volume 2

reviews in NUMBER THEORY

as printed in
MATHEMATICAL REVIEWS
1940 through 1972
volumes 1—44 inclusive

edited by

WILLIAM J. LeVEQUE

AMERICAN MATHEMATICAL SOCIETY · PROVIDENCE · RHODE ISLAND · 1974

Reviews reprinted from
MATHEMATICAL REVIEWS
volumes 1—44 published during 1940—1972

AMS (MOS) classification numbers (1970).
Primary 10 – XX, 12 – XX; Secondary 00 – XX, 01 – XX.

Library of Congress Cataloging in Publication Data CIP

LeVeque, William Judson, comp.
Reviews in number theory.

1. Numbers, Theory of—Abstracts. I. Mathematical reviews. II. Title.
QA241.L577 512'.7'08 74-11335
ISBN 0-8218-0204-6 (v. 2)

SERIES CONTENTS

D DIOPHANTINE EQUATIONS 1

E FORMS AND LINEAR ALGEBRAIC GROUPS 191

CONTENTS

D. DIOPHANTINE EQUATIONS

For papers involving methods of algebraic geometry, see Chapter **G**. For equations over finite fields, see **T40** *ff*. For representations by forms, see Chapter **E**. For decidability questions, see **U05**.

D02 BOOKS AND SURVEYS

General texts which include standard material on Diophantine equations are to be found in **Z01** and **Z02** and are not cross-referenced here.

See also reviews D08-44, D12-30, D12-32, D12-33, D16-15, D24-49, D24-50, D32-28, D32-49, D40-32, D44-25, D44-28, D44-77, D52-13, D52-26, D52-43, D52-114, D72-53, D72-55, G05-11, P02-17, Z01-41, Z02-48, Z02-62, Z05-15.

D02-1 **(5, 254g)**

Mordell, L. J. Rational points on cubic curves and surfaces. Amer. Math. Monthly **51**, 332–339 (1944).

This is an exposition of various methods of solving in integers certain homogeneous cubic equations in three and four variables. This includes a description of some of the work of the author and B. Segre [J. London Math. Soc. **18**, 24–31, 31–34, 43–46 (1943); these Rev. **5**, 141, 154].

B. W. Jones (Ithaca, N. Y.).

Citations: MR 5, 141b = D32-12; MR 5, 154e = G35-1.

D02-2 **(13, 913c)**

Gel'fond, A. O. Rešenie uravenenii v celyh čislah. [The solution of equations in whole numbers.] Gosudarstv. Izdat. Tehn.-Teor. Lit., Moscow-Leningrad, 1952. 63 pp. 85 kopecks.

A booklet in the series, Popular Lectures in Mathematics.

Referred to in D02-3, D02-4, D02-6, D02-7, D02-8, D04-57.

D02-3 **(16, 335h)**

Gelfond, Alexander O. Ganzzahlige Lösungen von Gleichungen. Verlag von R. Oldenbourg, München, 1954. 59 pp. DM 7.80.

Gelfond, A. O. Die Auflösung von Gleichungen in ganzen Zahlen (Diophantische Gleichungen). Deutscher Verlag der Wissenschaften, Berlin, 1954. 59 pp.

Translations of the author's Rešenie uravnenii v celyh čislah [Gostehizdat, Moscow, 1952; these Rev. **13**, 913].

Citations: MR 13, 913c = D02-2.

Referred to in D02-7, D02-8.

D02-4 **(20# 6387)**

Гельфонд, А. О. Решение уравнений в целых числах. 2. Изд. [Gel'fond, A. O. Solution of equations in integers. 2nd ed.] Populyarnye Lekcii po Matematike, Vypusk 8. Gosudarstv. Izdat. Tehn.-Teor. Lit., Moscow, 1957. 63 pp. 0.85 rubles.

An essentially unchanged republication of the booklet listed in MR **13**, 913.

Citations: MR 13, 913c = D02-2.

Referred to in D02-5, D02-6, D02-7, D02-8, D04-57.

D02-5 **(21# 5607)**

Gelfond, A. O. The solution of equations in integers. Popular Lectures on Mathematics. Translated from the 2nd Russian edition by Leo F. Boron. P. Noordhoff, Ltd., Groningen, 1960. 72 pp. Paperbound.

The Russian original was listed as MR **20** #6387. The foreword to this American edition is a reproduction of a letter from the author; it remarks, in part: "This booklet is accessible to the more advanced high school students, . . . , to teachers of mathematics, and to engineers."

Citations: MR 20# 6387 = D02-4.

Referred to in D02-8, D04-57, D44-112.

D02-6 **(25# 5025)**

Gelfond, A. O. [Gel'fond, A. O.]

The solution of equations in integers.

Translated from the Russian and edited by J. B. Roberts.

W. H. Freeman and Co., San Francisco, Calif.-London, 1961. viii + 63 *pp.* $1.00.

The original Russian edition [2nd ed., GITTL, Moscow, 1957] was reviewed in MR **20** #6387; a review of the first edition (1952), was given in MR **13**, 913.

Citations: MR 13, 913c = D02-2; MR 20# 6387 = D02-4.

Referred to in D02-7, D02-8.

D02-7 **(37# 4002)**

Gelfond, A. O. [Gel'fond, A. O.]

Danklemlerin tam sayılarla cözülmesi (Diofant denklemleri). (Turkish) [The solution of equations in integers (Diophantine equations)]

Translated by Orhan İçen. Turkish Mathematical Society Publications, No. 8.

Türk Matematik Derneği, Istanbul, 1962. iv + 61 *pp.* 220 *Krş.*

Citations: MR 13, 913c = D02-2; MR 16, 335h = D02-3; MR 20# 6387 = D02-4; MR 25# 5025 = D02-6.

Referred to in D02-8.

D02-8 **(41# 3405)**

Gel'fond, A. O.

Die Auflösung von Gleichungen in ganzen Zahlen. Diophantische Gleichungen.

Aus dem Russischen übertragen von Gerhard Ränike. Dritte, durchgesehene Auflage. Kleine Ergänzungsreihe, V.

VEB Deutscher Verlag der Wissenschaften, Berlin, 1966. 59 *pp.* *MDN* 3.80.

Various earlier editions have been reviewed [Russian original, GITTL, Moscow, 1952; MR **13**, 913; German translations: VEB Deutsch. Verlag Wissensch., Berlin, 1954; MR **16**, 335; Oldenbourg, Munich, 1954; MR **16**, 335; Turkish translation, Türk Matematik. Derneği, Istanbul, 1962; MR **37** #4002; second Russian edition,

GITTL, Moscow, 1957; MR **20** #6387; English translations: Noordhoff, Groningen, 1960; MR **21** #5607; Freeman, San Francisco, Calif., 1961; MR **25** #5025].

Citations: MR 13, 913c = D02-2; MR 16, 335h = D02-3; MR 20# 6387 = D02-4; MR 21# 5607 = D02-5; MR 25# 5025 = D02-6; MR 37# 4002 = D02-7.

D02-9 (14, 19d)

Ξηρουδάκης, Γεώργιος Φ., καὶ Φασουλάκης, Κωνστ. Ν. Εἰσαγωγὴ εἰσ τὴν διοφαντικὴν ἀνάλυσιν ἀνωτέρου βαθμοῦ. [Xeroudakes, Georgios Ph., and Fasoulakes, Konst. N. Introduction to diophantine analysis of higher degree.] N. D. Phrantzeskakes, Athens, 1947. 148 pp. 12,000 drachmas.

This book was written with the aim of stimulating interest among young mathematicians in the direction of Diophantine Analysis. For this purpose the authors have written a very elementary book which presupposes only a bare minimum of background in the theory of numbers. No knowledge of quadratic residues or algebraic number fields is required.

The introduction is devoted to equations of the second degree. Parametric solutions are given of the three equations $x^2+ay^2=z^2$, $x^2+y^2=Az^2$, $x^2+y^2=z^2+w^2$. Then there is the usual discussion of numbers of the form $x^2+Axy+By^2$ with applications to solutions of such equations as $x^2+y^2=z^3$, $X^2+Y^2+Z^2=x^4+y^4+z^4+w^4$, $x^2+ay^2=z^2+aw^2$, $x^2-xy+y^2=z^2$, $x^2+y^2+z^2=w^2$. This is followed by a chapter on arithmetic triangles and parallelograms. The second chapter deals with a large number of equations of the third and fourth degree, most of which are of the form $f(x^3, y^3, z^3)=g(X^3, Y^3, Z^3)$ and $f(x^4, y^4, z^4)=g(X^4, Y^4, Z^4)$. In chapter III the study of third and fourth degree equations is continued, the principal types considered being of the form $f(x, y)=mz^2$, where f is a homogeneous polynomial of degree three or four. The fourth and final chapter introduces Fermat's method of infinite descent and applies it to prove the impossibility of certain equations, for instance: $x^4+y^4=z^4$, $x^4+6x^2y^2+y^4=2z^2$, $x^4+9x^2y^2+8y^4=z^2$, and other equations derivable from these. The book also contains fifty exercises. *T. M. Apostol* (Pasadena, Calif.).

D02-10 (16, 335j)

Utz, W. R. Diophantine equations. Pi Mu Epsilon J. **2**, 2–10 (1954).

D02-11 (17, 237h)

Skolem, Th. The use of a p-adic method in the theory of diophantine equations. Bull. Soc. Math. Belg. **1954**, 83–95 (1955).

Expository article.

D02-12 (22# 1546)

Davenport, H. Some recent progress in analytic number theory. J. London Math. Soc. **35** (1960), 135–142.

The paper is a presidential address delivered to the London Mathematical Society on November 19, 1959. Among other items concerning publications, the author announces that the collected papers of G. H. Hardy will be published by the Oxford University Press and that the publication will probably extend to ten volumes.

The author then goes on to discuss some problems in analytic number theory. After giving a brief outline of the Hardy-Littlewood method he describes two variants of Waring's problem. First one can treat the representation of N as $a_1x_1^k+\cdots+a_nx_n^k$ and in particular the number of solutions of the equation $a_1x_1^k+\cdots+a_nx_n^k=0$ in integers $x_1, \cdots, x_n$; if k is even it is necessary to suppose that not all the coefficients are of the same sign. It can be proved by the Hardy-Littlewood method that the equation has infinitely many solutions if n is greater than a certain function of k. For $k=2$ the conclusion holds for $n\geqq 5$ as was proved by Meyer in 1883.

Secondly, one can treat the solvability of an inequality such as $|\lambda_1x_1^k+\cdots+\lambda_nx_n^k|<1$, where $\lambda_1, \cdots, \lambda_n$ are real numbers, not all of the same sign when k is even. It was proved by Davenport and Heilbronn in 1946 that the inequality has infinitely many solutions in integers provided $n\geqq 2^k+1$.

A generalization of the first problem above is that of solving an equation $F(x_1, \cdots, x_n)=0$, when F is a homogeneous polynomial of degree k with integral coefficients (the first work on this problem, using the Hardy-Littlewood method, was that of Tartakovskiĭ in 1935). The corresponding generalization of the second problem is $|\Phi(x_1, \cdots, x_n)|<1$, where Φ is a form of degree k with real coefficients. These problems are referred to as the 'equation problem' and the 'inequality problem', respectively. In either case it is assumed that the form represents zero for real $x_1, \cdots, x_n$ not all zero. The immediate new difficulty is caused by the non-additive nature of F or Φ. For the inequality problem with $k=2$ the author reports on results due to himself, Birch, Heilbronn and Ridout. It was proved that $|\Phi|<1$ has an integral solution for $n\geqq 21$; presumably $n\geqq 5$ is the true solution. It is mentioned that "the case $k=3$ can also be solved, but that a new difficulty arises for $k>3$ which at present appears insuperable."

For the equation problem the first case of interest is $k=3$ since a quadratic form can be rationally transformed into a diagonal form. Davenport proved in 1957 that the cubic equation $F(x_1, \cdots, x_n)=0$ is solvable in integers (not all 0) if n is sufficiently large; D. J. Lewis had obtained a proof a little earlier. At about the same time Birch established the following more general result. Any system of equations

$$F_1(x_1, \cdots, x_n) = 0, \cdots, F_m(x_1, \cdots, x_n) = 0$$

of given odd degrees $k_1, \cdots, k_m$ is solvable in integers not all zero provided n is greater than a function of $k_1, \cdots, k_m$. For the case of a single cubic equation Davenport has proved that $n\geqq 29$ suffices, but presumably $n\geqq 10$ is the true condition.

Turning again to the work of Tartakovskiĭ it is noted that he proved that the 'general' equation, not necessarily homogeneous, of degree k in n variables is solvable, subject to the obvious necessary conditions, provided n is greater than a function of k. Birch has recently proved that the homogeneous equation $F(x_1, \cdots, x_n)=0$ is solvable in integers provided that the singular variety: $\partial F/\partial x_1=\cdots=\partial F/\partial x_n=0$ is of dimension $<n-(k-1)2^k$. In particular a non-singular cubic form in 17 or more variables represents zero.

In conclusion two problems concerning the singular variety of a primal are formulated.

L. Carlitz (Durham, N.C.)

Referred to in D72-30.

D02-13 (22# 9469)

Lang, Serge. Some theorems and conjectures in diophantine equations. Bull. Amer. Math. Soc. **66** (1960), 240–249.

In this address to the American Mathematical Society in February 1960 the author discusses known results and unsolved problems, in particular the connection between local and global theories. The following subjects are discussed. (1) Hasse's theorem on quadratic forms. (2) Peck's theorem on forms of arbitrary degree in a large number of variables over a totally imaginary ground field and forms over quasi-algebraically closed fields. (3) Principal homogeneous spaces, and the connection to cohomology theory. (4) The special case of curves, in particular the theorems of Siegel and of Mordell-Weil. A (rather incomplete) list of 27 papers closes the report.

K. Mahler (Manchester)

Referred to in D72-31, R08-45.

D02-14 **(22# 9471)**

Mordell, L. J. Recent work in number theory. Scripta Math. **25** (1960), 93–103.

The author discusses some recent results in number theory, most of which is his own work. (1) A simple proof that the multinomial coefficients are integral. (2) Let (u, t) denote the fundamental solution of the equation $y^2-Dx^2=-4$. The author has proved [see #9470] that if p is a prime $\equiv 1 \pmod 4$ and the number of classes of ideals in the cyclotomic field $k(e^{2\pi i/p})$ is not divisible by p, then $u\not\equiv 0 \pmod p$; whereas if p is a prime $\equiv 5 \pmod 8$, then $u\equiv 0 \pmod p$ if and only if the Bernoulli number $B_{(p-1)/4}\equiv 0 \pmod p$. Chowla has proved that the latter result holds for all prime $p\equiv 1 \pmod 4$. (3) Discussion of the following problem of J. J. Schoenberg. Given any quadrilateral $PQRS$, do there exist rational quadrilaterals $P'Q'R'S'$ (that is, quadrilaterals with rational sides and diagonals) whose vertices P', Q', R', S' are arbitrarily near to P, Q, R, S? (4) Integral solutions of two simultaneous homogeneous quadratic equations with rational coefficients. The author has proved the following result [Math. Sem. Univ. Hamburg Abh. **23** (1959), 126–143; MR **21** #3378]. Let $f(x)$, $g(x)$ be two quadratic forms with rational coefficients in n essential variables. Suppose that for real λ, μ not both zero, no member of the pencil $\lambda f(x)+\mu g(x)$ is either definite of rank $\leqq n$ or singular of rank <5 but that at least one member has more than four positive and more than four negative squares when expressed as a sum of squares of real linear forms. Then the system $f(x)=0$, $g(x)=0$ has an infinity of integral solutions with non-zero values of the variables when $n\geqq 13$. (5) Let $L_1, \cdots, L_n$ be linear forms in $u_1, \cdots, u_n$ with real coefficients and determinant 1 and let $C_1, \cdots, C_n$ be any real numbers. Put $M=\inf \prod_{r=1}^{n} |L_r+C_r|$, that is, the lower bound for all integers (u). The author has proved [J. London Math. Soc. **35** (1960), 91–97; MR **22** #1564] that

$$M \leqq 2^{-n/2}\{4-2(2-\tfrac{3}{4}\sqrt{2})^n-2^{-n/2}\}^{-1}.$$

L. Carlitz (Durham, N.C.)

Citations: MR 21# 3378 = D72-17; MR 22# 1564 = J40-27; MR 22# 9470 = D12-44.

D02-15 **(23# A1599)**

Landau, Edmund

Diophantische Gleichungen mit endlich vielen Lösungen.

Neu herausgegeben von A. Walfisz. Hochschulbücher für Mathematik, Bd. 44.

VEB Deutscher Verlag der Wissenschaften, Berlin, 1959. 87 *pp.* *DM* 7.20.

From the introduction: "Dieser Neuausgabe liegt § 4, Teil IX, Kapitel 2, der Landauschen *Vorlesungen über Zahlentheorie* zugrunde [Verlag Hirzel, Leipzig, 1927, S. 37–65]. Landau beweist dort den bekannten Siegelschen Näherungssatz und wendet ihn auf den Thueschen Problemkreis an. In der vorliegenden Neuausgabe wird der Siegelsche Satz durch den vor drei Jahren erschienenen hochbedeutenden Satz von Roth [Mathematika **2** (1955), 1–20, 168; MR **17**, 242] ersetzt. Der Umfang ist dadurch auf das Doppelte angewachsen, der elementare Charakter der Darstellung ist aber gewahrt geblieben; was an Algebra und Zahlentheorie vorausgesetzt wird, ist in den Anfängervorlesungen zu finden. Jeder Student in den mittleren Semestern, der über hinreichend Geduld verfügt (und zur Zahlentheorie muß man Geduld haben), kann also das Büchlein mit Nutzen lesen.

"Näheres über die Behandlung des Landauschen Textes findet man zu Beginn der Quellenangaben. Die Landausche Überschrift seines Paragraphen 'Der Thue-Siegelsche Satz' wurde, nach dem Vorbild von Dickson, durch einen neutralen Titel ersetzt, da Landau vor einundzwanzig Jahren starb und den Rothschen Satz nicht mehr erlebte. Freilich ließ es sich nicht vermeiden, daß im Texte selbst im Namen Landaus vom Rothschen Satz gesprochen wird."

D02-16 **(23# A2093)**

Underwood, R. S.

·Silhouette mathematics: Extended analytic geometry.

Published by the author, 1961; *distributed by Texas Tech. Bookstore, Lubbock, Texas.* iv + 148 *pp.* $2.00.

The author's interest in producing a simple visual counterpart for equations in more than three variables has resulted in this highly readable volume in which the ideas of an earlier paper [Amer. Math. Monthly **61** (1954), 525–542] are treated at length. After a detailed review of the conventional theory of curve-sketching, quadric surfaces and differentiation, the author establishes a many-one correspondence between polynomial equations in $x_1, \cdots, x_n$ and loci in the X, Y-plane, predominantly by means of linear relations of the form $X=\sum_{j=1}^{m} a_jx_j$, $Y=\sum_{j=m+1}^{n} a_jx_j$. By these means quadric surfaces are classified and identified by their "silhouettes" (i.e., plane regions bounded by conic sections). An extremely practical technique for rapid sketching of the loci of quadratics without cross-product terms is developed and used extensively. This geometric approach when applied to considerations of consistency in Diophantine systems of linear and quadratic equations produces such theorems as, "A linear and a quadratic equation are consistent if and only if the linear analogue touches the quadratic's silhouette". This concise result seems to be new.

Elementary methods and clear explanations develop the theory by stages which should be readilv understood by students beyond the sophomore level. Generous sets of exercises distributed throughout the text enable the reader periodically to test his comprehension of the theory.

Although no insight on classical problems in number theory seems to be obtainable by this system, its superiority to more conventional methods in other instances is convincingly demonstrated. Serious mathematicians, as well as the "dilettantes in ideas" to whom this paper-bound book is primarily directed, will find thought-provoking material therein regardless of their field of specialization. The final chapter contains suggestions for further investigations in adapting and applying this "extended analytic geometry".

D. C. B. Marsh (Golden, Colo.)

D02-17 **(23# A2370)**

Chatelet, François

Introduction à l'analyse diophantienne.

Enseignement Math. (2) **6** (1960), 3–17.

Expository paper.

J. W. S. Cassels (Cambridge, England)

Referred to in Z10-17.

D02-18 **(26# 6119)**

Mordell, L. J.

Rational points on cubic curves and surfaces.

Scripta Math. **26** (1963), 147–153.

An expository article concerning rational and integral points on cubic curves and on cubic surfaces. Throughout the paper many results are stated without proof and without reference to the literature. However, the author does give R. F. Whitehead's elementary algebraic proof of Segre's theorem: The general cubic equation $f(x, y, z)=0$ has either none or an infinity of rational solutions.

D. J. Lewis (Ann Arbor, Mich.)

D02-19 **(28# 3002)**

Davenport, H.

Analytic methods for Diophantine equations and Diophantine inequalities.

The University of Michigan, Fall Semester, 1962.

Ann Arbor Publishers, Ann Arbor, Mich., 1963. viii + 168 *pp.* $4.00.

The first ten sections of this course of lectures deal with the analytic theory of Diophantine equations of additive type; the other ten deal with the more recent application of the Hardy-Littlewood method to general Diophantine equations. It is convenient to describe these two halves separately.

After a couple of introductory sections, the author gives in §§ 3–6 the simplest available solution of Waring's problem: He proves that every large enough integer is a sum of (2^k+1) kth powers by using Hua's inequality. In §§ 7–8, asymptotic formulae are obtained for the number of solutions of equations of type $\sum_{i=1}^{s} c_i x_i^k = N$ for $s>2^k$. In § 9, Vinogradov's result that for $k>k_0(\delta)$ every large enough integer is a sum of at most $(6+\delta)k \log k$ kth powers is proved, following the account given by H. Heilbronn [Acta Arith. **1** (1936), 212–221]. In § 10, the author returns to the equation $\sum c_i x_i^k = 0$. Throughout this first part, the treatment of the singular series is unusually meticulous. These lectures were more or less contemporary with the proof by the author and D. J. Lewis [Proc. Roy. Soc. Ser. A **274** (1963), 443–460; MR **27** #3617] that for $k>16$ every diagonal equation $\sum c_i x_i^k = 0$ with $s>k^2$ is soluble in integers; in this problem, the singular series caused the principal difficulty.

The author then turns to general homogeneous equations. First, in § 11, he proves a theorem of the reviewer [Mathematika **4** (1957), 102–105; MR **20** #3828] that a rational equation of odd degree has a zero so long as it involves enough variables. §§ 12–18 contain the main meat of the lectures; the author gives a complete exposition of his theorem that every rational cubic in s variables has a rational zero for $s \geqq 17$. This is in fact much the clearest presentation of this important work. The proof given here contains an extra idea and so is simpler than the author's original proof [Philos. Trans. Roy. Soc. London Ser. A **251** (1959), 193–232; MR **21** #4136] valid for $s \geqq 32$; on the other hand, one avoids the extra difficulties of detail in the author's proof valid for $s \geqq 16$ [Proc. Roy. Soc. Ser. A **272** (1963), 285–303; MR **27** #5734]. § 19 describes related work of the reviewer. § 20 contains a result of a different character, the theorem of the author and H. Heilbronn [J. London Math. Soc. **21** (1946), 185–193; MR **8**, 565] that for every real $\lambda_1, \cdots, \lambda_5$, not all of the same sign, one can find integers $x_1, \cdots, x_5$ so that $|\sum_{i=1}^{5} \lambda_i x_i^2| < 1$.

These notes are almost completely self-contained; there is even a section proving relevant lemmas from the Geometry of Numbers. The author normally chooses the simplest available proofs—these are often his own, and often simpler than those available elsewhere; but he refers to alternative lines of attack when they exist. Plenty of references are given, both historical and to current work. These notes should be very valuable both to those starting research and to more experienced workers.

B. J. Birch (Manchester)

Citations: MR 8, 565e = D76-1; MR 20# 3828 = D72-16; MR 21# 4136 = D72-19; MR 27# 3617 = D72-31; MR 27# 5734 = D72-33.

Referred to in D72-56, D72-60, N32-49.

D02-20 **(30# 4725)**

Schafarewitsch, I. R. [Šafarevič, I. R.] 4725

Einige Anwendungen der Galoisschen Theorie auf Diophantische Gleichungen.

Bericht von der Dirichlet-Tagung, pp. 81–82. *Akademie-Verlag, Berlin*, 1963.

An expository lecture presented in 1959.

D02-21 **(36# 6347)**

Karanikolov, Hr. [Караниколов, Хр.]

Tonkov, T. [Тонков, Т.]

Indeterminate equations [Неопределени уравнения]. (Bulgarian)

Nauka i Izkustvo, Sofia, 1967. 123 *pp.* (*loose errata*) 0.38 *lv.*

From the authors' preface: "In the present book are included the more basic results from the theory of indeterminate equations of the first, second and third degrees. Also included are a large number of third and fourth degree indeterminate equations of a special form. We have tried to assemble the largest possible number and the most interesting equations from the classical literature as well as the most accessible modern results in this domain. The theory of quadratic forms is presented according to Gauss, but for the sake of brevity not all questions are touched upon. Since the equations of third and higher degrees are harder to investigate, and the proofs in these cases are not of an elementary nature, the results in most of these cases are stated purely for information."

D02-22 **(39# 2699)**

Lewis, D. J.

Diophantine equations: p-adic methods.

Studies in Number Theory, pp. 25–75. *Math. Assoc. Amer.* (*distributed by Prentice-Hall, Englewood Cliffs, N.J.*), 1969.

This is a very interesting and valuable paper on Diophantine equations in general and, in particular, on the p-adic methods used in their treatment. The paper tries to give a panoramic view of an enormous amount of material in less than 50 pages and the thankless task of the present review is to try to summarize still further such a condensed summary. For this reason in what follows the definitions of the symbols (all are standard) and all quotations of references have been suppressed even at the risk of some ambiguity, when speaking, e.g., of "Chevalley's theorem" or "Artin's conjecture". After the title of each section follows only the briefest indication of content and, occasionally, a few comments. (1) Introduction (examples of a large and representative variety of Diophantine problems); (2) Reality conditions (integral solutions cannot exist, if there are no real ones); (3) Congruence conditions (the existence of integral solutions implies the solvability of the corresponding congruences; Chevalley's theorem; some ideas of Hensel); (4) The ring $\mathfrak{O}_p$; (5) Zeros in $\mathfrak{O}_p^{(m)}$ (the existence of a zero in $\mathbf{Z}^{(m)}$ implies the existence of a zero in $R^{(m)}$ and in $\mathfrak{O}_p^{(m)}$ for every prime p); (6) The p-adic field (valuations; the field $\mathbf{Q}_p$; p-adic limits; the approximation theorem; local fields); (7) Equivalent sets of polynomials; (8) Linear polynomials ("a set of linear polynomials with coefficients in $\mathbf{Z}$ has a zero in $\mathbf{Z}^{(m)}$ if and only if it has a zero in each $\mathfrak{O}_p^{(m)}$"); (9) Quadratic polynomials ("if $a \in \mathbf{Z}$, then $x^2 - a$ has a zero in $\mathbf{Z}$ if and only if it has a zero in each $\mathfrak{O}_p$"); (10) One quadratic form ("a quadratic form with coefficients in $\mathbf{Q}$ has a zero in $\mathbf{Q}$ if and only if it has a zero in each local field of $\mathbf{Q}$"; "an indefinite quadratic form in $m \geqq 5$ variables, with coefficients in $\mathbf{Z}$ has a zero in $\mathbf{Z}$"; the Hilbert symbol is introduced); (11) Several quadratic forms (work of Swinnerton-Dyer, Demjanov, Birch and Lewis is presented; from here on, the author's own work comes prominently to the fore in many sections); (12) Integral zeros of quadratic polynomials (work of Eichler, O'Meara and especially G. L. Watson is presented); (13) Polynomials of higher degree (R. Brauer's and Birch's work on non-trivial zeros of forms of odd degrees in sufficiently many variables is presented; results of Davenport and the author are quoted; the Artin conjecture is stated and Terjanian's counterexample to the conjecture is given; Browkin's theorem is indicated and the theorem of Ax and Kochen (a form of degree d in $n \geqq d^2+1$ variables has a zero in $\mathbf{Q}_p$ for p sufficiently (depending on d) large) is stated; the theorem of Demjanov and the author (a cubic form in $m \geqq 10$ variables with coefficients in $\mathbf{Q}_p$ has a zero in $\mathbf{Q}_p$) is stated and proved; many other important results, especially on cubics (due to, besides the author, Davenport, Swinnerton-Dyer and G. L. Watson) are quoted with comments, but without proofs); (14) Algebraic number fields ($\mathfrak{P}$-adic fields $K_{\mathfrak{P}}$); (15) Power series over $K_{\mathfrak{P}}$ (Strassman's theorem, with proof); (16) A Weierstrass expansion for continuous functions (Mahler's theorem on continuous functions from $\mathfrak{O}_p$ to $\mathfrak{O}_{\mathfrak{P}}$); (17) Exponential equations; (18) Linear recurrences (order; companion polynomial; several important theorems on exponential polynomials, too long to quote); (19) Representation by cubic forms (several theorems culminating in the result by Delone and Nagell that if $C(x, y)$ is an irreducible binary cubic form with integral coefficients and exactly one real zero, then $C(x, y) = 1$ has at most five integral solutions and, except for special forms, actually only at most 3 integral solutions); (20) The equation $x^3 - dy^3 = 1$ ("d cube free implies that $x^3 - dy^3 = 1$ has at most one non-trivial integral solution"; Skolem's p-adic method, work of Nagell); (21) Generalizations and extensions. This last section is filled with interesting and important results, either quoted, or barely indicated. Among these are theorems of Skolem, Chabauty, the Thue-Siegel-Roth theorem, Mahler's p-adic version of it and work by Ljunggren. On the last half-page of this last section, mention is made also of the extremely important recent work of A. Baker (explicit bounds for the zeros of $F(x, y) = a$, where $F(x, y)$ is a form of degree $m \geqq 3$); most of this must have been available to the author only in manuscript form. The paper ends with an excellent bibliography of 38 entries (oldest: Thue in 1909; latest: Watson in 1967; A. Baker, 1968, could not yet be included).

E. Grosswald (Philadelphia, Pa.)

D02-23 **(40# 2600)**

Mordell, L. J.
Diophantine equations.
Pure and Applied Mathematics, Vol. 30.
Academic Press, London-New York, 1969. xi + 312 *pp.* 90 *s.*; $13.50.

The author's researches in the field of diophantine equations are well-known; they have exercised a profound influence in many fields of mathematics. In particular, the reviewer has in mind the "finite-basis" theorem for the rational points on a plane cubic curve of genus 1. This theorem was generalized by A. Weil. The theorem also forms a background for the highly important work of Birch and Swinnerton-Dyer on the zeta functions of cubic curves. The author's work on diophantine equations also led to the recent startling results of A. Baker on bounds for the largest integers x and y such that (the author's equation) $y^2 = x^3 + k$ $(k \neq 0)$ and for $f(x, y) = m[m \neq 0, f$ homogeneous of degree $\geqq 3$ and irreducible over $Q]$.

Needless to say, the author's book on diophantine equations will be welcomed by students of mathematics all over the world. We shall now list chapter by chapter a selection from the contents.

Chapter 1: Introduction. Let $f = f(x_1, \cdots, x_n)$ be a polynomial in these variables. Problem: To find some or all of the solutions of $f = 0$ in (I) rational numbers, i.e., in the field Q; (II) rational integers, i.e., in the ring Z. Section 2 gives some necessary conditions for solvability of $f = 0$.

Chapter 2: Equations proved impossible by congruence considerations. This chapter concludes by stating "a non-constructive proof has been given of the" theorem: For every natural number r, there exists a fixed set $S(r)$ of primes such that for every prime p not in $S(r)$, every homogeneous equation $f(x_1, \cdots, x_n)$ of degree r and with $n > r^2$ variables, always has a non-trivial solution in the p-adic fields. This theorem is due to J. Ax and S. Kochen [Amer. J. Math. **87** (1965), 605–630; MR **32** #2401].

Chapter 3: Equations involving sums of squares.

Chapter 4: Quartic equations with only trivial solutions. Example: $x^4 + y^4 = z^2$ has no integer solutions with $xy \neq 0$. Theorem 3: There cannot be 4 squares in arithmetical progression. The author mentions that most of the results on the impossibility of non-trivial integer solutions of $ax^4 + by^4 = cz^2$ are due to H. C. Pocklington [Proc. Cambridge Philos. Soc. **17** (1914), 110–118], T. Nagell [Norsk. Mat. For. Skr. (1) **1923**, no. 13 (1924)] and C. E. Lind ["Untersuchungen über die rationalen Punkteder ebenen kubischen Kurven vom Geschlecht Eins", Ph.D. Thesis, Uppsala, Appelberg, 1940], and mostly by the method of infinite descent. Details are given for $x^4 + 2py^4 = z^2$ $(x, y, z > 0)$, where $p \equiv \pm 3 \pmod 8$.

Chapter 5: Some linear equations.

Chapter 6: Properties of congruences. Example: Theorems on the solvability of $f(x) = a_1x_1^{l_1} + \cdots + a_nx_n^{l_n} + a \equiv 0 \pmod p$.

Chapter 7: Homogeneous equations of the second degree. This chapter includes the classical $ax^2 + by^2 + cz^2 = 0$ with a slightly weaker form of a theorem due to Holzer giving bounds for the solutions (when solutions exist). Also, the theorem that every indefinite quadratic form in 5 variables represents 0 (non-trivially).

Chapter 8: Pell's equation. Amongst other topics, the author mentions the conjecture of Artin, Ankeny and the reviewer that $u \not\equiv 0 \pmod p$, where $\varepsilon = (t + u\sqrt{p})/2 > 1$ is the fundamental unit of $Q(\sqrt{p})$, where p is a prime $\equiv 1 \pmod 4$. This is equivalent to $B_{(p-1)/4} \not\equiv O(p)$, where B_n is the nth Bernoulli number. Let p be a prime $\equiv 3$ (4) and so now $y^2 - px^2 = 1$. Let u be the least positive value of x. Then (Mordell's conjecture) $u \not\equiv 0 \pmod p$. This is equivalent to $E_{(p-3)/4} \not\equiv O(p)$, where E_n is the nth Eulerian number.

Chapter 9: Rational solutions derived from given ones. Example: Theorem 5: All the integer solutions of $x^4 - 2y^4 = -z^2$ $(x, y, z > 0; (x, y) = 1)$ can be "derived" from rational functions of one solution.

Chapter 10: Rational points on some cubic curves. Example: Theorem 2: If the quartic curve $y^2 = ax^4 + bx^3 + cx^2 + dx + e$ has a rational point, it is "equivalent" to a cubic curve $Y^2 = 4X^3 - g_2X - g_3$.

Chapter 11: Rational points on cubic surfaces. Example: Theorem 1: All the rational points on a cubic surface can be found if it contains two lines whose equations are defined by conjugate numbers of a quadratic field and, in particular, by rational numbers. Example: Theorem 3: The theorem of Cassells and Guy that the equation $5x^3+9y^3+10z^3+12w^3=0$ is solvable everywhere locally but has no rational solutions except (0, 0, 0, 0).

Chapter 12: Rational and integer points on quartic surfaces. Example: Euler's treatment of the equation $x^4+y^4=z^4+w^4$.

Chapter 13: Integer solutions of some cubic equations in 3 variables. Example: The theorem of Segre: The equation $ax^3+by^3+cz^3+d=0$ $(abcd\neq 0)$, where a, b, c, d are integers, has in general no solutions with x, y, z as relatively prime polynomials with rational coefficients of degree $\leqq 4$ in a parameter t. (This is stated without proof.)

Chapter 14: Simple algebraic considerations. Example: Discussion of the equation $ax^2+by^2=cz^2$. "Many of these results are classical, and are due to Euler and Lagrange."

Chapter 15: Applications of algebraic number theory (contains some classical results of algebraic number theory). There is also a discussion of some equations $x^3+y^3=az^3$ which have (for special values of a) no rational solutions. Many of these results go back to Sylvester. Also: $x^3+y^3+z^3=0$ has no non-trivial solutions in $Q(e^{2\pi i/3})$. The theorem of Cassello and Sansone that the diophantine equation $x^3+y^3+z^3=xyz$ has only the solutions $x+y=0$, $z=0$, etc.

Chapter 16: Finite basis theorem for the rational points on a cubic curve $f(x, y, z)=0$ of genus 1. Example: Theorem 1: All the rational points of a cubic curve $f(x, y, z)=0$ of genus 1 can be found from a finite number by the chord and tangent process.

For this important theorem the author gives a sketch of the original proof by Mordell, and a full account of A. Weil's proof [Bull. Sci. Math. (2) **54** (1930), 182–191]. In passing, we may mention that in a special case an elementary proof is given in the reviewer's book [*The Riemann hypothesis and Hilbert's tenth problem*, Gordon and Breach, New York, 1965; MR **31** #2201].

This chapter also mentions the exciting conjectures of B. Birch and H. P. F. Swinnerton-Dyer [J. Reine Angew. Math. **212** (1963), 7–25; MR **26** #3669; ibid. **218** (1965), 79–108; MR **31** #3419], especially one that states that a Hecke L-series $L(S)$ has a zero at $s=1$ precisely of order g, where g is the "Mordell-Weil" number of a certain cubic curve whose zeta-function is $\zeta(s)\zeta(s-1)/L(s)$. Let p denote a prime and let N_p-1 be the number of solutions of $y^2\equiv x^3-Ax-B \pmod p$. The zeta-function takes the form $f(x)=\prod_p \{1+(N_p-p-1)p^{-s}+p^{1-2s}\}$, where the "exceptional" primes are excluded from the product. By a theorem of Hasse the product converges absolutely for $R(s)>\frac{3}{2}$, and it has been conjectured by Hasse that $f(s)$ can be continued meromorphically over the whole s-plane. The Birch–Swinnerton-Dyer conjecture is that $f(s)$ has at $s=1$ a pole of order g, where g is the number of generators of the rational points of infinite order. The author also mentions that A. Wiman [Acta Math. **80** (1948), 223–257; MR **10**, 472] found an infinity of non-equivalent cubic curves with $g=4$, $g=5$ and a number with $g=6$.

Chapter 17: Rational points on curves of genus $g=0$ or 1 and $g>1$. Example: Mordell put forward, in 1922, the following conjecture: There are only a finite number of rational points on a curve of genus $g>1$. We are probably very far from a proof of this difficult conjecture. References in this chapter are to D. Hilbert and A. Hurwitz [ibid. **14** (1890), 217–224], H. Poincaré [J. Math. (5) **7** (1901), 161–233], V. A. Dem'janenko [Izv. Akad. Nauk SSSR Ser. Mat. **30** (1966), 1373–1396; MR **34** #5816], and Ju. I. Manin [ibid. **28** (1964), 1363–1390; MR **30** #3886].

Chapter 18: Representation of numbers by homogeneous forms in 2 variables. An account of some work of C. Hermite [J. Reine Angew. Math. **36** (1848), 357–364; reprinted in *Œuvres*. Tome 1, pp. 84–93, Gauthiers-Villars, Paris, 1905] and G. Julia [Mem. Acad. Sci. France (2) **55** (1917), 1–296].

Chapter 19: Representation of numbers by special binary quadratic and quaternary quadratic forms. This chapter contains classical results, treated by the author's method.

Chapter 20: Representation of numbers by homogeneous forms in several variables. A proof is sketched of the theorem that numbers $\not\equiv 4^a(8k+7)$ are sums of 3 squares.

Chapter 21: Representations of numbers by polynomials. Example: Theorem 2: Every integer can be expressed as a sum of 5 integer cubes. Conjecture: Every integer can be expressed as a sum of 4 cubes of integers. Schinzel's theorem that there does not exist a representation of $9k\pm 4$ as a sum of cubes of 4 quartic polynomials, is mentioned. Theorem 4 concerns the so-called "easier" Waring's problem.

Chapter 22: Thue's theorem on the integer solutions of $f(x, y)=m$. The author gives a detailed proof of this "fundamental" theorem of Thue (1904). A. Baker's theorem is mentioned.

Chapter 23: Local methods or p-adic applications. "One of the most important applications of p-adic numbers to diophantine equations deals with the following problem. Let $\omega_1, \cdots, \omega_n$ be a basis of the integers in an algebraic number field $K=Q(\theta)$. Denote by $N(\omega)$, the norm of ω in the field. It is required to discuss the solution in rational integers $x_1, \cdots, x_n$ of the equation $N(x_1\omega_1+\cdots+x_n\omega_n)=a$, where the x's satisfy the $n-m$ equations $q_l(x_1, \cdots, x_n)=0$ $(l=1, 2, \cdots, n-m)$ for given $m\leqq n$ and the q's are polynomials in the x's with rational coefficients."

This chapter contains an account of the important methods of Skolem.

In Theorem 6 the author gives Hasse's treatment of the diophantine equation $2^n=x^2+7$ (there is no solution for $n>15$). This result was first proved by Nagell; various authors (D. J. Lewis, M. Dunton, the reviewer) have given other solutions.

This chapter also mentions work of W. Ljunggren [Acta Math. **75** (1942), 1–21; MR **8**, 135] and W. Schmidt [Mathematika **14** (1967), 113–120; MR **36** #3722] on some diophantine equations in 3 variables.

Chapter 24: Binary cubic forms. Example: The equation $x^3+dy^3=1$ $(d>1)$ has at most one integer solution with $xy\neq 0$. This is given by the fundamental unit in the ring when it is a binomial unit, i.e., takes the form $x+y\sqrt[3]{d}$.

This is Theorem 5. For another account of this topic see also W. J. LeVeque [*Topics in the theory of numbers*, 2 vols., Addison-Wesley, Reading, Mass., 1956; MR **18**, 283].

Chapter 25: Binary quartic forms. Contains the theorem: The number N of solutions of $f(x, y)=ax^4+bx^3y+cx^2y^2+dxy^3+ey^4=1$ is always even and $N\leqq 8$. Also, $n=i$ if and only if $f(x, y)=(1, 0, -1, 0, 1)$, etc. (a finite number of cases, which are enumerated).

Chapter 26: The equation $y^2=x^3+k$. "This has played a fundamental role in the development of number theory." This chapter contains Fueter's Theorem 6: The equation $y^2=x^3+k$ has no rational solutions if k is a negative integer free from 6th power factors and contains all odd prime factors to an odd power and if also $k\equiv 2 \pmod 9$, $k\not\equiv 1 \pmod 4$, $k\not\equiv 4 \pmod{16}$ and the class-number of $Q(\sqrt{k})$ is not divisible by 3.

Three similar theorems (7, 8, 9) were found by Chang and the author. On p. 248, the author mentions the following "deep result from the theory of relative fields".

Lemma: If $Q(\sqrt{k})$ and $Q(\sqrt{(-3k)})$ are two quadratic fields and if the class-number for the imaginary field is prime to 3, then so also is the class-number of the real field.

Chapter 27: The equation $y^2=ax^3+bx^2+cx+d$. "The study of this equation has led to important developments and great advances in diophantine analysis." Theorem 1: The equation above ($a\neq 0$), where the right-hand-side has no squared factor, has only a finite number of solutions in integers.

A number of special equations are treated, e.g., $y(y+1)=x(x+1)(x+2)$ [no solutions when $|x|>5$].

Chapter 28: Some equations of degree >3. Theorem 4 concerns the finite number of solutions of $ay^2+by+c=dx^n$ except in special cases. Theorem 6 (Erdős, Erdős and Selfridge, unpublished): The equation $y^m=x(x+1)\cdots(x+n-1)$ has only the integer solutions given by $y=0$. Theorems of Ljunggren, Delone and Faddeev, Podsypanin, J. H. E. Cohn. Addendum (some work of Schinzel, suggested by Davenport and Lewis).

Chapter 29: Fermat's last theorem. An account of some of the classical work of Kummer, Wieferich and others.

Chapter 30: Miscellaneous results. Conjecture (Erdős, Straus): The equation $4/n=1/x+1/y+1/z$, where n is an integer >3, is solvable in positive integers x, y, z.

(References to works of L. Bernstein, R. Obláth, K. Yamamoto, L. A. Rosati, S. Selberg and others.)

S. Chowla (University Park, Pa.)

Citations: MR 8, 135k = D24-10; MR 10, 472c = G05-20; MR 18, 283b = Z01-38; MR 26# 3669 = G05-63; MR 30# 3886 = G10-24; MR 31# 2201 = Z02-48; MR 31# 3419 = G05-75; MR 32# 2401 = D72-44; MR 34# 5816 = G30-40; MR 36# 3722 = D56-30.

Referred to in T55-46.

D02-24 (40# 4201)

LeVeque, W. J.
A brief survey of diophantine equations.
Studies in Number Theory, pp. 4–24. *Math. Assoc. Amer.* (*distributed by Prentice-Hall, Englewood Cliffs, N.J.*), 1969. \$6.00.

"This article is devoted to a description, mostly informal, of some of the broad principles which have influenced research in the theory of diophantine equations during recent years." The article is divided into five sections (1) pre-nineteenth century work, (2) equations in two variables, (3) rational points on curves of genus 1, (4) equations in many variables, (5) equations with many solutions.

The first section contains a brief description of the pythagorean theorem, works of Diophantos, the Fermat equation $x^n+y^n=z^n$, the Pell equation $x^2-dy^2=c$ and other related problems.

In Section 2, Hilbert's, Hurtwitz' and Poincaré's algebraic-geometric methods of attacking Diophantine problems are discussed in some detail, with special reference to curves of genus zero. Thue's method, the Mordell-Weil finite basis theorem, Mordell's conjecture (there are only finitely many rational points on a curve of genus greater than 1), the Thue-Siegel theorem and related problems are considered.

Section 3 deals with problems of rational points on curves and the number of generators, while in Section 4 both kinds of Waring problem together with various recent variations of the Waring problem are discussed. The paper concludes with a discussion of the equation $y^2=f(x)$ and its generalizations.

J. M. Gandhi (Macomb, Ill.)

D04 LINEAR EQUATIONS

For linear inequalities, see **P28**.

See also Section A10.

See also reviews A04-4, B44-58, B56-5, B56-6, J16-24, N56-13, N56-16, P16-20, P28-30, P28-33, P28-35, P28-38, P28-46, P28-47, P28-48, P28-49, P28-50, P28-51, P28-52, P28-62, P28-66, P28-80, P28-81, P56-2.

D04-1 (2, 34e)

Pillai, S. S. On a linear Diophantine equation. Proc. Indian Acad. Sci., Sect. A. **12**, 199–201 (1940).

The Diophantine equation $a_1x_1+\cdots+a_nx_n=1$, where $a_1, a_2, \cdots, a_n$ are integers with no common factor greater than 1, has solutions in integers $x_1, \cdots, x_n$. This note establishes an upper bound for $F=F(a_1, a_2, \cdots, a_n)$ defined as the least value (if any) of $|x_1|+\cdots+|x_n|$.

R. D. James (Saskatoon, Sask.).

D04-2 (2, 247k)

Lehmer, D. H. A note on the linear Diophantine equation. Amer. Math. Monthly **48**, 240–246 (1941).

A solution in integers x, y of the linear Diophantine equation $a_0x-a_1y=K$, where $0<a_1<a_0$ and $(a_0, a_1)=1$, may be found by writing a_0/a_1 as a continued fraction and computing the convergents. The author points out that this method is twice as laborious as necessary and gives instead the following result. The equation $a_0x-a_1y=1$, where $0<a_1<a_0$ and $(a_0, a_1)=1$, has a solution $x=(-1)^nC_{n-1}$, $y=(-1)^nC_n$, where $C_0=0$, $C_1=1$, $C_{k+1}=q_{n-k}C_k+C_{k-1}$, and the q's are the partial quotients in the continued fraction development of a_0/a_1. It is noted that other sets of q's may be used, the only requirement being that the sequence terminate with $a_{n-1}=q_na_n$, $|a_n|=1$.

R. D. James.

Referred to in D04-3.

D04-3 (3, 161b)

Rosser, Barkley. A note on the linear Diophantine equation. Amer. Math. Monthly **48**, 662–666 (1941).

This paper presents an alternative to the methods presented in a paper by Lehmer [Amer. Math. Monthly **48**, 240–246 (1941); these Rev. **2**, 247]. It leads to a general solution with smaller coefficients.

R. D. James.

Citations: MR 2, 247k = D04-2.

Referred to in J12-19.

D04-4 (3, 270d)

Brauer, Alfred. On a problem of partitions. Amer. J. Math. **64**, 299–312 (1942).

The author considers the Diophantine linear equation

$$a_1x_1+a_2x_2+\cdots+a_kx_k=n,$$

in which the letters are positive integers and the a's are without common factor. The problem discussed is that of determining a bound $F=F(a_1, \cdots, a_k)$ such that for all $n>F$ we are assured of the existence of the k unknown x's. For $k=2$ a bound $F(a_1, a_2)=a_1a_2$ was given by Sylvester. This bound is the best possible. For $k>2$ a bound F is given by $S=a_1a_k+a_2+a_3+\cdots+a_{k-1}$. This is a previously unpublished result of I. Schur. If $d_\nu=(a_1, a_2, a_3, \cdots, a_\nu)$ is the greatest common divisor of the first ν a's, so that $d_1=a_1$, $d_k=1$, then an alternative bound is given by

$$T=\sum_{\nu=2}^{k} a_\nu d_{\nu-1}/d_\nu.$$

It is shown that T is at least as good as S and that the two bounds are equally good when and only when S is the best possible. The question of when T is the best bound is further discussed. In the special case in which the a's are the k consecutive integers from m to $m+k-1$, the best bound is given by the greatest integer not exceeding $\frac{1}{2}(k^2-k-2)+[(m+k^2-3)/(k-1)]m$. *D. H. Lehmer.*

Referred to in D04-20, D04-30, D04-31, D04-38.

D04-5 (5, 92a)

Bell, E. T. Interpolated denumerants and Lambert series. Amer. J. Math. **65**, 382–386 (1943).

Let $D(n)=D(n|a_1, a_2, \cdots, a_r)$ be the number of sets $(x_1, \cdots, x_r)$ of nonnegative integers x such that $a_1x_1+\cdots+a_rx_r=n$. This numerical function was called by Sylvester the denumerant of n with respect to the positive integers $a_1, \cdots, a_r$. Sylvester and Cayley showed that $D(n)=A(n)+U(n)$, where $A(n)$ is a polynomial in n of degree $r-1$ and $U(n)$ is a periodic function of period a, the least common multiple of $a_1, \cdots, a_r$. This paper gives an elementary proof of the fact that, for any fixed b, $D(am+b)$ is a polynomial in m of degree $r-1$. Hence, if we compute once for all the values of $D(aj+b_j)$, $0\leqq b_j<a$; $j=1, \cdots, r$, and regard these as known constants, an explicit formula for $D(am+b)$ may be found by the straightforward application of Lagrange's interpolation formula. As an application the author considers the problem of expanding in powers of x the function $L(x)$ defined by the r-fold Lambert series

$$L(x)=\sum_{n=1}^{\infty}\frac{f(n)x^{ns}}{(1-x^{a_1n})\cdots(1-x^{a_rn})},$$

where $s=a_1+\cdots+a_r$. *D. H. Lehmer* (Berkeley, Calif.).

D04-6 (7, 148a)

Skolem, Th. Verallgemeinerungen der Betti-Guidiceschen Formel. Avh. Norske Vid. Akad. Oslo. I. **1940**, no. 1, 18 pp. (1940).

Let K be an algebraic number field, R its ring of integers. For elements $a_1, \cdots, a_n$ from R, define their g.c.d. as follows: let $\mathfrak{a}=(a_1, \cdots, a_n)$ and let h be the class number so that $\mathfrak{a}^h=(a)$, a principal ideal in R; then the g.c.d. of $a_1, \cdots, a_n$ is the algebraic integer $a^{1/h}$, which may not be in R. Let Kd designate the set of all products xd, where $x\varepsilon K$. Then the general solution of a system

$$\sum_{i=1}^{n}a_{ij}x_i=0, \qquad j=1, \cdots, m,$$

all a_{ij} in R, $m<n$, in numbers $x_i\varepsilon R$ can be written in the form

$$x_i=\sum\pm A_{i_1, \cdots, i_m}u_{i, i_1, \cdots, i_m}/d.$$

The sum is over $i_1, \cdots, i_m$ different from i, and $1\leqq i_1<\cdots<i_m\leqq n$; $A_{i_1, \cdots, i_m}$ designates the determinant formed from columns $i_1, \cdots, i_m$ of the matrix of coefficients of the system; d is the g.c.d. of these determinants; $u_{i, i_1, \cdots, i_m}$ are parameters whose values range over the algebraic integers belonging to the set Kd, and two parameters whose index numbers are the same except for order are identical. The sign is $+$ or $-$ according as the permutation

$$\begin{bmatrix}1, 2, \cdots, & n\\ i, i_1, \cdots, i_m, & \cdots\end{bmatrix}$$

is even or odd, the integers to the right of i_m in the lower row being in their natural order. This is the author's most general theorem for homogeneous systems. Nonhomogeneous systems are also discussed. *I. Niven.*

D04-7 (7, 365c)

Simmons, H. A. Note on use of matrices in solving linear Diophantine equations. Tôhoku Math. J. **48**, 71–74 (1941).

The Diophantine equation $\sum_{i=1}^{n}a_ix_i=k$ has been solved by a method of substitutions [cf. É. Cahen, Théorie des Nombres, vol. 1, Hermann, Paris, 1914, chaps. 9, 10] and by various methods employing continued fractions. The writer outlines the method of substitutions using matrix notation, so that "one can see at a glance the nature and number of non-singular linear transformations that one uses in solving a general equation." *I. Niven.*

D04-8 (8, 6d)

Griffiths, L. W. A note on linear homogeneous Diophantine equations. Bull. Amer. Math. Soc. **52**, 734–736 (1946).

The solution of the Diophantine system

(1) $$a_{i1}x_1+\cdots+a_{in}x_n=0, \qquad i=1, \cdots, m,$$

of rank r is well known if $r=m=n-1$ $(x_j=(-1)^jtE_j/e$, where t is an arbitrary integer, E_j is the jth minor of order $n-1$ and $e=(E_1, \cdots, E_j))$. The author proves that, if $r=m<n-1$, the complete solution can be obtained by applying this to the system formed by (1) and the equations $\xi_{i1}x_1+\cdots+\xi_{in}x_n=0$, $i=1, \cdots, n-m-1$, where the ξ_{ij} are arbitrary integer parameters. [Reviewer's note. A simpler proof of this result may be obtained by application of its analogue in the rational number field.] *N. G. de Bruijn.*

Referred to in D04-10.

D04-9 (8, 196a)

Veress, Paul. Graphische Lösung von Diophantischen Gleichungen. Mat. Fiz. Lapok **48**, 393–397 (1941). (Hungarian. German summary)

Es wird durch einfache elementargeometrische Überlegungen folgender bekannte Satz bewiesen. Ein Gitterparallelogramm hat dann und nur dann einen Flächeninhalt gleich 1, wenn auf dem Gitterparallelogramm (Begrenzung mit inbegriffen) ausser seinen Eckpunkten keine weiteren Gitterpunkte vorhanden sind. Aus diesem Satz werden die bekannten Sätze über die Diophantische Gleichung $ay-bx=1$ auf geometrischem Wege hergeleitet und eine graphische Methode zur Auffindung der Grundlösung von dieser Gleichung angegeben. *Author's summary.*

D04-10 (9, 78f)

Givens, Wallace. Parametric solution of linear homogeneous Diophantine equations. Bull. Amer. Math. Soc. **53**, 780–783 (1947).

The following stronger form of a result of L. W. Griffiths [Bull. Amer. Math. Soc. **52**, 734–736 (1946); these Rev. **8**, 6] is proved. The solutions of the Diophantine system $\sum_{i=1}^{n}a_{\alpha i}x_i=0$ $(\alpha=1, 2, \cdots, r)$ of rank r admit the representation $x_i=\Delta_i/a$ in terms of integer parameters $p_{\alpha i}$ $(\alpha=r+1, \cdots, n-1; i=1, \cdots, n)$; a is the g.c.d. of the r-rowed minors of the matrix $A=\|a_{\alpha i}\|$ and Δ_i is the ith $(n-1)$-rowed minor of the matrix $\|q_{\alpha i}\|$ $(q_{\alpha i}=a_{\alpha i}$ for $1\leqq\alpha\leqq r$, $q_{\alpha i}=p_{\alpha i}$ for $r<\alpha\leqq n-1)$. *N. G. de Bruijn* (Delft).

Citations: MR 8, 6d = D04-8.

D04-11 (9, 568j)

Aude, Herman T. R. The pattern for the distribution of the numbers c when the Diophantine equation $ax+by=c$ has exactly n solutions. Bull. École Polytech. Jassy [Bul. Politehn. Gh. Asachi. Iași] **2**, 10–18 (1947).

Let $f(c)$ denote the number of positive integral solutions of the equation indicated in the title, where a, b, c are positive integers with $(a, b)=1$. It is proved that $f(c+ab)=1+f(c)$, $f(c)=0$ for $1\leqq c\leqq a+b-1$, and $f(c)=1-f(ab+a+b-c)$ for $a+b\leqq c\leqq ab$. The proofs are based on the classical result that the least and greatest values of c for which $f(c)=n$ are $(n-1)ab+a+b$ and $(n+1)ab$, respectively. *I. Niven.*

D04-12 (10, 13a)

Pettineo, B. Sull'analisi indeterminata di primo grado. I. Matematiche, Catania **1**, 33–37 (1945).

Betti's formula for the integral solutions of (1) $c_1x_1+\cdots+c_mx_m=k$ has the defect of giving the same solution for an infinity of values of the parameters. The author gives a method of avoiding this defect. First it is proved that every integral solution of (1) for $k=0$ has the form

$$x_i=a_i-\alpha_i(c_1a_1+\cdots+c_ma_m),$$

$i=1, \cdots, m$, where $a_1, \cdots, a_m$ are arbitrary parameters and $\alpha_1, \cdots, \alpha_m$ is a given integral solution of (1) for $k=1$. Let h be the smallest index for which $\alpha_h>0$; if we take for a_h a member of a complete system of residues (mod α_h) then to every integral solution of (1) for $k=0$ there exists one and only one system $a_1, a_2, \cdots, a_{h-1}, a_{h+1}, \cdots, a_m$. If $k\neq 1$ in (1), $k\alpha_1, \cdots, k\alpha_m$ is a solution of (1) and hence all solutions of (1) may be found from

$$c_1(x_1-k\alpha_1)+\cdots+c_m(x_m-k\alpha_m)=0.$$

N. G. W. H. Beeger (Amsterdam).

D04-13 (10, 13b)

Pettineo, B. Sull'analisi indeterminata di primo grado. II. Matematiche, Catania **1**, 38–41 (1945).

The number a_h [see the preceding review] is now eliminated. The equation is (1) $c_1x_1+\cdots+c_mx_m=0$. Let δ_m be the greatest common divisor of $c_1, \cdots, c_{m-1}$ and $\gamma_i=c_i/\delta_m$, $i=1, \cdots, m-1$; (δ_m, c_m) being 1, $x_m=\delta_my_m$ and (1) becomes (2) $\gamma_1x_1+\cdots+\gamma_{m-1}x_{m-1}+c_my_m=0$. Let $\alpha_1, \cdots, \alpha_{m-1}$ be an integral solution of $\gamma_1x_1+\cdots+\gamma_{m-1}x_{m-1}=1-c_m$; then $\gamma_1\alpha_1+\cdots+\gamma_{m-1}\alpha_{m-1}+c_m\cdot 1=1$. Hence $\alpha_1, \cdots, \alpha_{m-1}, 1$ is a solution of (2) (with second member 1). For α_h of the preceding review we can therefore take 1 and we can infer a solution of (1) with $m-1$ parameters and $a_h=0$ by the method of the preceding review. *N. G. W. H. Beeger.*

D04-14 (12, 481i)

Thomas, J. M. The linear Diophantine equation in two unknowns. Math. Mag. **24**, 59–64 (1950).

The algorithm for solving $ax+by=c$ in integers x, y is discussed by means of second order determinants with special reference to minimizing x^2+y^2. When $c=1$ the author shows that the minimum solution comes from the penultimate convergent when a/b is developed in its shorter continued fraction. *D. H. Lehmer* (Berkeley, Calif.).

Referred to in D68-7, D68-15, D68-16.

D04-15 (12, 675a)

von Mises, Richard. Über "kleinste" Lösungen diophantischer Gleichungen. Math. Nachr. **4**, 97–105 (1951).

An integral solution $(x_1, \cdots, x_n)$ of the $m<n$ inhomogeneous equations $\sum_{\nu=1}^n a_{\mu\nu}x_\nu=b_\mu$ $(1\leqq\mu\leqq m)$ is a "smallest" solution if there is no distinct solution $(y_1, \cdots, y_n)$ for which $0\leqq y_\nu \operatorname{sgn} x_\nu\leqq|x_\nu|$ $(\nu=1, \cdots, n)$. Such solutions have an application in probability theory [cf. the author, Rev. Fac. Sci. Univ. Istanbul (N.S.) **4**, 145–163 (1939)]. It is almost intuitive that only a finite number of smallest solutions exist since the solutions form a $k\leqq n-m$ dimensional inhomogeneous lattice. Explicit bounds for the x_ν are given for $m=1, 2$ in terms of the $a_{\mu\nu}$, b_μ. *J. W. S. Cassels.*

D04-16 (14, 950c)

Kontorovič, P. G., and Mil'man, D. I. On a method of N. I. Lobačevskiĭ for finding integer solutions of linear homogeneous equations with integer coefficients. Uspehi Matem. Nauk (N.S.) **8**, no. 1(53), 145–149 (1953). (Russian)

The general integer solution of $a_1x_1+\cdots+a_nx_n=0$, where $a_1, \cdots, a_n$ are integers, as given in Skolem's Diophantische Gleichungen [Springer, Berlin, 1938] and ascribed to Betti (1862; cf. Skolem, op. cit., p. 4, 121) is to be found already in Lobačevskiĭ's course "Algebra" [Kazan Univ., 1834], although this point has not been made before. It is shown that his method also gives the most general solution of the independent equations $\sum_{i=1}^n a_{ji}x_i=0$ $(1\leqq j\leqq m<n)$ in the form

$$x_i=d^{-1}\sum(-1)^{i+\gamma}A_{\alpha_1,\alpha_2,\cdots,\alpha_{n-m-1},i}t_{\alpha_1,\cdots,\alpha_{n-m-1}}$$

where the t's are independent integer parameters, $A_{\alpha_1,\cdots,\alpha_{n-m}}$ is the determinant obtained by deleting columns $\alpha_1, \cdots, \alpha_{n-m}$ of the matrix of the equations, d is the greatest common divisor of the A's, and γ is the number of inversions in $\alpha_1, \cdots, \alpha_{n-m-1}, i$. *J. W. S. Cassels.*

D04-17 (14, 1063f)

Rivier, William. A propos de la résolution en nombres entiers de l'équation à coefficients entiers $rx+sy=m$. Bull. Sci. Math. (2) **77**, 51–55 (1953).

Let $r>0$, $s>0$, $k\geqq 0$ be fixed integers with $(r, s)=1$, and let I_k be the interval $(krs, krs+rs-1)$. For m in the interval I_k the equation $rx+sy=m$ has either k or $k+1$ solutions, there being exactly k solutions for $(r-1)(s-1)/2$ values of m in I_k. *I. Niven* (Eugene, Ore.).

D04-18 (15, 288e)

Duparc, H. J. A., and Peremans, W. On certain representations of positive integers. Nieuw Arch. Wiskunde (3) **1**, 92–98 (1953).

Let u and v be positive integers, with $(u, v)=1$. A non-negative integer n is said to be representable if $n=ux+vy$, where x and y are non-negative integers. Let Q^k denote the sum of the kth powers of the integers which are not representable. The authors derive a formula for Q^k in terms of Bernoulli numbers, and give a short proof of some known results. *N. J. Fine* (Princeton, N. J.).

D04-19 (15, 404a)

Rumney, Max. Equations in polynomials. Math. Gaz. **37**, 261–264 (1953).

The paper contains a brief discussion of some properties of polynomials in a single indeterminate with rational coefficients. In particular the solution of the equation $AU+BV=k$ by continued fractions is indicated; the case in which the coefficients are integral is also mentioned. As an application the following result is obtained. If U_1, V_1; $\cdots$; U_{n+1}, V_{n+1} denote solutions of $AU+BV=P$ and $H_i(u, v)$ are homogeneous polynomials, then one has, for the determinant of order $n+1$, $|H_i(U_j, V_j)|\equiv 0$ (mod $P^{\frac{1}{2}n(n+1)}$). *L. Carlitz* (Durham, N. C.).

D04-20 (15, 777a)

Brauer, Alfred, and Seelbinder, B. M. On a problem of partitions. II. Amer. J. Math. **76**, 343–346 (1954).

The linear Diophantine equation in k unknowns

$$a_1x_1+a_2x_2+\cdots+a_kx_k=n,$$

where the letters represent positive integers and the a's have no common factor, has a solution for n sufficiently large. This paper is a continuation of a previous one [Brauer, same J. **64**, 299–312 (1942); these Rev. **3**, 270; **5**, 328] in which bounds $F(a_1, \cdots, a_k)$ such that $n>F$ implies that the equation is solvable are discussed. One bound proposed is

$$T(a_1, \cdots, a_k)=\sum_{\nu=2}^{k}a_\nu d_{\nu-1}/d_\nu,$$

where d_ν is the greatest common divisor of the first ν a's. It was shown previously that in case the a's are such that

$$(1) \qquad a_\nu/d_\nu = \left(\sum_{\lambda=1}^{\nu-1} a_\lambda y_{\nu\lambda}\right) \Big/ d_{\nu-1},$$

where the y's are non-negative integers, then T is the best bound possible. In the present paper it is shown conversely that (1) is a necessary condition for T to be best possible. In case (1) does not hold, a better bound is given by $T-\min(a_1, a_2, \cdots, a_k)$. *D. H. Lehmer.*

Citations: MR 3, 270d = D04-4.
Referred to in D04-30.

D04-21 (15, 934e)

Salié, Hans. Zur Verteilung natürlicher Zahlen auf elementfremde Klassen. Ber. Verh. Sächs. Akad. Wiss. Leipzig. Math.-Nat. Kl. **101**, no. 4, 26 pp. (1954).

Let

$$(1) \qquad \sum_{v=1}^{n} a_{u,v} x_v = 0, \quad u=1, 2, \cdots, m, \quad n>m$$

be a system of homogeneous equations with rational coefficients. Rado calls (1) regular, if for any division of the integers into k classes (k arbitrary) (1) is solvable in at least one of the classes. He calls (1) precisely l-regular if this holds for any $k \leqq l$, but fails for $k=l+1$, i.e., if there exists a division of the integers into $l+1$ classes so that in none of the classes is (1) solvable.

Rado conjectured that there exists an l_n so that if (1) is l_n-regular, then it is regular. He proved that it will suffice to prove this conjecture for $m=1$. The author proves this conjecture in several special cases; he also conjectures that $l_n < cn \log n$. If (1) is l-regular, there exists an s_l such that, if one splits the integers $\leqq s_l$ into l classes, (1) is solvable in at least one of the classes. The author determines s_l in some special cases, e.g., he shows that, for $2(x+y)=3z$, $s_3=54$. [Reviewer's remark: This later result was also proved by E. Straus in an unpublished letter to the reviewer.] *P. Erdös.*

D04-22 (16, 335k)

Rivier, William. Sur les solutions entières et non négatives de l'équation $rx+sy=m$. Bull. Sci. Math. (2) **78**, 147–155 (1954).

Let $\omega(m)$ denote the number of non-negative integral solutions of $rx+sy=m$. The writer continus his study [same Bull. (2) **77**, 51–55 (1953); these Rev. **14**, 1063] of properties of $\omega(m)$, proving such theorems as the following. Let $k>0$, m_1 and m_2 be any non-negative integers satisfying $m_1+m_2=krs-r-s$; assume that the integers $r>0$, $s>0$ satisfy $(r, s)=1$, and that $m\geqq 0$. Then $\omega(m_1)+\omega(m_2)=k$. *I. Niven* (Eugene, Ore.).

Citations: MR 14, 1063g = D48-22.

D04-23 (17, 829c)

Chowla, S.; and Mientka, W. E. The number of lattice points in an n-dimensional tetrahedron. Proc. Amer. Math. Soc. **7** (1956), 51–53.

Let $a_1, \cdots, a_n$ and ξ be positive integers. By a simple analytic argument it is shown that the number of solutions in integers $x_i \geqq 0$ of $\sum a_i x_i = \xi \prod a_i$ and of $\sum a_i x_i \leqq \xi \prod a_i$ are polynomials in the a_i, ξ with rational coefficients. *J. W. S. Cassels* (Cambridge, England).

D04-24 (17, 948d)

Sudan, Gabriel. Interprétation géométrique d'une certaine équation en nombre entiers. Rev. Univ. "C. I. Parhon" Politehn. București. Ser. Ști. Nat. **4** (1955), no. 6–7, 23–30. (Romanian. Russian and French summaries)

If $b>a>0$, $(a, b)=1$, then the diophantine equation $ax-by=z$ has at least one, and at most two solutions in integers x, y, z, satisfying $|x|<\sqrt{b}$, $|y|<\sqrt{b}$, $0<|z|<\sqrt{b}$, $(x, y)=1$ (the solutions (x, y, z) and $(-x, -y, -z)$ are not considered distinct). This theorem of Zeitz [Jber. Deutsch. Math. Verein. **42**, Abt. 2, 72 (1932), 110 (1933)] is proven by a geometrical argument, using Minkowski's theorem on convex figures. Furthermore, it is shown that if there is only one solution, this is a convergent of a/b, while if there are two solutions, at least one is a convergent. *E. Grosswald* (Philadelphia, Pa.).

D04-25 (18, 285a)

Ignat'eva, R. P. Number of integral solutions of $x+2y+3z+4u+5v+6w=m$. Kabardinskiĭ Gos. Ped. Inst. Uč. Zap. **8** (1955), 53–59. (Russian)

D04-26 (18, 285b)

Ignat'eva, R. P. Number of integral solutions of the equations $x+2y+3z+4u=m$, $x+2y+3z+4u+5v=m$. Kabardinskiĭ Gos. Ped. Inst. Uč. Zap. **8** (1955), 45–52. (Russian)

D04-27 (18, 379c)

Levit, R. J. A minimum solution of a diophantine equation. Amer. Math. Monthly **63** (1956), 646–651.

It is traditional in treating the solution of the linear diophantine equation $ax+by=c$ to consider first the equation $a\xi+b\eta=1$. Once this is solved by a continued fraction algorithm, ξ and η are multiplied by c to give x, y. This often results in unnecessarily large values. The author proposes a variant of the traditional process in which a sequence of c's is obtained and which leads directly to minimum solutions of $ax+by=c$. In its "absolutely least" form the algorithm produces two sets of partial quotients (b_i, c_i) defined by $b_0=a$, $b_i=b$, $c_0=c$, $b_{i-1}=q_i b_i+b_{i+1}$, $c_{i-1}=g_i b_i+c_i$, where $|b_{i+1}|$ and $|c_i|$ do not exceed $\frac{1}{2}|b_i|$. The process terminates at $i=n$, where for the first time either $c_n=0$ or $c_n=\pm\frac{1}{2}b_n$. Following Gauss, a single sequence x_k now gives both $x=x_i$ and $y=x_0$. The recurrence is

$$x_{i-1}=g_i-q_i x_i+x_{i+1},$$

where intially $x_n=c_n$ and $x_{n+1}=-\operatorname{sgn} c_n[\frac{1}{2}b_{n+1}]$. Conditions on c for the existence of solutions (x, y) in which $|x|$ and $|y|$ both attain their least possible values are found. Such solutions when they exist are onbtaied by the algorithm. *D. H. Lehmer* (Berkeley, Calif.).

D04-28 (18, 561f)

Ballantine, J. P. Integral approximate solutions of systems of linear equations. Amer. Math. Monthly **63** (1956), 554–569.

The author considers the solution of several types of the equation $\sum_{j=1}^{n} a_{ij}x_j=b_i$ $(i=1, 2, \cdots, n)$. The equations to be solved are either exact, approximate, integral, least square or combinations of these. The author describes an approximate solution where the unknowns have integral value, i.e., type (ia) and similarly a type (lia). The latter signifies a type (ia) solution that is compared with other (ia) solutions and has the sum of the squares of its deviation a minimum. In order to obtain a type (lia) solution, recourse is made to the quadratic form approach proposed originally by Minkowski. Applying the aforementioned method, the author deftly suggests and demonstrates the utility of this approach. The procedure is unique in that a computer can initiate and continue with the solution of the above mentioned types by following the procedure as outlined in the sample examples. It is not necessary for him to understand the necessary mathematical proofs. *H. Saunders* (Philadelphia, Pa.).

D04-29 **(19, 730e)**

Ginatempo, Nicola. Su un teorema di Betti. Boll. Un. Mat. Ital. (3) 12 (1957), 312–315.

The general solution of the linear diophantine equation in n variables had already been stated by Betti in terms of parameters involving a skew-symmetric matrix. The author finds the same result by the method of induction [see Barnett and Mendel, Amer. Math. Monthly **49** (1942), 157–170, p. 158; MR 3, 268]. *I. A. Barnett.*

Citations: MR 3, 268g = D08-2.

D04-30 **(19, 1038d)**

Roberts, J. B. Note on linear forms. Proc. Amer. Math. Soc. 7 (1956), 465–469.

Frobenius proposed the problem of finding bounds $G(a_0, a_1, \cdots, a_s)$ such that the Diophantine equation $a_0x_0+a_1x_1+\cdots+a_sx_s=N$ has solutions in non-negative integers $x_0, x_1, \cdots, x_s$ for every $N\geqq G(a_0, a_1, \cdots, a_s)$. Such bounds were obtained by A. Brauer [Amer. J. Math. **64** (1943), 299–312; MR 3, 270] and by A. Brauer and B. Seelbinder [ibid. **76** (1954), 343–346; MR 15, 777]. In particular, in the first of these papers, the best possible bound was found for the special case that the a_ν are consecutive integers. The author generalizes this result for the case that the a_ν are in arithmetic progression. He proves that every integer $N_0\geqq N=\{[(a_0-2)/s]+1\}a_0+(d-1)(a_0-1)$ can be represented by $F=a_0x_0+(a_0+d)x_1+\cdots+(a_0+sd)x_s$ with non-negative x_ν if $(a_0, d)=1$, while $N-1$ cannot be represented. {The proof of the author can be simplified considerably. Let g be the greatest integer for which (*) $(a_0+sd)(g-d)<ga_0-d=K$. Then $K\equiv ga_0 \pmod d$. Assume that K could be represented by F with $x_0+x_1+\cdots+x_s=m$. Then $K\equiv ma_0 \pmod d$.] Hence $m\equiv g \pmod d$ since $(a_0, d)=1$. Since $(a_0+sd)(g-d)$ is the greatest number represented by F with $m=g-d$, and ga_0 is the smallest number represented with $m=g$, it follows from (*) that K is not represented, while all numbers greater than K and congruent to $K \pmod d$ are represented by F. From (*), we obtain $g<(a_0-1)/s+d$; hence $g=[(a_0-2)/s]+d$ and $K=a_0[(a_0-2)/s]+d(a_0-1)$. Now, let L be an integer greater than K. We determine h such that $L\equiv ha_0 \pmod d$ and $(h-d)a_0\leqq L<ha_0$; hence $L\leqq ha_0-d$. If $h>g$, then $(a_0+sd)(h-d)\geqq ha_0-d$, and all numbers congruent to L and greater than K are represented by F. Assume now that $h<g$. Then $L\leqq ha_0-d<ga_0-d=K$. This is impossible. Therefore all numbers greater than K can be represented by F.} *A. Brauer.*

Citations: MR 3, 270d = D04-4; MR 15, 777a = D04-20.

Referred to in D04-38, D04-39.

D04-31 **(19, 1038e)**

Roberts, J. B. On a Diophantine problem. Canad. J. Math. 9 (1957), 219–222.

It is proved that the Diophantine equation $mx_1+(m+a)x_2+(m+b)x_3=N$ always has solutions in non-negative integers x_1, x_2, x_3 if

$$N\geqq m(b-2+[m/b])+(a-1)(b-1).$$

This bound for N is in some cases less and in others greater than the bound obtained by A. Brauer [Amer. J. Math. **64** (1942), 299–312; MR 3, 270; **5**, 328; see also the preceding review]. *A. Brauer.*

Citations: MR 3, 270d = D04-4.

Referred to in D04-39.

D04-32 **(20# 834)**

Egerváry, E. Auflösung eines homogenen linearen diophantischen Gleichungssystems mit Hilfe von Projektormatrizen. Publ. Math. Debrecen 4 (1956), 481–483.

Let small Roman letters represent n-partite vectors whose components are rational integers, and let, further, $a\cdot x$ stand for the inner product $a_1x_1+a_2x_2+\cdots+a_nx_n$. The greatest common divisor of the n integers $a_1, a_2, \cdots, a_n$ is denoted by $\Delta(a)$. It was shown by Giundice [Giorn. Mat. Battaglini (2) **5**(**36**) (1898), 225–232] that the general solution x of the equation $a\cdot x=0$ can be expressed in terms of a and $n-1$ integral parameters. A simpler expression for x was given by Barnett and Mendel [Amer. Math. Monthly **49** (1942), 157–170; MR 3, 268]. A system of m linear homogeneous equations $a^{(i)}\cdot x=0$, $i=1, 2, 3, \cdots, m$, $m<n$, $\Delta(a^{(i)})=1$, was completely solved by Heger [Denkschr. Akad. Wiss. Wien. Math.-Nat. Cl. **14** (1858), Abt. 2, 1–122], who proved that the general solution x can be expressed in terms of $a^{(i)}$ and $n-m$ integral parameters, if the equations are linearly independent. The author gives a short proof of this theorem and a simple expression for the general solution. When $m=1$, this solution is the same as that of Barnett and Mendel. The author makes use of a method more thoroughly dealt with in his paper: "Rank-diminishing operations and the solution of linear equations by finite iteration" (to be published in Acta Sci. Math. Szeged). *W. Ljunggren* (Bergen)

Citations: MR 3, 268g = D08-2.

D04-33 **(20# 839)**

Ignat'eva, R. P. The number of non-negative integral solutions of the equations $x+2y+3z+4u=m$, $x+2y+3z+4u+5v=m$ (a new method of solution). Kabardin. Gos. Ped. Inst. Uč. Zap. 8 (1955), 45–52. (Russian)

D04-34 **(20# 840)**

Ignat'eva, R. P. The number of non-negative integral solutions of the equation $x+2y+3z+4u+5v+6w=m$. Kabardin. Gos. Ped. Inst. Uč. Zap. 8 (1955), 53–59. (Russian)

D04-35 **(20# 3816)**

Nilov, G. N. The number of non-negative integer solutions of the equation $\sum_{k=1}^{n-1} x_k+p\cdot x_n=m$. Kabardin. Gos. Ped. Inst. Uč. Zap. 12 (1957), 21–23. (Russian)

D04-36 **(20# 3817)**

Tkačev, M. I. The number of non-negative integer solutions of the equation $\sum_{i=1}^{7} i\cdot x_i=m$. Kabardin. Gos. Ped. Inst. Uč. Zap. 12 (1957), 75–82. (Russian)

D04-37 **(20# 3819)**

Tkačev, M. I. The generating function $p_n(m)$. (Method and formulas for $n=8, 9$). Kabardin. Gos. Ped. Inst. Uč. Zap. 12 (1957), 86–98. (Russian)

The function $p_n(m)$ is defined as the number of solutions in natural numbers x_i of the Diophantine equation $x_1+2x_2+3x_3+\cdots+nx_n=m$.

An inductive method is presented for calculating $p_{n+1}(m)$ from $p_n(m)$, and finite, closed (rather lengthy) formulas are obtained, for the first time, for $n=8, 9$.

D04-38 **(21# 25)**

Bateman, P. T. Remark on a recent note on linear forms. Amer. Math. Monthly 65 (1958), 517–518.

Generalizing a result of A. Brauer for the case $d=1$ [Amer. J. Math. **64** (1942), 299–312; MR 3, 270], J. B. Roberts [Proc. Amer. Math. Soc. **7** (1956), 465–469; MR **19**, 1038] determined the largest integer N for which the Diophantine equation

$$N = ax_0+(a+d)x_1+\cdots+(a+sd)x_s$$

has no solution in non-negative integers. The author gives a simpler proof for this result. (See also the review of Roberts' paper.) *A. Brauer* (Chapel Hill, N.C.)

Citations: MR 3, 270d = D04-4; MR 19, 1038d = D04-30.

D04-39 **(22# 12074)**

Johnson, S. M. A linear diophantine problem. Canad. J. Math. **12** (1960), 390–398.

Let $a_1, a_2, \cdots, a_k$ be positive relatively prime integers. Several authors [see, for instance, J. B. Roberts, Proc. Amer. Math. Soc. **7** (1956), 465–469; Canad. J. Math. **9** (1957), 219–222; MR **19**, 1038] obtained bounds $F(a_1, a_2, \cdots, a_k)$ such that the equation $a_1x_1+a_2x_2+\cdots+a_kx_k=n$ has solutions in positive integers $x_1, x_2, \cdots, x_k$ for every integer $n>F(a_1, a_2, \cdots, a_k)$. For $k=2$ the best bound is $a_1 \cdot a_2$. The author studies the case $k=3$. He reduces the problem to the case that a_1, a_2, a_3 are relatively prime in pairs. He develops a method to compute the best possible bound $F(a_1, a_2, a_3)$. He states without a proof that some of his results hold for the case $k>3$. *A. Brauer* (Chapel Hill, N.C.)

Citations: MR 19, 1038d = D04-30; MR 19, 1038e = D04-31.

D04-40 **(23# A89)**

Weinstock, Robert

Greatest common divisor of several integers and an associated linear diophantine equation.

Amer. Math. Monthly **67** (1960), 664–667.

The author gives a numerical method for computing the g.c.d. $d=(a_1, \cdots, a_n)$ of several integers and for finding a solution of the Diophantine equation $a_1x_1+\cdots+a_nx_n=N$. *O. Ore* (New Haven, Conn.)

Referred to in D04-63.

D04-41 **(23# A1621)**

Jeger, M.

Ein Partitionsproblem und seine funktionentheoretische Lösung.

Elem. Math. **13** (1958), 97–104.

The author poses the problem of the number of solutions, A_n, of the Diophantine equation

$$\mu_1+2\mu_2+5\mu_3+10\mu_4+20\mu_5+50\mu_6 = n$$

in non-negative integers μ_i. Considering a generating series and applying the Cauchy residue theorem, the author obtains the formula

$$A_n = \sum_{k=0}^{[n/10]} B_k B_{n-10k},$$

where $B_n=[2n^2+16n+27+5(-1)^n+8\Omega(n)]/40$; $\Omega(n)=0$ if $n\equiv 1 \pmod 5$, 1 if n is congruent to 0 or 2 (mod 5), and -1 otherwise. *B. V. Levin* (RŽMat **1959** #5485)

D04-42 **(24# A1874)**

Avanesov, E. T.

Équations diophantiques linéaires contenant 3 et 4 inconnues. (Romanian. Russian and French summaries)

Gaz. Mat. Fiz. Ser. A **13 (66)** (1961), 360–367.

Author's summary: "Dans cette note on considère une équation diophantique linéaire indéterminée avec n inconnues ($n=3$, 4) pour laquelle on trouve, par une sommation, les formules effectives du nombre des solutions entières non-négatives."

D04-43 **(26# 2386)**

Nagata, Masayoshi; Matsumura, Hideyuki

A theorem in elementary arithmetic. (Japanese)

Sûgaku **13** (1961/62), 161.

Theorem: Let $a_1, a_2, \cdots, a_n$ be integers such that $1\leq a_1<a_2<\cdots<a_n\leqq 2n-1$. Then the additive semi-group generated by $a_1, a_2, \cdots, a_n$ contains all integers $\geqq 2n$. A corollary of this theorem has to do with the gaps of a point on a closed Riemann surface.

K. Nomizu (Providence, R.I.)

D04-44 **(26# 6113)**

Brauer, Alfred; Shockley, James E.

On a problem of Frobenius.

J. Reine Angew. Math. **211** (1962), 215–220.

Theorems on the problem of finding the largest positive integer not representable in the form $x_1a_1+x_2a_2+\cdots+x_ka_k$, where $a_1, a_2, \cdots, a_k$ are given relatively prime positive integers and $x_1, x_2, \cdots, x_k$ positive integers.

B. Stolt (Stockholm)

Referred to in D04-71.

D04-45 **(27# 3596a; 27# 3596b)**

Ehrhart, Eugène

Sur le nombre de solutions non négatives d'une équation diophantienne linéaire.

C. R. Acad. Sci. Paris **256** (1963), 4566–4569.

Ehrhart, Eugène

Sur le nombre de solutions non négatives d'une équation diophantienne linéaire à k inconnues.

C. R. Acad. Sci. Paris **256** (1963), 4801–4803.

Let $k\geqq 2$ and $a_1, \cdots, a_k, n$ be positive integers; let C_n be the number of solutions in non-negative integers $x_1, \cdots, x_k$ of the equation $a_1x_1+\cdots+a_kx_k=n$. The author gives an explicit formula for C_n as the sum of a polynomial in n and a term periodic in n; to keep his formula tidy, he restricts himself to the case where the a's are coprime by pairs, though his method works as well without this condition. The reviewer was surprised to hear that the result was new; the method is very simple and may be regarded as a degenerate case of the circle method. The first paper contains a treatment of the cases $k=2$, 3.

B. J. Birch (Manchester)

Referred to in P28-62.

D04-46 **(28# 1161)**

Motzkin, T. S.

Rational points on linear subspaces. Representation of an integer as a sum of squares with accessory conditions.

Canad. J. Math. **15** (1963), 206–213.

An exposition of some simple properties of rational points in planes. *A. C. Woods* (Columbus, Ohio)

D04-47 **(29# 2208)**

Avanesov, E.

Elementary solution of an arithmetic problem. (Bulgarian)

Fiz.-Mat. Spis. Bŭlgar. Akad. Nauk. **6 (39)** (1963), 206–208.

Let n be a positive integer, and let $f(n)$ $[F(n)]$ be the number of solutions in non-negative integers of the equation $x+2y+5z=n$ $[x+2y+5z+10(u+2v+5t)=n]$. Then $f(n)=1+[20^{-1}n(n+8)]$, and $F(n)=\sum f(i)f(n-10i)$, i running from 0 to $[n/10]$. An obvious application is the determination of the number of ways in which a given integral dollar sum can be made up by using one-, two-, five-, ten-, twenty-, and fifty-dollar bills.

F. Haimo (Belmont, Mass.)

D04-48 **(29# 5778)**

Ehrhart, Eugène

Sur un problème de partition d'un nombre.

C. R. Acad. Sci. Paris **259** (1964), 2746–2747.

Let $a_1=2, \cdots, a_{16}=53$ be the first 16 primes, and write C_n for the number of solutions of the equation $\sum_{i=1}^{16} a_iX_i=0$ in integers $X_i \geqq 0$. There is a polynomial $P(n)$ of degree 15 such that C_n is the nearest integer to $P(n)$. *B. J. Birch* (Manchester)

Referred to in D04-49.

D04-49 **(30# 3860)**

Ehrhart, Eugène

Sur un problème de partition d'un nombre.

C. R. Acad. Sci. Paris **260** (1965), 3237.

Correction of a paper with the same title [same C. R. **259** (1964), 2746–2747; MR **29** #5778].

Citations: MR 29# 5778 = D04-48.

D04-50 **(29# 5779)**

Ehrhart, Eugène

Sur la partition des nombres.

C. R. Acad. Sci. Paris **259** (1964), 3151–3153.

Author's summary: "The functions C_n, C_n' which count, respectively, the non-negative and the positive solutions of the diophantine equation $\sum_{i=1}^{k} a_iX_i=n$ are related by $C_n'=(-1)^{k-1}C_{-n}$. Application: If the a's are coprime by pairs, then $C_n=P(n)+\psi(n)$, where $\psi(n)$ is periodic; $P(n)$ can now be given a relatively concise form."

{The reviewer presumes that the a's are positive integers and that, for $-n<0$, C_{-n} is defined to be $P(-n)+\psi(-n)$; owing to the lack of a definition for C_{-n}, the proof appears incomplete, though the results are essentially correct.}

B. J. Birch (Manchester)

D04-51 **(30# 4689)**

Heap, B. R.; Lynn, M. S.

A graph-theoretic algorithm for the solution of a linear Diophantine problem of Frobenius.

Numer. Math. **6** (1964), 346–354.

A suitable directed graph (and a corresponding matrix A) is defined which enables one to compute the solution to the following number-theoretic problem. Let $p(1), p(2), \cdots, p(k)$ be a set of positive integers whose greatest common divisor is 1, and let g be the largest integer not expressible in the form $\sum a(i)p(i)$, where each $a(i)$ is a non-negative integer. The problem is to compute g. The number g is easily obtained when it is known which is the smallest power of A whose entries are all non-zero. Since one is only concerned with Boolean powers of A, the computation by machine is quite rapid.

N. S. Mendelsohn (Winnipeg, Man.)

D04-52 **(31# 1227)**

Heap, B. R.; Lynn, M. S.

On a linear Diophantine problem of Frobenius: An improved algorithm.

Numer. Math. **7** (1965), 226–231.

If A is a matrix whose entries are non-negative, its index of primitivity $\gamma(A)$ is the smallest power of A which has no zero entries. $\gamma(A)$ is easily computed using only Boolean arithmetic. The index of primitivity is useful in solving the following Diophantine equation. Let $1<p_1<p_2<\cdots<p_k$ be a set of relatively prime integers, and let $g[p_1, p_2, \cdots, p_k]$ be the largest integer not representable in the form $\sum_{s=1}^{k} a_sp_s$, where the a_s are non-negative integers. The computation of $g[p_1, p_2, \cdots, p_k]$ is reduced to the computation of the index of primitivity of a suitable matrix B. In this paper the authors show that B can always be taken as a matrix of order p_k.

N. S. Mendelsohn (Winnipeg, Man.)

D04-53 **(31# 5832)**

Avanesov, E. T.

A generalization of the method of V. P. Ermakov. (Romanian. French and Russian summaries)

Gaz. Mat. Ser. A **69** (1964), 26–29.

Author's summary: "En généralisant cette méthode, on obtient une formule pour le nombre des solutions entières non-négatives d'une équation diophantienne linéaire à coëfficients donnés."

D04-54 **(32# 5579)**

Kelisky, R. P.

Concerning the Euclidean algorithm.

Fibonacci Quart. **3** (1965), 219–223.

The author shows that if a and b are coprime integers, $a>b>1$, the solution of the Diophantine equation $ax+by=1$ obtained by the Euclidean algorithm is the lattice point on the line $ax+by=1$ which is nearest the origin. *T. M. Apostol* (Pasadena, Calif.)

Referred to in A06-28.

D04-55 **(33# 130)**

Cheema, M. S.

Integral solutions of a system of linear equations.

Amer. Math. Monthly **73** (1966), 487–490.

The author presents an elementary elimination method for solving the system of equations (*) $\sum_{j=1}^{n} a_{ij}x_j=b_i$ $(i=1, 2, \cdots, m)$ in integers, and gives some numerical examples to illustrate his method. A system of linear inequalities of type (*) may be solved by the same method by introducing slack variables to convert the inequalities to equations. The author also shows how information about the primal problem can be made to give information about the dual problem. *R. Finkelstein* (Tucson, Ariz.)

D04-56 **(33# 2658)**

Jambunathan, M. V.

Solution of indeterminate equations of the first degree in positive integers by the vector method.

J. Karnatak Univ. Sci. **9–10** (1964/65), 236–239.

Exposé d'une technique d'orthogonalisation pour résoudre des systèmes linéaires en nombres entiers.

N. Gastinel (Grenoble)

D04-57 **(33# 3990)**

Price, H. E.

Solution of the diophantine equation $ax+by=c$.

Math. Gaz. **50** (1966), 144–147.

According to A. O. Gel'fond [*The solution of equations in integers*, Noordhoff, Groningen, 1960; MR **21** #5607; Russian original, GITTL, Moscow, 1952; MR **13**, 913; second edition, 1957; MR **20** #6387], the solutions (x, y) of $ax+by=c$ are given by $x=x_0-bn$, $y=y_0+an$, where (x_0, y_0) is any solution and $n=0, \pm 1, \pm 2, \cdots$. The author gives an algorithm for constructing the solution for fixed a and all pairs (b, c).

A. A. Armendáriz (Ann Arbor, Mich.)

Citations: MR 13, 913c = D02-2; MR 20# 6387 = D02-4; MR 21# 5607 = D02-5.

D04-58 (33# 3997)

Avanesov, È. T.

Estimate for the number of solutions of a linear diophantine equation. (Russian)

Ivanov. Gos. Ped. Inst. Učen. Zap. **34** (1963), *vyp. mat.*, 3–7.

The author gives explicit (non-recurrent) formulae for the number of solutions in positive integers of the equation $\sum_1^n a_jx_j = M$, for $n = 4, 5, 6$, where M and a_j $(j = 1, 2, \cdots, n)$ are positive integers. He also gives an estimate for the number of such solutions for an arbitrary n and a large M.

G. Biriuk (Ann Arbor, Mich.)

D04-59 (33# 3998)

Avanesov, È. T.

A problem of decomposition of numbers. (Russian)

Ivanov. Gos. Ped. Inst. Učen. Zap. **34** (1963), *vyp. mat.*, 8–14.

The author gives an elementary method for solving the equation $x + 2y + 5z + 10u + 20v + 50t = n$, n a positive integer, in positive integers. A generalization of this method is given for other linear Diophantine equations.

G. Biriuk (Ann Arbor, Mich.)

D04-60 (34# 126)

Dumitriu, Anton

Congruences du premier degré.

Rev. Roumaine Math. Pures Appl. **10** (1965), 1201–1234.

Author's summary: "L'auteur donne des méthodes nouvelles pour résoudre l'équation diophantienne $ax + by = c$ et les congruences du premier degré. Il démontre d'abord la loi de réciprocité des restes des puissances $a^{\phi(b)-1}$ et $b^{\phi(a)-1}$ et trouve l'égalité fondamentale: $aR_b + bR_a = ab + 1$, où $b^{\phi(a)-1} \equiv R_a \pmod a$ et $a^{\phi(b)-1} \equiv R_b \pmod b$. L'auteur fait ensuite la théorie des restes des puissances et démontre plusieurs propriétés dont: $p^{q-1} + q^{p-1} \equiv 1 \pmod{pq}$ et $(\frac{1}{2}(p-1))^{p-2} \equiv p - 2 \pmod p$, $p > 2$.

"Cet article est l'introduction de notre livre en manuscrit *La théorie des congruences.*"

J. W. S. Cassels (Cambridge, England)

D04-61 (34# 5792)

Hofmeister, Gerd Rolf

Zu einem Problem von Frobenius.

Norske Vid. Selsk. Skr. (Trondheim) **1966**, *no.* 5, 37 *pp.*

Let $a_1, \cdots, a_k$ be relatively prime positive integers. Then for every sufficiently large integer n there exist non-negative integers $x_1, \cdots, x_k$ such that $n = a_1x_1 + \cdots + a_kx_k$. One puts $g(a_1, \cdots, a_k)$ for the largest n not so representable. The problem of Frobenius is to determine this quantity.

If $c_1, \cdots, c_k$ satisfy (1) $c_1 = 0$, $c_2 = 1 < c_3 < \cdots < c_k$, then defining $e_k^{(n)}, e_{k-1}^{(n)}, \cdots, e_2^{(n)}$ by $0 \leqq n - \sum_{i=j}^k e_i^{(n)}c_i < c_j$ $(2 \leqq j \leqq k)$, one sees that (2) $n = \sum_{i=2}^n e_i^{(n)}c_i$, and this is called the Euclidean representation of n relative to the c_i. If (3) $a_{i+1} = \gamma_ia_i - \sum_{k=1}^{i-1} \beta_k^{(i)}a_k$ $(2 \leqq i \leqq k-1)$, and $\sum_{i=0}^{h-1} \sum_{j=h}^N \beta_{m+i}^{(m+j)} \leqq 1$ $(2 \leqq m < m + N \leqq k - 1,\ 1 \leqq h \leqq N)$, where all $\gamma_i \geqq 2$ and all $\beta_k^{(i)} \geqq 0$, then $c_1, \cdots, c_k$ satisfying (1) may be defined by (4) $c_1 = 0$, $c_2 = 1$, $c_{i+1} = \gamma_ic_i - \sum_{k=1}^{i-1} \beta_k^{(i)}c_k$ $(2 \leqq i \leqq k-1)$. Thus, each set of positive relatively prime integers $a_1, \cdots, a_k$ satisfying (3) leads, via (4), to a Euclidean representation (2) for each non-negative integer n.

The main theorem of the paper is as follows: If $a_1, \cdots, a_k$ are relatively prime positive integers satisfying (3), and L is a complete system of residues modulo a_1, then $g(a_1, \cdots, a_k) = \min \max \sum_{i=2}^k e_i^{(n)}a_i - a_1$, where the min is taken over $l \in L$ and the max over $n \equiv la_2^{-1} \pmod{a_1}$.

From this theorem the author deduces many interesting results, among which are many previously obtained in quite different ways by other workers. One previously known result deduced is the following: If $d \geqq 1$, $(a_1, d) = 1$, then $g(a_1, a_1 + d, \cdots, a_1 + (k-1)d) = [(a_1 - 2)/(k-1)]a_1 + (a_1 - 1)d$. We confine ourselves to stating but a single further example here. Let $a_3 = \gamma a_2 - \beta a_1$, where γ is the smallest integer $\geqq 2$ for which such an equality is possible. Then

$$g(a_1, a_2, a_3) \leqq [(a_1 - 1)/\gamma]a_3 - a_2 - a_1 + \max\{\beta a_1, a_2(a_1 - [(a_1 - 1)/\gamma]\gamma)\},$$

and the equality holds when a_2 is greater than or equal to the product of β and the smallest integer greater than or equal to a_1/γ.

Finally, in an appendix, it is proved that the largest n for which all integers $0, \cdots, n$ may be written $n = \sum_{i=2}^k x_ic_i$ with $\sum_{i=2}^k x_i \leqq h$ (the c_i as in (1)) is unchanged if one adds the additional restriction that the representations be Euclidean.

J. B. Roberts (Dar es Salaam)

D04-62 (35# 146)

Rudert, W. S.; Lill, H. G.

Über Partitionen und ein lineares diophantisches Problem.

Numer. Math. **8** (1966), 407–411.

A problem of considerable interest in number theory is the following: Let $d_1, d_2, \cdots, d_k$ be a set of positive integers and let $f(d_1, d_2, d_3, \cdots, d_k)$ be the largest integer which cannot be expressed in the form $c_1d_1 + c_2d_2 + \cdots + c_kd_k$, where $c_1, c_2, \cdots, c_k$ are non-negative integers; what can be said about $f(d_1, d_2, \cdots, d_k)$? The authors use generating functions of the partition function to obtain some information about f. In particular, the results are applicable to the case where $d_1, d_2, \cdots, d_k$ are a block of consecutive integers.

N. S. Mendelsohn (Winnipeg, Man.)

D04-63 (36# 2552)

Bond, James

Calculating the general solution of a linear Diophantine equation.

Amer. Math. Monthly **74** (1967), 955–957.

R. Weinstock gave a numerical method for computing the g.c.d. $d = (a_1, a_2, \cdots, a_n)$ of several integers and for finding a solution of the Diophantine equation $a_1x_1 + \cdots + a_nx_n = N$ [Amer. Math. Monthly **67** (1960), 664–667; MR **23** #A89]. He concluded his paper with the remark that his algorithm gives only particular solutions of the equation (*) $a_1x_1 + \cdots + a_nx_n = d$.

The present author obtains a general solution of the equation (*) by applying Weinstock's algorithm $n - 1$ times.

L. M. Chawla (Lahore)

Citations: MR 23# A89 = D04-40.

D04-64 (37# 2421)

Newman, Morris

Solving equations exactly.

J. Res. Nat. Bur. Standards Sect. B **71B** (1967), 171–179.

Author's summary: "A congruential method for finding the exact solution of a system of linear equations with integral coefficients is described, and complete details of the program are given. Typical numerical results obtained with an existing program are given as well."

D04-65 (37# 6241)

Avanesov, È. T.

On the question of a certain theorem of Skolem. (Russian. Armenian and English summaries)

Izv. Akad. Nauk Armjan. SSR Ser. Mat. **3** (1968), no. 2, 160–165.

In a well-known work [Eighth Scand. Math. Congr. (Stockholm, 1934) (Swedish), pp. 163–188, Ohlssons Boktryckeri, Lund, 1935] T. A. Skolem proved the following theorem: Let

$$F_j(x_1, x_2, \cdots, x_k) = \sum_{i=0}^{\infty} p^i f_{i,j}(x_1, x_2, \cdots, x_k),$$

where p is an odd prime and all the $f_{i,j}$ are polynomials in $x_1, x_2, \cdots, x_k$ with integral coefficients. If for each t ($t=1, 2, \cdots, k$) there exists a polynomial with integral coefficients $h_{j,t}(x_1, x_2, \cdots, x_k)$ such that the function congruence $\sum_{j=1}^{k} f_{0,j}(x_1, x_2, \cdots, x_k)h_{j,t}(x_1, x_2, \cdots, x_k) \equiv h_t(x_t) \pmod p$ holds, where h_t depends only on x_t and not all coefficients of $h_{j,t}(x_1, x_2, \cdots, x_k)$ are congruent to 0 modulo p, then the system of equations $F_j=0$, $j=1, 2, \cdots, k$, has only a finite number of integral (and, in fact, p-adic integral) solutions.

Further, Skolem conjectured on the possibility of determining an exact upper bound for the number of such solutions.

In the present paper the author establishes Skolem's conjecture for systems of linear forms in local fields with nonvanishing determinant and proves that such systems have at most one p-adic integral solution. In addition, he uses his results to find the exact number of representations of unity by certain classes of semireal binary quartic forms. *R. Finkelstein* (Bowling Green, Ohio)

Referred to in D24-85.

D04-66 (38# 2077)

Onari, Setsuo

On Diophantine equation of 1st degree.

Hitotsubashi J. Arts Sci. **9** (1968), 44–49.

Verfasser untersucht mit elementaren Methoden Mengen $S(a_1, \cdots, a_n)$ von natürlichen Zahlen, welche so definiert sind: a_j, x_j seien natürliche Zahlen ($j=1, \cdots, n$); es sei g.g.T. $(a_1, \cdots, a_n)=1$. $S(a_1, \cdots, a_n)=\{\sum_{j=1}^{n} a_jx_j\}$. Als Beispiel sei das folgende Ergebnis genannt. Setzt man $a_j^{(0)}=a_j$, $d_r=(a_{r+1}^{(r-1)}, \cdots, a_n^{(r-1)})$, $a_j^{(r-1)}=d_r a_j^{(r)}$, $r+1\leqq j\leqq n$, $r=1, \cdots, n-1$; dann enthält $S(a_1, \cdots, a_n)$ alle natürlichen Zahlen $>\sum_{j=1}^{n-1} a_jd_j$. *H. J. Kanold* (Braunschweig)

D04-67 (41# 141)

Zeĭnalov, B. A.

A criterion for the solvability of an arbitrary system of linear equations in integers. (Russian)

Dagestan. Gos. Univ. Učen. Zap. **5** (1959), 159–165 (1960).

D04-68 (42# 221)

Mendelsohn, N. S.

A linear diophantine equation with applications to non-negative matrices.

International Conference on Combinatorial Mathematics (1970).

Ann. New York Acad. Sci. **175** (1970), 287–294.

The paper deals with a discussion of applications involving the function $F(a_1, a_2, \cdots, a_n)$. This function is defined as the largest positive integer which cannot be expressed in the form $c_1a_1+c_2a_2+\cdots+c_na_n$, where $c_i\geqq 0$, $i=1, 2, \cdots, n$, and $a_1, a_2, \cdots, a_n$ are positive integers. A simple proof of the fact that $F(a_1, a_2)=a_1a_2-a_1-a_2$ is not expressible as a linear combination of a_1 and a_2 is given. Page 292 line 9 should read $N>k+F(a_1, a_2, \cdots, a_t)$. *Diane Johnson* (Winnipeg, Man.)

D04-69 (43# 2840)

Sarčimelija, R. A.

A method of solving systems of linear algebraic equations by means of integral representation of the unknowns. (Russian. Georgian summary)

Thbilis. Sahelmç. Univ. Gamoqeneb. Math. Inst. Šrom. **1** (1969), 17–24.

The author considers the problem of solving systems of linear algebraic equations with integral coefficients and right-hand sides. Consider such a problem of the form $\sum_{j=1}^{m} a_{ij}x_j=b_i$, $i=1, \cdots, m$. A method of transforming any integral system to this form was given in an earlier paper of the author [Èkon. i Mat. Metody **1** (1965), no. 5, 760–771]. In the following, $\bar a=1$ if a is odd, and $\bar a=0$ if a is even. Let b_i^k be defined by the iterative process $b_i^{k+1}=\frac{1}{2}(b_i^k-\sum_{j=1}^{m} a_{ij}\bar b_j^k)$, $b_i^0=b_i$, $i=1, \cdots, m$. It is clear that the b_i^k are integers for all i and k. Theorem: There exist indices l and r such that $b_i^{l+r}=b_i^l-\sum_{j=1}^{m} a_{ij}(\overline{b_j^{l+r}-b_j^l})$, $i=1, \cdots, m$, and the solution x of the system $Ax=b$ is then given by

$$x_j = \sum_{k=0}^{l-1} 2^k\bar b_j^k+(1-2^r)^{-1}\left(\sum_{k=0}^{r-1} 2^{l+k}\bar b_j^{l+k}-2^{l+r}\overline{(b_j^{l+r}-b_j^l)}\right).$$

Corollary: The system $Ax=b$ has an integral solution x if and only if $b_i^{l+1}=b_i^l$ for some l and all i, and a nonnegative integral solution if and only if $b_i^l=0$ for some l and all i. In the latter case $x_j=\sum_{k=0}^{l-1} 2^k\bar b_j^k$ (i.e., the $\bar b_j^k$ are the binary digits of x_j). *B. T. Poljak* (Moscow)

D04-70 (43# 4751)

Laborde, P.

On sets S.

Gac. Mat. (*Madrid*) (1) **22** (1970), 144–147.

A set S is a collection of integers with gcd 1 having no proper subset with gcd 1. In the present paper the author improves his results from an earlier paper [Amer. Math. Monthly **70** (1963), 855–856] and also gives the following necessary and sufficient condition for a given set of integers to be a set S. Theorem: A necessary and sufficient condition that a set R of $n(n>2)$ integers a_i ($i=1, 2, \cdots, n$) not be a set S is that the coefficients of the parameters in the representation of some component x_j ($1\leqq j\leqq n$) in the general solution of the Diophantine equation $\sum_{i=1}^{n} a_ix_i=1$ be relatively prime.

The author also gives some equivalent forms of this result. *R. Finkelstein* (Bowling Green, Ohio)

D04-71 (44# 5274)

Nijenhuis, Albert; Wilf, Herbert S.

Representations of integers by linear forms in non-negative integers.

J. Number Theory **4** (1972), 98–106.

The linear form $f=a_1x_1+a_2x_2+\cdots+a_nx_n$, where the a's are given relatively prime natural numbers and the x's run independently over nonnegative integers, assumes a certain set of nonnegative integral values which form a semigroup. This simple fact is used by the authors to evolve an ingenious argument which enables them to prove theorems regarding the number of positive integers which f does not represent and the largest of such integers. Some of the results were given by A. Brauer and J. E. Shockley [J. Reine Angew. Math. **211** (1962), 215–220; MR **26** #6113]. *H. Gupta* (Allahabad)

Citations: MR 26# 6113 = D04-44.

D04-72 **(44# 6599)**

Mukaeva, L. M.
A certain class of solutions of the Diophantine equation $L_n(x)=\sum_{k=1}^n kx_k=A$ and a principle for numbering them. (Russian. Kazakh summary)
Izv. Akad. Nauk Kazah. SSR Ser. Fiz.-Mat. **1971**, *no.* 1, 58–62.

Let $L_n(X)=\sum_{k=1}^n kx_k$. The author gives two algorithms for finding all solutions of the equation $L_n(X)=A$ in integers $x_1, \cdots, x_n$ taking only the values ± 1. The problem is reduced to the solution of $L_n(X)=A_1$ in $x_1, \cdots, x_n$ taking only the values 0 and 1. A dyadic weight of such a solution is defined as $x_n 2^{n-1}+\cdots+x_1$ and an ordering of the set of solutions is induced by the ordering of their weights.

K. Szymiczek (Cambridge, England)

D08 QUADRATIC EQUATIONS: GENERAL

There is heavy overlap between quadratic equations and quadratic forms. Most papers concerning the existence of a representation of a number (including 0) by a quadratic form will be found in Chapter **E** (especially **E12, E 16, E20, E24, E28**).

See also reviews D12-2, D12-43, D24-14, D32-53, D48-54, D56-8, D72-17, D99-17, E12-5, E12-23, E12-70, E12-82, E12-107, E12-109, E12-119, E16-17, E20-7, E20-23, E20-27, E20-28, E20-29, E20-32, E20-43, E20-68, E24-130, E28-43, G30-11, G35-15, R14-9, R42-32, T15-34, Z15-71, Z15-84, Z30-10.

D08-1 **(1, 65e)**

Constantinescu, G. G. Integral solutions of the equation $\sum_{i=1}^n\sum_{j=1}^n a_{ij}x_ix_j=0$. Bol. Mat. **12**, 231–236 (1939). (Spanish)

A formula in $\frac{1}{2}n(n-1)$ parameters, giving integral solutions in terms of a given one, is derived by geometrical considerations.

G. Pall (Montreal, Que.).

D08-2 **(3, 268g)**

Barnett, I. A. and Mendel, C. W. On equal sums of squares. Amer. Math. Monthly **49**, 157–170 (1942).

The authors first solve the equation $\sum_1^n x_i^2=\sum_1^n y_i^2$ by writing it in the form $\sum_1^n(x_i-y_i)\cdot(x_i+y_i)=0$; this is a homogeneous linear Diophantine equation in x_i+y_i with coefficients x_i-y_i. If x_i-y_i are introduced as parameters one can solve for x_i+y_i in terms of these and the additional parameters that arise in the solution of such a linear equation. Finally one can solve for x_i, y_i in terms of all these parameters. This process must be modified considerably to make sure that x_i, y_i are integral; the authors succeed in doing this and thus obtain a general solution in terms of a set of parameters. To get a solution with a minimum number of parameters they first find a simple expression (which appears to be new) for the solution of $\sum_1^n a_ix_i=0$ in terms of $n-1$ parameters.

The result just explained is then used to solve the system $\sum_1^n x_i^2=\sum_1^n y_i^2$, $\sum_1^n x_i=\sum_1^n y_i$; this is done by determining the parameters in the solution of the first equation in such a way as to satisfy the second. Likewise a complete parametric solution of the more general equation $\sum_1^n x_i^2=\sum_1^m y_i^2$ $(m<n)$ is found by determining the parameters in such a way that $n-m$ of the values of y_i are zero. For $m=1$, that is, $y_1^2=\sum_1^n x_i^2$ the results are particularly simple.

H. W. Brinkmann (Swarthmore, Pa.).

Referred to in D04-29, D04-32.

D08-3 **(8, 851)**

de Rafael, Enrique. Exact axonometric scales. Publ. Inst. Mat. Univ. Nac. Litoral **6**, 145–167 (1946). (Spanish)

In the axonometric projection used in descriptive geometry three mutually perpendicular axes are projected orthogonally upon a plane. If the reductions in scale from each of the axes on the picture plane are m, n, p, respectively, it is known that (1) $m^2+n^2+p^2=2$, where in addition m, n, p are positive and less than unity. This paper deals with projections where the scales are rational ("exact"), that is, essentially, with rational solutions of (1) or integral solutions of the corresponding equation $m^2+n^2+p^2=2q^2$. Several special cases are discussed (for example, $m=n$); some of these lead to a Pell equation. [The author does not give the general solution of (1) in terms of rational parameters, although this would have at once made obvious the correctness of his conjecture that, given any axonometric projection (with rational or irrational scales), it is possible to find a projection with rational scales that differ from those of the given projection by less than an arbitrary amount.]

H. W. Brinkmann (Swarthmore, Pa.).

D08-4 **(8, 197c)**

Reitan, L. A solution of the equation $am^2=x^2+y^2+z^2$. Norsk Mat. Tidsskr. **24**, 43–47 (1942). (Norwegian)

D08-5 **(9, 270d)**

Boomstra, W. Quadrangles whose sides and diagonals can be represented by integers. Nieuw Tijdschr. Wiskunde **35**, 117–120 (1947). (Dutch)

D08-6 **(9, 498a)**

Kesava Menon, P. On the equation $ax^2\pm by^2=cz^2$. Math. Student **14** (1946), 77–80 (1948).

By means of hyperbolic sines and cosines, from an integral solution of $ax^2-by^2=1$ infinitely many solutions are derived. Using circular functions, from a solution of $ax^2+by^2=(cz^2)^q$ for $q=1$ there are derived solutions for $q>1$. Special cases.

N. G. W. H. Beeger (Amsterdam).

D08-7 **(10, 13e)**

Novikov, A. P. A new solution of the indeterminate equation $ax^2+by^2+cz^2=0$. Doklady Akad. Nauk SSSR (N.S.) **61**, 205–206 (1948). (Russian)

The author considers the Diophantine equation

$$(1) \qquad ax^2+by^2+cz^2=0,$$

a, b, c, integers, to be solved in integers x, y, z, which are relatively prime by pairs. He proves that if (2) $x=1$, $y=\beta$, $z=\gamma$, is a solution of (1), then all solutions are given by

$$(3) \qquad \begin{cases} \pm x=t_1+t_2, \\ \pm y=\beta(t_1-t_2)-2t_3\gamma c, \\ \pm z=\gamma(t_1-t_2)+2t_3\beta b, \end{cases}$$

where t_1, t_2, t_3 are parameters taking on integral values which satisfy (4) $t_1t_2=t_3^2bc$. From the fact that (2) satisfies (1) we have the condition (5) $a=-(b\beta^2+c\gamma^2)$. Using (4) and (5) one readily verifies that the x, y, z, given in (3), satisfy (1). Conversely, starting with an arbitrary solution x, y, z of (1), consider the equations

$$\begin{cases} \pm 2ax = t_1 + t_2, \\ \pm 2ay = \beta(t_1 - t_2) - 2t_3\gamma c, \\ \pm 2az = \gamma(t_1 - t_2) + 2t_3\beta b, \end{cases}$$

and solve for t_1, t_2, t_3, as

$$\begin{cases} t_1 = ax \pm (\beta by + \gamma cz), \\ t_2 = ax \mp (\beta by + \gamma cz), \\ t_3 = \beta z - \gamma y. \end{cases}$$

Then using (5) one can show that these t_i, $i = 1, 2, 3$, satisfy (4). Replacing t_i by $2at_i$, and noting that (4) still holds, completes the proof. *H. N. Shapiro* (New York, N. Y.).

Referred to in D08-8.

D08-8 (11, 328g)

Georgikopoulos, C. On the equation $ax^2 + by^2 + cz^2 = 0$. Bull. Soc. Math. Grèce **24**, 20–25 (1948). (English. Greek summary)

The problem is considered once again of finding all solutions of the Diophantine equation of the title, given any one solution [cf. Novikov, Doklady Akad. Nauk SSSR (N.S.) **61**, 205–206 (1948); these Rev. **10**, 13]. Several methods of achieving this are discussed, and several parametric formulae including all integral solutions of (*) are given. *H. N. Shapiro* (New York, N. Y.).

Citations: MR 10, 13e = D08-7.

D08-9 (12, 11b)

Holzer, L. Minimal solutions of Diophantine equations. Canadian J. Math. **2**, 238–244 (1950).

The author proves the following theorem. If a, b, c are integers, $ab > 1$, a, b, c relatively prime in pairs, and all free of squares, $-ab$ a quadratic residue of c, bc of a, ca of b, and if $F(x, y, z) = ax^2 + by^2 - cz^2$, we have nontrivial solutions of $F(x, y, z) = 0$ with the inequalities $|x| < (bc)^{\frac{1}{2}}$, $|y| < (ca)^{\frac{1}{2}}$, $|z| < (ab)^{\frac{1}{2}}$. The proof is based on the following result by Hecke [Math. Z. **1**, 357–376 (1918), p. 375; **6**, 11–51 (1920), p. 38; see also Hasse, Jber. Deutsch. Math. Verein. **35**, 1–55 (1926), p. 32]. In a field let j be any integer ideal, α a number prime to j. Then there are infinitely many prime ideals (π) of the first degree with $\pi \equiv \alpha \pmod{j}$.

T. Nagell (Uppsala).

Referred to in D08-25, D08-47, E20-32.

D08-10 (12, 79b)

van Wijngaarden, A. A table of partitions into two squares with an application to rational triangles. Nederl. Akad. Wetensch., Proc. **53**, 869–881 = Indagationes Math. **12**, 313–325 (1950).

This paper furnishes a table giving integral solutions (x, y), $0 \leqq x \leqq y$, of (1) $n = x^2 + y^2$ for each integer $n \leqq 10\,000$ for which (1) is possible. The table is used to solve the problem of finding the smallest triangle having integral sides and rational medians. The answer to the problem is Euler's example (68, 85, 87) with medians (79, 131/2, 127/2).

D. H. Lehmer (Berkeley, Calif.).

D08-11 (13, 111c)

Whitlock, W. P., Jr. The Diophantine equation

$$A^2 + 2B^2 = C^2 + D^2.$$

Scripta Math. **17**, 84–89 (1951).

Let N be a given number whose prime factors have the form $4n+1$. If N is a prime $= a^2 + b^2$, two sets of forms in two parameters a, b are given for each of the four unknowns. If N is a product of 2 primes $a^2 + b^2$, $c^2 + d^2$, 8 sets of forms in 4 parameters a, b, c, d are given for the 4 unknowns. The author explains how to find more sets in other cases. There are misprints in lines 5, 23 on p. 85, lines 1, 6, 7 on p. 86, and lines 8–11 on p. 87. The reviewer did not perform all the extensive calculations that are necessary to check the results. *N. G. W. H. Beeger* (Amsterdam).

D08-12 (13, 321l)

Skolem, Th. Remarks concerning the indeterminate equation $xy + yz + zx = k$, **k a positive integer, together with the analogue in several unknowns.** Norsk Mat. Tidsskr. **33**, 41–49 (1951). (Norwegian)

By use of the transformation $x' = x + 2z$, $y' = y + 2z$, $z' = -z$ which leaves the form $xy + xz + yz$ invariant, the author obtains a "least" solution from any known solution of the equation in the title. This least solution has $x \geqq y \geqq z \geqq 0$ and $z \leqq (k/3)^{1/2}$. The extension to n unknowns is discussed.

I. Niven (Eugene, Ore.).

D08-13 (13, 822e)

Boldyreff, A. W. Methods of solution of Diophantine equations by elementary means. Bol. Mat. **24**, 31–40 (1951).

D08-14 (14, 136g)

Gloden, A. Notes on Diophantine equations. Scripta Math. **18**, 87–89 (1952).

Comments are made on various Diophantine equations, such as how to obtain an infinity of solutions from one solution of $A(x^2 + y^2 + z^2) = B(xy + xz + yz)$. *I. Niven.*

D08-15 (16, 447f)

Gupta, Hansraj. On triangular numbers in arithmetical progression. Math. Student **22**, 141–143 (1954).

The general solution of the problem of three triangular numbers, $\frac{1}{2}n(n+1)$, in arithmetic progression is obtained in terms of three arbitrary parameters. *I. Niven.*

D08-16 (16, 1002c)

Cassels, J. W. S. Bounds for the least solutions of homogeneous quadratic equations. Proc. Cambridge Philos. Soc. **51**, 262–264 (1955).

Let $(a_1, a_2, \cdots, a_n)$ be a non-trivial solution in integers of the quadratic equation in $n \geqq 2$ variables $\sum f_{ij} x_i x_j = 0$, $1 \leqq i < j \leqq n$, with integral coefficients f_{ij}, such that max $|a_j|$ is a minimum. Let F denote max $|f_{ij}|$. It is proved that

$$0 < \max |a_j| \leqq \{\tfrac{1}{2}(3n^2 + n - 10)(n-1)^2 F\}^{(n-1)/2},$$

by a method of descent. There appears to be no earlier work on such bounds for $n > 3$; the author gives several references to papers on diagonal ternary forms. *I. Niven.*

Referred to in D08-17, D08-20, D08-21, D08-23, D76-8.

D08-17 (18, 380c)

Cassels, J. W. S. Addendum to the paper "Bounds for the least solutions of homogeneous quadratic equations". Proc. Cambridge Philos. Soc. 52 (1956), 602.

In the bound obtained by the writer [same Proc. **51** (1955), 262–264; MR **16**, 1002] for the least solution in integers of homogeneous quadratic equations in n variables, there appeared significantly the exponent $\frac{1}{2}(n-1)$, which is now shown to be best possible. *I. Niven.*

Citations: MR 16, 1002c = D08-16.

Referred to in D08-20, D08-21, D08-23, D76-8.

D08-18 (18, 718e)

Chalk, J. H. H. An estimate for the fundamental solutions of a generalized Pell equation. Math. Ann. 132 (1956), 263–276.

The author applies a method, used by Schur to obtain

an upper bound for the smallest solution of Pell's equation, to the equation

$$x^2+y^2-D(z^2+w^2)=1,$$

where D is any positive integer. He shows that there exist integers x, y, z, w satisfying this equation for which

$$(x^2+y^2)^{\frac{1}{2}}\leqq 1+D\prod_{\substack{p|D\\ p<2}}\left\{1+\left(\frac{-1}{p}\right)\frac{1}{p}\right\}.$$

Use is made of the group of proper automorphs of certain hermitian forms and the corresponding group of bilinear transformations which is Fuchsian of the first kind (horocyclic). Where Schur used Kronecker's form of the class-number formula, the author uses an identity of Humbert involving integrals over fundamental regions whose integrands involve the forms f_1 $(=x\bar{x}-Dy\bar{y})$, $f_2, \cdots, f_h$ which are properly primitive of determinant D, and no two of which are properly equivalent. The inequality (1) is obtained by ignoring the contributions from all the forms other than the first and by replacing the fundamental region by a smaller region outside a certain circle. By a more careful analysis, involving an application of the Siegel-Tsuji theorem on the non-Euclidean area of fundamental regions, the inequality (1) is sharpened by reducing the magnitude of the right-hand side by about 5 per cent. *R. A. Rankin* (Glasgow).

Referred to in D08-22.

D08-19 (19, 15c)

Ginatempo, Nicola. Problemi di analisi indeterminata in n variabili. Atti. Soc. Peloritana Sci. Fis. Mat. Nat. **1** (1955), 15–25.

"La risoluzione per via geometrica dei problemi di analisi indeterminata è feconda di risultati estremamente facilit a ritrovarsi". This dictum is illustrated by finding the general solution in integers of (I) $x_1^2+\cdots+x_n^2=x_0^2$, (II) the simultaneous pair

$$x_1^2+\cdots+x_n^2=x_0^2,\quad x_1+\cdots+x_n=x_0,$$

and (III) $x_0/x_1+\cdots+x_n/x_0=1/h$, where h is a given integer. The proofs are routine except that that of (II) is egregiously clumsy, the obvious way being to set $x_1=x_0+tm_1$, $x_j=tm_j$ $(1<j\leqq n)$, where the m_j are parameters subject to $\sum m_j=0$ and $t=-2m_1x_0/\sum m_j^2$.
J. W. S. Cassels (Cambridge, England).

D08-20 (19, 120c)

Watson, G. L. Least solutions of homogeneous quadratic equations. Proc. Cambridge Philos. Soc. **53** (1957), 541–543.

Let $f(x_1, \cdots, x_n)=\sum f_{ij}x_ix_j$ be an indefinite quadratic form with integral coefficients. Cassels [same Proc. **51** (1955), 262–264; **52** (1956), 602; MR **16**, 1002; **18**, 380] proved that if the equation $f(x_1, \cdots, x_n)=0$ has a nonzero integral solution, then it has one satisfying

$$\max |x_i|\leqq k_n(\max |f_{ij}|)^{(n-1)/2},$$

where k_n depends only on n. It is here shown that the exponent $\frac{1}{2}(n-1)$ can be replaced by $\max(2, \frac{1}{2}r, \frac{1}{2}s)$, where r is the number of positive squares and s the number of negative squares when f is expressed as a sum of squares (with signs) of real linear forms. Further, if for convenience we suppose $r\geqq s$, the exponent cannot be replaced by any number less than $\frac{1}{2}[rs^{-1}]$; this is an extension of a result of Kneser given by Cassels. Further negative results when $n=4$ or 5 are obtained by special constructions. *H. Davenport* (London).

Citations: MR 16, 1002c = D08-16; MR 18, 380c = D08-17.

D08-21 (19, 125d)

Davenport, H. Note on a theorem of Cassels. Proc. Cambridge Philos. Soc. **53** (1957), 539–540.

It is shown that if the quadratic form $\sum\sum_{1\leq i,j\leq n} f_{ij}x_ix_j$ with integer coefficients represents 0 at all, then there is a representation with

$$0<\sum x_i^2\leqq\gamma_{n-1}{}^{n-1}(2\sum_{i,j} f_{ij}^2)^{(n-1)/2},$$

where γ_{n-1} is Hermite's constant, in the usual notation, related to the minimum of positive definite quadratic forms in $n-1$ variables. Apart from the constant $\gamma_{n-1}{}^{n-1}$ this is equivalent to a result of the reviewer [same Proc. **51** (1955), 262–264; **52** (1956), 602; MR **16**, 1002; **18**, 380], but the author's proof is more elementary, since it does not require the theory of "successive minima".
J. W. S. Cassels (Cambridge, England).

Citations: MR 16, 1002c = D08-16; MR 18, 380c = D08-17.

Referred to in D08-23.

D08-22 (19, 837g)

Chalk, John. H. H. Quelques équations de Pell généralisées. C. R. Acad. Sci. Paris **244** (1957), 985–988.

The author extends the results obtained in an earlier paper [Math. Ann. **132** (1956), 263–276; MR **18**, 718] for the rational complex field $k(i)$ to the field $k(i\sqrt{P})$, where P is a square-free positive integer. By means of similar arguments and a corresponding identity of G. Humbert [C. R. Acad. Sci. Paris **171** (1920), 287–293, 377–382], he considers solutions of the equation $uu'-Dvv'=1$ in algebraic integers u, v and their conjugates u', v', where D is a fixed integer. He shows that there exists a solution for which $\sqrt{(uu')}$ is bounded above by an upper bound depending on D and P which is similar to, but more complicated than, the corresponding upper bound when $P=1$. When $P\equiv 3 \pmod 4$ this gives an upper bound for $\sqrt{(x^2+Py^2)}$, where x, y, z and w are rational integers for which

$$x^2+Pz^2-D(z^2+w^2)=1.$$

By transforming this equation upper bounds for small solutions of certain other equations are obtained.
R. A. Rankin (Glasgow).

Citations: MR 18, 718e = D08-18.

D08-23 (20# 3824)

Birch, B. J.; and Davenport, H. Quadratic equations in several variables. Proc. Cambridge Philos. Soc. **54** (1958), 135–138.

The following theorem, which has applications in the work of the authors on the representation of arbitrarily small numbers by quadratic forms in many variables, is proved. Theorem: Let $f(x_1, \cdots, x_n)$ be an indefinite quadratic form with integral coefficients, and let $g(x_1, \cdots, x_n)$ be a positive definite form with real coefficients. If the equation $f=0$ is properly soluble in integers, then it has a solution satisfying

$$0<g(x_1, \cdots, x_n)\leqq(\gamma_{n-1})^{n-1}(2\,\mathrm{Tr}(\mathbf{f}\mathbf{g}^{-1})^2)^{\frac{1}{2}(n-1)}(\det g).$$

Here **f** resp. **g** denotes the matrix of coefficients of the form f resp. g, Tr is the trace of a matrix, and γ_{n-1} is Hermite's constant which occurs in the theory of the minima of definite quadratic forms.

The proof is a modification of one given by Davenport [same Proc. **53** (1957), 539–540; MR **19**, 125] of a result by the reviewer [ibid. **51** (1955), 262–264; **52** (1956), 602; MR **16**, 1002; **18**, 380], of which the theorem here is a generalization. *J. W. S. Cassels* (Cambridge, England)

Citations: MR 16, 1002c = D08-16; MR 18, 380c = D08-17; MR 19, 125d = D08-21.

D08-24 **(20# 4522)**

Schinzel, André. Sur l'existence d'un cercle passant par un nombre donné de points aux coordonnées entières. Enseignement Math. (2) 4 (1958), 71–72.

Using the fact that the diophantine equation $x^2+y^2=5^k$ (k a suitable positive integer) has $4(k+1)$ solutions, the author solves in the affirmative sense the problem posed in the title. *C. G. Lekkerkerker* (Amsterdam)

D08-25 **(21# 2643)**

Kneser, Martin. Kleine Lösungen der diophantischen Gleichung $ax^2+by^2=cz^2$. Abh. Math. Sem. Univ. Hamburg **23** (1959), 163–173.

Let a, b, c be square-free positive integers which are relatively prime in pairs. Legendre found the necessary and sufficient conditions for the equation $ax^2+by^2=cz^2$ to have a solution in integers x, y, z, not all 0. Holzer [Canad. J. Math. **2** (1950), 238–244; MR **12**, 11] proved that, if the conditions are satisfied, there is a solution with $0<z\leqq(ab)^{1/2}$. The present paper contains a somewhat more elementary proof of a result which includes this and sometimes asserts more. For each positive integer n there is defined, by consideration of plane lattices and their sublattices, a number $k(n)$, and it is proved that the equation is soluble with $0<z\leqq k(n)(ab)^{1/2}$, where n is any divisor of the least common multiple of 2 and abc. Since $n=2$ is admissible, and $k(2)=1$, this includes Holzer's result. A process is described for determining $k(n)$, and a selection of numerical values is given.

H. Davenport (Cambridge, England)

Citations: MR 12, 11b = D08-9.

D08-26 **(22# 1557)**

Besicovitch, A. S. Rational polygons. Mathematika **6** (1959), 98.

The author proves that there is a right-angled triangle whose sides, all having rational lengths, are arbitrarily near to those of any given right-angled triangle. He proves, further, that there is a parallelogram whose sides and diagonals, all having rational lengths, are arbitrarily near to those of any given parallelogram. (The spelling "paralellogram" is unusual.)

H. S. M. Coxeter (Toronto)

D08-27 **(22# 5606)**

Browkin, J. Certain property of triangular numbers. Wiadom. Mat. (2) **2**, 253–255 (1959). (Polish)

The author proves that there exist infinitely many pairs of triangular numbers such that their sum and difference are also triangular numbers. The table of all pairs of triangular numbers (t_a, t_b) with this property is given for $a<250$ ($t_a<125250$).

J. W. Andrushkiw (Newark, N.J.)

D08-28 **(23# A108)**

Myller, A.

Triangles aréolaires-rationnaux. (Romanian. Russian and French summaries)

Gaz. Mat. Fiz. Ser. A **12** **(65)** (1960), 337–339.

Résumé de l'auteur: "On établit une formule qui donne le rayon du cercle circonscrit à un triangle en fonction des aires triangulaires formées par les côtés du triangle et le centre du cercle. Ces aires sont nommées longueurs aréolaires des côtés du triangle donné. Les triangles aréolaires-rationnaux sont ceux dont les longueurs aréolaires des côtés et le carré du rayon du cercle peuvent être exprimés par des nombres entiers." On établit une méthode pour déterminer ces triangles.

D08-29 **(23# A853)**

Battaglia, Antonio

Sull'equazione indeterminata: $x^2+y^2-x-y+k=kt^2$.

Archimede **13** (1961), 175–178.

D08-30 **(23# A1257)**

Supnick, Fred

Rational triangulations.

Amer. Math. Monthly **68** (1961), 95–102.

A rational triangle is one with rational sides and rational area. Let S_1 denote a set of three m.t. (mutually tangent) circles; and let S_i consist of S_{i-1} and all circles each of which is tangent to three m.t. circles of S_{i-1}. Let S denote the set of all circles of S_i ($i=1, 2, 3, \cdots$); and W the set of all triangles whose vertices are the centers of three m.t. circles of S. The author proves the theorem: Either all or none of the triangles of W are rational. He shows how this can be used to find solutions of the Diophantine equation $xy+yz+xz=R^2$ (R rational), and to find functions $f(x)$ for which there exist rational triples x_1, x_2, x_3 such that $f(x_1)f(x_2)f(x_3)(f(x_1)+f(x_2)+f(x_3))=R^2$ (R rational).

W. Moser (Winnipeg, Man.)

D08-31 **(23# A1592)**

Kulikowski, Thadée

Sur l'existence d'une sphère passant par un nombre donné de points aux coordonnées entières.

Enseignement Math. (2) **5** (1959), 89–90.

Le but de cette note est de démontrer le théorème: m étant un nombre naturel $\geqq 3$ et n un nombre naturel quelconque, il existe dans l'espace euclidien à m dimensions une sphère $\sum_{i=1}^{m}(x_i-a_i)^2=r^2$ passant précisément par n points aux coordinées entières $x_1, x_2, \cdots, x_m$.

D08-32 **(26# 6116)**

Muwafi, Amin

A quadratic Diophantine equation.

Monatsh. Math. **67** (1963), 32–35.

Results on a quadratic Diophantine equation containing a non-singular ternary quadratic form.

B. Stolt (Stockholm)

D08-33 **(27# 91)**

Sierpiński, W.

Sur les nombres triangulaires qui sont sommes de deux nombres triangulaires.

Elem. Math. **17** (1962), 63–65.

The author proves the following theorem: In order that a triangular number $t_n=(n(n+1))/2$ be a sum of two positive triangular numbers, it is necessary and sufficient that the number $n^2+(n+1)^2$ be composite. A. Schinzel and the author [Acta Arith. **4** (1958), 185–208; erratum, ibid. **5** (1959), 259; MR **21** #4936] have conjectured that there exists an infinity of primes that are sums of two consecutive squares; therefore an immediate consequence of this conjecture is the existence of an infinity of triangular numbers that are not the sums of two positive triangular numbers. *A. Sklar* (Chicago, Ill.)

Citations: MR 21# 4936 = N32-20.
Referred to in D08-53.

D08-34 **(27# 1405)**

Sierpinski, W. [Sierpiński, W.]

Sur l'équation $x=m^2y$ pour les nombres triangulaires.

Bull. Soc. Roy. Sci. Liège **32** (1963), 187–190.

The author determines all integer m's for which the

equation $x(x+1)=m^2y(y+1)$ has solutions in positive integers x, y. *S. Knapowski* (New Orleans, La.)

D08-35 **(27# 2480)**

Katzouraki, I. G.
A problem in Diophantine analysis. (Greek)
Bull. Soc. Math. Grèce (N.S.) **3** (1962), *no.* 2, 115–121.

R. Carmichael [*The theory of numbers and diophantine analysis*, p. 114, Dover, New York, 1959; MR **21** #4123] refers to a problem of Réalis which among other things requires the solution of the equation $A^2+B^2+C^2=K_1(A_1{}^2+B_1{}^2+C_1{}^2)$, where A, B, C, K_1, A_1, B_1, C_1 are all integers and $AB_1 \neq A_1B$. In this paper the case K_1 a perfect square and $C_1=A_1+B_1$ is studied. Several solutions are given.
L. A. Kokoris (Chicago, Ill.)

Citations: MR 21# 4123 = Z01-41.

D08-36 **(30# 4726)**

Shrikhande, S. S.; Raghavarao, D.
A note on the non-existence of symmetric balanced incomplete block designs.
Sankhyā Ser. A **26** (1964), 91–92.

The authors analyze, in terms of the Hilbert norm residue symbol, the conditions under which the Diophantine equation $x^2=(r-\lambda)y^2+(-1)^{(v-1)/2}\lambda z^2$, with v odd, possesses a nonzero solution in integers. The Diophantine equation under consideration is of importance in the study of symmetrical balanced incomplete block designs. *H. J. Ryser* (Syracuse, N.Y.)

D08-37 **(32# 85)**

Sierpiński, W.
On triangular numbers which are sums of two smaller triangular numbers. (Polish)
Wiadom. Mat. (2) **7**, 27–28 (1963).

The author proves the following theorem: The necessary and sufficient condition that a triangular number $t_n=\frac{1}{2}n(n+1)$ be the sum of two smaller triangular numbers is that $n^2+(n+1)^2$ be a composite number. From the hypothesis H of A. Schinzel [Schinzel and the author, Acta Arith. **4** (1958), 185–208; erratum, ibid. **5** (1959), 259; MR **21** #4936], it follows that there exist infinitely many triangular numbers which are not sums of two smaller triangular numbers.
J. W. Andrushkiw (S. Orange, N.J.)

Citations: MR 21# 4936 = N32-20.

D08-38 **(32# 2373)**

Davenport, H.; Lewis, D. J.; Schinzel, A.
Quadratic Diophantine equations with a parameter.
Acta Arith. **11** (1965/66), 353–358.

Let $f(t)$ be a polynomial with integral coefficients and suppose that every arithmetical progression contains an integer t such that the equation $F(x, y, t)=x^2+y^2-f(t)=0$ is soluble in integers x, y. The authors showed previously [same Acta **9** (1964), 107–116; MR **29** #1179] that then $F(x(t), y(t), t)=0$ identically, where $x(t)$ and $y(t)$ are polynomials with integral coefficients. Now let $F(x, y, t)$ be any polynomial with integral coefficients which is of degree at most two in x and y. Suppose that every arithmetical progression contains an integer t such that the equation $F(x, y, t)=0$ is soluble in rationals x, y. The authors show that there exist two rational functions $x(t)$ and $y(t)$ with rational coefficients such that $F(x(t), y(t), t)=0$ identically in t. The deepest earlier result used in the proof of this general and important theorem is a theorem concerning the density of the prime ideals in an algebraic number field for which a given number of the field has prescribed quadratic character.
J. B. Kelly (Tempe, Ariz.)

Citations: MR 29# 1179 = D56-23.

D08-39 **(33# 1274)**

Goodrich, Merton Taylor
On squares in arithmetic progression.
Math. Mag. **39** (1966), 87–88.

Formulae for three squares in arithmetic progression are given which do not differ from those of Fermat [cf. L. E. Dickson, *History of thetheory of numbers*, Vol. 2, Chapter 4, p. 435, Carnegie Inst. of Washington, Washington, D.C., 1920]. *A. Schinzel* (Warsaw)

D08-40 **(33# 1282)**

Blackburn, W. T.
A method of solving some Diophantine equations by means of the equation $a \cos\theta+b\sin\theta+c=0$.
Math. Gaz. **50** (1966), 40–43.

D08-41 **(33# 2599)**

Sinha, T. N.
Two simultaneous diophantine equations.
Math. Student **33** (1965), 59–61.

Two theorems on equations containing powers of a natural number having at least one prime factor of the form $6k+1$. *B. Stolt* (Stockholm)

D08-42 **(34# 7454)**

Simons, W. H.; Alder, H. L.
n and $n+1$ consecutive integers with equal sums of squares.
Amer. Math. Monthly **74** (1967), *no.* 1, *part I*, 28–30.

To solve $\sum(x+i)^2=\sum(y+j)^2$, where i runs from 0 to $n-1$ and j runs from 0 to n, let b be square-free and such that $n(n+1)=2a^2b$ if $n\equiv 1$ or 2 mod 4, and $n(n+1)=4a^2b$ if $n\equiv 0$ or 3 mod 4. Let $x=y+z$, $y-n(z-1)=abw$ and reduce the problem to $(2z-1)^2-2bw^2=1$, or to $(2z-1)^2-bw^2=1$, in the respective cases. These Pell equations may be solved by continued fractions and (with due attention in the second case to selecting w even) all solutions in positive integers x and y are obtained. The example $n=100$ has the solution with smallest x and y given by $x=20201$, $y=20100$. *B. M. Stewart* (E. Lansing, Mich.)

D08-43 **(38# 4404)**

Udrescu, Valeriu Şt.
A quadratic diophantine equation.
Rev. Roumaine Math. Pures Appl. **13** (1968), 885–886.

Let $u=a_1+a_2+\cdots+a_n$. Infinite systems of solutions are given of the integral diophantine equations $a_1x_1{}^2+a_2x_2{}^2+\cdots+a_nx_n{}^2=u^kx_{n+1}^2$ for k an odd integer or zero. The question of completeness of the solution set is left open. *J. D. Swift* (Los Angeles, Calif.)

D08-44 **(38# 5708)**

Adler, Irving
Three Diophantine equations. I.
Fibonacci Quart. **6** (1968), 360–369, 317.

Expository.

Referred to in D08-45.

D08-45 **(39# 4096)**

Adler, Irving
Three Diophantine equations. II.
Fibonacci Quart. **7** (1969), 181–193.
Part I of this expository article appeared in same Quart. **6** (1968), 360–369, 317 [MR **38** #5708].

Citations: MR 38# 5708 = D08-44.

D08-46 **(38# 5712)**

Hooley, Christopher
On the Diophantine equation $ax^2+by^2+cz^2+2fyz+2gzx+2hxy=0$.
Arch. Math. (*Basel*) **19** (1968), 472–478.
The general solution of the stated equation is obtained in the form $x=\kappa u(r,s)=\kappa(\xi r^2+2\lambda rs+\rho s^2)$, $y=\kappa v(r,s)=\kappa(\eta r^2+2\mu rs+\sigma s^2)$, $z=\kappa w(r,s)=\kappa(\zeta r^2+2\nu rs+\tau s^2)$, where κ runs through positive squarefree numbers. The invariants of the forms u, v, w are related to the coefficients of the original equation by $\lambda^2-\rho\xi=f^2-bc$ (not $bc-f^2$, as stated), $2\lambda\mu-\xi\sigma-\mu\rho=2(hc-fg)$, etc. Each solution is obtained twice if u, v, w run through a representative set.
H. J. Godwin (London)

D08-47 **(39# 2700)**

Mordell, L. J.
On the magnitude of the integer solutions of the equation $ax^2+by^2+cz^2=0$.
J. Number Theory **1** (1969), 1–3.
A simple elementary proof, using a descent method, is given that the equation $ax^2+by^2+cz^2=0$, if solvable in rational integers, has a solution satisfying $|x|\leqq|bc|^{1/2}$, $|y|\leqq|ac|^{1/2}$, $|z|\leqq|ab|^{1/2}$. This result was first proved by L. Holzer [Canad. J. Math. **2** (1950), 238–244; MR **12**, 11] using the existence of primes in arithmetic progressions in quadratic fields. *D. J. Lewis* (Ann Arbor, Mich.)

Citations: MR 12, 11b = D08-9.

D08-48 **(39# 4081)**

Alfred, Brother U. [Brousseau, Brother Alfred]
Sums of squares of consecutive odd integers.
Math. Mag. **40** (1967), 194–199.
The author obtains a number of necessary conditions on n in order that there exist n consecutive odd integers the sum of whose squares is itself a square. See also the paper reviewed below [#4082].

Referred to in D08-50.

D08-49 **(39# 4082)**

Sollfrey, William
Note on sums of squares of consecutive odd integers.
Math. Mag. **41** (1968), 255–258.
In his paper on the same subject, Brother Alfred Brousseau [#4081 above] treated the following question: Given a positive integer N, do there exist N consecutive odd integers the sum of whose squares is itself a square? He obtained a number of necessary conditions for N which enabled him to resolve all except eight cases $N\leqq 1000$, either by finding a solution or showing that none exists. In the present paper, the author answers the remaining eight cases and also finds smaller solutions for several of the previously solved cases. *F. Herzog* (E. Lansing, Mich.)

D08-50 **(41# 8330)**

Makowski, Andrzej
Remark on the paper "Sums of squares of consecutive odd integers" by Brother U. Alfred.
Math. Mag. **43** (1970), 212–213.
The author makes an addition and a correction to a paper by Brother Alfred Brousseau [same Mag. **40** (1967), 194–199; MR **39** #4081].

Citations: MR 39# 4081 = D08-48.

D08-51 **(39# 5469)**

Kelemen, József
On a ternary quadratic Diophantine equation. (Hungarian)
Mat. Lapok **19** (1968), 367–371.
Let (x_0, y_0, z_0) be a nontrivial solution in integers of $ax^2+by^2=cz^2$. The author determines all other solutions from the knowledge of the one solution (x_0, y_0, z_0). He also discusses some related questions.
{The author adds in proof that most of his results are to be found in T. A. Skolem's book *Diophantische Gleichungen*, pp. 30–31, Ergeb. Math. Grenzgeb. (N.F.), Heft 5, Springer, Berlin, 1938.} *P. Erdős* (Budapest)

D08-52 **(39# 6808)**

Shah, A. P.
On a relation between pentagonal and triangular numbers.
Vidya **11** (1968), *no.* 1, 174–177.
From the author's summary: "Let nth pentagonal and triangular numbers be denoted by P_n and T_n, respectively (i.e., $P_n=\frac{1}{2}n(3n-1)$ and $T_n=\frac{1}{2}n(n+1)$). In this paper, it is proved that if $P_a+P_b=P_c$ and if for some integer r, $b=r(c-a)$, then there exist integers t, m, n such that T_{a-b+t}, T_{c+m}, T_{a+b+n} are in arithmetic progression."

D08-53 **(40# 2601)**

Shah, S. M.
On triangular numbers which are sums of two triangular numbers.
Vidya **9** (1966), 161–163.
From the author's introduction: "Triangular numbers are defined by the relation $T_n=n(n+1)/2$, n being a positive integer. Many interesting properties have been given by D. B. Eperson [Math. Gaz. **47** (1963), 236–237]. It has been shown by W. Sierpiński [Elem. Math. **17** (1962), 63–65; MR **27** #91] that a necessary and sufficient condition that a triangular number T_n be the sum of two triangular numbers is that $n^2+(n+1)^2$ should be a composite number. In this note we give a systematic method of finding triangular numbers which are sums of two triangular numbers. It seems from this note that there is an infinite number of triangular numbers which are sums of two triangular numbers."

Citations: MR 27# 91 = D08-33.

D08-54 **(41# 5280)**

Rameswar Rao, D.
Rationals versus irrationals.
Proc. Nat. Acad. Sci. India Sect. A **36** (1966), 313–314.
The equilateral hyperbola $s(s+a)=t(t+b)$ is cut by the line $a(s-a)=b(t-b)$ in points (s_1, t_1), (s_2, t_2) with midpoint (a, b). Hence, the coordinates of these points define two triads in arithmetic progression which in terms of parameters $M=a$, $L=b/\sqrt{2}$ are given by $s_1=M-2L$, $a=M$, $s_2=M+2L$; $t_1=(L-M)\sqrt{2}$, $b=L\sqrt{2}$, $t_2=(L+M)\sqrt{2}$. Any such triad (s_1, a, s_2) of rational numbers, other than $(0,0,0)$, determines a corresponding triad (t_1, b, t_2) of irrational numbers, perhaps accounting for the cryptic title. Equations of other special conics with the same chord are $s^2+a^2=t^2+b^2$, $s^2-a^2=2tb$, $2sa=t^2-b^2$.
B. M. Stewart (E. Lansing, Mich.)

D08-55 **(41# 5293)**

Owings, James C., Jr.
An elementary approach to Diophantine equations of the second degree.
Duke Math. J. **37** (1970), 261–273.

If x is a root of the equation $ax^2+bx+c=0$, then x', where x' is defined by the relation $ax'=-ax-b$, is also a root. According to the author this simple observation is the basis for a very elementary, and apparently little-explored approach to the solution of diophantine equations in the second degree with any number of unknowns.

The classical method of solving the general second degree equation (1) $ax^2+bxy+cy^2+dx+ey+f=0$ is to reduce it to one of the form (2) $u^2-Dv^2=k$, and then use the theory of the Pell equation $s^2-Dt^2=1$, since $D>0$ and square-free is the only case of interest. It may also be reduced to the form (3) $Ax^2+Bxy+Cy^2=k$ [see, for example, T. A. Skolem, *Diophantische Gleichungen*, Ergeb. Math. Grenzgeb., Band 5, Heft 4, Springer, Berlin, 1938; reprint, Chelsea, New York, 1950].

T. Nagell [*Introduction to number theory*, second edition, Chelsea, New York, 1964; MR **30** #4714] has shown that it is possible to determine all the solutions of (2) in an elementary way without using the theory of quadratic forms or the theory of quadratic fields. There is a finite number of classes of associated solutions, and a so-called fundamental solution in each class can be found by means of inequalities.

His investigations have been continued by B. Stolt in three papers [Ark. Mat. **2** (1952), 1–23; MR **14**, 247; ibid. **2** (1952), 251–268; MR **14**, 354; ibid. **3** (1955), 117–132; MR **16**, 903]. He found an upper bound for the number of classes $C(N)$ for arbitrary N. If N is square-free, then $C(N)$ is a power of 2. An exact value is obtained in case N is a power of a prime. Stolt extended Nagell's theory to equation (3) [ibid. **3** (1957), 381–390; MR **18**, 791].

E. Grosswald [Boll. Un. Mat. Ital. (4) **1** (1968), 382–392; MR **38** #1058] obtained formulae yielding an infinite set of integral solutions of the diophantine equation $x^2+bx+c=ky^2$, with emphasis on formulae that yield all solutions in integers.

The author of the paper under review does not mention these investigations, due to Stolt and Grosswald. He proves two theorems concerning equation (1), the first of them being the following: Let a, b, c, d, e, f be integers such that $a>0$, $c>0$, $a+b+c<0$; $a|b$, $a|d$, $c|b$, and $c|e$. Let $X=\{x|ax^2+dx+f\leqq 0\}$, $Y=\{y|cy^2+ey+f\leqq 0\}$, $W=\{w|(a+b+c)\omega^2+(e+d)\omega+f\geqq 0\}$, $X'=X\cup W$, $Y'=Y\cup W$. Then X', Y' are finite sets of integers such that every chain of solutions in integers to (1) contains some member of X' as an x-value or some member of Y' as a y-value. The author's chains of solutions are of course related to Nagell's classes of solutions.

His second theorem (number 3 in the paper) is a more general one, but it is too complicated to be given here.

The author illustrates his procedure by examples. The first is the equation (4) $x^2+y^2-3xy-2y=1$. It seems to me that (4) is more easily solved by the classical method, since it may be written $(5x+6)^2-5(2y-3x-2)^2=-4$, from which it is immediately concluded that x and y can be given in terms of Fibonacci numbers. However, the equation $x^2+3xy-y^2+2x+y=0$ is an example of interest.

It is asserted that if Theorem 3 does not apply to a particular equation, then the classical method of solving it is at least as good as the method developed in this paper. In particular, if there is a cross term present and if certain divisibility conditions hold, there seems to be much saving in computation.

Some equations in three variables are also discussed, but no complete theory is developed.

W. Ljunggren (Oslo)

Citations: MR 14, 247e = D12-21; MR 14, 354a = D12-22; MR 16, 903e = D12-31; MR 18, 791d = D12-37; MR 30# 4714 = Z01-14; MR 38# 1058 = D12-62.

D08-56 **(41# 6776)**

Zelichowicz, W.
On the equation $x^2+y^2-z^2=k$. (Polish. English and Russian summaries)
Fasc. Math. No. 4 (1969), 79–90 (1970).

The author finds all integral solutions of the equation in the title and also all (with finitely many exceptions in the case of negative k) integral non-zero solutions.

W. Narkiewicz (Wrocław)

D08-57 **(42# 1761)**

Sinha, T. N.
A diophantine problem.
Math. Student **37** (1969), 131–135.

Let $n\geqq 2$ and put $f_n=\sum_{i=1}^n x_i^2+\sum_{i<j} x_ix_j$, $g_n=\sum_{i=1}^n \binom{i}{2} y_i^2$. The author derives a parametric solution for the Diophantine equation $f_n=x^2$. Then, by showing that the quadratic form g_n is congruent to f_n, he derives a parametric solution of the equation $g_n=x^2$. (It is easy to check that a natural modification of this solution will work when the coefficients of $y_2, y_3, \cdots, y_n$ are arbitrary integers.) There is no discussion of completeness.

J. B. Kelly (Tempe, Ariz.)

D08-58 **(43# 3204)**

Belkner, Horst
Die Diophantische Gleichung $a^2+kb^2=kc^2$.
Wiss. Z. Pädagog. Hochsch. Potsdam Math.-Natur. Reihe **14** (1970), 187–193.

A method of F. J. M. Barning [Math. Centrum Amsterdam Afd. Zuivere Wisk. **1963**, ZW-011; MR **32** #7491] for generating the complete set of Pythogorean triangles from (3, 4, 5) by unimodular matrices is extended to $2a^2+b^2=c^2$ from (2, 1, 3) and $a^2+2b^2=2c^2$ from (4, 1, 3).

J. D. Swift (Los Angeles, Calif.)

Citations: MR 32# 7491 = D16-32.

D08-59 **(44# 1621)**

Bundschuh, Peter
Zwei Resultate über Trigonalzahlen.
Elem. Math. **26** (1971), 12–14.

Denote the hth triangular number by $t_h=h(h+1)/2$. M. N. Khatri [Scripta Math. **21** (1955), 94] found several triples of triangular numbers $t_x+t_y=t_z$. The present author generalizes the result, using constructive elementary methods to show that for each Pythagorean triple (p_1, p_2, p_3) satisfying $p_1{}^2+p_2{}^2=p_3{}^2$ there are exactly two different (q_1, q_2, q_3) such that $t_{p_1\cdot k+q_1}+t_{p_2\cdot k+q_2}=t_{p_3\cdot k+q_3}$ $(k=0, 1, \cdots, n)$.

Also, a problem of Sierpiński is answered in the affirmative; namely, there are infinitely many triangular numbers that can be written in m ways as the sum of triangular numbers $(m=0, 1, \cdots, n)$.

S. I. Gendler (Clarion, Pa.)

D12 QUADRATIC EQUATIONS: PELL AND OTHER BINARY EQUATIONS

See also Sections E16, R14.

See also reviews A50-68, A56-24, A56-34, A56-60, D02-14, D08-18, D08-22, D08-24, D20-3, D20-7, D20-16, D20-25, D24-55, D56-38, D64-18, E16-7, E16-52, E16-53, E16-69, E24-124, E28-7, N24-70, R14-9, R14-28, R14-36, R14-97, Z15-2, Z15-12, Z15-13, Z15-51, Z15-102, Z30-52.

D12-1 (3, 161g)

Aigner, Alexander. Die Zerlegung einer arithmetischen Reihe in summengleiche Stücke. Deutsche Math. **6**, 77–89 (1941).

The paper contains an interesting examination of questions centered around the following problem: consider an arithmetical progression with the νth term $a_\nu = a+(\nu-1)d$, $d \geqq 1$, $a \gtreqless 0$, $(a, d)=1$, all numbers rational integers. The progression is called zweiteilig when it has the property that for some $k>1$ and $n>k$ we have $a_1+\cdots+a_k=a_{k+1}+\cdots+a_n$. Letting $\sum_\nu$ be the sum of the first ν terms, we have $\sum_n=2\sum_k$, from which $(d-2a)(n-2k)=d(n^2-2k^2)$. This shows that the problem has no solution for $d=2a$ or $n=2k$. If n, k have assigned values, there is always one solution, from $a:d=(n^2-2k^2-2):(4-2n)$, except when $n=2k$. Assuming next a, d given, and solving the quadratic equation for n, the discriminant is found to be $D=2(2a-d+2dk)^2-(2a-d)^2$. With $D=x^2$ (since n must be an integer), $2a-d+2dk=y$, we are led to the Diophantine equation $x^2-2y^2=-(2a-d)^2$; $2n=(x-2a+d)/d$, $2k=(y-2a+d)/d$; $2a_n=x-d$, $2a_k=y-d$. The investigation is thus reduced to the examination of a Pell equation. It is proved that to every $d(>0)$ and every $a>d/2$ there exist an infinite number of zweiteilig progressions (solutions). The case $a \leqq d/2$ leads to arithmetical difficulties. It is found: (I) $a<-3d$: infinite number of solutions, or a finite number, or no solutions; (II) $-3d \leqq a \leqq d/2$: infinite number of solutions, or no solution. These possibilities are discussed in detail. Examples: impossible $(a, d)=(1, 4)$, $(-1, 4)$, $(1, 7)$, $(3, 7)$; possible: $1+4+\cdots+13$; $3+7+\cdots+27$; $2+3+\cdots+7$; $2+3+\cdots+43$.

A second part deals with the size of the solution n, k, or a_k, a_n in the cases when an infinite number of solutions exist for a given a, d. Here $\lim k/n=\lim a_k/a_n=1/\sqrt{2}$, independently of a, d. This follows from $n=(x-2a+d)/2d$, $k=(y-2a+d)/2d$; $2a_n=x-d$, $2a_k=y-d$, $x^2-y^2=-(2a-d)^2$, and the known behavior of solutions of Pell's equation. Part 3 considers the set of natural numbers, the progression $1+2+3+\cdots$. Now $x^2-2y^2=-1$, $2n=x-1$, $2k=y-1$, and the solutions are given by $(x+y\sqrt{2})=(1+\sqrt{2})^{2h+1}$, $h>0$. The first six solutions are $(x, y; n, k)=(7, 5; 3, 2)$; $(41, 29; 20, 14)$; $(239, 169; 119, 84)$; $(1393, 985; 696, 492)$; $(8119, 5741; 4059, 2870)$; $(47321, 33461; 23660, 16730)$. For the second, for example, $41^2-2\cdot 29^2=-1$, $n=(41-1)/2=20$, $k=(29-1)/2=14:1+2+\cdots+14=15+\cdots+20$. Part 4 proves the impossibility of $a_1+\cdots+a_k=a_{k+1}+\cdots+a_n=a_{n+1}+\cdots+a_m$ except for the trivial case $d=0$ (dreiteilig impossible).

Finally, general arithmetical progressions a, $a+d$, $a+2d$, $\cdots$, with arbitrary real or complex a, d, are considered. It is easily shown that every zweiteilig arithmetical progression of real or complex numbers is a zweiteilig progression of real integers, multiplied by a constant factor. Any arithmetical progression $(d\neq 0)$ of real or complex numbers is at most zweiteilig (never dreiteilig or μ-teilig, $\mu>2$).

A. J. Kempner (Boulder, Colo.).

D12-2 (4, 34b)

Niven, Ivan. Quadratic Diophantine equations in the rational and quadratic fields. Trans. Amer. Math. Soc. **52**, 1–11 (1942).

The author studies the number of integral solutions of the general quadratic equation

$$ax^2+bxy+cy^2+dx+ey+f=0,$$

where coefficients and solutions are from the field of rational numbers or from some quadratic field. Thus if $A=b^2-4ac<0$ and the field is that of the rational numbers, there is at most a finite number of solutions; if $A\geqq 0$ and there is one solution, then there must be an infinite number, aside from certain exceptional cases that are stated in detail. Similarly detailed results are given for real quadratic fields (in this case a finite number of solutions occurs if A is totally negative) and for imaginary quadratic fields (here one solution implies infinitely many, aside from certain exceptions). The exceptions essentially deal with the cases where the left hand side of the equation can be factored. As might be expected the whole discussion depends upon the study of the generalization of the Pell equation in quadratic fields. In this connection it is proved that the equation $\xi^2-\gamma\eta^2=1$ ($\gamma\neq 0$ an integer in a quadratic field F) has an infinite number of integral solutions in F if and only if γ is not a square in F when F is imaginary, and γ is not totally negative when F is real. The proof of this depends in part upon a theorem of Hilbert on the existence of relative units in a field over F. Aside from this theorem the entire treatment is elementary. *H. W. Brinkmann.*

Referred to in D12-4.

D12-3 (4, 130f)

Hua, Loo-keng. On the least solution of Pell's equation. Bull. Amer. Math. Soc. **48**, 731–735 (1942).

Let x_0, y_0 be the least positive solution of $x^2-dy^2=4$, where d is a positive integer, not a square, congruent to 0 or 1 mod 4. Let $\epsilon=(x_0+y_0d^{\frac{1}{2}})/2$. The class-number formula $(d^{\frac{1}{2}}/\log\epsilon)\cdot\sum(d|n)(1/n)$ is used to prove that $\log\epsilon<d^{\frac{1}{2}}(\frac{1}{2}\log d+1)$, whence one can easily get Schur's inequality $\epsilon<d^{d^{\frac{1}{2}}}$. The proof gives another application of the averaging of character sums, here with $\chi(n)=(d|n)$, introduced in the article reviewed above.* *G. Pall.*

*See MR 4, 130d = N76-1.

Citations: MR 4, 130d = N76-1.

Referred to in D12-16, R14-73.

D12-4 (4, 240b)

Niven, Ivan. The Pell equation in quadratic fields. Bull. Amer. Math. Soc. **49**, 413–416 (1943).

The author [Trans. Amer. Math. Soc. **52**, 1–11 (1942); these Rev. **4**, 34] has shown that, if γ is an integer of a quadratic field F, then the equation $\xi^2-\gamma\eta^2=1$ has an infinite number of integral solutions in F if and only if γ is not totally negative when F is a real field, and γ is not the square of an integer of F when F is imaginary. Here he considers the possibility of representing the solutions in the form

$$\xi=\{(\xi_1+\gamma^{\frac{1}{2}}\eta_1)^n+(\xi_1-\gamma^{\frac{1}{2}}\eta_1)^n\}/2,$$
$$\eta=\{(\xi_1+\gamma^{\frac{1}{2}}\eta_1)^n-(\xi_1-\gamma^{\frac{1}{2}}\eta_1)^n\}/(2\gamma^{\frac{1}{2}}),$$

where ξ_1, η_1 is, in a sense, a minimal solution. The result is that such a representation can be found whenever the equation has an infinite number of solutions if and only if γ is not a totally positive nonsquare integer of F. In the statement of the theorem the value $n=0$ should be allowed in order to include the trivial solution $\xi=1$, $\eta=0$.

H. S. Zuckerman (Seattle, Wash.).

Citations: MR 4, 34b = D12-2.

D12-5 **(8, 7f)**

Skolem, Th. A theorem on the equation $\zeta^2-\delta\eta^2=1$ where δ, ζ, η are integers in an imaginary quadratic field. Avh. Norske Vid. Akad. Oslo. I. **1945**, no. 1, 13 pp. (1945).

Let k be an imaginary quadratic field different from $R(\sqrt{(-1)})$ and $R(\sqrt{(-3)})$ and let δ be any integer in k not having any of the forms τ^2, $-\tau^2$, $-3\tau^2$, for τ in k. Say that a solution of $\zeta^2-\delta\eta^2=1$ in k has property P when all prime ideals which divide η also divide δ. It is proved that the number of essentially different solutions which have property P never exceeds two. If there is only one such solution it is α, β, where $\alpha+\beta\sqrt{\delta}$ is a fundamental unit for the group of all units in the field $k(\sqrt{\delta})$ having the relative norm $+1$. If there are two solutions they are α, β and α_3, β_3, determined by $\alpha_3+\beta_3\delta=(\alpha+\beta\sqrt{\delta})^3$. Furthermore, only the solution α, β can have property P if 3 is a prime number in k or the square of a prime ideal in k. Necessary and sufficient conditions for only α, β to have property P are given in case 3 is the product of two different prime ideals in k.

I. Niven (West Lafayette, Ind.).

D12-6 **(8, 7g)**

Skolem, Th. A remark on the equation $\zeta^2-\delta\eta^2=1$, $\delta>0$, $\delta', \delta'', \cdots<0$, where δ, ζ, η belong to a total real number field. Avh. Norske Vid. Akad. Oslo. I. **1945**, no. 12, 15 pp. (1945).

Let k be an algebraic number field of degree n which contains a totally real element δ such that $\delta>0$; $\delta', \delta'', \cdots, \delta^{(n-1)}<0$; then δ is necessarily primitive in k and $[k(\sqrt{\delta}):k]=2$. The group of units of $k(\sqrt{\delta})$ having norm $+1$ relative to k is cyclic, as is the subgroup of such units of the form $\zeta+\eta\sqrt{\delta}$, ζ, η integers in k, and hence the solutions of the equation $\zeta^2-\delta\eta^2=1$ may be obtained from the powers of the unit which generates this subgroup. The author shows that there is only a finite number of solutions of this equation such that every prime ideal divisor of η also divides δ, that an upper bound to the number of these solutions may always be found, and that in certain cases all such solutions may be effectively obtained. As a consequence of these results he deduces the following theorem. Let $A, A_1, \cdots, A_m, B, B_1, \cdots, B_n$ be integers in a totally real algebraic number field K with $AB>0$, $A'B'<0$, $A''B''<0, \cdots$; $A_1, \cdots, A_m, B_1, \cdots, B_n$ totally positive. Then the equation $AA_1^{x_1}\cdots A_m^{x_m}-BB_1^{y_1}\cdots B_n^{y_n}=1$ has only a finite number of solutions in rational integers $x_1, \cdots, x_m, y_1, \cdots, y_n$. If none of A_i or B_j is a unit in K, then all solutions can be obtained, while in general an upper bound to the number of solutions may be found. Similar theorems are shown to hold in any field which is quadratic, cyclic cubic or cubic with negative discriminant.

S. A. Jennings (Vancouver, B. C.).

D12-7 **(8, 136c)**

Kuroda, Sigekatu. Über die Pellsche Gleichung. Proc. Imp. Acad. Tokyo **19**, 611–612 (1943).

Let $D>0$ be the discriminant of a quadratic field and let k_0 be the largest odd or even integer not exceeding $\sqrt{D}$, according as $D\equiv1$ or 0 (mod 4). Then

$$\theta=\tfrac{1}{2}(k_0+\sqrt{D})=k_0+\frac{1}{k_1+}\cdots\frac{1}{+k_{n-1}+}\frac{1}{\theta}=\frac{p_n\theta+p_{n-1}}{q_n\theta+q_{n-1}},$$

$$k_\nu=k_{n-\nu}\ (\nu=1, \cdots, n-1).$$

The least positive solution t, u of $t^2-Du^2=\pm4$ is obtained from the equation $E_0=q_n\theta+q_{n-1}=\frac{1}{2}(t+u\sqrt{D})$. If E_0 has norm $+1$, then $n=2m$. Let

$$\eta=k_m+\frac{1}{k_{m-1}+}\cdots\frac{1}{+k_1+}\frac{1}{\theta}=\frac{p\theta+p'}{q\theta+q'}=\frac{-b+\sqrt{D}}{2a}.$$

Then $a>0$, $\sqrt{E_0}=(q\theta+q')/\sqrt{a}=(q_m\theta+q_{m-1})\sqrt{a}$ is a biquadratic unit, and a is the norm of the primitive ambiguous ideal $[a, a\eta]\neq[1]$ of $R(\sqrt{D})$, which divides E_0+1 or E_0-1 according as m is even or odd. If E_0 has norm -1, then n is odd, and a result pertaining to the field $R(\sqrt{(-1)}, \sqrt{D})$ is obtained.

R. Hull (Lincoln, Neb.).

D12-8 **(8, 315b)**

Candido, Giacomo. Le equazioni di Fermat $x^2-2y^2=\pm1$. Boll. Mat. (4) **1**, 85–91 (1940).

Referred to in D12-21.

D12-9 **(8, 315c)**

Nagell, Trygve. An elementary method for the determination of lattice points on a hyperbola. Norsk Mat. Tidsskr. **26**, 60–65 (1944). (Norwegian)

The author investigates the solutions in integers of the Diophantine equation (1) $x^2-Dy^2=\pm N$ (D and N are positive integers, $\sqrt{D}$ is irrational). The solutions of (1) are classified. Two solutions (x_i, y_i) and (x_j, y_j) belong to the same class if $x_i+y_i\sqrt{D}=(x_j+y_j\sqrt{D})(A+B\sqrt{D})$, where (A, B) is a solution in integers of (2) $u^2-Dv^2=1$. Let (u_0, v_0) be the solution of (2) in the least positive integers. The following results are proved. (I) In each class of solutions of (3) $x^2-Dy^2=+N$ there is a solution (x, y) with $0<y\leqq v_0\sqrt{N}$, $0<|x|\leqq u_0\sqrt{N}$. (II) In each class of solutions of (4) $x^2-Dy^2=-N$ there is a solution (x, y) with $0<y\leqq v_0/\{\frac{1}{2}(u_0-1)N\}^{\frac{1}{2}}$, $0<|x|\leqq\{\frac{1}{2}(u_0-1)N\}^{\frac{1}{2}}$. In consequence of this the class-numbers of the solutions of (3) and (4) are finite and the representatives of these classes (the fundamental solutions (x_m, y_m)) are found by a finite number of operations. All solutions of (3) or (4) are formed by $(x_m+y_m\sqrt{D})(a+b\sqrt{D})$, where the solutions (x_m, y_m) run through the system of fundamental solutions and (a, b) run through all solutions of (2).

S. C. van Veen (Delft).

D12-10 **(9, 9c)**

Ţino, O. N. Sur la réduction de l'équation indéterminée du second degré $x^2-\rho y^2=l$ ($\rho>0$) aux équations $x^2-\rho y^2=\pm1$ et $\alpha x^2-\beta y^2=\pm1$. Bull. Sci. École Polytech. Timişoara **10**, 43–68 (1941).

In this paper the author outlines a method for reducing the indeterminate equation $x^2-\rho y^2=l$, where x, y, ρ, l denote integers with $\rho>0$ and $|l|>\sqrt{\rho}$, to an equation of the same form, with $|l|<\sqrt{\rho}$, or to one of the forms $u^2-\rho v^2=\pm1$, $\alpha u^2-\beta v^2=\pm1$, where α, β, u, v are integers and $\alpha\beta=\rho$. Noting that when the given equation is possible in integers, a transformation employed by Lagrange always permits us to obtain one or more solutions, the author discusses various cases in detail. He first considers $x^2-\rho y^2=l$, with $|l|>\sqrt{\rho}$, l a prime, $\rho>0$ and prime to l. It is shown that in this case the equation is resolved into one of $u^2-\rho v^2=-\epsilon$, $k_1^2u^2-\rho_1v^2=-\epsilon$, $u^2-\rho v^2=-2\epsilon$, $k_1u^2-\rho_1v^2=-2\epsilon$, where $\rho=k_1\rho_1$ and ϵ is a definite one of $-1, +1$. Since the general solutions of the first two, and of the last two for $2<\sqrt{\rho}$, have been fully treated by Lagrange [Dickson, History of the Theory of Numbers, v. 2, Washington, 1920, pp. 358–362], it remains only to consider the last two for $\rho\leqq4$. When integer solutions are possible, it is proved that for $\rho\leqq4$ these equations are reducible to the form $u^2-\rho v^2=-\epsilon$. The author finally applies to his method to $x^2-ly^2=\rho$ with $|l|>\sqrt{\rho}$, where ρ (not a square) is greater than zero and prime to l, and l is the product of two primes l_1, l_2, both of which are different from 2. In all cases the analysis is similar to that in the first case. He remarks that the treatment in the cases given can be applied without essential modification to the general case with $|l|>\sqrt{\rho}$, where $\rho>0$ is not a square and is prime to l, and l is the product of n factors $l_1, l_2, \cdots, l_n$. *W. H. Gage.*

D12-11 (9, 78e)

Bucher, J. Neues über die Pell'sche Gleichung. Mitt. Naturforsch. Ges. Luzern **14**, 1–18 (1943).

Let p, q be primes of the form $4n+1$, h the class number of the field $R(\sqrt{(pq)})$, and t, u the least positive integral solution of $t^2-pqu^2=4$. Using Dirichlet's results on the norm of the fundamental unit, the author proves that, if h is divisible by 4, then $\left(\frac{p}{q}\right)_4 \equiv (\frac{1}{2}t)^{h/4} \pmod{p}$, where $\left(\frac{p}{q}\right)_4$ is the biquadratic character of p modulo q. Define $M=\prod(4\sin^2 x\pi/p-4\sin^2 y\pi/q)$, where the product ranges over all positive $x<p/2$ and positive $y<q/2$ for which $\left(\frac{x}{p}\right)=\left(\frac{y}{q}\right)=1$, and define λ by $\lambda M=|M|$. Let ϵ designate the conjugate of the fundamental unit in $R(\sqrt{p})$, define e by $e=-\epsilon\sqrt{p}$, and let $q=\alpha\alpha'$ be the factorization of q in $R(\sqrt{p})$. If h is divisible by 8, say $h=8h_1$, then $\lambda\left(\frac{e}{\alpha}\right)_4 \equiv (\frac{1}{2}t)^{h_1} \pmod{q}$, and $\{(t-u\sqrt{(pq)})/2\}^{h_1}=|M|$. Finally, the coefficients of u in $\prod(u-4\sin^2 x\pi/p)$, the range of x in this product being the same as in M above, are integers in $R(\sqrt{p})$, and divisible by $\sqrt{p}$. Corresponding results are obtained throughout the paper for the case $q=2$.

I. Niven (Eugene, Ore.).

D12-12 (9, 270c)

Skolem, Th. Solutions of the equation $axy+bx+cy+d=0$ in algebraic integers. Avh. Norske Vid. Akad. Oslo. I. **1946**, no. 3, 8 pp. (1947).

Let K be a field of finite degree over the rationals, K_n a field of degree n over K, R and R_n the rings of integers in K and K_n. Consider the equation (*) $axy+bx+cy+d=0$ with coefficients in R, $(a, b, c)=1$, $a\neq 0$, $D=ad-bc\neq 0$. The principal results proved are: (*) is solvable in the residue class ring of any ideal in R; if R has a finite number of units, the number of solutions of (*) in R is finite, possibly zero; if R has an infinite number of units, the number of solutions of (*) in R is infinite or zero; for given R there exist n and R_n such that (*) has a solution in R_n (the proof gives an upper bound for the least value of n); if $(a, c)=1$, (*) is solvable in R if and only if D has a divisor congruent to $c \pmod{a}$; if $(a, c)=1$, there exists a ring R_n in which (*) is solvable if and only if D^n has a divisor $D_1\equiv c^n \pmod{a}$ in R. *I. Niven* (Eugene, Ore.).

D12-13 (10, 353j)

Palamà, G. Tabelle della soluzione minima dell'equazione di Pell-Fermat. Boll. Mat. (5) **2**, 40–42 (1948).

Bibliographical note.

D12-14 (10, 430b)

Nyberg, Michael. Remark on the indeterminate equation $x^2-Dy^2=\pm L$. Norsk Mat. Tidsskr. **30**, 69–71 (1948). (Norwegian)

The author shows that the two equations

$$x^2-(m^2+4)y^2=\pm m$$

are both solvable for every odd integer m. For an even m the equations are simultaneously solvable only when m is a square, $m\neq 0$. *T. Nagell* (Uppsala).

D12-15 (11, 642f)

Patz, Wilhelm. Über die Gleichung $X^2-DY^2=\pm c\cdot(2^{31}-1)$, wo c möglichst klein. S.-B. Math.-Nat. Kl. Bayer. Akad. Wiss. **1948**, 21–30 (1949).

The author illustrates by three examples a continued fraction method of solving $x^2-Dy^2=cp$. The examples considered are $x^2+3y^2=p$, $x^2+5y^2=2p$, and $x^2-13y^2=-p$, where $p=2^{31}-1$. Fermat's theorem is used to solve $z^2\equiv D \pmod{p}$ and then the convergents of the continued fraction for $(D^{\frac{1}{2}}-z)/p$ give the solution (x, y). *D. H. Lehmer.*

D12-16 (11, 714k)

Nagell, Trygve. Über die Darstellung ganzer Zahlen durch eine indefinite binäre quadratische Form. Arch. Math. **2**, 161–165 (1950).

From a solution (u, v) of (1) $u^2-Dv^2=N$ an associated solution $u'=ux+vyD$, $v'=uy+vx$ can be obtained by using a solution (x, y) of (2) $x^2-Dy^2=1$, where D is a positive nonsquare integer. A complete set of associated solutions of (1) is an equivalence class; define the fundamental solution of a class as that one with least positive v and the corresponding u (the positive one in case of ambiguity). It is proved that the fundamental solution of a class satisfies the inequality $v\leqq\frac{1}{2}y_1\{2|N|/(x_1\pm 1)\}^{\frac{1}{2}}$, with sign chosen to match that of N, and where (x_1, y_1) is a fundamental solution of (2). Thus (1) has only a finite number of classes. If N is a prime p, then (1) has at most one nonnegative solution satisfying this inequality on v, and (assuming the existence of a solution) there are one or two classes according as $p|2D$ or not. It should be pointed out that inequalities for the least positive solution of $x^2-Dy^2=4$, $D\equiv 0$ or $1 \pmod 4$, have been given by L. K. Hua [Bull. Amer. Math. Soc. **48**, 731–735 (1942); these Rev. **4**, 130]. Earlier work was done by I. Schur. *I. Niven* (Eugene, Ore.).

Citations: MR 4, 130f = D12-3.

Referred to in D12-20, D12-21.

D12-17 (12, 393d)

Schogt, C. A theorem of Petr from number theory. Math. Centrum, Amsterdam. Rapport **ZW-1950-009**, 10 pp. (1950). (Dutch)

A new proof is given of the following theorem of Petr [Časopis Pěst. Mat. Fys. **56**, 57–66 (1927)]: If D is a positive integer, not a square, then there is exactly one triple $(D_1, D_2, e)\neq(1, D, 1)$, with $D_1D_2=D$, $D_1<D_2$, $e=\pm 1$ or ± 2, for which there are integers u, v such that $D_1u^2-D_2v^2=e$ and $(u, D_2)=(v, D_1)=1$. Petr's proof used continued fractions; the present proof uses only properties of the units in the quadratic field $k(\sqrt{D})$. *W. J. LeVeque.*

D12-18 (13, 535b)

Jarden, Dov. On a sequence with separate recurring formulas for members with even and odd subscripts. Riveon Lematematika **5**, 39–40 (1951). (Hebrew. English summary)

The author remarks that a sequence $\{W_n\}$ satisfying the pair of 2nd order recursion relations:

$$W_{2n+2}=aW_{2n+1}+bW_{2n},$$
$$W_{2n+3}=cW_{2n+2}+dW_{2n+1},$$

satisfies the single 4th order recursion relation

$$W_n=(b+ac+d)W_{n-2}-bdW_{n-4}.$$

It is noted that use of this fact would have simplified the work of Tuchman and Kalai [see the following review].

E. G. Straus (Los Angeles, Calif.).

D12-19 **(13, 535c)**

Tuchman, Zevulun, and Kalai, Shraga. Application of recurring sequences for solving Diophantine equations. Riveon Lematematika **5**, 23–31 (1951). (Hebrew. English summary)

The authors prove: If the sequences $\{u_n\}$, $\{v_n\}$ are determined by

$$u_0=0,\quad u_1=1,\quad u_{2n}=u_{2n-1}+u_{2n-2},\quad u_{2n+1}=(k-2)u_{2n}+u_{2n-1},$$

and $v_0=2$, $v_1=1$, $v_{2n}=(k-2)v_{2n-1}+v_{2n-2}$, $v_{2n+1}=v_{2n}+v_{2n-1}$, then the pairs $x=u_{2m}$, $y=u_{2m+2n}$ $(m=0, \pm1, \pm2, \cdots)$ yield (except for signs) all integer solutions of the Diophantine equations $x^2-v_{2n}xy+y^2=u_{2n}^2$. Similar relations are mentioned for the various other combinations of the u and v with even or odd indices and the corresponding quadratic Diophantine equations. The authors' work would have been greatly simplified by noticing that each of the sequences $\{u_{2n}\}$, $\{u_{2n-1}\}$, $\{v_{2n}\}$, $\{v_{2n-1}\}$ satisfies the difference equation $X_n=kX_{n-1}-X_{n-2}$, as remarked by Jarden [see the preceding review]. *E. G. Straus* (Los Angeles, Calif.).

D12-20 **(14, 19h)**

Nagell, Trygve. Bemerkung über die Diophantische Gleichung $u^2-Dv^2=C$. Arch. Math. **3**, 8–9 (1952).

Referring to previous work [Arch. Math. **2**, 161–165 (1950); these Rev. **11**, 714] the author indicates that a simpler formulation results if the fundamental solution of a class were defined as that one with least non-negative v instead of least positive v. *I. Niven* (Eugene, Ore.).

Citations: MR 11, 714k = D12-16.

Referred to in D12-21.

D12-21 **(14, 247e)**

Stolt, Bengt. On the Diophantine equation $u^2-Dv^2=\pm 4N$. Ark. Mat. **2**, 1–23 (1952).

It has been shown by T. Nagell [Norsk Mat. Tidsskr. **26**, 60–65 (1944); Arch. Math. **2**, 161–165 (1950); Introduction to number theory, Wiley, New York, 1951, pp. 195–212; Arch. Math. **3**, 8–9 (1952); these Rev. **8**, 315; **11**, 714; **13**, 207; **14**, 19] that $u^2-Dv^2=\pm N$, where D is a positive nonsquare integer, can be solved without the use of either the theory of quadratic forms or the theory of quadratic fields. The author extends this theory to (1) $u^2-Dv^2=\pm 4N$, not simply by replacing N by $4N$, but by relating the equation to $x^2-Dy^2=4$ where Nagell used $x^2-Dy^2=1$. Thus from one solution (u, v) of (1) is obtained an associated solution $u'=\frac{1}{2}(ux+vyD)$, $v'=\frac{1}{2}(uy+vx)$ where (x, y) satisfies $x^2-Dy^2=4$. A complete set of associated solutions forms a class, and each class has a fundamental (minimal) solution. Any equation (1) has but a finite number of classes of solutions, in fact at most 2^n classes in case N is square-free with n prime factors. (The author has carried this part of the theory beyond Nagell's formulation.) The number of classes is given a better bound in many special cases, with exact values being given if N is a prime or the product of two primes. *I. Niven* (Eugene, Ore.).

Citations: MR 8, 315b = D12-8; MR 11, 714k = D12-16; MR 13, 207b = Z01-13; MR 14, 19h = D12-20.

Referred to in D08-55, D12-22, D12-31, D12-32, D12-37, D12-59.

D12-22 **(14, 354a)**

Stolt, Bengt. On the Diophantine equation $u^2-Dv^2=\pm 4N$. II. Ark. Mat. **2**, 251–268 (1952).

Continuing his previous work [Ark. Mat. **2**, 1–23 (1952); these Rev. **14**, 247] the author now determines an upper bound for the number of classes of solutions of the equation of the title for general N, where in the earlier work he treated the cases with N square-free. The detailed results are too lengthy for summary here. It is also established that for fixed N the equation has at most one ambiguous class, that is, a class which contains the solution $(u, -v)$ whenever it contains (u, v). *I. Niven* (Eugene, Ore.).

Citations: MR 14, 247e = D12-21.

Referred to in D08-55, D12-31, D12-59.

D12-23 **(14, 537c)**

Val'fiš, A. Z. Elementary solution of Pell's equation. Akad. Nauk Gruzin. SSR. Trudy Mat. Inst. Razmadze **18**, 116–132 (1951). (Russian. Georgian summary)

The author (whose name is also spelled Walfisz) claims that all previous treatments of Pell's equation $x^2-ky^2=1$ depend tacitly on limiting processes as they either operate in the field of real numbers or use cyclotomy (Kreisteilung). Here he shows how known proofs can be modified to avoid this dependence. To prove the existence of solutions he first proves that for any positive integer m there is a rational r with $k<r^2<k+m^{-2}$ and then uses the Schubfachprinzip to show the existence of integers x, y with $|x-ry|<m^{-1}$, $0<y\leqq m$. Then $|x^2-ky^2|\leqq 4k$; and infinitely many such pairs x, y can be obtained. The proof now runs on familiar lines. To demonstrate the existence of a fundamental solution the author works in the abstractly defined field of elements $a+b\sqrt{k}$. He shows at great length that this can be ordered (the order is that obtained by giving $\sqrt{k}$ its real-number value; but this interpretation is avoided). The proofs are now again the familiar ones. *J. W. S. Cassels* (Cambridge, England).

D12-24 **(14, 537d)**

Val'fiš, A. Z. Pell's equation in imaginary quadratic fields. Akad. Nauk Gruzin. SSR. Trudy Mat. Inst. Razmadze **18**, 133–151 (1951). (Russian. Georgian summary)

The equation in question is $\xi^2-\kappa\eta^2=1$, where κ is a given nonsquare integer in the imaginary quadratic field $K(\sqrt{d})$, $d<0$, and ξ, η are variable integers in the field. Using the method of Dirichlet for $K(\sqrt{-1})$ [J. Reine Angew. Math. **24**, 291–371 (1842) = Werke, Bd. I, Reimer, Berlin, 1889, pp. 533–618], the author shows the existence of nontrivial solutions and of a fundamental solution ξ_0, η_0 such that every other solution is of the form $\xi+\eta\sqrt{\kappa}=\pm(\xi_0+\eta_0\sqrt{\kappa})^n$ (or if $d\neq -1$ and $\kappa=-1$ or $d=-3$ and $\kappa=\frac{1}{2}(1\pm\sqrt{(-3)})$ of the form $\pm i(\xi_0+\eta_0\sqrt{\kappa})^n$). The methods are elementary throughout. There is an account of other recent work, but no reference to the relation with the units of the quartic field $K(\sqrt{d}, \sqrt{\kappa})$. *J. W. S. Cassels* (Cambridge, England).

Referred to in D12-28.

D12-25 **(14, 725e)**

Moessner, Alfred. On the equation $x^m=py^m+(-1)^m$, $m=1, 2$. Euclides, Madrid **13**, 119 (1953). (Spanish)

D12-26 **(14, 950d)**

Gloden, A. Une méthode de résolution de l'équation diophantienne $2x^2+1=ay^2$, $(a=2b^2+1)$. Bull. Soc. Roy. Sci. Liège **22**, 195–196 (1953).

D12-27 **(15, 10b)**

Gloden, A. Une méthode de résolution de l'équation diophantienne $2x^2+1=ay^2$, $(a=2b^2+1)$. Bull. Soc. Roy. Sci. Liège **22**, 195–196 (1953).

D12-28 **(15, 202h)**

Fjellstedt, Lars. On a class of Diophantine equations of the second degree in imaginary quadratic fields. Ark. Mat. **2**, 435–461 (1953).

The author shows that the classical treatment of Pell's equation can be extended to the equation $x^2-\delta y^2=\pm 1$, where δ is a fixed integer in an imaginary quadratic field and x, y are to be found. He proves the existence of a fundamental solution and also gives sufficient (but not necessary) criteria for a solution to the fundamental. Finally he applies the results to the equation $x^2-\delta y^2=\gamma$. The paper has similarities with A. Z. Val'fiš, Akad. Nauk Gruzin. SSR. Trudy Mat. Inst. Razmadze **18**, 133–151 (1951) [these Rev. **14**, 537]. *J. W. S. Cassels.*

Citations: MR 14, 537d = D12-24.

D12-29 (15, 854e)

Nagell, Trygve. On a special class of Diophantine equations of the second degree. Ark. Mat. **3**, 51–65 (1954).

The author proves the following results using the elementary theory of quadratic fields but without using ideals. (I) Let $D>1$ be squarefree and consider equations of the type $Ax^2-By^2=E$ where $AB=D$ and $E=\pm 1$, ± 2 with the supplementary conditions $1<A<B$ for $E=+1$, $1\leqq A<B$ otherwise. Further, $E\neq\pm 2$ if D is even. Then precisely one of these equations is soluble. If $x=\xi$, $y=\eta$ is the least solution, then $|E|^{-1}(\xi\sqrt{A}+\eta\sqrt{B})^2=U+V\sqrt{D}$ is a fundamental solution of Pell's equation $U^2-DV^2=4$. (II) Suppose that Pell's equation $U^2-DV^2=4$ admits a solution with odd U, V. Then for $1\leqq A<B$, $AB=D$, precisely one of the equations $Ax^2-By^2=\pm 4$ other than Pell's equation is soluble in odd integers x, y. If ξ, η is the least solution of this other equation then $\frac{1}{4}(\xi\sqrt{A}+\eta\sqrt{B})^2=U+V\sqrt{D}$ is a fundamental solution of Pell's equation. It is remarked that these results follow readily from known results of ideal theory; and that the author has already proved something rather analogous for cubic fields [J. Math. Pures Appl. (9) **4**, 209–270 (1925)]. *J. W. S. Cassels.*

Referred to in D12-74, R14-83.

D12-30 (16, 903c)

Surányi, János. Equations diophantiques et fractions continues. Mat. Lapok **5**, 79–100 (1954). (Hungarian. Russian and French summaries)

Expository article. *P. Erdös.*

D12-31 (16, 903e)

Stolt, Bengt. On the Diophantine equation $u^2-Dv^2=\pm 4N$. III. Ark. Mat. **3**, 117–132 (1955).

Continuing his previous work [Ark. Mat. **2**, 1–23, 251–268 (1952); MR **14**, 247, 354] the author determines the number of classes of solutions of the equation of the title in the following two cases: (1) N is square-free, and (2) N is a power of a prime. The details are too extensive for reproduction here; however, in case (1) the number of classes is a power of 2. Among the solutions in a class, that one with smallest non-negative v is called the fundamental solution of the class. The paper treats various bounds on the fundamental solutions of the equation. These bounds or inequalities on the fundamental solutions can be obtained in an elementary way as well as by algebraic number theory, and it is established that the elementary methods give better results. *I. Niven* (Berkeley, Calif.).

Citations: MR 14, 247e = D12-21; MR 14, 354a = D12-22.

Referred to in D08-55, D12-59.

D12-32 (17, 13b)

Nagell, Trygve. Contributions to the theory of a category of Diophantine equations of the second degree with two unknowns. Nova Acta Soc. Sci. Upsal. (4) **16**, no. 2, 38 pp. (1955).

Throughout the discussion D will denote a positive integer not a perfect square, and C a square-free integer. The first part of the paper treats the elementary properties of the Diophantine equations $u^2-Dv^2=\pm 4$ without the use of the theory of quadratic fields or binary quadratic forms. This development parallels the author's treatment of $x^2-Dy^2=\pm 1$ as given in his book [Introduction to number theory, Wiley, New York, 1951; MR **13**, 207]. Next it is established that if (1) $u^2-Dv^2=C$ has an ambiguous class of solutions (definitions may be found in the book cited above, pp. 204–208) then C divides $2D$. On the other hand, if C divides $2D$, then equation (1) has at most one class of solutions, and this class, if it exists, is ambiguous.

A parallel result is obtained for the equation (2) $u^2-Dv^2=4C$. A basic theory for (2) along lines similar to Nagell's work on (1) has been given by B. Stolt [Ark Mat. **2**, 1–23 (1952); MR **14**, 247]. Throughout the present paper much use is made of the parallel between equations (1) and (2), so that almost every theorem has an analogue; in several instances one member of such a pair of analogous theorems is an already known result.

Say that C is admissible if it is a divisor of $2D$, with $C\neq 1$ and $C\neq -D$. If C is admissible then any solution u, v of (1) gives a solution $x=(u^2+Dv^2)/|C|$, $y=2uv/|C|$ of $x^2-Dy^2=1$; moreover, if the solution u, v is least positive among solutions of (1), then the corresponding x, y is also least positive. Furthermore, for a given D which is not square-free, there is at most one admissible value of C for which (1) is solvable. For a given D which is square-free there are exactly two admissible values of C for which (1) is solvable; the product of these two values of C is $-4D$ when D is odd and C is even, and the product is $-D$ in all other cases.

Next we assume that D is odd and that C divides D. If a solution u, v in positive odd integers of (2) has the property that all prime factors of v are factors of D, then it is the least positive solution in odd integers of (2); exception must be made in the case $D=5$, $C=-1$, which is fully treated. This is an analogue of a result of K. Mahler [Arch. Math. Naturvid. **41**, no. 6 (1935)]. These results are generalized (we omit the details) and also applied to obtain an analogue of another result of Mahler, as follows. A method is given of finding all solutions, there being only a finite number, in positive integers x, z_1, z_2, $\cdots$, z_m of the equation $Ax^2-4E=q_1^{z_1}q_2^{z_2}\cdots q_m^{z_m}$, where $E=\pm 1$, A is positive, odd, and square-free, and $q_1, q_2, \cdots, q_m$ are any given distinct odd primes which do not divide A.

Application is also made to obtain the following result. We are given n odd, $n\geq 3$, A odd, square-free, $A\geq 3$; assume that n is not a divisor of the class number of the field $R(\sqrt{-2A})$. Then $Ax^2+2=y^n$ has no solutions in integers. Related equations were treated earlier by the writer and by W. Ljunggren [Norske Vid. Selsk. Forh., Trondhjem **15**, no. 30, 115–118 (1942); MR **8**, 442]. Another analogue of a result of Mahler deals with any polynomial $f(x)=Ax^2\pm 4$, where A is a positive integer. For any integer x define $P(x)$ as the greatest prime factor of $f(x)$. Then $\liminf P(x)/\log\log x\geq 1$.

The paper is partly expository, with new proofs of various known results, and provides a fairly unified treatment of the subject. *I. Niven* (Eugene, Ore.)

Citations: MR 8, 442g = D40-11; MR 13, 207b = Z01-13; MR 14, 247e = D12-21.

D12-33 (17, 237g)

Skolem, Th. On relative Pell's equations. Bull. Soc. Math. Belg. **1954**, 96–105 (1955).

Expository article.

D12-34 **(17, 1055j)**

Schinzel, A.; et Sierpiński, W. Sur l'équation $x^2+x+1=3y^2$. Colloq. Math. **4** (1956), 71–73.

All solutions of $x^2+x+1=3y^2$ in positive integers are given by the recursion formulas $x_{n+1}=7x_n+12y_n+3$, $y_{n+1}=4x_n+7y_n+2$, with $x_1=y_1=1$. *I. Niven.*

Referred to in D12-38, D12-58.

D12-35 **(18, 561b)**

Thébault, Victor. Sur des suites de Pell. Mathesis **65** (1956), 390–395.

The paper starts from the following known property of the Pell equation: If we form the two sequences $x_{n+1}=2x_n+1x_{n-1}$, $x_0=1$, $x_1=1$ and $y_{n+1}=2y_n+1y_{n-1}$, $y_0=0$, $y_1=1$, then (x_{2k}, y_{2k}) yield all solutions of

$$x^2-2y^2=+1,$$

and (x_{2k}, y_{2k}) all solutions of $x^2-2y^2=-1$. Several relations between the x's and y's are established by elementary considerations, for example

$$y_{n+1}^2-y_n^2-2y_n\cdot y_{n+1}=(-1)^n;$$

$$x_{n+1}+x_n=2y_{n+1};\ y_n\cdot y_{n+1}-y_{n-1}\cdot y_{n+2}=2\cdot(-1)^{n-1}$$

(misprint in paper);

$$x_{n-1}\cdot x_n\cdot x_{n+1}\cdot x_{n+2}+4=(x_n\cdot x_{n+1}+2\cdot(-1)^{n+1})$$

(misprint in paper); etc. Similar types of relations are established for the sequences $y_{n+1}=p\cdot y_n+1\cdot y_{n-1}$, p a positive integer. For some reason the importance of this sequence for Pell's equation (for suitably chosen p) is not mentioned. *A. J. Kempner* (Boulder, Colo.).

D12-36 **(18, 791c)**

Hunter, John. A note on integer solutions of the Diophantine equation $x^2-dy^2=1$. Proc. Glasgow Math. Assoc. **3** (1956), 55–56.

The purpose of this note is to establish a procedure for obtaining solutions of the Fermat equation (1) $x^2-dy^2=1$ by Newton's method of approximating to the root $\sqrt{d}$ of the equation $f(x)=x^2-d=0$. If x_1 is any positive rational number, then Newton's method gives a sequence (x_n) of rational numbers defined by the relation

$$x_{n+1}=x_n-\frac{f(x_n)}{f'(x_n)}=\frac{x_n^2+d}{2x_n}\ (n\geqq 1).$$

It is shown that each x_1 provides a sequence of positive rational solutions (p_n, q_n), $n=2, 3, \cdots$, of (1), which are such that

(2) $$p_{n+1}+q_{n+1}\sqrt{d}=(p_2+q_2\sqrt{d})^m\ (m=2^{n-1}),$$

where

$$p_2=\frac{x_1^2+d}{|x_1^2-d|},\quad q_2=\frac{2x_1}{|x_1^2-d|}.$$

If p_2 and q_2 are integers, then (2) gives a sequence of positive integer solutions of (1). Putting $d=m^2+r$, where $r\neq 0$ and $-m+1\leqq r\leqq m$, $m>0$, the author then gives a new proof of the well-known theorem that p_2, q_2 give the minimum positive integer solution of (1) in the following two cases: $r=-1$, $x_1=m-1$; and r divides $2m$, $r\neq -1$, $x_1=m$. *W. Ljunggren* (Blindern).

D12-37 **(18, 791d)**

Stolt, Bengt. On a Diophantine equation of the second degree. Ark. Mat. **3** (1957), 381–390.

For solving an equation of the type $x^2-Dy^2=\pm N$, where D and N are positive rational integers, one may use either the theory of quadratic forms or the theory of quadratic fields. T. Nagell has shown [e.g. Introduction to number theory, Wiley, New York, 1951, pp. 195–212; MR **13**, 207] how it is possible to determine all solutions in rational integers x and y independently of these theories and completely elementarily. His investigations have been continued by the author [e.g. Ark. Mat. **2** (1952), 1–23; MR **14**, 247]. In this paper the following equation is considered: (1) $Au^2+Buv+Cv^2=\varepsilon N$, where A, B, C and N are rational integers, $A>0$, $N>0$, $\varepsilon=\pm 1$, and where $B^2-4AC=D$ is a positive integer which is not a perfect square. It is shown how it is possible to avoid the usual linear transformations and congruences in order to obtain all the integral solutions of (1). If $u=t/A$ is a fractional number and v is an integer which satisfy (1), the number $f(u, v)=(2Au+Bv+\sqrt{D})/2$ is called a solution of (1). The set of all solutions associated with each other forms a class of solutions of (1). If u and v are two integers satisfying (1), $f(u, v)$ is called an integral solution of (1). It is proved that if one solution of a class K is an integral solution, then every solution of K is integral. If $f(u, v)$ is the fundamental solution (in a sense defined) of (1), then one has the following inequality:

$$0<v\leqq\frac{AN}{D}(x_1-2\varepsilon)^{\frac{1}{2}},$$

where $v=0$ also may be possible if $\varepsilon=1$, (x_1, y_1) denoting the fundamental solution of $x^2-Dy^2=4$. If in $f(u, v)$ the number $(2Au+Bv)v/N$ is an integer, the class is said to be quasi-ambiguous. Some theorems concerning such classes are proved. Finally, examples are given.

W. Ljunggren (Blindern).

Citations: MR 13, 207b = Z01-13; MR 14, 247e = D12-21.

Referred to in D08-55.

D12-38 **(19, 941g)**

Palamà, Giuseppe. Sulla risoluzione completa in numeri naturali dell'equazione indeterminata $x^2+mx+p=(p+m+1)y^2$, nei casi $m=1$, 2. Boll. Un. Mat. Ital. (3) **12** (1957), 636–647.

As a generalization of a recent note by Schinzel and Sierpinski [Colloq. Math. **4** (1956), 71–73; MR **17**, 1055] the author gives the complete solution of the diophantine equation in the title. Since there is the initial solution $x=y=1$, all solutions can be found from the well-known theory of the Pell equation $t^2-(p+m+1)u^2=1$ with some attention to parity when $m=1$. The author does not explain why he restricted m to the values 1 and 2. There is, as a matter of fact, no difficulty to be encountered for a general integer m.

D. H. Lehmer.

Citations: MR 17, 1055j = D12-34.

Referred to in D12-58.

D12-39 **(20# 1660)**

Zeckendorf, E. Équations quadratiques à discriminant atypique. Bull. Soc. Roy. Sci. Liège **27** (1958), 28–40.

In an earlier paper [same Bull. **26** (1957), 112–122; MR **19**, 730] the author studied equations of the type $A^2-MB^2=k_1(-m)^x$, $M=v^2+m$, and showed how to express solutions in integers A and B as terms of certain recurring series. Now the more general case $M\neq v^2+m$ is considered. *W. Ljunggren* (Blindern)

Citations: MR 19, 730b = B36-22.

Referred to in B36-24, E28-21.

D12-40 **(20# 3820)**

Labutin, D. N. Refinement of an algorithm of I. Čistyakov. Kabardin. Gos. Ped. Inst. Uč. Zap. **12** (1957), 63–64. (Russian)

The article points out that without proper care some of the solutions of the Diophantine equation

$$ax^2+bxy+cy^2+dx+ey=0$$

with integral non-zero coefficients may be lost in making the substitution $y=xt$.

D12-41 (20# 6390)

Lánský, Miloš. On prime lattice points lying on the conics. Mat.-Fyz. Časopis. Slovensk. Akad. Vied 7 (1957), 121–127. (Czech. Russian and English summaries)

Es sei r eine rationale Zahl. Gibt es einen nicht zerfallenden Kegelschnitt, der durch den Punkt $[0, r]$ hindurchgeht und unendlich viele Punkte $[x, y]$ besitzt, wobei x eine Primzahl und y eine ganze Zahl ist, so stellt er eine Parabel dar, deren Achse zu der y-Achse parallel ist. Aus dem Satz werden einige Folgerungen abgeleitet, u.a.: Es gibt keinen nicht zerfallenden Kegelschnitt, der die Koordinatenachsen in Punkten mit rationalen Koordinaten schneidet und auf dem unendlich viele Punkte liegen, deren beide Koordinaten Primzahlen sind.

M. Novotný (Brno)

D12-42 (21# 1951)

Copley, G. N. Recurrence relations for solutions of Pell's equation. Amer. Math. Monthly **66** (1959), 288–290.

Making use of the usual expression for solutions of the Pell equation in terms of the fundamental one, the author quickly deduces some recurrence relations. Relationships with the circular and hyperbolic functions are exploited.

B. W. Jones (Boulder, Colo.)

D12-43 (22# 1540)

Steuerwald, Rudolf. Über die Gleichung $x^2-Dy^2=Cz$. Math. Z. **73** (1960), 382–385.

The equation (*) of the title has a non-trivial solution in rational integers x, y, z if and only if $C\neq 0$, and the congruence $u^2\equiv D \pmod{C}$ is solvable (D not a square). The author discusses the problem of finding that solution of (*) for which $|z|$ has the smallest positive value. He presents a continued fraction method which yields an upper bound (depending only on D) for the smallest attainable value of $|z|$.

A. L. Whiteman (Princeton, N.J.)

D12-44 (22# 9470)

Mordell, L. J. On a pellian equation conjecture. Acta Arith. **6** (1960), 137–144.

Let p be a prime $\equiv 1 \pmod 4$ and let $\varepsilon=\frac{1}{2}(t+u\sqrt{p})>1$ be the fundamental unit in the quadratic field $R(\sqrt{p})$. It has been conjectured by Ankeny, Artin and Chowla [Ann. of Math. (2) **56** (1952), 479–493; MR **14**, 251] that $u\not\equiv 0 \pmod p$.

The following results are proved in the present paper. (1) If p is a regular prime (that is, the number of classes of ideals in the cyclotomic field $R(e^{2\pi i/p})$ is not divisible by p), then $u\not\equiv 0 \pmod p$. (2) If $p\equiv 5 \pmod 8$, then $u\equiv 0 \pmod p$ if and only if the Bernoulli number $B_{(p-1)/4}\equiv 0 \pmod p$.

L. Carlitz (Durham, N.C.)

Citations: MR 14, 251h = R14-19.

Referred to in D02-14, D12-45, R14-44, R14-50.

D12-45 (23# A3707)

Mordell, L. J.

On a Pellian equation conjecture. II.

J. London Math. Soc. **36** (1961), 282–288.

Let p be a prime $\equiv 3 \pmod 4$ and denote by T, U the fundamental solution of the equation $y^2-px^2=1$. It is proved in this paper that $U\equiv 0 \pmod p$ if and only if the Euler number

$$E_{(p-3)/4}\equiv 0 \pmod p,$$

where E_n is defined by

$$\sec t=\sum_0^\infty E_n\frac{t^{2n}}{(2n)!}.$$

This result may be compared with a like result concerning the equation $y^2-px^2=-4$ where p is a prime $\equiv 5 \pmod 8$ obtained recently by the author [Acta Arith. **6** (1960), 137–144; MR **22** #9470].

L. Carlitz (Durham, N.C.)

Citations: MR 22# 9470 = D12-44.

Referred to in R04-39.

D12-46 (25# 2030)

Jensen, Chr. U.

On the solvability of a certain class of non-Pellian equations.

Math. Scand. **10** (1962), 71–84.

This paper is concerned with the determination of criteria for the solvability of the equation $x^2-dm^2y^2=-1$ when the equation is assumed solvable for $m=1$. This problem is equivalent to assuming that the quadratic field $Q(\sqrt{d})$ has a unit ε of negative norm and determining criteria for the existence of units of negative norm in the order I_m.

The equation is shown to be solvable for an odd m if and only if it is solvable for all prime divisors of m. When m is a prime, solvability is shown to depend on the sign of $\varepsilon^{(m-1)/2}$ modulo m. By studying the impact of the representations of the prime m by quadratic forms on the sign of $\varepsilon^{(m-1)/2}$ modulo m, conditions (usually for the case d a prime) are given for solvability of the equation, e.g., if $d=5$, and $m=u^2-5v^2\equiv 1 \pmod 4$, then a necessary condition for the solvability of the equation is $|u|\equiv 1 \pmod 4$. If $m\equiv 5 \pmod 8$, this condition is sufficient.

Rédei [Acta Math. Acad. Sci. Hungar. **4** (1953), 31–87; MR **16**, 450] has given a solution to this problem in terms of the ideal class groups of quadratic fields. While the results given here are not as complete, they have the advantage of being arrived at by elementary methods. The author's methods and results, arrived at independently, bear a resemblance to those of Furuta [J. Math. Soc. Japan **11** (1959), 139–145; MR **22** #3716].

D. J. Lewis (Ann Arbor, Mich.)

Citations: MR 16, 450e = R14-28; MR 22# 3716 = R14-38.

Referred to in D12-47.

D12-47 (25# 3905)

Jensen, Chr. U.

Über eine Klasse nicht-Pellscher Gleichungen.

J. Reine Angew. Math. **209** (1962), 36–38.

This is a résumé of some theorems on conditions for the existence of an integral solution of the Pell-type equation $\xi^2-D\eta^2=-1$, where D is any non-square integer, the detailed proofs of which are given by the author in Math. Scand. **10** (1962), 71–74 [MR **25** #2030]. The following example is fairly typical and, incidentally, augments a classical theorem of J. Perott [J. Reine Angew. Math. **102** (1888), 185–223] for the case $D=2p^2$, p a prime $\equiv 1 \pmod 8$.

Let p be a prime $\equiv 1 \pmod{16}$, representable as $x_1^2+128y_1^2$ and as x^2+64y^2 for suitable integers x, y, x_1, y_1. If $\xi^2-2p^2\eta^2=-1$ is solvable, then

$$y+y_1\equiv\frac{p-1}{16} \bmod 2.$$

If $p\equiv 17 \pmod{32}$, this condition is also sufficient.

J. H. H. Chalk (Toronto)

Citations: MR 25# 2030 = D12-46.

D12-48 **(25# 3900)**

Chowla, S.

A remarkable solution of the Pellian equation $x^2-py^2=-4$, in the case when $p\equiv 1|(4)|$ and the class-number of $R(\sqrt{p})$ is 1.

J. Indian Math. Soc. (*N.S.*) **25** (1961), 43–46.

If the class-number of the real quadratic field $R(\sqrt{p})$, where p is a prime of the form $4k+1$, be 1 (as is the case more often than not at least when $p\leq 10009$), then the author proves that u in the Pellian $t^2-pu^2=-4$ is given by one of the two congruences

$$\pm A^2Bu \equiv A^2+B^2 \pmod{2^p-1}, \qquad 0<u<2^p-1,$$

where $A=\sum_r 2^r-\sum_n 2^n$, $B=\prod_n(2^n-1)$ and r and n run respectively over the quadratic residues and non-residues of p, $0<r$, $n<p$.

There is an obvious misprint in the value of B given in the paper. *H. Gupta* (Chandigarh)

D12-49 **(26# 3667)**

Jensen, Chr. U.

On the Diophantine equation $\xi^2-2m^2\eta^2=-1$.

Math. Scand. **11** (1962), 58–62.

The author continues his study of criteria for the solvability of equations of the type $\xi^2-dm^2\eta^2=-1$. This time he considers the equation (*) $\xi^2-2p^2\eta^2=-1$, where p is an odd prime and he outlines a proof of the following: If $p\equiv 1 \pmod{16}$ and representable in the form $p=u^2+128v^2$, then it is also representable in the form $p=x^2+64y^2$. For such p, a necessary condition for the solvability of (*) is that $y+v\equiv(p-1)/16 \pmod 2$; in case $p\equiv 17 \pmod{32}$ this condition is also sufficient. He also proves that there does not exist a residue class of integers such that (*) is solvable by all p in the class. The proofs make use of class field theory. *D. J. Lewis* (Ann Arbor, Mich.)

D12-50 **(26# 4955)**

Zeckendorf, E.

Les nombres triangulaires carrés.

Bull. Soc. Roy. Sci. Liège **30** (1961), 23–29.

The author makes some elementary remarks concerning factorization of A^2+1 and concerning the Diophantine equation $m^2-m=2s^2$, whose complete solution, $s=0, 1, 6, 35, 204, \cdots$, is easy and has been known for a long time. *J. L. Selfridge* (Seattle, Wash.)

D12-51 **(26# 4958)**

Sierpiński, W.

Sur les nombres triangulaires carrés.

Bull. Soc. Roy. Sci. Liège **30** (1961), 189–194.

A nice demonstration of the solution of the quadratic Diophantine equation $x(x+1)=2y^2$. An infinite sequence of rational right triangles is described whose legs are consecutive triangular numbers. The only known right triangle whose sides are all triangular numbers is given by $132^2(133)^2+143^2(144)^2=164^2(165)^2$. The paper concludes with some remarks about primes of the form x^2+1 and related questions. *J. L. Selfridge* (Seattle, Wash.)

D12-52 **(26# 4959)**

Sierpiński, W.

Sur les nombres triangulaires carrés.

Univ. Beograd. Publ. Elektrotehn. Fak. Ser. Mat. Fiz. *No.* 65–69 (1961), 1–4.

A new version of the paper reviewed above [#4958] minus the concluding section. *J. L. Selfridge* (Seattle, Wash.)

D12-53 **(29# 2242)**

Rodriquez, Gaetano

Forme canoniche quadratiche e cubiche nei domini d'integrità p-adici.

Ist. Lombardo Accad. Sci. Lett. Rend. A **97** (1963), 881–898.

Using simple p-adic approximations, the author discusses necessary and sufficient conditions for the solvability of equations like $x^2-\alpha y^2=\beta$ and $x^3+\alpha y^3=\beta$ for given p-adic integers α, β by p-adic integers. (The author is dealing with power series in one variable.) *O. F. G. Schilling* (Lafayette, Ind.)

D12-54 **(32# 2375)**

Schinzel, A.; Sierpiński, W.

On the equation $x^2-2y^2=k$. (Polish)

Wiadom. Mat. (2) **7**, 229–232 (1964).

The authors prove in an elementary way the following (known) theorems. Theorem 1: Let k be a natural number, q the greatest square by which k is divisible, and $r=k/q$. Equation (1) $x^2-2y^2=k$ is solvable in natural numbers x, y if and only if r is not divisible by a prime number of the form $8t\pm 3$. Theorem 2 [I. A. H. Hunter, Amer. Math. Monthly **69** (1962), 316–317, Problem 5020]. If the equation (1) is solvable in natural numbers, then the equation (2) $(x^2-k)(z^2-k)=(y^2-k)^2$ has infinitely many solutions in different natural numbers x, y, z. It follows that for $k=1$, equation (2) has infinitely many solutions in different odd natural numbers. It is not known whether even different solutions exist in this case. {Equation $t_{(x-1)/2}\cdot t_{(z-1)/2}=t_{(y-1)/2}$ on page 282 should read $t_{(x-1)/2}\cdot t_{(z-1)/2}=t^2_{(y-1)/2}$.} From this equation it follows that there exist infinitely many geometric progressions whose first three terms are three different triangular numbers. *J. W. Andrushkiw* (S. Orange, N.J.)

D12-55 **(33# 5557)**

Maurer, G. V.

Solution of certain indeterminate equations of the second degree by means of continued fractions of general type. (Russian)

Mari. Gos. Ped. Inst. Učen. Zap. **26** (1965), 431–441.

Considering convergents of the continued fractions of the form

$$\sqrt{D} = m+\frac{D-m^2}{2m}\,\frac{}{+}\,\frac{D-m^2}{2m}\,\frac{}{+}\cdots,$$

the author studies the solution of the indeterminate second degree equations (1) $x^2-Dy^2=(m^2-D)^{n+1}$, (2) $x^2-Dy^2/B=(Bm^2-D)^{2n}$, (3) $x^2+Bx-Dy^2=0$, and (4) $x^2\pm x-Dy^2=0$, where D, B and m are integers. *T. T. Tonkov* (Sofia)

D12-56 **(33# 5560)**

Selenius, Clas-Olof

Kriterien für diophantische Ungleichungen, indefinite Hauptformen und Hauptideale quadratischer Zahlkörper.

Ark. Mat. **6**, 467–483 (1966).

Let D be a positive integer which is not a square. The author shows that the integer solutions x, y of $|x^2-y^2D|<\sqrt{D}$ with $(x,y)=1$ are completely characterized by the condition that $|x|/|y|$ be a convergent of the diagonal continued fraction expansion of $\sqrt{D}$. A similar condition is obtained for the diophantine inequality

$$|x^2+xy-\tfrac14(d-1)y^2| < \tfrac12\sqrt{d},$$

where $d-1$ is a positive integer divisible by 4. Obvious

consequences for the norms in quadratic number fields are drawn. The proofs are elementary, and make use of well-known properties of continued fractions.

O. H. Körner (Marburg)

Referred to in D12-57.

D12-57 (34# 2559)

Selenius, Clas-Olof

Kriterien für Zahlen quadratischer Zahlkörper mit Normbetrag kleiner als die Quadratwurzel aus der Diskriminante.

Acta Acad. Åbo. Ser. B **26** (1966), *no.* 3, 23 *pp.*

Let $x+\omega y$ be an integer of the real quadratic field $K=Q(\sqrt{d})$, where 1, ω denotes an integral basis for K, which is equal to $[1, \frac{1}{2}\sqrt{d}]$ or $[1, \frac{1}{2}(1+\sqrt{d})]$ in case $d\equiv 0$ or 1 (mod 4), respectively. The norm of $x+\omega y$ may then be written in the form $N(x+\omega y)=N_\eta(x, y)=x^2+\eta xy-\frac{1}{4}(d-\eta)y^2$, $\eta=0$ or 1, respectively.

The author considers the question of the integers whose norms are less than $\sqrt{d}$ in absolute value, i.e., the solution of the inequality (*) $N(x+\omega y)<\sqrt{d}$, $\eta=0, 1$; $(x, y)=1$.

In a previous work [Ark. Mat. **6**, 467–483 (1966); MR **33** #5560] the author derived a general necessary and sufficient condition for the solution of the inequality $|N(x+\omega y)|<\frac{1}{2}\sqrt{d}$ and also replaced a necessary condition of Lagrange [*Œuvres de Lagrange*, Vol. 7, pp. 5–180, Gauthiers-Villars, Paris, 1877] for the solutions of the equation $x^2-Dy^2=L$, $0<|L|<\frac{1}{2}\sqrt{d}=\sqrt{D}$, by a more general criterion.

Hurwitz [Math. Ann. **44** (1894), 417–436] found a necessary but not sufficient condition for the solutions of (*). In the present paper the author uses a method of convergence approximation to derive a necessary and sufficient condition for the solutions of (*). These conditions are based upon the properties of the neighboring fractions of the number $\frac{1}{2}(-\eta \operatorname{sgn} xy+\sqrt{d})$.

R. Finkelstein (Tucson, Ariz.)

Citations: MR 33# 5560 = D12-56.

D12-58 (34# 7449)

Battaglia, Antonio

Sulla risoluzione in numeri naturali dell'equazione indeterminata $x^2+x+1=ky^2$.

Archimede **18** (1966), 312–316.

Generalizing a procedure of A. Schinzel and W. Sierpiński [Colloq. Math. **4** (1956), 71–73; MR **17**, 1055], G. Palamà determined all integral solutions of $x^2+mx+p=(p+m+1)y^2$ for integral p and $m=1, 2$ [Boll. Un. Mat. Ital. (3) **12** (1957), 636–647; MR **19**, 941]. D. H. Lehmer, in his review of Palamà's paper, pointed out a generalization to all integral m; the present author generalizes Schinzel's and Sierpiński's result in a different direction. The equation in the title is obtained from $x^2-zx+z^2=ky^2$ for $z=-1$. Setting $X=x/y$, $Y=z/y$, the equation becomes $X^2-XY+Y^2=k$. Knowledge of one rational point on this ellipse permits one to find all of them, the integers x, y and z being represented each by a quadratic polynomial in two integral variables α, β. The author restricts himself (needlessly, it seems to the reviewer) to two cases in which the condition $z=z(\alpha, \beta)=-1$ is equivalent to the classical Pell equation. One knows how to obtain all solutions (α_n, β_n) of the latter and each pair (α_n, β_n) yields corresponding solutions $x=x(\alpha_n, \beta_n)$, $y=y(\alpha_n, \beta_n)$ of the equation in the title. {The paper is marred by a very large number of small (presumably typographical) errors.}

E. Grosswald (Philadelphia, Pa.)

Citations: MR 17, 1055j = D12-34; MR 19, 941g = D12-38.

D12-59 (35# 2829)

Walker, D. T.

On the diophantine equation $mX^2-nY^2=\pm 1$.

Amer. Math. Monthly **74** (1967), 504–513.

The paper develops a formula for all solutions in natural numbers of the equation of the title. {Reviewer's remark: This result can be obtained from a formula for the solutions of the Diophantine equation $u^2-Dv^2=\pm N$, or $=\pm 4N$, proved by T. Nagell [*Elementary number theory* (Swedish), Almqvist and Wiksells, Uppsala, 1950; MR **11**, 640] and extended by the reviewer [Ark. Mat. **2** (1952), 1–23; MR **14**, 247; ibid. **2** (1952), 251–268; MR **14**, 354; ibid. **3** (1955), 117–132; MR **16**, 903].} The author also proves a theorem on the prime factors of Y and n.

B. Stolt (Stockholm)

Citations: MR 11, 640d = Z01-12; MR 14, 247e = D12-21; MR 14, 354a = D12-22; MR 16, 903e = D12-31.

D12-60 (35# 6623)

Schmidt, Hermann

Über das Kettenbruchverfahren von Patz und Arwin zur Darstellung von Zahlen durch positiv definite binäre quadratische Formen.

Bayer. Akad. Wiss. Math.-Natur. Kl. S.-B. **1966**, *Abt. II*, 5–12 (1967).

A theorem is given on the solutions (x, y) of $x^2+Dy^2=L$, $|x|$, $|y|\in N$, $(x, y)=1$, $(y, L)=1$, where D, L are in the region N of natural numbers. A second theorem deals with solutions of $x^2+Dy^2=Q_0z$, $L=Q_0$.

E. Frank (Chicago, Ill.)

D12-61 (38# 112)

Lind, D. A.

The quadratic field $Q(\sqrt{5})$ and a certain Diophantine equation.

Fibonacci Quart. **6** (1968), *no.* 3, 86–93.

The author gives an elementary treatment of the diophantine equation (1) $x^2-5y^2=\pm 4$, and expresses the solutions by means of Fibonacci and Lucas numbers. Finally he investigates the binomial coefficients equation $\binom{n}{k}=\binom{n-1}{k+1}$, the solution of which is shown to depend on the solution of an equation of type (1). *W. Ljunggren* (Oslo)

D12-62 (38# 1058)

Grosswald, Emil

On a classical Diophantine equation.

Boll. Un. Mat. Ital. (4) **1** (1968), 382–392.

In the present paper the author obtains formulae which yield an infinite set of integral solutions of the Diophantine equation (1) $ax^2+bx+c=ky^2$, subject to the conditions $k\neq g^2$, $d=b^2-4ac\neq m^2$, $d+4k=q^2$. In particular, he proves the following theorem: Let b, c and k be positive integers, with k and $d=b^2-4c$ not squares, but such that $d+4k=q^2$ for some integer q; set $q_1=\frac{1}{2}(q-b)$. Then (1) has an infinite set of integral solutions given by (2) $x=P_1(\alpha, \beta)$, $y=\pm P_2(\alpha, \beta)$, or equivalently by (2′) $x=P_1'(\alpha, \beta)$, $y=\pm P_2(\alpha, \beta)$, where $P_1(\alpha, \beta)=-(q_1+b)\beta^2-2c\alpha\beta+cq_1\alpha^2$, $P_1'(\alpha, \beta)=q_1\beta^2+2(c+bq_1)\alpha\beta+(bc+q_1b^2-q_1c)\alpha^2$, $P_2(\alpha, \beta)=\beta^2+b\alpha\beta+c\alpha^2$, and where α, β run through the coprime integral solutions of the system $\gamma^2-k\alpha^2=1$, $\gamma>0$, $\beta=\gamma+q_1\alpha$.

Further, the author proves several additional theorems which yield further restrictions on (1) such that no solutions other than (2) exist.

Finally, some particular cases of (1) are solved, and the author discusses some open problems connected with (1) when the restriction $d+4k=q^2$ is dropped.

R. Finkelstein (Bowling Green, Ohio)

Referred to in D08-55.

D12-63 **(38# 3224)**

Mrowka, Erwin

Die Frage der Lösbarkeit von diophantischen Gleichungen der Gestalt $x^2+qy^2=p$ für $-q\equiv 1$ (8) und Angabe von Lösungen für auflösbare Gleichungen (p und q ungerade Primzahlen und $p\neq q$).

Wiss. Z. Hochsch. Verkehrswesen "Friedrich List" Dresden **12** (1965), 15–16.

The author gives solvability conditions for the equation in the title. *B. Stolt* (Stockholm)

D12-64 **(39# 171)**

Mordell, L. J.

The integer solutions of the equation $ax^2+by^2+c=0$ in quadratic fields.

Bull. London Math. Soc. **1** (1969), 43–44.

Let a, b, and c be rational integers that are relatively prime in pairs, and let a and b be square-free. Necessary and sufficient conditions are found for the existence of integer solutions of the equation $ax^2+by^2+c=0$ in a quadratic field $Q(t)$. *W. H. Mills* (Princeton, N.J.)

D12-65 **(39# 2697)**

Emersleben, Otto

Über zweite Binomialkoeffizienten, die Quadratzahlen sind, und Anwendung der Pellschen Gleichung auf Gitterpunktanordnungen.

Wiss. Z. Ernst-Moritz-Arndt-Univ. Greifswald Math.-Natur. Reihe **16** (1967), 279–296. (*Loose errata*)

This paper contains a lengthy elementary discussion of the Diophantine equations $n(n+1)=2u^2$ and $n^2+(n+1)^2=u^2$, with remarks on lattice arrangements, and some notes on Landau's work. {Not all numerical errors are noted in the errata sheet.} *H. J. Godwin* (London)

D12-66 **(41# 1628)**

Emerson, Edgar I.

Recurrent sequences in the equation $DQ^2=R^2+N$.

Fibonacci Quart. **7** (1969), *no.* 3, 231–242.

For a given $D>1$ and not a square, the complete Pell equations are of one of the two forms $DY_n^2=X_n^2-(-1)^n$ or $DY_n^2=X_n^2-1$, $n\geqq 0$. In terms of the non-trivial fundamental solution (X_1, Y_1), the general solution is given by $X_n+Y_n\sqrt{D}=(X_1+Y_1\sqrt{D})^n$. The author shows how this implies that $X_{n+1}=2X_1X_n\pm X_{n-1}$, $Y_{n+1}=2X_1Y_n\pm Y_{n-1}$ with $X_0=1$, $Y_0=0$, the + or − sign being taken according as the fundamental equation is $DY_1^2=X_1^2+1$ or $DY_1^2=X_1^2-1$. The Lagrange equation the author proposes to consider in a later communication.

H. Gupta (Allahabad)

D12-67 **(42# 183)**

Kočegura, V. K.

Pell's equation and certain arithmetic semigroups. (Russian)

Orenburg. Gos. Ped. Inst. Učen. Zap. Vyp. 21 (1967), 81–91.

Purports to use the elementary theory of semi-groups to prove the existence of a non-trivial solution of Pell's equation. *J. W. S. Cassels* (Cambridge, England)

D12-68 **(42# 1760)**

Ginatempo, Nicola

Ulteriore abbassamento del limite superiore dei tentativi da fare avere per la soluzione minima della equazione di Pell-Fermat. (English summary)

Atti Soc. Peloritana Sci. Fis. Mat. Natur. **14** (1968), 513–522.

Let (x_1, y_1) be the fundamental solution of the Pell equation $x^2-Dy^2=1$. The author considers the problem of obtaining an upper bound for x_1. {His results are invalidated by his assumption that the length of the period of the regular continued fraction for $\sqrt{D}$ cannot exceed $\sqrt{D}$. He is apparently unaware of the fact that when $D=10009$ this length is 131.}

D. H. Lehmer (Berkeley, Calif.)

D12-69 **(43# 154)**

Nagell, Trygve

Über die Lösbarkeit gewisser diophantischer Gleichungen zweiten Grades.

Arch. Math. (*Basel*) **21** (1970), 487–489.

Let D and p denote given natural numbers, $D>1$ and p an odd prime where $(p, D)=1$. Further, let A and B denote variable natural numbers such that $AB=D$ and $A<B$. It is proved that among the diophantine equations $Ax^2+By^2=Cp$, $C=1$ or 2, at most one is solvable in natural numbers x and y if $(C, D)=1$. *W. Ljunggren* (Oslo)

D12-70 **(43# 4760)**

Ginatempo, Nicola

Il metodo dei tentativi per la risoluzione della equazione di Pell-Fermat.

Istituto di Matematica dell'Università di Messina, Pubblicazione No. 1.

Nicola Ginatempo, Catania, 1966. 5 *pp.* *n.p.*

The author uses the theory of the continued fraction of $\sqrt{D}$, D not a square, to show that the equation $x^2-Dy^2=1$ always has a non-trivial solution satisfying $x<(q+1)E$, $y<E$ where $E=2(q+1)(\frac{2}{3}q+1)^{2q}$ and $q=[\sqrt{D}]$.

R. F. Churchhouse (Cardiff)

D12-71 **(43# 6156)**

Finkelstein, Raphael; Karst, Edgar; London, Hymie

Application of recursive sequences to Diophantine equations.

Fibonacci Quart. **8** (1970), *no.* 5, 463–469.

The authors show how to solve various diophantine equations by linear recurrence algorithms, analogous to the solution of the Pell equation (essentially) by multiplying by a unit. Some typical cases are $3a^2-2b^2=1$, $1+2a^2=b^2$, $x^2+y^2+z^2=w^2$, etc.

Harvey Cohn (New York)

D12-72 **(44# 149)**

Chowla, S.

A note concerning a problem related to Hilbert's tenth problem.

Norske Vid. Selsk. Skr. (*Trondheim*) **1970**, *no.* 5, 2 *pp.*

The author states that he recently proved the following theorem: Let p denote a prime $\equiv 1 \pmod 4$ and let $p=a^2+b^2$, $2|b$; then the equation (1) $x^2-py^2=2b$ is solvable with x and y in Z. By means of this theorem and on the assumption that for any even b there exist infinitely many primes p such that $p=a^2+b^2$, the author gives a positive answer to the following question: Let A be an arbitrary large positive number; do there exist infinitely many primes p satisfying (1) with $x > p^A$, x being the smallest positive solution of (1)? *W. Ljunggren* (Oslo)

D12-73 **(44# 2695)**

Chowla, S.
Some results and problems in number theory.
Acta Arith. **18** (1971), 273–274.
A brief announcement of results, one of which will appear in a paper in J. Reine Angew. Math.

D12-74 **(44# 5273)**

Nagell, Trygve
Sur la solubilité en nombres entiers des équations du second degré à deux indéterminées.
Acta Arith. **18** (1971), 105–114.
Let D be a square-free integer greater than 1, and let p be a prime not dividing D. We consider the set of all Diophantine equations of the form $Ax^2 - By^2 = Ep$, where $1 \leq A < B$, $AB = D$, and $E = \pm 1$ if D is even, $E = \pm 1$ or ± 2 if D is odd. If any of these equations has integer solutions, then it is shown that exactly two of them have integer solutions. The same methods can be used to study the set of equations $Ax^2 - By^2 = EN$, where A, B and E satisfy the same conditions as before and N is composite. The proofs are based on earlier results of the author on the case $N = 1$ [Ark. Mat. **3** (1954), 51–65; MR **15**, 854].
W. H. Mills (Princeton, N.J.)

Citations: MR 15, 854e = D12-29.

D16 QUADRATIC EQUATIONS: PYTHAGOREAN EQUATIONS

See also reviews B36-39, B36-103, D08-3, D08-19, D08-59, D12-51, D12-71, D20-2, D20-12, D20-13, D20-20, D20-22, D32-32, D32-60, D36-7, D36-29, D60-32, D60-41, D60-48, D60-66, E24-7, E24-43, E24-72, E24-120, N52-42, Z15-2, Z15-11, Z15-15, Z15-29, Z15-52, Z15-79, Z15-82, Z15-87, Z30-24.

D16-1 **(2, 247g)**

Reitan, L. Some considerations on a problem in number theory. Norsk Mat. Tidsskr. **22**, 110–115 (1940). (Norwegian)
Elementary considerations connected with the Diophantine equation $m^2 = x^2 + y^2 + z^2$. *W. Feller.*

Referred to in A26-3.

D16-2 **(3, 161c)**

Barnett, I. A. and Mendel, C. W. Pythagorean points lying in a plane. Amer. Math. Monthly **48**, 610–616 (1941).
The authors study the system of Diophantine equations $x^2 + y^2 = z^2$, $Ax + By + Cz = D$, with A, B, C relatively prime, that is, they determine the lattice points on a certain conic section in space. By using the solutions $x = \frac{1}{2}\rho(u^2 - v^2)$, $y = \rho uv$, $z = \frac{1}{2}\rho(u^2 + v^2)$ of the first equation, the second equation becomes $(C+A)u^2 + 2Buv + (C-A)v^2 = 2D/\rho$. Hence $2D/\rho$ has to be represented by this binary quadratic form in u, v; the discriminant of this form is $\Delta = A^2 + B^2 - C^2$. In addition certain conditions of parity have to be satisfied. When $D = 0$ (degenerate conic) the system is homogeneous and solutions exist if and only if Δ is a perfect square. When $D \neq 0$ there are three cases: (1) $\Delta < 0$ (ellipse), the number of solutions is finite (possibly 0); (2) $\Delta = 0$ (parabola), there are infinitely many solutions; (3) $\Delta > 0$ (hyperbola), there are infinitely many solutions or none at all. These results are obtained without explicit use of the theory of quadratic forms, although properties of the Pellian equation are used in the discussion of case 3.
H. W. Brinkmann (Swarthmore, Pa.).

D16-3 **(3, 268a)**

Aude, H. T. R. Primitive integral triangles. Nat. Math. Mag. **16**, 280–283 (1942).
This paper is concerned with the parametric representation of the sides a, b, c of an integral triangle in which the cosine of the angle C between a and b has a specified rational value r/s. It is found that

$$a : b : c = 2n(ms - nr) : s(m^2 - n^2) : (m^2 s - 2mnr + n^2 s),$$

where m, n are a pair of coprime integers. A similar triangle is given by $m' = (m+n)s - 2nr$, $n' = (m-n)s$. The cases of $C = 120°$, $60°$ and arccos $(-1/4)$ are considered in detail.
D. H. Lehmer (Berkeley, Calif.).

D16-4 **(3, 268f)**

Olds, C. D. On the number of representations of the square of an integer as the sum of three squares. Amer. J. Math. **63**, 763–767 (1941).
By using a Liouville identity of J. V. Uspensky [Bull. Acad. Sci. USSR **20**, 327–348 (1926)] an elementary proof is obtained of the formula for the number of solutions of $n^2 = x^2 + y^2 + z^2$. *G. Pall* (Montreal, P. Q.).

D16-5 **(5, 199c)**

Whitlock, W. P., Jr. Rational right triangles with equal areas. Scripta Math. **9**, 155–161 (1943).

Referred to in D16-6, D16-17.

D16-6 **(6, 36b)**

Whitlock, W. P., Jr. Rational right triangles with equal areas. Scripta Math. **9**, 265–267 (1943).
Continuation of the article in the same journal **9**, 155–161 (1943); these Rev. **5**, 199.

Citations: MR 5, 199c = D16-5.

D16-7 **(7, 242b)**

Levi, Beppo. On a Diophantine problem. Math. Notae **5**, 108–119 (1945). (Spanish)
The paper concerns a problem proposed in the same journal: find integral sides of a right-angled triangle which again form a right-angled triangle when a digit is prefixed. The two answers submitted claimed that 5, 12, 13; 15, 112, 113 is the only solution. The author shows that, on the contrary, there are an infinite number of families of solutions. For example, one such family is $6 \cdot 10^{n+2}$, $1125 \cdot 10^{2n+1} \pm 8$ for $n = 0, 1, \cdots$, with 2 the digit to be prefixed. The method is an elementary case by case reduction. *I. Kaplansky.*

Referred to in D16-9.

D16-8 **(7, 242c)**

Santaló, L. A. Addendum to the note "On a Diophantine problem." Math. Notae **5**, 162–171 (1945). (Spanish)
Continuing Levi's analysis [cf. the preceding review], the author shows that the prefixed digit a must satisfy $1 \leqq a \leqq 7$, in each of which cases there are an infinite number of solutions. *I. Kaplansky* (Chicago, Ill.).

Referred to in D16-9.

D16-9 **(7, 413c)**

Sagastume Berra, Alberto E. New considerations on a Diophantine problem. Math. Notae **5**, 215–224 (1945). (Spanish)

The problem discussed for radix 10 by Levi and Santaló [Math. Notae **5**, 108–119, 162–171 (1945); these Rev. **7**, 242] is generalized to arbitrary radix. *I. Kaplansky.*

Citations: MR 7, 242b = D16-7; MR 7, 242c = D16-8.

D16-10 (9, 568b; 9, 568c)

Carrese, Pietro. Alcune proprietà delle terne pitagoriche intere. Matematiche, Catania **1**, 163–170 (1946).
Carrese, Pietro. Qualche altra proprietà delle terne pitagoriche intere. Matematiche, Catania **2**, 80–83 (1947).

D16-11 (10, 431c)

Lehmer, D. H. A conjecture of Krishnaswami. Bull. Amer. Math. Soc. **54**, 1185–1190 (1948).

Let $T(N)$ denote the number of right triangles whose perimeters do not exceed $2N$ and whose sides are relatively prime. Krishnaswami Ayyangar [Tôhoku Math. J. **27**, 332–348 (1926)] conjectured that $T(N) \sim N/7$. In the present paper it is proved that $T(N) = \pi^{-2}N \log 4 + O(N^{\frac{1}{2}} \log N)$.
W. H. Simons (Vancouver, B. C.).

Referred to in D16-17.

D16-12 (11, 82a)

Buquet, A. Comparaison de différentes solutions de l'équation diophantienne (1) $x^2+y^2+z^2=t^2$. Mathesis **58**, 70–73 (1949).

D16-13 (13, 436g)

Droop, Goswin. On the classification of Pythagorean triples. Revista Soc. Cubana Ci. Fís. Mat. **2**, 163–169 (1950). (Spanish)

D16-14 (14, 724d)

Moessner, Alfred. A property of Pythagorean numbers. Riveon Lematematika **6**, 27 (1953). (Hebrew)

D16-15 (16, 447i)

Sierpiński, Wacław. Trójkąty pitagorejskie. [Pythagorean triangles.] Państwowe Wydawnictwo Naukowe, Warszawa, 1954. 94 pp. zł. 7.50.

This is an expository account of some dozen problems connected with rational right triangles considered by Diophantus, Fermat, Euler and others. The booklet is intended to stimulate the interest of teachers of elementary mathematics. *D. H. Lehmer* (Berkeley, Calif.).

Referred to in D16-16.

D16-16 (33# 97)

Sierpiński, Wacław
Pythagorean triangles.
Translated by Ambikeshwar Sharma. The Scripta Mathematica Studies, No. 9.
Published by Graduate School of Science, Yeshiva University, New York, 1962. viii + 107 *pp.* $2.50.

This is a very readable translation of the Polish original [Państ. Wydawn. Nauk., Warsaw, 1954; MR **16**, 447], with some six pages of additional material.
E. S. Barnes (Adelaide)

Citations: MR 16, 447i = D16-15.

D16-17 (16, 796h)

Lambek, J., and Moser, L. On the distribution of Pythagorean triangles. Pacific J. Math. **5**, 73–83 (1955).

Let $P_h(n)$, $P_p(n)$ and $P_a(n)$ denote respectively the number of primitive Pythagorean triangles whose hypotenuses, perimeters and areas do not exceed n. D. N. Lehmer [Amer. J. Math. **22**, 293–335 (1900)] showed that

$$P_h(n) \sim n/(2\pi), \quad P_p(n) \sim n \log 2/\pi^2.$$

Recently the reviewer proved that

$$(1) \qquad P_p(n) = n \log 2/\pi^2 + O(n^{1/2} \log n)$$

[Bull. Amer. Math. Soc. **54**, 1185–1190 (1948); MR **10**, 431]. W. P. Whitlock [Scripta Math. **9**, 155–161 (1943); MR **5**, 199] conjectured that $P_a(n) \sim \frac{1}{2}n^{1/2}$. The inspection of an unpublished table of F. L. Miksa showed the authors that $P_a(n)$ behaves more like $.53n^{1/2}$. By a uniform method the authors prove not only (1) but

$$(2) \qquad P_h(n) = n/(2\pi) + O(n^{1/2} \log n), \quad P_a(n) = cn^{1/2} + O(n^{1/3}),$$

where $c = \{\Gamma(1/4)\}^2/(2\pi^5)^{1/2} = .531340$. All three problems are replaced, as usual, by that of determining the number of lattice points in appropriate regions of the plane.

In the case of $P_a(n)$ the region is $xy(x^2-y^2)<n$, $0<x<y$. The number of lattice points in this region is found to be

$$L(n) = n^{1/2}\{\Gamma(1/4)\}^2/(32\pi)^{1/2} + O(n^{1/3})$$

from which (2) follows easily. It is conjectured that

$$P_a(n) = cn^{1/2} - c'n^{1/3} + O(n^{1/3}),$$

where c' is about .295. *D. H. Lehmer* (Berkeley, Calif.).

Citations: MR 5, 199c = D16-5; MR 10, 431c = D16-11.

D16-18 (16, 797a)

Wild, Roy E. On the number of primitive Pythagorean triangles with area less than n. Pacific J. Math. **5**, 85–91 (1955).

Referring to the preceding review, the author proves the conjecture about $P_a(n)$, namely that the number of primitive Pythagorean triangles whose area does not exceed n is

$$P_a(n) = cn^{1/2} - c'n^{1/3} + O(n^{1/4} \log n)$$

where

$$c = \{\Gamma(1/4)\}^2/(2\pi^5)^{1/2}, \quad c' = -\frac{(1+2^{-1/3})\zeta(1/3)}{(1+4^{-1/3})\zeta(4/3)} = .297.$$

The author considers the number of lattice points in the first quadrant and under the curve $xy(x+y)(2x+y)=n$. This transformed region is much more like the classical hyperbolic region $xy \leqq n$ and by a judicious choice of a rectangle with one corner in the origin an estimate with an error of only $O(n^{1/4})$ for the number of lattice points is found via the Euler-MacLaurin formula. *D. H. Lehmer.*

D16-19 (18, 380b)

Steiger, Franz. Über die Grundlösungen der Gleichung $a^2+b^2+c^2=d^2$. Elem. Math. **11** (1956), 105–108.

A set of formulas involving four integral parameters is announced for the solutions in integers of $a^2+b^2+c^2=d^2$. The formulas give each fundamental solution (such that $(a, b, c, d)=1$) exactly once. Proofs will be given later.

I. Niven (Eugene, Ore.).

D16-20 (19, 250a)

Dittmann, Gerd. Über eine Verallgemeinerung der Pythagoreischen Zahlen. Wiss. Z. Pädagog. Hochschr. Potsdam. Math.-Nat. Reihe **2** (1955/1956), 261–263.

D16-21 (20# 20)

Pignataro, Salvatore. Sulle terne pitagoriche. Ricerca, Napoli (2) **8** (1957), Gennaio-Giugno, 73–98.

The author has considered the integral right triangles whose legs are consecutive integers [Archimede **6** (1954), 185]. In the present paper he studies triangles whose legs

...ffer by a constant. Sequences of such triangles arise out of the multiple solutions of the Pell equation and hence have sides satisfying second order linear recurrences. The treatment is in great detail.

D. H. Lehmer (Cambridge, England)

D16-22 **(20# 1659)**

Barreneche, Rodrigo Noguera. The problem of rational quadrature of the right triangle with integral sides and other minutiae. Stvdia. Rev. Univ. Atlantico **2** (1957), 211–221. (Spanish)

D16-23 **(20# 3808)**

Hazanov, M. B. Formulas for Pythagorean numbers. Kabardin. Gos. Ped. Inst. Uč. Zap. **12** (1957), 14. (Russian)

An elementary method is given for determining all Pythagorean triples x, y, z; that is, such that $x^2+y^2=z^2$.

D16-24 **(21# 4125)**

Sierpiński, W. On Pythagorean triangles with equal areas. Wiadom. Mat. (2) **1** (1955/56), 163–168. (Polish)

The author generalizes Fermat's theorem on incongruent equiareal Pythagorean triangles to: if among $n \geqq 1$ equiareal Pythagorean triangles with distinct hypothenuses at least one has a hypothenuse of odd length, then there exist $n+1$ equiareal Pythagorean triangles with distinct hypothenuses one of which has odd length. Some questions concerning primitive, isoperimetric, minimal, etc., sets of Pythagorean triangles are also considered and answered.

Z. A. Melzak (Murray Hill, N.J.)

D16-25 **(22# 4655)**

Świerczkowski, S. On Pythagorean angles. Colloq. Math. **7** (1959), 103–105.

An angle α is called Pythagorean if it is congruent modulo $\pi/2$ to an angle of a right triangle, the lengths of whose sides are integers. The author proves that the Pythagorean angles are precisely those that are sums (modulo $\pi/2$) of the Pythagorean angles that arise from primes of the form $p=4k+1$ in the well-known way (i.e.. the uniquely determined Pythagorean angles which correspond to triangles whose hypotenuse is p).

L. A. Rubel (Urbana, Ill.)

D16-26 **(23# A105)**

Sierpiński, W.

On a certain problem of Fermat. (Polish)

Wiadom Mat. (2) **4**, 177–181 (1961).

Fermat raised the following problem: to find right triangles with integer sides such that sum of the legs is a given number A. The author shows that a necessary and sufficient condition that an integer A be a sum of legs of a Pythagorean triangle is that A be divisible at least by one prime of the form $8k \pm 1$.

S. Knapowski (Poznań)

D16-27 **(23# A106)**

Sierpiński, W.

A remark on Pythagorean triangles. (Polish)

Wiadom. Mat. (2) **4**, 185 (1961).

The author proves the following theorem: For every Pythagorean triangle (a, b, c) and for every positive integer n there exists a triangle similar to (a, b, c), each side of which is an integer power with exponent $\geqq n$.

S. Knapowski (Poznań)

D16-28 **(24# A2549)**

Mariani, J.

The group of the Pythagorean numbers.

Amer. Math. Monthly **69** (1962), 125–128.

The author considers the group $\bar{G}$ of all homogeneous linear transformations of integers x, y, z with integral coefficients, which leave $x^2+y^2-z^2$ invariant. Calling three integers x, y, z a proper Pythagorean triplet if they have no common divisor $\neq \pm 1$, if x is even, $z>0$ and if $x^2+y^2=z^2$, the author defines a subgroup G of $\bar{G}$ including in G those transformations which map proper Pythagorean triplets onto proper Pythagorean triplets and have determinant ± 1. He then proves some simple properties of the groups G and $\bar{G}$.

S. Knapowski (Poznań)

Referred to in E28-43.

D16-29 **(24# A2564)**

Mjakišev, V. P.

Distribution of primitive integral points on certain cones. (Russian)

Dokl. Akad. Nauk SSSR **143** (1962), 785–786.

The author proves the following theorem. Let $A(h)$ denote the number of points (x, y, z), where x, y, z are integers and have no common divisor >1, which satisfy $x^2+y^2-z^2=0$ and $0<z\leqq h$. Then $A(h)=(4/\pi)h+O(h^{1/2})$ as $h\to\infty$. Also some more general results are formulated.

S. Knapowski (Poznań)

D16-30 **(25# 3006)**

Spira, Robert

The Diophantine equation $x^2+y^2+z^2=m^2$.

Amer. Math. Monthly **69** (1962), 360–364.

In this elementary expository note, the author proves the known parametric expression for the primitive integral solutions of the title equation. He applies this expression to the important equation $x^4+y^4+z^4=m^4$, but does not go very far.

B. J. Birch (Manchester)

D16-31 **(26# 4975)**

Sárközy, András

Lattice cubes in 3-space. (Hungarian. Russian summary)

Mat. Lapok **12** (1961), 232–245.

Let R be a cube whose vertices have integral coordinates and one of whose vertices is the origin. R is called oblique (skew) if none of its edges is perpendicular to any of the axes, and it is simple if the coordinates of all the vertices have no common factor. Denote by n the length of the edge of our cube. The author proves among others that a simple cube of length n exists if and only if n is odd, a simple and oblique cube of length n exists if and only if n is odd and $n\neq 1$, $n\neq 5$, $n\neq 25$. Finally an oblique cube of length n exists if and only if $n\neq 2^\alpha$, $n\neq 5\cdot 2^\alpha, n\neq 25\cdot 2^\alpha$ $(\alpha=0, 1, \cdots)$. The author also determines the number of these cubes of length n and gives methods for their construction.

P. Erdős (London)

D16-32 **(32# 7491)**

Barning, F. J. M.

On Pythagorean and quasi-Pythagorean triangles and a generation process with the help of unimodular matrices. (Dutch)

Math. Centrum Amsterdam Afd. Zuivere Wisk. **1963**, ZW-011, 37 *pp.*

The author considers the set P of all irreducible Pythagorean triangles (x, y, z), where the x, y, z are positive integers with $x^2+y^2=z^2$, such that $(x, y)=1$ and x is even.

In order to generate the set P he considers each triple (x, y, z) as a vector and then introduces the unimodular transformations

$$A_1=\begin{pmatrix}1 & 2 & 2\\ 2 & 1 & 2\\ 2 & 2 & 3\end{pmatrix},\quad A_2=\begin{pmatrix}1 & -2 & 2\\ 2 & -1 & 2\\ 2 & -2 & 3\end{pmatrix},\quad A_3=\begin{pmatrix}-1 & 2 & 2\\ -2 & 1 & 2\\ -2 & 2 & 3\end{pmatrix},$$

which leave the quadratic form $x^2+y^2-z^2$ invariant. By a method of infinite descent, he shows that every element of P can be generated in exactly one way by starting from (4, 3, 5) and applying the transformations A_1, A_2, A_3 successively.

His method allows him to treat in a similar way the set BP of quasi-Pythagorean triangles (x, y, z), where the x, y, z are positive integers such that $x^2+y^2=z^2\pm 1$.

Much attention is paid to certain subsets of P and BP which arise in a natural way by means of the generating process described above. *J. Popken* (Amstelveen)

Referred to in D08-58.

D16-33 (34# 1268)

Sexauer, N. E.

Pythagorean triples over Gaussian domains.

Amer. Math. Monthly **73** (1966), 829–834.

The Diophantine equation $x^2+y^2=z^2$ is studied over certain Gaussian domains of characteristic zero. As an application, the complete solution of this equation over the Gaussian integers is obtained.

W. H. Mills (Princeton, N.J.)

D16-34 (35# 6618)

Henneman, F.

A theorem of D. N. Lehmer from the theory of numbers. (Dutch)

Nieuw Arch. Wisk. (3) **15** (1967), 7–10.

D. N. Lehmer's paper [Amer. J. Math. **22** (1900), 293–335] contains, as a very special case of a general theorem, the following result: The relative frequency as $N\to\infty$ of all primitive Pythagorean triangles with hypotenuse $\leqq N$ is $1/2\pi$ [pp. 327–328].

The author tries to give a simple and direct proof of this result. {However, this attempt is not more than an intuitive probabilistic approach. For instance, the author uses without proof that the three sets of relative prime positive integers (i, j) with $i^2+j^2\leqq N$ given by (1) i and j both odd, (2) i odd and j even, and (3) i even and j odd, have the same relative frequency as $N\to\infty$.}

J. Popken (Amstelveen)

D16-35 (37# 4003)

Sexauer, N. E.

Pythagorean triples over Gaussian domains with fundamental units.

Amer. Math. Monthly **75** (1968), 278–279.

Formulas for primitive solutions of $x^2+y^2=z^2$ over certain Gaussian domains are presented. The complications, as contrasted with the rational integral case, arise from the fact that 2 is no longer necessarily prime.

J. B. Kelly (Tempe, Ariz.)

D16-36 (38# 5713)

Šindelář, Karel

A note on Pythagorean triangles. (Slovak. English summary)

Mat. Časopis Sloven. Akad. Vied **18** (1968), 144–147.

The author shows that if n is a natural number, then there are $\varepsilon(n)$ Pythagorean triangles (i.e., triples of natural numbers (a, b, c) such that $a^2+b^2=c^2$) with one side equal to n, where, if n is odd, $\varepsilon(n)$ is the number of natural numbers $h<n$ that divide n^2, and $a=n$, $b=(n^2-h^2)/(2h)$, $c=(n^2+h^2)/(2h)$, while, if n is even, $\varepsilon(n)$ is the number of natural numbers $h<\frac{1}{2}n$ that divide $(\frac{1}{2}n)^2$, and $a=n$, $b=h^{-1}(\frac{1}{2}n)^2-h$, $c=h^{-1}(\frac{1}{2}n)^2+h$.

D16-37 (39# 5475)

Nobusawa, Nobuo

On the distribution of integer solutions of $f(x, y)=z^2$ for a definite binary quadratic form f.

Canad. Math. Bull. **10** (1967), 755–756.

Let f be a positive definite binary quadratic form with rational coefficients. An integral point (x, y) in the plane is called a Pythagorean point of f if $f(x, y)$ is the square of a positive integer. It is proved that inside a region of the plane bounded by two parallel lines one of which passes through the origin and a Pythagorean point of f, there are at most finitely many Pythagorean points of f.

A. C. Woods (Columbus, Ohio)

D16-38 (41# 3388)

Fraser, Owen; Gordon, Basil

On representing a square as the sum of three squares.

Amer. Math. Monthly **76** (1969), 922–923.

The authors give an elementary proof of the following theorem stated by A. Hurwitz [*Mathematische Werke. Band 2. Zalentheorie,. Algebra und Geometrie*, p. 751, Birkhäuser, Basel, 1933; reprinting, 1963; MR **27** #4723b]: The equation $n^2=x^2+y^2+z^2$ has a solution in positive integers x, y, z if and only if n is not of the form 2^k or $2^k\cdot 5$. *T. Hayashida* (Yokohama)

Citations: MR 27# 4723b = Z25-18.

D16-39 (42# 7591)

Heller, Siegfried

Untersuchungen über die Lösungen der Fermatschen Dreiecksaufgabe.

Rev. Mat. Hisp.-Amer. (4) **29** (1969), 195–210; *ibid.* (4) **30** (1970), 68–98.

In diesem ersten Teil seiner Ausführungen gibt der leider inzwischen verstorbene Verfasser das in einem Aufsatz des Referenten [dieselbe Rev. (4) **29** (1969), 13–50; MR **39** #3952] entwickelte und mutmaßlich Hauptgedanken Fermats enthaltende Verfahren zur Ermittlung aller Pythagoreischen Dreiecke wieder, deren Hypotenuse und deren algebraische Kathetensumme Quadratzahlen sind. Weiterschreitend, vermag er durch ein wohlausgedachtes Abkürzungsverfahren über die aufeinanderfolgenden Lösungen der in Frage stehenden Hilfsgleichung $(a^2-b^2)\alpha^2+2ab\alpha\beta-(2a^2+b^2)\beta^2=0$, aus der die gesuchten Seitenzahlen $x=\frac{1}{2}(b^2+c)$, $y=\frac{1}{2}(b^2-c)$, $z=a^2$ hervorgehen, wesentliche numerische Aussagen zu machen. Er unterscheidet zwischen negativen Lösungen (eine der Katheten negativ) und positiven Lösungen 1. und 2. Art (je nachdem die ungeradzahlige Kathete größer oder kleiner ist als die geradzahlige), und stellt fest, daß in der "Kleinreihe" der ersten 41 Lösungen 28 negative und 13 positive auftreten, nämlich 7 1. und 6 2. Art. Die kleinstzahlige Lösung 1. Art gibt 13-stellige Zahlen (schon Fermat bekannt), die 2. Art 165-stellige. Innerhalb der nachfolgenden Kleinreihen wiederholt sich diese Verteilung mit kleinen Veränderungen.

Der zweite Teil bezieht sich auf die eigentümlichen Verschiebungen, die sich hinsichtlich der Verteilung der Einzellösungen bei Zusammenfassen von je drei aufeinanderfolgenden Kleinreihen zu einer "Großreihe" ergeben. Die anschließend mit größter Sorgfalt berechneten Zahlentabellen und graphischen Darstellungen (sie beziehen sich jeweils auf die ersten 5 Stellen der beteiligten Zahlen, die zur Kennzeichnung hinreichen) sind deshalb von hohem Interesse, weil sie den Gesamtüberblick in einem Fall vermitteln, der wegen des komplizierten Aufbaus des in Frage stehenden Gleichungsgefüges schwerlich allgemein durchgeführt werden kann.

J. E. Hofmann (Ichenhausen)

Citations: MR 39# 3952 = Z15-87.

D20 QUADRATIC EQUATIONS: SYSTEMS

See also reviews D16-7, D24-46, D36-19, D56-11, D99-8, E04-21, E16-90, E20-61, Z15-39.

D20-1 (2, 248b)

Bell, E. T. Note on a certain type of Diophantine system. Bull. Amer. Math. Soc. **47**, 155–159 (1941).

The author gives necessary and sufficient conditions that the system of Diophantine equations $ax^2+bx=y^2$, $cx^2+dx=z^2$ shall have integral solutions. These conditions are that b and d be simultaneously representable in two forms of degree seven, and the solution of the original system is given in terms of the coefficients of these forms. The method is made to depend on the fact that the given system is equivalent to a pure multiplicative system [author's paper, Amer. J. Math. **55**, 50–56 (1933)]. The results are generalized to systems of s equations whose members involve certain polynomials. *I. A. Barnett* (Urbana, Ill.).

D20-2 (8, 6e)

Kraitchik, Maurice. On certain rational cuboids. Scripta Math. **11**, 317–326 (1945).

The Diophantine system $x^2+y^2=Z^2, y^2+z^2=X^2, z^2+x^2=Y^2$ is discussed. Among other results, Euler's formulas [see L. E. Dickson, History of the Theory of Numbers, vol. 2, Washington, 1920, p. 498] are proved. A table of 50 solutions not derivable from Euler's formulas is given.

I. Niven (West Lafayette, Ind.).

D20-3 (8, 314g)

Ljunggren, W. A note on simultaneous Pell equations. Norsk Mat. Tidsskr. **23**, 132–138 (1941). (Norwegian)

This paper treats the problem of finding the integral solutions of the simultaneous equations

$$x^2-Dy^2=1, \quad y^2-D_1z^2=1.$$

The author proves that there is only a finite number of solutions and that it is possible to determine an upper limit for this number; in the special case $D=2$, $D_1=3$ he shows that the only solution is $x=3$, $y=2$, $z=1$. The proof depends on the properties of the units of quadratic and special biquadratic fields. *T. Nagell* (Uppsala).

Referred to in D24-46.

D20-4 (8, 314h)

Ljunggren, W. Proof of a theorem of de Jonquières. Norsk Mat. Tidsskr. **26**, 3–8 (1944). (Norwegian)

The theorem states that the only solution in integers n, x and y of the simultaneous Diophantine equations $n=x^2+(x+1)^2$, $n^2=y^2+(y+1)^2$ is $n=5$, $x=1$, $y=3$. The author gives the first proof of this theorem. He uses some of his own results on the units in quadratic and biquadratic fields [Avh. Norske Vid. Akad. Oslo. I. **1942**, no. 5; these Rev. **8**, 6] and, in addition, the p-adic method of T. Skolem [C. R. Huitième Congrès Math. Scandinaves (Stockholm, 1934), Lund, 1935, pp. 163–188]. *T. Nagell* (Uppsala).

Citations: MR 8, 6f = D24-8.

D20-5 (8, 314i)

Størmer, Carl. A number-theoretical problem. Norsk Mat. Tidsskr. **26**, 109–115 (1944). (Norwegian)

The author discusses the following problem: $f(x)$ being a polynomial in x, which takes integral values for every integral value of x, determine all the solutions of the equation $f(x_0)=f(x_1)^{k_1}f(x_2)^{k_2}\cdots f(x_\nu)^{k_\nu}$ in positive integers $x_0, \cdots, x_\nu$, $k_1, \cdots, k_\nu$. Using two results of W. Ljunggren [see the preceding review] he shows that, in the case $f(x)=x^2+(x+1)^2$, $\nu=1$, the only solutions are given by the relations $3^2+4^2=(1^2+2^2)^2$ and $119^2+120^2=(2^2+3^2)^4$. *T. Nagell.*

D20-6 (9, 175d)

Bell, E. T. The problems of congruent numbers and concordant forms. Proc. Nat. Acad. Sci. U. S. A. **33**, 326–328 (1947).

The author indicates necessary and sufficient forms of r, m, s, n in order that there shall exist X, Y, Z, W all different from zero, satisfying $rX^2+mY^2=rZ^2$, $sX^2+nY^2=sW^2$, where all letters denote rational integers and solutions are complete solutions in such integers. Altogether there are 41 parameters. Each of m, n is of degree 3 in these parameters; each of r, s is of degree 71; each of X, Z, W is of degree 49, and Y is of degree 83. It is noted that for $r=s=Y^2=1$, $n=-m$ (m a given constant) and for $r=s=1$ the Diophantine system above includes a classical problem on congruent numbers and concordant forms, respectively. Both problems (the first for m arbitrarily assigned) are still unsolved. The author remarks that "the inherent complexity of the solution" given in his paper "may suggest why these two old and apparently simple problems are still not completely solved." *W. H. Gage* (Vancouver, B. C.).

D20-7 (11, 500b)

Gloden, A. Impossibilités diophantiennes. Euclides, Madrid **9**, 476 (1949).

Si l'on a $2x^2+1=y^2$, pour cette même valeur de x l'équation $3x^2+1=z^2$ est impossible, sauf au cas trivial où $x=0$; alors $y=z=\pm 1$. *Extract from the paper.*

D20-8 (13, 913f)

Chudyniv-Bohun, Volodymyr. Solution of the Euler's problem. Ukrainian Free Academy of Science. Series: Mathematics. Publ. no. 1. Privately printed, Regensburg, 1947. 20 pp.

The problem of the title is one that Euler proposed to Lagrange in 1770. It consists in finding 16 numbers A_{ij}, $i, j=1, 2, 3, 4$, satisfying the 22 relations

$$\sum_{j=1}^{4} A_{ij}^2=\sum_{i=1}^{4} A_{ij}^2=\sum_{i=1}^{4} A_{ii}^2=\sum_{i=1}^{4} A_{i,5-i}^2=S,$$

$$\sum_{i=1}^{4} A_{ki}A_{ji}=\sum_{i=1}^{4} A_{ik}A_{ij}=0.$$

A two-parameter family of solutions of this problem is given. The parameters however are not free but must satisfy 11 other conditions. However, these latter conditions are fairly easy to meet. Many examples are worked out in which the elements A_{ij} are integers, complex numbers, quaternions, octonions, and sedecimions. *D. H. Lehmer.*

D20-9 **(14, 950e)**

Mills, W. H. A system of quadratic Diophantine equations. Pacific J. Math. **3**, 209–220 (1953).

The system is $x|y^2+ay+1$; $y|x^2+ax+1$, where a is a fixed integer. If x, y satisfy these relations, then so do y, z, where $xz=y^2+ay+1$. In this way solutions occur in chains $\cdots, u_{-1}, u_0, u_1, u_2, \cdots$ with $u_{n+1}u_{n-1}=u_n^2+au_n+1$. Each such chain satisfies a linear relation $u_{n+1}-bu_n+u_{n-1}+a=0$, where b is a constant characteristic of the chain: and the number of chains is finite for $a\neq\pm2$. Possible b are listed for $0\leqq a\leqq 10$. *J. W. S. Cassels* (Cambridge, England).

Referred to in D32-44, D32-52, D32-53, D48-27.

D20-10 **(17, 1121i)**

Froda, Alexandru. Sur les triangles rationnels. Com. Acad. R. P. Romîne **5** (1955), 1695–1701. (Romanian. Russian and French summaries)

The classical relations

(*) $$a/(m^2+n^2)=b/(m^2-n^2)=c/2mn=\varrho$$

(ϱ rational, $m>n>0$, rational integers), necessary and sufficient, in order to have a right triangle with rational sides a, b, c is generalized for arbitrary triangles. The conditions

(**) $$a/((m^2+n^2)q-mnp)=\varepsilon b/(m^2-n^2)q=\varepsilon c/n(2mq-np)=\varrho$$

($\varrho>0$, rational, m, n coprime integers, $n>0$, p, q coprime integers, $q>0$, $\varepsilon=\pm1$) are necessary and sufficient for the existence of a non-degenerate triangle of rational sides a, b, c. In the particular case $p=0$, (**) reduce to (*). *E. Grosswald* (Philadelphia, Pa.).

D20-11 **(20# 3823)**

Venkatachalam Iyer, R. Sur les formes concordantes. Mathesis **66** (1957), 138–144.

Two forms ax^2+by^2, cx^2+dy^2 are called concordant (Euler) if they can be made simultaneously square for certain positive integers x and y. Various known cases of concordant forms are given, and a number of new cases are found. For example, it is shown that if $a+b$ and $c+d$ are squares, then the forms are concordant. In fact, the forms are squares for $x=4bd(a+b)(c+d)-(ac-bd)^2$ and $y=4ac(a+b)(c+d)-(ac-bd)^2$. As yet unsolved is the problem of finding all n for which x^2+y^2 is concordant with x^2+ny^2. *L. Moser* (Edmonton, Alta.)

D20-12 **(21# 2939)**

Sierpiński, W. Sur les ensembles de points aux distances rationnelles situés sur un cercle. Elem. Math. **14** (1959), 25–27.

Let r^2 be a rational number. Then the author proves that there exists on the circle of radius r a dense set of points so that the distance between any two of them is rational. He further remarks that if on a circle of radius r there are three points whose mutual distances are rational then r^2 is rational.

{Remark by the reviewer: About 15 years ago Ulam asked if there is a dense set in the plane so that the distance between any two of its points is rational. This problem is still unsolved.} *P. Erdös* (Budapest)

D20-13 **(23# A1594)**

Bromhead, T.

On square sums of squares.

Math. Gaz. **44** (1960), 219–220.

The author considers "Mahatma's problem" of finding three integers a, b, c such that a^2+b^2, a^2+c, b^2+c, and a^2+b^2+c are all squares. He shows that there are an infinity of solutions to the problem, by giving polynomials $a(t)$, $b(t)$, $c(t)$ with integral coefficients which make the above expressions squares of polynomials. These yield, for $t=1$, the smallest known solution $a=124$, $b=957$, $c=13852800$. *T. Hayashida* (Kanagawa)

D20-14 **(24# A1875)**

Stamatis, Evang

Verallgemeinerung eines Problems unbestimmter Analytik des Diophantos. (Greek. German summary)

Prakt. Akad. Athēnōn **35** (1960), 423–428.

Diophantus showed that one can always find four rational numbers such that the product of every pair, increased by 1, is the square of a rational number. The author considers the more general problem of finding n rational numbers with the same property. Denote the n unknowns by $x, x_1, x_2, \cdots, x_{n-1}$. If we take $x_k=k^2x+2k$ for $k=1, 2, \cdots, n-1$, then for any choice of a rational x the numbers xx_k+1 and $x_kx_{k+1}+1$ will be squares of rational numbers. For each $m\geqq2$ the choice $x=(m^2-1)/[4k(k+m)(2k+m)]$ will make $x_kx_{k+m}+1$ a square of a rational number. *T. M. Apostol* (Pasadena, Calif.)

D20-15 **(24# A3116)**

Sierpiński, W.

Sur une propriété des nombres triangulaires.

Elem. Math. **17** (1962), 28.

This note contains an elementary proof that there exists an infinity of pairs of triangular numbers such that both the sum and the difference are also triangular numbers. *R. D. James* (Vancouver, B.C.)

D20-16 **(30# 1970)**

Sierpiński, W.

Sur les nombres pentagonaux.

Bull. Soc. Roy. Sci. Liège **33** (1964), 513–517.

For positive integral k, $t_k=\frac{1}{2}k(k+1)$ and $\omega_k=\frac{1}{2}k(3k-1)$ are known, respectively, as triangular and pentagonal numbers. (For the geometric origins of these terms see L. E. Dickson [*History of the theory of numbers*, Vol. II, p. 1, Carnegie Institution of Washington, Washington, D.C., 1920].) In this paper it is shown that a triangular number t_x is at the same time a pentagonal number ω_y if and only if for some positive integer n, $x=x_n$, $y=y_n$, where the sequences (x_n) and (y_n) are defined recursively by the equations $x_1=y_1=1$; $x_{n+1}=7x_n+12y_n+1$, $y_{n+1}=4x_n+7y_n+1$. Thus, there are infinitely many pentagonal numbers which are also triangular. A similar result is obtained for pentagonal numbers which are also squares. The proofs are by induction and are elementary and self-contained. A corollary, attributed to A. Rotkiewicz, establishes the existence of infinitely many pentagonal numbers which are also hexagonal (i.e., of the form $k(2k-1)$) and incidentally triangular as well. For a contrasting result by A. Rotkiewicz see the following review [#1971]. *R. J. Levit* (San Francisco, Calif.)

Referred to in D20-18.

D20-17 **(30# 1971)**

Rotkiewicz, A.

Sur les nombres a la fois triangulaires, carrés et pentagonaux.

Bull. Soc. Roy. Sci. Liège **33** (1964), 518–519.

In contrast with Sierpiński's paper (see the preceding review [#1970]), the author proves that there are only a finite number of numbers which are simultaneously pentagonal, triangular, and square. The proof depends on Thue's theorem that for integral a, b, c, d, n, if $a\neq 0$, $d\neq 0$, $b^2-4ac\neq 0$, $n\geqq 3$, the equation $ay^2+by+c=dx^n$ has only a finite number of solutions in integers (x, y).

R. J. Levit (San Francisco, Calif.)

D20-18 **(31# 1223)**

Makowski, A.

Remarque à une note de A. Rotkiewicz sur les nombres à la fois triangulaires, carrés et pentagonaux.

Bull. Soc. Roy. Sci. Liège **34** (1965), 27.

The author proves that 1 is the only positive integer which is simultaneously triangular, square, and pentagonal, using a necessary condition for an integer to have all three properties given by Rotkiewicz [same Bull. **33** (1964), 518–519; MR **30** #1971], who showed that there are only a finite number of such integers. The proof utilizes Ljunggren's theorem that the Diophantine equation $x^2-Dy^4=1$ has at most two positive integral solutions [Skr. Norske Vid.-Akad. Oslo I Mat.-Naturv. Kl. **1936**, no. 12]. *R. J. Levit* (San Francisco, Calif.)

Citations: MR 30# 1971 = D20-17.

D20-19 **(31# 3380)**

Sierpiński, W.

Sur trois nombres triangulaires en progression arithmétique à différence triangulaire.

Elem. Math. **20** (1965), 79–81.

The author establishes the existence of an infinite collection of triples of triangular numbers forming an arithmetic progression in which the common difference is triangular. Using the fact that a typical triangular number is $t_k=[(2k+1)^2-1]/8$, he shows that m, n, r, s exist with $t_n-t_m=t_r-t_n=t_s$ if and only if there exist integers $x>1$, $y\neq x$, z and u satisfying $x^2+z^2=2y^2$ and $y^2-x^2=u^2-1$. Solutions to this latter system are then obtained from solutions to the Diophantine equation $g^2-24h^2=1$.

T. M. Apostol (Pasadena, Calif.)

D20-20 **(32# 4082)**

Lal, M.; Blundon, W. J.

Solutions of the Diophantine equations $x^2+y^2=l^2$, $y^2+z^2=m^2$, $z^2+x^2=n^2$.

Math. Comp. **20** (1966), 144–147.

A table of 130 solutions is given.

D20-21 **(34# 4204)**

Smirnov, G. P.

On the solution of systems of Diophantine equations containing quadratic forms. (Russian)

Baškir. Gos. Univ. Učen. Zap. Vyp. 20 (1965), *Ser. Mat. No.* 2, 114–118.

Let there be given, in n-dimensional space, the m quadratic forms $A_\kappa(x,x)=\sum_{i=1,j=1}^n a_{ij}^{(\kappa)}x_ix_j$ $(\kappa=1,2,\cdots,m)$ with integral coefficients $a_{ij}^{(\kappa)}$, and let $A_\kappa(x,y)=\frac{1}{2}\sum_{j=1}^n A_{\kappa x_j}y_j$, $x=(x_1,\cdots,x_n)$, $y=(y_1,\cdots,y_n)$, be the symmetric bilinear form corresponding to the form $A_\kappa(x,x)$, where $A_{\kappa x_j}$ is the derivative of the function $A_\kappa(x,x)$ with respect to x_j.

The author considers the system of equations (*) $A_\kappa(x,x)=A_\kappa(y,y)$ $(\kappa=1,2,\cdots,m)$ and derives general formulas for obtaining all integral solutions of (*), where an integral solution of (*) is any set of $2n$ integers $x_{01},\cdots,x_{0n}$, $y_{01},\cdots,y_{0n}$ satisfying all the equations (*). The author also obtains some analogous results for the equations $\sum_{i=1}^n b_\kappa^{(i)}x_i^2=\sum_{i=1}^n b_\kappa^{(i)}y_i^2$ $(\kappa=1,2,\cdots,m;\ 1\leqq m\leqq n-1)$ and gives some numerical examples which illustrate his derived formulas.

R. Finkelstein (Tucson, Ariz.)

D20-22 **(36# 1387)**

Dimiev, Veselin

Right triangles whose sides are triangular numbers. (Bulgarian. Russian and French summaries)

Godišnik. Visš. Tehn. Učebn. Zaved. Mat. **1** (1964), *kn.* 3, 9–14 (1965).

Author's summary: "On démontre le théorème suivant: Il existe au plus un nombre fini des triangles, dont les côtés sont des nombres triangulaires, qui sont semblables à un triangle rectangulaire dont les côtés sont $a=m^2-n^2$, $b=2mn$ et $c=m^2+n^2$, où $m>n$, $(m,n)=1$, m est un nombre paire arbitraire et n est un nombre impaire arbitraire."

D20-23 **(37# 4004)**

Sierpiński, W.

Un théorème sur les nombres triangulaires.

Elem. Math. **23** (1968), 31–32.

From the author's introduction: "Les nombres triangulaires sont des nombres $t_n=n(n+1)/2$, où $n=1,2,\cdots$. Le but de cette note est de démontrer d'une façon élémentaire le théorème suivant: Il existe une infinité de nombres triangulaires qui sont à la fois sommes, différences et produits de deux nombres triangulaires >1."

D20-24 **(39# 154)**

van Lint, J. H.

On a set of diophantine equations.

T. H.-Report 68-WSK-03.

Department of Mathematics, Technological University Eindhoven, Eindhoven, 1968. 8 *pp.*

Author's summary: "The system $N+1=x^2$, $3N+1=y^2$, $8N+1=z^2$ has no solutions N with $120<N<10^{1700000}$."

D20-25 **(40# 1333)**

Baker, A. [Baker, Alan]; Davenport, H.

The equations $3x^2-2=y^2$ and $8x^2-7=z^2$.

Quart. J. Math. Oxford Ser. (2) **20** (1969), 129–137.

The four numbers 1, 3, 8, 120 have the property that the product of any two, increased by 1, is a perfect square. The authors consider the question of whether there exists any other positive integer N that can replace 120. Such an integer N must be of the form $N=x^2-1$, and the conditions are equivalent to solving the simultaneous Diophantine equations $3x^2-2=y^2$ and $8x^2-7=z^2$. The authors show that no such N exists by using the theory of Diophantine approximations to prove that the only solutions are $x=0$ and $x=11$ (corresponding to $N=0$ and $N=120$, respectively).

At one point in their proof the authors were required to compute four reals θ, q, β, β' accurately to 1040, 520, 600, 600 decimal places, respectively. These constants were computed by a computer at the Atlas Computing Laboratory in England. Special note should be taken of the closing comments of the authors: "Briefly, we may say that the present method fails only if $\|q\beta\|$ is exceptionally small and also q is exceptionally small relative to its upper bound."

Here $\|z\|$ denotes the distance of a real number z from the nearest integer. *H. London* (Montreal, Que.)

Referred to in G05-101.

D20-26 **(41# 1630)**

Hansen, Rodney T.
Arithmetic of pentagonal numbers.
Fibonacci Quart. **8** (1970), *no.* 1, 83–87.

From the author's introduction: "The pentagonal numbers are the integers $p_n=(n/2)(3n-1)$, $n=1, 2, \cdots$. Each number p_n can also be derived by summing the first n terms of the arithmetic progression $1, 4, 7, 10, 13, \cdots, 3m-2$. Geometrically, considering regular pentagons homothetic with respect to one of the vertices and containing $2, 3, 4, \cdots, n$ points at equal distances along each side, the sum of all points for a given n yields p_n. In this paper we shall give several algebraic identities involving pentagonal numbers of different orders. The principal result is that an infinite number of pentagonal numbers exist which are, at the same time, the sum and difference of distinct pentagonal numbers."

D24 CUBIC AND QUARTIC CURVES: INTEGRAL POINTS

Papers in the relevant special case of Siegel's theorem (curves of genus 1) are to be found in **G05**.

See also reviews D02-18, D04-65, D12-53, D32-74, D36-2, D36-35, D40-12, D40-35, D40-58, E76-21, E76-22, G05-101, G05-102, G15-21, J68-45, R02-3, R14-59, R16-53, R20-50, Z10-35, Z10-47, Z15-45.

D24-1 **(2, 347b)**

Trost, Ernst. Über eine Verallgemeinerung eines Satzes von Fermat. Vierteljschr. Naturforsch. Ges. Zürich **85** Beiblatt (Festschrift Rudolf Fueter), 138–142 (1940).

If $M=N(N+1)$, where N is a natural number, the Diophantine equation $(Mx^2-N)^2=My^2-N$ has the trivial solution $x=0$, $y=1$, and it is readily seen that $x=2$, $y=4N+1$ is also a solution. The author proves that, if $N=D^2$ $(D\neq 1)$, these are the only solutions in non-negative integers. For $D=1$ this is a well-known conjecture of Fermat, which was proved by Genocchi [Nouv. Ann. Math. (3) **2**, 306–310 (1883)]. The proof is accomplished by means of a theorem about the equation $Ax^4-By^4=\pm 1$ which Ljunggren proved by using the theory of units. *H. W. Brinkmann.*

Referred to in D24-13.

D24-2 **(3, 161d)**

Podsipanin, W. D. Über eine unbestimmte Gleichung wo $\sigma=1, 2, 4, 8, 16$ ist. Bull. Acad. Sci. URSS. Sér. Math. [Izvestia Akad. Nauk SSSR] **5**, 305–324 (1941). (Russian. German summary)

The exact English translation of the title is "On a certain indeterminate equation."

The equation considered is (1) $ax^2-by^4=\sigma$, $\sigma=1, 2, 4, 8, 16$, or rather (2) $px^2-my^4=16$ with $p=16a/\sigma$, $m=16b/\sigma$. The author shows that for a given (p, m) only a finite number of quartic fields K need be considered. In each of these fields the author finds a fundamental unit ϵ. For $K\neq R((-m)^{\frac{1}{4}})$ one constructs the number $\mu=(\epsilon(-m)^{\frac{1}{4}})^{\frac{1}{2}}$. If this number satisfies a quadratic equation of the form $\mu^2-w(-m)^{\frac{1}{4}}\mu-(-m)^{\frac{1}{2}}=0$, then $y=w$ is a solution of (2) whose corresponding x can then be found. A finite number of other solutions (usually none) can be found by considering the quadratic equations satisfied by $\mu^{2n+1}(-m)^{-n}$, where n is an integer such that $\epsilon^{2n+1}=\epsilon$. If μ satisfies no such quadratic equation then (2) is impossible in integers. In case $K=R((-m)^{\frac{1}{4}})$ the equation reduces to $a'x^4-b'y^4=\sigma$, $\sigma=1, 2, 4, 8$, already considered by Faddeev [Uchenye Zapiski Leningrad. Gosudarstvennogo Pedagogicheskogo Inst. im. Hertzena **28**, 141–145 (1939)]. There are a number of special exceptional equations which are all disposed of, except the equation $17x^2-y^4=16$, which may or may not have solutions other than $x=\pm 1$, $y=\pm 1$. The casual reader should be warned that the a, b used in the body of the paper are not the coefficients of (1).

D. H. Lehmer (Berkeley, Calif.).

D24-3 **(6, 169e)**

Ljunggren, Wilhelm. Sätze über unbestimmte Gleichungen. Skr. Norske Vid. Akad. Oslo. I. no. **9**, 53 pp. (1942).

It was proved by Mordell [Proc. London Math. Soc. (2) **21**, 415–419 (1923)] that the Diophantine equation

$$Ax^4+Bx^2+C=Dy^2,$$

where the left-hand side has no squared factor in x, has only a finite number of solutions; however, his method does not give the solutions themselves or a bound for their number. The author obtains bounds for the number of integral solutions for some special equations of this type. If the fundamental units of certain biquadratic fields are known, then all the solutions can be determined. For instance, the following theorems are proved. Let a and D be square-free integers with $(a, 6)=(D, 3)=1$. The four equations $A^2x^4+2Ax^2+4=Dy^2$ with $D>1$ and $A=a$ or $A=3a$ have together at most four positive integral solutions unless $a=1$, $D=7$. In this case, $x^4+2x^2+4=7y^2$ has the solutions $x=y=1$; $x=9$, $y=31$; $x=2$, $y=2$; $x=6$, $y=14$; and $9x^4-6x^2+4=7y^2$ has the solution $x=1$, $y=1$. The three equations $a^2x^4\pm 2ax^2+2=Dy^2$ and $a^2x^4+1=Dy^2$ have together at most one positive integral solution. Some other similar theorems are proved. [It may be remarked that the special case $A=D=1$ was solved completely by T. Nagell [Norsk Mat. Forenings Skrifter (I) no. **17** (1927)].]

With the same method, the author obtains results on equations of the form $x^3+b^3=Dy^2$. For $b=1$, this equation was studied by Nagell [Tôhoku Math. J. **24**, 48–53 (1924)] and by C. E. Lind [Untersuchungen über die rationalen Punkte der ebenen kubischen Kurven vom Geschlecht eins, Uppsala, 1940]. Nagell proved that this equation has only the solution $x=-1$, $y=0$ if D is an integer, different from 1, which is only divisible by primes of the form $12n+5$ or by 3. For $b=-1$, it was proved by Nagell [Norsk Mat. Forenings Skrifter (I) no. **13** (1923)] that the equation has no solution for which x is odd if the class number h of the quadratic field $P(\sqrt{-D})$ is relatively prime to 3. However, Nagell was not able to solve the equation if $h\equiv 0 \pmod 3$ or to determine the solutions with even x. For instance, he obtained certain results for $D=23$ and he found three positive solutions with even x for $D=7$, but he could not decide whether there are further solutions. In this paper the author proves that this equation has no solution for $D=23$ and exactly three positive solutions for $D=7$. Moreover, he proves the following theorem. Let $D>2$ be a square-free integer which is not divisible by 3 or primes of the form $6n+1$; then the eight equations $x^3+b^3=Dy^2$, $x^3+b^3=3Dy^2$, where $b=\pm 1$ and $b=\pm 2$, have together at most one solution in positive integers x, y. *A. Brauer* (Chapel Hill, N. C.).

Referred to in D24-25, D24-76.

D24-4 **(7, 47l)**

Ljunggren, Wilhelm. Über die Gleichung $x^4-Dy^2=1$. Arch. Math. Naturvid. **45**, no. 5, 61–70 (1942).

It is proved that for any positive integer D the equation $x^4-Dy^2=1$ has at most two solutions in positive integers x and y. [The author imposes the further hypothesis that D is square-free, which seems unnecessary.] The proof, which furnishes a procedure for calculating the possible solutions, is based on earlier work of the author [Skr. Norske Vid. Akad. Oslo. I, **1936**, no. 12 (1937)] on the units of quadratic and biquadratic fields. The result is the best possible: the equation with $D=1785$ has the solutions $x=13$, $y=4$ and $x=239$, $y=1352$. *I. Niven.*

D24-5 (7, 244e)

Ljunggren, Wilhelm. A theorem of diophantine equations of the fourth degree. Avh. Norske Vid. Akad. Oslo. I. **1943**, no. 9, 13 pp. (1943).

Let a, b, c, d be integers; a, b, c positive, $d\neq 0$; a and c squarefree; d^2+4acb^2 not a perfect square. For every pair of natural numbers b_1, b_2 satisfying $b_1b_2=b$, the equations

(1) $$ab_1^2x^4-cb_2^2y^4-dx^2y^2=\pm 1,$$

(1′) $$a^3b_1^2x^4-c^3b_2^2y^4+acdx^2y^2=\pm 1$$

are considered. If $a=c=1$, the equations (1′) are omitted, each of them being equivalent to an equation in the set (1). For fixed a, b, c, d, all equations in this set are insoluble in natural numbers x, y, except possibly one, which has exactly one solution. This is proved by showing that at most one unit of the field $K(\sqrt{a}, \sqrt{(-c)}, \theta)$, $\theta=\sqrt{(d+2b\sqrt{(-ac)})}$, has the form $p\sqrt{a}+q\sqrt{(-c)}+(s+t\sqrt{(-ac)})\theta$, where p, q, s, t are nonnegative rational integers, and $st=0$, $s+t\neq 0$.
N. G. de Bruijn (Eindhoven).

D24-6 (7, 244f)

Ljunggren, Wilhelm. Sur la résolution de quelques équations diophantiennes cubiques dans certains corps quadratiques. Avh. Norske Vid. Akad. Oslo. I. **1943**, no. 14, 23 pp. (1944).

The following theorem is proved. Let $D>1$ be a rational integer other than 3, such that neither the number of ideal classes of $K(\sqrt{D})$ nor of $K(\sqrt{-D})$ is congruent to 0 (mod 3). Let $E>1$ be the fundamental unit of $K(\sqrt{D})$, and let $s=0$ or 1. Then the numbers of solutions of

$$\eta^2+1=E^s\xi^3, \quad \xi\not\equiv 0 \pmod 2,$$
$$\eta^2+1=2E^s\xi^3, \quad \xi\not\equiv 0 \pmod 2,$$
$$\eta^2+1=4E^s\xi^3$$

in integral numbers ξ, η of $K(\sqrt{D})$ are finite, and upper bounds can be found for the numbers of solutions. In some special cases the author obtains more precise results.
N. G. de Bruijn (Eindhoven).

D24-7 (7, 506c)

Podsypanin, V. On the equation $ax^4+bx^2y^2-cy^4=1$. Rec. Math. [Mat. Sbornik] N.S. **18(60)**, 105–114 (1946). (Russian. English summary)

The author proves that the equation of the title, where a, b, c are integers, a and c positive, has at most one solution in positive integers. The proof is based on a study of special units in a field of order 8. The result generalizes one of B. N. Delaunay and Faddeev. [See Skolem, Diophantische Gleichungen, Ergebnisse der Math., v. 5, no. 4, Springer, Berlin, 1938, pp. 113 f.; B. N. Delone, Izvestiya Rossiĭskoĭ Akad. Nauk [Bull. Acad. Sci. Russie] (6) **16**, 253–272 (1922); D. K. Faddeev, Učenye Zapiski Leningrad. Gos. Pedagog. Inst. **28**, 141–145 (1938); Delone and Fadeev, Theory of irrationalities of third degree, Acad. Sci. URSS. Trav. Inst. Math. Stekloff, v. 11, 1940, pp. 289–313; these Rev. **2**, 349.] *K. Mahler* (Manchester).

Citations: MR 2, 349d = R02-3.

D24-8 (8, 6f)

Ljunggren, Wilhelm. Zur Theorie der Gleichung $x^2+1=Dy^4$. Avh. Norske Vid. Akad. Oslo. I. **1942**, no. 5, 27 pp. (1942).

It is proved that, if the fundamental unit of the real quadratic field $R(\sqrt{D})$ is not also the fundamental unit of the ring of integers of the field, then $x^2+1=Dy^4$ has at most two solutions in positive integers. It is shown how the possible solutions may be found. The result is best possible: for $D=2$ the solutions are $x=1$, $y=1$ and $x=239$, $y=13$. The proof depends on earlier work of the author [Skr. Norske Vid. Akad. Oslo. I. **1936**, no. 12] on the units of quadratic and biquadratic fields. *I. Niven.*

Referred to in D20-4, D24-60, D24-81.

D24-9 (8, 7d)

Skolem, Th. Unlösbarkeit von Gleichungen, deren entsprechende Kongruenz für jeden Modul lösbar ist. Avh. Norske Vid. Akad. Oslo. I. **1942**, no. 4, 28 pp. (1942).

It is known that linear homogeneous quadratic Diophantine equations have solutions if the corresponding congruences are solvable for every modulus. This is, however, not correct for inhomogeneous quadratic equations and equations of higher degree. The author shows that, for instance, $(x^2-2)(x^2+7)(x^2+14)\equiv 0 \pmod m$ is solvable for every m while the corresponding equation has no rational root.

Let $f(x, y)$ be a cubic form. In an earlier paper [same Avh. **1937**, no. 12] it was mentioned by the author that the equation $f(x, y)=$constant may have no solution while the corresponding congruence is solvable for every modulus m. He gave the example $x^3-2y^3=47$. He now states that this example is not correct since $x=63$, $y=50$ is a solution. In order to obtain correct examples he proves the following theorems. Let p be a prime of form $3n+2$ and $(a, b)=(a, c)=(b, c)=1$; then $ax^3+by^3\equiv c \pmod{p^n}$ has solutions for every n. Moreover, this congruence has solutions if $p\neq 7$ is an arbitrary prime and $3abc\not\equiv 0 \pmod p$. Using these results the author proves that $x^3+3y^3=22$ and $u^3+4v^3=55$ have no solutions while the corresponding congruences are solvable for every m. Moreover, he proves criteria for the solvability of congruences of the form $N(\alpha_1x+\alpha_2y)\equiv 1 \pmod{p^n}$, where α_1 and α_2 are integers of a cubic field.
A. Brauer (Chapel Hill, N. C.).

Referred to in G05-31.

D24-10 (8, 135k)

Ljunggren, Wilhelm. Einige Bemerkungen über die Darstellung ganzer Zahlen durch binäre kubische Formen mit positiver Diskriminante. Acta Math. **75**, 1–21 (1943).

Skolem [Skr. Norske Vid. Akad. Oslo. I. **1933**, no. 6] obtained a method for solving cubic Diophantine equations with positive discriminant. He considered, in particular, the equation (1) $x^3-3xy^2-y^3=1$ and conjectured that his method would solve (1) completely. However, he did not carry out the necessary tedious calculations. The author proves that (1) has only the following 6 solutions: (1, 0); (0, −1); (−1, 1); (1, −3); (−3, 2); (2, 1).

Nagell [Norsk Mat. Forenings Skr. (I) no. **2** (1921)] proved that the equation (2) $x^2+x+1=y^n$ has only trivial solutions unless n is a power of 3. For $n=3$ he showed that the solutions of (2) can be obtained if the solutions of (1) are known. It was proved by the reviewer [Bull. Amer. Math. Soc. **49**, 712–718 (1943); these Rev. **5**, 90] that (2) has no solution for which x is a positive prime number. The author proves that (2) has only two nontrivial solutions, namely $y=7$, $x=18$ or $x=-19$ for $n=3$.

In addition, the author considers the more general equation $x^3-ax^2y-(a+3)xy^2-y^3=1$. *A. Brauer.*

Citations: MR 5, 90b = A32-5.

Referred to in D02-23, D24-19, D24-61, D28-24, D40-15.

D24-11 **(8, 314j)**

Ljunggren, Wilhelm. On the representation of integers by binary biquadratic forms of a special class. Norsk Mat. Tidsskr. **26**, 51–59 (1944). (Norwegian)

Using the p-adic method of T. Skolem [C. R. Huitième Congrès Math. Scandinaves (Stockholm, 1934), Lund, 1935, pp. 163–188] the author proves the following theorem. The Diophantine equation

$$F(x, y)=x^4+px^3y+qx^2y^2+pxy^3+y^4=\pm 1,$$

where $F(t, -1)$ has exactly two real roots, and where $q\neq 2|p|-3$, has at most 8 solutions in integers x and y, including the 4 trivial solutions $x=\pm 1$, $y=0$ and $x=0$, $y=\pm 1$. If $q=2|p|-3$ the equation has at most 10 solutions. *T. Nagell* (Uppsala).

D24-12 **(8, 368h)**

Ljunggren, Wilhelm. Sur la solution de quelques équations diophantiennes biquadratiques à deux inconnues. Norske Vid. Selsk. Forh., Trondhjem **16**, no. 28, 103–105 (1944).

The equations $(ax^2+bx+c)^2-Dy^2=-N$ and

$$x^2-D(ay^2+by+c)^2=N$$

with integral coefficients, $a>0$, $N>0$ and $D>1$, are considered. By a p-adic method of T. Skolem [C. R. Huitième Congrès Math. Scandinaves (Stockholm, 1934), Lund, 1935, pp. 163–188] it is proved that there is an upper bound, which can be determined, to the number of integral solutions x and y. *I. Niven* (West Lafayette, Ind.).

D24-13 **(8, 442f)**

Ljunggren, Wilhelm. Über die Gleichung $(Mx^2-N)^2=My^2-N$. Norske Vid. Selsk. Forh., Trondhjem **15**, no. 18, 67–70 (1942).

It was shown by E. Trost [Vierteljschr. Naturforsch. Ges. Zürich **85** Beiblatt (Festschrift Rudolf Fueter), 138–142 (1940); these Rev. **2**, 347] that in the case $M=N(N+1)$, $N=D^2$ $(D\neq 1)$ the equation $(Mx^2-N)^2=My^2-N$, where M and N are positive integers, has no nonnegative integral solutions except $x=0$, $y=1$ and $x=2$, $y=4N+1$. In the present paper it is shown that this result also holds for any integer $N>1$. In his proof, which depends upon unit theory, the author uses results which he obtained in an earlier paper [Skr. Norske Vid.-Akad. Oslo. I. **1936**, no. 12]. *W. H. Gage* (Vancouver, B. C.).

Citations: MR 2, 347b = D24-1.

D24-14 **(9, 498d)**

Moessner, Alfred. Einige Diophantische Probleme und Resultat. Bull. Calcutta Math. Soc. **39**, 73–78 (1947).

Solutions of some equations $x^n+y^n=(x-y)^{n+1}$, $x^3+y^3=(x+y)^2$, $\sum_{i=1}^4 a_i^n=\sum_{i=1}^4 b_i^n$, $n=1, 2, 4$. Numerical examples. *N. G. W. H. Beeger* (Amsterdam).

D24-15 **(9, 498e)**

Pompeiu, D. Les sommes de nombres entiers. Acad. Roum. Bull. Sect. Sci. **23**, 225–228 (1942).

Elementary proof of the impossibility of $(x-a)^3+x^3=(x+a)^3$ in integers. *N. G. W. H. Beeger* (Amsterdam).

D24-16 **(12, 80d)**

Nagell, Trygve. Über die Anzahl der Lösungen gewisser diophantischer Gleichungen dritten Grades. Math. Z. **52**, 750–757 (1950).

Consider the equation $ax^3+bx^2y+cxy^2+dy^3=k$, the cubic form having negative discriminant. It is proved that this equation has at most 6 integral solutions when $k=2$, at most 12 when $k=4$. This result is improved in many special cases, of which only one is reproduced here. If $k=2$ or 4 there are at most 2 solutions in case $a\equiv d\equiv b+1\equiv c+1\equiv 1 \pmod 2$. The method used is reduction of cubic forms to simpler equivalent ones. Use is also made of the author's earlier results of a similar kind for $k=1$ [Math. Z. **28**, 10–29 (1926)]. *I. Niven* (Eugene, Ore.).

D24-17 **(12, 481g)**

Häggmark, Per. On an unsolved question concerning the Diophantine equation $Ax^3+By^3=C$. Ark. Mat. **1**, 279–294 (1950).

T. Nagell [J. Math. Pures Appl. (9) **4**, 209–270 (1925)] proved that $Ax^3+By^3=C$ has at most one solution under the conditions $C=1$ or 3, both $A>1$ and $B>1$ if $C=1$, and $(AB, 3)=1$ if $C=3$. Furthermore if $A=ac^2$ and $B=bd^2$ where a, b, c, d are square-free and relatively prime in pairs, then any solution has the property that $(xA^{\frac{1}{3}}+yB^{\frac{1}{3}})/C=\xi^{2^r}$, where ξ is the fundamental unit of the field $R((ab^2c^2d)^{\frac{1}{3}})$. Nagell determined the values of r in certain cases, and others are treated in the present paper. With all hypotheses as stated above, for $C=3$ it is proved that $r\leqq 1$ in each of the following three cases: Neither A nor B has more than 2 prime factors; A and B are odd, and neither has more than 4 prime factors; $4|A$, and A has at most 3 odd prime factors. Some similar results for $C=1$ are stated in terms of the fundamental unit of the ring generated by 1, $(ab^2c^2d)^{\frac{1}{3}}$, $(a^2bcd^2)^{\frac{1}{3}}$. *I. Niven* (Eugene, Ore.).

Referred to in R16-17.

D24-18 **(12, 590b)**

Gloden, A. Sur une méthode inédite pour transformer en un carré une forme binaire du 4e degré. (Méthode des équations adjointes). Inst. Grand-Ducal Luxembourg. Sect. Sci. Nat. Phys. Math. Arch. N.S. **19**, 239–242 (1950).

Given one rational solution of the equation $f(x)=y^2$, where $f(x)$ is a polynomial of degree 4 with rational coefficients, further solutions are found by means of an associated quadratic equation whose coefficients are quadratic in x and whose discriminant is $f(x)$. However, the problems of the existence and determination of the associated equation are not discussed. *I. Niven* (Eugene, Ore.).

D24-19 **(12, 590d)**

Obláth, Richard. Über die diophantische Gleichung $x^3-1=2y^2$. Acta Math. Acad. Sci. Hungar. **1**, 113–117 (1950). (German. Russian summary)

It is proved that $x^3-1=3y^2$ and $x^3-1=2y^n$ $(n\geqq 2)$ have no integral solutions with $|x|\neq 1$. Results of Nagell [Norsk Mat. Forenings Skr. (I) no. **2**, (1921)] and Ljunggren [Acta Math. **75**, 1–21 (1943); these Rev. **8**, 135] concerning the equations $x^2+x+1=3v^n$ and $x^2+x+1=v^n$ are employed. *I. Niven* (Eugene, Ore.).

Citations: MR 8, 135k = D24-10.

Referred to in D24-20.

D24-20 **(13, 625h)**

Obláth, Richard. Berichtigung zum Aufsatze "Über die diophantische Gleichung $x^3-1=2y^2$." Acta Math. Acad. Sci. Hungar. **1**, 321–322 (1950).

The earlier paper [Acta Math. Acad. Sci. Hungar. **1**, 113–117 (1950); these Rev. **12**, 590] contained the proposition that $x^2+x+1=3v^2$ has no non-trivial solution in integers, on which two other results were based. This is false, T. Nagell having pointed out the solution $x=313$, $v=181$. However, all the other results in the earlier paper appear to be correct, new proofs being given in the present work. Thus it is shown that $x^3=1+2y^2$ and $x^3=1+3y^2$ have no nontrivial solutions by a discussion of factorizations in the quadratic fields $R(\sqrt{-2})$ and $R(\sqrt{-3})$. *I. Niven.*

Citations: MR 12, 590d = D24-19.

D24-21 (14, 19i)

Skolem, Th. Application of 3-adic analysis and "cofields" to the proof of some theorems concerning certain cubic equations. Norsk Mat. Tidsskr. **34**, 45–51 (1952). (Norwegian)

Through the application of 3-adic expansions and the author's concept of cofields certain results by Delaunay and Nagell concerning the integral solutions of the Diophantine equations $x^3+Dy^3=1$ and $Ax^3+By^3=1$ or 3 are derived in a very simple manner. *O. Ore* (New Haven, Conn.).

D24-22 (14, 136j)

Ljunggren, Wilhelm. On the Diophantine equation $x^2+4=Ay^4$. Norske Vid. Selsk. Forh., Trondheim **24** (1951), 82–84 (1952).

It is proved that the equation $x^2+4=Ay^4$ has at most one solution in positive integers x and y with x odd. The proof employs properties of units in the quadratic field $R(\sqrt{A})$. *I. Niven* (Eugene, Ore.).

D24-23 (14, 353h)

Ljunggren, Wilhelm. New solution of a problem proposed by E. Lucas. Norsk Mat. Tidsskr. **34**, 65–72 (1952).

G. N. Watson [Messenger of Math. **48**, 1–22 (1918)] proved, by use of elliptic functions, that the only integral solutions of $\sum_{j=1}^{n} j^2=q^2$ are $n=q=1$ and $n=24$, $q=70$, thus settling a question proposed by E. Lucas [Nouvelles Ann. Math. (2) **14**, 336 (1875)]. The present paper gives a proof employing only arithmetic considerations, and sketches two other such proofs. The study of the units of certain biquadratic fields is involved. *I. Niven* (Eugene, Ore.).

D24-24 (14, 354b)

Hemer, Ove. On the Diophantine equation $y^2-k=x^3$. Thesis, University of Uppsala, Almqvist & Wiksells, Uppsala, 1952. 101 pp.

The first chapter contains results on binary cubic forms and cubic rings, and the correspondence between (1) $y^2-kf^2=x^3$ and binary cubic forms. The binary cubic forms arise from equating irrational parts in

$$\pm y+f\sqrt{k}=\epsilon(a+b\sqrt{k})^3,$$

ϵ being a unit in $R(\sqrt{k})$, in order to solve (1). There are special theorems giving bounds for the number of solutions (x, y) of (1) in terms of the number of prime factors of f, under suitable hypotheses on k, f, and the class number of $R(\sqrt{k})$. Extensions and refinements are made to the theory of binary cubic forms with negative discriminant of B. Delaunay and T. Nagell; this theory relates the forms to fundamental units of cubic fields, and has been summarized by Nagell [L'analyse indéterminée de degré supérieur, Gauthier-Villars, Paris, 1929].

Applications are made in the second chapter to 37 equations with $0<kf^2\leqq 100$ which yield to the various methods and criteria of Chapter I, complete solutions being obtained. The other cases satisfying this inequality are treated, but for these the solutions obtained are not shown to be complete. Seven equations with $0<-kf^2\leqq 100$ are treated. In Chapter III the writer uses results of Billing [Nova Acta Soc. Sci. Upsaliensis (4) **11**, no. 1 (1938)], Cassels [Acta Math. **82**, 243–273 (1950); these Rev. **12**, 11], and Fueter [Comment. Math. Helv. **2**, 69–89 (1930)] to determine all solutions of 89 of the 100 equations $y^2+27k=x^3$ with $0<|k|\leqq 50$. Tables of solutions and fundamental units of the cubic fields are given. An extensive bibliography can be obtained from the works of Cassels and Nagell cited above, and from Th. Skolem [Diophantische Gleichungen, Springer, Berlin, 1938]. *I. Niven* (Eugene, Ore.).

Citations: MR 12, 11a = G05-22.
Referred to in D24-29.

D24-25 (14, 450d)

Ljunggren, Wilhelm. Eine elementare Auflösung der diophantischen Gleichung $x^3+1=2y^2$. Acta Math. Acad. Sci. Hungar. **3**, 99–101 (1952). (Russian summary)

The author's theorem [Skr. Norske Vid. Akad. Oslo. I. no. **9** (1942); these Rev. **6**, 169] that the only integral solutions of $x^3+1=2y^2$ have x values ± 1 and 23 is proved now by elementary methods. *I. Niven* (Eugene, Ore.).

Citations: MR 6, 169e = D24-3.

D24-26 (14, 846k)

Obláth, Richard. Über einige unmögliche diophantische Gleichungen. Mat. Tidsskr. A. **1952**, 53–62 (1952).

It is established that the following equations have no integral solutions with $|x|>1$: $x^3-1=2y^2$, $x^3-1=3y^n$ $(n\geqq 2)$, $48x^4+1=y^2$, $12x^4+1=y^4$, $x^3+1=3y^2$, $x^4\pm x^2+1=3y^2$. The first two of these equations (with $n=2$) were treated earlier by the author [Acta Math. Acad. Sci. Hungar. **1**, 321–322 (1950); these Rev. **13**, 625, 1140] but the present work avoids the use of quadratic fields. *I. Niven.*

D24-27 (14, 1063d)

Hall, Marshall, Jr. Some equations $y^2=x^3-k$ without integer solutions. J. London Math. Soc. **28**, 379–383 (1953).

In this paper the author gives two new methods for obtaining equations of the type mentioned in the title. In the first method he uses factorisation in $K(\sqrt{-k})$ in certain cases when $h(\sqrt{-k})\equiv 0 \pmod 3$. In the second, use is made of a representation $k=3a^2+rb^3$, applying cubic reciprocity to the equation in the form $x^3-rb^3=y^2+3a^2$. Three theorems are proved, and applications of these theorems are given. The equation is impossible for $k=24$, 31, and 77. The same principles can be used to determine other insoluble equations $(k=92, -60)$. *W. Ljunggren* (Bergen).

Referred to in D24-42, D28-38.

D24-28 (15, 400d)

Ljunggren, Wilhelm. On an improvement of a theorem of T. Nagell concerning the Diophantine equation $Ax^3+By^3=C$. Math. Scand. **1**, 297–309 (1953).

T. Nagell [J. Math. Pures Appl. (9) **4**, 209–270 (1925)] proved that $Ax^3+By^3=C$ has at most one solution in integers if $C=1$ or 3, both $A>1$ and $B>1$ if $C=1$, and $(AB, 3)=1$ if $C=3$; exception must be made in the one case $2x^3+y^3=3$ with the two solutions (1, 1) and (4, −5), but this case is ignored in what follows. Any solution has the property that $C^{-1}(xA^{1/3}+yB^{1/3})=\xi^{2^r}$, where ξ is the fundamental unit in the field $R((AB^2)^{1/3})$. Nagell determined an upper limit for the non-negative rational integer r in certain cases, and P. Häggmark [Ark. Mat. **1**, 279–294 (1950); these Rev. **12**, 481] treated some others. In the present paper the best possible result $r\leqq 1$ is established for all cases. *I. Niven* (Eugene, Ore.).

Citations: MR 12, 481h = D68-5.

D24-29 **(15, 776h)**

Hemer, Ove. Notes on the Diophantine equation $y^2-k=x^3$. Ark. Mat. **3**, 67–77 (1954).

This paper gives some additions and corrections to the author's dissertation [Univ. of Uppsala, 1952; these Rev. **14**, 354]. In addition to refinements of the theory, there are corrections in application of the theory in a few instances, and the removal of one or two numerical errors. The Diophantine equation $y^2-k=x^3$ is now solved completely in all cases $0<k\leqq 100$, and in all but 22 of the cases $0<-k\leqq 100$. Corrected tables of solutions and of the fundamental units of the cubic fields are given. *I. Niven* (Eugene, Ore.).

Citations: MR 14, 354b = D24-24.

Referred to in D24-35, D24-57, D24-59.

D24-30 **(16, 220f)**

Bini, Umberto. Sul numero delle soluzioni intere dell'equazione $x^3+y^3=K$. Archimede **6**, 187–195 (1954).

Observations are made on the number of solutions in integers of $x^3+y^3=K$, based on ideas such as the following. If $K=ab$ where $3(4b-a^2)$ is a perfect square, say $9A^2$, then $x, y=\frac{1}{2}(a\pm A)$ is a solution. Conversely, any solution x, y determines a, A and b, and thus a correspondence and a counting procedure can be established. *I. Niven.*

D24-31 **(16, 448a)**

Ljunggren, Wilhelm. Ein Satz über die diophantische Gleichung $Ax^2-By^4=C$ ($C=1, 2, 4$). Tolfte Skandinaviska Matematikerkongressen, Lund, 1953, pp. 188–194 (1954). 25 Swedish crowns (may be ordered from Lunds Universitets Matematiska Institution).

Let A, B be positive integers and $C=1$, 2, or 4, such that AB is odd if C is even; A square-free and AB not a perfect square; and let $C=2$ when $A=1$. Further, only such values of A, B, C are considered for which $Ax^2-Bz^2=C$ has a solution, $(x, z)=(a, b)$ being the least positive. If $3+4Bb^2/C$ is not a perfect square, then $Ax^2-By^4=C$ has at most one solution in positive integers x, y. The equation $Ax^2-By^4=4$ has at most one solution in positive relatively prime integers x, y. These are extensions of earlier work by the author [Arch. Math. Naturvid. **41**, no. 10 (1938)]. *I. Niven.*

Referred to in D24-81.

D24-32 **(16, 450a)**

Wiman, A. Über die Punkte mit ganzzahligen Koordinaten auf gewissen Kurven dritter Ordnung. Tolfte Skandinaviska Matematikerkongressen, Lund, 1953, pp. 317–323 (1954). 25 Swedish crowns (may be ordered from Lunds Universitets Matematiska Institution).

The present paper deals with the class of cubic curves

(1) $y^2=x^3+px+q$ (p, q integers)

which are met in triplets of integer points

$$(-(a+b), t),\ (a, t),\ (b, t);\quad (-b, s),\ (-a, s),\ (a+b, s)$$

by two lines $y=s$, $y=t$, as e.g.:

(2) $y^2=x^3-7x+10$ ($a=1, b=2, s=4, t=2$),

(3) $y^2=x^3-172x+820$ ($a=2, b=12, s=34, t=22$),

(4) $y^2=x^3-172x+505$ ($a=2, b=12, s=29, t=13$),

(5) $y^2=x^3-112x+2320$ ($a=4, b=8, s=52, t=44$).

For some of them, it may happen that the tangent and chord processes lead to new integer points; for instance, if (x_1, y_1), (x_2, y_2) are any two integer points of the curve (1) (with $x_1\neq x_2$), their join meets (1) at an integer point if, and only if, x_1-x_2 divides y_1-y_2. It is thus deduced that the curves (3)–(5) contain 24, 60, 58, 70 integer points respectively, in pairs symmetrical with respect to the x-axis. *B. Segre.*

D24-33 **(16, 998k)**

Lorent, H. Sur l'équation indéterminée $x^2+l=y^3$. I, II. Bull. Soc. Roy. Sci. Liège **24**, 72–76, 192–197 (1955).

D24-34 **(17, 237i)**

Schinzel, André. Sur l'équation indéterminée $x^2+l=y^3$. Bull. Soc. Roy. Sci. Liège **24** (1955), 271–274.

D24-35 **(18, 379j)**

Hemer, Ove. On some diophantine equations of the type $y^2-f^2=x^3$. Math. Scand. **4** (1956), 95–107.

This paper is based on some previous work by the same author [Ark. Mat. **3** (1954), 67–77; MR **15**, 776; see also L. J. Mordell, Proc. London Math. Soc. (2) **13** (1913), 60–80; T. Nagell, Math. Z. **28** (1928), 10–29]. If the cubic form $AU^3+BU^2V+CUV^2+DV^3$ is denoted by (A, B, C, D) then, as the author has previously shown, an equation $y^2-f^2=x^3$ may be replaced by the equation $(1, 0, 0, 1)=2f$ and $\frac{1}{2}(3^r-1)$ equations $(A, 0, 0, D)=2fA^{-1}D^{-1}$, if $2f$ contains r distinct primes. Using the methods of algebraic numbers the author finds all the solutions of the equations $y^2-f^2=x^3$ for the fifteen values of $f=11, 12, \cdots, 25$.

I. A. Barnett (Cincinnati, Ohio).

Citations: MR 15, 776h = D24-29.

Referred to in D24-55.

D24-36 **(20# 6388)**

Bombieri, Enrico. Sulle soluzioni intere dell'equazione $4x^3=27y^2+N$. Riv. Mat. Univ. Parma **8** (1957), 199–206.

All integral solutions (x, y) of the title equation are determined for $-22\leqq N\leqq 80$ except $N=49$. The argument turns on the fact that, for the values of N involved, the cubic t^3-xt+y in the indeterminate t must have a rational integral root (for otherwise the roots would generate a cubic field, which contradicts what is known about the possible values of the discriminants of cubic fields. *J. W. S. Cassels* (Cambridge, England)

Referred to in D24-37.

D24-37 **(21# 4131)**

Toscano, Letterio. Sulle soluzioni intere dell'equazione $4x^3=27y^2+N$. Riv. Mat. Univ. Parma **8** (1957), 405–406.

The author modifies the method of Bombieri [same Riv. **8** (1957), 199–206; MR **20** #6388] to give a simpler proof of the same result.

J. W. S. Cassels (Cambridge, England)

Citations: MR 20# 6388 = D24-36.

D24-38 **(23# A103)**

Gross, Oliver

On the elementary approach to Diophantine equations.

Math. Mag. **34** (1960/61), 259–267.

The author rightly advocates the use of elementary methods when these are available. Examples:

$$x^6+3=y^3+z^3;\quad x^3=y^2+3;\quad x^3+x^2+x=y^2+y.$$

S. Chowla (Boulder, Colo.)

D24-39 **(23# A2373)**

G.-Rodeja F., E.

On the diophantine equations $x^3+y^3=kx^2$, $k=1, 2, 3$. (Spanish)

Rev. Mat. Hisp.-Amer. (4) **19** (1959), 84–91.

Several 2-parameter solutions are given for each of the equations of the title, and small triples x, y, z are deducted.

This paper continues and provides corrections for earlier ones by the author [e.g., same Rev. (4) **13** (1953), 229–240; MR **15**, 506]. *W. J. LeVeque* (Ann Arbor, Mich.)

Citations: MR 15, 506f = D32-42.

D24-40 (27# 1413)

Sprindžuk, V. G.

On the number of solutions of the Diophantine equation $x^3=y^2+A$. (Russian)

Dokl. Akad. Nauk BSSR **7** (1963), 9–11.

Let A be an integer of the form $A=f^2g$, where $g\neq -1$ and is square-free. The author proves that the number of solutions of the Diophantine equation $x^3=y^2+A$ is smaller than $c(\varepsilon)3^{\sigma(-g)}|A|^\varepsilon$ for each $\varepsilon>0$, where $c(\varepsilon)$ is a constant depending only on ε, and $\sigma(-g)$ is the class number of ideals of the field $R(\sqrt{-g})$, the third powers of which are principal. *J. Kubilius* (Vilnius)

D24-41 (27# 3590)

Mordell, L. J.

On the integer solutions of $y(y+1)=x(x+1)(x+2)$.

Pacific J. Math. **13** (1963), 1347–1351.

The author shows that the only solutions in integers (x, y) of the equation of the title are for the following values of x: $x=5, 1, 0, -1, -2$. His proof makes use of the properties of the cubic field $R(\theta)$ generated by the equation: $x^3-4x+2=0$. This field has class number 1, all integers are of the form $a+b\theta+c\theta^2$, where a, b, c are integers and the two fundamental units may be taken to be $\theta-1$ and $2\theta-1$. By this means the problem is reduced to solving four pairs of simultaneous quadratic equations of the form $f(P, Q, R)=0$, $G(P, Q, R)=1$. *Burton W. Jones* (Boulder, Colo.)

D24-42 (28# 2082)

Ljunggren, W.

On the diophantine equation $y^2-k=x^3$.

Acta Arith. **8** (1962/63), 451–463.

The author remarks that the finding of the solutions of the title equation in positive rational integers is more difficult when the integer k is negative and that, although a complete solution is known for every positive $k\leqq 100$, there are 22 negative values of k with $-k\leqq 100$ for which the complete solution was unknown. He solves completely the problem for the two smallest outstanding negative k by showing that the only solutions with $k=-7$ are (2, 1) and (32, 181) and the only solution with $k=-15$ is (4, 7). The elaborate and laborious proofs depend on the fact that the solution of the title equation in integers is equivalent to the solution of a finite number of equations $f(x, y)=1$, where f is a binary quartic with rational integer coefficients [Mordell, Messenger of Math. **51** (1922), 169–171]. If k is negative, the equation $f(x, 1)=0$ has precisely two real roots and so there is an equation of the type $x+y\eta=\varepsilon_1^{n_1}, \varepsilon_2^{n_2}$, where $f(\eta, -1)=0$ and $\varepsilon_1, \varepsilon_2$ is a pair of basic units for the quartic field. This is dealt with by Skolem's p-adic method [Math. Ann. **111** (1935), 399–424]. There is a useful list of references to which might be added Hall [J. London Math. Soc. **28** (1953), 379–383; MR **14**, 1063]. *J. W. S. Cassels* (Cambridge, England)

Citations: MR 14, 1063d = D24-27.

Referred to in D24-57, D24-85.

D24-43 (28# 2083)

Mordell, L. J.

The Diophantine equation $y^2=ax^3+bx^2+cx+d$, or fifty years after.

J. London Math. Soc. **38** (1963), 454–458.

Using linear and quadratic congruence arguments, the author constructs several families of Diophantine equations of the form $y^2=xg(x)$ which either have no solutions in rational integers or have only finitely many effectively computable solutions of this kind. The technique is that developed by the author fifty years ago [Proc. London Math. Soc. (2) **13** (1913/14), 60–80]. The interest lies in the computability of the solution, since Siegel has shown [J. London Math. Soc. **1** (1926), 66–68] that the equation $y^2=f(x)$ has only finitely many solutions in integers if the polynomial $f(x)$ has at least three distinct zeros. *W. J. LeVeque* (Boulder, Colo.)

Referred to in D24-48, D24-77.

D24-44 (29# 65)

Mordell, L. J.

The Diophantine equation $y^2=Dx^4+1$.

J. London Math. Soc. **39** (1964), 161–164.

W. Ljunggren [Skr. Norske Vid.-Akad. Oslo I Mat.-Naturv. Kl. **1936**, no. 12] has shown that the equation of the title has at most two solutions when D is a positive non-square integer, and that these can be found explicitly. In the present paper, the author obtains, by elementary methods, two sets of sufficient conditions that the equation have no solution. One is that $D\not\equiv 0, -1, 3, 8 \pmod{16}$, and that D have no factorization $D=pq$, where $p>1$, p is odd, $(p, q)=1$, and such that $p\equiv\pm1$, $p-q\equiv\pm1$, $p-4q\equiv\pm1 \pmod{16}$. The other is similar. *W. J. LeVeque* (Ann Arbor, Mich.)

Referred to in D24-47, D24-60, D24-87.

D24-45 (29# 1180)

Schinzel, A.; Sierpiński, W.

Sur l'équation diophantienne

$$(x^2-1)(y^2-1)=\left[\left(\frac{y-x}{2}\right)^2-1\right]^2.$$

Elem. Math. **18** (1963), 132–133.

The authors give the complete solution of the title equation in natural numbers x, y, $x<y$, showing that this equation can be written $(x+y)^2(x^2-6xy+y^2+8)=0$, which for, $x>0$, $y>0$, is equivalent to $x^2-6xy+y^2+8=0$, or $x^2-2(\frac14(y-3x))^2=1$. A similar problem was proposed by J. A. Hunter [Amer. Math. Monthly **69** (1962), 316–317] and solved by R. Venkatchalam Iyer [ibid. **70** (1963), 574]. The complete solution of the more general equation $(x^2-1)(y^2-1)=(z^2-1)^2$ is unknown. *W. Ljunggren* (Oslo)

Referred to in D28-35.

D24-46 (31# 2200)

Cassels, J. W. S.

Integral points on certain elliptic curves.

Proc. London Math. Soc. (3) **14a** (1965), 55–57.

The author remarks that when an elliptic curve is given as the intersection of two quadratics in three-dimensional space, it may be useful to consider the singular quadratics in the pencil. As an illustration he shows that the only triangular numbers which are the squares of triangular numbers are 0, 1, and 36. This was first proved by the reviewer [Arch. Math. Naturvid. **48**, no. 7 (1946); MR **8**, 442]. The new proof is simpler in the sense that no use is made of the p-adic method. The author's general considerations have some similarities with those introduced in an earlier paper by the reviewer [Norsk Mat. Tidsskr. **23** (1941), 132–138; MR **8**, 314]. *W. Ljunggren* (Oslo)

Citations: MR 8, 314g = D20-3; MR 8, 442h = D40-12.

Referred to in D32-85, D32-89.

D24-47 (31# 2202)

Cohn, J. H. E.
Lucas and Fibonacci numbers and some Diophantine equations.
Proc. Glasgow Math. Assoc. **7**, 24–28 (1965).

Define the Lucas numbers v_n and the Fibonacci numbers u_n by $v_1=1$, $v_2=3$, $v_{n+2}=v_{n+1}+v_n$ and $u_1=u_2=1$, $u_{n+2}=u_{n+1}+u_n$ for all integers n. The following theorems are proved. (1) If $v_n=x^2$ then $n=1$ or 3. (2) If $v_n=2x^2$ then $n=0$ or ± 6. (3) If $u_n=x^2$ then $n=0$, ± 1, 2 or 12. (4) If $u_n=2x^2$ then $n=0$, ± 3 or 6. Theorem 3 had been proved earlier by the author [J. London Math. Soc. **39** (1964), 537–540; MR **29** #1166].

In the remainder of the paper the author applies these results to eight Diophantine equations. For example, he proves that the equation $y^2=5x^4+1$ has only the solutions $x=0$, ± 2. This result has been proved also by L. J. Mordell [ibid. **39** (1964), 161–164; MR **29** #65].

L. Carlitz (Durham, N.C.)

Citations: MR 29# 65 = D24-44; MR 29# 1166 = B36-53.

D24-48 (31# 3379)

Mordell, L. J.
The Diophantine equation $y^2=ax^3+bx^2+cx+d$.
Rend. Circ. Mat. Palermo (2) **13** (1964), 249–256.

Recently, the author [J. London Math. Soc. **38** (1963), 454–458; MR **28** #2083] has given various sets of conditions on the integers a, b, c, d which will ensure that all the solutions of the equation of the title are less than some computable bound. He generalises the method as follows. Suppose that one can write $ax^3+bx^2+cx+d=g(x)h(x)-k(f(x))^2$, where f, g, h are polynomials with integer coefficients and k divides 210. Then the equation of the title becomes $y^2+kf^2=gh$, and by making the coefficients of f, g, h satisfy suitable conditions one can ensure that all the integer solutions x, y of the equation make $h(x)$ negative, so that x is bounded by the largest root of h.

B. J. Birch (Manchester)

Citations: MR 28# 2083 = D24-43.
Referred to in D24-77.

D24-49 (31# 4760)

Mordell, L. J.
The Diophantine equation $y^2=ax^3+bx^2+cx+d$.
Scripta Math. **27** (1964), 205–211 (1965).

This is an expository article about the well-known Diophantine equation $y^2=ax^3+bx^2+cx+d$, with particular emphasis on recent work of the author.

W. H. Mills (Princeton, N.J.)

D24-50 (32# 1165)

Mordell, L. J.
The Diophantine equation $y^2=ax^3+bx^2+cx+d$. (Polish)
Wiadom. Mat. (2) **7**, 203–210 (1964).

An expository lecture presented in 1963.

S. Knapowski (Gainesville, F'a.)

D24-51 (32# 4079)

Birch, B. J.; Chowla, S.; Hall, Marshall, Jr.; Schinzel, A.
On the difference x^3-y^2.
Norske Vid. Selsk. Forh. (*Trondheim*) **38** (1965), 65–69.

It is a well-known consequence of Thue's theorem that for integers x and y, the expression $|x^3-y^2|$ tends to infinity with $\max\{|x|, |y|\}$. However, the existing proofs provided no estimate for $|x^3-y^2|$. The authors prove that there is an absolute constant $C>0$ such that $0<|x^3-y^2|<Cx^{3/5}$ for infinitely many x and y. (In fact, C can be taken to be 1/9.) Their proof consists in showing the existence of polynomials $f(t)$, $g(t)$ of degrees 6 and 9, respectively, such that f^3-g^2 is of degree 4. Other examples are also given, some of which give results such as $|(8158)^3-(736{,}844)^2|=24$. The authors make a number of conjectures related to their work.

D. J. Lewis (Ann Arbor, Mich.)

Referred to in D24-70.

D24-52 (32# 4080)

Davenport, H.
On $f^3(t)-g^2(t)$.
Norske Vid. Selsk. Forh. (*Trondheim*) **38** (1965), 86–87.

The author proves a conjecture of Birch, Chowla, M. Hall, Jr., and Schinzel [see #4079 above]; namely, if $f(t)$, $g(t)$ are polynomials with complex coefficients, then either $f^3=g^2$ or $\deg(f^3-g^2)\geqq 1+\frac{1}{2}\deg f$. The proof is elementary, using linear equations arising from equating coefficients. A generalization is also given. The question of whether $\deg(f^3-g^2)=1+\frac{1}{2}\deg f$ holds for a sequence of f with increasing degrees is left open. (See loc. cit. for some cases of equality.)

D. J. Lewis (Ann Arbor, Mich.)

D24-53 (32# 7492)

Cohn, J. H. E.
Eight Diophantine equations.
Proc. London Math. Soc. (3) **16** (1966), 153–166.

Let d be an integer such that the equation $X^2-dY^2=-4$ has solutions with X and Y odd. The eight Diophantine equations $y^2=dx^4+1$, $dy^2=x^4-1$, $y^2=4dx^4+1$, $y^2=dx^4-1$, $dy^2=4x^4+1$, $y^2=dx^4+4$, $y^2=dx^4-4$, and $dy^2=x^4+4$ are treated by means of a careful study of the solutions of $X^2-dY^2=-4$. Except for the equation $y^2=5x^4+4$, which has three non-negative integral solutions, none of these eight equations has more than two non-negative integral solutions for fixed d.

W. H. Mills (Princeton, N.J.)

Referred to in D24-54, D24-78, D24-80, D24-81.

D24-54 (34# 5748)

Cohn, J. H. E.
Addendum: "Eight Diophantine equations".
Proc. London Math. Soc. (3) **17** (1967), 381.

This note contains minor corrections and additions to the author's paper in same Proc. (3) **16** (1966), 153–166, [MR **32** #7492].

W. H. Mills (Princeton, N.J.)

Citations: MR 32# 7492 = D24-53.
Referred to in D24-81.

D24-55 (32# 7493)

Finkelstein, Raphael
The house problem.
Amer. Math. Monthly **72** (1965), 1082–1088.

An integer N is said to be the kth power numerical center for the positive integer n if $1^k+\cdots+N^k=N^k+\cdots+n^k$. It is easily verified that N is the first power numerical center for n exactly when N, n is a solution of the Pellian equation $(2n+1)^2-8N^2=1$. Hence, infinitely many n have first power numerical centers. On the other hand, as the author also proves, 1 is the only integer with a second power numerical center. The proof is achieved by showing (for $k=2$) that N, n are solutions of a certain cubic diophantine equation, which in turn are associated with certain solutions of the Diophantine equations $a^3+2b^3=1, 3, 11, 33$. Solutions of these last equations are found by use of basic algebraic number theory and by references to Nagell [J. Math. Pures Appl. (9) **4** (1925),

209–270] and Hemer [Math. Scand. **4** (1956), 95–107; MR **18**, 379]. *D. J. Lewis* (Ann Arbor, Mich.)

Citations: MR 18, 379j = D24-35.

D24-56 **(32# 7497)**

Nagell, Trygve

Sur les représentations de l'unité par les formes binaires biquadratiques du premier rang.

Ark. Mat. **5**, 477–521 (1965).

Let $\sum_{i=0}^{4} a_i x^{4-i} y^i = f(x, y)$ be a binary quartic form where the coefficients are rational integers and the form is irreducible over the rational field. The form is defined to be of rank 1 if all the roots of $f(x, 1)=0$ are imaginary. This paper contains a very complete and careful discussion of the integer solutions of the diophantine equation

$$x^4 - px^3y + qx^2y^2 - xy^3 + sy^4 = 1$$

where the underlying form $g(x, y) = x^4 - px^3y + qx^2y^2 - xy^3 + sy^4$ is of rank 1. Since statements of the theorems proved involve a fair amount of technical details, only the following results will be stated here: Except possibly for one category of forms, the number of integer solutions of $g(x, y) = 1$ is at most equal to eight; there are eight solutions precisely for two classes of forms; there are infinitely many classes of forms for which the number of solutions is six.

The paper concludes with a discussion of some forms of higher degree. The following theorem, amongst others, is proved: Let θ be an algebraic integer of degree 6 over the rationals. Suppose that $Q(\theta)$ contains a quadratic imaginary subfield different from $Q(\sqrt{-1})$ and $Q(\sqrt{-3})$. Then the number of solutions in integers with $\mathrm{Norm}_{Q(\theta)/Q}(x - \theta y) = 1$ is at most equal to six.

J. K. Goldhaber (College Park, Md.)

Referred to in D24-79.

D24-57 **(33# 91)**

Lal, M.; Jones, M. F.; Blundon, W. J.

Tables of solutions of the diophantine equation $y^3 - x^2 = k$.

Department of Mathematics, Memorial University of Newfoundland, St. John's, Newfoundland, 1965.

iii + 162 *pp.* $10.00.

This is a table of all integral solutions of the title equation with $|k| \leqq 9999$ and $0 \leqq x < 10^{10}$. The authors claim that it is probable from the run of the figures that the set of solutions is complete for most of the k in the stated range. In the range $|k| \leqq 100$ all solutions have been determined except for 20 values of k [O. Hemer, Ark. Mat. **3** (1954), 67–77; MR **15**, 776; W. Ljunggren, Acta Arith. **8** (1962/63), 451–463; MR **28** #2082], and for the missing values of k in this range the computations have not thrown up any solutions that were not already known [loc. cit.]. The largest solutions are $(1{,}775{,}104)^3 - (2{,}365{,}024{,}826)^2 = -5412$ and $(939{,}787)^3 - (911{,}054{,}064)^2 = 307$, for negative and positive k, respectively.

J. W. S. Cassels (Cambridge, England)

Citations: MR 15, 776h = D24-29; MR 28# 2082 = D24-42.

D24-58 **(33# 98)**

Lal, M.; Jones, M. F.; Blundon, W. J.

Numerical solutions of the Diophantine equation $y^3 - x^2 = k$.

Math. Comp. **20** (1966), 322–325.

D24-59 **(33# 4004)**

Finkelstein, Raphael

On a Diophantine equation with no nontrivial integral solution.

Amer. Math. Monthly **73** (1966), 471–477.

A problem proposed in the Monthly and outstanding since 1940 [V. V. Johnston, same Monthly **47** (1940), Problem 3951, p. 182] asks for the complete solution in positive integers (m, n) of the equation $m(m+1)(m+2) = n(n+1)(2n+1)$. The author remarks that this is equivalent to the solution of $x^3 + 4y^3 = x + 4y$ in integers x, y with $x > 0 > y$ and x odd, and he proves that the only such solutions are $[x, y] = [1, -1]$ and $[3, -2]$. To do this, he writes $\gcd(x, y) = d$, so that $x = ad$, $y = bd$ with $d^2(a^3 + 4b^3) = a + 4b$, and shows that $a^3 + 4b^3$ must divide 15. Thus, there are four cases, according as $a^3 + 4b^3 = \pm 1, \pm 3, \pm 5, \pm 15$. The complete rational solution of $a^3 + 4b^3 = 1$ is well known, and there are no rational solutions of $a^3 + 4b^3 = 15$ [Selmer, Acta Math. **85** (1951), 203–362; MR **13**, 13]; it is a particular case of a theorem of Nagell that $a^3 + 4b^3 = 3$ has at most one integral solution. There remains the case $a^3 + 4b^3 = 5$; by using Skolem's method as described by Hemer [Ark. Mat. **3** (1954), 67–77; MR **15**, 776] in the field $Q(\sqrt[3]{2})$, the author shows that the only solutions of this are $[a, b] = [1, 1]$ and $[-3, 2]$. A difficult example, treated by a nice assortment of standard tools.

B. J. Birch (Oxford)

Citations: MR 13, 13i = G05-31; MR 15, 776h = D24-29.

D24-60 **(33# 5555)**

Ljunggren, W.

Some remarks on the diophantine equations $x^2 - \mathscr{D}y^4 = 1$ and $x^4 - \mathscr{D}y^2 = 1$.

J. London Math. Soc. **41** (1966), 542–544.

Improving a result of Mordell [same J. **39** (1964), 161–164; MR **29** #65], the author proves that if $p \neq 5$ is a prime congruent to 1 (mod 4), then $x^2 - py^4 = 1$ has no solution with x, y positive integers. He goes on to show that if p is any prime other than 5 or 29, then $x^4 - py^2 = 1$ has no solution in positive integers. The proofs are superficially simple, but depend on the author's difficult theorem that the only solutions in positive integers of $x^2 - 2y^4 = -1$ are $(x, y) = (1, 1), (13, 239)$ [Avh. Norske Vid.-Akad. Oslo I No. 5 (1942); MR **8**, 6]. *B. J. Birch* (Oxford)

Citations: MR 8, 6f = D24-8; MR 29# 65 = D24-44.
Referred to in D24-81, D24-87.

D24-61 **(33# 7298)**

Baulin, V. I.

On an indeterminate equation of the third degree with least positive discriminant. (Russian)

Tul'sk. Gos. Ped. Inst. Učen. Zap. Fiz.-Mat. Nauk Vyp. 7 (1960), 138–170.

It is shown that the only integral solutions of the equation $x^3 + x^2y - 2xy^2 - y^3 = 1$ are $(1, 0)$, $(0, -1)$, $(-1, 1)$, $(5, 4)$, $(4, -9)$, $(-9, 5)$, $(2, -1)$, $(-1, -1)$ and $(-1, 2)$. The proof is said to follow Ljunggren's treatment [Acta Math. **75** (1942), 1–21; MR **8**, 135] of $x^3 - 3xy^2 - y^3 = 1$ and is very elaborate, depending on a knowledge of the units of the field $\mathbf{Q}(\eta^{1/2})$, where $\eta^3 - \eta^2 - 2\eta + 1 = 0$.

J. W. S. Cassels (Cambridge, England)

Citations: MR 8, 135k = D24-10.

D24-62 **(35# 4158)**

Cohn, J. H. E.

The Diophantine equation $y^2 = Dx^4 + 1$.

J. London Math. Soc. **42** (1967), 475–476.

Let D be a positive integer such that either $D \equiv 9$, 10, or 13 (mod 16); or $D \equiv 2$ (mod 16) and D has a factor $\equiv 5$ (mod 8). Suppose further that $v^2 - Du^2 = -1$ has solutions in integers u, v. It is shown that neither $y^2 = Dx^4 + 1$ nor $y^2 = 4Dx^4 + 1$ has any solutions in positive integers.

W. H. Mills (Princeton, N.J.)

D24-63 **(35# 6619)**

Avanesov, È. T.

Solution of a problem on figurate numbers. **(Russian)**

Acta Arith. **12** (1966/67), 409–420.

A tetrahedral number is one of the form $\frac{1}{6}(x)(x+1)(x+2)$, and a triangular number is one of the form $\frac{1}{2}y(y+1)$, where x and y are natural numbers. A famous problem is that of determining which tetrahedral numbers are also triangular [cf. W. Sierpiński, *A selection of problems in the theory of numbers*, Problem 98, Macmillan, New York, 1964; MR **30** #1078]. The author solves this problem by proving that 1, 10, 120, 1540 and 7140 are the only tetrahedral numbers which are also triangular. The problem is equivalent to finding all the integral solutions of the Diophantine equation (1) $3y(y+1)=x(x+1)(x+2)$, and the substitution $X=2x+2$, $Y=2y+1$ transforms (1) into (2) $6Y^2=X^3-4X+6$. The elaborate and laborious solution of (2) depends upon the fact that its solution is equivalent to the solution of a finite number of equations $f(m,n)=1$, where f is a semi-real binary quartic form with rational integral coefficients. The corresponding equation $f(\eta,-1)=0$ then has two real roots and thus there exists an equation of the form (3) $m+n\eta=\pm\varepsilon_1^{n_1}\varepsilon_2^{n_2}$, where ε_1, ε_2 is a pair of fundamental units for the ring $R(1,\eta,\eta^2,\eta^3)$. (3) may then be treated by Th. Skolem's p-adic method [Eighth Scand. Math. Congr. (Stockholm, 1934) (Swedish), pp. 163–188, Ohlssons Boktryckeri, Lund, 1935].

R. Finkelstein (Tucson, Ariz.)

Citations: MR 30# 1078 = Z05-8.

D24-64 **(36# 106)**

Cohn, J. H. E.

The Diophantine equation $x^3=dy^3+1$.

J. London Math. Soc. **42** (1967), 750–752.

It is known that the equation of the title, where $d\neq 0$ is an integer, has at most one solution in integers x, y, where $y\neq 0$, and that this solution, if it exists, can be found when the fundamental unit of the cubic field $R(d^{1/3})$ is known [see, e.g., W. J. LeVeque, *Topics in number theory*, Vol. II, Section 3.9, Addison-Wesley, Reading, Mass., 1956; MR **18**, 283]. In the present paper the author proves the following theorems, which provide conditions of a simple type under which no such nontrivial solution exists. (In each theorem d may be considered positive, since if d is negative, the minus sign can be absorbed into y.)

(1) With the single exception $d=9$, the equation has no nontrivial solution when $9|d$, unless $d=pq$, where p and q are positive integers satisfying (i) $(p,q)=1$, (ii) if $p_1|p$ then $p_1\equiv 1 \pmod 6$, and (iii) $p\neq p_1^3$. If $27|d$, then one must also have (iv) $p\equiv 1 \pmod{18}$.

(2) If $d\equiv\pm 3$ or $\pm 4 \pmod 9$ the equation has no nontrivial solution unless $d=pq$, where p,q are positive integers satisfying (i)–(iv) above.

(3) With exactly six exceptions, namely $d=1, 2, 17, 20$, 5831 and 6860, the equation has no nontrivial solution when $d\equiv\pm 1$ or $\pm 2 \pmod 9$, unless $d=pq$, where p,q are positive integers satisfying (i)–(iii) above.

The author uses these theorems to determine those values of d not exceeding 100 for which the equation has a nontrivial solution.

R. Finkelstein (Tempe, Ariz.)

Citations: MR 18, 283b = Z01-38.

Referred to in D24-89.

D24-65 **(36# 1388)**

Dyšlis, A. D.

A solution in integers for some equations of the form $Ay^4+By^2+C=Px^2$. **(Russian)**

Sverdlovsk. Gos. Ped. Inst. Učen. Zap. **31** (1965), 73–86.

The author studies the diophantine equation $m^2y^4+2(a+4)my^2+(a-4)^2=px^2$ for $a=1, 2, 3$. As in Ljunggren's work, there is, via a deep study of the fundamental unit in a certain algebraic number-field, a contribution to the problem stated in the title. Examples of results: (1) $33x^2=4y^4+20y^2+9$ has no integral solutions, and (2) $13x^2=9y^4+42y^2+1$ has the solutions $x=2$, $y=1$ and $x=3098$, $y=61$. Thue was the first to prove that such equations have only a finite number of solutions; but, in general, there is not yet a finite algorithm to determine all the solutions. A special case can be extremely troublesome, sometimes hopelessly hard and time-consuming.

S. Chowla (University Park, Pa.)

D24-66 **(36# 2559)**

Faddeev, D. K.

On a paper by A. Baker. **(Russian)**

Zap. Naučn. Sem. Leningrad. Otdel. Mat. Inst. Steklov. (LOMI) **1** (1966), 128–139.

A. Baker has proved an effective version of Thue's approximation theorem for certain special irrationalities and has deduced a bound for all integer solutions of $x^3-2y^3=C$ [Quart. J. Math. Oxford Ser. (2) **15** (1964), 375–383; MR **30** #1977]. The author investigates thoroughly the possibilities of Baker's method in the case of cubic irrationalities and obtains an effective method of solving the equations $x^3+x^2y-y^3=C$, $x^3+x^2y+xy^2-y^3=C$, $x^3+x^2y-2xy^2-y^3=C$. Although the results are formulated in terms of Diophantine equations, the proof furnishes estimations similar to those of Baker related to Thue's theorem.

A. Schinzel (Warsaw)

Citations: MR 30# 1977 = J68-45.

Referred to in Z10-48.

D24-67 **(37# 1312)**

Avanesov, È. T.

The representation of numbers by binary cubic forms of positive discriminant. **(Russian)**

Acta Arith. **14** (1967/68), 13–25.

The author studies the equation (*) $x^3+qx^2y-rxy^2+sy^3=1$, where the left side is an irreducible binary cubic form with integer coefficients and with discriminant $\mathscr{D}$.

The well-known method of B. N. Delone and T. Nagell is applicable in the case $\mathscr{D}<0$, but generally not if $\mathscr{D}>0$.

The latter case ($\mathscr{D}>0$), is discussed in the present paper. By means of his own method, the author reduces the problem of the solution of (*) to the problem of finding the representations of finitely many integers by integer binary forms of sixth degree and with negative discriminants.

In the corresponding rings of sixth degree it is possible to apply Th. Skolem's local method.

T. T. Tonkov (Leningrad)

D24-68 **(37# 1313)**

London, Hymie

On the Diophantine equation $y^2+p^2=x^3$.

Amer. Math. Monthly **75** (1968), 56.

Let p be an odd prime. Explicit nonnegative integer solutions of $y^2+p^2=x^3$ are given for $p=12a^2-1$ and $p^2=3a^2+1$. If $p\equiv 3 \pmod 4$ the given solutions are the only possible solutions. For $p\equiv 1 \pmod 4$ all solutions are given in terms of solutions of another equation.

B. Garrison (San Diego, Calif.)

D24-69 **(37# 2682)**

Aigner, Alexander

Die diophantische Gleichung $x^2+4D=y^p$ im Zusammenhang mit Klassenzahlen.

Monatsh. Math. **72** (1968), 1–5.

Let $D > 1$ be odd and squarefree, x and y be odd and positive, p be an odd prime, and h be the class number of $K(\sqrt{-D})$. Following work by W. Ljunggren [Pacific J. Math. **14** (1964), 585–596; MR **28** #5035] and considering various power residues, the author shows that if $3 \nmid h$ then there is more than one solution of $x^2 + 4D = y^3$ only for $D = 19$ and 91 (there being then two solutions in each case), and that $x^2 + 4D = y^p$ has no solution for $D < 47$ and $p > 3$. He conjectures that there is no solution for $p > 3$ such that $p \nmid h$. *H. J. Godwin* (Swansea)

Citations: MR 28# 5035 = D40-38.

D24-70 (37# 4006)

Baker, A. [**Baker, Alan**]

Contributions to the theory of Diophantine equations. II. The Diophantine equation $y^2 = x^3 + k$.

Philos. Trans. Roy. Soc. London Ser. A **263** (1967/68), 193–208.

If $k \neq 0$, Mordell (1922) used Thue's famous (1909) theorem to show that the equation $y^2 = x^3 + k$ has only a finite number of solutions in integers x, y. However, no general algorithm was established which would enable one to find all the solutions for any prescribed k. Using the result of Part I of this paper [see #4005 above], the author obtains the following remarkable Theorem 1: For any integer $k \neq 0$ all solutions of $y^2 = x^3 + k$ in integers x, y satisfy (1) $\max(|x|, |y|) < \exp\{10^{10}|k|^{10^4}\}$. An alternative way of expressing the theorem is the assertion (2) $|x^3 - y^2| > 10^{-10}(\log x)^{10^{-4}}$, the range of validity of this inequality extending to all positive integers x, y with $x^3 \neq y^2$.

The author is to be congratulated on solving an outstanding problem of great importance.

{Reviewer's remarks: In Norske Vid. Selsk. Forh. (Trondheim) **38** (1965), 65–69 [MR **32** #4079], B. J. Birch, M. Hall, A. Schinzel and the reviewer proved the following theorem in the opposite direction to (2) above: There exists an absolute constant $C > 0$ such that the inequality $0 < |x^3 - y^2| < Cx^{3/5}$ has infinitely many solutions in integers x, y. In a paper following the paper by Birch et al., Davenport proved that given any positive integer $k > 5$ there exist polynomials $f(t)$, $g(t)$ of degree $2k$, $3k$, respectively, such that the degree of $f^3(t) - g^2(t)$ is $k + 1$. Here the polynomials $f(t)$ and $g(t)$ have complex coefficients.

Probably this theorem is true with the word "complex" replaced by "rational". Finally, M. Hall, in the Forhandlinger paper cited above [see the immediately preceding reference], conjectured the surprisingly strong: There are only a finite number of integral pairs (x, y) such that $0 < |x^3 - y^2| < \sqrt{|x|}$.} *S. Chowla* (University Park, Pa.)

Citations: MR 32# 4079 = D24-51; MR 37# 4005 = D40-50.

Referred to in D24-71, D40-52.

D24-71 (37# 6247)

Sprindžuk, V. G.

Effectivization in certain problems of Diophantine approximation theory. (Russian)

Dokl. Akad. Nauk BSSR **12** (1968), 293–297.

Making use of the work of A. Baker [Mathematika **13** (1966), 204–216; ibid. **14** (1967), 102–107; ibid. **14** (1967), 220–228; MR **36** #3732] on effectively computable bounds for linear forms in the logarithms of algebraic numbers, and of certain p-adic analogues of this work, the author indicates how a number of previously non-effective methods and bounds in the theory of Diophantine approximations may be made effective. For instance, in the first of seven catalogued examples, an explicit upper bound for $\max(|x|, |y|)$ taken over the finite set of solutions of $f(x, y) = A$, where A is an integer and f is an irreducible binary form of degree $\geqq 3$, is obtained. Similar applications were announced by Baker in his third paper listed above. They have appeared in Philos. Trans. Roy. Soc. London Ser. A **263** (1967/68), 173–191 [MR **37** #4005]; ibid. **263** (1967/68), 193–208 [MR **37** #4006].

J. B. Roberts (Portland, Ore.)

Citations: MR 36# 3732 = J80-26; MR 37# 4005 = D40-50; MR 37# 4006 = D24-70.

Referred to in D60-78, N32-67.

D24-72 (38# 111)

Baker, A. [**Baker, Alan**]

The Diophantine equation $y^2 = ax^3 + bx^2 + cx + d$.

J. London Math. Soc. **43** (1968), 1–9.

In this paper, appearing in a volume of the journal dedicated to L. J. Mordell on his 80th birthday, the author solves an important problem relating to "one of Mordell's best known and most long-standing interests", namely, the diophantine equation of the title. If the right-hand side contains no squared linear factor in x, a famous theorem of Thue tells us that the equation in question has only a finite number of solutions. But the method of Thue is not effective and so "cannot lead to the explicit determination of the totality of solutions of the equation". The author proves that if $a \neq 0$, b, c, d are rational integers with absolute values at most H, then all solutions of the equation in integers x, y satisfy $\max(|x|, |y|) < \exp\{(10^6 H)^{10^6}\}$. This paper prepares some of the groundwork for a complete proof. For the greater part of the proof one must refer to the author's paper in Philos. Trans. Roy. Soc. London Ser. A **263** (1967/68), 173–191 [MR **37** #4005]. One cannot over-emphasize the importance of the author's theorem, which solves an outstanding problem of number-theory [see the reviewer's book, *The Riemann hypothesis and Hilbert's tenth problem*, Gordon and Breach, New York, 1965; MR **31** #2201]. See also a paper by B. J. Birch, the reviewer, M. Hall, Jr. and A. Schinzel [Norske Vid. Selsk. Forh. (Trondheim) **38** (1965), 65–69; MR **32** #1079] which contains results in the opposite direction, e.g., Theorem: There exists an absolute constant $C > 0$ such that the inequality $0 < |x^3 - y^2| < Cx^{3/5}$ has infinitely many solutions in integers x, y.

S. Chowla (University Park, Pa.)

Citations: MR 31# 2201 = Z02-48; MR 37# 4005 = D40-50.

Referred to in D60-77, D60-78.

D24-73 (38# 113)

Mordell, L. J.

The diophantine equations $y^2 = x^4 \pm 1$ in quadratic fields.

J. London Math. Soc. **44** (1969), 112–114.

Bekanntlich sind die einzigen rationalen Lösungen von (1) $y^2 = x^4 + 1$ bzw. (2) $y^2 = x^4 - 1$ gegeben durch $x = 0$, $y = \pm 1$ bzw. $x = \pm 1$, $y = 0$. Verfasser untersucht (1) und (2) im Hinblick auf Lösungen, die in einem quadratischen Zahlkörper $K = Q(d)$ liegen. Die Lösungen, für die wenigstens eine der beiden Zahlen x, y rational ist, werden als triviale Lösungen von den Betrachtungen ausgeschlossen. Dann gilt der Satz: Nichttriviale Lösungen von (1) bzw. (2) existieren nur für $K = Q(b^4 \pm 12b^2 + 4)^{1/2}$ bzw. $K = Q(b^4 - 12b^2 + 32b - 28)^{1/2}$ (b rational). Eine Folgerung lautet: Die einzige Lösung von (1) in $Q(i)$ ist $x = 0$; die einzigen Lösungen von (2) in $Q(i)$ sind $x = 0$, ± 1, $\pm i$.

H. J. Kanold (Braunschweig)

D24-74 (38# 4401)

Cohn, J. H. E.

Five Diophantine equations.

Math. Scand. **21** (1967), 61–70 (1968).

Let d be an integer such that $X^2-dY^2=-4$ has no solutions and $X^2-dY^2=4$ has solutions with X and Y odd. The five Diophantine equations $y^2=dx^4+1$, $y^2=4dx^4+1$, $dy^2=x^4-4$, $y^2=dx^4+4$, and $dy^2=x^4-1$ are studied. None of the first three of these has more than one solution in positive integers. The fourth has at most two such solutions. The last one has no solution with $x\neq 1$ except when $d=725$, in which case there is a solution with $x=99$.

W. H. Mills (Princeton, N.J.)

Referred to in D24-78.

D24-75 (38# 4405)

Lal, Mohan; Dawe, James

Solutions of the diophantine equation $x^2-Dy^4=k$.

Math. Comp. **22** (1968), 679–682.

Positive integral solutions of $x^2-Dy^4=k$ are found for 37 values of D, in the range $2\leq D\leq 43$, where D is not a perfect square, $y\leq 2(10^5)$ and $|k|\leq 999$. Out of 6275 solutions found, 1453 are imprimitive. For example, $(x, y)=(16, 2)$, $(44, 4)$, $(96, 6)$, and $(1524, 24)$ are imprimitive solutions for $D, k=7, 144$ since they can be derived from the four primitive solutions for $D, k=7, 9$. A copy of the tables of these solutions has been submitted to the Unpublished Mathematical Tables file. {Reviewer's remark: A recent Ph.D. dissertation by R. P. Finkelstein ["On the units in a quartic field with applications to Mordell's equation", Ph.D. Thesis, Arizona State Univ., Tempe, Ariz., 1968] is relevant.}

E. Karst (Tucson, Ariz.)

D24-76 (38# 5714)

Avanesov, Èduard T.

A certain property of the number seven. (Bulgarian)

Fiz.-Mat. Spis. B"lgar. Akad. Nauk. **11 (44)** (1968), 277.

The author proves that the only integer solutions of the Diophantine equation (1) $p^3+p^2+p+1=q^2$ with p odd are $p=1$, $q=2$ and $p=7$, $q=20$.

After some elementary algebra, the problem reduces to solving (2) $x^2=2y^4-2y^2+1$, and by a result of W. Ljunggren [Skr. Norske Vid. Akad. Oslo I No. 9 (1942); MR **6**, 169], the only positive integer solutions of (2) are $x=y=1$ and $x=5$, $y=2$, which yields the author's result on (1).

R. Finkelstein (Bowling Green, Ohio)

Citations: MR 6, 169e = D24-3.

D24-77 (39# 2701)

Mordell, L. J.

The diophantine equation $dy^2=ax^4+bx^2+c$.

Acta Arith. **15** (1968/69), 269–272.

In two previous papers [J. London Math. Soc. **38** (1963), 454–458; MR **28** #2083; Rend. Circ. Mat. Palermo (2) **13** (1964), 249–256; MR **31** #3379], the author showed how to find, by elementary means, the integral solutions of equations of the form $y^2=ax^3+bx^2+cx+d$. In the present paper the same method is applied to equations of the form $dy^2=ax^4+bx^2+c$. Thus, for example, it is shown that the equation $y^2+1=(4x^2-17)(8x^2-10)$ has only the solutions $x=0, x=\pm 1$. As an example of an equation with three solutions, the author gives $y^2+1=(4x^2-17)(60x^2-1025)$, which has the solutions $y_0=132$, $y_1=112$, $y_2=28$.

L. Carlitz (Durham, N.C.)

Citations: MR 28# 2083 = D24-43; MR 31# 3379 = D24-48.

D24-78 (39# 2702)

Cohn, J. H. E.

Some quartic Diophantine equations.

Pacific J. Math. **26** (1968), 233–243.

The author in his previous paper [Proc. London Math. Soc. (3) **16** (1966), 153–166; MR **32** #7492] discussed the existence of the values of d for which the equation $x^2-dy^2=-4$ has a pair of solutions x, y both of which are odd. Using these values of d, the author obtains solutions of the equation $x^2=dy^4+m$ for various positive and negative values of m.

Then the author studies solutions of the equation $x^2=dy^4+m$, where m is an integer, positive or negative, and d is a positive integer with the property that the equation $x^2-dy^2=4$ has at least one solution x, y where both x and y are odd. For the cases $m=\pm 1, \pm 4$, complete solutions were obtained by the author [Math. Scand. **21** (1967), 61–70 (1968); MR **38** #4401]. In the present paper an attempt is made to cover other values of m. In many cases a complete solution of the problem is obtained.

J. M. Gandhi (Toronto, Ont.)

Citations: MR 32# 7492 = D24-53; MR 38# 4401 = D24-74.

D24-79 (39# 5511)

Nagell, Trygve

Sur les unités dans les corps biquadratiques primitifs du premier rang.

Ark. Mat. **7**, 359–394 (1968).

Let $\sum_{i=0}^{4} a_i x^{4-i}y^i=f(x, y)$ be a binary quartic form, where the coefficients are rational integers and the form is irreducible over the rational field. The form is defined to be of rank 1 if all the roots of $f(x, 1)=0$ are imaginary. The quartic field generated by these roots is also said to be of rank 1.

Continuing his earlier research [same Ark. **5**, 477–521 (1965); MR **32** #7497] the author proves a number of results on the representation of units of primitive quartic fields of rank 1 by forms of the type $f(x, 1)=x^4-px^3+qx^2-rx+s$, where $s=1$. In a future paper he will consider the problem for arbitrary s.

B. Stolt (Stockholm)

Citations: MR 32# 7497 = D24-56.

Referred to in R04-39.

D24-80 (39# 6818)

Bumby, Richard T.

The Diophantine equation $3x^4-2y^2=1$.

Math. Scand. **21** (1967), 144–148 (1968).

It is shown that the only solutions of the Diophantine equation $3x^4-2y^2=1$ in positive integers are $x=y=1$ and $x=3$, $y=11$. This result was conjectured by J. H. E. Cohn [Proc. London Math. Soc. (3) **16** (1966), 153–166; MR **32** #7492].

W. H. Mills (Princeton, N.J.)

Citations: MR 32# 7492 = D24-53.

Referred to in D32-89.

D24-81 (39# 6820)

Ljunggren, W.

On the diophantine equation $Ax^4-By^2=C$ $(C=1, 4)$.

Math. Scand. **21** (1967), 149–158 (1969).

In a previous paper [Avh. Norske Vid. Akad. Oslo I **1942**, no. 5; MR **8**, 6] the author gave a method which can be used to solve the Diophantine equation $Ax^4-By^2=1$ with A, B integers and B not a perfect square. The only difficulty is that the method involves a great deal of computation. In this paper the author combines an idea of J. H. E. Cohn [Proc. London Math. Soc. (3) **16** (1966), 153–166; MR **32** #7492] with a method of his own [Tolfte Skandinaviska Matematikerkongressen (Lund, 1953), pp. 188–194, Ohlissons, Lund, 1954; MR **16**, 448].

Let A and B be odd positive integers such that the Diophantine equation $Az_1{}^2-Bz_2{}^2=4$ has solutions in odd, positive integers z_1 and z_2. Let $z_1=a$, $z_2=b$ be the smallest solution. With these assumptions, the author proves Theorem 1: The Diophantine equation $Ax^4-By^2=4$

has at most two solutions in positive integers x, y. If $a=h^2$ and $Aa^2-3=k^2$, there are only two solutions, namely, $x=h$ and $x=hk$. If $a=h^2$ and $Aa^2-3\neq k^2$, then $x=h$ is the only solution. If $a=5h^2$ and $A^2a^4-5Aa^2+5=5k^2$, then the only solution is $x=5hk$. Otherwise there are no solutions. (The last assertion, although proved, was omitted in the text.) Theorem 2: The Diophantine equation $Ax^4-By^2=1$ has at most one solution in positive integers x, y. If $x=x_1$, $y=y_1$ is a solution, then (with a typographical error corrected) $x_1{}^2A^{1/2}+y_1B^{1/2}=(\frac{1}{2}(aA^{1/2}+bB^{1/2}))^3$.

The following references are also pertinent: J. H. E. Cohn [Proc. London Math. Soc. (3) **17** (1967), 381; MR **34** #5748], the author [J. London Math. Soc. **41** (1966), 542–544; MR **33** #5555]. *H. London* (Montreal, Que.)

Citations: MR 8, 6f = D24-8; MR 16, 448a = D24-31; MR 32# 7492 = D24-53; MR 33# 5555 = D24-60; MR 34# 5748 = D24-54.

Referred to in D24-82.

D24-82 (40# 2602)

Ljunggren, W.

A remark concerning the paper "On the diophantine equation $Ax^4-By^2=C(C=1,4)$".

Math. Scand. **22** (1968), 282 (1969).

In this paper the author clears up the proof of a theorem given in his earlier paper [Math. Scand. **21** (1967), 149–158 (1969); MR **39** #6820]. The author also corrects a misprint which occurs in the first two lines of page 158.

H. London (Montreal, Que.)

Citations: MR 39# 6820 = D24-81.

D24-83 (40# 87)

Faddeev, D. K.

The ascent algorithm of B. N. Delone. (Russian)

Zap. Naučn. Sem. Leningrad. Otdel. Mat. Inst. Steklov. (LOMI) **1** (1966), 123–127.

B. N. Delone applied a remarkable "ascent algorithm" to study indeterminate equations $f(x, y)=1$, where $f(x, y)$ is an integer-valued cubic form of negative discriminant and the solutions are to be integers [Izv. Akad. Nauk SSSR (6) **16** (1922), 273–280; Ž. Leningrad. Fiz.-Mat. Obšč. **1** (1927), 257–267]. In the present note the author interprets this algorithm in terms of the theory of rings.

N. Timofeev (RŽMat **1968** #9 A127)

D24-84 (40# 4208)

Dem'janenko, V. A.

The representation of numbers by binary biquadratic forms. (Russian)

Mat. Sb. **80 (122)** (1969), 445–452.

The author studies the difficult question about the representation of numbers by forms with positive discriminants. He proves the following theorem: Let the rank of the equation $ax^4+bx^2y^2+cy^4=kz^2$ over the field $R(1)$ be $\leqq 1$, and let k be biquadratic free and prime to the discriminant. Then for sufficiently large values of $(b^2-4ac)/\max\{|a|, |c|\}$, the equation $ax^4+bx^2y^2+cy^4=k$ has $\leqq 3$ positive integer solutions. *T. T. Tonkov* (Sofia)

D24-85 (42# 3019)

Finkelstein, Raphael; London, Hymie

On Mordell's equation $y^2-k=x^3$: An interesting case of Sierpiński.

J. Number Theory **2** (1970), 310–321.

It is proved that when $k=-18$ the only integer solutions of the equation of the title are $x=3$, $y=\pm 3$. If $(x, y)=1$ it is easily shown that there are no solutions. In case $(x, y)=3$ the problem is transferred to the problem of finding all integer solutions (u, v) of the equation (1) $f(u, v)=u^4-18u^2v^2+24uv^3-27v^4=1$. Since $f(\eta, -1)=0$ has two real and two complex roots, (1) implies $u+v\eta=\pm\varepsilon_1{}^m\cdot\varepsilon_2{}^n$, where ε_1 and ε_2 denote a pair of fundamental units in the number field $Q(\eta)$. The further method of attack is exactly that of the reviewer [Acta Arith. **8** (1962/63), 451–463; MR **28** #2082]. This paper is not mentioned, but there are two references to joint papers of the authors, not yet published. They make use of a theorem due to È. T. Avanesov [Izv. Akad. Nauk Armjan. SSR Ser. Mat. **3** (1968), no. 2, 160–165; MR **37** #6241]. However, for the exponential equations in question, this was already proved by Skolem in 1934.

N. M. Stephens and F. B. Coghlan have shown ("The diophantine equation $x^3-y^2=k$", Proc. Atlas Sympos., 1968, to appear) that the only integer solutions of the title equation in case $0<-k\leqq 100$ are the known ones.

W. Ljunggren (Oslo)

Citations: MR 28# 2082 = D24-42; MR 37# 6241 = D04-65.

D24-86 (42# 5902)

Nagell, Trygve

Remarques sur une classe d'équations indéterminées.

Ark. Mat. **8**, 199–214 (1969).

Cet article donne un exposé sur l'histoire des résultats concernant les équations diophantiennes du type $ax^3+by^3=c$ et en général $ax^n-by^n=c$ $(n\geqq 4)$, obtenus principalement par l'auteur et par d'autres mathématiciens scandinaves. Les découvertes et les méthodes en question sont rangées dans l'ordre chronologique. Le travail contient une bibliographie détaillée de ce domaine.

K. Győry (Debrecen)

D24-87 (42# 7592)

Mordell, L. J.

The diophantine equation $y^2=Dx^4+1$.

Number Theory (Colloq., János Bolyai Math. Soc., Debrecen, 1968), *pp.* 141–145. *North-Holland, Amsterdam*, 1970.

The author extends his results of an earlier paper [J. London Math. Soc. **39** (1964), 161–164; MR **29** #65] relating to the above equation to cover the case where D is a prime $\equiv 1$ (4). He proves that in this case the equation has only the trivial integer solution $x=0$ unless $D=5$, when there is also a solution $x=2$. This new proof is simpler than the one given by W. Ljunggren [ibid. **41** (1966), 542–544; MR **33** #5555]. The author also conjectures that if D is a prime $\equiv 5$ (8) then the equation always has a rational solution. *R. F. Churchhouse* (Cardiff)

Citations: MR 29# 65 = D24-44; MR 33# 5555 = D24-60.

D24-88 (43# 3207)

Williams, H. C.

Note on a diophantine equation.

Elem. Math. **25** (1970), 123–125.

Let a and b be given integers. The author obtains the complete solution in integers x, y of the equation

$$(x^2+a)(y^2+a) = (a[(y-x)/(2b)]^2+b^2)^2$$

in terms of the representations of certain integers by certain binary quadratic forms. This gives a (not necessarily complete) solution of $(x^2+a)(y^2+a)=(az^2+b^2)^2$ in integers x, y, z. When $z=b=1$ direct computation shows that this solution is complete at least for $1\leqq y\leqq x\leqq 300$.

J. W. S. Cassels (Cambridge, England)

D24-89 **(43# 4759)**

Bernstein, Leon
Infinite non-solubility classes of the Delaunay-Nagell diophantine equation $x^3+my^3=1$.
J. London Math. Soc. (2) **3** (1971), 118–120.

J. H. E. Cohn [same J. **42** (1967), 750–752; MR **36** #106] has found necessary conditions for the solubility of the equation in the title for every rational integer m and sufficient conditions for its non-solubility. The author proves that if $m=D^3+k$, $|k|\neq 1$, where $k=d$, $D\geqq 1$; $k=3d$, $D\geqq 3d$; $k=3D$, $D\geqq 2$; $k=d$, $D\geqq 4d$; $k=-3d$, $D\geqq 12d$; or $k=6D$, $D\geqq 4$ then the equation has no solutions. He then shows that an infinite set of pairs (d, D) can be found that satisfy Cohn's necessity conditions for solubility and the author's sufficiency conditions for non-solubility and hence that Cohn's necessity conditions are "far from being sufficient" for solubility. The proof is based on Nagell's theorem that any solution of the equation in the title arises either from a fundamental unit in $R(\sqrt[3]{m})$ or the square of such a fundamental unit. *R. F. Churchhouse* (Cardiff)

Citations: MR 36# 106 = D24-64.

D24-90 **(44# 5275)**

Trost, E.
Eine Bemerkung zur Diophantischen Analysis.
Elem. Math. **26** (1971), 60–61.

The author notes that an equation $at^2+bt+c=0$ has a rational solution t only if the discriminant is a square. On applying this remark to the equation $x^4t^2-2y^4t-1=0$, he deduces that there is an integral solution of $x^4-2y^4=1$ with $y\neq 0$ if and only if there is an integral solution of (*) $x^4+y^4=z^2$ with $xy\neq 0$, which is notoriously insoluble. In fact, however, there is no nontrivial integral solution of $x^4-2y^4=z^2$ and the equivalence of this insolubility with that of (*) is well-known [e.g., G. H. Hardy and E. M. Wright, *An introduction to the theory of numbers*, Theorem 226, first edition, Clarendon Press, Oxford, 1938; third edition, 1954; MR **16**, 673; German translation, Oldenbourg, Munich, 1958; MR **20** #828]. [Vom höherem Standpunkt aus we have two isogenous elliptic curves.] There is a second application of the same trick which shows that there are no non-trivial rational points on a certain elliptic curve if there are none on its jacobian. *J. W. S. Cassels* (Cambridge, England)

Citations: MR 16, 673b = Z01-28; MR 20# 828 = Z01-29.

D28 CUBIC AND QUARTIC CURVES: RATIONAL POINTS

Papers on the Mordell-Weil group of rational points on an elliptic curve are in **G05**, even when they involve little or no algebraic geometry.

See also reviews D02-18, D40-31, D48-51, D52-41, D56-13, E24-130, G30-11, J12-57, R02-3, R14-23, Z10-18, Z15-84.

D28-1 **(1, 25c)**

Goodstein, R. L. Rational triangles. Math. Gaz. **23**, 264–269 (1939).

A general formula giving such triangles was stated by Gauss; we propose to find a general formula giving prime solutions, that is, a formula giving integral sides and circumradius, a, b, c, R, which have highest common factor unity. *Extract from the paper.*

Referred to in D28-43.

D28-2 **(2, 34g)**

Reichardt, Hans. Über die Diophantische Gleichung $ax^4+bx^2y^2+cy^4=ez^2$. Math. Ann. **117**, 235–276 (1940).

The solutions of the Diophantine equation

(1) $$ax^4+bx^2y^2+cy^4=ez^2$$

form a module under a certain rule of combination. This rule can be obtained either from the addition theorem for the elliptic functions corresponding to the equation (1) or from the law for the multiplication of the classes of divisors in the function field defined by (1). Mordell has proved [Proc. Cambridge Philos. Soc. **21**, 179–192 (1922)] that this module has a finite basis, but his proof gives no method of determining such a basis or of deciding the solubility of (1).

The author proves that the following problems are essentially equivalent. (1) The decision of the solubility and the determination of one solution. (2) The determination of a basis for the solutions of a solvable equation. (3) The determination of all the equations which are birationally transformable into the equation

$$x^4+bx^2y^2+cy^4=z^2.$$

To solve one of these problems for a fixed equation of the form (1), it is sufficient to solve one of the other two problems for certain equations of the form (1), finite in number. *A. Brauer* (Princeton, N. J.).

Referred to in D32-13.

D28-3 **(2, 346f)**

Billing, G. A Diophantine equation with seven solutions. Ark. Mat. Astr. Fys. **27A,** no. 14, 7 pp. (1941).

La courbe $x_2^2x_3=x_1^3-43x_1x_3^2+166x_3^3$ possède exactement les sept points rationnels (0, 1, 0), (3, ±8, 1), (−5, ±16, 1), (11, ±32, 1). Pour la démonstration on applique avant tout un théorème établi par l'auteur dans sa thèse [Uppsala, 1938] qui permet, au moyen d'une factorisation dans le corps déterminé par la racine réelle de l'équation $\xi^3-43\xi+166=0$, d'assurer que le nombre des solutions rationnelles est fini et impair; un théorème de T. Nagell permet alors d'affirmer que toutes les solutions doivent correspondre à la valeur de x_3 0 ou 1, et à x_2^2 diviseur du discriminant de cette équation. La discussion des cas que par lá résultent encore possibles est omise. On signale une observation fondée sur la considération du paramètre elliptique qui permet de réducir notablement ces tentatives. *B. Levi* (Rosario).

D28-4 **(2, 346h)**

Billing, G. A Diophantine equation with nine solutions. Ark. Mat. Astr. Fys. **27B,** no. 8, 5 pp. (1941).

Par la même méthode de la note précédente, l'auteur démontre que la courbe $x_2^2x_3=x_1^3-219x_1x_3^2+1654x_3^3$ possède exactement les 9 points rationnels (0, 1, 0), (3, ±32, 1), (11, ±24, 1), (−13, ±48, 1), (35, ±192, 1). *B. Levi.*

D28-5 **(9, 270b)**

Mordell, L. J. On some Diophantine equations $y^2=x^3+k$ with no rational solutions. Arch. Math. Naturvid. **49,** no. 6, 143–150 (1947).

The equation of the title (k being an integer) has been much discussed with reference to its integral solutions. Much less is known about the possible rational solutions of such an equation. Fueter has, among other things, given certain classes of such equations with no rational solutions [Comment. Math. Helv. **2**, 69–89 (1930)]. The author proves the following result. The equation of the title has no rational solutions if k is a square-free positive integer and (1) $k\equiv 6$, 15 (mod 36); (2) the class number of the field $R(\sqrt{k})$ is not divisible by 3; (3) if T, U is the fundamental solution of the equation $t^2-ku^2=1$, so that U is the least positive value of u, then $U\not\equiv 0, \pm 1 \pmod 9$; (4) the class number h of the field $R(\sqrt{(-k/3)})$ is not divisible by 3; (5) the integer solutions of $p^2+(k/3)q^2=3^{2h}$, when $h\equiv 1 \pmod 3$, do not satisfy $q\equiv \pm 1 \pmod 9$; when $h\equiv -1 \pmod 3$, do not satisfy $q\equiv \pm 2(k/3)^2 \pmod 9$. It is noted that the values $k=6$, 42, 51 satisfy all of these conditions. The proof is quite straightforward and makes use only of the theory of ideals in quadratic fields.

H. W. Brinkmann (Swarthmore, Pa.).

Referred to in D28-6, D28-19, D28-33, D28-45.

D28-6 (10, 101d)

Chang, K. L. On some Diophantine equations $y^2=x^3+k$ with no rational solutions. Quart. J. Math., Oxford Ser. **19**, 181–188 (1948).

Using a method of L. J. Mordell [Arch. Math. Naturvid. **49**, no. 6, 143–150 (1947); these Rev. **9**, 270] the writer proves that $y^2=x^3+k$ has no rational solutions if k satisfies certain conditions. These conditions are similar to those obtained by Mordell for the same Diophantine equation. However, the values of k satisfying the conditions of the present paper are completely distinct from those satisfying Mordell's conditions. *I. Niven* (Eugene, Ore.).

Citations: MR 9, 270b = D28-5.
Referred to in D28-19, D28-33.

D28-7 (13, 437b)

Verkaart, H. G. A. Deriving a general formula for finding positive and negative integers which satisfy the relation $(-a+b+c)(a-b+c)(a+b-c)=abc$, where a, b and c represent three distinct numbers different from zero. Nieuw Tijdschr. Wiskunde **39** (1951/52), 153–157 (1952). (Dutch)

D28-8 (15, 933e)

Cavallaro, Vincenzo G. Equazioni diofantee brocardiane. Giorn. Mat. Battaglini (5) **2**(**82**), 301–308 (1954).

D28-9 (16, 113a)

Kesava Menon, P. On the equation

$$y^2=x^3-3\lambda\mu x-\lambda^3 a-\mu^3 a^{-1}.$$

Math. Student **22**, 85–88 (1954).

The equation of the title has no known rational solutions x, y for arbitrarily given values of a, λ and μ. From one known solution others can be found, for example by the tangent and chord process. This paper gives a procedure by means of algebraic transformations for finding other solutions from a given one. As corollaries, parametric solutions are obtained for two special equations where a particular solution is obvious. *I. Niven* (Eugene, Ore.).

D28-10 (16, 674e)

Selmer, Ernst S. The diophantine equation

$$ax^3+by^3+cz^3=0.$$

Completion of the tables. Acta Math. **92**, 191–197 (1954).

The author continues his studies [Acta Math. **85**, 203–362 (1951); MR **13**, 13] of the equations (1) $x^3+y^3=Az^3$ and (2) $ax^3+by^3+cz^3=0$. The tables of basic solutions of equation (2) are completed for all positive cube-free $abc\leqq 500$, with extensions beyond 500 in some cases. Part of this was done by work with an electronic computer. These tables, together with cases proved unsolvable by the method of J. W. S. Cassels [ibid. **82**, 243–273 (1950); MR **12**, 11] enable the writer to complete the solutions of (1) for all positive cube-free $A\leqq 500$. *I. Niven* (Eugene, Ore.).

Citations: MR 12, 11a = G05-22; MR 13, 13i = G05-31.
Referred to in G05-88.

D28-11 (16, 903f)

Utz, W. R. Two diophantine cubics. Portugal. Math. **13**, 121–123 (1954).

The following theorem is proved: The diophantine equation (1) $x^3+y^3=xyz$ has no integral solutions (x, y, z) for $z=1$ or for z an odd prime unless z is of the form $3n^2+3n+1$, n an integer. In case $z=2$, there is exactly one solution $(1, 1, 2)$. When the prime z is of the form $3n^2+3n+1$, (1) has only the solutions $(x, y, z)=(p, q, r)$ and (q, p, r), where $p=n^2(n+1)$, $q=-n(n+1)^2$ and $r=3n^2+3n+1$. The trivial solutions $(0, 0, z)$ and $(x, -x, 0)$ are neglected. All integral solutions of $x^3+y^3=z(x-y)$ are also obtained.

W. Ljunggren (Bergen).

D28-12 (16, 1088d)

Selmer, Ernst S. The indeterminate equation

$$X^3+Y^3=AZ^3.$$

Nordisk Mat. Tidskr. **3**, 48–56, 80 (1955). (Norwegian. English summary)

The author gives an account of some results from an earlier paper [Acta Math. **85**, 203–362 (1951); MR **13**, 13].

W. Ljunggren (Bergen).

Citations: MR 13, 13i = G05-31.

D28-13 (19, 1160e)

Wakulicz, A. On the equation $x^3+y^3=2z^3$. Colloq. Math. **5** (1957), 11–15.

A proof of the well-known theorem (first published by Euler in 1770 and included, with generalizations, in a number of standard undergraduate texts) that rational integral solutions of the equation in the title require $x=\pm y$. *J. D. Swift* (Los Angeles, Calif.).

D28-14 (22# 6771)

Cassels, J. W. S. On a diophantine equation. Acta Arith. **6** (1960), 47–52.

The theory of the set of rational points on cubics of genus one is used to show that the system of equations $r+s+t=rst=1$ is insoluble in rational numbers.

G. B. Huff (Athens, Ga.)

Referred to in D28-17, D28-18.

D28-15 (23# A1593)

Mordell, L. J.

Rational quadrilaterals.

J. London Math. Soc. **35** (1960), 277–282.

The following theorem is proved. To any quadrilateral there exist arbitrarily near rational quadrilaterals (i.e., with rational sides and diagonals). The problem of rational quadrilaterals is very old and was reduced by Kummer to the solution in rationals ξ, η, x, y, c of

$$\frac{(\xi+c)^2-1}{\xi}\,\frac{(x-c)^2-1}{x}=\frac{(\eta-c)^2-1}{\eta}\,\frac{(y+c)^2-1}{y}.$$

This is re-proved here more simply, in modified form. The solution is then transformed to the solution in rationals of a cubic equation, which is achieved.

O. Taussky-Todd (Pasadena, Calif.)

Referred to in D28-20, D28-25.

D28-16 (23# A3708)

Buquet, A.

Sur l'équation diophantienne

$$aX^3+bX^2Y+cXY^2+dY^3=Z^3.$$

Mathesis **69** (1960), 304–311.

Elementary considerations concerning the solutions of indeterminate equations of the form mentioned in the title. The procedure is illustrated by means of three examples.

W. Ljunggren (Oslo)

D28-17 **(24# A80)**

Sierpiński, W.

Remarques sur le travail de M. J. W. S. Cassels "On a diophantine equation".

Acta Arith. **6** (1960/61), 469–471.

The author documents the history of the conjecture of Werner Mnich [proved by the reviewer, Acta Arith. **6** (1960), 47–52; MR **22** #6771]. He gives several results which were known to be equivalent. He also gives an "elementary" proof, following A. Schinzel, that there are no integer points on $y^2=x^3+(x+4)^2$ $(x\neq 0)$, the conjecture of Werner Mnich being equivalent to the nonexistence of rational points with $x\neq 0$. The reviewer notes that G. Sansone independently found a proof of Mnich's conjecture which is more "elementary" (in the vague sense used by the author) than the reviewer's [see Sansone and the reviewer, Acta Arith. **7** (1961), 187–190; MR **24** #A2550].

J. W. S. Cassels (Cambridge, England)

Citations: MR 22# 6771 = D28-14; MR 24# A2550 = D28-18.

Referred to in D28-40.

D28-18 **(24# A2550)**

Sansone, G.; Cassels, J. W. S.

Sur le problème de M. Werner Mnich.

Acta Arith. **7** (1961/62), 187–190.

The authors give another, simpler, proof of the ancient conjecture that three rational numbers cannot have sum and product both equal to one. Their ingenious proof is by an infinite descent using nothing more highbrow than factorization in the Eisenstein field. Cassels' first proof [Acta Arith. **6** (1960), 47–52; MR **22** #6771] used a fairly complicated cubic extension.

B. J. Birch (Cambridge, England)

Citations: MR 22# 6771 = D28-14.

Referred to in D28-17, D28-40.

D28-19 **(25# 3007)**

Edgar, Hugh

On some diophantine equations $y^2=x^3+k$ with no rational solutions.

Norske Vid. Selsk. Forh. (Trondheim) **34** (1961), 96–99.

It is shown that if k satisfies either of two rather lengthy sets of conditions, then the equation $y^2=x^3+k$ has no rational solutions. The proofs are straightforward modifications of arguments of Mordell [Arch. Math. Naturvid. **49** (1947), no. 6, 143–150; MR **9**, 270] and Chang [Quart. J. Math. Oxford Ser. **19** (1948), 181–188; MR **10**, 101].

D. J. Lewis (Ann Arbor, Mich.)

Citations: MR 9, 270b = D28-5; MR 10, 101d = D28-6.

D28-20 **(26# 4963)**

Almering, J. H. J.

Rational quadrilaterals.

Nederl. Akad. Wetensch. Proc. Ser. A **66** = *Indag. Math.* **25** (1963), 192–199.

Mordell [J. London Math. Soc. **35** (1960), 277–282; MR **23** #A1593] established the existence of a rational quadrilateral (i.e., one with rational sides and diagonals) whose vertices are arbitrarily close to the vertices of any given quadrilateral. The author generalizes this result by proving that if A, B, C are distinct points with rational distances AB, BC, CA, then the set of points P for which PA, PB, PC are rational is everywhere dense in any plane containing A, B, C. The conditions on the point P lead to the consideration of a plane cubic curve which is shown, by a method similar to that of Mordell, to contain an everywhere dense set of rational points.

E. S. Barnes (Adelaide)

Citations: MR 23# A1593 = D28-15.

Referred to in D28-28.

D28-21 **(27# 3582)**

Hofmann, J. E.

Über Fermats Behandlung des Vierkubenproblems.

Math. Ann. **150** (1963), 45–49.

Fermat indicated with several examples a process of obtaining an infinity of positive rational solutions of $x^3+y^3=A$ from one solution (A is an arbitrary given rational number), employing three formulas:

$$a^3-b^3=\left[b\cdot\frac{2a^3-b^3}{a^3+b^3}\right]^3-\left[a\cdot\frac{2b^3-a^3}{a^3+b^3}\right]^3$$

and others [L. E. Dickson, *History of the theory of numbers*, Vol. II, pp. 550–561, Carnegie Inst., Washington, D.C., 1920]. The author gives a short historical account of the problem of four cubes [the author, Arch. Internat. Hist. Sci. **14** (1961), 35–63] and confirms Fermat's treatment by proving that the process is in all cases applicable (provided that A is not twice a cube).

T. Hayashida (Yokohama)

D28-22 **(28# 1158)**

Sedláček, Jiří

Some remarks on the problem of W. Mnich. (Czech. Russian and German summaries)

Mat.-Fyz. Časopis Sloven. Akad. Vied **13** (1963), 97–102.

Author's summary: "Es sei das Gleichungssystem

$$(1)\qquad x_1+x_2+x_3=1,\qquad x_1x_2x_3=1$$

gegeben. In diesem Beitrag wird zuerst die Lösbarkeit des Systems (1) in einigen quadratischen Zahlkörpern untersucht. Das allgemeinere System $x_1+x_2+x_3=r$, $x_1x_2x_3=r$ (wo r eine gegebene rationale Zahl ist) hat unendlich viele Lösungen in dem nichtkommutativen Quaternionkörper über dem Körper aller rationalen Zahlen. Schließlich wird das Kongruenzsystem

$$(2)\qquad x_1+x_2+x_3\equiv 1 \pmod p,\qquad x_1x_2x_3\equiv 1 \pmod p,$$

wo p eine gegebene ungerade Primzahl ist, untersucht. Für $p\equiv 1 \pmod 4$ und für $p\equiv 7 \pmod 8$ ist das System (2) lösbar. Es bleiben noch die Primzahlen $p\equiv 3 \pmod 8$. Für $p=3$ besitzt das System (2) keine Lösung, aber für $p=11$ und für $p=19$ z. B., ist das System (2) lösbar."

A. J. Lohwater (Providence, R.I.)

Referred to in D28-40.

D28-23 **(28# 1159)**

Schwarz, Štefan

On a system of congruences. A remark on the preceding paper of J. Sedláček. (Slovak)

Mat.-Fyz. Časopis Sloven. Akad. Vied **13** (1963), 103–104.

The author shows that the system (1) of the preceding paper [#1158 above] has a solution in the field T_p for each $p\neq 3$, where T_p is the field of residues (mod p).

A. J. Lohwater (Providence, R.I.)

D28-24 **(29# 2216)**

Dimovski, Ivan

On the rational solutions of the equation $1+x+x^2=y^3$. (Bulgarian)

Fiz.-Mat. Spis. Bŭlgar. Akad. Nauk. **6 (39)** (1963), 209–211.

Starting from results due to Nagell [Norsk Mat. Forenings Skr. (1) No. 2 (1921)], Ljunggren proved in 1942 [Acta Math. **75** (1942), 1–21; MR **8**, 135] that the only integral solutions of the equation

(1) $$1+x+x^2 = y^3$$

are (0, 1), (−1, 1), (18, 7), and (−19, 7). In this paper the author gives an elementary geometric proof of the theorem that equation (1) has infinitely many solutions in rational numbers. *R. Finkelstein* (Tucson, Ariz.)

Citations: MR 8, 135k = D24-10.

D28-25 (30# 63)

Daykin, D. E.

Rational polygons.

Mathematika **10** (1963), 125–131.

The following theorems are proved: Any parallelogram can be approximated arbitrarily closely by a parallelogram with rational sides, diagonals and area; and the same is true if we substitute quadrilateral for parallelogram throughout. The author initially follows the ideas of Mordell [J. London Math. Soc. **35** (1960), 277–282; MR **23** #A1593], using results on rational points on cubic curves, of the type "one rational point implies many"; to produce the one rational point, he utilizes a family of rational parallelograms due to Schubert. There are some trivial errors of sign in the final section. *H. T. Croft* (Cambridge, England)

Citations: MR 23# A1593 = D28-15.

Referred to in D28-34.

D28-26 (30# 3061)

Schmidt, Hermann

Über einige diophantische Aufgaben 3. und 4. Grades.

Jber. Deutsch. Math.-Verein. **67** (1964/65), *Abt.* 1, 2–13.

The author uses the method of descent to discuss the rational points on certain curves of genus 1; in particular, he shows that (*) $z^2=p^2x^4+px^2y^2+y^4$ has no solution in positive integers if $p=3$ or if $p\equiv 7$ (24) ($p=$prime). As a byproduct he shows that the only rational solutions of

$$x_1^2+x_2^2 = x_3^2+x_4^2, \quad x_1^3+x_2^3 = x_3^3+x_4^3$$

are the trivial ones in which the x's are equal in pairs. This is stronger than the corresponding result of Segre for three pairs [Colloque de Géométrie Algébrique, Liège, 1949, pp. 123–142, Thone, Liège; MR **12**, 200] (not cited by the author). The author's methods seem to have something in common with those of Reichardt [J. Reine Angew. Math. **184** (1942), 12–18; MR **5**, 141] (also not cited). Finally, it is shown that if the equation (*) has nontrivial rational solutions, then it has infinitely many (i.e., there are in any case no nontrivial points of finite order). *J. W. S. Cassels* (Cambridge, England)

Citations: MR 5, 141c = D32-13; MR 12, 200e = G05-25.

Referred to in D28-27.

D28-27 (36# 107)

Schmidt, Hermann

Nachtrag zu: "Über einige diophantische Gleichungen 3. und 4. Grades".

Jber. Deutsch. Math.-Verein. **70** (1967), *Heft* 1, *Abt.* 1, 51–52.

The author acknowledges the priority of L. Gatteschi and L. A. Rosati [Boll. Un. Mat. Ital. (3) **5** (1950), 43–48; MR **11**, 714] for Satz 4 of his paper [Jber. Deutsch. Math.-Verein. **67** (1964/65), Abt. 1, 2–13; MR **30** #3061] and adds a few minor comments to other points. *J. W. S. Cassels* (Cambridge, England)

Citations: MR 11, 714h = D52-56; MR 30# 3061 = D28-26.

D28-28 (31# 3375)

Almering, J. H. J.

Rational quadrilaterals. II.

Nederl. Akad. Wetensch. Proc. Ser. A **68** = *Indag. Math.* **27** (1965), 290–304.

Let ABC be a rational triangle. The author has previously shown [same Proc. Ser. A **66** (1963), 192–199; MR **26** #4963] that the set of points E for which the distances EA, EB, EC are rational is everywhere dense in the plane ABC. Here, by a detailed consideration of rational points on a certain plane cubic curve, he obtains quantitative results on the distribution of such points E (called "convenient" points). He proves in particular that, in any given circle in the plane, the number of convenient points E, for which the least common denominator of the rational numbers EA, EB, EC does not exceed G, has order of magnitude at least $\log\log G$. *E. S. Barnes* (Adelaide)

Citations: MR 26# 4963 = D28-20.

D28-29 (32# 7496)

Hunter, J. A. H.

The Diophantine equation $X^3+Y^3=9Z^3$.

Math. Mag. **38** (1965), 305–306.

In his *Canterbury puzzles* [Dover, New York, 1959; MR **21** #4088], H. Dudeney declared that he found by trial a negative basic solution of the equation of the title in smaller numbers than Fermat's solution (1,88479; −36520; 90391), which led him to the solution (67,67024,67503; 41,52805,64497; 34,86716,82660). However, Dudeney did not give his basic solution nor the method for deriving it. The author of the present work proves that the basic solution of Dudeney is (919; −271; 438) and gives two theoretical methods for deriving it. *R. Finkelstein* (Tucson, Ariz.)

D28-30 (33# 5559)

Mordell, L. J.

The infinity of rational solutions of $y^2=x^3+k$.

J. London Math. Soc. **41** (1966), 523–525.

The author gives a new and simpler proof for a theorem due to R. Fueter [Comment. Math. Helv. **2** (1930), 69–89] concerning the problem mentioned in the title. The proof is based on an idea of Bachet. *W. Ljunggren* (Oslo)

D28-31 (33# 7301)

Mordell, L. J.

Some quartic diophantine equations of genus 3.

Proc. Amer. Math. Soc. **17** (1966), 1152–1158.

The author produces families of quartic curves of genus 3 with rational coefficients but no rational points. They are given by equations $f(x, y, z)=0$, where $f(x, y, z)=g(x^2, y^2, z^2)$ and g is a quadratic form. The detailed enunciations are too elaborate to quote here. The proof depends on writing $g(X, Y, Z)=0$ in the shape $L_1L_2=L_3^2$, where the L_j are linear forms in X, Y, Z, and considering possible factorisations, the resulting equations being then considered locally (i.e., as congruences). It is, apparently, implied that at least some of the equations $f(x, y, z)=0$ are soluble everywhere locally (since otherwise they are

trivially insoluble), but it would have added to the value of the paper to give an explicit numerical example of this.
J. W. S. Cassels (Cambridge, England)

Referred to in D28-32, D28-44.

D28-32 **(34# 4202)**

Mordell, L. J.
Addendum to: "Some quartic diophantine equations of genus 3".
Proc. Amer. Math. Soc. **18** (1967), 190.

The original article appeared in same Proc. **17** (1966), 1152–1158 [MR **33** #7301].

Citations: MR 33# 7301 = D28-31.

D28-33 **(34# 4196)**

Edgar, Hugh M.
Classes of equations of the type $y^2 = x^3 + k$ having no rational solutions.
Nagoya Math. J. **28** (1966), 49–58.

Let k denote any positive rational integer, not a square, and, further, let (T, U) denote the fundamental solution of the Pellian equation $Y^2 - kX^2 = 1$. The author proves three theorems concerning the equations mentioned in the title. The results are too complicated to be given here. The first theorem is an immediate generalization of a theorem of L. J. Mordell [Arch. Math. Naturvid. **49** (1947), no. 6, 143–150; MR **9**, 270]. It is obtained by replacing the third of Mordell's five conditions, namely $U \not\equiv \pm 1, 0 \pmod 9$, by $U \equiv \pm 3 \pmod 9$. The second theorem follows in a similar way from a proposition due to K. L. Chang [Quart. J. Math. Oxford Ser. **19** (1948), 181–188; MR **10**, 101]. The third theorem requires a more detailed investigation and applies to the case $k \equiv 33 \pmod{72}$. No examples are given.
W. Ljunggren (Oslo)

Citations: MR 9, 270b = D28-5; MR 10, 101d = D28-6.

D28-34 **(34# 7463)**

Sheng, T. K.; Daykin, D. E.
On approximating polygons by rational polygons.
Math. Mag. **39** (1966), 299–300.

I. J. Schoenberg's problem "Can any given polygon be approximated as closely as we like by a rational polygon?", and other related problems, have previously been discussed for triangles, parallelograms and quadrilaterals [see, e.g., D. E. Daykin, Mathematika **10** (1963), 125–131; MR **30** #63]. The authors prove two general results. Theorem 1: A polygon $\mathscr{P}$ is rational (with rational area) if and only if every triangle formed by producing the sides and diagonals of $\mathscr{P}$ is rational (with rational area). Theorem 2: (i) The set of all rational cyclic n-gons with one tangential angle and $n-2$ interior angles in given rational ratios is dense in the set of all such cyclic n-gons. (ii) When n is odd, the same result holds for $n-1$ interior angles. {The word "rational" is omitted from the enunciation of Theorem 2. In the next-to-last line on page 299, "$\mathscr{C}$" is presumably a misprint for "$\sigma(\mathscr{C})$".}
J. F. Rigby (Cardiff)

Citations: MR 30# 63 = D28-25.

D28-35 **(35# 128)**

Szymiczek, K.
On a Diophantine equation.
Elem. Math. **22** (1967), 37–38.

Formulas are given furnishing all integer solutions of the equation $(x^2-t^2)(y^2-t^2) = ((\frac{1}{2}(y-x))^2 - t^2)^2$. (For $t=1$, see the reviewer and W. Sierpiński [Elem. Math. **18** (1963), 132–133; MR **29** #1180].)
A. Schinzel (Warsaw)

Citations: MR 29# 1180 = D24-45.

D28-36 **(35# 137)**

Sheng, T. K.
Rational polygons.
J. Austral. Math. Soc. **6** (1966), 452–459.

By considering first the rational roots of $y^2 = x^4 + 2mx^2 + 1$, where $m > 1$ and rational, the author exhibits polygons with rational sides, diagonals and area, that approximate arbitrarily closely certain polygons that have all their vertices except two on a unit circle, these two points being the centre and a general point. {The last phrase of Lemma 1 should read: if and only if $\phi \pm \psi \in \Theta$; this does not affect the argument.}
H. T. Croft (Cambridge, England)

Referred to in D28-42.

D28-37 **(37# 1314)**

Stefani, V. N.
The equation $x^3 + 6xyz + y^3 - mz^3 = 0$, and certain other equations related to it. (Russian)
Rjazansk. Gos. Ped. Inst. Učen. Zap. **42** (1967), 60–84.

Working in algebraic fields of degree 3 over the rational numbers, the author deduces rather complicated conditions for the unsolvability of the equation in the title and of the relation equation $xy^2 + x^2z + myz^2 - 6xyz = 0$. As an example these equations are unsolvable (in rational integers distinct from 0) when $m = 5$.
J. B. Roberts (Portland, Ore.)

D28-38 **(37# 2684)**

Mordell, L. J.
Equations $ax^3 + bx^2y + cxy^2 + dy^3 = e$ with no rational solutions.
J. London Math. Soc. **43** (1968), 433–438.

A method due to M. Hall [same J. **28** (1953), 379–383; MR **14**, 1063] is extended to cover integral solutions of the homogeneous version of the equation in the title. Four theorems are given covering four types of equations; Theorem 1 will serve as an example: The equation $(px+qy)^3 + kz^3 = (rx+sy)(x^2+xy+7y^2)$, where $k=2$ or 4 and the coefficients p, q, r, s are integers has no integer solution except $(0,0,0)$ if (A) $p - r \equiv 1 \pmod 2$, $p + q \not\equiv 0 \pmod 3$. (B) Denote by P_2 the primes $\equiv 1 \pmod 3$ for which 2 is a noncubic residue. We suppose that if $q^2 - qp + 7p^2 \equiv 0 \pmod{P_2}$, then $s^2 - sr + 7r^2 \not\equiv 0 \pmod{P_2}$.

Among the specific equations covered is the Selmer example, $x^3 + 11y^3 + 20z^3 = 0$, of an equation locally soluble everywhere but possessing globally the single solution $(0,0,0)$.
J. D. Swift (Los Angeles, Calif.)

Citations: MR 14, 1063d = D24-27.
Referred to in D28-39.

D28-39 **(40# 2603)**

Schinzel, A.
A remark on a paper of Mordell.
J. London Math. Soc. (2) **1** (1969), 765–766.

The paper of L. J. Mordell mentioned in the title appeared in the same J. **43** (1968), 433–438 [MR **37** #2684]. The purpose of the present note is to show that the hypotheses on one of the four types of equations considered may be drastically simplified. The result is then applied to obtain an example, originally given by E. S. Selmer [Acta Math. **85** (1951), 203–362; MR **13**, 13], $10x^3 + 51y^3 + z^3 = 0$, solvable nontrivially for all positive moduli as a congruence but having only the trivial solution in integers.
J. D. Swift (Los Angeles, Calif.)

Citations: MR 13, 13i = G05-31; MR 37# 2684 = D28-38.

D28-40 **(37# 4001)**

Avanesov, Èduard Tigranovič

Remarks on the problem of W. Mnich. (Russian. English summary)

Mat. Časopis Sloven. Akad. Vied **17** (1967), 85–91.

It is shown that the numbers $u_k = s^{-1}(1+\varepsilon_k(s^s-1)^{1/s})$, $\varepsilon_k^s = (-1)^{s+1}$, satisfy the equations (*) $u_1 + \cdots + u_s = u_1 \cdots u_s = 1$. A new proof is given that there are no rational solutions of (*) with $s=3$ (Mnich's problem; see W. Sierpiński [Acta Arith. **6** (1960/61), 469–471; MR **24** #A80] and the reviewer and G. Sansone [ibid. **7** (1961/62), 187–190; MR **24** #A2550]). It is well-known that the solubility of (*) in rationals with $s=3$ is equivalent to the existence of a rational r such that all the solutions of $u^3-u^2+ru-1=0$ are rational. It is shown that there is no rational r such that all three roots lie in the same purely cubic field (cf. J. Sedláček [Mat.-Fyz. Časopis Sloven. Akad. Vied **13** (1963), 97–102; MR **28** #1158] for the similar problem for real quadratic fields).

J. W. S. Cassels (Cambridge, England)

Citations: MR 24# A80 = D28-17; MR 24# A2550 = D28-18; MR 28# 1158 = D28-22.

D28-41 **(37# 5148)**

Mordell, L. J.

The Diophantine equation $x^4+y^4=1$ in algebraic number fields.

Acta Arith. **14** (1967/68), 347–355.

The author gives a complete solution of the problem of finding all solutions of (1) $x_1^4+x_2^4=1$, $x_1x_2 \neq 0$, in quadratic and cubic number fields K. In a quadratic field solutions can only occur if $K=Q(\sqrt{-7})$, $x_1=\frac{1}{2}\varepsilon_1(1+\varepsilon\sqrt{-7})$, $x_2=\frac{1}{2}\varepsilon_2(1-\varepsilon\sqrt{-7})$, where $\varepsilon^2=\varepsilon_1^2=\varepsilon_2^2=1$. In a cubic field there are no solutions.

The result for quadratic fields is due to A. Aigner [Jber. Deutsch. Math.-Verein. **43** (1934), 226–229].

The same proposition is to be found as a corollary in a paper by D. K. Faddeev [Dokl. Akad. Nauk SSSR **134** (1960), 776–777; translated as Soviet Math. Dokl. **1** (1961), 1149–1151; MR **23** #A1641].

The author gives an elementary proof for quadratic and cubic fields. A solution of (1) is given parametrically by (2) $x_1^2=(1-t^2)/(1+t^2)$, $x_2^2=2t/(1+t^2)$. It is easily shown that t rational gives $x_1x_2=0$. Let then t be a root of the irreducible equation $F(t)=t^2+Bt+C=0$, B and C being rational constants. Putting $X_1=(1+t^2)x_1x_2$, $X_2=(1+t^2)x_2$, he finds $X_i^2=2t(1+(-1)^it^2)$, $i=1, 2$. Since $K=Q(t)$, then $X_i=a_i+b_it$, when a_i, b_i are also rational constants. This gives the identities $(a_i+b_iz)^2-2z(1+(-1)^iz^2)=F(z)(P_i+Q_iz)$, P_i, Q_i rational constants. The left-hand side must vanish for rational values of z, from which it follows that $z=0$, $z=\pm 1$ for $i=1$ and $z=0$, $z=1$ for $i=2$. The remainder of the proof consists now in working out details. The cubic case can be handled in the same way.

W. Ljunggren (Oslo)

Citations: MR 23# A1641 = G30-25.

D28-42 **(39# 6816)**

Ang, D. D.; Daykin, D. E.; Sheng, T. K.;

On Schoenberg's rational polygon problem.

J. Austral. Math. Soc. **9** (1969), 337–344.

Extending the result of the third author [same J. **6** (1966), 452–459; MR **35** #137], certain classes of polygons with rational sides, diagonals and area are constructed; all except 2 of the vertices are concyclic, one of these being the centre O of the circle, the other a point P; for some rational ratios OP/(radius), e.g. 2, such a construction cannot be performed.

H. T. Croft (Cambridge, England)

Citations: MR 35# 137 = D28-36.

D28-43 **(40# 4202)**

Rameswar Rao, D.

Application of Goodstein's solution in solving some Diophantine equations.

Proc. Nat. Acad. Sci. India Sect. A **38** (1968), 185–188.

From the author's introduction: "The solution of the equation (A) $q(p^2-q^2)=Q(p^2-Q^2)$ was given by R. L. Goodstein [Math. Gaz. **23** (1939), 264–269, especially 266; MR **1**, 25] as (B) $p=h^2+hk+k^2$, $q=h^2-k^2$, $Q=2hk+k^2$. The author uses the above solution for finding two-parameter solutions of certain Diophantine equations."

Citations: MR 1, 25c = D28-1.

D28-44 **(41# 3393)**

Mordell, L. J.

The diophantine equation $Ax^4+By^4+Cz^4=0$.

Proc. Cambridge Philos. Soc. **68** (1970), 125–128.

Some fifty years ago the author conjectured that a curve of genus greater than one contained only a finite number of rational points, but this has never been proved. In a recent paper [Proc. Amer. Math. Soc. **17** (1966), 1152–1158; MR **33** #7301] he proved that certain diophantine equations of the type $Ax^4+By^4+Cz^4=0$, A, B, C integers, $ABC\neq 0$, had only the trivial solution (0, 0, 0) in integers (x, y, z). Based on considerations concerning this problem, Mordell now deduces the following more simple theorem: The equation (1) $2^\beta Lx^4+My^4-Nz^4=0$ ($\beta = 0, 1, 2, 3$) has only the integer solution (0, 0, 0) if the integers L, M, N are odd, positive, relatively prime in pairs and have only factors $\equiv 1 \pmod 8$, and if also the equation (2) $2^{4\alpha-\beta}LX^2+MY^2-NZ^2=0$, $\beta=0$, $\alpha\geqq 1$; $\beta>0$, $\alpha \geqq 2$, has positive integer solutions with $(X, Y)=(Y, Z)=(Z, X)=1$, $X\equiv Y\equiv Z\equiv -1 \pmod 8$. The question whether (1) can be proved impossible by congruence considerations is left open. It is only proved that this is not so mod 16.

W. Ljunggren (Oslo)

Citations: MR 33# 7301 = D28-31.

D28-45 **(41# 5294)**

Mordell, L. J.

On some diophantine equations $y^2=x^3+k$ with no rational solutions. II.

Number Theory and Analysis (Papers in Honor of Edmund Landau), pp. 223–232. *Plenum, New York*, 1969.

A number of detailed conditions are given under which the equation of the title has no rational solution. All of these depend on properties of the class number of one of the quadratic fields $Q(\sqrt{k})$ or $Q(\sqrt{(-3k)})$, as well as properties of fundamental solutions of certain Pell equations. Instances of values of k to which one of these conditions apply are: $k=7, 14, -5, -14, -33, -34, -42$ and others.

{Part I appeared in Arch. Math. Naturvid. **49** (1947), no. 6, 143–150 [MR **9**, 270].}

H. W. Brinkmann (Wallingford, Pa.)

Citations: MR 9, 270b = D28-5.

D32 CUBIC AND QUARTIC SURFACES

See also Sections E76, G35.

See also reviews C05-38, D02-18, D24-88, D28-21, D28-26, D36-5, D36-18, D36-36, D48-1, D48-15, D56-7, D99-17, E24-27, E76-29, G25-25, G35-1, G35-5, G35-6, G35-7, G35-9, G35-12, G35-14, G35-24, G35-26, G35-28, G35-32, G35-38, G35-52, P04-48, P04-51, Z10-1, Z10-7, Z15-64.

D32-1 (1, 134f)

Rédei, L. Die Diophantische Gleichung $mx^2+ny^2=z^4$. Monatsh. Math. Phys. **48**, 43–60 (1939).

Let m and n be quadratfrei integers, $mn\neq -1$; assume that the greatest common divisor d of m and n is 1 or 2, and assume that in the latter case $mn\equiv 4 \pmod{16}$. The author studies the solvability of the Diophantine equation

$$(1)\qquad mx^2+ny^2=z^4,$$

where z is odd and where x, y are relatively prime integers in the case $d=1$, and where x, y are rational numbers in the case $d=2$ such that $2x$ and $2y$ are relatively prime integers. Let D be the discriminant of a quadratic field. The author calls $D=D_1D_2$ a D-decomposition of the second kind [D-Zerfällung zweiter Art], if D_1 and D_2 are also discriminants, and if for all primes p of D either Kronecker's symbol $(D_1/p)=1$ or $(D_2/p)=1$. Let a_1, a_2 be discriminants of quadratic fields, $a_3>1$ quadratfrei, and $k_1=\mathrm{P}(a_1^{\frac{1}{2}})$. Suppose that it is possible to choose an integer α_2 in k_1 and an ideal $\mathfrak{a}_3$ in k_1 as follows: (1) The norm of α_2 is $N_{k_1}(\alpha_2)=a_2g^2$, where g is a rational integer. (2) If we put $k_{12}=k_1(\alpha_2^{\frac{1}{2}})$, then the norm of the relative discriminant of k_{12} over k_1 is $N_{k_1}(D_{k_{12}|k_1})=a_2$. (3) If $a_3=p_1p_2\cdots p_r$ is the factorization of a_3, let $\mathfrak{a}_3$ be the product of the ideals $\mathfrak{p}_1\mathfrak{p}_2\cdots\mathfrak{p}_r$, where $\mathfrak{p}_\rho$ is a prime ideal and a divisor of p_ρ $(\rho=1, 2, \cdots, r)$. (4) Suppose that $(\alpha_2/\mathfrak{a}_3)$ has a value independent of the special choice of α_2 and $\mathfrak{a}_3$, and also that it is not zero. Then the author defines

$$\{a_1, a_2, a_3\}=(\alpha_2/\mathfrak{a}_3)=\pm 1.$$

The conditions for the existence of this symbol and methods for its determination were given by the author previously [J. Reine Angew. Math. **180**, 1–43 (1939)].

Using these definitions the author proves: Equation (1) has solutions in the sense defined above if and only if $\{D_1, D_2, m\}=+1$ for every D-decomposition $D=D_1D_2$ of the second kind admitted by the discriminant D of the quadratic field $\mathrm{P}((-mn)^{\frac{1}{2}})$. This result shows that the solvability of (1) essentially depends on the solvability of certain ternary homogeneous quadratic Diophantine equations. Moreover the author considers the equation $mx^2+ny^2=z^l$.

A. Brauer (Princeton, N. J.).

Referred to in A14-42.

D32-2 (2, 34f)

Venkatarama Ayyar, M. and Bhimasena Rao, M. Types of solutions of $x^3+y^3+z^3=1$ in integers (I). J. Indian Math. Soc. (N.S.) **4**, 47–70 (1940).

The authors begin by deriving a solution of the equation $x^3+y^3=z^3+w^3$ involving four parameters a, b, l, m. Here x, y, z, w are quadratic forms in a, b with coefficients that are functions of l, m. By specializing l, m they thus obtain various types of solutions. For example, if we use (L, M, N) as an abbreviation for $La^2+2Mab+Nb^2$, one solution is $(-14, -6, -54)^3+(14, -6, 54)^3=(7, -24, -27)^3+(-7, -24, 27)^3$; this particular one can be transformed into an identity due to Ramanujan. To solve the equation mentioned in the title, it is sufficient to have one of the four quadratic forms represent unity, either directly or after a common factor has been removed. Thus the illustration given above can be transformed into $(-12, 4, -8)^3+(10, 0, 8)^3=(1, 9, -4)^3+(-9, 7, 4)^3$ and $a=1$, $b=0$ gives us the solution $-12^3+10^3+9^3=1$ of the proposed equation. Many numerical solutions are given, among them a number that had been found by Ramanujan.

H. W. Brinkmann (Swarthmore, Pa.).

D32-3 (2, 346d)

Aucoin, A. A. Solution of a quartic Diophantine equation. J. Math. Pures Appl. (9) **20**, 17–21 (1941).

A particular quartic equation in four integral unknowns is studied. Each side of this Diophantine equation is composed of two linear and one quadratic factor. All integral solutions proportional to a given solution are found.

I. A. Barnett (Cincinnati, Ohio).

D32-4 (3, 65e)

McKeon, R. P. and Goldstine, H. H. A generalized Pell equation. I. Trav. Inst. Math. Tbilissi [Trudy Tbiliss. Mat. Inst.] **8**, 165–172 (1940). (English. Russian summary)

The authors consider the Pellian cubic

$$(1)\qquad x^3+Dy^3+D^2z^3-3Dxzy=1$$

in the case $D=2$. The paper is a partial rediscovery of the results of Meissel and Mathews, for a general D [Dickson, History of the Theory of Numbers, v. 2, p. 594], of which the authors are apparently unaware. A second paper is promised dealing with the general equation (1).

D. H. Lehmer (Berkeley, Calif.).

Referred to in J12-57.

D32-5 (3, 161e)

Venkata Rama Ayyar, M. A note on three allied problems of Ramanujan. J. Mysore Univ. Sect. B. **1**, 109–114 (1941).

Ramanujan has given special sets of integral solutions of the Diophantine equations (1) $x^3+y^3+z^3=u^3$, (2) $x^3+y^3+z^3=1$, (3) $x^3+y^3+z^3=u^6$. He found for x, y, z and u quadratic expressions in two variables which satisfy (1) identically. Equation (2) has been discussed by Mitra [Amer. Monthly **32**, 506–509 (1925)] and by Mahler [J. London Math. Soc. **11**, 136–138 (1936)]. The author gives an interesting method modeled along the lines of Mitra yielding solutions of $x^3+y^3=k^3(z^3+w^3)$ for $k=2, 3, 4$.

I. A. Barnett (Cincinnati, Ohio).

D32-6 (4, 189d)

Mordell, L. J. On sums of three cubes. J. London Math. Soc. **17**, 139–144 (1942).

The known rational solutions of

$$x^3+y^3+z^3=\lambda a^3$$

for $\lambda=1, 2$ are given by x, y and z as certain quartic polynomials in a parameter t with rational coefficients. This led the author to the following theorem whose proof is the object of the paper: The equation

$$x^3+y^3+z^3=n$$

has no solutions with x, y, z as quartic polynomials in a parameter t with rational coefficients unless $n=2a^3$ or $n=a^3$, where a is a rational number, and then the only solutions are those previously known. *B. W. Jones.*

D32-7 (4, 265c)

Mordell, L. J. Note on cubic Diophantine equations $z^2=f(x, y)$ with an infinity of integral solutions. J. London Math. Soc. **17**, 199–203 (1942).

The author notes that "many equations of the type $z^2=f(x, y)$, where $f(x, y)$ is a polynomial of the third degree in x, y, have an infinity of integer solutions" and supports this statement by geometrical considerations. He illustrates his methods by showing in detail that certain equations of the form $z^2 = ax^3 + by^3 + c$ have infinitely many integer solutions, where each of a, b, c is a nonzero integer. The methods are essentially elementary. *B. W. Jones* (Ithaca, N. Y.).

Referred to in D32-22, D32-34, D32-37.

D32-8 (4, 265d)

Mordell, L. J. On Ryley's solution of $x^3+y^3+z^3=n$. J. London Math. Soc. **17**, 194–196 (1942).

The author quotes a result of S. Ryley, published in 1825, namely, that the equation

$$x^3+y^3+z^3=n, \qquad n \text{ rational},$$

has an infinity of rational solutions expressible as rational functions of a parameter. Using a device of Ryley, the author shows that the same statement can be made about the following equation:

$$(x+y+z)^3-dxyz=m,$$

where $d\neq 0$ and m are rational numbers. *B. W. Jones.*

D32-9 (4, 265e)

Richmond, H. W. A note upon Prof. Mordell's paper. J. London Math. Soc. **17**, 196–199 (1942).

The author looks at Ryley's result [see the preceding review] from a geometrical point of view and refers to a fuller account of this argument and its results [Proc. Edinburgh Math. Soc. (2) **2**, 92–100 (1930)].

B. W. Jones (Ithaca, N. Y.).

D32-10 (5, 89c)

Sispánov, Sergio. A problem in Diophantine analysis. Revista Union Mat. Argentina **9**, 41–48 (1943). (Spanish)

The author solves the Diophantine equation

$$(1) \qquad x^3+y^3+z^3-3xyz=kt^3$$

in the following way. Let $(x-z, y-z, t)=r$. Hence

$$(2) \qquad x=z-ar, \quad y=z-br, \quad t=cr,$$

where $(a, b, c)=1$, Put

$$(3) \qquad \frac{r}{3(a^2-ab+b^2)}=\frac{h}{d}, \qquad (h, d)=1.$$

Then

$$(4) \qquad z=\frac{r(kc^3+a^3+b^3)}{3(a^2-ab+b^2)}=\frac{h}{d}(kc^3+a^3+b^3).$$

Similar formulas follow from (2), (3) and (4) for x, y, t. We have from (3) and (4)

$$d\,|\,d'=(kc^3+a^3+b^3,\ 3(a^2-ab+b^2)).$$

If we drop the assumption $(h, d)=1$, we may put $d=d'$. Then we obtain the general solution of (1) depending upon the four parameters a, b, c, h. *P. Scherk.*

D32-11 (5, 89e)

Dyer, P. S. A solution of $A^4+B^4=C^4+D^4$. J. London Math. Soc. **18**, 2–4 (1943).

Euler gave solutions of the Diophantine equation $A^4+B^4=C^4+D^4$. A simpler solution was obtained by Gérardin [Intermédiaire des Math. **24**, 51 (1917)]. In both solutions A, B, C, D are homogeneous polynomials in two variables of degree seven with integral coefficients. The author gives a very simple proof for Gérardin's result. *A. Brauer.*

Referred to in D48-32.

D32-12 (5, 141b)

Segre, B. On a parametric solution of the equation $x^3+y^3+az^3=b$, and on ternary forms representing every rational number. J. London Math. Soc. **18**, 31–34 (1943).

It is shown that the equation $x^3+y^3+az^3=b$, a and b rational numbers, $ab\neq 0$, has an infinity of rational solutions which are rational functions of two parameters. This result is applied to the problem of representing a given rational number r by a given ternary cubic form $f(x, y, z)$. Outside of the trivial case in which f is a product of three linear factors, it is found that the cubic surface $f(x, y, z)=r$ always has infinitely many rational solutions at finite distance, except when the cubic curve $f=0$ has no rational points. *O. Zariski* (Baltimore, Md.).

Referred to in D02-1.

D32-13 (5, 141c)

Reichardt, Hans. Einige im Kleinen überall lösbare, im Grossen unlösbare diophantische Gleichungen. J. Reine Angew. Math. **184**, 12–18 (1942).

The author applies his results on Diophantine equations [Math. Ann. **117**, 235–276 (1940); these Rev. **2**, 34] to the special equation (1) $x^4+17y^4=z^2$. In order to obtain a basis for the solution of (1) in the field of rational numbers we have to determine which of the following equations have solutions in rational integers: (2) $x^4-68y^4=z^2$, $68x^4-y^4=z^2$, $x^4-17y^4=2z^2$, $17x^4-y^4=2z^2$. While it is trivial that (1) and the first equation (2) have solutions, it seems to be difficult to answer this question for the other three equations. Therefore the author's earlier method is not directly applicable. However, he succeeds by considering the more general problem of finding a basis for the solutions of (1) in the field $\mathfrak{P}(\sqrt{-2})$. It follows from this result that (1) and the first equation (2) have only trivial integral rational solutions while the other three equations (2) have no solutions in rational integers. *A. Brauer.*

Citations: MR 2, 34g = D28-2.
Referred to in D28-26, D32-83.

D32-14 (6, 37g)

Segre, B. A parametric solution of the indeterminate cubic equation $z^2=f(x, y)$. J. London Math. Soc. **18**, 226–233 (1943).

The author proves the following theorem. Let $f(x, y)$ be any given cubic polynomial in x, y with rational coefficients, which is not expressible as a polynomial in a single linear function of x and y. Then the equation $z^2=f(x, y)$ has an infinity of rational solutions in x, y, z, given rationally in terms of one or more parameters. From this theorem these results follow. (1) If a rational solution of a given indeterminate cubic equation $F(x, y, z)=0$ is known, which does not annul all the first and second partial derivatives of $F(x, y, z)$, so that $F=0$ is not a curve for any choice of coordinates, then it is possible to obtain an infinity of rational solutions, expressed in terms of one or more parameters. (2) An indeterminate ternary cubic equation which cannot be reduced to an equation involving less than three variables has either no rational solution or an infinity of rational solutions. Both cases are in fact possible.

B. W. Jones (Ithaca, N. Y.).

Referred to in D32-16, D32-41, D32-51.

D32-15 **(6, 37h)**

Mordell, L. J. A rational parametric solution of $z^2-k=ax^3+bx^2y+cxy^2+dy^3$. J. London Math. Soc. **18**, 222–226 (1943).

The author finds a parametric solution of the equation

$$z^2-k(1+px)^2=ax^3+bx^2y+cxy^2+dy^3,$$

whose existence for $k=1$ has been proved by Segre. A short resume of recent results is also given. *B. W. Jones.*

Referred to in D32-16, H20-5, H20-7, J08-2, J52-10.

D32-16 **(6, 258c)**

Whitehead, R. F. A rational parametric solution of the cubic indeterminate equation $z^2=f(x, y)$. J. London Math. Soc. **19**, 68–71 (1944).

A simple proof is given of the existence of a rational parametric solution of the equation $z^2=ax^3+bx^2y+cxy^2+dy^3+\phi$, where ϕ denotes $ex^2+fxy+gy^2+hx+ky+m$, and all coefficients are rational. The problem reduces to the case

$$z^2=x^3+x(a_1y^2+b_1y+c_1)+d_1y^3+e_1y^2+f_1y+g_1.$$

Putting $x=y^2+2ty$ gives $z^2=(y^3+3ty^2+\cdots)^2+Py^2+Qy+R$, with P, Q, R certain polynomials in t. Solving $Py^2+Qy+R=0$ gives expressions of the form $y=\beta\pm\beta'\sqrt{\Delta}$, $x=\alpha\pm\alpha'\sqrt{\Delta}$, $z=\gamma\pm\gamma'\sqrt{\Delta}$; the straight line $x=\alpha+\alpha'\theta$, $y=\beta+\beta'\theta$, $z=\gamma+\gamma'\theta$ intersects the cubic surface in points given by $\theta=\pm\sqrt{\Delta}$, and in a third point with rational coordinates. Unless all of a_1, b_1, d_1, e_1, f_1 vanish (when $f(x, y)$ reduces to a function of one variable), this point is not at infinity. Segre gave a geometrical proof in the case $\phi=(1+ex+fy)^2$ [same J. **18**, 24–31, 88–100 (1943); these Rev. **5**, 154], Mordell an algebraic proof with $\phi=g(1+ex+fy)^2$ [same J. **18**, 43–46, 222–226 (1943); these Rev. **5**, 154; **6**, 37], and Segre extended Mordell's method to the general case [same J. **18**, 226–233 (1943); these Rev. **6**, 37]. *G. Pall.*

Citations: MR 5, 154e = G35-1; MR 5, 154f = G35-1; MR 6, 37g = D32-14; MR 6, 37h = D32-15.

D32-17 **(6, 259e)**

Ward, Morgan. Euler's three biquadrate problem. Proc. Nat. Acad. Sci. U. S. A. **31**, 125–127 (1945).

This famous unsolved problem is to prove or disprove the existence of three positive integral fourth powers whose sum is a fourth power. The author indicates a method by means of which he has shown that the Diophantine equation

$$x^4+y^4+z^4=w^4, \qquad xyz\neq 0,$$

has no solution for $w<10000$. This equation is replaced by another equation

$$u^4+v^4=2\epsilon kl(e^8l^2+2^{18+8\sigma+2\epsilon}d^8k^2), \tag{1}$$

whose derivation is not given and which the reviewer fears is misprinted. With $w<10000$, the new variables are subject to inequalities and congruence conditions with respect to the moduli 8, 5 and 13. There results a finite set of numbers represented by the right member of (1). To show that none of these numbers is the sum of two biquadrates each number is expressed in all possible ways as the sum of two squares with the aid of factor tables and the factor stencils of D. N. Lehmer and J. D. Elder. The details of the proof are promised in another paper. *D. H. Lehmer.*

Referred to in D32-23.

D32-18 **(7, 414c)**

Kesava Menon, P. On the equation $x_1^3+x_2^3=y_1^3+y_2^3$. Math. Student **13**, 52–54 (1945).

The general solution of the Diophantine equation

$$x_1^3+x_2^3=y_1^3+y_2^3 \tag{1}$$

in rational numbers x_1, x_2, y_1, y_2 was found by Euler and simplified by Binet. This solution can be written in the form

$$x_1=c\{(a+3b)(a^2+3b^2)-1\}, \quad x_2=c\{-(a-3b)(a^2+3b^2)+1\},$$
$$y_1=c\{(a^2+3b^2)^2-(a-3b)\}, \quad y_2=c\{-(a^2+3b^2)^2+(a+3b)\},$$

where a, b, c are arbitrary rational numbers. Since the right-hand sides are not of the same degree, integral solutions exist for which the corresponding values of a and b are not integers. Therefore it is of interest to find a solution where the right-hand sides are of the same degree. Ramanujan [Hardy and Wright, An Introduction to the Theory of Numbers, Oxford University Press, 1938, p. 201] gave the particular solution

$$x_1=3a^2+5ab-5b^2, \quad x_2=4a^2-4ab+6b^2,$$
$$y_1=3b^2+5ab-5a^2, \quad y_2=4b^2-4ab+6a^2.$$

The author generalizes this result by proving the following theorem. Let a_1, a_2, b_1, b_2 be rational numbers satisfying the conditions that $a_1^3+a_2^3+b_1^3+b_2^3=0$ and $-(a_1+b_1)/(a_2+b_2)$ is the square of a rational number d. Then

$$x_1=a_1a^2\pm(a_2-b_2)ab/d-b_1b^2, \quad x_2=a_2a^2\pm(a_1-b_1)abd-b_2b^2,$$
$$y_1=a_1b^2\pm(a_2-b_2)ab/d-b_1a^2, \quad y_2=a_2b^2\pm(a_1-b_1)abd-b_2a^2$$

is a solution of (1), but not the general solution. For instance, we may choose $a_1=1$, $a_2=12$, $b_1=-9$, $b_2=-10$. From each such set a_1, a_2, b_1, b_2, infinitely many other such sets may be obtained. *A. Brauer* (Chapel Hill, N. C.).

D32-19 **(7, 415g)**

Srinivasan, A. K. Residual types of partitions of "0" into four cubes. Math. Student **13**, 47–48 (1945).

Elementary remarks. *A. Brauer* (Chapel Hill, N. C.).

D32-20 **(7, 505g)**

Potts, D. H. Solution of a Diophantine system proposed by Bhaskara. Bull. Calcutta Math. Soc. **38**, 21–24 (1946).

Bhaskara's problem of finding integers x, y such that $x-y$ is a square and x^2+y^2 a cube is essentially the problem of solving the Diophantine system $x-y=t^2$, $x^2+y^2=z^3$. The author considers, separately, two general solutions $x=r^3-3rs^2$, $y=3r^2s-s^3$ and $x=r(r^2+s^2)$, $y=s(r^2+s^2)$ of the second equation and imposes on each the condition $x-y=t^2$. With the aid of results of Kronecker, Desboves, and Legendre [Dickson's History of the Theory of Numbers, vol. 2, Washington, 1920, pp. 169, 405, 570], he derives formulas which may be used to obtain an infinite number of numerical solutions. Several numerical solutions, including those of Bhaskara, are given. *W. H. Gage.*

Referred to in D32-33.

D32-21 **(7, 505h)**

Duarte, F. J. On the equation $x_1^3+x_2^3=y_1^3+y_2^3$. Estados Unidos de Venezuela. Bol. Acad. Ci. Fís. Mat. Nat. **7**, 855–866 (1943). (Spanish)

The solution of this equation in integers is reduced to the problem of representing a certain integer by a quadratic form of the type v^2-Au^2. A solution equivalent to the well-known formulas of Euler and Binet is then obtained and it is shown that this furnishes all integral solutions of the equation. *H. W. Brinkmann* (Swarthmore, Pa.).

D32-22 **(8, 564g)**

Prasad, Sarveshwar, and Chariar, V. R. On certain Diophantine equations. Patna Univ. J. **2**, 66–71 (1946).

L. J. Mordell [J. London Math. Soc. **17**, 199–203 (1942); these Rev. **4**, 265; **6**, 334] has discussed certain Diophantine equations having an infinite number of solutions; in particular, a set of solutions was exhibited for $z^2=x^3+y^3-1$. The present paper exhibits other infinite sets of solutions of this equation and also of the equation $2z^2=x^3+y^3-1$. The method used is similar to Mordell's. *I. Niven.*

Citations: MR 4, 265c = D32-7.

D32-23 (10, 283f)

Ward, Morgan. Euler's problem on sums of three fourth powers. Duke Math. J. **15**, 827–837 (1948).

The famous problem referred to in the title is that of proving or disproving that a biquadrate is not the sum of three biquadrates. This paper proves that the Diophantine relation

$$(1)\qquad x^4+y^4+z^4=w^4, \qquad xyw\neq 0,$$

implies (2) $w>10^4$. The basic idea of the proof is set forth in a previous paper [Proc. Nat. Acad. Sci. U. S. A. **31**, 125–127 (1945); these Rev. **6**, 259]. In the present paper a full account of the details is given. The assumption that (1) has a solution leads to the equation

$$(3)\qquad u^4+v^4=2^\epsilon kl(2^{8\sigma+2\epsilon+18}d^8k^2+e^8l^2).$$

The denial of (2) gives corresponding restrictions on the variables on the right side of (3). All numbers of this form, with these restrictions, are shown not to be the sum of two biquadrates either by using lemmas, small moduli, or in stubborn cases by examining all representations as sums of two squares. The extensive calculations involved do not invite further efforts in this direction. *D. H. Lehmer*

Citations: MR 6, 259e = D32-17.

D32-24 (10, 430c)

Rosenthall, E. Diophantine systems suggested by Bhascara's problem. Duke Math. J. **15**, 921–928 (1948).

By the use of two lemmas, one given by Uspensky and Heaslet [Elementary Number Theory, McGraw-Hill, New York, 1939, p. 393; these Rev. **1**, 38], and the other proved by Dickson [Introduction to the Theory of Numbers, University of Chicago Press, 1929, pp. 44–47], the author proves that all rational integers satisfying the system $x^2+y^2=z^3$, $x-y=t^2$, where $(x,y)=1$, are given without duplication by $x=r^3-3rs^2$, $y=3r^2s-s^3$, where r and s are expressed by three sets of formulas. In each set r and s are polynomials in integral parameters p, q having integral coefficients. The range of these parameters is also obtained. Similar results are likewise given for $x^3+y^3=z^2$, $(x,y)=1$, where x and y are obtained as polynomials in parameters p, q, these parameters being restricted to a precise range. Finally, by using results in an earlier paper [Amer. J. Math. **65**, 663–672 (1943); these Rev. **5**, 90] the author obtains the complete integral parametric representation of $x^3+y^3=z^2$ without the restriction $(x,y)=1$. *W. H. Gage.*

Citations: MR 1, 38c = Z01-2; MR 5, 90a = D36-5.

D32-25 (10, 510c)

Swift, J. D. Diophantine equations connected with the cubic Fermat equation. Amer. Math. Monthly **56**, 254–256 (1949).

All solutions of $u^3-z^3=3uv$ are given in terms of 3 parameters, 3 sets of formulas being employed. Further results are then obtained by using known theory of the Fermat equation $x^3+y^3=z^3$, derived from the previous equation by the substitution $u=x+y$, $v=xy$. An application is also made to the cubic Fermat equation in quadratic fields. *I. Niven* (Eugene, Ore.).

D32-26 (10, 592d)

Hlaváček, Miloslav. Again on the solution of the equation $x^4-y^4=z^4-u^4$ in integers. Časopis Pěst. Mat. Fys. **73**, D43–D46 (1949). (Czech)

Denote by $\xi(v)$, $\eta(v)$, $\zeta(v)$ the quotients $\vartheta_i(v,\tau)/\vartheta_0(v,\tau)$ $(i=1,2,3)$ of the Jacobi theta-functions. If $\xi(v)$, $\eta(v)$, $\zeta(v)$ are rational, then $\xi((2k+1)v)=a_k/d_k$, $\eta((2k+1)v)=b_k/d_k$, $\zeta((2k+1)v)=c_k/d_k$ $(k=1,2,3,\cdots)$ are also rational, and the integers a_k, b_k, c_k, d_k therefore give a series of solutions of the equation of the title (since $\xi^4-\eta^4=1-\zeta^4$), for which $(a_k^2+d_k^2)/(c_k^2-b_k^2)$ is independent of k. See also Hlaváček [same Časopis **67**, D1–D4 (1938)], where an analogous result is obtained with the aid of the $\wp$-function. *V. Jarník* (Prague).

Referred to in Z02-44.

D32-27 (11, 82b)

Zahlen, Jean-Pierre. Sur l'équation Diophantienne $X^3+Y^3+Z^3=hT^3$. Euclides, Madrid **9**, 139–142 (1949).

Infinitely many solutions X, Y, Z, T of the indicated equation are given in terms of 3 independent parameters and h. *I. Niven* (Eugene, Ore.).

D32-28 (11, 82h)

Mordell, L. J. Rational points on cubic surfaces. Publ. Math. Debrecen **1**, 1–6 (1949).

Lecture at the University of Debrecen.

Referred to in D32-41, D32-51, D36-33.

D32-29 (11, 328f)

Georgikopoulos, C. Rational integral solutions of the equations $x^3+4y^3=z^2$ and $x^3+2y^3=z^2$. Bull. Soc. Math. Grèce **24**, 13–19 (1948). (English. Greek summary)

It is proved that all the rational integral solutions of the equation

$$(1)\qquad x^3+4y^3=z^2,$$

for x, y, z, relatively prime by pairs, are included in the parametric solution

$$\pm x=x_1(x_1^3+4y_1^3),$$
$$\pm y=y_1(y_1^3-2x_1^3),$$
$$\pm z=x_1^6-2y_1^6+10x_1^3y_1^3.$$

A similar result is worked out for the equation

$$(2)\qquad x^3+2y^3=z^2.$$

The method used depends on (a) the fact that the class number of $K(\sqrt[3]{2})$ (K the field of rational numbers) is 1, (b) that 1, $\sqrt[3]{2}$, $\sqrt[3]{4}$, form a minimal basis for $K(\sqrt[3]{2})$, and (c) that $\sqrt[3]{2}-1$ is a fundamental unit. Knowing this, one is completely informed concerning the arithmetic of $K(\sqrt[3]{2})$, and the results are obtained by comparing the factorizations into integers of $K(\sqrt[3]{2})$ of both sides of (1), (2), respectively. *H. N. Shapiro* (New York, N. Y.).

D32-30 (11, 714i)

Mordell, L. J. Note on cubic equations in three variables with an infinity of integer solutions. Ann. Mat. Pura Appl. (4) **29**, 301–305 (1949).

The equation $z^3=ax^2+by^2+c$ has an infinite number of integral solutions in x, y, z if a, b, c are odd, $(a,b)=1$, $c\not\equiv a^3 \pmod 7$ when $7|b$, and $c\not\equiv b^3 \pmod 7$ when $7|a$. The proof is based on the lemma that $y^3\equiv x^3+k \pmod a$ is solvable if a is odd; in fact it is solvable with $(y,a)=1$ except when $7|a$ and $7|(k+1)$. *I. Niven* (Eugene, Ore.).

Referred to in D32-31, D32-34.

D32-31 (12, 675d)

Mordell, L. J. Note on cubic equations in three variables with an infinity of integer solutions. Algèbre et Théorie des Nombres. Colloques Internationaux du Centre National de la Recherche Scientifique, no. 24, pp. 77–79. Centre National de la Recherche Scientifique, Paris, 1950.

Reprinted from Ann. Mat. Pura Appl. (4) **29**, 301–305 (1949); these Rev. **11**, 714.

Citations: MR 11, 714i = D32-30.

D32-32 **(12, 159c)**

Xeroudakes, Georgios F. On some problems of indeterminate analysis. Bull. Soc. Math. Grèce **24**, 28–50 (1949). (Greek)

Summaries of known results on various problems in Diophantine analysis. The early part of the paper deals with some examples studied by Fermat which arise from seeking Pythagorean right triangles whose sides satisfy certain auxiliary conditions. Among the other problems discussed are the equations $x^4+y^4+\alpha^2z^4=X^4+Y^4+\alpha^2Z^4$, and $x^4+mx^2y^2+ny^4=kz^2$, with complete solutions given in some special cases. *T. M. Apostol* (Pasadena, Calif.).

D32-33 **(12, 675c)**

Potts, D. H. The Diophantine equation $x^2+y^2=z^3$. Bull. Calcutta Math. Soc. **42**, 99–100 (1950).

In this paper the author gives an elementary derivation of the complete solutions in rational integers of the Diophantine equation $x^2+y^2=z^3$, $xyz\neq 0$. [Cf. same Bull. **38**, 21–24 (1946); these Rev. **7**, 505.] *W. H. Gage.*

Citations: MR 7, 505g = D32-20.

D32-34 **(13, 822g)**

Mordell, L. J. On cubic equations $z^2=f(x, y)$ with an infinity of integer solutions. Proc. Amer. Math. Soc. **3**, 210–217 (1952).

The author continues his investigations [J. London Math. Soc. **17**, 199–203 (1942); Ann. Mat. Pura Appl. (4) **29**, 301–305 (1949); these Rev. **4**, 265; **6**, 334; **11**, 714] on certain classes of cubic Diophantine equations. It is proved that the equation

$$z^2=p^2+\lambda x+ax^2+bxy+2py^2+Ax^3+Bx^2y+Cxy^2+Dy^3,$$

with $p\neq 0$, has infinitely many solutions if $p^2(b^2-8ap)+2p\lambda^2$ is positive and not a square. Also the same equation with quadratic terms in x and y deleted, $\lambda p\neq 0$, has infinitely many solutions if the congruence

$$2\lambda^3+2p(8Ap^3+4Bp^2t+2Cpt^2+Dt^3)\equiv 0 \pmod{\lambda^4}$$

is solvable for t. The equation $z^3=p^3+\lambda x+ax^2+bxy+cy^2$ with $\lambda p\neq 0$ has infinitely many solutions if

$$(9a+3bt+ct^2)p^4-3\lambda^2 p\equiv 0 \pmod{\lambda^3}$$

is solvable. Note the unconditional results in these last two cases if $\lambda=1$. Finally, let L_1, M_1 be homogeneous polynomials in x, y, z of the first degree, L_2, M_2 similarly of the second degree, integral coefficients throughout. Then $L_1+L_2+M_1{}^3+L_1M_2=0$ has infinitely many solutions if $L_1=0$, $M_1=1$ are solvable in integers. It is conjectured in general that if the cubic equation $g(x, y, z)=0$ has one integral solution, then there are infinitely many solutions if $g(x, y, z)-a$ is irreducible for all a. *I. Niven.*

Citations: MR 4, 265c = D32-7; MR 11, 714i = D32-30.

D32-35 **(14, 20a)**

Alef. On a diophantine equation. Revista Mat. Hisp.-Amer. (4) **12**, 3–8 (1952). (Spanish)

The equation $x^3+y^3=2z^2$ is found to have solutions $x, y=2^{2\alpha}3^{2\gamma+1}r^2\pm s$, $z=2^{\alpha+\beta}3^{\gamma+1}rq$, where the integral parameters satisfy the relation $2^{2\beta}q^2-s^2=2^{4\alpha}3^{4\gamma+1}r^4$. It is asserted that these include all relatively prime solutions, but an error in the interpretation of the writer's formulas [9] leads him to overlook another class of solutions. For example the solution $x=253$, $y=85$, $z=2899$ does not arise from the above formulas, which give only values with $z\equiv 0 \pmod 3$). *I. Niven* (Eugene, Ore.).

Referred to in D32-42.

D32-36 **(14, 354c)**

Duarte, F. J. General solution of a Diophantine equation of the third degree. Estados Unidos de Venezuela. Bol. Acad. Ci. Fís. Mat. Nat. **14**, no. 45, 3–7 (1951). (Spanish)

With arbitrary integral parameters a, b, c the formulas

$$x, y=(a^2+3b^2)^2+(a\pm 3b)c^3,$$
$$z=(a^2+3b^2)^2-2ac^3, \quad v=3(a^2+3b^2)c^2$$

give solutions of $x^3+y^3+z^3-3xyz=v^3$. Conversely, to any integral solution x_1, y_1, z_1, v_1 of this equation there correspond integers a, b, c giving values x, y, z, v in the formulas such that $x/x_1=y/y_1=z/z_1=v/v_1$. *I. Niven.*

D32-37 **(14, 536f)**

Mordell, L. J. The congruence $ax^3+by^3+c\equiv 0 \pmod{xy}$, and integer solutions of cubic equations in three variables. Acta Math. **88**, 77–83 (1952).

It is proved that the congruence of the title has an infinity of solutions for which $(cx, y)=1$; the solutions obtained are polynomials in a, b, c. The result also holds if ax^3 and by^3 are replaced by any polynomials $f(x)$ and $g(y)$ respectively, with integral coefficients and $f(0)=g(0)=0$. With this it is proved that $z^2-(27abc)^2=ab^2x^3+y^3$ has an infinity of integral solutions, a, b, c being integers; a similar result was obtained earlier by the author [J. London Math. Soc. **17**, 199–203 (1942); these Rev. **4**, 265; **6**, 334]. These results support a conjecture of the author that if $F(x,y,z)=0$ is a cubic with integral coefficients, not representing a cone in three-space, and if $F-a$ is irreducible for all integers a, then one integral solution of $F=0$ implies an infinity of such solutions. However, the author added in proof two counterexamples to this conjecture; for example, $x^2+y^2+z^2+4xyz=1$ is said to have only solutions typified by $y=z=0$. Remark by reviewer: the author seems to assume in the proofs that certain coefficients are not zero, without formal hypotheses in the statements of the theorems. *I. Niven.*

Citations: MR 4, 265c = D32-7.

Referred to in D32-38, D48-64.

D32-38 **(14, 725f)**

Barnes, E. S. On the Diophantine equation $x^2+y^2+c=xyz$. J. London Math. Soc. **28**, 242–244 (1953).

A solution $x=u_0$, $y=u_1$, $z=v$ of the equation of the title is called fundamental if $u_0\leqq u_1$, and $0<u_0\leqq c$ or $0\leqq u_0\leqq\sqrt{-c}$ according as c is positive or negative, all solutions being subject to the condition $(xy, c)=1$. It is proved that any solution with $0\leqq x\leqq y$ is either a fundamental solution or generated therefrom by the recurrence relation $u_{r+1}=vu_r-u_{r-1}$; thus $x=u_r$, $y=u_{r+1}$, $z=v$ for some positive integer r. The proof is by descent, similar to one of L. J. Mordell [Acta Math. **88**, 77–83 (1952); these Rev. **14**, 536]. *I. Niven.*

Citations: MR 14, 536f = D32-37.

Referred to in D32-44, D32-53, D48-27.

D32-39 **(14, 950f)**

Xeroudakes, Georgios F. On the equation

$$x^4+mx^2y^2+ny^4=z^2.$$

Bull. Soc. Math. Grèce **27**, 85–91 (1953). (Greek. English summary)

Let p, q, m be given integers, $q\neq 1$, $(p, q)=1$, and assume the congruence $z^2\equiv p^2(p^2+mq^2) \pmod{q^4}$ has a solution z_0. The author proves that $x=p$, $y=q$ is a solution of the equation in the title if and only if n has the form

$$n=q^4X^2+2z_0X+[z_0{}^2-p^2(p^2+mq^2)/q^4],$$

where X is an integer. *T. Apostol* (Pasadena, Calif.).

D32-40 **(15, 102b)**

Mordell, L. J. On the integer solutions of the equation $x^2+y^2+z^2+2xyz=n$. J. London Math. Soc. **28**, 500–510 (1953).

It is proved that the equation of the title has no solutions in integers if $n\equiv 3 \pmod 4$, $n\equiv 6 \pmod 8$, $n\equiv \pm 3 \pmod 9$, $n=1-4k^2$ with $k\not\equiv 0 \pmod 4$ and k has no prime factors of the form $3+4j$, or $n=1-3k^2$ with $(k,4)=2$, $(k,3)=1$ and k has no prime factors of the form $2+3j$. On the other hand, one solution of the equation implies an infinitude of solutions, except possibly when n is a perfect square having no prime factors of the form $1+4j$. Also there are infinitely many solutions if $n=2^r$ and r is odd, but only the solutions typified by $x=y=0$ when r is even. Proofs are given of A. Hurwitz' theorem that the equation has only the solution $x=y=z=0$ in case $n=0$, and of P. Bachmann's complete parametric solution for the case $n=1$. For any odd n it is established by explicit formulas that the solutions of the equation can be put into one-to-one correspondence with simultaneous solutions of $x^3+y^3+z^3+w^3=m$, $x+y+z+w=2$, with $m=\frac{1}{2}(3n+1)$. *I. Niven* (Eugene, Ore.).

Referred to in D32-62.

D32-41 **(15, 290b)**

Selmer, Ernst S. Sufficient congruence conditions for the existence of rational points on certain cubic surfaces. Math. Scand. **1**, 113–119 (1953).

It is known that, if a ternary non-homogeneous cubic equation with rational coefficients cannot be homographically reduced to one involving less than three variables, and if it has one rational solution, then the equation has an infinity of rational solutions [B. Segre, J. London Math. Soc. **18**, 226–233 (1943); these Rev. **6**, 37]. Necessary and sufficient conditions for the existence of one solution are not known; but L. J. Mordell [Publ. Math. Debrecen **1**, 1–6 (1949); these Rev. **11**, 82] has conjectured that the required conditions coincide with the elementary congruence conditions.

The present paper proves Mordell's conjecture for the (homogeneous quaternary) equation

(1) $$a_1x_1^3+a_2x_2^3+a_3x_3^3+a_4x_4^3=0 \quad (a_1a_2a_3a_4\neq 0),$$

under the assumption that (for instance) $(a_3a_4)/(a_1a_2)$ is a rational cube. Then the equation (1) can be transformed into $x^3+my^3=n(u^3+mv^3)$, with integer cubefree m and n. The solubility of this equation when the congruence conditions are satisfied is first obtained by means of elementary methods of ideal theory, involving class-number considerations, in the hypothesis that a not-too-high power of 3 divides the class number. Then an alternative proof, unrestrictedly valid, is given by using a deep result due to Hasse [Nachr. Ges. Wiss. Göttingen. Math.-Phys. Kl. **1931**, 64–69] concerning norms in a cyclic field. The same method can also be applied for proving Mordell's conjecture for the cubic equation $f(x,y)=nf(u,v)$—where f is an arbitrary cubic form with rational coefficients, and so this equation includes the last one—but it fails for the more general equation (1). However, the author affirms to have verified the solubility of equation (1) in all cases, satisfying the congruence conditions, for which $|a_1a_2a_3a_4|\leqq 500$, and he points out some considerations suggesting the same result as highly probable also in remaining cases. *B. Segre.*

Citations: MR 6, 37g = D32-14; MR 11, 82h = D32-28.
Referred to in D36-33.

D32-42 **(15, 506f)**

Rodeja, F., E. G.-. On the diophantine equation $x^3+y^3=2z^2$. Revista Mat. Hisp.-Amer. (4) **13**, 229–240 (1953). (Spanish)

The equation $x^3+y^3=2z^2$ is solved completely in the cases $(x,y)=1$ or 2, three sets of formulas being given in the first case and four in the second. Each set of formulas is in terms of two relatively prime parameters. An earlier set of formulas for the case $(x,y)=1$ by Alef [same Revista (4) **12**, 3–8 (1952); these Rev. **14**, 20] was noted to be incomplete by this reviewer. *I. Niven* (Eugene, Oreg.).

Citations: MR 14, 20a = D32-35.
Referred to in D24-39.

D32-43 **(15, 855b)**

Đerasimović, B. Eine Diophantische Gleichung vom dritten Grade. Bull. Soc. Math. Phys. Serbie **5**, no. 3–4, 61–77 (1953). (Serbo-Croatian. German summary)

The author generalizes that part of the A. Markov theory of minima of indefinite binary quadratic forms which relates the so-called Markov numbers to the diophantine cubic

(1) $$x^2+y^2+z^2=3xyz.$$

The author considers the cubic $x^2+\epsilon_1y^2+\epsilon_2z^2=\alpha xyz$, where $\epsilon_1^2=\epsilon_2^2=1$. Solutions are given in terms of cumulants quite similar to those which generate the Markov numbers. The special role played by the number 2 in the case of (1) is now played by $\alpha-1$. [For the Markov theory see L. E. Dickson, Studies in the theory of numbers, Univ. of Chicago Press, 1930, Ch. 7.] *D. H. Lehmer.*

D32-44 **(16, 13e)**

Mills, W. H. A method for solving certain Diophantine equations. Proc. Amer. Math. Soc. **5**, 473–475 (1954).

The Diophantine equation $x^2+xyz+\epsilon y^2+ax+by+c=0$, where $\epsilon=\pm 1$, a, b, c are given integers and x, y, z are to be determined can be treated by methods evolved independently by the author [Pacific J. Math. **3**, 209–220 (1953); these Rev. **14**, 950] and E. S. Barnes [J. London Math. Soc. **28**, 242–244 (1953); these Rev. **14**, 725] but going back in essence to Hurwitz [Math. Werke, Bd 2, Birkhäuser, Basel, 1933, pp. 410–421]. If either of the polynomials x^2+ax+c, ϵy^2+by+c is factorizable over the rational field then solutions exist for all integers z; but otherwise all solutions belong to a finite number of "chains" (defined by recurrence relations); and, in particular, the equation is soluble for only a finite number of given values of z. *J. W. S. Cassels* (Cambridge, England).

Citations: MR 14, 725f = D32-38; MR 14, 950e = D20-9.
Referred to in D32-53, D48-27.

D32-45 **(16, 17d)**

Ramasarma, B. V. Partitions of zero into 4 cubes. Math. Student **22**, 102–103 (1954).

D32-46 **(16, 335l)**

Sansone, G. Soluzioni intere delle equazioni $3y^4-2x^4=z^2$, $\lambda^4-6g^4=v^2$. Formule di Pepin e loro inversione. Matematiche, Catania **8**, no. 2, 3–10 (1953).

The infinitude of solutions in integers of $3y^4-2x^4=z^2$ is obtained by a geometric procedure. This contrasts with the recursion method of solution by T. Pepin [Atti Accad. Pont. Nuovi Lincei **31**, 397–427 (1878)]. Pepin's procedure is outlined in the present paper, and then transformed in order to obtain the infinitude of solutions of $\lambda^4-6g^4=v^2$, a related equation which was also solved by Pepin.
I. Niven (Eugene, Ore.).

D32-47 **(16, 797e)**

Miller, J. C. P., and Woollett, M. F. C. Solutions of the Diophantine equation $x^3+y^3+z^3=k$. J. London Math. Soc. **30**, 101–110 (1955).

At the suggestion of L. J. Mordell, the authors have programmed the EDSAC to search for small sums of three integer cubes. The results are tabulated and give all primitive nontrivial solutions of

(1) $$x^3+y^3+z^3=k$$

with $|k|\leqq 100$, $|z|\leqq|y|\leqq|x|\leqq 3164$, in all 345 solutions. The number of solutions for a given k is highly irregular. For $k=9n\pm 4$ the equation is impossible. There are 21 such solutions for $k=1$ and only 2 for $k=3$, namely (1, 1, 1) and (−5, 4, 4). A further search up to $|x|=10000$ is planned for the case $k=3$. In almost all cases where the number of solutions is small, the solutions themselves are small, giving support to the conjecture that, for some k, (1) has only a finite number of solutions. No primitive solutions were found for $k=24, 30, 33, 39, 42, 52, 74, 75, 80, 84, 87, 96$. All solutions found for $k=2$ are given by

$$x=6t^3+1,\quad y=-6t^3+1,\quad z=-6t^2.$$

There are many solutions when k is itself a cube.
D. H. Lehmer (Berkeley, Calif.).

Referred to in D32-77.

D32-48 (16, 798a)

Mordell, L. J. On an infinity of integer solutions of $ax^3+ay^3+bz^3=bc^3$. J. London Math. Soc. **30**, 111–113 (1955).

The author remarks on the table of Miller and Woollett [see preceding review] that the case $k=1$ and more generally $k=c^3$ give rise to many solutions of $x^3+y^3+z^3=k$. He then proceeds to show that the more general equation in the title has an infinity of non-trivial solutions. This is done by writing the equation in the form

$$a(x+y)(x^2-xy+y^2)=b(c-z)(c^2+cz+z^2).$$

After a change and specialization of variables and a cancellation of a non-zero factor the condition becomes an indeterminate equation of the second degree of hyperbolic type having an infinity of solutions. The more general equation $xF(x,y,z)=yG(x,y,z)$, where F, G are quadratic polynomials, as discussed briefly. *D. H. Lehmer.*

Referred to in D32-57, D32-65.

D32-49 (16, 998l)

Mordell, L. J. Integer solutions of cubic equations in three variables. Rend. Mat. e Appl. (5) **14**, 431–438 (1955).

This is an expository paper reviewing the work of the author and others on cubic Diophantine equations in three variables with integral coefficients. *I. Niven.*

D32-50 (17, 461b)

Kesava Menon, P. On the equation $X^3+Y^3=U^3+V^3$. Math. Student **23** (1955), 101–103.

All solutions in integers of $X^3+Y^3=U^3+V^3$ are obtained explicitly in terms of four unrestricted integer parameters. We omit the details. The method involves the quadratic field generated by the cube roots of unity. [The following minor error occurs in the final solution: equations (8) lack the factor 3 in the terms qr and ps.]
I. Niven (Berkeley, Calif.).

D32-51 (17, 464c)

Skolem, Th. Einige Bemerkungen über die Auffindung der rationalen Punkte auf gewissen algebraischen Gebilden. Math. Z. **63** (1955), 295–312.

There are, first of all, a few remarks on rational points upon a rational unicursal curve, and others concerning the points of such a curve belonging to an algebraic field and the existence of parametric solutions, accompanied by a number of interesting examples, where the rational points are given by transcendental functions of a parameter varying in a module. The rational points on a cubic rational surface are then studied, considering both the singular non-ruled surfaces and the non-singular ones. Particularly noteworthy is the proof for the singular cubic surfaces of Mordell's conjecture [Publ. Math. Debrecen **1** (1949), 1–6; MR **11**, 82], according to which the equation $f(x,y,z,u)=0$, where f is a cubic form, has rational solutions if the congruence $f(x,y,z,u)\equiv 0$ is solvable for every module.

Also a very simple proof is given of the theorem [B. Segre, J. London Math. Soc. **18** (1943), 226–233; MR **6**, 37] which affirms that every rational cubic surface containing a rational simple point has an infinity of these points. The result is obtained by a geometric construction, which is then applied for solving Ryley's equation $x^3+y^3+z^3=r$; by another simple method, solutions of

$$xy(x+y)+z^3=r,\quad x^3+y^2+z^2=r,\quad x^3+y^3+z^2=r$$

are also deduced. Finally, the cubic equation

$$x^3+2y^3+3z^3+6u^3=0$$

is solved completely in the rational field, by applying the transformation

$$x:y:z:u=-t_0t_1+2t_2^2:-t_1^2+t_0t_2:-t_1t_3:t_2t_3,$$

which reduces it to the cubic equation

$$t_0^3+2t_1^3+4t_2^3-6t_0t_1t_2+3t_3^3=0;$$

the success of the method is due to the fact that, while the first cubic surface is non-singular, the second one possesses three (irrational cubic conjugate) double points; and the author asks whether the method can be extended. [The reviewer will give an answer to this question in a forthcoming paper.] *B. Segre* (Rome).

Citations: MR 6, 37g = D32-14; MR 11, 82h = D32-28.
Referred to in D36-33, G35-31.

D32-52 (17, 711e)

Schinzel, A.; et Sierpinski, W. Sur l'équation $x^2+y^2+1=xyz$. Matematiche, Catania **10** (1955), 30–36.

It is proved by the method of descent that $x^2+y^2+1=xyz$ has no solutions in integers except when $z=3$, in which case all solutions are given essentially by consecutive pairs x, y of the sequence obtained by deleting the even-numbered terms of the Fibonacci sequence. Applications are given of the theorem and the method of proof. It is shown that $u^2-(z^2-4)v^2=-4$ has solutions only if $z=3$. The set of all pairs x, y such that x divides y^2+1 and y divides x^2+1 is obtained; this result, in more general form, was derived in a different way by W. H. Mills [Pacific J. Math. **3** (1953), 209–220; MR **14**, 950]. Finally it is established that for any given $n\geqq 2$ there are infinitely many pairs of integers x, y such that x divides y^n+1 and y divides x^n+1. *I. Niven* (Eugene, Ore.).

Citations: MR 14, 950e = D20-9.
Referred to in D48-29.

D32-53 (17, 712a)

Mills, W. H. Certain Diophantine equations linear in one unknown. Canad. J. Math. **8** (1956), 5–12.

Let

$$F(x,y)=\alpha x^2+\beta xy+\gamma y^2+\delta x+\varepsilon y+\xi$$

where α, β, γ, δ, ϵ, ξ are integers and $\alpha|(\beta,\delta)$, $\gamma|(\beta,\varepsilon)$. If x_1, y_1 are integers and $F(x_1,y_1)=0$, the other solutions x_0, y_2 of $F(x,y)=0$, $F(x_1,y)=0$ are also integers. In this way each integer solution of $F(x,y)=0$ gives rise, in general, to a sequence of infinitely many. This process goes back at least to A. Hurwitz [Math. Werke, Bd. II, Birkhauser, Basel, 1933, pp. 410–421; ignored by the author] and has been recently exploited by several workers [E. S. Barnes, J. London Math. Soc. **28** (1953), 242–244; MR **14**, 725; A. and R. Brauer, Jber. Deutsch. Math. Verein. **36** (1927), Abt. 2, 90–92; K. Goldberg, M. Newman, E. G. Straus and J. D. Swift, Arch. Math. **5** (1954), 12–18; MR **15**, 857; W. H. Mills, Pacific J. Math. **3** (1953), 209–220; Proc. Amer. Math. Soc. **5** (1954), 473–475; MR **14**, 950; **16**, 13]. The author considers $F(x, y)=N(x, y)-zD(x, y)$, where $N(x, y)=ax^2+bxy+cy^2+dx+ey+f$, $D(x, y)=pxy+qx+ry+s$ and z is a variable integer. Here $a, \cdots, s$ are integers and

$$a|(b, d, p, q), c|(b, e, p, r).$$

A sequence of solutions is said to be of type I if it contains a solution of $N(x, y)=D(x, y)=0$; of type II if it contains a solution with $y=-q/p$ or with $x=-r/p$. If sequences types I, II exist, they exist for infinitely many values of z. An infinite-descent argument shows that other sequences of solutions exist for at most a finite number of z. The author specifies those values of z for which infinitely many sequences of solutions exist. He shows that if a sequence is periodic its period is one of 1, 2, 3, 4, 6, 8, 12, all these cases actually occurring.

J. W. S. Cassels (Cambridge, England).

Citations: MR 14, 725f = D32-38; MR 14, 950e = D20-9; MR 15, 857a = E16-17; MR 16, 13e = D32-44.

D32-54 (17, 1185f)

Mordell, L. J. The diophantine equation $x^3+y^3+z^3+kxyz=0$. Colloque sur la Théorie des Nombres, Bruxelles, 1955, pp. 67–76. Georges Thone, Liège; Masson and Cie, Paris, 1956.

The equation of the title is shown to have, for $k=1$, no solutions in relatively prime integers (x, y, z) other than the trivial ones $(1, 1, -1)$, $(1, -1, -1)$, $(1, -1, 0)$ and the obvious permutation thereof. For $k=-5$ there are no solutions other than $(1, -1, 0)$ $(1, 1, 2)$, $(-1, -1, -2)$ and their permutations. These results apparently fill a hiatus left by A. Hurwitz [Vierteljschr. Naturforsch. Ges. Zürich **62** (1917), 207–229] in his study of homogeneous cubic equations. *I. Niven* (Eugene, Ore.).

Referred to in D40-31.

D32-55 (17, 1187c)

Lehmer, D. H. On the Diophantine equation $x^3+y^3+z^3=1$. J. London Math. Soc. **31** (1956), 275–280.

The author shows how the theory of Pell's equation can be used for constructing infinite sequences of integral solutions (x, y, z) of $x^3+y^3+z^3=1$. Every such sequence is obtained from a set of recurrence formulas of the type $x_{k+1}=ax_k-x_{k-1}+b$, $y_{k+1}=ay_k-y_{k-1}+b$, $z_{k+1}=az_k-z_{k-1}+c$, and for every such sequence $1-z_k$ is a constant integral multiple of x_k+y_k. In particular, starting from the known parametric solution $(9t^4, 3t-9t^4, 1-9t^3)$, he derives an infinite sequence of new parametric solutions, the simplest being

$$(2^4 3^5 t^{10}-3^3 5t^4,\ -2^4 3^5 t^{10}-2^4 3^4 t^7-3^4 t^4+3t,\ 2^4 3^5 t^9+2^3 3^4 t^6-3^2 t^3+1).$$

N. G. de Bruijn (Amsterdam).

Referred to in D32-65, D36-42.

D32-56 (18, 641e)

Oppenheim, A. On the Diophantine equation

$$x^2+y^2+z^2+2xyz=1.$$

Amer. Math. Monthly **64** (1957), 101–103.

The solution of the equation $x^2+y^2+z^2+2xyz=1$ in rationals was recently given by the reviewer [same Monthly **62** (1955), 251–252]. The present note gives the most general solution in rational integers. If the triple of integers p, q, r has a g.c.d. equal to unity, with one of these integers equal to the sum of the other two, then $x=\pm\cosh p\theta$, $y=\pm\cosh q\theta$, $z=\pm\cosh r\theta$, where

$$\theta=\log(u+(u^2-1)^{\frac{1}{2}}),$$

u an integer $\geqq 1$, gives the most general non-trivial solution in rational integers. The ambiguous signs must be chosen so that $xyz=-1$. [See also Marsh, ibid. **64** (1957), 122, wherein the most general solution is found by reducing the problem to a Pell equation.]

I. A. Barnett (Cincinnati, Ohio).

D32-57 (18, 641f)

Mordell, L. J. Note on the integer solutions of

$$z^2-k^2=ax^3+by^3.$$

Ganita **5** (1954), 103–104 (1955).

The author considers the equation in the title in the case in which $k=4abc^3$, and proves that in this case there are infinitely many solutions in integers (x, y, z). The proof consists in transforming the given equation into

$$A(t^3+u^3)+Bv^3=Bc^3$$

which by the author's previous paper [J. London Math. Soc. **30** (1955), 111–113; MR **16**, 798] has an infinity non-trivial integer solutions. The reader should be on the look out for two misprints. *D. H. Lehmer.*

Citations: MR 16, 798a = D32-48.

D32-58 (18, 718c)

Thébault, V. Equations diophantiennes. Mathesis **65** (1956), 421–423.

The author gives special parametric solutions of four diophantine equations. As an example we mention the equation $ab(a+b)=cd(c+d)$ with the solutions

$$a=xy(x+y),\ b=(z-x-y)(xy+xz-z^2),$$
$$c=x(z^2-xy-xz),\ d=y[(x-z)^2-yz].$$

At last some solutions of $A^4+B^4+C^4=D^4+E^4$ are noted. *W. Ljunggren* (Blindern).

D32-59 (18, 873c)

Christofferson, Stig. Über eine Klasse von kubischen diophantischen Gleichungen mit drei Unbekannten. Ark. Mat. **3** (1957), 355–364.

The author considers the Diophantine equation

$$(*)\qquad u^3+ab^2v^3+a^2bw^3-3abuvw=c$$

in integers u, v, w when the integers a, b, c are given. This may be regarded as an equation $\mathrm{Norm}(u+v\alpha+w\beta)=c$ where $\alpha=(ab^2)^{\frac{1}{3}}>0$ and $\beta=(a^2b)^{\frac{1}{3}}>0$ are numbers of the same cubic field. In the first part it is shown, by a direct modification of a method of Dirichlet, that when $c=1$ there is always a solution in which, u, v, w are less than a rather elaborate bound which is given explicitly in terms of a, b. In the second part the author shows that if c is positive and $u+v\alpha+w\beta>c^{\frac{1}{3}}$ then $u\geqq 0$, $v\geqq 0$, $w\geqq 0$ with strict inequality if either $c\geqq 16$ or $u+v\alpha+w\beta\geqq(4c)^{\frac{1}{3}}$. An example is given with $c=15$, $u+v\alpha+w\beta>c^{\frac{1}{3}}$ but $uvw=0$. In the third part it is shown that if $\varepsilon>1$ is the fundamental unit of the ring of $u+v\alpha+w\beta$ then to every solution of (*) there is an 'associated' solution in which u, $v\alpha$, $w\beta$ lie between the bounds $-\frac{1}{3}(2-\varepsilon^{-1})(c\varepsilon)^{\frac{1}{3}}$ and $(c\varepsilon)^{\frac{1}{3}}$. This is better than the direct application of the well-known bounds of Hecke [Vorlesungen über die Theorie der algebraischen Zahlen, 2. Aufl., Akademische Verlagsgesellschaft, Leipzig, 1954; MR **16**, 571] and Nagell [Math. Z. **34** (1931), 183–193, p. 191] but is obtained by an immediate modification of their general method applied to this particular case. *J. W. S. Cassels.*

Citations: MR 16, 571b = R02-14.

D32-60 **(19, 15b)**

Ginatempo, Nicola. Sulla risoluzione in numeri interi della equazione $x^4-8y^4-8y^2z=z^2$ Atti Soc. Peloritana Sci. Fis. Mat. Nat. **2** (1955–56), 13–25.

A proof at great length that the complete solution of the title equation in integers is equivalent to the complete solution in rationals h, ω of $2h^3+4h=\omega^2$, and also to the finding of all integral Pythagorean triangles with sides M, P, Q (so $M^2=P^2+Q^2$) such that $P+Q$ is a square and $M-(P-Q)$ is twice a square. *J. W. S. Cassels.*

D32-61 **(19, 730c)**

Godwin, H. J. A note on $x^3+y^3+z^3=1$. J. London Math. Soc. **32** (1957), 501–503.

This paper supplements a note by the reviewer on the diophantine equation in the title. The sets of solutions for which $\alpha=(1-z)/(x+y)$ has a fixed value are recursively related via the theory of the Pell equation to the indeterminate equation

$$3v^2-(4\alpha^3-1)u^2=4(1-\alpha^3).$$

The author considers the general case of rational α which lead to integer solutions (x, y, z). For the case $\alpha=4$ a new set of solutions represented by $x=67402$, $y=-83802$, $z=65601$ is found. For $\alpha=7$, four new sets are added to the four already known. *D. H. Lehmer.*

D32-62 **(19, 942a)**

Schwartz, H.; and Muhly, H. T. On a class of cubic Diophantine equations. J. London Math. Soc. **32** (1957), 379–382.

The equation referred to in the title is $x^2+y^2+z^2-axyz=b$, where all the letters stand for integers and $a>0$, $b\geqq 0$. This had been studied by A. Hurwitz in the case $b=0$ [Arch. Math. Phys. (3) **11** (1907), 185–196]. Hurwitz remarked, without proof, that similar results could be obtained for the case $b>0$. The case $b>0$ was treated, in passing, by Mordell in a recent paper [J. London Math. Soc. **28** (1953), 500–510; MR **15**, 102]; this treatment contains an oversight which is briefly corrected in the paper reviewed below. The authors of this paper give a complete treatment of the case $b>0$ along the lines of Mordell's argument and they find that Hurwitz's conjectures were correct, with a few exceptions. They show that, except for two exceptions, if a solution with at most one number x, y, or z equal to zero exists, then all such solutions can be obtained from a finite set of "fundamental" solutions by a sequence of so-called elementary operations. The exceptions are $a=1$, $b=4$ and $a=2$, $b=1$; in each of these cases there are infinitely many fundamental solutions. It is also proved that, except for the case $a=1$, $b=2$ (where the set of solutions is finite), the existence of one solution with at most one number x, y, or z equal to zero implies the existence of infinitely many solutions. *H. W. Brinkmann* (Swarthmore, Pa.).

Citations: MR 15, 102b = D32-40.

D32-63 **(19, 942b)**

Mordell, L. J. Corrigendum: Integer solutions of the equation $x^2+y^2+z^2+2xyz=n$. J. London Math. Soc. **32** (1957), 383.

This is a correction of the oversight in the paper mentioned above; the resulting treatment of the Diophantine equation in question is still incomplete. *H. W. Brinkmann* (Swarthmore, Pa.).

D32-64 **(20# 4525)**

Boico, I. Note sur le théorème de Fermat. Gaz. Mat. Fiz. Ser. A (N.S.) **10**(63) (1958), 609–612. (Romanian. French and Russian summaries)

Etant donné que l'équation $x^3+y^3=z^3$ n'a pas de solutions en nombres entiers, l'auteur donne quelques solutions de l'équation $x^3+y^3=z^3+1$ et montre qu'on peut obtenir des solutions en nombres entiers arbitrairement grands. *Résumé de l'auteur*

D32-65 **(22# 4674)**

Chandra, K. R. A note on the integer solutions of Mordell's cubic $ax^3+by^3=z^2-k^2$. J. London Math. Soc. **35** (1960), 78–80.

Various cases of the equation in the title are considered and for each it is proved that the equation has an infinity of parametric solutions (x, y, z). Some examples are

$$ax^3+y^3 = z^2-c^{18},$$
$$ax^3+by^3 = z^2-(b^2c^3)^2,$$
$$ax^3+by^3 = z^2-(4abc^3)^2.$$

The latter case, for example, is transformed into a special case of $A(x^3+y^3)+B(z^3-c^3)=0$, which in turn gives rise to $d(x^3+y^3)+z^3=1$. This is a generalization of the case $d=1$ studied recently by Mordell [same J. **30** (1955), 111–113; MR **16**, 798] and by the reviewer [same J. **31** (1956), 275–280; MR **17**, 1187] and is shown to possess an infinite set of parametric solutions. *D. H. Lehmer* (Berkeley, Calif.)

Citations: MR 16, 798a = D32-48; MR 17, 1187c = D32-55.

D32-66 **(24# A1248)**

Schinzel, A.

On the equation $x^4+ax^2y^2+by^4=z^2$. **(Polish. Russian and English summaries)**

Prace Mat. **4** (1960), 53–57.

The author proves the following theorem. Let $\langle a, b\rangle\neq\langle -3, 3\rangle$, $b=2$, 4 or p^α (where p is a prime >2), $\Delta=a^2-4b$. If for each $d\neq 1$, $d|\Delta/(a, 2)$, the system

$$q^2-br^2 = dx^2,$$
$$2qr+ar^2 = dy^2,$$
$$q^2+aqr+br^2 = dz$$

has no solutions in positive integers x, y, z, q, r satisfying $(x, z)=(y, z)=(q, r)=1$, then the equation

$$x^4+ax^2y^2+by^4 = z^2$$

has no solutions in positive integers with $(x, b)=1$. *S. Knapowski* (Poznań)

D32-67 **(24# A3118)**

Sierpiński, W.

Sur un propriété des nombres tétraédraux.

Elem. Math. **17** (1962), 29–30.

This note contains an elementary proof that there exists an infinity of pairs of tetrahedral (pyramidal) numbers whose sum is also a tetrahedral number. *R. D. James* (Vancouver, B.C.)

Referred to in D32-74, D32-80.

D32-68 **(25# 3413)**

Swinnerton-Dyer, H. P. F.

Two special cubic surfaces.

Mathematika **9** (1962), 54–56.

One might conjecture that a cubic surface which has points in every p-adic field must also have rational points. A counter-example is furnished by the surface whose equation is $t(t+x)(2t+x)=\prod(x+\theta y+\theta^2 z)$, where the product on the right is taken over the roots of the equation $\theta^3-7\theta^2+14\theta-7=0$. There is also an example of a cubic surface consisting of two parts, one of which contains an infinite number of rational points and the other contains no rational points. *G. B. Huff* (Athens, Ga.)

Referred to in D32-73, D36-33, G25-23.

D32-69 (26# 1279)

Kiss, Ernest

Résolution en nombres naturels de l'équation diophantienne $x^2+y^3=z^4$. (Romanian. Russian and French summaries)

Studia Univ. Babeş-Bolyai Ser. I Math. Phys. **1960**, *no.* 1, 15–19.

Author's summary: "L'auteur recherche des solutions relativement premières pour l'équation. Il démontre que celle-ci admet une infinité de solutions de ce genre et il expose la manière de les obtenir, en donnant aussi des exemples numériques."

D32-70 (26# 4957)

Sierpiński, W.

Trois nombres tétraédraux en progression arithmétique.

Elem. Math. **18** (1963), 54–55.

Author's summary: "Le but de cette note est de donner une démonstration élémentaire de la proposition suivante: Théorème. Il existe une infinité de progressions arithmétiques formées de trois nombres tétraédraux distincts."

D32-71 (26# 6115)

Wunderlich, M.

Certain properties of pyramidal and figurate numbers.

Math. Comp. **16** (1962), 482–486.

The author discusses the equation

$$a^3+b^3+c^3 = a+b+c \tag{1}$$

and lists a large number of integral solutions. His computations led the reviewer and others to prove that (1) has an infinity of "non-trivial" solutions (the same result has been proved by Sierpiński [Elem. Math. **16** (1961), 27–30; MR **23** #A2374]). The author also raises some interesting unsolved questions related to the equation (1). *S. Chowla* (Boulder, Colo.)

Citations: MR 23# A2374 = E24-85.
Referred to in D32-74, D32-80, D64-27.

D32-72 (29# 4733)

Oppenheim, A.

The rational integral solution of the equation $a(x^3+y^3)=b(u^3+v^3)$ and allied Diophantine equations.

Acta Arith. **9** (1964), 221–226.

A method of solving the Diophantine equation

$$a(x^3+y^3) = b(u^3+v^3), \qquad (a, b) = 1, ab \neq 0,$$

in rational integers x, y, u, v, is presented. Apart from exceptional cases when $a(x+y)^3=b(u+v)^3$, the remaining solutions are associated with those of a diagonal ternary quadratic equation

$$X^2+3Y^2-3nZ^2 = 0$$

by means of the expression

$$4g^2\{a(x^3+y^3)-b(u^3+v^3)\}-k(a\lambda^3-b\mu^3)\{X^2+3Y^2-3nZ^2\},$$

which vanishes identically under the substitutions

$$(X, Y, Z) = (gk, e, f), \qquad n = ab\lambda\mu,$$
$$x+y = k\lambda, \qquad u+v = k\mu,$$
$$g(x-y) = e\lambda+bf\mu^2, \qquad g(u-v) = e\mu+af\lambda^2.$$

It is indicated that a similar method applies to more general equations of the types:

$$aL^n(x, y)Q(x, y) = bL^n(u, v)Q(u, v) \tag{1}$$

when n is an integer $\neq -2$, L is an integral linear form and Q is an integral quadratic form,

$$p(x, u)Q(x, y) = q(x, u)Q(u, v), \tag{2}$$

where p and q are integers, depending on x and u. *J. H. H. Chalk* (Toronto, Ont.)

Referred to in D36-34.

D32-73 (30# 58)

Mordell, L. J.

On the conjecture for the rational points on a cubic surface.

J. London Math. Soc. **40** (1965), 149–158.

The author gives three families of cubic surfaces which have no rational points, though they have non-singular p-adic points for every p. They are all close relatives of the specimen produced by Swinnerton-Dyer [Mathematika **9** (1962), 54–56; MR **25** #3413]. *B. J. Birch* (Manchester)

Citations: MR 25# 3413 = D32-68.

D32-74 (30# 1094)

Edgar, Hugh Maxwell

Some remarks on the Diophantine equation $x^3+y^3+z^3=x+y+z$.

Proc. Amer. Math. Soc. **16** (1965), 148–153.

The author proves that if A, B, C, D are given non-zero integers with $(A, B)=(C, D)=1$ and $C|A^2$, then the Diophantine equation $A(Cx^3-Dx)=B(z^3-z)$ has at most $5\sum(2\sigma(c)+1)$ solutions in positive integers x, z, where the summation is over all $c|B(A^2D^3-CB^2)A^3C^3$ and $\sigma(c)=\sum_{d|c} d$. The method is a generalization of an observation of the reviewer [Amer. Math. Monthly **69** (1962), 637–638] that $2(x^3-x)=z^3-z$ has only two solutions in positive integers. The bound is obtained by applying theorems of Delone (Delaunay) and Nagell on the solutions of

$$pX^3+qX^2Y+rXY^2+sY^3 = 1,$$

and can be improved by quoting stronger results of these authors than those cited in the paper [see, e.g., B. N. Delone and D. K. Faddeev, *The theory of irrationalities of the third degree*, Section 75, Amer. Math. Soc., Providence, R.I., 1964; MR **28** #3955].

The author also constructs two new infinite classes of solutions of

$$x^3+y^3+z^3 = x+y+z,$$

$x>0$, $y>0$, $z<0$, modelled on an idea of Chowla for reducing construction of such classes satisfying further side conditions to the solution of a Pellian. The author cites an unpublished paper of Chowla and others, apparently unaware of its anticipation by W. Sierpiński [Elem. Math. **17** (1962), 29–30; MR **24** #A3118], who constructed a similar infinite class of solutions.

{The paper by M. Wunderlich [Math. Comp. **16** (1962), 482–486; MR **26** #6115] should also be added to the bibliography.} *S. L. Segal* (Rochester, N.Y.)

Citations: MR 24# A3118 = D32-67; MR 26# 6115 = D32-71; MR 28# 3955 = R02-4.
Referred to in D32-80.

D32-75 (30# 1969)

Sierpiński, W.

Sur un problème de A. Makowski concernant les nombres tétraédraux.

Publ. Inst. Math. (Beograd) (N.S.) **2** (**16**) (1962), 115–119 (1963).

A. Makowski has raised the following question. Does there exist an infinite number of solutions in positive integers x, y, z of the equation

$$(*) \qquad T_x + T_y = kT_z,$$

where k is a given positive integer and

$$T_n = n(n+1)(n+2)/6?$$

The author proves that there exist infinitely many values of k for which (*) has infinitely many solutions; in particular, (*) has infinitely many solutions for $1 \leqq k \leqq 7$. It is noted that A. Schinzel has proved that (*) has infinitely many solutions for $k = 8, 9, 10$.

L. Carlitz (Durham, N.C.)

D32-76 (30# 3864)

Szymiczek, Casimir

L'équation $uv = w^2$ en nombres triangulaires.

Publ. Inst. Math. (Beograd) (N.S.) **3** (**17**) (1963), 139–141.

The author proves the existence of infinitely many geometrical progressions formed of three distinct triangular numbers. According to L. E. Dickson [*History of the theory of numbers*, Vol. II, p. 36, Carnegie Inst., Washington, D.C., 1920] a similar proof was given by A. Gérardin [Sphinx-Oedipe **9** (1914), 75, 145–146].

A. Schinzel (Warsaw)

D32-77 (31# 119)

Gardiner, V. L.; Lazarus, R. B.; Stein, P. R.

Solutions of the diophantine equation $x^3 + y^3 = z^3 - d$.

Math. Comp. **18** (1964), 408–413.

At the suggestion of L. J. Mordell, who wished to know if the equation $x^3 + y^3 + z^3 = 3$ has any solution other than (1, 1, 1) and (4, 4, −5), the reviewer and M. F. C. Woollett [J. London Math. Soc. **30** (1955), 101–110; MR **16**, 797] investigated on EDSAC all solutions of $x^3 + y^3 + z^3 = d$ for $0 < d \leqq 100$ and $|x| \leqq |y| \leqq |z| \leqq 3200$, and listed primitive solutions found. The paper now reviewed describes an extended search for $|d| < 1000$, d not a cube, and $0 < x \leqq y \leqq 2^{16}$, for solutions of the equation $x^3 + y^3 = z^3 - d$.

Neither search gives any new solution for $d = 3$, but the list of solutions indicates several interesting cases where even one solution is lacking, apart from $d = 9m \pm 4$, when obviously no solution is possible. It is suggested that values of d may possibly, even probably, exist, for which there is no solution (x, y, z) in integers. A list of the solutions found has been deposited in the UMT File of Math. Comp.; the paper gives a table listing the number of solutions N_+ (with $d > 0$) and N_- (with $d < 0$), for relevant d from 2 to 1000.

J. C. P. Miller (Cambridge, England)

Citations: MR 16, 797e = D32-47.

D32-78 (31# 5834)

Ögmundsson, Vilhjálmur

A complete integral solution of $x^3 + y^3 = u^3 + v^3$.

Nordisk Mat. Tidskr. **13** (1965), 88–90.

Author's summary: "Apart from the trivial solution $x = -y$, $u = -v$, a complete integral solution of the title equation is given in terms of three parameters. In contrast with earlier methods, based on quadratic fields, the author utilizes a simple algebra of order two."

D32-79 (32# 5589)

Machado Cardoso, Jayme

Solution of $X^2 - Y^2 = Z^3$ in integers. (Portuguese)

Gac. Mat. (Madrid) (1) **17** (1965), 119–120.

D32-80 (32# 5590)

Oppenheim, A. [Oppenheim, Alexander]

On the Diophantine equation $x^3 + y^3 + z^3 = x + y + z$.

Proc. Amer. Math. Soc. **17** (1966), 493–496.

The author shows how, given a solution of the equation in the title, others may be generated from it by use of a classical result on indefinite binary quadratic forms. In particular, if $|h| \geqq 2$, any trivial solution $(x, y, z) = (h, 1, -h)$ generates by the author's method infinitely many non-trivial solutions. The method rests on the fact that if integers m, n, a, c are defined by

$$x + y = am, \quad z = -cm, \quad x - y = n, \quad (a, c) = 1, \quad m \geqq 1,$$

then one has the identity

$$4(x^3 + y^3 + z^3 - x - y - z) = m(3an^2 + (a^3 - 4c^3)m^2 - 4(a - c)).$$

Isolated infinite classes of solutions have been found earlier by Sierpiński [Elem. Math. **17** (1962), 29–30; MR **24** #A3118] and Edgar [Proc. Amer. Math. Soc. **16** (1965), 148–153; MR **30** #1094].

As the author remarks, the difficult problem now remains, namely, determining criteria for when two solutions can be connected by a finite number of binary forms in the manner described in the paper.

{Reviewer's remarks: The paper of Chowla and others referred to by the author (following Edgar) has never appeared, having been anticipated by Sierpiński's paper cited above. A table of all solutions of the title equation for $|z| \leqq 12825$, $x > 0$, $y > 0$, is given (in slightly different notation) by M. Wunderlich [Math. Comp. **16** (1962), 482–486; MR **26** #6115].}

S. L. Segal (Vienna)

Citations: MR 24# A3118 = D32-67; MR 26# 6115 = D32-71; MR 30# 1094 = D32-74.

Referred to in D32-86.

D32-81 (34# 1267)

Mordell, L. J.

On some ternary quartic diophantine equations.

Elem. Math. **21** (1966), 89–90.

This note presents the following theorem: The equation $z^2 = U_1{}^2 + U_2U_3$, where $U_r = a_rx^2 + h_rxy + b_ry^2 + f_ry + g_rx$ $(r = 1, 2, 3)$ and the coefficients are integers, has an infinity of integer solutions if for either $r = 2$ or 3, $h_r{}^2 - 4a_rb_r > 0$ and is not a perfect square and U_2 or U_3 is absolutely irreducible.

W. T. Scott (Tempe, Ariz.)

D32-82 (34# 4201)

Mordell, L. J.

The diophantine equation $z^2 = ax^4 + 2bx^2y^2 + cy^4$.

Math. Ann. **168** (1967), 138–141.

If x, y, z, w are integers with $x^2 + y^2 + z^2 + w^2 \equiv 0$ (8), then x, y, z, w are all even. The author exploits this, to show that certain Diophantine equations $z^2 = ax^4 + 2bx^2y^2 + cy^4$ have no integral solution with $xy \neq 0$. For instance, this is so of the equation $z^2 = (lx^2 + my^2)^2 - k(l_1x^2 + m_1y^2)^2$ if l, m, k are all positive, $l \equiv m \equiv -1$ (8), all the positive odd factors of $\delta = lm_1 - l_1m$ and of k are $\equiv 1$ (8), and k is divisible by an even power of 2.

B. J. Birch (Oxford)

D32-83 (35# 1545)

Mordell, L. J.

The diophantine equation $x^4 + my^4 = z^2$.

Quart. J. Math. Oxford Ser. (2) **18** (1967), 1–6.

The following theorem is proved. Let $m > 0$ be a prime $\equiv 1$ (mod 8) such that 2 is a non-biquadratic residue of m. Then the set of equations $ax^4 + cy^4 = z^2$, $ac = m$, $-4m$, $(x, y) = 1$, where a and c are rational numbers, includes only two essentially different ones, namely, $x^4+my^4=z^2$ and $x^4-4my^4=z^2$. These two equations have only the integer solutions $x=\pm 1$, $y=0$, $z=\pm 1$.

This generalizes a theorem of H. Reichardt [J. Reine Angew. Math. **184** (1942), 12–18; MR **5**, 141]. The proof is simple and elementary. The paper contains further some remarks concerning related results due to C. E. Lind ["Untersuchungen über die rationalen Punkte der ebenen kubischen Kurven vom Geschlecht Eins", Thesis, Univ. Uppsala, Uppsala, 1940; MR **9**, 225] and K. Heegner [Math. Z. **56** (1952), 227–253; MR **14**, 725].

W. Ljunggren (Oslo)

Citations: MR 5, 141c = D32-13; MR 9, 225b = G05-16; MR 14, 725j = R14-23.

D32-84 (37# 2685)

Swinnerton-Dyer, H. P. F.

$A^4+B^4=C^4+D^4$ revisited.

J. London Math. Soc. **43** (1968), 149–151.

The following theorem is proved. Given any real solution of $A^4+B^4=C^4+D^4$, we can find a rational solution as close as we please to it.

B. Stolt (Stockholm)

D32-85 (38# 4400)

Blanpain, M.

Sur le problème de Zarankiewicz.

Elem. Math. **23** (1968), 135.

Let n denote any positive integer and $t_n=\frac{1}{2}n(n+1)$ the nth triangular number. The problem mentioned in the title consists then in determining all x, y, z satisfying the equation (1) $t_x{}^2+t_y{}^2=t_z{}^2$. It is proved that (1) is impossible if at least two of the integers x, y, z are consecutive numbers. In the short proof use is made of results due to T. Nagell and the reviewer and J. W. S. Cassels. See, for example, W. J. LeVeque [*Topics in number theory*, Vol. II, Addison-Wesley, Reading, Mass., 1956; MR **18**, 283] and Cassels [Proc. London Math. Soc. (3) **14a** (1965), 55–57; MR **31** #2200].

W. Ljunggren (Oslo)

Citations: MR 18, 283b = Z01-38; MR 31# 2200 = D24-46.

Referred to in D32-89.

D32-86 (39# 126)

Oppenheim, A. [Oppenheim, Alexander]

On the Diophantine equation $x^3+y^3-z^3=px+py-qz$.

Univ. Beograd. Publ. Elektrotehn. Fak. Ser. Mat. Fiz. *No.* 230–241 (1968), 33–35.

Continuing some earlier work [Proc. Amer. Math. Soc. **17** (1966), 493–496; MR **32** #5590; erratum, MR **32**, p. 1755], the author obtains parametric solutions for the Diophantine equation $x^3-x+y^3-y=z^3-z$, and under suitable conditions on p and q, for the Diophantine equation $x^3+y^3-z^3=p(x+y)-qz$. These polynomial solutions, while incomplete, appear to be the first which have been published.

S. L. Segal (Rochester, N.Y.)

Citations: MR 32# 5590 = D32-80.

D32-87 (39# 6819)

Lal, M.; Russell, W.; Blundon, W. J.

A note on sums of four cubes.

Math. Comp. **23** (1969), 423–424.

An investigation by the authors on an IMB 1620, Model 1, shows that there are now just 19 values of k in the range $0<k<10^3$ for which no solution of $x^3+y^3+2z^3=k$, for $|x|$, $|y|$, and $|z|<10^5$, is known. These are listed and are: 76, 148, 183, 230, 253, 356, 418, 428, 445, 482, 491, 519, 580, 671, 734, 788, 923, 931, and 967.

E. Karst (Tucson, Ariz.)

D32-88 (40# 2604)

Zelichowicz, W.

On the equation $(x^2-1)(z^2-1)=(y^2-1)^2$.

Prace Mat. **13** (1969), 113–118.

The Diophantine equation in question is studied for the case x, y and z even. An error in the last equation invalidates the result.

W. H. Mills (Princeton, N.J.)

D32-89 (40# 7195)

Blanpain, M. E.

Sur l'équation diophantienne $(x^2-1)^2+(y^2-1)^2=(z^2-1)^2$.

Elem. Math. **24** (1969), 134–135.

Assuming $x<y<z$ it is proved that the equation of the title has no solutions in rational, positive integers x, y, z if (i) $y-x=1$ or (ii) $y-x$ or $z-y$ or $z-x=2$. In case $z-y=1$ there is the unique solution $(x, y, z)=(10, 13, 14)$. The proof is elementary. However, use is made of some deep results due to Ljunggren-Cassels in case (i) and due to R. T. Bumby if $z-y=1$ [J. W. S. Cassels, Proc. London Math. Soc. (3) **14a** (1965), 55–57; MR **31** #2200; R. T. Bumby, Math. Scand. **21** (1967), 144–148 (1968); MR **39** #6818]. For a related equation see the author's paper [Elem. Math. **23** (1968), 135; MR **38** #4400].

W. Ljunggren (Oslo)

Citations: MR 31# 2200 = D24-46; MR 38# 4400 = D32-85; MR 39# 6818 = D24-80.

D32-90 (40# 7196)

Shimizu, Tamon

On the Diophantus equation $x^3+y^3=mz^2$.

J. College Arts Sci. Chiba Univ. **5** (1968), *no.* 2, 205–206 (1969).

The integral solutions of $x^3+y^3=z^2$ are obtained in parametric form by factoring the left-hand side in the field $K((-3)^{1/2})$. Multiplying these solutions by m, one gets the solutions of the equation of the title.

B. Stolt (Stockholm)

D32-91 (42# 1762)

Ginatempo, Nicola

Risoluzione in numeri interi della equazione pitagorica cubica. (English summary)

Atti Soc. Peloritana Sci. Fis. Mat. Natur. **14** (1968), 591–594.

The equation mentioned in the title is $x_1{}^3+x_2{}^3+x_3{}^3-3x_1x_2x_3=x_4{}^3$ and rational solutions are meant. A parametric solution is given in the form $qx_1=a^3+b^3+c^3+6abc$, $qx_2=3(a^2b+b^2c+c^2a)$, $qx_3=3(a^2c+b^2a+c^2b)$, $qx_4=a^3+b^3+c^3-3abc$, where q, a, b, c are integers, $q\neq 0$.

The paper has numerous misprints.

D. H. Lehmer (Berkeley, Calif.)

D32-92 (43# 6155)

Subbarao, M. V.

Perfect triangles.

Amer. Math. Monthly **78** (1971), 384–385.

Let $N(\lambda)$ denote the number of triangles (a, b, c) whose integer-valued sides a, b, c add up to λ times their area. The author proves that $N(\lambda)$ is finite for all positive values of λ; moreover, $N(\lambda)=0$ for all $\lambda>\sqrt{8}$ with the exception of $N(2\sqrt{3})=1$ (in which case the triangle is $(2, 2, 2)$). Since it is known that $N(1)=5$ and $N(2)=1$ this completes the problem on perfect triangles. The author adds that it would be interesting to consider a similar problem for a quadrilateral, and in general, a polygon of n sides.

E. M. Horadam (Armidale)

D36 HIGHER DIMENSIONAL CUBIC AND QUARTIC VARIETIES

See also Sections D72, E76, G35.

See also reviews D32-32, D32-58, D48-32, D48-54, D99-16, E76-15, E76-17, G35-8, G35-16, P04-48.

D36-1 (1, 65f)

Gloden, A. Sur une méthode de résolution d'équations diophantiennes homogènes du troisième degré. Mathesis **53**, 233–235 (1939).

Referred to in D40-13.

D36-2 (1, 291i)

Fogels, E. Über die Möglichkeit diophantischer Gleichungen in relativ quadratischen Zahlenkörpern. Acta Univ. Latviensis **3**, 273–284 (1940) = Publ. Sem. Math. Univ. Lettonie, no. 15 (1940). (German. Latvian summary)

Let $f(x, y, z, \cdots)=0$ be a Diophantine equation of degree three with coefficients in the field K. The author proves some theorems on the solubility of $f=0$ in quadratic fields over K. For instance, he gives a new proof for the following theorem of Nagell [Ark. Mat. Astr. Fys. **25**, no. 5 (1935)]. If the equation $x^3+y^3+a=0$ with $a\neq 0$ has a solution in $K(\sqrt{-3})$, then there exists a solution in K too. Theorems 7 and 8 are not quite correct; this is shown by the following example: $f=x^3+2y^3-ax=0$, $x=y=X-Y=g(X, Y)$, $f[g(X, Y)]=0$ for $X=Y$. *A. Brauer* (Princeton, N. J.).

D36-3 (4, 33e)

Patterson, J. O. A note on the Diophantine problem of finding four biquadrates whose sum is a biquadrate. Bull. Amer. Math. Soc. **48**, 736–737 (1942).

In 1753 Euler conjectured the existence of 4 biquadrates whose sum is a biquadrate; 158 years later Norrie discovered that

$$30^4+120^4+272^4+315^4=353^4.$$

This note gives the second example:

$$240^4+340^4+430^4+599^4=651^4$$

and describes an exclusion method by which the author plans to search for further solutions of this Diophantine equation. *D. H. Lehmer* (Berkeley, Calif.).

D36-4 (5, 89f)

Rosenthall, E. Diophantine equations reducible in biquadratic fields. Duke Math. J. **10**, 463–470 (1943).

This paper gives the "complete solution in rational integers" of the Diophantine equations $x^3+y^3=u^2+v^2$ and $x^4+y^4=u^2+v^2$. The method, which is applicable to equations completely reducible in the special bi-quadratic field produced by the adjunction of $a^{\frac{1}{2}}$ and $b^{\frac{1}{2}}$ to the rationals, consists in the application of the fundamental lemma to the effect that all integer solutions of $XY=ZW$ are given by $X=AB$, $Y=CD$, $Z=AD$, $W=CB$, where A, B, C, D are arbitrary integers with B, D coprime. The solutions of the two equations given above are far from explicit since they are expressed in terms of parameters which are not rational integers and in terms of solutions of linear equations in bi-quadratic fields. The author shows how these linear equations can be reduced to the solution of linear equations in rational integers. The complete solutions of the equations originally proposed, in terms of rational integer parameters, could be obtained from results of this paper. *D. H. Lehmer* (Berkeley, Calif.).

D36-5 (5, 90a)

Rosenthall, E. On some cubic Diophantine equations. Amer. J. Math. **65**, 663–672 (1943).

The cubic equations considered in this paper are $x^3+y^3=z^3+w^3$, $x^3+y^3=z^2$, $x^3+y^3+z^3-3xyz=u^3+v^3+w^3-3uvw$. These equations are written in multiplicative form by the use of integers of the form $a+b\rho$, where ρ is an imaginary cube root of unity, and are then completely solved by applying the lemma to the effect that all solutions, in integers of the above type, of the equation $XY=ZW$ are given by $X=US$, $Y=VT$, $Z=UT$, $W=VS$. Unfortunately the solutions are far from explicit since they are given in terms of parameters which are not rational integers but integers of the above-mentioned quadratic field. Rules have to be given for selecting these integers so that the resulting values of $x, y, z, \cdots$ are rational integers [see also the paper reviewed above]. *D. H. Lehmer.*

Referred to in D32-24.

D36-6 (9, 411f)

Caris, P. A. Rational solutions of a Diophantine equation. Amer. Math. Monthly **55**, 238–240 (1948).

This paper is concerned with the Diophantine equation

$$u^3+v^3+w^3-3uvw=x^3+y^3.$$

The author derives in a simple manner the following general nontrivial rational solution: $u=acq-3bcq-cp^2-dp^2+adq+bdq$, $v=acq-3bcq-cp^2+dp^2+adq+bdq$, $w=acq-3bcq+2cp^2+adq+bdq$, $x=3acp-3bcp+adp+3bdp$, $y=2adp-6bcp$, where $pq=a^2+3b^2$. *A. L. Whiteman.*

D36-7 (9, 497e; 9, 497f)

Whitlock, W. P., Jr. Pythagorean variations. Scripta Math. **12**, 259–265 (1946).

Bell, E. T. A Pythagorean variation. Scripta Math. **13**, 163–168 (1947).

In the second paper Bell gives a complete solution of the Diophantine equation $(x^2-w)^2+(y^2-w)^2=(z^2-w)^2$ explicitly in terms of nine independent integral parameters. An infinitude of solutions is given by Whitlock in the first paper. *I. Niven* (Eugene, Ore.).

D36-8 (9, 568h)

Rosenthall, E. On the sum of cubes. Bull. Amer. Math. Soc. **54**, 366–370 (1948).

A method is given for obtaining the complete rational integer solution for the Diophantine equation $\sum_{i=1}^m z_i^3=0$ $(m>3)$. The solution is of the form $z_i=tu_i/d$, $u_i=P_i(p_1, \cdots, p_M)$, where $t, p_1, \cdots, p_M$ are integral parameters, $P_1, \cdots, P_m$ are polynomials with integral coefficients and d is the greatest common divisor of the numbers $u_1, \cdots, u_m$. *N. G. de Bruijn* (Delft).

D36-9 (10, 353i)

Bell, E. T. A Diophantine equation. Amer. Math. Monthly **56**, 1–4 (1949).

Complete solutions of the Diophantine equation $x^2-y^2=z^3-w^3$ are given in terms of 9 independent parameters. The results are in two parts and are obtained by using complete solutions of the equations $rs=tv$, $r^2+3s^2=tv$ and $x_1y_1+x_2y_2+x_3y_3=0$. *I. Niven* (Eugene, Ore.).

D36-10 (10, 510d)

Gloden, A. A solution of a Diophantine equation. Scripta Math. **14**, 185–186 (1948).

It is announced without proof that formulas [to be published elsewhere] have been derived for solving $\sum_{i=1}^3(x_i^4-y_i^4)=0$ and the equation obtained by the substitution $x_i-y_i=2u_i$, $x_i+y_i=2v_i$. Examples involving two free parameters are given. *I. Niven* (Eugene, Ore.).

D36-11 (10, 510e)

Campbell, R. C. A simple solution of the Diophantine equation $x^3+y^3=z^2+t^2$. Bull. Amer. Math. Soc. **55**, 442–446 (1949).

By completely factoring the indicated equation in the field $R(i, \sqrt{3})$ the author obtains a complete solution in rational numbers in terms of parameters λ, p, q, r, thus: $x=\lambda^2uvw(p+r)$, $y=2\lambda^2ruvw$, $z=\lambda^3ru^2v^2w$, $t=\lambda^3qu^2v^2w$, where $u=p+3r$, $v=p^2+3r^2$, $w=r^2+q^2$. Since x, y, z, w are invariant under the transformation $p=kp'$, $q=kq'$, $r=kr'$, $\lambda=k^{-3}\lambda'$, clearly p, q, r can be taken as integral parameters.

I. Niven (Eugene, Ore.).

D36-12 (11, 11a)

Storchi, Edoardo. Uguaglianze fra somme di biquadrati. Boll. Un. Mat. Ital. (3) **3**, 220–223 (1948).

Identities are given for yielding integral solutions of the equations $\sum_{i=1}^n x_i^4=\sum_{i=1}^n y_i^4$ for $n=3$, 4 and 5. An identity is also given for obtaining solutions of the problem of finding two fourth powers whose difference is the sum of two sixth powers. With slight modification this identity can be used to obtain integral solutions of the equation $x^4=y^4+z^4+t^{6n}$ when n is odd. *W. H. Simons.*

D36-13 (11, 82c)

Gloden, A. Résolution d'un système diophantien. Euclides, Madrid **9**, 218–219 (1949).

Five different sets of 2-parameter families of solutions are given for the simultaneous solution of the Diophantine system $A^4+B^4+C^4=D^4+E^4+F^4$, $A^2+B^2=D^2$, $C^2=E^2+F^2$. [Equation (2) should be $A^2+B^2=D^2$ and the fourth subsequent equation should be $D=\rho(a^2+b^2)$.] *I. Niven.*

D36-14 (11, 642i)

Palamà, Giuseppe. Somme uguali di biquadrati. Boll. Un. Mat. Ital. (3) **4**, 417–422 (1949).

A solution in integers is obtained for the equation

$$x_1^4+\cdots+x_n^4=y_1^4+\cdots+y_m^4$$

when $n\geqq 2$, $m\geqq 3$. *W. H. Simons* (Vancouver, B. C.).

D36-15 (12, 80c)

Nicolesco, G. Sur quelques équations diophantiennes. Mathesis **59**, 95–98 (1950).

Identities are given which solve certain Diophantine equations, such as the sum of n squares equal to a cube. The question of completeness of solutions is not raised.

I. Niven (Eugene, Ore.).

D36-16 (12, 159b)

Gloden, A. Note d'analyse diophantienne. Sur l'équation biquadratique $x_1^4+x_2^4+x_3^4=y_1^4+y_2^4+y_3^4$. Bull. Inst. Polytech. Jassy [Bul. Inst. Politech. Iași] **4**, 54–57 (1948).

Various two parameter families of solutions of the equation indicated in the title are given. *I. Niven.*

D36-17 (18, 561a)

Straus, E. G.; and Swift, J. D. The representation of integers by certain rational forms. Amer. J. Math. **78** (1956), 62–70.

The authors consider the Diophantine equations

(1) $f(x)=z$, where $f(x)=N(x)/D(x)$

and $N(x)$ and $D(x)$ are polynomials in $x=(x_1, x_2, \cdots, x_n)$ of degree no higher than 2 in each x_i and the degree of $D(x)$ is at least as great as that of $N(x)$. If $D_1(x)$ is the homogeneous polynomial consisting of the terms of highest degree of $D(x)$ they call the locus $D_1(x)=0$, the critical cone $\mathscr{C}$. A conical neighborhood of $\mathscr{C}$ is an open set of rays originating at the origin and containing $\mathscr{C}$. A conjugate lattice point of $(x_1, x_2, \cdots, x_n, z)$ is obtained by replacing one x_i for which (1) is quadratic in x_i by x_i' the conjugate of x_i when all the other x_i in (1) are considered fixed.

The authors prove: If every lattice point x satisfying (1) has a conjugate lattice point in the exterior of some conical neighborhood of the critical cone, then (1) has solutions for at most a finite number of z. The cases $n=2$ and $n=3$ are considered in more detail and possible extensions indicated. *B. W. Jones* (Boulder, Colo.).

D36-18 (19, 837f)

Leech, John. Some solutions of Diophantine equations. Proc. Cambridge Philos. Soc. **53** (1957), 778–780.

The author considers the Diophantine equation

$$f(x)+f(y)=f(z)+f(t),$$

where $f(x)$ is a power of x or a binomial coefficient $\binom{x}{n}$, n fixed. A search for solutions was carried out on EDSAC 1½ at the University Mathematical Laboratory, Cambridge. Thus for example the author finds that the equation

$$\binom{x}{5}+\binom{y}{5}=\binom{z}{5}+\binom{t}{5}$$

has three solutions in integers less than 500, given by

x	y	z	t
9	9	10	
118	117	133	78
197	160	209	53.

Other cases treated were

$$f(x)=x^3,\ x^4,\ \binom{x}{3},\ \binom{x}{4}.$$

A consequence of the author's work is that the solution

$$158^4+59^4=134^4+133^4,$$

due to Euler, is in fact the one with the smallest integers.

M. Newman (Washington, D.C.).

D36-19 (19, 942c)

Xeroudakes, George; and Moessner, Alfred. Three Diophantine systems. Euclides, Madrid **17** (1957), 63–71.

The three systems of the title are: $x^3+y^3+z^3=0$, $x^2+y^2=z^2$ in integers of $K(\sqrt{-2})$; $x+y+z=u+w$, $x^2+y^2+z^2=u^2+w^2$, $x^2+y^2=z^2$ in rational integers; $x+y+z=u+w$, $x^2+y^2+z^2=u^2+w^2$, $x^3+y^3+z^3=3xyz=u^3+w^3$, $x+y=x^2+y^2=z^2$ in rational numbers. The systems are solved by elementary methods. The solutions are presented implicitly and recursively. No argument for completeness is offered. *J. D. Swift.*

D36-20 (19, 1160d)

Mordell, L. J. Corrigendum: On the four integer cubes problem. J. London Math. Soc. **32** (1957), 383.

The derivation in J. London Math. Soc. **11** (1936), 208–218, of sufficient conditions that $x^3+y^3+z^3+w^3=a^3+b^3+c^3+d^3$ (a, b, c, d given integers) have an infinity of integer solutions, is invalid if $a=b$, $c=d$, etc.

D36-21 (20# 835)

Gloden, A. Note d'analyse Diophantienne sur l'équation biquadratique $x_1^4+x_2^4+x_3^4=y_1^4+y_2^4+y_3^4$. Bul. Inst. Politech. Iași **4** (1949), 54–57.

The author discusses an elementary method for finding

solutions of the equation $x_1^4+x_2^4+x_3^4=y_1^4+y_2^4+y_3^4$ in terms of binary quadratic forms with integral coefficients; e.g.,

$$x_1=(4, -46, 202),\ x_2=(8, -74, 206),\ x_3=(15, -24, 69),$$
$$y_1=(10, 2, 28),\quad y_2=(14, -26, 32),\ y_3=(9, -72, 243),$$

where

$$(\lambda, \mu, \nu)=\lambda p^2+\mu pq+\nu q^2.$$

He also gives the solution,

$$x_1=128p^9+pq^8,\ x_2=64p^8q-12p^4q^5-q^9,\ x_3=0,$$
$$y_1=3pq^8,\ y_2=128p^9-2pq^8,\ y_3=64p^8q+12p^4q^5-q^9.$$

K. Mahler (Manchester)

D36-22 (20# 2301)

Leech, John. On $A^4+B^4+C^4+D^4=E^4$. Proc. Cambridge Philos. Soc. **54** (1958), 554–555.

Using EDSAC II, the author finds all solutions to the equation in the title, for $|E|\leq 4303$, a limitation imposed by the word length of the machine. The computation, although clearly finitary, is reduced a million-fold by the use of 16 and 5 as exclusion moduli; for instance, it then follows that three of the four quantities A, B, C, D are divisible by 2, and another three of them are divisible by 5, while E is divisible by neither (for a primitive solution). The smallest of eight primitive solutions found is the quintuple (30, 120, 272, 315, 353), discovered by Norrie [Univ. St. Andrews 500th Anniv. Mem. Vol., Edinburgh, 1911, pp. 87–89].

H. Cohn (Tucson, Ariz.)

Referred to in D36-28.

D36-23 (22# 4656)

Battaglia, Antonio. Formule parametriche per triangoli eroniani. Archimede **11** (1959), 163–167.

Using the formula of Heron (more correctly, of Archimedes), $S^2=p(p-a)(p-b)(p-c)$, for the area of a triangle having a, b, c for sides, the author derives the formulas

$$(*)\qquad \begin{aligned} a &= \lambda^2+9\mu^2, & b &= 2(\lambda^2+3\mu^2),\\ c &= 3(\lambda^2+\mu^2), & S &= 6(\lambda^2+\mu^2)\lambda\mu, \end{aligned}$$

which, for integral values of λ, μ give integers for a, b, c, and S (i.e., a Heronian triangle, by definition); furthermore, a, b, c form an arithmetic progression. By expressing S in terms of two sides and the sine of the included angle the author obtains another set of formulas having the same properties as (*).

N. A. Court (Norman, Okla.)

D36-24 (23# A107)

Bradis, V. M.; Sîcikov, A. F.

Sur les triangles de Héron. (Romanian. Russian and French summaries)

Gaz. Mat. Fiz. Ser. A **11 (64)** (1959), 325–334.

Authors' summary: "On appelle triangle de Héron tout triangle dont les côtés et l'aire s'expriment par des nombres naturels. Le problème de trouver tous les triangles de Héron revient à résoudre en nombres naturels l'equation $uvw(u+v+w)=s^2$ (u, v, w sont les mesures des segments déterminés sur les côtés du triangle par les points de contact du cercle inscrit et s est l'aire du triangle). On ne connaît pas encore la solution générale de cette équation. Dans cet article, on donne une solution partielle du problème, en dressant un tableau de tous les triangles de Héron, tels que la mesure de chaque côté ne dépasse pas la valeur 100. Pour cela, on établit préalablement quelques propriétés des triangles de Héron. On s'appuie sur le fait que tout triangle de Héron peut être placé de manière que ses sommets aient comme coordonnées rectangulaires des nombres entiers."

D36-25 (25# 5028)

Sierpiński, W.

Sur les sommes égales des cubes distincts de nombres naturels. (Bulgarian and Russian summaries)

Bŭlgar. Akad. Nauk Izv. Mat. Inst. **4**, *no.* 1, 7–11 (1959).

From the author's introduction: "Le but de cette communication est de démontrer d'une façon tout à fait élémentaire le théorème suivant: Quels que soient les nombres naturels m et $n\geqq m$, sauf les cas $m=n=1$ et $m=1$, $n=2$, il existe $m+n$ nombres naturels distincts $a_1, a_2, \cdots, a_m, b_1, b_2, \cdots, b_n$, tels que

$$a_1^3+a_2^3+\cdots+a_m^3 = b_1^3+b_2^3+\cdots+b_n^3."$$

D36-26 (26# 4956)

Mjakišev, V. P.

On a third-degree Diophantine equation. (Russian)

Dokl. Akad. Nauk SSSR **148** (1963), 1020–1021.

The author determines all primitive solutions of a Diophantine equation in four variables (the proof is only sketched). He also states without proof an asymptotic formula for the number of those solutions which lie on a certain cubic surface. *S. Knapowski* (New Orleans, La.)

D36-27 (27# 4792)

Trau, Z.

On the Diophantine equation $uvw(u+v+w)-s^2=0$.

Gaz. Mat. Fiz. Ser. A **14 (67)** (1962), 74–75.

D36-28 (29# 3429)

Brudno, Simcha

A further example of $A^4+B^4+C^4+D^4=E^4$.

Proc. Cambridge Philos. Soc. **60** (1964), 1027–1028.

The example is $A=955$, $B=1770$, $C=2634$, $D=5400$, $E=5491$. The author outlines the search method on an IBM 709 by which this solution was found. See also J. Leech [same Proc. **54** (1958), 554–555; MR **20** #2301].

O. Taussky-Todd (Pasadena, Calif.)

Citations: MR 20# 2301 = D36-22.

D36-29 (31# 121)

Popovič, Konstantin P. [Popovici, C. P.]

Heronian triangles. (Russian)

Rev. Math. Pures Appl. (Bucarest) **7** (1962), 439–457.

A Heronian triangle is one whose sides and area are natural numbers. The main result of this paper is the following theorem: If $d, f, t, u, v, z, \theta, \varepsilon, \eta, \chi$ are natural numbers such that $uv\theta^2-tz\eta^2>0$ and f is the greatest common divisor of the integers $uz\chi^2+tv\varepsilon^2$ and $uv\theta^2-tz\eta^2$, then the natural numbers a, b, c satisfying the conditions

$$(1)\qquad \begin{aligned} a &= [(t\varepsilon\eta)^2+(u\theta\chi)^2]vzd:f\\ b &= [uv\theta^2-tz\eta^2][uz\chi^2+tv\varepsilon^2]d:f\\ c &= [(z\eta\chi)^2+(v\theta\varepsilon)^2]utd:f \end{aligned}$$

are the sides of a Heronian triangle. Conversely, if a, b, c are the sides of a Heronian triangle, then one can find natural numbers $d, f, t, u, v, z, \theta, \varepsilon, \eta, \chi$ for which $uv\theta^2-tz\eta^2>0$ and $f=(uz\chi^2+tv\varepsilon^2,\ uv\theta^2-tz\eta^2)$, such that conditions (1) are satisfied. The author extends this result by proving a similar result for Pythagorean triangles, where a Pythagorean triangle is a right-angled Heronian triangle satisfying any one of the conditions $a^2=b^2+c^2$, $b^2=c^2+a^2$, or $c^2=a^2+b^2$. The author concludes with a few remarks about the still unsolved problem of determining all the rational triangles from the Heronian triangles, where a rational triangle is one whose sides and area are positive rational numbers.

R. Finkelstein (Tucson, Ariz.)

D36-30 **(32# 7494)**

Gabowicz, J. A.

Solutions of the equation $x^3+y^3+z^3-t^3=1$ in natural numbers. (Polish)

Wiadom. Mat. (2) **7**, 63–64 (1963).

The author shows that the equation $x^3+y^3+z^3-t^3=1$ has infinitely many solutions in positive integers.

J. Kubilius (Vilnius)

D36-31 **(34# 2525)**

Dem'janenko, V. A.

Sums of four cubes. (Russian)

Izv. Vysš. Učebn. Zaved. Matematika **1966**, *no.* 5 (54), 64–69.

It is proved, by means of highly ingenious identities, that the equation (*) $x^3-y^3+z^3-t^3=A$ has infinitely many solutions in positive integers x, y, z, t if $A \equiv \pm 2 \pmod{18}$. Since the same is true for $A \equiv \pm 1, 3, 6, 7, 9 \pmod{18}$ [cf. H. W. Richmond, Messenger Math. (2) **51** (1921), 177–186; L. J. Mordell, J. London Math. Soc. **11** (1936), 208–218; and W. Sierpiński and the reviewer, Acta Arith. **4** (1958), 20–30; MR **20** #1664] and for $A = \pm 4, 5 \pmod{18}$, the equation (*) cannot be solved by identities (Richmond [loc. cit.] and Mordell [loc. cit.]), the result achieved is final for this line of investigation. In addition, the author proves that the equation (*) has infinitely many solutions for all positive $A \leqq 1000$, and gives a method of finding all integral solutions of the system $x^3+y^3+z^3+t^3=A$, $x+y+z+t=\pm 1, \pm 2, \pm 4$.

A. Schinzel (Warsaw)

Citations: MR 20# 1664 = P04-43.

Referred to in D36-34.

D36-32 **(34# 4195)**

Dani, Ernest

On the rational Diophantine solution of the equation $\sum_{i=1}^4 a_i x_i^4 = ax^4(\prod_{i=1}^4 a_i = b^2)$. (Romanian. Russian and English summaries)

Studia Univ. Babeș-Bolyai Ser. Math.-Phys. **11** (1966), *no.* 1, 7–11.

Rational solutions of the Diophantine equation $\sum_{i=1}^4 a_i x_i^4 = ax^4$ have been indicated by R. Norrie [see, e.g., L. E. Dickson, *History of the theory of numbers*, Vol. 2, p. 646, Carnegie Institute, Washington, D.C., 1920], H. Richmond [J. London Math. Soc. **19** (1944), 193–194; MR **7**, 244] and B. Segre [ibid. **19** (1944), 195–200; MR **7**, 244] under various restrictions on the coefficients. The author generalizes previous results to the case when the only restriction is $\prod_{i=1}^4 a_i = b^2$. His method is inductive; starting from a rational solution corresponding to $a=0$ (obtained by using the results of Richmond and Segre), he constructs solutions for the case $\prod_{i=1}^4 a_i = b^2$, $a \neq 0$, and shows that his method will yield an infinite sequence of distinct solutions. In case Norrie's conditions are satisfied, these reduce to Norrie's solutions. {The reviewer is unable to follow the details of the proofs.}

E. Grosswald (Philadelphia, Pa.)

Citations: MR 7, 244c = G35-9; MR 7, 244d = G35-10.

D36-33 **(35# 2841)**

Cassels, J. W. S.; Guy, M. J. T.

On the Hasse principle for cubic surfaces.

Mathematika **13** (1966), 111–120.

It had been conjectured by L. J. Mordell [Publ. Math. Debrecen **1** (1949), 1–6; MR **11**, 82] that the Hasse principle holds for a cubic surface in 3-dimensional projective space which is not a cone; i.e., if the cubic surface is defined over the rational field Q and has points defined over each p-adic field Q_p, then it has a rational point. T. Skolem [Math. Z. **63** (1955), 295–312; MR **17**, 464] verified this conjecture in the case of singular cubic surfaces and E. S. Selmer [Math. Scand. **1** (1953), 113–119, MR **15**, 290] verified it for surfaces $ax^3+by^3+cz^3+dw^3=0$ with $ab=cd$. H. P. F. Swinnerton-Dyer [Mathematika **9** (1962), 54–56; MR **25** #3413] showed the conjecture to be false for cubic surfaces in general. On the basis of computation, Selmer conjectured that the conjecture held whenever the equation of the curve could be diagonalized over Q. The authors disprove this conjecture by demonstrating that the surface $5x^3+12y^3+9z^3+10w^3=0$ has p-adic points, for all p, but no rational point. The particular equation was found by searching for such forms with no small integral points. The proof that it has no rational point depends on the factorization of prime ideals in certain cubic fields. There is an appendix on the class number of fields $Q(\sqrt[3]{a}, \sqrt[3]{b})$, which while perhaps known in principle, has not appeared in print earlier.

D. J. Lewis (Ann Arbor, Mich.)

Citations: MR 11, 82h = D32-28; MR 15, 290b = D32-41; MR 17, 464c = D32-51; MR 25# 3413 = D32-68.

D36-34 **(35# 4159)**

Klarner, D. A.

Representation of an integer as a sum of four integer cubes and related problems.

Amer. Math. Monthly **74** (1967), 531–537.

Let f be an integral cubic form, $k=f(a_1, a_2)+f(a_3, a_4)$, where the a_i are integers. The author produces a solution of the equation $f(x_1, x_2)+f(x_3, x_4)=kx_5^3$ in which the x_i are integral binary quadratic forms, relatively prime provided certain polynomials in the a_i do not vanish. This result is applied to the investigation of the Diophantine equations $x_1^3+x_2^3+x_3^3+x_4^3=k$ and $ax_1^3+dx_2^3=ax_3^3+dx_4^3$.

{Reviewer's remarks: Concerning the two aforesaid equations, a reference should be made to V. A. Dem'janenko [Izv. Vysš. Učebn. Zaved. Matematika **1966**, no. 5 (54), 64–69; MR **34** #2525] and A. Oppenheim [Acta Arith. **9** (1964), 221–226; MR **29** #4733], respectively. In Theorem 1, the assumption $(a_1+a_2)(a_3+a_4)<0$ is missing and only one of the assumptions $a_1 \neq a_2$, $a_3 \neq a_4$ is needed.}

A. Schinzel (Warsaw)

Citations: MR 29# 4733 = D32-72; MR 34# 2525 = D36-31.

D36-35 **(35# 6621)**

Sierpiński, W.

Tetrahedral numbers. (Polish)

Wiadom. Mat. (2) **9**, 209–217 (1966/67).

This article is a continuation of the study made in the author's book *Trigonal numbers* (Polish) [Państw. Zakł. Wydawn. Szkoln., Warsaw, 1962], concerning the numbers of the form $T_n = n(n+1)(n+2)/6$ $(n=1, 2, \cdots)$, called tetrahedral numbers. All theorems are proved by elementary methods. The first two theorems are the following: Theorem 1: There exist infinitely many tetrahedral numbers that are sums of two squares of positive integers. Theorem 2: There exist infinitely many square numbers that are sums of tetrahedral numbers.

T. T. Tonkov (Leningrad)

D36-36 **(37# 1315)**

Dem'janenko, V. A.

L. Euler's hypothesis. (Russian)

Izv. Vysš. Učebn. Zaved. Matematika **1968**, *no.* 3 (70), 37–42.

The Euler conjecture in question asserts that for $n \geqq 3$ the equation $x_1^n + \cdots + x_n^n = x_{n+1}^n$ has a solution in rational numbers distinct from 0 while $x_1^n + \cdots + x_{n-1}^n = x_n^n$ does not. In this paper the author gives explicit, but very involved, recurrence relations leading from any given rational solution of $x^4=(y+z)^4+(y-z)^4+t^4$ to infinitely many others. He also shows that in $R(u, v)$ the sole respective solutions of $x^4+(u^4+v^4)y^4=z^4$ and $(u^4+v^4)x^4-y^4=z^4$ are multiples of the triples (1, 0, 1) and (1, u, v). Finally, recurrence relations are given that yield an infinite parametric family of solutions for the equation $x^4-y^4+z^2=1$.

{In a recent paper by L. J. Lander and T. R. Parkin [Math. Comp. **21** (1967), 101–103; MR **36** #3721] the Euler conjecture is shown to be false. In particular, $27^5+84^5+110^5+133^5=144^5$.} *J. B. Roberts* (Portland, Ore.)

Citations: MR 36# 3721 = D48-58.

D36-37 **(40# 7197)**

Shimizu, Tamon

On the Diophantus equation $x^3+y^3+z^3-3xyz=mt^2$.

J. College Arts Sci. Chiba Univ. **5** (1968), *no.* 2, 207–208 (1969).

Solutions in rational integers are obtained by factoring in the field $K((-3)^{1/2})$. *B. Stolt* (Stockholm)

D36-38 **(41# 6808)**

Davenport, H.; Landau, E.

On the representation of positive integers as sums of three cubes of positive rational numbers.

Number Theory and Analysis (Papers in Honor of Edmund Landau), pp. 49–53. *Plenum, New York,* 1969.

H. W. Richmond [Proc. London Math. Soc. (2) **21** (1923), 401–409] showed that for every integer $R>0$, the Diophantine equation $R=x^3+y^3+z^3$ has solutions in rational (clearly, in general non-integral) x, y, z. In the present paper, the authors show that those rationals can be selected so that they have a common denominator T, satisfying $T=O(R^2)$. The (fairly simple) proof is based on (1) Richmond's identities, and (2) a strong form of Bertrand's postulate (for sufficiently large A, the interval $(A, 2A)$ contains at least one prime $p\equiv 2 \pmod 3$). Richmond's identities state that if we set $x+y+z=3\rho(1-\theta)\{1+\theta+3p-3p^3(1-\theta)\}$, $y+z=\rho\{1-9p^2(1-\theta)-9p^3(1-\theta)^2(1+\theta)\}$, $z=\theta(x+y+z)$, where ρ and θ are explicitly given (rather complicated) rational functions of the two arbitrary (rational) parameters p and λ, then x, y, and z are solutions of the preceding Diophantine equation. {Reviewer's remark: This joint paper had been written (but was not published) in 1935. Shortly before his own death, the first author contributed it to the volume dedicated to the memory of the second author.}

E. Grosswald (Philadelphia, Pa.)

Referred to in D36-41.

D36-39 **(41# 8337)**

Lagrange, Jean

Sommes égales de trois bicarrés.

Enseignement Math. (2) **16** (1970), 1–3.

It is shown that, for any natural number h, the system $x_1^4+y_1^4+z_1^4=x_2^4+y_2^4+z_2^4=\cdots=x_h^4+y_h^4+z_h^4$ has nontrivial positive integer solutions, that is, solutions for which the triples (x_i, y_i, z_i) are all distinct.

B. Garrison (San Diego, Calif.)

D36-40 **(43# 7402)**

Legendre, Robert

Remarques sur un théorème de Sophie Germain.

C. R. Acad. Sci. Paris Sér. A-B **271** (1970), A425–A426.

This brief note unfortunately contains no reference enabling the reader to identify the theorem of Sophie Germain referred to in the title, nor is the theorem quoted. The author considers relations connecting solutions of the diophantine equation $x^3=rx^2+sx+t$, $(s, t)=1$ and shows that in certain cases a pair of polynomials involving s and t must satisfy congruence conditions that in general admit only a limited class of solutions.

R. F. Churchhouse (Cardiff)

D36-41 **(44# 6601)**

Mordell, L. J.

On the representation of positive integers as sums of three cubes of positive rational numbers.

Mathematika **18** (1971), 98–99.

Let n denote any positive rational integer. It was proved by H. Davenport and E. Landau [*Number theory and analysis* (Papers in Honor of Edmund Landau), pp. 49–53, Plenum, New York, 1969; MR **41** #6808] that the Diophantine equation (1) $x^3+y^3+z^3=n$ has positive rational solutions with denominators of order of magnitude $O(n^2)$. The author gives a proof for the poorer result $O(n^{8/3})$, but his proof is elementary, simple and self-contained.

W. Ljunggren (Oslo)

Citations: MR 41# 6808 = D36-38.

D36-42 **(44# 6602)**

Podsypanin, V. D.

The equation $x^3+y^3+z^3=1$. **(Russian)**

Tul. Gos. Ped. Inst. Učen. Zap. Mat. Kaf. **1968**, 4–9.

Using D. H. Lehmer's method [see J. London Math. Soc. **31** (1956), 275–280; MR **17**, 1187] the author gives new formulae, which lead to an infinity of solutions of the Euler equation $x^3+y^3+z^3=1$. *B. Novák* (Prague)

Citations: MR 17, 1187c = D32-55.

D40 HIGHER DEGREE CURVES: GENERAL

See also Sections D60, G30.

See also reviews B40-38, C05-31, D12-32, D24-26, D24-67, D24-86, D28-31, D44-42, D52-41, D56-23, D60-78, D64-6, E24-130, J02-27, J68-15, J68-68, N32-67, R04-17, R04-27, R08-50.

D40-1 **(1, 291d; 1, 291e)**

Obláth, Richárd. Sur les nombres x^2-1. Mat.-Fiz. Lapok **47**, 58–77 (1940). (Hungarian. French summary)

Obláth, Richárd. Über die Zahl x^2-1. Mathematica, Zutphen. B. **8**, 161–172 (1940).

The author studies the solubility of the Diophantine equation

$$(1) \qquad x^2-1=y^n.$$

Using theorems of Lubelski [Prace Mat.-Fiz. **42**, 11–44 (1935)], Nagell [Norsk Vid. Selsk. Forh. **7**, 136–139 (1934)] and Vandiver [Monatsh. Math. Phys. **43**, 317–320 (1936)], the author obtains criteria for the insolubility of (1). It follows from these results that (1) has no solutions in certain cases in which the theorems of Nagell are inapplicable. In particular, the following theorem is proved. Let $p>3$ be a prime and let 2^{p-2} and 2^{p-3} be non-residues of the pth power (mod p^2). Then, if $n=p$, (1) has no solutions in integers x, y different from zero. Moreover, using a theorem of Siegel [Math. Ann. **114**, 57–68 (1937)] the author proves that (1) has at most one solution in integers different from zero. [In the proof of theorem 3 the term $+1$ is missing twice.] *A. Brauer* (Princeton, N. J.).

D40-2 **(4, 130c)**

Aucoin, Anthony A. Homogeneous and nonhomogeneous Diophantine equations. Bull. Amer. Math. Soc. **48**, 933–937 (1942).

In a previous paper [Bull. Amer. Math. Soc. **45**, 330–333 (1939)], Aucoin and Parker discussed the Diophantine equation $f(x)=g(y)$, where f and g are homogeneous polynomials whose degrees are relatively prime. In the present paper the results are extended to obtaining integral solutions of the equation $f(x)=g(x)$, where f and g are homogeneous polynomials with integral coefficients of an arbitrary number of variables, each polynomial involving the same number of variables. The results depend on the degrees of the polynomials in a specified number of these variables or their reciprocals. The solutions are given in terms of polynomials (with integral coefficients) involving arbitrary parameters. *I. A. Barnett* (Cincinnati, Ohio).

D40-3 **(5, 33d)**

Sispánov, Sergio. On the indetermined equation $ax^n+by^n+cz^n=0$. Bol. Mat. **16**, 71–73 (1943). (Spanish)

D40-4 **(7, 273g)**

Oblath, Richard. On impossible Diophantine equations of the form $x^m+1=y^n$. Revista Mat. Hisp.-Amer. (4) **1**, 122–140 (1941). (Spanish)

The principal theorems proved are the following. (I) The Diophantine equation $x^2-1=y^n$ is impossible in nonzero integers if n is a prime ($n>3$) satisfying either of the conditions $2^{n-1}\not\equiv 1 \pmod{n^2}$ or $3^{n-1}\not\equiv 1 \pmod{n^2}$ (hence if $3<n<16000$). (II) Hence the equation is impossible (save for trivial cases) if n is a prime factor of numbers of the form $2^\alpha\pm1$, $2^\alpha3^\beta\pm1$, $2^\alpha\pm3^\beta$ or $3^\beta\pm1$. (III) The equation is impossible if either (i) $y=2^\alpha p$ (p prime), (ii) $y=2^\alpha3^\beta5^\gamma$ or (iii) y is a product of primes less than 32000. (IV) The equation $x^m+1=y^n$ is impossible if y consists only of primes of the form $2^\alpha+1$ or $2^\alpha3^\beta+1$. Gérono [Nouv. Ann. Math. (2) **9**, 469–471 (1870); **10**, 204–206 (1871)] had considered the last equation with x or y prime. Use is made of the work of Nagell on $x^2-1=y^n$ [latest reference, Norsk. Vidensk. Selsk. Forh. **7**, 136–139 (1934)] and Lubelski on $x^n+y^n=cz^n$ [Prace Mat. Fiz. **42**, 11–34 (1935), in particular, p. 29]. *G. Pall* (Montreal, Que.).

Referred to in D60-55.

D40-5 **(7, 506d)**

Banerjee, D. P. On the rational solutions of the Diophantine equation $ax^n-by^n=k$. Proc. Benares Math. Soc. (N.S.) **5**, 29–30 (1943).

S. Chowla [Indian Phys.-Math. J. **5**, 5–6 (1934)] has proved the following theorem. If Euler's conjecture is true, that $x_1^r+\cdots+x_m^r\neq y^r$ where $1<m<r$ and $r>2$, then the Diophantine equation $ax^n-by^n=k$, $n>2$, has at most one rational solution if n is odd and $|a|+|b|<n/2$. The author proves some simple corollaries of this result. *A. Brauer* (Chapel Hill, N. C.).

D40-6 **(8, 136a)**

Ljunggren, Wilhelm. On a Diophantine equation. Norske Vid. Selsk. Forh., Trondhjem **18**, no. 32, 125–128 (1945).

The author discusses the equation $Cx^2+D=y^n$, where the product of the odd positive integers C, D contains no squared factor greater than 1 and the number of classes of ideals of the field $K(\sqrt{(-CD)})$ is indivisible by the odd positive integer n. For $n>1$ and $D+(-1)^{(D+1)/2}$ exactly divisible by an odd power of 2, the equation is shown to be impossible in integers x, y if $CD\equiv1 \pmod 4$ or if $CD\equiv3 \pmod 8$ with $n\not\equiv0 \pmod 3$. For $n=q>3$, where q is prime, $D+(-1)^{(D+1)/2}=2^{2\lambda}D_1$, $(D_1, 2)=1$, and $CD\not\equiv7 \pmod 8$, it is also shown to be impossible if $q\not\equiv CD \pmod 8$. *W. H. Gage* (Vancouver, B. C.).

Referred to in D40-10, D40-25, D40-38.

D40-7 **(8, 315a)**

Ljunggren, Wilhelm. Some theorems on indeterminate equations of the form $\dfrac{x^n-1}{x-1}=y^q$. Norsk Mat. Tidsskr. **25**, 17–20 (1943). (Norwegian)

Completing a result of the reviewer [Norsk Mat. Forenings Skr. (I) no. **3** (1921)] the author proves the following theorem. The Diophantine equation of the title is, for $q=2$, impossible in integers x, y, $|x|>1$, except when $n=4$, $x=7$ and $n=5$, $x=3$. Another result is that the equation of the title is impossible in integers when q is divisible by 3, except in the case $n=3$, $x=18$ or $x=-19$, $q=3$. *T. Nagell.*

D40-8 **(8, 368i)**

Ljunggren, Wilhelm. A Diophantine equation with two unknowns. C. R. Dixième Congrès Math. Scandinaves 1946, pp. 265–270. Jul. Gjellerups Forlag, Copenhagen, 1947.

The Diophantine equation $x^2-Dy^{2n}=1$ with $n>3$ and $D+1$ not a square has at most 2 solutions in positive integers x and y. These solutions can be found readily if the fundamental unit of $R(\sqrt{D})$ is known. If $n=3$, the result holds for all D. The result also holds when $D+1$ is a square if D exceeds a certain limit depending only on n. The proof employs work of Siegel [Math. Ann. **114**, 57–68 (1937)] on the equation $ax^n-by^n=c$ and Tartakowsky [Bull. Acad. Sci. URSS [Izvestia Akad. Nauk SSSR] (6) **20**, 301–324 (1926)] on the equation $x^{2n}-Dy^{2n}=1$. *I. Niven.*

D40-9 **(8, 442d)**

Ljunggren, Wilhelm. On the Diophantine equation $x^2+p^2=y^n$. Norske Vid. Selsk. Forh., Trondhjem **16**, no. 8, 27–30 (1943).

Let p be a prime such that p^2-1 is exactly divisible by an odd power of 2. Then the equation of the title has only a finite number of solutions in x, y and n with $n>1$. The proof provides a method for finding all solutions. *I. Niven* (Eugene, Ore.).

Referred to in D60-49.

D40-10 **(8, 442e)**

Ljunggren, Wilhelm. On the Diophantine equation $x^2+D=y^n$. Norske Vid. Selsk. Forh., Trondhjem **17**, no. 23, 93–96 (1944).

The author shows that the equation $x^2+D=y^n$ ($n>1$ and odd; $D\equiv1 \pmod 4$, squarefree and positive) is not satisfied by any integers x and y if $D-1$ is exactly divisible by an odd power of 2, and if n does not divide the class number of the field $K\sqrt{(-D)}$. The method of proof is similar to that used by the author in an earlier paper [see the preceding review; see also the author's later paper in the same Forh. **18**, no. 32, 125–128 (1945); these Rev. **8**, 136]. *R. A. Rankin* (Cambridge, England).

Citations: MR 8, 136a = D40-6.

D40-11 **(8, 442g)**

Ljunggren, Wilhelm. Über die Gleichungen $1+Dx^2=2y^n$ und $1+Dx^2=4y^n$. Norske Vid. Selsk. Forh., Trondhjem **15**, no. 30, 115–118 (1942).

If the number h of ideal classes in $R(\sqrt{(-D)})$ is not divisible by n, then the Diophantine equations of the title, with $D\equiv1 \pmod 4$ and $D\equiv3 \pmod 4$, respectively, have no solutions in integers x, y with $y>1$. *I. Niven.*

Referred to in D12-32.

D40-12 **(8, 442h)**

Ljunggren, Wilhelm. Solution complète de quelques équations du sixième degré à deux indéterminées. Arch. Math. Naturvid. **48**, no. 7, 35 pp. (1946).

Consider the Diophantine equation (1) $Ax^6-By^6=C$, where $A>0$, $B>0$, $(AB, C)=1$, AB is not a square or a cube and AB is not divisible by the 6th power of a prime. If $R((-27A/B)^{1/6})$ and $R((-27A_1/B_1)^{1/6})$ are identical fields, say that (1) and $A_1x^6-B_1y^6=C_1$ belong to the same family. Then, for C restricted to 1, 2, 3, 4, 6 or 12, at most one equation in a family is solvable. If $C=1$, 2, 3, 4 or 6, equation (1) has at most one solution in positive integers; and if ξ is the fundamental unit of $R((-27A/B)^{1/6})$ of relative norm 1 with respect to the subfields $R((A/B)^{1/3})$ and $R((-3A/B)^{1/3})$, then ξ or ξ^2 is given by an explicit formula involving A, B, C and the solution of (1) if it exists (except in case $A=5$, $B=4$, $C=1$, when ξ^4 is so expressed). The proofs involve detailed discussions of units of the various fields. The methods are also applied to the equation $x^3+Dy^3=1$ which has been treated by B. Delaunay [C. R. Acad. Sci. Paris **162**, 150–151 (1916)] and T. Nagell [J. Math. Pures Appl. (9) **4**, 209–270 (1925)] and to the more general equation (2) $Ax^3+By^3=C$ which is discussed in Nagell's paper. The author states that he simplifies Nagell's procedure for solving (2). *I. Niven.*

Referred to in D24-46.

D40-13 **(10, 13c)**

Pettineo, B. Sull'analisi indeterminata di grado superiore al primo. Matematiche, Catania **1**, 42–48 (1945).

Parametric solutions of homogeneous Diophantine equations of degree greater than 2 are derived under special hypotheses; a method by Gloden [Mathesis **53**, 233–235 (1939); these Rev. **1**, 65] is generalized.

N. G. W. H. Beeger (Amsterdam).

Citations: MR 1, 65f = D36-1.

D40-14 **(10, 14b)**

Vandiver, H. S. Congruence methods as applied to Diophantine analysis. Math. Mag. **21**, 185–192 (1948).

[The author's initials are misprinted H. V. in the original.] This paper contains a simple account of the author's method of constructing Diophantine equations that have no solutions, by making sure that the corresponding congruences have no solution for a properly chosen prime modulus [see, for example, Proc. Nat. Acad. Sci. U. S. A. **32**, 101–106 (1946); these Rev. **7**, 414]. Thus it is shown how to find Diophantine equations of the form $Au^m+Bv^m=1$ that have no solutions; the modulus used is a prime of the form $mc+1$. An example is the equation $7u^4-10v^4=1$, where the modulus is the prime 13. A general method is also given whereby impossible Diophantine equations are obtained by a certain process of addition from other impossible equations and congruences. *H. W. Brinkmann.*

Citations: MR 7, 414f = D48-10.

D40-15 **(11, 328e)**

Persson, Bengt. On a Diophantine equation in two unknowns. Ark. Mat. **1**, 45–57 (1949).

It was proved by T. Nagell [Norsk Mat. Forenings Skr. (I) no. **2** (1921)] that the equation (1) $x^2+x+1=y^q$ has only trivial integral solutions unless q is a power of 3. W. Ljunggren [Acta Math. **75**, 1–21 (1943); these Rev. **8**, 135] proved that the only nontrivial solution of (1) is $y=7$ for $q=3$. The present paper discusses the equation (2) $x^2+x+\frac{1}{4}(D+1)=y^q$, where q is an odd prime, $D\equiv 3 \pmod 4$, $D\geqq 7$, D square-free. Let h denote the number of ideal classes in the field $K(\sqrt{(-D)})$. The following results are proved. If $q\nmid h$, there is only a finite number of values of D for which (2) is solvable, and any solution must satisfy the inequality $y<1+\frac{1}{4}D\operatorname{cosec}^2\pi/q$. If (2) has a solution with $y<\frac{1}{4}(D+1)$, then $q\,|\,h$. If $q=D$, (2) is not solvable. If $q=3$ and $3\nmid h$, then (2) has only the solution $y=\frac{1}{3}(D-1)$ if $D=3c^2+4$, only the solution $y=\frac{1}{3}(D+1)$ if $D=3c^2-4$, and no solutions for other values of D. If $q=3$ and $3\,|\,h$, there are other solutions: the examples $D=23$, 31, 59, 85 are discussed. If $q=5$ and $5\nmid h$, then (2) has only the solutions $D=7$, $y=2$ and $D=11$, $y=3$. If $q=7$ and $7\nmid h$, then (2) has at most one solution y for a given D. A table of solutions of (2) is given for prime $D<100$ and $q=3$.

I. Niven (Eugene, Ore.).

Citations: MR 8, 135k = D24-10.
Referred to in D40-29.

D40-16 **(13, 202d)**

Mahler, K. On algebraic relations between two units of an algebraic field. Algèbre et Théorie des Nombres. Colloques Internationaux du Centre National de la Recherche Scientifique, no. 24, pp. 47–55. Centre National de la Recherche Scientifique, Paris, 1950.

The principal result of this paper is this theorem: Let $\mathfrak{K}$ be a field of finite degree over the rational field, and let $F(x, y)$ be a polynomial with coefficients in $\mathfrak{K}$ which is irreducible over the field of all complex numbers. Assume that the curve C: $F(x, y)=0$ is not a line parallel to either of the coordinate axes. (A) If there are infinitely many points (x, y) on C for which x is an integer and y a unit in $\mathfrak{K}$, then the curve may be expressed parametrically in the form $x=P(z)=\sum_{h=-m}^{+m}a_hz^h$, $y=Q(z)=\beta z^d$, where m and d are two positive integers, all coefficients a_h and $\beta\neq 0$ are in R, and where $P(z)$ is not a constant. (B) If there are infinitely many points (x, y) on C such that x and y are integers in $\mathfrak{K}$, the norm of y is unbounded, and y is divisible only by a finite set $\mathfrak{P}=\{\mathfrak{p}_1, \mathfrak{p}_2, \cdots, \mathfrak{p}_s\}$ of prime ideals, then the curve can be expressed parametrically in the form $x=\sum_{h=0}^{m}a_hz^h$, $y=\beta z^d$ where m and d are two positive integers, all coefficients a_h and $\beta\neq 0$ are in $\mathfrak{K}$, and $P(z)$ is not a constant.

This is an extension of a theorem of Siegel [Abh. Deutsch. Akad. Wiss. Math.-Nat. Kl. **1929**, 1–70 (1930)] in which the additional assumptions about the integers y lead to additional information about the parametric representation. The author first shows that for each sufficiently large prime N there is an integer $\alpha\neq 0$ of K such that the curve C_N: $F(x, \alpha y^N)=0$ also satisfies the hypotheses of Siegel's theorem, from which his result is quickly derived. He further extends the theorem by subjecting x as well as y to the additional hypotheses, obtaining the theorem: Let $\mathfrak{K}$ be a field of finite degree over the rational field, and let $F(x, y)$ be a polynomial with coefficients in $\mathfrak{K}$ which is irreducible over the complex field. Let the curve C: $F(x, y)=0$ contain an infinite set of points (x, y) where x and y are units in $\mathfrak{K}$, or where, more generally, both x and y are divisible only by a finite set of given prime ideals $\mathfrak{p}_1, \mathfrak{p}_2, \cdots, \mathfrak{p}_s$ in $\mathfrak{K}$. Then the polynomial $F(x, y)$ consists of exactly two non-vanishing terms. *H. Levi* (New York, N. Y.).

D40-17 **(13, 208c)**

Obláth, Richard. Une équation diophantienne de M. Segre. Bull. Soc. Roy. Sci. Liège **20**, 199–204 (1951).

A straightforward proof that $y^n=3x(x^2+x+1)$ $(n\geqq 2)$ has no nontrivial integer solutions, together with trivial remarks on the possibility of rational solutions. Errera [same Bull. **19**, 177–186, 213–214 (1950); these Rev. **12**, 200] and Siegel [Errera, ibid. **19**, 404–405 (1950); these Rev. **12**, 853] have already shown that there are no nontrivial rational solutions for $n=2$. *J. W. S. Cassels* (Cambridge, England).

Citations: MR 12, 200f = G05-26; MR 12, 200g = G05-26; MR 12, 853a = G05-27.
Referred to in D40-18.

D40-18 **(13, 321j)**

Oblath, R. Une équation diophantienne de M. Segre (addition). Bull. Soc. Roy. Sci. Liège **20**, 378 (1951).

A correction to the author's paper [same Bull. **20**, 199–204 (1951); these Rev. **13**, 208]. *J. W. S. Cassels.*

Citations: MR 13, 208c = D40-17.

D40-19 **(14, 137a)**

Bini, Umberto. La risoluzione delle equazioni $x^n \pm y^n = M$ e l'ultimo teorema di Fermat. Archimede **4**, 50–57 (1952).

The author gives a number of equations of the form $x^n + y^n = M$ which are impossible in positive coprime integers x, y. The arguments are based on inequalities for $x+y$ and on certain divisibility properties of x^n+y^n.

D. H. Lehmer (Los Angeles, Calif.).

D40-20 **(14, 354d)**

Häggmark, Per. On a class of quintic Diophantine equations in two unknowns. Thesis, University of Uppsala, Almqvist & Wiksells, Uppsala, 1952. 91 pp.

It is proved that (1) $u^5+mv^5=1$ has at most two integral solutions with $v \neq 0$, m being any rational integer. For $|m| \geqq 2060$ it has been established by C. L. Siegel [Math. Ann. **114**, 57–68 (1937)] that this equation, among others, has at most one solution. The author uses a p-adic method developed by Skolem in a series of four papers [we cite the last: Math. Ann. **111**, 399–424 (1935)]. Each solution of (1) gives a corresponding unit $u+v\sqrt[5]{m}$ of $R(\sqrt[5]{m})$. It is established that if (1) has two non-trivial solutions, then the corresponding units form a system of independent units of $R(\sqrt[5]{m})$, and this result is employed in proving the central theorem. *I. Niven* (Eugene, Ore.).

Referred to in D40-22.

D40-21 **(15, 855a)**

Nagell, Trygve. Verallgemeinerung eines Fermatschen Satzes. Arch. Math. **5**, 153–159 (1954).

The Diophantine equation $x^2+2=y^n$ has no solutions for $n>1$ except $x=\pm 5$, $y=3$ in case $n=3$. This is proved with the aid of a theorem of K. Mahler [Arch. Math. Naturvid. **41**, no. 6 (1935)] on the Pell equation. It is also established that for $n>2$, the equation $x^2+8=y^n$ has no solutions except perhaps when n is a prime of the form $8k\pm 1$, and for any such value of n there is at most one solution. *I. Niven.*

Referred to in D40-24.

D40-22 **(16, 13c)**

Domar, Yngve. On the Diophantine equation

$$|Ax^n - By^n| = 1, \quad n \geqq 5.$$

Math. Scand. **2**, 29–32 (1954).

Modifications of a method of Siegel [Math. Ann. **114**, 57–68 (1937)] are used to prove the following two theorems. The Diophantine equation $|Ax^n-By^n|=1$ where A and B are positive integers and $n \geqq 5$ has at most two solutions in positive integers x and y. The equation $|x^n-My^n|=1$ with M positive and $n\geqq 5$ has at most one solution in positive integers, except possibly when $M=2$, and if $n=5$ or 6 when $M=2^n\pm 1$. The latter is, for $n=5$, an improvement of a result of P. Häggmark [Thesis, Univ. of Uppsala, 1952; these Rev. **14**, 354]. *I. Niven* (Eugene, Ore.).

Citations: MR 14, 354d = D40-20.

D40-23 **(16, 13d)**

Obláth, R. Über die Gleichung $x^m+1=y^n$. Ann. Polon. Math. **1**, 73–76 (1954).

Observations on the Diophantine equation $x^m+1=y^n$ under the restriction $|x-y|=1$. *I. Niven.*

D40-24 **(16, 903d)**

Nagell, Trygve. On the Diophantine equation $x^2+8D=y^n$. Ark. Mat. **3**, 103–112 (1955).

Let n be an odd integer >3, and suppose that the class number of $R((-2D)^{1/2})$ is not divisible by n. If $D\equiv 1 \pmod 3$ then the equation $x^2+8D=y^n$ has no solution in integers x and y. This result enables the author to improve an earlier theorem [Arch. Math. **5**, 153–159 (1954); MR **15**, 855] and establish that $x^2+8=y^n$ has no solution in positive integers with $n\geqq 3$; this follows from the general theorem above and the facts that $x^2+8=y^2$ has only the solutions $|x|=1$, $|y|=3$, and $x^2+8=y^3$ only the solution $x=0$, $y=2$. Many other results concerning the equation $x^2+8D=y^n$ are proved, such as the following. Let n be a power of an odd prime of the form $8k\pm 1$, and suppose that the class number of $R((-2D)^{1/2})$ is not divisible by n. Then the equation has at most one solution in positive integers. *I. Niven.*

Citations: MR 15, 855a = D40-21.

D40-25 **(17, 1185g)**

Ljunggren, Wilhelm. New theorems concerning the diophantine equation $Cx^2+D=y^n$. Norske Vid. Selsk. Forh., Trondheim **29** (1956), 1–4.

Let C and D be positive integers such that CD is squarefree, $CD\not\equiv 7 \pmod 8$, D of the form $1+4^m d$ with d odd. Assume further that either $Cd\equiv 5 \pmod 8$ or $C=1$ and $d\equiv 3 \pmod 8$. Then the equation $Cx^2+D=y^p$ has only a finite number of solutions (x, y, p) in positive integers x, y and primes $p>3$ such that p does not divide the class number of the field $R(\sqrt{-CD})$. This extends an earlier result by the writer [Norske Vid. Selsk. Forh., Trondheim **18** (1945), no. 32, 125–128; MR **8**, 136]. It is also proved that $x^2+21=y^n$ and $x+13=y^n$ are impossible in positive integers x, y, $n>2$ apart from the solution $x=70$, $y=17$, $n=3$ of the second equation. *I. Niven.*

Citations: MR 8, 136a = D40-6.
Referred to in D40-38.

D40-26 **(17, 1187a)**

Schäffer, Juan J. The equation $1^p+2^p+3^p+\cdots+n^p=m^q$. Acta Math. **95** (1956), 155–189.

The author shows that for fixed p, q the title equation has an infinite number of solutions only in the following cases. (I) $q=1$ or $p=3$, $q=2$; when every n gives a solution. (II) $p=1$, $q=2$ or $p=3$, $q=4$; when all the solutions are given by $n=\frac{1}{2}(x-1)$, $m=\frac{1}{2}y$ and $x+y\sqrt{2}=(1+\sqrt{2})^r$. (III) $p=5$, $q=2$; when all the solutions are given by $n=\frac{1}{2}(x-1)$, $m=\frac{1}{4}y(3y^2+1)$, $x+y\sqrt{6}=(3+\sqrt{6})(5+2\sqrt{6})^r$.

In all other cases the number of solutions is bounded by a constant depending only on p. The author conjectures that the only other solutions have $m=n=1$ apart from $p=q=2$, $n=24$, $m=70$ and verifies this for extensive classes of (p, q).

The main line of attack is as follows. The left hand side of the title equation may be written

$$n(n+1)(2n+1)P_p(n)/k(p) \qquad (p \text{ even}),$$

$$n^2(n+1)^2P_p(n)/k(p) \qquad (p \text{ odd}),$$

where $k(p)$ is an integer and $P_p(x)$ is a polynomial in x with integer coefficients which have no common factor. Further, $P_p(x)$ has no factor x, $x+1$ or $2x+1$. For, say, even p the title equation implies that n, $n+1$, $2n+1$ are all perfect qth powers multiplied by bounded factors, the bound depending only on p. (And similarly for odd p.) The resulting equations may then be shown insoluble by a wide variety of methods based on an extensive knowledge of the literature.

Of independent interest is the fact that $P_p(x)$ is a polynomial in $y=x(x+1)$ which, for odd p, is neither of the shape $\{T(y)\}^2$ nor $(Ay+B)\{T(y)\}^2$, where $T(y)$ is a polynomial, except for $p=3$, 5 respectively.

J. W. S. Cassels (Cambridge, England).

Referred to in A64-9, B64-35.

D40-27 (18, 565d)

Mahler, K. A remark on Siegel's theorem on algebraic curves. Mathematika 2 (1955), 116–127.

Siegel has proved that an irreducible curve $f(x, y)=0$, of genus $\geqq 1$, where f is a polynomial with algebraic coefficients, has only a finite number of points (x, y) satisfying the following conditions: y is in some preassigned algebraic number field K, and, for some fixed integer $j>0$, jx is an integer in K. This theorem is generalized as follows: let $f(x, y)=0$ be an arbitrary irreducible algebraic curve of genus $\geqq 1$ (the coefficients of f being complex numbers); let X be a finitely generated additive subgroup of the field C of complex numbers, and let Y be a vector subspace of finite dimension of C (considered as a vector space over the field of rationals); then $f(x, y)=0$ has only a finite number of points such that $x \in X$, $y \in Y$. The proof consists in reducing this statement to the statement of Siegel's theorem by a suitable specialisation of the coefficients of f and of the generators of X and Y.

C. Chevalley (Paris).

Referred to in G30-26.

D40-28 (19, 115b)

Shapiro, Harold S. The range of an integer-valued polynomial. Amer. Math. Monthly **64** (1957), 424–425.

A proof of the following theorem. Let $P(x)$ and $Q(x)$ be polynomials which are integer-valued at the integers, of degrees p and q respectively. If $P(n)$ is of the form $Q(m)$ for all n, or even for infinitely many blocks of consecutive integers of length $\geqq p/q+2$, then there is a polynomial $R(x)$ such that $P(x)=Q[R(x)]$.

From the author's summary.

D40-29 (21# 1952)

Stolt, Bengt. Die Anzahl von Lösungen gewisser diophantischer Gleichungen. Arch. Math. **8** (1957), 393–400.

The author discusses the equation (1) $x^2+x+\frac{1}{4}(D+1)=y^q$, where q is an odd prime and D a positive integer, $D\equiv 3 \pmod 4$ and square-free. Let h denote the number of ideal classes in the field $K(\sqrt{-D})$ and $D_1=\frac{1}{4}(D+1)$. For given values of D and q the following theorem is proved: (1) has at most one solution in positive integers x, y if $(h, q)=1$, and either D_1 is even or D_1 is odd and at the same time $q\equiv 5 \pmod 6$. (1) has at most three solutions if D_1 is odd and $q\equiv 1 \pmod 6$. This generalizes a result due to B. Persson [Ark. Mat. **1** (1949), 45–57; MR **11**, 328]. In the proof use is made of an idea of Persson.

W. Ljunggren (Oslo)

Citations: MR 11, 328e = D40-15.

D40-30 (22# 1541)

Stolt, B. Über einen verallgemeinerten Fermatschen Satz. Acta Arith. **5**, 267–276 (1959).

The author treats the Diophantine equation $Cx^2+D=y^q$, where q is an odd prime, C and D are positive integers such that CD is square free, $CD\not\equiv 7 \pmod 8$, and q does not divide the class number $h(\sqrt{-CD})$. For certain values of C, D, and q the equation is shown to have no integer solutions. Let q and D be fixed, $D\neq 1, 3$. If $q\equiv 3 \pmod 4$ and $q>3$, or if $q=3$ and D is even, then there is at most one value of C, such that the above conditions are satisfied, for which the equation has solutions. For that value of C there is at most one solution in positive integers x, y. If $q=3$ and D is odd, then as C runs through all admissible values there are at most two solutions in positive integers. If $q\equiv 1 \pmod 4$, then D must be odd, and there is at most one solution for which C is odd and at most one solution for which $CD\equiv 6 \pmod 8$.

W. H. Mills (Berkeley, Calif.)

D40-31 (22# 1544)

Ward, Morgan. The vanishing of the homogeneous product sum of the roots of a cubic. Duke Math. J. **26** (1959), 553–562.

Let H_n denote the homogeneous product sum of x_1, x_2, x_3 of degree n:

$$H_n = \sum_{r_1+r_2+r_3=n} x_1^{r_1}x_2^{r_2}x_3^{r_3}.$$

The following results are proved. (1) If $n>1$, the diophantine equation $H_n=0$ has a non-trivial solution if and only if for this value of n there exists a trinomial $\phi(t)=t^{n+2}+pt+q$ with p and q relatively prime and $q\neq 0$ which has three integral roots. (2) If n is even the diophantine equation $H_n=0$ has only trivial solutions. (3) The diophantine equation $H_3=0$ has only trivial solutions.

The proof of the third result is by descent and makes use of properties of the field $R(\sqrt{-3})$. The author remarks that by the same method it can be proved that each of the equations $x_1^2x_2+\cdots+x_2x_3^2=0$ and $x^3+y^3+z^3=5xyz$ has only trivial solutions. The last result was obtained by Mordell [*Colloque sur la théorie des nombres, Bruxelles, 1955*, pp. 67–76, Thone, Liège, 1956; MR **17**, 1185] by a different method. *L. Carlitz* (Durham, N.C.)

Citations: MR 17, 1185f = D32-54.

Referred to in D40-33.

D40-32 (22# 1545)

af Ekenstam, Adolf. Contributions to the theory of the Diophantine equation $Ax^n-By^n=C$. Inaugural dissertation, Univ. of Uppsala. Almqvist & Wiksells Boktryckeri AB, Uppsala, 1959. 63 pp.

Let A_i, B_i, C_i be positive integers, for $i=1, 2, \cdots, g$. If all the numbers $(A_i/B_i)^{1/n}$ define the same extension of the field K of rational numbers, the Diophantine equations $|A_ix^n-B_iy^n|=C_i$, for $i=1, 2, \cdots, g$, are said to belong to the same class. In the first chapter it is shown that at most one of a set of equations of the same class is solvable in relatively prime x and y, under the following hypotheses: $(A_iB_i, C_i)=1$, A_iB_i nth power free, $n\geqq 4$, and $\min_i(A_iB_i)$ larger than an explicitly given function of n and $\max_i(C_i)$. More precise results are obtained in the special cases $C_i=1$ for all i and $A_i=C_i=1$ for all i. In the second chapter the inequality $|Ax^n-By^n|\leqq C$ is considered, where A, B and C are fixed, and x and y are variable, integers of $K(\sqrt{-m})$, in the cases $n=m=3$ and $n=4$, $m=1$. It is shown that there is essentially at most one solution if $(A, B)=1$, $|A/B|^{2/n}$ is irrational, and $|AB|$ is larger than an explicit function of $|C|$. The first two chapters use the method of Siegel [Math. Ann. **114** (1937), 57–68] depending on identities between hypergeometric functions.

In Chapter 3 the following assertion of Tartakovskiĭ is proved: Let n be $\geqq 3$ and M a positive integer, not a square. If the equation $x^{2n}-My^{2n}=1$ has a solution $x=x_1$, $y=y_1$ in positive integers, then $x_1^n+y_1^n\sqrt{M}$ is the fundamental unit ε of $K(\sqrt{M})$, or its square, the latter occurring for only finitely many M. If $N(\varepsilon)=-1$, the equation has no solution with $y_1\neq 0$. The proof depends on a result of Siegel in the paper cited above.

W. J. LeVeque (Ann Arbor, Mich.)

D40-33 (22# 5609)

Ward, Morgan. The vanishing of the homogeneous product sum on three letters. Duke Math. J. **27** (1960), 619–624.

By the homogeneous product sum $H_n = H_n(x, y, z)$ is understood the sum of all the symmetric functions of weight n. In a previous paper [same J. **26** (1959), 553–562; MR **22** #1544] the author showed that for n even the equation $H_n = 0$ has only trivial solutions. He proved also by descent that $H_3 = 0$ has only trivial solutions. In the present paper the following theorem is proved:

The diophantine equation $H_n(x, y, z) = 0$ has only trivial solutions whenever $n+2$ is a prime number >3.

The proof is by contradiction and makes use of the cyclotomic field $R(e^{2\pi i/p})$, where $p = n+2$.

L. Carlitz (Durham, N.C.)

Citations: MR 22# 1544 = D40-31.

D40-34 (22# 9472)

Makowski, A.; Schinzel, A. Sur l'équation indéterminée de R. Goormaghtigh. Mathesis **68** (1959), 128–142.

R. Goormaghtigh conjectured that the only solution of $N = 1+x+\cdots+x^m = 1+y+\cdots+y^n$, $m>n>1$, $y>x>1$, are $N=31$, $y=5$, $x=2$, $m=4$, $n=2$ and $N=8191$, $y=90$, $x=2$, $m=12$, $n=2$. The authors prove several special cases of this conjecture. *P. Erdös* (Budapest)

D40-35 (22# 10952)

Lewis, D. J.; Mahler, K. On the representation of integers by binary forms. Acta Arith. **6** (1960/61), 333–363.

The authors improve earlier results of Davenport and Roth [Mathematika **2** (1955), 160–167; MR **17**, 1060] and Mahler [Math. Ann. **107** (1933), 691–730; **108** (1933), 37–55] concerning the number of solutions of the diophantine equation $F(x, y) = m$, where $F(x, y)$ is a form of degree n at least 3, with integral coefficients numerically smaller than a and with nonzero discriminant, and m is an integer different from 0. Specifically, it is shown that there are not more than $c_1(an)^{c_2\sqrt{n}} + (c_3n)^{t+1}$ pairs x, y with $x \neq 0$, $y>0$, and $(x, y)=1$, for which $F(x, y) \neq 0$ has at most t given prime factors $p_1, \cdots, p_t$. Here c_1, c_2, c_3 are positive absolute constants (of the order of magnitude of 100). It follows that if $|m| > m_0(a, n)$, then the number of primitive solutions of $F(x, y) = m$ is not greater than $(c_3n)^{t+1}$; this bound is independent of the coefficients of the form. The proof depends on the Mahler-Parry p-adic Thue-Siegel theorem.

As an application, an upper bound is obtained for the number of solutions of an equation of the form

$$p_{11}^{x_{11}}\cdots p_{1r}^{x_{1r}} + p_{21}^{x_{21}}\cdots p_{2s}^{x_{2s}} = p_{31}^{x_{31}}\cdots p_{3t}^{x_{3t}},$$

where the p_{ij} are fixed distinct primes.

W. J. LeVeque (Ann Arbor, Mich.)

Citations: MR 17, 1060d = J68-15.

Referred to in D60-49.

D40-36 (23# A2369)

Fried, Ervin; Surányi, János

Neuer Beweis eines zahlentheoretischen Satzes über Polynome. (Hungarian. Russian and German summaries)

Mat. Lapok **11** (1960), 75–84.

The authors give a new elementary proof for the following known result: Let $f(x)$ be a polynomial, k an integer and $\{u_m\}$ a sequence of integers sueh that $f(m) = u_m^k$, $m = 0, 1, \cdots$; then $f(x) \equiv [g(x)]^k$ for some polynomial $g(x)$.

G. Freud (Budapest)

D40-37 (25# 1152)

Davenport, H.; Lewis, D. J.; Schinzel, A.

Equations of the form $f(x) = g(y)$.

Quart. J. Math. Oxford Ser. (2) **12** (1961), 304–312.

Let f, g be two polynomials with integral coefficients; in view of Siegel's theorem that a curve of positive genus has only finitely many integral points, it is clear that the equation $f(x) = g(y)$ will have only finitely many integral solutions if the curve $f(x) = g(y)$ is irreducible and of positive genus. However, it seems to be a difficult and interesting problem to characterise the cases in which $f(x) - g(y)$ is reducible. The authors give a non-obvious case of reducibility, and a reasonably weak condition which ensures irreducibility. They apply their results to the particular equation $1+x+\cdots+x^n = 1+y+\cdots+y^m$, showing that if $n>m>1$, this equation has at most a finite number of solutions.

B. J. Birch (Cambridge, England)

Referred to in D40-39, R08-59.

D40-38 (28# 5035)

Ljunggren, W.

On the Diophantine equation $Cx^2 + D = y^n$.

Pacific J. Math. **14** (1964), 585–596.

The author extends his results [see Norske Vid. Selsk. Forh. (Trondjhem) **18** (1945), no. 32, 125–128; MR **8**, 136; ibid. **29** (1956), 1–4; MR **17**, 1185] on the number of integral triples x, y, z such that $Cx^2 + D = y^z$. Typical of his results is the following. Let D be an odd square-free integer greater than 1. If z is an odd prime, prime to the class number of $Q(\sqrt{-D})$ and $\not\equiv 3 \pmod 8$, then the equation $x^2 + 4D = y^z$ has no integral solutions with y odd. Furthermore, for a given D, there are but finitely many x, y, and prime z such that $x^2 + 4D = y^z$, and bounds can be given on the size of y and z after finitely many arithmetical operations. The author's theorems lead to generalizations and extensions of results of the reviewer [Pacific J. Math. **11** (1961), 1063–1076; MR **25** #3005] for the cases $C=1$, $D=7$ and 28. The proofs make use of Skolem's p-adic method as refined by the author. The paper concludes with a short historical review of the general problem.

D. J. Lewis (Ann Arbor, Mich.)

Citations: MR 8, 136a = D40-6; MR 17, 1185g = D40-25; MR 25# 3005 = D60-49.

Referred to in D24-69.

D40-39 (29# 3428)

Karanicoloff, Chr.

Sur une équation diophantienne considérée par Goormaghtigh.

Ann. Polon. Math. **14** (1963), 69–76.

Let $g_n(x) = 1+x+\cdots+x^n$. The author is concerned with integral solutions of equations of the type $g_m(x) = g_n(y)$, where $m>n>1$, $y>x>1$. Goormaghtigh [Intermód. Math. **24** (1917), 88; errata, p. 153] proved that there were exactly two 4-tuples (m, n, x, y) such that $g_m(x) = g_n(y) < 10^6$. Kanold [Math. Ann. **132** (1956), 246–255; MR **18**, 718] proved that for fixed x and y there are finitely many m and n such that $g_m(x) = g_n(y)$. Davenport, Lewis and Schinzel [Quart. J. Math. Oxford Ser. (2) **12** (1961), 304–312; MR **25** #1152] proved that for fixed m and n there are finitely many x and y such that $g_m(x) = g_n(y)$, and in case $(n, m) = d > 1$ or $m = n+1$, the solutions could be enumerated by use of Runge's method. In this paper the author shows that the only solution of $g_{2n}(x) = g_n(y)$ is $n=2$, $y=5$, $x=2$. The proof is elementary.

D. J. Lewis (Ann Arbor, Mich.)

Citations: MR 18, 718a = A32-63; MR 25# 1152 = D40-37.

D40-40 (30# 56)

LeVeque, W. J.

On the equation $y^m = f(x)$.

Acta Arith. **9** (1964), 209–219.

Verfasser gibt eine vollständige Beschreibung der Fälle in welchen die Gleichung $\mathcal{G}$ im Titel eine unendliche sogenannte quasi-ganze Menge von Lösungen in einem algebraischen Zahlkörper K hat. Die unendliche Teilmenge $G_K \subset K$ heisst quasi-ganz wenn für eine passende ganze Zahl $\eta \in K$, ηG_K aus lauter ganzen Zahlen besteht. Folgendes ist bewiesen: k sei ein algebraischer Zahlkörper, O_k der Ring der ganzen Zahlen aus k und $f(x) \in O_k[x]$. $\mathcal{G}$ hat eine unendliche Menge von Lösungen in einer endlichen algebraischen Erweiterung K von k, wo die Menge X der x-Werte eine quasi-ganze Menge ist nur in den folgenden drei Fällen ($f_i(x)$ bezeichnet für $i = 1, 2, 3, 4$ Polynome aus $O_k[x]$): (i) $f(x) = \lambda^m f_1{}^m(x)$, $\lambda \in K$, $\lambda^m \in k$; (ii) $f(x) = \lambda^{m/s}(x-\alpha)^{mt/s} f_2{}^m(x)$, $s|m$, $(t, s) = 1$, $\lambda \in K$, $\lambda^{m/s}, \alpha \in k$; (iii) $f(x) = \lambda^{m/2} f_3{}^{mt/2}(x) f_4{}^m(x)$, m gerade, t ungerade, $\lambda \in K$, $\lambda^{m/2} \in k$, wo $f_3(x)$ von zweitem Grad ist und im Falle (iii) noch zwei Arten von Ausnahmen angegeben sind. In diesen Fällen gibt Verfasser auch eine Übersicht der quasi-ganzen Mengen von Lösungen und einige Abschätzungen an. Die Beweise knüpfen C. L. Siegels [J. London Math. Soc. **1** (1926), 66–68], elementaren idealtheoretischen Überlegungen an. *J. Surányi* (Budapest)

D40-41 **(30# 1975)**

Chowla, S.

Remarks on two theorems of Siegel.

Acta Arith. **9** (1964), 417–418.

If the equation $ax^n - by^n = c$ has three solutions (x_1, y_1), (x_2, y_2), (x_3, y_3), then clearly

$$\begin{vmatrix} x_1{}^n & y_1{}^n & 1 \\ x_2{}^n & y_2{}^n & 1 \\ x_3{}^n & y_3{}^n & 1 \end{vmatrix} = 0.$$

The author points out that this determinant cannot vanish for $n \geqq 7$ if the following conjecture (C) holds: The equation $\sum_{m=1}^{n} \pm X_m{}^n = 0$ is impossible in positive integers X_m, unless it is trivially possible (i.e., by "cancellation"). *W. J. LeVeque* (Ann Arbor, Mich.)

Referred to in D48-70.

D40-42 **(31# 3377)**

Inkeri, K.; Hyyrö, S.

Über die Anzahl der Lösungen einiger Diophantischer Gleichungen.

Ann. Univ. Turku. Ser. A I No. 78 (1964), 10 *pp.*

By a method resembling that of Siegel, for $m = 2$ [J. London Math. Soc. **1** (1926), 66–68], it is shown that there are only a finite number of integral solutions of the equation $f(x) = y^m$ for $m \geqq 2$, where $f(x)$ is a polynomial of degree $n \geqq 2$. There are applications to equations of the type $x^m + y^n = z^n$, which are also discussed by elementary means. *J. W. S. Cassels* (Cambridge, England)

D40-43 **(32# 1164)**

Chao Ko

On the Diophantine equation $x^2 = y^n + 1$, $xy \neq 0$.

Sci. Sinica **14** (1965), 457–460.

In an earlier paper [Acta Sci. Natur. Univ. Szechuan. **2** (1960), 57–64] the author proved that the Diophantine equation in the title has no solutions when n is a prime $p \equiv 5$ or 7 (mod 8). In this paper he proves that it has no solutions for all remaining primes $p > 3$. The treatment in these cases is brief and elementary. Nagell [Norsk Math. Forenings Skr. (1) No. 4 (1921)] discussed the same equation and showed its impossibility in a large number of special cases. Ko's work now shows that there are no solutions other than $n = 3$, $x = \pm 3$, $y = 2$. *T. M. Apostol* (Pasadena, Calif.)

Referred to in D40-55.

D40-44 **(34# 4200)**

Ljunggren, W.

On the diophantine equation $Cx^2 + D = 2y^n$.

Math. Scand. **18** (1966), 69–86.

A. Thue [Ark. Mat. Naturv. (Kristiania) **34** (1917)] has proved that the equation $a + bx + cx^2 = dy^n$ (where $n \geqq 3$, $a \neq 0$, b, c, $d \neq 0$ are integers such that $b^2 - 4ac \neq 0$) has only finitely many integral solutions. However, no general method is known for determining the solutions for any given equation of that type. Various special cases have been discussed by V. A. Lebesgue, C. Störmer, T. Nagell, the author and others (see the relatively long bibliography to this paper). In this paper, the author discusses the equations $x^2 + D = 2y^n$, where n is a power of an odd prime q, D is a square-free integer greater than one and $D \equiv 1 \pmod 4$, and the class number of the complex quadratic field $Q(\sqrt{-D})$ is not divisible by n. His results include the following. If $q \equiv 1 \pmod 4$ and $D^2 - 1 = 2^{2m+1} D_1$, D_1 odd or $D^2 - 1 = 2^{2m} D_2$, D_2 odd and $\not\equiv q \pmod 8$, then $x^2 + D = 2y^n$ has no integral solutions. If $q \equiv \pm 3 \pmod 8$ then the finitely many solutions of $x^2 + D = 2y^n$ can be obtained in a finite number of steps. The proofs make use of the "Skolem p-adic" method, various polynomial identities, and a result of J. W. S. Cassels [Ark. Mat. **4** (1961), 231–233; MR **24** #A84] on an effective method for solving certain binary quadratic polynomials. *D. J. Lewis* (Ann Arbor, Mich.)

Citations: MR 24# A84 = D60-44.

D40-45 **(35# 6622)**

Dimiev, Veselin

A generalization of a theorem of Thue. **(Bulgarian)**

Fiz.-Mat. Spis. B"lgar. Akad. Nauk. **9 (42)** (1966), 222–224.

A. Thue proved the following theorem: If $f(z) = a_0 z^n + a_1 z^{n-1} + \cdots + a_n$ is a polynomial of degree $n \geqq 3$ and $f(z)$ is irreducible in the field of rational numbers, then the equation $F(x, y) = a_0 x^n + a_1 x^{n-1} y + \cdots + a_n y^n = c$ (with c an integer) has at most a finite number of zeros.

By using this theorem and some considerations about divisibility, the author proves the following theorem: If $n > m$, $n \geqq 3$ and if the polynomial $f(z) = a_0 z^n + a_1 z^{n-1} + \cdots + a_n$ is irreducible in the field of rational numbers, the equation $F(x, y) = G(x, y)$, where $F(x, y) = a_0 x^n + a_1 x^{n-1} y + \cdots + a_n y^n$, $G(x, y) = b_0 x^m + b_1 x^{m-1} y + \cdots + b_m y^m$ ($a_0 \neq 0$, $a_1, \cdots, a_n, b_0, b_1, \cdots, b_m$ are integers), has at most a finite number of zeros in integers.

{Reviewer's remark: The last theorem was also proved by Thue [Vid. Selsk. Skrift. (Kristiania) Mat. Naturvid. Kl. No. 3 (1911)], but this fact evidently was not known to the author and he discovered it anew.}

T. T. Tonkov (Leningrad)

D40-46 **(36# 3720)**

Babaev, G.

The number of solutions of the indeterminate equation $f(x, y) = F(x, y)$, and the connection with continued fractions. **(Russian)**

Tadžik. Gos. Univ. Učen. Zap. **26** (1963), *vyp.* 1, 21–30.

Die Form $f(x, y) = a_0 x^n + a_1 x^{n-1} y + \cdots + a_n y^n$, $a_0 \neq 0$, habe ganze Koeffizienten; $F(x, y)$ sei ein ganzzahliges Polynom vom Grade $m < n$. Der Autor gibt—gestützt auf den Approximationssatz von K. F. Roth [Mathematika **2** (1955), 1–20; corrigendum, ibid. **2** (1955), 168; MR **17**, 242]—hinreichende Bedingungen dafür, daß die Gleichung (*) $f(x, y) = F(x, y)$ höchstens endlich viele ganzzahlige Lösungen x, y besitzt. So beweist der Autor etwa: Es bezeichne k die größte Vielfachheit der reellen Wurzeln von $f(x, 1)$; es sei $F(ay, y) \not\equiv 0$ für jede rationale Wurzel a von $f(x, 1) = 0$. Ist $m \leqq n - 2k - 1$, so hat (*) höchstens endlich viele ganzzahlige Lösungen x, y.

Eine Folgerung aus einem weiteren Satz verdient Erwähnung: Ist $[q_1, q_2, \cdots]$ der (periodische) Kettenbruch für $\sqrt{D}$, so ist $\max_\nu q_\nu > 2\sqrt{D}-2$.

W. Schwarz (Freiburg)

Citations: MR 17, 242d = J68-14.

D40-47 **(36# 3724)**

Nagell, Trygve

Sur quelques propriétés arithmétiques des formes binaires à coefficients entiers.

Ark. Mat. **7**, 241–248 (1967).

Let $F(x, y) = a_0x^n + a_1x^{n-1}y + \cdots + a_ny^n$, $a_0, \cdots, a_n$ rational integers, be a binary form irreducible over the rationals. If K is a field of nth degree generated by the equation $a_0x^n + a_1x^{n-1} + \cdots + a_n = 0$ then $F(x, y)$ is said to be constructed on K. It is shown that if K is an algebraic field of nth degree, $n \geqq 3$, and c is any nonzero rational integer, then there exist infinitely many classes of binary forms of the nth degree constructed on K which cannot represent c. If $F(x, y)$ is an irreducible binary form having the fixed maximal divisor δ then there exist infinitely many integers, pairwise relatively prime, which cannot be represented by the form $F(x, y)/\delta$. Upper bounds for the number of nonassociated solutions in relatively prime rational integers x and y for equations $N(x-\theta y) = a$ are given for certain fields $K(\theta)$. Here a is a natural

D40-48 **(36# 5077)**

Győry, K.

Note sur un théorème de H. Davenport et de K. F. Roth.

Publ. Math. Debrecen **14** (1967), 331–335.

The following generalization of the theorems of A. Thue [Skr. Vid. Selsk. Christiania **1908**, no. 7] and H. Davenport and K. F. Roth [Mathematika **2** (1955), 160–167; MR **17**, 1060] is proved: Let $f(x, y) = a_0x^n + a_1x^{n-1}y + \cdots + a_ny^n$ be a homogeneous polynomial of degree $n \geqq 3$ with rational integer coefficients such that $a_0a_n \neq 0$. Let $g(x, y) \neq 0$ be a polynomial with rational coefficients of degree s. Suppose f and g are relatively prime. Let l = maximum of the multiplicities of the rational roots of $f(x, 1)$ and let k = maximum of the multiplicities of the real irrational roots of $f(x, 1)$. Assume $l < n$, $2k < n$ and $s < n - \max(l, 2k)$. Then the diophantine equation $f(x, y) = g(x, y)$ has only finitely many solutions in rational integers x, y. The proof, of course, reduces this problem to the theorem of K. F. Roth [ibid. **2** (1955), 1–20; corrigendum, ibid. **2** (1955), 168; MR **17**, 242] on the rational approximations of algebraic numbers.

W. W. Adams (Berkeley, Calif.)

Citations: MR 17, 242d = J68-14; MR 17, 1060d = J68-15.

D40-49 **(37# 151)**

Vinogradov, A. I.; Sprindžuk, V. G.

The representation of numbers by binary forms. (Russian)

Mat. Zametki **3** (1968), 369–376.

If A is a rational integer and $f(x, y)$ is an integral binary form of degree greater than 2, irreducible over the rationals, then by a well known theorem of Thue the equation $f(x, y) = A$ has only a finite number of rational integer solutions. In this paper the authors give an effective procedure for the determination of all rational solutions whose denominators contain only primes belonging to given fixed finite sets of primes. The results are based on those of A. Baker [Mathematika **13** (1966), 204–216; ibid. **14** (1967), 102–107; ibid. **14** (1967), 220–228; MR **36** #3732] and p-adic generalizations due to the second author [Dokl. Akad. Nauk BSSR **11** (1967), 767–769; MR **36** #1396].

J. B. Roberts (Portland, Ore.)

Citations: MR 36# 1396 = J80-24; MR 36# 3732 = J80-26.

D40-50 **(37# 4005)**

Baker, A. [Baker, Alan]

Contributions to the theory of Diophantine equations. I. On the representation of integers by binary forms.

Philos. Trans. Roy. Soc. London Ser. A **263** (1967/68), 173–191.

An effective algorithm is established for solving in integers x, y any diophantine equation of the type $f(x, y) = m$, where f denotes an irreducible binary form with integer coefficients and degree at least 3. Thue (1909) proved that the number of solutions is finite, but his method was not effective. Thue deduced this result from his investigation (sharpening Liouville's 1844 result) of the accuracy with which algebraic numbers can be approximated by rationals. Later improvements by Siegel (1921) and Roth (1955) suffered from the same defect. A proof of Thue's theorem, in the case when $f(x, 1)$ has at least one complex zero, was given by Skolem (1935) by means of a $\mathfrak{p}$-adic argument very different from the original, but also noneffective. The present paper is "devoted to a new proof" of Thue's theorem, "which proceeds by an argument that is effective". Let $f(x, y)$ denote a homogeneous polynomial in x, y with degree $n \geqq 3$ and with integer coefficients, irreducible over the rationals. Suppose that $\kappa > n+1$ and let m be any positive integer. The author's first theorem states that all solutions of $f(x, y) = m$ in integers x, y satisfy $\max(|x|, |y|) < Ce^{(\log m)^\kappa}$, where C is an effectively computable number depending only on n, κ and the coefficients of f. This is certainly a remarkable theorem. The proof depends essentially on the methods developed by the author in two recent papers for the study of linear forms in the logarithms of algebraic numbers [Mathematika **13** (1966), 204–216; ibid. **14** (1967), 102–107; ibid. **14** (1967), 220–228; MR **36** #3732].

The second theorem of the author is an immediate deduction: Suppose that α is an algebraic number with degree $n \geqq 3$ and that $\kappa > n+1$. Then there is an effectively computable number $c = c(\alpha, \kappa) > 0$ such that $|\alpha - p/q| > cq^{-n}e^{(\log q)^{1/\kappa}}$ for all integers p, q $(q > 0)$. This is the "first generally effective improvement" on the well-known result of Liouville.

We emphasize that the author has solved an outstanding problem. {Reviewer's remarks: As the author remarks, he has solved Hilbert's tenth problem in a special case, $f(x, y) = m$, where f is a "form" of degree $\geqq 3$. It is generally believed that Hilbert's tenth problem has a negative answer in the general case, i.e., there exist diophantine equations $f(x, y) = 0$, where f is a polynomial in x, y of degree $\geqq 3$, for which no finite algorithm exists to find all solutions (supposed finite in number). In the case of "exponential" diophantine equations, it has been proved by H. Putnam, M. Davis and J. Robinson that a finite algorithm does not, in general, exist. We also quote the result of Putnam and Davis that Hilbert's tenth problem has a negative answer if the following is true: For arbitrary $A > 0$ there exists a "d" such that the equation $x^3 - dy^3 = 1$ has a solution with $x > d^A$.}

S. Chowla (University Park, Pa.)

Citations: MR 36# 3732 = J80-26.

Referred to in D24-70, D24-71, D24-72, D40-52, D60-78, J80-28, J80-39.

D40-51 **(38# 3226)**

Baker, A. [Baker, Alan]

Bounds for the solutions of the hyperelliptic equation.

Proc. Cambridge Philos. Soc. **65** (1969), 439–444.

Der Autor beweist folgende zwei Sätze über diophantische Gleichungen: Satz 1: (1) Sei $y^m = a_0x^n + a_1x^{n-1} + \cdots + a_n$ mit $m \geqq 3$, $n \geqq 3$; $a_0 = 0$, $a_1, \cdots, a_n$ ganz, wobei das Polynom auf der rechten Seite von (1) mindestens 2 einfache Nullstellen habe und sei $H = \max|a_j|$. Dann gilt für jede ganzzahlige Lösung x, y von (1),

$$\max\{|x|, |y|\} < \exp\exp\{(5m)^{10}(n^{10n}H)^{n^2}\}.$$

Satz 2: Ist $m = 2$ und hat das Polynom auf der rechten Seite von (1) mindestens 3 einfache Lösungen, dann gehorchen alle ganzzahligen Lösungen x, y von (1), $\max\{|x|, |y|\} < \exp\exp\exp\{(n^{10n}H)^{n^2}\}$.

J. M. Wills (Berlin)

Referred to in G05-101.

D40-52 **(39# 4095)**

Coates, J.

An effective p-adic analogue of a theorem of Thue.

Acta Arith. **15** (1968/69), 279–305.

In 1909 A. Thue [J. Reine Angew. Math. **135** (1909), 284–305] proved that the diophantine equation (1) $f(x, y) = m$, where f denotes an irreducible binary form with integral coefficients and degree at least 3, m an integer, has only a finite number of solutions in integers x, y. A. Baker [Philos. Trans. Roy. Soc. London Ser. A **263** (1967/68), 173–191; MR **37** #4005; ibid. **263** (1967/68), 193–208; MR **37** #4006] gave another proof of Thue's theorem, obtaining an explicit upper bound for the size of all integral solutions of (1). In the present paper p-adic analogues of Baker's results are proved by the method used by him. *B. Stolt* (Stockholm)

Citations: MR 37# 4005 = D40-50; MR 37# 4006 = D24-70.

Referred to in D40-57, D40-58.

D40-53 **(40# 7226)**

Lovász, László

Connections between number theoretic properties of polynomials and their substitutional values. (Hungarian)

Mat. Lapok **20** (1969), 129–132.

A proof is given for the well-known fact that a polynomial over the integers is the kth power of a polynomial if its substitutional values at integers are kth powers.

L. Fuchs (New Orleans, La.)

D40-54 **(41# 148)**

Blanpain, M. E.

Sur l'équation diophantienne $x^n - d^2y^n = 2d$.

Elem. Math. **25** (1970), 35.

From the author's introduction: "Dans cette note, nous prouvons le théorème suivant. Théorème: L'équation: $x^n - d^2y^n = 2d$, x, y, d, n dans Z, $xy \neq 0$, $n > 1$, ne possède, outre les solutions triviales $x = -y = d = \pm 1$, n impair, que les quatre solutions $x = 2\varepsilon$, $y = \varepsilon$, $d = 2\varepsilon$ ou -4ε, $n = 3$ ($\varepsilon = \pm 1$)."

D40-55 **(41# 3391)**

Nagell, Trygve

Remarques sur une catégorie d'équations diophantiennes à deux indéterminées.

Ark. Mat. **8**, 49–62 (1969).

Let a, b and n denote natural numbers. The author discusses the solvability of some equations of the type (1) $y^2 - a^2 = bz^n$ in natural numbers y and z. In case $a = b = 1$ he partly reproduces investigations from 1921 and 1935, feeling that the results there obtained have been overlooked. He now proves: Let $n > 3$ and suppose that $y^2 - 1 = z^n$ has the solution $y = y_1$, $z = z_1$, in natural numbers. Then n must be a prime $n \equiv 1 \pmod 8$ such that 2 is not a biquadratic rest mod n, and there are no other solutions in natural numbers. However, as remarked in a footnote at the end of the paper, the Chinese mathematician Chao Ko has shown the impossibility in case $n \equiv 1 \pmod 8$ [Sci. Sinica **14** (1965), 457–460; MR **32** #1164].

The author also obtains some results in the cases (i) $a = 1$, $b > 1$, $n \geqq 5$ and (ii) $b = 1$, n and a being primes. At last he gives the complete solution of the equation $x^3 - 1 = bz^n$ in case $b > 1$, b without any prime factors $\equiv 1 \pmod 6$, n odd. *W. Ljunggren* (Oslo)

Citations: MR 32# 1164 = D40-43.

D40-56 **(41# 3442)**

Berstel, Jean

Sur des fractions rationnelles particulières.

C. R. Acad. Sci. Paris Sér. A-B **270** (1970), A304–A306.

A subset A of the natural numbers N is "arithmetically dense" if A contains a member of every arithmetic progression. The author proves the following theorem: Let $f \in Q(X)$ be a rational function with rational coefficients and let A be an arithmetically dense subset of N. Then (a) if, for some $g \in Q(X)$, we have $f(A) \in g(N)$, then there is a polynomial $r \in Q[X]$ such that $f = g \circ r$, (b) if, for some monic polynomial $p \in Z[X]$, we have $f(A) \in p(Q)$, then there is a rational function $h \in Q(X)$ such that $f = p \circ h$.

Setting $p(X) = X^k$, one deduces as a corollary that a rational function with rational coefficients whose values on an arithmetically dense set are kth powers of rational numbers must itself be the kth power of a rational function with rational coefficients.

The theorem is a fairly elementary consequence of the corresponding theorem for polynomials established by H. Davenport, D. J. Lewis and A. Schinzel [Acta Arith. **9** (1964), 107–116; MR **29** #1179].

J. B. Kelly (Tempe, Ariz.)

Citations: MR 29# 1179 = D56-23.

D40-57 **(41# 8341)**

Coates, J.

An effective p-adic analogue of a theorem of Thue. II. The greatest prime factor of a binary form.

Acta Arith. **16** (1969/70), 399–412.

In 1909 A. Thue [J. Reine Angew. Math. **135** (1909), 284–305] proved that the diophantine equation (1) $f(x, y) = m$, where f denotes an irreducible binary form with integral coefficients and degree at least 3, m an integer, has only a finite number of solutions in integers x, y. The author continues his work on p-adic analogues on this theorem [Acta Arith. **15** (1968/69), 279–305; MR **39** #4095], giving an upper bound for $|x|$, $|y|$ of the solutions of (1), when certain conditions are satisfied. *B. Stolt* (Stockholm)

Citations: MR 39# 4095 = D40-52.

Referred to in N32-67.

D40-58 **(41# 8342)**

Coates, J.

An effective p-adic analogue of a theorem of Thue. III. The diophantine equation $y^2 = x^3 + k$.

Acta Arith. **16** (1969/70), 425–435.

The author applies the method of his earlier papers of the same title [Part I; MR **39** #4095; Part II; #8341 above] to the diophantine equation $y^2 = x^3 + k$, giving an upper bound for $|x|$, $|y|$ of integral solutions satisfying certain conditions. *B. Stolt* (Stockholm)

Citations: MR 39# 4095 = D40-52.
Referred to in N32-67.

D40-59 **(42# 4491)**

Tartakovskiĭ, V. A.
A uniform estimate of the number of representations of unity by a binary form of degree $n \geq 3$. (Russian)
Dokl. Akad. Nauk SSSR **193** (1970), 764.

The following theorem is announced without proof. Let $f(x, y)$ be an irreducible binary form of degree $n > 3$ with rational integral coefficients. Then the number of integral representation of 1 by f is at most $235n^6$.

{This article has appeared in English translation [Soviet Math. Dokl. **11** (1970), 1026–1027].}

J. W. S. Cassels (Cambridge, England)

D40-60 **(43# 1922)**

Schinzel, A.
An improvement of Runge's theorem on Diophantine equations. (Latin summary)
Comment. Pontificia Acad. Sci. **2** (1969), *no.* 20, 1–9.

The author proves the following improvement of the theorems of C. Runge [J. Reine Angew. Math. **100** (1887), 425–435] and C. L. Siegel [Abh. Preuss. Akad. Wiss. Phys.-Math. Kl. **1929**, no. 1] concerning the infinity of integral points on plane affine curves: If $f(x, y)$ is a polynomial with integer coefficients that is irreducible in the rational field and the equation $f(x, y) = 0$ has an infinity of integer solutions, then the highest homogeneous part of $f(x, y)$ is, up to a constant factor, a power of a linear or an irreducible indefinite quadratic form. Furthermore, if the degree of $f(x, y)$ is m in x and n in y, then (1) the highest terms in x and y appear separately as ax^m and by^n, (2) each branch of the algebraic function y of x defined by the equation $f(x, y) = 0$ tends to infinity with x and is of order $x^{m/n}$, and (3) every term $cx^s y^t$ has $ns + mt \leq mn$ and the sum $g(x, y)$ of all terms $cx^s y^t$ with $ns + mt = mn$ is of the form $bh(x^{m/d}, y^{n/d})^u$, where $d = (m, n)$ and h is either a linear or an irreducible indefinite quadratic form.

D. J. Lewis (Ann Arbor, Mich.)

D40-61 **(43# 3206)**

Remorov, P. N.
The spectrum of a certain diophantine equation. (Russian)
Leningrad. Gos. Ped. Inst. Učen. Zap. **302** (1967), 32–42.

The author proves that the equation $m^p + n^p = p^2 \Delta z^p$, $(mnz\Delta, p) = 1$, does not have solutions in integers (m, n, z) for prime $p \geq 3$ and $\Delta = PQ^p$, where $P = p_1^{m_1} \cdots p_r^{m_r}$, $p_i \not\equiv 1 \pmod p$, $1 \leq i \leq r$, $Q = q_1^{n_1} \cdots q_s^{n_s}$, and $q_j \equiv 1 \pmod p$, $1 \leq j \leq s$. He computes the asymptotic behavior of the number of $\Delta \leq x$.

A. I. Vinogradov (RŽMat **1968** #6 A196)

D40-62 **(43# 4761)**

Kanold, Hans-Joachim
Über eine spezielle Klasse von diophantischen Gleichungen.
J. Reine Angew. Math. **245** (1970), 165–171.

After publication the author found that he uses methods already used by T. Nagell in treating the same equation* [Norsk Mat. Forenings Skr. (1) **1921**, no. 3]. His results are somewhat better than those of Nagell. On the other hand the author only treats positive x, while Nagell also considers the case when x is negative. *B. Stolt* (Stockholm)

*[Namely, $y^2 = (x^n - 1)/(x - 1)$.]

D44 HIGHER DEGREE CURVES: FERMAT'S EQUATION, AND THE EQUATION $x^n + y^n = cz^n$

For $2^{p-1} \equiv 1(p^2)$ and similar congruences, see **A16**.

See also Sections B68, R18.

See also reviews A50-9, A50-75, A52-12, A99-10, B68-61, C20-32, D32-25, D40-61, D48-25, D48-35, D80-7, D80-76, E76-1, G05-116, G05-125, G30-22, G30-25, G30-28, G30-40, G30-42, R10-11, R40-24, Z01-70, Z10-32, Z15-45, Z15-70, Z15-73, Z30-28, Z30-51.

D44-1 **(1, 5b)**

Rosser, Barkley. On the first case of Fermat's last theorem. Bull. Amer. Math. Soc. **45**, 636–640 (1939).

Employing a theorem of Morishima [Jap. J. Math. **11**, 241–252 (1935)], the author proves that for no prime $p < 8$, 332, 403 will the equation (1) $x^p + y^p + z^p = 0$ have integral solutions x, y, z in the field of the pth roots of unity, with xyz prime to p. The method of proof consists in a comparison of the number of solutions x, $0 < x < p^2/2$, of the congruence (2) $x^{p-1} \equiv 1 \pmod{p^2}$ with the number of numbers (M), within the same limits, generated by the first eleven primes. For, should the equation (1) possess solutions of the above mentioned kind for a given p, then by Morishima's theorem all numbers (M) satisfy congruence (2). Should, therefore, the number of numbers (M) between 0 and $p^2/2$ exceed the number of possible solutions of (2) within the same limits, then the corresponding equation (1) would have no solution. A lower bound $f_n(\log N)$ for the number $\phi_n(N)$ of positive integers not greater than N and having no prime factor greater than the nth prime, is determined in the paper and the case $n = 11$ with $N = p^2/2$ is used in the comparison. *A. E. Ross* (St. Louis, Mo.).

Referred to in D44-6.

D44-2 **(1, 65d)**

Beeger, N. G. W. H. On the congruence $2^{p-1} \equiv 1 \pmod{p^2}$ and Fermat's last theorem. Nieuw Arch. Wiskde **20**, 51–54 (1939).

The author gives a table of Fermat's quotient $q_2 = (2^{p-1} - 1)/p$ modulo p for all primes between 14000 and 16000. There is also given for each such p the residue index of 2. This table is an extension of the author's table to 14000 [Messenger of Math. **51**, 149–50; **55**, 17–26] and shows that except for the primes 1093 and 3511, q_2 is not divisible by p for $p < 16000$. By Wieferich's criterion, the first case of Fermat's last theorem is proved for exponents up to 16000. *D. H. Lehmer* (Bethlehem, Pa.).

D44-3 **(1, 200d)**

Vandiver, H. S. Note on Euler number criteria for the first case of Fermat's last theorem. Amer. J. Math. **62**, 79–82 (1940).

Take $m = 4$ in a formula of the writer [Ann. of Math. **26**, 88–94 (1924)], note that

$$-w\frac{w^{4l}-1}{(w-1)^2} \equiv w + 2w^2 + \cdots + (4l-1)w^{4l-1} = F_2(w) \pmod l,$$

and let $w = t : \rho^{(w-1)^2}$, $\rho^4 = 1$, $\rho \neq 1$, then

$$(1) \qquad \sum_\rho \rho(t^2 + (\rho+1)t + \rho)^2 \cdot \frac{f_{l-2}(\rho)}{\rho^l - 1} \equiv 0 \pmod l.$$

Now, if

(2) $x^l+y^l+z^l=0, \quad t\equiv x:y \pmod l,$

the six numbers t, $1/t$, $t-1$, $1/(t-1)$, $(t-1)/t$, $t/(t-1)$ are roots of the congruence (1) of 4th degree. Hence $t^2-t+1\equiv 0$ [which is inconsistent with (2); cf. Pollascek, Akad. Wiss. Wien, S.-B. **126**, 1–15 (1917)] or $t=-1, \frac{1}{2}, 2$. Let $t=\frac{1}{2}$ and $t=2$ in (1) and take the difference of the results. From this, by formulas of Frobenius [S.-B. Preuss. Akad. Wiss. **1914**, 653–681], follows $E_{(l-3)/2}\equiv 0 \pmod l$ if (2) exists.
N. G. W. H. Beeger (Amsterdam).

Referred to in D44-41.

D44-4 (1, 291j)

Krasner, Marc. Sur le théorème de Fermat. C. R. Acad. Sci. Paris **210**, 92–94 (1940).

In a paper [C. R. Acad. Sci. Paris **208**, 1468–1471 (1939)] the author has proved that the equation $x^p+y^p+z^p=0$, the class number of $K(\rho)$, $\rho=2^{1/p}$, being odd, has a rational solution, $xyz\neq 0$, z even, $x\not\equiv y \pmod p$, if and only if there exist an even number z and an odd number M so that $\alpha=z^2-\rho^2M$ is the square of a number of $K(\rho)$. The suppositions z even and $x\not\equiv y \pmod p$ were only used in that part of the demonstration in which the residue symbol of Hilbert $(\alpha, 1-\rho\,|\,(\rho))_2$ was proved to have the value -1. The author now shows that in the case z odd, $x\not\equiv y \pmod p$, from the hypothesis $M\not\equiv 0 \pmod 4$ also follows the value -1 for this symbol. *N. G. W. H. Beeger* (Amsterdam).

D44-5 (1, 291k)

Krasner, M. À propos du critère de Sophie Germain-Furtwängler pour le premier cas du théorème de Fermat. Mathematica, Cluj **16**, 109–114 (1940).

The author makes use of an idea due to Sophie Germain to prove that the Fermat equation $x^p+y^p+z^p=0$ cannot be satisfied by integers x, y, z which are all non-divisible by p, if there exists a prime q of the form $q=up+1$, where u is not a multiple of 3 and $3^{u/4}<q$, $2^u\not\equiv 1 \pmod q$. The proof uses a theorem of Furtwängler but is otherwise "elementary." He concludes that we may expect to be able to prove the first case of Fermat's theorem when the theory of primes has been sufficiently developed. *H. W. Brinkmann.*

D44-6 (1, 292a)

Rosser, Barkley. A new lower bound for the exponent in the first case of Fermat's last theorem. Bull. Amer. Math. Soc. **46**, 299–304 (1940).

In the author's notation an odd prime p is called improper if there are integers α, β and γ in the field of the pth roots of unity such that $\alpha\beta\gamma$ is prime to p and $\alpha^p+\beta^p+\gamma^p=0$. It was proved in a previous paper [Bull. Amer. Math. Soc. **45**, 636–640 (1939); cf. these Rev. **1**, 5] that there are no improper primes less than 8,332,403. The proof was based on the following theorem of Morishima: If p is an improper prime then, for each prime $m\leqq 31$, we have $m^{p-1}\equiv 1 \pmod{p^2}$. In the present paper the fact that p must exceed 8,000,000 is used to show that the theorem of Morishima holds also when $m=37$ or 41. From this it follows that there are no improper primes less than 41,000,000. The process could be repeated with the possibility of showing that the theorem of Morishima holds for all primes $m\leqq N_1$, where $N_1\geqq 43$, thus obtaining a still higher bound. However, an argument is advanced which appears to rule out the possibility of obtaining an indefinitely large bound by this method. *R. D. James* (Saskatoon, Sask.).

Citations: MR 1, 5b = D44-1.

Referred to in D44-8.

D44-7 (2, 34d)

Grün, Otto. Eine Kongruenz für Bernoullische Zahlen. Jber. Deutsch. Math. Verein. **50**, 111–112 (1940).

The congruence mentioned in the title is a special case of a theorem of Voronoi (1889) [see Uspensky and Heaslet, Elementary Number Theory, New York and London, 1939, p. 261]. Substituting this congruence into Kummer's celebrated criterion for Fermat's last theorem, the author obtains the equivalent criterion:

$$\sum_{n=1}^{l-1}\left[\frac{kn}{l}\right]\frac{t^n}{n}\equiv 0 \pmod l.$$

D. H. Lehmer (Berkeley, Calif.).

D44-8 (2, 250e)

Rosser, Barkley. An additional criterion for the first case of Fermat's last theorem. Bull. Amer. Math. Soc. **47**, 109–110 (1941).

In a previous paper [Bull. Amer. Math. Soc. **46**, 299–304 (1940); these Rev. **1**, 292] it was shown that if p is an odd prime and $a^p+b^p+c^p=0$ has a solution in integers prime to p then $m^{p-1}\equiv 1 \pmod{p^2}$ for each prime $m\leqq 41$. From this it followed that $p>41,000,000$. In the present paper the result is extended by similar methods to $m\leqq 43$ thus increasing the lower bound for p. *R. D. James* (Saskatoon, Sask.).

Citations: MR 1, 292a = D44-6.

D44-9 (2, 250f)

Lehmer, D. H. and Lehmer, Emma. On the first case of Fermat's last theorem. Bull. Amer. Math. Soc. **47**, 139–142 (1941).

A number is called an "A_n number" if it is divisible by no prime exceeding the nth prime p_n. Let $\phi_n(x)$ and $\phi_n^*(x)$ denote, respectively, the number of A_n numbers less than x and the number of odd A_n numbers less than x. If $a^p+b^p+c^p=0$ has a solution in integers prime to p and if $m^{p-1}\equiv 1 \pmod{p^2}$ for each prime $m\leqq p_n$, it is shown that $\phi_n(p^2/3)+\phi_n^*(p^2/3)\leqq(p-1)/2$. In order to apply this inequality, polynomials $P_n(x)$, $P_{n-1}^*(x)$ of degree n and $n-1$, respectively, giving lower bounds for $\phi_n(10^x)$ and $\phi_n^*(10^x)$ have been constructed by D. H. Lehmer [Duke Math. J. **7**, 341–353 (1940); these Rev. **2**, 149]. Rosser has shown that $m^{p-1}\equiv 1 \pmod{p^2}$ holds for each prime $m\leqq 43=p_{14}$ [see the preceding review]. The polynomials $P_{14}(x)$ and $P_{13}^*(x)$ are then calculated and it is found that the inequality $P_{14}(\log p^2/3)+P_{13}^*(\log p^2/3)\leqq(p-1)/2$ is satisfied only if $p\geqq 253,747,889$. Hence there is no solution of $a^p+b^p+c^p=0$ in integers prime to p if p is an odd prime $<253,747,889$.
R. D. James (Saskatoon, Sask.).

Citations: MR 2, 149g = P28-1.

Referred to in A50-75, D44-49.

D44-10 (3, 67g)

Wachs, Sylvain. Sur certains aspects analytiques du théorème de Fermat. C. R. Acad. Sci. Paris **211**, 55–57 (1940).

This note contains three "analytic" theorems that are equivalent to Fermat's last theorem. For example, to prove Fermat's theorem is equivalent to proving that, if a, b, c are integers, then no one of the coefficients in the power series expansion in terms of z of the function

$$\frac{d}{dz}\log(1-az)(1-bz)(1-cz)$$

can be zero. *H. W. Brinkmann* (Swarthmore, Pa.).

Referred to in D44-15.

D44-11 (3, 68a)

Bitterlich-Willmann, Johann. Eine Verallgemeinerung der Fermatschen Vermutung. J. Reine Angew. Math. **183**, 251–252 (1941).

The author conjectures that the number of solutions (in

positive integers) of $x^k+y^k=z^n$ with $z\leqq M$ is asymptotic to $C\cdot M^{1+2n/k-n}$. This is true for $(n, k)=(2, 2)$, $(3, 3)$, $(2, 4)$, but it seems difficult to make it plausible in general. If true, it would obviously imply Fermat's famous theorem.

H. W. Brinkmann (Swarthmore, Pa.).

D44-12 (3, 269f)

Vandiver, H. S. Certain congruence criteria connected with Fermat's last theorem. Proc. Nat. Acad. Sci. U. S. A. **28**, 144–150 (1942).

The author derives congruences that must hold if Fermat's equation $x^l+y^l+z^l=0$ (l an odd prime) has solutions. They are derived by an extension of a method used previously by the author to obtain similar criteria [Proc. Nat. Acad. Sci. U. S. A. **15**, 43–48 (1929), in particular, p. 45]. As an illustration let xyz be prime to l (the "first case"). Certain principal prime ideals $\mathfrak{p}$, each dividing a prime p, are described, and it is found that there are infinitely many of these. It turns out that $N(\mathfrak{p})=p=1+cl$ and by applying the theorem of reciprocity one gets $(x+y\zeta^s/\mathfrak{p})=1$, so that $(x+y\zeta^s)^c\equiv 1 \pmod{\mathfrak{p}}$; here $\zeta^l=1$, $\zeta\neq 1$, $s=0, 1, \cdots, l-1$. These congruences are then combined to yield various congruences free from ζ and the resulting congruences then hold modulo p. Similar congruences are derived for the "second case." Finally, by a process of elimination, congruences modulo p are found that do not contain x, y.

H. W. Brinkmann (Swarthmore, Pa.).

D44-13 (5, 141d)

Niedermeier, Franz. Ein elementarer Beitrag zur Fermatschen Vermutung. J. Reine Angew. Math. **185**, 111–112 (1943).

Proof that $x^{2\lambda}+y^{2\lambda}=z^{2\lambda}$ is impossible for λ an odd prime such that $\lambda\not\equiv 1 \pmod 8$, x, y, z odd and not divisible by λ. In an addendum the author notes that this result was proved by Kummer [1837] by elementary methods.

L. Carlitz (Durham, N. C.).

D44-14 (5, 254c)

Pierre, Charles. Sur le théorème de Fermat $a^n+b^n=c^n$. C. R. Acad. Sci. Paris **217**, 37–39 (1943).

Abel and Legendre proved that, if Fermat's theorem is true for a prime $n>2$ (with a, b, c relatively prime), then we must have $a+b=C^n/\eta$, $c-a=B^n/\eta'$, $c-b=A^n/\eta''$, where A, B, C are divisors of a, b, c, respectively, and η, η', η'' are, respectively, n or 1 according as c, b, a are divisible by n or not. The writer proves that $\eta c/C$, $\eta' b/B$ and $\eta'' a/A$ are quadratic residues of one another. As a consequence it is shown that one of a, b, c must be divisible by 4.

I. Niven (Lafayette, Ind.).

D44-15 (5, 254d)

Roussel, André. Remarques sur un énoncé de Fermat. C. R. Acad. Sci. Paris **217**, 39–41 (1943).

Six statements in analysis equivalent to Fermat's last theorem are given. Other statements of this sort were given by S. Wachs [C. R. Acad. Sci. Paris **211**, 55–57 (1940); these Rev. **3**, 67]. *I. Niven* (Lafayette, Ind.).

Citations: MR 3, 67g = D44-10.

Referred to in A50-9.

D44-16 (6, 117e)

Vandiver, H. S. On trinomial congruences and Fermat's last theorem. Proc. Nat. Acad. Sci. U. S. A. **30**, 368–370 (1944).

The author states and generalizes certain results of König and of Dickson on the number of distinct roots of an equation in a finite field. Thus he obtains a formula for the number of solutions in the finite field $F(p^n)$ of the equation $f(x_1, \cdots, x_n)=0$, f being a polynomial with coefficients in F. He then applies these results to obtain criteria for Fermat's last theorem. It is possible to do this since such criteria have been found in terms of the solubility of certain congruences, that is, equations in a finite field. A formula is also obtained for the number of distinct solutions (u^m, v^m) of the congruence $au^m+bv^m+1\equiv 0 \pmod p$, where m is odd and the prime p is prime to $abuv$. *H. W. Brinkmann.*

Referred to in T99-4.

D44-17 (6, 117f)

Vandiver, H. S. Some theorems in finite field theory with applications to Fermat's last theorem. Proc. Nat. Acad. Sci. U. S. A. **30**, 362–367 (1944).

The result on the trinomial congruence referred to in the preceding review is here applied to the first case of Fermat's equation $x^l+y^l+z^l=0$, p being a prime of the form $p=cl+1$. Using a method due to H. H. Mitchell it is also proved that Fermat's equation is impossible (in the first case) if c is even and not divisible by 3, $l>c$, and $p>3^{\varphi(c)}$.

H. W. Brinkmann (Swarthmore, Pa.).

Referred to in T50-1, T99-4.

D44-18 (6, 169d)

Jonah, Harold F. S. Congruences connected with the solution of a certain Diophantine equation. Bull. Amer. Math. Soc. **51**, 137–147 (1945).

Transformations of some congruences connected with Fermat's last theorem are obtained from a functional equation. *H. S. Zuckerman* (Seattle, Wash.).

D44-19 (7, 47h; 7, 47i)

Racliş, N. Démonstration du grand théorème de Fermat pour des grandes valeurs de l'exposant. Bull. École Polytech. Bucarest [Bul. Politechn. Bucureşti] **15**, 3–21 (1944).

Racliş, N. Lemmes pour le théorème de Fermat. Bull. École Polytech. Bucarest [Bul. Politechn. Bucureşti] **14**, 145–156 (1943).

The author proves several results, of which the following is typical: if $x^n+y^n=z^n$ in positive integers $x<y<z$, then $n<y$. [That $n<x$ was noted in 1856 by Grunert; cf. Dickson, History of the Theory of Numbers, vol. 2, Washington, 1920, p. 744.] The statement in a summary that he proves $n<y/(1+2^n)$ is not upheld in the text. He hopes to base a proof of Fermat's theorem on the conjecture that, for n prime, $nxyz\,|\,(z^n-x^n-y^n)$ if and only if $z=x+y$. The conjecture seems doubtful: for example, for $n=3$, (7, 3, 1) or (39, 7, 2). *I. Kaplansky* (Chicago, Ill.).

Referred to in A52-6, D44-35.

D44-20 (7, 47j)

Pierre, Charles. Remarques arithmétiques en connexion avec le dernier théorème de Fermat. C. R. Acad. Sci. Paris **218**, 23–25 (1944).

For a prime $p=6k-1$ the solving of $x^p+y^p+z^p=0$ in integers prime to p is shown to be equivalent to the problem of solving a certain system of congruences (modulo p), whose details are too complicated to reproduce here.

I. Niven (West Lafayette, Ind.).

D44-21 (7, 415a)

Yamada, Kaneo. Berichtigung zu der Note: Eine Bemerkung zum Fermatschen Problem. Tôhoku Math. J. **48**, 193–198 (1941).

Corrections of erroneous [Zentralblatt für Math. **23**, 8 (1941)] congruences of a former paper [same J. **45**, 249–251 (1939)], relating to Fermat's quotient. The reviewer has found the new congruences to be correct [the factor p in (9) must be cancelled]. The author also gives a proof of the theorem of Gottschalk [Math. Ann. **115**, 157–158 (1938)] that if, for the odd prime p, $mp=a\pm b$, $(p, m)=1$, and a and b are not divisible by primes other than 2, 3, 5, 11, 17 (if $p=6n-1$ by no prime greater than 19), then $x^p+y^p+z^p=0$, $(xyz, p)=1$ has no solution. Let $Q(a)\equiv(a^{p-1}-1)/p \pmod p$; from the congruences of Eisenstein,

$$Q(g)+Q(h)\equiv Q(gh) \pmod p,$$
$$Q(mp\pm b)\equiv Q(b)\mp m/b \pmod{p^2},$$

it follows that $Q(2)\equiv Q(3)\equiv Q(5)\equiv\cdots\equiv 0 \pmod p$ is impossible; hence, from theorems of Wieferich, Mirimanoff and others, that $x^p+y^p+z^p=0$ is impossible with $(xyz, p)=1$.
N. G. W. H. Beeger (Amsterdam).

D44-22 (7, 506a)

Duarte, F. J. On the equation $x^3+y^3+z^3=0$. Estados Unidos de Venezuela. Bol. Acad. Ci. Fís. Mat. Nat. **8**, 971–979 (1944). (Spanish)

A simple proof is given of the impossibility of solving the Fermat equation in the title in nonzero integers. It is based on writing the equation in the form

$$(x+y+z)^3=(x+y)(y+z)(z+x)$$

and then showing that it is possible to set $x=3t+u$, $y=6t-u$. The proof avoids the usual discussion of the divisibility of x, y, z by 2 and 3. A solution of the equation in terms of numbers in certain quadratic fields is also given.
H. W. Brinkmann (Swarthmore, Pa.).

D44-23 (7, 506b)

Bussi, C. Osservazione sull'ultimo teorema di Fermat. Boll. Un. Mat. Ital. (2) **5**, 42–43 (1943).

If $a^n+b^n=c^n$, $(a, b)=(b, c)=(c, a)=1$, then (I) $a-A$, $b-A$, $c-A$, A arbitrary, have no common factor; (II) from $\varphi(a^n+b^n)\equiv 0 \pmod n$, n prime, $n>2$, follows $\varphi(a^n)\equiv\varphi(b^n)\equiv\varphi(c^n)\equiv 0 \pmod n$ and hence a, b, c have, respectively, prime factors p, q, r for which $p\equiv q\equiv r\equiv 1$ or $p=n$, $q\equiv r\equiv 1 \pmod n$. Elementary proofs. *N. G. W. H. Beeger.*

D44-24 (8, 195b)

Niedermeier, Franz. Zwei Erweiterungen eines Kummerschen Kriteriums für die Fermatsche Gleichung. Deutsche Math. **7**, 518–519 (1944).

The author proves two extensions of an early result of Kummer [J. Reine Angew. Math. **17**, 203–209 (1837)]. Let q be 3 or 5 and let p be a prime quadratic nonresidue of q; then the equation $x^{2p}+y^{2p}=z^{2p}$ has no solution in integers x, y, z for which none of x, y, z is divisible by pq.
D. H. Lehmer (Berkeley, Calif.).

D44-25 (8, 313e)

Vandiver, H. S. Fermat's last theorem. Its history and the nature of the known results concerning it. Amer. Math. Monthly **53**, 555–578 (1946).

Fermat's "last theorem" still awaits a proof or disproof. The author first discusses early proofs for the special exponents 4, 3, 5, 7 and criteria obtained by elementary methods, indicating proofs. To prove Fermat's statement it is sufficient to demonstrate the impossibility of (1) $x^l+y^l=z^l$, l prime, $l>2$. Although the condition that (1) is satisfied may be expressed in the form that there exists a rational r for which $(1+r^l)^{1/l}$ is rational, all known methods begin by assuming that (1) is satisfied in integers and then investigate their properties. From (1) follows $(x+y)(x+\zeta y)\cdots(x+\zeta^{l-1}y)=-z^l$, ζ a primitive lth root of unity. The author gives an introduction to algebraic number fields, rings, ideals and principal ideals; he considers in some detail the cyclotomic field and shows how Kummer obtained his set of congruences, known as the Kummer criteria. He discusses the results derived from them. The author then considers criteria governing both the cases when x, y, z are prime to l, and x, y or z divisible by l. He indicates a proof of the celebrated theorem of Kummer: if l is a "regular" prime (that is, a prime not divisible into one of the first $(l-3)/2$ Bernoulli numbers) then (1) is impossible. Then he describes theorems of his own for irregular primes. At the end of the paper there is a bibliography of 74 articles.
N. G. W. H. Beeger (Amsterdam).

Referred to in D44-26.

D44-26 (14, 725a)

Vandiver, H. S. A supplementary note to a 1946 article on Fermat's last theorem. Amer. Math. Monthly **60**, 164–167 (1953).

Additions to the bibliographical references to papers on the first case of Fermat's last theorem, given in a former article [same Monthly **53**, 555–578 (1946); these Rev. **8**, 313] by the same author. *N. G. W. H. Beeger.*

Citations: MR 8, 313e = D44-25.

D44-27 (8, 313f)

Fell, J. Elementare Beweise des grossen Fermatschen Satzes für einige besondere Fälle. Deutsche Math. **7**, 184–186 (1943).

Elementary proof of the first case of the Fermat theorem for exponents 3, 5, 11, 17 and 23. *M. Hall, Jr.*

D44-28 (8, 313h)

Pizá, Pedro A. Fermagoric Triangles. Polytechnic Institute of Puerto Rico, San Germán, P. R., 1945. viii+155 pp.

A fermagoric triangle is one whose sides a, b, c satisfy the Fermat equation $a^n+b^n=c^n$. In the first few chapters the cases $n=3, 4, 5$ are discussed at length; parametric solutions of the equation are given in a form involving square roots only, so that the author is able to give a construction of such triangles with ruler and compass, and many numerical examples are given. The author then attempts an attack on Fermat's theorem by similar methods. He does not claim to give a proof but his method seems, in the opinion of the reviewer, to be doomed to failure. Even for the cases $n=3, 4, 5$ the formulas given are of no visible use in proving Fermat's theorem in those cases.

The last two chapters deal with the curves that are the loci of the vertex of a fermagoric triangle whose "hypotenuse" c is fixed, n being any constant (not necessarily an integer). It is conjectured that these curves are certain plane sections of the surface (the "fermatoid") obtained by revolving a certain segment of a circle about its bounding chord. This conjecture is incorrect and the interesting speculations that the author bases on it are therefore useless also.

The reader has to be warned that the book is full of conjectures (like the one just mentioned) and it is not always clear just what is being guessed and what is being proved.
H. W. Brinkmann (Swarthmore, Pa.).

Referred to in B60-2.

D44-29 (8, 314a)

Pizá, P. A. Elliptic fermagoric triangles. Amer. Math. Monthly **53**, 317–323 (1946).

L'auteur renvoie, en note, à son ouvrage, analysé ci-dessus, dont l'article constitue une sorte de dixième chapitre et il précise que la lecture de l'article nécessite la connaissance du livre. On appelle triangles elliptiques fermagoriques une famille de triangles dont les côtés a, b, c satisfont à l'équation de Fermat $a^n+b^n=c^n$, l'un d'eux, b ou c, étant constant, et dont le périmètre $a+b+c$ est aussi constant. En donnant à tous les triangles de la famille la même base, les troisièmes sommets se placent sur une ellipse. La relation entre l'exposant n et le point de l'ellipse n'a pas été découverte mais

la détermination des triangles fermagoriques correspondant aux valeurs entières successives de n est entreprise.
M. Decuyper (Lille).

D44-30 **(8, 502c)**

Schmid, F. Über die Gleichung $x^3+y^3+z^3=0$. Akad. Wiss. Wien, S.-B. IIa. **152**, 7–14 (1944).

The author gives a proof of the impossibility in rational integers of the equation of the title, based on the theorem that the discriminant of a cubic algebraic number field is divisible by at least one rational prime. Since Kronecker proved that the impossibility of the cubic Fermat equation implies the cubic case of the Minkowski discriminant theorem, the essential equivalence of the former with the latter follows. *R. Hull* (Seattle, Wash.).

D44-31 **(8, 564i)**

Pizá, Pedro A. Cubic and quintic triangles. Revista Soc. Cubana Ci. Fís. Mat. **2**, 92–97 (1946). (Spanish)

Formulas in terms of parameters are derived for the sides a, b, c of a Fermat triangle of orders 3 and 5, i.e., one whose sides satisfy the equation $a^n+b^n=c^n$ ($n=3, 5$). These formulas involve square roots only. A ruler and compass construction is given for the case $n=5$. *H. W. Brinkmann.*

D44-32 **(8, 564j)**

Pizà, Pedro A. Construction euclidienne de triangles de Fermat. Mathesis **55**, 5–8 (1947).

Two constructions, by ruler and compass, are given for a Fermat triangle of order 3, i.e., a triangle whose sides a, b, c satisfy the equation $a^3+b^3=c^3$. *H. W. Brinkmann.*

D44-33 **(9, 411l)**

Inkeri, K. Untersuchungen über die Fermatsche Vermutung. Ann. Acad. Sci. Fennicae. Ser. A. I. Math.-Phys. no. **33**, 60 pp. (194?).

This memoir is concerned with a large number of rather unconnected results on the Fermat problem, dealing mostly with conditions on the integers x, y, z in (1) $x^l+y^l+z^l=0$ (l an odd prime) and (2) $x^m+y^m+z^m=0$ ($m=l^n$). The main results are as follows. (a) If x is not divisible by l but is divisible by the prime p then $p^{l-1}-1$ is divisible by l^2, in case (2) holds. This is a generalization of a theorem of Furtwängler ($m=1$). Three other generalizations of the same sort are given. (b) If $l\not\equiv 1, 9 \pmod{20}$, one of x, y, z in (1) is divisible by 5. (c) If $(n \log l)^2>l$ then (2) has no solution. Other results involve inequalities. It is shown that x, y, z in (1) all exceed $(30l^2+1)^l$ and in case one of x, y, z is divisible by l they all exceed $\frac{1}{2}l^{3l-4}$. In particular, x, y, z each have more than 5000 digits and in case they are prime to l they have more than 4.6×10^9 digits. There is a bibliography of 38 titles, mostly recent. *D. H. Lehmer.*

Referred to in D44-55.

D44-34 **(9, 568i)**

Kahanoff, Boris. Sur le théorème de Fermat. Bull. Inst. Égypte **28**, 11–20 (1947).

The author attempts to prove that in case integers x, y, z exist satisfying the Fermat equation $x^n+y^n=z^n$, then the smallest one of them must contain at least 27 digits, no matter what the value of n may be. The proof is not valid, however. The paper also contains some unconvincing remarks about the impossibility of the Fermat equation in case n is nonintegral but rational. *H. W. Brinkmann.*

D44-35 **(10, 353k)**

Racliş, Nicolas. Recherches sur le grand théorème de Fermat. Ann. Roumaines Math. **5**, 61 pp. (1944).

This is a collection of the author's papers. Cf. these Rev. **7**, 47.

Citations: MR 7, 47g = A52-5; MR 7, 47h = D44-19; MR 7, 47i = D44-19.

D44-36 **(11, 81b)**

Inkeri, K. Some extensions of criteria concerning singular integers in cyclotomic fields. Ann. Acad. Sci. Fennicae. Ser. A. I. Math.-Phys. no. **49**, 15 pp. (1948).

Let l be an odd prime and write $\zeta=\exp(2i/l)$. An integer in the cyclotomic field $K(\zeta)$ is said to be singular if it is equal to the lth power of a nonprincipal ideal in K. Necessary conditions for an integer to be singular have been given by Fueter, Hasse, Takagi and Vandiver. In the present paper these criteria are extended to the case in which l is replaced by $m=l^\nu$. Criteria of Kummer and Furtwängler for the equation $x^l+y^l+z^l=0$ are extended to cover the case of $x^m+y^m+z^m=0$. *D. H. Lehmer* (Berkeley, Calif.).

D44-37 **(11, 81c)**

Kapferer, Heinrich. Über ein Kriterium zur Fermatschen Vermutung. Comment. Math. Helv. **23**, 64–75 (1949).

The following theorem is proved: the Fermat equation $x^p+y^p+z^p=0$ (p a prime greater than 7) has no integral solution with the restriction

$$xyz(x-y)(y-z)(z-x)(x^2+y^2+z^2)\not\equiv 0 \pmod p$$

provided the discriminant of the polynomial

$$\sum_{(r)}\binom{\frac{1}{2}(p-3)-r}{2r}(2r+1)^{-1}t^r$$

is not divisible by p. This criterion is proved in an entirely elementary manner by deriving a necessary and sufficient condition that the congruence $x^p+y^p+z^p\equiv 0 \pmod{p^2}$ have a solution with the restriction on x, y, z mentioned above; this condition comes out in terms of the discriminant of the theorem. The author notes that, for $p<100$, the discriminant in question is divisible by p only for $p=59$, 79, 83.
H. W. Brinkmann (Swarthmore, Pa.).

D44-38 **(11, 81d)**

Izvekoff, J. Sur une propriété des nombres premiers. Bull. Soc. Math. Phys. Serbie **1**, no. 1, 41–43 (1949). (Serbian. Russian and French summaries)

The author shows that there are no solutions of Fermat's equation, $a^n=b^n+c^n$, $n>2$; a, b, c rational integers, for which a is a prime. [Cf. Abel, Oeuvres, v. 2, 1881, p. 254.]
R. Bellman (Stanford University, Calif.)

D44-39 **(11, 500c)**

Vivanti, Giulio. Un teorema di aritmetica e la sua relazione colla ipotesi di Fermat. Ist. Lombardo Sci. Lett. Rend. Cl. Sci. Mat. Nat. (3) **11(80)** (1947), 239–246 (1949).

The author proves the known facts that if $(x, y)=1$, $x\pm y$ and $(x^p\pm y^p)/(x\pm y)$ are relatively prime if $p\nmid(x\pm y)$ and that if $p\mid(x\pm y)$ then p, but not p^2, divides $(x^p\pm y^p)/(x\pm y)$. From this theorem he derives several observations concerning Fermat's last theorem, e.g., if $(x, y)=1$ and $x\pm y$ is a product of different odd primes, then there is no odd m for which $x^m\pm y^m$ is equal to an mth power. He concludes that the probability of the failure of Fermat's last theorem is very small. *N. G. W. H. Beeger* (Amsterdam).

D44-40 **(11, 500d)**

Inkeri, K. On the second case of Fermat's last theorem. Ann. Acad. Sci. Fennicae. Ser. A. I. Math.-Phys. no. **60**, 32 pp. (1949).

The author extends results of Vandiver on the equation (1) $\alpha^l+\beta^l+\gamma^l=0$, where l is an odd prime. Many of the theorems contain complicated assumptions about the nature of primes p for which the congruence $x^l+y^l+z^l\equiv 0 \pmod p$ has no solution in integers x, y, z, prime to p. These are employed to prove that if $l\leqq 617$ then equation (1) is impossible if α, β, γ are integers, none zero, in the field $K(\zeta+1/\zeta)$, where $\zeta=\exp(2\pi i/l)$. *D. H. Lehmer.*

D44-41 **(12, 243d)**

Gut, Max. Eulersche Zahlen und grosser Fermat'scher Satz. Comment. Math. Helv. **24**, 73–99 (1950).

The connection between the last theorem of Fermat and the Bernoulli numbers was indicated by Kummer more than a century ago. This is the basis of a number of criteria that have proved useful. The author shows that a similar connection exists between the Fermat problem and the Euler numbers E_n. As a parallel to a theorem of Mirimanoff, it is proved that if l is a prime the equation (1) $X^{2l}+Y^{2l}=Z^{2l}$ has no solution in rational integers X, Y, Z, prime to l if at least one of E_{l-3}, E_{l-5}, E_{l-7}, E_{l-9}, E_{l-11} is divisible by l [cf. Vandiver, Amer. J. Math. **62**, 79–82 (1940); these Rev. **1**, 200]. The familiar Kummer criteria involving the polynomials $\sum_{m=1}^{l} m^{n-1}t^m$ and Bernoulli numbers have parallel criteria involving the polynomials $\sum_{m=1}^{l}(2m-1)^{n-1}t^m$ and Euler numbers. *D. H. Lehmer* (Berkeley, Calif.).

Citations: MR 1, 200d = D44-3.

Referred to in R18-26.

D44-42 **(12, 392d)**

Dénes, Peter. Über die Unlösbarkeit der Diophantischen Gleichung $x^{np}+y^{np}=p^m\cdot z^{np}$ in ganzen Zahlen x, y, z, m, n, wenn p eine reguläre Primzahl ist und $p>3$. Monatsh. Math. **54**, 175–182 (1950).

The equation in the title is shown to have no nonzero integer solutions x, y, z, if m and n are positive integers; also, if $p=3$ and $m\not\equiv 2 \bmod 3$. More generally, in the real subfield $k(\zeta+\zeta^{-1})$, if E_1, E_2, and E_3 are units and ξ, χ, ψ are prime to the ideal $[\Lambda]$, $\Lambda=(1-\zeta)(1-\zeta^{-1})$, and s is an integer greater than p, then the equation $E_1\xi^p+E_2\chi^p+E_3\Lambda^s\psi^p=0$ is impossible. *G. Pall* (Chicago, Ill.).

Referred to in D44-73.

D44-43 **(12, 392e)**

Birman, Abraham. Proof and examples that the equation of Fermat's last theorem is solvable in integral quaternions. Riveon Lematematika **4**, 62–64 (1950). (Hebrew. English summary)

An infinitude of solutions of $x^n+y^n=z^n$ in Lipschitz integral quaternions is constructed for each positive integer $n\equiv 1$ or $5 \pmod 6$ and for $n=3$, x and y being conjugate quaternions in each solution. *I. Niven* (Eugene, Ore.).

D44-44 **(12, 482e)**

Dénes, Peter. Über den ersten Fall des letzten Fermatschen Satzes. Monatsh. Math. **54**, 161–174 (1950).

Conditions are obtained under which the equation $x^p+y^p=z^p$ has no solutions prime to p, not merely in rational integers x, y, z, but in integers in the cyclotomic field $k(\zeta)$, $\zeta=\exp(2\pi i/p)$. This generalizes the work of Furtwängler [Nachr. Ges. Wiss. Göttingen-Math.-Phys. Kl. **1910**, 554–562]. The original congruence conditions of Kummer are shown to hold in the extended sense. Mirimanoff's four congruence conditions are augmented by one. The simplest concluding theorem is that if the class-number of $k(\zeta)$ is not divisible by p^5, then the equation has no solutions prime to p in $k(\zeta)$. *G. Pall* (Chicago, Ill.).

D44-45 **(12, 482f)**

Hasse, Helmut. Über den algebraischen Funktionenkörper der Fermatschen Gleichung. Acta Univ. Szeged. Sect. Sci. Math. **13**, 195–207 (1950).

The author discusses the Fermat equation $x^n+y^n+z^n=0$ as the generating equation of a function field F of one variable with a coefficient field which is to contain $2n$ distinct $2n$th roots of unity. The genus and a basis for the differentials of the first kind of F are determined. After some remarks on the connection between the solutions of Fermat's equation with the algebraic prime divisors, the author estimates the weights of the Weierstrass points and sets down some explicit formulas for the multiplication of divisor classes. *O. F. G. Schilling* (Chicago. Ill.).

D44-46 **(13, 321i)**

Turán, Paul. A note on Fermat's conjecture. J. Indian Math. Soc. (N.S.) **15**, 47–50 (1951).

Let $R_q(N)$ denote the number of solutions of $x^q+y^q=z^q$ in integers x, y, z with $1\leqq x\leqq N$, $1\leqq y\leqq N$, $1\leqq z\leqq N$ where x and y are coprime and q is an odd prime. According to Fermat's last theorem $R_q(N)=0$ for all $N\geqq 1$. The author shows that there is a c_1 depending on q alone such that $R_q(N)<c_1N(\log N)^h$ where $h=2+(q-1)^{-1}$. This result is made to follow from the form of the prime factors of x^q+y^q and from the prime number theorem for primes in arithmetical progression. *D. H. Lehmer.*

Referred to in D44-75.

D44-47 **(13, 626e)**

Duarte, F. J. Sur l'équation $\xi^3+\eta^3+\zeta^3=0$. Ann. Soc. Sci. Bruxelles. Sér. I. **65**, 87–92 (1951).

The impossibility of finding rational integral solutions of the Fermat equation given in the title is proved in a simple fashion without using the method of descent. The main lemma used for this purpose deals with the general solution, in integers, of the equation $Z^3-3XYZ+X^3+Y^3=T^3$ $(XYZT\neq 0)$. *H. W. Brinkmann* (Swarthmore, Pa.).

D44-48 **(13, 726e)**

Morishima, Taro. On Fermat's last theorem (thirteenth paper). Trans. Amer. Math. Soc. **72**, 67–81 (1952).

In this paper the author continues his own and Vandiver's investigations of the first case of Fermat's last theorem, that is, he considers the equation (*) $\alpha^l+\beta^l+\gamma^l=0$ where α, β, γ are integers in the cyclotomic field $k(\zeta)$ that are prime to $1-\zeta$, l is an odd prime and ζ is a primitive lth root of unity. Thus he proves that, under the conditions just mentioned, at least one of the first half of the set of Bernoulli numbers $B_1, B_2, \cdots, B_{(l-3)/2}$ must be divisible by l if (*) has a solution; he also proves that at least seven of this set of Bernoulli numbers must be divisible by l. As another result he proves that if α, β, γ are integers in the field $k(\zeta+\zeta^{-1})$ prime to $1-\zeta$, then the first factor of the class number of $k(\zeta)$ is divisible by l^{13}; he had previously proved that it is divisible by l^{12} [Jap. J. Math. **11**, 241–252 (1935), p. 251]. There are also results concerning the irregular class group; thus it is proved that if in a normal basis of this group the number of quadratic non-residues (mod l) exceeds the number of quadratic residues by less that seven, then Fermat's equation (*) cannot be satisfied under the conditions given above. *H. W. Brinkmann* (Swarthmore, Pa.).

D44-49 **(13, 822h)**

Dénes, Peter. An extension of Legendre's criterion in connection with the first case of Fermat's last theorem. Publ. Math. Debrecen **2**, 115–120 (1951).

By Legendre's criterion is meant the theorem that if both l and $2l+1$ are primes, then the equation (*) $x^l+y^l+z^l=0$ has no solutions x, y, z, prime to l. The present paper extends this result to cover 35 different cases as follows: Let u be any even number less than 104 not divisible by 6. If both l and $ul+1$ are primes, then (*) has no solutions prime to l. This theorem is also proved for $u=110$. The results follow from the fact that this first case of Fermat's last theorem is proved for $l<253747899$ [D. H. and Emma Lehmer, Bull.

Amer. Math. Soc. **47**, 139–142 (1941); these Rev. **2**, 250]. The following lemma is used: Let u be a positive integer and ρ a primitive uth root of unity. Let $N_u(z)$ denote the norm of a number z in the cyclotomic field generated by ρ. If both l and $p=ul+1$ are primes and if $N_u(1+\rho^a+\rho^b)$ is divisible by p for no choice of the integers a and b, then (*) has no solution prime to l. If u is not divisible by 6, then $N_u(1+\rho^a+\rho^b)$ cannot vanish. Furthermore, for a fixed u, if $N_u(1+\rho^a+\rho^b)$ does not exceed p, then the hypothesis of the lemma is satisfied. The author finds upper bounds for $N_u(1+\rho^a+\rho^b)$ which, for the u's mentioned above, are in each case less than $253747899u$. *D. H. Lehmer.*

Citations: MR 2, 250f = D44-9.

D44-50 (14, 20f)

Mihaljinec, Mirko. Une contribution au problème de Fermat. Hrvatsko Prirodoslovno Društvo. Glasnik Mat.-Fiz. Astr. Ser. II. **7**, 12–18 (1952). (Serbo-Croatian. French summary)

The author uses quite elementary methods to prove two results about the equation (1) $x^n+y^n=z^n$ $(n>2)$. (I) The equation (1) cannot be solved in integers x, y, z which are in arithmetical progression. (II) If the equation (1) has a solution for which $z-x$ is square-free, then $x<n^3$ and $y<n^3+n$, so that (1) has only a finite number of such solutions. Unfortunately, Peter Barlow [Theory of numbers, Johnson, London, 1811] proved that $z-x$ is not square-free when n is a prime, the really interesting case.

D. H. Lehmer (Los Angeles, Calif.).

D44-51 (14, 20g)

Natucci, Alpinolo. Osservazioni sul problema di Fermat. Boll. Un. Mat. Ital. (3) **6**, 245–248 (1951).

Let $y=x+u$, and $z=x+u+v$. Then the function

$$z^n-(x^n+y^n)$$

becomes

$$F_n=F_n(x,u,v)=(x+u+v)^n-\{x^n+(x+u)^n\}.$$

The author observes that with x, u, v fixed and positive, $F_n\to-\infty$ as $n\to\infty$. From this fact he concludes that it is extremely improbable that F_n can be made to vanish. A small table of $F_n(x,u,v)$ for $v=1$, $u=1$, 2, and $n=3$, 4, 5 is given. The variable x ranges over integers in each case as far as the place where F becomes negative.

D. H. Lehmer (Los Angeles, Calif.).

D44-52 (14, 354g)

Ankeny, Nesmith C. The insolubility of sets of Diophantine equations in the rational numbers. Proc. Nat. Acad. Sci. U. S. A. **38**, 880–884 (1952).

Denote by $M(T, a_1, a_2, \cdots, a_n)=M(T)$ the set of all positive integers $m<T$ for which the equation

$$(*)\qquad a_1X_1^m+a_2X_2^m+\cdots+a_nX_n^m=0$$

has a non-trivial solution in the rational integers. (A non-trivial solution is one in which not all of the X's are zero.) Theorem I: If $\sum_{j=1}^n a_j\epsilon_j\neq0$, where $\epsilon_j=\pm1$ or 0, then $M(T)=o(T)$ as $T\to\infty$, i.e., for almost all m equation (*) has no non-trivial solution. Theorem I excludes the important case $n=3$, $a_1=a_2=a_3=1$. However, some information can be gathered but only in the "first case" of Fermat's theorem. Theorem II: The density of integers $m<T$ for which the equation $X_1^m+X_2^m+X_3^m=0$ has a rational solution and for which $(X_1X_2X_3, m)=1$ is $o(T)$ as $T\to\infty$. The The author sketches the proofs of a number of lemmas from which Theorems I and II follow. A main lemma states that if $a_1, a_2, \cdots, a_n$ satisfy the conditions of Theorem II, then for a given m there exist no non-trivial rational solutions of (*) provided we can find a rational prime $p\not\equiv1 \pmod{n!}$ such that $m\,|\,p-1$, $mr=p-1$, $(r, n!)=1$ or 2, $\phi(r)<\alpha^{-1}\log p$, where $\alpha=\log(|a_1|+|a_2|+\cdots+|a_n|)$, and $\phi(r)$ is the Euler function. The proof is based upon ideas of algebraic number theory. There are also two lemmas which use tools of analytic number theory, namely the Brun-Selberg sieve methods and certain "probability" theorems regarding the density of numbers having a fixed number of prime factors.

A. L. Whiteman (Princeton, N. J.).

D44-53 (14, 451e)

Dénes, Peter. Beweis einer Vandiver'schen Vermutung bezüglich des zweiten Falles des letzten Fermat'schen Satzes. Acta Sci. Math. Szeged **14**, 197–202 (1952).

Let p be an odd prime, let $\Omega(\zeta)$ be the cyclotomic field of pth roots of unity, $\zeta=e^{2\pi i/p}$, $\lambda=1-\zeta$, $\Lambda=(1-\zeta)(1-\zeta^{-1})$, ϵ_0 a unit in $\Omega(\zeta)$. Vandiver [Trans. Amer. Math. Soc. **31**, 613–642 (1929)] proved the theorem: If (1) the second factor of the class-number of $\Omega(\zeta)$ is not divisible by p, and (2) none of the Bernoulli numbers B_{np} $(n=1, \cdots, (p-3)/2)$ is divisible by p^3, then the Fermat equation $\xi^p+\eta^p=\epsilon_0\Lambda^{mp}\psi^p$ has no non-zero solutions ξ, η, ψ in the real subfield $\Omega(\zeta+\zeta^{-1})$ of $\Omega(\zeta)$, which are relatively prime in pairs, and such that $\xi\eta\psi\equiv0 \pmod p$ [this is the so-called second case]. He later conjectured [Proc. Nat. Acad. Sci. U. S. A. **16**, 298–304 (1930)] that there is no solution even when the restriction is removed that ξ, η, and ψ be relatively prime in pairs. This is the conjecture proved by the author. *R. Hull.*

D44-54 (14, 452a)

Aigner, Alexander. Weitere Ergebnisse über $x^3+y^3=z^3$ in quadratischen Körpern. Monatsh. Math. **56**, 240–252 (1952).

The author first shows that any solution of the title equation in integers of a quadratic field $k(m^{\frac12})$ can be reduced by permuting the variables and multiplying them by a common factor to the type in which x, y are conjugates and z is rational. This was previously regarded by Fueter as a specially simple particular case [S.-B. Heidelberger, Akad. Wiss. **4A**, no. 25 (1913)]. The equation with $|m|\equiv1$ (3), $m<0$, was especially treated by Fueter (loc. cit.). Here the equation with $m\equiv1$ (3), $m>0$, is proved insoluble if the class-number of $k((-3m)^{\frac12})$ is prime to 3 (a similar criterion to Fueter's). The proof is by infinite descent and is elementary, except that it uses results of Scholz on the connection between the class-number of $k((-3m)^{\frac12})$ and the class-number and fundamental unit of $k(m^{\frac12})$ [J. Reine Angew. Math. **166**, 201–203 (1932)]. The method sheds light on the more difficult cases $|m|\equiv2$ (3). The equation is also shown insoluble if m contains only prime factors of which 2 is a cubic non-residue. In particular, the title equation is insoluble in some fields with class-number divisible by 3, disproving a conjecture of Fueter. In conclusion there is a list of solutions in quadratic fields complementary to one of Fueter. *J. W. S. Cassels* (Cambridge, England).

Referred to in D44-56, D44-79, D44-91.

D44-55 (14, 536d)

Obláth, Richard. Untere Schranken für Lösungen der Fermatschen Gleichung. Portugaliae Math. **11**, 129–132 (1952).

Lower bounds are given for x, y, and z in the equation $x^n+y^n=z^n$ where n is an odd prime. In the so-called first case (n does not divide xyz) the author gives

$$x>4n^2+1,\qquad y>2(4n^2+1),\qquad z\geqq2(10n^2+1).$$

Here the author could have made use of a theorem of Peter Barlow and obtained practically the nth powers of the above lower bounds. In fact, Inkeri [Ann. Acad. Sci. Fennicae. Ser. A. I. Math.-Phys. no. **33** (1946); these Rev. **9**, 411] has shown that $x>n(30n^2+1)^n$. In the second case (n divides x) the author uses a theorem of Vandiver, which states that n^3 divides x, to show that $z>n^{3n-1}$. Since $n>619$

in the second case and $n>253747889$ in the first case, x, y, and z are extremely large in either case.

The author calls attention to a statement of Dickson to the effect that R. Sauer proved that neither x, y, nor z can be "a power of a prime." Apparently the theorem has not been really proved. *D. H. Lehmer* (Los Angeles, Calif.).

Citations: MR 9, 411l = D44-33.

Referred to in D44-59.

D44-56 **(14, 621d)**

Aigner, Alexander. Ein zweiter Fall der Unmöglichkeit von $x^3+y^3=z^3$ in quadratischen Körpern mit durch 3 teilbarer Klassenzahl. Monatsh. Math. **56**, 335–338 (1952).

Developing the ideas of his earlier paper [Monatsh. Math. **56**, 240–252 (1952); these Rev. **14**, 452] the author proves that $x^3+y^3=z^3$ is insoluble in $k(m^{1/2})$ if $m=\pm 2^v qP$; $v>0$, P contains only primes $\equiv 1$ (6) with 2 a cubic non-residue and $q\equiv -1$ (6) is a prime of which $(2^{1/3}-1)$ is a quadratic non-residue. This furnishes further examples of fields $k(m^{1/2})$ whose class-number is divisible by 3 but in which $x^3+y^3=z^3$ is insoluble. *J. W. S. Cassels.*

Citations: MR 14, 452a = D44-54.

Referred to in D44-79.

D44-57 **(14, 846f)**

Thébault, Victor. A note on number theory. Amer. Math. Monthly **60**, 322–323 (1953).

D44-58 **(14, 949d)**

Griselle, Thomas. Proof of Fermat's last theorem for $n=2(8a+1)$. Math. Mag. **26**, 263 (1953).

D44-59 **(15, 200a)**

Duparc, H. J. A., and van Wijngaarden, A. A remark on Fermat's last theorem. Nieuw Arch. Wiskunde (3) **1**, 123–128 (1953).

In a recent paper [Portugaliae Math. **11**, 129–132 (1952); these Rev. **14**, 536] Obláth discussed lower bounds for x, y, and z in $x^n+y^n=z^n$ but failed to notice a relation of Barlow which allows one to replace these bounds by practically their nth powers. This fact is pointed out by the present authors. Since n exceeds 253747888 in the "first case" of Fermat's Last Theorem this advantage pays off lavishly. The authors show that for the first case $\log\log z>23.3$. A result of Inkeri gives similarly $\log\log x>23$.

D. H. Lehmer (Los Angeles, Calif.).

Citations: MR 14, 536d = D44-55.

Referred to in D44-62, D44-63.

D44-60 **(15, 288c)**

Ghoshal, S. C. Solution of Fermat's Last Theorem. Privately printed, Lucknow, 1953. ii+12 pp.

An error has been made in the proof of Lemma 2.

D. H. Lehmer (Berkeley, Calif.).

D44-61 **(15, 401e)**

de Beaumont, Henry du Boscq. Démonstration du dernier théorème de Fermat. Editions Industrielles, Techniques et Littéraires, Paris, 1953. ii+18 pp. (unnumbered)

The author begins his proof by introducing the birational transformation $(u-v^2)x=v$, and $(u+v^2)y=v$, where $x^n+y^n=1$. Unfortunately there is a rather serious non-sequitur in the paragraph common to pages 6 and 7 which the reviewer has been unable to rectify.

D. H. Lehmer (Berkeley, Calif.).

D44-62 **(15, 401f)**

Inkeri, K. Abschätzungen für eventuelle Lösungen der Gleichung im Fermatschen Problem. Ann. Univ. Turkuensis. Ser. A. **16**, no. 1, 9 pp. (1953).

This paper improves upon results recently obtained by Duparc and van Wijngaarden [Nieuw Arch. Wiskunde (3) **1**, 123–128 (1953); these Rev. **15**, 200] for lower bounds for x and z in Fermat's equation

$$x^l+y^l=z^l \ (x, y, z)=1, \quad 0<x<y<z.$$

It is shown that in Case I (xyz not divisible by l)

$$x>\{(2l^3+1)/\log (3l)\}^l,$$

while in Case II

$$x>l^{3l-4}, \quad z>\tfrac{1}{2}l^{3l-1}.$$

These inequalities lead to inconceivably large numbers when the known lower limits for l in the two cases are substituted. Incidentally in Case II, Vandiver's old lower limit 619 may now be replaced by 2521. *D. H. Lehmer.*

Citations: MR 15, 200a = D44-59.

Referred to in D44-102.

D44-63 **(15, 602c)**

Duparc, H. J. A., and van Wijngaarden, A. Note on a previous paper on Fermat's Last Theorem. Nieuw Arch. Wiskunde (3) **2**, 40–41 (1954).

In the previous paper [same Arch. (3) **1**, 123–128 (1953); these Rev. **15**, 200] the authors obtained a lower bound for z in the Fermat relation $x^n+y^n=z^n$. In the present note similar results are obtained for x and y. *D. H. Lehmer.*

Citations: MR 15, 200a = D44-59.

D44-64 **(15, 602d)**

Natucci, Alpinolo. Ricerche sistematiche sull'ultimo teorema di Fermat. Giorn. Mat. Battaglini (5) **1**(**81**), 171–179 (1953).

The author describes and illustrates a quite impractical method for looking for solutions of Fermat's equation $x^n+y^n=z^n$. Denoting $y-x$ by $\delta>0$, the author writes $d_{\delta,y}^{(n)}$ for the difference between $(y-\delta)^n+y^n$ and the nearest nth power. For each δ, n he finds the minimum absolute value with respect to y of d. If this is zero the Fermat problem is solved! *D. H. Lehmer* (Berkeley, Calif.).

D44-65 **(15, 778b)**

Carlitz, L. Note on irregular primes. Proc. Amer. Math. Soc. **5**, 329–331 (1954).

A prime p is irregular if it divides the numerator of at least one of the numbers $B_2, B_4, \cdots, B_{p-3}$, where B_m denotes a Bernoulli number in the even-suffix notation. Jensen has proved that there exist infinitely many irregular primes of the form $4n+3$ [for the proof see H. S. Vandiver, Bull. Nat. Res. Council no. **62**, 28–111 (1928), p. 82]. In this note the author gives a simple proof of the weaker result that the number of irregular primes is infinite. He also proves a like result corresponding to the prime divisors of Euler numbers. *A. L. Whiteman.*

Referred to in D44-126.

D44-66 **(15, 778f)**

Lehmer, D. H., Lehmer, Emma, and Vandiver, H. S. An application of high-speed computing to Fermat's last theorem. Proc. Nat. Acad. Sci. U. S. A. **40**, 25–33 (1954).

In connection with the proof of Fermat's Last Theorem, it is necessary to investigate the regularity or irregularity of the prime p which appears as the exponent in $x^p+y^p=z^p$. A prime p is regular if it does not divide any of the first $(p-3)/2$ Bernoulli numbers. The truth of Fermat's conjecture for the case of regular primes was settled by Kummer [J. Reine Angew. Math. **40**, 93–116, 117–129, 130–138 (1850)]. Kummer also devised criteria which apply to some irregular primes. In the years 1928–1936, H. S. Vandiver and a number of collaborators developed further criteria for irregular primes. Since the arithmetic labor of examining these criteria was enormous, the calculations were carried out only for the 36 irregular primes less than 619.

The purpose of the present note is to indicate how the original criteria of Vandiver can be adapted to the SWAC (the high-speed computing machine at the Institute for Numerical Analysis at UCLA). The coding was performed by D. H. and Emma Lehmer. The result of the calculation is that Fermat's Last Theorem is true for all primes less than 2000. However, as the authors point out, calculations of this type are of great use in the theory of cyclotomic fields, regardless of their applicability to Fermat's problem.

R. Bellman (Santa Monica, Calif.).

Referred to in D44-76, D44-155, R18-20.

D44-67 (15, 778g)

Vandiver, H. S. New types of trinomial congruence criteria applying to Fermat's last theorem. Proc. Nat. Acad. Sci. U. S. A. **40**, 248–252 (1954).

The criteria discussed are concerned with the second case of Fermat's Last Theorem. An attempt is made to obtain conditions which involve the exponent l in

(1) $$x^l+y^l+z^l=0$$

rather than x, y or z. The main result is as follows. Let (1) be solvable in non-zero integers one of which is divisible by the prime l. Let p be a prime of the form $1+cl$ not dividing xyz. Let q be a primitive root of p and let the exponent of the prime ideal in $K(\exp 2\pi i/l)$ dividing the ideal (p) not be a multiple of l. Then there are integers i and j such that the number (ij) of solutions α, β of the congruence

$$1+g^{i+c\alpha}\equiv g^{i+l\beta} \pmod P$$

is equal to l. Here g is a primitive root of p. Since $\sum_{j=0}^{l-1}(ij)\leq l$, the criterion $(i\ j)=l$ is indeed a strong one. Unfortunately it is not strong enough to be impossible. It holds for $l=3$, $p=109$ and $l=5$, $p=61051$. No further cases with $l>5$ are known. *D. H. Lehmer* (Berkeley, Calif.).

Referred to in D44-69.

D44-68 (15, 855c)

Grey, L. D. A note on Fermat's last theorem. Math. Mag. **27**, 274–277 (1954).

The author considers the equation $x^{2p}+y^{2p}=z^{2p}$ in the case where p does not divide xyz. It is shown that p must be of the form $3n+1$ and that all odd prime factors of $p+1$ must be of the form $4m+1$. *D. H. Lehmer.*

D44-69 (16, 13f)

Vandiver, H. S. Examination of methods of attack on the second case of Fermat's last theorem. Proc. Nat. Acad. Sci. U. S. A. **40**, 732–735 (1954).

In a previous paper [same Proc. **40**, 25–33 (1954); these Rev. **15**, 778], D. and E. Lehmer and the author proved that the equation $x^n+y^n=z^n$ had no nonzero solutions in rational integers for $2<n<2003$. In this paper, the upper limit is raised to 2521, combining as before the analytic-arithmetic criteria of Kummer and Vandiver with the computational celerity of the SWAC under the supervision of J. Selfridge. A discussion is given of the procedure to follow in the case the criteria so far employed fail.

R. Bellman (Santa Monica, Calif.).

Citations: MR 15, 778g = D44-67.
Referred to in D44-76, D44-155.

D44-70 (16, 222b)

Dénes, P. Über den letzten Fermatschen Satz in relativzyklischen Zahlkörpern. Ann. Polon. Math. **1**, 77–80 (1954).

Let ζ be a primitive pth root of unity, where p is an odd regular prime, so that the class number of the field k_0 generated by ζ over the rational number field is not divisible by p. For $i\geq 1$, let k_i be a field obtained by adjoining to k_{i-1} a pth root of a unit of k_{i-1}. In a previous paper [Monatsh. Math. **55**, 229–232 (1951); these Rev. **13**, 324], the author has shown that the class number of k_i is not divisible by p, and that, in k_i, (p) is a power of a prime ideal P_i (which, furthermore, is principal). Let H be any unit of k_i, and let n be any positive rational integer. The author shows here that there are no integers A_1, A_2 and A_3 in k_i which are prime to P_i and satisfy the equation

$$A_1{}^p+A_2{}^p=H(1-\zeta)^{np}A_3{}^p.$$

G. Hochschild (Urbana, Ill.).

Citations: MR 13, 324c = R20-11.

D44-71 (16, 674g)

Araujo, Roberto. Fermat's theorem for even exponent. Rev. Acad. Ci. Zaragoza (2) **8**, no. 2, 21–24 (1953). (Spanish)

The paper, in two parts, contains arguments purporting to show that $x^4+y^4=z^4$ and $x^{2n}+y^{2n}=z^{2n}$ (n, odd >1) have no solutions in integers $\neq 0$. The first part of the argument does not use Fermat's celebrated descent method but arrives at the conclusion by omitting one case. The second part is difficult to follow because of many typographical errors. The reviewer succeeded in finding his way to equation (7) where omission of a term vitiates the rest of the argument.

D. H. Lehmer (Berkeley, Calif.).

D44-72 (16, 903a)

Vandiver, H. S. Divisibility problems in number theory. Scripta Math. **21**, 15–19 (1955).

Expository paper.

D44-73 (16, 903g)

Dénes, Peter. Über die Diophantische Gleichung

$$x^{np}+y^{np}=p^m\cdot z^{np}.$$

Czechoslovak Math. J. **1**(76) (1951), 179–185 (1952) = Čehoslovack. Mat. Ž. **1**(76) (1951), 205–211 (1952).

In a previous paper [Monatsh. Math. **54**, 175–182 (1950); MR **12**, 392] the author showed that the equation in the title has no solution in non-zero integers x, y, z when $p>3$ is a regular prime. The object of this paper is to consider the case in which p is an irregular prime. By using certain results of H. S. Vandiver, the author proves that if p is irregular but does not divide the second factor of the class number of the cyclotomic field $K(\exp 2\pi i/p)$ and further if p^3 does not divide the Bernoulli number B_{rp} for $r=1$, $2, \cdots, (p-3)/2$ and finally if $m\neq 3$, then the equation in the title has no solution with $xyz\neq 0$. *D. H. Lehmer.*

Citations: MR 12, 392d = D44-42.

D44-74 **(16, 903h)**

Dénes, Peter. Über die Diophantische Gleichung

$$x^l+y^l=cz^l.$$

Acta Math. **88**, 241–251 (1952).

Nine theorems giving conditions under which the equation of the title has no nontrivial solutions are proved by the theory of cyclotomic fields, special attention being given to the case c a prime or prime power and in particular, $c=2$. For this latter case the author proves the theorem: Let l be a regular prime, not dividing $(2^l-2)/l$, for which the exponent of 2 is either $(l-1)/2$ or even; then $x^l+y^l=2z^l$ implies $xyz=0$ or 1. The regular primes <617 all satisfy these hypotheses with the 7 exceptions

$$31, 73, 89, 127, 151, 223, 281.$$

The author is unaware of the facts that $l=389$ and 613 are irregular since they divide B_{100} and B_{261}.

D. H. Lehmer (Berkeley, Calif.).

D44-75 **(16, 1089b)**

Dénes, P., and Turán, P. A second note on Fermat's conjecture. Publ. Math. Debrecen **4**, 28–32 (1955).

As in a previous paper [Turán, J. Indian Math. Soc. (N.S.) **15**, 47–50 (1951); MR **13**, 321], the authors denote by $R_q(N)$ the number of solutions (x, y, z) of the system

$$x^q+y^q-z^q=0, \quad 1\leqq x, y, z\leqq N,$$

where q is an odd prime and $qh=1$. An improved inequality

$$R_q(N)<q(1+3\cdot 2^h)N^{2h}$$

is established by an elementary argument about the prime factors of $(z^q-x^q)(z-x)$. By using a deeper theorem of Furtwängler and some results on Dirichlet L-functions the author proves that

$$R_q(N)<cN^{2h}(\log N)^{2(h-1)}.$$

He conjectures that the state of the art permits a proof of $R_q(N)<cN^h$, but feels that $R_q(N)=O(N^\epsilon)$ $(\epsilon>0)$, is very deep. *D. H. Lehmer* (Berkeley, Calif.).

Citations: MR 13, 321i = D44-46.

Referred to in D44-147.

D44-76 **(17, 348a)**

Selfridge, J. L., Nicol, C. A., and Vandiver, H. S. Proof of Fermat's last theorem for all prime exponents less than 4002. Proc. Nat. Acad. Sci. U.S.A. **41** (1955), 970–973.

Two previous papers [D. H. Lehmer, E. Lehmer, and H. S. Vandiver, same Proc. **40** (1954), 25–33; Vandiver, ibid. **40** (1954), 732–735; MR **15**, 778; **16**, 13] describe calculations made on the SWAC which extend the proof of Fermat's Last Theorem to exponents up to 2521. In the present note the extension is made to 4001 using routines modified to give the greater speeds required for these larger exponents. Of the 183 prime exponents considered, 72 are irregular, thus perpetuating a probability of about $.39=1-e^{-\frac{1}{2}}$ that a prime be irregular. All irregular primes so far discovered are properly irregular. *D. H. Lehmer* (Berkeley, Calif.).

Citations: MR 15, 778f = D44-66; MR 16, 13f = D44-69.

Referred to in D44-88, D44-155, R18-41.

D44-77 **(17, 445b)**

Famous Problems and other monographs. Famous problems of elementary geometry, by F. Klein. From determinant to tensor, by W. F. Sheppard. Introduction to combinatory analysis, by P. A. MacMahon. Three lectures on Fermat's last theorem, by L. J. Mordell. Chelsea Publishing Co., New York, 1955. i+338 pp. \$3.25.

Reprint by photo-offset of the four books of the subtitle above [2nd ed., Stechert, New York, 1930; Oxford, 1923; Cambridge, 1920; Cambridge, 1921].

D44-78 **(17, 463f)**

Vandiver, H. S. Relation of the theory of certain trinomial equations in a finite field to Fermat's last theorem. Proc. Nat. Acad. Sci. U.S.A. **41** (1955), 770–775.

By the use of a theorem of reciprocity the author relates the study of the possibility of the Fermat equation $x^l+y^l+z^l=0$ (l an odd prime) to the study of equations of the form $g^{i+sc}+g^{j+tl}=1$ in a finite field $F(p^n)$; here $p^n=1+cl$, $c\equiv 0 \pmod l$, g is a multiplicative generator of the nonzero elements of $F(p^n)$ and $0\leqq s<l$, $0\leqq t<c$. The study of Fermat's last theorem can then be continued by making use of the author's many relations between the number of solutions, s, t of the equation just given.

H. W. Brinkmann (Swarthmore, Pa.).

D44-79 **(17, 464b)**

Aigner, Alexander. Die kubische Fermatgleichung in quadratischen Körpern. J. Reine Angew. Math. **195** (1956), 3–17 (1955).

The author continues his studies [Monatsh. Math. **56** (1952), 240–252, 335–338; MR **14**, 452, 621] whether quadratic extensions $K(m^{\frac{1}{2}})$ of the rational field ($m=$ square-free rational integer) contain a solution of (*) $x^3+y^3=z^3$, and, in particular, he shows how to construct numbers k such that (*) is insoluble for all $m=\pm Rk$ where $R=1$ or contains only prime factors of which k is a cubic non-residue. As he has shown (loc. cit.), one can assume $3\nmid m$ and a solution exists if and only if there is a rational integer solution of $X(X^3+4Y^3)=mZ^2$, $(X, Y)=1$ [this is substantially a special case of Nagell's theorem that $4x^3-g_2x-g_3=y^2$ (g_2, g_3 rational) is soluble in $K(m^{\frac{1}{2}})$ if and only if $4x^3-g_2x-g_3=my^2$ is soluble in rationals, Nova Acta Soc. Sci. Upsal. (4) **13** (1942), no. 3; MR **8**, 315]. Hence $X^3+4Y^3=m_1Z_1^2$, $X=m_2Z_2^2$ where $m_1m_2=m$, $Z_1Z_2=Z$ and m_1 is odd and positive; and so

$$m_2Z_2^2+2^{\frac{2}{3}}Y=\alpha\xi^2$$

where α, $\xi\in K(2^{\frac{1}{3}})$ and norm $\alpha=m_1$. Here $\alpha=1$ leads to an infinite descent and the remaining cases may often be excluded by taking congruences to the prime divisors of m in $K(2^{\frac{1}{3}})$. The author develops a systematic process for this. He works largely by expressing the numbers of $K(2^{\frac{1}{3}})$ in terms of the basis 1, $2^{\frac{1}{3}}$, $2^{\frac{2}{3}}$ and then applies the law of quadratic reciprocity in the rational field, but the reviewer suspects that some of the ingenuity would not be necessary if he had used the reciprocity law for $K(2^{\frac{1}{3}})$. The author concludes with the (rash) conjecture that (*) is soluble in all m not excluded by the criteria of this and previous papers and, in particular, when $|m|\equiv 2$ (3).

J. W. S. Cassels (Cambridge, England).

Citations: MR 8, 315d = G05-10; MR 14, 452a = D44-54; MR 14, 621d = D44-56.

Referred to in D44-82.

D44-80 **(17, 586j)**

Möller, Kurt. Untere Schranke für die Anzahl der Primzahlen, aus denen x, y, z der Fermatschen Gleichung $x^n+y^n=z^n$ bestehen muss. Math. Nachr. **14** (1955), 25–28.

Generalizing a theorem of Lucas, the author shows that in case n is odd and divisible by r distinct primes, the conditions $x^n+y^n=z^n$, $x<y<z$ imply that x contains at least r, and y and z each at least $r+1$ distinct prime factors. The method uses essentially Lucas' function $U_n=(\alpha^n-\beta^n)/(\alpha-\beta)$ and its algebraic factorization when n is composite. [For previous theorems for $r=1$ see L. E. Dickson, History of the theory of numbers, v. 2, Carnegie Inst. Washington, 1920, pp. 754–761.] *D. H. Lehmer.*

D44-81 (17, 827e)

Vrănceanu, G. On a theorem equivalent to Fermat's theorem. Gaz. Mat. Fiz. Ser. A. **8** (1956), 23–24. (Romanian)

D44-82 (17, 945a)

Aigner, Alexander. Unmöglichkeitskernzahlen der kubischen Fermatgleichung mit Primfaktoren der Art $3n+1$. J. Reine Angew. Math. **195** (1955), 175–179 (1956).

The author continues his investigation of quadratic fields $K(\sqrt{m})$ in which $x^3+y^3+z^3=0$ is insoluble [same J. **195** (1956), 3–17; MR **17**, 464], this time with particular reference to the m divisible by several primes for which 2 is a cubic residue. [Note that the correct English translation of "Diese Gleichung ist in Prinzip möglich" is "I have so far been unable to disprove the existence of solutions of this equation".] *J. W. S. Cassels.*

Citations: MR 17, 464b = D44-79.

D44-83 (17, 946a)

de Fraga Torrejón, Eduardo. Note on Fermat's Last Theorem. Las Ciencias **21** (1956), 5–13. (Spanish)

Referred to in D44-84.

D44-84 (18, 194b)

Rodeja F., E. G.-. On Fermat's last theorem. Las Ciencias **21** (1956), 382–383. (Spanish)

An error is pointed out in the proof offered in the article listed in MR **17**, 946.

Citations: MR 17, 946a = D44-83.

D44-85 (18, 381b)

Remorov, P. N. On Kummer's theorem. Leningrad. Gos. Univ. Uč. Zap. **144.** Ser. Mat. Nauk **23** (1952), 26–34. (Russian)

The author forms estimates for the magnitude of primes p associated with a counter-example to Fermat's last theorem, i.e., $x^p+y^p=z^p$, $(p, xyz)=1$. The estimates are of the type $N_k<p<M_k$ where k is the degree of irregularity, i.e., $p^k|h_1$, $p^{k+1}\nmid h_1$, for h_1 the first factor of the class number of $R(\exp 2\pi i/p)$. [See Vandiver, Bull. Nat. Res. Council no. **62** (1928), 28–111]. The value of M_k, (or the fact that $\lim k=\infty$, as $p\to\infty$), follows from results of Vandiver and Kummer [op. cit., p. 85] that

$$h_1\equiv\pm p\prod B_{\frac{1}{2}(sp^K+1)}2^{-\frac{1}{2}(p-3)} \pmod{p^K},$$

whereas, as $p\to\infty$, more and more of these B_n are necessarily divisible by p, [op. cit., p. 65]. The value of N_k $(=2k+\text{const})$ follows even more simply from formulas: $p^k\leqq h_1\leqq(2p)^{-\frac{1}{2}(p-3)}\prod\sum_j$. [op. cit., p. 35]. No discussion of numerical data is given. *H. Cohn* (St. Louis, Mo.).

D44-86 (18, 381c)

Remorov, P. N. On indeterminate equations of form $a^p+Db^p=c^p$. Dokl. Akad. Nauk SSSR (N.S.) **106** (1956), 395–398. (Russian)

The author considers the values of the prime $p\geqq 3$ and the integer D such that a non-trivial integer solution of $x^p+y^p=Dz^p$ exists and generalizes results about the Fermat case $D=1$. He finds it necessary to restrict D by the condition $\sum f_j^{-1}<1$, where the f_j are the exponents to which the distinct prime divisors of D belong to modulus p. The following results are stated and proofs of (I), (II), (V) are sketched.

(I)
$$\left[\frac{d^{p-1}}{d\nu^{p-1}}\log(x+e^\nu y)\right]_{\nu=0}\equiv\frac{(x+y)^{p-1}-1}{p}\ (p),$$
$$B_n\left[\frac{d^{p-2n}}{d\nu^{p-2n}}\log(x+e^\nu y)\right]_{\nu=0}\equiv 0\ (p)\ (1\leqq n\leqq\tfrac{1}{3}(p-1))$$

[cf. Kummer, Abh. Akad. Wiss. Berlin **1857**, Math. Abh., 41–74]. (II) If $x\not\equiv y$ (p), then

$$3^p-3\equiv\frac{5p}{2}\sum_{k=0}^{p-1}(-1)^k k^{p-2}\ (p^2).$$

(III) If $x\equiv y$ (p), then

$$2^{p-1}\equiv D^{p-1}\ (p^2)$$

[cf. Frobenius, S.-B. Preuss. Akad. Wiss. **1914**, 653–681]. (IV) There is an N_k such that if $p>N_k$ and the first factor of the class-number of the pth cyclotomic field is exactly divisible by p^k, then $Dxyz(x-y)\equiv 0$ (p) [see the paper reviewed above]. (V) If $x\equiv 0$ (r), $r\not\equiv 1$ (p), then $r^{p-1}\equiv 1$ (p^2). *J. W. S. Cassels.*

Referred to in D44-115.

D44-87 (18, 642a)

Oeconomou, Georges. Sur le premier cas du théorème de Fermat pour les exposants pairs. C. R. Acad. Sci. Paris **243** (1956), 1588–1591.

The impossibility of (1) $x^{2n}+y^{2n}=z^{2n}$, $(xyz, n)=1$, n odd, in integers is investigated. The result is that (1) is impossible for a prime q, $(n, q-1)=1$, $(n/q)=-1$ or $n\neq 8v+1$. By the aid of this criterion the author calculated that (1) is impossible for all $n<100000$, with the exception of possibly two numbers. Finally, it is mentioned that (1) is impossible for an infinity of primes n.

N. G. W. H. Beeger (Amsterdam).

D44-88 (18, 719c)

Inkeri, K. Uber eine Verallgemeinerung des letzten Fermatschen Satzes. Ann. Univ. Turku. Ser. A. **23** (1956), 16 pp.

Extending a result of J. L. Selfridge, C. A. Nicol and H. S. Vandiver [Proc. Nat. Acad. Sci. U.S.A. **41** (1955), 970–973; MR **17**, 348], the author proves that, if l is a prime, $2<l\leqq 4001$, and α, β, γ are real integers of the field of the primitive lth roots of unity, such that $\alpha\beta\gamma\neq 0$, then $\alpha^l+\beta^l+\gamma^l\neq 0$. *T. Estermann* (London).

Citations: MR 17, 348a = D44-76.

D44-89 (19, 16d)

Zeckendorf, E. L'équation de Fermat. Bull. Soc. Roy. Sci. Liège **25** (1956), 414–425.

D44-90 (19, 16e)

Noguera Barreneche, Rodrigo. General solution of the algebraico-exponential equation $X^v+Y^v=Z^v$. Stvdia. Rev. Univ. Atlantico **2** (1957), nos. 11–12, 119–126. (Spanish)

D44-91 (19, 120e)

Aigner, Alexander. Die Unmöglichkeit von $x^6+y^6=z^6$ **und** $x^9+y^9=z^9$ **in quadratischen Körpern.** Monatsh. Math. **61** (1957), 147–150.

Using techniques of Fogels [Comment. Math. Helv. **10** (1938), 263–269] as developed by himself [Monatsh. Math. **56** (1952), 240–252; MR **14**, 452], the author shows that the title equations have no solutions in any field quadratic over the rationals. *J. W. S. Cassels.*

Citations: MR 14, 452a = D44-54.

D44-92 (19, 251f)

Villaseñor Z., Francisco. El celebre teorema de Fermat y su demostración. [The celebrated theorem of Fermat and its proof.] Mexico, D. F., 1957. v+127 pp.

D44-93 (19, 731c)

Yahya, Q. A. M. M. Complete proof of Fermat's last theorem. With a foreword by Dr. Razi-Ud-Din Siddiqui. Available from the author, Pakistan Air Force, Kohat,

West Pakistan, 1958. 14 pp. Mimeographed appendix, 3 pp.

D44-94 (20# 1656)

Barreneche, Rodrigo Noguera. Solution of an equation related to Fermat's last theorem. Stvdia. Rev. Univ. Atlantico **2** (1957), 91–101. (Spanish)

D44-95 (20# 1657)

Barreneche, Rodrigo Noguera. Elementary discussion of Fermat's last theorem. Stvdia. Rev. Univ. Atlantico **2** (1957), 103–198. (Spanish)

D44-96 (20# 1658)

Barreneche, Rodrigo Noguera. Historically the first proof incontrovertible, complete and universal, of the grand theorem of Fermat with the Davidic algebra of the "principle of the amateurs" in mathematical investigation. Stvdia. Rev. Univ. Atlantico **2** (1957), 199–209. (Spanish)

D44-97 (20# 4548)

Thierrin, Gabriel. Sur les idéaux fermatiens d'un anneau commutatif. Comment. Math. Helv. **32** (1958), 241–247.

An ideal M in a commutative ring A is $(n\text{-}r)$ fermatian, where n, r are integers such that $n>1$, $r\geqq 1$, if any relation $\sum_{i=1}^{r} a_i^n \in M$ implies $\sum_{i=1}^{r} a_i \in M$. If (0) is $(n\text{-}r)$ fermatian, A is called an $(n\text{-}r)$ fermatian ring. If M is $(n\text{-}r)$ fermatian for all r, M is termed n-fermatian. Fermat's last theorem may be expressed: The ring of integers is not $(n\text{-}r)$ fermatian for any odd n.

The author employs the $(n\text{-}r)$ fermatian radical of an arbitrary ideal M, defined as the intersection of all (n, r) ideals containing M (and shown to be the intersection of all $(n\text{-}r)$ fermatian minimal prime ideals dividing M), to show that every non-trivial $(n\text{-}r)$ fermatian ring is the subdirect sum of $(n\text{-}r)$ fermatian integral domains. Fermat's last theorem for odd n is equivalent to the statement that an infinite number of primes can not be expressed in the form $(a^n+b^n+c^n)/d$, with $a+b+c=1$.

Results analogous to those for $(n\text{-}r)$ fermatian ideals are obtained for n-fermatian ideals. The characteristic of an n-fermatian ring divides q^n-q for all integers q.

{The letter A in theorem 7 should be C.}

J. D. Swift (Los Angeles, Calif.)

D44-98 (21# 2618)

Pérez-Cacho, T. On some questions in the theory of numbers. Mem. Mat. Inst. "Jorge Juan", no. 20, 29 pp. (1958). (Spanish)

Same as article below.

D44-99 (21# 2619)

Pérez-Cacho, L. On some questions in the theory of numbers. Rev. Mat. Hisp.-Amer. (4) **18** (1958), 10–27, 113–124. (Spanish)

The largest part of these two papers deals with the derivation of certain consequences of the assumption that the Fermat equation $x^n+y^n=z^n$ can be satisfied by positive integers x, y, z relatively prime in pairs (n an odd prime). Thus in the case where n is prime to x, y, z the author sets $x=aA$, where $(a, A)=1$ and $z-y=a^n$. He then proves that each prime factor of A is of the form Kn^2+1. A simple proof of Wieferich's theorem that $2^{n-1}\equiv 1 \pmod{n^2}$ results from this and the similar facts about y and z. A further exploitation of the nature of the prime factors of x, y, z enables him to derive lower bounds for x and y. Thus for $n=1093$, y would have to be a number with at least 21860 digits. Similar results are derived in case n divides x; for $n=1093$ it then turns out that y would have to be a number with at least 14000 digits. Another typical result states that if n is of the form $6k-1$, then one of the numbers x, y, z must be divisible by 3.

In addition there are a few miscellaneous items mainly dealing with rather specialized arithmetic functions. For example, the author discusses the equation

$$n = \varphi(n)+\varphi(\varphi(n))+\cdots,$$

where $\varphi(n)$ is the Euler function.

H. W. Brinkmann (Swarthmore, Pa.)

D44-100 (21# 2620)

Nagell, Trygve. Sur l'équation $x^5+y^5=z^5$. Ark. Mat. **3** (1958), 511–514.

The author gives a new proof of the non-existence of solutions of the Fermat equation

$$(*) \qquad x^5+y^5 = z^5$$

in non-zero integers of the quadratic field $\mathbf{K}(\sqrt{5})$. The author's proof is independent of the general theory of Kummer, and is effected by considering, instead of (*), the more general equation

$$(**) \qquad x^5-y^5 = E\cdot(\sqrt{5})^{5+\mu}z^5.$$

The non-existence of solutions of (**) is shown under the conditions that μ be a non-negative rational integer, E a unit of $\mathbf{K}(\sqrt{5})$, and x, y, z non-zero integers of $\mathbf{K}(\sqrt{5})$. The non-existence of solutions of (*) then follows from the fact, established in a lemma, that in any solution of (*) in non-zero integers of $\mathbf{K}(\sqrt{5})$, at least one of x, y, z is divisible by $\sqrt{5}$. *A. Sklar* (Chicago, Ill.)

D44-101 (22# 7974)

Carlitz, L. A determinant connected with Fermat's last theorem. Proc. Amer. Math. Soc. **11** (1960), 730–733.

Let $a_{ij}=\binom{p-1}{K}$ where p is a prime and $K\equiv j-i \pmod{p-1}$, and let Δ be the determinant of the matrix a_{ij}. This circulant is connected with the first case of Fermat's last theorem and Fermat's quotient $q(a)=(a^{p-1}-1)/p$. It is known that if $x^p+y^p+z^p=0$ is solvable in integers x, y, z not divisible by p, then $q(a)$ is divisible by p for all integers $a<47$. The author proves that in this case Δ is divisible by p^{p+43}. This result is significant when $p=6n+5$. For $p=6n+1$, $\Delta=0$. [See also Carlitz, same Proc. **10** (1959), 686–690; MR **21** #7182.]

D. H. Lehmer (Berkeley, Calif.)

Citations: MR 21# 7182 = C20-32.

D44-102 (22# 9473)

Lewandowski, Z. Proof of a special case of Fermat's last theorem. Wiadom. Mat. (2) **2**, 249–252 (1959). (Polish)

The author proves the following theorem: if x, y, z, n are integers, $n>2$ and $x\leqq 2n$ or $y\leqq 2n$ then $x^n+y^n\neq z^n$. A stronger theorem has been proved, however, in a more complicated way, by K. Inkeri [Ann. Univ. Turku. Ser. A **16** (1953), no. 1; MR **15**, 401]. *S. Knapowski* (Poznań)

Citations: MR 15, 401f = D44-62.

D44-103 (22# 9474)

Rotkiewicz, A. Une remarque sur le dernier théorème de Fermat. Mathesis **69** (1960), 135–140.

By an elementary method the author proves that if n is an integer >2, and the positive integers x, y, z satisfy $x^n+y^n=z^n$, then $x>3^n$ and $y>3^n$. The author distinguishes four cases: (I) n is odd, and (1) at least one of $(x+y, n)$, $(z-x, n)$, $(z-y, n)$ is greater than 1, or (2) $(x+y, n)=(z-x, n)=(z-y, n)=1$; (II) $n=2n_1$, where

n_1 is odd, since Fermat's last theorem is true for $n=4n_2$, and (1) at least one of $(x^2+y^2, n/2)$, $(z^2-x^2, n/2)$, $(z^2-y^2, n/2)$ is greater than 1, or (2) $(x^2+y^2, n/2)=(z^2-x^2, n/2)=(z^2-y^2, n/2)=1$; and in each case applies the following lemma: Let a and b be relatively prime integers, and let p be an odd prime; also let n be a positive odd integer. Let α be an integer $\geqq 0$, and let λ be an integer $\geqq 1$. Then $p^\lambda | a\pm b$, $p^{\lambda+1}\nmid a\pm b$, $p^\alpha | n$, $p^{\alpha+1}\nmid n$ imply $p^{\lambda+\alpha} | a^n \pm b^n$, $p^{\lambda+\alpha+1}\nmid a^n\pm b^n$. *T. Morishima* (Tokyo)

D44-104 (23# A104)

Breusch, Robert

A simple proof of Fermat's last theorem for $n=6$ and $n=10$.

Math. Mag. **33** (1959/60), 279–281.

D44-105 (23# A854)

Long, Louis

A note on Fermat's theorem.

Math. Gaz. **44** (1960), 261–262.

An elementary proof is given of the fact that Fermat's equation $a^n+b^n=c^n$ with $n=2p$ has no solution with none of a, b, c divisible by p, if p is a prime not of the form $120m+1$ or $120m+49$.

D44-106 (23# A1595)

Beauvois, F.-Henri-A.

Le problème de Fermat et la formule du binome. Aide-Mémoire des principaux résultats.

Chez l'auteur, Pessac, 1960. 7 *pp.* 1 *NF.*

D44-107 (23# A2375)

Draeger, Max

Das Fermat-Problem.

Wiss. Z. Techn. Hochsch. Dresden **8** (1958/59), 941–946.

First, the author proves that if $x^p+y^p=z^p$, $(x, y)=1$, has nonzero rational integral solutions for an odd prime p, then, putting $z-y=h$, $z-x=k$, in the case $(hk, p)=1$ (Case 1), $h=d^p$, $k=\delta^p$, $x=\nu pd\delta+d^p$, $y=\nu pd\delta+\delta^p$, $(\nu, hk)=1$, $\nu^2>((p-1)/p)(d\delta)^{p-2}$; in the case $(h, p)=p$ (Case 2), $h=p^{p-1}d^p$, $k=\delta^p$, $x=\nu pd\delta+p^{p-1}d^p$, $y=\nu pd\delta+\delta^p$, $\nu=p\nu'$, $\nu^2>(p-1)(pd\delta)^{p-2}$, where d, δ, ν, ν' are rational integers. However, in the latter case, the proof of $\nu=p\nu'$ is incorrect. Using these results, the author proves, in Case 1, that $h^p-(h-k)^p$ is divisible by k and y, that is, $h^p-(h-k)^p=kD'=my$ with rational integers D', m; that $k^p-(k-h)^p$ is divisible by h and x, that is, $k^p-(k-h)^p=h\Delta'=nx$ with rational integers Δ', n; here m and n cannot take the values 1, q, qr (q, r primes, $q\neq r$), and also $m=q^\beta$ or $q^\beta r^\gamma$ and $n=s^\delta$ or $s^\delta t^\varepsilon$ (s, t primes, $s\neq t$; β, γ, δ, $\varepsilon>1$) imply $y=\delta D'$ and $x=d\Delta'$, which is impossible. For general m and n, no results are given. In Case 2 the author treats analogous problems, but the proof of the main result depends on $\nu=p\nu'$, so is incorrect. The method of proof used in this paper, which is additive and multiplicative, is called the "h-method" by the author.

T. Morishima (Tokyo)

D44-108 (23# A3112)

Vandiver, H. S.

Some aspects of the Fermat problem. I, II.

Proc. Nat. Acad. Sci. U.S.A. **47** (1961), 202–209, 585–590.

Concerning the equation $x^l+y^l+z^l=0$, where x, y, z are nonzero rational integers and l is an odd prime, the author proves the following results. (I) Let R_ζ be the ring of integers in the cyclotomic field defined by $\zeta=e^{2i\pi/l}$, and let α be a primary integer in R_ζ, that is, $\alpha\equiv\delta^l \pmod{(1-\zeta)^l}$ with an integer δ in R_ζ, such that the principal ideal (α) is prime; also, let p be a rational prime which is divisible by (α). If $x^l+y^l+z^l=0$ has solutions in Case I, that is, in the case $(xyz, l)=1$, then $x+y\zeta\equiv\theta^l \pmod p$ with an integer $\theta=b_0+b_1\zeta+\cdots+b_{l-2}\zeta^{l-2}$ in R_ζ, where $(p, xyz)=1$ and the b's are rational integers. Further, let $\theta^l=M_0+M_1\zeta+\cdots+M_{l-1}\zeta^{l-1}$. Then the M's are homogeneous expressions of the lth degree in the b's, and $M_i-M_{l-1}\equiv 0 \pmod p$ for $i=2, 3, \cdots, l-2$. Also, $x\equiv M_0-M_{l-1} \pmod p$, $y\equiv M_1-M_{l-1} \pmod p$, and $v^l\equiv M_0+M_1-2M_{l-1} \pmod p$, where $v^l=x+y$. It is always possible to find the above-mentioned prime p. Thus there exists a set of homogeneous simultaneous congruences of the lth degree in b_0, b_1, $\cdots$, b_{l-2}, v; in other words, there exists a set of $l-2$ homogeneous conditional congruences in l unknowns, each of degree l, which must be satisfied. In the above results, if the pair (x, y) is replaced by (x, z) or (y, z), then the similar relations are obtained. Further, the author obtains a similar set of criteria for Case II, that is, the case $(xyz, l)=l$. In this case α need not necessarily be primary.

In the second paper, the author proves the following results. (II) If $x^l+y^l+z^l=0$, $(x, y)=1$, $(z, l)=1$, has solutions, then $\prod_s (x+\zeta^{s_1}y)=\zeta^g\omega^l$ with an integer ω in R_ζ, where $ss_1\equiv 1 \pmod l$ and s ranges over the positive integers $h<l$ such that $h+\{ch\}<l$, where c is any positive integer with $(c(+1), l)=1$ and $\{ch\}$ is the least positive residue of ch modulo l; and if $c<44$ in Case I or $y\equiv 0 \pmod l$ in Case II, then $\prod_s (x+\zeta^{s_1}y)=\omega^l=(b_0+b_1\zeta+\cdots+b_{l-2}\zeta^{l-2})^l$ with rational integers b_i. By the same idea as in (I), the following result is obtained, on expanding this equation: There exists a set of conditional equations in $l+1$ quantities, x, y, b_0, b_1, $\cdots$, b_{l-2}, each of degree l; and in Case II, for a given c, the conditions with $x+y=v^l$ are necessary and sufficient for the existence of a solution of $x^l+y^l+z^l=0$. Similarly, the author reduces known criteria involving algebraic integers, which concern $x^l+y^l+z^l=0$, $(y, l)=l$, and the second factor of the class number of the cyclotomic field, to criteria which consist of conditional equations involving rational integers alone. Further, in the last paragraph the author gives another result concerning the Fermat problem in Case II without proof, which is obtained by the use of a different method from the above. *T. Morishima* (Tokyo)

Referred to in D44-110.

D44-109 (24# A1921)

Barnett, I. A.; Weitkamp, H. M.

The equation $X^n+Y^n+Z^n=0$ in rational binary matrices. (Romanian and Russian summaries)

An. Şti. Univ. "Al. I. Cuza" Iaşi Secţ. I (N.S.) **7** (1961), 1–64.

From the authors' introduction: "It is our purpose here to study the solutions of the matric equation

(1.1) $$X^n+Y^n+Z^n = 0 \qquad (n \geqq 2),$$

where X, Y and Z are taken to be 2×2 matrices, viz.,

(1.2) $$X = \begin{pmatrix} x_1 & x_2 \\ x_3 & x_4 \end{pmatrix}, \quad Y = \begin{pmatrix} y_1 & y_2 \\ y_3 & y_4 \end{pmatrix}, \quad Z = \begin{pmatrix} z_1 & z_2 \\ z_3 & z_4 \end{pmatrix}.$$

Let t_i be their traces

(1.3) $$t_1 = x_1+x_4,\ t_2 = y_1+y_4,\ t_3 = z_1+z_4;$$

and let d_i be their determinants

(1.4) $$d_1 = x_1x_4-x_2x_3, d_2 = y_1y_4-y_2y_3, d_3 = z_1z_4-z_2z_3,$$

respectively. Unless otherwise stated, the t_i and d_i will be taken as rational numbers. From the Hamilton-Cayley

Equation, we have

$$(1.5)\quad X^2 = t_1X-d_1I,\ Y^2 = t_2Y-d_2I,\ Z^2 = t_3Z-d_3I,$$

$$I = \begin{pmatrix}1 & 0\\ 0 & 1\end{pmatrix};$$

and in general,

$$(1.6)\quad X^n = \alpha_n^{(1)}X+\beta_n^{(1)}I,\ Y^n = \alpha_n^{(2)}Y+\beta_n^{(2)}I,$$

$$Z^n = \alpha_n^{(3)}Z+\beta_n^{(3)}I.$$

"In the first six sections we study the properties of $\alpha_n^{(i)}$, $\beta_n^{(i)}$ $(i=1,2,3)$, as well as the trace of X^n, as functions of their arguments t_i, d_i. In Sect. 7 we use some of these properties to discuss the special equation $X^n+Y^n=0$, and the Fermat equation $X^n+Y^n+Z^n=0$ where one or more of the $\alpha_n^{(i)}$ or $\beta_n^{(i)}$ is zero. It turns out that when $\alpha_n^{(1)}=\alpha_n^{(2)}=\alpha_n^{(3)}=0$, the matric problem is reducible to the classical Fermat conjecture in the rational t_i and d_i except for the case $n=2$ and 4. We next consider the general case of (1.1) where the elements of the matrices are rational. We find necessary and sufficient conditions that the equation (1.1) have rational solutions (Sect. 8), and we give a procedure for finding these solutions when $n=3$. Finally, in Section 9, we study the solutions of (1.1) when X, Y, and Z are commutative in pairs. For $n=3$ this is made to depend on the work of Burnside for $x^3+y^3+z^3=0$ in quadratic fields."

R. P. Bambah (Chandigarh)

D44-110 (24# A2557)

Vandiver, H. S.

Some aspects of the Fermat problem. III.

Proc. Nat. Acad. Sci. U.S.A. **47** (1961), 1831–1838.

In connection with the results stated in the last paragraph of the author's previous paper II [same Proc. **47** (1961), 585–590; MR **23** #A3112], the author proves the following theorems.

(I) Let k be the cyclotomic field defined by $\zeta=e^{2\pi i/l}$, where l is an odd prime, and let $\mathfrak{p}$ be a prime ideal in k such that $\mathfrak{p}^h$ is principal for $(h,l)=1$. If $x^l+y^l+z^l=0$ has non-zero rational integral solutions x,y,z such that $(xz,l)=1$ and $(y,l)=l$, and $\zeta^a r^l+(x+\zeta^a y)s^l$ is divisible by $\mathfrak{p}$, where r,s,a are non-zero rational integers such that $(rsa,l)=1$, $(r,sz)=1$ and $(r+sx,l)=1$, then the norm p of $\mathfrak{p}$ is congruent to 1 modulo l^2.

(II) If $x^l+y^l+z^l=0$ has non-zero rational integral solutions x, y, z such that $(xz,l)=1$ and $(y,l)=l$, then every prime divisor q of $w=\{(xs^l)^l+(r^l+s^ly)^l\}/(xs^l+r^l+s^ly)$ has the form $1+gl^2$ unless this integer is divisible by q^l, where r, s are defined as before. (II) follows immediately from (I).

(III) Assuming that $x^l+y^l+z^l=0$ is solvable in non-zero rational integers x,y,z such that $(xz,l)=1$ and $(y,l)=l$, let V be $\zeta^a Ar^l+Bs^l$ and let A be $\Pi_i\,(x+\zeta^{t_i}y)^{b_i}$, where t_i are distinct integers in the set $0,1,\cdots,l-1$, and b_i are any non-negative integers $<l$, but not all zero; also, let B be an expression of the same type as A, but such that no factor of the form $x+\zeta^c y$ is contained in both A and B, with $rsa\neq 0$, $(rsa,l)=1$, among other restrictions depending on the particular values of A and B. If V is divisible by $\mathfrak{p}$, then $p\equiv 1 \pmod{l^2}$, where $\mathfrak{p}$, p are defined as before.

The author gives some results in special cases of (III) and another particularly simple case, and results related to the above but obtained from a bit different standpoint.

In (I) and (II) there exists an infinite set of values r, s, and, if r and s increase, then the density of composite values for W increases, and therefore chances should be enhanced of finding a divisor of it which is not of the form $1+gl^2$.

T. Morishima (Tokyo)

Citations: MR 23# A3112 = D44-108.

Referred to in D44-112.

D44-111 (26# 4961)

Orts Aracil, D. José M.ª

A conjecture concerning Fermat's last theorem. (Spanish)

Mem. Real Acad. Ci. Art. Barcelona **34** (1961), 17–25.

The conjecture consists in supposing that Fermat tried to find solutions of the equation $x^n+y^n=z^n$ in the form $x=a^p$, $y=a^q$, $z=a^r$. This leads to an equation of the form $N^X+N^Y=N^Z$ which is a sort of dual of the original Fermat equation; it is easily seen that integral solutions exist only for $N=2$, with $X=Y$, $Z=X+1$. It is suggested that Fermat was led to his conjecture by this fact.

H. W. Brinkmann (Swarthmore, Pa.)

D44-112 (27# 104)

Vandiver, H. S.

Some aspects of the Fermat problem. IV.

Proc. Nat. Acad. Sci. U.S.A. **49** (1963), 601–608.

Part III appeared in same Proc. **47** (1961), 1831–1838 [MR **24** #A2557]. The author discusses statements involving methods of attack on Fermat's last theorem as considered by A. L. Gelfond who stated in his book, *The solution of equations in integers*, p. 61 [Noordhoff, Groningen, 1960; MR **21** #5607]: ". . . [that] at the present time, the proof of Fermat's last theorem, especially a proof constructed on the considerations of the divisibility theory of numbers, can have only sporting interest. Of course, if this proof can be obtained by a new and fruitful method, then its significance, connected with the significance of the method itself, could be very great. One must note that present-day attempts by mathematicians to prove the Fermat theorem by completely elementary means are doomed to failure. Elementary considerations based on the theory of divisibility of integers were already used by Kummer and the subsequent development of them by the most prominent mathematicians have not yet yielded anything important. We shall now give the proof of Fermat's theorem for the case $n=4$ inasmuch as the method of infinite descent, on which this proof is based, is very interesting."

Concerning this quotation, the author states the following: "When a mathematician of the caliber of Gelfond makes assertions involving a mathematical subject, they definitely should be considered if the reader is also interested in the subject. It may be that some young mathematician who has great ability in connection with number theory but little acquaintance with the history of the Fermat problem will be steered away from it in view of such assertions. Hence, the present paper will be devoted to the examination of several of the statements Gelfond made in the quotation above so that the young mathematician will be in a better position to choose for himself."

Further, quoting five theorems which have been proved, the author discusses the statements of Gelfond concerning the divisibility theory of numbers and the method of infinite descent. In conclusion, the author states: "I am now definitely of the opinion that Fermat's last theorem is entirely correct."

T. Morishima (Tokyo)

Citations: MR 21# 5607 = D02-5; MR 24# A2557 = D44-110.

D44-113 **(27# 1681)**

R.-Salinas, Baltasar

On Fermat's last theorem and the equation

$$\frac{\partial^n u}{\partial x^n}+\frac{\partial^n u}{\partial y^n} = \frac{\partial^n u}{\partial z^n}.$$

(Spanish)

Univ. Lisboa Revista Fac. Ci. A (2) **9** (1961/62), 35–43.

Let p, q, r be integers satisfying Fermat's equation $p^n+q^n=r^n$ with even n; then

$$u(x, y, z) = \sin 2\pi px\cdot\sin 2\pi qy\cdot\sin 2\pi rz$$

is a non-trivial solution of the equation

$$(*)\qquad \frac{\partial^n u}{\partial x^n}+\frac{\partial^n u}{\partial y^n} = \frac{\partial^n u}{\partial z^n},$$

periodic in x, y, z (period one) and vanishing on the faces of the unit cube Q ($0 \leqq x, y, z \leqq 1$). The purpose of the paper is to prove (under the additional condition C: the partial derivatives occurring in (*) are uniformly bounded) a non-trivial converse, which follows as a corollary from the stronger statements of two theorems proven here. These are essentially (the exact statements are too long for verbatim quotation) the following. Theorem 3: Let n be an even integer for which Fermat's equation has no non-trivial solution; if $u(x, y, z)$ is periodic with period one in each of the independent variables, satisfies (*) and condition C, then u vanishes identically, provided only that it vanishes on any one among 45 (specifically indicated) quadruples of edges and diagonals of Q. Theorem 4 is the corresponding statement for odd n; the additional condition requires only that u vanish on one among 49 triplets of edges and diagonals of Q. The proof is based on the Fourier expansion $u\sim\sum_{p,q,r} A_{p,q,r}\, e^{2\pi i(px+qy+rz)}$.

{The reviewer is unable to understand the meaning of the last sentence in Theorems 3 and 4, according to which u—already shown to vanish identically—need not vanish on certain edges and diagonals.}

E. Grosswald (Philadelphia, Pa.)

D44-114 **(27# 2475)**

Slavutskiĭ, I. Š.

On irregular primes. (Russian)

Acta Arith. **8** (1962/63), 123–125.

An odd prime p is called irregular if $B_2B_4\cdots B_{p-3}\equiv 0 \pmod p$, where the B_i are Bernouilli numbers in even suffix notation. K. L. Jensen [Nyt. Tidsskr. Math. Afd. B **26** (1915), 73–83] proved that there are infinitely many such $p\equiv 3 \pmod 4$. A proof is now offered that there are infinitely many irregular $p\equiv 2 \pmod 3$. The proof is incorrect, first because T may be divisible by some p_i, thus invalidating the inference from equation (*), and secondly because $B_{4Q}<0$, invalidating equation (1). To correct this, construct a prime $q\equiv 1 \pmod{33\prod_{i=1}^{s} p_i(p_i-1)}$, and work with B_{10q}. The reviewer also notes that the congruence $3B_{2n}\equiv -1 \pmod 3$, here deduced from a result of Voronoĭ and Grün, is contained in the Staudt-Clausen Theorem. Also, the same method shows that for $3\leqq m\leqq 100$ there are infinitely many irregular $p\not\equiv 1 \pmod m$.

B. Gordon (Los Angeles, Calif.)

Referred to in D44-126.

D44-115 **(27# 2481)**

Remorov, P. N.

The problem of representing integers as the sum of two powers. (Russian)

Izv. Vysš. Učebn. Zaved. Matematika **1963**, *no.* 1 (32), 145–149.

The author proves a criterion for the unsolvability of the modified Fermat equation (**) $\Delta z^p=x^p+y^p$, where Δ is an integer of type $\prod q_i^{m_i}$ and where q_i belongs to $f_i \pmod p$ and $\sum 1/f_i<1$. Solutions are restricted by $\Delta zxy(x+y)\not\equiv 0 \pmod p$. The criteria of Wieferich and Miriamanoff are still valid, e.g., (**) is unsolvable if $r^{p-1}\equiv 1 \pmod{p^2}$ for r a prime divisor of $xy(x+y)$ and/or $r=2$ and 3. Thus (**) is unsolvable for $3<p<10^5$. The author's proof assumes the classically known Eisenstein reciprocity theorem as well as the lemma that (**) leads to the situation where one factor $(x+hy)$ is a pth power of an ideal in $K(h)$ for h a primitive pth root of unity. The lemma was established in the author's earlier work [Dokl. Akad. Nauk SSSR **106** (1956), 395–398; MR **18**, 381], where the special case $r=3$ is also established.

H. Cohn (Tucson, Ariz.)

Citations: MR 18, 381c = D44-86.

D44-116 **(28# 5036)**

Inkeri, K.

Über die Lösbarkeit einiger Diophantischer Gleichungen.

Ann. Acad. Sci. Fenn. Ser. A I No. 334 (1963), 15 *pp.*

Let l be an odd prime, n a positive integer, and c_1 and c_2 relatively prime positive integers. The author derives a sequence of necessary conditions that the equation

$$c_1(x^{l^n}+y^{l^n}) = c_2 z^{l^n}$$

should have integral solutions. Typical of his results is the following: If $n>((l-1)\log c)/(\log l)-1$ and $c=\max(c_1, c_2)>1$, then the equation has no integral solutions with $(l, z)=1$. The methods used are closely related to those used previously in studying Fermat's conjecture.

D. J. Lewis (Ann Arbor, Mich.)

D44-117 **(29# 68)**

Ferentinou-Nicolacopoulou, Jeanne

Une propriété des diviseurs du nombre $r^{r^m}+1$. Applications au dernier théorème de Fermat.

Bull. Soc. Math. Grèce (N.S.) **4** (1963), *no.* 1, 121–126.

Let r, m, n be integers, $r\geqq 2$, $m\geqq 0$, $n\geqq 2$, let n^k be the largest power of n which divides $r^{r^m}+1$. The author proves that if r is even, then $r^{n^k-1}\not\equiv \pm 1 \pmod{n^{k+1}}$, while if r is odd, $r^{n^k-1}\not\equiv(-1)^{n+1} \pmod{n^{k+1}}$. The proofs are straightforward. Corollaries involving Fermat's Last Theorem are derived from the result (with n an odd prime and $k=1$) in an obvious fashion by using the well-known results of Morishima, Rosser and Furtwangler.

S. L. Segal (Rochester, N.Y.)

D44-118 **(29# 69)**

Kapferer, Heinrich

Verifizierung des symmetrischen Teils der Fermatschen Vermutung für unendlich viele paarweise teilerfremde Exponenten E.

J. Reine Angew. Math. **214/215** (1964), 360–372.

The author proves the following theorem: Let E and n be positive rational integers, and let $(E, 6)=1$. If $x^E+y^E+z^E=0$ has nonzero rational integral solutions x, y, z such that $(x, y)=(y, z)=1$, and, for a divisor $a>0$ of x, $a^n-1=EF$ with $(E, F)=1$, where F is a rational integer, then x is divisible by E. Now, let $K_n(a)=\prod_{t\mid n}(a^{n/t}-1)^{\mu(t)}$, $n=1, 2, 3, \cdots$, where the notation indicates a product over all the divisors of n, $\mu(t)$ is the Möbius function and a is a positive integer. Then a^n-1 is divisible by $K_n(a)$. Using $K_{n_1}(a)$ or $K_{n_2}(a)/p$ with a prime p, the author proves that there exist infinitely many E and that any two of these E are prime to each other. Further, using the above theorem, the author proves the following result: Let g be any even positive integer and prime to 3, and let π_i be a prime such that $\pi_i>3^{\varphi(g)}$ and $\pi_i-1=E_i g$ with $(E_i, g)=1$, where $\varphi(g)$ is the Euler function. If $x^{E_i}+y^{E_i}+z^{E_i}=0$, $(x, y)=(y, z)=1$

has nonzero rational integral solutions, then one of x, y, z is divisible by E_i. There exist infinitely many such E_i and any two of these E_i are relatively prime.

T. Morishima (Tokyo)

D44-119 **(29# 5781)**

Pignataro, Salvatore

Una osservazione sull'ultimo teorema di Fermat. (English summary)

Rend. Accad. Sci. Fis. Mat. Napoli (4) **30** (1963), 281–286.

On sait que le dernier (ou grand théorème) de Fermat s'énonce comme suit: L'équation diophantienne

$$(1) \qquad x^n = y^n + z^n,$$

n entier > 2, est impossible en entiers rationnels tous $\neq 0$. On sait que ce théorème n'a pas encore été démontré pour tout nombre premier n.

Dans cette note, l'auteur établit un critère pour l'existence éventuelle de solutions de l'équation (1) en entiers positifs tous $\neq 0$. Il y expose en effet une méthode ramenant la recherche de solutions éventuelles de (1) à celle des solutions représentant un certain nombre impair positif moyennant une forme canonique (quadratique binaire), m étant un nombre positif impair, il s'agit d'une représentation de la forme

$$(2) \qquad m = \xi x^2 - \eta y^2.$$

L'auteur note cette forme $(\xi, -\eta)$, où ξ et η sont supposés premiers entre eux, et où x et y sont des entiers positifs premiers entre eux et respectivement premiers avec η et ξ. Il démontre le théorème suivant: Si un nombre positif impair est représentable par (2), alors il est représentable, d'une infinité de façons, par des nombres positifs qui peuvent être rangés, à partir de deux solutions minimales, en deux suites de nombres croissants. Moyennant ce théorème, il arrive à un critère pour l'existence éventuelle d'une solution (ξ^k, η^k, ζ^k), qui représente ζ^{2k+1} par la forme $(\xi, -\eta)$, $2k+1 \geqq 3$, ξ et η étant supposés de parité différente, donc ζ impair (ξ^k, η^k, ζ^k) étant une solution primitive en entiers positifs de l'équation (1) que nous écrirons sous la forme

$$(1') \qquad x^n - y^n = z^n,$$

$$(1'') \qquad \xi^{2k+1} - \eta^{2k+1} = \zeta^{2k+1}.$$

(1″) peut évidemment s'écrire sous la forme $\xi(\zeta^k)^2 - \eta(\eta^k)^2 = \zeta^{2k+1}$ d'où il résulte que (ξ^k, η^k) est une solution représentant ζ^{2k+1} moyennant la forme canonique $\xi x^2 - \eta y^2$.

A propos de l'équation $\xi x^2 - \eta y^2 = \zeta^{2k+1}$, il est connu, d'après la théorie des formes quadratiques, que le produit $\xi\eta$ doit être un résidu quadratique de ζ^{2k+1}, et partant, de ζ. L'auteur démontre finalement que, s'il existe une solution ξ^k, η^k de l'équation $\xi x^2 - \eta y^2 = \zeta^{2k+1}$, (ξ^k, η^k) doit être la solution minimale absolue parmi l'infinité de solutions représentant ζ^{2k+1} par cette forme. Ainsi le critère de l'auteur réduit le problème de Fermat à la détermination d'une méthode donnant la solution minimale absolue pour tout nombre impair ζ^{2k+1} représentable par une certaine forme canonique, quadratique binaire $(\zeta, -\eta)$ pour laquelle le produit $\xi\eta$ est un résidu quadratique de ζ, où x et y désignent toujours deux entiers positifs premiers entre eux et premiers respectivement, avec η et ξ.

A. Gloden (Luxembourg)

D44-120 **(30# 1088)**

Gandhi, J. M.

On Fermat's last theorem.

Amer. Math. Monthly **71** (1964), 998–1006.

The author discusses the following two statements. Conjecture 1: The equation $x^n + y^n = pz^n$ has no integral solution. Conjecture 2: The equation $x^n - y^n = pz^n$ has no integral solution. Here x, y, z are nonzero, unequal coprime integers, $n > 2$ and p is a positive integer $\leqq n$. It is recalled that Legendre [A. M. le Gendre, *Essai sur la théorie des nombres*, p. 409, Duprat, Paris, 1798] showed that $x^3 + y^3 = 2z^3$ implies $x = \pm y$. Also it is known [Uspensky and Heaslet, *Elementary number theory*, problem 7, McGraw-Hill, New York, 1939; MR **1**, 38] that $x^3 + y^3 = 3z^3$ has no integral solution. Thus the stated conjectures are true for $n = 3$. The author proves that the conjectures hold in a number of special cases. For example, he shows that Conjecture 1 holds for all powers of the form $n^c(n-1)$, n odd prime, $p \neq 1$ or 2. He also states that Conjecture 1 is true for $n = 8, 20, 24, 32, 44, 48, 56, 80, 84$.

The author also states that the equation

$$x^n + y^n = (n+1)z^n$$

has no integral solution for a large number of even values of $n \leqq 1000$, in particular, for $n = 34, 94, 118, 142, 202, \cdots, 982, 994$. Also it is stated that the equation

$$x^n + y^n = (n+2)z^n$$

has no integral solution for many even values of n.

L. Carlitz (Durham, N.C.)

Citations: MR 1, 38c = Z01-2.

Referred to in D44-162.

D44-121 **(30# 3053)**

Waldal, Per

Die Symmetrie am Fermat-Satz. (English summary)

H. Akerets Erben AG, Dielsdorf ZH, 1963. 107 *pp.* *sFr.* 12.00.

This book contains various remarks, mostly trivial, on the nature of number, such as the importance of commutativity in the process of addition (symmetry) and the difficulty of understanding the Fermat theorem since it deals with a non-linear problem. The author clearly does not understand what would be involved in a proof of the theorem. Some historical remarks (of a very general sort) are included.

H. W. Brinkmann (Swarthmore, Pa.)

D44-122 **(30# 4724)**

Eichler, M.

Eine Bemerkung zur Fermatschen Vermutung.

Acta Arith. **11** (1965), 129–131.

The following theorem is proved. Let l be a prime > 3. Let l^H denote the highest power of l that divides the first factor of the class number of the cyclotomic field $R(\zeta)$, where $\zeta = e^{2\pi i/l}$. Then if $H < [l^{1/2}] - 1$, the equation $x^l + y^l + z^l = 0$ has no solutions in rational integers prime to l.

L. Carlitz (Durham, N.C.)

Referred to in D44-123.

D44-123 **(32# 90)**

Eichler, M.

Errata zur Arbeit "Eine Bemerkung zur Fermatschen Vermutung".

Acta Arith. **11** (1965), 261.

Two misprints are noted in the paper which appeared in same Acta **11** (1965), 129–131 [MR **30** #4724].

L. Carlitz (Durham, N.C.)

Citations: MR 30# 4724 = D44-122.

D44-124 **(31# 3595)**

Legendre, Robert

Uniformisation de la relation $x^p + y^p = 1$.

C. R. Acad. Sci. Paris **261** (1965), 21–24.

It is shown that the curve $x^p + y^p = 1$, where p is a positive

integer, admits a uniformisation of the form $x=f(z)$, $y=f(ze^{i\pi/p})$. For $p=1, 2, 3$, explicit formulas for f are given. For $p>3$, the existence of such a uniformisation is deduced from potential-theoretic considerations, and ways of obtaining f explicitly are suggested.
H. H. Martens (Blindern)

D44-125 **(31# 4761)**

Morishima, Taro; Miyoshi, Takeo
On the Diophantine equation $x^p+y^p=cz^p$.
Proc. Amer. Math. Soc. **16** (1965), 833–836.

The authors obtain elegant criteria generalising the classical Wieferich and Mirimanoff criteria for the first case of Fermat's equation. In particular, if $x^p+y^p=cz^p$ with x, y, z coprime by pairs and prime to p, then either $p|\phi(c)$ or $c^{p-1}\equiv 2^{p-1}$ (p^2) or $2^{p-1}\equiv 3^{p-1}\equiv 1$ (p^2). Unfortunately, the authors' indications of proofs are brief and sometimes misleading, though the reviewer believes that the arguments are correct in essentials. It would be hard to read this paper without Hasse's "Klassenkörpertheorie" [Jber. Deutsch. Math.-Verein. **6** (1930), Abt. 2, 1–204] handy. *B. J. Birch* (Manchester)

Referred to in D44-137, D44-142.

D44-126 **(31# 5861)**

Montgomery, Hugh L.
Distribution of irregular primes.
Illinois J. Math. **9** (1965), 553–558.

An odd prime p is regular provided that it does not divide any of the numerators $N_2, N_4, \cdots, N_{p-3}$, where $B_{2n}=N_{2n}/D_{2n}$, $(B_{2n}, D_{2n})=1$ and B_{2n} denotes the Bernoulli number in the even suffix notation. K. L. Jensen [Nyt. Tidsskr. Math. Afd. B **26** (1915), 73–83] proved that there are infinitely many irregular primes of the form $4m+3$; the reviewer [Proc. Amer. Math. Soc. **5** (1954), 329–331; MR **15**, 778] gave a simpler proof of the existence of infinitely many irregular primes. In the present paper the author proves the following theorem. If P is a fixed odd prime, then there exist infinitely many irregular primes not of the form $mP+1$. The author notes that I. Š. Slavutskiĭ [Acta Arith. **8** (1962/63), 123–125; MR **27** #2475] asserted that there is an infinite number of irregular primes of the form $3m+2$, but that his proof contained an error. However, this assertion is contained in the theorem quoted above. *L. Carlitz* (Durham, N.C.)

Citations: MR 15, 778b = D44-65; MR 27# 2475 = D44-114.
Referred to in D44-161.

D44-127 **(32# 89)**

Dittmann, Gerd
Untersuchungen über höhere Potenzen natürlicher Zahlen.
Inauguraldissertation zur Erlangung der Würde des Dr. rer. nat. der Mathematisch—Naturwissenschaftlichen Fakultät der Pädagogischen Hochschule Potsdam.
Dissertation, Potsdam, 1964. ii + 56 *pp.*

In the first part of the dissertation, the author gives some necessary conditions for the solutions of Fermat's equation $x^p+y^p=z^p$, p prime. His main theorem gives bounds for $c=(z, 2z-x-y)$, from which several corollaries follow. The theorem is too complicated to state here. In particular, divisibility relations between x, y, z, $(x-y)^p+(z-x)^p$, $(z-y)^p-(x-y)^p$, $(z-y)^p+(z-x)^p$ are investigated. In the second part, necessary conditions are obtained for the special cases (i) $x=y+1$, (ii) $z=x+1$. In particular, there are no solutions with $p\nmid xy$ in the first case and $p\nmid xyz$, $p\geqq 3$ in the second. Some necessary conditions are also obtained for $x>y$, $z>x+1$, $p\nmid xyz$. Finally, the author studies the equation $P_m+P_n=P_s$, where $\{P_r\}$ is a sequence of order 2, and obtains the complete solution. He concludes with some remarks on special cases of $a_0+a_1x_1^l+\cdots+a_kx_k^l=0$ and $x_1^l+y_1^l=\cdots=x_n^l+y_n^l$.
R. J. Hans (Columbus, Ohio)

D44-128 **(32# 2595)**

Gross, Fred
On the equation $f^n+g^n=1$.
Bull. Amer. Math. Soc. **72** (1966), 86–88.

The author considers the problem of the existence of meromorphic functions $f(z)$, $g(z)$, such that $f^n+g^n=1$, n an integer $\geqq 2$.

As immediate consequences of a theorem on uniformization (or alternatively, Nevanlinna theory), he observes that there are no such solutions for $n\geqq 4$, elliptic function solutions for $n=3$, and gives all solutions for $n=2$.

An explicit example of an elliptic function solution which is given is apparently erroneous, and may be corrected as follows: on page 87, line 7, F and G should be interchanged; formula (3) on page 86 will then read $f=(1+3^{-1/2}\wp')/2\wp$, $g=(1-3^{-1/2}\wp')/2\wp$, which does in fact form a solution for $n=3$, with $\wp$ as in the text.

The problem of determining all meromorphic solutions for $n=3$ apparently remains open. *S. L. Segal* (Vienna)

D44-129 **(32# 7499)**

Simmons, G. J.
Some results pertaining to Fermat's conjecture.
Math. Mag. **39** (1966), 18–21.

This paper collects several results of the Fermat equation (1) $x^n+y^n=z^n$ which are obtainable by purely elementary means from an equivalent expression of (1) discovered by G. Reis in 1959 and published for the first time in this paper:

$$(2) \qquad (K+a)^n+(K+b)^n = (K+a+b)^n,$$

where K, a and b are integers. In addition, the author uses the results obtained and (2) to derive an alternate form of the well-known solution for the case $n=2$.
R. Finkelstein (Tucson, Ariz.)

D44-130 **(33# 1273)**

Gandhi, J. M.
On Fermat's last theorem.
Math. Gaz. **50** (1966), 36–39.

D44-131 **(33# 1283)**

Domiaty, R. Z.
Lösungen der Gleichung $x^n+y^n=z^n$ mit $n=2^m$ im Ring gewisser ganzzahliger Matrizen.
Elem. Math. **21** (1966), 5–7.

Let G_k be the ring of $k\times k$ matrices with integral elements. It is shown that if $n=2^m$, then there exist x, y, z in $G_{2^{m-1}}$ such that $x^n+y^n=z^n$, $x^n\neq 0$, $y^n\neq 0$, $z^n\neq 0$. {The reviewer notes that this equation can already be solved in G_2 for any n. For example, take

$$x=\begin{pmatrix} a & 0\\ 0 & 0\end{pmatrix}, \quad y=\begin{pmatrix} 0 & 0\\ 0 & d\end{pmatrix}, \quad z=\begin{pmatrix} a & 0\\ 0 & d\end{pmatrix},$$

or the conjugates of these by any invertible $t\in G_2$. Hence, a new definition of non-triviality (perhaps non-singularity of x, y, z) is needed to make the author's results more significant.} *B. Gordon* (Los Angeles, Calif.)

D44-132 **(33# 4006)**

Krishnasastry, M. S. R.; Perisastri, M.
On some diophantine equations.
Math. Student **33** (1965), 73–76.

Proof of the impossibility of two equations related to Fermat's last theorem, and a proof that the only integral solutions of $x^y - y^x = \phi(x)$ are $x = q$ (a prime), $y = 1$.
B. Stolt (Stockholm)

D44-133 **(33# 5553)**

Bergmann, G.
Über Eulers Beweis des grossen Fermatschen Satzes für den Exponenten 3.
Math. Ann. **164** (1966), 159–175.

The author gives a critical analysis of Euler's "proof" of Fermat's last theorem for exponent 3. At a crucial point, one needs to show that if p, q are coprime integers and p^2+3q^2 is a cube, then $p+q\sqrt{-3}=(t+u\sqrt{-3})^3$ with integers t, u. Euler's explanation of this in his *Algebra* is inadequate; he refers to it "wie oben gezeigt worden", though earlier sections of the *Algebra* appear to prove no more than that p^2+3q^2 is a cube whenever $p+q\sqrt{-3}=(t+u\sqrt{-3})^3$. However, the author finds, elsewhere in Euler's works, tools sufficient for a correct treatment of this point; he suggests that "wie oben gezeigt worden" refers not to earlier sections of the *Algebra*, but to a precise account which has been lost. The author gives rather complete quotations, to make it possible to follow his arguments without the original. *B. J. Birch* (Oxford)

D44-134 **(33# 5645)**

Domiaty, R. Z.
Solutions of $x^4+y^4=z^4$ in 2 × 2 integral matrices.
Amer. Math. Monthly **73** (1966), 631.

It is observed that the matrices

$$A=\begin{bmatrix}0 & 2mn\\ 1 & 0\end{bmatrix},\quad B=\begin{bmatrix}0 & m^2-n^2\\ 1 & 0\end{bmatrix},\quad C=\begin{bmatrix}0 & m^2+n^2\\ 1 & 0\end{bmatrix},$$

where m and n are integers, satisfy $A^4+B^4=C^4$.
C. G. Cullen (Pittsburgh, Pa.)

D44-135 **(34# 138)**

Rossi, Francesco Saverio
Osservazioni intorno a una celebre equazione indeterminata.
Archimede **17** (1965), 142–147.

Some observations concerning Fermat's last theorem, of the following type: If (x, y, z) is a Pythagorean triple of positive integers, then $x^n+y^n-z^n<0$ for $n\geqq 3$.
C. G. Lekkerkerker (Amsterdam)

D44-136 **(34# 4198)**

Gandhi, J. M.
A note on Fermat's last theorem.
Amer. Math. Monthly **73** (1966), 1106–1107.

If p and $4p+1$ are primes with $p>3$ and $a^p+b^p+c^p=0$, where a, b, c are nonzero integers and are relatively prime in pairs, then an elementary proof shows that precisely one of the integers a, b, c is divisible by $4p+1$.
B. M. Stewart (E. Lansing, Mich.)

Referred to in D44-139, D44-145.

D44-137 **(34# 4199)**

Győry, Kálmán
Über die diophantische Gleichung $x^p+y^p=cz^p$.
Publ. Math. Debrecen **13** (1966), 301–305.

Let $p>3$ be an arbitrary prime and c a rational integer. The author proves two theorems, thereby continuing the work of T. Morishima and T. Miyoshi [Proc. Amer. Math. Soc. **16** (1965), 833–836; MR **31** #4761]. (I) If $(\phi(c), p)=1$, $c^{p-1}\not\equiv 2^{p-1} \pmod{p^2}$, then $x^p+y^p=cz^p$, $p\nmid z$, has a solution only if $r^{p-1}\equiv 1 \pmod{p^2}$ for an arbitrary divisor r of c. (II) If c has no prime divisor of the form $pt+1$, then $x^p+y^p=cz^p$, $p\nmid x$, has a pairwise co-prime solution only if $r^{p-1}\equiv 1 \pmod{p^2}$ for an arbitrary divisor r of x. The main tool is the Eisenstein reciprocity theorem (see, e.g., E. Landau [*Vorlesungen über Zahlentheorie*, Band 3, pp. 277–311, S. Hirzel, Leipzig, 1927]). *H. J. Godwin* (Swansea)

Citations: MR 31# 4761 = D44-125.

D44-138 **(34# 5738a; 34# 5738b)**

Ferentinou-Nikolakopoulou, Ioanna
A new necessary condition for the existence of a solution to the equation $x^p+y^p=z^p$ of Fermat. (Greek. French summary)
Bull. Soc. Math. Grèce (N.S.) **6 I** (1965), *fasc.* 2, 222–236.

Ferentinou-Nikolakopoulou, Ioanna
Remarks on the article: "A new necessary condition for the existence of a solution to the equation $x^p+y^p=z^p$ of Fermat". (Greek. French summary)
Bull. Soc. Math. Grèce (N.S.) **6 II** (1965), *fasc.* 2, 356–357.

In the first paper the author proves that if the Fermat equation $x^p+y^p=z^p$ has a solution with $(x, y, z)=1$ and $(xyz, p)=1$, where p is a prime >5, then there exists an integer a in the interval $1\leqq a\leqq (p-5)/2$ satisfying the congruence $(a+1)^{p^2}-a^{p^2}-1\equiv 0 \pmod{p^4}$. In the second paper she acknowledges priority of this result to A. Trypanis, who announced the same condition in an abstract [Proc. Internat. Cong. Mathematicians (Cambridge, Mass., 1950), Vol. I, pp. 301–302, Amer. Math. Soc., Providence, R.I., 1951]. *T. M. Apostol* (Pasadena, Calif.)

D44-139 **(35# 1544)**

Christilles, W. E.
A note concerning Fermat's conjecture.
Amer. Math. Monthly **74** (1967), 292–294.

The author obtains some elementary results related to Fermat's conjecture. In particular, it is shown that $x^p+y^p+z^p=0$ has a solution under certain normalization conditions if and only if $x^{3p}+y^{3p}+z^{3p}-3x^py^pz^p=0$ has a solution. From this he obtains another proof of Stone's theorem which states that if p and $2p+1$ are odd primes and $a^p+b^p+c^p=0$, where a, b, c are non-zero pairwise prime integers, then precisely one of the integers a, b, c is divisible by $2p+1$ [D. E. Stone, same Monthly **70** (1963), 976–977]. Another result similar to Stone's result is obtained, i.e., if a, b, c and p are integers satisfying certain conditions with both p and $4p+1$ odd primes and $(abc, 4p+1)=1$, then Fermat's equation has no solution. J. M. Gandhi [ibid. **73** (1966), 1106–1107; MR **34** #4198] obtained this result by different elementary considerations. {There is a minor printing error in the proof of Theorem 2.}
M. S. Cheema (Tucson, Ariz.)

Citations: MR 34# 4198 = D44-136.
Referred to in D44-145.

D44-140 **(35# 4149)**

Gandhi, J. M.
A note on Fermat's last theorem.
Math. Notae **20** (1965), 107–108.

The author proves that if $p(>3)$ and $4p+1$ are odd primes and $a^p+b^p+c^p=0$, where a, b, c are nonzero, pairwise prime integers, then precisely one of the integers a, b, c is divisible by $4p+1$. *H. Gupta* (Allahabad)

D44-141 **(36# 108)**

Le Lidec, Paul
Sur une forme nouvelle des congruences de Kummer-Mirimanoff.
C. R. Acad. Sci. Paris Sér. A-B **265** (1967), A89–A90.

Let a, b, c be a solution in rational integers of Fermat's equation $a^p+b^p+c^p=0$, $p\nmid abc$, $p\geqq 3$, prime. D. Mirimanoff has shown that Kummer's congruences imply $f_i(t)f_{p-i}(t) \equiv f_{p-1}(t) \equiv 0 \pmod p$ for $t \equiv -b/a \pmod p$, where $f_i(x) = \sum_{s=1}^{p-1} s^{i-1}x^{p-s}$ and i is odd, $3 \leqq i \leqq p-2$. The purpose of the present paper is to show that Mirimanoff's $\frac{1}{2}(p-1)$ congruences are equivalent to the $p-1$ congruences $P_n(t) \equiv f_{p-1}(t) \equiv 0 \pmod p$ $(1 \leqq n \leqq p-2)$. Here

$$P_n(x) = \sum_{1 \leqq s \leqq p-1;\, \overline{(n+1)}ns < s} \bar{s}x^{p-1-s},$$

$\bar{n}$ stands for the arithmetic inverse of n $(1 \leqq \bar{n} \leqq p-1$, $n\bar{n} \equiv 1 \pmod p)$ and the summation condition $\overline{(n+1)}ns < s$ means that the smallest positive integer congruent to $\overline{(n+1)}ns \pmod p$ is less than s.

E. Grosswald (Philadelphia, Pa.)

D44-142 (36# 6349)

Miyoshi, Takeo
On the Diophantine equation $x^l + y^l = cz^l$. II.
TRU Math. **2** (1966), 53–54.

Let l be a prime greater than 3, and let c be an integer such that $(\varphi(c), l) = 1$ and $c^{l-1} \not\equiv 2^{l-1} \pmod{l^2}$. It is shown that if the Diophantine equation $x^l + y^l = cz^l$ has a solution in integers x, y, z not divisible by l, then the numerator of the Bernoulli number $B_{(l-3)/2}$ is divisible by l.

{Part I, by T. Morishima and the author, appeared in Proc. Amer. Math. Soc. **16** (1965), 833–836 [MR **31** #4761].}

W. H. Mills (Princeton, N.J.)

Citations: MR 31# 4761 = D44-125.

D44-143 (36# 6350)

Yamaguchi, Itaru
On Fermat's last theorem.
TRU Math. **3** (1967), 13–18.

Let l be a prime, $l > 5$, $l \equiv 1 \pmod 4$, let ζ be a primitive lth root of unity, and let $k(\zeta)$ be the corresponding cyclotomic field. The author derives additional necessary conditions for the solvability of Fermat's equation $x^l + y^l = z^l$ in integers of $k(\zeta)$ that are relatively prime to $1-\zeta$. These conditions involve Bernoulli numbers and the irregular class group of $k(\zeta)$. *W. H. Mills* (Princeton, N.J.)

D44-144 (37# 149)

Christilles, W. E.
On Fermat's conjecture.
Amer. Math. Monthly **75** (1968), 53.

In this note the author announces that he has proved the following result relating to Fermat's last theorem. Let α, β, π and p be integers, with $p \neq 3$ an odd prime, such that α, β and π are pairwise coprime, and $\pi < 0 < \alpha < \beta < |\pi|$. Moreover, let $\gamma > 2$ be the largest integer, where $\gamma = jq$ and $j > 2$, such that $q | \frac{1}{2}(\alpha^{2p} + \beta^{2p} + \pi^{2p})$, $j | \alpha\beta\pi$, and $(p, \phi(\gamma)) = 1$. Then the equation $\alpha^p + \beta^p + \pi^p = 0$ holds only if $\alpha > |\alpha + \beta + \pi| > \gamma$. *A. L. Whiteman* (Princeton, N.J.)

D44-145 (37# 1316)

Perisastri, M.
A note on Fermat's last theorem.
Amer. Math. Monthly **75** (1968), 170.

Author's text: "In this paper we give an extension of the results proven by D. E. Stone [same Monthly **70** (1963), 976–977], J. M. Gandhi [ibid. **73** (1966), 1106–1107; MR **34** #4198], and W. E. Christilles [ibid. **74** (1967), 292–294; MR **35** #1544]. Theorem: If $p > 51$ and $8p+1$ are primes, and a, b, and c are pairwise coprime integers such that $(abc, 8p+1) = 1$, then $a^p + b^p + c^p \neq 0$."

Citations: MR 34# 4198 = D44-136; MR 35# 1544 = D44-139.

D44-146 (37# 5149)

Linkovski, Josef
Sharpening of a theorem of Wieferich. (Russian)
Math. Nachr. **36** (1968), 141.

Let p be an odd prime > 3 and let x, y, z be integers such that $(x, y, z) = (xyz, p) = 1$. From $x^p + y^p + z^p = 0$ Vandiver (see E. Landau [*Vorlesungen über Zahlentheorie*, Vol. 3, p. 327, Hirzee, Leipzig, 1927]) deduced $x^3 \equiv x$, $y^3 \equiv y$, $z^3 \equiv z \pmod{p^3}$ and Grebenuk [Dokl. Akad. Nauk UzSSR **1956**, no. 8, 9–11] deduced that every divisor of $x+y+z$ which is prime to xyz must divide $2^{p-1}-1$. The author observes that these results together yield the further deduction that $2^{p-1} \equiv 1 \pmod{p^3}$, which is a sharpened form of Wieferich's theorem.

J. B. Roberts (Portland, Ore.)

D44-147 (38# 2085)

Győry, Kálmán
On the Diophantine equation $x^p + y^p = cz^p$. (Hungarian. German summary)
Mat. Lapok **18** (1967), 93–96.

The author considers the Diophantine equation (*) $x^p + y^p = cz^p$, $(x, y) = (y, z) = (z, x) = 1$, where p is a prime and c a natural number. Because of the difficulty of the problem whether (*) is soluble for $p \geqq 3$, it is of interest to give upper estimates for the possible solutions of (*) below N, that is, for the number of solutions of (*) for which (**) $1 \leqq x, y, z \leqq N$ holds.

P. Dénes and P. Turán [Publ. Math. Debrecen **4** (1955), 28–32; MR **16**, 1089] showed that for $c = 1$ we have $R_p(N) \leqq p(1 + 3 \cdot \sqrt{2})N^{2/p}$ and

$$R_p(N) \leqq c_1(p)N^{2/p}(\log^{2-2/p} N)^{-1},$$

where $R_p(N)$ is the number of solutions of (*) satisfying (**) and $c_1(p)$ is a constant depending only on p.

In the present note it is shown that for general c, $R_p(N) \leqq c_2N$, c_2 depending only on c and p, but not on N.

P. Szüsz (Stony Brook, N.Y.)

Citations: MR 16, 1089b = D44-75.

D44-148 (38# 3285)

Bolker, E. D.
Solutions of $A^k + B^k = C^k$ in $n \times n$ integral matrices.
Amer. Math. Monthly **75** (1968), 759–760.

Let $Z(n)$ be the ring of $n \times n$ matrices with integer entries; $Z(1) = Z$. The author proves that the equation $A^{pn} + B^{pn} = C^{pn}$ has a nonsingular solution in $Z(n)$ whenever $\alpha^p + \beta^p = \gamma^p$ has a nonzero solution in Z. In fact, $A = \operatorname{diag}(\alpha, 1, \cdots, 1)P$, $B = \operatorname{diag}(\beta, 1, \cdots, 1)P$ and $C = \operatorname{diag}(\gamma, 1, \cdots, 1)P$, where P is a cyclic permutation matrix in $Z(n)$. *B. N. Moyls* (Vancouver, B.C.)

D44-149 (38# 4409)

Puccioni, Silvano
Un teorema per una risoluzione parziale del famoso problema di Fermat.
Archimede **20** (1968), 219–220.

Der Verfasser führt eine gewisse Menge N von Primzahlen ein und zeigt: (1) Ist N unendlich, so ist für unendlich viele Primzahlen l die Fermatgleichung $x^l + y^l + z^l = 0$, $(x, y, z) = 1$, $l \nmid xyz$, unlösbar. (2) Ist N endlich, so gibt es für jede Primzahl $p \leqq 43$, $p \not\equiv \pm 1 \bmod 8$, unendlich viele Primzahlen l mit $p^{l-1} - 1 \equiv 0 \bmod l^3$.

W. Schwarz (Freiburg)

D44-150 (38# 5697)

Thérond, Jean-Daniel
L'hypothèse de Fermat pour les exposants négatifs.
Enseignement Math. **13** (1967), 247–252 (1968).

Let $F_n(x, y, z) \equiv x^n + y^n + z^n$, with $x, y, z \in Q$ and $n \in Z$. By purely elementary methods the author proves several results for $n < 0$. *H. London* (Montreal, Que.)

Referred to in D44-151.

D44-151 **(41# 6766)**

Thérond, Jean-Daniel

L'hypothèse de Fermat pour les exposants négatifs.

Enseignement Math. (2) **14** (1968), 195–196 (1970).

The author improves the results of his previous paper of the same title [Enseignement Math. **13** (1967), 247–252 (1968); MR **38** #5697]. *H. London* (Montreal, Que.)

Citations: MR 38# 5697 = D44-150.

D44-152 **(39# 1404)**

Swistak, J. M.

A note on Fermat's last theorem.

Amer. Math. Monthly **76** (1969), 173–174.

The following theorem is proved. If $x^n+y^n=z^n$, where n is prime, $x>0$, $y>0$, $z>0$, $(x,y)=1$, then $n|\phi(x)$, $n|\phi(y)$, $n|\phi(z)$, where ϕ is the Euler function.

L. Carlitz (Durham, N.C.)

D44-153 **(39# 5471)**

Perisastri, M.

On Fermat's last theorem.

Amer. Math. Monthly **76** (1969), 671–675.

Let $a^p+b^p+c^p=0$. By elementary methods it is proved that (i) if p and $2p+1$ are primes, then exactly one of the integers a, b, c is divisible by p^2 and (ii) if p and $3p+1$ are primes, then one of the integers a, b, c is divisible by $3p+1$. Some inequalities involving a, b, c and p have also been derived. {Reviewer's remark: The proof of Theorem 2 could have been shortened if the author would have started from his equations (4)–(6), which are well known [L. J. Mordell, *Three lectures on Fermat's last theorem*, Cambridge Univ. Press, Cambridge, Mass., 1921; French translation, Les Presses Universitaires de France, Paris, 1929].} *J. M. Gandhi* (Macomb, Ill.)

D44-154 **(40# 4204)**

Greenleaf, Newcomb

On Fermat's equation in $\mathscr{C}(t)$.

Amer. Math. Monthly **76** (1969), 808–809.

The author gives an elementary proof, using Fermat descent, of the known result that for $n>2$, $X^n+Y^n=Z^n$ has no trivial solution in $C(t)$, where $C(t)$ is the field of rational functions over the complex numbers.

Fred Gross (Washington, D.C.)

D44-155 **(41# 3363)**

Kobelev, V. V.

A proof of Fermat's last theorem for all prime exponents less than 5500. (Russian)

Dokl. Akad. Nauk SSSR **190** (1970), 767–768.

The aim of the title is fulfilled by the table of a computation concerning irregular primes L (which divide the denominator of B_{2a}, $2a<L-1$). The criterion of Vandiver is applied [see D. H. Lehmer, E. Lehmer and H. S. Vandiver, Proc. Nat. Acad. Sci. U.S.A. **40** (1954), 25–33; MR **15**, 778] to extend the range to $4002<L<5500$. The earlier range, up to 4002 [loc. cit. and J. L. Selfridge, C. A. Nicol and Vandiver, ibid. **41** (1955), 970–973; MR **17**, 348; also Vandiver, ibid. **40** (1954), 732–735; MR **16**, 13] was rechecked and errors are claimed for $L=1381, 1597, 1663, 1887, 1933, 3631$. There are 66 irregular primes in the new range out of 174 (still close to the conjectured 39%). Primes of double and triple degree of irregularity (i.e., number of divisible Bernoullian denominators) still occur. The computer used is the BESM-6 with basic speed of 10^6 operations per second and running time of 31 minutes for this calculation.

{This article has appeared in English translation [Soviet Math. Dokl. **11** (1970), 188–190].}

Harvey Cohn (Tucson, Ariz.)

Citations: MR 15, 778f = D44-66; MR 16, 13f = D44-69; MR 17, 348a = D44-76.

D44-156 **(41# 6768)**

Le Lidec, Paul

Nouvelle forme des congruences de Kummer-Mirimanoff pour le premier cas du théorème de Fermat.

Bull. Soc. Math. France **97** (1969), 321–328.

From the author's introduction: "Soient p un nombre premier impair, et (a,b,c) une solution de l'équation de Fermat (F) $x^p+y^p+z^p=0$ telle que $abc\not\equiv 0 \pmod p$. Mirimanoff a déduit des congruences de Kummer les congruences suivantes: (M) $f_i(t)f_{p-i}(t)\equiv 0 \pmod p$, $i=3, 5, \cdots, (p-2)$, $t\equiv -b/a \pmod p$, auxquelles il faut ajouter la congruence $f_{p-1}(t)\equiv 0 \pmod p$, qui n'est autre que le développement de $((t+1)^p-t^p-1)/p\equiv 0 \pmod p$.

"Le développement de $f_i(x)$ est le suivant: $f_i(x)=x^{p-1}+2^{i-1}x^{p-2}+3^{i-1}x^{p-3}+\cdots+(p-2)^{i-1}x^2+(p-1)^{i-1}$, c'est-à-dire, $f_i(x)=\sum_{s=1}^{p-1} s^{i-1}x^{p-s}$.

"Le présent mémoire a pour but de déduire des congruences (M) d'autres congruences équivalentes de forme remarquable et qui semblent permettre l'application de méthodes combinatoires susceptibles d'aboutir à la démonstration du premier cas du théorème de Fermat."

J. H. H. Chalk (Toronto, Ont.)

D44-157 **(41# 8339)**

Rameswar Rao, D.

Some theorems on Fermat's last theorem.

Math. Student **37** (1969), 208–210.

Let x, y, z denote non-negative integers, $n\geqq 2$ and $x^n+y^n=z^n$. It is proved: (i) x, y, z cannot be in arithmetical progression; (ii) $\mu(x+y)=0$, μ denoting Möbius' function; (iii) $(x+y)|(z, x+y-z)^p$, $n=p>2$. The proofs are elementary. *W. Ljunggren* (Oslo)

D44-158 **(42# 1802)**

Riekstin'š, Ja. È. [Riekstiņš, J.]

The solution of the Fermat equation for matrices. (Russian. Latvian and English summaries)

Latvian Math. Yearbook, 5 (*Russian*), *pp.* 133–138. *Izdat. "Zinatne", Riga*, 1969.

The author considers the equation $X^n+Y^n=Z^n$, where X, Y, and Z are matrices whose elements are integers. He gives a number of interesting constructions for solutions where X, Y, and Z satisfy the following additional constraints: (1) their order is $\leqq n$, (2) their elements are non-negative, and (3) they have no row or column consisting entirely of zeros. *B. Gordon* (Los Angeles, Calif.)

D44-159 **(42# 4482)**

Karamatsu, Yoshikazu; Abe, Shuichi

On Fermat's last theorem and the first factor of the class number of the cyclotomic field.

TRU Math. **4** (1968), 1–9.

In 1925 H. S. Vandiver [Ann. of Math. (2) **26** (1925), 217–232] proved: If $x^p+y^p+z^p=0$ is satisfied by integers x, y, z, prime to the odd prime p, then the first factor of the class number of the cyclotomic field $k(e^{2\pi i/p})$ is divisible by p^8.

In 1932 T. Morishima [Proc. Imp. Acad. Tokyo **8** (1932), 63–66] improved this by showing that p^8 can be replaced by p^{12} if p does not divide $75571\cdot 20579903$. Later in 1932 D. H. Lehmer [Bull. Amer. Math. Soc. **38**

(1932), 723–724] showed that the proviso of Morishima's result is unnecessary by showing that $x^p+y^p+z^p=0$ is not satisfied by the prime factors of $7551\cdot 20579903$. In this paper the authors prove that p^{12} can be replaced by p^{14} if p does not divide 3,547,114,323,481. The authors claim that the proviso is actually unnecessary. They plan to show that $x^p+y^p+z^p=0$ is not satisfied by the prime factors of 3,547,114,323,481, presumably in a manner similar to that of Lehmer, that is, by using Wieferich's criterion. *K. S. Williams* (Ottawa, Ont.)

D44-160 **(42# 4483)**

Sarantopoulos, Spyridon
Du premier cas du théorème de Fermat.
Bull. Soc. Math. Grèce (N.S.) **10** (1969), *fasc.* 1, 76–115.

An elementary proof is given of the first case of the Fermat theorem, that is, it is shown that there do not exist positive integers x, y, z, μ such that $x^\mu+y^\mu=z^\mu$, $\mu\geqq 3$, and μ is relatively prime to each of the integers x, y, z.
B. Garrison (San Diego, Calif.)

The reviewer wishes to add the following remarks. "Professor E. G. Straus has pointed out that Théorème 11 of this paper is false (counterexamples are easily constructed). Thus the first case of the Fermat conjecture appears to remain open."

D44-161 **(43# 168)**

Metsänkylä, Tauno
Note on the distribution of irregular primes.
Ann. Acad. Sci. Fenn. Ser. A I No. 492 (1971), 7 *pp.*

Generalising a theorem of H. L. Montgomery [Illinois J. Math. **9** (1965), 553–558; MR **31** #5861], it is proved that if T is an integer, $T>4$, $T\neq 6$, then there are infinitely many irregular primes (in the sense of Kummer) which do not lie in the two residue classes $\pm 1 \pmod T$. The method is similar to that in the above paper.
I. Danicic (Aberystwyth)

Citations: MR 31# 5861 = D44-126.

D44-162 **(44# 2701)**

Gandhi, J. M.
Generalized Fermat's last theorem and regular primes.
Proc. Japan Acad. **46** (1970), 626–629.

The author has conjectured [Amer. Math. Monthly **71** (1964), 998–1006; MR **30** #1088] that $x^n+y^n=cz^n$ has no nontrivial solution in integers if $n>2$ and $0<c\leqq n$. In addition to giving several references having a bearing on the conjecture the author proves the following: Let $p>3$ be a regular prime, and let c satisfy $(c\phi(c),p)=1$ and $c^{p-1}\not\equiv 1, 2^{p-1} \pmod{p^2}$. Then $x^p+y^p=cz^p$ has no nontrivial solutions. The author notes that for $0<c\leqq p$ the condition $(c\phi(c),p)=1$ is unnecessary since $x^p+y^p=pz^p$ is known to have no nontrivial solutions for regular p.
S. A. Burr (Whippany, N.J.)

Citations: MR 30# 1088 = D44-120.

D44-163 **(44# 2724)**

Erdős, P.; Ulam, S.
Some probabilistic remarks on Fermat's last theorem.
Rocky Mountain J. Math. **1** (1971), *no.* 4, 613–616.

Suppose $\alpha>1$. A measure μ_α is introduced on the space of increasing sequences of integers $A=\{a_n\}$ such that for μ_α-almost all such sequences, $a_n\sim cn^\alpha$ for a suitable constant c. It is shown that for μ_α-almost all A the equation $a_i+a_j=a_r$ has only finitely many solutions if $\alpha>3$, but infinitely many solutions for $\alpha\leqq 3$. Since $x^3+y^3=z^3$ has no solution, the sequence $\{n^3\}$ belongs to the exceptional set of μ_3-measure 0. There is a corresponding statement for k summands, the dichotomy then being $\alpha>k+1$ or $\alpha\leqq k+1$. The proof invokes the Borel-Cantelli lemmas.
W. J. LeVeque (Claremont, Calif).

D44-164 **(44# 6598)**

Hellegouarch, Yves
Sur l'équation diophantienne $x_1^{p^h}+x_2^{p^h}=q^a x_3^{p^h}$.
C. R. Acad. Sci. Paris Sér. A-B **273** (1971), A1194–A1196.

The author's serious discussion starts with the (believable, to say the least) conjecture (*) for p (odd) and q primes and $a>0$, there exists an integer $N(p,q^a)$ (depending on the number field K) such that (**) $X_1^{p^h}+X_2^{p^h}=q^aX_3^{p^h}$ has no rational points over K if $h>N(p,q^a)$. The state of the art being what it is, attempts at Mordell's conjecture for any equation must assume special properties of K; the author takes $K=\mathbf{Q}$. Of course, if (**) has finitely many solutions for some h, then for large h it will have no (non-trivial) solutions.

The author establishes a lemma (whose conclusion is valid under restrictive conditions, for example, when p is a regular prime and q is a primitive root mod p, while mod p^2 the period of q is $\neq p-1$) and then establishes (*) when the conclusion of the lemma holds.
M. Fried (Ann Arbor, Mich.)

D48 HIGHER DEGREE VARIETIES: GENERAL

See also Sections D56, D60, E76, G35.
See also reviews A32-27, A44-16, D24-14, D24-19, D24-38, D24-56, D28-15, D28-20, D28-40, D32-52, D36-12, D36-19, D40-41, D40-42, D44-52, D44-86, D44-127, D52-7, D52-35, D52-72, D52-75, D52-118, D56-2, D56-3, D56-5, D56-6, D56-7, D56-8, D56-14, D56-15, D56-17, D56-19, D56-22, D56-24, D56-30, D56-32, D80-34, E12-108, E76-12, G35-7, G35-41, J68-42, J68-52, P08-13, P08-42, R14-9, R18-26, R42-32, T25-3, U05-7, U05-19, U05-35, U05-42, U05-43, U05-46.

D48-1 **(1, 4f)**

Ward, Morgan. Note on the general rational solution of the equation $ax^2-by^2=z^3$. Amer. J. Math. **61**, 788–790 (1939).

The author finds the general rational solution of

$$a_0x^m+a_1x^{m-1}y+\cdots+a_my^m=z^n,$$

where m and n are co-prime integers and $a_0, a_1, \cdots, a_m$ are rational, by reducing it to the form $Y^m=Z^n$. This last equation is a particular case of an equation previously discussed by the author [Amer. J. Math. **55**, 67–76 (1933); **59**, 921–926 (1937)]. The case $m=2$, $n=3$, $a_0=a$, $a_1=0$, $a_2=-b$, $a_3=a_4=\cdots=a_m=0$ leads to an equation solved by Fogels by the method of algebraic numbers [Amer. J. Math. **60**, 734–736 (1938)]. *I. A. Barnett* (Cincinnati, Ohio).

Referred to in D48-71.

D48-2 **(1, 200b)**

Tchacaloff, Lhristo et Karanicoloff, Chr. Résolution de l'équation $Ax^m+By^n=z^p$ en nombres rationnels. C. R. Acad. Sci. Paris **210**, 281–283 (1940).

Let A and B be given rational numbers, and let m, n, p be integers, relatively prime in pairs. The author considers the problem of finding all rational solutions of the equation $Ax^m+By^n=z^p$. He shows that all rational solutions of this equation may be deduced from the rational solutions of the simple equation $AX+BY=Z$. Here x, y, z and X, Y, Z are connected by a functional relation which depends on m, n and p. *A. C. Schaeffer* (Palo Alto, Calif.).

Referred to in D48-6, D48-8, D48-14, D48-46.

D48-3 (1, 291a)

Bang, A. S. On sums of powers of the sixth degree. Mat. Tidsskr. B. **1939**, 52–65 (1939). (Danish)

The author indicates three identities of type $A_1^6+\cdots+A_m^6=B_1^6+\cdots+B_n^6$, where A_i and B_i are forms in two variables. He deduces many numerical identities and, for different couples m, n, the existence of infinitely many integers representable both as sums of m and of n sixth powers. In particular, if $n\geqq 13$, there is a sixth power which is the sum of n sixth powers. *W. Feller.*

D48-4 (1, 291c)

Moessner, A. Einige Diophantische Probleme und zahlentheoretische Untersuchungen. Bol. Mat. **13**, 41–47 (1940).

D48-5 (2, 145d)

Aucoin, A. A. Diophantine equations of degree n. Bull. Amer. Math. Soc. **46**, 334–339 (1940).

This is a generalization of a paper by the author and W. V. Parker on "Cubic Diophantine Equations" in the Nat. Math. Mag. **13**, 115–117 (1938). The present paper has to do with the integral solutions of the equation $f(x_1, \cdots, x_p)=g(y_1, \cdots, y_q)$ when f and g are homogeneous polynomials with integral coefficients of degrees n and m, and such that there exist a set of integers $a_1, \cdots, a_p$ not all zero for which the partial derivatives of f of all orders less than $n-1$ vanish when $x_i=a_i$. The discussion is incomplete since the condition (2) on page 334 is frequently not satisfied and the case $\sum_{j=1}^{p} a_j\partial f/\partial x_j\equiv 0$ has not been considered. In the corollary on page 338 the phrase "is given by" should be changed to "an equivalent solution may be obtained from." *I. A. Barnett* (Cincinnati, Ohio).

D48-6 (2, 145e)

Vijayaraghavan, T. The general rational solution of some Diophantine equations of the form $\sum_{r=1}^{k+1} A_r x_r^{n_r}=0$. Proc. Indian Acad. Sci., Sect. A. **12**, 284–289 (1940).

Let i range over $1, \cdots, k$; r, s over $1, \cdots, k+1$. The general solution in rational nonzero x_r of $\sum A_i x_i^{n_i}=x_{k+1}^{n_{k+1}}$, where n_{k+1} is prime to $n_1\cdots n_k$ $(\neq 0)$, is given by $x_r=[X_r\Pi X_s^{M_s}]^{1/m_r}$, where the X_i are arbitrary nonzero l_ith powers of rational numbers, and $X_{k+1}=\sum A_i X_i$. Here $\alpha_0=(n_1, \cdots, n_k)$, $\alpha_0\alpha_i=(n_1, \cdots, n_{i-1}, n_{i+1}, \cdots, n_k)$, $\alpha_{k+1}=\alpha_0\cdots\alpha_k$, $l_r=\alpha_{k+1}/\alpha_r$, $m_r=n_r/l_r$, $N=m_1\cdots m_{k+1}$, N_r are integers such that $N_r\equiv -1 \pmod{m_r}$, $N_r\equiv 0 \pmod{\alpha_r N/m_r}$; $1+\sum N_r=aN$, b and c satisfy $b\alpha_1+c\alpha_2=1-a$; $M_1=N_1+b\alpha_1 N$, $M_2=N_2+c\alpha_2 N$, $M_j=N_j$ $(j=3, \cdots, k+1)$. L. Tchacaloff and C. Karanicoloff [C. R. Acad. Sci. Paris **210**, 281–283 (1940); these Rev. **1**, 200] treated the case $k=2$ with n_r coprime in pairs. *G. Pall* (Princeton, N. J.).

Citations: MR 1, 200b = D48-2.

D48-7 (2, 247d)

Bang, A. S. Some algebraic identities. Mat. Tidsskr. B. **1940**, 62–65 (1940). (Danish)

From the known identity

$$2(a^2+ab+b^2)^4=(a^4-b^4)^4+(a^2+2ab)^4+(2ab+b^2)^4$$

is derived for each n an identity of the form

$$2(a^2+ab+b^2)^{4n}=A^4+B^4+C^4,$$

where A, B, C are polynomials in a and b with integral coefficients. *B. Jessen* (Copenhagen).

D48-8 (3, 268e)

Basu, N. M. On a Diophantine equation. Bull. Calcutta Math. Soc. **32**, 15–20 (1940).

In a recent note Tchacaloff and Karanicoloff [C. R. Acad. Sci. Paris **200**, 281–283 (1940); these Rev. **1**, 200] have obtained the general parametric solution, in nonzero rational numbers, of the equation $Ax^m+By^n=z^p$, where m, n, p are relatively prime in pairs and A and B are any rational numbers. For example, in the case of the equation $x^2-y^3=z^5$, the solution obtained is

$$(x, y, z)=(a^8b^{10}(a-b)^{-3}, a^5b^7(a-b)^{-2}, a^3b^4(a-b)^{-1}),$$

where the parameters a, b run over all nonzero rationals with $a\neq b$. Solving for a and b in terms of x, y, z gives $a=xy^{-2}z$, $b=x^{-1}yz$, so that the solution is general.

In the present note the method is extended to the general equation

$$A_1x_1^m+A_2x_2^n+\cdots+A_kx_k^l=x_{k+1}^r,$$

where the A's are rational and the integers $m, n, \cdots, l$ are prime to r and are such that any pair of them have the same greatest common divisor g. The general solution is given in terms of the solutions $(y_1, \cdots, y_{k+1})$ of

$$A_1y_1^g+A_2y_2^g+\cdots+A_ky_k^g=y_{k+1}.$$

D. H. Lehmer (Berkeley, Calif.).

Citations: MR 1, 200b = D48-2.

D48-9 (4, 240a)

Bell, E. T. Note on a conjecture due to Euler. Bull. Amer. Math. Soc. **49**, 393–394 (1943).

The conjecture referred to is to the effect that the equation

$$x_1^n+x_2^n+\cdots+x_t^n=x^n$$

has no solution $(x_1, \cdots, x_t, x)$ in rational numbers (different from zero) in case $n>3$ and $2<t<n$. The author points out that this equation has solutions in algebraic numbers for $n>3$ and for any $t>1$. This solution is (to within a factor of homogeneity) as follows:

$$\begin{aligned} x_1&=1,\\ x_2&=r_1,\\ x_3&=r_2(1+r_1),\\ x_4&=r_3(1+r_2)(1+r_1),\\ &\cdots\cdots\\ x_t&=r_{t-1}(1+r_{t-2})\cdots(1+r_1),\\ x&=(1+r_{t-1})\cdots(1+r_1),\end{aligned}$$

where the r's are chosen in any way from among those roots of $(1+x)^n=1+x^n$ which are different from 0 and -1. *D. H. Lehmer* (Berkeley, Calif.).

D48-10 (7, 414f)

Vandiver, H. S. On classes of Diophantine equations of higher degrees which have no solutions. Proc. Nat. Acad. Sci. U. S. A. **32**, 101–106 (1946).

In many cases the impossibility of a Diophantine equation may be shown by the use of congruences with respect to a convenient modulus. The author uses this principle for constructing general classes of Diophantine equations which have no solutions or no nonzero solutions. His main result is the following. If c is a prime and m is an integer such that $p=1+mc$ with p prime, then

$$a_1x_1^m+a_2x_2^m+\cdots+a_sx_s^m=0$$

has only the solution $x_1=x_2=\cdots=x_s=0$ provided that $s\leqq c-2$; the sum of no n of the integers a is zero, $0<n\leqq s$; and

$$\left(\sum_{i=1}^{s}|a_i|\right)^{\varphi(c)}<p.$$

The condition that the sum of no n of the a's is zero is necessary since, if $a_1+a_2+\cdots+a_j=0$, the Diophantine equation is satisfied with $x_1=x_2=\cdots=x_j=1$ and $x_{j+1}=x_{j+2}=\cdots=x_s=0$. *T. Nagell* (Uppsala).

Referred to in D40-14.

D48-11 (8, 313g)

Gentile, Giovanni. Sulla rappresentazione della potenza n-esima di un numero primo con le forme $x^m \pm y^m$. Boll. Mat. (4) **4**, 19–21 (1943).

It is shown that the Diophantine equation $x^m+y^m=p^n$, where x and y are positive integers, p is a prime and m contains at least one odd prime factor, has solutions only when $p=2$, $n\equiv 1 \pmod m$, or when $p=3$, $n\equiv 2 \pmod 3$. This was proved by Gegenbauer by a similar method in a paper which the author states that he has been unable to consult [Akad. Wiss. Wien, S.-B. IIa. **97**, 271–276 (1888)]. It is also shown that the equation $x^m-y^m=p^n$ possesses no solutions for even $m>2$. *R. A. Rankin.*

D48-12 (10, 353e)

Pettineo, B. Sull'equazione indeterminata: $x^2+y^2=kz^n$. Matematiche, Catania **1**, 180–210 (1946).

The author considers the Diophantine equation $x^2+y^2=kz^n$, and for any fixed k and n gives criteria for the existence of integral solutions. This is done by considering the factorization of both sides of the equation in the ring of Gaussian integers. In the special case $n=2$, well-known theorems of Gauss and Dirichlet are obtained. *H. N. Shapiro.*

D48-13 (10, 510a)

Moessner, Alfred. Verschiedene zahlentheoretische Untersuchungen und Diophantische Probleme. Bull. Calcutta Math. Soc. **40**, 147–152 (1948).

Numerical solutions of some special systems of Diophantine equations. *N. G. W. H. Beeger* (Amsterdam).

D48-14 (10, 510f)

Karanikolov, Chr. On a class of indeterminate equations. Spisanie Bulgar. Akad. Nauk. **65**, 291–293 (1942). (Bulgarian)

Cf. Tchakaloff and the author, C. R. Acad. Sci. Paris **210**, 281–283 (1940); these Rev. **1**, 200.

Citations: MR 1, 200b = D48-2.

D48-15 (12, 804c)

Moppert, Karl-Felix. Über eine diophantische Identität. Comment. Math. Helv. **25**, 71–74 (1951).

The author discusses identities (1) $P_1^{k_1}+P_2^{k_2}+P_3^{k_3}\equiv 0$, where k_1, k_2, k_3 are integers greater than 1, and P_1, P_2, P_3 are relatively prime nonconstant polynomials over the field of complex numbers. He obtains as a necessary condition for the existence of (1) that (2) $k_1^{-1}+k_2^{-1}+k_3^{-1}>1$; the set of solutions of (2) is: $(2, 2, k)$, $k>1$; $(2, 3, 3)$, $(2, 3, 4)$, and $(2, 3, 5)$. For each triple (k_1, k_2, k_3) in the above set he shows that the Schwarz triangle function mapping the circular arc triangle with angles π/k_1, π/k_2, π/k_3 onto the upper half plane—which is a rational function—can be set equal to $P_1^{k_1}/P_3^{k_3}$ and (1) is satisfied. The identity obtained from (2, 3, 3) reads:

$$p(px^4-64qxy^3)^3+q(8px^3y+512qy^4)^3 = (p^2x^6+160pqx^3y^3-512q^2y^6)^2,$$

where the letters appearing are arbitrary complex numbers. By specialization to integers one obtains infinitely many solutions of the diophantine equation $pX^3+qY^3=Z^2$. The remaining identities are treated similarly. *J. Lehner.*

D48-16 (13, 13h)

Ward, Morgan. A class of soluble Diophantine equations. Proc. Nat. Acad. Sci. U. S. A. **37**, 113–114 (1951).

Let $F(x_1, \cdots, x_t)$ be a homogeneous polynomial of degree n with integer coefficients, and let $m>0$ be prime to n. Then the diophantine equation $F(x)=z^m$ has the trivial family of integer solutions $x_i=y_iF^k(y)$, $z=F^l(y)$, where $k>0$, $l>0$ is any solution of $nk+1=lm$ and $y_1, \cdots, y_t$ are any integers. *J. W. S. Cassels* (Cambridge, England).

Referred to in T40-15.

D48-17 (13, 111d)

Moessner, Alfred. Due sistemi diofantei. Boll. Un. Mat. Ital. (3) **6**, 117–118 (1951).

A two parameter solution of the Diophantine equation $\sum_{i=1}^{6} x_i^5=0$ is given, and also another two parameter solution which satisfies the additional condition $\sum_{i=1}^{6} x_i=0$. *I. Niven* (Eugene, Ore.).

D48-18 (13, 626b)

Moessner, Alfred. Sopra alcune equazioni diofantee. Boll. Un. Mat. Ital. (3) **6**, 318–319 (1951).

A two-parameter family of integral solutions is given for $\sum_{i=1}^{n} x_i^j=0$ with $n=6$, $j=5$, and a three-parameter family for the simultaneous system of equations with $j=1$, 3, and 5, $n=7$. A one-parameter family is given for the simultaneous system $\sum_{i=1}^{n}(x_i^j-y_i^j)=0$ with $n=3$, $j=2$ and 3. *I. Niven* (Eugene, Ore.).

D48-19 (14, 354e)

Georgiev, G. Résolution de l'équation

$$\sum_{k=1}^{n} A_k \prod_{i=1}^{n} x_i^{a_{ki}}=A_0$$

en nombres rationnels. Acta Math. Acad. Sci. Hungar. **2**, 229–246 (1951). (French. Russian summary)

The equation of the title, with rational coefficients A_k and integral exponents a_{ki} with determinant $|a_{ki}|\neq 0$, is studied by use of the transformation (1) $x_i=\prod_{r=1}^{n} X_r^{\lambda_{ri}}$, $i=1, 2, \cdots, n$, with integral exponents having determinant $|\lambda_{ri}|=\pm 1$. Necessary and sufficient conditions that a transformation (1) exist which reduces the original equation to $\sum_{k=1}^{n} A_kX_k=A_0$ are that $|a_{ki}|=\pm 1$. Necessary and sufficient conditions are also given for reduction to $\sum A_kX_k^{m_k}=A_0$. These results lead to sufficient conditions for solving the equation in rational integers. In case one or more of the coefficients A_k are zero, stronger results are obtained. *I. Niven* (Eugene, Ore.).

D48-20 (14, 950h)

Georgiev, G. On the solution in rational numbers of the indeterminate equation

$$\sum_{k=1}^{n} A_k x_k^{m_k}=0.$$

Uspehi Matem. Nauk (N.S.) **8**, no. 1(53), 127–130 (1953). (Russian)

If the integer indices m_k of the title equation can be divided into two nonvacuous sets, every element of the one set being coprime to every element of the other, then there is a reversible transformation of the type $x_i=\prod_{r=1}^{n} X_r^{\lambda_{ri}}$, where the λ_{ri} are integers and $\det(\lambda_{ri})=\pm 1$ such that in the transformed equation X_n occurs only to the powers λ, $\lambda+1$ (λ, some integer). Hence, if $X_1, \cdots, X_{n-1}$ are given, then X_n is determined by a linear equation, and so there is a parametric solution. This improves results of Chr. Karanikolov [Thesis, Sofia, 1942]. *J. W. S. Cassels.*

D48-21 (14, 950i)

Georgiev, G. On the indeterminate equation

$$\sum_{k=1}^{m} A_k \prod_{i=1}^{n} x_i^{a_{ki}}=A_0.$$

Uspehi Matem. Nauk (N.S.) **8**, no. 1(53), 131–134 (1953). (Russian)

A typical result is: if $m=n-1$, then a necessary and sufficient condition for the title equation to be reducible to $\sum A_k X_k = A_0$ by a transformation of the type considered in the preceding review is that the $m \times n$ minors of the matrix (a_{ik}) be relatively prime. *J. W. S. Cassels.*

D48-22 **(14, 1063g)**

Georgiev, G. On the solution in rational numbers of the indeterminate equation $\sum_{k=1}^n A_k \prod_{i=1}^n x_i^{a_{ki}} = A_0$. Uspehi Matem. Nauk (N.S.) **8**, no. 2(54), 115–118 (1953). (Russian)

The title equation may be solved by a transformation of the type $x_i = \prod_{r=1}^n X_r^{\lambda_{ri}}$ if the integers λ_{ri} can be chosen so that det $(\lambda_{ri}) = \pm 1$ and so that $\sum_i \lambda_{ni} a_{ki}$ is 0 or 1 for each k, with at least one 1. For these the equation becomes a linear equation in X_n; and the x_i are uniquely determined by the X_i. *J. W. Cassels* (Cambridge, England).

Referred to in D04-22, D48-23.

D48-23 **(17, 586f)**

Georgiev, G. On the solution in rational numbers of certain Diophantic equations. Prace Mat. **1** (1955), 201–238. (Polish. Russian and English summaries)

An exhaustive elaboration of the method expounded more briefly in Uspehi Mat. Nauk (N.S.) **8** (1953), no. 2(54), 115–118; MR **14**, 1063. *J. W. S. Cassels.*

Citations: MR 14, 1063g = D48-22.

Referred to in D48-39.

D48-24 **(15, 400a)**

Moessner, Alfred. Einige zahlentheoretische Untersuchungen und Resultate. Hrvatsko Prirodoslovno Društvo. Glasnik Mat.-Fiz. Astr. Ser. II. **8**, 129–132 (1953). (Serbo-Croatian summary)

The author shows how an application of the identity

$$(a^2+b^2)^2 = (a^2-b^2)^2 + (2ab)^2$$

can produce solutions in integers of such systems as

$$2(A^{2n}-C^{2n}) = B+D, \quad 2(A^{6n}-C^{6n}) = B^3+D^3$$

and

$$2(P^n+Q^n) = x+y+z+w$$
$$2(P^{2n}+Q^{2n}) = x^2+y^2+z^2+w^2$$
$$2(P^{3n}+Q^{3n}) = x^3+y^3+z^3+w^3.$$

D. H. Lehmer (Berkeley, Calif.).

D48-25 **(15, 934a)**

Ankeny, N. C., and Erdös, P. The insolubility of classes of diophantine equations. Amer. J. Math. **76**, 488–496 (1954).

Proofs of the following two theorems. Theorem I. Let $a_1, \cdots, a_n$ be rational integers and suppose that

$$e_1 a_1 + \cdots + e_n a_n = 0,$$

with $e_j = 0$ or ± 1, implies $e_1 = e_2 = \cdots = e_n = 0$. Then the Diophantine equation

$$a_1 X_1^m + \cdots + a_n X_n^m = 0$$

has a non-trivial rational integer solution for almost no integers $m>0$ (in the sense that the number of $m \leqq M$ for which a solution exists is $o(M)$ as $M \to \infty$). Theorem II. The equation $X_1^m + X_2^m + X_3^m$ has a rational integer solution with g.c.d. $(X_1 X_2 X_3, m) = 1$ for almost no integers $m>0$. The argument extends to general algebraic number fields, and is stated to be capable of replacing $o(M)$ by an explicit estimate $O(M(\log M)^{-c})$ for some $c>0$. The reviewer remarks that the methods appear to say little about the relative density of the primes $p=m$, for which the equations are soluble, in the set of all primes. *J. W. S. Cassels.*

D48-26 **(17, 586e)**

Moessner, Alfredo. Problemi diofantei. Boll. Un. Mat. Ital. (3) **10** (1955), 574–576.

D48-27 **(17, 944h)**

Fjellstedt, Lars. On a class of Diophantine equations. Ark. Mat. **3** (1956), 223–227.

The author applies to the equation

$$\sum_{i \leqq u} (x_i + a_i)^2 + c = x \prod_{i \leqq u} x_i \neq 0 \quad (c \geqq 0)$$

the methods of Hurwitz [Math. Werke, Bd. II, Birkhäuser, Basel, 1933, pp. 410–421] which have been applied recently by other authors to so many problems [Barnes, J. London Math. Soc. **28** (1953), 242–244; MR **14**, 725; Mills, Pacific J. Math. **3** (1953), 209–220; Proc. Amer. Math. Soc. **5** (1954), 473–475; MR **14**, 950; **16**, 13]. The equation has a solution $x_1, \cdots, x_u$ for only a finite number of x and these can be obtained from only a finite number of fundamental solutions in the now familiar way. The case $c<0$ is said to require more complication in detail and will be the subject of another paper.

J. W. S. Cassels (Cambridge, England).

Citations: MR 14, 725f = D32-38; MR 14, 950e = D20-9; MR 16, 13e = D32-44.

D48-28 **(19, 391c)**

Brčić-Kostić, Mato. Solution of the diophantine equation $x^4+y^4=z^6$. Bull Soc. Math. Phys. Serbie **8** (1956), 125–136. (Serbo-Croatian. Esperanto summary)

D48-29 **(19, 391d)**

Palamà, Giuseppe. Sull'equazione indeterminata $x_1^2 + \cdots + x_n^2 + y^2 = (n+1)x_1 \cdots x_n$ e su altre analoghe. Riv. Mat. Univ. Parma **7** (1956), 89–123.

The author considers the general equation in the title as an outgrowth of the equation

$$x^2+y^2+1=3xy$$

studied recently by Schinzel and Sierpiński [Matematiche Catania **10** (1955), 30–36; MR **17**, 711] whose solutions are $(x, y) = (U_{2r-1}, U_{2r+1})$, where U_k is the kth term of the Fibonacci sequence $U_1=1$, $U_2=1$, $U_k=U_{k-1}+U_{k-2}$. The same general method of solving the quadratic equation for the unknown x_n, requiring that the discriminant be a perfect square and proceeding inductively, is used throughout. For example, the equation

$$x_1^2+x_2^2+x_3^2+x_4^2+y^2=4x_1x_2x_3x_4$$

has as solution

$$(A_k, A_{k+1}, A_{k+2}, A_{k+3}, [A_{k+3}-A_{k+2}][A_{k+1}-A_k]),$$

where A_k is the kth term of the sequence

$$1, 1, 3, 11, 41, 153, 571, 2131, 7953, \cdots$$

in which $A_k = 4A_{k-1} - A_{k-2}$. Numerous similar equations such as $x^2+y^2+20=7xy$ are solved in the same manner. *D. H. Lehmer* (Berkeley, Calif.).

Citations: MR 17, 711e = D32-52.

D48-30 **(19, 941f)**

Battaglia, Antonio. Un caso d'impossibilità dell'equazione indeterminata: $x^{2n}+y^{2n}=z^2$. Boll. Un. Mat. Ital. (3) **12** (1957), 689–694.

The equation in the title is discussed for the case in which n is a prime and x^2+y^2 is the square of a power of a prime. The argument that the equation is impossible in integers x, y, z, none zero, is valid only if z is a prime or the square of a prime. *D. H. Lehmer.*

Referred to in D48-37.

D48-31 (20# 2302)

Schönheim, Ioan. Détermination d'une solution de l'équation $\sum_{j=1}^{N} x_j^2 = N \prod_{j=1}^{N} x_j$ pour un entier $N>2$ quelconque, x_j étant des nombres premiers deux à deux. Acad. R. P. Romîne. Fil. Cluj. Stud. Cerc. Mat. Fiz. **7** (1956), no. 1–4, 59–63. (Romanian. Russian and French summaries)

The author shows that the recurrence

(i) $$a_n = a_1 a_2 \cdots a_{n-1} + k,$$

where the a_i and k are relatively prime in pairs, defines numbers a_i which are also relatively prime in pairs, Formula (i) is equivalent to (ii) $a_n = a_{n-1}^2 - k a_{n-1} + k$, $n>2$, and (iii) $a_2 = a_1 + k$. Furthermore, $x_j = a_{j+1}$ is the solution of the diophantine equation $\sum_{j=1}^{N} x_j^2 = N \prod_{j=1}^{N} x_j$, for an arbitrary $N>2$, where the x_j are relatively prime in pairs. He utilizes the sequence defined by (i) to generalize the proof of Pólya and Szegö for the existence of an infinite number of primes.

I. A. Barnett (Cincinnati, Ohio)

D48-32 (20# 3100)

Moessner, Alfred. Über die Gleichung $A^{2n}+B^2=C^{2n}+D^2$. Glasnik Mat.-Fiz. Astr. Društvo Mat. Fiz. Hrvatske Ser. II. **12** (1957), 21–22. (Serbo-Croatian summary)

For $A>C$, $A\equiv C \pmod 2$, let s and k be determined by $s-k=A^n$, $s+k=C^n$. If $sk=mp$ with $m>p$, then the identity $A^{2n}+(m+p)^2=C^{2n}+(m-p)^2$ yields solutions of the Diophantine equation of the title. When $n=2$ one may be able to choose A, C, m, p so that $m+p$ and $m-p$ are squares. One thus obtains solutions of (1) $A^4+B^4=C^4+D^4$, including the smallest known solution $134^4+133^4=158^4+59^4$, due to P. S. Dyer [J. London Math. Soc. **18** (1943), 2–4; MR **5**, 89]. A two parameter solution of (1) was found by Euler, but the complete solution is not known. *L. Moser* (Edmonton, Alta.)

Citations: MR 5, 89e = D32-11.

D48-33 (20# 4521)

Campbell, J. G. Diophantine problems having no solution. Amer. Math. Monthly **65** (1958), 204.

The author gives a criterion that the Diophantine equation

$$A_1 x_1^{r_1(p-1)} + A_2 x_2^{r_2(p-1)} + \cdots + A_n x_n^{r_n(p-1)} = B,$$

where p is a prime, has no solution. His result is an immediate consequence of Fermat's theorem and well known. *A. Brauer* (Chapel Hill, N.C.)

D48-34 (20# 5774)

Morelock, J. C.; and Perry, N. C. A note concerning homogeneous polynomials. Math. Mag. **31** (1957/58), 75–79.

Il s'agit de trouver toutes les équations homogènes

$$F(x_1, x_2, x_3, x_4)=0,$$

de degré p, qui restent invariantes dans la transformation

$$T:(x_1', x_2', x_3', x_4')=(x_1, Ex_2, E^2x_3, E^3x_4)$$

où p est un nombre premier et $E^p=1$. Il faudra que les termes $x_1^a x_2^b x_3^c x_4^d$ du polynome F se transforment en acquérant un facteur E^s dont l'exposant s est le même pour tous les termes. On écrit et on résout très facilement en nombres entiers les équations exprimant cette propriété en supposant connus, par exemple, les valeurs de a et de d. Les auteurs donnent les formules résolutives générales et ils les appliquent au cas $p=5$ (on a dans ce cas 5 solutions). *E. G. Togliatti* (Genoa)

D48-35 (21# 26)

Battaglia, Antonio. L'equazione indeterminata $x^{2n}+y^{2n}=z^3$ e l'ultimo teorema di Fermat. Archimede **10** (1958), 120–125.

It is shown that the equation $x^{2n}+y^{2n}=z^3$ has no integral solutions x, y, z subject to the conditions that n is an odd prime and $(z, n)=(x, y)=1$. In the reviewer's opinion, the derivations of equations (21)–(24) requires more justification than is given. *R. A. Rankin* (Glasgow)

D48-36 (21# 5606)

Subba Rao, K. Some properties of arithmetic progressions. Amer. Math. Monthly **66** (1959), 582–584.

By means of identities and the well-known procedure of making a^2+kd^2 a perfect nth power, the author proves that the diophantine equation $\sum_{i=1}^{m} x_i^2 = mz^n$, where $x_1, x_2, \cdots, x_m$ are integers in arithmetic progression and z, n are integers, has infinitely many solutions. The same result is obtained for the equations $\sum_{i=1}^{m} x_i^s = z^n$ in the cases $s=2$, n odd and $s=3$, $n \not\equiv 0 \pmod 3$.

W. Ljunggren (Oslo)

D48-37 (22# 4673a; 22# 4673b)

Battaglia, Antonio. Sull'equazione indeterminata $x^{2n}+y^{2n}=z^2$. Boll. Un. Mat. Ital. (3) **14** (1959), 498–499.

Ricci, Giovanni. Una osservazione sulla precedente Nota "A. Battaglia, Sull'equazione indeterminata $x^{2n}+y^{2n}=z^2$". Boll. Un. Mat. Ital. (3) **14** (1959), 499–500.

In a previous paper [same Boll. (3) **12** (1957), 689–694; MR **19**, 941] Battaglia showed that integers x, y, z satisfying the conditions $x^{2n}+y^{2n}=z^2$, $(x, y, z)=1$, $(n, z)=1$ $(n>1)$, and such that x^2+y^2 is the square of a power of a prime, do not exist. In the present note he attempts to remove the last condition. The validity of his reasoning is questioned in the note by Ricci.

D. H. Lehmer (Berkeley, Calif.)

Citations: MR 19, 941f = D48-30.

D48-38 (23# A1596)

Thébault, Victor

Sur deux équations en nombres entiers.

Mathesis **67** (1958), 220–224.

The author considers the Diophantine equations

(1) $$x^n+y^n = p^m$$

and

(2) $$x^n-y^n = p^m.$$

For $n=2$, well-known results are stated. The case $n=2^t$, for $t>1$, is not considered. The author wants to show that if n is not a power of 2, and x and y are relatively prime, then (1) has only the solution $x=2$, $y=1$, $p=3$, $n=3$, $m=2$. For (1) and (2) he uses the same method. But his method is not completely correct. Let n be an odd prime. For equation (1) he obtains $(x+y)[N(x+y)+ny^{n-1}]=p^m$, where N is a certain integer. Without using other properties of N, and without using $x>y$, he concludes that $y=1$. A counterexample is $(5+2)[279(5+2)+7\cdot 2^6]=7^5$. That the equation (1) has only the mentioned solution was proved by L. Gegenbauer [S.-B. Akad. Wiss. Wien Math.-Phys. Kl. Abt. IIa **97** (1888), 271–276]. The result obtained by the author for equation (2) is not correct. The solution $x=8$, $y=7$, $p=13$, $n=3$, $m=2$ was found by J. Collins [T. Leyburn, *The mathematical questions proposed in the Ladies' Diary*, v. IV, London, 1817, p. 149] and by S. Parlour [ibid., p. 150]. Other solutions with $n=3$ and $m=2$ were given by W. B. Davis [*Mathematical questions with their solutions*, from the "Educational Times", **23** (1875), 85] and W. J. Greenfield [ibid., 86], for instance, $x=3932761$, $y=3932760$, $p=6811741$.

A. Brauer (Chapel Hill, N.C.)

D48-39 (24# A1247)

Schinzel, A.

On the diophantine equation $\sum_{k=1}^{n} A_k x_k^{\vartheta_k}=0$. (Polish. Russian and French summaries)

Prace Mat. **4** (1960), 45–51.

The author gives some results concerning equivalence of diophantine equations $\sum_{k=1}^{n} A_k x_k^{\vartheta_k}=0$, $\sum_{k=1}^{n} A_k X_k^{m_k}=0$, in the sense of a birational transformation [for its definition see G. Gheorghiu, Prace Mat. **1** (1955), 201–238; MR **17**, 586] of one into another. *S. Knapowski* (Poznań)

Citations: MR 17, 586f = D48-23.

D48-40 (26# 2421)

Birch, B. J.; Davenport, H.; Lewis, D. J.

The addition of norm forms.

Mathematika **9** (1962), 75–82.

Es sei K ein algebraischer Zahlkörper vom Grad k und $\omega_1, \cdots, \omega_k$ eine Ganzheitsbasis von K. Es bezeichne $\omega_r^{(1)}, \cdots, \omega_r^{(k)}$ die Konjugierten von ω_r $(r=1, \cdots, k)$ und $d(K)$ die Diskriminante von K.

$$N(K; x_1, \cdots, x_k) = \prod_{n=1}^{k} (x_1\omega_1^{(n)} + \cdots + x_k\omega_k^{(n)})$$

heisse die Normform von K. Satz: K_1 und K_2 seien algebraische Zahlkörper vom Grad k, nicht beide total-komplex; hat dann die Gleichung $N(K_1; x_1, \cdots, x_k)+N(K_2; y_1, \cdots, y_k)+z^k=n$ (n ganzrational) für jede Primzahl p mit $p|d(K_1)$ und $p|d(K_2)$ eine nichtsinguläre Lösung im p-adischen Zahlkörper, so hat diese Gleichung unendlich viele ganzrationale Lösungen. Der Beweis wird analytisch geführt (Farey-Zerschneidung, trigonometrische Summen, singuläre Reihe). Auf einige Verallgemeinerungen wird hingewiesen. *G. J. Rieger* (Munich)

D48-41 (26# 3668)

Busulini, Franca

Alcuni problemi di analisi diofantea di grado superiore.

Ist. Veneto Sci. Lett. Arti Atti Cl. Sci. Mat. Nat. **119** (1960/61), 267–285.

By simple algebra, parametric solutions are obtained for the following Diophantine equations:

$$x_1^4+x_2^4+x_3^4-x_4^4-x_5^4-x_6^4+f_4(x_7, \cdots, x_m) = 0,$$

$$x_1^5+\cdots+x_4^5-x_5^5-\cdots-x_8^5+f_5(x_9, \cdots, x_m) = 0,$$

$$x_1^6+\cdots+x_8^6-x_9^6-\cdots-x_{16}^6+f_6(x_{17}, \cdots, x_m) = 0,$$

$$x_1^n+\cdots+x_{2s}^n = x_{2s+1}^n+\cdots+x_m^n \qquad (m \geqq 4s = 6\cdot 2^{n-4}),$$

where f_n denotes an arbitrary form with integer coefficients, of degree n in its arguments. *B. Segre* (Rome)

D48-42 (27# 90)

Mano, Kenji

On the integral solutions of $\sum_{i=1}^{r} x_i^n=\sum_{i=1}^{r} y_i^n$.

Sci. Rep. Fac. Lit. Sci. Hirosaki Univ. **8** (1961), 57.

The author starts from Hankel's determinant of order $n+2$, whose value is zero, and whose sub-diagonal is the single maximum term. Obviously this determinant will have $\frac{1}{2}(n+2)!$ positive terms and as many negative terms, so that this provides integral solutions of equations of the type $\sum_{i=1}^{r} x_i^n=\sum_{i=1}^{r} y_i^n$, where $r=\frac{1}{2}(n+2)!$. The author then quotes known results with $r=2$ and $n=2, 3, 4$, and adds the remark that for $n>4$ it is still not clear how low r can be made and still obtain solutions of the above type.

Some slight hints as to how the results were arrived at would have materially enhanced the utility of the paper.

Q. M. Husain (Dacca)

D48-43 (27# 1410)

Dani, Ernest

Über die rationale diophantische Lösung der Gleichungen, die in gewissen zyklischen Determinanten linear sind.

Math. Nachr. **24** (1962), 331–348.

Let $a_1, \cdots, a_n$ and b denote integers. Let

$$|X_k| = \begin{vmatrix} x_{k0}\cdots x_{km-1} \\ \cdots\cdots \\ x_{k1}\cdots x_{k0} \end{vmatrix} \qquad (k = 1, \cdots, n)$$

denote a circulant determinant of order m, where the x_{ki} are integers. The author discusses a straightforward method for finding Diophantine solutions of the equation $\sum_{k=1}^{n} a_k|X_k|=b$. For example, in the case $m=2$, $n=5$, $a_1=1$, $a_2=2$, $a_3=3$, $a_4=4$, $a_5=5$, $b=0$ his method yields the solution $x_{10}=-31$, $x_{11}=-29$, $x_{20}=7$, $x_{21}=-5$, $x_{30}=10$, $x_{31}=-6$, $x_{40}=8$, $x_{41}=2$, $x_{50}=7$, $x_{51}=-13$.

A. L. Whiteman (Los Angeles, Calif.)

D48-44 (28# 5042)

Schmidt, Wolfgang M.

Über Gitterpunkte auf gewissen Flächen.

Monatsh. Math. **68** (1964), 59–74.

The author shows that under quite mild restrictions there cannot be too many integral points (x, y, z) on a surface $z=f(x, y)$, or, more generally, that there cannot be too many integral points for which the difference $z-f(x, y)$ is very small. Theorem 1 is concerned with integral points for which (*) $1\leqq x\leqq A$, $\phi_1(x)\leqq y\leqq\phi_2(x)$, where $A\geqq 2$ is an integer, the $\phi_j(x)$ are differentiable and $\phi_2(x)-\phi_1(x)\leqq B$ for some constant B. Suppose that f_y is monotone on each of the curves $y=\phi_j(x)$ and that $|f_y|\leqq c$ for some constant c throughout (*). Suppose, further, that f has continuous second derivatives and that the f_{yy} and the Hessian $\begin{vmatrix} f_{xx} & f_{xy} \\ f_{yx} & f_{yy} \end{vmatrix}$ do not vanish in (*). Then the number of pairs (x, y) of integers in (*) for which $f(x, y)$ is an integer is at most

$$150(1+c)^{2/3}A^{5/6}B^{2/3}+4A.$$

The theorems about the more general problem when $f(x, y)$ is near an integer z are too elaborate to be reproduced here. A special case is that the number of integral solutions (x, y, z) of

$$|\rho y^{\alpha+1}x^{-\alpha}-z| < x^{-\mu}$$

in $\lambda_1 x\leqq y\leqq\lambda_2 x$, $1\leqq x\leqq q$, where λ_1, λ_2, ρ, $\alpha\neq -1$, $1<\mu\leqq\frac{3}{2}$ are constants, is majorized by a constant multiple of $q^{3/2+(3/2-\mu)/7}$, the constant being independent of q. The proofs are technically elementary but very elaborate.

J. W. S. Cassels (Cambridge, England)

Referred to in J84-35.

D48-45 (28# 5050)

May, Warren L.

Binary forms over number fields.

Ann. of Math. (2) **79** (1964), 597–615.

Let K be a number field and let M_K be the set of absolute values of K normalized to agree with the usual absolute values on **Q**. Denote by S any finite subset of M_K containing all the archimedean ones. By an (S, d)-parallelotope, d being a positive integer, is meant a parallelotope P in K such that $P(v)=1$ if $v\notin S$ and $P(v)\in$ (the value group of $v)^d$ if $v\in S$. Denote by I_S the ring of S-integers of K. The object of the paper is a polynomial $F(X, Y) \in I_S[X, Y]$ which is homogeneous of degree d. In the main part of the paper $F(X, Y)$ is subject to the following condition (C): $d > 2$, $F(X, 1)$ has no repeated roots and no root lies in K. Under (C) the author considers the number $n(P)$ of pairs $(x, y) \in I_S \times I_S$ such that $F(x, y) \in P$ for an (S, d)-parallelotope P and proves the formula: $n(P) = c\|P\|^{2/d} + O(\|P\|^a)$, where c is a constant depending on the original data K, F and S, a is a positive real number depending on the original data such that $a < 2/d$, and

$$\|P\| = \prod_{v \in M_K} P(v)^{[K_v : \mathbf{Q}_v]}.$$

At the end of the paper, the author drops the condition (C) on $F(X, Y)$ and considers a subset T of $K \times K$ stable under the operation by coordinate-wise multiplication of S-units U_S: Denoting by $n'(P)$ the number of pairs $(x, y) \in T$ such that $F(x, y) \in P \cap U_S$ for an $(S, 1)$-parallelotope P, he proves that $n'(P) = c'(\log \|P\|)^{s-1} + O((\log \|P\|)^{s-2})$, where c' is a constant depending on K, F, S and T, and s is the number of elements in S. A condition is given which insures that, for certain T, c' is finite.
T. Ono (Philadelphia, Pa.)

D48-46 (30# 57)

Nagell, T.
Sur quelques catégories d'équations diophantiennes résolubles par des identités.
Acta Arith. **9** (1964), 227–235.

We quote two theorems from the author's investigations of categories of Diophantine equations solvable by identities. Theorem 1: Let m be an arbitrary natural number. Let $F(y, z)$ be a form of degree $n \geqq 2$ with coefficients in a field K. The equation

$$X^{mn+1} = F(Y, Z) \tag{1}$$

is identically satisfied by the system of formulas

$$X = F(U, V),$$
$$Y = U[F(U, V)]^m,$$
$$Z = V[F(U, V)]^m.$$

As U, V run independently over the numbers of K, one obtains the general solution of (1) with X, Y, Z in K. Theorem 5: Let a, b, c be non-zero numbers of K. Let $P = MNt + 1$. Then the general solution of the equation

$$ax^M + by^N = cz^P$$

(with x, y, z in K) is given by

$$x = u(au^M + bv^N)^{Nt} c^{-Nt},$$
$$y = v(au^M + bv^N)^{Mt} c^{-Mt},$$
$$z = (au^M + bv^N)c^{-1},$$

where u, v run independently over K, except for the case $z = 0$.

{Regarding Theorems 4, 5 and 6, the reviewer observes that the author has overlooked a paper by Tchacaloff and Karanicoloff [C. R. Acad. Sci. Paris **210** (1940), 281–283; MR **1**, 200], where the general solution of $ax^m + by^n = z^p$ in integers was obtained when m, n, p are mutually co-prime.}
S. Chowla (University Park, Pa.)

Citations: MR 1, 200b = D48-2.
Referred to in D48-71.

D48-47 (31# 3381)

Utz, W. R.
Some fifth degree Diophantine equations.
Math. Mag. **38** (1965), 161–163.

The author observes that if n, s are positive integers and $P(x)$, $Q(x)$ are polynomials, then the solution of the Diophantine equation $y^n = [P(x)]^{s \cdot n} Q(x)$ can be reduced in an obvious way to those of $P(x) = 0$, $z^n = Q(x)$. He illustrates the use of this remark in a couple of examples.
R. P. Bambah (Columbus, Ohio)

D48-48 (32# 2372)

Brčić-Kostić, Mato
On the solution of the generalized Fermat equation. (Esperanto. Serbo-Croatian summary)
Bull. Soc. Math. Phys. Serbie **11** (1959), 17–22.

The author uses a class of identities to construct solutions of various diophantine equations of the type $x^m \pm y^n = z^r$.
H. Halberstam (Nottingham)

D48-49 (32# 7495)

Gorzkowski, W.
On the equation $x_0^2 + x_1^2 + \cdots + x_n^2 = x_{n+1}^k$.
Prace Mat. **10** (1966), 75–79.

The author investigates the Diophantine equation $x_0^2 + x_1^2 + \cdots + x_n^2 = x_{n+1}^k$, for $k \geqq 2$, and obtains a family of solutions given by

$$x_0 = \sum_{r=0}^{[k/2]} \binom{k}{2r} a_0^{k-2r}(-A)^r,$$

$$x_i = a_i \sum_{r=0}^{[(k-1)/2]} \binom{k}{2r+1} a_0^{k-2r-1}(-A)^r$$

for $1 \leqq i \leqq n$, and $x_{n+1} = A$, where $a_0, a_1, \cdots, a_n$ are parameters and $A = a_0^2 + a_1^2 + \cdots + a_n^2$. He shows that $x_0 x_1 \cdots x_n \neq 0$ if and only if $a_0^2/(a_1^2 + a_2^2 + \cdots + a_n^2) \neq \frac{1}{3}$, 1, 3 and $a_0 a_1 \cdots a_n \neq 0$.
D. G. Cantor (Los Angeles, Calif.)

Referred to in D48-73.

D48-50 (33# 102)

Mitrinović, Dragoslav S.
Congruence où interviennent des polynomes homogènes.
Univ. Beograd. Publ. Elektrotehn. Fak. Ser. Mat. Fiz. No. 143–155 (1965), 1–2.

If h_p and H_q are forms with integer coefficients in n integer variables $a_1, a_2, \cdots, a_n$ of degrees p and q, respectively, it is noted that, for $q \geqq p+1$, $H_q/h_p \equiv 0 \pmod 1$ whenever a_ν ($\nu = 1, 2, \cdots, n$) is of the shape $a_\nu = kb_\nu h_p(b_1, b_2, \cdots, b_n)$ with integral values for $k, b_1, b_2, \cdots, b_n$. Special cases are investigated and the question as to whether the above substitution gives a complete solution of the congruence $H_q(a_1, a_2, \cdots, a_n) \equiv 0 \pmod{h_p(a_1, a_2, \cdots, a_n)}$ is raised. The analogous problem, where the coefficients and variables are natural numbers, is also treated.
J. H. H. Chalk (Nottingham)

D48-51 (33# 3999)

Avanesov, Eduard T.
On a problem of W. Mnich. (Russian. English summary)
Mat.-Fyz. Časopis Sloven. Akad. Vied **15** (1965), 280–284.

Author's summary: "We consider the system of equations (1) $x_1 + x_2 + \cdots + x_s = 1$, $x_1 x_2 \cdots x_s = 1$, and (2) $x_1 + x_2 + \cdots + x_s = r$, $x_1 x_2 \cdots x_s = r$, where r is a given rational number. First, the existence of quadratic fields $R(\sqrt{d})$ over the field of rational numbers is proved for which (1) with $s = 4$ has a solution. (Here, $d > 0$ is a non-square.) Some particular cases of (1) having solutions in fields of higher order than 2 are given. Further, for an odd s and any $r \in R$, the existence of an infinite number of solutions of (2) in the field of quaternions over the rational numbers is shown. Finally, in the field of residue classes mod p, a constructive proof for the existence of solutions of (1) is given."

D48-52 **(33# 4005)**

Gorodničiĭ, V. V.

On the problem of solving the indeterminate equation $x^{p^n}+y^{p^n}=Dz^{p^n}$. (Russian)

Volž. Mat. Sb. Vyp. 1 (1963), 52–61.

The paper is devoted to proving the following theorem: If D is a suitable rational integer and the prime p does not divide $Dxyz$, where x, y, z is a solution of the equation in question, then either of (1) $r|xy$ or (2) $r|x-y$, $p\nmid x-y$ implies $r^{p-1}\equiv 1 \pmod{p^{n+1}}$. Heavy use is made of definitions and results of Šafarevič [Mat. Sb. (N.S.) **26 (68)** (1950), 113–146; MR **11**, 230], which are not restated in the present paper and which make use of the properties of p-adic numbers. *J. B. Roberts* (Dar es Salaam)

Citations: MR 11, 230f = R40-2.

D48-53 **(33# 5554)**

Lander, L. J.; Parkin, T. R.

Counterexample to Euler's conjecture on sums of like powers.

Bull. Amer. Math. Soc. **72** (1966), 1079.

The text of the article follows: "A direct search on the CDC 6600 yielded $27^5+84^5+110^5+133^5=144^5$ as the smallest instance in which four fifth powers sum to a fifth power. This is a counterexample to a conjecture by Euler [see L. E. Dickson, *History of the theory of numbers*, Vol. 1, p. 648, Chelsea, New York, 1952] that at least n nth powers are required to sum to an nth power, $n>2$."

D48-54 **(34# 4205)**

Watson, G. L.

Diophantine equations reducible to quadratics.

Proc. London Math. Soc. (3) **17** (1967), 26–44.

This paper is one of a series, whose original aim was the proof of results on non-homogeneous cubic Diophantine equations complementary to those of H. Davenport and D. J. Lewis [J. London Math. Soc. **39** (1964), 657–671; MR **29** #4731]. Consider the equation (*) $f(x_1,\cdots,x_n)+\sum_{i=1}^n Q_i(y_1,\cdots,y_k)x_i+R(y_1,\cdots,y_k)=0$, where f is an integral quadratic form and $Q_1,\cdots,Q_n$, R are polynomials of any degree with integer coefficients. The author solves (*) by a technique of choosing integers $\mathbf{y}$ so that it reduces to a soluble equation of shape $f(\mathbf{x})+\sum b_ix_i+c=0$. He proves various theorems, which vary in difficulty and in detail according as $n=2,3,4$ or $n\geqq 5$; the greatest difficulty is for $n=3$. For instance, writing $P(\mathbf{x},\mathbf{y})$ for the left-hand side of (*), the author proves for $n=4$ that (*) is soluble in integers if P is indefinite, f is a non-singular form representing zero, and $P(\mathbf{x},\mathbf{y})\equiv 0$ (det f) is soluble; in particular, for $n\geqq 4$, $P=0$ is soluble in integers whenever f is non-singular, P has odd degree, and $P(\mathbf{x},\mathbf{y})\equiv 0$ (det f) is soluble. *B. J. Birch* (Oxford)

Citations: MR 29# 4731 = D72-37.

Referred to in D72-51.

D48-55 **(34# 5750)**

Hyyrö, Seppo

Über die Gleichung $ax^n-by^n=z$ und das Catalansche Problem.

Ann. Acad. Sci. Fenn. Ser. A I No. 355 (1964), 50 *pp.*

The author proves a number of rather sharp theorems on the effective solution of Diophantine equations of the type $ax^n-by^n=z$, where z is to be small compared with ax^n, by^n. His results are descended from the method of C. L. Siegel [Math. Ann. **114** (1937), 57–68] using hypergeometric functions. One of his main theorems is as follows. Given integers $n\geqq 3$, a, b, there exist numbers $\sigma_0(n)$, $C_0(n,ab)$ with the following properties. For any positive numbers σ, C with either $\sigma>\sigma_0$, $C>0$ or $\sigma=\sigma_0$, $C>C_0$, one may compute explicitly a number $G(n,\sigma,C,ab)$ such that the Diophantine equation $|ax^n-by^n|=z$ has at most one solution with $(x,y)=1$, $\max\{|ax^n|,|by^n|\}=M>G$, $z<CM^{1-\sigma}$. Explicit expressions are given for σ_0, C_0, G—e.g., $\sigma_0=1/2+1/n$ for $n\geqq 9$; unfortuntely, $\sigma_0(3)=1$.

The interest of the results is in the sharpness of the explicit estimates; for instance, it is a corollary that, given a, b and $n\geqq 7$, the equation $|ax^n-by^n|=1$ has at most one solution with $|ax^n|>2^n$. The author applies his results to Catalan's problem, and deduces Cassels' theorem that if $x^p-y^q=1$ with p, q prime and $x\geqq 1$, $y\geqq 1$, then $p|y$ and $q|x$. *B. J. Birch* (Manchester)

Referred to in J68-59, J68-66.

D48-56 **(35# 4164)**

May, Warren

Representation by binary forms.

J. Algebra **6** (1967), 157–184.

Let K be a number field of degree N over the rationals and $F: K\times K\to K$ a binary form of degree d; furthermore, let S be a finite set of absolute values of K containing the Archimedean absolute values of K. For J a fractional ideal, the author estimates the number $n(B)$ of classes of solutions (x,y) in $J\times J$, modulo the action of S-units, which satisfy $\prod_{v\in S}\|F(x,y)\|_v\leqq B$. It is found that $n(B)=c\bar{B}^{2/d}+O(\bar{B}^a(\log\bar{B})^b)$, where $\bar{B}=B\|J\|_S^{-d}$, and $\|J\|_S=\prod_{v\notin S}\|J\|_v^{-1}$. The constant c depends on the ideal class of J, a and b depend on K, F and S. The condition $d>4N$ is necessary in order that the error term be of smaller order than the main term. *H. Gross* (Zürich)

D48-57 **(36# 2551)**

Aucoin, A. A.

Diophantine systems.

Pacific J. Math. **23** (1967), 419–425.

The system of simultaneous Diophantine equations $\sum_{i=1}^n(a_ix_i-b_iy_i)=0$, $c\prod_{i=1}^n x_i=d\prod_{i=1}^n y_i$, and two similar systems are discussed. The non-trivial solutions are proportional to solutions given in terms of integral parameters. *W. H. Mills* (Princeton, N.J.)

D48-58 **(36# 3721)**

Lander, L. J.; Parkin, T. R.

A counterexample to Euler's sum of powers conjecture.

Math. Comp. **21** (1967), 101–103.

A computer search was conducted for nontrivial solutions in non-negative integers for the Diophantine equation $\sum_{i=1}^n x_i^5=y^5$, $n\leqq 6$. Among the new solutions the authors have obtained a counterexample to Euler's conjecture that at least k positive kth powers (excluding the trivial case) are required to sum to a kth power. They obtain $27^5+84^5+110^5+133^5=144^5$. Primitive solutions of $\sum_{i=1}^6 x_i^5=y^5$, $y\leqq 100$ and of $\sum_{i=1}^5 x_i^5=y^5$, $y\leqq 250$ are also listed. *M. S. Cheema* (Tucson, Ariz.)

Referred to in D36-36.

D48-59 **(36# 5060)**

Lander, L. J.; Parkin, T. R.; Selfridge, J. L.

A survey of equal sums of like powers.

Math. Comp. **21** (1967), 446–459.

From the authors' introduction: "The Diophantine equation (*) $x_1^k+x_2^k+\cdots+x_m^k=y_1^k+y_2^k+\cdots+y_n^k$, $1\leqq m\leqq n$, has been studied by numerous mathematicians for many years and by various methods. We recently conducted a series of computer searches using the CDC 6600 to identify the sets of parameters k, m, n for which solutions exist and to find the least solutions for certain sets. This paper outlines the results of the computation, notes some previously published results, and concludes with a table showing, for various values of k and m, the least n for which a solution to (*) is known."

D48-60 **(36# 5078)**

Möller, Kurt

Über Summen gleichhoher Potenzen. **(Serbo-Croatian summary)**

Glasnik Mat. Ser. III **2** **(22)** (1967), 29–37.

Some facts found experimentally about Diophantine equations of the form $\sum_{i=1}^{m} a_i^k = \sum_{j=1}^{n} b_j^k$, where $b_1 = a_1 + 1$.

P. Szüsz (Stony Brook, N.Y.)

D48-61 **(37# 2683)**

Battaglia, Antonio

Impossibilità dell'equazione $x^{2n} + y^{2n} = z^2$ **quando** z **è divisibile per** n.

Rend. Circ. Mat. Palermo (2) **15** (1966), 169–178.

The equation of the title is well known to be insoluble when the Fermat equation is insoluble for n. The author attempts to prove it insoluble in general for n a prime of the form $4k+1$ when z is divisible by n. The proof is marred by unstated assumptions. For example, n is not explicitly assumed prime until half a page after its primality has been implicitly used. The proof appears to be irreparably damaged by the assumption (in paragraph 9) that the only representations of a product of sums of two squares as a sum of two squares are those given by the Euler identities. An earlier similar assumption in paragraph 4 is not fatal. *J. D. Swift* (Los Angeles, Calif.)

D48-62 **(37# 4007)**

Dem'janenko, V. A.

The indeterminate equations $x^6 + y^6 = az^2$, $x^6 + y^6 = az^3$, $x^4 + y^4 = az^4$. **(Russian)**

Izv. Vysš. Učebn. Zaved. Matematika **1968**, *no.* 4 (71), 26–32.

The main theorem asserts that if the rank of the elliptic curve $u^3 + a^3 = v^2$ over the field of rational numbers does not exceed one, then the curve $x^6 + 1 = ay^2$ has no rational points, with the exceptions of the cases $a = 1$, $\{x, y\} = \{0, \pm 1\}$; $a = 2$, $\{x, y\} = \{\pm 1, \pm 1\}$. The proof makes use of four mappings between the curves $(u, v) = (ax^2, a^2y)$, $(a/x^2, a^2y/vx^3)$, $(a(2x^2-1)/(x^2+1), 3a^2xy/(x^2+1)^2)$, $(a(2-x^2)/(x^2+1), 3a^2y/(x^2+1)^2)$.

A similar theorem relates the curves $u^3 - a^2 = v^2$ and $x^6 + 1 = ay^3$; another relates the curves $x^4 - ay^4 = z^2$ and $x^4 + y^4 = a$. *S. Stein* (Davis, Calif.)

D48-63 **(38# 4406)**

Mordell, L. J.

On some sextic diophantine equations of genus 2.

Proc. Amer. Math. Soc. **21** (1969), 347–350.

Let (*) $z^2 = f(x, y)$, where $f(x, y)$ is a homogeneous polynomial of degree six, with integer coefficients. For the particular case $f(x, y) = \prod_{i=1}^{3} (a_i x^2 + b_i y^2)$ (either all a's and all b's positive, or else $a_i b_i < 0$ for at least some i $(1 \leq i \leq 3)$, thus insuring the positivity of all factors of $f(x, y)$), the author proves that (*) has no integer solution, except $(0, 0, 0)$, provided that the following conditions hold (the index i runs from 1 to 3): $\sum a_i + 1 \equiv \sum b_i \equiv 0 \pmod 4$; only one b_i is even; the sets (a_i) and $(a_i + b_i)$ are not congruent (mod 4) to either $(1, 1, 1)$ or a permutation of $(0, 1, 2)$; the minors of the matrix $\begin{pmatrix} a_1 & a_2 & a_3 \\ b_1 & b_2 & b_3 \end{pmatrix}$ have no common divisor $\neq 1$ and their odd factors are $\equiv 1 \pmod 4$. The proofs are elementary and the interest of the result is enhanced by the fact that (for special values of the coefficients) (*) may be everywhere locally solvable. The author illustrates this on the examples $(a_1, a_2, a_3) = (4a+1, 3, 4b+3) \equiv (1, 3, 3) \pmod 4$, $(b_1, b_2, b_3) = (2, 1, 1)$, for various values of a and b.

E. Grosswald (Philadelphia, Pa.)

D48-64 **(38# 4408)**

Osgood, Charles F.

The diophantine equation $P(x, y) = (xy + d)z$.

J. Res. Nat. Bur. Standards Sect. B **72B** (1968), 23–28.

L. J. Mordell [Acta Math. **88** (1952), 77–83; MR **14**, 536] suggested the problem of finding all solutions of the diophantine equation $ax^3 + by^3 + c = z(xy + d)$, where a, b, c and d are rational integers. In this paper it is proved that under certain conditions the diophantine equation (1) $P(x, y) = z(xy + d)$ has an infinite number of solutions, where $P(x, y)$ denotes a polynomial in x and y with integral coefficients.

There is no restriction in writing $P(x, y) \equiv P_1(x) + P_2(y) \bmod (xy + d)$ and supposing that $P_2(0) = 0$. Let $P_1(x)$ and $P_2(y)$ have degrees β and α, respectively, and put $P_2(y) = \beta_0 y^\alpha + \beta_1 y^{\alpha-1} + \cdots$. Then the author proves: The equation (1) has an infinite number of solutions if $\alpha + \beta \geqq 4$, $\alpha \geqq \max(\beta, 3)$, $d \neq 0$, $\beta_0 | \beta_1^k$ for some $k \geqq 1$ and $(P_1(t), d) = 1$ whenever $(t, d) = 1$. If $d = \pm 1$ then $(0, y, \pm P(0, y))$ is an infinite collection of solutions, and in the following it is assumed that $|d| > 1$.

It can be shown that (1) is implied by (2) $R(x) = z''(xy + d)$, where $(xy, d) = 1$ and $R(x) = a_n x^n + \cdots + a_j x^j + \cdots + a_3 x^3 + a_2 d x^2 + a_1 d^2 x + a_0 d^3$, a_i integers, $a_n \neq 0$, $a_0 \neq 0$ and $n \geqq 4$. Further (2) is equivalent to (3) $\sum_{k=0}^{n} A_k^0 x^k = z''(xy + r_0)$, where r_0 and the coefficients A_k^0 are given by (2). In order to show that (3) has an infinite number of solutions, the author proves that there exists an infinite sequence of equations $\{E_{2i}\}$ with $E_0 = (3)$ and $E_{2i} \leftrightarrow E_{2i+2}$ in the sense that there is a sequence of reversible steps taking one equation into the other and inducing a one-to-one correspondence of solutions. The equation E_{2m} is (4) $\sum_{k=0}^{n} A_k^{2m} x^k = v_1(xy + r_{2m})$, where it is necessary to introduce the numerical function $\beta(m) = (n-2)\beta(m-1) - \beta(m-2)$, $\beta(0) = 0$, $\beta(1) = 1$, in order to define r_m and the coefficients A_k^{2m}. Finally, it is shown, putting $xy + r_{2m} = 1$, that for a given $N > 0$, $1 - r_{2m}$ has at least N distinct pairs of factors. There are some misprints among the numerous details. *W. Ljunggren* (Oslo)

Citations: MR 14, 536f = D32-37.

D48-65 **(38# 5709)**

Győry, K.

Sur une classe des équations diophantiennes.

Publ. Math. Debrecen **15** (1968), 165–179.

Der Autor geht aus von der folgenden Vermutung, die das simultane Analogon zum Satz von Thue-Siegel-Roth ist, und die durch den Satz von Dirichlet über simultane diophantische Approximation und Ergebnisse von W. Schmidt [Acta Math. **114** (1965), 159–206; MR **31** #2206] nach Meinung des Autors wahrscheinlich richtig ist. Vermutung: Seien $\alpha_1, \cdots, \alpha_k$ reelle algebraische Zahlen so, daß $1, \alpha_1, \cdots, \alpha_k$ linear unabhängig über dem Körper der rationalen Zahlen sind und seien $c > 0$, $\varepsilon > 0$ beliebig. Dann hat $\max_{1 \leq i \leq n} \|q\alpha_i\| < c \cdot q^{-1/k - \varepsilon}$ nur endlich viele Lösungen in ganz-rationalen $q > 0$. ($\|x\|$ bedeutet Abstand von x zur nächsten ganz-rationalen Zahl.) Der Autor fragt dann nach der Anzahl der ganz-rationalen Lösungen $x = (x_1, \cdots, x_m)$ der diophantischen Gleichung $F(x_1, \cdots, x_m) = G(x_1, \cdots, x_m)$ wo G ein Polynom mit rationalen Koeffizienten ist und F gewisse algebraische Eigenschaften hat. Der Autor zeigt dann, daß unter Annahme der Richtigkeit der obigen Vermutung für jedes $k < m$ diese diophantische Gleichung höchstens endlich viele ganz-rationale Lösungen hat. Die Arbeit knüpft an die von H. Davenport und K. F. Roth [Mathematika **2** (1955), 81–96; MR **17**, 829] an, in der aus dem Thue-Siegel-Rothschen Satz Folgerungen über Anzahl und Schranken ganz-rationaler Lösungen einer diophantischen Gleichung vom Typ $F(x_1, x_2) = G(x_1, x_2)$ gezogen werden.

J. M. Wills (Berlin)

Citations: MR 17, 829f = D76-7; MR 31# 2206 = J68-46.

D48-66 **(38# 5710)**

Lander, L. J.

Geometric aspects of Diophantine equations involving equal sums of like powers.

Amer. Math. Monthly **75** (1968), 1061–1073.

Algebraic and geometric methods are discussed for determining integer solutions to Diophantine equations of the form $x_1^k + x_2^k + \cdots + x_n^k = y_1^k + y_2^k + \cdots + y_n^k$ for $(k, n) = (4, 2)$, $(5, 4)$, and $(5, 3)$. In each case parametric solutions are developed through a geometric approach. Some of the parametric solutions were indicated by examining numerical solutions found by computer search. There is an excellent bibliography. *H. London* (Montreal, Que.)

D48-67 **(38# 5711)**

Liff, Allan I.

On solutions of the equation $x^a + y^b = z^c$.

Math. Mag. **41** (1968), 174–175.

A family of solutions of the equation $x^a + y^b = z^c$ is found.

H. London (Montreal, Que.)

D48-68 **(38# 5715)**

Bartoš, Pavel

A note on a problem of Fermat. (Slovak. English summary; loose Russian summary)

Mat. Časopis Sloven. Akad. Vied **18** (1968), 21–24.

Author's summary: "The article deals with the solution of the equation $xy[x^{2kn} + (-1)^m y^{2kn}] = kz^2$ in integers (n is an arbitrary natural number, $k, m = 1, 2$). It is shown that the equation has only trivial solutions (i.e., at least one of x, y and z is zero) in the cases $k = m = 1$; $k = 1, m = 2$; $k = 2, m = 1$. In the case $k = m = 2$ there is a solution $x = y = a$, $z = \pm a^{2n+1}$, where a is an arbitrary integer. It is shown further that for an arbitrary natural number m there exists a natural number $k(m)$ such that the equation $xy(x^{2^k n} - y^{2^k n}) = m$ is not solvable for any $k \geqq k(m)$."

D48-69 **(39# 1405)**

Battaglia, Antonio

Impossibilità dell'equazione indeterminata: $x^{2n} + y^{2n} = z^5$.

Archimede **20** (1968), 300–305.

The author seeks to establish the nonexistence of integral solutions of the equation of the title under the conditions that n is an odd prime, $(n, z) = (x, y, z) = 1$. A number of unexplained assumptions are made which, at the very least, require additional hypotheses. For example, on the first page, it is concluded from $(\lambda^2 + \mu^2)^2 = a^2 + b^2$ that $a = \lambda^2 - \mu^2$, $b = 2\lambda\mu$. In context, the conclusion can be justified only by the additional assumption that z is a prime power. *J. D. Swift* (Los Angeles, Calif.)

D48-70 **(41# 3398)**

Udrescu, Valeriu Șt.

On a theorem of Chowla.

Rev. Roumaine Math. Pures Appl. **14** (1969), 1633–1634.

In a previous note [Acta Arith. **9** (1964), 417–418; MR **30** #1975] S. Chowla put forward the conjecture: The diophantine equation $\sum_{m=1}^{n-1} \pm X_m{}^n = 0$, where n is an integer $\geqq 3$, is impossible in positive integers X_m, unless it is trivially possible (i.e., by "cancellation"). In this paper the author proves: Let $a_1, a_2, \cdots, a_{n+1}$ be integers. If Chowla's conjecture is true, then the diophantine equation $a_1 x_1{}^n + a_2 x_2{}^n + \cdots + a_r x_r{}^n = a_{r+1}$ has at most r solutions in positive integers if $n \geqq (r+1)! + 1$. This theorem was proved by Chowla in case $r = 2$. The proof is an immediate extension of that of Chowla.

W. Ljunggren (Oslo)

Citations: MR 30# 1975 = D40-41.

D48-71 **(42# 5901)**

Grytczuk, Aleksander

Sur quelques équations diophantiennes du type $cZ^N = F_1(X, Y) + F_2(U, V)$.

Rend. Circ. Mat. Palermo (2) **17** (1968), 328–332.

Let $f_i(U_i, V_i)$ be forms of degree $m_i \geqq 2$ $(i = 1, 2)$, with coefficients in a field K. Further, let t denote any natural number and put $N = m_1 m_2 t + \varepsilon$, $\varepsilon = \pm 1$. Then it is proved that one obtains the complete solution of the diophantine equation $cz^N = f_1(x_1, x_2) + f_2(y_1, y_2)$ in x_i, y_i and z in K by the identities $x_i = \mu_i F^{m_2 r} c^{-m_2 r}$, $y_i = \lambda_i F^{m_1 r} c^{-m_1 r}$, $z = F^\varepsilon c^{-\varepsilon} \neq 0$ as μ_1, μ_2, λ_1 and λ_2 run independently over all elements of K, where $F = f_1(\mu_1, \mu_2) + f_2(\lambda_1, \lambda_2)$ and $r = t\varepsilon$.

This theorem generalizes results obtained by T. Nagell [Acta Arith. **9** (1964), 227–234; MR **30** #57]. Some other theorems are indicated. The reviewer remarks that in case $c = 1$, $f_2(u_2, v_2) = 0$, the more general problem with $(N, m_1) = 1$ was solved by M. Ward [Amer. J. Math. **61** (1939), 788–790; MR **1**, 4]. *W. Ljunggren* (Oslo)

Citations: MR 1, 4f = D48-1; MR 30# 57 = D48-46.

D48-72 **(42# 5903)**

Brudno, Simcha

On generating infinitely many solutions of the Diophantine equation $A^6 + B^6 + C^6 = D^6 + E^6 + F^6$.

Math. Comp. **24** (1970), 453–454.

Author's summary: "A method of generating infinitely many solutions of the Diophantine equation $A^6 + B^6 + C^6 = D^6 + E^6 + F^6$ is presented. The technique is to reduce the equation to one of fourth degree and to use the known recursive solutions to the fourth-order equations."

D48-73 **(43# 3203)**

Belkner, Horst

Die Diophantische Gleichung $x_1{}^2 + x_2{}^2 + \cdots + x_n{}^2 = x_{n+1}^k$.

Wiss. Z. Pädagog. Hochsch. Potsdam Math.-Natur. Reihe **14** (1970), 181–186.

A set of solutions for the equation of the title was given by W. Gorzkowski [Prace Mat. **10** (1966), 75–79; MR **32** #7495]. These solutions are not complete; for example, no nontrivial solutions of $x_1{}^2 + x_2{}^2 + x_3{}^2 = 13^{2m+1}$ are available. The present author gives a more general set of solutions using integral matrices, which do give solutions to the trinomial equation above. He gives a list of these solutions for $m = 2$. No claim of completeness is made.

J. D. Swift (Los Angeles, Calif.)

Citations: MR 32# 7495 = D48-49.

D48-74 **(44# 5271)**

Adler, A.

A reduction of homogeneous diophantine problems.

J. London Math. Soc. (2) **3** (1971), 446–448.

Let $P(x_1, x_2, \cdots, x_n)$ be any homogeneous integral polynomial of degree d. If $\mathbf{a} = (a_1, a_2, \cdots, a_n)$ is any n-tuple of non-negative integers, let $|\mathbf{a}| = a_1 + a_2 + \cdots + a_n$. Further, let S be the set of n-tuples $\mathbf{a}$ such that $|\mathbf{a}| = d$, and T the set of $\mathbf{a}$ such that $|\mathbf{a}| \leqq d$. Denote by $\mathbf{0}$ the n-tuple $(0, 0, \cdots, 0)$, and by $\mathbf{a} + \mathbf{b}$ the usual vector sum of $\mathbf{a}$ and $\mathbf{b}$. Then it is proved that we can effectively find homogeneous quadratic integral polynomials $Q_i(y_1, y_2, \cdots, y_m)$ $(i = 1, 2, 3, \cdots, k)$, such that the equation (1) $P = \sum_{\mathbf{a} \in S} c_{\mathbf{a}} x_1{}^{a_1} \cdot x_2{}^{a_2} \cdots x_n{}^{a_n} = 0$ has a non-trivial solution in integers if and only if the system $Q_j = 0, j = 1, 2, \cdots, k$ has a non-trivial solution in integers.

Dropping the word homogeneous everywhere, we have a theorem due to T. A. Skolem [*Diophantische Gleichungen*, pp. 2–3, Ergeb. Math. Grenzgeb., Band 5, Heft 4, Springer, Berlin, 1938; reprint, Chelsea, New York, 1950].

A crucial point in the proof is to show that (1) has a non-trivial solution if and only if the following system of equations and inequalities in the variables $y_{\mathbf{a}}(\mathbf{a} \in T)$ has a non-trivial solution: $y_{\mathbf{a}}y_{\mathbf{b}} = y_{\mathbf{c}}y_{\mathbf{d}}(\mathbf{a}+\mathbf{b}=\mathbf{c}+\mathbf{d})$; $\sum_{\mathbf{a}\in S} c_{\mathbf{a}}y_{\mathbf{a}}=0$; $\sum_{\mathbf{a}\in S} y_{\mathbf{a}}^2 \leqq y_0^2 \leqq 2^{2d} \sum_{\mathbf{a}\in S} y_{\mathbf{a}}^2$. *W. Ljunggren* (Oslo)

D52 HIGHER DEGREE VARIETIES: MULTIGRADE SYSTEMS

See also reviews A62-42, C05-16, D24-14, D48-4, D48-13, D48-24, D56-1, D56-10, D80-5, D80-8, D80-30, D99-14, L02-5, L15-7, L15-10, L15-35, P02-6, P08-2, P08-13, P08-28, P08-42, P44-17.

D52-1 (1, 5a)

Gloden, A. Sur la résolution en nombres entiers du système $A^{kx}+B^{kx}+C^{kx}+D^{kx}=E^x+F^x+G^x+H^x$ ($x=1$, 2 **et** 3). Bol. Mat. **12**, 118–122 (1939).

D52-2 (1, 133c)

Moessner, Alfred. Einige numerische Identitäten. Proc. Indian Acad. Sci., Sect. A. **10**, 296–306 (1939).

The author considers the two systems of Diophantine equations

$$\sum_{i=1}^{3} G_i^n = \sum_{i=1}^{3} J_i^n, \qquad n=1, 3,$$

and

$$\sum_{i=1}^{2} K_i^n = \sum_{i=1}^{4} L_i^n, \qquad n=1, 3.$$

He exhibits "general solutions" in terms of a certain number of parameters but does not prove that these solutions are really general. It is pointed out by S. Chowla that the author has given a solution of the system

$$\sum_{i=1}^{3} x_i = \sum_{i=1}^{3} y_i, \quad \sum_{i=1}^{3} x_i^5 = \sum_{i=1}^{3} y_i^5,$$

namely, 49, 75, 107; 39, 92, 100. This result is new [cf. Hardy and Wright, Introduction to the Theory of Numbers, p. 333]. There are a few misprints in the writing of the exponents. *I. A. Barnett* (Cincinnati, Ohio).

Referred to in D52-3.

D52-3 (8, 564h)

Moessner, Alfred. Einige numerische Identitäten. Bull. Sci. École Polytech. Timişoara **9**, 245–255 (1940).

The paper also appeared in Proc. Indian Acad. Sci., Sect. A. **10**, 296–306 (1939); these Rev. **1**, 133.

Citations: MR 1, 133c = D52-2.

D52-4 (1, 291b)

Moessner, Alfred. Zahlentheoretische Untersuchungen und Resultate. Tôhoku Math. J. **46**, 234–238 (1940).

D52-5 (2, 247c)

Moessner, Alfred. Verschiedene Diophantische Probleme und numerische Identitäten. Tôhoku Math. J. **47**, 188–200 (1940).

The author gives certain algebraic identities which yield some solutions of various diophantine systems involving equal sums and products of like powers. For example, he points out that certain cubic polynomials in four variables satisfy the system $X_1+X_2+X_3=Y_1+Y_2+Y_3$; $X_1\cdot X_2\cdot X_3 = Y_1\cdot Y_2\cdot Y_3$, identically. *I. A. Barnett.*

D52-6 (2, 347a)

Sastry, S. On Tarry's problem. J. Indian Math. Soc. (N.S.) **4**, 167–168 (1940).

The problem of finding, for a fixed k, sets of integers x_i, y_i ($i=1, 2, \cdots, n$) such that $\sum_{i=1}^n x_i^m = \sum_{i=1}^n y_i^m$, for all $m=1, 2, \cdots, k$, is known as Tarry's problem. It is only interesting to consider the case where all x_i are different from all y_i, and it is obvious that the least possible number n for a given k is then $k+1$. For $1\leqq k\leqq 7$ solutions are known for this least value of n. The author constructs a new solution for $k=7$ with $n=8$, by a method similar to that used by Tarry [see Dickson, History of the Theory of Numbers, vol. 2, p. 710]. From this he deduces the relation $9^{2k}+47^{2k}+49^{2k}+67^{2k}=23^{2k}+31^{2k}+61^{2k}+63^{2k}$, for all $k=1, 2, 3$. *H. W. Brinkmann* (Swarthmore, Pa.).

D52-7 (5, 90e)

Bell, E. T. Algebraic identities in the theory of numbers. Amer. Math. Monthly **50**, 535–541 (1943).

This paper is concerned with identities which express numbers in an arithmetical progression as sums of like powers of linear functions, as, for example, the identity

$$6m+3=4(m+1)^3-(2m+1)^3+4m^3,$$

from which it follows that every integer is of the form

$$x^3+y^3+4(z^3+w^3),$$

the letters being integers $\gtreqless 0$. Such identities have an extensive history in connection with the problem of representing numbers as sums of like powers. The author gives some very general identities of this kind. These are derived from the binomial expansions

$$\sum_{r=1}^{n-1} \binom{n}{r} a_i^{n-r} b_i^r x^{n-r} y^r \equiv (a_i x+b_i y)^n - a_i^n x^n - b_i^n y^n,$$

where the a's and b's are integer parameters. Solving this system of $n-1$ equations for $x^{n-1}y=N$, it is clear that, unless its determinant $D=0$, DN can be expressed as a sum of nth powers. Other identities follow by differentiation and other devices. Many special cases are exhibited, including some giving sets of integers having equal sums of sth powers for $s=0, 1, \cdots, n-2$, as, for example, $(x+5)^s+5(x+3)^s+10(x+1)^s=(x-5)^s+5(x-3)^s+10(x-1)^s$, $s=0, 1, 2, 3, 4$. Solutions involving three parameters are given of such Diophantine equations as

$$x_1^3+x_2^3+x_3^{3n}+3x_4^{3n}=y_1^3+y_2^3+y_3^{3n}+3y_4^{3n}$$

for every integer $n>0$. Applications in which the parameters of the identities are algebraic are mentioned. *D. H. Lehmer* (Berkeley, Calif.).

D52-8 (7, 47a)

Grossman, Howard D. Applications of an operator to algebra and to number-theory, with comments on the Tarry-Escott problem. Nat. Math. Mag. **19**, 385–390 (1945).

The problem is to find two sets of numbers with the same sum of kth powers ($k=1, \cdots, m$). The author derives a solution briefly by using a series expansion of the operator D. Comparison is made with various solutions in the literature. *I. Kaplansky* (Chicago, Ill.).

D52-9 (8, 135g)

Gloden, A. Un nouveau théorème sur les multigrades. Euclides, Madrid **6**, no. 64, 377–379 (1946).

In the original, the author's name was spelled Glooden.

D52-10 (8, 315e)

Malengreau, Julien. Considerazione sulla teoria delle potenze. Boll. Mat. (4) **3**, 35–41 (1942).

The author considers some special solutions of the problem of Tarry on equal sums of like powers: to find two sets of nonnegative integers $x_1, \cdots, x_M; y_1, \cdots, y_M$ such that

$$(1)\qquad \sum_{i=1}^{M} x_i^k = \sum_{i=1}^{M} y_i^k, \qquad k=0, 1, \cdots, n-1.$$

Consider the sums taken k at a time from the set of n arbitrary integers $m_1, \cdots, m_n$ for $k=0, 1, \cdots, n-1$. Then those sums for which k is even may be taken for x's in (1) and the others for y's. As a special case we may take $m_r=2^r$ and the above result may be modified as follows. Let $s=s(h)$ be the sum of the digits of the integer h in the binary scale and let $e(h)=(-1)^s$; then for every arithmetical progression $a+hd$, $d=0, 1, \cdots, 2^n-1$, of 2^n terms we have $\sum e(h)(a+hd)^k=0$, $k=0, 1, \cdots, n-1$. If we transpose to the left those terms for which $e(h)=-1$ we obtain an example of (1). Other corollaries are also stated. No proofs are given.

D. H. Lehmer (Berkeley, Calif.).

D52-11 (8, 315f)

Palamà, G. Osservazioni sulla nota "Considerazione sulla teoria delle potenze" di J. Malengreau. Boll. Mat. (4) **3**, 64–66 (1942).

Comments on the note of the preceding review. Proofs are given of some of the theorems and their connection with some results of Barbette is traced [Assoc. Française Avancement Sci., C. R. **1925**, 93–96]. *D. H. Lehmer.*

D52-12 (8, 315g)

Gloden, A. On multigrade Diophantine analysis. Euclides, Madrid **4**, 431–436, 514–519 (1944). (Spanish)

Expository article.

D52-13 (8, 441f)

Gloden, Albert. Mehrgradige Gleichungen. Mit einem Vorwort von Maurice Kraitchik. 2d ed. P. Noordhoff, Groningen, 1944. 104 pp. 2.50 florins; bound, 3.25 florins.

By a multigrade equation is meant a system of r equations

$$\sum_{\nu=1}^{p} a_\nu^{n_i} = \sum_{\nu=1}^{p} b_\nu^{n_i}, \qquad i=1, \cdots, r,$$

in which the a's and b's are unknown integers and the n's are given nonnegative integers. The problem of finding solutions of such a system is also known as the Tarry-Escott problem and has an extensive literature. The purpose of this book is to set forth the various methods of solving the problem and to treat the several applications of its solutions. In the more important and interesting problems the given integers n_i are the consecutive integers from 1 to n inclusive, in which case the above system is frequently written

$$(1)\qquad a_1, a_2, \cdots, a_p \overset{n}{=} b_1, b_2, \cdots, b_p.$$

The contents of the eight chapters may be described briefly as follows. Chapters I and II contain definitions and general properties of solutions and their transformations. In case $n=p-1$ the equations (1) are called normal (ideal). Chapter III is devoted to such equations. The present state of this problem is as follows. For $n\leqq 3$ the problem is completely solved. For $4\leqq n\leqq 7$ parametric solutions are known. For $n=8$ only two essentially different numerical solutions are known, from which infinitely many examples with $n=9$ may be found. Chapter IV deals with various abnormal cases of $n\geqq 10$ and the possible bounds for p. Chapters V and VI are concerned with other types of related Diophantine systems. Chapter VII treats the more general problem of finding more than two sets of integers having equal sums of like powers. These are called chains. For example, in each of the four sets (1, 17, 18), (2, 13, 21), (3, 11, 22), (6, 7, 23) the sum is 36 and the sum of squares is 614. The final chapter gives applications of multigrade equations. These include problems in the theory of equations, the calculation of logarithms and arccotangents of integers, irreducible polynomials and Waring's problem. Copious references to recent literature are given throughout the text. This work is a translation of a first edition in French which appeared in Luxembourg in 1938. *D. H. Lehmer.*

Referred to in D52-17, D52-18, D52-31, D52-49, D52-64, D52-91, P08-13.

D52-14 (8, 441g)

Gloden, A. Un théorème sur les multigrades. Inst. Grand-Ducal Luxembourg. Sect. Sci. Nat. Phys. Math. Arch. N.S. **16**, 61–63 (1945).

This note has to do with the so-called Tarry-Escott problem [cf. the preceding review]. The theorem shows how to find two sets of five integers having equal sums of mth powers for $m=1, 3, 5$ and 7 given six integers $a_1, a_2, a_3, b_1, b_2, b_3$ such that

$$a_1^2+a_2^2+a_3^2=b_1^2+b_2^2+b_3^2,$$
$$a_1^4+a_2^4+a_3^4=b_1^4+b_2^4+b_3^4,$$
$$a_1+a_2-a_3=2(b_1+b_2-b_3)\neq 0.$$

D. H. Lehmer (Berkeley, Calif.).

D52-15 (8, 442a)

Dorwart, H. L. Sequences of ideal solutions in the Tarry-Escott problem. Bull. Amer. Math. Soc. **53**, 381–391 (1947).

For a statement of the problem and notations see the second preceding review. A solution (of degree k) is represented as

$$(1)\qquad a_1, a_2, \cdots, a_s \overset{k}{=} b_1, b_2, \cdots, b_s$$

and it implies $Ma_i+K\overset{k}{=}Mb_i+K$, $i=1, 2, \cdots, s$, and

$$(2)\qquad a_1, a_2, \cdots, a_s, b_1+h, b_2+h, \cdots, b_s+h \overset{k+1}{=} b_1, b_2, \cdots, b_s, a_1+h, a_2+h, \cdots, a_s+h$$

with arbitrary M, K and h. The set of all the differences $|a_i-a_j|$, $|b_i-b_j|$ is called the difference table of (1); (1) is an ideal solution if $s=k+1$. If in its difference table a number h appears exactly h times, then (2) is reduced to an ideal solution (of degree $k+1$) that is said to be in sequence with the ideal solution of degree k. All sequences of ideal solutions beginning with $k=1, 2, 3$ are determined and arranged in a table. Certain substitution groups in the solutions are noted. No new solutions are given. [See also Dorwart and Brown, Amer. Math. Monthly **44**, 613–626 (1937); Chernick, ibid., 626–633 (1937); and Gloden's book reviewed above.] *N. G. W. H. Beeger* (Amsterdam).

Referred to in D52-29.

D52-16 (8, 442b)

Palamà, G. Contributo alla ricerca di soluzioni intere di sistemi indeterminati. Ist. Lombardo Sci. Lett. Cl. Sci. Mat. Nat. Rend. (3) **6(75)**, 437–452 (1942).

The author is concerned with finding integral solutions of a system of equations of the form

$$\sum_{j=1}^{n} u_j^{m_i} = \sum_{j=1}^{n'} v_j^{m_i}, \qquad i=1, 2, \cdots, r,$$

particularly for the cases where $n=n'$ and $m_i=i$, $2i$ or $2i-1$. Following a procedure due to Barbette [Association Française Avancement Sci. C. R. **49**, 93–96 (1925)] solutions can easily be obtained for sufficiently large n (e.g., $n=2^r$ will suffice in the case $m_i=i$). The author obtains solutions for $m_r\leqq 12$ for which n does not exceed 26. *F. A. Behrend.*

D52-17 **(9, 9d)**

Moessner, Alfred, und Gloden, Albert. Einige zahlentheoretische Untersuchungen und Resultate. Bull. Sci. École Polytech. Timişoara **11**, 196–219 (1944).

Examples of the determination of numerical solutions of several Diophantine systems such as

(1) $x_1, \cdots, x_k \overset{n}{=} y_1, \cdots, y_k$

or $x_1, \cdots, x_6 \overset{n}{=} y_1, \cdots, y_6 \overset{n}{=} z_1, \cdots, z_6 \overset{n}{=} u_1, \cdots, u_6$, $n=2, 4$, and of more complicated systems such as $u_1, \cdots, u_6 \overset{4}{=} v_1, \cdots, v_6$, $u_4 \cdot u_5 \cdot u_6 \overset{n}{=} v_4 \cdot v_5 \cdot v_6$, $u_1 \cdot u_2 \cdot u_3 \overset{n}{=} v_1 \cdot v_2 \cdot v_3$, $n=1, 4$. Two parametric solutions of (1) for $k=6$, $n=1, 3, 5, 7$. Some numerical solutions of the Tarry-Escott problem [Dorwart and Brown, Amer. Math. Monthly **44**, 613–633 (1937)]. Parametric solutions of $y^2-z^2=u^2$, $x^2-z^2=v^2$, $x^2-y^2=w^2$. See for theorems, A. Gloden, Mehrgradige Gleichungen [Noordhoff, Groningen, 1944; these Rev. **8**, 441].

N. G. W. H. Beeger (Amsterdam).

Citations: MR 8, 441f = D52-13.

D52-18 **(9, 9e)**

Palamà, G. Generalizzazione di due teoremi sulle uguaglianze multigrade, su delle trasformazioni di esse e sulle multigrade a catena. Univ. Roma. Ist. Naz. Alta Mat. Rend. Mat. e Appl. (5) **6**, 95–120 (1947).

The main theorem is as follows. From

(1) $a_1, \cdots, a_r \overset{n}{=} b_1, \cdots, b_r, \qquad r>n,$

follows: if n is even,

$$a_1, \cdots, a_r, k-a_1, \cdots, k-a_r \overset{n+3}{=} b_1, \cdots, b_r, k-b_1, \cdots, k-b_r;$$

if n is odd,

$$a_1, \cdots, a_r, k-b_1, \cdots, k-b_r \overset{n+3}{=} b_1, \cdots, b_r, k-a_1, \cdots, k-a_r,$$

where

$$k=\frac{2(T_{n+2}-S_{n+2})}{(n+2)(T_{n+1}-S_{n+1})}, \quad T_m=\sum_i b_i^m, \quad S_m=\sum a_i^m$$

[for notation see these Rev. **8**, 441 (review of Gloden's "Mehrgradige Gleichungen")]. Proof by the binomial theorem. The theorem is proved to be a generalization of two known theorems. Further theorems on transformation of multigrade equalities, for example: from (1) follows $a_1+a_2, a_1+a_3, \cdots, a_1+a_r, a_2+a_3, \cdots, a_2+a_r, \cdots, a_{r-1}+a_r \overset{n}{=} b_1+b_2$, etc. Construction of chains of equalities (1), for example: from (1) follows $\lambda_i a_1+\alpha_i, \lambda_i a_2+\alpha_i, \cdots, \lambda_i a_r+\alpha_i \overset{n}{=} \lambda_i b_1+\alpha_i$, etc., $i=1, \cdots, m$. Now interchanging the members of 0, then of 1, then of 2, $\cdots$, then of m equalities of this system we get 2^m systems. We may form a chain whose members are the 2^m sums of the members of each system. Each member has nr terms. *N. G. W. H. Beeger* (Amsterdam).

Citations: MR 8, 441f = D52-13.

Referred to in D52-50.

D52-19 **(9, 10a)**

Palamà, G. Metodi per avere soluzioni parametriche della $a_1, \cdots, a_p \overset{2,4}{=} b_1, \cdots, b_p$, nei casi $p=3$, $p=4$. Univ. Roma. Ist. Naz. Alta Mat. Rend. Mat. e Appl. (5) **6**, 48–64 (1947).

Methods for deriving parametric solutions of

$$a_1, a_2, a_3 \overset{2,4}{=} b_1, b_2, b_3$$

and of $a_1, a_2, a_3, a_4 \overset{2,4}{=} b_1, b_2, b_3, b_4$. Relations between them.

N. G. W. H. Beeger.

D52-20 **(9, 10b)**

Palamà, G. Quelques théorèmes sur les multigrades. Inst. Grand-Ducal Luxembourg. Sect. Sci. Nat. Phys. Math. Arch. N.S. **16**, 98–103 (1946).

This paper is concerned with the Tarry-Escott problem of finding two sets of integers with equal sums of like powers. The solutions are special in that each set is such that its members can be grouped in pairs having a constant sum. Given two such sets the author obtains two others as linear combinations of the members of the first sets. Thus two-parameter solutions can be set down. For example, from the fact that the two sets

$$1, 6, 7, 17, 18, 23;$$
$$2, 3, 11, 13, 21, 22$$

have equal sums of kth powers, for $k=0, 1, \cdots, 5$, it is deduced that the two sets

$$p+2q, 6p+3q, \cdots, 23p+22q;$$
$$2p+q, 3p+6q, \cdots, 22p+23q$$

have the same property. Applications are given to the problem of 3 or more sets with equal sums of like powers.

D. H. Lehmer (Berkeley, Calif.).

D52-21 **(9, 78d)**

Lehmer, D. H. The Tarry-Escott problem. Scripta Math. **13**, 37–41 (1947).

Let $b>1$ and $\mu_1, \cdots, \mu_n>0$ be given. Let S_r denote the set of all the numbers $S=\mu_1 a_1+\cdots+\mu_n a_n$ for which $a_1+\cdots+a_n \equiv r \pmod b$, where every a_i ranges independently over all the integers $0, 1, \cdots, b-1$. Then the sums of the numbers of each set $S_0, S_1, \cdots, S_{b-1}$ are equal and so are the sums of the second powers, the sums of the third powers, $\cdots$, the sums of the $(n-1)$th powers. They constitute a chain of solutions of the Tarry-Escott problem of degree n (not $n+1$). In the proof of the theorem the author uses the function

$$F(x)=\prod_{\nu=1}^{n}(1+\epsilon e^{\mu_\nu x}+\epsilon^2 e^{2\mu_\nu x}+\cdots+\epsilon^{b-1}e^{(b-1)\mu_\nu x});$$

$\epsilon \neq 1$ is a bth root of unity. *N. G. W. H. Beeger.*

Referred to in D52-32, D52-37, D52-58, D52-82, D52-112, D52-125, D52-126.

D52-22 **(9, 331d)**

Gloden, A. Parametric solutions of two multi-degreed equalities. Amer. Math. Monthly **55**, 86–88 (1948).

Six solutions of $x_1^n+\cdots+x_3^n=y_1^n+\cdots+y_3^n$, $n=2, 4$, in which x_i and y_i are homogeneous forms of the fourth degree in two variables. Each solution provides a solution of $x_1^n+\cdots+x_7^n=y_1^n+\cdots+y_7^n$, $n=1, 2, 4, 6, 8$.

N. G. W. H. Beeger (Amsterdam).

D52-23 **(9, 331e)**

Dorwart, H. L. Note on multi-degree equalities. Inst. Grand-Ducal Luxembourg. Sect. Sci. Nat. Phys. Math. Arch. N.S. **17**, 121–122 (1947).

Consider the four sets of integers (A) 1, 19, 28, 59, 65, 90, 102; (B) 2, 14, 39, 45, 76, 85, 103; (C) 1, 25, 31, 84, 87, 134, 158, 182, 198; (D) 2, 18, 42, 66, 113, 116, 169, 175, 199. Then Escott and Letac have shown that (A) and (B) have the same sums of pth powers for $0 \leqq p \leqq 6$, and the same is true of (C) and (D) for $0 \leqq p \leqq 8$. This note shows how these results may be derived by successive application of the following theorem. Let $a_1, \cdots, a_r$ and $b_1, \cdots, b_r$ be two sets of integers having the above property for $0 \leqq p \leqq n$; then for every k the sets $a_1, \cdots, a_r, b_1+k, \cdots, b_r+k$ and $b_1, \cdots, b_r, a_1+k, \cdots, a_r+k$ have the property for $0 \leqq p \leqq n+1$. *D. H. Lehmer* (Berkeley, Calif.).

D52-24 **(9, 411g)**

Guttman, Solomon. Universal magic squares and multigrade equations. Scripta Math. **13**, 187–202 (1947).

A natural magic square is defined as a square containing

in its cells the integers 1, 2, 3, $\cdots$ in their natural order. Most of its properties do not belong to magic squares in the ordinary sense. A pattern is defined as a figure containing any number of cells marked − and an equal number of cells marked +. Many illustrations of such patterns are given. They are divided in groups according to their ranks and rules are given for the determination of the rank. When a pattern of rank k is applied to a natural square and the integers in the − cells are denoted by a_i, those in the + cells by b_i, then $\sum_i a_i^m = \sum_i b_i^m$ for $m=1, 2, \cdots, k$. Hence patterns yield solutions of the Tarry-Escott problem (multigrade equalities). When a pattern is moved from one position to another within the same square each a_i and b_i is increased by the same number h and $\sum_i(a_i+h)^m = \sum_i(b_i+h)^m$ for $m=1, 2, \cdots, k$. Natural squares possess a "magic constant" $c=\sum_i a_i^{k+1} - \sum_i b_i^{k+1}$. The numbers (a, b) may represent $ax+by$; hence patterns yield general solutions of the Tarry-Escott problem. *N. G. W. H. Beeger.*

D52-25 (9, 411h)

Palamà, G. Teoremi relativi alle uguaglianze multigrade. Univ. Roma. Ist. Naz. Alta Mat. Rend. Mat. e Appl. (5) **6**, 366–394 (1947).

Proofs of known elementary theorems on multi-degree equalities (Tarry-Escott problem) and some new theorems inferred from them. Numerical examples.

N. G. W. H. Beeger (Amsterdam).

D52-26 (9, 411i)

Gloden, A., et Palamà, G. Bibliographie des Multigrades avec Quelques Notices Biographiques. A. Gloden, Luxembourg, 1948. iv+64 pp. 50 Belgian francs.

D52-27 (9, 498b)

Kesava Menon, P. Some Diophantine equations. Math. Student **14** (1946), 65–68 (1948).

Elementary theorems on systems $\sum_{i=1}^n A_i x_i^r = 0$, $r=0, 1, \cdots, m-1$. For example, if $x_i = a_i$ $(i=1, \cdots, n)$ is a solution, then

$$x_i = (m+1)a_i \sum_{j=1}^n A_j a_j^m - \sum_{j=1}^n A_j a_j^{m+1}, \quad i=1, \cdots, n,$$

is a solution of the system for $r=0, 1, \cdots, m-1, m+1$.

N. G. W. H. Beeger (Amsterdam).

D52-28 (9, 498c)

Palamà, Giuseppe. Multigrade fattoriali. Revista Unión Mat. Argentina **13**, 3–11 (1948).

If $\sum_{i=1}^p a_i^k = \sum_{i=1}^p c_i^k$, $k=1, \cdots, n$, then for any $\alpha_1, \cdots, \alpha_n$:

$$\sum_{i=1}^p (a_i+\alpha_1)(a_i+\alpha_2)\cdots(a_i+\alpha_k) = \sum_{i=1}^p (c_i+\alpha_1)\cdots(c_i+\alpha_k), \quad k=1, \cdots, n.$$

The author calls such a system a "factorial multigrade equality" and gives some theorems.

N. G. W. H. Beeger (Amsterdam).

D52-29 (10, 13d)

Maggio, Oreste. Sistemi equitotali. Matematiche, Catania **1**, 88–93 (1946).

Known proofs of known theorems: from

$$\sum_{i=1}^n x_i^k = \sum_{i=1}^n y_i^k,$$

$k=1, \cdots, g$, follows

$$\sum_{i=1}^n x_i^k + \sum_{i=1}^n (y_i+c)^k = \sum_{i=1}^n y_i^k + \sum_{i=1}^n (x_i+c)^k,$$

$k=1, \cdots, g+1$, for every c; $g<n$, otherwise the y_i are, in a certain order, identical with the x_i [cf. Dorwart, Bull. Amer. Math. Soc. **53**, 381–391 (1947); these Rev. **8**, 442, and the references given in that review].

N. G. W. H. Beeger (Amsterdam).

Citations: MR 8, 442a = D52-15.

D52-30 (10, 101c)

Wright, E. M. Equal sums of like powers. Bull. Amer. Math. Soc. **54**, 755–757 (1948).

Let $P(k, s)$ denote the smallest j for which there exists a nontrivial solution of the system

$$\sum_{i=1}^j a_{i1}^h = \sum_{i=1}^j a_{i2}^h = \cdots = \sum_{i=1}^j a_{is}^h, \qquad h=1, \cdots, k,$$

for given k and s. It is known that $P(k, s) \geqq k+1$ and $P(k, 2) \leqq (k^2+4)/2$. The author now proves that

$$P(k, s) \leqq (k^2+k+2)/2$$

and, for k odd, $P(k, s) \leqq (k^2+3)/2$. He makes the conjecture that $P(k, s) = k+1$ (for $k=2, 3, 5$, and for $s=2$, $k=1, 2, \cdots, 9$, this has been proved).

N. G. W. H. Beeger (Amsterdam).

Referred to in D52-37, D52-42, D52-66, D52-96.

D52-31 (10, 283b)

Palamà, G. Sul problema di Escott-Tarry. Boll. Mat. (5) **2**, 25–26 (1948).

This paper gives the previously known ideal solutions of the Tarry-Escott problem [see Gloden, Mehrgradige Gleichungen, Noordhoff, Groningen, 1944; these Rev. **8**, 441] for degrees less than 10. For $n=10(1)25$ the author gives the smallest known number of integers in each of the two sets which have equal sums of like powers up to and including the nth powers. For n beyond 15 these numbers of integers are considerably greater than the ideal $n+1$.

D. H. Lehmer (Berkeley, Calif.).

Citations: MR 8, 441f = D52-13.

D52-32 (10, 283c)

Mirsky, L. A remark on D. H. Lehmer's solution of the Tarry-Escott problem. Scripta Math. **14**, 126–127 (1948).

An alternative proof is given of a theorem of Lehmer having to do with equal sums of like powers of integers [Scripta Math. **13**, 37–41 (1947); these Rev. **9**, 78]. Instead of using a generating function, the author makes a simple application of the multinomial theorem.

D. H. Lehmer (Berkeley, Calif.).

Citations: MR 9, 78d = D52-21.

Referred to in D52-82.

D52-33 (10, 431i)

Gloden, A. Sur la multigrade $A_1, A_2, A_3, A_4, A_5, \overset{k}{=} B_1, B_2, B_3, B_4, B_5$ $(k=1, 3, 5, 7)$. Euclides, Madrid **8**, 383–384 (1948).

Announcement of two solutions each with two parameters, to be proved later. Numerical results are deduced.

N. G. W. H. Beeger (Amsterdam).

D52-34 (10, 431j)

Gloden, A. Un nouveau procédé de résolution de la sextigrade normale $A_1, A_2, A_3, A_4, A_5, A_6, A_7 \overset{6}{=} B_1, B_2, B_3, B_4, B_5, B_6, B_7$. Bull. Soc. Roy. Sci. Liége **17**, 252–256 (1948).

D52-35 (10, 431k)

Rai, T. On a problem of additive theory of numbers. Math. Student **15** (1947), 25–28 (1948).

Let $\beta(k)$ denote the least number of kth powers whose sum is equal to the sum of a smaller number of kth powers. Improvements of $\beta(k)$ for 4 values of k are derived. To this aim Tarry's theorem on multigrade equalities [see

Dickson, History of the Theory of Numbers, v. 2, Carnegie Institution of Washington, 1920, p. 710] is applied to $2+5=3+4$ with $x=3, 5, 7, 8, 13, 11, 9, 19, 17, 25$ in succession, finally diminishing every term by 62. The result is an equality, giving $\beta(10)\leqq 11$. In an analogous manner improvements for $k=14, 15, 16$ are derived.

N. G. W. H. Beeger (Amsterdam).

Referred to in D52-75.

D52-36 (10, 432a)

Sastry, S. On equal sums of like powers. Math. Student **15** (1947), 29–32 (1948).

Tarry's theorem [see the preceding review] is applied to $0+(a+b)=a+b$ with $x=a+b$ and $x=a+2b$ in succession. Then $a=3m-n$, $b=2n-m$ is substituted. Again $a=3n-m$, $b=2m-n$. The two results give a solution of

$$\sum_{i=1}^{h} x_i^l=\sum_{i=1}^{h} y_i^l=\sum_{i=1}^{h} z_i^l, \qquad l=1, 2, 3;\ h=4.$$

Similarly a solution for $h=6$; $l=1, 2, \cdots, 5$, is derived and 3 equal sums of 3 fourth powers are found.

N. G. W. H. Beeger (Amsterdam).

D52-37 (10, 510b)

Wright, E. M. The Prouhet-Lehmer problem. J. London Math. Soc. **23**, 279–285 (1948).

The problem to which the title refers is that of finding sets of integers having equal sums of like powers. More precisely one seeks to solve the system of $k(s-1)$ simultaneous Diophantine equations

$$(1)\qquad \sum_{i=1}^{j}(x_{i1})^h=\sum_{i=1}^{j}(x_{i2})^h=\cdots=\sum_{i=1}^{j}(x_{is})^h \qquad (h=0, 1, \cdots, k)$$

for the s sets of j integers x_{iu}. To avoid triviality one requires that no set of x's is a mere permutation of another set. The case of $s=2$ is known as the Tarry-Escott problem [1912]. The general case was considered by E. Prouhet as long ago as 1851 [C. R. Acad. Sci. Paris **33**, 225]. Three numbers $P(k, s)$, $L(k, s)$, $W(k, s)$ are defined as follows: P is the least value of j for which (1) has a solution; L is the least value of j for which (1) has a solution such that not all the s sums (2) $\sum_{i=1}^{j}(x_{iu})^{k+1}$ ($u=1, 2, \cdots, s$) are equal, that is, the sets fail to have equal sums of $(k+1)$th powers. Finally W is the least value of j for which (1) has a solution such that the s sums (2) are distinct. Obviously $P\leqq L\leqq W$. Prouhet showed that $P(k, s)\leqq s^k$. Recently the author has shown that $P(k, s)\leqq(k^2+k+2)/2$ [Bull. Amer. Math. Soc. **54**, 755–757 (1948); these Rev. **10**, 101]. The present paper obtains similar results for L and W. Lehmer proved that $L(k, s)\leqq s^k$ [Scripta Math. **13**, 37–41 (1947); these Rev. **9**, 78]. The author proves that

$$L(k, s)\leqq(k+1)H(k, 2),$$
$$W(k, s)\leqq(k+1)H(k, s),$$

where $H(k, s)$ is the greatest integer not exceeding

$$\log((k+1)(s+1)/2-k+k^{-1})/\log(1+k^{-1}),$$

which is asymptotic to $k \log k$ for large k. Whether $L(k, s)$ is ever equal to $W(k, s)$ is an open question.

D. H. Lehmer (Berkeley, Calif.).

Citations: MR 9, 78d = D52-21; MR 10, 101c = D52-30.

Referred to in D52-38, D52-82.

D52-38 (11, 82f)

Hua, Loo-Keng. Improvement of a result of Wright. J. London Math. Soc. **24**, 157–159 (1949).

The result referred to is in a paper by E. M. Wright [same J. **23**, 279–285 (1948); these Rev. **10**, 510] on a problem of sets of integers having equal sums of like powers. The functions $L(k, s)$ and $W(k, s)$ used below are defined there. Wright has shown that if $H(k, s)$ is the greatest integer not exceeding

$$\log\{\tfrac{1}{2}(k+1)(s+1)+k^{-1}-k)\}/\log(1+k^{-1})\sim k\log k$$

then $L(k, s)\leqq(k+1)H(k, 2)$ for all s and

$$W(k, s)\leqq(k+1)H(k, s)$$

but was unable to find an upper bound for $W(k, s)$ independent of s, as in the case of $L(k, s)$. The present paper proves that Wright's result for $L(k, s)$ holds also for $W(k, s)$ although $L(k, s)\leqq W(k, s)$.

D. H. Lehmer.

Citations: MR 10, 510b = D52-37.

D52-39 (11, 82g)

Gupta, Hansraj. A solution of the Tarry-Escott problem of degree r. Proc. Nat. Inst. Sci. India **15**, 37–39 (1949).

The Tarry-Escott problem of order q and of degree precisely r is that of finding q sets $S_1, S_2, \cdots, S_q$ of s integers each such that the members of each set have equal sums of kth powers for $k=0, 1, \cdots, r$ but distinct sums for $k=r+1$. The least s for which this problem is possible depends on r and possibly also on q and is denoted by $M_q(r)$. It is known that $M_q(r)=r+1$ for $r=1, 2, 3, 5$. The author proves that $M_q(r+1)\leqq qM_q(r)$ so that $M_q(4)\leqq 4q$, $M_q(r)\leqq 6q^{r-5}$ ($r\geqq 5$). [For a much stronger inequality see the paper by E. M. Wright cited in the preceding review.] It is conjectured that $M_q(r)$ is not a function of q. [An upper bound for $M_q(r)$ independent of q has been obtained by Hua in the paper reviewed above.]

D. H. Lehmer (Berkeley, Calif.).

D52-40 (10, 514h)

Sprague, R. Über Zerlegungen in n-te Potenzen mit lauter verschiedenen Grundzahlen. Math. Z. **51**, 466–468 (1948).

Let $P_n(k)$ denote the number of partitions of k into distinct parts taken from $1, 2^n, 3^n, \cdots$. The author proves that there is a positive integer N_n depending only on n such that $P_n(k)>0$ for all $k>N_n$. In other words, for each n there are only a finite number of integers which are not the sums of distinct nth powers. This result for $n=2$ has already been obtained by the author [same vol., 289–290 (1948); these Rev. **10**, 283]. The method of proof is an application of the Tarry-Escott problem.

D. H. Lehmer (Berkeley, Calif.).

Citations: MR 10, 283d = E24-31.

Referred to in A46-7, A46-8, P99-3.

D52-41 (10, 592b)

Moessner, A. Alcune ricerche di teoria dei numeri e problemi diofantei. Boll. Mat. (5) **2**, 36–39 (1948).

Ten miscellaneous results on Diophantine equations are given. Parametric solutions in rational numbers are given of the equations

$$x^n+y^n=(x-y)^{n+1},$$
$$x+y=x^n+y^n,$$
$$x-y=x^3-y^3,$$
$$x^3+y^3=(x+y)^2,$$
$$x^2+y^2+z^2=(x+y-z)^2=w^4.$$

All integers X_i ($i=1, 2, \cdots, 6$) less than 1000 in absolute value whose sum and sum of 5th powers both vanish are given. Other results involve the Tarry-Escott problem in special cases. A parametric ideal solution is given of the 7th degree problem. The reader should be on the alert for misprints.

D. H. Lehmer (Berkeley, Calif.).

D52-42 (10, 592c)

Gupta, Hansraj. On $N_q(r)$ in the Tarry-Escott problem. Proc. Nat. Inst. Sci. India **14**, 335–336 (1948).

The function $N_q(r)$ is the least value of s for which there exist q sets of s integers each, no set a mere permutation of another, which have the same sums of kth powers for $k=0, 1, \cdots, r$. The author proves that $N_q(r) \leqq (r^2+r+2)/2$, a result obtained also by E. M. Wright [Bull. Amer. Math. Soc. **54**, 755–757 (1948); these Rev. **10**, 101] by a similar argument. *D. H. Lehmer* (Berkeley, Calif.).

Citations: MR 10, 101c = D52-30.

D52-43 (10, 681h)

Palamà, Giuseppe. Saggio di una nuova trattazione delle multigrade. Boll. Un. Mat. Ital. (3) **3**, 263–278 (1948).

An expository article giving known results and numerical examples in the problem, known as the Tarry-Escott problem, of finding two sets of integers $a_1, \cdots, a_p$ and $b_1, \cdots, b_q$ such that

$$(1) \qquad \sum_{i=1}^{p} a_i^k = \sum_{i=1}^{q} b_i^k, \qquad k=(m_1, \cdots, m_r),$$

where the m_i are positive integers. Mention is made of the application of multigrade equations to (a) Waring's problem, (b) the calculation of logarithms, (c) equations having unity as a multiple root and (d) the theory of irreducible polynomials. The paper contains copious references. *W. H. Simons* (Vancouver, B. C.).

D52-44 (10, 682a)

Palamà, Giuseppe. Un teorema analogo a quello di Tarry. Osservazioni su altri noti. Applicazioni. Atti Sem. Mat. Fis. Univ. Modena **2**, 116–142 (1948).

This paper is concerned with the so-called Tarry-Escott problem of equal sums of like powers. The theorem mentioned in the title is the following. If $\sum_{i=1}^{p} a_i^k = \sum_{i=1}^{p} b_i^k$ $(k=0, 1, \cdots, n)$, then

$$\sum_{i=1}^{p} a_i^k + (s-c_i)^k = \sum_{i=1}^{p} b_i + (s-d_i)^k, \qquad k=0, 1, \cdots, n+1,$$

where s is an arbitrary parameter and $(c_i, d_i)=(a_i, b_i)$ or (b_i, a_i) according as n is even or odd. The theorem is illustrated by numerous numerical examples. *D. H. Lehmer* (Berkeley, Calif.).

D52-45 (11, 82d)

Gloden, A. Zwei Parameterlösungen einer mehrgradigen Gleichung. Arch. Math. **1**, 480–482 (1949).

By application of theorem 2 [Amer. Math. Monthly **53**, 205–206 (1946)] with the additional condition $a_3-a_1=b_2-b_1$ or $a_2-a_1=b_3-b_2$ two-parameter solutions of

$$\sum_{i=1}^{5} x_i^n = \sum_{i=1}^{5} y_i^n,$$

$n=1, 3, 5, 7$, are deduced. *N. G. W. H. Beeger.*

D52-46 (11, 82e)

Gloden, A. Über mehrgradige Gleichungen. Arch. Math. **1**, 482–483 (1949).

Solution of $\sum_{i=1}^{5} x_i^n = \sum_{i=1}^{5} y_i^n$, $n=1, 2, \cdots, 5$, and of $\sum_{i=1}^{4} x_i^n = \sum_{i=1}^{4} y_i^n$, $n=1, 3, 5$. *N. G. W. H. Beeger.*

D52-47 (11, 329a)

Sastry, S., and Rai, T. On equal sums of like powers. Math. Student **16** (1948), 18–19 (1949).

If a nontrivial solution in positive integers of the k equations

$$x_1^h + \cdots + x_j^h = y_1^h + \cdots + y_j^h, \qquad 1 \leqq h \leqq k,$$

is denoted by

$$(1) \qquad [a_1, a_2, \cdots, a_j]_k = [b_1, b_2, \cdots, b_j]_k,$$

then it is known that the existence of a solution (1) implies the existence of solutions

$$(2) \qquad [a_1+z, \cdots, a_j+z]_k = [b_1+z, \cdots, b_j+z]_k$$

and

$$(3) \qquad [a_1, \cdots, a_j, b_1+d, \cdots, b_j+d]_{k+1} = [b_1, \cdots, b_j, a_1+d, \cdots, a_j+d]_{k+1},$$

z and d being arbitrary integers. Burchnall and Chaundy have given a one-parameter solution of (1) when $k=7$ [Quart. J. Math., Oxford Ser. **8**, 119–130 (1937)]. Applying the results (2) and (3) to this solution, with suitable choice of z and d, the authors have obtained a one-parameter solution of the equation

$$x_1^7 + \cdots + x_6^7 = y_1^7 + \cdots + y_6^7.$$

[Correction: page 19 line 1 should read, ". . . that (4) implies . . .". Line 4 should read, "From (5) and (6) . . .".] *W. H. Simons* (Vancouver, B. C.).

D52-48 (11, 329b)

Zahlen, J. P. Sur les égalités multigrades en nombres tous premiers. Euclides, Madrid **9**, 283–286 (1949).

The following theorems and their converses are proved. If a_i and b_j are primes such that

$$(1) \qquad a_1, a_2, \cdots, a_k \stackrel{n}{=} b_1, b_2, \cdots, b_k \qquad (n \geqq k+1),$$

then for all $1 \leqq r \leqq n$

$$(2) \qquad \int (a_1)^r + \int (a_2)^r + \cdots + \int (a_k)^r = \int (b_1)^r + \cdots + \int (b_k)^r,$$

where the notation $\int (a_i)^r$, attributed to Euler, denotes the sum of the divisors of a_i^r. Moreover the existence of a multigrade equation (1) implies the existence of

$$(3) \qquad \left(\int a_1\right), \cdots, \left(\int a_k\right) \stackrel{n}{=} \left(\int b_1\right), \cdots, \left(\int b_k\right),$$

and conversely (3) implies (1). The result (2) is obtained by adding successively the equations of (1) with $n=1, 2, \cdots$ and using the fact that if p is a prime then $\int p^r = 1+p+p^2+\cdots+p^r$. The result (3) is obtained by applying the theorem of Frolov to (1). The author concludes the paper with some unanswered problems. *W. H. Simons* (Vancouver, B. C.).

D52-49 (11, 329c)

Gloden, A. Analyse diophantienne et analyse multigrade. Euclides, Madrid **9**, 329–331 (1949).

Solution of $ab(a+b)=cd(c+d)$ by substitution of $a=pq$, $b=rs$, $a+b=tu$, $c=ps$, $d=qt$, $c+d=ru$. Every solution also satisfies $(a+b)^k+(-a)^k+(-b)^k=(c+d)^k+(-c)^k+(-d)^k$ for $k=1, 3$. Applying a theorem [Mehrgradige Gleichungen, Noordhoff, Groningen, 1944, p. 22, Satz V; these Rev. **8**, 441] to this equality, we get a solution of $\sum_{i=1}^{6} A_i^k = \sum_{i=1}^{6} B_i^k$, $k=1, 2, 3, 4$. *N. G. W. H. Beeger* (Amsterdam).

Citations: MR 8, 441f = D52-13.

D52-50 (11, 499g)

Palamà, Giuseppe. Somma termine a termine e sequenze di multigrade. Partizione dei numeri. Multigrade a catena. Applicazioni. Atti Sem. Mat. Fis. Univ. Modena **3**, 162–190 (1949).

In this paper, which is divided into five parts, methods of combining solutions of multigrade equations are considered. Thus in part I it is shown under what conditions, when $n=2$, 3 or 5, two solutions

$$a_1, \cdots, a_p \stackrel{n}{=} b_1, \cdots, b_p,$$
$$a_1', \cdots, a_p' \stackrel{n}{=} b_1', \cdots, b_p'$$

may be combined to form a solution

$$ma_1+m'a_1', \cdots, ma_p+m'a_p' \stackrel{n}{=} mb_1+m'b_1', \cdots, mb_p+m'b_p',$$

m, m' being arbitrary integers. In part II a generalized Tarry's theorem [see the author, Univ. Roma Ist. Naz. Alta Mat. Rend. Mat. e Appl. (5) **6**, 95–120 (1947); these Rev. **9**, 9] is used to partition the first p integers into multigrade equation chains. Other methods of obtaining chains are discussed in part III. The methods of part III are used in part IV to construct an 8×8 magic square and a 4×8 magic rectangle using the integers $1, 2, \cdots, 64$ and $1, 2, \cdots, 32$ respectively. Finally, in part V, sequences of solutions of multigrade equations are discussed. The paper contains many numerical examples to illustrate the theory.
W. H. Simons (Kingston, Ont.).

Citations: MR 9, 9e = D52-18.

D52-51 (11, 500a)

Moessner, Alfred. On equal sums of powers. Math. Student **15** (1947), 83–88 (1949).

This paper gives a parametric solution, with many examples, of the Tarry-Escott problem including two sets of 20 linear functions in 6 variables having the same sum of nth powers for $n=0, 1, \cdots, 10$. *D. H. Lehmer.*

D52-52 (11, 571h)

Gloden, A. Aperçu historique des multigrades. Soc. Nat. Luxembourgeois. Bull. Mensuels. N.S. **43**, 18–23 (1949).

D52-53 (11, 581a)

Palamà, G. Numero di termini minimo di un membro di multigrade non banali. Boll. Un. Mat. Ital. (3) **4**, 310–317 (1949).

The author proves the following two theorems and gives some consequences of them. (1) A nontrivial multigrade equation

$$a_1, \cdots, a_{n+m} \overset{n}{=} b_1, \cdots, b_{n-1}$$

$(m\geqq 1)$ is impossible if all the terms are positive. (2) A nontrivial solution in integers,

$$a_1, \cdots, a_{n+m} \overset{n}{=} b_1, \cdots, b_{n-2}$$

$(m\geqq 1)$ is impossible if some of the a's and b's are positive and some negative. *W. H. Simons* (Kingston, Ont.).

D52-54 (11, 642g)

Moessner, Alfred. Some Diophantine problems. Euclides, Madrid **9**, 423–426 (1949). (Spanish)

Various relations among sums of powers of integers are obtained which are based essentially upon a parametric solution of the Diophantine system $3A=B+C+D$, $A^3=BCD$.
H. W. Brinkmann (Swarthmore, Pa.).

D52-55 (11, 643a)

Palamà, G. Multigrade con termini uguali o primi. Generalizzazione di teoremi delle multigrade. Univ. Roma. Ist. Naz. Alta Mat. Rend. Mat. e Appl. (5) **8**, 60–76 (1949).

A multigrade equation of the type

$$m_1A_1^k+\cdots+m_pA_p^k=q_1\beta_1^k+\cdots+q_p\beta_p^k, \qquad k=n_1, \cdots, n_r$$

is denoted by

$$[m_1]A_1, \cdots, [m_p]A_p \overset{k}{=} [q_1]\beta_1+\cdots+[q_p]\beta_p, \quad k=n_1, \cdots, n_r.$$

In the first part of the paper equations of the type

$$A_1, \cdots, [m]A_n \overset{4}{=} \beta_1, \cdots, [m]\beta_n$$

are obtained by applying Tarry's theorem to identities of the form $m_1^2+\cdots+m_n^2=p^2$, the M_i, A_i, B_i being quadratic forms. In part II are given numerical examples of multigrade equations whose terms are all primes. Finally, in part III, compound multigrade equations are defined and the theorems of Tarry and Frolov are generalized for such equations. [The paper contains some typographical omissions. The last term of equation (5) page 62 should be $\{3, 2, -1\}$. The fourth line from the bottom of page 62 should be $a_{i+1}=a_i+\alpha$. In the fifth line from the bottom of page 63 r should be $\{1, 0, -11\}$.] *W. H. Simons.*

D52-56 (11, 714h)

Gatteschi, L., e Rosati, L. A. Risposta ad una questione proposta da A. Moessner. Boll. Un. Mat. Ital. (3) **5**, 43–48 (1950).

In reply to a question proposed by A. Moessner [same Boll. (3) **4**, 146 (1949)] the authors show that the Diophantine system

$$A_1^2+B_1^2=A_2^2+B_2^2=A_3^2+B_3^2,\quad A_1^3+B_1^3=A_2^3+B_2^3=A_3^3+B_3^3$$

has no real solutions in which the pairs (A_1, B_1), (A_2, B_2), (A_3, B_3) are distinct. Moreover, the Diophantine system $A_1^2+B_1^2=A_2^2+B_2^2$, $A_1^3+B_1^3=A_2^3+B_2^3$ has no nontrivial integer solutions. *W. H. Simons* (Kingston, Ont.).

Referred to in D28-27, D52-65.

D52-57 (11, 714j)

Gloden, A. Une méthode de résolution du système trigrade normal. Bull. Soc. Roy. Sci. Liége **18**, 516–518 (1949).

A solution in integers of the system of equations

$$\sum_{i=1}^{s} x_i^k=\sum_{i=1}^{s} y_i^k, \qquad k=1, \cdots, m,$$

is called normal (or ideal) when $s=m+1$. Methods for obtaining all solutions of the normal trigrade equation $\sum_{i=1}^4 x_i^k=\sum_{i=1}^4 y_i^k$, $k=1, 2, 3$, have been given by Dickson [Introduction to the Theory of Numbers, University of Chicago Press, 1929, pp. 49–52] and Buquet [Sciences, Revue de l'Association Française pour l'Avancement des Sciences **75**, no. 60, 456 (1948)]. In the present paper the author gives another method which results in a complete solution in terms of 8 arbitrary parameters.
W. Simons (Vancouver, B. C.).

D52-58 (12, 11e)

Wright, E. M. Equal sums of like powers. Proc. Edinburgh Math. Soc. (2) **8**, 138–142 (1949).

The reviewer [Scripta Math. **13**, 37–41 (1948); these Rev. **9**, 78] presented the following theorems. (A) If $\mu_1, \mu_2, \cdots, \mu_n$ are any n integers $(n>1)$ then the sum

$$S(r, n, h)=\sum_{r,n}(\mu_1a_1+\cdots+\mu_na_n)^h,$$

extended over all sets of n integers $(a_1, \cdots, a_n)$ for which $a_1+a_2+\cdots+a_n\equiv r \pmod s$, $0\leqq a_i<s$, is not dependent upon r for $h=0, 1, 2, \cdots, n-1$. (B) If $\mu_1\cdots\mu_n\neq 0$, then $S(r, n, n)$ depends on r. The proofs were made to depend on formal power series and roots of unity. In the present paper the author gives two very simple proofs of (A) depending only on the multinomial theorem and the factor theorem for polynomials. Use is made of a lemma to the effect that if $\phi(x_1, \cdots, x_n)$ is not really a function of all its variables then the sum $\sum_{r,n}\phi(a_1, \cdots, a_n)$ is independent of r. The author proves (B) via the lemma: The sum $\sum_{r,n}a_1a_2\cdots a_n$ is not independent of r. The proof here is not as immediate as the proofs of (A). By a simple argument the author shows how to construct sets of fewer than s^k numbers having equal sums of like powers up through the kth power.
D. H. Lehmer (Berkeley, Calif.).

Citations: MR 9, 78d = D52-21.

Referred to in D52-112, D52-122.

D52-59 (12, 318c)

Gloden, A. Une extension des systèmes multigrades. Euclides, Madrid **10**, 289–290 (1950).

Three known theorems concerning equal sums of like powers are stated. *I. Niven* (Eugene, Ore.).

D52-60 **(12, 589k)**

Moessner, Alfred. Some Diophantine problems with their solutions. Simon Stevin **27**, 196–200 (1950).

D52-61 **(12, 590a)**

Gloden, A. Normal trigrade and cyclic quadrilateral with integral sides and diagonals. Amer. Math. Monthly **58**, 244–247 (1951).

D52-62 **(12, 675b)**

Pietrosanti, Aldo. Sopra una questione proposta da A. Moessner. Boll. Un. Mat. Ital. (3) **6**, 32–35 (1951).

The author proves that the system of Diophantine equations $A^2+B^2=C^2+D^2$, $A^3+B^3=C^3+D^3$ has no solution in integers other than the trivial one $A=C$, $B=D$.

W. H. Simons (Vancouver, B. C.).

D52-63 **(12, 675h)**

Jabotinsky, Eri. The minimal Tarry-Escott problem. Riveon Lematematika **4**, 41–58 (1950). (Hebrew. English summary)

The minimum Tarry-Escott equalities

$$\sum_{i=1}^{M} A_i^k = \sum_{i=1}^{k} B_i^k \quad (k=0, 1, \cdots, M-1),$$

where the A's and B's are integers, are replaced by congruences in which the A's and B's are polynomials in five parameters and the modulus is, in reality, Sylvester's cyclotomic polynomial $\psi_M(z)$ whose roots are $z=2\cos 2\pi r/M$ with $r\leqq\frac{1}{2}M$ and r prime to M. By choosing as one of the five parameters a root of $\psi_M(z)=0$ and the other four parameters integers, the congruences become equalities and one obtains a minimum solution of the Tarry-Escott problem of any degree $M-1$. Unfortunately, the solution is not in rational integers but in algebraic integers belonging to the real subfield of the cyclotomic field $K(\exp(2\pi i/M))$. Thus, for $M=12$ the solution is in the field $K(\sqrt{3})$. If one permits general algebraic integral solutions the Tarry-Escott problem disappears. *D. H. Lehmer* (Berkeley, Calif.).

D52-64 **(13, 14a)**

Palamà, G. Multigrade normali del 9° ordine. Inverso del teorema di Gloden. Univ. Roma. Ist. Naz. Alta Mat. Rend. Mat. e Appl. (5) **9**, 228–236 (1950).

In A. Gloden's "Mehrgradige Gleichungen" [Noordhoff, Groningen, 1944; these Rev. **8**, 441] it is explained [pp. 54–55] how from a solution of a normal (ideal) multigrade equality of the 9th order a solution of

$$m^2(1089p^2-1053n^2)=q^2(13p^2-9n^2)$$

may be deduced, and conversely. J. P. Flad [Intermédiaire Recherches Math. **5**, 8 (1949)] gave numerical solutions of this last equation without indicating the manner in which he found them. The present author exposes a method of obtaining such solutions. Also a proof is given of the converse of a theorem by Gloden [loc. cit., pp. 45–46].

N. G. W. H. Beeger (Amsterdam).

Citations: MR 8, 441f = D52-13.

D52-65 **(13, 111e)**

Palamà, Giuseppe. Sistemi indeterminati impossibili. Boll. Un. Mat. Ital. (3) **6**, 113–117 (1951).

The set of simultaneous equations

$$x_1^k+\cdots+x_n^k=y_1^k+\cdots+y_n^k$$

($k=m, m+1, \cdots, m+n-1$) has no non-trivial real positive solutions for $m=2$, n arbitrary and for $m=3$, $n=2$. The proofs are only sketched and depend on expressing the sums of powers in terms of the elementary symmetric functions. Previously, L. Gatteschi and L. A. Rosati [Same Boll. (3) **5**, 43–48 (1950); these Rev. **11**, 714] have shown there are no real solutions at all for $n=m=2$. *J. W. S. Cassels.*

Citations: MR 11, 714h = D52-56.

D52-66 **(13, 535e)**

Sastry, S. On Prouhet-Lehmer problem. J. Sci. Res. Benares Hindu Univ. **1** (1950–1951), 1–4 (1951).

Let $P(k, s)$ denote the least number j such that s sets of j numbers each have equal sums of nth powers for $n=1, 2, \cdots, k$. The author proves in an elementary way that $P(4, 3)\leqq 8$, $P(4, 4)\leqq 10$, $P(6, 3)\leqq 13$, and in general $P(4, q)\leqq 3q+1$. These results are to be compared with the following of Wright [Bull. Amer. Math. Soc. **54**, 755–757 (1948); these Rev. **10**, 101]: $P(4, q)\leqq 11$, $P(6, q)\leqq 22$.

D. H. Lehmer (Los Angeles, Calif.).

Citations: MR 10, 101c = D52-30.

Referred to in D52-96, D52-103.

D52-67 **(13, 625c)**

Kaprekar, D. R. Reversible number sets with equal sums of powers. Math. Student **18**, 127–129 (1950).

The author constructs palindromic numbers like

9847653223567489

which are such that when the digits are pointed off in pairs and placed in two sets:

(I) 98, 47, 65, 32; (II) 23, 56, 74, 89

the numbers in (I) and (II) have the same sum and same sum of squares. The examples are constructed from solutions of the Tarry-Escott problem. *D. H. Lehmer.*

Referred to in B60-20.

D52-68 **(13, 625d)**

Venkatachalam Iyer, R. Reversible number sets with equal sums of like powers. Math. Student **18**, 123–127 (1950).

The problem of the preceding review is extended to allow a cyclic permutation of the digits of one number. Thus in the case of the two numbers, 1356424675434532 and 3564246754345321, we obtain the two sets (I) 13, 56, $\cdots$, 32, (II) 35, 64, $\cdots$, 21 which have equal sums of kth powers for $k=0, 1, 2, 3$. *D. H. Lehmer* (Los Angeles, Calif.).

D52-69 **(13, 626c)**

Moessner, Alfred. The identity

$$6PD^{\nu}=E_1^{\nu}+E_2^{\nu}+\cdots+E_{6p}^{\nu}, \quad (\nu=1, 2, \cdots, 6p-1).$$

Math. Student **19**, 48–49 (1951).

Algebraic identities in the Euler tradition. *I. Niven.*

D52-70 **(13, 822d)**

Rosati, Luigi Antonio. Risoluzione di un sistema diofanteo. Boll. Un. Mat. Ital. (3) **7**, 69–70 (1952).

D52-71 **(13, 913e)**

Swinnerton-Dyer, H. P. F. A solution of

$$A^5+B^5+C^5=D^5+E^5+F^5.$$

Proc. Cambridge Philos. Soc. **48**, 516–518 (1952).

Two three-parameter families of solutions are given for the equation indicated in the title, each of which also satisfies $A+B+C=D+E+F$. *I. Niven* (Eugene, Ore.).

D52-72 **(14, 20c)**

Palamà, Giuseppe. Sulle somme di K^{me} potenze e su di un teorema relativo alle multigrade. Boll. Un. Mat. Ital. (3) **7**, 19–29 (1952).

Let $\beta(k)$ and $\gamma(k)$ denote the smallest value of n for which the equation

(1) $$x_1^k+\cdots+x_n^k=y_1^k+\cdots+y_m^k,\quad (x_1,\cdots,x_n,y_1,\cdots,y_n)=1,$$

has one or infinitely many non-negative integral solutions respectively when $m<n$. Moreover, let $\beta'(k)$, $\gamma'(k)$ denote the smallest value of n for which (1) has one or infinitely many solutions respectively when $m<n-1$. Then $\beta(k)\leqq\gamma(k)$, $\beta(k)\leqq\beta'(k)$ and $\gamma(k)\leqq\gamma'(k)$. In the first part of this paper the author obtains some upper bounds for $\beta(k)$, $\beta'(k)$, $\gamma(k)$ and $\gamma'(k)$ for $k\leqq 24$. In the second part of the paper the author gives a theorem regarding the combination of two multigrade equations of degree n to form a multigrade equation of degree $n+1$. *W. H. Simons.*

D52-73 (14, 136e)

Moessner, Alfred. On the multiple identity

$$x_1^n+x_2^n+x_3^n+x_4^n+x_5^n=y_1^n+y_2^n+y_3^n+y_4^n+y_5^n$$

for $n=1, 3, 5, 7$. Scripta Math. **18**, 90–91 (1952).

D52-74 (14, 136f)

Moessner, Alfred. Alcuni problemi diofantei elementari. Boll. Un. Mat. Ital. (3) **7**, 185–187 (1952).

D52-75 (14, 138a)

Rai, T. On a problem of additive theory of numbers. II. Math. Student **19** (1951), 113–116 (1952).

Methods and aims are analogous to those of a previous paper of the same author [Math. Student **15**, 25–28 (1948); these Rev. **10**, 431]. Let $N(k)$ be the least value of n such that (1) $\sum_{i=1}^m x_i^k=\sum_{i=1}^n y_i^k$ has a solution with $m<n$. Let $\delta(k)$, resp. $\theta(k)$, be the least value of s such that there exists a constant $c=c(k)\neq 0$ and $c=\sum_{i=1}^s \epsilon_i x_i^k$, $\epsilon_i=\pm 1$, has infinitely many integer, resp. rational, solutions. Let $\gamma(k)$ be the least value of n such that (1) has infinitely many solutions with $m<n$. From numerical identities the author derives inequalities such as $N(18)\leqq 54$, $\beta(17)\leqq 29$, $\gamma(23)\leqq 83$, $\delta(9)\leqq 15$, $\theta(13)\leqq 21$. *N. G. W. H. Beeger* (Amsterdam).

Citations: MR 10, 431k = D52-35.

D52-76 (14, 138b)

Gupta, Hansraj. A note on sums of powers. Math. Student **19** (1951), 117 (1952).

Addendum to a paper with the same title and by the same author [Proc. Indian Acad. Sci., Sect. A. **4**, 571–574 (1936)]. $M(k)$ denotes the least value of n for which $\sum_{i=1}^n a_i^m=\sum_{i=1}^n b_i^m$, $m=1, 2, 3, \cdots, k(\neq k+1)$ has a solution. By means of two numerical identities he proves $M(21)\leqq 80$. Proceeding as in Rai's paper [see the preceding review] it can be shown that $\gamma(23)\leqq 81$.

N. G. W. H. Beeger (Amsterdam).

D52-77 (14, 450f)

Leonardi, Raffaele. Sulla formazione dei sistemi di numeri equitotali. Boll. Un. Mat. Ital. (3) **7**, 345–350 (1952).

Various observations concerning systems of equations $\sum_{i=1}^n(x_i^\alpha-y_i^\alpha)=0, \alpha=1, 2, \cdots, k.$ *I. Niven.*

D52-78 (14, 450g)

Gloden, A. Systèmes multigrades remarquables. Mathesis **61**, 278–280 (1952).

D52-79 (14, 725c)

Moessner, Alfred. A Diophantine problem. Riveon Lematematika **6**, 26–27 (1953). (Hebrew)

D52-80 (14, 725d)

Moessner, Alfredo. Due problemi diofantei. Boll. Un. Mat. Ital. (3) **8**, 71–73 (1953).

D52-81 (14, 726c)

Rai, T. On a problem of additive theory of numbers. IV. J. Sci. Res. Banaras Hindu Univ. **2**, 219–220 (1952).

$W(k, s)$ is the least value of j for which

$$\sum_{i=1}^j x_{i_1}^l=\cdots=\sum_{i=1}^j x_{i_s}^l,\quad 1\leqq l\leqq k,$$

have a nontrivial solution such that no two of the sums $\sum$ are equal. Application of a known theorem to known (numerical) solutions yields new solutions from which follow $W(4, 3)\leqq 7$ and $W(6, 3)\leqq 12$.

N. G. W. H. Beeger (Amsterdam).

D52-82 (14, 1065a)

Palamà, G. On a theorem of D. H. Lehmer concerning the Tarry-Escott problem. Scripta Math. **19**, 19–23 (1953).

The theorem in question concerns b sets of integers all having equal sums of like powers. The precise statement of the theorem is given in Lehmer, Scripta Math. **13**, 37–41 (1947); these Rev. **9**, 78. The original method of proof was by use of a certain generating function. Simpler proofs have been given by Wright [J. London Math. Soc. **23**, 279–285 (1948); these Rev. **10**, 510] and Mirsky [Scripta Math. **14**, 126–127 (1948); these Rev. **10**, 283]. The author gives a simple proof for the case $b=2$ and indicates how it may be extended to case of any b using a theorem of Tarry. A variant of Tarry's theorem is given. *D. H. Lehmer.*

Citations: MR 9, 78d = D52-21; MR 10, 283c = D52-32; MR 10, 510b = D52-37.

D52-83 (15, 199f)

Palamà, G. Diophantine systems of the type

$$\sum_{i=1}^p a_i^k=\sum_{i=1}^p b_i^k,\quad (k=1, 2, \cdots, n, n+2, n+4, \cdots, n+2r).$$

Scripta Math. **19**, 132–134 (1953).

D52-84 (15, 400e)

Palamà, Giuseppe. Su di una questione relativa a somme uguali di potenze simili. Boll. Un. Mat. Ital. (3) **8**, 286–293 (1953).

Denote by $M(n, r)$ the smallest value of p for which the diophantine equations

(1) $$a_1^s+\cdots+a_p^s=a_p^s+\cdots+b_p^s\quad (s=1, \cdots, n, n+2, n+4, \cdots, n+rn)$$

has solutions $a_1, \cdots, b_p$ in which the a's are not a permutation of the b's. Let $\alpha(k)$ denote the least value of p for which (1) has solutions for $s=k, k-2, \cdots, s\geqq 0$, so that $M(0, r)=\alpha(2r)$, and $M(1, r)=\alpha(2r+1)$. It is shown that

$$M(2, 2)=4,\quad M(2, 3)=5,\quad M(2, 4)\leqq 7,$$
$$M(2, 5)\leqq 15,\quad M(2, 6)\leqq 15,\quad M(2, 7)\leqq 24,\quad M(2, 8)\leqq 29.$$

It is conjectured that $M(2, r)=\alpha(2r+2)$. Furthermore

$M(3, 2)=\alpha(7)=5$, $M(3, 3)\leqq 7$, $M(3, 4)\leqq 11$, $M(3, 5)\leqq 17$, $M(3, 6)\leqq 21$, $M(3, 7)\leqq 30$, $M(4, 2)\leqq 8$, $M(4, 3)\leqq 11$, $M(5, 2)\leqq 11$.

D. H. Lehmer (Berkeley, Calif.).

D52-85 (15, 400f)

Gloden, A. Un procédé de formation de systèmes multigrades normaux. Bull. Soc. Roy. Sci. Liège **22**, 474–480 (1953).

Given two sets of n numbers having equal sums of like powers, say $\sum a_i^k=\sum b_i^k$ for $k=1, \cdots, n$, a procedure is sketched for extension to $n+1$, i.e., to obtain two sets of

$n+1$ numbers having equal sums of kth powers for all positive integers $k \leqq n+1$. *I. Niven* (Eugene, Ore.).

D52-86 **(15, 400g)**

Singh, Raghuraj. On multigrade equations of the third order. J. Sci. Res. Benaras Hindu Univ. **3**, 1–4 (1953).

If a_1, a_2, a_3 and b_1, b_2, b_3 are two solutions of $x_1^2+x_2^2+x_3^2=n$, then

$$\sum_{i=1}^{3}\{(c+a_i)^j+(c-a_i)^j\}=\sum_{i=1}^{3}\{(c+b_i)^j+(c-b_i)^j\}, \quad j=1, 2, 3.$$

This device clearly provides a class of solutions of the simultaneous system $\sum_{i=1}^{6}x_i^j=\sum_{i=1}^{6}y_i^j$ for $j=1, 2, 3$, but it is not clear that, as the author claims, all solutions are thus obtained. *I. Niven* (Eugene, Ore.).

D52-87 **(15, 601h)**

Moessner, Alfred. Drei diophantische Probleme. Hrvatsko Prirodoslovno Društvo. Glasnik Mat.-Fiz. Astr. Ser. II. **8**, 191–193 (1953). (Serbo-Croatian summary)

D52-88 **(16, 112g)**

Xeroudakes, George, and Moessner, Alfred. A theorem of the elementary arithmetic. Jber. Deutsch. Math. Verein. **57**, Abt. 1, 89–92 (1954).

The following result is proved. If $n \geqq 1$ and N has at least one prime divisor of the form $4k+1$, then there exist integers x, y, z, t such that $2(N^n)^m=x^m+y^m+z^m+t^m$ ($m=1, 2, 3$).

L. Carlitz (Durham, N. C.).

D52-89 **(16, 220d)**

Moessner, Alfred, and Xeroudakes, George. On some sets of integers with equal sums of like powers. Acad. Serbe Sci. Publ. Inst. Math. **6**, 125–136 (1954).

Solutions are given of the following systems:

$$\sum_{i=1}^{3}A_i^n=\sum_{i=1}^{3}B_i^n=\sum_{i=1}^{3}C_i^n \ (n=1, 3), \quad \sum_{i=1}^{3}X_i^n=\sum_{i=1}^{3}Y_i^n \ (n=2, 4),$$

$$\sum_{i=1}^{2}A_i^n=\sum_{i=1}^{3}B_i^n \ (n=1, 3), \quad \sum_{i=1}^{4}X_i^n=\sum_{i=1}^{4}Y_i^n \ (n=1, 3).$$

L. Carlitz (Durham, N. C.).

D52-90 **(16, 337c)**

Hua, Loo-Keng. On the number of solutions of Tarry's problem. Acta Sci. Sinica **1**, 1–76 (1952).

Let $r_t(P, k)$ be the number of integral solutions of the system of equations

$$x_1^h+\cdots+x_t^h=y_1^h+\cdots+y_t^h, \quad h=1, \cdots, k,$$

subject to the restriction that all variables lie in the closed interval $[1, P]$. The main result is that if $k \geqq 2$ and $t>t_0(k)$, then for large P

$$r_t(P, k)=\vartheta_t(k)\mathfrak{S}_t(k)P^{2t-k(k+1)/2}+O(P^{2t-k(k+1)/2-c(k)})$$

for some $c(k)>0$ and for certain positive $\vartheta_t(k)$, $\mathfrak{S}_t(k)$, $t_0(k)$, formulas for which are given. Here $t_0(2)=3$ and $t_0(k)\sim 3k^2 \log k$ for large k. This improves a result given in the first edition of the author's book (see the following review) where the result was proved for $t>t_1(k)\sim \frac{3}{2}k^3 \log k$. The sharpening of the lower bound for t results from the use of an improved form of Vinogradov's mean-value theorem proved earlier by the author [Quart. J. Math., Oxford Ser. **20**, 48–61 (1949); these Rev. **10**, 597].

In connection with the singular series $\mathfrak{S}_t(k)$, whose terms are non-negative, the author proves that it converges for $t>\frac{1}{4}k(k+1)+1$ if $k \geqq 3$ and diverges for all other t. The proof of divergence is rather easy. For $t>k^2$, and even for $t>\frac{1}{2}k(k+1)$, the proof of convergence is not too difficult and depends on earlier results of the author which are now well known. But the complete result on convergence is based on a very detailed study of the singular series and ultimately depends on an analysis of the solutions of the polynomial congruence $g(x)\equiv 0 \pmod p$.

The factor $\vartheta_t(k)$ is a k-fold infinite integral with non-negative integrand. By using the Young-Hausdorff theorem regarding a function and its Fourier transform, the author is able to show that $\vartheta_t(k)$ converges for $t>\frac{1}{4}k(k+2)$.

A number of remarks and statements of results are made concerning the Prouhet problem and the number

$$r_t(N_1, \cdots, N_k; P)$$

of solutions of

$$(*) \qquad x_1^h+\cdots+x_t^h=N_h \quad (h=1, \cdots, k)$$

subject to $1 \leqq x_j \leqq P$. Finally an asymptotic result is obtained for $r'(N)$ which is defined as the number of solutions of

$$x_1+x_2+x_3=y_1+y_2+y_3, \quad x_1^2+x_2^2+x_3^2=y_1^2+y_2^2+y_3^2 \leqq N.$$

This result is

$$r'(N)=35(3/4)^{1/2}N^{3/2} \log N+O(N^{3/2} \log^{1/2} N).$$

The proof depends on the fact that $r'(N)$ is the sum of squares of terms $r_3(N_1, N_2; N)$. Each of these terms is closely connected with $\Psi(m)$, the number of solutions of $X_1^2+X_1X_2+X_2^2=m$. Finally, $\Psi(m)$ is six times the sum of the Jacobi symbol $(-3|l)$ taken for $l|m$. By using these results and careful estimations, the result for $r'(N)$ is obtained. *L. Schoenfeld* (Princeton, N. J.).

Citations: MR 10, 597d = P08-11.

Referred to in D52-119, D52-130, D99-14.

D52-91 **(16, 1089a)**

Gloden, A. Théorèmes nouveaux sur les systèmes multigrades d'ordre n et applications. IIIe Congrès National des Sciences, Bruxelles, 1950, Vol. 2, pp. 80–84. Fédération belge des Sociétés Scientifiques, Bruxelles.

Various elementary theorems are given concerning the Tarry-Escott problem; for definitions see Gloden's book on the subject or the review thereof [Mehrgradige Gleichungen, Noordhoff, Groningen, 1944; MR **8**, 441]. The applications are to geometry, such as the determination of a quadrilateral inscribed in a circle with rational values for sides, diagonals, and area. *I. Niven* (Berkeley, Calif.).

Citations: MR 8, 441f = D52-13.

D52-92 **(17, 461a)**

Palamà, G. Congruenze multigrade. Period. Mat. (4) 33 (1955), 230–234.

D52-93 **(17, 586g)**

Sastry, S. On some systems of Diophantine equations. J. Sci. Res. Banaras Hindu Univ. 5 (1955), no. 2, 1–6.

The author shows how a representation of an integer r^2 in the form a^2+ab+b^2 can be used to obtain integer solutions of the system of equations

$$x_1^j+\cdots+x_i^j=y_1^j+\cdots+y_8^j \ (1 \leqq j \leqq 6).$$

W. H. Simons (Vancouver, B.C.).

D52-94 **(17, 586h)**

Dutta Mishra, Shiva. On Prouhet-Lehmer problem. J. Sci. Res. Banaras Hindu Univ. 5 (1955), no. 2, 7–10.

Let $P(k, s)$ be the least value of j such that the $k(s-1)$ Diophantine equations

$$\sum_{i=1}^{j}x_{i1}^h=\sum_{i=1}^{j}x_{i2}^h=\cdots=\sum_{i=1}^{j}x_{is}^h \ (1 \leqq h \leqq k),$$

have a solution in positive integers. Numerical examples

are used to obtain the following bounds for $P(k, s)$: $P(4, 3)\leq 8$, $P(6, 3)\leq 14$, $P(7, 3)\leq 26$, $P(4, 5)\leq 12$, $P(5, 5)\leq 36$. *W. H. Simons* (Vancouver, B.C.).

D52-95 (17, 586i)

Prakash Srivastava, Om. On Prouhet-Lehmer problem. J. Sci. Res. Banaras Hindu Univ. **5** (1955), no. 2, 59–62.

$P(k, s)$ being defined as in the previous review, it is shown here that $P(4, q)\leq 2q+2$. Numerical examples are given to show that $P(4, 5)\leq 10$, $P(4, 6)\leq 12$.

W. H. Simons (Vancouver, B.C.).

Referred to in D52-103.

D52-96 (17, 828a)

Sastry, S. On Prouhet-Lehmer problem. II. J. Sci. Res. Banaras Hindu Univ. **6** (1955–56), 90–92.

Let $P(k, s)$ denote the least number j such that there exist s different sets of j positive integers each having equal sums of nth powers for $n=1, 2, \cdots, k$. It is conjectured by Wright [Bull. Amer. Math. Soc. **54** (1948), 755–757; MR **10**, 101, 855] that $P(k, s)=k+1$ and this has been proved for $k<6$. In the author's previous paper he proved that $P(6, s)\leq 5s+1$ [J. Sci. Res. Benares Hindu Univ. **1** (1950–1951), 1–4; MR **13**, 535]. In this paper the result is improved to $P(6, s)\leq 4s$. Wright has proved that $P(6, s)\leq 22$. *D. H. Lehmer* (Berkeley, Calif.).

Citations: MR 10, 101c = D52-30; MR 13, 535e = D52-66.

D52-97 (18, 380d)

Gloden, A. Construction de systèmes multigrades remarquables. Mathesis **65** (1956), 230–234.

Identities are given for obtaining equal sums of like powers of integers. *I. Niven* (Eugene, Ore.).

D52-98 (18, 466d)

Palamà, Giuseppe. Su taluni problemi che si riducono a quello ideale di Escott-Tarry o di Prouhet-Tarry. Boll. Un. Mat. Ital. (3) **11** (1956), 569–577.

Referred to in D52-122.

D52-99 (18, 641a)

Venkataraman, L. V. On multigrade equations of degree 3 and order δ. J. Sci. Res. Banaras Hindu Univ. **6** (1955–56), 211–213.

The author observes that it is known that the identity in t

$$(t+x_1)^3+(t-x_1)^3+(t+y_1)^3+(t-y_1)^3=(t+x_2)^3+(t-x_2)^3+(t+y_2)^3+(t-y_2)^3$$

follows from $x_1^2+y_1^2=x_2^2+y_2^2$. Using facts about integers representable as the sum of two squares, he shows how to obtain an infinite number of equations of degree 3 of the form stated above. A number of numerical examples are given. *R. D. James* (Vancouver, B.C.).

D52-100 (18, 718d)

Xeroudakes, George. The Diophantine system

$$\sum A_i=\sum B_i, \sum A_i^3=\sum B_i^3 (i=1, 2, 3).$$

Applications and significant conclusions. (Greek). Athens, 1955. 48 pp.

D52-101 (18, 718g; 18, 718h; 18, 718i)

Xiroudakis, Georges. Surd es systèmes multigrades. Mathesis **65** (1956), 371–378.
Gloden, A. Formation de chaînes trigrades avec cinq termes par maillon. Mathesis **65** (1956), 412–414.
Venkatachalam Iyer, R. Analyse multigrade. Mathesis **65** (1956), 416–417.

Additional examples of relations involving equal sums of like powers of integers mentioned MR **8**, 441 and **16**, 1089. *I. Niven* (Eugene, Ore.).

D52-102 (19, 15e)

Srivastava, Om Prakash. On the number of representations as sum of four squares of numbers of the form $4^a(8b+7)$. J. Sci. Res. Banaras Hindu Univ. **6** (1955–56), 278–285.

The author investigates the numbers which have precisely three partitions into four positive squares. These numbers are 55, 79, 95 and $4^k m$, where $k>0$ and $m=7$, 15 and 23. These facts are applied in an interesting way to the Tarry-Escott problem to derive three sets of eight numbers having equal sums of kth powers for $k=1, 2, 3$. The same questions are answered about numbers which have precisely h partitions into four positive squares for $h=1$, 2 and 4. [See also Lehmer, Amer. Math. Monthly **55** (1948), 476–481; MR **10**, 182.] The reader may be assisted in following the paper if it is here noted that "$s(n)$" denotes the sum of the odd divisors of n and that "representation" usually means "partition".

D. H. Lehmer (Berkeley, Calif.).

Citations: MR 10, 182c = E24-30.

D52-103 (19, 120d)

Din, Deota. On Prouhet Lehmer problem. J. Sci. Res. Banaras Hindu Univ. **6** (1955–56), 221–226.

Denote, as usual, by $P(k, s)$ the least value of j such that the $k(s-1)$ diophantine equations

$$\sum_{i=1}^{j} x_{1i}^h=\sum_{i=1}^{j} x_{2i}^h=\cdots=\sum_{i=1}^{j} x_{si}^h \quad (0\leq h\leq k)$$

have a non-trivial solution in integers. Improving on recent results of Prakash Srivastava [same J. **5** (1955), no. 2, 59–62; MR **17**, 586] and S. Sastry the author shows that $P(4, s)\leq 2s+1$ and $P(6, s)\leq 3s+2$. Numerical examples show that $P(4, 3)\leq 7$, $P(4, 6)\leq 13$, $P(6, 3)\leq 11$, $P(6, 6)\leq 20$. The method is based on a device of Sastry [ibid. **1** (1950–1951), 1–4; MR **13**, 535]. *D. H. Lehmer.*

Citations: MR 13, 535e = D52-66; MR 17, 586i = D52-95.

D52-104 (19, 531e)

Xiroudakis, Georges. Les systèmes multigrades dont les termes sont formés au moyen des nombres de Pythagore. Mathesis **66** (1957), 7–16.

A solution in integers of $A^2=B^2+C^2$ provides a solution of the diophantine system

$$A, A, 2A \overset{3}{=} A+B, A-B, A+C, A-C.$$

In this paper the author discusses the solutions of the above and similar systems of diophantine equations obtained from solutions of $A^2=B^2+C^2$. Numerous numerical examples are given. *W. H. Simons.*

D52-105 (19, 635c)

Moessner, Alfred. Zwei diophantische Probleme. Glasnik Mat.-Fiz. Astr. Ser. II. **11** (1956), 249–252. (Serbo-Croatian summary)

Various identities, involving equal sums of like powers, are established. *W. H. Mills* (New Haven, Conn.).

D52-106 (20# 19)

Moessner, Alfred. Einige zahlentheoretische Untersuchungen und diophantische Probleme. Bul. Inst. Politech. Iaşi **4** (1949), 143–154.

Many systems of the Tarry-Escot type are discussed, and numerous numerical solutions are given. For example a non-trivial integer solution is given for the system

$$\sum_{i=1}^{20} E_i^n=\sum_{i=1}^{20} F_i^n, \quad 1\leq n\leq 10.$$

W. H. Mills (New Haven, Conn.)

D52-107 **(20# 3099)**

Tewari, Krishna. On equal sums of powers. J. Sci. Res. Banaras Hindu Univ. 8 (1957/58), 81–85.

A solution of the equation (*) $\sum_{s=1}^{m} x_s^k = \sum_{t=1}^{n} y_t^k$ in positive integers $x_1, \cdots, x_m, y_1, \cdots, y_n$ is said to be nontrivial if $(x_1, \cdots, x_m, y_1, \cdots, y_n) = 1$. If $m = n$ and the y's are not a permutation of the x's, let $N(k)$ denote the least value of n such that (*) has a nontrivial solution; let $\beta(k)$ denote the least value of n such that (*) has a nontrivial solution with $m < n$; and let $\gamma(k)$ denote the least value of n such that (*) has infinitely many solutions with $m < n$. Using elementary methods, the author proves ten results, of which $N(18) \leqq 50$, $\beta(22) \leqq 51$, $\gamma(24) \leqq 83$ are examples.

R. D. James (Vancouver, B.C.)

D52-108 **(20# 4523)**

Moessner, Alfred. Folgerungen aus den Gleichungen $A \cdot B = C \cdot D$ und $a^2 + b^2 = c^2$. Bul. Inst. Politehn. Iaşi (N.S.) 3 (1957), 7–14. (Russian and Romanian summaries)

Various identities, involving equal sums of like powers, are established. *W. H. Mills* (New Haven, Conn.)

D52-109 **(20# 5752)**

Moessner, Alfred. Ein Diophantisches Problem. Euclides, Madrid, 17 (1957), 115–120.

The author gives some solutions of the simultaneous system $\sum_{i=1}^{r} x_i^n = \sum_{i=1}^{s} y_i^n$ for $n = 1, 2, 3$ and for $n = 1, 2, 3, 4$. *W. Ljunggren* (Blindern)

D52-110 **(20# 6389)**

Moessner, Alfred; and Xeroudakes, George. On the solutions of the system $2A^m = B^m + C^m + (B+C)^m$ ($m = 2,4$). Glasnik Mat.-Fiz. Astr. Društvo Mat. Fiz. Hrvatske. Ser. II. 13 (1958), 89–96. (Serbo-Croatian summary)

Various identities, involving equal sums of like powers, are established. Numerical illustrations are given.

W. H. Mills (New Haven, Conn.)

D52-111 **(21# 20)**

Xeroudakes, George; and Moessner, Alfred. On equal sums of like powers. Proc. Indian Acad. Sci. Sect. A. 48 (1958), 245–255.

D52-112 **(21# 3375)**

Wright, E. M. Prouhet's 1851 solution of the Tarry-Escott problem of 1910. Amer. Math. Monthly **66** (1959), 199–201.

The author gives historical proof of the fact that the problem generally known as the Tarry-Escott problem was anticipated in more general form by Prouhet by the amount indicated in the title. Prouhet's result may be stated as follows. Consider all j^k integers $n \geqq 0$ that have k (or fewer) digits when written in the scale of j. Two such integers are considered equivalent if the sums of their digits are congruent modulo j. Then the j equivalence classes are such that the sums of the mth powers of the members of each class are all the same, this for $m = 0(1)k-1$. The author gives a new proof of this using the finite difference operator $E = 1 + \Delta$ and jth roots of unity. [For three other proofs by the reviewer and the author see Lehmer, Scripta Math. **13** (1947), 37–41; MR **9**, 78; Wright, Proc. Edinburgh Math. Soc. (2) **8** (1949), 138–142; MR **12**, 11]. *D. H. Lehmer* (Berkeley, Calif.)

Citations: MR 9, 78d = D52-21; MR 12, 11e = D52-58.

D52-113 **(23# A100)**

Roberts, J. B.

Polynomial identities.

Proc. Amer. Math. Soc. **11** (1960), 723–730.

This paper further generalizes the author's previous extension of a known theorem about sets of numbers having equal sums of like powers [Canad. J. Math. **10** (1958), 191–194; MR **20** #3092]. To indicate the degree of generality, we may state the main result as follows. Let m be a positive integer and let $\alpha_1, \alpha_2, \cdots, \alpha_m$ be integers $\geqq -1$. Let $P(x)$ be a polynomial of degree less than $m + \alpha_1 + \cdots + \alpha_m$. Let $n_1, n_2, \cdots$ be an arbitrary set of integers $\geqq 2$ and write $p_k = n_1 n_2 \cdots n_k$. For each integer n define the digits $a_i^{(n)}$ of n by $n = a_0^{(n)} + a_1^{(n)} p_1 + a_2^{(n)} p_2 + \cdots$ $(0 \leqq a_i^{(n)} < n_{i+1})$. Let $\beta_0, \beta_1, \beta_2, \cdots$ be an arbitrary sequence of complex numbers and let $A_n = a_0^{(n)}\beta_0 + a_1^{(n)}\beta_1 + \cdots$. For each $j \leqq m$ select a numerical function f_j such that $\sum_{n=0}^{n_j-1} f_j(n) n^t = 0$ $(0 \leqq t \leqq \alpha_j)$. Then

$$\sum_{n=0}^{p_m-1} \left\{ \prod_{j=1}^{m} f_j(a_{j-1}^{(n)}) \right\} P(x + A_n) \equiv 0$$

is an identity in x. There are a number of interesting special cases. *D. H. Lehmer* (Berkeley, Calif.)

Referred to in A66-15, D52-128.

D52-114 **(23# A2371)**

Palamà, Giuseppe

I problemi di Escott-Tarry e di Prouhet-Tarry.

Giorn. Mat. Battaglini (5) **4** (**84**) (1956), 189–247.

Expository. *D. H. Lehmer* (Berkeley, Calif.)

Referred to in D52-122.

D52-115 **(23# A2372)**

Palamà, Giuseppe

I problemi di Escott-Tarry e di Prouhet-Tarry.

Giorn. Mat. Battaglini (5) **5** (**85**) (1957), 80–94.

Expository. *D. H. Lehmer* (Berkeley, Calif.)

Referred to in D52-122.

D52-116 **(23# A3108)**

Palamà, Giuseppe

I problemi di Escott-Tarry e di Prouhet-Tarry.

Giorn. Mat. Battaglini (5) **5** (**85**) (1957), 271–295.

Referred to in D52-122.

D52-117 **(24# A1880)**

Melzak, Z. A.

A note on the Tarry-Escott problem.

Canad. Math. Bull. **4** (1961), 233–237.

Let $K = K(n)$ be the smallest positive integer k such that the system

$$\sum_{i=1}^{k} a_i^j = \sum_{i=1}^{k} b_i^j, \qquad j = 1, \cdots, n,$$

has a non-trivial solution in integers a_i, b_i [$K(n) = P(n, 2)$ in the notation of Hardy and Wright, *An introduction to the theory of numbers*, 3rd ed., p. 328, Clarendon, Oxford, 1954; MR **16**, 673]. For a polynomial $P(x) = \sum_{i=0}^{m} a_i x^i$, a_i integers, not all zero, define $S(P) = \sum_{i=0}^{m} |a_i|$. Then the author proves that

$$K(n) = \tfrac{1}{2} \min_{P \in \mathbf{a}} S[P(x)(1-x)^{n+1}],$$

where **a** is the class of all polynomials with integral coefficients.

Using a particular $P(x)$ and computing $S[P(x)(1-x)^{n+1}]$ on the IBM 704, the author obtains an upper bound for $K(n)$ for $n \leqq 29$. This bound is better than the bound $\frac{1}{2}(n^2+4)$, valid for all n, due to E. M. Wright [Quart. J. Math. Oxford Ser. **6** (1935), 261–267].

R. P. Bambah (Chandigarh)

Citations: MR 16, 673b = Z01-28.

Referred to in D52-129.

D52-118 (24# A2558)

Moessner, Alfred

Einige zahlentheoretische Untersuchungen und diophantische Probleme. (Serbo-Croatian summary)
Glasnik Mat.-Fiz. Astronom. Društvo Mat. Fiz. Hrvatske Ser. II **14** (1959), 177–182.

The author gives various multigrade identities of which the following is typical. If $K=(A^2+B^2-2C^2)/(A+B-2C)$, then

$$2C^n+2(K-C)^n = A^n+B^n+(K-A)^n+(K-B)^n \quad (n = 1, 2, 3).$$

Various algebraic identities which yield solutions to such Diophantine systems as $a^2+b^2+c^2=2d^6$, $a^4+b^4+c^4=2d^{12}$, are given. It is stated that the equation $A^6=B_1^6+B_2^6+\cdots+B_r^6$ was previously known to have solutions only for $r\geqq 28$. Solutions are given here for $r=16$, 18, 20 and 23.

L. Moser (Edmonton, Alta.)

D52-119 (26# 70)

Karacuba, A. A.

Tarry's problem for a system of congruences. (Russian)
Mat. Sb. (N.S.) **55 (97)** (1961), 209–220.

Let $N_k(P)$ be the number of solutions of the system of congruences

$$\sum_{\nu=1}^{k} x_\nu^r \equiv \sum_{\nu=1}^{k} y_\nu^r \pmod q,$$

where $1\leqq x_\nu\leqq P$, $1\leqq y_\nu\leqq P$, $1\leqq r\leqq n$, and $2kP^r<q\leqq 2kP^{r+1}$. An upper bound for $N_k(P)$ was obtained by N. M. Korobov [Dokl. Akad. Nauk SSSR **118** (1958), 231–232; MR **20** #6393]. In the corresponding version of the problem for equations (instead of congruences), I. M. Vinogradov had previously obtained an upper bound, and Loo-Keng Hua [Acta Sci. Sinica **1** (1952), 1–76; MR **16**, 337] obtained an explicit limiting result as $P\to\infty$. It is a result of this latter kind that the author now proves for the congruence problem. Subject to certain conditions, which include the conditions $\lim_{P\to\infty} qP^{-r}=C$ and $k>n^2\{2+\log(20rn(n+1)\log n)\}$, he shows that

$$\lim_{P\to\infty} P^{-2K+\frac{1}{2}r(2n-r+1)}N_k(P) = C^{r-n}\Theta_r\mathfrak{S}_0,$$

where Θ_r is a certain r-fold multiple integral and $\mathfrak{S}_0$ is the limit of a certain multiple series. *R. A. Rankin* (Glasgow)

Citations: MR 16, 337c = D52-90; MR 20# 6393 = L15-18.

D52-120 (26# 4962)

Karacuba, A. A.; Korobov, N. M.

A mean-value theorem. (Russian)
Dokl. Akad. Nauk SSSR **149** (1963), 245–248.

Let $N_k(P)$ denote the number of solutions in integers of the system

$$(1)\quad x_1^\nu+\cdots+x_k^\nu = y_1^\nu+\cdots+y_k^\nu,\quad 0\leqq x,y\leqq P-1, \quad (\nu = 1, 2, 3, \cdots, n).$$

The authors prove Theorem 1: For $\tau\geqq 1$, $k\geqq n^2+n\tau$, we have

$$(2)\quad N_k(P) < (3k^{2n})^\tau(1+2\theta)^{2k(n+\tau)}P^w,$$

where

$$(3)\quad w = 2k-\tfrac{1}{2}(n(n+1))+\tfrac{1}{2}(n(n+1))(1-1/n)^\tau, \quad 0<\theta\leqq 1.$$

Theorem 2: There exist absolute constants α and C such that for $n\geqq 11$, $1\leqq\tau\leqq 2n\log(n+1)+1$, $k\geqq 2n^2+n\tau$, $P\geqq n^{\alpha n(1+1/(n-1))^\tau}$ we have the estimate

$$(4)\quad N_k(P)\leqq CP^w,$$

where w is given by (3) above.

A postscript to this theorem says that we may take $\alpha=86$, $C\leqq 1$. These estimates give new proofs of the mean value theorems of Vinogradov [whose papers appeared in Izv. Akad. Nauk SSSR Ser. Mat. **15** (1951), 109–130; MR **13**, 328; ibid. **22** (1958), 161–164; MR **21** #2624]; see also L. K. Hua, Quart. J. Math. Oxford Ser. **20** (1949), 48–61 [MR **10**, 597].

The proofs are based on an estimate for the number of solutions of a system of congruences with certain bounds for the variables. The authors operate with Weyl's sums.

S. Chowla (Boulder, Colo.)

Citations: MR 10, 597d = P08-11; MR 13, 328e = L15-14; MR 21# 2624 = M15-19.
Referred to in D52-121, D52-140.

D52-121 (38# 1062)

Karacuba, A. A.

A certain system of indeterminate equations. (Russian)
Mat. Zametki **4** (1968), 125–128.

A version of Vinogradov's mean value theorem similar to that of the author and N. M. Korobov [Dokl. Akad. Nauk SSSR **149** (1963), 245–248; MR **26** #4962] except that it is valid for all positive P at the expense of a somewhat weaker inequality. An estimate for a trigonometric sum is said to be deducible in the usual way. The results are too complicated to be stated in full.

J. W. S. Cassels (Cambridge, England)

Citations: MR 26# 4962 = D52-120.

D52-122 (28# 2086)

Palamà, Giuseppe

Problema di Prouhet-Tarry. II.
Giorn. Mat. Battaglini (5) **6 (86)** (1958), 187–208.

Der aus drei Mitteilungen bestehende Teil I des Übersichtsberichtes des Verfassers zu den Problemen von Escott-Tarry und Prouhet-Tarry über mehrgradige Gleichungen ist [dasselbe Giorn. (5) **4 (84)** (1956), 189–247; MR **23** #A2371; Boll. Un. Mat. Ital. (3) **11** (1956), 569–577; MR **18**, 466; Giorn. Mat. Battaglini (5) **5 (85)** (1957), 80–94; MR **23** #A2372; ibid. (5) **5 (85)** (1957), 271–295; MR **23** #A3108] referiert worden. Der nun vorliegende Teil II umfaßt vier Kapitel. Kapitel 1: "Einführung. Möglichkeit der Lösung des Problems." Das Prouhet-Tarrysche Problem betrifft die Frage der Lösbarkeit einer Kette mehrgradiger Gleichungen (*) $x_{11}^k+\cdots+x_{1p}^k=x_{21}^k+\cdots+x_{2p}^k=\cdots=x_{m1}^k+\cdots+x_{mp}^k$ für $k=1,\cdots,n$ in ganzen rationalen Zahlen $x_{\mu\nu}$. Von Prouhet wurde 1851 die Lösung

$$1^k+6^k+8^k+12^k+14^k+16^k+20^k+22^k+27^k$$
$$= 2^k+4^k+9^k+10^k+15^k+17^k+21^k+23^k+25^k$$
$$= 3^k+5^k+7^k+11^k+13^k+18^k+19^k+24^k+26^k \quad (k = 1, 2)$$

angegeben, E. M. Wright [Proc. Edinburgh Math. Soc. (2) **8** (1949), 138–142; MR **12**, 11] bewies (1949), daß man die ersten m^{n+1} positiven ganzen Zahlen in m Gruppen von je m^n Zahlen einteilen kann, so daß sie eine Lösung von (*) für $p=m^n$ ergeben.

Bezeichnet man mit $P(n,m)$ den kleinsten Wert von p, für den eine nicht triviale Lösung von (*) existiert, d. h., wobei $x_{\alpha 1},\cdots,x_{\alpha p}$ nicht bloß eine Permutation von $x_{\beta 1},\cdots,x_{\beta p}$ ist, so sieht man leicht ein, daß $P(n,m)\geqq$

$P(n, 2) \geqq n+1$ ist, und es entsteht die Frage, ob ideale Lösungen existieren, d. h., ob es mehrgradige Ketten der Ordnung n mit $P(n, m)=n+1$ gibt. Spezielle Ergebnisse zu dieser allgemein nicht gelösten Frage werden zusammengestellt.

Kapitel 2: "Sätze über Ketten mehrgradiger Gleichungen." Es werden u. a. Verfahren angegeben, die z. T. bereits auf Frolov (1888) zurückgehen und z. T. Verallgemeinerungen der Betrachtungen von Escott (1910) und Tarry (1912) darstellen und mit denen aus Ketten der Ordnung n solche der Ordnung $n+1$ gewonnen werden können. Kapitel 3: "Methoden zur Aufstellung idealer Ketten der Ordnungen 2, 3 und 5." Kapitel 4: "Kuriose Anwendungen." (a) Verschiedene Einteilungen der ersten N natürlichen Zahlen—z. B., für $N=3^{r-1}q$ und $N=4^{r-1}q$, so daß mehrgradige Ketten entstehen (Verallgemeinerungen des oben angeführten Beispiels von Prouhet). (b) Zusammenhang der mehrgradigen Ketten mit der Frage nach Polynomen des Grades $2n+1$, die an $2n+1$ Stellen $2m$ ganzzahlige Werte $\pm N_1, \pm N_2, \cdots, \pm N_m$ annehmen. Auf den Zusammenhang der Frage nach der Reduzibilität von Polynomen der Form $f(x)=A(x-c_1)\cdots(x-c_n)+p$, wo p eine Primzahl ist und $c_1, \cdots, c_n$ ganze rationale Zahlen sind, mit dem Problem von Escott-Tarry hat (1935) H. L. Dorwart [Duke Math. J. **1** (1935), 70–73] hingewiesen, nachdem Polynome dieser Art ohne Eingehen auf den Zusammenhang mit dem Escott-Tarryschen Problem —was Verfasser in seinem Bericht nicht erwähnt—zuerst (1919) von G. Pólya [Jber. Deutsch. Math.-Verein. **28** (1919), Abt. 1, 31–40] und 1933 von A. Brauer [ibid. **43** (1933), Abt. 1, 124–129] untersucht worden waren.

W. Schulz (Zbl **87**, 39)

Citations: MR 12, 11e = D52-58; MR 18, 466d = D52-98; MR 23# A2371 = D52-114; MR 23# A2372 = D52-115; MR 23# A3108 = D52-116.

D52-123 (28# 3001)

Möller, Kurt

Über mehrgradige Gleichungen und Quadrate.

Math. Nachr. **27** (1963), 67–75.

Ayant rappelé la définition d'un système multigrade, système diophantien de la forme $\sum_{v=1}^{s} a_v^k = \sum_{v=s+1}^{2s} a_v^k$, k étant un entier naturel prenant successivement les valeurs $k_1, k_2, \cdots, k_r$, l'auteur définit un carré multigrade comme la matrice carrée $a_{\mu,v}$ ($\mu, v = 1, 2, \cdots, s, s+1, \cdots, 2s$) telle qu'on ait simultanément $\sum_{v=1}^{s} a_{\mu,v}^k = \sum_{v=s+1}^{2s} a_{\mu,v}^k$, et $\sum_{\mu=1}^{s} a_{\mu,v}^k = \sum_{\mu=s+1}^{2s} a_{\mu,v}^k$ ($k=k_1, k_2, \cdots, k_r$). À l'instar d'un système multigrade d'ordre r ($k=1, 2, \cdots, r$), et d'un système multigrade normal d'ordre r ($s=r+1$), il définit les carrés multigrades d'ordre r et les carrés multigrades normaux d'ordre r.

Il démontre ensuite le théorème: Si des fonctions linéaires $l_v(x, y)=\alpha_v x+\beta_v y$ ($v=1, 2, \cdots, s, s+1, \cdots, 2s$) vérifient la relation $\sum_{v=1}^{s} l_v^k(x, y) \equiv \sum_{v=s+1}^{2s} l_v^k(x, y)$, dans laquelle k est un entier naturel, et si l'on pose $a_{\mu,v}=\alpha_\mu\beta_v-\alpha_v\beta_\mu$, on a $\sum_{v=1}^{s} a_{\mu,v}^k = \sum_{v=s+1}^{2s} a_{\mu,v}^k$ et $\sum_{\mu=1}^{s} a_{\mu,v}^k = \sum_{\mu=s+1}^{2s} a_{\mu,v}^k$. L'auteur applique ce théorème pour obtenir, à partir de théorèmes sur les multigrades donnés par M. Frolov, G. Tarry, A. Gloden, des théorèmes analogues pour les carrés multigrades. En particulier, il démontre qu'il existe des carrés multigrades de tout ordre.

En construisant des systèmes multigrades normaux d'ordre 2, 3, 4, 5, dont les termes sont des fonctions linéaires, il en déduit respectivement des carrés multigrades normaux du même ordre. *A. Gloden* (Luxembourg)

D52-124 (29# 2217)

Moessner, Alfred; Sinha, T. N.

Some Diophantine problems.

Math. Student **31** (1963), 35–39 (1964).

Using some identities and relations the authors find some solutions to certain systems of Diophantine equations, e.g., $2(x^m+y^m+z^m)=u_1^m+\cdots+u_6^m$ ($m=1, 2, 3, 4, 5$).

D. J. Lewis (Ann Arbor, Mich.)

D52-125 (29# 3435)

Roberts, J. B.

Relations between the digits of numbers and equal sums of like powers.

Canad. J. Math. **16** (1964), 626–636.

The author derives a general identity involving the digits of integers in an arbitrary system of notation and deduces a few solutions of the Tarry-Escott problem [Lehmer, Scripta Math. **13** (1947), 37–41; MR **9**, 78]. For instance, we have Theorem 4: The integers from 0 to db^m-1, inclusive, whose base d expansions do not have a units digit equal to any one of a fixed, but arbitrary, set of $d-b$ of the integers $0, 1, \cdots, d-1$, may be split into b classes such that the sum of the tth powers of the elements in a given class is the same for all classes for all t from 0 to $m-1$, inclusive, and the splitting may be accomplished in $(b-1)!^{m-1}$ ways. Theorem 7: For each t, $0 \leqq t < m$, the sum of the tth powers of the integers from 0 to 3^m-1, inclusive, having no 1's and an odd number of 2's in their base 3 expansions equals the sum of the tth powers of those integers in the same range having no 1's and an even number of 2's. A numerical example for $m=3$ is

$$0^t+8^t+20^t+24^t = 2^t+6^t+18^t+26^t, \qquad t = 0, 1, 2.$$

J. W. Andrushkiw (S. Orange, N.J.)

Citations: MR 9, 78d = D52-21.

D52-126 (31# 117)

Wright, E. M.

Equal sums of like powers.

Canad. Math. Bull. **8** (1965), 193–202.

The author discusses the Tarry-Escott problem. Put $S_h=S_h(a)=a_1^h+\cdots+a_s^h$ and consider the system of k equations (*) $S_h(a)=S_h(b)$ ($1 \leqq h \leqq k$). When $s \leqq k$, all solutions are trivial, that is, the b's are a permutation of the a's. When $s>k$, there may be non-trivial solutions. Let $P(k, 2)$ denote the least s such that the equations (*) have a non-trivial solution. Then $P(k, 2) \geqq k+1$, a result due to Bastien. Somewhat more generally, if $P(k, j)$ denotes the least value of s such that the set of $k(j-1)$ equations (**) $S_{h1}=S_{h2}=\cdots=S_{hj}$ ($1 \leqq h \leqq k$), where $S_{hu}=a_{1u}^h+a_{2u}^h+\cdots+a_{su}^h$, has a non-trivial solution, then $P(k, j) \geqq P(k, 2)$. The author shows by an enumerative argument that $P(k, j) \leqq \frac{1}{2}k(k+1)+1$, and indeed, for odd k, that $P(k, j) \leqq \frac{1}{2}(k^2+3)$. He remarks that it seems probable that $P(k, j)=k+1$ for all j. Gloden [*Mehrgradige Gleichungen*, zweite Auflage, Noordhoff, Groningen, 1944; MR **8**, 441] proved this for $k=2$, 3, 5 and any j by exhibiting a solution of (**). The result $P(k, 2)=k+1$ is known for $k \leqq 9$. Prouhet [C. R. Acad. Sci. Paris **33** (1851), 225] announced a rule for finding a solution of (**) for any j and $s=j^k$. Lehmer [Scripta Math. **13** (1947), 37–41; MR **9**, 78] proved a generalized form of this result. A proof of Lehmer's result is given. Finally, the author makes some remarks related to the so-called "easier" Waring problem, namely, finding a solution of (*) such that $S_{k+1}(a) \neq S_{k+1}(b)$. *L. Carlitz* (Durham, N.C.)

Citations: MR 9, 78d = D52-21.

D52-127 (32# 5588)

Karacuba, A. A.

Congruence systems and equations of Waring type. (Russian)

Dokl. Akad. Nauk SSSR **165** (1965), 274–276.

The author studies the following system of $r \geqq 1$ equations and $n-r$ congruences: $x_1^\nu+\cdots+x_k^\nu=y_1^\nu+\cdots+y_k^\nu$ for $1\leqq\nu\leqq r$, $x_1^\nu+\cdots+x_k^\nu=y_1^\nu+\cdots+y_k^\nu \pmod{q_\nu}$ for $r<\nu\leqq n$. Let $N_{k,n}$ be the number of solutions such that $1\leqq x_i, y_i\leqq P$. It is shown that if $k\geqq 6rn\ln n$, if ε and ε_0 are given positive numbers, and if the product $Q=q_{r+1}\cdots q_n$ is prescribed, then there are at least $Q(1-Q^{-\varepsilon_0})$ choices of $(q_{r+1},\cdots,q_n)$ such that

$$N_{k,n} \leqq C_1(n)P^{2k-rn+r(r-1)/2+\varepsilon}Q^{\varepsilon_0}.$$

If, on the other hand, there is a prime $p<P/2$ such that $q_\nu=p^{\alpha_\nu}q_\nu'$, where $1\leqq\alpha_\nu\leqq\nu$, $p\nmid q_\nu'$, then

$$N_{k,n} \geqq C_2(n)P^{2k-rn+r(r-1)/2}p^{-2k+\alpha_{r+1}+\cdots+\alpha_n}.$$

Next it is shown that if $k\geqq c_1r^2$, $1\leqq r\leqq n/3$, or if $k\geqq c_2n^2\ln n$, $n/3<r\leqq n$, then the number $I_{k,n}$ of solutions of the equation $x_1^n+\cdots+x_k^n=y_1^n+\cdots+y_k^n$, $1\leqq x_i, y_i\leqq P$, satisfies $I_{k,n}\leqq C_3(n)P^{2k-r}$. Finally, the inequality $I_{k,n}\leqq C_4(n)I_{k,m}$ is proved under the assumption that $k=c_3m^2\ln m$, $2\leqq m\leqq n$.

{This article has appeared in English translation [Soviet Math. Dokl. **6** (1965), 1439–1441].}

B. Gordon (Los Angeles, Calif.)

D52-128 (32# 5591)

Roberts, J. B.

Splitting consecutive integers into classes with equal power sums.

Amer. Math. Monthly **71** (1964), 25–37.

In an earlier paper [Proc. Amer. Math. Soc. **11** (1960), 723–730; MR **23** #A100] the author proved that if q is a factorization of n whose factors have least common multiple L_q, then the first n nonnegative integers can be split into L_q classes with equal tth power sums for all t satisfying $0\leqq t<T$, where $T=q^*-\max_{0<s<L_q}\nu_s$. Here q^* is the number of factors in q, and ν_s is the number of them that divide s. In this paper he calls T the t-range of the factorization q, and proves that the maximum value of T for all factorizations q is the smallest exponent occurring in the canonical prime factorization of n. He also gives an algorithm which determines, for a given q, a splitting with given t-range. The problem of determining the number of such splittings is still open.

T. M. Apostol (Pasadena, Calif.)

Citations: MR 23# A100 = D52-113.

D52-129 (33# 1281)

Barrodale, Ian

A note on equal sums of like powers.

Math. Comp. **20** (1966), 318–322.

The author gives details of an extension of the search by Z. A. Melzak [Canad. Math. Bull. **4** (1961), 233–237; MR **24** #A1880] for the minimum Tarry-Escott set with less than 30 elements to as many as 85 elements.

D. H. Lehmer (Berkeley, Calif.)

Citations: MR 24# A1880 = D52-117.

D52-130 (33# 1296)

Karacuba, A. A.

Theorems on the mean and complete trigonometric sums. (Russian)

Izv. Akad. Nauk SSSR Ser. Mat. **30** (1966), 183–206.

Tarry's problem is that of finding non-trivial solutions of the system of equations

$$\begin{aligned} x_1+\cdots+x_k &= y_1+\cdots+y_k,\\ x_1^2+\cdots+x_k^2 &= y_1^2+\cdots+y_k^2,\\ &\cdot\\ &\cdot\\ &\cdot\\ x_1^n+\cdots+x_k^n &= y_1^n+\cdots+y_k^n, \end{aligned}$$

with, say, $1\leqq x_i, y_i\leqq P$ $(1\leqq i\leqq k)$. It is conceivable that such solutions exist even when $k=n+1$ for P sufficiently large, and for any fixed n. The author uses the deep results of I. M. Vinogradov [*Selected Works* (Russian), Izdat. Akad. Nauk SSSR, Moscow, 1952; MR **14**, 610; Proc. Third All-Union Math. Congress, Vol. III (Russian), pp. 3–13, Izdat. Akad. Nauk SSSR, Moscow, 1958] on estimates for exponential sums, and the result of A. Weil that if $(a_1,\cdots,a_n,p)=1$ then

$$\left|\sum_{x=1}^{p}\exp\left(\frac{2\pi i}{p}(a_1x+\cdots+a_nx^n)\right)\right| \leqq n\sqrt{p}$$

(this is the author's Lemma 2; actually $n\sqrt{p}$ can be replaced by $(n-1)\sqrt{p}$; p is a prime) to get estimates for the number of solutions in integers x_i, y_i of the above system of equations as a function of P. The dominant term in this estimate is a constant times the "singular series" (of Hardy-Littlewood) multiplied by a certain power of P. If one sets (for example) $r=n-1$ in his results (which are too long to quote here), one gets an asymptotic formula for the number of solutions when k is greater than (essentially) a constant times n^2. The proofs use, besides the methods of Hardy-Littlewood and I. M. Vinogradov, lemmas due to van der Corput [Math. Ann. **84** (1921), 53–79] and L. K. Hua [J. Chinese Math. **2** (1940), 301–312; MR **2**, 347; Acta Sci. Sinica **1** (1952), 1–76; MR **16**, 337].

S. Chowla (University Park, Pa.)

Citations: MR 2, 347h = L05-2; MR 14, 610i = Z25-9; MR 16, 337c = D52-90.

D52-131 (33# 5558)

Möller, Kurt

Einige mehrgradige Gleichungen. (Serbo-Croatian summary)

Glasnik Mat.-Fiz. Astronom. Ser. II Društvo Mat. Fiz. Hrvatske **20** (1965), 39–42.

Gloden [*Liste des formes linéaires des nombres dont le carré se termine dans le système décimal par une tranche donnée de 4 chiffres*, A. Gloden, Luxembourg, 1947; MR **8**, 441] noted that the two sets 1, 4, 6, 12, 14, 17 and 2, 2, 9, 9, 16, 16 have equal sums of kth powers for $k=0(1)5$, while the sets 1, 4, 6, 12, 14, 17, 23, 23 and 2, 2, 8, 11, 13, 19, 21, 24 have equal sums of kth powers for $k=0(1)6$. The author gives a one-parameter family of such instances.

D. H. Lehmer (Berkeley, Calif.)

D52-132 (35# 2826)

Sinha, T. N.

A diophantine problem.

Math. Student **34** (1966), 31–32.

The author gives a parametric solution (involving three parameters) of the Diophantine system $A^r, A^r, A^r, B_1, B_2, B_3={}^nC_1, C_2, C_3, D^r, D^r, D^r$ $(n=1,2,3,4)$, where the separation of two sets by the symbol $=^n$ denotes that they have the same sum of the nth powers, and r is an arbitrary integer.

{See also #2827 below.} *T. Hayashida* (Yokohama)

D52-133 (35# 2827)

Kaprekar, D. R.; Moessner, Alfred

On a new type of Diophantine identity.

Math. Student **34** (1966), 33–34.

With the notation of the article reviewed above [#2826], the authors give a parametric solution of the Diophantine system: $x, y, z={}^nu, v, w$ $(n=2,4)$. {In fact, this gives one form of the general solution of the system with the condition $x+y+z=u+v+w=0$ [cf. Dickson, *History of the theory of numbers*, Vol. II, Chapter XXIV, Carnegie Inst., Washington, D.C., 1920; reprint, Chelsea, New York, 1952].} Moreover, they make a short remark on the Diophantine system $u_1, u_2, \cdots, u_{n+1} \stackrel{k}{=} v_1, v_2, \cdots, v_{n+1}$ ($k = 1, 2, \cdots, n$).

{See also #2828 below.} *T. Hayashida* (Yokohama)

D52-134 (35# 2828)

Moessner, Alfred

Remarks on a note by D. R. Kaprekar and R. V. Iyer.

Math. Student **34** (1966), 35–36.

A note on the Diophantine system $A_1, A_2, A_3, A_4 \stackrel{n}{=} B_1, B_2, B_3, B_4$ ($n=1, 2$). (For the notation, see #2826 above.)

{The original note by Kaprekar and Iyer appeared in Scripta Math. **16** (1950), 160. An additional note by them also appears on page 36 immediately following the note under review.} *T. Hayashida* (Yokohama)

D52-135 (36# 1389)

Sinha, T. N.

Some systems of diophantine equations of the Tarry-Escott type.

J. Indian Math. Soc. (*N.S.*) **30** (1966), 15–26 (1967).

The Tarry-Escott problem is that of finding solutions in integers of the system of equations $\sum_{i=1}^{s} a_i^x = \sum_{i=1}^{s} b_i^x$, for $x = 1, 2, \cdots, k$. This system is denoted by the notation (1) $a_1, a_2, \cdots, a_s \stackrel{x}{=} b_1, b_2, \cdots, b_s$ ($x = 1, 2, \cdots, k$).

In the present paper the author first finds lower bounds of the minimum s such that (1) has nontrivial solutions for odd powers $x = 1, 3, \cdots, k_0$ (k_0 odd) and for even powers $x = 2, 4, \cdots, k_0$ (k_0 even), respectively. He then obtains parametric solutions of certain types of equations similar to (1).

Although a parametric solution of the system

$$(2) \qquad A_1, A_2, A_3, A_4, A_5 \stackrel{x}{=} B_1, B_2, B_3, B_4, B_5 \qquad (x = 2, 4, 6, 8)$$

has not as yet been found, the author gives a new method of handling (2) which yields the only known numerical solution of Letac, and shows that (2) has an infinity of solutions. Some numerical examples of the author's results are also given. *R. Finkelstein* (Tempe, Ariz.)

D52-136 (37# 1311)

Gupta, Hansraj

A system of equations having no nontrivial solutions.

J. Res. Nat. Bur. Standards Sect. B **71B** (1967), 181–182.

Author's summary: "The object of this note is to prove the theorem: The system of equations $a_1^r + a_2^r + \cdots + a_{n-1}^r = b_1^r + b_2^r + \cdots + b_{n-1}^r$, $r = 2, 3, \cdots, n$, has no nontrivial solutions in positive integers."

D52-137 (38# 1419)

Negoescu, N. C.

On a class of numerical equalities. (Romanian. Russian and French summaries)

An. Univ. Timișoara Ser. Ști. Mat.-Fiz. No. 5 (1967), 135–139.

The author proves a well-known result on the effect of a finite-difference operator on a polynomial and deduces some arithmetical results, e.g., that $1^m - 2^m - 3^m + 4^m - 5^m + 6^m + 7^m - 8^m = 0$, $m = 0, 1, 2$.

D52-138 (38# 2109)

Katzourakes, Iason

Equal sums of like powers of real integers and Gaussian integers. (Greek. English summary)

With comment by Konstantinos Papaïoannes.

Prakt. Akad. Athēnōn **40** (1965), 242–247 (1966).

The author considers the Diophantine system $(x+iy)^n + (x-iy)^n + z^n = (x_1+iy_1)^n + (x_1-iy_1)^n + z_1^n$ for $n=1$ and $n=3$. He finds two families of solutions, each depending on two integer parameters p and q. One of them is given by $x = 4p^2+q^2$, $x_1 = 8p^2+4pq+q^2$, $y = 2p^2+3pq+q^2$, $y_1 = pq+q^2$, $z = 10p^2+6pq+q^2$, $z_1 = 2p^2-2pq+q^2$. The second family has different formulas for y and y_1. Applications are given to other Diophantine systems. His method yields the following theorem: If N is a positive integer $\neq 1$, 2 or 4, then $2N$ can be expressed as the sum of two pairs of conjugate Gaussian integers, the sum of whose squares is equal to $2N^2$, and the sum of whose cubes is equal to $2N^3$. *T. M. Apostol* (Pasadena, Calif.)

D52-139 (40# 4236)

Eda, Yosikazu; Kitayama, Toshiko

Note on the generalized Prouhet-Tarry problem in an algebraic number field.

Sci. Rep. Kanazawa Univ. **14** (1969), 21–28.

Let k, s denote natural numbers. Consider the solutions in rational integers x_i, y_i, $i = 0, \cdots, s$, of the system of equations (*) $x_1^h + \cdots + x_s^h = y_1^h + \cdots + y_s^h$, $1 \leq h \leq k$. A solution of (*) is called a trivial one if the y_i are a permutation of the x_i. If $s \leq k$, there are only trivial solutions. One is interested in the least natural number $s_0(k) > k$ for which (*) is nontrivially soluble. This problem and related problems (e.g., in (*) integral coefficients $a_{ij} > 1$ are allowed) are generalized to arbitrary algebraic number fields K of finite degree n over the field of rationals. The theorems are too long to be stated here.

W. G. H. Schaal (Marburg)

D52-140 (41# 171)

Eda, Yoshikazu

On the mean-value theorem in an algebraic number field.

Japan. J. Math. **36** (1967), 5–21.

The author proves an analogue to I. M. Vinogradov's mean-value theorem [Trudy Mat. Inst. Steklov. **23** (1948); MR **10**, 599] where the system of equations is considered in a certain algebraic number field. The proof is executed by means of the p-adic method, as in the work of the reviewer and N. M. Korobov [Dokl. Akad. Nauk SSSR **149** (1963), 245–248; MR **26** #4962]. As in the work just mentioned, one of the basic statements in the proof of the mean-value theorem is analogous to the lemma of Ju. V. Linnik [ibid. **34** (1942), 184–186, Lemma 7; MR **4**, 211]. Basic theorem: Let k be an algebraic number field of degree n, where, as always, $n = n_1 + 2n_2$. By $\gamma^{(i)}$ ($1 \leq i \leq n$) we denote the coordinates $\gamma \in k$.

Furthermore, $\|\gamma\| = \max_{1 \leq i \leq n} |\gamma^{(i)}|$, and if $\|\gamma\| \leq T$, $\gamma^{(l)} \geq 0$ at $1 \leq l \leq n$, then we write $0 \prec \gamma \prec T$. Furthermore, let A be the set of all integers k, $Q^n = P$ and N_s is the number of solutions of the following system of equations:

$$\begin{cases} \lambda_1 + \lambda_2 + \cdots + \lambda_s = \mu_1 + \mu_2 + \cdots + \mu_s \\ \lambda_1^2 + \lambda_2^2 + \cdots + \lambda_s^2 = \mu_1^2 + \mu_2^2 + \cdots + \mu_s^2 \\ \cdot \quad \cdot \quad \cdot \quad \cdot \quad \cdot \quad \cdot \quad \cdot \quad \cdot \quad \cdot \quad \cdot \\ \lambda_1^k + \lambda_2^k + \cdots + \lambda_s^k = \mu_1^k + \mu_2^k + \cdots + \mu_s^k, \end{cases}$$

where $0 \prec \lambda_j$, $\mu_j \prec Q$, $\lambda_j, \mu_j \in A$.

The mean value theorem: Let $0 < \theta \leq 1$ and $k \geq 2$, k be an integer, R be a "sufficiently large" number, where $R > \max(k, (2^n\theta^{-1})^{1/k})$, $Q = Q_0$ is a positive number such that $(2R)^{k(1+1/(k-1))^{\tau-1}} < Q = Q_0$ with integral $\tau \geq 1$. Let s be an integer, $s \geq \frac{1}{2}k(k+1) + \tau - 1$. Then the following estimate holds: $N_s \leq CP^{2s-(1/2)k(k+1)+\delta}$, where

$$\delta = \tfrac{1}{2}k(k+1)(1-1/k)^\tau,$$

$$C = e^{(k^2+2s+((\tau-1)/k)s-(1/4)(\tau-1)(k+1))\tau n} \times (1+2\theta)^{2s\tau+(1/k)\tau(\tau-1)s-(1/4)\tau(\tau-1)(k+1)} 8^{2k\tau}.$$

A. Karacuba (RŽMat **1969** #5 A163)

Citations: MR 4, 211g = L15-7; MR 10, 599a = L02-2; MR 26# 4962 = D52-120.

D52-141 **(41# 1646)**

Brudno, Simcha

Some new results on equal sums of like powers.

Math. Comp. **23** (1969), 877–880.

Author's summary: "The Diophantine equations $\sum_{i=1}^{M} x_i^n = \sum_{i=1}^{M} y_i^n$ is examined for $n=3$, 4 and 6 and $M=[(n+1)/2]$. A method for generating parametric solutions for $n=4$ is derived and several new numerical examples for $n=4$, 6 are given. The method also applies for all other values of M and possibly for values of n greater than 6, too." *J. D. Swift* (Los Angeles, Calif.)

D52-142 **(42# 1765)**

Sinha, T. N.

A relation between the coefficients and roots of two equations and its application to diophantine problems.

J. Res. Nat. Bur. Standards Sect. B **74B** (1970), 31–36.

Let $\{a_1, a_2, \cdots, a_n\}$ and $\{b_1, b_2, \cdots, b_n\}$ be two sets of numbers and let p_k $[q_k]$ be the kth elementary symmetric function of the a's [b's]. Let $p_0 = q_0 = 1$ and $p_k = q_k = 0$ when $k>n$. Set $A_r = \sum_{i=1}^{n} a_i^r$, $B_r = \sum_{i=1}^{n} b_i^r$ and let $A_r - B_r = h_r$. Inverting Newton's formulas, the author obtains a determinantal formula for p_r in terms of $A_1, A_2, \cdots, A_r$. Let H_r denote the number obtained by replacing A_j by h_j $(1 \leqq j \leqq r)$ in this formula. Finally, let $c_r = r!p_r$ and $d_r = r!q_r$. An inductive proof is given of the equation (*) $c_r = \sum_{i=1}^{r} \binom{r}{i} H_i d_{r-i}$. (*) is then used to show that the system of equations $A_r = B_r$ $(r=1, 2, \cdots, j-1, j+1, \cdots, n+1)$ has no non-trivial solutions in positive integers $a_1, a_2, \cdots, a_r, b_1, b_2, \cdots, b_r$. (The proof actually shows that the system has no non-trivial positive real solution.) Next the system $a_1^s + a_2^s = b_1^s + b_2^s$, $a_1^t + a_2^t = b_1^t + b_2^t$, $1 \leqq s < t \leqq 4$, is discussed, and it is shown, using (*), that it has no non-trivial integer solutions. {It is not clear exactly what the author means by "non-trivial" here. When s and t are odd, there are, besides the "trivial" solutions in which the b's are a permutation of the a's, also the "trivial" solutions in which $a_2 = -a_1$, $b_2 = -b_1$. Moreover, it seems to the reviewer that the restriction $1 \leqq s < t \leqq 4$ could be removed and the general case treated by a geometric argument involving a consideration of the intersections of the curves $x+y=\alpha$, $x^{t/s} + y^{t/s} = \beta$; α, β real.} *J. B. Kelly* (Tempe, Ariz.)

D52-143 **(42# 4515)**

Mehrotra, S. N.

On sums of powers.

Math. Student **35** (1967), 73–77 (1969).

Let $N(k)$ denote the least value of n for which a non-trivial solution of the system of equations $\sum_{i=1}^{n} a_i^x = \sum_{i=1}^{n} b_i^x$ $(x=1, 2, \cdots, k)$ exists. In this note the author improves some of the known results about upper bounds for the values of $N(k)$. In particular, it is proved that $N(a) \leqq b$, where $b=28$, 72, 96, 106, 120, 140, 148, 164, 164, 192 for $a=13$, 21, 23, 24, 25, 26, 27, 28, 29, 30, respectively. Further, let $\beta(k)$ denote the least value of n for which a solution of the equation $\sum_{i=1}^{m} a_i^k = \sum_{i=1}^{n} b_i^k$ exists with $m<n$ and $(a_1, \cdots, a_m, b_1, \cdots, b_n) = 1$ and let $\nu(k)$ denote the value of n for which the last equation has infinitely many solutions. It is proved that $\beta(a) \leqq b$, where $b=23$, 27, 42, 50, 58, 27, 94, 84, 98 for $a=15$, 16, 21, 22, 23, 25, 26, 27, respectively. The author proves also that $\nu(k+2) \leqq N(k)+1$. *A. Rotkiewicz* (Warsaw)

D52-144 **(42# 4516)**

Mehrotra, S. N.

On sums of powers.

Math. Student **37** (1969), 204–205.

Using the notation of his paper reviewed above [#4515], the author proves the following results: $N(16) \leqq 34$, $N(17) \leqq 42$, $\beta(15) \leqq 18$, $\beta(16) \leqq 25$, $\nu(18) \leqq 35$, $\nu(19) \leqq 43$. This is an improvement of the results of the author and H. Gupta. *A. Rotkiewicz* (Warsaw)

D52-145 **(43# 4798)**

Klamkin, M. S.;

Newman, D. J. [**Newman, Donald J.**]

Uniqueness theorems for power equations.

Elem. Math. **25** (1970), 130–134.

The authors discuss several problems concerning systems of equations of the form $\sum_{i=1}^{n} x_i^k = a_k$, where k runs through a sequence of consecutive integers or, alternatively, through a sequence of consecutive odd integers. For example, if $\sum_{i=1}^{n} x_i^k = 0$ $(k=1, 2, \cdots, n-2; n \geqq 4)$, then $\sum_{i=1}^{n} x_i^p = 0$, where $p = rn+s$ and $1 \leqq r \leqq n-3$, $1 \leqq s \leqq n-r-2$. *W. Ledermann* (Brighton)

D56 HIGHER DEGREE VARIETIES: MULTIPLICATIVE EQUATIONS AND NORM FORMS

See also Sections D40, E24.

See also reviews D20-1, D24-56, D36-4, D36-5, D40-47, D48-1, D48-40, D48-57, G35-4, J36-20, L25-26, R08-22, R08-35, R16-54, R52-18.

D56-1 **(1, 39e)**

Gloden, A. Sur le système diophantien $x+y+z=u+v+w$, $xyz=uvw$. Bol. Mat. **12**, 205–209 (1939).

D56-2 **(1, 291h)**

Bell, E. T. Compound multiplicative Diophantine systems. Proc. Nat. Acad. Sci. U. S. A. **26**, 462–466 (1940).

The author considers the system of simultaneous Diophantine equations $\sum_{p=1}^{t} a_p(x, a, n)_p = 0$, $\sum_{q=1}^{j} b_q(y, b, m)_q = 0$, $\cdots$, $\sum_{r=1}^{k} c_r(z, c, t)_r = 0$, where (x, a, n) denotes the product $x_{i_1}^{a_{i_1}} \cdots x_{in_i}^{a_{in_i}}$, $a, b, \cdots, c$ are constant integers and the $x, y, \cdots, z$ are the unknowns. The definition of this compound multiplicative system is given in terms of the simple multiplicative system already studied by the author [Amer. J. Math. **55**, 50–66 (1933)]. It is proved that the problem of finding the complete solution of the above compound system is reduced to that of a simple system and that the solution of the compound system may be written as polynomials with rational integral coefficients in a certain minimum number of parameters. *I. A. Barnett.*

D56-3 **(2, 346e)**

Aucoin, A. A. Solution of a quartic Diophantine equation. Bol. Mat. **14**, 36–39 (1941).

The author considers the quartic Diophantine equation $\Pi_{i=1}^{4} \sum_{j=1}^{3} a_{ij} x_j = f(y_1, y_2, \cdots, y_a)$, where $f(y)$ is a given polynomial with integral coefficients of degree $n \not\equiv 0 \pmod 4$. He shows that all integral solutions, apart from those satisfying certain linear relations, are given (in a sense discussed in the paper) by three sets of formulas according as $n-1$, $n-2$, $n-3$ is divisible by 4, respectively. The solutions depend in a complicated manner upon the determinant and cofactors of the integral matrix $\|a_{ij}\|$ and upon $a+3$ integral parameters. *I. A. Barnett* (Cincinnati, Ohio).

Referred to in D56-4.

D56-4 **(13, 626a)**

Benner, Charles P. The solution of a Diophantine equation. Proc. Amer. Math. Soc. **3**, 41–43 (1952).

An immediate generalisation of a result of A. A. Aucoin

[Bol. Mat. **14**, 36–39 (1941); these Rev. **2**, 346].
J. W. S. Cassels (Cambridge, England).
Citations: MR 2, 346e = D56-3.

D56-5 (3, 65d)

Bell, E. T. Transformed multiplicative diophantine equations. Trav. Inst. Math. Tbilissi [Trudy Tbiliss. Mat. Inst.] **8**, 1–21 (1940). (English. Russian summary)

Let $P_i(x_1, x_2, \cdots, x_n)$ $(i=1, \cdots, m)$ be m polynomials with rational integral coefficients in the n indeterminates $x_1, x_2, \cdots, x_n$. Suppose, further, that the system (1) $P=0$ has the known complete solution (2) $x_j=Q_{ij}(t_1, t_2, \cdots, t_r)$ $(j=1, \cdots, n)$, where $t_1, t_2, \cdots, t_r$ are integral parameters. Let (3) $P(x_1, x_2, \cdots, x_n)=0$ be a given diophantine equation which can be written in the form (4) $P_1 \cdot P_2 \cdots P_m=0$. Then the complete solution of (4) is called the disjunction of the complete solutions of (1) and is the set of m independent solutions (2) for $i=1, 2, \cdots, m$. If the equation (3) can be written in the form $P_1^{s_1}+P_2^{s_2}+\cdots+P_m^{s_m}=0$ ($s_i>0$ and even), then the complete solution of (3) is the $[s_1, s_2, \cdots, s_m]$ conjunction of the complete solutions (2) and is the complete solution of the system (1) considered as a simultaneous system in $x_1, x_2, \cdots, x_n$. The author shows in this paper that the solutions of many of the classical diophantine equations and various new equations are conjunctions and disjunctions of linear or non-linear transforms of equations or systems of equations involving the indeterminates in a multiplicative form. The latter may be solved by the method of reciprocal arrays considered by the author in a previous paper [Amer. J. Math. **55**, 50–66 (1933)]. *I. A. Barnett.*

D56-6 (4, 34a)

Bell, E. T. Parametric solutions of certain Diophantine equations. Duke Math. J. **9**, 431–435 (1942).

One of the Diophantine equations considered by the author is $a_1x_1 \cdots x_{i_1}+a_2y_1 \cdots y_{i_2}+\cdots+a_nz_1 \cdots z_{i_n}$ in the $i_1+i_2+\cdots+i_n$ variables. The solution of this is reduced to that of $\sum_{i=1}^n x_iy_i=0$ (whose complete parametric solution is known) and an associated multiplicative system. The other equation is $Q(x_1, \cdots, x_n)=\sum_{i=1}^n a_ix_iy_i$, where Q is the general homogeneous quadratic form in n variables with integral coefficients. To solve this last equation the author first finds the complete integral solution with all the $a_i=1$. It is also pointed out how a parametric solution of $Q(x_1, \cdots, x_{n-1})=uv$ may be obtained. [The special case $n=3$ has already been considered by Dickson and Latimer.]
I. A. Barnett (Cincinnati, Ohio).

D56-7 (6, 57a)

Bell, E. T. A method in rational diophantine analysis. Proc. Nat. Acad. Sci. U. S. A. **30**, 355–359 (1944).

By means of rational substitutions involving auxiliary Diophantine equations, the author is able to reduce rational Diophantine systems to those of multiplicative type. In this way he finds all or only some of the solutions of the original system according as the substitutions are or are not rationally reversible. The method is illustrated by means of two examples. The first is the classical ternary cubic leading to Ryley's theorem on the decomposition of every rational number as the sum of three rational cubes, while, in the second, the auxiliary equation reduces the given equation to one of multiplicative type by rendering the equation algebraically reducible. *I. A. Barnett.*

D56-8 (6, 256c)

Bell, E. T. Separable Diophantine equations. Trans. Amer. Math. Soc. **57**, 86–101 (1945).

An equation of the type

$$(1) \qquad \sum_{i=1}^{n} m_iX_i=0, \qquad n>2; \prod m_i\neq 0,$$

where the m_i are integral constants and the X_i are independent elementary monomials, is called an extended multiplicative equation. (An elementary monomial is an expression of the form $x_1^{a_1} \cdots x_n^{a_n}$, a_i positive integers, $n>1$, in which at least one exponent a_i is equal to unity.) By considering first the case in which the X_i are of the form $x_{i1}x_{i2} \cdots x_{is_i}$, where the x_{ij} are independent variables, the author shows that the solution of the Diophantine equation (1) is equivalent to that of a finite system of simple linear Diophantine equations. The solution of the latter is known. A system is said to be separable if its solution is equivalent to one or more of the following: (a) the solution of independent extended equations, (b) the solution of simple systems, (c) the solution of systems of linear Diophantine equations, the total number of systems in (a), (b), (c) being finite. From the results concerning equation (1) it follows that separable equations are solvable. The equation

$$(2) \qquad \sum_{i=1}^{n} a_ix_i^2=\sum_{i=1}^{s} b_iu_iv_i,$$

where the a_i and b_i are integral constants and the x_i, u_i, v_i are independent variables, is a separable equation. The same is true when the left member of (2) is replaced by a general quadratic form. Many well-known problems which have been considered in the literature are solved as special cases of these results. [The following typographical errors were noted. Page 90, line 8, replace "second" by "first"; in formulas (7.6) and (7.101), the upper limits of the first and second summations should be $i-1$ and $n-i$, respectively; formula (8.3) should read $\alpha\alpha_i=m_iX'_{i1}X_{i2} \cdots X_{it_i}$.]
I. A. Barnett (Cincinnati, Ohio).
Referred to in D56-10, D56-13.

D56-9 (6, 256d)

Rosenthall, E. On some special Diophantine equations. Bull. Amer. Math. Soc. **50**, 753–758 (1944).

Let R be an algebraic number field. Then all solutions of $\xi\eta=\zeta\vartheta$ in integers of R are given by $\xi=\kappa\lambda/e$, $\eta=\mu\nu/e$, $\zeta=\kappa\nu/e$, $\vartheta=\lambda\mu/e$, where κ, λ, μ, ν are arbitrary integers of R and e takes only the finite set of rational integral values each equal to the norm of a representative ideal from each class. This result is proved by the author and used for the proof of the following theorem. Let R be a quadratic number field, ξ an integer of R, and $\bar{\xi}$ the conjugate of ξ. Then all the solutions of $\xi\bar{\xi}=z^{2n+1}$ are given by

$$f^{2n+1}\xi=\varphi_1^{2n+1}\varphi_2^{2n}\bar{\varphi}_2\cdots\varphi_{n+1}^{n+1}\bar{\varphi}_{n+1}^{n},$$

$$f^2z=\varphi_1\bar{\varphi}_1\varphi_2\bar{\varphi}_2\cdots\varphi_{n+1}\bar{\varphi}_{n+1},$$

where $f=e_1^{n+1}e_2^n \cdots e_n^2$, and each of $e_1, e_2, \cdots, e_n$ is equal to the norm of a representative ideal from each class.
A. Brauer (Chapel Hill, N. C.).

D56-10 (8, 369a)

Bell, E. T. Mahavira's Diophantine system. Bull. Calcutta Math. Soc. **38**, 121–122 (1946).

The complete integer solution is given for a system noted by B. Datta in his account of Mahavira's work in Diophantine analysis [Bull. Calcutta Math. Soc. **20**, 267–294 (1930), in particular, pp. 283–288]. This system, consisting of the equations $m(x+y)=n(u+v)$, $pxy=quv$, where m, n, p, q are any constant integers and x, y, u, v are the unknowns, is separable [E. T. Bell, Trans. Amer. Math. Soc. **57**, 86–101 (1945); these Rev. **6**, 256]. The regular and singular solutions which make up the complete integer solution fall into sets according to the divisors of m, n, p, q.
W. H. Gage (Vancouver, B. C.).
Citations: MR 6, 256c = D56-8.

D56-11 (8, 442c)

Bell, E. T. Diophantine equations suggested by elementary geometry. Ann. of Math. (2) **48**, 43–50 (1947).

The problem of finding complete solutions (i.e., solutions with exactly the right number of parameters) of even very simple looking Diophantine equations is a delicate task. The present paper gives such solutions for several types of equations which arise in elementary geometry. For example, the complete solution of $xyzw=t^2$, which is connected with the problem of finding triangles with integral sides and areas, contains ten rational integral parameters:

$$x=1\cdot a_{11}^2\cdot a_{12}a_{13}a_{14},\quad y=a_{12}\cdot a_{22}^2\cdot a_{23}a_{24},\quad z=a_{13}a_{23}\cdot a_{33}^2\cdot a_{34},$$
$$w=a_{14}a_{24}a_{34}\cdot a_{44}^2,\quad t=a_{11}a_{12}a_{13}a_{14}a_{22}a_{23}a_{24}a_{33}a_{34}a_{44}.$$

The general solution of $x_1x_2\cdots x_n=t^2$ is built similarly and contains $n(n+1)/2$ parameters.

As another example, the equation $\sum z_j^2=0$, $j=1,\cdots,n$, $z_j=x_j+iy_j$, x, y rational integers, is equivalent to the Diophantine system $\sum x_j^2=\sum y_j^2$, $\sum x_jy_j=0$, $j=1,\cdots,n$. For $n=4$ the general solution contains eight rational integral parameters: $2x_1=a_1b_1-a_2b_2+a_3b_3-a_4b_4$. For x_2, x_3, x_4, y_1, y_2, y_3, y_4 the a's occur in the same order as in x_1 and the indices of the b's and the signs of the summands of $2x_1, 2x_2, \cdots, 2y_4$ are, respectively, as follows: $(1,-2,3,-4)$, $(2,1,-4,-3)$, $(3,-4,-1,2)$, $(4,3,2,1)$, $(2,1,4,3)$, $(-1,2,3,-4)$, $(4,3,-2,-1)$, $(-3,4,-1,2)$. Misprints noticed: (2.1), in product read $r=1$ instead of $r=i$; (2.4), in x_4 read a_{21}^2 instead of a_{11}^2. *A. J. Kempner.*

Referred to in D56-20.

D56-12 (10, 353h)

Bell, E. T. The basic lemma in multiplicative Diophantine analysis. Math. Gaz. **32**, 182–183 (1948).

The general solution of the Diophantine equation $xy=zw$ is $x=af$, $y=bk$, $z=ak$, $w=bf$, where f, k may be taken relatively prime. It is proved that this result holds in any integral domain all of whose ideals are principal.

I. Niven (Eugene, Ore.).

D56-13 (10, 592a)

Bell, E. T. Derived Diophantine systems. Revista Ci., Lima **50**, 69–84 (1948).

Let $P(X)$, $X=(X_1,\cdots,X_m)$ denote a system (one or more) of Diophantine equations whose complete solution is known explicitly, say $X=X'$. Let $D(x)$, $x=(x_1,\cdots,x_n)$ be a second Diophantine system such that when $x=x'$ ranges over the complete solution of $D(x)$, $X_i=f_i(x)$ ranges over the complete solution of $P(X)$. Then the complete solution of $D(x)$ is the solution of $f_i(x)=X_i'$; if $P(X)$ has no solutions, neither has $D(x)$. Several examples are given showing how to derive $D(x)$ from a system $P(X)$ which is separable in a sense defined in a previous paper [Trans. Amer. Math. Soc. **57**, 86–101 (1945); these Rev. **6**, 256]. For example, if $P(X)$ is $X^3+Y^3=AZ^3$, then $D(x)$ can be taken as $yz^2(4bw^3-a^2x^6y^3)=3u^2$, $ab=A$, where the $X_i=f_i(x)$ are $X=\frac{1}{2}(ax^3y^2z+u)$, $Y=\frac{1}{2}(ax^3y^2z-u)$, $Z=xyzw$. In this case $D(x)$ was obtained from $P(X)$ by treating the latter as a multiplicative equation $RS=AZ^3$, whose complete solution is $R=ax^3y^2z$, $S=byz^2w^3$, $A=ab$, $Z=xyzw$. The rest follows by identifying R and $X+Y$, and writing u for $X-Y$. By thus taking known equations for $P(X)$ the author solves the derived equations $D(x)$. [Reviewer's remark: (6.1) and (6.2) are incorrect, because their solutions corresponding to certain trivial solutions of their primitive were omitted; e.g., the equation in (6.2) has the solution $c=3$, all other symbols equal to one.] *I. Niven* (Eugene, Ore.).

Citations: MR 6, 256c = D56-8.

D56-14 (13, 321k)

Aucoin, A. A. Systems of Diophantine equations. Proc. Amer. Math. Soc. **2**, 760–765 (1951).

Three theorems on diophantine equations of which the most impressive is that if $L_{ij}(x)$ $(i, j=1,\cdots,n)$ are n^2 homogeneous linear forms in q variables $(x)=(x_1,\cdots,x_q)$ with integer coefficients and if $f_i(y)$ are homogeneous polynomials of degree m prime to n then in some cases a general solution of (*) $\prod_j L_{ij}(x)=f_i(y)$ can be given. The author assumes (tacitly) that the n^2-n forms L_{ij} $(j\neq n)$ are linearly dependent on at most $q-n$ of them. If these and the (y) are taken as parameters, then (*) become n linear equations in (x). Thus we have $(q-n)+n=q$ linear equations in (x); which can be solved, the solution being rational if the parameters are. Finally, integer solutions are obtained by homogeneity. *J. W. S. Cassels* (Cambridge, England).

D56-15 (14, 247c)

Morgantini, E. Sulla ricerca delle soluzioni intere di un tipo notevole di equazioni diofantee. Rend. Sem. Mat. Univ. Padova **21**, 44–57 (1952).

The author discusses a technique for obtaining classes of solutions in integers of Diophantine equations of the form

$$\sum_{i=1}^{r} a_ix_i^{m_i}=\sum_{j=1}^{s} b_jy_j^{n_j},\quad m_i,\ n_j\geqq 1.$$

It depends ultimately upon reducing the equation to the simpler multiplicative type $au^m=bv^n$ by suitable parametrization of x_i and y_j. *R. Bellman* (Santa Monica, Calif.).

Referred to in D56-18.

D56-16 (14, 725g)

Morgantini, Edmondo. Sulla risoluzione dell'equazione diofantea: $\sum_i a_ix_i^2=x_0^{2m}\sum_i a_i$. Ann. Univ. Ferrara. Sez. VII. (N.S.) **1**, 93–101 (1952).

This is substantially a special case of the treatment in the paper next reviewed. *J. W. S. Cassels.*

D56-17 (14, 725h)

Morgantini, Edmondo. Sulla risoluzione dell'equazione diofantea: $\sum_i a_ix_i^2=\sum_i a_iy_i^{2m_i}$. Ann. Triestini. Sez. 2. (4) **5(21)** (1951), 35–45 (1952).

A parametrisation of the title equation where the a_i are rational integers and the m_i are natural numbers in terms of variables y_i, α_i is obtained by putting $x_i+y_i^{m_i}=\alpha_it$ and solving the resultant linear equation for t. The problem of finding all integer solutions thus leads to a multiplicative diophantine equation [Skolem, Diophantische Gleichungen, Springer, Berlin, 1938, Kap. IV]. *J. W. S. Cassels.*

D56-18 (14, 725i)

Morgantini, Edmondo. Sulla rappresentazione parametrica di un'ampia classe di varietà unirazionali e sulle sue applicazioni all'analisi diofantea. Univ. Roma. Ist. Naz. Alta Mat. Rend. Mat. e Appl. (5) **11**, 238–267 (1952).

The author considers integer solutions of the diophantine equation

$$\sum_{i=1}^{r} a_ix_i^{\rho m_i}=\sum_{i=1}^{s} b_iy_i^{\sigma n_i}$$

where the a_i, b_i are polynomials with integer coefficients in variables $z_1,\cdots,z_t$ and ρ, m_i, σ, n_i are natural numbers [cf. Morgantini, Rend. Sem. Mat. Univ. Padova **21**, 44–57 (1952); these Rev. **14**, 247]. On putting $x_i=A_ix^{\mu_i}$, $y_i=B_iy^{\nu_i}$, where the μ_i, ν_i are chosen so that $m_1\mu_1=m_2\mu_2=\cdots=m$, $n_1\nu_1=n_2\nu_2=\cdots=n$, and the A_i, B_i, z_i are taken as parameters, there results an equation of the type

$$U(A,B,z)x^{m\rho}=V(A,B,z)y^{n\sigma};$$

which gives a parametrisation of the surface if $m\rho$ is prime to $n\sigma$. Integer solutions are discussed. As with the two preceding papers, the discussion is cloaked in an impressive geometrical terminology. *J. W. S. Cassels.*

Citations: MR 14, 247c = D56-15.

D56-19 (15, 14a)

Rosenthall, E. Diophantine equations separable in cyclotomic fields. Duke Math. J. **20**, 217–232 (1953).

The author generalizes his method for solving certain cubic diophantine equations by means of corresponding multiplicative ideal equations in the number field $R(e^{2\pi i/3})$ and corresponding multiplicative equations in the rational field. Here he considers diophantine equations which can be given as multiplicative ideal equations in a suitable form, for instance, as an equality between two norms of linear forms in the field $R(e^{2\pi i/l})$ where l is an odd prime. The fundamental theorem reduces the solving of these equations to the solving of multiplicative equations in the rational domain. In this way the complete solution of some diophantine equations are obtained. For instance, the equation $\sum_{i=1}^{2n} x_i^l = 0$ is solved. The solution of this diophantine equation is reduced to the solution of a system of $n(l-2)$ linear equations in $\frac{1}{2}(n^2-n)+l-1$ unknowns.

H. Bergström (Göteborg).

D56-20 (16, 998g)

Schinzel, A. On the equation $x_1x_2\cdots x_n=t^k$. Bull. Acad. Polon. Sci. Cl. III. **3**, 17–19 (1955).

The totality of solutions in natural numbers is given in parametric form for the equation listed in the title. The case $k=2$ had been done by E. T. Bell [Ann. of Math. (2) **48**, 43–50 (1947); MR **8**, 442].

I. Niven.

Citations: MR 8, 442c = D56-11.

D56-21 (16, 1088e)

Rosenthall, E. Reducible diophantine equations and their parametric representations. Canad. J. Math. **7**, 328–336 (1955).

The diophantine equation

$$(*)\qquad \prod(\mathrm{Norm}_{K_i/R}\,\kappa_i)^{c_i}=1$$

is to be solved in $\kappa_i \in \mathfrak{K}_i$, where the $\mathfrak{K}_i$ $(1\leqq i\leqq I)$ are given algebraic fields over the rational field $\mathfrak{R}$ and the c_i are given nonzero integers in $\mathfrak{R}$. The author shows that the linear factors into which the left side of (*) splits in the least normal extension $\mathfrak{N}/\mathfrak{R}$ containing the $\mathfrak{K}_i$ must have ideal factorisations of one of a finite number of parametric shapes; but he does not consider when these ideal factorisations correspond to solutions κ_i of (*).

J. W. S. Cassels.

D56-22 (25# 2033)

Moĭšezon, B. G.

A representation of numbers by factorizable forms. (Russian)

Mat. Sb. (N.S.) **56 (98)** (1962), 173–206.

Let $\eta_1, \cdots, \eta_m$ be elements of an algebraic number field K which are linearly independent over the rational field Q. Following Skolem [Math. Ann. **111** (1935), 399–424] and Chabauty [Ann. Mat. Pura Appl. (4) **17** (1938), 127–168], the author considers when the form

$$\prod_{1\leq i\leq n}(x_1\eta_1^{(i)}+\cdots+x_m\eta_m^{(i)})$$

represents the same element $c\neq 0$ of Q for infinitely many sets of rational integer values of the variables $x_1, \cdots, x_m$, where the product is over all sets of conjugates (so that the degree of K/Q is n). In particular, he gives general conditions under which there is only a finite number of representations when $m=4$ and $m=5$. He does not use p-adic methods but takes as his starting point the algebraic-geometric criteria which Chabauty [loc. cit.] obtained by p-adic analysis.

J. W. S. Cassels (Cambridge, England)

D56-23 (29# 1179)

Davenport, H.; Lewis, D. J.; Schinzel, A.

Polynomials of certain special types.

Acta Arith. **9** (1964), 107–116.

It is well known that if $f(x)$ is a polynomial with integral coefficients such that $f(x)$ is a kth power for every positive integer x, then $f(x)=g(x)^k$, where $g(x)$ is a polynomial with integral coefficients. The authors show that the conclusion holds under the weaker hypothesis that every arithmetic progression contains an integer x such that $f(x)$ is a kth power. This result, in turn, is a corollary of the following more general theorem: Let $F(x,y)$ be a polynomial with integral coefficients. Suppose that every arithmetic progression contains an integer x such that $F(x,y)=0$ has an integral solution in y. Then there exists a polynomial $h(x)$ with rational coefficients such that $F(x,h(x))=0$ identically.

The second principal result of the paper is the following. Let K be any normal algebraic number field of degree n with integral basis $w_1, w_2, \cdots, w_n$ and let $N(u_1, u_2, \cdots, u_n)$ $=\mathrm{norm}\,(u_1w_1+u_2w_2+\cdots+u_nw_n)$ be the norm-form corresponding to K. Let $f(x)$ be a polynomial with rational coefficients and suppose that every arithmetic progression contains an integer x such that $f(x)=N(u_1, u_2, \cdots, u_n)$ for rational $u_1, u_2, \cdots, u_n$. Suppose further that either K is cyclic or the multiplicity of every zero of $f(x)$ is relatively prime to n. Then $f(x)=N(v_1(x), v_2(x), \cdots, v_n(x))$ identically, where $v_1(x), v_2(x), \cdots, v_n(x)$ are polynomials with rational coefficients. An example shows that if K is not cyclic and the multiplicities are not prime to n, the conclusion need not follow. An interesting corollary, proved by letting $K=Q(i)$ (Q is the rational field), is that if $f(x)$ is a polynomial with integral coefficients such that every arithmetic progression contains an integer x for which $f(x)$ is a sum of two squares, then $f(x)=v_1^2(x)+v_2^2(x)$ identically, where $v_1(x)$ and $v_2(x)$ are polynomials with integral coefficients. The authors do not know what happens when $f(x)$ is a sum of two cubes for every sufficiently large x.

The highly original proofs involve classical (1930) algebraic number theory. Among the tools employed are Hilbert's irreducibility theorem and a theorem of Bauer [Math. Ann. **77** (1916), 353–356].

J. B. Kelly (Tempe, Ariz.)

Referred to in D08-38, D40-56, D56-24, D56-39, R08-39, R08-58.

D56-24 (32# 4081)

Chowla, S.

Some problems of elementary number theory.

J. Reine Angew. Math. **222** (1966), 71–74.

Let $g(x)$ be a polynomial with integer coefficients. The author proves that if $g(x)$ is a sum of two squares for every sufficiently large integer x, then there exist two polynomials $P_1(x)$ and $P_2(x)$ with integer coefficients such that $g(x)=P_1(x)^2+P_2(x)^2$ for all x. As the author points out in a postscript, this result is contained in a theorem of Davenport, Schinzel and Lewis [Acta Arith. **9** (1964), 107–116; MR **29** #1179], in which they get the same conclusion under the weaker assumption that every arithmetic progression contains an integer x such that $g(x)$ is the sum of two squares. The author also makes a number of conjectures concerning related problems.

T. M. Apostol (Pasadena, Calif.)

Citations: MR 29# 1179 = D56-23.

D56-25 (32# 7544)

Schinzel, A.

On a theorem of Bauer and some of its applications.

Acta Arith. **11** (1965/66), 333–344.

For any algebraic number field K, let $P(K)$ denote the set of all rational primes p which have a prime ideal factor of the first degree in K. Write $P(\Omega)\leqq P(K)$ if the set $P(\Omega)-P(K)$ is finite. The field K is called Bauerian if $P(\Omega)\leqq P(K)$ implies that Ω contains at least one of the conjugates of K. Every normal field is Bauerian [M. Bauer, Math. Ann. **77** (1916), 353–356]. Let $\bar{K}$ be the normal closure of K. Let $\mathfrak{H}$ and $\mathfrak{J}$ be the subgroups of the Galois group $\mathfrak{G}$ of $\bar{K}$ belonging to K and $\Omega \cap \bar{K}$, respectively. Let $\mathfrak{H}_1, \cdots, \mathfrak{H}_m$ be the conjugates of $\mathfrak{H}$ in $\mathfrak{G}$. It is shown that $P(\Omega) \leqq P(K)$ if and only if $\mathfrak{J} \subseteq \bigcup \mathfrak{H}_i$. This implies that the field K is Bauerian if and only if every subgroup of $\mathfrak{G}$ that is contained in $\bigcup \mathfrak{H}_i$ is contained in one of the $\mathfrak{H}_i$. In particular, all cubic and quartic fields are Bauerian. If K is a solvable field such that the degree of $\bar{K}$ over K is relatively prime to the degree of K over the rationals, then K is Bauerian. On the other hand, for $n \geqq 5$, a field of degree n is not Bauerian if its Galois group contains the alternating group $\mathfrak{A}_n$. The author uses these results to attack the problem of characterizing those polynomials and rational functions $f(x)$ over the rationals, for which every arithmetic progression contains an integer x such that $f(x)$ is the norm of an element in a fixed field K.

W. H. Mills (Princeton, N.J.)

Referred to in D56-27.

D56-26 (32# 7545)

Lewis, D. J.; Schinzel, A.; Zassenhaus, H.

An extension of the theorem of Bauer and polynomials of certain special types.

Acta Arith. **11** (1965/66), 345–352.

An algebraic number field K is said to have property (N) if there exists a normal field L of degree relatively prime to the degree of K such that the composition KL is the normal closure of K. It is shown that if K has property (N), then it is Bauerian (see the preceding review #7544).

Let $N_{K/Q}(\omega)$ denote the norm from K to the rational field Q. Let $f(x)$ be a polynomial over Q such that the multiplicity of each zero of $f(x)$ is relatively prime to the degree of K. The authors show that if K has property (N) and if in every arithmetical progression there is an integer x such that $f(x) = N_{K/Q}(\omega)$ for some ω in K, then $f(x) = N_{K/Q}(w(x))$ for some $w(x)$ in $K[x]$.

W. H. Mills (Princeton, N.J.)

D56-27 (35# 1570)

Schinzel, A.

Corrigendum to the paper: "On a theorem of Bauer and some of its applications".

Acta Arith. **12** (1966/67), 425.

The original paper appeared in same Acta **11** (1965/66), 333–344 [MR **32** #7544].

Citations: MR 32# 7544 = D56-25.

D56-28 (33# 2594)

Gabovič, Ja.

On arithmetic progressions with equal products of terms. (Russian)

Colloq. Math. **15** (1966), 45–48.

Consider the problem of finding two arithmetic progressions, of equal length, of positive integers $a_1, a_2, \cdots, a_n$ and $b_1, b_2, \cdots, b_n$, such that the products of their terms are equal, $a_1 a_2 \cdots a_n = b_1 b_2 \cdots b_n$. It is known that for $n = 3$ the problem has infinitely many solutions. In the present article the author shows that there are also infinitely many solutions for $n = 4$. He also states that the problem is open for $n \geqq 5$. *G. Biriuk* (Ann Arbor, Mich.)

D56-29 (34# 7450)

Bernstein, Leon

The generalized Pellian equation.

Trans. Amer. Math. Soc. **127** (1967), 76–89.

Let $D(m; x_1, x_2, \cdots, x_n)$ be a determinant of the nth order, obtained from the circulant $C(x_1, x_2, \cdots, x_n)$ by multiplying all entries below the main diagonal by m. The equation (1) $D(m; x_1, x_2, \cdots, x_n) = \pm 1$ is called the generalized Pellian equation, since for $n = 2$ it becomes $x_1^2 - mx_2^2 = \pm 1$. Further, let m and $x_i \in Q$, $m > 0$, $i = 1, 2, \cdots, n$, and suppose that $\theta = m^{1/n}$ is a positive, real nth degree irrational. First the author proves that $N(X) = \mathrm{Norm}(x_1 + x_2\theta + \cdots + x_n\theta^{n-1}) = D(m; x_1, x_2, \cdots, x_n)$. However, this special formula is not new—it was first proved by Muir in 1881, and later on by several authors. The main result of the paper is that it is possible to find an infinite system of integral solutions x_i of the equations (2) $N(X) = (-1)^{k(n-1)} d^k$ in case $m = D^n + d$, D and d denoting natural numbers, $d|D$ and $k = 0, 1, 2, \cdots, n-1$, by generalizing the usual continued fraction method for $n = 2$. In the proof use is made of the author's investigations concerning the periodic Jacobi-Perron algorithm [J. Reine Angew. Math. **213** (1963/64), 31–38; MR **27** #5727]. The case $m = D^n - d$ is also considered. In some concluding remarks it is mentioned that the same results for equation (2) can be obtained by means of the theory of algebraic numbers, noting that $d^{-1}(\theta - m)^n$ is a unit in $R[\theta]$ and that $N(D - \theta) = \mp d$. *W. Ljunggren* (Oslo)

Citations: MR 27# 5727 = A60-22.

D56-30 (36# 3722)

Schmidt, Wolfgang M.

Some diophantine equations in three variables with only finitely many solutions.

Mathematika **14** (1967), 113–120.

Let K be an algebraic number field of degree $n > 3$ over the field of rationals Q. For ξ in K, let $\xi^{(i)}$, $1 \leqq i \leqq n$, denote the conjugates of ξ, and let $N(\xi)$ denote the norm $N_{K/Q}(\xi)$. Let α, β, γ be three elements of K, linearly independent over Q, such that $K = Q(\alpha/\gamma, \beta/\gamma)$. Set $L = \alpha x + \beta y + \gamma z$, and $L^{(i)} = \alpha^{(i)}x + \beta^{(i)}y + \gamma^{(i)}z$, $1 \leqq i \leqq n$. Let l be the maximum number of forms $L^{(i)}$ which are linear combinations of two given forms, and let m be the maximum number of forms $L^{(i)}$ which are linear combinations of a given rational form R and a given real form S. Set $r = \max\{n - 3l/2, n - 2m\}$. Using his recent results on the simultaneous approximations of two algebraic numbers by rationals [Acta Math. **119** (1967), 27–50; MR **36** #6357], the author proves that for every $\varepsilon > 0$ there are only finitely many triples of rational integers x, y, z such that $|N(\alpha x + \beta y + \gamma z)| \leqq \max\{|x|, |y|, |z|\}^{r-\varepsilon}$. This theorem implies that many diophantine equations in three variables have only a finite number of solutions. For example, if $f(x, y, z)$ is a polynomial of total degree less than r, then $N(\alpha x + \beta y + \gamma z) = f(x, y, z)$ has at most a finite number of solutions in rational integers x, y, z.

W. H. Mills (Princeton, N.J.)

Citations: MR 36# 6357 = J68-56.

Referred to in D02-23, D56-34, D56-35.

D56-31 (38# 4407)

Nagell, Trygve

Remarques sur les formes à plusieurs variables décomposables en facteurs linéaires.

Ark. Mat. **7**, 313–329 (1968).

Let K be an algebraic field of degree n over the rationals Q, r the rank of the group of units of K, and let N denote the norm in K over Q. The author considers equations of the type (*) $N(x_1\alpha_1 + \cdots + x_m\alpha_m) = A$, where $m \leqq n$, $\alpha_1, \cdots, \alpha_m$ are linearly independent integers of K such that $K(\alpha_2\alpha_1^{-1}, \cdots, \alpha_m\alpha_1^{-1}) = K$, A is a rational integer, and the x_i are to be rational integers; in particular, he considers the problem of whether or not (*) has infinitely many solutions. A survey of known results is given and some conjectures made; in particular, it is conjectured that (*) has only finitely many solutions if $m < n$ and K is primitive. Among the new results established are: (i) (*) has only finitely many solutions when $m=3$, $n=4$, $r=1$ and K has only 1 imaginary quadratic subfield (and no real quadratic subfield); (ii) $N(x_1\xi+x_2\xi^2+x_3\xi^3+x_4\xi^4)=1$ has only finitely many solutions when ξ is a primitive pth root of unity, $p\geqq 7$ and $K=Q(\xi)$.

E. S. Barnes (Adelaide)

D56-32 (39# 4113)

Sirovich, Carole

On the distribution of elements belonging to certain subgroups of algebraic numbers.

Trans. Amer. Math. Soc. **141** (1969), 93–98.

If an algebraic number field is regarded in a natural way as a subset of a real vector space, then the units are contained in a hypersurface having a finite number of asymptotic hyperplanes. From this geometrical viewpoint, the author investigates more general, finitely generated, multiplicative groups in a number field, and obtains various results on their asymptotic behavior. Furthermore, the author derives as corollaries some Diophantine results concerning the finiteness of the number of elements of these groups belonging to algebraic varieties. The theorem of A. Baker [Mathematika **14** (1967), 102–107; MR **36** #3732] is used as an effective tool. *T. Kubota* (Nagoya)

Citations: MR 36# 3732 = J80-26.

D56-33 (40# 1334)

Ramachandra, K.

A lattice-point problem for norm forms in several variables.

J. Number Theory **1** (1969), 534–555.

In a series of papers [see, e.g., Acta Math. **62** (1933), 91–166] K. Mahler developed an asymptotic formula for the following problem: Let $F(x, y)$ be an irreducible binary form of degree $n\geqq 3$ over the rationals with rational integer coefficients and let $P_1, \cdots, P_t$ $(t\geqq 0)$ be a (possibly void) set of distinct primes. Let k be a large real number and let $N(F; P_1, \cdots, P_t; k)$ be the number of lattice points (x, y) subject to the inequality

$$|F(x, y)| \prod_{\tau=1}^{t} |F(x, y)|_{P_\tau} \leqslant k.$$

Then Mahler showed in the above mentioned paper that $N(F; P_1, \cdots, P_t; k)$ is finite for all k and obtained an asymptotic formula for it as k approaches infinity.

In the present paper the author obtains the following result: Let $F(x, y)$ be as above, let α run over the zeros of $F(x, 1)$ and let a_0 be the coefficient of x^n in $F(x, 1)$. Let $\Phi(\tilde{x})=a_0{}^h \prod_j (x_0\alpha^h+\cdots+x_h)$. Then if n is sufficiently large with respect to h the number of lattice points satisfying the condition $|\Phi(\tilde{x})|\leqq k$ is finite and asymptotic to a constant times $k^{(h+1)/n}$, the constant depending on $F(x, 1)$. The proof depends on some previous results of the author [Nachr. Akad. Wiss. Göttingen Math.-Phys. Kl. II **1966**, 45–52; MR **36** #112].

R. Finkelstein (Bowling Green, Ohio)

Citations: MR 36# 112 = J68-54.

D56-34 (41# 3392)

Győry, K.

Note on the paper of W. M. Schmidt "Some diophantine equations in three variables with only finitely many solutions".

Ann. Univ. Sci. Budapest. Eötvös Sect. Math. **12** (1969), 67–71.

Let K be an algebraic number field of degree $n\geqq 4$ over the rationals Q. For ξ in K, let $\xi^{(i)}$, $1\leqq i\leqq n$, denote the conjugates of ξ, and let $N(\xi)$ denote the norm $N_{K/Q}(\xi)$. Let α, β, γ be three elements of K, linearly independent over Q, such that $K=Q(\alpha/\gamma, \beta/\gamma)$. We write $\mathbf{x}=(x, y, z)$ and $|\mathbf{x}|=\mathrm{Max}\{|x|, |y|, |z|\}$. Set $L(\mathbf{x})=\alpha x+\beta y+\gamma z$ and $L^{(i)}(\mathbf{x})=\alpha^{(i)}x+\beta^{(i)}y+\gamma^{(i)}z$, $1\leqq i\leqq n$. Suppose that r is the maximal number for which there exist $i_1, \cdots, i_r$ and a non-zero element $\mathbf{a}$ of real euclidean 3-space satisfying $L^{(i_1)}(\mathbf{a})=\cdots=L^{(i_r)}(\mathbf{a})=0$, and m is the maximal number of forms $L^{(i)}$ which can be written simultaneously as linear combinations with complex coefficients of a rational linear form R and a real linear form S. We set $t=\mathrm{Min}\{n-\frac{3}{2}r, n-2m\}$. It is shown that there are infinitely many triples of rational integers x, y, z having the property $|N(L(\mathbf{x}))|\leqq c|\mathbf{x}|^t$ with a suitable constant $c>0$, but for every $\varepsilon>0$ there are only finitely many triples of rational integers x, y, z such that $|N(L(\mathbf{x}))|\leqq|\mathbf{x}|^{t-\varepsilon}$. This is an improvement of a result of W. M. Schmidt [Mathematika **14** (1967), 113–120; MR **36** #3722].

W. H. Mills (Princeton, N.J.)

Citations: MR 36# 3722 = D56-30.

D56-35 (42# 192)

Győry, K.

Représentation des nombres par des formes décomposables. I.

Publ. Math. Debrecen **16** (1969), 253–263.

K sei ein algebraischer Zahlkörper eines Grades $n\geqq 2$; sei $m\geqq 2$ und $\alpha_2, \cdots, \alpha_m\in K$ derart, daß $K=R(\alpha_2, \cdots, \alpha_m)$ (R der Körper der rationalen Zahlen) und daß $1, \alpha_2, \cdots, \alpha_m$ über R linear unabhängig sind. Es bezeichne N die Norm in K. Der Autor betrachtet diophantische Gleichungen der Form (1) $N(x_1+\alpha_2x_2+\cdots+\alpha_mx_m)=a$ mit $a\in R$ und gibt einige hinreichende Bedingungen dafür an, daß solche Gleichungen höchstens endlich viele verschiedene Lösungen $(x_1, \cdots, x_m)$ mit ganzen $x_i\in R$ haben. Dabei beschränkt er sich auf die beiden Spezialfälle: (a) K ist nicht reell und hat eine abelsche Galois-Gruppe; (b) K ist Kreisteilungskörper. Im Fall (a) mit $m=4$ und $3\nmid n$ sowie $4\nmid n$ beweist er die im Buch von Z. I. Borevič und I. R. Šafarevič [German translation, *Zahlentheorie*, p. 322, Birkhäuser, Basel, 1966; MR **33** #4000; English translation, Academic Press, New York, 1966; MR **33** #4001] ausgesprochene Vermutung, daß (1) höchstens endlich viele Lösungen hat, falls der von $1, \alpha_2, \cdots, \alpha_m$ erzeugte Modul nicht ausgeartet ist. Diese Vermutung ist für $m=2$ von A. Thue [J. Reine Angew. Math. **135** (1909), 284–305] und für $m=3$ von W. M. Schmidt [Mathematika **14** (1967), 113–120; MR **36** #3722] bewiesen. Im Fall (b) ist folgendes Resultat interessant: Sei $p>37$ eine Primzahl und ζ eine primitive p-te Einheitswurzel. Dann hat $N(x_1+\zeta x_2+\cdots+\zeta^7x_8)=1$ höchstens endlich viele Lösungen $(x_1, \cdots, x_8)$ mit ganzen $x_i\in R$. Ferner wird unter denselben Voraussetzungen für p und ζ eine explizite, nur von p abhängige Schranke für die Lösungsanzahl von $N(x_1+\zeta x_2+\zeta^2x_3+\zeta^3x_4)=1$ angegeben. *P. Bundschuh* (Freiburg)

Citations: MR 33# 4000 = Z02-45; MR 33# 4001 = Z02-46; MR 36# 3722 = D56-30.

D56-36 (42# 5919)

Gafurov, N.

Distribution of integral points on the surface $xyz=m$. (Russian. Tajiki summary)

Dokl. Akad. Nauk Tadžik. SSR **11** (1968), *no.* 11, 3–5.

The author gives the asymptotics of the number of integral points on parts of the surface shown in the title when $m=p_1{}^{\alpha_1}p_2{}^{\alpha_2}$, $\alpha_1\to\infty$, $\alpha_2\to\infty$.

A. I. Vinogradov (RŽMat **1969** #7 A139)

D56-37 (42# 7590)

Fel'dman, N. I.

Effective bounds for the number of solutions of certain Diophantine equations. (Russian)

Mat. Zametki **8** (1970), 361–371.

The author gives an effective proof of the finiteness of the number of solutions of the Diophantine equation $\mathrm{Norm}(z_1\omega_1+\cdots+z_m\omega_m)=f(z_1,\cdots,z_m)$, where $\omega_1,\cdots,\omega_m$ are algebraic numbers of a special form, the left side of the equation is the norm relative to an imaginary quadratic field, and f is a polynomial of small degree.

{This article has appeared in English translation [Math. Notes 8 (1970), 674–679].}

R. Finkelstein (Bowling Green, Ohio)

D56-38 **(43# 3205)**

Pitti, Christian

Sur un problème diophantien relatif au corps diédraux. *C. R. Acad. Sci. Paris Sér. A-B* **272** (1971), A92–A94.

Let $k(\vartheta)$ be a quadratic extension of a field k. The author constructs the solutions of the diophantic equation $N_{k(\vartheta)/k}(\beta)=1$ with $\beta\in k(\vartheta)$, using elements of a field $K\supset k(\vartheta)$ such that the Galois group of K over k is a dihedral group of order $2p$. The cases p odd and p even are treated separately. *F. van der Blij* (Bilthoven)

D56-39 **(44# 185)**

Berstel, Jean

Sur des fractions rationnelles particulières. *Séminaire M. P. Schützenberger, A. Lentin et M. Nivat, 1969/70: Problèmes Mathématiques de la Théorie des Automates, Exp. 2, 9 pp. Secrétariat mathématique, Paris,* 1970.

The author's starting point is the following well-known theorem: (*) If $f\in Q[x]$ is an integer-valued polynomial that is a kth power for every integer in the set N of positive integers, then $f=g^k$, where $g\in Q[x]$ is integer-valued. The author first discusses various known generalizations and refinements of (*), in particular, the far-reaching extension obtained by H. Davenport, D. J. Lewis and A. Schinzel [Acta Arith. **9** (1964), 107–116; MR **29** #1179], of which one consequence is that the set N in the hypothesis of (*) may be replaced by any set of integers A having the property that it contains an integer in every arithmetic progression. (Such sets A are called arithmetically dense in this paper and several of their properties are developed.) The author's principal objective is to extend some of this previous work to rational functions. Thus, to quote several typical results, he proves that if $f\in Q(x)$ is the kth power of a rational number for every integer in an arithmetically dense set A, then $f=g^k$ with $g\in Q(x)$. This result, in turn, is a corollary of the following more general theorem: Suppose that $f\in Q(x)$ and that $p\in Z[x]$, with p monic; if A is an arithmetically dense set for which $f(A)\subset p(Q)$, then there exists a $g\in Q(x)$ such that $f=p\circ g$.

Another interesting variant of (*) for the case $k=2$ is the following: Let $f\in Z[x]$ have all its irreducible factors over Q of degree ≥ 3; if f is a square for an infinite set of positive integers, then $f=g^2$, where $g\in Z[x]$. This result is noteworthy since, in general, (*) need not hold when N is replaced by an arbitrary infinite subset.

The author's proofs are elementary, but they depend on deeper results obtained previously, notably by Davenport, Lewis and Schinzel in the paper cited above [op. cit.].

I. Gerst (Stony Brook, N.Y.)

Citations: MR 29# 1179 = D56-23.

D60 EXPONENTIAL EQUATIONS: GENERAL

An equation such as $x^2+1=y^n$, with n unspecified, may be regarded as defining a collection of algebraic curves ($n=3,4,\ldots$), or as an exponential equation $x^2+1=y^z$.

The former viewpoint has been adopted for certain papers in **D40**, **D44** and **D48**, the latter in **D64**.

See also Sections D40, D48.

See also reviews A50-35, B40-32, B40-38, B40-52, B72-31, B99-6, C15-6, C15-49, D12-32, D20-5, D24-47, D24-69, D40-7, D40-38, D44-90, D44-111, D44-132, D48-55, D64-16, J68-65, J80-1, J80-29, K15-50, K25-16, K25-17, K25-20, K30-23, N32-1, N32-6, Q05-34, U05-7, U05-14, U05-18, U05-23, U05-42, U05-43, Z10-30.

D60-1 **(1, 292d)**

Gelfond, A. Sur la divisibilité de la différence des puissances de deux nombres entiers par une puissance d'un idéal premier. Rec. Math. [Mat. Sbornik] N.S. **7** (49), 7–25 (1940). (French. Russian summary)

The author makes use of $\mathfrak{p}$-adic analysis to study the expression $\alpha^n\pm\beta^m$, where α,β are numbers in an algebraic field R such that $\alpha^n\neq\beta^m$ for any rational integers m,n with $mn\neq 0$. Thus he proves that, if $\mathfrak{p}$ is a prime ideal of R not contained in the numerator and denominator of α and β, then for any $\epsilon>0$ there exists a $n_0=n_0(\alpha,\beta,\mathfrak{p},\epsilon)$ such that $\alpha^n\pm\beta^m$ with $n>n_0$, $n\geqq m>0$ is not divisible by $\mathfrak{p}^\gamma$ if $\gamma>\log^{3+\epsilon}n$. Using this result and a previous one [cf. these Rev. **1**, 295] the author proves that the equation $\alpha^x+\beta^y=\gamma^z$ (α,β,γ are in R, none equals 0, ± 1 and at least one of them is not a unit) has at most a finite number of integral solutions x,y,z except when $\alpha=\pm 2^{n_1}$, $\beta=\pm 2^{n_2}$, $\gamma=\pm 2^{n_3}$ (n_1,n_2,n_3 rational). *H. W. Brinkmann.*

Referred to in D60-72, J02-3, J80-10.

D60-2 **(2, 346i)**

Ko, Chao. Note on the Diophantine equation $x^xy^y=z^z$. J. Chinese Math. Soc. **2**, 205–207 (1940).

The reviewer conjectured that the equation $x^xy^y=z^z$ has no solutions in integers, $x,y,z>1$. The author proves that this conjecture holds only if $(x,y)=1$. If $(x,y)\neq 1$ there are infinitely many solutions, say

$$x=2^{2^{n+1}(2^n-n-1)+2n}(2^n-1)^{2(2^n-1)},$$
$$y=2^{2^{n+1}(2^n-n-1)}(2^n-1)^{2(2^n-1)+2},$$
$$z=2^{2^{n+1}(2^n-n-1)+n+1}(2^n-1)^{2(2^n-1)+1}.$$

P. Erdös (Philadelphia, Pa.).

D60-3 **(6, 169f)**

Pillai, S. S. On $a^X-b^Y=b^y\pm a^x$. J. Indian Math. Soc. (N.S.) **8**, 10–13 (1944).

In two previous papers [J. Indian Math. Soc. (1) **19**, 1–11 (1931); same J. (N.S.) **2**, 119–122, 215 (1936)] the author proved that for given positive integers a and b the equation $a^x-b^y=c$ has only a finite number of solutions x,y for any c and at most one solution for sufficiently large c. It follows at once that $a^x-b^y=a^z-b^w$ has only a finite number of solutions x,y,z,w. In this paper the author intends to prove the same result for $a^x-b^y=b^z\pm a^w$. However, this result is correct only if $(a,b)=1$, although the author also considers the case $(a,b)>1$. This can be seen by the following examples:

$$3^{k+1}-3^k=3^k+3^k \quad\text{and}\quad 2^{\alpha k+2}-(2^\alpha)^k=(2^\alpha)^k+2^{\alpha k+1},$$

where $a=b=3$ and $a=2$, $b=2^\alpha$, respectively. *A. Brauer.*

D60-4 **(7, 145i)**

Pillai, S. S. On the equation $2^x-3^y=2^X+3^Y$. Bull. Calcutta Math. Soc. **37**, 15–20 (1945).

The following Diophantine equations are solved completely:

$$2^x-3^y=3^Y-2^X,\quad 2^x-3^y=2^X+3^Y,\quad 3^y-2^x=2^X+3^Y.$$

A. Brauer (Chapel Hill, N. C.).

D60-5 (7, 147b)

Chabauty, Claude. Démonstration nouvelle d'un théorème de Thue et Mahler sur les formes binaires. Bull. Sci. Math. (2) 65, 112–130 (1941).

The author gives a new proof, independent of Diophantine approximation, for the following theorem of K. Mahler [Math. Ann. **107**, 691–730 (1933)]. Let λ, μ, ν be three different algebraic integers generating a field K of degree k over the rational field R. There exists at most a finite number of pairs of rational relatively prime integers a, b such that the principal ideals $(a-\lambda b)$, $(a-\mu b)$, $(a-\nu b)$ have only a finite number of given prime factors $\mathfrak{p}_1, \cdots, \mathfrak{p}_h$ in K. The proof uses a $\mathfrak{p}$-adic method due to T. Skolem [Math. Ann. **111**, 399–424 (1935)]. It runs as follows. Let the assertion be false. Then there exists an infinite sequence E of pairs of rational integers a, b with $(a, b)=1$ such that $(a-\lambda b)$, $(a-\mu b)$, $(a-\nu b)$ have only the prime factors $\mathfrak{p}_1, \cdots, \mathfrak{p}_h$. Without loss of generality, an infinite subsequence E_1 of E can be chosen in which $|a-\lambda b|_{\mathfrak{p}_i}\geqq c_0>0$, $|a-\mu b|_{\mathfrak{p}_i}\geqq c_0>0$, $|a-\nu b|_{\mathfrak{p}_i}\to 0$, $i=1, \cdots, h'$; $h'\leqq h$, and such that a/b tends to a limit, α say. Choose a prime number n greater than $4k(k^5+h+3)^2$ and greater than the exponents of the roots of unity contained in K. Then there is an infinite subsequence E_2 of E_1 such that $a-\lambda b=\varphi_0\varphi^n$, $a-\mu b=\psi_0\psi^n$ with constant integers φ_0, ψ_0 and variable integers φ, ψ in K satisfying $|\varphi|_{\mathfrak{p}_i}\geqq c_1>0$, $|\psi|_{\mathfrak{p}_i}\geqq c_1>0$, $i=1, \cdots, h'$. Denote by θ a root of $z^n=\psi_0(\lambda-\nu)/\varphi_0(\mu-\nu)$ not in K, and by H the field $H=K(\theta)$. Then an infinite subsequence E_3 of E_2 exists such that the principal ideal (Δ) in H generated by $\Delta=\varphi-\theta\psi$ is of the form $(\Delta)=\mathfrak{A}\mathfrak{P}_1^{l_1}\cdots\mathfrak{P}_j^{l_j}$, $l_1, \cdots, l_j$ nonnegative integers, where $\mathfrak{A}$ is one of a finite number of ideals and $\mathfrak{P}_1, \cdots, \mathfrak{P}_j$ are $j\leqq h$ fixed prime ideals in H. Put

$$\Omega(x, y; u, v, w; \zeta^g)=\sqrt[n]{(x-uy)(v-w)}-\zeta^g\sqrt[n]{(x-vy)(u-w)},$$

where ζ is a primitive nth root of unity, $g=0, 1, \cdots, n-1$, and the nth roots have their principal values. Then

$$\Delta=\zeta^{-g_1}\Omega(a, b; \lambda, \mu, \nu; \zeta^{g_0})/\sqrt[n]{\varphi_0(\mu-\nu)}$$

with g_0 and g_1 depending on a, b. Hence there exists an infinite subsequence E_4 of E_3 such that, if a_1, b_1 is a fixed and a, b a variable pair in E_4, then a_1/b_1 and a/b lie on the same side of α and are near α; furthermore, the quotient $\Gamma=\Delta/\Delta_1$ of the corresponding numbers Δ and Δ_1 takes the form

$$\Gamma=\Omega(a, b; \lambda, \mu, \nu; \zeta^{g_0})/\Omega(a_1, b_1; \lambda, \mu, \nu; \zeta^{g_0}),$$

g_0 fixed. Choose for M the smallest subfield of H, say of degree m, which contains Γ for some infinite subset E_5 of E_4. Then all m conjugates $\Gamma^{(t)}$ of Γ over R can be written as

$$\Gamma^{(t)}=\Omega(a, b; S\lambda, S\mu, S\nu; \zeta^g)/\Omega(a_1, b_1, S\lambda, S\mu, S\nu; \zeta^g),$$

where g runs over $0, \cdots, n-1$, and S over the automorphisms which change K into the conjugate fields; we can write, instead

$$\Gamma^{(t)}=\Omega(a, b; \lambda_t, \mu_t, \nu_t; \zeta^{g_t})/\Omega(a_1, b_1; \lambda_t, \mu_t, \nu_t; \zeta^{g_t}),$$

$t=1, \cdots, m$, and choose the notation so that $\lambda_t=\lambda_\tau$, $\mu_t=\mu_\tau$, $\nu_t=\nu_\tau$, $g_t=g_\tau$ or $\lambda_t=\mu_\tau$, $\mu_t=\lambda_\tau$, $\nu_t=\nu_\tau$, $g_t=g_\tau$ only if $t=\tau$. Of the fields conjugate to M, let r_1 be real and $2r_2$ complex; hence $r_1+2r_2=m$. One can show that, if θ was chosen suitably, then $r_2\geqq k^5+h+2$; hence, by Dirichlet's theorem, the rank r of the group of units in M is

$$r=r_1+r_2-1=m-r_2-1\leqq m-k^5-h-3.$$

By construction, the principal ideal (Γ) is of the form

$$(\Gamma)=(\Delta/\Delta_1)=(\mathfrak{A}/\mathfrak{A}_1)\mathfrak{P}_1^{l_1-l_1'}\cdots\mathfrak{P}_j^{l_j-l_j'}.$$

Hence there is an infinite subsequence E_6 of E_5 in which $\Gamma=A_0\Gamma^*$, where A_0 is a fixed number in M and Γ^* belongs to a multiplicative group in M of rank

$$\rho=r+j\leqq r+h\leqq m-k^3-3.$$

Let $P=(X_1, \cdots, X_m)$ be the point in m-dimensional space S of coordinates $H_1=\Gamma^{(1)}/A_0^{(1)}, \cdots, H_m=\Gamma^{(m)}/A_0^{(m)}$; here the upper indices denote the conjugates with respect to M. The points belong to a multiplicative group of rank ρ and lie on the algebraic variety in S of dimension $\sigma=2$ defined by

$$H_t=\omega_t\Omega(x, y; \lambda_t, \mu_t, \nu_t; \zeta^{g_t}),\qquad t=1, \cdots, m,$$

where the ω_t are constants. A general theorem of the author [Ann. Mat. Pura Appl. (4) **17**, 127–168 (1938), theorem 2.4] implies, therefore, the existence of an infinite subsequence E_7 of E_6 for which the points P satisfy a system of homogeneous multiplicative relations of the form

$$\prod_{t=1}^{m}\Omega(a, b; \lambda_t, \mu_t, \nu_t; \zeta^{g_t})^{C_{tq}}=\text{constant},\quad \sum_{t=1}^{m}C_{tq}=0,\quad q=1, \cdots, \kappa,$$

where the matrix of the integral exponents C_{tq} is at least of rank $m-\rho-\sigma\geqq k^5+1$. On putting $c=a/b$, by homogeneity for the pairs in E_7,

$$\prod_{t=1}^{m}\Omega(c, 1; \lambda_t, \mu_t, \nu_t; \zeta^{g_t})=\text{constant},\quad q=1, \cdots, \kappa.$$

Now c tends to α and so the last equations imply the system of identities

$$\prod_{t=1}^{m}\Omega(z, 1; \lambda_t, \mu_t, \nu_t; \zeta^{g_t})=\text{constant},\quad q=1, \cdots, \kappa.$$

But a direct discussion shows that at most k^5 independent equations of this type can hold, whence a contradiction.

K. Mahler (Manchester).

D60-6 (8, 7a)

Skolem, Th. On certain exponential equations. Norske Vid. Selsk. Forh. **18**, no. 18, 71–74 (1945).

The Diophantine equation $a^x-1=p_1^{x_1}\cdots p_m^{x_m}$ (a a given integer, $p_1, \cdots, p_m$ given primes) is proved to have at most a finite number of solutions in nonnegative integers $x, x_1, \cdots, x_m$. This is a special case of a theorem of Størmer. The method used here can be extended to algebraic number fields. The following theorem is obtained. If α is a given algebraic integer, no conjugate of which has the absolute value 1, and $\mathfrak{p}_1, \cdots, \mathfrak{p}_m$ are given prime ideals in a field containing α, then an upper bound can be found for the natural numbers x with the property that the decomposition of α^x-1 contains only $\mathfrak{p}_1, \cdots, \mathfrak{p}_m$. *N. G. de Bruijn.*

D60-7 (8, 7b)

Skolem, Th. On the prime divisors of the values of certain functions. Norske Vid. Selsk. Forh. **18**, no. 19, 75–78 (1945).

Generalizing a theorem concerning the prime divisors of a^x-1 [cf. the preceding review] the author proves the following theorem. Let $f(x)$ attain rational integral values for all rational integers x, let $p_1, \cdots, p_m$ denote different primes and let $r_1, \cdots, r_l$ be l integers. For $j=1, \cdots, m$; $n=1, 2, 3, \cdots$, suppose that $f(x)\equiv 0 \pmod{p_j^n}$ implies that x belongs to one of the l residue classes $x\equiv r_i \pmod{\psi_j(n)}$. Now if f and ψ_j satisfy

$$\liminf_{x\to\pm\infty}\,(\log|f(x)|)/\log|x|>m,$$

$$\liminf_{n\to\infty}\,n^{-1}\log\psi_j(n)\geqq\log p_j,\qquad j=1, \cdots, m,$$

then the equation $f(x)=kp_1^{x_1}\cdots p_m^{x_m}$ has, for a given value

of k, at most a finite number of solutions in rational integers $x, x_1, \cdots, x_m$. A second theorem deals with the same equation under slightly different conditions.
N. G. de Bruijn (Eindhoven).

D60-8 **(8, 7c)**

Skolem, Th. A method for the solution of the exponential equation $A_1^{x_1}\cdots A_m^{x_m}-B_1^{y_1}\cdots B_n^{y_n}=C$. Norsk. Mat. Tidsskr. **27**, 37–51 (1945). (Norwegian)

Using a lemma on the Pell equation, Størmer showed [Nyt Tidsskr. Math. B. **19**, 1–7 (1908)] how to obtain all integral solutions x_i, y_j of the exponential equation of the title when $C=\pm1$ or ±2 and A_i, B_j are given integers. The author treats the general case $|C|\geqq3$ and shows how it is possible to solve the more general problem: find all integral solutions X, Y of the Diophantine equation $X^3-DY^3=E$, when D, E and the prime divisors of Y are all given. There is only a finite number of solutions. In his proof the author uses the properties of p-adic numbers and of the cubic field generated by $D^{\frac{1}{3}}$. In the case $C=\pm3$ the proof is not complete.
T. Nagell (Uppsala).

D60-9 **(8, 8a)**

Skolem, Th. Extension of two theorems of C. Størmer. Norsk. Mat. Tidsskr. **26**, 85–95 (1944). (Norwegian)

Let α, β, δ be integers in a totally real field K of algebraic numbers, α and $\beta\neq0$, δ totally positive, prime to α and to the discriminant of the field K and not a square in K. The author shows that, if $A=\alpha+\beta\sqrt{\delta}$, $A^x=\alpha_x+\beta_x\sqrt{\delta}$, x a positive integer, and if every prime ideal factor of β_x divides δ, then $x=1$, 2 or 3.

This result is a generalization of a theorem of Størmer [Skr. Norske Vid.-Selsk. Christiania. I. **1897**, no. 2] in the rational field R. The author conjectures that an analogous result holds for any field without restrictions; a proof is given only for an imaginary quadratic field. A consequence of the results is an extension to algebraic fields of a theorem of Størmer on the solutions of a certain type of exponential Diophantine equation in the rational field R [C. R. Acad. Sci. Paris **127**, 752–754 (1898); Nyt Tidsskr. Mat. B. **19**, 1–7 (1908)]. The number of solutions is finite; the solutions may all be determined by a finite number of operations.
T. Nagell (Uppsala).

D60-10 **(13, 822f)**

LeVeque, Wm. J. On the equation $a^x-b^y=1$. Amer. J. Math. **74**, 325–331 (1952).

For fixed positive integers a, b the title equation has at most one integer solution x, y except that $a=3$, $b=2$ has $3-2=3^2-2^3=1$. The proof for $2|a$ is simple, that for $2\nmid a$ is elaborate. The solution, if it exists, is specified entirely by certain congruences. As a corollary it is shown that the only identity $\sum^n k^s=(\sum^n k^t)^r$ with integer s, r, t is $s=3$, $t=1$, $r=2$.
J. W. S. Cassels (Cambridge, England).

Referred to in A28-9, D60-11, D60-33, D60-67.

D60-11 **(14, 536e)**

Cassels, J. W. S. On the equation $a^x-b^y=1$. Amer. J. Math. **75**, 159–162 (1953).

It was shown by the reviewer [same J. **74**, 325–331 (1952); these Rev. **13**, 822] that the equation of the title has at most one solution if $(a,b)\neq(3,2)$, and this solution was effectively specified. The present author gives a simpler proof of the following slightly stronger theorem: Suppose that x, y, $a>1$, $b>1$ are positive integers, and the equation is not $3^2-2^3=1$. Suppose also that ξ, η are the least positive solutions of $a^\xi\equiv1 \pmod B$, $b^\eta\equiv-1 \pmod A$, where A and B are the products of the odd prime divisors of a, b respectively. Then $x=\xi$, $y=\eta$, except that $x=2$, $y=1$ may occur if $\xi=\eta=1$ and $a+1$ is a power of 2. In the course of the proof it is also shown that any prime divisor of y which is less than x divides a, and vice versa.
W. J. LeVeque.

Citations: MR 13, 822f = D60-10.
Referred to in D60-33.

D60-12 **(15, 933f)**

Natucci, Alpinolo. Ricerche sistematiche intorno al "teorema di Catalan". Giorn. Mat. Battaglini (5) **2**(**82**), 297–300 (1954).

Catalan's theorem states that 8 and 9 are the only powers of positive integers which differ by unity. No proof or disproof is known. The author describes and illustrates a somewhat pedestrian method of systematic search for two such powers. He concludes that the probability of the truth of Catalan's assertion is very great.
D. H. Lehmer.

D60-13 **(16, 675b)**

Ward, Morgan. On the number of vanishing terms in an integral cubic recurrence. Amer. Math. Monthly **62**, 155–160 (1955).

Let (T): T_0, T_1, T_2, $\cdots$ be an integral cubic recurrence; that is, the initial values T_0, T_1, T_2 are integers and $T_{n+3}=PT_{n+2}-QT_{n+1}+RT_n$, where P, Q, R are fixed integers and $R\neq0$. The polynomial $f(z)=z^3-Pz^2+Qz-R$ and the recurrence (T) are said to be associated; also both (T) and $f(z)$ are degenerate or non-degenerate according as the ratio of any pair of different roots of $f(z)$ is, or is not, a root of unity. By a result of Mahler [Nederl. Akad. Wetensch. **38**, 50–60 (1935)], if (T) is non-degenerate, $|T_n|$ tends to infinity with n; hence the total number of zeros of any non-degenerate (T) is finite. The present paper contains a proof of the following theorem. If the associated polynomial of (T) is non-degenerate and has integral roots which are co-prime in pairs, then at most three terms of (T) can vanish.
L. Carlitz (Durham, N. C.).

Referred to in D60-14.

D60-14 **(17, 826e)**

Smiley, M. F. On the zeros of a cubic recurrence. Amer. Math. Monthly **63** (1956), 171–172.

The cubic recurrence $(T)=(T_1, T_2, T_3, \cdots)$ is defined by real numbers T_0, T_1, T_2 and

$$T_{n+3}=PT_{n+2}-QT_{n+1}+RT_n \quad (n=0, 1, 2, \cdots),$$

where P, Q, R are real. It is assumed that the roots, u v, w of z^3-Pz^2+Qz-R are nonzero, real and have distinct absolute values. If $T_k=0$, k is called a zero of (T). The following theorem is proved. The cubic recurrence (T) has at most three zeros. Ward [same Monthly **62**(1955), 155–160; MR **16**, 675] had proved this result under the restriction that u, v, w were integers relatively prime in pairs. The proof of the theorem of the paper makes use of Descartes' rule of signs.
L. Carlitz.

Citations: MR 16, 675b = D60-13.
Referred to in D60-35.

D60-15 **(18, 285d)**

Vandiver, H. S. Diophantine equations in certain rings. Proc. Nat. Acad. Sci. U.S.A. **42** (1956), 656–665.

In addition to several observations on the solution of Diophantine equations in rings, the following theorem is proved by considerations in the field generated by a primitive mth root of unity. The equation

$$da+k_1p+(db+k_2p)x^c=(d+k_3p)y^m$$

with a, b and m fixed such that $(a,b)=1$ and m is an odd prime, is impossible for an infinity of integers c such that $cm+1\equiv0 \pmod p$, $d\not\equiv0 \pmod p$, and none of a, $a+b$, $(a^m+b^m)/(a+b)$ is an mth power.
I. Niven.

D60-16 **(19, 9e)**

Vandiver, H. S. Errata: Diophantine equations in certain rings. Proc. Nat. Acad. Sci. U.S.A. **43** (1957), 252–253.

Corrections to the article reviewed in MR **18**, 285.

D60-17 **(18, 561c)**

Hampel, R. On the solution in natural numbers of the equation $x^m - y^n = 1$. Ann. Polon. Math. **3** (1956), 1–4.

The author proves that the equations

$$n^{\alpha+s} - (n+1)^\alpha = \pm 1$$

with $n \geqq 2$, $\alpha \geqq 2$, $s \geqq 1$ are not solvable except in the trivial case $n=2$, $\alpha=2$, $s=1$. The case with $+1$ on the right hand side is readily reduced to the solubility of $2^{\alpha+s} - 3^\alpha = 1$, and it is then not difficult to see that the expansions of 3^α and $2^{\alpha+s}-1$ in the scale of 2 always fail to agree in the last three digits. The case with -1 on the right is more difficult, but the author disposes of it by showing that the representation of $(n+1)^\alpha$ in the scale of n cannot, except in the trivial case, have as many zero digits as $n^{\alpha+s}+1$. The paper concludes with a slight generalisation.

H. Halberstam (Exeter).

D60-18 **(18, 561d)**

Schinzel, A. Sur l'équation $x^z - y^t = 1$, **où** $|x-y|=1$. Ann. Polon. Math. **3** (1956), 5–6.

The author gives a shorter proof of the theorem reviewed above by a method based on primitive roots and a result of B. A. Hausmann [Amer. Math. Monthly **48** (1941), 482] which states that 2^m+1 for $m>3$ cannot be the power of an integer with exponent greater than 1.

H. Halberstam (Exeter).

D60-19 **(18, 561e)**

Rotkiewicz, A. Sur l'équation $x^z - y^t = a^t$, **où** $|x-y|=a$. Ann. Polon. Math. **3** (1956), 7–8.

A theorem of G. D. Birkhoff and Vandiver [Ann. of Math. (2) **5** (1904), 173–180] states that if a, b, n are natural numbers, $a>b$, $(a, b)=1$, $n>2$, then $a^n - b^n$ is divisible by at least one prime p such that p does not divide any of the integers $a^r - b^r$ $(r=1, 2, \cdots, n-1)$; the case $a=2$, $b=1$, $n=6$ provides the sole exception. From this the author concludes, by a very short and simple argument, that the equation $x^z - y^t = a^t$, where a is an integer, has no integer solutions x, y, z, t greater than 1, other than $x=3$, $y=2$, $z=2$, $t=3$, such that $|x-y|=a$ and $(x, y)=1$. If $a=1$, we arrive again at the theorem discussed in the preceding two reviews. *H. Halberstam* (Exeter).

Referred to in B40-38.

D60-20 **(18, 641b)**

Obláth, Richard. Une propriété des puissances parfaites. Mathesis **65** (1956), 356–364.

If the digit a is written k times in juxtaposition, is it possible to find a $k>1$ so that the number $\underbrace{aa\cdots a}_{k}$, interpreted in the denary scale with be a perfect nth power? For the numbers $a=2$, 4, 5, 6 the answer is easily seen to be in the negative. For $a=7$ the proof of the impossibility is more involved and is based on results by T. Nagell and W. Ljunggren. The impossibility for $a=3$ and $a=8$ depends on the fact that $\underbrace{11\cdots 1}_{k}$ can never be a cube. For $a=1$ the author proves that $\underbrace{11\cdots 1}_{k}$ is never a power if k is even or divisible by 3. It is never a fifth power if k is divisible by 5 and is never a seventh power if k is divisible by 7. Some results on bases other than 10 are given. *I. A. Barnett* (Cincinnati, Ohio).

D60-21 **(18, 717g)**

Wall, C. T. C. A theorem on prime powers. Eureka no. 19 (1957), 10–11.

The only (non-prime) prime powers which differ by unity are 8 and 9. The proof is extremely short.

Referred to in D60-26.

D60-22 **(20# 3098)**

Edmonds, Sheila M. Sums of powers of the natural numbers. Math. Gaz. **41** (1957), 187–188.

The well-known identity $\sum_{n=1}^N n^3 = (\sum_{n=1}^N n)^2$ is derived by partial summation and it is shown that there is no other identity of the form $\sum_{n=1}^N Cn^p = (\sum_{n=1}^N n^q)^2$, where C is a constant and p, q are non-negative integers.

{Concerning this last observation, it might be worth noting that even the Diophantine equation $1+2^p = (1+2^q)^r$ has no solution in positive integers p, q, r with $r>1$ except $p=3$, $q=1$, $r=2$. To prove this we consider this equation successively modulo $1+2^q$, 2^{q+1} and 3 to obtain $p \equiv 0 \pmod{q}$, $r \equiv 0 \pmod{2^q}$ and $p \equiv q \equiv 1 \pmod{2}$. Now let $q = 3^s q_1$, where $(3, q_1)=1$. Then, $1+2^q \equiv 0 \pmod{3^{s+1}}$ and hence $1+2^p \equiv 0 \pmod{3^{(s+1)r}}$. Hence, $p \equiv 0 \pmod{3^{(s+1)r-1} q_1}$. Thus,

$$(1+2^q)^r = 1+2^p > 2^{q_1 3^{(s+1)r-1}} = (2^{3^s q_1})^{3^{(s+1)(r-1)-1}} > (1+2^q)^{3^{(s+1)(r-1)-1}}.$$

This is possible only if $r > 3^{(s+1)(r-1)-1}$; in other words, if $s=0$, $r=2$; and hence $q=1$, $p=3$.}

E. G. Straus (Los Angeles, Calif.)

The reviewer adds, also: "By similar means it can be shown that the only non-trivial prime powers which differ by 1 from a proper power are 8 and 9."

D60-23 **(20# 3101)**

Green, John W. On the computation of certain roots by the use of the binomial series. Amer. Math. Monthly **64** (1957), no. 8, part II, 34–36.

It is suggested that there are "very few" integers K for which $q^k K = p^k \pm 10^{-n} p^k$ has solutions in integers p, q, $n>0$; here $k=2$, 3. Motivation, and numerical evidence.

D60-24 **(20# 3815)**

Cestari, R. Risoluzione della diofantea $X^y - Z^t = 1$. Giorn. Mat. Battaglini (5) **5** (**85**) (1957), 197–208.

This paper purports to prove "Catalan's conjecture" that the equation in the title has no integer solutions other than $3^2 - 2^3 = 1$. There is a fallacy in the remark B_1 below equation (20) on page 207.

J. W. S. Cassels (Cambridge, England)

D60-25 **(21# 2621)**

Nagell, Trygve. Sur une classe d'équations exponentielles. Ark. Mat. **3** (1958), 569–582.

The bulk of this paper is devoted to a case by case examination of the set of solutions in non-negative integers x, y, z of the exponential equations $a^x = b^y + c^z$, where a, b, c are distinct primes $\leqq 7$. There are nine cases to consider (obviously one of a, b, c must be 2). Five cases can be settled by elementary arguments based primarily on the set of values assumed by powers of one prime modulo a fixed power of another. Two, $(a, b, c) = (3, 5, 2)$ and $(3, 7, 2)$, require an argument based on the solutions of equations of the type $X^2 - DY^2 = C$. The cases $(2, 5, 3)$ and $(2, 5, 7)$ are dealt with by algebraic number theory using standard divisibility arguments involving ideals in quadratic fields and, for the equation $2^x = 5^y + 3$, the cubic field generated by $2^{1/3}$. All solution sets are finite, the maximum number of distinct solutions being 5 for $(a, b, c)=(2, 5, 3)$.

The detailed examination is preceded by some remarks on more general systems of exponential equations; in particular, a simple proof is given of the fact that

$$AM_1^{x_1}M_2^{x_2}\cdots M_m^{x_m}-BN_1^{y_1}N_2^{y_2}\cdots N_n^{y_n} = C$$

has only a finite number of non-negative integer solutions, $x_1, \cdots, x_n, y_1, \cdots, y_n$ where A, B, C, the M_i and the N_i are positive integers coprime in pairs.

J. D. Swift (Los Angeles, Calif.)

D60-26 (21# 3374)

Sierpiński, W. Sur une question concernant le nombre de diviseurs premiers d'un nombre naturel. Colloq. Math. **6** (1958), 209–210.

Let $\nu(n)$ be the number of distinct prime factors of n. It is shown simply that if $\nu(n)=\nu(n+1)=1$ and $n\neq 8$ then n is a Mersenne prime or $n+1$ is a Fermat prime. This was previously shown in essentially the same way by C. T. C. Wall [Eureka no. 19 (1957), 10–11; MR **18**, 717]. It is not known whether there are infinitely many solutions of $\nu(n)=\nu(n+1)$, though according to a conjecture of Schinzel there exist infinitely many solutions to $\nu(n)=\nu(n+1)=\cdots=\nu(n+k)$ for every k.

L. Moser (Edmonton, Alta.)

Citations: MR 18, 717g = D60-21.

D60-27 (21# 4126)

Sierpiński, W. On the equation $3^x+4^y=5^z$. Wiadom. Mat. (2) **1** (1955/56), 194–195. (Polish)

Working modulo 2 the author proves that the only solution in positive integers is $x=y=z=2$.

Z. A. Melzak (Murray Hill, N.J.)

Referred to in D60-32.

D60-28 (21# 4132)

Chowla, P.; Chowla, S.; Dunton, M.; and Lewis, D. J. Some diophantine equations in quadratic number fields. Norske Vid. Selsk. Forh. **31** (1958), 181–183.

The authors are interested in the following general problem. For $n\geqq 3$, let $S_n+aS_{n-1}+bS_{n-2}=0$, with a, b, S_1, S_2 arbitrary but fixed integers. Determine an explicit $f=f(a, b, c, S_1, S_2)$ such that the equation $S_n=c$ has no solutions for $n>f$. This note deals with the special case $a=-1$, $b=\lambda\geqq 2$, $S_1=1$, $S_2=1-2\lambda$, $c=1$. For $\lambda>2$, $f=1$. For $\lambda=2$, $f=4$. This result was proved but not published by Artin and Fox, and the methods used were quite different.

N. J. Fine (Princeton, N.J.)

D60-29 (21# 4133)

Chowla, Paromita. A class of Diophantine equations. Proc. Nat. Acad. Sci. U.S.A. **45** (1959), 569–570.

Let $\alpha=\frac{1}{2}(1+\sqrt{7})$, $\beta=\frac{1}{2}(1-\sqrt{7})$ and $s(g)=\alpha^g+\beta^g$. The author outlines the proof of the result that for $n>2$ the only solution of $s(g)=s(2^n)$ is $g=2^n$.

She also can prove that $s(g)=c$ has at most two solutions, but does not give the proof.

P. Erdös (Budapest)

D60-30 (22# 25)

Skolem, Th.; Chowla, S.; Lewis, D. J. The diophantine equation $2^{n+2}-7=x^2$ and related problems. Proc. Amer. Math. Soc. **10** (1959), 663–669.

Ramanujan [*Collected papers*, Cambridge Univ. Press, 1927, p. 327] conjectured that the above equality has no rational integral solutions for n and x except for $n=1, 2, 3, 5, 13$. Using Skolem's p-adic method [8te Skand. Mat. Kongr. Forh., Stockholm, 1934, pp. 163–188] the authors prove this conjecture and some related results. Consider the sequence $\{a_n\}$ for which $a_0=a_1=1$; $a_n=a_{n-1}-2a_{n-2}$ for $n\geqq 2$. Then $a_{n-1}^2=1$ exactly for those values of n such that $2^{n+2}-7=x^2$ has a solution. An integer appears in the sequence $\{a_n\}$ at most three times.

J. F. Koksma (Amsterdam)

Referred to in A52-67, B40-32, D60-37, D60-42, D60-43, D60-52, D60-54.

D60-31 (22# 688)

Mąkowski, A. On the diophantine equation $2^x+11^y=5^z$. Nordisk Mat. Tidskr. **7** (1959), 81, 96.

The author states: "The purpose of the present note is to prove the following theorem. The only solutions in non-negative integers x, y, z of the equation $2^x+11^y=5^z$ are given by $x=2$, $y=0$, $z=1$ and $x=y=2$, $z=3$."

A. Sklar (Chicago, Ill.)

D60-32 (22# 1537)

Jeśmanowicz, L. Several remarks on Pythagorean numbers. Wiadom. Mat. (2) **1** (1955/56), 196–202. (Polish)

W. Sierpiński [Wiadom. Mat. (2) **1** (1955/56), 194–195; MR **21** #4126] showed that the equation $3^x+4^y=5^z$ has $x=y=z=2$ as its only solution in natural x, y, z. The integers 3, 4, 5 constitute a triad of Pythagorean numbers, integral solutions of the equation $a^2+b^2=c^2$. The author proves that Sierpiński's result holds also for the following sets of Pythagorean numbers: $2n+1$, $2n(n+1)$, $2n(n+1)+1$ with $n=2, 3, 4, 5$ ($n=1$ is Sierpiński's case).

H. Halberstam (London)

Citations: MR 21# 4126 = D60-27.

Referred to in D60-41, D60-66.

D60-33 (22# 5610)

Cassels, J. W. S. On the equation $a^x-b^y=1$. II. Proc. Cambridge Philos. Soc. **56** (1960), 97–103.

Corrigendum, 57 (1961), 187.

The equation of the title, in which a and b are regarded as known, arises as a special case of Catalan's conjecture, according to which 8 and 9 are the only two consecutive positive integers which are integral powers of smaller integers. The reviewer showed [Amer. J. Math. **74** (1952), 325–331; MR **13**, 822] that the equation of the title has at most one solution, which solution can be found explicitly if it exists, and the author showed [ibid. **75** (1953), 159–162; MR **14**, 536] that if p and q are prime, $p>q\geqq 2$, and $a^p-b^q=\pm 1$ with $a>1$, $b>1$, then $q|a$. It is shown here that under these same conditions, also $p|b$. An account of the history of the larger conjecture is also given.

The reader should note that the letters a and b have been interchanged on p. 98, lines 2 and 4 up, p. 99, line 8, and p. 100, lines 14 and 15 up.

W. J. LeVeque (Ann Arbor, Mich.)

Citations: MR 13, 822f = D60-10; MR 14, 536e = D60-11.

Referred to in D60-57.

D60-34 (22# 6770)

Leszczyński, B. The equation $n^x+(n+1)^y=(n+2)^z$. Wiadom. Mat. (2) **3**, 37–39 (1959). (Polish)

Theorem: If $y>1$, the equation given in the title of the paper has only two solutions in the natural numbers: (1) $n=1$, x arbitrary, $y=3$, $z=2$; (2) $n=3$, $x=y=z=2$. The author states that the question whether the equation has a solution for $y=1$ remains open (meaning, probably, a solution different from $n=x=y=z=1$).

J. W. Andrushkiw (Newark, N.J.)

Referred to in D60-71.

D60-35 **(22# 9467)**

Scott, S. J. On the number of zeros of a cubic recurrence. Amer. Math. Monthly **67** (1960), 169–170.

Let $(T)=(T_0, T_1, T_2, \cdots)$ denote the cubic recurrence defined by the real numbers T_0, T_1, T_2 and the relation

$$T_{n+3} = PT_{n+2}-QT_{n+1}+RT_n \quad (n = 0, 1, \cdots),$$

where P, Q, R are real. When $T_k=0$, k is said to be a zero of (T). It is proved that a recurrence (T), distinct from (T'): $T_n'=Uu^n(1-(-1)^n)$, can have no more than three zeros when the zeros of x^3-Px^2+Qx-R are non-vanishing real numbers. This extends a result of Smiley [Amer. Math. Monthly **63** (1956), 171–172; MR **17**, 826].

L. Carlitz (Durham, N.C.)

Citations: MR 17, 826e = D60-14.

D60-36 **(22# 9468)**

Rotkiewicz, A. Sur le problème de Catalan. Elem. Math. **15** (1960), 121–124.

Theorem: Let x, y, z, t be integers greater than 1 such that (*) $x^z-y^t=1$ but $(x, y, z, t)\neq(3, 2, 2, 3)$. Then each of x, y is divisible by two prime factors, one of which is greater than 11. Further, at least one prime divisor of x is congruent to 1 modulo t and at least one prime divisor of y is congruent to 1 modulo z. If $z=2$, then y is also divisible by a prime congruent to 1 modulo t. The author concludes by giving a simple proof of the theorem of Moret-Blanc that the only solution of (*) with $x=t$ and $y=z$ is $(x, y, z, t)=(3, 2, 2, 3)$.

J. W. S. Cassels (Cambridge, England)

Referred to in B40-38, D60-40, D60-45, D60-55.

D60-37 **(22# 10950)**

Apéry, Roger. Sur une équation diophantienne. C. R. Acad. Sci. Paris **251** (1960), 1451–1452.

The author considers the diophantine equation (1) $p^n=x^2+A$ $(n\geqq 0)$, where A is a positive integer and p is an odd prime not dividing A (both p and A are given in advance). He proves that (1) has at most 2 solutions. (The case $p=2$, $A=7$ was considered by Skolem, Chowla and Lewis in Proc. Amer. Math. Soc. **10** (1959), 663–669 [MR **22** #25]. In this case (1) has 5 solutions, where x is restricted to be positive.) *S. Chowla* (Boulder, Colo.)

Citations: MR 22# 25 = D60-30.

D60-38 **(22# 10951)**

Apéry, Roger. Sur une équation diophantienne. C. R. Acad. Sci. Paris **251** (1960), 1263–1264.

The diophantine equation (1) $2^{n+2}=x^2+A$ $(n\geqq 0)$, where A is a given positive integer congruent to 7 (mod 8), has at most 2 solutions in integers provided $A\neq 7$. (When $A=7$, it was proved that (1) has 5 solutions. See #10950.)

S. Chowla (Boulder, Colo.)

D60-39 **(23# A109)**

Postnikov, A. G.

Ein Analogen des Tarryschen Problems für die Exponentialfunktion. (Russian summary)

Sammelband zu Ehren des 250. *Geburtstages Leonhard Eulers, pp.* 281–283. *Akademie-Verlag, Berlin,* 1959.

Direct counting arguments are used to show that the number of solutions of the equation

$$g^{x_1}+\cdots+g^{x_n} = g^{y_1}+\cdots+g^{y_n}$$

for x_i, y_i non-negative and less than P is $n!P^n+O(P^{n-1})$ for any positive n. *J. D. Swift* (Princeton, N.J.)

D60-40 **(23# A1597)**

Rotkiewicz, A.

Sur le probléme de Catalan. II.

Elem. Math. **16** (1961), 25–27.

The author shows that any solutions of Catalan's equation $x^z-y^t=1$ in integers other than the known solutions must have $x>10^3$, $y>10^3$. He states that he can show similarly that if z and t are primes, then 10^3 can be replaced by 10^6. The proofs are an elaboration of those in his previous note [Elem. Math. **15** (1960), 121–124; MR **22** #9468].

J. W. S. Cassels (Cambridge, England)

Citations: MR 22# 9468 = D60-36.

Referred to in D60-45.

D60-41 **(24# A81)**

Józefiak, T.

On a hypothesis of L. Jeśmanowicz concerning pythagorean numbers. (Polish. Russian and English summaries)

Prace Mat. **5** (1961), 119–123.

The author proves a hypothesis of L. Jeśmanowicz [Wiadom. Mat. (2) **2** (1955/56), 196–202; MR **22** #1537] for a class of Pythagorean numbers: If $a=2^{2r}p^{2s}-1$, $b=2^{r+1}p^s$, $c=2^{2r}p^{2s}+1$, where r, s are natural numbers and p is a prime number, then $x=y=z=2$ is the only integral solution of the equation $a^x+b^y=c^z$.

J. W. Andrushkiw (Newark, N.J.)

Citations: MR 22# 1537 = D60-32.

D60-42 **(24# A82)**

Browkin, J.; Schinzel, A.

On the equation $2^n-D=y^2$. (Russian summary, unbound insert)

Bull. Acad. Polon. Sci. Sér. Sci. Math. Astronom. Phys. **8** (1960), 311–318.

The equation $2^n-7=x^2$ was treated independently by (1) T. Nagell [Nordisk Mat. Tidskr. **30** (1948), 62–64], (2) Skolem, Lewis and the reviewer [Proc. Amer. Math. Soc. **10** (1959), 663–669; MR **22** #25], and (3) G. Browkin and A. Schinzel [C. R. Acad. Sci. Paris **242** (1956), 1780–1781; MR **17**, 1055]. In this paper the authors use their method in (3) to prove the following. Theorem: If $D\not\equiv 0, 4, 7 \pmod 8$, the equation (*) $2^n-D=y^2$ has one solution at the most. If any solution exists, then $n\leqq 2$. In four more theorems the authors achieve quite deep information on the equation (*).

S. Chowla (Boulder, Colo.)

Citations: MR 17, 1055d = D64-16; MR 22# 25 = D60-30.

D60-43 **(24# A83)**

Nagell, T.

The diophantine equation $x^2+7=2^n$.

Ark. Mat. **4** (1961), 185–187.

The author points out that he had published [Nordisk Mat. Tidskr. **30** (1948), 62–64] a solution of the problem in the title much earlier than Skolem, Lewis and the reviewer [Proc. Amer. Math. Soc. **10** (1959), 663–669; MR **22** #25]. *S. Chowla* (Boulder, Colo.)

Citations: MR 22# 25 = D60-30.

Referred to in D60-52.

D60-44 **(24# A84)**

Cassels, J. W. S.

On a class of exponential equations.

Ark. Mat. **4** (1961), 231–233.

From a result by A. O. Gel'fond [*Transcendental and*

algebraic numbers (Russian), GITTL, Moscow, 1952; p. 157; MR **15**, 292] the author deduces an effective method of finding all non-negative integral solutions $x_1, \cdots, x_{r+s}$ of the equation

$$p_1^{x_1} \cdots p_r^{x_r} - p_{r+1}^{x_{r+1}} \cdots p_{r+s}^{x_{r+s}} = C,$$

where $C \neq 0$ is a given integer, and $p_1, \cdots, p_{r+s}$ are given distinct primes; that this equation has only finitely many solutions was proved many years ago by G. Pólya. The author bases his construction on the following lemma. Let K be a (finite) algebraic number field; let a and b be two elements of K for which $(\log a)/(\log b)$ is irrational; and let $\mathfrak{p}$ be a prime ideal in K such that both a and b are $\mathfrak{p}$-adic units. By means of a finite number of steps it is possible to determine a constant $x_0 = x_0(a, b, \mathfrak{p})$ with the following property: If $x \geqq x_0$, then the congruence $a^u \equiv b^v \pmod{\mathfrak{p}^m}$ has no solutions in integers u, v, m satisfying $0 < |u| + |v| \leqq x$, $m \geqq [\log^7 x]$. *K. Mahler* (Manchester)

Citations: MR 15, 292e = J02-6.

Referred to in D40-44.

D60-45 (24# A712)

Hampel, R.

On the problem of Catalan. (Polish. Russian and English summaries)

Prace Mat. **4** (1960), 11–19.

A history is given of the so-called problem of Catalan, i.e., the impossibility of the diophantine equation $x^y - z^t = 1$ $(x, y, z, t > 1, \langle x, y, z, t \rangle \neq \langle 3, 2, 2, 3 \rangle)$. The author proves, as his own contribution, that the equation is impossible if x or y is of the form 10^r or $2^r 3^s$. It follows from these and earlier results that the equation is impossible if (*) $14 \neq \min(x, y) < 20$. These theorems have been recently surpassed by the results of A. Rotkiewicz [Elem. Math. **15** (1960), 121–124; MR **22** #9468; ibid **16** (1961), 25–27; MR **23** #A1597] who proved, e.g., that condition (*) can be replaced by $\min(x, y) \leqq 1000$. *A. Schinzel* (Warsaw)

Citations: MR 22# 9468 = D60-36; MR 23# A1597 = D60-40.

D60-46 (24# A1879)

Hausner, Alvin

Algebraic number fields and the Diophantine equation $m^n = n^m$.

Amer. Math. Monthly **68** (1961), 856–861.

Euler showed that the only integral solutions of the equation $m^n = n^m$ with $m < n$ are $(m, n) = (2, 4)$ and $(m, n) = (-4, -2)$. The author generalises the problem to algebraic number fields in two ways. First, he gives a complete solution of the equation $\alpha^{N\beta} = \beta^{N\alpha}$ in integers α, β of a number field K; he splits the problem into three main cases: case (a) $N\alpha = 2$, $\beta = \pm\alpha^2$; case (b) $N\alpha = -2$, $\beta = -\alpha^2$; and case (c) $N\alpha = N\beta$. Second, he considers the equation $A^{NB} = B^{NA}$ in integral ideals A, B of K; there are only finitely many solutions with $A \neq B$, and these all have $NA = 2$, $B = A^2$.

His discussion is clear and thoroughly elementary.

B. J. Birch (Cambridge, England)

D60-47 (25# 39)

Chowla, S.; Dunton, M.; Lewis, D. J.

Linear recurrences of order two.

Pacific J. Math. **11** (1961), 833–845.

The recurrences are $f(n+2) = Af(n+1) - Bf(n)$, $B \neq 0$, $f(0) = a$, $f(1) = b$, with A, B, a, b rational integers and $(a, b) \neq (0, 0)$. The authors study the number, $M(c)$, of values of n for which $f(n) = c$. When $\Delta = A^2 - 4B \geqq 0$, they show in an elementary way that $M(c)$ is infinite for some c, or $M(c) \leqq 3$ for all c. The case $\Delta < 0$ is far more difficult. Write $\|x\|_p = \max\{k; p^k | x\}$ for integers x, and $\lambda_p = \|\Delta\|_p$. The main result of this paper is that if $\lambda_p \geqq 1$ for some prime $p \geqq 5$, then $M(c) \leqq p^e$ with $e = \lambda_p$ for all c. The same conclusion holds for $p = 2$, respectively, $p = 3$, if we have $\lambda_2 \geqq 3$, respectively, $\lambda_3 \geqq 2$ and $(A, 3) = 1$. The proof involves p-adic analysis and rests on a theorem of R. Strassmann [J. Reine Angew. Math. **159** (1928), 13–28]. Certain more special results are obtained, such as: if there is a prime p for which $0 < 2\|A\|_p < \|B\|_p$, then $M(c) \leqq 2$ for all c and $M(c) = 2$ for only finitely many c.

M. F. Smiley (Riverside, Calif.)

Referred to in D60-58, D60-69.

D60-48 (25# 1130)

Podsypanin, V. D.

On a property of Pythagorean numbers. (Russian)

Izv. Vysš. Učebn. Zaved. Matematika **1962**, *no.* 4 (29), 130–133.

Remarks concerning the solubility of the Diophantine equations $a^x - b^y = c^z$, where a, b, c are Pythagorean numbers. *S. Knapowski* (Poznań)

Referred to in D60-66.

D60-49 (25# 3005)

Lewis, D. J.

Two classes of Diophantine equations.

Pacific J. Math. **11** (1961), 1063–1076.

Several authors showed that $x^2 + 7 = 2^y$ has exactly 5 solutions in integers [Mordell, Skolem, Lewis, Nagell, Browkin, Schinzel, and the reviewer]. The author shows that $x^2 + 7 = N^y$ has at most 2 solutions if N is odd, and has no solution when N is odd and not a power of a prime. Using a p-adic argument he also gets an upper bound in terms of M and n, on the number of "primitive" solutions of the equation $x^2 + 7M^2 = y^n$ $(M \geqq 1, n \geqq 3)$. For other related literature see also Lewis and Mahler [Acta Arith. **6** (1960/61), 333–363; MR **22** #10952] and Ljunggren [Norske Vid. Selsk. Forh. (Trondhjem) **16** (1943), no. 8, 27–30; MR **8**, 442; ibid. **17** (1944), no. 23, 93–96; MR **8**, 442]. *S. Chowla* (Boulder, Colo.)

Citations: MR 8, 442d = D40-9; MR 22# 10952 = D40-35.

Referred to in D40-38.

D60-50 (25# 5032)

Makowski, A.

On the equation $13^x - 3^y = 10$.

Math. Student **28** (1960), 87 (1962).

From the author's introduction: "The purpose of this note is to solve in non-negative integers the equation

(1) $$13^x - 3^y = 10.$$

It is proved that equation (1) has exactly two solutions in non-negative integers: $x = y = 1$ and $x = 3$, $y = 7$."

D60-51 (26# 73)

Makowski, A.

Three consecutive integers cannot be powers.

Colloq. Math. **9** (1962), 297.

It is proved that the simultaneous equations $x^p - y^q = y^q - z^r = 1$ have no solution in natural numbers x, y, z, p, q, r with $p > 1$, $q > 1$ and $r > 1$. *T. Estermann* (London)

D60-52 (26# 74)

Mordell, L. J.

The diophantine equations $2^n = x^2 + 7$.

Ark. Mat. **4**, 455–460 (1962).

The author presents one more proof of the fact that the only integral solutions of the equation $x^2 + 7 = 2^n$ are given by $n = 3, 4, 5, 7$ and 15. This result was first proved by

Nagell [Nordisk Mat. Tidskr. **30** (1948), 62–64]. Nagell republished this proof [Ark. Mat. **4** (1961), 185–187; MR **24** #A83]. Other proofs were given by Skolem, Chowla and Lewis [Proc. Amer. Math. Soc. **10** (1959), 663–669; MR **22** #25] and Chowla, Dunton and Lewis [Norske Vid. Selsk. Forh. Trondheim **33** (1960), 37–38]. All of these proofs appear to be more elementary than this one, which relies on the arithmetic of the cubic fields $Q(\sqrt[3]{7})$ and $Q(\sqrt[3]{28})$. *D. J. Lewis* (Ann Arbor, Mich.)

Citations: MR 22# 25 = D60-30; MR 24# A83 = D60-43.

D60-53 (26# 76)

Townes, S. B.

Notes on the Diophantine equation $x^2+7y^2=2^{n+2}$.

Proc. Amer. Math. Soc. **13** (1962), 864–869.

Define integer sequences $\{a_n\}$, $\{b_n\}$ by $\frac{1}{2}(a_n+\sqrt{(-7)}b_n)=[\frac{1}{2}(1+\sqrt{(-7)})]^n$, so that $a_n^2+7b_n^2=2^{n+2}$; alternatively, one may define the sequences to be the solutions of a pair of quadratic recurrences. Recently, several authors have tested their techniques by investigating the sequence $\{a_n\}$, and have proved amongst other things that $|a_n|=1$ has exactly five solutions; this is harder than might be expected. The author's main result is that for $|c|>1$ the equation $a_n=c$ has at most one solution, except that $a_4=a_8=-3$; he also exhibits a function $N(c)$ such that $a_n\neq c$ for $n>N(c)$; the proofs use congruences and ingenious identities. The results slightly overlap those of Schinzel [Ark. Mat. **4** (1962), 413–416; MR **25** #2999], although the methods are entirely different; references are given by Schinzel. *B. J. Birch* (Manchester)

Citations: MR 25# 2999 = B40-32.
Referred to in D60-58.

D60-54 (26# 6118)

Chowla, S.; Dunton, M.; Lewis, D. J.

All integral solutions of $2^n-7=x^2$ are given by $n=3, 4, 5, 7, 15$.

Norske Vid. Selsk. Forh. (Trondheim) **33** (1960), 37–38.

Ramanujan conjectured and Nagell [Norsk. Mat. Tidsskr. **30** (1948), 62–64] proved the assertion in the title of this note. This is a neat proof, an improvement of the proof of Skolem, Chowla and Lewis [Proc. Amer. Math. Soc. **10** (1959), 663–669; MR **22** #25]. {The problem has application in the theory of error correcting codes; see Shapiro and Slotnick [IBM J. Res. Develop. **3** (1959), 25–34, Eq. (4); MR **20** #5092].} *J. L. Selfridge* (Seattle, Wash.)

Citations: MR 20# 5092 = R99-6; MR 22# 25 = D60-30.

D60-55 (27# 103)

Inkeri, K.; Hyyrö, S.

On the congruence $3^{p-1}\equiv 1 \pmod{p^2}$ and the Diophantine equation $x^2-1=y^p$.

Ann. Univ. Turku. Ser. A I No. 50 (1961), 4 *pp.*

It is known that $p=1093$ and $p=3511$ are the only primes $<100\,000$ for which $2^{p-1}\equiv 1\ (p^2)$ [see Kravitz, Math. Comp. **14** (1960), 378; MR **22** #12073]. At the Turku Computation Centre it was found that $p=11$ is the only prime $<100\,000$ for which $3^{p-1}\equiv 1\ (p^2)$. These results imply that the Catalan equation $x^2-1=y^p$ (p a prime, $x>3$) can only be solved for $p>100\,000$ [see Obláth, Rev. Math. Hisp.-Amer. (4) **1** (1941), 122–140; MR **7**, 273], while $p>50\,000$ was already established by Rotkiewicz [Elem. Math. **15** (1960), 121–124; MR **22** #9468]. It is shown here that $x\equiv 0\ (p^2)$, $y\equiv -1\ (p^2)$. Further, greatly improving a result of Obláth it is shown that $2v-u>5\cdot 10^9$ when $x\mp 1=2u^p$, $x\pm 1=2^{p-1}v^p$, $y=2uv$. The estimates of Obláth for x and y are also greatly improved. *O. Taussky-Todd* (Pasadena, Calif.)

Citations: MR 7, 273g = D40-4; MR 22# 9468 = D60-36; MR 22# 12073 = A16-29.

D60-56 (27# 4791)

Chowla, Paromita

Some diophantine equations in quadratic number fields.

Calcutta Math. Soc. Golden Jubilee Commemoration Vol. (1958/59), *Part II, pp.* 373–378. *Calcutta Math. Soc., Calcutta,* 1963.

The author considers the Diophantine equation (1) $S_n=\frac{1}{2}(\alpha^n+\beta^n)=c$, where $\alpha=1+i\sqrt{2}$, $\beta=1-i\sqrt{2}$ and $c=\pm 1$, corresponding to the linear recurrence $S_n+aS_{n-1}+bS_{n-2}=0$, $n\geqq 3$, with $a=-2$, $b=3$, $S_1=1$ and $S_2=-1$. It is proved that (1) has no solutions for $n>5$ in case $c=1$ and for $n>2$ if $c=-1$. However, (1) is only a special case of a more general equation, completely solved by T. Nagell [see, for example, T. Nagell, *L'analyse indéterminée de degré supérieur*, p. 58, Mémor. Sci. Math., Fasc. XXXIX, Gauthier-Villars, Paris, 1929]. *W. Ljunggren* (Oslo)

Referred to in D60-77.

D60-57 (28# 62)

Hyyrö, Seppo

On the Catalan problem. (Finnish)

Arkhimedes **1963**, *no.* 1, 53–54.

From the author's summary: "As far as we are aware [W. J. LeVeque, *Topics in number theory*, Vol. 2, p. 154, Addison-Wesley, Reading, Mass., 1956; MR **18**, 283], it has not been proved previously that there are no three consecutive integers, except the integers -1, 0, 1, which are powers of integers with integral exponents greater than unity. In this note a short proof based on a result of J. W. S. Cassels [Proc. Cambridge Philos. Soc. **56** (1960), 97–103; corrigendum, ibid. **57** (1961), 187; MR **22** #5610; errata, MR **22**, p. 2546] is given. Moreover, some known results relating to Catalan's conjecture are presented. We will show that the Diophantine equations

$$(1)\qquad x^p-y^q=1,\qquad y^q-z^r=1\qquad (p>1, q>1, r>1, y\neq 0)$$

have no common solution. There is no loss in generality in assuming that p, q, r are prime and $x>1$, $y>1$, $z>1$. Now, by Cassels [loc. cit.] the equations (1) imply $q|x$ and $q|z$. Hence, it follows from $x^p-z^r=2$ that $q^2|2$, which is a contradiction."

Citations: MR 18, 283b = Z01-38; MR 22# 5610 = D60-33.

D60-58 (28# 1160)

Chowla, P.; Chowla, S.; Dunton, M.; Lewis, D. J.

Diophantine equations in quadratic number fields.

Calcutta Math. Soc. Golden Jubilee Commemoration Vol. (1958/59), *Part II, pp.* 317–322. *Calcutta Math. Soc., Calcutta,* 1963.

Let $\lambda>1$ be a positive integer, and let α, β be the roots of $X^2-X+\lambda=0$. Define $S(g)=\alpha^g+\beta^g$, $t(g)=(\alpha^g-\beta^g)/(\alpha-\beta)$. The authors prove that $|S(g)|>\exp[c(\log\log g)^{1/2}]$ for some determinable constant c, and they state a similar result for $t(g)$, but only in case $\lambda=2$. Though this note was published only recently, it was submitted four years ago; since then, several other papers by the authors, by A. Schinzel, and by S. B. Townes [see, in particular, P. Chowla, M. Dunton, D. J. Lewis, Pacific J. Math. **11** (1961), 833–845; MR **25** #39; A. Schinzel, Ark. Mat. **4** (1962), 413–416; MR **25** #2999; S. B. Townes, Proc. Amer. Math. Soc. **13** (1962), 864–869; MR **26** #76] have been written and published, so the authors' methods are no longer the best available. The explicit result for $t(g)$ has been superseded by that of Townes, but the result for $S(g)$ still seems to be the best published.

B. J. Birch (Manchester)

Citations: MR 25# 39 = D60-47; MR 25# 2999 = B40-32; MR 26# 76 = D60-53.

D60-59 **(28# 2072)**

Lehmer, D. H.

On a problem of Störmer.

Illinois J. Math. **8** (1964), 57–79.

Let $q_1 < q_2 < \cdots < q_t$ be a set of primes, and let a pair of consecutive integers n, $n+1$ be called 'admissible' if all prime divisors of both n and $n+1$ belong to this set. (This is not the author's terminology.) C. Størmer [Vid. Skr. I Math.-Natur. Kl. (Christiania) **1897**, no. 2] developed an algorithm for finding all admissible pairs (for a given set of q's). This algorithm depends on the solution of $3^t - 2^t$ Pell equations and shows, in particular, that the number of admissible pairs cannot exceed $3^t - 2^t$. The object of the paper under review is to present an alternative to Størmer's algorithm and to reduce to $2^t - 1$ the number of Pell equations that need to be solved. It follows from the new procedure that, if $q_t > 3$, then the number of admissible pairs does not exceed $(q_t + 1)(2^t - 1)/2$. Moreover, an upper bound is obtained, in terms of the q's, for the largest admissible pair. Several tables are appended to the paper and, in particular, all 869 admissible pairs corresponding to the set $q_1 = 2$, $q_2 = 3$, $q_3 = 5$, $\cdots$, $q_{13} = 41$ are listed.

L. Mirsky (Sheffield)

D60-60 **(29# 5780)**

Inkeri, K.

On Catalan's problem.

Acta Arith. **9** (1964), 285–290.

Catalan's equation $x^p - y^q = 1$ is discussed for the case p, q prime, $p > 3$, $q > 3$, $p \equiv 3 \pmod 4$, and q does not divide the class number $h(p)$ of the quadratic field $k(\sqrt{-p})$. If these conditions hold and if there is a non-zero integral solution x, y, then it is shown that $p^q \equiv p \pmod{q^2}$, $x \equiv 0 \pmod{q^2}$, and $y \equiv -1 \pmod{q^{2p-1}}$. If we also have $p > q$ and $q \equiv 3 \pmod 4$, then the roles of p and q can be reversed to obtain additional conditions. These results imply that Catalan's equation is unsolvable for a large number of pairs p, q. *W. H. Mills* (Princeton, N.J.)

D60-61 **(29# 5783)**

Rumsey, Howard, Jr.; Posner, Edward C.

On a class of exponential equations.

Proc. Amer. Math. Soc. **15** (1964), 974–978.

The purpose of the paper is the proof of the following theorem. Let a be an odd integer or $a = 2$, and let q_s $(1 \leq s \leq j)$ and r_t $(1 \leq t \leq k)$ be $j + k$ distinct primes, all prime to a. Then the equation $a^x = B + C$ $(B = q_1^{y_1} \cdots q_j^{y_j}$, $C = r_1^{z_1} \cdots r_k^{z_k})$ has only a finite number of solutions in non-negative integers x; $y_1, \cdots, y_j$; $z_1, \cdots, z_k$. All such solutions may be found in a finite number of steps. The fact that the number of solutions is finite follows from a more general statement in Gel'fond [*Transcendental and algebraic numbers* (Russian), GITTL, Moscow, 1952; MR **15**, 292; English transl., p. 37, Dover, New York, 1960; MR **22** #2598]. The fact that all solutions may be found constructively seems new. The proof is based on the factorization of a^{2x} in the field $R((-BC)^{1/2})$ (R is the field of rationals) and follows readily from the following lemma. Let D be a positive integer, H an algebraic integer in $R((-D)^{1/2})$, not a unit, u a unit in $R((-D)^{1/2})$ and $(p_1, p_2, \cdots, p_m)$ a fixed set of rational primes, all relatively prime to H. Then there exist effectively computable constants $X_1, \cdots, X_m$ such that $x_i \geq X_i$ $(1 \leq i \leq m)$ implies that $uH^r - \bar{u}\bar{H}^r = p_1^{x_1} p_2^{x_2} \cdots p_m^{x_m}(-D)^{1/2}$ has no solutions in non-negative integers r; $x_1, \cdots, x_m$. The proof of the lemma is obtained by considering separately the three particular cases: $u = \pm 1$; $u = \pm i$, $D = 1$; $u = \frac{1}{2}(\pm 1 \pm i3^{1/2})$, $D = 3$.

{Misprints: in (7) replace i by 1, and reference [3] should read reference [2].} *E. Grosswald* (Paris)

Citations: MR 15, 292e = J02-6; MR 22# 2598 = J02-7.

D60-62 **(30# 1093)**

Chidambaraswamy, J.

On a conjecture of A. Makowski.

Math. Student **31** (1963), 5–6 (1964).

It is proved that $13^x - 3^y = 10^z$ is not solvable in non-negative integers x, y, z unless $z = 1$.

E. Cohen (Knoxville, Tenn.)

D60-63 **(30# 1972)**

Rotkiewicz, A.; Sierpiński, W.

Sur l'équation diophantienne $2^x - xy = 2$.

Publ. Inst. Math. (*Beograd*) (*N.S.*) **4** **(18)** (1964), 135–137.

It is proved that the equation in the title has but one solution with both x and y prime, infinitely many with both x and y composite, infinitely many with x prime and y composite, and none with x composite and y prime. The last case offers the principal difficulty. When x is composite, it is pseudoprime, that is, it divides $2^x - 2$.

J. B. Kelly (Tempe, Ariz.)

Referred to in A18-32.

D60-64 **(31# 3378)**

Hyyrö, Seppo

Über das Catalansche Problem.

Ann. Univ. Turku. Ser. A I No. 79 (1964), 10 *pp.*

Catalan's problem is to show that there are no integral solutions x, y, p, q (p, q prime) of the equation $x^p - y^q = 1$ except $3^2 - 2^3 = 1$. In this paper it is shown that any other solution must be very large: $x > 10^{11}$, $y > 10^{11}$. More generally, in any solution of $x^m - y^n = 1$ $(m > 1, n > 1)$, if m is composite, then $x > 10^{84}$, and similarly $y > 10^{84}$ if n is composite; and if both m and n are composite, then the numbers x^m and y^n contain more than 10^9 digits. Finally, it is deduced from work of Davenport and Roth [Mathematika **2** (1955), 81–96; MR **17**, 829; ibid. **2** (1955), 160–167; MR **17**, 1060] that for fixed m and n the number of solutions of $x^m - y^n = 1$ is at most $\exp(631 m^2 n^2)$.

J. W. S. Cassels (Cambridge, England)

Citations: MR 17, 829f = D76-7; MR 17, 1060d = J68-15.

D60-65 **(32# 1166)**

Szymiczek, K.

On the equation $a^x - b^x = (a-b)c^y$. (Polish)

Wiadom. Mat. (2) **7**, 233–236 (1964).

An elementary proof of the theorem that the equation $a^x - b^x = (a-b)c^y$ has at most one solution in natural x, y. *S. Knapowski* (Gainesville, Fla.)

D60-66 **(33# 92)**

Dem'janenko, V. A.

On Jeśmanowicz' problem for Pythagorean numbers. (Russian)

Izv. Vysš. Učebn. Zaved. Matematika **1965**, *no.* 5 (48), 52–56.

The problem of Jeśmanowicz consists in showing that if $a^2 + b^2 = c^2$ (a, b, c positive integers), then $a^x + b^y = c^z$ has no solution in integers $x, y, z \geq 0$ other than $x = y = z = 2$ [L. Jeśmanowicz, Wiadom. Mat. (2) **1** (1955/56), 196–202;

MR **22** #1537]. Using the results of K'o Chao ["Note on Pythagorean numbers" and "A premise of Jeśmanowicz", both in Acta Sci. Natur. Univ. Szechuan. **1958**, no. 2] and Podsypanin [Izv. Vysš. Učebn. Zaved. Matematika **1962**, no. 4 (29), 130–133; MR **25** #1130], the author solves the problem for (I) $c=b+1$, and for (II) $a=m^2-1$, $b=2m$, $c=m^2+1$.

{Reviewer's remarks: (1) The proof of a lemma and the proof related to the case (II), m odd, contain gaps which, however, can be filled in. (2) The case (II), m even, has been already settled by Lu Wen-twan in Acta Sci. Natur. Univ. Szechuan. **1959**, no. 2, 39–42.}

A. Schinzel (Warsaw)

Citations: MR 22# 1537 = D60-32; MR 25# 1130 = D60-48.

D60-67 (33# 2600)

Szymiczek, K.

On the equations $a^x \pm b^x = c^y$.

Amer. J. Math. **87** (1965), 262–266.

It follows from a theorem of Birkhoff and Vandiver [Ann. of Math. **5** (1903/04), 173–180] on the existence of primitive prime divisors of numbers a^n-b^n that each of the equations in the title has at most one solution in integers x, y, aside from $x=y=1$. Here the author determines the only possible solution rather explicitly, using methods similar to, but simpler than, those applied by the reviewer for the equation $a^x-b^y=1$ [Amer. J. Math. **74** (1952), 325–331; MR **13**, 822].

W. J. LeVeque (Ann Arbor, Mich.)

Citations: MR 13, 822f = D60-10.

D60-68 (34# 136)

Hasse, Helmut

Über eine diophantische Gleichung von Ramanujan-Nagell und ihre Verallgemeinerung.

Nagoya Math. J. **27** (1966), 77–102.

Over the years a sizable literature has been developed regarding the nonnegative integral solutions (for x and n) of the equation $x^2-D=l^n$, where D and $l>0$ are specified integers. It is well known that such equations have only finitely many solutions [see Satz 698 (Pólya) of E. Landau, *Vorlesungen über Zahlentheorie*, Vol. 3, p. 65, Hirzel, Leipzig, 1927]. However, no general method is known which will give the solutions for any given equation, although, in principle, an adept application of "Skolem's p-adic" method should give a bound on the number of solutions. The most popular example of this type of problem is the conjecture of Ramanujan (first proved by T. Nagell [Nordisk. Mat. Tidskr. **30** (1948), 62–64]) that the equation $x^2+7=2^n$ has $n=3, 4, 5, 7, 15$ as its only solutions. The first part of this paper is a thorough survey of the literature regarding the equation $x^2-D=l^n$, and especially the case $l=2$, D odd. In the last part of the paper various necessary conditions for the existence of a solution to $x^2-D=2^n$, D odd, are given in terms of congruence conditions for a solution n and the smallest solution x_1.

D. J. Lewis (Ann Arbor, Mich.)

D60-69 (34# 7489)

Laxton, R. R.

Linear recurrences of order two.

J. Austral. Math. Soc. **7** (1967), 108–114.

It has long been conjectured that a linear recurrence of rational numbers $\{f(n)\}$ of order 2, whose companion polynomial $y^2-ay-b\in Q[y]$ has no zero and no ratio of zeros a root of unity, can represent any one rational number at most five times. As a step in this direction, the author proves: Let p be the smallest prime such that a is a p-adic integer and b is a p-adic unit; then no rational number is represented more than M times, where $M=8$ if $p=2$, $M=10$ if $p=3$, and $M=p^2$ otherwise. The proof relies heavily on Skolem's p-adic method for exponential sums. For earlier results, see S. Chowla, M. Dunton and the reviewer [Pacific J. Math. **11** (1961), 833–845; MR **25** #39]. The author comments that his method also yields results on related conjectures for recurrences of order 3.

D. J. Lewis (Ann Arbor, Mich.)

Citations: MR 25# 39 = D60-47.

D60-70 (35# 127)

Hurwitz, Solomon

On the rational solutions of $m^n=n^m$ with $m\neq n$.

Amer. Math. Monthly **74** (1967), 298–300.

It is shown that all the rational solutions of the well-known Diophantine equation $m^n=n^m$ with $|m|>|n|$ are given by $m=(1+1/s)^{1+s}$, $n=(1+1/s)^s$, with s a positive integer, and $m=-(1+1/s)^{1+s}$, $n=-(1+1/s)^s$, with s a positive odd integer.

M. S. Cheema (Tucson, Ariz.)

D60-71 (35# 4156)

Mąkowski, A.

On the equation $n^x+(n+1)^y=(n+2)^z$. (Polish)

Wiadom. Mat. (2) **9**, 221–224 (1966/67).

Some necessary conditions are given for the solubility of the Diophantine equation $n^x+(n+1)^y=(n+2)^z$ with $y=1$. All the solutions of this equation with $y>1$ have been found by B. Leszczyński [Wiadom. Mat. (2) **3**, 37–39 (1959); MR **22** #6770].

A. Schinzel (Warsaw)

Citations: MR 22# 6770 = D60-34.

D60-72 (35# 6627)

Schneider, Th.

Anwendung eines abgeänderten Roth-Ridoutschen Satzes auf diophantische Gleichungen.

Math. Ann. **169** (1967), 177–182.

Let X, Y, Z be, respectively, of the form $hP_1^{\alpha_1}\cdots P_s^{\alpha_s}$, $qQ_1^{\beta_1}\cdots Q_t^{\beta_t}$, $fR_1^{\gamma_1}\cdots R_n^{\gamma_n}$, where $P_1,\cdots,P_s$, $Q_1,\cdots,R_n$ are distinct primes and where $0<|h|\leq c|X|^\mu$, $0<|q|\leq c|Y|^\nu$, $0<|f|\leq c|Z|^\lambda$, $\lambda+\mu+\nu<1$. Then there are at most finitely many pairwise prime triplets X, Y, Z such that $X+Y+Z=0$. The proof entails a fairly standard application of Ridout's extensions [D. Ridout, Mathematika **4** (1957), 125–131; MR **20** #32] of Roth's theorem [K. F. Roth, ibid. **2** (1955), 1–20; corrigendum, p. 168; MR **17**, 242] to simultaneous approximations of an algebraic number by a real and several p-adic numbers. The case where $\lambda=\mu=\nu=0$ and h, q, r are fixed was first solved by A. Gel'fond [Mat. Sb. (N.S.) **7** **(49)** (1940), 7–25; MR **1**, 292].

D. J. Lewis (Ann Arbor, Mich.)

Citations: MR 1, 292d = D60-1; MR 17, 242d = J68-14; MR 20# 32 = J68-18.

D60-73 (36# 127)

Usol'cev, L. P.

An additive problem with an increasing number of terms with the exponential function. (Russian)

Izv. Vysš. Učebn. Zaved. Matematika **1967**, *no.* 3 (58), 96–104.

Let $g\geq 4$ be a natural number. An asymptotic formula is given for the number $A_g(N)$ of solutions of the diophantine equation $g^{x_1}+\cdots+g^{x_n}=g^{y_1}+\cdots+g^{y_n}$, where $x_1,\cdots,x_n$, $y_1,\cdots,y_n$ are nonnegative integers not exceeding $N-1$. The proof is based on an estimate of the exponential sum $(1/p)\sum_{k=0}^{N-1}\exp(2\pi ixg^k)$ and on an argument similar to that used in proving the local form of the central limit theorem of probability theory.

A. Rényi (Budapest)

D60-74 (36# 5062)

Cohen, Edward L.

On the sum of the squares of two consecutive integers.

Math. Comp. **21** (1967), 460–465.

The primes or prime powers 5, 5^2, 13, 13^4, 29^2, 41 and 61 are sums of the squares of consecutive integers. The result of the present work is that, for primes $q \leq 109$, there are no further solutions of $n^2+(n+1)^2=q^k$. The cases $q=17$ and 41 are discussed in detail and information is given on the computations required for other cases.

{The exposition is disorganized. Neither the theorem nor the two lemmas are true as stated although they are easily patched up. The distinction that the author draws between Case 1 and Case 2 primes is nowhere clearly stated but appears to rest on the fact that a Case 2 prime requires one less step in the proof (which may involve considerable computation) than a Case 1 prime. The simplification makes it possible to extend the result to some 28 Case 2 primes between 110 and 1000.}

J. D. Swift (Los Angeles, Calif.)

D60-75 (37# 5185)

Laxton, R. R.

Linear p-adic recurrences.

Quart. J. Math. Oxford Ser. (2) **19** (1968), 305–311.

Let $\{f(n)\}$ be a linear recurrence of p-adic integers, not all divisible by p, of order $k: f(n+k)=\sum_{i=0}^{k-1} c_i f(n+i)$, where $c_0, \cdots, c_{k-1}; f(0), \cdots, f(k-1)$ are p-adic integers. Suppose further that the companion polynomial $G(y)=y^k-\sum_{i=0}^{k-1} c_i y^i$ is irreducible over the p-adic field, has no root of unity as zero, and has discriminant prime to p. Then, using Skolem's p-adic method, the author proves: If α is a p-adic unit, then $f(n)=\alpha$ has at most $k(p^k-1)p^s$ positive rational integer solutions n, where $p^s \| (k+1)!$. The case of linear recurrences of order 2 had been studied earlier by M. Ward [Illinois J. Math. **6** (1962), 40–52; MR **25** #2028].

D. J. Lewis (Ann Arbor, Mich.)

Citations: MR 25# 2028 = B40-30.

D60-76 (38# 4403)

Udrescu, Valeriu Şt.

An elementary proof of a conjecture of Ramanujan.

Rev. Roumaine Math. Pures Appl. **13** (1968), 887–890.

An attempt at an elementary proof that the only integral solutions of $2^n=7+x^2$ are for $n=3, 4, 5, 7, 15$. The fallacy occurs at the bottom of page 889 where it is concluded that, since a quadratic function is negative at $2^{n-1}-1$ and positive at 2^n-1, its zero cannot be integral. There are a number of previous errors and misprints but these are correctible.

J. D. Swift (Los Angeles, Calif.)

D60-77 (40# 1360)

Chowla, Paromita

Remarks on a previous paper.

J. Number Theory **1** (1969), 522–524.

Let a, b and g be given integers, $|g|>1$. Further, let $\{s_n\}$ be defined by the linear recurrence $s_n=as_{n-1}-bs_{n-2}$. Then it is proved that $s_n=g$ implies $n<|g|^B$, where B is an effectively computable constant depending only on a, b, s_1 and s_2. In the proof use is made of a recent result due to A. Baker [J. London Math. Soc. **43** (1968), 1–9; MR **38** #111]. The author gives details only in the special case $a=2$, $b=3$, $s_1=1$ and $s_2=-1$, thereby generalizing a result in a previous paper [*Calcutta math. soc. golden jubilee commemoration vol. (1958/1959)*, Part II, pp. 373–378, Calcutta Math. Soc., Calcutta, 1963; MR **27** #4791].

W. Ljunggren (Oslo)

Citations: MR 27# 4791 = D60-56; MR 38# 111 = D24-72.

D60-78 (40# 5538)

Sprindžuk, V. G.

Effective estimates in "ternary" exponential diophantine equations. (Russian)

Dokl. Akad. Nauk BSSR **13** (1969), 777–780.

The author makes use of earlier work by himself [same Dokl. **11** (1967), 767–769; MR **36** #1396; ibid. **12** (1968), 293–297; MR **37** #6247; Vescī Akad. Navuk BSSR Ser. Fīz.-Mat. Navuk **1968**, no. 4, 5–14] and A. Baker [Philos. Trans. Roy. Soc. London Ser. A **263** (1967/68), 173–191; MR **37** #4005; J. London Math. Soc. **43** (1968), 1–9; MR **38** #111] to give effective bounds for the solutions of Diophantine equations of the following types. (I) $A\alpha\alpha_1^{x_1}\cdots\alpha_e^{x_e}+B\beta\beta_1^{y_1}\cdots\beta_m^{y_m}+C\gamma\gamma_1^{z_1}\cdots\gamma_n^{z_n}=0$, where the unknowns are the non-negative rational integers x_i, y_i, z_i and the algebraic integers α, β, γ (the $\alpha_i, \beta_i, \gamma_i, A, B, C$ being fixed algebraic integers); (II) $f(x,y)=A$, where f is an irreducible integral binary form of degree at least 3 and A is a rational integer; (III) $f(x,y)=Ap_1^{z_1}\cdots p_s^{z_s}$, where the z_i are non-negative integers and the p_i are primes dividing neither the discriminant of f nor the rational integer A.

J. B. Roberts (Halifax, N.S.)

Citations: MR 36# 1396 = J80-24; MR 37# 4005 = D40-50; MR 37# 6247 = D24-71; MR 38# 111 = D24-72.

D60-79 (40# 5539)

Suryanarayana, D.

Certain diophantine equation.

Math. Student **35** (1967), 197–199 (1969).

In the present paper the author proves the following Theorem: Let p be a prime and q an integer greater than 1. If $1+q+q^2+\cdots+q^{\mu-1}$ is a power of p, then μ is unique and equal to 2 if $p=2$ and is a prime divisor of $p-1$ if p is odd.

R. Finkelstein (Bowling Green, Ohio)

D60-80 (41# 8338)

Perisastri, M.

A note on the equation $a^x-b^y=10^z$.

Math. Student **37** (1969), 211–212.

It is proved in an elementary way that the equation of the title has no solutions in non-negative integers if $a\equiv 13 \pmod{20}$, $b\equiv 3 \pmod{20}$ and $z\neq 1$.

W. Ljunggren (Oslo)

D60-81 (42# 1759)

Madhavarao, B. S.

On a conjecture of Ramanujan and some simple deductions.

Indian J. Math. **9** (1967), 447–450 (1968).

It is known that $2^{n+2}-7=u^2$ has just five solutions: $(n,u)=(1,1), (2,3), (3,5), (5,11), (13,181)$. The author proposes a new proof based on certain convergents of the continued fraction for $\sqrt{2}$, but at the final, crucial steps the argument is poorly expressed and not convincing. Several misprints appear and the notation $(2n+1)C_k$ for the binomial coefficient $\binom{2n+1}{k}$ is confusing.

B. M. Stewart (E. Lansing, Mich.)

D60-82 (42# 5910)

Sprindžuk, V. G.

A new application of p-adic analysis to representations of numbers by binary forms. (Russian)

Izv. Akad. Nauk SSSR Ser. Mat. **34** (1970), 1038–1063.

The author investigates the problem of estimating solutions of a Diophantine equation (1) $f(x, y)=Ap_1^{z_1}\cdots p_s^{z_s}$, $(x, y)=1$.

In (1) $f(x, y)$ is an integral irreducible binary form of power $n\geqq 3$, $p_1, \cdots, p_s$ are fixed distinct prime numbers, and A is an integer.

With special assumptions on the form $f(x, y)$ and the numbers $A, p_1, \cdots, p_s$, the author shows that all the solutions $x, y, z_1\geqq 0, \cdots, z_s\geqq 0$ of the Diophantine equation (1) satisfy $\max(|x|, |y|, p_1^{z_1}, \cdots, p_s^{z_s})<c\exp(\ln|A|)^k$, where $k>2$, c an effectively determined value, not dependant on A.

The author's method is based on estimates of bounds of linear forms of algebraic number logarithms in various metrics. *L. A. Kogan* (Tashkent)

D60-83 (44# 3953)

Ljunggren, W.
On the diophantine equation $x^2+D=4y^q$.
Monatsh. Math. **75** (1971), 136–143.

The author proves the following result. Let $D\equiv 15 \pmod{72}$; then the equation in the title has only a finite number of solutions in positive integers x and y and odd primes q, provided $(h, q)=1$. If there are solutions these can be effectively found. A similar theorem is also proved for $D\equiv 7 \pmod{24}$. In the proof use is made of a lemma due to Cassels. *B. Stolt* (Stockholm)

D60-84 (44# 5272)

Sato, Daihachiro
Algebraic solution of $x^y=y^x$ $(0<x<y)$.
Proc. Amer. Math. Soc. **31** (1972), 316.

The author proves the theorem: The solutions of $x^y=y^x$ $(0<x<y)$ in the real algebraic field are parametrized by $x=s^{s/(s-1)}$, $y=s^{1/(s-1)}$, where s is any rational number in the open unit interval $0<s<1$ and the solutions in the ring of algebraic integers are parametrized by $x=(k+1)^{1/k}$, $y=(k+1)\times(k+1)^{1/k}$ where $k=1, 2, 3, \cdots$.

This is an extension of the result that the only solution to the equation in rational integers is $2^4=4^2$. The proof is very short and effectively follows from the Gel'fond-Schneider theorem. *R. F. Churchhouse* (Cardiff)

D64 EXPONENTIAL EQUATIONS: PRODUCT OF CONSECUTIVE INTEGERS OR BINOMIAL COEFFICIENTS MADE A POWER

For more on triangular numbers, see **D08**.
See also reviews B64-59, D12-51, D12-65.

D64-1 (1, 4d)

Erdös, P. Note on products of consecutive integers. J. London Math. Soc. **14**, 194–198 (1939).

The purpose of this note is to prove that the product of k consecutive integers is never a perfect square. The proof makes use of the theorem (due to Sylvester) that such a product is divisible by a prime greater than k [Mess. of Math. **21** (1892); Sylvester's Collected Mathematical Papers **4**, 687]. The author has given an elementary proof of Sylvester's theorem [J. London Math. Soc. **9**, 282–288 (1934)]; the methods used in this note are again elementary and somewhat similar to those used in the paper just referred to. The proof is given for $k\geqq 100$; the remaining cases are taken care of by referring to a paper by S. Narumi who had already given the proof for $k\leqq 202$ [Tôhoku Math. J. **11**, 128–142 (1917)]. The author states that the same method can be used to prove that a product of consecutive odd integers is never a power. *H. W. Brinkmann.*

Referred to in D64-13.

D64-2 (1, 39d)

Erdös, P. Note on the product of consecutive integers (II). J. London Math. Soc. **14**, 245–249 (1939).

The author proves that for every $l>2$ there exists a $k_0=k_0(l)$, such that, when $k\geqq k_0$, the product of k consecutive integers cannot be a perfect lth power. He had previously shown that such a product is never a perfect square [J. London Math. Soc. **14**, 194–198 (1939); Math. Reviews **1**, 4]. The method used here is very similar to that used in the earlier paper; in addition the well-known theorem of Thue is employed at one point. The author also shows in a very simple way that the binomial coefficient $C_{n,k}$ $(n\geqq 2k)$ is not a perfect lth power if $k\geqq 2^l$ $(l>1)$ or if $l=3$ $(k>1)$. It would be possible to prove this for any $l\geqq 3$ $(k>1)$ if one could show that the equations

$$x^l\pm 1=2y^l, \quad x^l\pm 1=2^{l-1}y^l$$

have no solution in positive integers (except $x=y=1$ for the first equation). *H. W. Brinkmann* (Swarthmore, Pa.).

Referred to in D64-5, D64-9, D64-12, D64-13.

D64-3 (1, 291f)

Johnson, L. Louise. On the Diophantine equation $x(x+1)\cdots(x+n-1)=y^k$. Amer. Math. Monthly **47**, 280–289 (1940).

Let the product of n consecutive integers be

$$P_n=x(x+1)\cdots(x+n-1).$$

The author proves that $P_k=y^{2k}$ is impossible and that the equation $P_n=y^k$, for $n=4, 5, 6, 7$ and $k>7$ prime, has at most one solution. The proof of the first result is elementary and uses a result of Sylvester and Schur. The proof of the second result is based on a deep theorem of Siegel. *P. Erdös* (Princeton, N. J.).

Referred to in A40-3, D64-7, D64-13.

D64-4 (1, 291g)

Pillai, S. S. On m consecutive integers. II. Proc. Indian Acad. Sci., Sect. A. **11**, 73–80 (1940).

The greater part of this paper is devoted to the proof of the fact that the equation

$$(1) \qquad n(n+1)\cdots(n+m-1)=y^r$$

has no solutions n and y for the case $2\leqq m\leqq 16$, $r\geqq(m+3)/2$. The proof depends on an interesting theorem proved in the first communication [in the same vol., pp. 6–12; these Rev. **1**, 199]. This states that for $m\leqq 16$, in every set of m consecutive integers, there is at least one which is prime to every other integer in the set. Two further theorems are given with outlines of their proofs. The first states that, for $r\geqq 3$, the equation (1) has at most a finite number of solutions. The second states that there is a number $c(m)$ such that (1) has no solution for $r>c(m)$. Here the author clearly intends that the condition $m\geqq 2$ shall hold. The proofs are accomplished by making use of theorems of Thue and Siegel. *H. S. Zuckerman* (Seattle, Wash.).

Citations: MR 1, 199g = A40-1.
Referred to in D64-13.

D64-5 (2, 145c)

Rigge, Olov. On a diophantine problem. Ark. Mat. Astr. Fys. **27A**, no. 3, 10 pp. (1940).

The main result of this paper is as follows. If q is a prime and c an integer which is only divisible by primes not greater than $n/2$, then the diophantine equation

$$c(x+1)(x+2)\cdots(x+n)=y^q$$

is, for $q=5$, $n=50q^3$, solvable in integers x, y only when $y=0$. Essentially this says that, if $q\geqq 5$ is a prime and x and n are integers for which $x\geqq n\geqq 50q^3$, then there is at least one number in the set $x+1, x+2, \cdots, x+n$ which is divisible by a prime $\geqq n$ to a power whose exponent is not divisible by q. The proof of this theorem is extremely involved and rests on a result of Thue concerning equations of the form $ax^r-by^r=f$. The author confines himself to the case $q\geqq 17$, where the proof is actually given, while the result for $q=5, 7, 11, 13$ is merely stated. The paper is closely connected with one previously published by Erdös [J. London Math. Soc. **14**, 245–249 (1939); cf. these Rev. **1**, 39]. *I. A. Barnett* (Cincinnati, Ohio).

Citations: MR 1, 39d = D64-2.

Referred to in D64-17.

D64-6 (5, 90d)

Oblath, Richard. On products of consecutive integers. Revista Mat. Hisp.-Amer. (4) **2**, 190–210, 253–270 (1942). (Spanish)

This paper contains various contributions to the conjecture that the product

$$P_k(x)=x(x+1)\cdots(x+k-1)$$

of k consecutive integers $(k>1)$ cannot be a perfect nth power $(n>1)$. For example, the author proves that P_5 cannot be an nth power if n is a prime for which $2^{n-1}\not\equiv 1 \pmod{n^2}$; this proves the conjecture for P_5 if n(prime) <16000 with the possible exceptions of $n=1093$, 3511. Similar results are obtained for P_4, P_6, P_7. Again it is proved that $P_5(x)=y^n$ can have at most one solution (for given n); similar results are given for P_4, P_6, P_7. All of these special results have been superseded by the proof of the conjecture for $k\leqq 9$ which has been given by G. Szekeres. This result has apparently not been published but was communicated to the author.

Some of the lemmas used in the proofs are themselves of interest. For example, it is proved that the equations $x^n\pm 1=2^{n-2}y^n$ have no solutions in positive integers if n is a prime for which $2^{n-1}\not\equiv 1 \pmod{n^2}$. In the theorem concerning the number of solutions a theorem of Siegel is used to establish the uniqueness. A few independent results may be quoted: (1) P_k cannot be a cube or a fifth power if $k\leqq 23$; (2) $P_k(x)$ cannot be an nth power if $k>\frac{1}{2}\sqrt{x}$; (3) $P_k(x)$ can be a perfect cube for at most $3^{3k/(\log k)}$ values of x; (4) $P_k(x)$ can be an nth power $(n\geqq 5)$ for at most $2^{(7/2)k+6\sqrt{k}}$ values of x. *H. W. Brinkmann.*

Referred to in D64-13.

D64-7 (6, 170a)

Pillai, S. S. On m consecutive integers. IV. Bull. Calcutta Math. Soc. **36**, 99–101 (1944).

[The first three notes appeared in Proc. Indian Acad. Sci., Sect. A. **11**, 6–12, 73–80 (1940); **13**, 530–533 (1941); these Rev. **1**, 199, 291; **3**, 66.] The theorem of the third note of this series is proved in a much simpler way. *H. S. Zuckerman* (Seattle, Wash.).

Citations: MR 1, 199g = A40-1; MR 1, 291f = D64-3; MR 3, 66g = A40-3.

D64-8 (10, 3d)

Correnti, Salvatore. Problemi inversi in analisi combinatoria. Matematiche, Catania **1**, 72–80 (1946).

The problems considered are all related to the following: find r consecutive integers whose product is a given integer. Conditions for the existence of a solution and rough bounds for the solution when it exists are given. *J. Riordan.*

D64-9 (10, 353l)

Obláth, Richard. Note on the binomial coefficients. J. London Math. Soc. **23**, 252–253 (1948).

P. Erdös [same J. **14**, 245–249 (1939); these Rev. **1**, 39] has shown that the binomial coefficient $\binom{n}{k}$ for $n\geqq 2k>2$ is not a perfect jth power if the equations $x^j\pm 1=2y^j$, $x^j\pm 1=2^{j-1}y^j$ have no solutions in positive integers (except $x=y=1$ for the first equation), a well-known fact for $j=3$. The writer points out that the impossibility of these equations has been proved for $j=4$ by Legendre, for $j=5$ by Dirichlet and V. A. Lebesgue. *I. Niven* (Eugene, Ore.).

Citations: MR 1, 39d = D64-2.

Referred to in D64-12.

D64-10 (12, 10f)

Obláth, Richard. Une remarque sur la progression arithmétique. Mat. Lapok **1**, 138–139 (1950). (Hungarian. Russian and French summaries)

The author proves that if $(a, d)=1$ then $a(a+d)(a+2d)$ is never a cube, fourth power, or fifth power. *P. Erdös* (Aberdeen).

D64-11 (12, 590e)

Obláth, Richard. Über das Produkt fünf aufeinander folgender Zahlen in einer arithmetischen Reihe. Publ. Math. Debrecen **1**, 222–226 (1950).

Let $(a, d)=1$. The author proves that

$$a\cdot(a+d)(a+2d)(a+3d)(a+4d)=x^2$$

is impossible. *P. Erdös* (Aberdeen).

D64-12 (12, 804d)

Erdös, P. On a Diophantine equation. J. London Math. Soc. **26**, 176–178 (1951).

The equation $\binom{n}{k}=x^j$ with the natural restrictions $n\geqq 2k$, $j>1$, $k>1$ is proved impossible in integers for all $k>3$. The author [same J. **14**, 245–249 (1939); these Rev. **1**, 39] established the impossibility in case $j=3$, and Obláth [ibid. **23**, 252–253 (1948); these Rev. **10**, 353] extended this to $j=4$ and $j=5$. It can be readily proved that there are infinitely many solutions in case $j=k=2$, and Erdös recalls that there is only one solution $(n=50, x=140)$ in case $k=3$, $j=2$, although the reference is forgotten. Thus it appears that the cases $k=2$ and $k=3$ with $j\geqq 6$ remain open. *I. Niven* (Eugene, Ore.).

Citations: MR 1, 39d = D64-2; MR 10, 353l = D64-9.

Referred to in D64-17.

D64-13 (13, 823a)

Oblath, Richard. Eine Bemerkung über Produkte aufeinander folgender Zahlen. J. Indian Math. Soc. (N.S.) **15** (1951), 135–139 (1952).

It is proved that the product $P_k(x)=x(x+1)\cdots(x+k-1)$ of k consecutive integers cannot be a perfect nth power y^n for $2\leqq k\leqq 17$, $y\neq 0$, $n>1$. The author had treated some cases previously [Revista Mat. Hisp.-Amer. (4) **2**, 190–210, 253–270 (1942); these Rev. **5**, 90], and attributes part of his method to Szekeres. The proof employs Pillai's theorem [Proc. Indian Acad. Sci., Sect. A. **11**, 6–12 (1940); these Rev. **1**, 199] that in every set of 16 or fewer consecutive integers there is one which is prime to all the others, and the exceptions to this for 17 integers noted by Pillai. The result overlaps various earlier contributions to the conjecture that $P_k(x)$ cannot be an nth power by Erdös [J. London Math. Soc. **14**, 194–198, 245–249 (1939); these Rev. **1**, 4, 39], Johnson [Amer. Math. Monthly **47**, 280–289 (1940);

these Rev. **1**, 291] and Pillai [Proc. Indian Acad. Sci., Sect. A. **11**, 73–80 (1940); these Rev. **1**, 291]. *I. Niven.*

Citations: MR 1, 4d = D64-1; MR 1, 39d = D64-2; MR 1, 199g = A40-1; MR 1, 291f = D64-3; MR 1, 291g = D64-4; MR 5, 90d = D64-6.

D64-14 **(16, 335a)**

Thébault, Victor. Sur des produits de nombres entiers consécutifs. Mathesis **63**, 254–261 (1954).

Elementary proofs are given of special cases of known results on the impossibility of the product of consecutive integers being a square or a small multiple of a square.

I. Niven (Eugene, Ore.).

D64-15 **(16, 797d)**

Erdös, P. On the product of consecutive integers. III. Nederl. Akad. Wetensch. Proc. Ser. A. **58** = Indagationes Math. **17**, 85–90 (1955).

It has been conjectured for a long time that the product of k consecutive integers is never an mth power ($m>1$). In this paper the author proves that there exists a constant c such that the conjecture is correct for $k>c$. The proof is entirely elementary. The author states that an earlier (unpublished) proof of this fact by Siegel and himself had made use of the well known theorem of Thue-Siegel.

H. W. Brinkmann (Swarthmore, Pa.).

Referred to in D64-17.

D64-16 **(17, 1055d)**

Browkin, Georges; et Schinzel, André. Sur les nombres de Mersenne qui sont triangulaires. C. R. Acad. Sci. Paris **242** (1956), 1780–1781.

It is proved that the only solutions in positive integers of $2^x-1=y(y+1)/2$ are (1, 1), (2, 2), (4, 5) and (12, 90).

I. Niven (Eugene, Ore.).

Referred to in A52-67, B36-31, D60-42.

D64-17 **(19, 251c)**

Stolt, Bengt. Über die diophantische Gleichung $\binom{n}{k}=Mx^m$. Arch. Math. **7** (1957), 446–449.

Let $n\geqq 2k$, $m>1$, and $k>3$. The reviewer proved* [Mat. Lapok **1** (1950), 192–210; MR **13**, 208] that $\binom{n}{k}=x^m$ has no solutions in integers x, k, m and n. Let now $M=\prod p_\nu^{\alpha_\nu}$, $\alpha_\nu<m$. The author proves the existence of a $k_0=k_0(m, M)$ such that for $k>k_0$ the equation $\binom{n}{k}=Mx^m$ has no integer solutions.

[For further literature see V. Rigge, Nionde Skand. Matematiker Kongrenen, Helsingfors, 1938, Mercator, Helsingfors, 1939, pp. 155–160; Ark. Mat. Astr. Fys. **27A** (1940), no. 3; MR **2**, 145; also Erdös, Nederl. Akad. Wetensch. Proc. Ser. A. **58** (1955), 85–90; MR **16**, 797.]

P. Erdös (Toronto, Ont.).

*See instead MR 12, 804D = D64-12.

Citations: MR 2, 145c = D64-5; MR 12, 804d = D64-12; MR 16, 797d = D64-15.

D64-18 **(22# 4654)**

Khatri, M. N. Triangular numbers which are also squares. Math. Student **27** (1959), 55–56.

D64-19 **(25# 2031)**

Makowski, A.

Remarks on triangular and tetrahedral numbers.

Boll. Un. Mat. Ital. (3) **17** (1962), 20–21.

The author notes trivially that the only triangular numbers of the form p^k+1, with p prime, are 3, 6, 10 and 28, and that 1 is the only tetrahedral number of the form $2^k\pm 1$.

B. J. Birch (Manchester)

Referred to in D64-20.

D64-20 **(26# 3666)**

Simpson, Harold

On tetrahedral numbers.

Boll. Un. Mat. Ital. (3) **17** (1962), 357.

Author's summary: "A. Makowski [same Boll. (3) **17** (1962), 20–21; MR **25** #2031] considers the equations

$$n(n+1)(n+2) = 6(p^k+1),$$

$$n(n+1)(n+2) = 6(p^k-1),$$

where n, k, and p are positive integers, in the case $p=2$. His methods can readily be extended to the case in which p is any prime number, and we find that the only solutions of the first equation are those given by $n=2$, 3, 4, 7 and the only solutions of the second equation are those given by $n=1$, 2, 3, 8, 19."

Citations: MR 25# 2031 = D64-19.

D64-21 **(27# 5724)**

Moser, L.

Notes on number theory. V. Insolvability of $\binom{2n}{n}=\binom{2a}{a}\binom{2b}{b}$.

Canad. Math. Bull. **6** (1963), 167–169.

Part IV appeared in the same Bull. **6** (1963), 163–166 [MR **28** #76]. It is shown that the Diophantine equation $\binom{2n}{n}=\binom{2a}{a}\binom{2b}{b}$ has no solutions.

W. H. Mills (Princeton, N.J.)

Citations: MR 28# 76 = B16-20.

Referred to in D64-22.

D64-22 **(30# 52)**

Erdős, P.

On some divisibility properties of $\binom{2n}{n}$.

Canad. Math. Bull. **7** (1964), 513–518.

L. Moser [same Bull. **6** (1963), 167–169; MR **27** #5724] proved that the equation $\binom{2n}{n}=\binom{2a}{a}\binom{2b}{b}$ has no solutions in positive integers. In the present paper it is proved that for $a>n/2$, $\binom{2a}{a}\nmid\binom{2n}{n}$, which implies that

$$\binom{2n}{n} = \prod_{j=1}^{r}\binom{2a_j}{a_j}^{\alpha_j} \qquad (\alpha_j \geqq 1, n > a_j \geqq 1)$$

has no solutions. The author proves that if $g(m)$ is the smallest integer $n>m$ such that $\binom{2m}{m}\Big|\binom{2n}{n}$, then $g(m)\geqq 2m$ for all m, and

$$m^{1+c} < g(m) < (2m)^{\log m/\log 2} \qquad (m > m_0),$$

where c is an absolute constant >0.

L. Carlitz (Durham, N.C.)

Citations: MR 27# 5724 = D64-21.

D64-23 **(30# 3059)**

Győry, Kálmán

On the Diophantine equations $\binom{n}{2}=a^l$ **and** $\binom{n}{3}=a^l$.

(Hungarian. English summary)

Mat. Lapok **14** (1963). 322–329.

The author proves that for $n>2$ and $l>1$ the equation $\binom{n}{2}=a^{2l}$ has no solutions. He obtains some results about the unsolvability of $\binom{n}{3}=a^p$, where p is an odd prime.

P. Erdős (Budapest)

D64-24 **(41# 145)**

Stahl, Wolfgang
Bemerkung zu einer Arbeit von Hering.
Arch. Math. (*Basel*) **20** (1969), 580.

The author gives a very short and elementary proof that $\binom{n}{k}$, $1<k<n-1$, is not a power of a prime.

{The paper by F. Hering mentioned in the title appeared in same Arch. **19** (1968), 411–412 [MR **38** #1010].}

J. B. Roberts (Halifax, N.S.)

Citations: MR 38# 1010 = B64-59.

D64-25 **(41# 146)**

Scheid, Harald
Die Anzahl der Primfaktoren in $\binom{n}{k}$.
Arch. Math. (*Basel*) **20** (1969), 581–582.

The author shows that $\omega\left(\binom{n}{k}\right)$, the number of distinct prime factors in $\binom{n}{k}$, is greater than $(k \log 2)/(\log 2k)$ when $2<2k\leqq n$. This generalizes the result in the preceding paper [#145 above]. He also observes: (i) the above result is off by no more than a factor of three; (ii) $\omega\left(\binom{n}{2}\right)=2$ for n a Fermat prime or one more than a Mersenne prime; (iii) $\omega\left(\binom{n}{3}\right)=3$ for $n=6p+1$ when p, $6p-1$, $6p+1$ are all prime.

J. B. Roberts (Halifax, N.S.)

D64-26 **(42# 193)**

MacLeod, R. A.; Barrodale, I.
On equal products of consecutive integers.
Canad. Math. Bull. **13** (1970), 255–259.

Writing $a^{\bar b}$ for $a(a+1)(a+2)\cdots(a+b-1)$, a and b positive integers, the main theorem proved in this paper can be stated in the form: The equation $n^{\bar k}=m^{\overline{2k}}$, $k>1$, has at most a finite number of solutions in positive integers.

The proof given by the authors can be simplified if we note that for $0\leqq j\leqq k-1$, $n\geqq(k-2)^2/4$, we have $(n+(k-2)/2)^2\leqq(n+j)(n+k-j-1)\leqq(n+(k-1)/2)^2$, the equality sign on the right holding only when k is odd and $j=(k-1)/2$. Hence $(n+(k-2)/2)^{2k}\leqq(n^{\bar k})^2<(n+(k-1)/2)^{2k}$; so that $[(n^{\bar k})^{1/k}]=n+[(k-2)/2]$. The authors conjecture that the product of two consecutive positive integers cannot be equal to the product of four or more consecutive positive integers.

{Remark. The solutions of the equation $n^{\bar k}=m^{\bar t}$, $k<t$, would be of interest only with $n>(m+t-1)$.}

H. Gupta (Allahabad)

D64-27 **(43# 6157)**

Makowski, Andrzej
Remark on a conjecture of Erdős on binomial coefficients.
Math. Comp. **24** (1970), 705.

M. Wunderlich [Math. Comp. **16** (1962), 482–486; MR **26** #6115] ascribes the following conjecture to Erdős: (*) $2\binom{x+n-1}{n}=\binom{y+n-1}{n}$ has only one solution in positive integers x and y. The author remarks that (*) has infinitely many solutions for $n=2$ (see A. Boutin in L. E. Dickson's *History of the theory of numbers, Vol. II: Diophantine analysis*, p. 30, Carnegie Inst., Washington, D.C., 1920; reprinted, Chelsea, New York, 1966 [MR **39** #6807b]) and uses this to obtain infinitely many counterexamples to the conjecture. He feels that (*) may have no solutions with $y-x\geqq 3$.

R. P. Bambah (Chandigarh)

Citations: MR 26# 6115 = D32-71; MR 39# 6807b = Z15-88.

D68 RATIONAL NUMBERS AS SUMS OF FRACTIONS

See also Section A66.

See also reviews A66-13, A66-14, E24-127, P80-43, Z02-36, Z15-72.

D68-1 **(1, 134c)**

Nakayama, Masayosi. On the decomposition of a rational number into "Stammbrüche." Tôhoku Math. J. **46**, 1–21 (1939).

A positive proper fraction a/b can be expressed as the sum of reciprocals of natural numbers, usually in several ways. This paper deals with the minimum number $N(a, b)$ of reciprocals necessary for a given fraction. For example, necessary conditions that $N(a, b)=a$ are derived. The number of fractions $G(a, n, x)$ with $a<b\leqq x$ such that $N(a, b)>n$ $(2\leqq n<a)$ is also estimated.

H. W. Brinkmann.

Referred to in D68-15.

D68-2 **(3, 269a)**

Simmons, H. A. Classes of maximum numbers associated with two symmetric equations. Bull. Amer. Math. Soc. **48**, 295–303 (1942).

One of the Diophantine equations studied in this paper is

$$\sum_{n,\,n-1}(1/x)+\sum_{i=1}^{m}a_i[\pi(x)]^{-i}=k,$$

where $\sum_{i,j}(1/x)$ stands for the elementary symmetric function of the jth order of the i reciprocals $1/x_p$, $\pi(x)=x_1x_2\cdots x_n$, $a_i\geqq 0$ and $k=b/[(c+1)b-1]$, b and c positive integers. The second of the equations, not written here, includes as special instances certain equations previously considered by the author [Simmons and Block, Duke Math. J. **2**, 317–339 (1936)]. The solution $x=(x_1, x_2, \cdots, x_n)$ of either of these equations obtained by minimizing the variables $x_1, x_2, \cdots, x_{n-1}$ in this order, one at a time, among the positive integers is called the Kellogg solution w, while an E-solution is one in which $x_1\leqq x_2\leqq\cdots\leqq x_n$, where $x_1, x_2, \cdots, x_{n-1}$ are positive integers. He proves that for either of these equations (1) the Kellogg solution contains the largest number that exists in any E-solution, and (2) if $X\neq w$ is an E-solution, then $P(x)<P(w)$, where $P(x)=P(x_1, x_2, \cdots, x_n)$ is a symmetric polynomial, not a constant, having no negative coefficients. Both of these results have already been announced by the author for the more special equations referred to above.

I. A. Barnett.

Referred to in D68-10.

D68-3 **(7, 413d)**

Erdös, Paul, and Niven, Ivan. Some properties of partial sums of the harmonic series. Bull. Amer. Math. Soc. **52**, 248–251 (1946).

It was shown by the reviewer [T. Nagell, Skr. Norske Vid. Akad. Kristiania. I. **1923**, no. 13, 10–15 (1924)] that $\sum_{k=0}^{n}(m+kd)^{-1}$ cannot be an integer. The authors prove the following theorem of a similar nature. There is only a finite number of integers n for which one or more of the elementary symmetric functions of $1, \frac{1}{2}, \frac{1}{3}, \cdots, \frac{1}{n}$ is an integer. The proof is based on the result of A. E. Ingham [Quart. J. Math., Oxford Ser. **8**, 255–266 (1937)] that there is a prime between x and $x+x^{5/8}$. The authors assert, without proof, that the same result holds for the elementary symmetric functions of $1/m, 1/(m+1), \cdots, 1/n$ and of $1/m, 1/(m+d), 1/(m+2d), \cdots, 1/(m+nd)$. The second result of this paper is the following theorem. No two partial sums of the harmonic series can be equal; that is, it is not possible that $\sum_{k=m}^{n} k^{-1} = \sum_{k=x}^{y} k^{-1}$. The proof depends on the application of the following theorem of I. Schur [cf. Erdös, J. London Math. Soc. **9**, 282–288 (1934)]. When $n>k$, there is in the set $n, n+1, \cdots, n+k-1$ at least one integer containing a prime divisor greater than k. *T. Nagell* (Uppsala).

D68-4 (8, 443b)

Simmons, H. A. Classes of maximum numbers associated with symmetric equations in n reciprocals. IV. Proc. Phys.-Math. Soc. Japan (3) **23**, 687–695 (1941).

[Part III, by Simmons and Block, appeared in Duke Math. J. **2**, 317–339 (1936).] Let b, c, m and $n>1$ be arbitrary positive integers, and a_i, $i=1, \cdots, m$, any positive real numbers. The equation

$$\sum_{j=1}^{n} 1/x_j + \sum_{i=1}^{m} a_i \lambda^{-i} = b/a,$$

where $a=(c+1)b-1$ and λ is the product of the x_j, is discussed. Say that an E-solution of this equation is one such that $x_1 \leqq \cdots \leqq x_n$, with all these except x_n required to be positive integers. One E-solution is

$$w_1 = c+1, \quad w_{j+1} = aw_1w_2 \cdots w_j + 1, \quad j=1, \cdots, n-2,$$

and w_n determined by solving the equation for x_n. It is proved that the maximum λ among E-solutions is λ_w, which is the product of the w_j; that, among E-solutions for which (1) $\sum_{i=2}^{m} a_i \lambda^{1-i} < \sum_{i=2}^{m} a_i \lambda_w^{1-i} + 1$, the largest value of x is w_n; that, under hypothesis (1), $P(x_j) < P(w_j)$, where $P(x_j)$ is any symmetric polynomial in the x_j, not a constant and with no negative coefficients. *I. Niven.*

D68-5 (12, 481h)

Obláth, Richard. Sur l'équation diophantienne

$$\frac{4}{n} = \frac{1}{x_1} + \frac{1}{x_2} + \frac{1}{x_3}.$$

Mathesis **59**, 308–316 (1950).

Erdös is said to have conjectured that the indicated Diophantine equation is solvable for any given integer $n>1$. This conjecture is verified for all $n \leqq 106{,}128$ by means of various identities and calculations. One general result obtained is that the equation is solvable if $n+1$ is divisible by a prime of the form $4k+3$. *I. Niven* (Eugene, Ore.).

Referred to in D24-28.

D68-6 (13, 208b)

Erdös, Pál. On a Diophantine equation. Mat. Lapok **1**, 192–210 (1950). (Hungarian. Russian and English summaries)

For given integral a, b with $1 \leqq a < b$ let $N(a, b)$ denote the smallest integer n such that

$$(1) \qquad a/b = \sum_{r=1}^{n} 1/x_r, \quad \text{with} \quad x_1 < x_2 < \cdots < x_n,$$

is soluble in positive integers x_r. Sharpening a result and the method of N. G. de Bruijn he proves that

$$N(a, b) = O(\log b / \log \log b).$$

He conjectures that the true result is $N(a, b) = O(\log \log b)$, and he in fact establishes the inequalities

$$\sum_{a=1}^{b-2} N(a, b) > \tfrac{1}{2}(b-2)(\log \log b - 1), \quad N(b-1, b) > \log \log b - 1.$$

Other problems discussed include that of the greatest proper fraction a/b for which $N(a, b) \leqq n$, for given n, and that of the equation

$$(2) \qquad 1 = \sum_{r=1}^{n} 1/x_r, \quad \text{with} \quad x_1 < x_2 < \cdots < x_n,$$

and positive integral x_r. For (2) he conjectures that $x_n/x_1 \geqq 3$, with equality only when $n=3$, $x_1=2$, $x_2=3$, $x_3=6$, and further that $\lim_{n\to\infty} x_n/x_1 = \infty$. He also proves that (2) has only a finite number of solutions for given n. He also announces that he has proved that the "practical numbers" [Srinivasan, Current Sci. **17**, 179–180 (1948); these Rev. **10**, 356] have zero asymptotic density. *F. V. Atkinson.*

Citations: MR 10, 356e = A32-18.

Referred to in D68-15, D68-20.

D68-7 (15, 684c)

Rosati, Luigi Antonio. Sull'equazione diofantea

$$4/n = 1/x_1 + 1/x_2 + 1/x_3.$$

Boll. Un. Mat. Ital. (3) **9**, 59–63 (1954).

It is established that the Diophantine equation of the title is solvable for integers x_1, x_2, x_3 for all n in the range $106{,}129 \leqq n \leqq 141{,}648$. This had been verified for all smaller positive $n \neq 1$ by R. Obláth [Mathesis **59**, 308–316 (1950); these Rev. **12**, 481]. *I. Niven* (Eugene, Ore.).

Citations: MR 12, 481i = D04-14.

Referred to in D68-15, D68-16.

D68-8 (17, 1185d)

Sierpiński, W. Sur les décompositions de nombres rationnels en fractions primaires. Mathesis **65** (1956), 16–32.

Let a, b, x_1, x_2, $\cdots$ be positive integers. Denote by $f(a, b)$ the smallest value of s for which

$$\frac{a}{b} = \pm\frac{1}{x_1} \pm \frac{1}{x_2} \pm \cdots \pm \frac{1}{x_s}$$

is solvable, and by $g(a, b)$ the smallest integer s' for which

$$\frac{a}{b} = \frac{1}{x_1} + \frac{1}{x_2} + \cdots + \frac{1}{x_r}$$

is solvable. The author proves (among other results) that $f(18, 23) = 4$ and that the set of rational numbers a/b with $f(a, b) \leqq s$ is nowhere dense for every s. Schinzel conjectured that for every a there exists a constant $c = c(a)$ so that for $b > c$, $f(a, b) \leqq 3$.

The reviewer and Straus conjectured some years ago that $g(4, n) \leqq 3$ for every $n > 1$. Schinzel conjectures that for every a there exists a $c' = c'(a)$ so that for $b < c'$, $f(a, b) \leqq 3$. (The author first conjectured $g(5, n) \leqq 3$ and proved it for $1 < n \leqq 1000$). *P. Erdös* (Haifa).

Referred to in D68-11, D68-12.

D68-9 (18, 284a)

Schinzel, André. Sur quelques propriétés des nombres $3/n$ et $4/n$, où n est un nombre impair. Mathesis **65** (1956), 219–222.

Using several identities, two of which are attributed to Sierpiński, the author proves three theorems of which the following is typical: For every positive integer $n>1$ there exist distinct odd integers x, y, z, such that

$$\frac{3}{2n+1} = \frac{1}{x} + \frac{1}{y} + \frac{1}{z}.$$

L. Moser (Edmonton, Alta.).

Referred to in D68-23.

D68-10 **(18, 791e)**

Simmons, H. A. Classes of maximum numbers associated with two symmetric equations in N reciprocals. Proc. Amer. Math. Soc. **8** (1957), 169–175.

In the present paper the author generalizes results obtained in a series of previous papers [e.g. Bull. Amer. Math. Soc. **48** (1942), 295–303; MR 3, 269]. Let $\sum_{i,j}(1/x)$ stand for the elementary symmetric function of the jth order of the i reciprocals $1/x_p$, $p=1, 2, \cdots, i$, $i>0$, with $\sum_{i,j}(1/x)\equiv 0$ when $i<j$ or $j<0$, and $\sum_{i,j}(1/x)\equiv 1$ when $j=0$. Let further

$$(1)\quad \varphi_p\left(\frac{1}{x}\right)=\sum_{p,r}\left(\frac{1}{x}\right)+\sum_{k=r+1}^{s}L_k\sum_{p,k}\left(\frac{1}{x}\right)\ (r\leqq p\leqq n).$$

At first the author considers the equation

$$(2)\quad \varphi_n\left(\frac{1}{x}\right)=\frac{b}{a},\ a=(c+1)b-1,$$

in which r, s, n are positive integers with $r<s\leqq n$; each L_k is a non-negative integer; and b, c are arbitrary positive integers. The solution $x=(x_1, x_2, \cdots, x_n)$ of (2), obtained by minimizing the variables $x_1, x_2, \cdots, x_{n-1}$ in this order, one at time, among the positive integers is called the Kellogg solution ω, while an E-solution is one in which

$$(3)\quad x_1\leqq x_2\leqq x_3\leqq\cdots\leqq x_n,$$

where $x_1, x_2, \cdots, x_{n-1}$ are positive integers. Further a solution of (2) is called admissible if the elements x_j in x are real numbers $\geqq 1$, satisfying (3), and such that

$$(4)\quad \varphi_p\left(\frac{1}{x}\right)\leqq\frac{b}{a}-\frac{1}{ax_1x_2\cdots x_p}\ (p=r, \cdots, n-1).$$

When x is an E-solution of (2), (4) holds for each indicated value of p. Furthermore, one readily finds that when $x=\omega$, the equality sign applies in (4) for each value of p. Being an E-solution of (2), ω is admissible. Relative to (2) the following theorem is proved. If x is an admissible solution and $x\neq\omega$, then $x_n<\omega_n$ and $P(x)<P(\omega)$, where $P(x)\equiv P(x_1, x_2, \cdots, x_n)$ denote any nonconstant, symmetric polynomial in $x_1, x_2, \cdots, x_n$ with no negative coefficients. Finally, a similar result is proved for an equation obtained by multiplying the first term in the right member of (1) by L_r, L_r being a positive integer, in case $a=b=1$. *W. Ljunggren* (Blindern).

Citations: MR 3, 269a = D68-2.

D68-11 **(20# 3821)**

Palamà, Giuseppe. Su di una congettura di Sierpiński relativa alla possibilità in numeri naturali della $5/n=1/x_1+1/x_2+1/x_3$. Boll. Un. Mat. Ital. (3) **13** (1958), 65–72.

W. Sierpiński [Mathesis **65** (1956), 16–32; MR **17**, 1185] conjectured that the equation

$$\frac{5}{n}=\frac{1}{x_1}+\frac{1}{x_2}+\frac{1}{x_3}$$

is soluble in positive integers x_1, x_2, x_3, for every positive integer n, and verified that this is so for $n\leqq 1000$. By a detailed consideration of the form of n, and with the aid of a criterion due to G. Mignosi [Rend. Sem. Fac. Sci. Univ. Cagliari **1** (1931), 97–107], the author proves that this equation is always soluble if n is not of the form $1260m+1$, and verifies that, even for n of this form, it is soluble if $n\leqq 922321$. *R. A. Rankin* (Glasgow)

Citations: MR 17, 1185d = D68-8.

D68-12 **(22# 7989)**

Palamà, Giuseppe. Su di una congettura di Schinzel. Boll. Un. Mat. Ital. (3) **14** (1959), 82–94.

Let x_i be positive integers and let A_s be positive rationals m/n of the form

$$\frac{1}{x_1}\pm\frac{1}{x_2}\pm\cdots\pm\frac{1}{x_s},$$

where the signs + and − may be chosen arbitrarily. It has been conjectured by Andrzej Schinzel that every positive rational number m/n, with n greater than a certain natural number k_m, dependent on m, is an A_3 [W. Sierpiński, Mathesis **65** (1956), 16–32; MR **17**, 1185]. This conjecture has been verified for all $m<20$. For some m's this proof is quite complicated. For example, Schinzel has verified that for $n>23$, the number $18/n$ is an A_3. In the present paper the author proves a result [Th. III, p. 92] from which follows readily the conjecture of Schinzel for $m=19, 20, 21, 22, 23$. *I. A. Barnett* (Cincinnati, Ohio)

Citations: MR 17, 1185d = D68-8.

D68-13 **(23# A829)**

Sedláček, Jiří

Über die Stammbrüche. (Czech. Russian and German summaries)

Časopis Pěst. Mat. **84** (1959), 188–197.

Let s be a natural number and B_s the set of all rationals representable in the form $\sum_{i=1}^{s}1/x_i$, where $x_1, x_2, \cdots, x_s$ are integers. Schinzel [Sierpiński, *On the decomposition of rational numbers into unit fractions* (Polish), Państwowe Wydawnictwo Naukowe, Warsaw, 1957] has conjectured that, corresponding to every natural number m there exists a number l_m such that m/n belongs to B_3 for $n\geqq l_m$, and he and Sierpiński have verified this conjecture for $m\leqq 18$. The author shows that it is true for $m=19, 20, 21$; he also proves several results about the structure of the sets B_s. *H. Halberstam* (London)

D68-14 **(23# A1590)**

Benson, Arne

Resistance circuits and things synthesized by number theory.

Math. Mag. **34** (1960/61), 125–130.

An incomplete solution of the 'optical equation', $1/n=1/x+1/y$. For a full solution, see solution to Problem 1, Part I, 1960 Putnam examination, Amer. Math. Monthly **68** (1961), 634–635. For the history of the equation, see Dickson's *History of the theory of numbers, Vol. II*, p. 689 [Stechert, New York, 1934]. The error in the present paper occurs in the restriction at line 7, p. 128. *J. D. Swift* (Princeton, N.J.)

D68-15 **(23# A2376)**

Kiss, Ernest

Quelques remarques sur une équation diophantienne. (Romanian. Russian and French summaries)

Acad. R. P. Romîne Fil. Cluj Stud. Cerc. Mat. **10** (1959), 59–62.

For integral a, b denote by $N(a, b)$ the smallest integer n for which the Diophantine equation $a/b=\sum_{k=1}^{n}x_k^{-1}$ has solutions. Nakayama [Tôhoku Math. J. **46** (1939), 1–21; MR **1**, 134], Erdös [Mat. Lapok **1** (1950), 192–210; MR **13**, 208], Obláth [Mathesis **59** (1950), 308–316; MR **12**, 481] and Rosati [Boll. Un. Mat. Ital. (3) **9** (1954), 59–63; MR **15**, 684] proved various theorems concerning $N(a, b)$. In the present paper it is shown that the inequality $N(4, b)\leqq 3$ (conjectured by Erdös and Strauss) holds for $b<200{,}000$. This is obtained with some numerical work, on the basis of the following theorem of the author: $a/b=1/x_1+1/x_2$

has integral solutions if, and only if, $b = kb_1b_2$ with $(b_1, b_2) = 1$ and $b_1 + b_2 = ma$.

E. Grosswald (Philadelphia, Pa.)

Citations: MR 1, 134c = D68-1; MR 12, 481i = D04-14; MR 13, 208b = D68-6; MR 15, 684c = D68-7.

D68-16 (26# 77)

Bernstein, Leon

Zur Lösung der diophantischen Gleichung $m/n = 1/x + 1/y + 1/z$, insbesondere im Fall $m = 4$.

J. Reine Angew. Math. **211** (1962), 1–10.

P. Erdős has formulated the following two conjectures. For every integer $n > 1$ the equation (1) $4/n = 1/x + 1/y + 1/z$ is solvable in positive integers x, y, z. A system of congruences $a_i \pmod{n_i}$, $n_1 < n_2 < n_3 < \cdots < n_k$, is called a covering congruence system if every integer n satisfies at least one of these congruences. Does there exist to every c a covering congruence system with $n_1 > c^2$?

In the present paper it is shown that there is an intimate connection between these problems and conjectures. At first the author gives the general form of the solutions of the generalized equation (1), where 4 is replaced by m, $(m, n) = 1$. Then the solutions of (1) are furnished by means of a system S consisting of an infinite number of congruences, in a sense defining a generalized covering system. In order to get solutions, a practical method is given, and finally it is conjectured that the system S contains every integer n. This is not proved, but it is shown to be correct for all integers $n < 8000$. Two papers due to Obláth [Mathesis **59** (1950), 308–316; MR **12**, 481] and Rosati [Boll. Un. Mat. Ital. (3) **9** (1954), 59–63; MR **15**, 684] ought to be mentioned. *W. Ljunggren* (Oslo)

Citations: MR 12, 481i = D04-14; MR 15, 684c = D68-7.

Referred to in D68-18, D68-21.

D68-17 (26# 1278)

Kiss, Ernest

Remarques relatives à la représentation des fractions subunitaires en somme des fractions ayant le numérateur égal à l'unité. (Romanian. Russian and French summaries)

Acad. R. P. Romîne Fil. Cluj Stud. Cerc. Mat. **11** (1960), 319–323.

Author's summary: "On démontre le théorème: Lorsque $b < 10{,}000$, si $a = 5, 6, 7$, la fraction a/b peut être décomposée en trois fractions ayant le numérateur égal à l'unité, lorsque $b < 10{,}000$, la fraction $12/b$ et lorsque $b < 200{,}000$ la fraction $8/b$ peuvent être décomposées en quatre fractions ayant le numérateur égal à 1. En guise de conclusion on énonce la conjecture: Si $4 \leqq a \leqq 7$, alors $N(a, b) \leqq 3$, et si $8 \leqq a \leqq 12$, alors $N(a, b) \leqq 4$."

D68-18 (28# 3969)

Aigner, Alexander

Brüche als Summe von Stammbrüchen.

J. Reine Angew. Math. **214/215** (1964), 174–179.

The paper is concerned with the problem of representing a given fraction as the sum of r unit fractions, in other words, with the Diophantine equation

$$\frac{m}{n} = \frac{1}{x_1} + \cdots + \frac{1}{x_r} \qquad (x_j \geqq 1),$$

where $m \geqq 1$, $n \geqq 1$, $(m, n) = 1$. The case $r = 3$ is of particular interest. L. Bernstein [same J. **211** (1962), 1–10; MR **26** #77] discussed the case $m = 4$. The present paper contains some criteria for the representation of a fraction of the type m/p, p prime, as a sum of three unit fractions; in particular, it is shown that the criteria are the same for primes in reciprocal residue classes (mod m), that is, $kp + 1 \equiv 0$, $p + k \equiv 0 \pmod{m}$. The cases $m = 5, 6, 7$ are discussed at some length. It is shown that $5/p$ is not a sum of three unit fractions only when the numbers $(p+1)/2$, $(p+2)/3$, $(2p+1)/3$ are products of primes of the form $10x + 1$; in particular, $5/p$ is such a sum for $p < 30000$. Finally, $6/p$ and $7/p$ are certainly sums of three unit fractions for $p < 2000$ ($p > 2$ when $m = 7$).

L. Carlitz (Durham, N.C.)

Citations: MR 26# 77 = D68-16.

D68-19 (30# 1968)

Yamamoto, Koichi

On a conjecture of Erdős.

Mem. Fac. Sci. Kyushu Univ. Ser. A **18** (1964), 166–167.

At the 1963 Number Theory Conference in Boulder, Erdős conjectured that every positive fraction less than 1 can be written as the sum of three unit fractions. The author shows that this is not the case. He proves that if m is a given positive integer, then every neighborhood of $1/m$ contains infinitely many reduced fractions that cannot be expressed as a sum of three unit fractions. The proof makes use of the following lemma. Let k/n be a reduced positive fraction. Then it can be expressed as the sum of two unit fractions if and only if there exist relatively prime positive integers a, b such that $k | a + b$ and $ab | n$. The author notes that if p is a prime $\geqq 11$, then $(p-1)/p$ cannot be written as a sum of three unit fractions; similarly for $(p-1)/2p$, where $p \geqq 29$. *L. Carlitz* (Durham, N.C.)

Referred to in D68-21.

D68-20 (30# 3060)

Popovici, Constantin P.

On the Diophantine equation

$$\frac{a}{b} = \frac{1}{x_1} + \frac{1}{x_2} + \frac{1}{x_3}.$$

(Romanian. Russian and French summaries)

An. Univ. București Ser. Şti. Natur. Mat.-Fiz. **10** (1961), *no.* 29, 29–44.

Author's summary: "Dans cet article, l'auteur donne dans le § 1 la solution générale de l'équation diophantienne $a/b = 1/x_1 + 1/x_2 + 1/x_3$ dans le cas où a, b, x_1, x_2, x_3 sont des inconnues et l'en cherche les solutions entières de cette équation diophantienne. Dans le § 2, en considérant que a et b sont des nombres naturels tandis que x_1, x_2, x_3 sont des inconnues, on donne la condition nécessaire et suffisante pour que l'équation diophantienne considérée admette des solutions en nombres naturels. Dans le § 3 sont analysés les travaux consacrés à l'hypothèse de P. Erdős [Mat. Lapok **1** (1950), 192–210; MR **13**, 208], qui affirme que l'équation diophantienne $a/b = 1/x_1 + 1/x_2 + \cdots + 1/x_n$, où a et b sont des nombres naturels, admet des solutions en nombres naturels pour lesquelles $n \geqq 3$. Dans § 4 on démontre que si l'équation diophantienne $a/b = 1/x_1 + 1/x_2 + 1/x_3$, où a et b sont des nombres naturels, admet des solutions en nombres naturels, alors le nombre de ces solutions est fini." *E. Grosswald* (Paris)

Citations: MR 13, 208b = D68-6.

D68-21 (31# 2203)

Yamamoto, Koichi

On the Diophantine equation $\frac{4}{n} = \frac{1}{x} + \frac{1}{y} + \frac{1}{z}$.

Mem. Fac. Sci. Kyushu Univ. Ser. A **19** (1965), 37–47.

Erdős and Straus conjectured that if $n > 1$ the equation (*) $4/n = 1/x + 1/y + 1/z$ has a solution in positive integers. L. Bernstein [J. Reine Angew. Math. **211** (1962), 1–10; MR **26** #77] proved that (*) is solvable for $1 < n < 8000$. The present author has announced [Mem. Fac. Sci. Kyushu Univ. Ser. A **18** (1964), 166–167; MR **30** #1968] the existence of solutions for $1<n<10{,}000{,}000$. The present paper is a detailed report concerning this result. It suffices to restrict the discussion to the case n prime. The details are too involved for a brief summary. The author remarks that there is a connection between the equation (*) and the Kronecker symbol, and that this connection is peculiar to the numerator 4; if the 4 is replaced by 5, 6, $\cdots$, the connection is less apparent.

L. Carlitz (Durham, N.C.)

Citations: MR 26# 77 = D68-16; MR 30# 1968 = D68-19.

D68-22 (32# 7498)

Rav, Yehuda

On the representation of rational numbers as a sum of a fixed number of unit fractions.

J. Reine Angew. Math. **222** (1966), 207–213.

The author considers the solubility in integers $n_1, \cdots, n_k$ of the equation (*) $m/n=\sum_{i=1}^{k} 1/n_i$, where k is fixed and m, n are given coprime integers. He proves a necessary and sufficient condition for the solubility of (*); this condition looks superficially more complicated than the original equation, but leads one to a relatively efficient decision algorithm. As a corollary, he proves that (*) is soluble if and only if there exist M, N with $M/N=m/n$ and divisors N_i $(i=1,\cdots,k)$ of N such that $(N_1,\cdots,N_k)=1$ and $N_1+\cdots+N_k\equiv 0\ (M)$.

B. J. Birch (Oxford)

D68-23 (34# 2521)

Suryanarayana, D.; Rao, N. Venkateswara

On a paper of André Schinzel.

J. Indian Math. Soc. (*N.S.*) **29** (1965), 165–167.

Let n be an integer >1. A. Schinzel [Mathesis **65** (1956), 219–222; MR **18**, 284] showed that $3/(2n+1)$ can be written as the sum of reciprocals of three distinct odd positive integers. The authors give a second solution to this problem and also show that $2/(2n+1)$ can be expressed as the sum of two such reciprocals if and only if $2n+1$ is not a prime $\equiv 3 \pmod 4$. {On page 166, line 11, the parenthesis after 7 should be after 3; on line 16, s should be q, and q should be n. See also W. Sierpiński [*Theory of numbers*, Part II (Polish), pp. 85–88, 236–238, Pánst. Wydawn. Nauk., Warsaw, 1959; MR **22** #2572; English translation, 1964; MR **31** #116].}

R. Spira (Knoxville, Tenn.)

Citations: MR 18, 284a = D68-9; MR 22# 2572 = Z01-17; MR 31# 116 = Z01-59.

D68-24 (39# 1340)

Bende, Sándor

The Diophantine equation $\sum_{i=1}^{n} 1/2^{x_i}=1$ and its connection with graph theory and information theory. (Hungarian)

Mat. Lapok **18** (1967), 323–327.

Denote by $\tau(n)$ the number of solutions of $1=\sum_{i=1}^{n} 1/2^{x_i}$, $x_1\leqq\cdots\leqq x_n$, where the x_i are positive integers. The author gives a graph theoretic interpretation of $\tau(n)$ and obtains a recursion formula for it; further, he discusses some connection with information theory. It would be desirable to obtain an asymptotic formula for $\tau(n)$.

P. Erdős (Budapest)

D68-25 (41# 1639)

Webb, William A.

On $4/n=1/x+1/y+1/z$.

Proc. Amer. Math. Soc. **25** (1970), 578–584.

P. Erdős has conjectured that the equation $4/n=1/x+1/y+1/z$ is solvable in positive integers for all integers $n\geqq 2$. Using Selberg's sieve, it is shown that the number of positive integers $n\leqq N$ for which this Diophantine equation is not solvable is less than a constant times $N/(\log N)^{7/4}$.

W. H. Mills (Princeton, N.J.)

D68-26 (42# 7589)

Bartoš, Pavel

On prolongable solutions of the optical equation. (Slovak. German summary)

Časopis Pěst. Mat. **95** (1970), 278–289.

The author studies the diophantine equation $\sum_{j=1}^{n} 1/x_j=1/a$ in positive integers x_j of the form $x_1=\alpha_1$, $x_2=\alpha_2, \cdots, x_{n-1}=\alpha_{n-1}$, $x_n=\alpha_n-k_{n-1}$, where $\{\alpha_j\}_0^\infty$ and $\{k_j\}_0^\infty$ are given series of positive integers.

T. T. Tonkov (Sofia)

D68-27 (43# 1919)

Bartoš, Pavel

A remark on the number of solutions of the equation $1/x+1/y=a/b$ in natural numbers. (Czech. German summary)

Časopis Pěst. Mat. **95** (1970), 411–415.

The following theorem is given an elementary proof. All the solutions in positive integers x and y of the equation in the title (a and b are given positive integers) are given by $x=(b+k_1)/a$ and $y=(b+k_2)/a$, where k_1 and k_2 are positive integers, $k_1k_2=b^2$, $a|b+k_1$ and $a|b+k_2$. From this theorem the author easily derives some assertions about the number $n(a/b)$ of all solutions. For example, if p is prime and $p\nmid a$ then $n(a/p)\leqq 2$ and, in addition, $n(a/p)=2$ $[=1]$ if and only if $a=1$ or 2 $[a>2$ and $a|p+1]$.

B. Novák (Prague)

D68-28 (44# 6596)

Bartoš, Pavel; Pehartzová-Bošanská, Katarína

On the solution of the Diophantine equation $1/x+1/y+1/z=a/b$. (Slovak. German summary)

Časopis Pěst. Mat. **96** (1971), 294–299.

Main theorem: The general integer solution of the equation (*) $1/x+1/y+1/z=a/b$, $0<x\leqq y\leqq z$, $(a,b)=1$, is given by $x=\gamma uv/(ab)$, $y=\gamma bv(u+v)/a(\gamma uv-b^2)$, $z=(u/v)y$, where the positive integers γ, u, v $(u\geqq v,\ (u,v)=1)$ are such that $b^2<\gamma uv\leqq 3b^2$, $(\gamma uv-b^2)^2\leqq b^2(b^2+\gamma v^2)$, $ab/\gamma uv$, $a(\gamma uv-b^2)/\gamma b(u+v)$. (This theorem implies that if there exists an integer t, $t\geqq 1$, such that $(at-r)|b(b+1)$, where $b\equiv r \pmod a$, $0<r<a$, then the equation (*) has an integer solution.)

B. Novák (Prague)

D68-29 (44# 6600)

Vaughan, R. C.

On a problem of Erdős, Straus and Schinzel.

Mathematika **17** (1970), 193–198.

Let a, n, x, y, z and p denote natural numbers, p a prime and $a>1$. A. Schinzel has conjectured that the Diophantine equation (1) $a/n=1/x+1/y+1/z$ is soluble for every a if $n>n_0(a)$. When $a=4$ this conjecture has been verified for $n<10^7$ and when $a=5$ for $n<922321$.

Let $E_a(N)$ denote the number of natural numbers n not exceeding N for which (1) is insoluble. The author proves the following theorem: $E_a(N)\ll N\exp\{-(\log N)^{2/3}/C(a)\}$, where $C(a)$ is a positive number depending at most on a, and $F\ll G$ denotes $F=0(G)$. This theorem implies that almost every n is representable in the form (1).

By means of a theorem of H. L. Montgomery [J. London Math. Soc. **43** (1968), 93–98; MR **37** #184] the author first proves that $E_a(N)\leqq 4N/S$, where $S=\sum_{s\leqq\sqrt{N}}\mu^2(s)\prod f(p)/(p-f(p))$, $f(p)$ denoting a certain arithmetical function of a and p. Then he shows that for sufficiently large X (2) $(\log X)^2/C_1(a)<\sum_{p\leqq X} f(p)/p<C_2(\log X)^2$. In proving (2) the author uses a theorem due to E. Bombieri [Mathematika **12** (1965), 201–225; MR **33**

#5590].

The estimate for N/S then follows by means of a method due to R. A. Rankin. *W. Ljunggren* (Oslo)

Citations: MR 33# 5590 = M55-43; MR 37# 184 = M55-56.

D72 EQUATIONS IN MANY VARIABLES

For Waring's problem, see **P04** and the sections referred to there. For representations by quadratic forms, see the next following chapter, especially **E12, E24, E28.**

See also reviews D02-12, D02-14, D02-19, D02-22, D52-140, D76-9, D76-22, D80-35, D80-36, D80-63, E12-52, E24-88, E24-108, E76-30, G25-33, G35-46, P04-34, P04-50, S25-19, S25-24, T40-28, T40-29, T45-8, T45-13, T50-19, T50-20, T50-24, U02-2, U05-34, Z10-7, Z10-47.

D72-1 (7, 108i)

Brauer, Richard. A note on systems of homogeneous algebraic equations. Bull. Amer. Math. Soc. **51**, 749–755 (1945).

The author considers systems of equations

(1) $$f_i(x_1, \cdots, x_n)=0, \qquad i=1, \cdots, h,$$

where each f_i is a homogeneous polynomial of degree r_i with coefficients in a field K. He proves that, if m is any integer and the number n of unknowns exceeds a certain bound $\Phi(r_1, \cdots, r_h, m)$, then we can find a soluble extension field K_2 of K in which (1) has an m-dimensional linear family of solutions. The degree $(K_2:K)$ is less than a bound depending only on the r_i, and each prime factor of $(K_2:K)$ is at most equal to max (r_i). The proof is by induction: (1) is reduced to an equation

(2) $$a_1u_1^s+a_2u_2^s+\cdots+a_tu_t^s=0,$$

together with a system of lower degree. If K has the property that, for some function $\Psi(s)$, every equation (2) with $t\geqq\Psi(s)$ has a nontrivial solution, then K itself contains an m-dimensional linear family of solutions whenever n exceeds a bound of the above type. All $\mathfrak{P}$-adic number fields have this property.

These theorems have application to Hilbert's resolvent problem: if l_n is the least number such that the roots of the general equation of degree n can be expressed in terms of the coefficients by using algebraic functions of l_n parameters, then it follows that $\lim_{n\to\infty}(n-l_n)=\infty$. *G. Whaples.*

Referred to in D72-2, D72-3, D72-15, D72-19, D72-21, D72-36.

D72-2 (10, 231c)

Segre, B. Sulle irrazionalità da cui può farsi dipendere la determinazione di S_k appartenenti a varietà intersezioni complete di forme. Atti Accad. Naz. Lincei. Rend. Cl. Sci. Fis. Mat. Nat. (8) **4**, 149–154 (1948).

Some years ago, the author and the reviewer found independently that a system of homogeneous equations $f_1=0$, $f_2=0, \cdots, f_k=0$ of degrees $n_1, n_2, \cdots, n_k$ in r unknowns with coefficients in a field K has a nontrivial solution in a suitable soluble extension field K^*, provided that the number r of unknowns lies above a certain integer m depending on $n_1, n_2, \cdots, n_k$. The author here proves a generalization given by the reviewer [Bull. Amer. Math. Soc. **51**, 749–755 (1945); these Rev. **7**, 108]. The proof gives a recursive construction of a possible value of m and of a field K^*. *R. Brauer* (Ann Arbor, Mich.).

Citations: MR 7, 108i = D72-1.

D72-3 (10, 515e)

Peck, L. G. Diophantine equations in algebraic number fields. Amer. J. Math. **71**, 387–402 (1949).

Soient K un corps (de degré fini) de nombres algébriques, $\mathfrak{J}$ son domaine d'intégrité, n son degré. L'auteur prouve les résultats suivants: (I) $f_i(x_1, x_2, \cdots, x_q)=0$ $(i=1, 2, \cdots, h)$ étant un système d'équations en $x_1, x_2, \cdots, x_q$, où f_i est un polynome homogène d'un degré m_i à coefficients dans $\mathfrak{J}$, si K est totalement complexe (c'est-à-dire n'a aucun corps conjugué réel), et si m est un entier naturel, il existe un nombre positif $Q=Q(m; m_1, \cdots, m_h; n)$ tel que, si $q\geqq Q$, le système $f_i=0$ a m solutions dans $\mathfrak{J}$ qui sont linéairement indépendentes; (II) si $\alpha_1, \alpha_2, \cdots, \alpha_q \varepsilon \mathfrak{J}$, si la forme $f=\alpha_1z_1^m+\alpha_2z_2^m+\cdots+\alpha_qz_q^m$ est indéfinie (c'est-à-dire, dans tout corps conjugué réel K' de K, la forme conjuguée $f'=\alpha_1'z_1^m+\alpha_2'z_2^m+\cdots+\alpha_q'z_q^m$ de f peut s'annuler pour des valeurs réelles non toutes nulles des $z_1, z_2, \cdots, z_q$) et si $q\geqq 1+\max[4m^{2n+3}, (2^{m-1}+n)mn]$, l'équation $f=0$ a des solutions non-triviales dans $\mathfrak{J}$. Le résultat (I) se trouve être, en vertu d'un résultat de R. Brauer [Bull. Amer. Math. Soc. **51**, 749–755 (1945); ces Rev. **7**, 108], une conséquence de (II). L'auteur démontre (II) par des méthodes apparentées à celles de Siegel [Ann. of Math. (2) **46**, 313–339 (1945); ces Rev. **7**, 49] qui consistent à mettre sous forme d'une intégrale le nombre de solutions de $f=0$ dans $\mathfrak{J}$ telles que tous les conjugués des valeurs des $z_1, z_2, \cdots, z_q$ ne dépassent pas, en valeur absolue, un nombre positif T, et de montrer que, quand $T\to+\infty$, cette intégrale devient positive. Pour le faire, le domaine d'intégration est décomposé en deux parties, dont une est la réunion des voisinages convenables $B(\gamma)$ des éléments γ de K, parcourant un système complet de restes modulo δ^{-1}, où δ est la différente de K, dans le sous-ensemble de K, formé par ses éléments dont la norme est bornée, d'une manière convenable, en fonction des m, n, α_i $(i=1, 2, \cdots, q)$ et T. Il est prouvé que la contribution à l'intégrale de cette partie est, à $o(T^{n(q-m)})$ près, de la forme $\sigma(T)I(1)T^{n(q-m)}$, où $I(1)$ est un certain intégrale multiple, et où $\sigma(T)$ est une certaine somme finie, et que la contribution de la partie restante est $o(T^{n(q-m)})$. Ensuite, il est montré que $I(1)>0$ (méthode surtout analytique) et que $\sigma(T)>0$ (méthode surtout algébrique). *M. Krasner* (Paris).

Citations: MR 7, 49b = R48-5; MR 7, 108i = D72-1.
Referred to in D72-15.

D72-4 (12, 315d)

Dem'yanov, V. B. On cubic forms in discretely normed fields. Doklady Akad. Nauk SSSR (N.S.) **74**, 889–891 (1950). (Russian)

Hasse has shown [J. Reine Angew. Math. **152**, 129–148 (1923)] that every quadratic form in more than 4 variables over the field Q_p of p-adic numbers has a nontrivial zero in Q_p. Mordell has shown [J. London Math. Soc. **12**, 127–129 (1937)] that for any $n>0$ there exists a form over Q_p of degree n in n^2 variables which has no nontrivial zero in Q_p. There arose thus the conjecture that every form over Q_p of degree n in n^2+1 variables has a nontrivial zero in Q_p. In the present note the author verifies this conjecture for $n=3$, $p\neq 3$. The first step is to prove the lemma that if a cubic form F over a field K of characteristic $\neq 3$ has no nontrivial zero in K, then F can be transformed by a reversible linear transformation over K into a form in which every $x_i^2x_j$ $(i<j)$ has coefficient 0. Next the author considers any field K complete with respect to a discrete valuation and with residue class field P of characteristic $\neq 3$. Using the lemma

he shows that if every cubic form over P in more than t variables has a nontrivial zero in P, then every cubic form over K in more than $3t$ variables has a nontrivial zero in K. By virtue of Chevalley's result [Abh. Math. Sem. Hamburg. Univ. **11**, 73 (1935)] that every form over a finite field of degree n in more than n variables has a nontrivial zero in that field, this implies that if P is finite, then every cubic form over K in more than 9 variables has a nontrivial zero in K.

E. R. Kolchin (New York, N. Y.).

Referred to in D72-7, D72-19, D72-21, D72-39.

D72-5 (13, 102d)

Samuel, Pierre. Corps valués quasi algébriquement clos. C. R. Acad. Sci. Paris **232**, 1985–1987 (1951).

A field K is said to be quasi algebraically closed (q.a.c.) if every homogeneous equation of degree d in s unknowns with coefficients in K and with $d<s$ has a non-trivial solution in K. In this note it is shown that if k is an algebraically closed field, the fields $k(T)$ and $k\{\{T\}\}$ of rational functions and formal power series in one variable over k are q.a.c. Also, the field of power series with complex coefficients which converge in the neighborhood of the origin is q.a.c. There is a partial converse to these results: the residue class field of a q.a.c. field with a discrete valuation is algebraically closed.

B. N. Moyls (Vancouver, B. C.).

D72-6 (13, 726d)

Lang, Serge. On quasi algebraic closure. Ann. of Math. (2) **55**, 373–390 (1952).

A field F is called C_i if every form in F in n variables and degree d with $n>d^i$ has a non-trivial zero in F; C_0 is Artin's quasi-algebraic closedness; for general C_i cf. C. Tsen, J. Chinese Math. Soc. **1**, 81–92 (1936). If F is C_i and admits a normic form of order i (=a form with $n=d^i$ possessing no non-trivial zero in F) then an extension of transcendency h over F is C_{i+h}; this refines Tsen [loc. cit.] and the proof uses Tsen's argument as well as a lemma of Artin. Modifications for (single or several) polynomials without constant term (as in Tsen, loc. cit.) are given. The power series field $k\{t\}$ over a finite field k is C_2; the proof depends on Chevalley's theorem [Abh. Math. Sem. Univ. Hamburg **11**, 73–75 (1935)]. A complete valuated field with algebraically closed residue field, the maximal unramified extension of a complete field with perfect residue field (Artin's conjecture), the absolutely algebraic subfield of the maximal unramified extension of an ordinary p-adic field, and the field of convergent power series over an algebraically closed valuated constant field are all C_1; the proof uses expansion structures of the fields and some approximation and specialization processes for forms and zeros. Application to the cohomology approach to local class field theory [Hochschild, same Ann. **51**, 331–347 (1950); these Rev. **11**, 490] is observed; the treatment avoids the direct proof of the 2nd inequality but proceeds similarly as in the hypercomplex approach.

T. Nakayama (Nagoya).

Citations: MR 11, 490a = S30-4.

Referred to in D72-10, D72-14, D72-47, E24-108, G25-33, S02-3, U02-2.

D72-7 (14, 251g)

Lewis, D. J. Cubic homogeneous polynomials over p-adic number fields. Ann. of Math. (2) **56**, 473–478 (1952).

Let K be a complete discretely-valued field with finite residue field. For each integer $r\geqq 1$ there exists a smallest integer $\varphi(r)>0$ such that every form over K in n arguments and of degree r has a nontrivial zero in K if $n\geqq\varphi(r)$ [R. Brauer, Bull. Amer. Math. Soc. **51**, 749–755 (1945); these Rev. **7**, 108]; it is known that $\varphi(r)>r^2$, and [Hasse, J. Reine Angew. Math. **153**, 113–130 (1923)] that $\varphi(2)=5$. Dem'yanov showed [Doklady Akad. Nauk SSSR (N.S.) **74**, 889–891 (1950); these Rev. **12**, 315] that $\varphi(3)=10$ provided the residue field characteristic $p\neq 3$. The present paper contains a different proof (arrived at independently and at the same time as Dem'yanov's) that $\varphi(3)=10$, valid even if $p=3$.

E. R. Kolchin (New York, N. Y.).

Citations: MR 12, 315d = D72-4.

Referred to in D72-19, D72-21, D72-48, D72-53.

D72-8 (17, 232c)

Springer, T. A. Some properties of cubic forms over fields with a discrete valuation. Nederl. Akad. Wetensch. Proc. Ser. A. **58**=Indag. Math. **17** (1955), 512–516.

This note generalizes to cubic forms some previous results of the author on quadratic fields [same Proc. **58** (1955), 352–362; MR **17**, 17]. Let K be a commutative field and E a vector space over K, of finite dimension and having basis vectors e_i. Then with each vector $x=\sum_i \xi_i e_i$ may be associated cubic forms

$$f(x)=\sum_{i\leq j\leq k}\alpha_{ijk}\xi_i\xi_j\xi_k \quad (\alpha_{ijk}\in K).$$

The form is called definite if $f(x)\neq 0$ whenever $x\neq 0$. The author proves the following. 1. If f is definite then $|f(x)|^{\frac{1}{3}}$ is a norm over E. 2. Suppose that the residue class field $\bar{K}$ has the following property: There is an integer n_0 such that the dimension of any definite cubic form over $\bar{K}$ is $\leqq n_0$. Then the dimension of a definite cubic form over K is $\leqq 3n_0$. (The bar over the K is omitted, an obvious misprint. 3. If f is of dimension greater than 3 over a field K which is complete under a discrete valuation with finite residue class field, then f has a non-trivial zero in the unramified cubic extension L of K.

B. W. Jones.

Citations: MR 17, 17a = E08-10.

Referred to in D72-21.

D72-9 (17, 578e)

Dem'yanov, V. B. On representation of a zero of forms of the form $\sum_{i=1}^m a_ix_i^n$. Dokl. Akad. Nauk SSSR (N.S.) **105** (1955), 203–205. (Russian)

Let K be any field. Let A_n denote the order of the multiplicative group of K, modulo nth powers. Let C_n be the smallest integer such that any form $\sum a_ix_i^n$ in more than C_n variables represents 0. Theorem: If -1 is a sum of nth powers in K, then $C_n\leqq A_n$. For $n=2$ this was a conjecture of the reviewer [J. Math. Soc. Japan **5** (1953), 200–207; MR **15**, 500], proved by Kneser as reported in the review, and also proved by Tsuzuku [ibid. **6** (1954), 325–331; MR **16**, 669]. Dem'yanov's proof is similar to Kneser's. For the field of p-adic numbers the author notes the value of A_n, observes that C_n may be smaller, and finds the exact value of C_n if $p=2$ and n is a power of 2. An application is given to the solution of congruences $\sum a_ix_i^n\equiv 0$ with integral coefficients. Full proofs are included.

I. Kaplansky (Chicago, Ill.).

Citations: MR 15, 500a = E04-5; MR 16, 669e = E04-10.

D72-10 (18, 284g)

Dem'yanov, V. B. Pairs of quadratic forms over a complete field with discrete norm with a finite field of residue classes. Izv. Akad. Nauk SSSR. Ser. Mat. **20** (1956), 307–324. (Russian)

Let $f_j(x_1,\cdots,x_m)$ $(1\leqq j\leqq n)$ be homogeneous forms in m variables of respective degrees r_j and coefficients in a field K. When K is the field of formal power series over a finite field it was shown by Lang [Ann. of Math. (2) **55** (1952), 373–390; MR **13**, 726] that there is always a solution in K, other than the trivial one, of the simultaneous system $f_j=0$ provided that $m>\sum r_j^2$: and it has been conjectured that a similar result holds when K is a finite algebraic extension of a p-adic field. The author verifies this conjecture for the simplest simultaneous case, namely $n=r_1=r_2=2$, $m=9$. The proof is technically completely elementary but uses an elaborate induction hypothesis and must consider separately many different possibilities. Let $\mathfrak{p}$ denote the prime ideal of K. The greatest difficulty is to get from the solution of $f_1\equiv f_2\equiv 0$ ($\mathfrak{p}$) provided by the work of Chevalley [Abh. Math. Sem. Hamburg. Univ. **11** (1935), 73–75] to a solution of $f_1\equiv f_2\equiv 0$ ($\mathfrak{p}^2$). The induction from $\mathfrak{p}^N$ to $\mathfrak{p}^{N+1}$ ($N>1$), while still complicated, is rather simpler. A straightforward corollary is that if $\mathfrak{p}\nmid 2$ and $f(x_1, \cdots, x_m)$, $g(x_1, \cdots, x_m)$ do not represent 0 simultaneously, where $5\leqq m\leqq 8$, then there exist $m-4$ numbers c of K, the quotient of no two of them being a square, such that $f=g-c=0$ is simultaneously soluble. Frequent use is made of the lemma that if $\sum a_{ij}x_ix_j$, $\sum b_{ij}x_ix_j$ do not represent 0 simultaneously, where the a_{ij}, b_{ij} are integers of K and the diagonal coefficients a_{ii}, b_{ii} are divisible by $\mathfrak{p}$, then there exist integers λ, μ of K, not both divisible by $\mathfrak{p}$, such that every $\lambda a_{ij}+\mu b_{ij}$ is divisible by $\mathfrak{p}$.

J. W. S. Cassels (Cambridge, England).

Citations: MR 13, 726d = D72-6.

Referred to in D72-29, D72-38.

D72-11 (18, 467a)

Schwarz, Štefan. On a type of universal forms in discretely valued fields. Acta Sci. Math. Szeged 17 (1956), 5–29.

In a previous paper [Quart. J. Math. Oxford Ser. **19** (1948), 123–128; MR **9**, 572] the writer proved Theorem 1. Let $\delta=(p^f-1, k)\leqq p-1$, and suppose that $a_1, \cdots, a_\delta$ are elements of GF(p^f), $a_1a_2\cdots a_\delta\neq 0$. Then the equation $a_1x_1^k+\cdots+a_\delta x_\delta^k=b$ is solvable in GF(p^f) for every $b\in$ GF(p^f). The object of the present paper is to extend this theorem in various ways. It is pointed out, by means of a special example, that Th. 1 is not a consequence of Chevalley's theorem.

Let K denote a field complete with respect to a discrete non-archimedian valuation. Let I be the ring of integers $\in K$, π a prime of K, $\mathfrak{p}=\pi I$ the prime ideal generated by π; it is assumed that the residue class field $I=I/p$ is a finite field GF(p^f). Two cases are considered. (A) K has characteristic 0; it is the derived field of an algebraic number field $R(\theta)$ complete under a valuation corresponding to a prime ideal $\mathfrak{p}$ of $J[\theta]$, the ring of algebraic integers $\in R(\theta)$. (B) K has characteristic p and is the field of formal power series in x, containing only a finite number of negative powers, with coefficients $\in$ GF(p^p). In either case, every $a\in K$ is representable in the form

$$a=\pi^{-\nu}(a_0+a_1\pi+\cdots)\ (a_0\neq 0,\ a_i\in\mathfrak{R}).$$

In case (A) we choose $\pi\in J[\theta]$ such that $\mathfrak{p}/\pi$, $\mathfrak{p}^2\nmid\pi$; $\mathfrak{R}$ denotes a complete residue system (mod $\mathfrak{p}$). The principal results of the paper are the following.

Theorem 2. Let K be a complete field of type (A) or (B). Assume that (a) $k>1$, $(k, p)=1$, (b) $\delta=(k, p^f-1)\leqq p-1$, (c) $a_1, \cdots, a_{\delta+1}\in K$, $a_1a_2\cdots a_{\delta+1}\not\equiv 0$ (mod $\mathfrak{p}$). Then the equation

$$a_1x_1^k+\cdots+a_{\delta+1}{}^k=a$$

is solvable in K for every $a\in K$. Theorem 2a. Assume now that $a_1a_2\cdots a_\delta\not\equiv 0$ (mod $\mathfrak{p}$). Then if the congruence

$$a_1x_1^k+\cdots+a_\delta x_\delta^k\equiv 0 \pmod{\mathfrak{p}}$$

has at least one non-zero solution, then every $b\in K$ can be written in the form

$$b=a_1x_1^k+\cdots+a_\delta x_\delta^k\ (x_i\in K).$$

Put $k=k_0p^t$, $p\nmid k_0$, $t\geqq 0$. If $t\geqq 1$, then it is shown that in case (B) the equation

$$a=a_1x_1^k+\cdots+a_sx_s^k$$

need not be solvable in K for any $s\geqq 1$. For case (A) we have Theorem 3. Let $\delta=(k, p^f-1)\leqq p-1$,

$$s=(p^{f(t+1)}-1)\delta/(p^f-1),$$

and suppose that $a_1, \cdots, a_s$ are s element of $J[\theta]$ such that $a_1a_2\cdots a_s\not\equiv 0$ (mod $\mathfrak{p}$). Then the congruence

$$b\equiv a_1x_1^k+\cdots+a_sx_s^k \pmod{\mathfrak{p}^{t+1}}$$

is solvable for every $b\in J[\theta]$. Theorem 4. With the same notation as in the previous theorem and $\mathfrak{p}|p$, $\mathfrak{p}^2\nmid p$, the equation

$$b=a_1x_1^k+\cdots+a_{s+1}x_{s+1}^k$$

is solvable in K for every $b\in K$. Theorem 4a. Suppose now that $a_1a_2\cdots a_s\not\equiv 0$ (mod $\mathfrak{p}$). Then if the congruence

$$0\equiv a_1x_1^k+\cdots+a_sx_s^k \pmod{\mathfrak{p}^{t+1}}$$

has at least one non-zero solution, it follows that the equation

$$b=a_1x_1^k+\cdots+a_sx_s^k$$

is solvable in K.

{Reviewer's remark. In connection with Th. 3 reference may be made to a recent paper by Eckford Cohen, Congruences in algebraic number fields, Transactions of the American Math. Society, **83** (1956), 547–556. MR 18, 875.}

L. Carlitz (Durham, N.C.).

Citations: MR 9, 572f = T50-4; MR 18, 875b = D80-23.

D72-12 (18, 793e)

Lewis, D. J. Cubic congruences. Michigan Math. J. 4 (1957), 85–95.

It has been conjectured that every cubic form in at least 10 variables over an algebraic number field represents 0 in a non-trivial way. As a step in this direction the author proves the Theorem 3. If Γ is a finite extension of the field of rational numbers, if Δ is the ring of algebraic integers in Γ, and if $\mathfrak{m}$ is an ideal in Δ, then every congruence $\alpha_1x_1^3+\cdots+\alpha_nx_n^3\equiv 0$ (mod $\mathfrak{m}$), where $n>7$, $\alpha_i\in\Delta$, has a solution in Δ which is non-trivial modulo each prime factor of $\mathfrak{m}$. This result is derived from Theorem 2: If K is a complete field under a non-archimedean valuation and has a finite residue class field k, then every equation $\alpha_1x_1^3+\cdots+\alpha_nx_n^3=0$, where $\alpha_i\in K$, has a non-trivial solution if $n\geqq 7$, but there need not be a solution if $n=6$. Here the difficult case is when k has the characteristic 3, and then the construction of the solutions becomes very involved. *K. Mahler.*

Referred to in D72-36, T40-35.

D72-13 (19, 1040c)

Lewis, D. J. Strongly definite polynomials. Michigan Math. J. 4 (1957), 187–191.

A polynomial $F(X)=F(x_1, x_2, \cdots, x_n)$ over a ring R is said to be a definite polynomial over R provided it has the property that its only zero in R is the trivial one. Chevalley [Abh. Math. Sem. Hamburg. Univ. **11** (1935), 73–75] proved that for definite polynomials over finite fields, the number of indeterminates cannot exceed the degree of the polynomial. Let K be a field which is complete under a discrete valuation, and which has a finite residue class field. Let $\mathfrak{o}$ be the ring of integers of K, $\mathfrak{p}$ the prime ideal in $\mathfrak{o}$, π a prime in $\mathfrak{p}$, and q the number of elements in the residue class field $\mathfrak{o}/\mathfrak{p}$. A polynomial $F(X)$ of degree d over $\mathfrak{o}$ is said to be strongly definite over $\mathfrak{o}$ provided that, for a_i in $\mathfrak{o}$, $F(a_1, a_2, \cdots, a_n)\equiv 0$ (mod $\mathfrak{p}^d$) if and only if

$a_i \equiv 0 \pmod{\mathfrak{p}}$ $(i=1, 2, \cdots, n)$. Employing the method of Chevalley the author proves the following theorem. There exist polynomials $\phi_d(y)$, of degree $d-1$ over the ring of rational integers, such that if $F(X)$ is a strongly definite polynomial over $\mathfrak{o}$, of degree $d(d<q)$, then $n \leqq d^2\phi_d(q-1)$. *A. L. Whiteman* (Los Angeles, Calif.).

D72-14 (20# 853)

Nagata, Masayoshi. Note on a paper of Lang concerning quasi algebraic closure. Mem. Coll. Sci. Univ. Kyoto. Ser. A. Math. **30** (1957), 237–241.

A field K is called C_i [strongly C_i] if every homogeneous form [polynomial without constant term] in K of n variables and of degree d with $n>d^i$ has a nontrivial zero in K. The paper proves: 1a) if $f_1, \cdots, f_r$ are r homogeneous forms of degree d in n common variables in a C_i field K, and if $n>rd^i$, then the forms have a common non-trivial zero in K; 1b) similarly with polynomials $f_1, \cdots, f_r$, without constant term, of degree at most d, in a strongly C_i field K; 2a) if L is an extension field of a C_i field K with $\dim_K L=r$, then L is C_{i+r}; 2b) similarly with "C_i" replaced by "strongly C_i". The results generalize those of Lang [Ann. of Math. **55** (1952), 373–390; MR **13**, 726] who proved 1a), 2a), 2b) under the assumption that K admitted a "normic form" of order i. The paper offers also several problems and remarks in the context; for example, it is observed that if L is the function field of a normal curve having a rational point over K and if L is C_i, then K is C_{i-1}. *T. Nakayama* (Nagoya)

Citations: MR 13, 726d = D72-6.

D72-15 (20# 3827)

Lewis, D. J. Cubic forms over algebraic number fields. Mathematika **4** (1957), 97–101.

The author proves: For every algebraic number field K and for all integers $h>0$, $m\geqq 0$, there exists an integer $\Psi(K, h, m)$ such that every system of h cubic homogeneous polynomial equations in more than $\Psi(K, h, m)$ variables has an m-dimensional linear manifold of solutions in K. The proof depends on R. Brauer's reduction to the case of diagonal forms ($\sum \alpha_j y_j^3$) [Bull. Amer. Math. Soc. **51** (1945), 749–755; MR **7**, 108], applied over the field $K((-1)^{\frac{1}{2}})$ instead of K; use of the fact that every quadratic form in 5 variables over $K((-1)^{\frac{1}{2}})$ has a nontrivial zero; a result of L. G. Peck on diagonal forms [Amer. J. Math. **71** (1949), 387–402; MR **10**, 515]; and a lemma showing that if a cubic form over K has a nontrivial zero in $K((-1)^{\frac{1}{2}})$ then it has a nontrivial zero in K. A further lemma shows that the result of Peck is needed only for the field $Q((-1)^{\frac{1}{2}})$ (where Q=rational field), rather than for arbitrary fields K.

G. Whaples (Bloomington, Ind.)

Citations: MR 7, 108i = D72-1; MR 10, 515e = D72-3.

Referred to in D72-19, P02-17, P20-16.

D72-16 (20# 3828)

Birch, B. J. Homogeneous forms of odd degree in a large number of variables. Mathematika **4** (1957), 102–105.

The author proves the following. Let $h\geqq 1$ and $m\geqq 1$ be integers and let $r_1, \cdots, r_h$ be odd positive integers. Let K be an algebraic number field. Then there exists a number $\Psi(r_1, \cdots, r_h; m; K)$ such that every system of h homogeneous forms of degrees $r_1, \cdots, r_h$, respectively, in more than $\Psi(r_1, \cdots, r_h; m; K)$ variables, has an m-dimensional linear space of simultaneous solutions in K. The methods are very similar to those of Lewis, described in the preceding review, together with an induction on the maximum degree. *G. Whaples* (Bloomington, Ind.)

Referred to in D02-19, D72-19, D72-63, P02-17, P20-16.

D72-17 (21# 3378)

Mordell, L. J. Integer solutions of simultaneous quadratic equations. Abh. Math. Sem. Univ. Hamburg **23** (1959), 126–143.

The author proves the following theorem. Let

$$f_n(x) = f_n(x_1, x_2, \cdots, x_n), \quad g_n(x) = g_n(x_1, x_2, \cdots, x_n)$$

be two non-singular quadratic forms with rational coefficients in n variables. Suppose that for real λ, μ, no member of the pencil $\lambda f_n(x)+\mu g_n(x)$ is either definite of rank $\leqq n$, or singular of rank <5, but that at least one member has more than four positive and more than four negative squares when expressed as a sum of squares of real linear forms. Then the simultaneous equations $f_n(x)=0$, $g_n(x)=0$ have an infinity of integral solutions with non-zero values of the variables when $n\geqq 13$.

The author conjectures that the best possible result would be with 13 replaced by 10. He also gives conditions for the case when f has 11 variables and g has 12.

For $n=5$ or 6 and with the additional assumption that there is one nontrivial integral solution of the simultaneous equations $f_n(x)=0$, $g_n(x)=0$ he shows that there are infinitely many solutions provided that for no real values of λ, μ is $\lambda f_n(x)+\mu g_n(x)$ either a singular form of rank $<n-1$ or: (a) if $n=6$, a definite form of rank 5; (b) if $n=5$, of rank 4 for rational ratios of λ, μ.

B. W. Jones (Mayaguez, P.R.)

Referred to in D02-14, D72-38.

D72-18 (21# 3381)

Watson, G. L. Cubic forms representing arithmetic progressions. Proc. Cambridge Philos. Soc. **55** (1959), 270–273.

The author proves the following theorem. Let n_0 be an integer such that every cubic form with rational coefficients and at least n_0 variables represents zero nontrivially; then every non-degenerate cubic form with rational coefficients in at least n_0+2 integral variables represents an arithmetic progression. (The existence of n_0 between 10 and 32, has been shown by Lewis, Davenport and Birch.) *B. W. Jones* (Mayaguez, P.R.)

D72-19 (21# 4136)

Davenport, H. Cubic forms in thirty-two variables. Philos. Trans. Roy. Soc. London. Ser. A **251** (1959), 193–232.

D. J. Lewis [Mathematika, **4** (1957), 97–101; MR **20** #3827], B. J. Birch [ibid. 102–105; MR **20** #3828] and Davenport have independently proved the existence of a number N such that every cubic form in n variables, with integral coefficients, is a zero form if $n\geqq N$. Lewis' proof is based on a theorem of R. Brauer [Bull. Amer. Math. Soc. **51** (1945), 749–755; MR **7**, 108]; Birch proves the analogous result for all forms of odd degree with a value of N depending on the degree of the form. The present paper contains Davenport's proof, which leads to the value $N=32$. His result is as follows. Let

$$C(\mathbf{x}) = C(x_1, \cdots, x_n) = \sum_{i,j,k=1}^{n} c_{ijk}x_ix_jx_k$$

be a cubic form in n variables with integral coefficients. Then if $n\geqq 32$ there exist integers $x_1, \cdots, x_n$ such that

$$C(x_1, \cdots, x_n) = 0.$$

It is known [Mordell, J. London Math. Soc. **12** (1937), 127–129] that the theorem is false for $n<10$. Tartakowsky [Izv. Akad. Nauk SSSR **1935**, 483–524] had attempted to apply the Hardy-Littlewood method to "general" forms, but "his work appears to be incomplete". Most applications of the Hardy-Littlewood method are to additive problems; the difficulty now is that we are dealing with forms that contain product terms. In the next place, it is observed that the Hardy-Littlewood method, when it is effective, yields an asymptotic formula, the main term of which is the product of two factors. One of these essentially measures the density of the solutions in the real field. The other is an infinite product over the primes; each factor measures the density of the solutions in the p-adic field. For the present application it is necessary that the given equation have a non-singular solution both in the real field and in every p-adic field. It is observed that solvability in the p-adic field has been proved by Demyanov [Dokl. Akad. Nauk SSSR **74** (1950), 889–891; MR **12**, 315] and Lewis [Ann. of Math. (2) **56** (1952), 473–478; MR **14**, 251].

We now briefly sketch the proof of the theorem. § 1 of the paper is introductory. § 2 is devoted to the p-adic problem. Assume that $C(\mathbf{x})$ is not degenerate, that is, $C(\mathbf{x})$ is not equivalent to a cubic form in fewer than n variables; that is certainly the case if $C(\mathbf{x})$ does not represent zero. Let $N=\frac{1}{2}n(n+1)$ and let $\mathscr{C}$ denote the matrix of n rows and N columns (c_{ijk}), where i indicates the row and the pair j, k, with $j\leqq k$, indicates the column. Let $h(C)$ denote the greatest common divisor of all determinants of order n formed from $\mathscr{C}$; then it is proved that $h(C)$ is an invariant of C; that is, it has the same value for any two equivalent forms. Next if l is any positive integer, the form $C(\mathbf{x})$ is said to have the property $\mathscr{A}(p^l)$ if there exist integers $x_1, \cdots, x_n$ such that

$$C(x_1, \cdots, x_n) \equiv 0 \pmod{p^{2l-1}},$$
$$\frac{\partial C}{\partial x_1} \equiv \cdots \equiv \frac{\partial C}{\partial x_n} \equiv 0 \pmod{p^{l-1}},$$
$$\frac{\partial C}{\partial x_i} \not\equiv 0 \pmod{p^l} \text{ for some } i.$$

The main result of § 2 is that any non-degenerate cubic form in at least 10 variables has the property $\mathscr{A}(p^l)$ for every p and a suitable l depending on p. Moreover an upper bound for l is obtained that depends on $h(C)$ but not on p.

§ 3 is concerned with the general cubic exponential sum

$$S = \sum_{x_1, \cdots, x_n} e(\Gamma(x_1, \cdots, x_n)),$$

where $\Gamma(\mathbf{x})$ is a cubic form with real coefficients, $e(\alpha)=e^{2\pi i\alpha}$ and the summation is over all x_j such that $Px_j'\leqq x_j<Px_j''$. The aim is to investigate the consequences of the hypothesis $|S|\geqq P^{n-k}$, where k is a fixed positive number, small in comparison with n.

In § 4 the results of § 3 are applied to two types of exponential sums. The first type is the sum S with $\Gamma(\mathbf{x})=\alpha C(\mathbf{x})$, where α is real. The second sum is

$$S_{a,q}(\mathbf{l}) = \sum_{\mathbf{x}} e\left\{\frac{a}{q}C(\mathbf{x})+\frac{l_1x_1+\cdots+l_nx_n}{q}\right\},$$

where each x_j runs through a complete residue system $(\text{mod } q)$. It is assumed throughout that $C(\mathbf{x})$ does not represent zero.

§ 5. Approximation on major arcs.

§ 6. The choice of intervals. One of the lemmas in this section asserts the existence of a non-singular real solution of the equation $C(\mathbf{x})=0$.

§ 7. The singular series. This is defined by

$$\mathfrak{S} = \sum_{q=1}^{\infty} \sum_{\substack{a=1\\(a,q)=1}}^{q} q^{-n}S_{a,q}, \quad S_{a,q} = S_{a,q}(\mathbf{0}).$$

For $n\geqq 10$ and $C(\mathbf{x})$ non-degenerate it is proved that $\mathfrak{S}>0$.

§ 8. The proof of the theorem is now accomplished in several stages. It is proved first that if $C(\mathbf{x})$ does not represent zero then it represents a form of the type

$$C'(x_1, \cdots, x_{n-8})+d_1y_1^3.$$

Applying the same process to $C'(\mathbf{x})$ we ultimately arrive at a form

$$d_1y_1^3+\cdots+d_8y_8^3.$$

The final step is the proof that this form represents zero.

L. Carlitz (Durham, N.C.)

Citations: MR 7, 108i = D72-1; MR 12, 315d = D72-4; MR 14, 251g = D72-7; MR 20# 3827 = D72-15; MR 20# 3828 = D72-16.

Referred to in D02-19, D72-21, D72-27, D72-28, D72-30, D72-32, D72-33, E76-30, N32-49, P02-17.

D72-20 (23# A131a; 23# a131b)

Tartakovskiĭ, V. A.
The number of representations of large numbers by a form of "general type" with many variables. I. (Estimate of an integral by small intervals.) (Russian. English summary)
Vestnik Leningrad. Univ. **13** (1958), *no.* 7, 131–154.

Tartakovskiĭ, V. A.
The number of representations of large numbers by a form of "general type" with many variables. II. (Russian and English summary)
Vestnik Leningrad. Univ. **14** (1959), *no.* 7, 5–17.

The author extends the Hardy-Littlewood method used in Waring's problem to the problem of the number of representations of a large number n by a form $F(x_1, x_2, \cdots, x_s)$ of degree k, with $s\geqq\frac{3}{4}\{4(k+1)\}^{k+1}$ (the variables being further restricted to lie in a certain "cone"). The result is significant if the "singular series" is positive. The problem is a difficult one and it is to be expected that the methods used are heavy and complicated. The form F, besides having integer coefficients, must satisfy special conditions of "general type".

S. Chowla (Boulder, Colo.)

Referred to in D72-26.

D72-21 (23# A859)

Birch, B. J.; Lewis, D. J.
$\mathfrak{p}$-adic forms.
J. Indian Math. Soc. (*N.S.*) **23** (1959), 11–32 (1960).

It has been conjectured that a homogeneous polynomial in n variables of a given fixed degree d over a $\mathfrak{p}$-adic number field has a non-trivial zero in that field provided $n\geqq d^2+1$. Hasse [J. Reine Angew. Math. **153** (1924), 113–130] proved that this is true for $d=2$; the case $d=3$ has been treated independently by Dem'janov [Dokl. Akad. Nauk SSSR **74** (1950), 889–891; MR **12**, 315] and Lewis [Ann. of Math. (2) **56** (1952), 473–478; MR **14**, 251] and more recently by Davenport [Philos. Trans. Roy. Soc. London Ser. A **251** (1959), 193–232; MR **21** #4136]. Another approach to the cubic case is due to Springer [Nederl. Akad. Wetensch. Proc. Ser. A **58** (1955), 512–516; MR **17**, 232]. In the general case Brauer [Bull. Amer. Math. Soc. **51** (1945), 749–755; MR **7**, 108] has proved that there is a function $\psi(d)$ such that a $\mathfrak{p}$-adic form of degree d in more than $\psi(d)$ variables always has a non-trivial zero. The main result of the present paper is contained in the following theorem: Let $F(x)$ be a form over the $\mathfrak{p}$-adic field K of degree d in d^2+1 variables; then for $d=1$, 2, 3 or 5, if the residue class field is sufficiently large, $F(x)$ has a non-trivial zero. By the residue class field is meant $\mathfrak{o}/\mathfrak{p}$, where $\mathfrak{o}$ is the ring of integers of K. The proof of this theorem is too elaborate to describe briefly. However, we may mention one important point in the proof, namely, the result that if N is the number of zeros in GF(q) of an absolutely irreducible homogeneous polynomial F of degree d in n variables, F having coefficients in GF(q), then

$$|N-q^{n-1}| < A(n, d)q^{n-3/2},$$

where $A(n, d)$ depends only on n and d. This result is a corollary of a theorem of Lang and Weil [Amer. J. Math. **76** (1954), 819–827; MR **16**, 398]. The paper closes with some observations about what happens in general, and about the shape of those forms which involve a fairly large number of variables but, nevertheless, have no zero.

L. Carlitz (Durham, N.C.)

Citations: MR 7, 108i = D72-1; MR 12, 315d = D72-4; MR 14, 251g = D72-7; MR 16, 398d = G25-2; MR 17, 232c = D72-8; MR 21# 4136 = D72-19.

Referred to in D72-22, D72-41, D80-77, T05-34.

D72-22 (24# A3157)

Birch, B. J.; Lewis, D. J.

On $\mathfrak{p}$-adic forms.

Michigan Math. J. **9** (1962), 53–57.

The authors remark that in a previous paper [J. Indian Math. Soc. (N.S.) **23** (1959), 11–32; MR **23** #A859] they had difficulty proving a certain result (Lemma B) concerning the normalization of homogeneous forms with $\mathfrak{p}$-adic coefficients. In the present paper a sharper result is proved more simply. Since the statement of this sharper result requires considerable notation, it will not be given here.

L. Carlitz (Durham, N.C.)

Citations: MR 23# A859 = D72-21.

D72-23 (23# A1591)

Chowla, S.

A generalization of Meyer's theorem on indefinite quadratic forms in five or more variables.

Norske Vid. Selsk. Forh. Trondheim **33** (1960), 60.

This paper announces the following theorem: if k is an odd prime, there is an absolute constant $c>0$ such that the equation $\sum_{i=1}^{S} a_i x_i^k = 0$, where the a_i are integers $\neq 0$, has a non-trivial solution in rational numbers provided $S > ck \log k$.

B. W. Jones (Boulder, Colo.)

D72-24 (23# A2386)

Chowla, S.

On a conjecture of J. F. Gray.

Norske Vid. Selsk. Forh. Trondheim **33** (1960), 58–59.

On his Ph.D. thesis [Univ. of Notre Dame, Indiana, 1958] Gray conjectured that a diagonal form with rational coefficients of degree 5 in 16 variables represents the zero non-trivially in every p-adic field. The author sketches a proof of this conjecture.

H. B. Mann (Columbus, Ohio)

D72-25 (24# A1873)

Veidinger, L.

On the distribution of the solutions of diophantine equations with many unknowns.

Acta Arith. **5** (1958), 15–24 (1959).

Verfasser gibt eine obere Abschätzung für die Anzahl $R(P)$ der ganzzahligen Lösungen $x_1, \cdots, x_r$ mit $1 \leqq x_\nu \leqq P$, $\nu = 1, \cdots, r$, einer Gleichung $\Phi(x_1, \cdots, x_r) = 0$. Sind $n \geqq 3$, $r \geqq n2^{n-1}+1$,

$$\Phi(x_1, \cdots, x_r) = a_1 x_1^n + \cdots + a_r x_r^n + \varphi(x_1, \cdots, x_r),$$

a_ν ganze Zahlen $\neq 0$, φ ein Polynom vom Grade $\leqq n-3$ mit ganzen Koeffizienten, so beweist Verfasser, für jedes $\varepsilon > 0$ und genügend großes P, $R(P) \leqq (\rho+\varepsilon)|\mathfrak{S}|P^{r-n}$. Dabei hängen ρ und die "singuläre Reihe" $\mathfrak{S}$ nicht von P ab. Der Beweis folgt der Vinogradovschen Methode und benutzt Abschätzungen von Weyl und van der Corput.

H. -E. Richert (Zbl **83**, 39)

D72-26 (24# A3146)

Tartakovskiĭ, V. A.

On representability of large numbers by forms "of general type" with a large number of variables. (Russian)

Izv. Vysš. Učebn. Zaved. Matematika **1958**, *no.* 1 (2), 161–173.

Let

$$F(x) = F(x_1, \cdots, x_s) = \sum_{i_1,\cdots,i_k=1}^{s} a_{i_1\cdots i_k} x_{i_1} \cdots x_{i_k}$$

be a form with integral coefficients, of degree k and with discriminant D_F. Let H' be the Euclidean space of points $h' = (h_1^{(1)}, \cdots, h_s^{(1)}, \cdots, h_1^{(k-2)}, \cdots, h_s^{(k-2)})$, and form a square matrix $\Delta_F(h')$ with entries

$$\{\Delta_F(h')\}_{ij} = \sum_{j_1,\cdots,j_{k-2}=1}^{s} a_{ij_1\cdots j_{k-2}j} h_{j_1}^{(1)} \cdots h_{j_{k-2}}^{(k-2)},$$
$$i, j = 1, 2, \cdots, s.$$

Designate by $\Gamma_\nu(F)$ the algebraic manifold in H' defined by the condition rank $\Delta_F(h') \leqq \nu$, for $\nu = 0, 1, \cdots, s$, and let the dimension of $\Gamma_\nu(F)$ be $d_\nu(F)$. Then F is said to be of general type if $D_F \neq 0$ and $d_\nu(F) \leqq s(k-3)+\nu$, for $0 \leqq \nu \leqq s$.

Let $w(n)$ be the surface defined in the x-space E by the equation $F(x) = n$. Let $\sum$ be the unit sphere in E, and put $L = w(0) \cap \Sigma$. Let $\mathfrak{R}$ be the positive-coordinate s-hedron $x_1 \geqq 0, \cdots, x_s \geqq 0$, and put $\mathfrak{R}' = \mathfrak{R} \cap \Sigma$. $\mathfrak{R}$ is said to be of the first or second kind, according as $\mathfrak{R}' \cap L$ is or is not empty. It is always possible to choose coordinates in E so that $\mathfrak{R}$ is of the second kind.

The author proved earlier [Vestnik Leningrad. Univ. **13** (1958), no. 7, 131–154; MR **23** #A131a] that if F is of general type, if $\mathfrak{R}$ is of the second kind, and if $s \geqq \frac{3}{4}(4k+4)^{k+1}$, then the number of integral points in $\mathfrak{R}$ and on $w(n)$ is the form $v(n)\cdot\mathfrak{S}(n; F) + R(n, F)$. Here $v(n)$ is the volume of the body in $\mathfrak{R}$ bounded by $w(n-\frac{1}{2})$ and $w(n+\frac{1}{2})$, $\mathfrak{S}(n; F)$ is a certain "singular series", and the remainder term $R(n; F) = O(v(n)\cdot n^{-1/13k})$. In the present paper the singular series is investigated under the same hypotheses. It is shown that there is a positive integer ϕ such that for every integer n which is represented (mod ϕ) by F and which is prime to ϕ, the singular series is larger than a certain positive constant independent of n. The multiplicative structure of ϕ is explicitly given; it depends on the total prime structure of k and especially on the power of 2 dividing k.

W. J. LeVeque (Ann Arbor, Mich.)

Citations: MR 23# A131a = D72-20.

Referred to in Z10-22.

D72-27 (25# 50)

Davenport, H.

Cubic forms in 29 variables.

Proc. Roy. Soc. Ser. A **266** (1962), 287–298.

In an earlier paper [Philos. Trans. Roy. Soc. London Ser. A **251** (1959), 193–232; MR **21** #4136] the author had proved that every cubic form $C(x_1, \cdots, x_n)$ in $n \geqq 32$ variables with rational coefficients has a rational zero; in this note he improves the technique and obtains the result for $n \geqq 29$.

In the first paper, cubes were split off from the main form one by one until a form of diagonal type in 8 variables represented rationally by C was obtained. At each stage, several variables were lost; the author now manages to make some use of the lost variables at three of the stages of the reduction. He achieves this by re-examining the details of the earlier work, and by using a new version of Weyl's inequality for the exponential sum

$$U(z, \alpha) = \sum e[\alpha(fx^3+gxz^2)].$$

Subsequently, the author has found a comparatively simple proof that C has a rational zero if $n \geqq 17$.

B. J. Birch (Cambridge, England)

Citations: MR 21# 4136 = D72-19.

Referred to in D72-33.

D72-28 (25# 51)

Fowler, James

A note on cubic equations.

Proc. Cambridge Philos. Soc. **58** (1962), 165–169.

Davenport [Philos. Trans. Roy. Soc. London Ser. A **251** (1959), 193–232; MR **21** #4136] has proved that a cubic form in n variables with rational coefficients always represents zero if $n \geqq 32$; later he showed that $n \geqq 29$ suffices [see #50 above]. In the present paper it is proved that if $C(x_1, \cdots, x_n)$ is any non-degenerate cubic form with rational coefficients and N is any rational number different from 0, then if $n \geqq 21$, the equation

$$(*) \qquad C(x_1, \cdots, x_n) = N$$

is solvable in rational numbers $x_1, \cdots, x_n$. If C represents 0 rationally, it suffices if $n \geqq 3$. Moreover it is stated that (*) has infinitely many solutions.

Using the method of Birch [Proc. Roy. Soc. Ser. A **265** (1961/62), 245–263], it is proved that if the variety $C(x_1, \cdots, x_n) = 0$ has no singular points in complex space and $n \geqq 14$, then (*) is solvable in rational $x_1, \cdots, x_n$.

L. Carlitz (Durham, N.C.)

Citations: MR 21# 4136 = D72-19.

D72-29 (25# 52)

Birch, B. J.; Lewis, D. J.; Murphy, T. G.

Simultaneous quadratic forms.

Amer. J. Math. **84** (1962), 110–115.

In this paper a short proof is given of a theorem first proved by V. B. Dem'janov [Izv. Akad. Nauk SSSR Ser. Mat. **20** (1956), 307–324; MR **18**, 284] stating that two quadratic forms f and g in $n \geqq 9$ variables over a $\mathfrak{p}$-adic field k have a non-trivial common zero in k. The proof uses the corresponding result for a finite field k; there the appropriate condition is $n \geqq 5$ (this is a particular case of a theorem of Chevalley [Abh. Math. Sem. Hamburg Univ. **11** (1935), 73–75]). It is shown that for a general pair f, g, suitable reduction mod $\mathfrak{p}$ leads to forms over the finite residue class field which have a non-singular common zero in that field. This zero can be lifted to a non-trivial common zero of f and g by Hensel's lemma. Then a compactness argument is used to prove the theorem for arbitrary f and g. *T. A. Springer* (Utrecht)

Citations: MR 18, 284g = D72-10.

Referred to in D72-38, D72-40.

D72-30 (27# 132)

Birch, B. J.

Forms in many variables.

Proc. Roy. Soc. Ser. A **265** (1961/62), 245–263.

Using an adaptation of the classical Hardy-Littlewood method, Davenport [Philos. Trans. Roy. Soc. London Ser. A **251** (1959), 193–232; MR **21** #4136] has proved that every rational cubic form in at least 32 variables (he has subsequently reduced this number to 16 [Proc. Roy. Soc. Ser. A **272** (1963), 285–303]) has a rational zero. In the present paper the author gives a far-reaching generalization of Davenport's methods to obtain results about systems of homogeneous forms of given degree. An earlier attempt on this problem was made by Tartakowsky (references will be found in the present paper), but he restricted his considerations to 'general' forms, that is, to forms whose coefficients do not satisfy any one of a certain finite set of algebraic relations, relations which are not satisfied identically. Not only is the author's condition simpler, but also his final estimates for the number of variables required in terms of the degree are better.

The main theorem is as follows. Let $f_1, \cdots, f_R$ be R rational forms of degree d in n variables $x_1, \cdots, x_n$, where $n > R \geqq 1$. Let $V(\mu)$ be the variety $V(\mu)$: $f_1(x) = \mu_1, \cdots, f_R(x) = \mu_R$ and let $V^* = \bigcup_\mu V^*(\mu)$, where $V^*(\mu)$ is the locus of singularities of $V(\mu)$. [The μ_i run through some algebraically closed field; the most important conclusion refers to the case $\mu = 0$, but the significance of the hypothesis becomes apparent later on, especially in the discussion of the singular integral.] Then if $\dim[V(0)] = n - R$, and if $V(0)$ has non-singular real points and non-singular points in every p-adic completion of the rationals, and if

$$n - \dim[V^*] > R(R+1)(d-1)2^{d-1},$$

then $V(0)$ has a rational point other than the origin.

For a single form ($R = 1$) V^* is simply the locus of singularities of $V(0)$, that is, the variety $\partial f/\partial x_1 = \cdots = \partial f/\partial x_n = 0$, and in this case the sufficient condition (together with the obvious necessary conditions about real points and p-adic points) reads $n - \dim[V^*] > (d-1)2^d$. For $d = 3$, this implies that a non-singular cubic in 16 or more variables has a rational point. (Davenport's results refer to any cubic, singular or non-singular.)

The proof follows closely the work of Davenport, except that the device of splitting off cubes does not generalize and this is replaced by the discussion of singularities. The idea of the proof is to obtain an estimate for the number of integer points of $V(\nu)$ in a large box $P\mathscr{B}$, where ν is a vector with integer components, $\mathscr{B}$ is contained in the box $-1 \leqq x_j \leqq 1$ $(j = 1, \cdots, n)$ and $P \to \infty$. The number of such points is given by

$$\sum_{x \in P\mathscr{B}} \int_0^1 \cdots \int_0^1 e(\sum \alpha_i[f_i(x) - \nu_i])\, d\alpha_1 \cdots d\alpha_R.$$

In the usual way, one estimates this integral by looking at the exponential sums. It turns out that either one has a good estimate for these (minor arcs), or that $\alpha_1, \cdots, \alpha_R$ are well approximable by rationals (major arcs), or that the f_i satisfy a certain condition which implies that V^* has a high dimension. This last leads to the requirement that $\dim V^*$ is small.

The major arcs now lead to the singular integral and to the singular series. Following Siegel, the singular integral is evaluated by Fourier inversion, but this presents novel difficulties, which necessitate special consideration of the singular points in $\mathscr{B}$ and the use of estimates which depend ultimately on the appropriate form of Weyl's inequality. The singular integral is positive if $V(\mu)$ has a non-singular real point, and the singular series is positive if $V(\mu)$ has non-singular p-adic points for every p.

The paper concludes with an interesting discussion of some special cases and with a generalization to the case when the coefficients of the forms f_i are in an algebraic number field.

In conclusion, we ought to mention a paper of Davenport [J. London Math. Soc. **35** (1960), 135–142; MR **22** #1546] in which he proposes two problems to algebraic geometers arising out of the present work.

J. V. Armitage (Durham City)

Citations: MR 21# 4136 = D72-19; MR 22# 1546 = D02-12.

Referred to in D72-65.

D72-31 **(27# 3617)**

Davenport, H.; Lewis, D. J.

Homogeneous additive equations.

Proc. Roy. Soc. Ser. A **274** (1963), 443–460.

By an additive equation the authors mean an equation

(1) $$c_1x_1^k+\cdots+c_sx_s^k=0$$

in which there are no cross-point terms. It is clear that the solvability of such an equation in integers, not all zero, depends in part on a congruence condition: for every prime power p^ν, the congruence

(2) $$c_1x_1^k+\cdots+c_sx_s^k\equiv 0 \pmod{p^\nu}$$

has a solution with $x_1,\cdots,x_s$ not all divisible by p. Let $G^*(k)$ be the least number such that if $s\geqq G^*(k)$ and if $c_1,\cdots,c_k$ are such that the congruence condition is satisfied, then (1) has infinitely many solutions in integers. Further, let $\Gamma^*(k)$ be the smallest number such that if $s\geqq\Gamma^*(k)$ and $c_1,\cdots,c_s$ are any integers, then the congruence condition involving (2) is satisfied. Theorem 1: For all k, $\Gamma^*(k)\leqq k^2+1$, and there is equality whenever $k+1$ is prime. Theorem 2: If $k\geqq 12$, then $G^*(k)\leqq 2k-1+2l$, where l is the smallest integer such that

$$\left(1-\frac{1}{k}\right)^l<\frac{2k-1}{2k^3(2\log k+\log\log k+3)}.$$

In particular, for $\delta>0$, $G^*(k)<(4+\delta)k\log k$ if k is sufficiently large.

It follows from Theorem 2 that $G^*(k)\leqq k^2+1$ for $k\geqq 18$, and hence by Theorem 1 that (1) has infinitely many solutions whenever $k\geqq 18$ and $s\geqq k^2+1$. This represents a partial verification of Artin's conjecture; see S. Lang [Bull. Amer. Math. Soc. **66** (1960), 240–249; MR **22** #9469]. *W. J. LeVeque* (Boulder, Colo.)

Citations: MR 22# 9469 = D02-13.

Referred to in D02-19, D72-34, D72-35, D72-36, D72-59, D72-60, D80-63.

D72-32 **(27# 4793)**

Ramanujam, C. P.

Cubic forms over algebraic number fields.

Proc. Cambridge Philos. Soc. **59** (1963), 683–705.

The author proves the following theorem: Let K be an algebraic number field and let $C(x_1,\cdots,x_m)$ be a homogeneous cubic form with coefficients in K. If $m\geqq 54$, there exist $a_1,\cdots,a_m$ in K, not all zero, such that $C(a_1,\cdots,a_m)=0$. The proof follows ever so closely the general outline of H. Davenport's proof [Philos. Trans. Roy. Soc. London Ser. A **251** (1959), 193–232; MR **21** #4136] that a cubic form in $m\geqq 32$ variables with rational integer coefficients has a non-trivial rational zero. Davenport's proof consisted in an ingenious adaptation of the Hardy-Littlewood circle method to non-additive problems. In this paper, the author makes the now standard modifications of the circle method to algebraic number fields as developed by C. L. Siegel [Amer. J. Math. **66** (1944), 122–136; MR **5**, 200]. In most such applications, the degree of the field K enters into the bound on m. In this paper, the author carefully avoids this difficulty by applying a result of B. J. Birch [Proc. Cambridge Philos. Soc. **57** (1961), 449–459; MR **26** #1306].

It should be noted that Davenport [Proc. Roy. Soc. Ser. A **272** (1963), 285–303; MR **27** #5734; see also *Analytic methods for Diophantine equations and Diophantine inequalities*, Ann Arbor Publ., Ann Arbor, Mich., 1963] has recently shown that a cubic form in 16 or more variables with rational coefficients has a non-trivial rational zero. The reviewer sees no reason to stop these new arguments being extended, in like manner, to the algebraic number field case and so yielding a bound smaller than 54. *D. J. Lewis* (Ann Arbor, Mich.)

Citations: MR 5, 200c = R48-4; MR 21# 4136 = D72-19; MR 26# 1306 = R48-29; MR 27# 5734 = D72-33.

Referred to in D72-56.

D72-33 **(27# 5734)**

Davenport, H.

Cubic forms in sixteen variables.

Proc. Roy. Soc. Ser. A **272** (1963), 285–303.

The author has proved [Philos. Trans. Roy. Soc. London Ser. A **251** (1959), 193–232; MR **21** #4136] that if $C(x_1,\cdots,x_n)$ is a cubic form with integral coefficients, and if $n\geqq 32$, then $C(\mathbf{x})$ has a non-trivial rational zero; later, he was able to show that $n\geqq 29$ would suffice [Proc. Roy. Soc. Ser. A **266** (1962), 287–298; MR **25** #50]. He now finds a considerable simplification, which in the first place enables him to prove rather simply that any cubic form in $n\geqq 17$ variables has a rational zero; by a rather intricate argument, he in fact proves that $n\geqq 16$ is enough.

In this series of papers, the author uses the Hardy-Littlewood method of Fourier inversion; for $n\geqq 17$, one sees by fairly standard arguments that the crux of the matter is to show that a certain system of bilinear equations does not have too many integral solutions in a certain region. In his earlier papers, the author's method for investigating these equations was indirect and somewhat inefficient; he is now able to deal with them directly and precisely. His device is described in his § 2, which contains enough for the proof with $n\geqq 17$.

Since his proof with $n\geqq 17$ is now so simple, it is reasonable to hope that by scraping the barrel an extra variable may be saved. In the later sections of his paper, the author achieves this; but now several steps are critical, and arguments of ingenuity and delicacy are necessary. Some of the lemmas used in these extra arguments are of interest in their own right. *B. J. Birch* (Manchester)

Citations: MR 21# 4136 = D72-19; MR 25# 50 = D72-27.

Referred to in D02-19, D72-32, D72-37, D72-50, D72-51, D72-56.

D72-34 **(28# 3970)**

Chowla, S.

On a conjecture of Artin. I, II.

Norske Vid. Selsk. Forh. (*Trondheim*) **36** (1963), 135–141.

The author proves that there is an absolute constant c_1 such that if k is an odd prime, $s>c_1k\log k$, and $a_1,\cdots,a_s$ are rational integers, then the form $\sum_1^s a_ix_i^k=0$ has nontrivial solutions in each of the p-adic fields. The proof is based on ideas in an earlier paper [J. Indian Math. Soc. (N.S.) **25** (1961), 47–48; MR **25** #3893]. The author also states (but does not prove) that there is an absolute constant c_2 such that if k is an odd prime, $s>c_2k\log k$, $a_1,\cdots,a_s$ are rational integers, then $\sum a_ix_i^k=0$ has a nontrivial rational solution. Davenport and the reviewer have shown this result to hold for all integers $k\geqq 18$ when $s\geqq k^2+1$ [Proc. Roy. Soc. Ser. A **274** (1963), 443–460; MR **27** #3617]. *D. J. Lewis* (Ann Arbor, Mich.)

Citations: MR 25# 3893 = D80-36; MR 27# 3617 = D72-31.

D72-35 **(28# 3971)**

Chowla, S.; Shimura, G.

On the representation of zero by a linear combination of k-th powers.

Norske Vid. Selsk. Forh. (Trondheim) **36** (1963), 169–176.

Let $\Gamma^*(k)$ be the minimum integer s such that for every sequence $a_1, \cdots, a_s$ of rational integers the equation $\sum_{i=1}^s a_i x_i^k = 0$ has nontrivial solutions in each of the p-adic fields. Davenport and the reviewer [Proc. Roy. Soc. Ser. A **274** (1963), 443–460; MR **27** #3617] have shown that $\Gamma^*(k) \leqq k^2+1$, and it is well known that there are infinitely many k for which $\Gamma^*(k)=k^2+1$. The actual value of $\Gamma^*(k)$ depends in a complicated way on the arithmetic structure of k.

The authors prove that if k is an odd integer, then $\Gamma^*(k) < (2/\log 2+\varepsilon)k \log k$, provided $k > k_0(\varepsilon)$. Also, there are infinitely many odd integers k such that $\Gamma^*(k) > k \log k/\log 2$. The proofs rely on the box principle together with the usual Hensel-Newton method for obtaining solutions in p-adic fields.

D. J. Lewis (Ann Arbor, Mich.)

Citations: MR 27# 3617 = D72-31.

Referred to in D72-67, D80-63, D80-78, T40-29, T40-35, Z02-44.

D72-36 **(29# 4729)**

Birch, B. J.

Diagonal equations over $\mathfrak{p}$-adic fields.

Acta Arith. **9** (1964), 291–300.

Let K be a $\mathfrak{p}$-adic field. It is well known that to each positive integer d there is a constant $\varphi(K, d)$ such that every form of degree d over K in $n \geqq \varphi(K, d)$ variables has a non-trivial zero in K. It has long been conjectured that $\varphi(K, d)=d^2+1$, and this has been verified for $d=2$, 3 and for certain other d, provided the residue class field of K is sufficiently large. Brauer [Bull. Amer. Math. Soc. **51** (1945), 749–755; MR **7**, 108] has shown that a $\varphi(K, d)$ can be determined provided we are given a constant $\psi(K, d)$ such that every diagonal form of degree d over K in $n \geqq \psi(K, d)$ variables has a non-trivial zero in K. When d is a prime the reviewer [Michigan Math. J. **4** (1957), 85–95; MR **18**, 793] and Gray [Doctoral Dissertation, Univ. of Notre Dame, Notre Dame, Ind., 1958] have shown $\psi(K, d) \leqq d(d-1)+1$. When K is the p-adic completion of the rationals, Davenport and the reviewer [Proc. Roy. Soc. Ser. A **274** (1963), 443–460; MR **27** #3617] have shown that $\psi(K, d) \leqq d^2+1$. In this paper the author determines a function $\psi(d)$, which is essentially a dth power, and shows that $\psi(K, d) \leqq \psi(d)$ for all $\mathfrak{p}$-adic fields K. The proof involves a careful examination of the expansion of the series $(1+\sum_{t=1}^{\infty} \pi^t y_t)^d$, where π is a prime of K. The expansion varies greatly with the ramification index of K.

D. J. Lewis (Ann Arbor, Mich.)

Citations: MR 7, 108i = D72-1; MR 18, 793e = D72-12; MR 27# 3617 = D72-31.

D72-37 **(29# 4731)**

Davenport, H.; Lewis, D. J.

Non-homogeneous cubic equations.

J. London Math. Soc. **39** (1964), 657–671.

Let $\phi(\mathbf{x})$ be a cubic polynomial in n variables with integral coefficients, and let C be the part of ϕ that is homogeneous of degree 3. Define the invariant $h(C)$ as the codimension of the greatest rational linear space contained in the hypersurface $C=0$, so that, for instance, $h(C)=n$ if $C=0$ has no rational point. The authors prove that if $h(C) \geqq 17$ and if $\phi(\mathbf{x}) \equiv 0$ (m) is soluble for all m, then $\phi(\mathbf{x})=0$ has a solution in integers. Combining this with a theorem of Watson, it follows that $\phi=0$ is soluble in integers whenever $n \geqq 20$, $h(C) \geqq 4$, and the obvious necessary condition that $\phi \equiv 0$ (m) be soluble for all m is satisfied. The main part of the proof is essentially routine, using machinery developed by the authors [Amer. J. Math. **84** (1962), 649–665; MR **26** #2403] and by Davenport alone [Proc. Roy. Soc. Ser. A **272** (1963), 285–303; MR **27** #5734], but it should be added that their version of the machinery is exceedingly well-oiled. A new feature is the curious theorem that if a p-adic integral cubic ψ in at least 15 variables has a p-adic integral zero, then ψ has a non-singular p-adic zero; this can be false for a cubic polynomial in 14 variables.

B. J. Birch (Manchester)

Citations: MR 26# 2403 = L05-27; MR 27# 5734 = D72-33.

Referred to in D48-54, D72-42, D72-50, D72-51, N32-49.

D72-38 **(29# 4734)**

Swinnerton-Dyer, H. P. F.

Rational zeros of two quadratic forms.

Acta Arith. **9** (1964), 261–270.

Let f, g be quadratic forms in 11 variables defined over the rationals; and suppose that for all real λ, μ (not both 0) the form $\lambda f+\mu g$ is indefinite. The author proves that under these conditions f, g have a common non-trivial rational zero. The reality condition is obviously necessary. Previously, Mordell [Abh. Math. Sem. Univ. Hamburg **23** (1959), 126–143; MR **21** #3378] proved a related result assuming 13 variables. The idea behind the proof is to show that, in general, f can be expressed in the form $x_1x_2+\cdots+x_7x_8+h(x_9, x_{10}, x_{11})$ in such a way that $g(x_1, 0, x_3, 0, x_5, 0, x_7, 0, \cdots, 0)=k(x)$ has a non-trivial rational zero. The agreement that f can be so expressed is very intricate and involves some careful byplay between the real condition and the p-adic conditions necessary for the solubility of $k(x)$. Ad hoc arguments are needed when f cannot be so expressed.

Since quadratic forms in 4 variables over the rationals may not have non-trivial rational zeros, clearly 9 variables are needed. On the other hand, Dem'janov [Izv. Akad. Nauk SSSR Ser. Mat. **20** (1956), 307–324; MR **18**, 284] (see also Birch, Lewis and Murphy [Amer. J. Math. **84** (1962), 110–115; MR **25** #52]) has shown that two forms in 9 variables over the rationals have a common non-trivial p-adic zero for each p. Thus one might hope that 9 variables would suffice. The author discusses the possibilities of proving the existence of common non-trivial rational zeros of f, g assuming 9 or 10 variables and possibly a stronger real condition.

D. J. Lewis (Ann Arbor, Mich.)

Citations: MR 18, 284g = D72-10; MR 21# 3378 = D72-17; MR 25# 52 = D72-29.

D72-39 **(30# 1119)**

Medvedev, P. A.

On the representation of zero by a cubic form in a p-adic number field. **(Russian)**

Uspehi Mat. Nauk **19** (1964), *no.* 6 (120), 187–190.

It is known that every cubic form of more than nine variables with coefficients in the rational p-adic field R_p has a non-trivial zero in R_p [V. B. Dem'yanov, Dokl. Akad. Nauk SSSR **74** (1950), 889–891; MR **12**, 315]. In connection with this result, the author considers the general case and obtains a condition, necessary and sufficient, in order that a cubic form with coefficients in R_p have a non-trivial zero in R_p. If a given cubic form of s variables can be transformed so that at least one of the terms x_i^3, $i=1, \cdots, s$, vanishes, then it is clear that it has a non-trivial zero. If this is not the case, then it can be transformed into a form

$$b_1x_1^3+b_{12}x_1^2x_2+\cdots+b_{123}x_1x_2x_3+\cdots$$
$$+p^{h_2}(b_2x_2^3+b_{23}x_2^2x_3+\cdots)+\cdots+p^{h_s}x_s^3,$$

where all the coefficients are p-adic integers and b_i, $i=1,\cdots,s$, is not divisible by p. A cubic form of this type has a non-trivial zero in R_p if and only if it has a non-trivial zero modulo the

$$[2(h_2+1+2(h_3+1+\cdots+2(h_s+1))\cdots)+2^{s-1}]\text{th}$$

power of p. Furthermore, the author solves the problem whether a non-trivial zero modulo p^n of a cubic form is extensible or not. *E. Inaba* (Tokyo)

Citations: MR 12, 315d = D72-4.

D72-40 (30# 4723)

Birch, B. J.; Lewis, D. J.

Systems of three quadratic forms.

Acta Arith. **10** (1964/65), 423–442.

In this paper it is proved that three quadratic forms in at least 13 variables over a $\mathfrak{p}$-adic field k have a nontrivial common zero if the residue field has odd characteristic and has at least 49 elements. (This is a consequence of the unproved conjecture of E. Artin, that any form of degree d over k in n variables has a nontrivial zero if $n>d^2$.) The method used in this paper is an elaboration of that used by the authors and T. G. Murphy to deal with the case of 2 quadratic forms [Amer. J. Math. **84** (1962), 110–115; MR **25** #52].

The argument is roughly as follows. Let $\{f_1,\cdots,f_r\}$ be a set of quadratic forms over k. A set $\{g_1,\cdots,g_r\}$ is equivalent to the first one if, after a suitable invertible transformation of the coordinates, $\{f_1,\cdots,f_r\}$ and $\{g_1,\cdots,g_r\}$ span the same vector space. The authors introduce an invariant $\vartheta(f_1,\cdots,f_r)$. Now assume that the f_i have integral coefficients. Then define $\{f_1,\cdots,f_r\}$ to be a reduced set if $\vartheta(f_1,\cdots,f_r)\neq 0$ and if $|\vartheta(f_1,\cdots,f_r)|\leqq|\vartheta(g_1,\cdots,g_r)|$ for any set $\{g_1,\cdots,g_r\}$ of integral forms equivalent to $\{f_1,\cdots,f_r\}$.

Now let $\{f_1,f_2,f_3\}$ be a reduced set of integral forms in at least 13 variables. In order to prove the statement in the first paragraph, it suffices to show that the f_i ($i=1,2,3$) have a nontrivial common zero (k being subject to the restrictions mentioned before).

Let f_i^* be the form with coefficients in the residue field k^* defined by f_i; write the f_i^* as quadratic forms in $\rho\leqq 13$ variables, where ρ is as small as possible. The f_i^* define an algebraic variety V over k^* in $(\rho-1)$-dimensional projective space, and the authors show that V has a nonsingular point. Then Hensel's lemma finishes the proof. The existence of a nonsingular point of V is the crux of the proof and requires a long discussion of 12 pages. *T. A. Springer* (Utrecht)

Citations: MR 25# 52 = D72-29.

D72-41 (31# 160)

Laxton, R. R.; Lewis, D. J.

Forms of degrees 7 and 11 over $\mathfrak{p}$-adic fields.

Proc. Sympos. Pure Math., Vol. VIII, pp. 16–21. *Amer. Math. Soc., Providence, R.I.*, 1965.

Artin conjectured that a form F of degree d in n variables over a $\mathfrak{p}$-adic field k has a non-trivial zero in k, provided $n>d^2$. This has been proved for $d=1,2,3,5$, provided that the residue class field is large enough; the authors deal with the additional cases $d=7, 11$. Their methods are similar to those used in earlier papers [e.g., J. Indian Math. Soc. (N.S.) **23** (1959), 11–32 (1960); MR **23** #A859] by the reviewer and the second author, in the sense that this is what the reviewer and Lewis would have done had they thought of it at the time; unfortunately, the method is successful only when d is neither composite nor the sum of two composite numbers. It is less non-constructive than the (as yet unpublished) work of Ax and Kochen, which otherwise would supersede it. *B. J. Birch* (Manchester)

Citations: MR 23# A859 = D72-21.
Referred to in D72-44.

D72-42 (31# 5835a; 31# 5835b)

Watson, G. L.

Cubic Diophantine equations: The necessary congruence condition.

Mathematika **12** (1965), 30–38.

Watson, G. L.

Cubic Diophantine equations: A supplementary congruence condition.

Mathematika **12** (1965), 39–48.

Let $\phi(x_1,\cdots,x_n)$ be a cubic polynomial with integer coefficients; let C be the homogeneous cubic part of ϕ. One can write $C=L_1Q_1+\cdots+L_hQ_h$ identically, where the L_i, Q_i are linear and quadratic forms, respectively; the invariant $h(C)$ is defined as the least possible h in an identity of this type.

Davenport and Lewis [J. London Math. Soc. **39** (1964), 657–671; MR **29** #4731] have proved that the equation $\phi(\mathbf{x})=0$ is soluble in integers $\mathbf{x}$ if $h(C)\geqq 17$ and the necessary congruence condition (NCC), namely, that $\phi(\mathbf{x})\equiv 0(p^l)$ is soluble for all prime powers p^l, is satisfied. The author's eventual objective is to prove that $\phi(\mathbf{x})=0$ is soluble if $h(C)\geqq 4$, $n\geqq 20$, and the NCC is satisfied. His proof is long and involved, and will be spread over a series of papers not all of which have appeared yet. Roughly speaking, he will show that $\phi(\mathbf{x})=0$ is soluble if the NCC and a supplementary congruence condition (SCC) are satisfied, subject to some further conditions; an idea of how this is done is given in the second note under review. One then investigates the SCC.

The first note under review is not too difficult; the author shows that, given ϕ with $n\geqq 15$, one may compute a definite integer $m_0(\phi)$ such that the NCC holds if and only if the congruence $\phi(\mathbf{x})\equiv 0(m_0)$ is soluble; verification of the NCC is thus a finite problem.

The second note is much harder. The SCC is defined (part of the difficulty is that it appears so artificial) and its relevance is pointed out. It is proved, inter alia, that there is a finite process to decide whether or not the SCC is satisfied; that the SCC is always satisfied if $n\geqq 12$, ϕ is non-degenerate, and $h(C)\geqq 4$; and that for every $n\geqq 5$ there is a non-degenerate ϕ with $h(C)=3$ for which the NCC is satisfied, the SCC is not, and $\phi(\mathbf{x})=0$ is insoluble. *B. J. Birch* (Cambridge, England)

Citations: MR 29# 4731 = D72-37.
Referred to in D72-51.

D72-43 (32# 108)

Greenleaf, Newcomb

Irreducible subvarieties and rational points.

Amer. J. Math. **87** (1965), 25–31.

Let k be a field and V a k-closed subset of an affine space. Denote by $\mathbf{A}(V,k)$ the union of all those subvarieties of the affine space which are defined over k and contained in V. Let now k be an algebraic number field and p a prime divisor of k. Denote by k_p the p-adic-completion of k and by $\bar{k}_p$ the residue field of k_p. Denote also by $p(V)$ the reduction of a k-closed subset V of an affine space with respect to p. Then the author proves that if $\mathbf{A}(p(V),\bar{k}_p)$ is not empty for all but a finite set of the prime divisors p of k, there is a finite set $\{U_i\}$ of subvarieties of the affine space which are contained in V, such that some U_j is defined over

k_p for almost all p. From this, the existence of a rational point of V over k_p for almost all p follows under the same hypothesis. As an application of this theorem, the following result is obtained. Let k be again an algebraic number field and $f_1, \cdots, f_t$ polynomials of degrees $d_1, \cdots, d_t$ in n variables with coefficients in k. Suppose that $n > \sum d_i$ and that the constant terms of the f_i are zero. Then the f_i have a non-trivial common solution in k_p for almost all p.

T. Matsusaka (Waltham, Mass.)

Referred to in D72-54, D80-61.

D72-44 (32# 2401)

Ax, James; Kochen, Simon

Diophantine problems over local fields. I.

Amer. J. Math. **87** (1965), 605–630.

A conjecture of Artin states that every form f of degree d in $n > d^2$ variables over $\mathbf{Q}_p$ has a non-trivial zero in $\mathbf{Q}_p$. This has been proved for $d = 1, 2, 3, 5, 7, 11$ [see R. R. Laxton and D. J. Lewis, Proc. Sympos. Pure Math., Vol. VIII, pp. 16–21, Amer. Math. Soc., Providence, R.I., 1965; MR **31** #160]. In this paper it is proved that the conjecture is true "semi-globally", that is, for every p with the possible exception of a finite set $A = A(d)$.

As a by-product of their method, the authors obtain a proof of a conjecture of Lang. Let f be a polynomial, without constant term, of degree d in $n > d$ variables over $\mathbf{Z}$. Then there exists a finite set B of primes such that f has a non-trivial zero in $\mathbf{Q}_p$ for every $p \notin B$.

The obvious generalizations to $\mathfrak{p}$-adic fields hold.

Both these results are special cases of a powerful general principle which asserts that for problems of this type the field $\mathbf{Q}_p$ "behaves like" the field $S_p = \mathbf{F}_p((T))$ of formal power series for almost all p.

The proofs are based on a combination of ideas from logic and valuation theory, but they are presented in such a way that the reader who is expert in neither can follow the argument without too much preliminary reading.

From logic the authors introduce the idea of an ultraproduct [see the second author, Ann. of Math. (2) **74** (1961), 221–261; MR **25** #1992]. Let $(F_i)_{i\in I}$ be an indexed family of valued fields with valuation groups $(H_i)_{i\in I}$ and let ord denote the valuation map ord: $F \to H$. If D is an ultrafilter on I, then the ultraproduct $\prod_{i\in I} F_i/D$ is a valued field with valuation group $\prod_{i\in I} H_i/D$ which is a homomorphic image of the corresponding complete direct product $\prod F_i$ [$\prod H_i$] under the equivalence relation $f \equiv g$ if and only if $\{i \mid f(i) = g(i)\} \in D$ [$\gamma \equiv \delta$ if and only if $\{i \mid \gamma(i) = \delta(i)\} \in D$]. If $f^* \in \prod F_i/D$, then $\operatorname{ord}(f^*) = \gamma^*$ if $\{i \mid \operatorname{ord} f(i) = \gamma(i)\} \in D$.

The proofs of the main results are indirect and are based on a comparison of the ultraproducts $\mathscr{R} = \prod_{p\in P} \mathbf{F}_p/D$, $\mathscr{Q} = \prod_{p\in P} \mathbf{Q}_p/D$, $\mathscr{S} = \prod_{p\in P} S_p/D$, where D is an ultrafilter on the set of primes, defined in terms of an infinite set of primes for which the theorems are supposed not to hold.

Lang's conjecture follows from the existence of a monomorphism $\varphi: \mathscr{R} \to \mathscr{Q}$. The problem of solving $f(x_1, \cdots, x_n) = 0$ in $\mathbf{Q}_p$ is then equivalent (almost everywhere) to solving the corresponding equations in $\mathbf{F}_p$. The result now follows from a theorem of Chevalley.

The Artin conjecture lies much deeper, and its resolution is made to depend on the concept of an L-field, which is defined and studied in some detail. When combined with Kaplansky's theory of pseudo-Cauchy sequences [I. Kaplansky, Duke Math. J. **9** (1942), 303–321; MR **3**, 264], together with the continuum hypothesis, the concept leads to an analytic isomorphism $\mathscr{Q} \approx \mathscr{S}$ (that is, a field isomorphism in which the valuation groups are isomorphic). Now let $d_1, \cdots, d_r$ be positive integers such that $n > \sum d_i^2$ and suppose that S is an infinite subset of P such that for all $p \in S$ there exist homogeneous polynomials $f_1, \cdots, f_r$, of degrees $d_1, \cdots, d_r$, respectively, over $\mathbf{Q}_p$, for which the Artin conjecture is false. One constructs a related system $f_1^*, \cdots, f_r^*$ of polynomial equations over $\mathscr{Q}$ which have no non-trivial solution in $\mathscr{Q}$. Assuming the continuum hypothesis, the isomorphism $\mathscr{Q} \approx \mathscr{S}$ yields a system of equations over S with the same property. This contradicts Chevalley's theorem. Following a suggestion of Birch, it is shown that the continuum hypothesis can be eliminated, but not the axiom of choice.

The paper concludes with the general principle referred to. Let $\operatorname{ord}(\pi) = 1$ and let f, g be polynomials over $Z[\pi]$. The expressions $\operatorname{ord}(f) = \operatorname{ord}(g)$, $\operatorname{ord}(f) > \operatorname{ord}(g)$, $\operatorname{ord}(f) = \infty$ are called atomic formulas, and a formula which can be constructed from these by logical notions is called an elementary formula. An elementary statement is an elementary formula involving no free variables. The second author [loc. cit.] has proved that an elementary statement is true for an ultraproduct if and only if it is true almost everywhere on the components. Evidently it is this property which underlies the successful application of the concept to the Artin conjecture. Using this fact one can prove that $\mathscr{Q} \approx \mathscr{S}$ implies that every elementary statement is true in $\mathbf{Q}_p$ if and only if it is true in S_p (almost everywhere). The conjectures of Lang and Artin follow from this. On the other hand, the analytic isomorphism $\mathscr{Q} \approx \mathscr{S}$ is implied by this principle.

J. V. Armitage (Durham)

Citations: MR 31# 160 = D72-41.

Referred to in D02-23, D72-48, D72-53, D72-54, U02-2, U05-28, U05-30, U05-34, U05-36, U05-41.

D72-45 (33# 2626)

Terjanian, Guy

Sur les corps finis.

C. R. Acad. Sci. Paris Sér. A-B **262** (1966), A167–A169.

A field k is called C_1 [strongly C_1] if every homogeneous polynomial [polynomial with constant term 0] $f \in R_n = k[X_1 \cdots X_n]$ of degree $d > 0$ has a non-trivial zero in k^n whenever $n > d$. A well-known result of C. Chevalley [Abh. Math. Sem. Univ. Hamburg **11** (1935), 73–75] is that every finite field is C_1. The author calls a polynomial f of degree n in R_n normal over k if f has constant term 0 and has no non-trivial zero in k^n; he defines a field k to be C_1' if for every normal polynomial f and every polynomial p of degree $< n$ in R_n, there exists an $x \in k^n$ such that $f(x) = p(x)$. Then, using induction and Chevalley's result, he proves the following. Theorem 1: If k is C_1', then k is C_1. Theorem 2: Every finite field is C_1'. Finally, as a generalization of a lemma from Chevalley's paper, he proves Theorem 3: If k is a finite field of q elements, $\mathfrak{a}$ is an ideal of R_n, and $V(\mathfrak{a})$ is the variety of elements $M \in k^n$ such that $f(M) = 0$ for all $f \in \mathfrak{a}$, then the ideal of R_n whose elements vanish on $V(\mathfrak{a})$ is $\mathfrak{a} + \Gamma$, where Γ is the ideal such that $V(\Gamma) = k^n$.

John H. Hodges (Boulder, Colo.)

D72-46 (33# 5615)

Terjanian, Guy

Un contre-exemple à une conjecture d'Artin.

C. R. Acad. Sci. Paris Sér. A-B **262** (1966), A612.

Let p be a prime number, and let $\mathbf{Q}_p$ denote the field of p-adic numbers. Artin conjectured [see *Collected papers of Emil Artin*, p. x, Addison-Wesley, Reading, Mass., 1965; MR **31** #1159] that if $n > d^2$ then every homogenous polynomial of degree $d > 0$ in $\mathbf{Q}_p[X_1, \cdots, X_n]$ has a non-trivial zero in $\mathbf{Q}_p$. This note settles the conjecture in the negative by exhibiting a counterexample: an explicit homogeneous polynomial of degree 4 in 18 variables over $\mathbf{Q}_2$. Of course, the other conjectures of Artin concerning quasi-algebraically closed fields remain open.

E. Weiss (Boston, Mass.)

Citations: MR 31# 1159 = Z25-19.

Referred to in D72-48, D72-52, D72-53, D72-61.

D72-47 (33# 5619)

Eršov, Ju. L.

On the elementary theory of maximal normed fields. II. (Russian)

Algebra i Logika Sem. **4** (1965), *no.* 6, 47–48.

The present paper is a summary of a lecture given by the author in September, 1965. The author states his methods of proving some of his results in a previous work [same Sem. **4** (1965), no. 3, 31–70; MR **33** #1307] and states the following results on C_i fields, using the results on such fields given in an article by S. Lang [Ann. of Math. (2) **55** (1952), 373–390; MR **13**, 726]. (I) Let F be a C_i [strictly C_i] field of characteristic zero having at least one normed form of order i (for every positive integer i). Then the field of formal power series $F\{x_1\}\cdots\{x_\kappa\}$ is $C_{i+\kappa}$ [strictly $C_{i+\kappa}$]. More precisely, if the field F_1 possesses a valuation v_1 such that $\langle F_1, v_1, \gamma_1\rangle$ satisfies Hensel's lemma, F_1v_1 is arithmetically equivalent to F, and γ_1 is arithmetically equivalent to the group of rational rank κ, then F_1 is a $C_{i+\kappa}$ [strictly $C_{i+\kappa}$] field. (II) For any four natural numbers i, $S>1$, α, τ there exists a finite set of prime numbers $A=A(i,S,\alpha,\tau)$ such that for every prime P not in A and for any field F possessing a valuation such that $\langle F, v, \gamma\rangle$ satisfies Hensel's lemma, F is a C_i [strictly C_i] field of characteristic p having a normed form of order i and degree S [a normed form of order i of all degrees], and the group γ of the valuation is arithmetically equivalent to the group of rational rank τ for any form (polynomial without constant term) of degree α in $r>\alpha^{i+\tau}$ variables in F having a nontrivial zero.

R. Finkelstein (Tucson, Ariz.)

Citations: MR 13, 726d = D72-6; MR 33# 1307 = U05-30.

D72-48 (34# 2522)

Browkin, J.

On forms over p-adic fields. (Russian summary)

Bull. Acad. Polon. Sci. Sér. Sci. Math. Astronom. Phys. **14** (1966), 489–492.

It had been conjectured by E. Artin [see *The collected papers of Emil Artin*, Addison-Wesley, Reading, Mass., 1965; MR **31** #1159] that each form of degree d in $n>d^2$ variables over a p-adic field Q_p has a non-trivial zero in Q_p. This conjecture has been verified when $d=2$ [H. Hasse, J. Reine Angew. Math. **153** (1924), 113–130] and when $d=3$ [the reviewer, Ann. of Math. (2) **56** (1952), 473–478; MR **14**, 251]. J. Ax and S. Kochen [Amer. J. Math. **87** (1965), 605–630; MR **32** #2401] have shown this is the case if p is large compared with d. G. Terjanian [C. R. Acad. Sci. Paris Sér. A-B **262** (1966), A612; MR **33** #5615] disproved this conjecture when he gave an example where $d=4$, $n=18$ which had no non-trivial zero in Q_2. For a given field K, let S be the set of pairs of natural numbers (d, N), with $d>1$, such that there is a form of degree d in N variables over K having only the trivial zero in K. Let $\alpha(K)=\sup_{(d,N)\in S}\log_d N$. The author now gives examples to show that $\alpha(Q_p)\geqq 3$. The underlying idea is to find forms in n variables whose values are close to 1 on points $(x_1+py_1,\cdots,x_n+py_n)$ with $x_i=0,1$, not all 0, say $f(x+py)\equiv 1 \pmod{p^r}$. Put $g=f(x_1^{p-1},\cdots,x_n^{p-1})$, and let $G_j=g_{1j}+\cdots+g_{p^r-1}$, where $g_{ij}=g(x_{ij1},\cdots,x_{ijn})$ are forms in disjoint variables. Then $F=G_1+p^rG_2+\cdots+p^{rs}G_s$, where $s=[(\deg G)/r]-1$, has only the trivial zero in Q_p. In his examples, $\deg f$ is a power of p. The art in finding these examples is, for given d, to choose f so that n is large compared to r. It remains an open question whether or not $\alpha(Q_p)=3$.

D. J. Lewis (Ann Arbor, Mich.)

Citations: MR 14, 251g = D72-7; MR 31# 1159 = Z25-19; MR 32# 2401 = D72-44; MR 33# 5615 = D72-46.

Referred to in D72-52.

D72-49 (34# 5787)

Davenport, H.; Lewis, D. J.

Cubic equations of additive type.

Philos. Trans. Roy. Soc. London Ser. A **261** (1966), 97–136.

It is known that a diagonal cubic equation $\sum a_ix_i^3=0$ with integral coefficients in n variables has a non-trivial p-adic solution for every p if $n\geqq 7$, and has a non-trivial rational solution if $n\geqq 8$. The authors consider a pair of simultaneous diagonal cubic equations (*) $\Sigma a_ix_i^3=\sum b_ix_i^3=0$ with rational integral coefficients. Theorem 1: (*) has a non-trivial p-adic solution for every p if $n\geqq 16$. Theorem 2: (*) has a non-trivial rational solution if $n\geqq 18$. The authors show that Theorem 1 is best possible, by exhibiting an explicit example of a pair of forms in 15 variables with only the trivial 7-adic zero in common. Theorem 2 may not be best possible, but it is certainly false for cubic equations which are not diagonal.

The proof of Theorem 1 is decidedly difficult, and does not seem to work for degrees $k>3$; in particular, the case $p=3$ is by brute force. General theorems on the solubility of p-adic equations seem very hard to obtain. The deduction of Theorem 2 from Theorem 1 is a tour-de-force of technique; one imagines that the authors had great fun using all the tricks of the trade.

B. J. Birch (Oxford)

Referred to in D72-60.

D72-50 (35# 2844)

Pleasants, P. A. B.

The representation of integers by cubic forms.

Proc. London Math. Soc. (3) **17** (1967), 553–576.

Let $C(\mathbf{x})=C(x_1,\cdots,x_n)$ be a cubic form in n variables with integer coefficients. The invariant $h=h(C)$ is defined to be the least integer with the property that $C(\mathbf{x})$ is expressible in the form $C(\mathbf{x})=L_1(\mathbf{x})Q_1(\mathbf{x})+\cdots+L_h(\mathbf{x})Q_h(\mathbf{x})$, where $L_i(\mathbf{x})$ and $Q_i(\mathbf{x})$ $(i=1,\cdots,h)$ are, respectively, linear and quadratic forms with integer coefficients. The number $h^*=h^*(C)$ is defined to be the greatest integer with the property that there exists a non-singular rational linear transformation taking $C(\mathbf{x})$ into a cubic form $C'(\mathbf{y})$ of the shape $C'=C_1'+C_2'+\cdots+C_r'$, where $C_1',\cdots,C_r'$ are cubic forms in disjoint sets of variables and $\sum_{i=1}^r h(C_i')=h^*$.

The principal results of this paper are contained in the following two theorems. Theorem 1: Let $C(\mathbf{x})$ be a cubic form with integer coefficients and with $h^*(C)\geqq 12$. Then there exists a real number $\Delta>0$ such that for large X the number of integers N in the range $0\leqq N\leqq X$ for which the congruence $C(\mathbf{x})\equiv N \pmod m$ is soluble to every modulus m but the equation $C(\mathbf{x})=N$ is insoluble in integers $x_1,\cdots,x_n$ is $O(X^{1-\Delta})$. Theorem 2: Let $C(\mathbf{x})$ be a cubic form with integer coefficients and with $h^*(C)\geqq 8$, and let a_1, a_2 be two real numbers with $a_1<a_2$. Then there exist positive real numbers A, a and b, such that for all sufficiently large P there are more than aP^3 integers N in the range $a_1P^3\leqq N\leqq a_2P^3$ for which the equation $C(\mathbf{x})=N$ has more than bP^{n-3} solutions in integer points $\mathbf{x}$ in the region $|\mathbf{x}|<AP^3$.

This paper is an outgrowth of papers by H. Davenport [Proc. Roy. Soc. Ser. A **272** (1963), 285–303; MR **27**

#5734] and H. Davenport and D. J. Lewis [J. London Math. Soc. **39** (1964), 657–671; MR **29** #4731].

A. L. Whiteman (Princeton, N.J.)

Citations: MR 27# 5734 = D72-33; MR 29# 4731 = D72-37.

D72-51 **(35# 2846)**

Watson, G. L.

Non-homogeneous cubic equations.

Proc. London Math. Soc. (3) **17** (1967), 271–295.

Let $\phi(x_1, \cdots, x_n)$ be a cubic polynomial with integer coefficients. If ϕ is homogeneous and $n \geqq 16$, then the diophantine equation $\phi = 0$ has a non-trivial solution [H. Davenport, Proc. Roy. Soc. Ser. A **272** (1963), 285–303; MR **27** #5734]. However, when ϕ is non-homogeneous, regardless of the size of n, $\phi = 0$ need not be soluble in integers. One obviously needs the condition that for each prime power p^m, the congruence $\phi \equiv 0 \pmod{p^m}$ is soluble; this is called the necessary congruence condition (briefly, NCC). However, even this condition is not sufficient as the example $(2x_1 - 1)(1 + x_2^2 + \cdots + x_n^2) + x_1x_2 = 0$ shows. H. Davenport and the reviewer [J. London Math. Soc. **39** (1964), 657–671; MR **29** #4731] and the author, in a series of papers [principally Mathematika **11** (1964), 142–150; MR **30** #1967; ibid. **12** (1965), 39–48; MR **31** #5835b; ibid. **12** (1965), 151–160; MR **32** #7500; Proc. London Math. Soc. (3) **17** (1967), 26–44; MR **34** #4205], have investigated what additional conditions would imply solubility. This paper is the culmination of this study. The following is typical, but not as strong as the best results contained in the paper. Let C be the cubic part of ϕ and let $n - h(\phi)$ denote the maximal linear rational manifold on $C = 0$. (Equivalently, $h(\phi)$ is the minimal s such that C is the sum of s cubics each reducible over the rationals.) If ϕ is non-degenerate and satisfies NCC, then $\phi = 0$ is integrably soluble if either (a) $h(\phi) \geqq 17$ (H. Davenport and the reviewer [loc. cit.]), or (b) $n \geqq 5$ and $4 \leqq h(\phi) \leqq n - 3$. As a consequence, one has: A cubic polynomial in $n \geqq 19$ variables satisfying NCC and having $h(\phi) \geqq 4$ has an integral zero. The essential idea in the proof of (b) is that when $h(\phi)$ is small, one can specialize some of the variables and so obtain a quadratic polynomial in fewer variables. The trick is to specialize to a quadratic which is soluble. The proofs are quite involved and require all the earlier results and techniques of the author, as well as some refinements thereof.

D. J. Lewis (Ann Arbor, Mich.)

Citations: MR 27# 5734 = D72-33; MR 29# 4731 = D72-37; MR 30# 1967 = D80-52; MR 31# 5835b = D72-42; MR 32# 7500 = R08-44; MR 34# 4205 = D48-54.

Referred to in D72-64, N32-50.

D72-52 **(38# 139)**

Terjanian, Guy

Progrès récents dans l'étude de la propriété C_i des corps.

Séminaire Delange-Pisot-Poitou: 1966/67, Théorie des Nombres, Fasc. 2, Exp. 13, 7 *pp. Secrétariat mathématique, Paris*, 1968.

This is an expositive summary of some recent results on C_i fields obtained by M. J. Greenberg [Inst. Hautes Études Sci. Publ. Math. No. 31 (1966), 59–64; MR **34** #7515], the author [C. R. Acad. Sci. Paris Sér. A-B **262** (1966), A612; MR **33** #5615] and J. Browkin [Bull. Acad. Polon. Sci. Sér. Sci. Math. Astronom. Phys. **14** (1966), 489–492; MR **34** #2522]. The first half of the talk is devoted to explaining Greenberg's results cited above, and in the latter half the author shows some counter-examples for Artin's conjecture given by the author and Browkin.

H. Yanagihara (Hiroshima)

Citations: MR 33# 5615 = D72-46; MR 34# 2522 = D72-48; MR 34# 7515 = G25-33.

D72-53 **(38# 1057)**

Ribenboim, Paulo

La conjecture d'Artin sur les équations diophantiennes.

Queen's Papers in Pure and Applied Mathematics, No. 14.

Queen's University, Kingston, Ont., 1968. iii+163 *pp.* $2.50.

This paper is based on lectures given by J. Ax at Harvard University in 1966. A conjecture of E. Artin from 1936 states that every form f of degree d in $n > d^2$ variables over Q_p has a non-trivial zero in Q_p. For $d = 2$ this is a classical theorem about quadratic forms. A proof of the conjecture for $d = 3$ was given by D. J. Lewis [Ann. of Math. (2) **56** (1952), 473–478; MR **14**, 251]. Later on it has been proved for $d = 5$, 7 and 11. J. Ax and S. Kochen [Amer. J. Math. **87** (1965), 605–630; MR **32** #2401] have shown that Artin's conjecture is true if the prime p is large compared with d.

Let f have coefficients from a commutative field k. In the first chapter of this paper the author gives a series of definitions, thereby introducing certain numerical invariants which are intimately connected with the existence of non-trivial zeros for f. As examples we mention, i denoting any real number: The field k is a $C_i(d)$, or $k \in C_i(d)$, if f has a non-trivial zero in k if $n > d^i$. The diophantine d-dimension of k, denoted by $\mathrm{dd}_d(k)$, is defined by $\mathrm{dd}_d(k) = \inf\{i \mid k \in C_i(d)\}$, and $\mathrm{dd}(k) = \inf\{i \mid k \in C_i\}$ is called the diophantine dimension of k, $C_i = \bigcap_{d \geq 1} C_i(d)$. Artin's conjecture can then be written $\mathrm{dd}(Q_p) = 2$ for every prime p.

The author then gives some cases where invariants of these types are known and treats further cases where there exist relations between the diophantine dimensions of two fields. Counterexamples to Artin's conjecture are mentioned. The first of these was given by G. Terjanian in 1966, showing that $\mathrm{dd}_4(Q_2) \geqq \log_4 18 > 2$ [C. R. Acad. Sci. Paris Sér. A-B **262** (1966), A612; MR **33** #5615].

The last chapter is devoted to a proof of the theorem of Ax and Kochen: For every degree $d \geqq 1$ there exists a prime p_0 such that if the prime $p \geqq p_0$, then $Q_p \in C_2(d)$. The foundation is laid in Chapters II and III. In the main the proof follows the same lines as in the first paper of these two authors, but use is also made of results from their next two joint papers [Amer. J. Math. **87** (1965), 631–648; MR **32** #2402; Ann. of Math. (2) **83** (1966), 437–456; MR **34** #1262]. Thus the concept of an L-field is replaced by the simpler, but equivalent concept of a Hensel field of characteristic 0, and some simple applications of homological algebra also occur. *W. Ljunggren* (Oslo)

Citations: MR 14, 251g = D72-7; MR 32# 2401 = D72-44; MR 32# 2402 = U05-28; MR 33# 5615 = D72-46; MR 34# 1262 = U05-34.

D72-54 **(38# 5747)**

Tai, Yung-sheng

On a conjecture of Lang.

Hung-ching Chow Sixty-fifth Anniversary Volume, pp. 121–123. *Math. Res. Center Nat. Taiwan Univ., Taipei*, 1967.

The author gives a simple proof of the following theorem, previously proved by N. Greenleaf [Amer. J. Math. **87** (1965), 25–31; MR **32** #108] and J. Ax and S. Kochen [ibid. **87** (1965), 605–630; MR **32** #2401]. Let $f_1, \cdots, f_m$ be polynomials without constant term in n variables over an algebraic number field k. If $d_1 + \cdots + d_m < n$, where f_i has degree d_i, then the polynomials have a common nontrivial zero in all but a finite number of the completions of k. *L. R. McCulloh* (Urbana, Ill.)

Citations: MR 32# 108 = D72-43; MR 32# 2401 = D72-44.

D72-55 **(39# 2698)**

Greenberg, Marvin J.

Lectures on forms in many variables.

W. A. Benjamin, Inc., New York-Amsterdam, 1969. v+167 *pp.* $12.50; $3.95 *paperback.*

This is a most welcome little book concerning as it does a subject which is undergoing rapid advancement at the hands of enthusiastic workers. Part of the charm of this subject is that it mixes algebra, algebraic geometry, analysis, and arithmetic together in a cross stimulating brew. In this volume, the author treats the theory of forms in many variables mainly from the algebraic and arithmetic points of view, playing down the analysis and geometry. He keeps the exposition clear and relatively elementary, nevertheless, a considerable amount of material is covered and the reader will be well prepared to enter into a study of the available literature after finishing the book.

Chapter I is introductory and uses Tsen's theorem as the prime motivator of the subject. The reviewer feels that all students of algebra and number theory should read this chapter because it is beautifully concise yet touches on all the high points of the theory over a ground field: Tsen's theorem, Chevally-Warning's theorem, Wedderburn's theorem, Artin's conjectures, Birch-Peck's theorem, Lang's definition of C_i, the Ax-Kochen theorem and counter-examples due to Ax, Auslander, Terjanian, and Schanuel. All this in seven pages.

The rest of the book is a more detailed and leisurely view of the above mentioned topics. Specifically: Chapter II concerns finite fields and gives Ax's proof of Chevalley-Warning's theorem that finite fields are C_1. Chapter III discusses function fields and the author proves the following generalized form of Tsen's theorem: If the field k is C_i, then a function field of dimension d over k is C_{i+d}.

The three chapters IV, V, VI, entitled "Complete discrete valuation rings", "Hensel's lemma", and "Witt vectors", deal with matters indispensible to any working algebraist, number theorist or algebraic geometer. They are nicely presented, with many examples and some novel proofs such as the author's own result: If k is C_i and K is the field of one variable formal power series over k, then K is C_{i+1}. In addition, the chapter on Hensel's lemma is especially well-done for it gives the matrix form of the lemma, two proofs of it, examples, and excellent applications.

In the long Chapter VII on "p-adic fields", the Ax-Kochen theorem is stated, the low degree cases $d=2$, $=3$ are proved (theorems of Hasse and Lewis), and the ingenious counter-examples of Terjanian and Schanuel are discussed in detail. Chapter VIII is devoted to a proof of the celebrated theorem of Brauer and Birch on simultaneous zeros of forms over number-like fields. The proof is the most formidable in the book, but it is well worth while. Among the charming asides in the chapter is a short excursion into Hasse's principle and mention of Selmer's cubic counter-example. The last chapter deals with remarks on the Ax-Kochen theorem, methods of logic as used in algebra, remarks on a recent paper of P. J. Cohen in which the Ax-Kochen theorem is reproved in a simpler way; and the book closes with some well chosen words on real and p-adically closed fields. There is also a first class bibliography.

The reviewer heartily recommends this book to anyone with even the mildest interest in this fascinating area of mathematics. Thanks are due the author and publisher for a job well-done. *S. S. Shatz* (Philadelphia, Pa.)

D72-56 **(39# 5470)**

Ryavec, C.

Cubic forms over algebraic number fields.

Proc. Cambridge Philos. Soc. **66** (1969), 323–333.

The author proves: A cubic form in 17 or more variables with coefficients in an algebraic number field has a nontrivial zero in that field. His proof is based on the methods of H. Davenport [*Analytic methods for Diophantine equations and Diophantine inequalities*, Ann Arbor Publishers, Ann Arbor, Mich., 1962; MR **28** #3002] for a cubic form with rational coefficients and on the methods of C. P. Ramanujam [Proc. Cambridge Philos. Soc. **59** (1963), 683–705; MR **27** #4793] for a cubic form in 54 variables with coefficients in an algebraic number field. He leaves unanswered whether the methods can be adopted to handle cubic forms in 16 variables with algebraic numbers as coefficients. H. Davenport [Proc. Roy. Soc. Ser. A **272** (1963), 285–303; MR **27** #5734] has shown that in case of rational coefficients one can get a rational zero if there are 16 variables. *D. J. Lewis* (Ann Arbor, Mich.)

Citations: MR 27# 4793 = D72-32; MR 27# 5734 = D72-33; MR 28# 3002 = D02-19.

D72-57 **(39# 6821)**

Watson, G. L.

A cubic Diophantine equation.

J. London Math. Soc. (2) **1** (1969), 163–173.

The author applies a modification of the Hardy-Littlewood method to the cubic Diophantine equation (*) $\sum_{i=1}^{n-1}\{(a_iy+b_i)x_i^2+(a_i'y+b_i')x_i\}-c_0y^3-c_1y^2-c_2y-c_3=0$, in n variables x_i, y with integer coefficients. Let $\varphi(x_1, \cdots, x_{n-1}; y)$ denote the polynomial on the left side of (*). The author proves that the cubic equation (*) is solvable in integers x_i, y if the following conditions are satisfied: (i) $n \geqq 8$; (ii) $a_1, \cdots, a_{n-1}$ and c_0 are all strictly positive; (iii) no $n-3$ of the rational numbers b_i/a_i are equal; (iv) for each prime power p^t, the congruence $\varphi(x_1, \cdots, x_{n-1}; y) \equiv 0 \pmod{p^t}$ is solvable in integers x_i, y, possibly depending on φ, p and t.

H. London (Montreal, Que.)

D72-58 **(39# 6848)**

Davenport, H.; Lewis, D. J.

Simultaneous equations of additive type.

Philos. Trans. Roy. Soc. London Ser. A **264** (1969), 557–595.

Let $\mathscr{S}$ be a system of R simultaneous equations $a_{i1}x_1^k + \cdots + a_{iN}x_N^k = 0$, $i=1, \cdots, R$, where the a_{ij} are arbitrary integers. If k is an odd positive integer, and if $N \geqq [9R^2k \log 3Rk]$, then $\mathscr{S}$ has a solution in integers, not all 0. Conditions are given under which $\mathscr{S}$ has a solution in integers, not all 0, when k is an even integer greater than 2. For every prime p, $\mathscr{S}$ has a solution in p-adic integers, not all 0, if $N \geqq [9R^2k \log 3Rk]$ for k odd, and if $N \geqq [48R^2k^3 \log 3Rk^2]$ for k even. (Non-singular p-adic solutions are needed to ensure that $\mathscr{S}$ has a nontrivial solution in integers.) *B. Garrison* (San Diego, Calif.)

Referred to in D72-65.

D72-59 **(40# 1353)**

Dodson, M. M.

The average order of two arithmetical functions.

Acta Arith. **16** (1969/70), 71–84.

A method is established for finding the average orders of a certain class of arithmetic functions. The theory is applied to the function $\Gamma(k)$ of G. H. Hardy and J. E. Littlewood [Math. Z. **12** (1922), 161–188] and the function $\Gamma^*(k)$ of H. Davenport and D. J. Lewis [Proc. Roy. Soc. Ser. A **274** (1963), 443–460; MR **27** #3617]. The resulting average orders are, respectively, $5\pi^2k/12 \log k$ and $\pi^2k^2/6 \log k$.

D. Rearick (Boulder, Colo.)

Citations: MR 27# 3617 = D72-31.

D72-60 (40# 7198)

Davenport, H.; Lewis, D. J.

Two additive equations.

Number Theory (Proc. Sympos. Pure Math., Vol. XII, Houston, Tex., 1967), pp. 74–98.

Amer. Math. Soc., Providence, R.I., 1969.

Es sei Z der Ring der ganzen rationalen Zahlen. Die Verfasser untersuchen die simultanen Gleichungen (1) $f=\sum_{i=1}^N a_ix_i^k=0$, $g=\sum_{i=1}^N b_ix_i^k=0$ ($a_i, b_i, k \in Z$; $k \geqq 1$). Das Hauptziel der vorliegenden Arbeit ist u.a. der Beweis der folgenden Sätze. Satz 1: Wenn k ungerade und $N \geqq 2k^2+1$ erfüllt sind, dann besitzen (1) für alle Primzahlen p eine nichttriviale p-adische Lösung. Satz 3: Wenn $n \geqq 7k^2$, dann besitzen (1) für alle Primzahlen p eine nichttriviale p-adische Lösung.

Rationale Lösungen von (1) sollen in einer weiteren Arbeit untersucht werden.

Die Untersuchungen führen frühere Arbeiten [die Verfasser, Proc. Roy. Soc. Ser. A **274** (1963), 443–460; MR **27** #3617; der erste Verfasser, *Analytic methods for Diophantine equations and Diophantine inequalities*, Ann Arbor Publ., Ann Arbor, 1963; MR **28** #3002; die Verfasser, Quart. J. Math. Oxford Ser. (2) **17** (1966), 339–344; MR **34** #5749; Philos. Trans. Roy. Soc. London Ser. A **261** (1966), 97–136; MR **34** #5787] weiter.

H. J. Kanold (Braunschweig)

Citations: MR 27# 3617 = D72-31; MR 28# 3002 = D02-19; MR 34# 5749 = D80-60; MR 34# 5787 = D72-49.

D72-61 (41# 147)

Browkin, J.

On zeros of forms. (Loose Russian summary)

Bull. Acad. Polon. Sci. Sér. Sci. Math. Astronom. Phys. **17** (1969), 611–616.

G. Terjanian [C. R. Acad. Sci. Paris Sér. A-B **262** (1966), A612; MR **33** #5615] constructed a form which disproved Artin's conjecture that any form of degree d in $n > d^2$ variables over a p-adic field Q_p has a non-trivial zero in Q_p. The author considers a similar construction of forms with no non-trivial zero over a finite extension of Q_p, and shows that they all satisfy $n < d^3$. A generalization of the construction is finally discussed, indicating the possibility of finding forms over Q_p with $n > d^3$.

E. S. Barnes (Adelaide)

Citations: MR 33# 5615 = D72-46.

D72-62 (42# 195)

Maxwell, George

A note on Artin's diophantine conjecture.

Canad. Math. Bull. **13** (1970), 119–120.

Let Q_p be the field of p-adic numbers. The author gives a short elementary proof of the following theorem: Every form $a_1x_1^d+\cdots+a_nx_n^d$ with coefficients a_i in Q_p has a non-trivial zero in Q_p, if $n > d^2$ and if d is not divisible by p.

O. H. Körner (Marburg)

D72-63 (42# 1758)

Birch, B. J.

Small zeros of diagonal forms of odd degree in many variables.

Proc. London Math. Soc. (3) **21** (1970), 12–18.

The author proved [Mathematika **4** (1957), 102–105; MR **20** #3828] that for each odd integer k there exists an integer $N(k)$ such that any form of degree k in $N > N(k)$ variables with rational coefficients has a non-trivial rational zero. One would thus expect to be able to show that a form of odd degree k in sufficiently many variables with real coefficients can be made arbitrarily small for suitable non-trivial integer points. The late H. Davenport indicated to the author that this diophantine inequality conjecture would follow if one could prove: To each odd integer k and positive real number ε there is an integer $N(k, \varepsilon)$, such that whenever $N > N(k, \varepsilon)$, and $a_1, \cdots, a_N$ are given non-zero integers, there exist integers $x_1, \cdots, x_N$ such that $a_1x_1^k+\cdots+a_Nx_N^k=0$ and $0<\max|x_i|<(\max|a_j|)^\varepsilon$. This the author cannot yet prove, but he does prove the weaker result where he only requires $0<\max|x_i|<(\max|a_j|)^{1+\varepsilon}$. His proof uses the Hardy-Littlewood circle method in conjunction with Linnik's elementary method for Waring's problem.

D. J. Lewis (Ann Arbor, Mich.)

Citations: MR 20# 3828 = D72-16.

D72-64 (42# 1764)

Watson, G. L.

Cubic Diophantine equations with reducible cubic part.

Proc. London Math. Soc. (3) **21** (1970), 181–200.

Let P be a cubic polynomial in n variables with integer coefficients and C the cubic form consisting of all the terms of degree 3. The author has already treated the case when C is irreducible [same Proc. (3) **17** (1967), 271–295; MR **35** #2846]. He now supposes C reducible over the rational field and proves theorems on the solubility of the diophantine equation $P=0$.

B. Stolt (Stockholm)

Citations: MR 35# 2846 = D72-51.

D72-65 (43# 6158)

Lewis, D. J.

Systems of diophantine equations.

Symposia Mathematica, Vol. IV (INDAM, Rome, 1968/69), pp. 33–43. Academic Press, London, 1970.

Die vorliegende Arbeit befaßt sich mit der Lösbarkeit eines Systems homogener Gleichungen mit ganzen rationalen Koeffizienten in rationalen Zahlen, natürlich nichttrivialen Lösungen $\neq(0, \cdots, 0)$. B. J. Birch [Proc. Roy. Soc. Ser. A **265** (1961/62), 245–263; MR **27** #132] gab hinreichende Bedingungen dafür an, daß ein System von Formen $f_1, \cdots, f_R$ vom gleichen Grad k in N Variablen mit rationalen Koeffizienten eine gemeinsame rationale Nullstelle besitzt. Der Verfasser untersuchte zusammen mit H. Davenport [Philos. Trans. Roy. Soc. London Ser. A **264** (1969), 557–595; MR **39** #6848] Systeme von additiven Formen (*) $f_\rho=a_{\rho 1}x_1^k+a_{\rho 2}x_2^k+\cdots+a_{\rho N}x_N^k$ ($\rho=1, \cdots, R$; $a_{\rho\nu}$ rational für $\nu=1, \cdots, N$). Für ungerades k besitzt (*) eine Lösung $(x_1, \cdots, x_N)\neq(0, \cdots, 0)$ (x_ν ganz rational) und $f_\rho=0$ für $\rho=1, \cdots, R$, wenn

$$N \geqq |9R^2k\cdot\log 3Rk|$$

erfüllt ist. Bei geradem $k>2$ sind die hinreichenden Bedingungen komplizierter. Der Verfasser zeigt an zwei Beispielen, daß man bei geradem k nicht mit so einfachen Bedingungenen auskommt wie bei ungeradem. {Druckfehler: S. 37, Zeile 9 von oben. Statt $N \geqq |48R^2k^3 \log 3k^2|$ muß es heißen $N \geqq |48R^2k^3 \log 3Rk^2|$.}

H. J. Kanold (Braunschweig)

Citations: MR 27# 132 = D72-30; MR 39# 6848 = D72-58.

D72-66 (44# 3952)

Iskovskih, V. A.

A counterexample to the Hasse principle for systems of two quadratic forms in five variables. (Russian)

Mat. Zametki **10** (1971), 253–257.

As a counterexample to the would-be "Hasse principle" for pairs of quadratic forms, the author proves that the pair $x_1^2+x_2^2+x_3^2+x_3x_5=0$, $x_3x_5-x_4^2+3x_5^2=0$ has a nontrivial solution in every completion of the rational number field Q, but none in Q itself. This answers a question of Ju. I. Manin [Inst. Hautes Études Sci. Publ. Math. No. 30 (1966), 55–113; MR **37** #1373]. Geometrically, the example amounts to a rational surface whose Picard number (i.e., the dimension of the Picard group over the algebraic closure of Q) is equal to 6. The "Hasse principle" is apparently known for rational surfaces with Picard number $\leqq 5$. *G. Maxwell* (Vancouver, B.C.)

Citations: MR 37# 1373 = G35-46.

D72-67 (44# 5276)

Tietäväinen, Aimo

On a homogeneous congruence of odd degree.

Ann. Univ. Turku. Ser. A I No. 131 (1969), 6 *pp.*

Let p be a prime, k an odd positive integer. Let $\gamma^*(k)$ be the least integer s such that the congruence $\sum_{j=1}^{s} a_jx_j^k\equiv 0 \pmod p$ has a non-trivial solution for every prime p and all sets of integers a_j. Write $H'=\lim\sup(\gamma^*(k)/\log_2 k)$. The reviewer and G. Shimura [Norske Vid. Selsk. Forh. (Trondheim) **36** (1963), 169–176; MR **28** #3971] showed that $1\leqq H'\leqq 2$. K. K. Norton in his doctoral dissertation ["On homogeneous diagonal congruences of odd degree", Ph.D. Thesis, Univ. of Illinois, Urbana, Ill., 1966] sharpened this to $H'\leqq\frac{3}{2}$. In the present paper the author proves that $H'=1$. *S. Chowla* (Princeton, N.J.)

Citations: MR 28# 3971 = D72-35.

D72-68 (44# 6597)

Cook, R. J.

Simultaneous quadratic equations.

J. London Math. Soc. (2) **4** (1971), 319–326.

By using the Hardy-Littlewood method, H. Davenport and D. J. Lewis found an asymptotic formula for the number of solutions of a pair of cubic equations in $\geqq 18$ variables. V. B. Demjanov proved that if f and g are quadratic forms in $\geqq 9$ variables then they have a common zero in any p-adic field. The present author applies these results and methods and solves the problem for quadratic equations in $\geqq 9$ variables. In particular he proves the following theorem: Let $F(x)=\sum_{i=1}^{9} a_ix_i^2$ and $G(x)=\sum_{i=1}^{9} b_ix_i^2$ be quadratic forms with integer coefficients, and let $N(P)$ denote the number of simultaneous integer zeros of F and G in the domain $P\leqq x_i\leqq CP$, $i=1,\cdots,9$, where C is a constant; suppose that for all real λ, μ, not both zero, $\lambda F+\mu G$ is an indefinite form in at least 5 variables; then for some positive constant K_0 we have $N(P)=K_0P^5+o(P^5)$. *T. T. Tonkov* (Sofia)

D76 INEQUALITIES IN MANY VARIABLES

See also Sections J28, J32, J36, J40, J44, J48, J52, J56, J60, J64.

See also reviews C05-31, D02-12, D02-19, D72-63, E99-3, J99-4, R14-59.

D76-1 (8, 565e)

Davenport, H., and Heilbronn, H. On indefinite quadratic forms in five variables. J. London Math. Soc. **21**, 185–193 (1946).

It has been conjectured that any indefinite quadratic form in 5 variables with real coefficients assumes values that are arbitrarily small numerically (for integer values of the coefficients). The authors prove that this is the case when the form $Q(x_1,\cdots,x_5)=\lambda_1x_1^2+\cdots+\lambda_5x_5^2$. The corresponding problem for 3 and 4 variables has not been solved yet; the authors assert that their method, which is a modification of the Hardy-Littlewood method, also holds for the general case $Q(x_1,\cdots,x_s)=\lambda_1x_1^k+\cdots+\lambda_sx_s^k$, where $s=2^k+1$. Their exact result is as follows. Let $\lambda_1,\cdots,\lambda_5$ be real numbers, none of them zero, such that at least one of the ratios λ_s/λ_r is irrational. Then there exist arbitrarily large integers P, such that the inequalities $1\leqq x_1\leqq P,\cdots,1\leqq x_5\leqq P$, $|Q(x_1,\cdots,x_5)|<1$ have more than γP^3 solutions, where $\gamma=\gamma(\lambda_1,\cdots,\lambda_5)>0$. *J. F. Koksma* (Amsterdam).

Referred to in D02-19, D76-4, D76-6, D76-7, D76-8, D76-12, D76-21, D76-24, P12-6.

D76-2 (14, 955a)

Oppenheim, A. Values of quadratic forms. I. Quart. J. Math., Oxford Ser. (2) **4**, 54–59 (1953).

The following theorems are proved: (I) If $f(x_1,x_2,\cdots,x_n)$ is an indefinite quadratic form, such that for every $\epsilon>0$ the inequalities $0<f<\epsilon$ are solvable in integers x_ν, then, if $n\geqq 3$, the inequalities $0<-f<\epsilon$ are solvable in integers x_ν for every $\epsilon>0$. The theorem does not hold in general for $n=2$, as shown by a counter-example. (II) If f is an indefinite form with non-zero determinant $\Delta(f)$, then to every positive value a taken by f corresponds a negative value $-b$ taken by f such that $b^{2n-2}\leqq A_na^{n-2}|\Delta(f)|$, where the constant A_n depends only on n. Both a and b can be properly represented values. (III) If $P_1(f)$ denotes the lower bound of the positive values of a positive definite or indefinite form f, then $P_1^n(f)\leqq B_n|\Delta(f)|$, where B_n is a constant which depends only on n. Theorem (I) is a corollary of theorem (II). Theorems (II) and (III) are proved together by induction on n. A different proof of theorem (III), based on the adjoint form of f, is also given, establishing at the same time the inequality $B_n\leqq B_{n-1}^{n/(n-2)}$. For theorem (III) see also Blaney, J. London Math. Soc. **23**, 153–160 (1948); these Rev. **10**, 511. *E. Grosswald* (Philadelphia, Pa.).

Citations: MR 10, 511c = J48-4.

Referred to in D76-8.

D76-3 (14, 955b)

Oppenheim, A. Values of quadratic forms. II. Quart. J. Math., Oxford Ser. (2) **4**, 60–66 (1953).

It has been conjectured that if f is an incommensurable quadratic form in 5 or more variables, of non-vanishing determinant, then $0<|f(x_1,x_2,\cdots,x_n)|<\epsilon$ is solvable in integers x_ν for every $\epsilon>0$. The following weaker form of this statement is proved: If the indefinite form f in n ($\geqq 5$) variables and non-zero determinant represents zero properly and is not a multiple of a rational function, then the inequalities $0<|f|<\epsilon$ are solvable in integers x_ν for every $\epsilon>0$. Let $M(f)$ be the lower bound of the non-zero values of $|f|$. Then the preceding statement follows immediately from the following two theorems. (a) If f is a zero form and $M(f)>0$, then there exists a form

$$F=h(X_1X_2+\theta X_2^2+c_3X_3^2+c_4X_4^2+\cdots+c_nX_n^2)$$

such that $M(F)>0$, $c_3,\cdots,c_n$ are integers different from zero, θ is rational or irrational, and F is derived from f by rational, non-singular transformations. (b) If θ is irrational, $c_3,\cdots,c_n$ are integers, and $n\geqq 5$, then the inequalities $0<|X_1X_2+\theta X_2^2+c_3X_3^2+\cdots+c_nX_n^2|<\epsilon$ are solvable in integers X_ν for every $\epsilon>0$. The proof makes use of several lemmas, some of the author and some due to Jones [Trans. Amer. Math. Soc. **33**, 92–110, 111–124 (1931)], Ross [Proc. Nat. Acad. Sci. U. S. A. **18**, 600–608 (1932)], Smith [Collected Math. Papers, v. 1, Oxford, 1894, pp. 455–506] and Weyl [Math. Ann. **77**, 313–352 (1916)]. It is conjectured that the main statement remains true even for $n=3$.

E. Grosswald (Philadelphia, Pa.).

Referred to in D76-5, D76-8.

D76-4 **(14, 955c)**

Watson, G. L. On indefinite quadratic forms in three and four variables. J. London Math. Soc. **28**, 239–242 (1953).

If $\theta_1, \cdots, \theta_m$ are $m \geqq 1$ nonzero real numbers not of the same sign, whose ratios are not all rational, then one may ask whether for every $\epsilon > 0$ the inequality $|\theta_1 x_1^2 + \cdots + \theta_m x_m^2| < \epsilon$ is soluble in integers $x_1, \cdots, x_m$ not all zero. Davenport and Heilbronn [same J. **21**, 185–193 (1946); these Rev. **8**, 565] proved that the answer is affirmative for $m=5$ (and, therefore, for $m \geqq 5$). Now the author establishes the result for $m=3$ and $m=4$, considering, however, special types of forms only. For $m=3$ he considers forms

$$f(x, y, z) = x^2 - a\theta y^2 - (a\theta + 1)z^2,$$

where a is an arbitrary positive integer and θ denotes the positive root of the equation $\theta^2 = a\theta + 1$. He then even proves that for all integers $X > 0$ the simultaneous inequalities $0 < x \leqq X$, $0 < y \leqq X$, $0 < z \leqq X$, $|f| < CX^{-2}$, where $C = C(a)$ denotes a conveniently chosen constant, have an integer solution x, y, z. For $m=4$ he considers forms of the special kind $f(x, y, z, w) = x^2 + dy^2 - \theta^2(z^2 + dw^2)$, where d is an arbitrary positive integer and θ is any number of some quadratic fields (which depend on d). *J. F. Koksma.*

Citations: MR 8, 565e = D76-1.

D76-5 **(15, 106e)**

Oppenheim, A. Value of quadratic forms. III. Monatsh. Math. **57**, 97–101 (1953).

The following theorem has been proven by the author in a previous paper [Quart. J. Math., Oxford Ser. (2) **4**, 60–66 (1953); these Rev. **14**, 955]: If f represents zero for integers x_i not all zero, if f is not a multiple of a rational form and if $n \geqq 5$, then the inequalities $0 < f(x_1, x_2, \cdots, x_n) < \epsilon$ are solvable for integers $x_1, \cdots, x_n$ for every positive ϵ. For $n=2$ the theorem is false; for $n \geqq 3$ its proof can be reduced to that of the same statement for the particular quadratic form $Q = x_1x_2 + \vartheta x_2^2 + c_3x_3^2 + \cdots + c_nx_n^2$ with ϑ irrational and $c_3, \cdots, c_n$ non-zero integers. In the present paper the theorem is proven for $n=4$; the case $n=3$ is left unsettled. In the proof use is made of (i) the equidistribution (mod 1) of ϑp_n^2 for primes p_n; and (ii) the fact that an integral binary quadratic form represents the numbers $\sigma^2 p$, where σ is a fixed integer, while p runs through the primes of an arithmetic progression. (i) follows from Weyl's theorem on equidistribution (mod 1) [Math. Ann. **77**, 313–352 (1916)] and a paper by Vinogradov [C. R. (Doklady) Acad. Sci. URSS (N.S.) **17**, 165–166 (1937)], while (ii) is proven using the properties of integral binary quadratic forms. *E. Grosswald* (Philadelphia, Pa.).

Citations: MR 14, 955b = D76-3.

Referred to in H15-81.

D76-6 **(15, 291g)**

Watson, G. L. On indefinite quadratic forms in five variables. Proc. London Math. Soc. (3) **3**, 170–181 (1953).

Davenport and Heilbronn proved that any indefinite quadratic form of the type $\lambda_1x_1^2 + \cdots + \lambda_5x_5^2$ with real coefficients whose ratios are not all rational, takes arbitrary small values for integers $(x_1, \cdots, x_5)$ not all zero [J. London Math. Soc. **21**, 185–193 (1946); these Rev. **8**, 565]. The author shows that the same result also holds for the form $\lambda_1x_1^2 + \cdots + \lambda_5x_5^2 + \lambda_6x_4x_5$, which is supposed indefinite with determinant $\neq 0$ such that the ratios of the real coefficients $\lambda_1, \cdots, \lambda_6$ are not all rational. His main theorem is similar to that of Davenport and Heilbronn [loc. cit.]. *J. F. Koksma* (Amsterdam).

Citations: MR 8, 565e = D76-1.

Referred to in P12-6.

D76-7 **(17, 829f)**

Davenport, H.; and Roth, K. F. The solubility of certain Diophantine inequalities. Mathematika **2** (1955), 81–96.

Let $\lambda_1, \cdots, \lambda_s$ be real numbers, not all of the same sign (say $\lambda_1\lambda_2 < 0$) and not all rational multiples of a single irrational number. Let $\varkappa$ be an arbitrary real number and let ε be positive. Improving a result of Davenport and Heilbronn [J. London Math. Soc. **21** (1946), 185–193; MR **8**, 565], it is shown that there is an absolute constant C such that if $k \geqq 12$ and $s > Ck \log k$, or if $k=3$ and $s=8$, the inequality

$$|\lambda_1x_1^k + \cdots + \lambda_sx_s^k + \varkappa| < \varepsilon$$

has infinitely many solutions in positive integers $x_1, \cdots, x_s$. *W. J. LeVeque* (Ann Arbor, Mich.).

Citations: MR 8, 565e = D76-1.

Referred to in D48-65, D60-64, D76-12, D76-21, D76-24, D76-26.

D76-8 **(19, 19a)**

Davenport, H. Indefinite quadratic forms in many variables. Mathematika **3** (1956), 81–101.

This paper is devoted to a proof of the following theorem. Let $Q(x_1, \cdots, x_n)$ be an indefinite quadratic form with real coefficients and index r. Suppose that

(3) $$r \geqq 37 \text{ and } n - r \geqq 37.$$

Then for each $\varepsilon > 0$, there exist integers $x_1, \cdots, x_n$, not all 0, such that

(2) $$|Q(x_1, \cdots, x_n)| < \varepsilon.$$

Using results of Oppenheim [Quart. J. Math. Oxford Ser. (2) **4** (1953), 54–59, 60–66; MR **14**, 955] it immediately follows that a quadratic form satisfying (3) is either a multiple of a form with integral coefficients or it assumes values that are everywhere dense among the real numbers. The proof uses: 1) a modification of the Hardy-Littlewood method used by Davenport and Heilbronn [J. London Math. Soc. **21** (1946), 185–193; MR **8**, 565] in proving (2) for $n=5$ where Q lacks cross product terms, and 2) a recent estimate of Cassels [Proc. Cambridge Philos. Soc. **51** (1955), 262–264; **52** (1956), 602; MR **16**, 1002; **18**, 380]. *B. W. Jones* (Boulder, Colo.).

Citations: MR 8, 565e = D76-1; MR 14, 955a = D76-2; MR 14, 955b = D76-3; MR 16, 1002c = D08-16; MR 18, 380c = D08-17.

Referred to in D76-9, D76-11.

D76-9 **(19, 1161a)**

Davenport, H. Indefinite quadratic forms in many variables. II. Proc. London Math. Soc. (3) **8** (1958), 109–126.

[For part I see Mathematika **3** (1956), 81–101; MR **19**, 19]. The author proves the following improvement of a previous result: Let $Q(x_1, \cdots, x_n)$ be an indefinite quadratic form with real coefficients. Suppose that when Q is written as a sum of squares of real linear forms with positive and negative signs, there are r positive signs and $n-r$ negative signs. Then the inequality $|Q(x_1, \cdots, x_n)| < \varepsilon$ is soluble in integers $x_1, \cdots, x_n$, not all 0, for any $\varepsilon > 0$, provided that either $r \geqq 16$ and $n - r \geqq 16$ or $13 \leqq r \leqq 15$ and $n > (9r-20)/(r-12)$.

The improvement is based partially on Minkowski's theory of successive minima in the geometry of numbers. In a note added in August, 1957, the author calls attention to a method of B. J. Birch which is more effective for small values of r and which will appear in a joint paper. *B. W. Jones* (Boulder, Colo.).

Citations: MR 19, 19a = D76-8.

Referred to in D76-11, D76-23.

D76-10 (20# 3103)

Danicic, I. An extension of a theorem of Heilbronn. Mathematatika **5** (1958), 30–37.

The author proves the following extension of a result of Heilbronn*: Let

$$Q(x_1, \cdots, x_n) = \sum_{i,j=1}^{n} \alpha_{ij} x_i x_j \ (\alpha_{ij} = \alpha_{ji})$$

be a real quadratic form in n variables. If $N > 1$ and $\varepsilon > 0$, then there exist integers $x_1, \cdots, x_n$, not all zero, satisfying

$$|x_j| \leqq N \ (j = 1, \cdots, n),$$

and

$$\|Q(x_1, \cdots, x_n)\| < CN^{-n/(n+1)+\varepsilon}$$

where C depends on n and ε only, and $\|\alpha\|$ denotes the difference between α and the nearest integer, taken positively.

The exponent of N cannot be improved beyond -2.

B. W. Jones (Boulder, Colo.)

Citations: MR 10, 284c = J04-5.

Referred to in J12-42.

D76-11 (20# 3104)

Birch, B. J.; and Davenport, H. Indefinite quadratic forms in many variables. Mathematika **5** (1958), 8–12.

This paper concerns the conjecture that any indefinite quadratic form Q in five or more variables and with real coefficients has, for every positive ε, the property that the inequality (1) $|Q| < \varepsilon$ is solvable non-trivially for integer values of the variables. Let n be the number of variables and r the index of the form. They prove the theorem: **If** $1 \leqq \min(r, n-r) \leqq 4$ **and** $n \geqq 21$, then (1) is soluble for any $\varepsilon > 0$ in integers not all 0. The conclusion holds also if $\min(r, n-r) > 4$ and $n \geqq 17 + \min(r, n-r)$.

This supplements recent results of the second author [Mathematika **3** (1956), 81–101; Proc. London Math. Soc. (3) **8** (1958), 109–126; MR **19**, 19, 1161]. This paper follows quite a different line of reasoning from the previous papers and requires an adaptation of methods of R. Brauer and of a result of Cassels.

B. W. Jones (Boulder, Colo.)

Citations: MR 19, 19a = D76-8; MR 19, 1161a = D76-9.

Referred to in D76-13, D76-25.

D76-12 (20# 3119)

Danicic, I. The solubility of certain Diophantine inequalities. Proc. London Math. Soc. (3) **8** (1958), 161–176.

Let $\lambda_1, \cdots, \lambda_{14}$ be non-zero real numbers, not all of the same sign, such that $\lambda_2^{-1}\lambda_1$ is irrational. It is proved that, for any real γ and any $\varepsilon > 0$, the inequality

$$|\lambda_1 x_1^4 + \cdots + \lambda_{14} x_{14}^4 + \gamma| < \varepsilon$$

has infinitely many solutions in positive integers $x_1, x_2, \cdots, x_{14}$. The number 14 corresponds to Davenport's result [Ann. of Math. **40** (1939), 731–747; MR **1**, 42] in Waring's problem that any sufficiently large positive integer incongruent to 15 or 16 modulo 16 is the sum of 14 integral fourth powers.

The proof stems from work of Davenport [loc. cit.], Davenport and Heilbronn [J. London Math. Soc. **21** (1946), 185–193; MR **8**, 565] and Davenport and Roth [Mathematika **2** (1955), 81–96; MR **17**, 829].

A. C. Woods (New Orleans, La.)

Citations: MR 1, 42a = P04-3; MR 8, 565e = D76-1; MR 17, 829f = D76-7.

D76-13 (20# 5166)

Birch, B. J.; and Davenport, H. On a theorem of Davenport and Heilbronn. Acta Math. **100** (1958), 259–279.

Davenport and Heilbronn have proved that if $\lambda_1, \cdots, \lambda_5$ are any real numbers not all of the same sign and none of them zero, there are integers $x_1, \cdots, x_5$ not all zero such that

$$(*) \qquad |\lambda_1 x_1^2 + \cdots + \lambda_5 x_5^2| < 1.$$

This paper sharpens this result by means of the following theorem. For $\delta > 0$ there exists C_δ with the following property. For any real $\lambda_1, \cdots, \lambda_5$, not all of the same sign and all of absolute value 1 at least, there exist integers $x_1, \cdots, x_5$ which satisfy both (*) and

$$0 < |\lambda_1| x_1^2 + \cdots + |\lambda_5| x_5^2 < C_\delta |\lambda_1 \cdots \lambda_5|^{1+\delta}.$$

This result is applied in another paper by the same authors [Mathematika **5** (1958), 8–12; MR **20** # 3104] to general indefinite quadratic forms.

B. W. Jones (Boulder, Colo.)

Citations: MR 20# 3104 = D76-11.

Referred to in D76-22, D76-24.

D76-14 (20# 5766)

Foster, D. M. E. On a class of quadratic polynomials in n variables. Quart. J. Math. Oxford Ser. (2) **9** (1958), 241–256.

Let $L_1, \cdots, L_n$ denote n homogeneous linear forms in n variables $u_1, \cdots, u_n$ with real coefficients and determinant $\Delta \neq 0$, and let c be any real number. Let $q = \pm L_1^2 \pm \cdots \pm L_{n-1}^2$ and $p = q + L_n + c$; let q be of rank $n-1$ and signature $s = 2r + 1 - n$, where r is the number of positive signs in the expression above for q. The author proves the following two theorems. Theorem 1: If the coefficients of $p - c$ are not all in a rational ratio, p assumes arbitrarily small values for integers $u_1, \cdots, u_n$. Theorem 2: If the coefficients of $p - c$ are in a rational ratio, then there are integers $u_1, \cdots, u_n$ satisfying $|p| \leqq (\frac{1}{2}|\Delta|)^{2/(n+1)}$ except possibly when $|s| = n-1$ and $n \geqq 10$. The second theorem is an improvement of a result of Macbeath.

B. W. Jones (Boulder, Colo.)

D76-15 (21# 2642)

Ridout, D. Indefinite quadratic forms. Mathematika **5** (1958), 122–124.

Let Q be an indefinite quadratic form in n variables with real coefficients. Let r be the index of the form (the number of positive terms in the diagonal form after a real transformation). The author proves that if $\min(r, n-r) = 5$ and $n \geqq 21$, then, for any positive ε, the inequality $|Q| < \varepsilon$ is solvable in integers not all zero. This fills a gap between results of Birch and Davenport (for $\min(r, n-r) \leqq 4$) and those of Davenport and the author.

B. W. Jones (Mayaguez, P.R.)

D76-16 (22# 28)

Davenport, H.; Ridout, D. Indefinite quadratic forms. Proc. London Math. Soc. (3) **9** (1959), 544–555.

Let $Q(x_1, \cdots, x_n)$ be an indefinite quadratic form in n variables with real coefficients. Suppose that when Q is expressed as a sum of squares of real linear forms with positive and negative signs, there are r positive signs and $n-r$ negative signs. The authors use results and extend methods of Birch, Davenport, Ridout and Oppenheimer to prove the following theorem: For any real indefinite quadratic form in 21 or more variables, the inequality

$$|Q(x_1, \cdots, x_n)| < \varepsilon$$

is solvable for arbitrary positive ε, in integers $x_1, \cdots, x_n$ not all zero. Further, if the coefficients of the form are not all in rational ratios, then the values assumed by the form for integers $x_1, \cdots, x_n$ are everywhere dense.

B. W. Jones (Boulder, Colo.)

D76-17 **(23# A114)**

Watson, G. L.

Distinct small values of quadratic forms.

Mathematika **7** (1960), 36–40.

Let $f = f(x_1, x_2, \cdots, x_n)$ be an indefinite, non-singular, quadratic form with real coefficients. The object of this paper is to prove the following theorem conjectured by Chalk: Let f be incommensurable (not a constant multiple of a form with integral coefficients) and $n \geqq 21$. Then f assumes, for integral x_i, an infinite sequence of positive values tending to zero. *B. W. Jones* (Boulder, Colo.)

D76-18 **(25# 1131)**

Watson, G. L.

Indefinite quadratic polynomials.

Mathematika **7** (1960), 141–144.

The author proves the following. Theorem 1: Let f be a quadratic form in $n \geqq 3$ variables with real coefficients. Suppose that f is indefinite and non-singular and takes arbitrarily small non-zero values (for integral $x_1, \cdots, x_n$). Let $\xi_1, \cdots, \xi_n, \alpha, \varepsilon$ be real numbers, ε being positive. Then the inequality

$$(*) \qquad |f(x_1+\xi_1, \cdots, x_n+\xi_n) - \alpha| < \varepsilon$$

is soluble in integers $x_1, \cdots, x_n$. Theorem 2: Suppose that $n \geqq 3$ and that f is non-singular, has all its coefficients in rational ratios, and represents zero non-trivially. Let $\xi_1, \cdots, \xi_n$ be real numbers, not all rational, and let α be any real number. Then (*) is soluble in integers $x_1, \cdots, x_n$ for every positive ε.

He discusses relations of these results with those of D. M. E. Foster [Mathematika **3** (1956), 111–116; MR **18**, 634]. *G. Whaples* (Bloomington, Ind.)

Citations: MR 18, 634a = J48-11.

D76-19 **(25# 1135)**

Watson, G. L.

On the gaps between the values of a rational quadratic polynomial.

J. London Math. Soc. **37** (1962), 235–241.

Let Q be an inhomogeneous quadratic polynomial with rational coefficients in $n \geqq 4$ variables, the homogeneous part of which is a primitive quadratic form f with integral coefficients and discriminant d. Consider the values taken by Q for integral values of the variables; there is a rational number G, the length of the longest gap containing none of these values; in particular, the inhomogeneous minimum of f is at most $\frac{1}{2}G$. The author obtains an estimate for G, a weak consequence of which is that $G \ll |d|^{1/(4n-4)+\varepsilon}$ for all $\varepsilon > 0$; this would clearly be impossible on grounds of homogeneity without the assumption that f is primitive. The proof is by reduction to a problem on quadratic congruences, ingenuity, and Burgess' estimate of character sums. *B. J. Birch* (Cambridge, England)

Referred to in D76-20.

D76-20 **(25# 3013)**

Watson, G. L.

Indefinite quadratic forms in many variables: the inhomogeneous minimum and a generalization.

Proc. London Math. Soc. (3) **12** (1962), 564–576.

This paper is a companion to an earlier paper [J. London Math. Soc. **37** (1962), 235–241; MR **25** #1135], and we use the same notation; but now f is merely an indefinite real quadratic form, no longer necessarily a primitive integral. The author considers estimates of the type $G \leqq A_{n,s}|d|^{1/n}$, $M_I \leqq B_{n,s}|d|^{1/n}$, for a given number of variables n and signature s; for $n \geqq 21$, he obtains the best-possible constants $A_{n,s}$ and $B_{n,s}$. The proofs are similar to those of the earlier paper, but Burgess' estimate is replaced by a weaker but more explicit result on quadratic residues; the nicest bit is a painless proof that $B_{n,s}$ depends only on the residue class of s modulo 8. The assumption that $n \geqq 21$ is not entirely essential, but avoids a lot of tedious complication; except for this, the author seems to have disposed of his problem completely. *B. J. Birch* (Cambridge, England)

Citations: MR 25# 1135 = D76-19.

D76-21 **(33# 110)**

Schwarz, Wolfgang

Über die Lösbarkeit gewisser Ungleichungen durch Primzahlen.

J. Reine Angew. Math. **212** (1963), 150–157.

H. Davenport and H. Heilbronn [J. London Math. Soc. **21** (1946), 185–193; MR **8**, 565] adapted the Hardy-Littlewood circle method to prove that if $\lambda_1, \cdots, \lambda_s$ are real numbers, not all of the same sign, and not all in rational ratio, then for every $\varepsilon > 0$, the inequality (*) $|\lambda_1 x_1{}^k + \cdots + \lambda_s x_s{}^k| < \varepsilon$ has infinitely many solutions in integers x_i provided that $s \geqq 2^k+1$. Later H. Davenport and K. F. Roth [Mathematika **2** (1955), 81–96; MR **17**, 829], using adaptations analogous to those of Vinagrodov for the Hardy-Littlewood method, proved that if $k \geqq 12$, $s \geqq ck \log k$ will suffice with a suitable absolute constant c. The author uses estimates of L. K. Hua [*Additive prime number theory* (Russian), Trav. Inst. Math. Stekloff **22** (1947); MR **10**, 597; erratum, MR **11**, p. 870; Chinese translation, Academia Sinica, Peking, 1953; MR **16**, 337; German translation, *Additive Primzahltheorie*, Teubner, Leipzig, 1959; MR **23** #A1620; English translation, *Additive theory of prime numbers*, Amer. Math. Soc., Providence, R.I., 1965; MR **33** #2614] for trigonometric sums involving primes to adapt the Davenport-Roth proof to show that if $s \geqq 2^k+1$ or $s \geqq 2k^2(2\log k + \log\log k + 2,5) - 1$, $k \geqq 12$, then (*) has an infinity of solutions with primes x_i. *R. P. Bambah* (Columbus, Ohio)

Citations: MR 8, 565e = D76-1; MR 10, 597e = P02-5; MR 17, 829f = D76-7.

Referred to in D76-24.

D76-22 **(35# 6620)**

Pitman, Jane; Ridout, D.

Diagonal cubic equations and inequalities.

Proc. Roy. Soc. Ser. A **297** (1967), 476–502.

The main result is as follows. For every $\theta > 0$ there exists a constant K_θ with the following property: If $\lambda_1, \cdots, \lambda_9$ are real numbers such that $|\lambda_i| \geqq 1$ for all i, then the inequality $|\lambda_1 x_1{}^3 + \cdots + \lambda_9 x_9{}^3| < 1$ has a solution in non-zero integers $x_1, \cdots, x_9$ such that $|\lambda_1 x_1{}^3| + \cdots + |\lambda_9 x_9{}^3| < K_\theta |\lambda_1 \cdots \lambda_9|^{(3/2)+\theta}$. (Compare this result with the result of B. J. Birch and H. Davenport [Acta Math. **100** (1958), 259–279; MR **20** #5166].) The authors conjecture that the general statement is true: If $n = 2^k+1$, and $\lambda_1, \cdots, \lambda_n$ are real numbers which satisfy $|\lambda_i| \geqq 1$ for all i and which are not all of the same sign if K is even, then for any $\theta > 0$ there is a solution of the inequality $|\lambda_1 x_1{}^k + \cdots + \lambda_n x_n{}^k| < 1$ in non-zero integers such that $|\lambda_1 x_1{}^k| + \cdots + |\lambda_n x_n{}^k| < C(\theta)|\lambda_1 \cdots \lambda_n|^{(k/2)+\theta}$. *V. Baulin* (Astrakhan)

Citations: MR 20# 5166 = D76-13.

Referred to in D76-25.

D76-23 **(36# 109)**

Danicic, I.

The distribution (mod 1) **of pairs of quadratic forms with integer variables.**

J. London Math. Soc. **42** (1967), 618–623.

Using methods and results of H. Davenport [Proc. London Math. Soc. (3) **8** (1958), 109–126; MR **19**, 1161], the author proves the following theorem: For every $\varepsilon > 0$, $N > 1$ and every pair of real quadratic forms $Q_i(x_1, \cdots, x_n)$ $(i=1, 2)$ in n variables, there exist integers $x_1, \cdots, x_n$, not all 0, such that $\|Q_i(x_1, \cdots, x_n)\| \ll N^{-\delta_n+\varepsilon}$ $(i=1, 2)$, $|x_j| \leqq N$ $(j=1, \cdots, n)$, where $\delta_n=(3+4n^{-1}+2\theta n^{-1})^{-1}$ with $\theta=\sum_{r=1}^{n} r^{-1}$, $\| \quad \|$ denotes distance to the nearest integer, and $F \ll G$ means that $F < cG$ for some $c=c(n, \varepsilon)$.

R. Jacobowitz (Lawrence, Kan.)

Citations: MR 19, 1161a = D76-9.

D76-24 (36# 111)

Baker, A. [Baker, Alan]

On some diophantine inequalities involving primes.

J. Reine Angew. Math. **228** (1967), 166–181.

Under suitable conditions on the real numbers λ_i, H. Davenport and H. Heilbronn [J. London Math. Soc. **21** (1946), 185–193; MR **8**, 565] proved the existence of infinitely many integers $x_1, \cdots, x_5$ such that

$$(*) \qquad |\lambda_1 x_1^2 + \cdots + \lambda_5 x_5^2| < 1,$$

and later on H. Davenport and K. F. Roth [Mathematika **2** (1955), 81–96; MR **17**, 829] proved a more general result {the reviewer [J. Reine Angew. Math. **212** (1963), 150–157; MR **33** #110] gave an analogous result for primes x_i}.

The present author is concerned with the more difficult problem of replacing the 1 in (*) by an explicit function of $x=\max|x_i|$, tending to zero for $x\to\infty$ [cf. B. J. Birch and H. Davenport, Acta Math. **100** (1958), 259–279; MR **20** #5166]. He proves the following result. Let the non-zero real numbers λ_1, λ_2, λ_3 be not all of the same sign, and let λ_1/λ_2 be irrational. For any $n>0$ there exist infinitely many primes p_i such that $|\lambda_1 p_1+\lambda_2 p_2+\lambda_3 p_3| < \{\log(\max p_i)\}^{-n}$.

W. Schwarz (Freiburg)

Citations: MR 8, 565e = D76-1; MR 17, 829f = D76-7; MR 20# 5166 = D76-13; MR 33# 110 = D76-21.

D76-25 (37# 154)

Pitman, Jane

Cubic inequalities.

J. London Math. Soc. **43** (1968), 119–126.

Let $C(x_1, \cdots, x_n)$ be a cubic form with real coefficients and γ the largest of the absolute values of the coefficients. The following theorems are proved. (1) There exists an absolute constant N such that, for every $\varepsilon>0$, the inequality $|C(x_1, \cdots, x_n)|<\varepsilon$ is soluble in integers $x_1, \cdots, x_n$ not all zero provided that $n \geqq N$. The constant N is less than $(1314)^{256}$. (2) For every $\theta>0$ there exist constants N_θ and $M(n, \theta)$ with the following property. If $n \geqq N_\theta$ and $\gamma \geqq 1$, then $|C(x_1, \cdots, x_n)|<1$ is soluble in integers $x_1, \cdots, x_n$ such that $0<\max|x_i| \leqq M(n, \theta)\gamma^{25/6+\theta}$. The proofs rely on an earlier result of the author and D. Ridout [Proc. Roy. Soc. Ser. A **297** (1967), 476–502; MR **35** #6620] concerning the solutions of a diagonal cubic inequality and use a reduction of a general form to an almost diagonal form similar in principle to that applied by B. J. Birch and H. Davenport [Mathematika **5** (1958), 8–12; MR **20** #3104] to quadratic inequalities. The conjectured value of N in Theorem 1 is 10.

A. Schinzel (Warsaw)

Citations: MR 20# 3104 = D76-11; MR 35# 6620 = D76-22.

D76-26 (39# 5480)

Ryavec, C. A.

Diophantine inequalities with a non-integral exponent.

Acta Arith. **14** (1967/68), 333–345.

Let $c_1, \cdots, c_s$ be nonzero real numbers not all of the same sign and let b be any real number. Let $t>12$ and not an integer. The author proves that there is an absolute constant $c>0$ such that if $s>ct\log t$ then the inequality $|c_1k_1^t+\cdots+c_sk_s^t+b|<e$ has infinitely many solutions in positive integers k_i for all $e>0$.

This result extends to nonintegral t a similar theorem due to H. Davenport and K. F. Roth [Mathematika **2** (1955), 81–96; MR **17**, 829] for integral t which requires, however, the additional necessary condition that some c_i/c_j is irrational. The proof is along similar lines.

A. C. Woods (Columbus, Ohio)

Citations: MR 17, 829f = D76-7.

D76-27 (41# 8343)

Raghavan, S.; Ramanathan, K. G.

On a Diophantine inequality concerning quadratic forms.

Nachr. Akad. Wiss. Göttingen Math.-Phys. Kl. II **1968**, 251–262.

Let K be an algebraic number field of finite degree, $\mathfrak{D}$ the ring of algebraic integers in K, and let $\bar{K}=K \otimes R$ be the tensor product of K and the real number field R. For any element a in $\bar{K}$, we put $\|a\|=\text{Max}(|a^{(1)}|, \cdots, |a^{(h)}|)$, where $a^{(i)}$ are the characteristic roots of the matrix representing the R-linear transformation L_a of $\bar{K}$ determined by $L_a(x)=a\cdot x$, for $x\in\bar{K}$. The following theorem is proved: Let $S=(s_{ij})$ be an $n\times n$ symmetric non-singular indefinite matrix such that $s_{ij}\in\bar{K}$, and $n\geqq 5$. We assume that S represents zero non-trivially over $\bar{K}$, and that S cannot be written as aT for $a\in\bar{K}$ and T a symmetric matrix with elements in K. Then, given $\varepsilon>0$, there exists a vector $\mathbf{x}\neq\mathbf{0}$ with elements in $\mathfrak{D}$ such that $0<\|\mathbf{x}'\cdot S\cdot\mathbf{x}\|<\varepsilon$.

The proof depends on an application of H. Weyl's result on uniform distribution [Math. Ann. **77** (1916), 313–352] and C. L. Siegel's results [Ann. of Math. (2) **38** (1937), 212–291] on the arithmetics of quadratic forms.

K. Iyanaga (Tokyo)

D76-28 (44# 2704)

Jackson, T. H.

Gaps between the values of quadratic polynomials.

J. London Math. Soc. (2) **3** (1971), 47–58.

Let $f(x_1, \cdots, x_n)$ be an indefinite quadratic form with discriminant $d(f)\neq 0$ and real coefficients. If $\xi_1, \cdots, \xi_n$ are given real numbers and $x_1, \cdots, x_n$ are integer variables define $Q(x_1, \cdots, x_n)=f(\xi_1+x_1, \cdots, \xi_n+x_n)$. The author considers the diophantine inequalities $\alpha<Q(x_1, \cdots, x_n)\leqq \alpha+\beta$ and defines $G(Q)$ as the least upper bound of the real β which, for suitable α, the inequalities are not simultaneously soluble in integers x_i. The main theorem of the paper is as follows. Let $f(x_1, \cdots, x_n)$ be a non-singular, indefinite zero form. Then for any given real numbers $\xi_1, \cdots, \xi_n$ the polynomial Q is defined and $G(Q)$ satisfies $G(Q)\leqq|c_n d(f)|^{1/n}$, where $c_n=2$ if n is odd, 1 if n is even.

For $n\geqq 4$ the author proves that there is strict inequality unless f is equivalent to certain specific quadratic forms which are stated explicitly.

The author conjectures that the above theorem is true, at least for $n\geqq 4$, without the hypothesis that f is a zero form.

W. J. Ellison (Talence)

D80 CONGRUENCES IN TWO OR MORE VARIABLES

For the number of solutions of $1 + g^s \equiv g^t \pmod p$ (p fixed, g a primitive root of p), see **T20**. For permutation polynomials, see **T10**.

Many of the results in **T40** ***ff***. specialize, for $q = p$, to theorems of interest here.

See also Section T40.

See also reviews A10-18, A12-24, A14-38, A36-11, A36-50, A36-53, A99-13, B08-73, D24-9, D28-22, D32-41, D40-14, D44-16, D48-51, D52-92, D52-119, D52-120, D52-127, D72-31, L05-28, L15-18, L99-8, N36-35, N72-50, P04-6, R08-44, T05-62, T25-36, T40-1, T50-26, T55-27, U05-22.

D80-1 **(1, 39g)**

van der Corput, J. G. Sur un certain système de congruences. I. Nederl. Akad. Wetensch., Proc. **42**, 538–546 (1939).

Let N be the number of incongruent solutions $y_1, \cdots, y_n$ of

$$\text{(I)} \qquad \sum_{\nu=1}^{n} b_{\mu\nu}\psi_\nu(y_\nu) \equiv g_\mu (\text{mod } v_\mu), \quad \mu=1, 2, \cdots, m,$$

where all $v_\mu = p^\alpha$, and α, $b_{\mu\nu}$, g_μ are integers, $\psi_\nu(y)$ polynomials with integral coefficients such that the derivatives $\psi_\nu'(y)$ have no zeros of higher multiplicities than s. The author intends to prove the following theorems: (1) If $n \geqq (s+2)m$, and if for every positive integer $\mu \leqq m$ the matrix $B=(b_{\mu\nu})_{\mu=1,2,\cdots,m;\,\nu=1,2,\cdots,n}$ retains at least the rank $m+1-\mu$ if $(s+2)\mu-1$ arbitrary columns are suppressed, then $N \leqq cp^{(n-m)\alpha}$, where c depends only on B and the $\psi_\nu(y)$. (2) The same conditions as under (1) are satisfied, but $v_1, \cdots, v_m$ are now arbitrary positive integers of product not greater than an integer X, and N is the number of solutions of (I) in positive integers $y_\nu \leqq X$. Then

$$N \leqq 2^n \tau(v_1 v_2 \cdots v_m)^\eta X^n (v_1 v_2 \cdots v_m)^{-1},$$

where $\tau(w)$ is the number of divisors of w, and η a constant depending only on B and the $\psi_\nu(y)$. (3) The less stringent conditions are made that $n \geqq m$ and that the rank of B is m. Then if N has the same meaning as under (2)

$$N \leqq 2^n X^n \prod_{\mu=1}^{m} \prod_{p \mid v_\mu} \omega p^{-1-(1/m)[\alpha/(s+3)]},$$

where p^α is the highest power of p which divides v_μ, and ω is a suitable number which depends alone on B and the $\psi_\nu(y)$. In this first note, the author begins with four lemmas which are necessary for the proof of (1). The fourth lemma gives upper bounds for the number of solutions of $\psi(y) \equiv g \ (\text{mod } p^\alpha)$. *K. Mahler* (Manchester).

Referred to in D80-2.

D80-2 **(1, 65c)**

van der Corput, J. G. Sur un certain système de congruences. II. Nederl. Akad. Wetensch., Proc. **42**, 707–712 (1939).

The proof of the theorems 1–3 of the first part [these Rev. **1**, 39 (1940)] is concluded. *K. Mahler.*

Citations: MR 1, 39g = D80-1.

D80-3 **(1, 39h)**

O'Connor, R. E., S.J. Quadratic and linear congruence. Bull. Amer. Math. Soc. **45**, 792–798 (1939).

This paper considers the number $N(p^m)$ of simultaneous solutions of a quadratic congruence

$$f(x) = \sum_1^n a_{ij}x_ix_j \equiv r \ (\text{mod } p^m)$$

and a linear congruence

$$g(x) = \sum_1^n c_ix_i \equiv s \ (\text{mod } p^m),$$

where f and g are integral forms, $n \geqq 2$, r and s are integers, and p is an odd prime. The author employs Minkowski's canonical form $F(x) = \sum_1^n a_ix_i^2$ of $f(x)$ [Minkowski: Gesammelte Abhandlungen, vol. 1, p. 14] and also a theorem of Jordan [C. R. Acad. Sci. Paris **62**, 687 (1866)] concerning the number of solutions of an integral quadratic congruence $\sum d_ix_i^2 \equiv h \ (\text{mod } p)$, to determine $N(p^m)$, for $m=1$, in terms of quadratic character symbols associated with the above forms. The author distinguishes between ordinary and singular solutions of the above system (a singular solution is a solution ξ such that, for some integer λ, p divides each of $\sum_j(a_{ij}\xi_j) - \lambda c_i$ for $i=1, \cdots, n$), determines the number $M(p^m)$ of the ordinary solutions for $m \geqq 1$, and indicates instances where these are the only solutions. An application to certain integral vectors is suggested in the last section. *A. E. Ross* (St. Louis, Mo.).

D80-4 **(3, 270a)**

Hua, Loo-keng and Min, Szu-hoa. On the number of solutions of certain congruences. Sci. Rep. Nat. Tsing Hua Univ. (A) **4**, 113–133 (1940).

Let $f(x) = a_kx^k + \cdots + a_1x + a_0$, the a_i integral, p a prime, $p \nmid (a_1, \cdots, a_k)$. The number $N(s, p, n)$ of integer solutions $x_1, \cdots, x_s$ of $f(x_1) + \cdots + f(x_s) \equiv n \ (\text{mod } p)$ is $p^{s-1} + p^{-1}E(s)$, where

$$|E(s)| \leqq T(s) = \sum_{a=1}^{p-1} \Big| \sum_{x=1}^{p} e^{2\pi i a f(x)/p} \Big|^s.$$

The object of this paper is to estimate $T(s)$ for large p. From a result of Davenport [J. Reine Angew. Math. **169**, 158–176 (1933)] is deduced $T(s) = O(p^{s-(s-2)/m})$ if $s \geqq 2$ and $k \geqq 3$; here $m = 8/3$ if $k=3$, and m is the largest integer of the form 2^σ or $3\cdot 2^\sigma$, and not exceeding k, if $k>3$. (Hence if $s>2$, $N(s, p, n) \sim p^{s-1}$; but this is false if $s=2$.) To obtain an improvement in certain cases, the authors show that $T(2t) = O(p^{2t-2})$ when $t=k$, and when $t = 2^r[k/2^r]$, where r is a positive integer such that $[k/2^r] = 3$, 4 or 5. Then by Hölder's inequality, or directly, follows $T(s) = O(p^{s-(s-2)/(t-1)})$ if $2 \leqq s \leqq 2t$, $T(s) = O(p^{s-2-(s-2t)/m})$ if $s>2t$. The paper contains hundreds of misprints. *G. Pall* (Montreal, Que.).

D80-5 **(5, 255f)**

Hua, Loo-keng and Min, Sze-hoa. An analogue of Tarry's problem. Acad. Sinica Science Record **1**, 26–29 (1942).

Asymptotic formulae are found for the number of solutions of the system of congruences (analogous to the equations of Tarry's problem)

$$x_1^h + \cdots + x_s^h \equiv y_1^h + \cdots + y_s^h, \quad 1 \leqq h \leqq k \ (\text{mod } p^n),$$

where p is a prime, $p>k$, $s \geqq k \geqq 2$, $n \geqq k^2$. Since this number is $p^{-kn}S$, where

$$S = \sum_{a_k=1}^{p^n} \cdots \sum_{a_1=1}^{p^n} \Big| \sum_{x=1}^{p^n} e^{2\pi i(a_kx^k + \cdots + a_1x)/p^n} \Big|^{2s},$$

the problem reduces to estimating sums

$$\sum \exp(2\pi i f(x)/p^n)$$

for various polynomials $f(x)$. Precise results are stated, but proofs will appear later. *G. Pall* (Montreal, Que.).

D80-6 **(7, 242g)**

Chowla, Inder. On Waring's problem (mod p). Proc. Nat. Acad. Sci. India. Sect. A. **13**, 195–220 (1943).

Let p denote a prime and k a positive integer. The paper deals mainly with the function $\gamma(k, p)$ defined as the least s such that the congruence $\sum_{m=1}^{s} x_m^k \equiv n \ (\text{mod } p)$ is solvable for every n. The main result is as follows. Let $p \equiv 1 \ (\text{mod } k)$, $p > 3k$, $C = (103 - 3\sqrt{641})/220$, and $\epsilon > 0$. Then $\gamma(k, p) = O(k^{1-C+\epsilon})$. The author applies this to the function $\Gamma(k)$ introduced by Hardy and Littlewood in connection with Waring's problem [Proc. London Math. Soc. (2) **28**, 518–542 (1928)], and obtains a result of the form

$\Gamma(k)=\max\{f(k), g(k)\}$, where $f(k)=O(k^{1-C+\epsilon})$ for every positive ϵ, and $g(k)$ is an elementary arithmetical function. This is an improvement on Hardy and Littlewood's results.
T. Estermann (London).

D80-7 (9, 8e)

Schupfer, Francesco. Su due proposizioni di teoria dei numeri. Univ. Roma. Ist. Naz. Alta Mat. Rend. Mat. e Appl. (5) **5**, 246–251 (1946).

(i) It is shown, by use of the quadratic reciprocity law, that a prime number n is a quadratic residue of all and only those primes of the form $p=4nk\pm(2m+1)^2$, where $2m+1$ ranges over the odd integers numerically less than n; if $n=4g+1$, this formula can be replaced by either of $p=2nh+(2m+1)^2$ or $p=2nh-(2m+1)^2$. (ii) If p is a prime number of the form $6k+1$ with $k>2$, then the congruence $x^3+y^3\equiv z^3 \pmod p$ has solutions with xyz prime to p. The proof considers the residue classes (a) the cubic residues $u_1, \cdots, u_r$; (b) $u_1v, \cdots, u_rv$; (c) $u_1v^2, \cdots, u_rv^2$, where $r=(p-1)/3$ and $1, v, v^2$ are the roots of the congruence $v^3\equiv 1 \pmod p$; and shows by examination of the numbers 1, 2, 3, 7, 13 and $p-1$ that there are three numbers in one residue class such that one is the sum of the other two. Thus, if 2 is in (a), take 2, $p-1$, $p+1$; if 2 is in (b) and 3 in (a), take 1, 8, 9; $\cdots$; if 2 is in (b) and 3 in (c), take 1, 6, 7, or 8, 28, 36, or 6, 8, 14, according as 7 is in (a), (b) or (c).
G. Pall (Chicago, Ill.).

D80-8 (9, 225a)

Min, Szu-hoa. On a system of congruences. J. London Math. Soc. **22**, 47–53 (1947).

Let p be a prime greater than 3, and consider the system of three congruences (mod p^α):

$$x_1+x_2+x_3\equiv y_1+y_2+y_3,$$
$$x_1^2+x_2^2+x_3^2\equiv y_1^2+y_2^2+y_3^2,$$
$$x_1^3+x_2^3+x_3^3\equiv y_1^3+y_2^3+y_3^3.$$

The author proves that the number of incongruent solutions of this system is, to within a factor $\{1+O(p^{-1})\}$, $p^{3\alpha+\alpha/3}$, $6p^{3\alpha+(\alpha-1)/3}$ or $16p^{3\alpha+(\alpha-2)/3}$ according as $p\equiv 0$, 1 or 2 (mod 3).
D. H. Lehmer (Berkeley, Calif.).

D80-9 (11, 229k)

Bagchi, Haridas. Note on the two congruences
$ax^2+by^2+e\equiv 0$, $ax^2+by^2+cz^2+dw^2\equiv 0 \pmod p$, where p is an odd prime and
$a\not\equiv 0$, $b\not\equiv 0$, $c\not\equiv 0$, $d\not\equiv 0 \pmod p$.
Rend. Sem. Mat. Univ. Padova **18**, 311–315 (1949).

It is pointed out that the existence of solutions of the first congruence mentioned in the title can be demonstrated by the method usually applied to the special case where $a=b=e=1$. It follows that the second congruence mentioned is also solvable nontrivially.
I. Niven.

D80-10 (11, 418b)

Verdenius, W. On generalized Gauss sums. Handelingen van het XXXIe Nederlands Natuur- en Geneeskundig Congres, pp. 93–94, Haarlem, 1949. (Dutch)

The following theorem is stated without proof. Let $\psi(y_1, \cdots, y_s)$ be a quadratic form (not necessarily homogeneous) with integral coefficients and assume the discriminant of the quadratic part to be different from 0. Then there exists a constant $C>0$ such that for any prime p, any $\alpha\geqq 1$ and any t the number $N(p^\alpha, t)$ of the solutions of $\psi(y_1, \cdots, y_s)\equiv t \pmod{p^\alpha}$ is either zero or greater than $Cp^{(s-1)\alpha}$. The same holds if the condition $p\nmid y_1\cdots y_s$ is added. The author states that he obtained these results by evaluation of generalised Gauss sums.
N. G. de Bruijn.

D80-11 (14, 353f)

Brčić-Kostić, Mato. L'extension de la congruence
$$(a+b)^n-a^n-b^n\equiv 0 \pmod n$$
(n un nombre premier). Hrvatsko Prirodoslovno Društvo. Glasnik Mat.-Fiz. Astr. Ser. II. **7**, 7–11 (1952). (Serbo-Croatian. French summary)

The author gives examples of the congruence

$$(1)\qquad (a+b)^n-a^n-b^n\equiv 0 \pmod{n^{2k+1}}$$

where n is a prime of the form $6m+1$. The function $(x+1)^n-x^n-1$ and its derivative vanish when x is a complex cube root of unity. Hence by the well-known divisibility property of the binomial coefficients, the form $(a+b)^n-a^n-b^n$ is divisible by $n(a^2+ab+b^2)^2$. Any power n^k can be represented by the form a^2+ab+b^2. Hence the congruence (1) has solutions (a, b) for every k. Five examples are given.
D. H. Lehmer (Los Angeles, Calif.).

D80-12 (14, 538e)

Cohen, Eckford. Sur les congruences du deuxième degré dans les corps algébriques. C. R. Acad. Sci. Paris **235**, 1358–1360 (1952).

The author considers the congruence $\rho=\alpha_1\xi_1^2+\cdots+\alpha_s\xi_s^2$ (mod A) in an algebraic number field when A is an odd ideal and $\alpha_1, \cdots, \alpha_s$ are integral numbers with $(\alpha_i, A)=1$. He gives (without proof) the number of solutions when A is a power of a prime ideal. The general case may be reduced to this case.
H. Bergström (Gothenberg).

D80-13 (14, 725k)

Cohen, Eckford. Representations by cubic congruences. Proc. Nat. Acad. Sci. U. S. A. **39**, 119–121 (1953).

In this paper the number $N_s(\alpha, p)$ of solutions of the congruence $\alpha\equiv x_1^3+\cdots+x_s^3 \bmod p$ is considered when p is a prime, $p\equiv 1 \bmod 3$. It is shown that $N_s(\alpha, p)$ can be computed by help of Gauss sums in the following special cases: 1) $s=3$, α cubic residue mod p; 2) $s=3$, $\alpha=0$.
H. Bergström (Gothenburg).

D80-14 (15, 200e)

Mordell, L. J. Note on the linear symmetric congruence in n variables. Canadian J. Math. **5**, 433–438 (1953).

Consider the congruence

$$f=a_0+a_1\sum x_1+a_2\sum x_1x_2+\cdots+a_nx_1x_2\cdots x_n\equiv 0 \pmod p.$$

The author has conjectured that, excluding certain exceptional cases, the number of solutions of $f\equiv 0 \pmod p$ satisfies $N=p^{n-1}+O(p^{\frac12(n-1)})$, where the constant implied in the O is independent of the a's. In the present paper he proves the conjecture for $n\leqq 4$.
L. Carlitz.

Referred to in D80-20.

D80-15 (15, 508c)

Cohen, Eckford. Congruence representations in algebraic number fields. Trans. Amer. Math. Soc. **75**, 444–470 (1953).

In two earlier papers [Duke Math. J. **19**, 115–129 (1952); C. R. Acad. Sci. Paris **234**, 787–788 (1952); these Rev. **13**, 823] the author has considered general arithmetic functions, defined on residue class rings in rational and algebraic fields. In this paper he gives some applications of the general theory to special arithmetic functions such as Rademacher sums, Ramanujan sums, Hecke sums and some sums that are related to Hecke sums. Then he uses these sums in order to get the number of solutions x_{ij} of congruences of the form $\rho\equiv\alpha_1x_{11}\cdots x_{l1}+\cdots+\alpha_sx_{1s}\cdots x_{ls}$ (mod A), where ρ is an arbitrary algebraic integer, α_i ($i=1, \cdots, s$) are given algebraic integers and A is an ideal in an algebraic field. In particular, the number of the solutions of the quadratic congruences $\rho=\alpha_1\xi_1^2+\cdots+\alpha_s\xi_s^2 \pmod A$ are given, when A is an odd prime and $\alpha_1, \cdots, \alpha_s$ are prime to A. All these applications depend on a theorem, which states that every arithmetic function considered here is a linear function of Hecke's exponential functions. *H. Bergström.*

Citations: MR 13, 823d = L05-7; MR 13, 823e = L05-8.
Referred to in D80-28.

D80-16 (15, 937a)

Cohen, Eckford. Rings of arithmetic functions. II. The number of solutions of quadratic congruences. Duke Math. J. **21**, 9–28 (1954).

In part I [same J. **19**, 115–129 (1952); these Rev. **13**, 823] sums of the form

$$c(n, r)=\sum_{\substack{(x, r)=1\\ 0<x<r}} \epsilon(xn, r), \quad \text{where} \quad \epsilon(xn, r)=e^{2\pi ixn/r},$$

were considered. Here the author studies quadratic functions of the form

$$T(n, r)=\sum_{\substack{(x, r)=1\\ 0<x<r}} \epsilon(x^2n, r), \quad r \text{ odd}, \quad T(n, 1)=1,$$

and sums of the form

$$J(n, r)=\sum_{\substack{(x, r)=1\\ 0<x<r}} \left(\frac{x}{r}\right)\epsilon(nx, r).$$

Connections between the J function and the c and T functions are given. It is shown that T has multiplicative properties. It is further shown that the number $N_s(n, r)$ of representations of a number n as a sum of s squares (mod r), $n=a_1x_1^2+\cdots+a_sx_s^2$ mod r, where r is odd and the a_i prime to r, is connected with a function $\mathfrak{S}_s(n, r)$ involving the c, J, and the ordinary Gauss sums $S(n, r)$. *H. Bergström.*

Citations: MR 13, 823d = L05-7.
Referred to in A36-53.

D80-17 (16, 220g)

Nagell, Trygve. On the solvability of some congruences. Norske Vid. Selsk. Forh., Trondheim **27**, no. 3, 5 pp. (1954).

The paper contains a very simple proof of the following theorem which had been previously stated by the author [Norsk Mat. Tidsskr. **22**, 28 (1940)]: If $abc\neq 0$ and p is a prime, $p\nmid 7ab$, then the congruence $ax^3+by^3\equiv c \pmod p$ is solvable. Several related results are also obtained. For example, it is proved that if q is an odd prime and N an arbitrary integer, then the congruence

$$y^2\equiv x^q+(-1)^{(q-1)/2}q \pmod N$$

is solvable; it is also shown that if $q\equiv 3 \pmod 8$ the corresponding equation is not solvable. *L. Carlitz.*

D80-18 (16, 798b)

Lehmer, Emma. On the number of solutions of $u^k+D\equiv w^2 \pmod p$. Pacific J. Math. **5**, 103–118 (1955).

Let $N_k(D)$ denote the number of solutions of the congruence $u^k+D\equiv w^2 \pmod p$ and let

$$\phi_k(D)=\sum_{u=1}^{p-1}\left(\frac{u}{p}\right)\left(\frac{u^k+D}{p}\right).$$

Improving a well-known result of Jacobsthal, the author shows that if $p=x^2+4y^2$, $x\equiv y\equiv 1 \pmod 4$, then

$$\phi_2(D)=\begin{cases} -2x\left(\frac{m}{p}\right) & (D\equiv m^2 \pmod p)),\\ -4y\left(\frac{m}{p}\right) & (D\equiv 2m^2 \pmod p));\end{cases}$$

$$N_4(D)=\begin{cases} p-1-2x\left(\frac{m}{p}\right) & (D\equiv m^2 \pmod p))\\ p-1-4y\left(\frac{m}{p}\right) & (D\equiv 2m^2 \pmod p)).\end{cases}$$

Similar improvements are obtained for results of Chowla [Proc. Nat. Acad. Sci. U. S. A. **35**, 244–246 (1949); MR **10**, 592] and Schrutka [J. Reine Angew. Math. **140**, 252–265 (1911)] and related theorems. The paper closes with a table of the cyclotomic numbers $(i, j)_8$. *L. Carlitz.*

Citations: MR 10, 592f = L10-2.

D80-19 (17, 16c)

Cohen, Eckford. The quadratic singular sum. Duke Math. J. **22**, 373–381 (1955).

Let F be any finite extension of the rational field, A an arbitrary odd ideal of F and α_i $(i=1, i, \cdots, s)$ integers of F which are prime to A. Then the number of solutions of the congruence

$$\varrho=\alpha_1\xi_1^2+\cdots+\alpha_s\xi_s^2 \pmod A$$

for any integer ϱ of F is equal to

$$\mathfrak{S}_s(\varrho, A, \alpha)=\begin{cases} N^{2m-1}(A)\sum_{D|A}\left(\frac{\alpha}{D}\right)\frac{R(\varrho, D)}{N^m(D)} & (s=2m),\\ N^{2m}(A)\sum_{D|A}\left(\frac{\alpha}{D}\right)\frac{J(\varrho, D)S(1, D)}{N^{m+1}(D)} & (s=2m+1),\end{cases}$$

$$\alpha=(-1)^m\alpha_1\alpha_2\cdots\alpha_s \quad \text{for } s=2m,$$
$$\alpha=(-1)^{m+1}\alpha_1\alpha_2\cdots\alpha_s \text{ for } s=2m+1,$$

and $R(S, D)$ is the Rademacher sum and $J(\varrho, D)$ a sum related to the Hecke sum. Further, $G_s(\varrho, A, \alpha)$ is given in an arithmetic form. These results generalize earlier results of the author. *H. Bergström* (Göteborg).

D80-20 (17, 947b)

Carlitz, L. A special symmetric equation in a finite field. Acta Math. Acad. Sci. Hungar. **6** (1955), 445–450. (Russian summary)

Let σ_r denote the rth elementary symmetric function of $x_1, \cdots, x_4$. Mordell [Canad. J. Math. **5** (1953), 433–438; MR **15**, 200] proved that the number of solutions of the congruence $a_1\sigma_1+\cdots+a_4\sigma_4\equiv a \pmod p$ is equal to $p^3+O(p^{3/2})$ except in certain excluded cases. The present author determines explicitly the number $M=M(a)$ of solutions of the equation $\sigma_3=a$, where $a, x_r \in GF(q)$, $q=p^n$ and p is an arbitrary prime. A particular case of the main result states that if q is odd, then

$$M(a)=q^3-2q \quad (a\neq 0,\ q\not\equiv 1 \pmod 3)),$$
$$M(a)=q^3-2q+(-1)^{n/2}tq^{3/2} \quad (a\neq 0,\ q\equiv 1,\ p\equiv 2 \pmod 3)),$$

where $t=-2$ or 1 according as a is or is not a cube of GF(q). *A. L. Whiteman* (Los Angeles, Calif.).

Citations: MR 15, 200e = D80-14.

D80-21 (18, 111d)

Cohen, Eckford. The number of solutions of certain cubic congruences. Pacific J. Math. **5** (1955), 877–886.

Formulas expressing the number of solutions of the

congruences $n\equiv ax^3+by^3$ and $n\equiv ax^3+by^3+cz^3 \pmod{p^\lambda}$ are given (p prime, a, b, c integers prime to p, n and λ integers). These formulas contain the integers A and B which are uniquely determined by the relations $4p=A^2+27B^2$, $A\equiv 1 \pmod 3$, $B>0$. In a special case, however, the formula is explicit. The main tools used in the paper are Gauss sums.

H. Bergström (Göteborg).

D80-22 (18, 114c)

Cohen, Eckford. Binary congruences in algebraic number fields. Proc. Nat. Acad. Sci. U.S.A. **42** (1956), 120–122.

Let P denote a prime ideal of norm p^f in a finite extension of the rational field F, let α, β and ρ be integers in F and m and λ positive integers. With some weak restrictions upon α, β, ρ, λ and m, the number of solutions of the congruence $\alpha X^m+\beta Y^m+\rho\equiv 0 \pmod{P^\lambda}$ is expressed by a formula containing the generalized Jacobi sum. It is also shown that the congruence $\alpha X^m+\beta Y^m+\gamma Z^m+\rho\equiv 0 \pmod{P^\lambda}$ is solvable for all P of sufficiently large norm, subject to the condition $(\alpha\beta\gamma, P)=1$ and some restrictions on m. *H. Bergström* (Göteborg).

D80-23 (18, 875b)

Cohen, Eckford. Congruences in algebraic number fields involving sums of similar powers. Trans. Amer. Math. Soc. **83** (1956), 547–556.

Let $Q_s(\rho)$ denote the number of solutions of the congruence $\alpha_1X_1^m+\cdots+\alpha_sX_s^m+\rho\equiv 0 \pmod{p^\lambda}$, where p is a prime ideal of a finite extension F of the rational field and $\alpha_1, \alpha_2, \cdots, \alpha_s, \rho$ are integers of F. Generalizing results which the author has obtained earlier in the case $s=2$ he gives exact formulas for $Q_s(\rho)$ involving the generalized Jacobi sums. In the general case these formulas are complicated but can be simplified in special cases.

H. Bergström (Göteborg).

Referred to in D72-11.

D80-24 (18, 380e)

Manin, Yu. I. On cubic congruences to a prime modulus. Izv. Akad. Nauk SSSR. Ser. Mat. **20** (1956), 673–678. (Russian)

Let $p>0$ be prime, k_p the field of p elements and a, b elements of k_p with $4a^3\neq 27b^2$. The author shows that the number N of solutions $x, y \in k_p$ of

$$(1)\qquad y^2=x^3+ax+b$$

satisfies

$$|N-p|<2p^{1/2}.$$

This is, of course, a particular case of the Riemann hypothesis for function fields [H. Hasse, J. Reine Angew. Math. **175** (1936), 55–62, 69–88, 193–208; A. Weil, Sur les courbes algébriques et les variétés qui s'en déduisent, Hermann, Paris, 1948; MR **10**, 262] but the author's proof is entirely elementary in its execution, though admittedly motivated by Hasse's ideas. The author points out that his proof can be extended to any function field over a finite field.

Departing somewhat from the author's notation for convenience consider the curve

$$(2)\qquad X^3+aX+b=(x^3+ax+b)Y^2$$

over the field $k_p(x)$ of rational functions of an indeterminate x. Two points on (2) with coordinates in $k_p(x)$ are $\mathfrak{p}$: $X=x$, $Y=1$ and $\mathfrak{P}$: $X=x^p$, $Y=(x^3+ax+b)^{\frac{1}{2}(p-1)}$. Define addition of points on (2) in the usual way with respect to the improper point $\mathfrak{O}$ corresponding to the point at infinity in the characteristic 0 case. For integer n put $d_n=0$ if $\mathfrak{P}+n\mathfrak{p}=\mathfrak{O}$. Otherwise d_n is to be the degree of the numerator of the X-coordinate of $\mathfrak{P}+n\mathfrak{p}$ when it is expressed as a quotient of polynomials in x with no common factor. The proof now runs in three steps. (I) $d_{-1}-d_0-1=N-p$. For

$$X_{-1}=-x-x^p+\frac{\{1+(x^3+ax+b)^{\frac{1}{2}(p-1)}\}^2(x^3+ax+b)}{(x-x^p)^2}.$$

Now $x^p-x=\prod_{j\in k_p}(x-j)$ and $(j^3+aj+b)^{\frac{1}{2}(p-1)}$ is the quadratic residue symbol of j^3+aj+b. Hence a factor $x-j$ divides $\{1+(x^3+ax+b)^{\frac{1}{2}(p-1)}\}$ if and only if j^3+aj+b is not a square in k_p. The result (I) now follows easily. (II) $d_{n-1}+d_{n+1}=2d_n+2$. If one of $\mathfrak{P}+n\mathfrak{p}$, $\mathfrak{P}+(n\pm 1)\mathfrak{p}$ is $\mathfrak{O}$, then (II) is trivial. Otherwise, let the x-coordinate of $\mathfrak{P}+n\mathfrak{p}$ be A_n/C_n, where A_n, C_n are polynomials with no common factor. By the formulae for addition we have

$$(3)\qquad \frac{A_{n-1}}{C_{n-1}}\frac{A_{n+1}}{C_{n+1}}=\frac{(A_nx-aC_n)^2-4bC_n(C_nx+A_n)}{(C_nx-A_n)^2}.$$

A detailed consideration of common factors shows that the numerator and denominator of (3) are equal; (II) now follows from the equality of the numerators since $d_n=$ degree A_n and it is not difficult to see that degree $C_n<$ degree A_n. (III) From (I), (II) we have

$$d_n=n^2-(N-p)n+p.$$

But $d_n\geqq 0$ by definition and if $d_n=0$ then $d_{n\pm 1}>0$. Hence $(N-p)^2-4p\leqq 0$: so $|N-p|<2p^{\frac{1}{2}}$, as asserted.

Postscript: Mr. B. J. Birch has pointed out to me that it is by no means obvious that the degree of A_n is greater than that of C_n, and that the author's proof of this contains an error on line 23 of page 675. Indeed it is easy to construct curves (2) with points (X, Y) where the degree of the numerator of X is less than that of the denominator, though I cannot show that they are thrown up by the author's construction of X_n. However the author's proof can be salvaged with some modifications by defining d_n to be the maximum of the degree of A_n and C_n. Closer examination shows that the author's proof can be considerably shortened, much of the detailed case-by-case discussion being unnecessary. *J. W. S. Cassels.*

Citations: MR 10, 262c = G20-8.

Referred to in D80-25, G20-26, G20-52.

D80-25 (22# 3711)

Manin, Yu. I. On cubic congruences to a prime modulus. Amer. Math. Soc. Transl. (2) **13** (1960), 1–7.

The Russian original [Izv. Akad. Nauk SSSR. Ser. Mat. **20** (1956), 673–678] has already been reviewed [MR **18** #380].

Citations: MR 18, 380e = D80-24.

D80-26 (19, 1039a)

Mordell, L. J. On the number of solutions in incomplete residue sets of quadratic congruences. Arch. Math. **8** (1957), 153–157.

Let p be an odd prime, and let $f(x, y)$ be an inhomogeneous quadratic form with integer coefficients, whose discriminant is not divisible by p. Let $h, k, \alpha, \beta, \gamma, \delta, \mu, \nu$ be integers, $0<h\leqq p$, $0<k\leqq p$, $\alpha\delta-\beta\gamma\not\equiv 0 \pmod p$. Let N denote the number of solutions of

$$f(\alpha\xi+\beta\eta+\mu, \gamma\xi+\delta\eta+\nu)\equiv 0 \pmod p,\ 0\leqq\xi<h,\ 0\leqq\eta<k.$$

The author shows that

$$|N-hk/p|<1+4p^{\frac{1}{2}}\log p+2p^{\frac{1}{2}}(\log p)^2$$

if f is equivalent to a canonical form ax^2+by^2+c ($abc\not\equiv 0 \pmod p$), and $|N-hk/p|<2p^{\frac{1}{2}}\log p+p^{\frac{1}{2}}(\log p)^2$ in the remaining case (equivalence with the canonical form y^2-x). In the first case the author uses Weil's inequality for Kloosterman sums. *N. G. de Bruijn.*

Referred to in D80-38, P20-41.

D80-27 (19, 1160c)

Mordell, L. J. Note on simultaneous quadratic congruences. Math. Scand. **5** (1957), 21–26.

With an odd prime p as the modulus, the author considers m simultaneous congruences

$$a_{r1}x_1^2+\cdots+a_{rn}x_n^2\equiv -a_{r0}\ (r=1,\cdots,m).$$

The number of solutions is denoted by N. Under certain conditions of linear independence in the coefficient matrix, the author estimates $N-p^{n-m}$. He suggests that the best possible result will be obtained by application of the following conjecture: If p is a prime and if $B_r=b_{1r}t_1+\cdots+b_{kr}t_k$ ($r=0, 1, \cdots, h$) are linear forms with integral coefficients, then the multiple sum of Legendre symbols $\sum\left(\frac{B_0B_1\cdots B_h}{p}\right)$ (summation is taken over complete residue sets mod p for $t_1, \cdots, t_k$) is $O(p^{\frac{1}{2}(k+1)})$ if h is odd, and zero if h is even. If $k=2$, the conjecture follows from a deep result by Weil [Proc. Nat. Acad. Sci. U.S.A. **27** (1941), 345–347; MR **2**, 345]. From the case $k=2$ the author derives estimates for cases with $k>2$, but these are quite far from the conjectured results. {It should be noted that there are exceptional cases, both in the conjecture for $k>2$ as in Weil's case $k=2$. These exceptional cases are neglected in the paper, and in the applications made by the author it may not always be easy to decide whether these exceptions do or do not cause difficulties.}

The author does not state explicitly that his formulas for general values of m are restricted to the case $m>2$, but the case $m=2$ is dealt with in detail at the end of his paper, and for this case he gives a number of explicit formulas. *N. G. de Bruijn* (Amsterdam).

Citations: MR 2, 345b = G20-3.

D80-28 (20# 5757)

Cohen, Eckford. Congruence representations in algebraic number fields. II. Simultaneous linear and quadratic congruences. Canad. J. Math. **10** (1958), 561–571.

[For part I, see Trans. Amer. Math. Soc. **75** (1953), 444–470; MR **15**, 508]. Let F be a finite algebraic extension of the rational number field and P an ideal in F of norm pt where p is odd. The author considers the pair of congruences

$$m\equiv\alpha_1x_1^2+\cdots+\alpha_sx_s^2,\ n\equiv\beta_1x_1+\cdots+\beta_sx_s\ (\text{mod } P^\lambda),$$

where m, n, α_i and β_i are integers of F and α_i and β_i prime to P. By the help of simple functions of the constants m, n, α_i and β_i he gives explicitely the number $N_s(m, n)$ of simultanous solutions of these congruences. The cases when $N_s(m, n)=0$ are separately described. For the computation of $N_s(m, n)$ generalized Cauchy-Gauss sums are used. *H. Bergström* (Göteborg)

Citations: MR 15, 508c = D80-15.

D80-29 (22# 7052)

Reiman, István. Geometrische Untersuchung einer quadratischen Kongruenz. Mat. Lapok **10** (1959), 122–126. (Hungarian. Russian and German summaries)

Der Verf. beweist auf geometrischem Wege den Bekannten Satz, wonach die quadratische Kongruenz

$$(1)\quad \sum_{\substack{i=1\\k=1}}^{3} a_{ik}x_ix_k\equiv 0\ (\text{mod } p)$$

$$(p \text{ prim},\ a_{ik}\equiv a_{ki},\ |a_{ik}|\not\equiv 0\ (\text{mod } p)),$$

p^2 Lösungen besitzt. Zum Beweis wird über dem Körper der Restklassen modulo p eine endliche projektive Ebene konstruiert. In dieser Ebene wird, ähnlich wie in der klassischen projektiven Geometrie, ein Begriff der Polarität eingeführt, und ein Punkt wird absolut genannt, wenn er auf seinen polaren Geraden liegt. Das zu einem absoluten Punkt gehörige Elemententripel (x_1, x_2, x_3) befriedigt (1). Indem wir nun die Anzahl der absoluten Punkte berücksichtigen, ergibt sich daraus die Behauptung des Satzes auf einfache Weise. Der Verfasser weist auch darauf hin, dass es sich ähnlich beweisen lässt, dass die Gleichung $\sum_{i,k=1}^3 a_{ik}x_ix_k=0$, in der $a_{ik}=a_{ki}$ und Det $|a_{ik}|\neq 0$, $p^{2\alpha}$ Lösungen besitzt über einem endlichen Körper der Ordnung p^α. *L. Gyarmathi* (Debrecen)

D80-30 (22# 7979)

Linnik, Yu. V. Some remarks on estimates of trigonometric sums. Uspehi Mat. Nauk **14** (1959), no. 3 (87), 153–160. (Russian)

The author proves that, given a prime $p>n$, an integer $\lambda\geqq 1$ and a set of n integers $N_1, N_2, \cdots, N_n$, the system of simultaneous congruences

$$x_1^r+x_2^r+\cdots+x_g^r\equiv N_r\ (\text{mod } p^\lambda)\quad (r=1, 2, \cdots, n)$$

possesses a solution in integers $x_1, x_2, \cdots, x_g$ if $g\geqq c_0n^2\log n$, where c_0 is a constant. The proof is based on I. M. Vinogradov's methods for trigonometric sums and A. Weil's famous inequality $|\sum_{x=0}^{p-1}\exp(2\pi if(x)/p)|\leqq(\nu-1)p^{1/2}$ (where f is a polynomial with integral coefficients and ν is the degree mod p of f) [Proc. Nat. Acad. Sci. U.S.A. **34** (1948), 204–207; MR **10**, 234]. The author remarks that if $p>c_1n^2$ his method also leads readily to an asymptotic formula for the number of solutions. The special case of a homogeneous system ($N_1=\cdots=N_n=0$) possessing a non-trivial solution if $g\geqq\frac{1}{2}n(n+1)+1$, follows, for $\lambda=1$, from a theorem of C. Chevalley [Abh. Math. Sem. Univ. Hamburg **11** (1935), 73–75]. The result of this paper is relevant to certain problems in Diophantine analysis; for instance, to the 'singular series' associated with the application of the Hardy-Littlewood-Vinogradov method to the simultaneous solubility of the Diophantine equations $x_1^r+\cdots+x_g^r=N_r$ ($r=1, 2, \cdots, n$) [see K. K. Mardžanišvili, Mat. Sb. (N.S.) **33 (75)** (1953), 630–675; MR **15**, 602]. *H. Halberstam* (London)

Citations: MR 10, 234e = T25-5; MR 15, 602l = P08-20.

D80-31 (23# A2385)

Chowla, S.

Some results in number-theory.

Norske Vid. Selsk. Forh. Trondheim **33** (1960), 43–44.

The author sketches the proof of a theorem asserting that every diagonal form in s variables represents the zero non-trivially if $s>c\log k$, $k>k_0$, provided -1 is a kth power residue. Two other theorems concerning the class number of quadratic fields are reported without proof. *H. B. Mann* (Columbus, Ohio)

D80-32 (23# A3113)

Dunton, M.

Non-trivial solutions of $ax^3+by^3=c$ mod p.

Norske Vid. Selsk. Forh. Trondheim **33** (1960), 45–46.

Implicit in the work of Gauss on exponential sums is the fact that the congruence $ax^3+by^3\equiv c$ (mod p) is always solvable, provided that p is a prime satisfying $p\nmid 7abc$. The author provides a simple direct proof of this, and if $p\nmid 7\cdot 13\cdot abc$, shows that there is a solution with $x\not\equiv 0$ (mod p), $y\not\equiv 0$ (mod p). *J. H. H. Chalk* (Toronto)

D80-33 (23# A3702)

D'Ambrosio, Ubiratan

The number of solutions of additive congruences. (Portuguese. English summary)

Soc. Parana. Mat. Anuário (2) **2** (1959), 5–15.

This is an expository paper on the number of solutions of congruences in the domain of the rational integers. The discussion makes systematic use of the Cauchy product (mod r) introduced by the reviewer [Duke Math. J. **19**

(1952), 115–129; MR **13**, 823]. Application is made to the congruence $ax^h+by^k\equiv 1 \pmod p$, p prime.

E. Cohen (Knoxville, Tenn.)

Citations: MR 13, 823d = L05-7.

D80-34 (25# 2995)

Chowla, S.

Some conjectures in elementary number theory.

Norske Vid. Selsk. Forh. (*Trondheim*) **35** (1962), 13.

The author offers the following conjectures. (1) To every fixed positive integer n, and to every large prime $p\equiv 1 \pmod n$, there exists an integer d such that the polynomial x^n-d is irreducible $\pmod p$. (2) To every large prime k there exists a prime $p\equiv 1 \pmod k$ such that $x^k+y^k+1\equiv 0 \pmod p$ has no non-trivial solution (the solutions $x=-1$, $y=0$ or $x=0$, $y=-1$ are called trivial solutions). (3) For $k>k_0$, the congruence $x^k+y^k+1\equiv 0 \pmod p$ has a non-trivial solution whenever $p>k^2$. (4) For odd $k\geqq 3$, the equation $\pm x_1^k\pm x_2^k\pm\cdots\pm x_k^k=0$ has no "non-trivial" solutions in integers x_n ($1\leqq n\leqq k$), e.g., $k=5$. The equation $a^5+b^5=c^5+d^5+e^5$ has no solutions in positive integers a, b, c, d, e.

{The reviewer thinks that (1) can be proved easily, as in this case x^n-d is irreducible $\pmod p$ if and only if d is not a qth power $\pmod p$ for any $q\mid n$, $q>1$.}

T. Hayashida (Yokohama)

D80-35 (25# 2996)

Chowla, S.

A generalization of Meyer's theorem on indefinite quadratic forms in five or more variables.

J. Indian Math. Soc. (*N.S.*) **25** (1961), 41.

The author announces the following two theorems for k an odd prime and $Q=\sum_{i=1}^s a_ix_i^k$ ($a_i\neq 0$). Theorem I: Let ε denote an arbitrary positive number. Then there exists a $k_0=k_0(\varepsilon)$ such that the congruence $Q\equiv 0 \pmod p$ has a non-trivial solution for all $s>(2+\varepsilon)\log k/\log 2$ and $k>k_0$, where the a_i are prime to p. Theorem II: There is an absolute constant $c>0$ such that the equation $Q=0$, where the a_i are integers, has a non-trivial solution in rational numbers provided $s>ck\log k$.

Burton W. Jones (Boulder, Colo.)

D80-36 (25# 3893)

Chowla, S.

On the congruence $\sum_{i=1}^s a_ix_i^k\equiv 0 \pmod p$.

J. Indian Math. Soc. (*N.S.*) **25** (1961), 47–48.

The author proves the following theorem. If -1 is a kth power residue of a prime p, then the congruence

$$\sum_{i=1}^s a_ix^k \equiv 0 \pmod p, \qquad a_i\not\equiv 0 \pmod p$$

has a non-trivial solution whenever $s\geqq c\log k$, where c is an absolute constant and k is large enough. The $c\log k$ in the theorem is a great improvement on $k+1$ of Chevalley and $2\sqrt{k}$ of Lewis and Gray.

H. Gupta (Chandigarh)

Referred to in D72-34.

D80-37 (25# 5037)

Mordell, L. J.

On a cubic congruence in three variables.

Acta Arith. **8** (1962/63), 1–9.

Let $f(x, y, z)$ be a cubic polynomial with coefficients in the field of residue classes $\pmod p$, f not being a polynomial in only two variables. Let N be the number of solutions of $f(x, y, z)\equiv 0 \pmod p$, where p is a large prime. It is well known that $|N-p^2|$ is of the exact order of magnitude $p^{3/2}$ when f is homogeneous and $f(x, y, 1)=0$ is of genus 1. The author conjectures that except in this case, $|N-p^2|=O(p)$. He proves the conjecture in the special case $f(x, y, z)=F(x, y)+k-z^2$, where $F(x, y)=ax^3+bx^2y+cxy^2+dy^3$ and $F(x, y)\not\equiv\nu(\lambda x+\mu y)^3$, with λ, μ, ν rational. He further shows that for such a binary cubic form F,

$$\sum_{x,y=0}^{p-1} e^{2\pi iF(x,y)/p} = O(p).$$

W. J. LeVeque (Ann Arbor, Mich.)

Referred to in D80-44, D80-47.

D80-38 (26# 3656)

Chalk, J. H. H.

The number of solutions of congruences in incomplete residue systems.

Canad. J. Math. **15** (1963), 291–296.

For an integer $m\geqq 2$, let C be the set of points $x=(x_i)\in\mathbf{Z}^n$ such that $0\leqq x_i<m$. Let S be a subset of C. The number of points in S is denoted by $M(S)$. For a function $f\colon \mathbf{Z}^n\to\mathbf{Z}$, denote by $N(S)$ the number of solutions $x\in S$ of the equation $f(x)\equiv 0 \pmod m$. $N(C)$ is therefore the number of solutions mod m. Put

$$E(S) = \sum_{y\in C-\{0\}}\Big|\sum_{z\in S}\exp(2\pi im^{-1}y\cdot z)\Big|.$$

The author, generalizing Mordell's inequality [Arch. Math. **8** (1957), 153–157; MR **19**, 1039], proves first the following. Theorem 1:

$$(1)\qquad N(S) = m^{-n}M(S)N(C)+\theta m^{-n-1}\Phi E(S),$$

where Φ is an upper bound of

$$\Big|\sum_{x\in C}\sum_{t=0}^{m-1}\exp(2\pi im^{-1}(tf(x)-x\cdot y))\Big|$$

and $|\theta|\leqq 1$. (Theorem 1 is actually stated in more general setting.) In Theorem 2, he applies (1) to $m=p$ (a prime), $f(x)=\sum_{i=1}^n a_ix_i^{k_i}+c$ with $(a_i, p)=(c, p)=1$, $2\leqq k_i\leqq p-2$ and $S=\{x=(x_i)\in\mathbf{Z}^n,\ 0<\nu_i\leqq x_i\leqq\nu_i+\delta_i<m,\ \delta_i\geqq 1\}$ to get the estimation: $N(S)=p^{-1}M(S)+O(p^{n/2}(\log p)^n)$, where Vinogradov's estimation [*Elements of number theory*, Ch. III, problem 11c, Dover, New York, 1954; MR **15**, 933], Weil's estimate for exponential sums [Proc. Nat. Acad. Sci. U.S.A. **34** (1948), 205–207; MR **10**, 234] and Mordell's asymptotic formula [Math. Z. **37** (1933), 193–209] are used. The paper concludes with some comments without details.

T. Ono (Vancouver, B.C.)

Citations: MR 10, 234e = T25-5; MR 15, 933c = Z01-6; MR 19, 1039a = D80-26.

Referred to in T40-38.

D80-39 (26# 3657)

Davenport, H.; Lewis, D. J.

Notes on congruences. I.

Quart. J. Math. Oxford Ser. (2) **14** (1963), 51–60.

D'après un théorème de A. Weil, si $F(x, y)$ désigne un polynôme à coefficients entiers $\pmod p$ absolument irréductible $\pmod p$, le nombre de solutions de la congruence $F(x, y)\equiv 0 \pmod p$ est $p+O(p^{1/2})$, la constante intervenant dans O dépendant uniquement du degré de F. Par des méthodes tout-à-fait élémentaires, les auteurs évaluent dans certains cas l'erreur si l'on fait varier un ou plusieurs paramètres figurant dans F.

Pour la congruence $y^2\equiv f(x)+m \pmod p$, si $f(x)$ est de degré $\geqq 3$ et si l'on désigne le nombre de solutions par $p+E(m)$, ils démontrent la relation (1) $\sum_m E^2(m)\gg p^2$, valable si f n'est pas exceptionnel, la sommation s'étendant à un système complet de restes $\pmod p$ et la notation $\gg$ étant celle de Vinogradov pour indiquer une inégalité dans laquelle entre un facteur constant non spécifié. Les polynômes exceptionnels $\pmod p$ sont ceux pour lesquels $\phi(x, y)=(f(x)-f(y))/(x-y)$ n'a aucun facteur $\pmod p$ absolument irréductible. Il est démontré ensuite que la relation (1) est valable pour la congruence $y^3\equiv f(x)+m$

(mod p), $f(x)$ étant de degré 3 ou 4. Si $F(x, y)=f(x, y)+lx+my+n$, et si le nombre de solutions est désigné par $p+E(l, m, n)$, on a $\sum_{l,m,n} E^2(l, m, n)=p^4-p^3$, pour tout $f(x, y)$. Pour $F(x, y)=f(x, y)+lx+n$, les auteurs démontrent, moyennant des hypothèses restrictives pour $f(x, y)$, la relation $\sum_{l,n} E^2(l, n)\gg p^3$, et, pour $F(x, y)=f(x, y)+n$, f étant un polynôme du 3ième degré, sous certaines conditions, la relation $\sum_n E^2(n)\gg p^2$.

A propos des polynômes exceptionnels (mod p), ils démontrent que $\phi(x, y)\equiv 0$ (mod p) a $O(1)$ solutions. Les auteurs signalent en plusieurs points la difficulté de démontrer les relations obtenues pour des polynômes f de degré plus élevé. Il semble difficile de déterminer explicitement les polynômes exceptionnels. La note se termine par quelques propriétés de ces polynômes.

A. Gloden (Luxembourg)

Referred to in D80-40, D80-52, T10-33, T10-34, T10-42.

D80-40 (26# 6117)

Davenport, H.; Lewis, D. J.

Notes on congruences. II.

Quart. J. Math. Oxford Ser. (2) **14** (1963), 153–159.

Pour la partie I, voir même J. (2) **14** (1963), 51–60 [MR **26** #3657]. Mordell a émis l'hypothèse que, si p est un grand nombre premier, $f(x, y, z)$ un polynôme non homogène du troisième degré à trois variables et à coefficients entiers, quelques cas exceptionnels mis à part, la congruence $f(x,y,z)\equiv 0 (\text{mod } p)$ a $p^2+O(p)$ solutions, la constante intervenant dans la notation O étant absolue. Il a démontré ce résultat pour certains types de congruences de la forme $z^2\equiv g(x, y)$ (mod p). L'objet de cette Note est la démonstration de l'hypothèse de Mordell. Exprimant leurs résultats en considérant, au lieu d'un polynôme non homogène à trois variables, une forme (polynôme homogène) à quatre variables, les auteurs démontrent les trois théorèmes suivants: Soit $F(x_1, x_2, x_3, x_4)$ une forme du troisième degré (mod p) non singulière, c'est-à-dire telle que les dérivées partielles $\partial F/\partial x_1, \cdots, \partial F/\partial x_4$ ne s'annulent pas simultanément dans une extension quelconque du corps mod p; des solutions ne différant que par un facteur de proportionalité étant considérées comme identiques, la congruence $F(x_1, x_2, x_3, x_4)\equiv 0$ (mod p) a $p^2+O(p)$ solutions. La démonstration de ce théorème se base sur un travail récent de Dwork concernant la fonction ζ d'une hypersurface; à part ceci, elle est tout-à-fait élémentaire. Du théorème précédent les auteurs déduisent le suivant: Soit $G(x_1, x_2, x_3)$ une forme du troisième degré (mod p) non singulière; la congruence non homogène $z^2\equiv G(x, y, 1)$ (mod p) a $p^2+O(p)$ solutions. Le troisième théorème se rapportant aussi à une congruence non homogène s'énonce comme suit: Soit $F(x, y)$ une forme binaire de degré n qui n'est pas identiquement congruente à une forme du type $a(F_1(x, y))^h$, $h>1$; si $k\not\equiv 0$ (mod p), le nombre des solutions de la congruence $z^m\equiv F(x, y)+k$ (mod p) est $p^2+O(p)$, la constante intervenant dans O ne dépendant que de n et de m. La démonstration se base sur le théorème de Weil concernant les sommes de caractères.

A. Gloden (Luxembourg)

Citations: MR 26# 3657 = D80-39.

Referred to in D80-60, G25-31.

D80-41 (27# 99)

Selberg, Sigmund

An upper bound for the number of solutions of $x^n\equiv y^n (\text{mod } M)$, $1\leq y<x\leq N$.

Norske Vid. Selsk. Forh. (Trondheim) **35** (1962), 96–98.

Theorem: Let n be a fixed natural number and S the number of solutions in x and y of

$$(1)\qquad x^n = y^n (\text{mod } M),\ 1\leq y<x\leq N.$$

Then $S<CN^2/M^{1/(n+1)}$, where C is a positive number not depending on N and M.

A. Sklar (Chicago, Ill.)

D80-42 (27# 2482)

Cross, J. T.

The number of solutions of a trinomial congruence involving a kth power and a square.

Bull. Amer. Math. Soc. **69** (1963), 83–86.

The author considers the number $Q_r(\rho)$ of incongruent solutions X, Y of the congruence $X^k+\alpha Y^2\equiv\rho$ (mod P^r), where P is an odd prime ideal of the finite extension K of the rationals and α, ρ are integers of K, $(\alpha, P)=1$. In a number of special cases explicit formulas for Q_r are given; in the others, evaluation of Q_r is reduced to the case $r=1$. The proof will be given in a later paper concerned with an extension of the problem of this note.

E. Cohen (Knoxville, Tenn.)

D80-43 (27# 3623)

Mordell, L. J.

On a special polynomial congruence and exponential sum.

Calcutta Math. Soc. Golden Jubilee Commemoration Vol. (1958/59), *Part I, pp.* 29–32. *Calcutta Math. Soc., Calcutta*, 1963.

The following results are proved. (I) Let N denote the number of solutions of the congruence

$$a_1x_1^{\lambda_1}+\cdots+a_nx_n^{\lambda_n}+bx_1^{\mu_1}\cdots x_n^{\mu_n}+c\equiv 0\ (\text{mod } p)$$

with $x_1x_2\cdots x_n\not\equiv 0$. Then

$$|N-(p-1)^n/p| < d_1\cdots d_np^{n/2},$$

where $d_j=(\lambda_j, p-1)$ and no $a\equiv 0$. (II) Let

$$S = \sum_{x_j=1}^{p-1} e(a_1x_1^{\lambda_1}+\cdots+a_nx_n^{\lambda_n}+bx_1^{\mu_1}\cdots x_n^{\mu_n}),$$

where $e(a)=e^{2\pi ia/p}$. Then if no $a\equiv 0$,

$$|S| \leq d_1\cdots d_np^{(n+1)/2}.$$

L. Carlitz (Durham, N.C.)

D80-44 (27# 3624)

Mordell, L. J.

On a cubic congruence in three variables. II.

Proc. Amer. Math. Soc. **14** (1963), 609–614.

Let $f(x, y, z)=z^2-F(x, y)-lx-my$, where $F(x, y)$ is a cubic form not a multiple of $(lx+my)^3$, and where l, m and the coefficients in $F(x, y)$ are integers, not all multiples of the prime p. Two proofs are given of the fact that if $f(x, y, z)$ cannot be expressed as a cubic polynomial in two independent variables, and if it is irreducible in any algebraic extension of the Galois field $G(p)$, then the number N of solutions of the congruence $f(x, y, z)\equiv 0$ (mod p) for large p satisfies $N=p^2+O(p)$, the implied constant being independent of f and p. For Part I, see Acta Arith. **8** (1962/63), 1–9 [MR **25** #5037].

W. J. LeVeque (Boulder, Colo.)

Citations: MR 25# 5037 = D80-37.

Referred to in D80-47.

D80-45 (27# 3625)

Mordell, L. J.

On a cubic congruence in three variables. III.

J. London Math. Soc. **38** (1963), 351–355.

The estimate $N=p^2+O(p)$, as in the preceding review [#3624] is obtained in the case $f(x, y, z)=ax^3+by^3+$

$cxy+d-z^2$, $b\not\equiv 0$. This extends unpublished work of S. Chowla. In the present case N can be expressed in elementary closed form. *W. J. LeVeque* (Boulder, Colo.)

Referred to in D80-47, G25-38.

D80-46 (27# 3626)

Mordell, L. J.

On a cubic exponential sum in two variables.

J. London Math. Soc. **38** (1963), 356–358.

It is shown that $\sum_{x,y=0}^{p-1} e^{2\pi i f(x,y)/p} = O(p)$ uniformly in f, when $f(x, y) = Ax^3 + By^3 + Cxy$, $AB \not\equiv 0 \pmod p$. The proof depends on the expression for N mentioned in the preceding review [#3625]. *W. J. LeVeque* (Boulder, Colo.)

Referred to in T25-24.

D80-47 (28# 2084)

Mordell, L. J.

On the congruence $ax^3+by^3+cz^3+dxyz \equiv n \pmod p$.

Duke Math. J. **31** (1964), 123–126.

The following conjecture is verified in the case indicated in the title: If p is prime and $f(x, y, z)$ is an irreducible cubic polynomial which is neither a function of two variables nor homogeneous in linear functions of x, y, z, then the number of solutions of the congruence $f(x, y, z) \equiv 0 \pmod p$ is $p^2 + O(p)$, where the implied constant is absolute. Other cases have been treated earlier by the author [Acta Arith. **8** (1962/63), 1–9; MR **25** #5037; Proc. Amer. Math. Soc. **14** (1963), 609–614; MR **27** #3624; J. London Math. Soc. **38** (1963), 351–355; MR **27** #3625]. *W. J. LeVeque* (Boulder, Colo.)

Citations: MR 25# 5037 = D80-37; MR 27# 3624 = D80-44; MR 27# 3625 = D80-45.

D80-48 (29# 1171)

Carlitz, L.; Whiteman, A. L.

The number of solutions of some congruences modulo a product of primes.

Trans. Amer. Math. Soc. **112** (1964), 536–552.

Let m be an odd integer with prime power decomposition $m = p_1^{\alpha_1} p_2^{\alpha_2} \cdots p_r^{\alpha_r}$. Suppose g_i is a primitive root $(\bmod\, p_i^{\alpha_i})$ and that g is an integer satisfying $g \equiv g_i \pmod{p_i^{\alpha_i}}$, $1 \leqq i \leqq r$; g is determined $(\bmod\, m)$ by the g_i. Put $d = \mathrm{lcm}(\phi_1(p_1^{\alpha_1}), \phi_2(p_2^{\alpha_2}), \cdots, \phi_r(p_r^{\alpha_r}))$. The authors are interested in determining the number $N(g)$ of solutions to the congruence $g^s + 1 \equiv g^t$, where $0 \leqq s, t \leqq d-1$. This has applications in the construction of difference sets. They consider the cases when m is the product of two primes, $m = pq$, and where $e = \gcd(p-1, q-1)$ is 2, 4, or 6. In addition, they consider the case when m is the product of three primes, $m = pqr$, and $e = \gcd(p-1, q-1) = \gcd(p-1, r-1) = \gcd(q-1, r-1) = 2$. Their answers are expressed in terms of Jacobi sums. When $e > 2$, the results depend upon the choice of primitive roots g_i. *D. G. Cantor* (Seattle, Wash.)

Referred to in T20-30, T20-40, T20-42.

D80-49 (29# 5782)

Postnikova, L. P.

Distribution of solutions of the congruence

$$x^2+y^2 \equiv 1 \pmod{p^n}.$$

(Russian)

Mat. Sb. (*N.S.*) **65** (**107**) (1964), 228–238.

Let p be a prime >3, n any natural number $\geqq 13$, and let $A(T, T_1)$ denote the number of solutions of the congruence $x^2+y^2 \equiv 1 \pmod{p^n}$ such that $y \not\equiv \pm 1 \pmod p$, $0 \leqq x \leqq T$, $0 \leqq y \leqq T_1$. It is proved that for $1 \leqq T \leqq p^n$ and $p^{(4n+13)/6} \leqq T_1 \leqq p^n$

$$A(T, T_1) - TT_1 p^{-n-1}\{p-2-(-1)^{(p-1)/2}\} \ll e^{7n \log^2 n} T_1^{1-1/(84n^3 \log 3n)}.$$

The proof is a combination of I. M. Vinogradov's method with an elementary form of p-adic analysis, no knowledge of the latter being presupposed.

{There are plenty of misprints and some minor inaccuracies such as $12(n-1)^2 \geqq 15n^2$ on p. 236, but they can be eliminated. A reference to Vinogradov's theorem [*Selected works* (Russian), p. 389, Izdat. Akad. Nauk SSSR, Moscow, 1952; MR **14**, 610] (where there are puzzling misprints) should be replaced by one to his original paper [Izv. Akad. Nauk SSSR Ser. Mat. **14** (1950), 199–214, p. 209; MR **12**, 161].} *E. Fogels* (Riga)

Citations: MR 12, 161a = L15-13; MR 14, 610i = Z25-9.

D80-50 (30# 1091)

Keller, Ott-Heinrich

Darstellungen von Restklassen $(\bmod\, n)$ als Summen von zwei Quadraten.

Acta Sci. Math. (*Szeged*) **25** (1964), 191–192.

It is shown that if $s \equiv 1 \pmod 4$ when $4|n$, and $(s, n) = 1$, then s has a representation $s = x^2 + y^2 \pmod n$ in which $(x, y, n) = 1$, and that then the number $\rho(n)$ of such representations is independent of s. More specifically, ρ is that multiplicative function such that $\rho(2) = 2$, $\rho(2^r) = 2^{r+1}$ for $r \geqq 2$, and for p odd, $\rho(p^r) = p^{r-1}(p - (-1/p))$, where $(-1/p)$ is the Legendre symbol. *W. J. LeVeque* (Ann Arbor, Mich.)

D80-51 (30# 1110)

Mordell, L. J.

Incomplete exponential sums and incomplete residue systems for congruences. (Russian summary)

Czechoslovak Math. J. **14** (**89**) (1964), 235–242.

Let l_i, $i = 1, 2, \cdots, n$, be n given integers, ξ_i, $i = 1, \cdots, n$, n integer variables, (ξ) and (l) the vectors $(\xi_1, \cdots, \xi_n)$ and $(l_1, \cdots, l_n)$, respectively, p a prime and $f(\xi)$, $f_1(\xi)$, $\cdots$, $f_m(\xi)$ $m+1$ polynomials in the ξ_i with integer coefficients. An inequality between two vectors or between a vector and scalar means that the inequality holds componentwise. Suppose $0 \leqq (l) < p$ and let $e(x) = \exp(2\pi i x/p)$. The author gives an expository account of the following two problems.

(1) Estimate

$$S_n' = \sum_{\xi} e(f(\xi_1, \cdots, \xi_n)), \qquad 0 \leqq (\xi) < (l),$$

in terms of

$$S_n = \sum_{x} e(f(x_1, \cdots, x_n)), \qquad 0 \leqq (x) < p.$$

(2) Estimate the number of solutions $N'_{n,m}$ of the m simultaneous congruences mod p

$$f_1(\xi) \equiv 0, \cdots, f_m(\xi) \equiv 0, \qquad 0 \leqq (\xi) < (l),$$

in terms of the number $N_{n,m}$ of solutions of

$$f_1(x) \equiv 0, \cdots, f_m(x) \equiv 0, \qquad 0 \leqq (x) < p.$$

Let $t \cdot x = \sum_{j=1}^n t_j x_j$ and $u \cdot f(x) = \sum_{j=1}^n u_j f_j(x)$. Assume in Problem (1) that there exist estimates of the form $|\sum_x e(f(x) + t \cdot x)| \leqq E_n^{(r)}$, and in Problem (2) estimates of the form $|\sum_{x,u} e(u \cdot f(x) + t \cdot x)| \leqq E_n^{(r)}$ which are independent of the t's, where all indices of summation take the values $0, 1, \cdots, p-1$, and r indicates the number of t's which are not zero. Estimates of the desired kind are obtained involving the $E_n^{(r)}$. The details of then estimating the $E_n^{(r)}$

are carried out for two cases of Problem (2), in both of which $m=1$ and f is quadratic.

S. L. Segal (Rochester, N.Y.)

D80-52 (30# 1967)

Watson, G. L.

Cubic congruences.

Mathematika **11** (1964), 142–150.

Soit p un nombre premier, et soit $\Phi=\Phi(x_1, \cdots, x_n)$ un polynôme du troisième degré à coefficients entiers avec un terme constant entier. L'auteur se propose d'étudier, par des méthodes élémentaires, la congruence du troisième degré

(1) $$\Phi(x_1, \cdots, x_n) \equiv 0 \pmod p.$$

Si la congruence (1) admet une solution en entiers x_i, on se pose la question si elle a une solution non singulière, c'est-à-dire une solution pour laquelle on a

(2) $$\frac{\partial\Phi}{\partial x_1}, \cdots, \frac{\partial\Phi}{\partial x_n} \not\equiv 0, \cdots, 0 \pmod p.$$

L'auteur considère ensuite, au lieu d'un p fixe, un p variable, et il examine ce qui peut être dit à propos de Φ s'il existe une infinité de p pour lesquels (1) n'a ou bien aucune solution ou admet seulement des solutions singulières. A ce propos, l'auteur obtient des résultats qui sont intéressants par leurs rapports avec l'équation cubique $\Phi=0$. On impose la condition restrictive (2) parce que, si (1) et (2) admettent des solutions simultanées, la congruence $\Phi\equiv 0 \pmod{p^t}$ est résoluble pour tout t, d'après un résultat bien connu. Il faut encore ici quelques remarques préliminaires pour énoncer les résultats obtenus d'une façon précise. Tout d'abord, nous avons toujours une identité de la forme (3) $\Phi=F(1, x_1, \cdots, x_n)$, où $F=F(x_0, \cdots, x_n)$ est homogène et est déterminée uniquement par Φ. Alors (4) $C=F(0, x_1, \cdots, x_n)$. La partie cubique de Φ, aussi homogène, est complètement déterminée par Φ. Nous avons encore, pour Q et L, respectivement, forme quadratique et forme linéaire en $x_1, \cdots, x_n$, et un certain entier N, les identités (5) $\Phi=C+Q+L+N$, (6) $F=C+Qx_0+Lx_0^2+Nx_0^3$. Sans préjudice de la généralité, on peut transformer Φ par une substitution entière unimodulaire (pas nécessairement homogène) portant sur les variables x_i. Si une telle substitution transforme Φ en P, on dit que Φ est équivalent à P (dans l'anneau des entiers); on note $\Phi\sim P$. Si Φ est équivalent à un certain P et si $\partial P/\partial x_n$ est identiquement 0, on dit que Φ est dégénéré (sur l'anneau des entiers). Dans ce cas, Φ peut être transformé en P avec $\partial P/\partial x=0$ par une substitution homogène. On peut certainement supposer, sans préjudice de la généralité, que Φ est non dégénéré, ou que $n\geqq 2$, puisque le cas de $n=1$ est banal.

Définissons encore une forme nulle modulo p. Nous considérons F comme une forme nulle modulo p si la congruence $F\equiv 0 \pmod p$ a une solution autre que la solution banale $x_0\equiv\cdots\equiv x_n\equiv 0 \pmod p$, bien que ceci se produise dans le cas banal que F est dégénéré mod p. L'auteur démontre maintenant les théorèmes suivants. Théorème I: Supposons $p\geqq 11$, $n\geqq 2$, Φ non dégénéré mod p et C non identiquement nulle mod p. Alors, ou bien, (1) est possible, ou $n=2$ et F n'est pas une forme nulle mod p. Théorème II: Supposons $p\geqq 5$, et n, Φ, C étant soumis aux mêmes hypothèses que dans le Théorème I, supposons que (1) soit possible. Alors, ou bien, (1) et (2) sont possibles simultanément, ou $n\leqq 3$, $\Phi\sim C \pmod p$, et C n'est pas une forme nulle mod p. Théorème III: Si $n\geqq 2$, si Φ est non dégénéré sur les entiers, et si C n'est pas identiquement nulle; on a les deux éventualités suivantes: (i) (1) est possible pour tout p appartenant au maximum à un ensemble fini de p; ou bien (ii) $n=2$, et F n'est pas une forme nulle sur les entiers. Au cas (i), l'auteur démontre encore les résultats suivants: (ia) (1) et (2) sont simultanément possibles pour toutes valeurs de p, sauf au maximum un nombre fini de p, ou bien (ib), $n\leqq 3$, Φ est équivalente à C sur le corps des rationnels, et C n'est pas une forme nulle sur les entiers (ou par équivalence sur les rationnels). Enfin, l'auteur remarque que, si l'on se contente de l'hypothèse $p\geqq p_0$ au lieu de l'hypothèse particulière $p\geqq 11$ ou $p\geqq 5$, alors ces resultats peuvent être déduire de ceux de Davenport et Lewis [Quart. J. Math. Oxford Ser. (2) **14** (1963), 51–60; MR **26** #3657]. Ceux-ci ont étés prouvés d'une manière moins élémentaire.

A. Gloden (Luxembourg)

Citations: MR 26# 3657 = D80-39.

Referred to in D72-51.

D80-53 (32# 5586)

Cohen, Eckford

Quadratic congruences with an odd number of summands.

Amer. Math. Monthly **73** (1966), 138–143.

If $B_m(n, r)$ denotes the number of distinct solutions mod r of the congruence $\sum_{i=1}^{2m+1} a_i x_i^2 = n \pmod r$, where a_i $(i=1, 2, \cdots, 2m+1)$ are integers prime to r, the author gives a short expository account of how Gaussian and related sums may be used to give explicit formulae for $B_m(n, r)$ in several important special cases.

J. H. H. Chalk (Nottingham)

D80-54 (32# 7526)

Chalk, J. H. H.; Williams, K. S.

The distribution of solutions of congruences.

Mathematika **12** (1965), 176–192.

Denote by $[p]$ the finite field with p elements (p odd). Let $f(\mathbf{x})$ be a homogeneous form of degree d in n variables over $[p]$. Let B be the box consisting of n-tuples $(x_1, \cdots, x_n)$ of integers satisfying $\nu_i \leqq x_i < \nu_i + h_i$, where $0\leqq \nu_i < \nu_i + h_i \leqq p$ are integers; let C be the box $0\leqq x_i < p$. For any integer x, denote by x^* its natural image in $[p]$. The authors seek to estimate $N(B)$, the number of solutions of $f(\mathbf{x}^*)=0$ with $x\in B$; $N(C)$ is thus the total number of solutions of $f(\mathbf{x}^*)=0$. Their main results are Theorem 1: If f has no linear factors, then

$$N(B) = h_1\cdots h_n p^{-n} N(C) + O(p^{n-2}\log p);$$

and Theorem 2: If f is non-singular and $n\geqq 2d+1$, then

$$N(B) = h_1\cdots h_n p^{-n} N(C) + O(p^{n-5/2}\log^n p).$$

They use the technique of "finite Fourier series", combined with estimates of Lang and Weil [Amer. J. Math. **76** (1954), 819–827; MR **16**, 398] and other estimates of their own, reminiscent of those of Lang and Weil, but obtained by more elementary arguments. Theorem 2 is the more interesting; it has about $p^{3/2}$ to spare, so is strong enough to give results about non-homogeneous forms (consider a flat box with say $h_1=1$).

{The expression "f is non-singular" is used to mean that the variety $f(\mathbf{x}^*)=0$ has no non-singular point with coordinates in $[p]$; if one gives the phrase the usual geometric meaning that $f(\mathbf{x}^*)=0$ has no non-singular point, then one may replace $n\geqq 2d+1$ in Theorem 2 by $n\geqq 5$, and dispense with an application of Chevalley's theorem. What one actually needs is that the intersection of $f(\mathbf{x}^*)=0$ with every rational hyperplane be absolutely irreducible. The reviewer did not follow Case (iii) of the proof of Lemma 7, though the result is correct.}

B. J. Birch (Oxford)

Citations: MR 16, 398d = G25-2.

Referred to in D80-55.

D80-55 **(40# 2595)**

Chalk, J. H. H.; Williams, K. S.

The distribution of solutions of congruences: Corrigendum and addendum.

Mathematika **16** (1969), 98–100.

The reviewer of the original paper [the authors, Mathematika **12** (1965), 176–192; MR **32** #7526] pointed out that the proof of Lemma 7 was incomplete. A new proof of the following stronger lemma is now given: Let k be the field of residue classes mod p, p an odd prime, f and g polynomials in $k[\underset{\sim}{x}]$, $\underset{\sim}{x}=(x_1, \cdots, x_n)$, without a common factor. Then the number of solutions of $f(\underset{\sim}{x})=g(\underset{\sim}{x})=0$ with $\underset{\sim}{x}\in k^n$ is less than cp^{n-2}, where c depends only on $\max(\deg f, \deg g)$. The proof is elementary. {It seems that the inequality in equation (4) and in the line after (7) should read $\deg \Omega \leqq 2\delta^2$.} *I. Danicic* (Aberystwyth)

Citations: MR 32# 7526 = D80-54.

D80-56 **(32# 7530)**

Karacuba, A. A.

On systems of congruences. (Russian)

Izv. Akad. Nauk SSSR Ser. Mat. **29** (1965), 935–944.

Let the following system of congruences be given:

$$(1)\quad \begin{array}{l} x_1+\cdots+x_k-y_1-\cdots-y_k \equiv \lambda_1,\\ \cdot\\ \cdot\\ \cdot\\ x_1^n+\cdots+x_k^n-y_1^n-\cdots-y_k^n \equiv \lambda_n, \end{array} \pmod q$$

$1 \leqq x_i,\ \ y_i \leqq P\ \ (i=1, 2, \cdots, k)$, and denote by $N_k(\lambda_1, \lambda_2, \cdots, \lambda_n)$ the number of solutions of system (1).

Let r be an integer satisfying the conditions $A_1P^r \leqq q \leqq A_2P^r$, A_1, A_2 constants depending on n.

The author establishes the estimate

$$N_k \geqq (2k)^{-r}A_2^{-n+r}P^{2k-rn+r(r-1)/2}.$$

It then follows easily (owing to the Vinogradov mean-value theorem) that

$$(2)\qquad N_k \leqq c(n, k)P^{2k-rn+r(r-1)/2},$$

with $k \geqq [4n^2 \ln n]$.

In the present paper a class of congruences (1) is obtained for which the inequality (2), with $k \geqq [6rn \ln n]$, holds. *C. Karanikolov* (Sofia)

D80-57 **(34# 137)**

Hayashi, H. S.

The number of solutions of certain quintic congruences.

Duke Math. J. **33** (1966), 747–756.

The author derives an exact formula for the number N_m of solutions of the quintic congruence (*) $n\equiv \sum_{1\leq i\leq m} a_iy_i^5 \bmod p^L$, $(a_i, p)=1$, $p\equiv 1 \bmod 5$, too complicated to be reproduced here. The formula is given in terms of x, u, v, and w, where (x, u, v, w) is an integral solution of the simultaneous diophantine equations $16p=x^2+50u^2+50v^2+125w^2$, $xw=v^2-4uv-u^2$; there are exactly four solutions (with $x\equiv 1 \bmod 5$), as L. E. Dickson [Amer. J. Math. **57** (1935), 391–424] showed.

The author deduces the solvability of (*) for $m\geqq 5$ (or for $m\geqq 4$, if $n=0$), and he gives necessary and sufficient conditions for solvability in the cases $1\leqq m\leqq 4$.

{Asymptotic formulae (with remainder) for the number of solutions of more general congruences were derived by Hua Lo-keng and H. S. Vandiver [Proc. Nat. Acad. Sci. U.S.A. **35** (1949), 94–99; MR **10**, 515] for $m>2$.}

W. Schwarz (Freiburg)

Citations: MR 10, 515c = T50-7.

D80-58 **(34# 139)**

Williams, K. S.

On the number of solutions of a congruence.

Amer. Math. Monthly **73** (1966), 44–49.

The author gives an expression for the number of solutions of the congruence $a_1x_1^3+a_2x_2^3+\cdots+a_nx_n^3+b\equiv 0 \pmod p$, where p is a prime and $p\nmid \prod_{i=1}^n a_i$, in terms of nonprincipal cubic characters χ_1, χ_2 mod p, Gaussian sums $\tau(\chi_1)$, $\tau(\chi_2)$ and the coefficients of the congruence.

T. Hayashida (Yokohama)

D80-59 **(34# 4203)**

Nageswara Rao, K.

On a congruence equation and related arithmetical identities.

Monatsh. Math. **71** (1967), 24–31.

Let $l=d_1<d_2<\cdots<d_r=m$ be the divisors of a positive integer m. Let $(n, m^k)_k$ denote the greatest common kth power divisor of n and m^k. Extending results of E. Cohen [Duke Math. J. **23** (1956), 623–630; MR **18**, 285] and P. J. McCarthy [J. Reine Angew. Math. **203** (1960), 55–63; MR **22** #2574], the author derives a formula for the number of solutions of the linear congruence $n\equiv \sum_{i=1}^t x_i \pmod{m^k}$, where s_i of the x's have the property $(x, m^k)_k=d_i^k$ and $\sum_i s_i=t$. The formula is expressed in terms of the extended Ramanujan sum of Cohen [Duke Math. J. **16** (1949), 85–90; MR **10**, 354]. The author also establishes several related arithmetical identities. Generalized Kronecker functions, Cauchy products and finite Fourier representations are systematically used in the proofs.

A. L. Whiteman (Los Angeles, Calif.)

Citations: MR 10, 354d = A36-10; MR 22# 2574 = A36-29.

Referred to in A36-61.

D80-60 **(34# 5749)**

Davenport, H.; Lewis, D. J.

Notes on congruences. III.

Quart. J. Math. Oxford Ser. (2) **17** (1966), 339–344.

Let $f_j(x_1, \cdots, x_n)$, $j=1, \cdots, r$, be polynomials in $GF(p^m)[x_1, \cdots, x_n]$ of degree k_j vanishing at $x_1=\cdots=x_n=0$. By Chevalley's theorem, the system $f_j=0$ will have a non-trivial solution if $n>k_1+\cdots+k_r$. It may happen that all solutions will be singular, i.e., that rank $[\partial f_j/\partial x_i]<r$. The existence of non-singular solutions appears to be a difficult question. The authors take up the special case of two equations of additive type over $GF(p)$: $f=a_1x_1^k+\cdots+a_nx_n^k\equiv 0 \pmod p$, $g=b_1x_1^k+\cdots+b_nx_n^k\equiv 0 \pmod p$, where not both a_i and b_i are $\equiv 0$ and $p\nmid k$. For $k>1$, if there are λ and μ, not both zero, such that $\lambda f+\mu g\equiv 0$ has only the trivial solution, then $f\equiv g\equiv 0$ has only singular solutions. The principal result is that for any k prime to p, if every non-trivial form $\lambda f+\mu g$ has more than k non-zero coefficients (and hence has a non-trivial zero) then $f\equiv g\equiv 0$ has a non-singular solution. The proof reduces k to $K=(k, p-1)$. Since $x^k\equiv a$ is soluble if and only if $y^K\equiv a$ is soluble, and such x and y must vanish together, non-trivial solutions correspond to non-trivial solutions, and non-singular to non-singular unless $k>K=1$, but even in this case there are non-singular solutions for K which correspond to such for k. On page 342, line 20, the change in notation also refers to a slight redefinition of r so that one can conclude all the $B_i\not\equiv 0 \pmod p$.

Finally, the authors show that an analogous theorem fails for more than two equations, mod p, and that a lemma for their theorem fails in some $GF(p^m)$ for $m>1$, but whether the theorem fails or not is an open question.

{Part II appeared in same J. (2) **14** (1963), 153–159 [MR **26** #6117].} *R. Spira* (Knoxville, Tenn.)

Citations: MR 26# 6117 = D80-40.
Referred to in D72-60, T50-24.

D80-61 (34# 7451)

Birch, B. J.; McCann, K.

A criterion for the p-adic solubility of diophantine equations.

Quart. J. Math. Oxford Ser. (2) **18** (1967), 59–63.

N. Greenleaf [Amer. J. Math. **87** (1965), 25–31; MR **32** #108] has proved that if $f(x_1, \cdots, x_n)$ is a polynomial with rational integral coefficients, then there is a finite set S of primes depending on f such that if $p \notin S$ then every solution of $f(x_1, \cdots, x_n) \equiv 0 \pmod p$ can be extended to a p-adic solution of $f(x_1, \cdots, x_n) = 0$. A. Nerode [Bull. Amer. Math. Soc. **69** (1963), 513–517; MR **29** #5723] gave a decision procedure by which one could decide whether $f(x_1, \cdots, x_n) = 0$ is solvable in p-adic integers. In the present paper, the authors show how to calculate a number $D_n(f)$ with the following property. Given a prime p and rational integers $x_1, \cdots, x_n$ such that the power of p dividing $f(x_1, \cdots, x_n)$ is greater than the power of p in $D_n(f)$, then $x_1, \cdots, x_n$ can be extended to a p-adic solution of $f(x_1, \cdots, x_n) = 0$. Moreover, an explicit upper bound for $D_n(f)$ is obtained; this bound is in terms of the degree, number of variables, and size of the coefficients of f.

L. Carlitz (Durham, N.C.)

Citations: MR 29# 5723 = U05-22; MR 32# 108 = D72-43.

D80-62 (35# 126)

Ax, James

Solving diophantine problems modulo every prime.

Ann. of Math. (2) **85** (1967), 161–183.

The author first treats congruences modulo primes, later states some conjectures extending these results to non-principal ultraproducts of prime fields, and obtains some results in the direction of the conjectures. If $f_1, \cdots, f_m$ are polynomials in n variables with rational integer coefficients, let $a(f_1, \cdots, f_m)$ denote the set of primes p such that $f_1 \equiv \cdots \equiv f_m \equiv 0 \pmod p$ is soluble. Let A_n denote the Boolean algebra of subsets of the primes generated by the $a(f_1, \cdots, f_m)$.

The author proves the following. (1) $A_n = A_1$. (Here his proof uses the Riemann hypothesis for curves (mod p).) (2) If $a(f_1, \cdots, f_m)$ is an infinite set then the Dirichlet density of $a(f_1, \cdots, f_m)$ is a finite rational number. (3) There is an algorithm to determine when $a(f_1, \cdots, f_m)$ is the set of all primes. (4) Let R be a non-principal ultraproduct of finite prime fields. A subfield K of the algebraic number field $\tilde{Q}$ is isomorphic to $\tilde{Q} \cap R$ if and only if $\mathrm{Gal}(\tilde{Q}/K)$ is procyclic. (5) An absolutely irreducible variety defined over a countable subfield K of R has a rational point in R which is generic over K. (6) If two non-principal ultraproducts R and R' contain isomorphic, countable, quasi-finite, relatively algebraic closed subfields, then (assuming the continuum hypothesis) the isomorphism can be lifted to one between R and R'.

D. J. Lewis (Ann Arbor, Mich.)

Referred to in U05-38.

D80-63 (35# 4160)

Dodson, M.

Homogeneous additive congruences.

Philos. Trans. Roy. Soc. London Ser. A **261** (1967), 163–210.

Let $\Gamma^*(k)$ denote the least integer s such that for each prime p, each integer n, and each s-tuple of integers $a_1, \cdots, a_s$, the congruence $a_1x_1^k + \cdots + a_sx_s^k \equiv 0 \pmod{p^n}$ has a solution with $(x_1, \cdots, x_s, p) = 1$. H. Davenport and the reviewer [Proc. Roy. Soc. Ser. A **274** (1963), 443–460; MR **27** #3617] showed that $\Gamma^*(k) \leqq k^2+1$, with equality holding if $k+1$ is a prime. S. Chowla and G. Shimura [Norske Vid. Selsk. Forh. (Trondheim) **36** (1963), 169–176; MR **28** #3971] showed that for odd k, $\Gamma^*(k) < [2/(\log 2)+\varepsilon]k \log k$; and for infinitely many k, $\Gamma^*(k) > k \log k/\log 2$. The author proves: (A) If $k+1$ is composite then $\Gamma^*(k) \leqq 49k^2/64+1$, and this bound can be improved if more is known about $\Gamma^*(8)$. In fact

$$\Gamma^*(k) \leqq \tfrac{1}{2}k^2[1+2/\sqrt{(1+4k)}]+1$$

if $k \neq 8, 32$. (B) For an infinity of even k, $\Gamma^*(k) < 12(\log k)^2k^{15/8}$. (C) For all k, $\Gamma^*(k) \geqq k+1$. (K. Norton has shown that for odd $k>1$, $\Gamma^*(k) > 2k+1$ ["On homogeneous diagonal congruences of odd degree", Ph.D. thesis, Univ. Illinois, Urbana, Ill., 1966].) The author's method of proof is to first find the least s such that the congruences modulo p are soluble. He then uses methods suggested by Davenport and the reviewer [loc. cit.] to lift to congruences with moduli a power of p. For the mod p problem he ingeniously combines results from additions of residue classes modulo p, exponential sums, and a combinatorial theorem of P. Erdős and R. Rado [J. London Math. Soc. **35** (1960), 85–90; MR **22** #2554].

D. J. Lewis (Ann Arbor, Mich.)

Citations: MR 27# 3617 = D72-31; MR 28# 3971 = D72-35.

D80-64 (36# 3710)

Nageswara Rao, K.

A congruence equation involving the factorisation in residue class ring mod n.

Publ. Math. Debrecen **14** (1967), 29–34.

Let $N_{r,s}(m, n)$ denote the number of solutions in $x_i^{(j)} \pmod n$ of the congruence $m \equiv \sum_{j=0}^{s} a_jx_1^{(j)}x_2^{(j)}\cdots x_{r+1}^{(j)} \pmod n$, $(a_j, n) = 1$. In this paper, the author obtains a formula for $N_{r,s}(m, n)$ and proves that $N_{r,s}(m_1m_2, n_1n_2) = N_{r,s}(m_1, n_1)N_{r,s}(m_2, n_2)$. Moreover, it is shown that $\sum_{m=1}^{n} N_{r,s}(m, n) = n^{(r+1)(s+1)}$. *H. Gupta* (Allahabad)

D80-65 (38# 4430)

Karacuba, A. A.

An asymptotic formula. (Russian)

Trudy Moskov. Mat. Obšč. **18** (1968), 77–82.

Let $I_k = I_k(n, P, q)$ be the number of solutions of the congruence $x_1^n + \cdots + x_k^n \equiv y_1^n + \cdots + y_k^n \pmod q$, where $1 \leqq x_i, y_j \leqq P$. The following theorem is proved. If $q = p^\alpha = P^r$, p prime, $1 \leqq r \leqq \sqrt[3]{n}$, $\alpha \geqq 4n\sqrt[3]{n}$, $k > Cn$, C an absolute constant, then $I_k = \psi P^{2k}q^{-1} + O(P^{2k-1}q^{-1})$,

$$\psi = \sum_{\nu=0}^{\infty} p^{-2\nu k} \sum_{a=1;\,(a,p)=1}^{p^\nu} \left| \sum_{x=1}^{p^\nu} \exp 2\pi i \frac{ax^n}{p^\nu} \right|^{2k}$$

and the constant in O depends on k, n, α only. The proof is based on estimations of trigonometric sums.

A. Schinzel (Warsaw)

D80-66 (39# 1432)

Varbanec, P. D.

The distribution of solutions of the congruence $x^2+y^2 \equiv 1 \pmod{p^l}$. (Russian)

Ukrain. Mat. Ž. **21** (1969), 96–98.

Let $p \equiv 3 \pmod 4$ be a prime, and let $B(T)$ denote the number of solutions of the congruence $x^2+y^2 \equiv 1 \pmod{p^l}$, $x^2+y^2 \leqq T$, $x \geqq 0$, $y \geqq 0$. The author states the formula $B(T) = \pi T(4p^l)^{-1}(p+1)/p + O(T^{5/6}/p^l)$, where the constant implied by the O is absolute. Next, suppose that $l > 3$, and that $p^{(3l+2)/(2-4\alpha)} \leqq x \leqq p^{2l}$, where $\alpha \leqq \frac{1}{8} - 1/4l$. Let φ_1, φ_2 be real numbers with $\varphi_2 - \varphi_1 > x^{-\alpha}$. It is stated that the number of solutions of the congruence $u^2+v^2\equiv 1 \pmod{p^l}$ subject to $u^2+v^2\leqq x$, $\varphi_1<\arg(u+iv)\leqq\varphi_2$, is equal to $\frac{1}{2}(\varphi_2-\varphi_1)xp^{-l}(p+1)/p+O((x^{1-\alpha}/p^l)\log^\alpha x)$, where the constant implied by the O depends only on l. Finally, suppose l and α are as above, and choose numbers T_1, T_2 such that $p^{(3l+2)/(4-8\alpha)}\leqq T_1\leqq p^l$, $T_1^{1-\alpha}\leqq T_2\leqq p^l$. The author states that the number of solutions of $x^2+y^2\equiv 1 \pmod{p^l}$ subject to $0\leqq x\leqq T_1$, $0\leqq y\leqq T_2$ is equal to $(T_1T_2/p^l)(p+1)/p+O((T_1^{1-\alpha}T_2/p^l)\log T_1^\alpha)$, where the constant implied by the O depends only on l.

B. Gordon (Los Angeles, Calif.)

D80-67 (39# 2721)

Rajwade, A. R.

On rational primes p congruent to 1 (mod 3 or 5).

Proc. Cambridge Philos. Soc. **66** (1969), 61–70.

Using classical methods of cyclotomy as developed by C. F. Gauss [*Disquisitiones arithmeticae*, G. Fleischer, Leipzig, 1801; German translation, Springer, Berlin, 1889; reprinting of German translation, especially pp. 446–447, article no. 365, Chelsea, New York, 1965; MR **32** #5488; English translation, Yale Univ. Press, New Haven, Conn., 1966; MR **33** #5545] and G. B. Mathews [*Theory of numbers*, Part 1, Deighton, Bell, 1892; second edition, especially the chapter on cyclotomy, Chelsea, New York, 1962; MR **23** #A3698] the author derives the following two theorems. Theorem 1: The number of solutions of the congruence $y^2\equiv x^3-a \pmod p$ is p if $p\equiv 2 \pmod 3$ and is $p-(-4a/\pi)_6\bar\pi-(-4a/\bar\pi)_6\pi$ if $p\equiv 1 \pmod 3$, where $(\cdots)_6$ is the sixth power residue symbol, and where $p=\pi\bar\pi$ is the decomposition of p in the ring of Eisenstein integers with π and $\bar\pi$ both normalized $\equiv 1 \pmod 3$. Theorem 2: Let $p\equiv$ (mod 5) be a rational prime. Let $\zeta=\exp(2\pi i/5)$ and let g be a fixed primitive root of p. Then there is a prime decomposition $p=\pi_1\pi_2\pi_3\pi_4$ in $Q(\zeta)$, where the π_j are conjugates ($\bar\pi_1=\pi_4$, $\bar\pi_2=\pi_3$) and ordered so that $(g/\pi_i)_5=\zeta^i$ ($i=1,2,3,4$). Moreover, the number of solutions of the congruence $y^2\equiv x^5-a \pmod p$ is

$$p+(-4a/\pi_1)_{10}{}^3\pi_2\pi_4+(-4a/\pi_2)_{10}{}^3\pi_3\pi_4+(-4a/\pi_3)_{10}{}^3\pi_2\pi_1+(-4a/\pi_4)_{10}{}^3\pi_3\pi_1,$$

where $(\cdots)_5$ and $(\cdots)_{10}$ are the fifth and the tenth power residue symbols, respectively. The following corollary of Theorem 2 is interesting. If $p=\pi_1\pi_2\pi_3\pi_4$ is the decomposition of a prime $p\equiv 1 \pmod 5$ given by Theorem 2, then $5[36p^2+4(\pi_1{}^3\pi_2+\bar\pi_2\bar\pi_1{}^3)(\bar\pi_2{}^3\pi_1+\bar\pi_1\bar\pi_2{}^3)]$ is a rational integer and is the sum of five rational integral biquadrates.

A. L. Whiteman (Los Angeles, Calif.)

Citations: MR 23# A3698 = Z02-37; MR 32# 5488 = Z25-20; MR 33# 5545 = Z25-21.

Referred to in T20-48.

D80-68 (39# 5459)

Stepanov, S. A.

Congruences modulo a power of a prime number. (Russian)

Dokl. Akad. Nauk SSSR **186** (1969), 43–46.

Let $F(x,y)=y^n+P_1(x)y^{n-1}+\cdots+P_{n-1}(x)y+P_n(x)$ be an irreducible polynomial with rational integral coefficients and discriminant $D(x)$. In this paper an estimate for the number of solutions of (*) $F(x,y)\equiv 0\ (p^m)$, where the x, y run over certain incomplete systems of residues modulo p^m, is given in terms of the total number $N(F,p)$ of solutions of this congruence in the case $m=1$. The main theorem is as follows: if m is suitably large, c is a positive constant, $p^{(m-1)/((c(m-1)-n)-1)}\leqq T_1\leqq p^m$, $1\leqq T_2\leqq p^m$ and $A(T_1,T_2)$ is the number of solutions of (*) such that $p\nmid D(x)$ and $0\leqq x<T_1$, $0\leqq y\leqq T_2$, then

$$A(T_1,T_2)=(T_1T_2/p^m)\cdot((N(F,p)+O(1))/p)+O(\exp\{7m\ln^2 m\}T_1{}^{1-1/12m^3\ln 12m^3}).$$

{This article has appeared in English translation [Soviet Math. Dokl. **10** (1969), 563–566].}

J. B. Roberts (Halifax, N.S.)

Referred to in D80-69.

D80-69 (41# 1634)

Stepanov, S. A.

Congruences modulo a power of a prime. (Russian)

Izv. Vysš. Učebn. Zaved. Matematika **1970**, *no.* 1 (92), 80–90.

This paper appears to be an expanded and rewritten version, with changed notations, of the author's earlier paper [Dokl. Akad. Nauk SSSR **186** (1969), 43–46; MR **39** #5459].

J. B. Roberts (Portland, Ore.)

Citations: MR 39# 5459 = D80-68.

D80-70 (40# 2598)

Williams, Kenneth S.

Small solutions of the congruence $ax^2+by^2\equiv c \pmod k$.

Canad. Math. Bull. **12** (1969), 311–320.

The author proves the following theorem: If k is an odd integer, there exist non-negative integers $x, y\leqq Ck^{3/4}d(k)^{1/2}$, where C is a positive absolute constant and $d(k)$ denotes the number of divisors of k, such that $ax^2+by^2\equiv c \pmod k$ provided $(abc,k)=1$.

The author's final remark is of special importance: It would be of interest to know if the method of this paper could be adapted to give a corresponding result for the congruence $ax^n+by^m\equiv c \pmod k$, where $n\geqq 2$, $m\geqq 3$ and $(abc,k)=1$.

H. London (Montreal, Que.)

D80-71 (40# 7199)

Rajwade, A. R.

A note on the number of solutions N_p of the congruence $y^2\equiv x^3-Dx \pmod p$.

Proc. Cambridge Philos. Soc. **67** (1970), 603–605.

This note contains a quick method of confirming the well-known formula for N_p [see, e.g., H. Davenport and H. Hasse, J. Reine Angew. Math. **172** (1934), 151–182], by using a theorem of M. Deuring [Abh. Math. Sem. Univ. Hamburg **14** (1941), 197–272; MR **3**, 104] on elliptic curves with complex multiplication. A table of the $(1+i)^n$ division points ($n=1,2,3,4,5$) on the elliptic curve $y^2=x^3-Dx$, which has complex multiplication by $i=\sqrt{(-1)}$, is included.

J. H. H. Chalk (Toronto, Ont.)

Citations: MR 3, 104g = G20-4.

D80-72 (41# 1683)

Kaplan, Pierre

Démonstration des lois de réciprocité quadratique et biquadratique.

J. Fac. Sci. Univ. Tokyo Sect. I **16** (1969), 115–145.

Let p and q be two distinct prime numbers. Let N_2 be the number of solutions of $x_1{}^2+\cdots+x_q{}^2\equiv q \pmod p$. Let N_4 be the number of solutions of $x_1^4+x_2^4+\cdots+x_q^4\equiv q$ (mod p), where $p\equiv 1 \pmod 4$. The numbers N_2 and N_4 are calculated using results of Gauss, Eisenstein, and Artin.

J. H. Jordan (Pullman, Wash.)

D80-73 (41# 6769)

Neumann, O.

Über die Kongruenz $ax^4+1=cz^2$ (mod. p).

Monatsb. Deutsch. Akad. Wiss. Berlin **11** (1969), 699–703.

Denote by n the number of prime divisors of first degree

of the function field $GF(p)(x, y)$, defined by $ax^4+1=cy^2$ for some fixed non-zero elements a and c of $GF(p)$. The author proves the well known estimate $|n-(p+1)| \leqq 2\sqrt{p}$ [S. H. Hasse, *Vorlesungen über Zahlentheorie*, § 10, 3–6, Zweite Auflage, Springer, Berlin, 1964; MR **32** #5569] in a way which is rather elementary, since it does not use sums of biquadratic characters. *O. H. Körner* (Marburg)

Citations: MR 32# 5569 = Z02-25.

D80-74 **(41# 6770)**

Williams, K. S.

On a result of Libri and Lebesgue.

Amer. Math. Monthly **77** (1970), 610–613.

In this note it is observed that a simple property of a primitive nth root of unity provides a counting function for the number of solutions of a congruence $f(x_1, x_2, \cdots, x_k) \equiv 0 \pmod n$. The idea is illustrated by taking $f(x_1, x_2, \cdots, x_k) = x_1^l + x_2^l + \cdots + x_k^l$ and a prime $n=p\equiv 1 \pmod l$. The number $N_p(k, l)$ of solutions of $x_1^l + x_2^l + \cdots + x_k^l \equiv 0 \pmod p$ is expressed in terms of the q-nomial periods of the pth roots of unity, where $q=(p-1)/l$. This yields an old result of Libri and Lebesgue, i.e., $N_p(k, l) = p^{k-1} + (q/p)\sum_{s=0}^{l-1}\{1+l\eta_s\}^k$, where $\eta_s = \sum_{u=0}^{q-1}\{\omega(p)\}^{s+lu}$, $\omega(p) = \exp(2\pi i/p)$. An alternative form of this result gives a generalization of an earlier result of the author when $l=3$. *M. S. Cheema* (Tucson, Ariz.)

D80-75 **(42# 4552)**

Stepanov, S. A.

Elementary method in the theory of congruences for a prime modulus.

Acta Arith. **17** (1970), 231–247.

Let $m, n \geqq 2$ be coprime natural numbers and let $p > 4m^2n(n-1)^2$ be any prime number. Further, let Z_p denote the finite field $GF(p)$ and I_p the number of solutions in $x, y \in Z_p$ of the equation (1) $y^n = f(x) = x^m + a_1x^{m-1} + \cdots + a_{m-1}x + a_m \in Z[x]$. It is proved that $|I_p - p| < (2qm)^{3/2}p^{1/2}$, $q=(n, p-1)$.

The method of proof is similar to that used by the author in a previous paper concerning the special case $n=2$ [Izv. Akad. Nauk SSSR Ser. Mat. **33** (1969), 1171–1181; MR **40** #5620].

All elements of Z_p are divided into three classes. The first class consists of those $\alpha \in Z_p$ for which $f(\alpha) \neq 0$ and (1) is solvable in Z_p for $x=\alpha$. The second class consists of $\beta \in Z_p$ for which (1) is insolvable in Z_p for $x=\beta$, the third class of $\gamma \in Z_p$ for which $f(\gamma)=0$. Let the number of members in these sets be denoted by I_{+1}, I_{-1} and I_0, respectively. Then (2) $p = I_{+1} + I_{-1} + I_0$ and $I_p = qI_{+1} + I_0$. The author proves the existence of a polynomial $R_0(x)$ of bounded degree such that all elements of the second class are roots of $R_0(x)$ of relatively high multiplicity, thereby obtaining an upper bound for I_{-1}. In a similar way he finds an upper bound for I_{+1}. The result then follows from (2).

The construction of $R_0(x)$ is very complicated. *W. Ljunggren* (Oslo)

Citations: MR 40# 5620 = G20-42.

D80-76 **(42# 7584)**

Klösgen, Willi

Untersuchungen über Fermatsche Kongruenzen.

BMBW-GMD-36.

Gesellschaft für Mathematik und Datenverarbeitung, Bonn, 1970. ii+124 *pp.* *DM* 14.00.

This is a thorough investigation of $F = x_1^{p^m} + \cdots + x_k^{p^m} \equiv 0 \pmod{p^{m+1}}$, $0 < x_i < p$, especially of Fermat's congruence $x^p + y^p + z^p \equiv 0 \pmod{p^2}$. It is shown that $x^{p^m} \equiv y^{p^m} \pmod{p^{m+1}}$ and that the last $m+1$ digits of $x^{p^{m+1}}$ agree with those of x^{p^m} in a number system with base p. An example with $p=13$ is given. Let $1 + x_2^{p^m} + \cdots + x_k^{p^m} \equiv 0 \pmod{p^{m+1}}$, $0 < x_i < p$, be designated by K. Then it is shown that F has a solution, if and only if K has a solution. Let the $p-1$ pth-power residues modulo p^2 be designated by $R(i) \equiv i^p \pmod{p^2}$, $R(i) = i + r(i)p$, $i = 1, \cdots, p-1$; then $r(i) \equiv (i^p - i)/p \pmod p$, $0 \leqq r(i) < p$, is called Fermat's remainder for $i \pmod p$. It is shown that Fermat's congruence has a solution if and only if Fermat's remainder is the same for two consecutive numbers. Again, an example with $p=13$, $i=1(1)12$, is given. There follow some isomorphisms from cyclotomy.

In $(x+1)^p - x^p - 1 = px(x+1)(x^2+x+1)^\varepsilon f_p(x)$, $\varepsilon=1$ for $p \equiv -1 \pmod 6$, $\varepsilon = 2$ for $p \equiv 1 \pmod 6$, we call $f_p(x)$ Fermat's polynomial. The first three are: $f_5 = f_7 = 1$, $f_{11} = x^6 + 3x^5 + 7x^4 + 9x^3 + 7x^2 + 3x + 1$, and $f_{13} = x^6 + 3x^5 + 8x^4 + 11x^3 + 8x^2 + 3x + 1$. The author finds, by means of an IBM 7090 computer, that f_p for $p \leqq 31$ is irreducible. Since the coefficients of f_p increase rapidly, $p > 31$ could not be investigated. A discussion about the zeros of $f_p(x)$ follows. Let f_{11} and f_{13} be combined to $P_T(x) = x^6 + 3x^5 + Tx^4 + (2T-5)x^3 + Tx^2 + 3x + 1$; then f_p contains P_T with $0 \leqq T < p$, where T may be any suitable parameter. A table is given showing which P_T divide f_p and which not, for $p < 500$. The ratio is 50:50; but only about $\frac{1}{4}$ of those dividing f_p are solutions of Fermat's congruence.

Next, a formula for the number of solutions of the various mentioned congruences is derived. A connection between exponential sums and Gauss' sums is found. Let g be a fixed primitive root $\pmod{p^2}$ and $g^{(p-1)a} \equiv 1 + p \pmod{p^2}$, $0 < a < p$; then $\operatorname{ind}(1+rp) \equiv -ra \pmod p$. Several asymptotic formulas for the number of solutions are given. The density of the number of those primes that have r equivalence classes of non-trivial solutions of Fermat's congruence is investigated. Numerous interesting tables, diagrams, and references conclude this remarkable paper. *E. Karst* (Tucson, Ariz.)

D80-77 **(42# 7636)**

Williams, Kenneth S.

A distribution property of the solutions of a congruence modulo a large prime.

J. Number Theory **3** (1971), 19–32.

Denote by $N_p(f)$ the number of solutions of the congruence (1) $f(x_1, x_2, \cdots, x_n) \equiv 0 \pmod p$, where $0 \leqq x_i < p$, $i = 1, 2, \cdots, n$, $x_i \in \mathbf{Z}$ (the domain of integers of the real number field R) and p is a prime determined by (2) $p \geqq (20d)^n$. The author proves the theorem: Let $f(x_1, \cdots, x_n) \in \mathbf{Z}[x_1, \cdots, x_n]$ be a homogeneous polynomial of degree $d \geqq 2$ in the $n \geqq 2$ indeterminates $x_1, x_2, \cdots, x_n$. If f is absolutely irreducible $\pmod p$ and $N_p(f) \geqq \frac{1}{2}p^{n-1}$ (this a consequence of the assumption that f is absolutely irreducible $\pmod p$) [see B. J. Birch and D. J. Lewis, J. Indian Math. Soc. (N.S.) **23** (1959), 11–32 (1960); MR **23** #A859; S. Lang and A. Weil, Amer. J. Math. **76** (1954), 819–827; MR **16**, 398]), then every subcube $S(i_1, \cdots, i_n) = \{X \in R^n(p) | i_j\mu \leqq x_j < (i_j+1)\mu, j = 1, 2, \cdots, n, i_1, \cdots, i_n = 0, 1, 2, \cdots, (\lambda-1)\}$, where $\lambda \equiv \lambda(p, n, d) = [p^{1/n}/10d] \in \mathbf{Z}$, $\mu \equiv \mu(p, n, d) = p/\lambda \in R$, contains a solution $(x_1, x_2, \cdots, x_n)$, $x_i \in \mathbf{Z}$ of (1). The author raises the question —does a similar result hold for nonhomogeneous polynomials? *J. M. Gandhi* (Macomb, Ill.)

Citations: MR 16, 398d = G25-2; MR 23# A859 = D72-21.

D80-78 **(44# 2702)**

Tietäväinen, Aimo

On a problem of Chowla and Shimura.

J. Number Theory **3** (1971), 247–252.

Let $\Gamma^*(k)$ denote the least integer S such that, for each prime-power p^h and each sequence of s integers $a_1, \cdots, a_s$, the congruence $a_1x_1^k + \cdots + a_sx_s^k \equiv 0 \pmod{p^h}$ has a solution with at least one x_j prime to p. It is known that $\Gamma^*(k) \leqq k^2+1$ and that it may be much smaller than this bound if k is odd and large. Thus, if

$$\delta = \limsup_{k\to\infty, k \text{ odd}} \{\Gamma^*(k)/(k \log k)\},$$

S. Chowla and G. Shimura [Norske Vid. Selsk. Forh. (Trondheim) **36** (1963), 169–176; MR **28** #3971] have proved that $1/\log 2 \leqq \delta \leqq 2/\log 2$ (see also the paper by K. K. Norton [Acta Arith. **15** (1968/69), 161–179; MR **39** #1419] for an improved upper bound). In this short note, the exact value of $\delta = 1/\log 2$ is determined and the proof depends upon the following interesting property of a finite additive abelian group G of, say, q elements. Let G_j $(j=1, \cdots, s)$ denote subsets of G of equal cardinality $r \geqq 3$ and such that $0 \in G_j$ and $a \in G_j \Rightarrow -a \in G_j$ for every j. Then the equation $g_1 + \cdots + g_s = 0$, $g_j \in G_j$ has a nontrivial solution, provided that $2^{s-2} > s^2(q-1)/(r-1)$.

J. H. H. Chalk (Toronto, Ont.)

Citations: MR 28# 3971 = D72-35; MR 39# 1419 = N72-40.

D80-79 **(44# 5297)**

Katz, Nicholas M.
On a theorem of Ax.
Amer. J. Math. **93** (1971), 485–499.

Let k be a finite field of characteristic p with $q=p^a$ elements. Let $\{f_i\}_{i=1,\cdots,r}$, be non-constant polynomials on n variables and let $d_i = $ degree of f_i, $i=1, \cdots, r$. The author proves that $N \equiv 0 \bmod (q^\mu)$, where N is the number of closed rational points of the closed subscheme of $\operatorname{Spec}(k[x_1, \cdots, x_n])$ defined by the annullation of the f_i, $i=1, \cdots, r$, and $\mu = \sup\{0, (n-\sum_{i=1}^r d_i)/(\sup\{d_i\}, i=1, \cdots, r)\}$. The author gives references to the congruences obtained previously by E. Warning [Abh. Math. Sem. Univ. Hamburg **11** (1935), 76–83] and J. Ax [Amer. J. Math. **86** (1964), 255–261; MR **28** #3986]. *P. Abellanas* (Madrid)

Citations: MR 28# 3986 = T40-27.

D80-80 **(44# 6631)**

Kocarev, B. G.
On the problem of an asymptotic formula for the number of solutions of a congruence of Waring type.
Dokl. Akad. Nauk SSSR **192** (1970), 976–979 (*Russian*); *translated as Soviet Math. Dokl.* **11** (1970), 758–762.

A. A. Karacuba [Vestnik Moskov. Univ. Ser. I Mat. Meh. **1962**, no. 1, 38–46; MR **25** #2053] obtained an asymptotic formula for the number of solutions of the congruence

$$(*) \qquad x_1^n + x_2^n + \cdots + x_t^n \equiv d \pmod{p^s}$$

in an incomplete residue system $0 \leqq M_j \leqq x_j \leqq M_j + Q_j - 1 < p^s$, $j=1, \cdots, t$. Here n, s and t are suitably related positive integers, p is a prime and d an arbitrary fixed integer.

The present author studies a generalization of (*) involving possibly fewer variables than in Karacuba's problem but replacing the constant d in (*) by a variable lying in a "short" interval. He obtains an asymptotic formula for the number of solutions of such a congruence in an incomplete residue system of the above type. The method is based on the Vinogradov theory of exponential sums. *H. G. Diamond* (Urbana, Ill.)

Citations: MR 25# 2053 = T50-21.

D84 EQUATIONS OVER p-ADIC AND POWER SERIES FIELDS

See reviews D02-11, D02-22, D04-65, D12-53, D12-64, D32-13, D32-68, D32-73, D36-33, D40-52, D44-154, D48-40, D48-63, D72-4, D72-5, D72-6, D72-7, D72-9, D72-10, D72-11, D72-12, D72-13, D72-19, D72-21, D72-24, D72-29, D72-31, D72-34, D72-35, D72-36, D72-37, D72-39, D72-40, D72-41, D72-43, D72-44, D72-46, D72-47, D72-48, D72-49, D72-52, D72-53, D72-54, D72-55, D72-58, D72-60, D72-61, D72-62, D72-66, D72-67, D80-61, E16-34, E16-40, E76-16, E76-21, E76-25, E76-26, E76-28, P08-44, Q25-36, R99-9, S05-11, U02-2, U05-28, U05-34

D99 NONE OF THE ABOVE, BUT IN THIS CHAPTER

See also reviews A32-28, B52-19, C15-4, E24-107, E24-113, E24-120, N32-52, U05-8, U05-9, U05-12, U05-15, U05-17, U05-20, U05-21, U05-39, U05-40, U05-44, U05-45, U05-50, U10-6, Z10-47, Z15-22, Z15-30, Z15-46, Z15-48, Z15-54, Z15-62, Z15-76, Z15-81.

D99-1 **(1, 134e)**

Barnett, I. A. and Szász, Otto. On a certain Diophantine problem. Amer. Math. Monthly **46**, 545–554 (1939).

The authors determine all real solutions x, y of the equation $\cos nx + \cos ny = 0$, for which $\cos x$ and $\cos y$ are rational, and all integers n for which such solutions exist. In generalization, the authors treat the case of certain systems of similar equations. Generalizing in another direction, the authors deal, for an arbitrary integer s, with the equation $\cos snx + \cos ny = 0$. *E. Rothe* (Oskaloosa, Iowa).

D99-2 **(3, 268h)**

Bell, E. T. Selective equations. Ann. of Math. (2) **42**, 1029–1036 (1941).

The author considers the systematic solution of certain general Diophantine systems which are shown to be completely solvable in a finite number of prescribed steps in terms of a finite (though sometimes extravagantly large) number of independent integer parameters. It is assumed that out of a finite number of arbitrary integers $n_1, n_2, \cdots, n_s$ it is possible to select the least and the greatest, denoted by $(n_1, n_2, \cdots, n_s)'$ and $[n_1, n_2, \cdots, n_s]'$, respectively. These operators $(\ )'$ and $[\ ]'$ are called the two simple selective operators. Compound selective operators are exemplified by such expressions as

$$(n_1, (n_2, n_3)', n_4)', \quad (n_1, [n_2, n_3]', n_4, (n_4, n_5, n_6)')'.$$

A selective system is a finite system of the type

$$\sum A_i x_i + \sum a_i X_i' = \cdots = \sum B_i y_i + \sum b_i Y_i',$$
$$\cdots\cdots\cdots\cdots,$$
$$\sum C_i x_i + \sum c_i Z_i' = \cdots = \sum D_i w_i + \sum d_i W_i',$$

where the X', Y', Z', W' are abbreviations for the results of certain specified compound selective operators on unknowns $x_{ik}, y_{ik}, \cdots, w_{ik}$ and where x_i, y_i, w_i, z_i are also unknown. The other letters are given. Such a system obviously has a dual in which $(\ )'$ and $[\ ]'$ are replaced by the greatest common divisor and least common multiple operators $(\ )$ and $[\ ]$, and addition in the above system is replaced by multiplication. This dual system is solved explicitly in terms of parameters subject to certain G.C.D. conditions. Compound operators are first reduced to simple ones and the resulting simple system is solved recursively. From this the solution of the original system can be written down, the complete solution being separated into sets of solutions by the dual of the G.C.D. conditions. *D. H. Lehmer.*

D99-3 (6, 39h)

Roussel, André. Sur les applications arithmétiques de certains théorèmes dus à É. Picard. C. R. Acad. Sci. Paris **216**, 227–229 (1943).

The title refers to results of É. Picard expressing in terms of integrals the number of solutions of $f(x, y) = g(x, y) = 0$ contained in a given domain. It is indicated that certain number-theoretic propositions can be stated in terms of the number of solutions of such a pair of equations. The author suggests that Fermat's last theorem can be treated thus, but admits the difficulty of studying the resulting integrals. *I. Niven* (Lafayette, Ind.).

D99-4 (6, 256f)

Ljunggren, Wilhelm. Über einige Arcustangensgleichungen die auf interessante unbestimmte Gleichungen führen. Ark. Mat. Astr. Fys. **29A**, no. 13, 11 pp. (1943).

C. Störmer [Skr. Vid.-Selsk. Christiania. I. **1895**, no. **11** (1895)] determined all the solutions of

$$m \arctan(1/x) + n \arctan(1/y) = k\pi/4$$

in integers m, n, x, y, k. The author solves the same problem for the similar equations

$$m \arctan(\sqrt{3}/x) + n \arctan(\sqrt{3}/y) = k\pi/6,$$
$$m \arctan(\sqrt{2}/x) + n \arctan(\sqrt{2}/y) = k\pi/2.$$

The first of them has 14 and the latter 10 nontrivial solutions. *A. Brauer* (Chapel Hill, N. C.).

Referred to in D99-6.

D99-5 (7, 145j)

Størmer, Carl. Sur un problème curieux de la théorie des nombres concernant les fonctions elliptiques. Arch. Math. Naturvid. **47**, no. 5, 83–85 (1943).

The author studies the Diophantine equation

$$m\int_x^\infty \frac{dt}{(4t^3 - g_2 t - g_3)^{\frac{1}{2}}} + n\int_y^\infty \frac{dt}{(4t^3 - g_2 t - g_3)^{\frac{1}{2}}} = k\omega,$$

where 2ω is the real period of the corresponding Weierstrass $\wp$-function. He obtains 9 solutions in integers x, y, m, n, and k, but he is not able to prove that there exist no other solutions. *A. Brauer* (Chapel Hill, N. C.).

D99-6 (8, 564k)

Ljunggren, Wilhelm. Sur une généralisation d'un théorème de C. Størmer. Arch. Math. Naturvid. **48**, no. 11, 145–152 (1944).

C. Størmer [Skr. Vid.-Selsk. Christiania. I. **1895**, no. 11] found all solutions of $m \arctan(1/x) + n \arctan(1/y) = k\pi/4$ in integers m, n, x, y, k. The author solves the same problem for $m \arctan(1/x\sqrt{D}) + n \arctan(1/y\sqrt{D}) = k\pi/2$, where $D > 1$ is square-free, there being 8 nontrivial solutions in integers m, n, x, y, k, D. The author [Ark. Mat. Astr. Fys. **29A**, no. 13 (1943); these Rev. **6**, 256] had previously solved the more general equation

$$m \arctan(\sqrt{D}/x) + n \arctan(\sqrt{D}/y) = k\pi/2$$

for the cases $D=2$ and $D=3$. *I. Niven* (Eugene, Ore.).

Citations: MR 6, 256f = D99-4.

D99-7 (11, 11c)

Claudian, Virgil. Identities and Diophantine analysis. Gaz. Mat., Bucureşti **54**, 292–309 (1949). (Romanian)

D99-8 (12, 444j)

Stosick, A. J. A method for indexing powder photographs, using linear Diophantine equations, and some tests for crystal classes. Acta Cryst. **2**, 271–277 (1949).

R. Hesse [Acta Cryst. **1**, 200–207 (1948)] has developed a numerical, as contrasted with graphical, method for the indexing of powder photographs of tetragonal and hexagonal classes of crystals. The method stems from expressing $q = \sin^2\theta$ (the $\sin\theta$ of Bragg's law) as a 2-dimensional vector over the field of rational numbers, whereas q in the standard theory is regarded as a quadratic form. In the present paper the vector q is shown to have dimension 1, 2, 3, 4, 6 in the cubic, tetragonal, or hexagonal, orthorhombic, monoclinic, triclinic classes of crystals, respectively. It then follows that a test for crystal class can be obtained from the linear dependence of sets of q values. The dimension, and hence the class, is decided by finding the rank of the matrix of integral coefficients of linear relations among various experimentally determined q values. The Hesse method is also extended by the use of linear Diophantine analysis, which gives an alternative numerical procedure. Finally, by applying such quadratic Diophantine analysis as the theory of the simultaneous equations $x^2+y^2=z^2$, $y^2+z^2=t^2$ to the quadratic form q, a criterion is developed for assigning a crystal to one of three types: cubic; tetragonal, hexagonal; orthorhombic, monoclinic, triclinic. *I. Niven.*

D99-9 (14, 950g)

Moser, Leo. On the diophantine equation

$$1^n + 2^n + 3^n + \cdots + (m-1)^n = m^n.$$

Scripta Math. **19**, 84–88 (1953).

By employing certain congruence properties of sums of nth powers, the author proves that the equation of the title has no solutions in positive integers m and $n > 1$ with $m \leqq 10^{10^6}$. P. Erdös has conjectured that there are no solutions. *I. Niven* (Eugene, Ore.).

D99-10 (15, 776g)

Storchi, Edoardo. Risoluzione generale in interi dell'equazione:

$$\operatorname{arctg}\frac{m}{n} = \operatorname{arctg}\frac{1}{x} + \operatorname{arctg}\frac{1}{y}.$$

Ist. Lombardo Sci. Lett. Rend. Cl. Sci. Mat. Nat. (3) **16(85)**, 191–206 (1952).

Integral solutions (x, y) are sought for the equation $\arctan(1/x) + \arctan(1/y) = \arctan(m/n)$, where m and n are given relatively prime positive integers. This equation can be rewritten in the form $(mx-n)(my-n) = m^2+n^2$, whence it follows that for each factorization $q\bar{q} = m^2+n^2$, $0 < q \leqq \bar{q}$, we have a solution if either $n+q$ or $n-q$ is divisible by m. When $m = 1, 2, 3, 4$, or 6, such solutions exist for all

n relatively prime to m, but for other values of m there are values of n for which no integral solutions exist, in particular if $n<m/3$. Similar arctangent relations have been discussed by Lehmer [Amer. Math. Monthly **45**, 657–664 (1938)] and Todd [ibid. **56**, 517–528 (1949); these Rev. **11**, 159].
J. S. Frame (East Lansing, Mich.).

Citations: MR 11, 159d = N32-6.

D99-11 **(17, 128c)**

Grammel, R. Diophantische Vektorgleichungen. Österreich. Ing.-Arch. **9** (1955), 126–147.

Greek letters will denote so-called vector integers, i.e., 3-dimensional vectors with integers for components. Given non-null vector integers α and β there exists ϱ such that $\alpha\times\varrho=\beta$ if and only if the g.c.d. of the components of α divides the g.c.d. of the components of β. Results are also obtained for other vector equations such as $\alpha\cdot\varrho=b$, $\alpha\times\beta\times\varrho=\gamma$, $\alpha\cdot(\beta\times\varrho)+\gamma\cdot\varrho=d$, where Roman letters denote scalar integers. Some systems of vector equations are discussed. In each case the problem reduces to a set of Diophantine equations, and so is tractable by classical methods. *I. Niven* (Berkeley, Calif.).

D99-12 **(18, 285c)**

Larsson, D. F. Quelques inégalités de la théorie élémentaire des nombres. Mathesis **65** (1956), 205–210.

By considering corresponding congruences (mod 9) several Diophantine equations are shown to be insolvable. A typical result is: For $m\not\equiv 0$ (mod 3), the equation

$$\sum_{v=n}^{n+3m-1}(1+3\lambda)^v=b^c$$

has no solution in integers. *L. Moser* (Edmonton, Alta.).

D99-13 **(18, 791b)**

Mitrinovitch, Dragoslav S. Sur une question d'analyse diophantienne. Univ. Beogradu. Publ. Elektrotehn. Fak. Ser. Mat. Fiz. no. **6** (1956), 4 pp. (Serbo-Croatian summary)

In a previous paper [Fac. Philos. Univ. Skopje. Sect. Sci. Nat. Annuaire **1** (1948), 49–95; MR **10**, 527] the author proposed the problem of finding all sets of rational numbers a_ν, p_ν ($\nu=1, 2, 3, \cdots, m$) such that the sum $\sum_{k=1}^{n}\prod_{\nu=1}^{m}(a_\nu+(k-1)p_\nu)$ could be written as a product of $m+1$ factors, linear in n and with rational coefficients. In the present paper some new sets of solutions are given in case $m=2$, each set containing an infinity of numbers a_1, a_2, p_1, p_2. *W. Ljunggren* (Blindern).

D99-14 **(21# 2632)**

Mineev, M. P. The Tarry problem for rapidly increasing functions. Mat. Sb. N. S. **46 (88)** (1958), 451–454. (Russian)

Theorem: Let $g_0=1$ and let $g_i\geqq 2$ ($i\geqq 1$) be integers. Put

$$F(x) = g_0g_1\cdots g_x.$$

Then for fixed n the number of solutions in positive integers of the diophantine equation $F(x_1)+\cdots+F(x_n)=F(y_1)+\cdots+F(y_n)$ with $0\leqq x_j<p$, $0\leqq y_i<p$, is $n!p^n+O(p^{n-1})$.

The author shows, in fact, quite easily, that the number of solutions for which the x_j are not a permutation of the y_i is $O(p^{n-1})$. The theorem generalizes a result of Postnikov [Festschrift anlässlich des 250. Geburtstages Leonhard Eulers, Berlin, 1957] for the case when the g_i are all equal, and also an estimate of Loo-keng Hua [Acta Sci. Sinica **1** (1952), 1–76; MR **16**, 337] for the ordinary Tarry problem $F(x)=x^k$. *J. W. S. Cassels* (Cambridge, England)

Citations: MR 16, 337c = D52-90.
Referred to in L99-6.

D99-15 **(22# 12075)**

Yaakson, H. On symmetric solutions of a Diophantine equation. Uč. Zap. Tartu Gos. Univ. **46** (1957), 63–84. (Russian. Estonian summary)

D99-16 **(25# 4403)**

Supnick, Fred; Keston, Jeanette F.
On the rational triangulation of a circle.
Proc. Amer. Math. Soc. **13** (1962), 768–770.

From the authors' introduction: "A triangle is called rational if its sides and area are rational. A set of rational triangles is referred to as a rational triangulation of a circle K if (a) each triangle is inscribed in K, (b) no two of the triangles have interior points in common, and (c) the sum of the areas of the triangles is equal to the area of K. Theorem: A circle can be rationally triangulated if and only if its radius is rational."
W. Moser (Winnipeg, Man.)

D99-17 **(27# 5725)**

Chawla, L. M.
On diophantine equations defining equivalence relations over the integers.
J. Natur. Sci. and Math. **3** (1963), 83–98.

The author considers binary quadratic and cubic polynomials f which have integral coefficients and which satisfy $f(x,y)=f(y,x)$. He wishes to determine those polynomials f for which the relation "there is an integer z such that $f(x,y)=f(z,z)$" is an equivalence relation between integers x and y; the property of equivalence that needs to be checked is transitivity. He solves this problem in the quadratic case, but only partially in the cubic case. *B. J. Birch* (Manchester)

Referred to in D99-19, D99-24.

D99-18 **(28# 2081)**

Andrews, George E.
On estimates in number theory.
Amer. Math. Monthly **70** (1963), 1063–1065.

A method for finding an upper bound for the number N of solutions* of a Diophantine equation of the form $y=f(x)$ is provided. If $f(x)$ is continuous and twice differentiable with continuous second derivative in $[a,b]$, then

$$N < c(d+1)\{(M-m)(b-a)\}^{1/3},$$

where $M=\max_{a\leqq x\leqq b}f(x)$, $m=\min_{a\leqq x\leqq b}f(x)$, c is an absolute constant and where d is the number of integers x in (a,b) for which $f''(x)=0$. *J. H. H. Chalk* (Toronto, Ont.)

*In $[a,b]$. Ed.

D99-19 **(29# 66)**

Chawla, L. M.; Shafaat
On certain classes of diophantine equations defining equivalence relations over integers.
J. Natur. Sci. and Math. **3** (1963), 163–173.

This paper continues the study of equivalence relations on subsets S of the integers, determined by solutions of particular types of Diophantine equations of the general form (*) $F(x, y, z)=0$ [L. M. Chawla, same J. **3** (1963), 83–98; MR **27** #5725]. Given x and y in S, if (*) holds for some integral z, then $x \sim y$. This will be an equivalence relation for certain S and F.

The following types of equivalence relation and corresponding Diophantine equation are considered: (1) $x-y \equiv a \pmod{m}$ for some a in S. These are associated with equations of the form $f(ax+by)=mz$; (2) $x \equiv ay \pmod{p}$ for some a in S, with p an odd prime. These are associated with Diophantine equations of the form:

$$(x-a_1 y)\cdots(x-a_k y) = pz,$$

$$((xy)^n - a_1)\cdots((xy)^n - a_k) = pz;$$

(3) $f(x) \sim f(y)$, where $f(x)$ is an integral polynomial, and $x \sim y$ is an equivalence relation of one of the previous types.

Necessary and sufficient conditions for each of these cases are obtained. The results are illustrated by examples.
O. Frink (University Park, Pa.)

Citations: MR 27# 5725 = D99-17.

D99-20 (29# 67)

Chawla, L. M.
On a determinantal diophantine equation.
J. Natur. Sci. and Math. **3** (1963), 175–178.

The author solves a generalization of the problem of finding all triangles with integral vertices whose areas are perfect squares; that of finding all r-dimensional simplexes whose vertices have integral coordinates, and with hypervolume a perfect rth power. More generally, he finds all integral solutions of the equation $D=m$, where D is an $(r+1)$-rowed determinant with 1 everywhere in the last column, the other elements being unknown integers; m is a given integer. The solutions are found explicitly, but are too complicated to list here. *O. Frink* (University Park, Pa.)

D99-21 (37# 150)

Newman, Morris
A diophantine equation.
J. London Math. Soc. **43** (1968), 105–107.

The equation of the title is $\prod_{j=1}^{t} \sin \pi x_j = r$, where r is a given positive rational and the solutions x_j are rational. We may assume $0 < x_1 \leqq x_2 \leqq \cdots \leqq x_t < 1$ or, setting $x_j = a_j/m$, where a_j, m are positive integral and $(a_1, a_2, \cdots, a_t, m)=1$, $0<a_1 \leqq a_2 \leqq \cdots \leqq a_t < m$. It is proved that $m < (\pi/r)^t$. Hence there are only a finite number of solution sets. The methods used are results from the basic theory of congruences and automorphisms of cyclotomic fields.
J. D. Swift (Los Angeles, Calif.)

D99-22 (39# 5468)

Newman, Morris
Some results on roots of unity, with an application to a diophantine problem.
Aequationes Math. **2** (1969), 163–166.

By means of several lemmas on cyclotomic fields the author provides a concise proof of the fact that the only positive rational solutions (x, y, z) of the equation $(\sin \pi x)\cdot(\sin \pi y) = z$, normalized without loss of generality so that $x \leqq y \leqq \frac{1}{2}$, are given by $(\frac{1}{2}, \frac{1}{2}, 1)$, $(\frac{1}{3}, \frac{1}{3}, \frac{3}{4})$, $(\frac{1}{4}, \frac{1}{4}, \frac{1}{2})$, $(\frac{1}{6}, \frac{1}{6}, \frac{1}{4})$, $(\frac{1}{10}, \frac{3}{10}, \frac{1}{4})$, $(\frac{1}{12}, \frac{5}{12}, \frac{1}{4})$. This settles a question raised by the reviewer [Proc. of the 1963 Number Theory Conf., p. 98, University of Colorado, Boulder, Colo., 1963] in connection with restricted compass constructions in the plane.
R. L. Graham (Murray Hill, N.J.)

D99-23 (40# 2638)

Chowla, S.
The nonexistence of nontrivial linear relations between the roots of a certain irreducible equation.
J. Number Theory **2** (1970), 120–123.

The author proves that if p is a prime $\equiv 3 \pmod 4$, and the a_r are integers, there is no relation of the form $\sum_{r=1}^{p-1/2} a_r \cot(r\pi/p) = 0$ unless each $a_r = 0$.

The proof, somewhat surprisingly, deduces this from the fact that $L(1, \chi) \neq 0$, where χ is a character mod p with $\chi(-1) = -1$. *S. L. Segal* (Rochester, N.Y.)

D99-24 (42# 191)

Dick, Elie; Muwafi, Amin
Equivalence classes associated with diophantine equations that define equivalence relations over the integers.
J. Natur. Sci. and Math. **9** (1969), 149–154.

Let (*) $f(x, y) = \varphi(z)$ be a diophantine equation, where f and φ are polynomials over the set of rational integers I, $x, y, z \in I$. Then L. M. Chawla [same J. **3** (1963), 83–98; MR **27** #5725] defined the following binary relation $\sim$ over a subset S of I: $a \sim b$ if and only if $f(a, b) = \varphi(z)$, $z \in S$. He investigated those equivalence relations over S which are subject to the following further conditions (i) $f(x, x) = \varphi(x)$, (ii) $f(x, y) = f(y, x)$. These conditions ensure the reflexive and the symmetric property of $\sim$. He then examined the eight possible equations (*) of degree $\leqq 2$. It turned out that only four of these equations defined equivalence relations over S. In this paper the authors determine the equivalence classes for the above-mentioned four equations. *W. Ljunggren* (Oslo)

Citations: MR 27# 5725 = D99-17.

D99-25 (42# 4481)

Cucurezeanu, Ion
Impossibility of solution of the Diophantine equation $1^n + 2^n + 3^n + \cdots + (m-1)^n = m^n$, where $m, n > 1$. (Romanian. French summary)
Stud. Cerc. Mat. **20** (1968), 1125–1129.

Referred to in D99-26.

D99-26 (42# 5904)

Dem'janenko, V. A.
A certain indeterminate equation. (Russian)
Rev. Roumaine Math. Pures Appl. **15** (1970), 817–818.

P. Erdős conjectured that the equation $1^n + 2^n + 3^n + \cdots + (m-1)^n = m^n$ has no solution in natural numbers $m, n > 1$. A proof was published by I. Cucurezeanu [Stud. Cerc. Mat. **20** (1968), 1125–1129; MR **42** #4481], but in the present note, the author shows that Cucurezeanu's proof is incorrect in the case $m = 4k+3$, $n = 2n'$.
S. E. Schuur (E. Lansing, Mich.)

Citations: MR 42# 4481 = D99-25.

E. FORMS AND LINEAR ALGEBRAIC GROUPS

Reviews of papers on Hermitian forms are in the corresponding sections for quadratic forms. All such papers are listed in **E52**. For papers on quadratic or Hermitian forms over finite fields, see **T35**.

For minima of forms, see **D76**, **J28**, **J32**, **J44**, **J48**, **J52**. Many Diophantine equations involve forms; see the appropriate sections of the preceding chapter. General principle: a paper giving conditions that $f(x, y, \ldots)$ represent n, or an estimate for the number of representations, would be in the present chapter, while results on the solutions themselves (parametric representations, bounds for the smallest solution, etc.) would occur in Chapter **D**.

See also Section J00.

E02 BOOKS AND SURVEYS

General texts which include standard material on quadratic forms are to be found in **Z01** and **Z02** and are not cross-referenced here.

See also reviews C20-35, D02-23, E12-19, E12-67, E12-90, E12-92, E12-126, E12-137, E16-36, E16-84, E20-45, E24-42, E24-48, E24-105, E24-120, E56-8, E60-12, E60-32, E64-5, E64-7, E64-15, E64-20, E64-28, E68-10, E68-14, E68-19, E68-20, E68-21, E72-11, H02-8, H02-20, Z02-73, Z10-25, Z10-45, Z30-59.

E02-1 **(3, 67c)**

Hull, Ralph. The representation of integers in forms. Nat. Math. Mag. **14**, 235–252 (1940).

Expository article.

E02-2 **(8, 285a)**

Tietze, H. Ein Kapitel Topologie. Zur Einführung in die Lehre von den verknoteten Linien. Hamburger Math. Einzelschr. **36**, vii+47 pp. (1942).

This book (originally an hour-lecture at a meeting) contains an introduction to Minkowski's theory of quadratic forms with rational coefficients and to Reidemeister's theory of the quadratic form associated with a knot. No proofs are given. Several examples are carefully worked out; there are many figures. *H. Samelson* (Ann Arbor, Mich.).

E02-3 **(12, 244a)**

Jones, Burton W. The Arithmetic Theory of Quadratic Forms. Carus Monograph Series, no. 10. The Mathematical Association of America, Buffalo, N. Y. (distributed by John Wiley and Sons, Inc., New York, N. Y.), 1950. x+212 pp. $3.00 (Members of The Mathematical Association of America may purchase one copy at $1.75, order to be placed with the Secretary-Treasurer).

This excellent monograph gives an introduction to the arithmetic parts of the theory of quadratic forms in self-contained form. It assumes only knowledge of the most elementary facts in the theory of numbers and the theory of matrices and, moreover, it is written in a very clear style. For these reasons it will make easy reading even for beginning students. Yet it leads up to the limits of what is known, taking into account recent work of Hasse, Pall, Ross, the author himself and others. In this respect it partly fills a gap in the existing literature, since no other exposition in book form of the more recent development of the arithmetic theory of quadratic forms exists. The general problem of the theory is that of the representation of quadratic forms in m variables by a given quadratic form in n variables ($1 \leqq m \leqq n$) or, in the language of matrices, the problem of the representation of symmetric $(m \times m)$-matrices B by a given symmetric $(n \times n)$-matrix A in the form $B = X^T A X$ by means of an $(n \times m)$-matrix X (X^T is the transposed matrix of X). The elements of these matrices can be restricted to given fields or rings. The titles and contents of the chapters are as follows. I: Forms with real coefficients. Conditions for the possibility of the representation of one quadratic form by another. Automorphs. II: Forms with p-adic coefficients. Definition of p-adic numbers. Relation between rational representability modulo a prime power p^t of a matrix B by a matrix A and p-adic representability of B by A. The symbols of Hilbert and Hasse. Zero forms. Conditions for p-adic representability of B by A. Universal forms. III: Forms with rational coefficients. Equivalence. Reduced forms. The fundamental theorem of Hasse (a rational nonsingular form is a zero form if and only if it is a p-adic zero form for all primes p and a real zero form). Rational equivalence and rational representation. IV: Forms with coefficients in $R(p)$ (the ring of p-adic integers). Canonical forms. Representation of numbers by forms and equivalence of forms in $R(p)$. Representation of one form by another. Zero forms. Universal forms. Automorphs. Binary forms. V: Genera and semi-equivalence. Representation without essential denominator. Existence of forms with integral coefficients and having given invariants. VI: Representation by forms. Siegel's representation function. Asymptotic results. VII: Binary forms. Automorphs. Representation by binary forms. Ideals in a quadratic field. Correspondence between ideal classes and classes of quadratic forms. Composition of classes of ideals and classes of forms. Genera. Reduction. Class number. VIII: Ternary quadratic forms. Numbers represented by ternary genera. One minor remark should be made here about the treatment of p-adic numbers in chapter II. This treatment is incomplete since it does not introduce the notion of p-adic convergence. In some places, however (e.g., on p. 22), where this notion is actually needed in the proofs, the author then uses the rather vague expression that a sequence of numbers "generates" its limit. There is a collection of 95 (for the greater part very interesting) problems at the end of the book as exercises for the reader. *H. D. Kloosterman.*

Referred to in E02-9, E04-15, E16-37, E20-83.

E02-4 **(14, 540a)**

Eichler, Martin. Quadratische Formen und orthogonale Gruppen. Die Grundlehren der mathematischen Wissenschaften in Einzeldarstellungen mit besonderer Berücksichtigung der Anwendungsgebiete. Band LXIII. Springer-Verlag, Berlin-Göttingen-Heidelberg, 1952. xii +220 pp. 24.60 DM; Bound, 27.60 DM.

The aim of the author is to develop in this book a thoroughgoing, self-contained theory of quadratic forms from a completely modern point of view. A familiarity with modern algebra and the elements of the theory of algebraic numbers is assumed. The quadratic forms are considered as metrics of a vector space in an arbitrary field and associated with such a metric is the orthogonal group in the broad sense of an automorphic transformation of the form. The reader familiar with the classical theory will miss some landmarks: reduction theory and some details of representation theory for forms with integral coefficients. But the spirit of the work of Hasse, Hecke, and Siegel pervade this volume and the power and beauty of the general modern methods is evident throughout. The author, in consideration for the reader recommends the omission of certain sections for those who wish to avoid the deeper ramifications of the theory. This is, however, not a book for the skimming reader.

The following partial list of chapter and section titles gives an idea of the content of the book: The metric space and its automorphisms; the spinor-representation of the orthogonal group; spaces of dimension 2 to 6; fundamental properties of perfect discrete valuation fields and their quadratic extensions; invariant characteristics of spaces and space types; lattices; units; ideals; the arithmetic of Clifford algebras; Theta functions and Gauss sums; elementary theory of mass; absolute mass of a p-adic unit group; the analytic mass formula for definite spaces and general spaces; the geometric theory of units. *B. W. Jones.*

Referred to in E12-48, E12-57, E12-66, E12-132, E20-85.

E02-5 **(14, 540b)**

Eichler, Martin. Idealtheorie der quadratischen Formen. Abh. Math. Sem. Univ. Hamburg **18**, 14–37 (1952).

The author gives a short and readable account of his work on quadratic forms (spinor representation of the "orthogonal" group of such a form; lattices belonging to quadratic forms over a field with a discrete non-archimedean valuation; ideals of lattices; the theory "in the large", i.e., over a finite algebraic field), as developed with all details in his recent book "Quadratische" Formen und orthogonale Gruppen" [see the preceding review]. *K. Mahler* (Manchester).

E02-6 **(18, 562e)**

van der Waerden, B. L. Die Reduktionstheorie der positiven quadratischen Formen. Acta Math. **96** (1956), 265–309.

This paper is a long-needed exposition, simplification, and unification of the reduction theory of positive quadratic forms, $f(x_1, x_2, \cdots, x_n)=\sum f_{ij}x_ix_j$. Chief attention is given to two definitions of reduced form. First, Hermite called a form reduced if $f_{ii}=N_i$ where the N_i are the "successive minima" of the form; that is, N_1 is the least positive value of f_{11} for all forms equivalent to f, N_2 is the least positive value of f_{22} for all forms equivalent to f and having $f_{11}=N_1$, etc. Second, Minkowski called a form f reduced if the following condition holds:

(D) $$f_{kk}\leqq f(s_1, s_2, \cdots, s_n)$$

for all integers $s_1, \cdots, s_n$ with $(s_k, \cdots, s_n)=1$. The fundamental inequalities are the following for the Minkowski reduced form

(E) $$\lambda_n f_{11}f_{22}\cdots f_{nn}\leqq D_n,$$

and the following for the successive minima:

(F) $$N_1N_2\cdots N_n\leqq \mu_n D_n.$$

After laying the basis for the reduction theory and proving inequality (F), the author sharpens Mahler's inequality, $f_{kk}\leqq\delta_k N_k$, to deduce inequality (E) with Remak's coefficient. He gives proofs of the two "Finiteness Theorems": For a given determinant, there is only a finite number of forms for which one or more equalities in (D) hold; there is only a finite number of integral transformations taking reduced forms into reduced forms. Special attention is given to binary, ternary, and quaternary forms.

In the second part of this paper, the author considers the geometrical phase of the reduction theory in which the set of reduced forms form a cell in the $\frac{1}{2}n(n+1)$ dimensional space of positive quadratic forms. The space is covered by these cells with overlapping on the boundaries.

The third part of the paper deals with "Extreme Forms" such that for each small variation of the variables which leaves fixed the first minimum, the discriminant increases. He proves the theorem of Korkine and Zolotareff: If f is an extreme form, the set of forms having its first minimum forms a linear subspace of the space of all forms of given discriminant. Again special attention is given to ternary and quaternary forms and a brief survey given of the results of Korkine, Zolotareff, Hofreiter, and Coxeter. *B. W. Jones* (Boulder, Colo.).

Referred to in Z10-45.

E02-7 **(20# 3118)**

Eichler, M. Quadratische Formen und Modulfunktionen. Acta Arith. **4** (1958), 217–239.

This is a helpful exposition of fundamental results by the author, particularly in generalized Abelian integrals [Math. Z. **67** (1957), 267–298; MR **19**, 740], the congruence zeta-function [Arch. Math. **5** (1954), 335–366; MR **16**, 116], and modular correspondences [J. Indian Math. Soc. (N.S.) **20** (1956), 163–206; MR **19**, 18]. The paper culminates in seven conjectures, some specific, but mostly constituting a vast program that can barely be sketched here. In the notation of the earlier papers, the author is concerned with (1) his conjecture that if $R_\chi{}^n(T_m)$ denotes the matrix of the modular correspondence of character χ belonging to a modular form of first type and degree $-n$, then its eigenvalues are less than const $\sqrt{p}$, for m=prime p; this includes Ramanujan's conjecture with $\Delta(\tau)=\sum\tau(m)\exp 2\pi im\tau$, $n=12$, $\chi\equiv 1$, $R=\tau(m)/m^5$; (2) generalization to principal congruence subgroups of the author's method of calculation of the trace of the matrices R; (3) further relations between theta series of a quadratic form and the field K of modular invariants of the principal congruence subgroups mod F; (4) the modular forms of a character $\chi\neq 1$ representable by theta series; (5) generalization (to definite quadratic forms in totally real fields with several complex variables) of the existence formulas for Abelian integrals, particularly for $n>2$; (6) modular correspondences in the automorphic forms belonging to the modular group of a totally real quadratic field; (7) a topological meaning for the matrices R for the case $n>2$

to correspond to the endomorphisms in the Betti group when $n \leqq 2$. *H. Cohn* (Tucson, Ariz.)

Citations: MR 16, 116d = G30-15; MR 19, 18a = F15-10; MR 19, 740a = F15-12.

E02-8 (22# 733)

Takahashi, Shuichi. Arithmetic of group representations. Tôhoku Math. J. (2) **11** (1959), 216–246.

This paper gives a complete account of all the basic facts known on integral representations. Its bibliography makes it possible to track down very easily virtually all the important literature on the subject to date. The author did not learn of the two fundamental papers of Maranda [Canad. J. Math. **5** (1953), 344–355; **7** (1955), 516–526; MR **15**, 100; **19**, 529] until his investigation was nearly complete, and a greater part of his work consists in an independent reconstruction of Maranda's results. In view of this, a detailed review would be inappropriate; we shall merely indicate some of the new ideas. For representations over Dedekind rings, the author uses Chevalley's version of the Steinitz elementary divisor theory, which is an improvement over the methods of Maranda's second paper. Zassenhaus' binding systems (Verbindungssysteme) have been replaced by appropriate cohomological devices complete with a "principal genus theorem". It has long been known that something homological was going on here but, to the reviewer's knowledge, this is the first time anybody has taken the trouble to write it all down. The slight amount of homology theory necessary is developed ab ovo so that the uninitiate need not be frightened away. The most interesting new idea in the paper is concerned with studying the classes of integral representations in a given genus. This is done by extending the representations to the adèle ring of the ground field and constructing a certain algebraic group, namely the group of all regular endomorphisms commuting with the extended representation. A one-to-one correspondence is constructed between the classes in a given genus and a particular family of double cosets of this algebraic group. This gives the relations between the local and global class numbers of the representations and the absolute ideal class number of the field; in particular, it gives the relations of this type that were obtained by Maranda. The theory of integral representations has perhaps not yet justified itself on the score of new group-theoretical results. However it has already produced some new invariants and there are high hopes for things to come. This paper is recommended, not only for its lucid account of what is already known, but also for its interesting and stimulating ideas suggestive of what the future may hold.
W. E. Jenner (Lewisburg, Pa.)

E02-9 (22# 9475)

Watson, G. L. Integral quadratic forms. Cambridge Tracts in Mathematics and Mathematical Physics, No. 51. Cambridge University Press, New York, 1960. xii+143 pp. $5.00.

This monograph is chiefly concerned with equivalence and representation of integers by quadratic forms with integral coefficients. A background of only elementary number theory and the rudiments of matrix theory is assumed. The methods are arithmetical and at times most ingenious. The first five chapters are mostly classical (if rational equivalence comes under that heading) and have much in common with the reviewer's *The arithmetic theory of quadratic forms* [Math. Assoc. of America, Buffalo, N.Y., 1950; MR **12**, 244]. They are concerned with reduction, the rational invariants (Hilbert and Hasse symbols), p-adic equivalence from the point of view of congruences, the congruence class, and genus.

The reader will notice one change in the beginning, wherein the quadratic form is written: $\frac{1}{2}x'Ax$, where the matrix A has elements $2a_{ii}$ along the diagonal and a_{ij} elsewhere. This is to prepare for the following definition of the discriminant of the form:

$$d = d(f) = (-1)^{n/2}|A| \quad (n \text{ even}),$$
$$= \tfrac{1}{2}(-1)^{(n-1)/2}|A| \quad (n \text{ odd}).$$

This definition simplifies other notations later.

The fifth chapter contains the author's beautiful result that an indefinite form in four or more variables represents properly an integer a if it represents it properly modulo d.

Chapter 6, which deals with rational transformations and automorphs, is largely preparation for the following chapter.

In chapter 7, the spinor norm of Eichler is defined in arithmetical terms. To accomplish this the author defines the weight, $w(R)$, of a rational transformation R, to be the least positive integer such that $w(R)e$ is integral when e ranges over all the minor determinants of R. The norm of R is the unique square-free positive integer such that the product of the norm and $w(R)$ is a square. Then two forms in n variables are said to be in the same spinor genus if one may be taken into the other by a rational transformation R whose determinant is $\neq 1$, whose norm is 1, and such that all the denominators of the elements of R are prime to d, the discriminant of the form. He then proceeds to prove the fundamental theorem: Two indefinite forms in three or more variables are equivalent if and only if they are in the same spinor genus. Simpler congruence conditions are given for spinor-relatedness.

In chapter 7 it is also shown that if f is a positive form in four or more variables, with discriminant d, and a is a positive integer such that the congruence $f(x) \equiv a \pmod d$ has a solution with x integral and primitive, then some form f' in the spinor genus of f represents a properly. For positive ternary quadratic forms there are so-called "exceptional" integers a which do not have this property. It is shown that if a is exceptional, ap^2 is exceptional for every prime p not dividing the discriminant.

Chapter 8 is concerned with factorization of the general rational automorph into reflexions with denominators prime to a given odd integer m. In particular, every rational automorph of a form with discriminant d, whose weight is prime to d, has the same norm as some product of rational reflexions of f, each reflexion having denominator prime to d.

Though in a number of spots this tract is very difficult reading, it is a notable contribution to the literature of quadratic forms and brings one to the threshold of much that is still unknown in the subject.
B. W. Jones (Boulder, Colo.)

Citations: MR 12, 244a = E02-3.
Referred to in E12-136.

E02-10 (23# A118)

Bromwich, T. J. I'A.
Quadratic forms and their classification by means of invariant-factors.
Reprinting of Cambridge Tracts in Mathematics and Mathematical Physics, No. 3. Hafner Publishing Co., New York, 1960. viii+100 *pp.* $3.00.

A reprinting of the 1906 edition.

E02-11 **(27# 2485)**

O'Meara, O. T.

Introduction to quadratic forms.

Die Grundlehren der mathematischen Wissenschaften. Bd. 117.

Academic Press, Inc., Publishers, New York; Springer-Verlag, Berlin-Göttingen-Heidelberg, 1963. xi+342 *pp.* $12.00.

The author states in the preface that "the main purpose of this book is to give an account of the fractional and integral classification problem in the theory of quadratic forms over the local and global fields of algebraic number theory", incorporating recent developments of the theory in the last decade. He also emphasizes that he does "not even touch upon the theory of hermitian forms, reduction theory and the theory of minima, composition theory, analytic theory, etc." so that "only a small part of the theory of quadratic forms is covered in this book". These words of the author himself seem to explain quite well the general scope of the present book.

The book is divided into four parts, each consisting of two or three chapters. An outline of each part is as follows.

Part I: Arithmetic theory of fields. This is an introduction to algebraic number theory via valuation theory. The theory for global fields is developed up to the Dirichlet unit theorem and the finiteness of class number by means of the product formula and idèle groups.

Part II: Abstract theory of quadratic forms. A vector space V, associated with a quadratic form on it, is called a quadratic space. Throughout the book, V is assumed to have a finite dimension over a field F of characteristic $\neq 2$. In this part, algebraic theory of such quadratic spaces is developed in a more or less standard manner. Topics such as the following are included: Witt's theorem, the Clifford algebra, the spinor norm, the Hasse algebra, the orthogonal group and its various subgroups.

Part III: Arithmetic theory of quadratic forms over fields. Here the field F is specialized to a local or global field studied in Part I, and the following main results are proved: (1) Let U and V be regular (=non-degenerate) quadratic spaces over a local field F. Then U is isometric to V if and only if U and V have the same dimension, the same discriminant, and the same Hasse invariant. (2) (Hasse-Minkowski) Let U and V be regular quadratic spaces over a global field F. Then U is isometric to V if and only if U is locally isometric to V at every (prime) spot of F. To prove the above, class field theory is developed for quadratic extensions up to the proof of Hasse norm theorem for such extensions. To define the Hasse symbol, Hilbert's norm residue symbol is also explained, and Hilbert's reciprocity law is proved.

Part IV: Arithmetic theory of quadratic forms over rings. First, the general theory of quadratic forms over a Dedekind domain is developed through the use of the notion of lattices in quadratic spaces. Then the lattices over the ring of integers of a local field are considered. So-called Jordan splittings of such lattices are defined, and a necessary and sufficient condition for the equivalence of two such lattices is given in terms of the components of Jordan splittings of those lattices. Finally, in the last chapter of the book, lattices over the ring of integers of a global field are studied. For such a lattice, the class, the genus, and the spinor genus are defined, as well as the class number of the genus. Then, by means of the idèle group associated with the given orthogonal group, theorems such as the following are proved: (1) The theorem of the finiteness of class number; (2) The approximation theorem for rotations; (3) The theorem that the class is equal to the spinor genus if dim $V \geqq 3$ and the quadratic form is isotropic at some archimedean spot.

Throughout the book, the presentation is clear and self-contained. It seems that the author, rather than including more advanced materials, has intended here to give an introduction to the theory of quadratic forms as neatly as possible, assuming little background on the part of the reader. We feel that he has succeeded in his purpose. Only a little more explanation in the bibliography, indicating the source of the results in the text and orienting further study in this area, would have made the book more valuable to the reader. *K. Iwasawa* (Cambridge, Mass.)

Referred to in E08-22, E08-24, E08-28, E08-38, E12-116, E12-131, E56-37.

E02-12 **(28# 3006)**

Siegel, Carl Ludwig

Lectures on the analytical theory of quadratic forms.

Notes by Morgan Ward. Third revised edition.

Buchhandlung Robert Peppmüller, Göttingen, 1963. iii+243 *pp.* *DM* 15.00.

This is a revision of the second edition [Inst. Advanced Study, Princeton, N.J., 1949]. A modern bibliography on the theory of modular functions and forms, abelian functions and abelian varieties has been included, with suitable references in the text, and a number of small errors and misprints have been eliminated. Otherwise the content, as before, is roughly this: the basic theorem on the density of representations of one definite quadratic form by the genus of a second; modular functions and forms, and the connection between the modular field and the moduli of an algebraic curve; extension of the basic theorem to indefinite forms; further extension to forms over totally real algebraic number fields.

W. J. LeVeque (Boulder, Colo.)

E02-13 **(34# 4372)**

Borel, Armand

Reduction theory for arithmetic groups.

Algebraic Groups and Discontinuous Subgroups (*Proc. Sympos. Pure Math., Boulder, Colo.*, 1965), *pp.* 20–25. *Amer. Math. Soc., Providence, R.I.*, 1966.

This expository paper is devoted to the statement of results concerning fundamental sets for arithmetic subgroups of linear algebraic groups defined over the rational field. Siegel domains and minimal principles are discussed, and many examples are given.

R. Steinberg (Los Angeles, Calif.)

E02-14 **(36# 171)**

Kneser, M.

Semi-simple algebraic groups.

Algebraic Number Theory (*Proc. Instructional Conf., Brighton*, 1965), *pp.* 250–265. *Thompson, Washington, D.C.*, 1967.

This is a rather comprehensive report on the status of the theory of semi-simple algebraic groups as of the middle of 1965. (1) Algebraic theory: e.g., work of Chevalley, Rosenlicht, Borel, Grothendieck on the classification of almost simple groups over algebraically closed, and perfect fields. (2) Galois cohomology: work of Serre, Steinberg, and the author on K-forms and the triviality of the appropriate first cohomology group, connections with the theorem of Minkowski and Hasse for the equivalence of quadratic forms over algebraic number fields. (3) Tamagawa numbers': starting with the basic work of Weil on the application of the theory of adèles to algebraic groups, the work of Tamagawa, Ono, Borel, Harish-Chandra, Mars, Bruhat, Tits and the author is reviewed; the important connections with Siegel's work on the representations of two quadratic forms by each other (Weil, and the author) are indicated. This valuable report is supplemented with a useful bibliography. *O. F. G. Schilling* (Lafayette, Ind.)

Referred to in Z10-29.

E02-15 **(39# 5577)**

Borel, Armand

Introduction aux groupes arithmétiques.

Publications de l'Institut de Mathématique de l'Université de Strasbourg, XV. Actualités Scientifiques et Industrielles, No. 1341.

Hermann, Paris, 1969. 125 *pp.*

This book, based on lectures given by the author in 1964 at the Institut Henri-Poincaré, is devoted mainly to the study of fundamental domains in a reductive algebraic group G defined over $\mathbf{Q}$, relative to an arithmetic subgroup $\Gamma\subset G_{\mathbf{Q}}$. (An earlier mimeographed version of the lectures also included a short chapter on automorphic forms.) Proofs are given for some of the results announced by the author [Colloque Théorie des Groupes Algébriques (Bruxelles, 1962), pp. 23–40, Librairie Universitaire, Louvain; MR **26** #6173]. These results improve earlier theorems of the author and Harish-Chandra [Ann. of Math. (2) **75** (1962), 485–535; MR **26** #5081], which are also discussed here. The present treatment does not include the case of adelic groups, but many of the techniques and proofs carry over to that situation as well.

The contents fall naturally into three parts, according to the (increasing) amount of information needed about algebraic groups. Chapter I, "Quelques groupes classiques", treats the reduction theory of quadratic forms by methods which can later be generalized, presupposing only a few standard facts (Iwasawa decomposition of $\mathrm{GL}(n,\mathbf{R})$, properties of Haar measure, ...). Let $G=\mathrm{GL}(n,\mathbf{R})$, $\Gamma=\mathrm{GL}(n,\mathbf{Z})$. In § 1 Siegel sets are introduced, relative to the standard Iwasawa decomposition $G=K\cdot A\cdot N$ ($K=\mathrm{O}(n)$), and it is proved that the right Γ-translates of a "big enough" Siegel set cover G. The proof involves showing that the function $\Phi(g)=\|g\cdot e_1\|$ (e_1 = first basis vector of $\mathbf{R}^n$) attains its minimum on $g\Gamma$ at a point of such a Siegel set. Mahler's criterion for compactness of a subset of G/Γ, viewed as the collection of lattices in $\mathbf{R}^n$, is obtained as a corollary. Next these considerations are adapted to $\mathrm{SL}(n,\mathbf{R})$; here the Haar measure of a Siegel set is finite, so that $\mathrm{SL}(n,\mathbf{R})/\mathrm{SL}(n,\mathbf{Z})$ has finite volume. § 2 places these results in their classical setting of reduction theory: The space of positive definite quadratic forms on $\mathbf{R}^n$ may be identified with the homogeneous space $\mathrm{O}(n)\backslash\mathrm{GL}(n,\mathbf{R})=K\backslash G$; then one obtains "Siegel sets" in $K\backslash G$ consisting of reduced forms in the sense of Hermite. (Minkowski's method is also worked out; the reduced forms in his sense are shown to lie in a Siegel set.) In § 3 the Bruhat decomposition of $\mathrm{GL}(n,k)$ (k a field) relative to the upper triangular group is computed explicitly. This yields a canonical form for elements of $G=\mathrm{GL}(n,\mathbf{R})$ which, together with the Iwasawa decomposition, is exploited in § 4 to prove the Siegel property: If $b\in\mathrm{GL}(n,\mathbf{Q})$ and $\mathfrak{S}$ is a Siegel set in G, then $\{\gamma\in\Gamma\mid\mathfrak{S}b\cap\mathfrak{S}\gamma\neq\varnothing\}$ is finite. (This is deduced from a theorem of Harish-Chandra, which appears in general form in § 15.) As a corollary, Γ is finitely-generated. The reduction of an indefinite quadratic form F relative to the arithmetic group $\mathrm{O}(F)\cap\mathrm{GL}(n,\mathbf{Z})$ is achieved in § 5, modulo a crucial finiteness lemma proved in § 6, by viewing the homogeneous space $\mathrm{O}(a)\times\mathrm{O}(b)\backslash\mathrm{O}(F)$ (where F has signature (a,b) and hence $\mathrm{O}(a)\times\mathrm{O}(b)$ is maximal compact in $\mathrm{O}(F)$) as the set of "minimal majorants" of F in the space of positive definite forms, and then adapting a suitable Siegel set in the latter to yield a fundamental set in the former. The method here goes back to Hermite, while the lemma of § 6 allows one to recover a classical theorem of Jordan on finiteness of the number of orbits of $\mathrm{SL}(n,\mathbf{Z})$ in the space of $\mathrm{SL}(n,\mathbf{R})$-transforms of a homogeneous form with integral coefficients.

Chapter II, "Groupes algébriques", begins with a brief summary of elementary facts about algebraic linear groups and a discussion (in characteristic 0) of the quotient of such a group by a reductive subgroup (§ 7). Let $G\subset\mathrm{GL}(n,\mathbf{C})$ be a $\mathbf{Q}$-group. A subgroup Γ of $G_{\mathbf{Q}}$ is called arithmetic if Γ is commensurable with $G_{\mathbf{Z}}=G\cap\mathrm{GL}(n,\mathbf{Z})$; this property of Γ is independent of the chosen linear representation of G. The author shows also that replacing $\mathbf{Q}$ in this set-up by a finite extension leads to nothing essentially new. In § 8 the following compactness criterion is proved: If G is connected reductive and $\Gamma\subset G_{\mathbf{Q}}$ is arithmetic, then $G_{\mathbf{R}}/\Gamma$ is compact if and only if $G_{\mathbf{Q}}$ consists of semi-simple elements and G is without $\mathbf{Q}$-characters. This generalizes some classical results on anisotropic quadratic forms, as well as Dirichlet's unit theorem. Conjectured by Godement for adelic groups, the theorem was proved by the author and Harish-Chandra [loc. cit.] and, in a different way, by G. D. Mostow and T. Tamagawa [ibid. (2) **76** (1962), 446–463; MR **25** #5069]; the latter proof, using Mahler's criterion, is given here. It is also shown in § 8 that $\mathbf{Q}$-isogeny preserves arithmetic subgroups. § 9 is devoted to the construction of a first type of fundamental set, due to the author and Harish-Chandra [loc. cit.]. If $G\subset\mathrm{GL}(n,\mathbf{C})$ is a reductive $\mathbf{Q}$-group, Γ an arithmetic subgroup, a set $\Omega\subset G_{\mathbf{R}}$ is called fundamental for Γ if: (F_0) $K\cdot\Omega=\Omega$ for some maximal compact subgroup K of $G_{\mathbf{R}}$; (F_1) $\Omega\cdot\Gamma=G_{\mathbf{R}}$; (F_2) if $b\in G_{\mathbf{Q}}$, $\{\gamma\in\Gamma\mid\Omega\cdot b\cap\Omega\cdot\gamma\neq\varnothing\}$ is finite. (The "Siegel property" (F_2) is stated not just for $b=e$, in order to insure that existence of a fundamental set for Γ will imply the same for any other arithmetic subgroup.) One first applies a theorem of Mostow to find $u\in\mathrm{GL}(n,\mathbf{R})$ such that $u\cdot G_{\mathbf{R}}\cdot u^{-1}$ is "self-adjoint" (closed under transposes) and then produces explicitly a fundamental set for Γ in $G_{\mathbf{R}}$ by adapting a suitable Siegel set for $\mathrm{GL}(n,\mathbf{R})$ relative to $\mathrm{GL}(n,\mathbf{Z})$. § 9 also establishes a finiteness theorem for the orbits of Γ in the set of integral points of a closed orbit of G (in the space of a linear representation of G), generalizing finiteness results of Jordan (cf. § 6).

The third chapter, "Ensembles fondamentaux à pointes", has as its main goal the construction of a second, more manageable type of fundamental set. Rationality properties of algebraic groups play an important role in the construction; the main results on tori and on parabolic subgroups of reductive groups (Borel-Tits theory) are summarized without proof in §§ 10–11, along with several illuminating examples and a detailed discussion of groups defined over $\mathbf{R}$ (Bruhat and Iwasawa decompositions, connectedness properties, compactness). For convenience, let G henceforth denote a connected reductive $\mathbf{Q}$-group, K a maximal compact subgroup of $G_{\mathbf{R}}$, P a minimal $\mathbf{Q}$-parabolic subgroup of G with unipotent radical U, S a maximal $\mathbf{Q}$-split torus of P, A the identity component of $S_{\mathbf{R}}$ (in the real topology), M the ($\mathbf{Q}$-anisotropic) derived group of $Z(S)$. In § 12 Siegel sets $\mathfrak{S}_{t,\omega}=K\cdot A_t\cdot\omega$ in $G_{\mathbf{R}}$ are introduced, analogous to those encountered in Chapter I; here A_t consists of the elements of A on which all simple $\mathbf{Q}$-roots take value $<t$, and ω is relatively compact in $M_{\mathbf{R}}\cdot U_{\mathbf{R}}$. If now $\Gamma\subset G_{\mathbf{Q}}$ is arithmetic, it is shown that, for suitable Siegel set $\mathfrak{S}$ and finite set $C\subset G_{\mathbf{Q}}$, $G_{\mathbf{R}}=\mathfrak{S}\cdot C\cdot\Gamma$ (§ 13). The proof makes full use of the Bruhat and Iwasawa decompositions, and is not easy. When G is semi-simple (or merely lacks $\mathbf{Q}$-characters), a Siegel set has finite Haar measure; so in this case, $G_{\mathbf{R}}/\Gamma$ has finite volume. Proof of the Siegel property (F_2) for $\mathfrak{S}\cdot C$ is deferred to § 15, following a dis-

cussion of functions of type (R, χ) (R parabolic, χ a character of R), which arise from certain representations of G and generalize the function Φ of § 1. These functions play a crucial role in the theorem of Harish-Chandra from which the Siegel property is deduced. Next an interpretation of the set C is given: a finite subset C of $G_{\mathbf{Q}}$ figures as above in a fundamental set if and only if $P_{\mathbf{Q}} \cdot C \cdot \Gamma = G_{\mathbf{Q}}$. An appendix to § 15 indicates how to strengthen (F_2) by passing from $G_{\mathbf{Q}}$ to the commensurability group of Γ, which in turn allows one to extend the principal results of the book to arbitrary subgroups of $G_{\mathbf{R}}$ commensurable with some arithmetic subgroup.

In the case of adelic groups, Godement and Weil used minimum arguments for functions of type (R, χ) to construct fundamental sets [R. Godement, Sém. Bourbaki (1962/63), Fasc. 3, No. 257; MR **33** #126]. The author modifies their procedure to give a second construction of his fundamental sets for Γ in $G_{\mathbf{R}}$ (§ 16). Besides Mahler's criterion (§ 1) and the compactness criterion (§ 8), the finiteness of $P_{\mathbf{Q}} \backslash G_{\mathbf{Q}} / \Gamma$ (§ 15) is needed; although this latter fact is here obtained as a consequence of his first construction, the author mentions that it can be gotten independently from the compactness criterion for adelic groups. The minimum argument for $G_{\mathbf{R}}$, similar in spirit to that in § 1, is more complicated than in the adelic case, because the finite set C intervenes (leading to a fundamental set with "pointes", analogous to the cusps of the classical fundamental domains for fuchsian groups). A technique of successive minima is also developed here.

§ 17 investigates the space $X = K \backslash G_{\mathbf{R}} / \Gamma$ in the special case when G has $\mathbf{Q}$-rank equal to 1 and Γ is "nice". The main result is that X is diffeomorphic to the interior of a compact variety $\bar{Y}$ with boundary; the connected components of the boundary correspond precisely to the points of the finite set C appearing in the construction of a suitable fundamental set. This discussion answers a question of Serre, whose condition of "niceness" for a matrix (the eigenvalues generate a torsion-free multiplicative group) is technically useful in the proof: one shows that any arithmetic subgroup Γ contains a subgroup of finite index whose elements are nice. {The conclusion of Proposition 17.4 should be weakened to: "Alors Γ possède un sous-groupe net d'indice fini."} A concluding remark relates the space $\bar{Y}$ to the Satake compactification of X.

This book is a valuable addition to the literature of arithmetic groups; although the style is concise and the proofs (in later sections) are often demanding of the reader, the author's introductory remarks and bibliographical notes serve well to place the main theorems in historical perspective and to indicate their logical interdependence.

James Humphreys (New York)

Citations: MR 25# 5069 = E60-3; MR 26# 5081 = E60-5; MR 26# 6173 = E60-6; MR 33# 126 = E68-15.

Referred to in E60-44.

E02-16 (41# 149)

Abel-Parry, Mireille

Une étude arithmétique des formes quadratiques.

D. E. A. de Mathématiques, Option Algèbre et Géométrie. Secrétariat des Mathématiques de la Faculté des Sciences de Montpellier, 1969–1970, Publication No. 66.

Université de Montpellier, Montpellier, 1970. i+39 *pp.* (*loose errata*) *n.p.*

These notes give a detailed survey with proofs of the theorems of the elementary parts of the theory of quadratic forms over fields. They give, moreover, some details concerning binary quadratic forms over the rational integers. The notes are based on a lecture of the reviewer given in a refresher course in Belgium [Bull. Soc. Math. Belg. **20** (1968), 205–212; MR **39** #2703].

F. van der Blij (Bilthoven)

Citations: MR 39# 2703 = E12-137.

E02-17 (41# 5296)

Manin, Ju. I.

On Hilbert's eleventh problem. (**Russian**)

Hilbert's Problems (*Russian*), *pp.* 154–158. *Izdat. "Nauka", Moscow*, 1969.

The eleventh problem of Hilbert was to develop a theory of quadratic forms over algebraic number fields comparable to the then existing theory of such forms over the rationals. As the author remarks, this has been achieved in the work of Hasse, Hecke and Siegel inter alios. The present expository article explains the Hasse principle and Siegel's quantitative results about integral representation by forms of a genus. After describing Witt's geometric formulation in terms of lattices and metric spaces, the author goes on to describe Kneser's and Tamagawa's reformulation and generalization of Siegel's theorem in terms of linear algebraic groups. He concludes by mentioning the conjectural generalizations to abelian varieties due to Birch, Swinnerton-Dyer and Tate. There is an adequate bibliography. *J. W. S. Cassels* (Cambridge, England)

E02-18 (42# 4574)

Scharlau, Winfried

Quadratic forms.

Queen's Papers in Pure and Applied Mathematics, No. 22.

Queen's University, Kingston, Ont., 1969. iii+162 *pp.*

These lecture notes give a competent introduction to the theory of quadratic forms in finitely many variables over fields of characteristic not 2. The first chapter introduces the basic definitions and readies tools such as Witt's theorem, Witt decompositions, Witt ring and Grothendieck ring. Chapter II presents the theory of Pfister in the elegant setting due to Witt: Multiplicative forms and applications to the structure of the Witt ring. The method of transfer (the author's different approach to parts of Pfister's theory). Pfister's local-global principle. Representation of definite functions as sums of squares. The theorems of Cassels. Fields of prescribed level.

For these materials one may also compare *Quadratische Formen über Körpern* by Falko Lorenz [Springer, New York, 1970].

Chapter III brings a neat presentation of Wedderburn theory based on a theorem by M. A. Rieffel [Proc. Nat. Acad. Sci. U.S.A. **54** (1965), 1513; MR **33** #4093], the Brauer group, the Clifford algebra (à la Atiyah-Bott-Shapiro) and other invariants of quadratic forms such as, e.g., Hasse algebra and Hasse invariant. In the last chapter most of the classical results on classification of quadratic forms are proved.

Beside the bibliography there is an appendix to each of the four chapters giving some additional (formal and informal) explanations about the material covered. The reading of the text is very pleasant and stimulating.

H. Gross (Zürich)

E02-19 (42# 5911)

Siegel, C. L.

Lectures on quadratic forms.

Notes by K. G. Ramanathan. Tata Institute of Fundamental Research Lectures on Mathematics, No. 7.

Tata Institute of Fundamental Research, Bombay, 1967. ii+192+iv *pp.* $2.00.

Die Ausarbeitung enthält zunächst einige Präliminarien

über Gitter und Charaktere mit einer Anwendung auf diophantische Approximation (Satz von Kronecker). Sodann wird die Reduktionstheorie der positiv definiten quadratischen Formen durchgeführt einschließlich der Endlichkeitssätze: Endlichkeit der Klassenzahl, Definierbarkeit der Minkowskipyramide durch endlich viele lineare Ungleichungen, Äquivalenz von Matrizen höchstens auf dem Rande.

Der größere Teil der Ausarbeitung ist den indefiniten Formen gewidmet und behandelt die in einer früheren Arbeit des Autors [Math. Ann. **124** (1951), 17–54; MR **16**, 800] entwickelte Theorie, deren Hauptresultat die Identität zwischen einer Eisensteinreihe

$$\psi_a(z) = \gamma_a + e^{\pi i(q-p)/4}\,\mathrm{abs}|2S|^{-1/2} \sum_{(\alpha,\gamma)=1,\gamma>0} \gamma^{-n} \times (z-\alpha/\gamma)^{-p/2}(\bar{z}-\alpha/\gamma)^{-q/2} \sum_{x \bmod \gamma} e^{2\pi i(\alpha/\gamma)S[x]}$$

und dem über einen Fundamentalbereich im Raum $\mathfrak{H}$ der Majoranten $\{H>0 | HS^{-1}H=S\}$ von S nach der Untergruppe Γ_a aller Einheiten U von S mit $Ua \equiv a \bmod 1$ erstreckten Integral

$$\varphi_a(z) = V^{-1} \int_{\mathfrak{H}/\Gamma_a} \sum_{x \equiv a \bmod 1} e^{\pi i(z(S+H)+\bar{z}(S-H))[x]}\,dv$$

einer Thetareihe ist. Dabei ist S eine indefinite quadratische Form der Signatur (p, q), $2S$ und $2Sa$ ganz, $n=p+q \geqq 4$; und für $n=4$ ist S keine Quaternionen—Nullform. Eine aus den Fourierentwicklungen herzuleitende arithmetische Konsequenz ist die Gleichung $M(S, a, t) = \mu_a(S) \prod_p \delta_p(S, a, t)$ zwischen dem "Darstellungsmaß" $M(S, a, t)$ von t durch $S[x+a]$ und den lokalen Faktoren $\delta_p(S, a, t) = \lim_{r\to\infty} p^{r(1-n)}$. Anzahl der mod p^r verschiedenen Lösungen von $S[x+a] \equiv t \bmod p^r$. Die Beweise sind ausgeführt für $n>4$.

S. Böge (Heidelberg)

E02-20 (44# 189)

Lorenz, Falko

Quadratische Formen über Körpern.

Lecture Notes in Mathematics, Vol. 130.

Springer-Verlag, Berlin-New York, 1970. ii+77 *pp.* *DM* 8.00; $2.20.

Diese Vorlesungsausarbeitung enthält im wesentlichen die jüngeren Pfisterschen Resultate aus der algebraischen Theorie der quadratischen Formen, und zwar in der Darstellung und mit den unveröffentlichten Beweisen von Witt, deren Haupthilfsmittel der Begriff der von Witt zu diesem Zweck eingeführten runden Form ist. U. a. kommen folgende Sätze vor: Das Produkt zweier Summen von 2^m Quadraten ist wieder eine solche. Die Stufe eines Körpers ist eine Zweierpotenz, und jede Zweierpotenz kommt als Stufe vor. Eine quadratische Form über einem formal reellen Körper k hat genau dann endliche Ordnung im Wittring über k, wenn sie im Wittring jeder reell abgeschlossenen Erweiterung von k verschwindet. Außerdem wird ein Satz von T. A. Springer [Nederl. Akad. Wetensch. Proc. Ser. A **58** (1955), 352–362; MR **17**, 17; errata, MR **17**, p. 1436] über die Struktur des Wittringes über einem diskret bewerteten, vollständigen Körper der Restklassencharakteristik $\neq 2$ bewiesen mit Hilfe der Beschreibung des Wittringes durch erzeugende und definierende Relationen [E. Witt, J. Reine Angew. Math. **176** (1936), 31–44]. Die Primideale des Wittringes werden beschrieben [der Autor und J. Leicht, Invent. Math. **10** (1970), 82–88; MR **42** #1851], und Aussagen über seine Einheiten, Nullteiler, nilpotenten und Torsionselemente gewonnen. Der letzte § 12 enthält weitere unveröffentlichte Ergebnisse von Pfister und Witt für Formen über Funktionenkörpern mit reell abgeschlossenem Grundkörper.

S. Böge (Heidelberg)

Citations: MR 17, 17a = E08-10; MR 42# 1851 = E04-32.

E04 QUADRATIC FORMS OVER GENERAL FIELDS

For special fields, see **E08**, **E32**, **T35**. For forms of lower dimension, see **E16** and **E20**.

See also reviews D80-53, E02-4, E02-11, E02-16, E02-20, E08-4, E08-25, E12-63, E12-100, E16-73, E16-74, E24-125, E60-7, G02-4, G05-25, M40-35, P02-22, Z10-4.

E04-1 (4, 237f)

Arf, Cahit. Untersuchungen über quadratische Formen in Körpern der Charakteristik 2. I. J. Reine Angew. Math. **183**, 148–167 (1941).

Let $F=\sum_{1\leqq i\leqq j\leqq n} a_{ij}x_ix_j$ be a quadratic form over a field k of characteristic 2. To study the equivalence of forms the author interprets F as the square of the norm of a vector in an n-dimensional vector space $\mathfrak{R}$ over k; similarly the bilinear form of F is considered to be the inner product on $\mathfrak{R}$. Then two forms F and F' are equivalent over k if and only if the associated vector spaces $\mathfrak{R}$ and $\mathfrak{R}'$ are isometric. Let $\mathfrak{R}^*$ be the invariant subspace of $\mathfrak{R}$ consisting of all $\mathfrak{x}^*$ with $(\mathfrak{x}^*, \mathfrak{y})=0$ for all $\mathfrak{y}$ in $\mathfrak{R}$. Then $\mathfrak{R}$ is the direct sum $\sum_{i=1}^n \langle \mathfrak{u}_i, \mathfrak{v}_i\rangle + \mathfrak{R}^*$, where $\dim \langle \mathfrak{u}_i, \mathfrak{v}_i\rangle = 2$, $\mathfrak{u}_i\mathfrak{v}_i \neq 0$ and $(\mathfrak{u}_i, \mathfrak{v}_i)$ has no subspace $\mathfrak{R}^*$; that is, they are completely regular. Passage to the quadratic forms then results in the equivalence

$$F \sim \sum_{i=1}^{n} (a_ix_i^2+b_ix_iy_i+c_iy_i^2) + \sum_{j=1}^{n^*} d_jz_j^2 = \sum f_i + F^*, \quad b_i \neq 0.$$

The form F^* is uniquely determined to within equivalence transformations. Similarly, the number $2n$ of the totally regular part $\sum f_i$ is unique, though $\sum f_i$ is not. To obtain further invariants the author studies the Clifford algebra $C(F)$ with $u_i^2=a_{ii}$, $u_iu_j+u_ju_i=a_{ij}$, $i<j$. Then $C(F) = \prod C(f_i)C(F^*)$. Reducing $C(F)$ modulo the radical, one finds that only $\prod C(f_i)$ and thus $C(f_i)$ have to be investigated. For totally regular forms $\sum f_i$ the algebra $\prod C(f_i)$ and residue class $\Delta(F) \equiv \sum (a_ic_i)/b_i^2 \pmod{a^2-a,\ a \text{ in } k}$ are invariants. To obtain complete sets of invariants the author studies the necessary and sufficient conditions which describe whether a form represents 0. These conditions depend on the number of variables. A typical result is this: "If each form $f_1+f_2+z^2$ represents 0 in k then the number of variables $2n$, $C(F)$ and $\Delta(F)$ form a complete set of invariants for equivalence." The author is unaware of the work of A. A. Albert [Ann. of Math. (2) **39**, 494–505 (1938); Trans. Amer. Math. Soc. **43**, 386–436 (1938)].

O. F. G. Schilling (Chicago, Ill.).

Referred to in E04-7, E04-8, E04-9, E04-17, E08-4, E08-25.

E04-2 (5, 30f)

Eckmann, Beno. Gruppentheoretischer Beweis des Satzes von Hurwitz-Radon über die Komposition quadratischer Formen. Comment. Math. Helv. **15**, 358–366 (1943).

This is a simplified proof using representation theory and group characters of the following theorem of A. Hurwitz and J. Radon. Let n be written $n=u\cdot 2^{4\alpha+\beta}$ (u odd; $\beta=0, 1, 2, 3$). There exist n complex bilinear forms $z_1, \cdots, z_n$ in the two sets of variables $x_1, \cdots, x_p$ and $y_1, \cdots, y_n$ such that

$$(x_1^2+\cdots+x_p^2)(y_1^2+\cdots+y_n^2)=z_1^2+\cdots+z_n^2$$

if and only if $p \leqq 8\alpha+2^\beta$. The forms z_i may always be chosen to be real.

C. C. MacDuffee (Madison, Wis.).

E04-3 (12, 585a)

Rédei, L. Ein Satz über quadratische Formen. Math. Ann. **122**, 340–342 (1950).

Let K be a formally real field and R a subring of K which is a principal ideal ring and which contains the unit element 1 of K. Let $f(x)=\sum a_{ij}x_ix_j$ $(i, j=1, \cdots, n)$ be a positive definite form with coefficients in K, and $n\geqq 2$. If $c_1, \cdots, c_n$ are elements of K, set $f(c, x)=\sum a_{ij}c_ix_j$. If the c_i are not all zero, then $\bar{f}(x)=f(c)f(x)-f^2(c, x)$ is equivalent to a positive definite quadratic form in $n-1$ indeterminates. If the c_i are relatively prime elements of R, there exists a homogeneous linear transformation with coefficients in R and of determinant 1, which transforms $\bar{f}(x)$ into a form containing $n-1$ indeterminates. If D is the determinant of $f(x)$, the determinant of the transformed form differs from $Df^{n-2}(c)$ by at most a factor which is a unit of R. *N. H. McCoy.*

Referred to in E04-11.

E04-4 (13, 815j)

Springer, Tonny Albert. Sur les formes quadratiques d'indice zéro. C. R. Acad. Sci. Paris **234**, 1517–1519 (1952).

The author proves the following conjecture of E. Witt [J. Reine Angew. Math. **176**, 31–44 (1937)]: Let f be a quadratic form over an arbitrary field K with characteristic $\neq 2$. If f has no zeros in K, then it has no zeros in any algebraic extension L of K of odd degree. Using Witt's results [loc. cit.] in conjunction with this, the author obtains the companion theorem: If the forms f and g are not equivalent over K, then they are not equivalent over L.

W. H. Durfee (Washington, D. C.).

E04-5 (15, 500a)

Kaplansky, Irving. Quadratic forms. J. Math. Soc. Japan **5**, 200–207 (1953).

Soit K un corps de caractéristique $\neq 2$ et qui ne soit pas réel au sens d'Artin-Schreier. Soient A l'indice du groupe multiplicatif $K^{(2)}$ des carrés des éléments non-nuls de K dans celui K^* des éléments non-nuls de K et soit C le plus petit entier n tel que toute forme quadratique de $n+1$ variables effectives et à coefficients dans K représente 0 d'une manière non-triviale. L'auteur émet l'hypothèse que $C\leqq A$ et la démontre dans les deux cas suivants: (1) $A\leqq 8$; (2) -1 est la somme d'au plus 4 carrés dans K. Dans une lettre personnelle, l'auteur a fait connaître aù référent que M. Kneser lui a signalé la démonstration simple suivante de son hypothèse: $f=\sum_{i=1}^n a_ix_i^2$ étant une forme quadratique dans K, soit f_r la somme de ses $r\leqq n$ premiers termes et soit M_r l'ensemble des valeurs de f_r quand les variables parcourent indépendemment K. Si $M_r=M_{r+1}$, on a, au sens de l'addition des sous-ensembles de K, $M_r+a_{r+1}K^{(2)}=M_r$, d'où, par induction, $M_r=M_r+a_r(K^{(2)}+K^{(2)}+\cdots+K^{(2)})$, quelque soit le nombre de termes $K^{(2)}$. Or K n'étant pas réel, tout $a \in K$ est une somme de carrés, donc appartient à la somme d'un certain nombre de $K^{(2)}$, d'où $M_r=M_r+a_{r+1}K=K$. Mais tout M_r est la réunion de $\{0\}$ et d'un certain nombre de classes (mod $K^{(2)}$) dans le groupe multiplicatif K^*, et, ainsi, le nombre des M_r distincts ne dépasse pas, puisque $M_r\subseteq M_{r+1}$, le nombre A de ces classes; ainsi, on a $M_r=K$ pour un $r\leqq A$, d'où résulte facilement $C\leqq A$. L'article contient encore le résultat suivant: si K n'admet, à l'isomorphie près, qu'une seule algèbre de quaternions, on a $C\leqq 4$. *M. Krasner.*

Referred to in D72-9, E04-10.

E04-6 (15, 936c)

Jones, Burton W., and Marsh, Donald. Automorphs of quadratic forms. Duke Math. J. **21**, 179–193 (1954).

A étant la matrice d'une forme quadratique non-dégénérée (c'est donc une matrice symétrique) à coefficients dans un corps F de caractéristique $\neq 2$, un procédé explicite de construction de tous les automorphes T de A (autrement dit, de toutes les matrices telles que $T'AT=A$, où T' est la transposée de T), exprimables comme polynômes à coefficients dans F en $L=T-T^{-1}$, est donné. La construction est définie quand on se donne une matrice antisymétrique R de même ordre que A et deux polynômes $h_1(x)$, $h_2(x) \in F[x]$ satisfaisant à certaines conditions explicites, qui ne font intervenir que la structure matricielle de A. Mais un même automorphe de A peut s'obtenir, par cette construction, à partir des R, h_1 et h_2 différents. En vue d'obtenir chaque automorphe T une seule fois, on normalise cette construction en imposant la condition $L=T-T^{-1}=RA/d$, où d est le déterminant de A, mais cette normalisation s'exprime d'une manière peu explicite en termes des R, h_1, h_2.

La forme des automorphes T tels que $L=0$ (autrement dit, tels que $T^2=I$) est également déterminée, ainsi que les conditions, auxquelles A doit satisfaire pour posséder de tels automorphes; et, dans le cas, où F est le corps rationnel, les conditions nécessaires et suffisantes sont données pour que A possède un tel automorphe à éléments entiers. Comme application, tous les automorphes à éléments entiers rationnels d'une forme quadratique ternaire à coefficients entiers sont determinés. *M. Krasner* (Paris).

E04-7 (16, 667b)

Witt, Ernst. Über eine Invariante quadratischer Formen mod 2. J. Reine Angew. Math. **193**, 119–120 (1954).

The invariant Δ mod $(\gamma^2+\gamma)$ [same J. **183**, 148–167 (1941); MR **4**, 237] of a quadratic form $\sum_{i=1}^{2m} a_ix_i^2+\sum_{i<k} a_{ik}x_ix_k$ in a field K of characteristic 2 is expressed as a rational function of the coefficients and a new and very simple proof of its invariance is given. For this purpose the author considers the field K as a residue field mod 2 in a domain of integrity of characteristic 0. He puts $A=(\alpha_{ik})$ with $\alpha_{ii}=2a_i$, $\alpha_{ik}=\alpha_{ki}=a_{ik}$ and $A^*=(\alpha^*_{ik})$ with $\alpha^*_{ii}=0$, $\alpha^*_{ik}=-\alpha^*_{ki}=a_{ik}$. Then Δ is given by $(-1)^m|A|\,|A^*|^{-1}=1+4\Delta$. *C. Arf.*

Citations: MR 4, 237f = E04-1.

E04-8 (16, 667c)

Klingenberg, Wilhelm, und Witt, Ernst. Über die Arfsche Invariante quadratischer Formen mod 2. J. Reine Angew. Math. **193**, 121–122 (1954).

The authors consider the quadratic form $\mathbf{x}'A\mathbf{x}$ in a field of characteristic 2. Assuming that $|A+A'|\neq 0$, a choice of the variables can be made in such a way that the matrices $A+A'$ and A assume the forms

$$\begin{pmatrix} 0 & E \\ E & 0 \end{pmatrix} \quad\text{and}\quad \begin{pmatrix} P & E \\ 0 & Q \end{pmatrix}.$$

Using the usual rules for the computing of traces, it is shown that Tr (PQ) mod $(\gamma^2+\gamma)$ is invariant with respect to the substitutions of the symplectic group. This invariant Tr (PQ) mod $(\gamma^2+\gamma)$ is the same as the one given by Arf [same J. **183**, 148–167 (1941); MR **4**, 237]. *C. Arf.*

Citations: MR 4, 237f = E04-1.

E04-9 (16, 667d)

Kneser, Martin. Bestimmung des Zentrums der Cliffordschen Algebren einer quadratischen Form über einem Körper der Charakteristik 2. J. Reine Angew. Math. **193**, 123–125 (1954).

The Clifford Algebra $\mathfrak{A}$ of a quadratic form $q(\mathbf{x})$ in a field K of characteristic 2 is defined independently of the choice of the variables. The products uv of the usual generators of $\mathfrak{A}$ generate a subalgebra the center of which is shown to be the residue ring $K[x]/(x^2+x+\Delta)$, where Δ mod $(\gamma^2+\gamma)$ is the invariant of the form $q(\mathbf{x})$ given by Arf [same J. **183**, 148–167 (1941); MR **4**, 237]. Thus an elegant proof of the invariance of Δ mod $(\gamma^2+\gamma)$ is given. *C. Arf* (Istanbul).

Citations: MR 4, 237f = E04-1.

E04-10 (16, 669e)

Tsuzuku, Tosirô. On a conjecture of Kaplansky on quadratic forms. J. Math. Soc. Japan 6, 325–331 (1954).

Let F be a field of characteristic different from 2 in which -1 is a sum of squares. Let A denote the order of the multiplicative group of F modulo squares. Let B denote the smallest integer such that -1 is a sum of B squares. Let C denote the smallest integer such that every quadratic form in $C+1$ variables is a null form. The reviewer [same J. **5**, 200–207 (1953); MR **15**, 500] conjectured $C\leqq A$ and proved it for $B\leqq 4$. In the review a proof of the conjecture by M. Kneser is given. Tsuzuku's method gives the sharper result that C is strictly smaller than A for $B>4$. For instance, $C\leqq 23A/32$ for $B=8$, and $C\leqq 301A/512$ for $B=16$. [Bibliographical note. H. Kneser [Jber. Deutsch. Math. Verein. **44**, 143–146 (1934)] proved among other things that B is a multiple of 16 if it is larger than 8. It is not known whether B can actually be larger than 4.]

I. Kaplansky (Los Angeles, Calif.).

Citations: MR 15, 500a = E04-5.
Referred to in D72-9, E04-20.

E04-11 (17, 820a)

van der Blij, F. A theorem on positive matrices. Nederl. Akad. Wetensch. Proc. Ser. A. **59**=Indag. Math. **18** (1956), 108–109.

An elementary matric proof is given of the following generalization of a result of Rédei [Math. Ann. **122** (1950), 340–342; MR **12**, 585]. Let K be a formally real field and let R be a principal-ideal subring of integral elements of K. If S is a positive symmetric n-by-n matrix over K and C is an integral n-by-m matrix $(n\geqq m)$ whose maximal minors are coprime, then $G=S-SC(C'SC)^{-1}C'S$ has rank $n-m$ and there is an integral unimodular transformation which replaces $x'Gx$ by a form in $n-m$ variables whose determinant is $|S|\cdot|C'SC|^{-1}$. *M. F. Smiley.*

Citations: MR 12, 585a = E04-3.

E04-12 (20# 1661)

Buzby, B.; and Whaples, G. Quadratic forms over arbitrary fields. Proc. Amer. Math. Soc. **9** (1958), 335–339; erratum, **10** (1959), 174.

The authors give another proof of a well-known theorem of E. Witt [J. Reine Angew. Math. **176** (1936), 31–44] to the effect that two binary or ternary quadratic forms over an arbitrary field (of characteristic not two) are equivalent if and only if they have the same determinant and Hasse invariant. The main idea of simplifying the proof is to replace the theory of simple algebras by the cohomology theory of finite groups.

Y. Kawada (Tokyo)

E04-13 (21# 66)

Jacobson, N. Composition algebras and their automorphisms. Rend. Circ. Mat. Palermo (2) **7** (1958), 55–80.

The problem of finding the quadratic forms permitting composition (Hurwitz's problem) and finding the algebras $\mathfrak{C}$ arising from such forms (these are called composition algebras) is solved completely even though it has been solved elsewhere [see Kaplansky, Proc. Amer. Math. Soc. **4** (1953), 956–960; MR **15**, 596] because the analysis of the composition algebras given here is essential to the study of the automorphisms. The study of the automorphisms is the main purpose of the paper. Following is a summary of what appear to be the main results obtained.

A "split composition algebra" is one which contains zero divisors, and it is proved that any two split composition algebras of the same dimension are isomorphic. The split algebras are then determined. An automorphism τ is called a reflection if $\tau^2=1$ and $\tau\neq 1$. A reflection is called split if the subalgebra $\mathfrak{B}$ of elements fixed by τ is split. If $\mathfrak{C}$ is a quaternion or Cayley algebra then every automorphism of $\mathfrak{C}$ is a product of reflections which may be taken to be split if $\mathfrak{C}$ is split Cayley; every automorphism is inner and is a rotation in $\mathfrak{C}$ (relative to N). If G is the automorphism group of $\mathfrak{C}$ and $\mathfrak{B}$ a subalgebra of $\mathfrak{C}$ then $G_{\mathfrak{B}}$, the Galois group of $\mathfrak{C}$ over $\mathfrak{B}$ is determined for several choices of $\mathfrak{C}$ and $\mathfrak{B}$. When $\mathfrak{C}$ is split Cayley, G is a simple group. For $\mathfrak{C}$ any composition algebra, the only invariant subspaces of $\mathfrak{C}$ relative to G are $\mathfrak{C}$, 0, $\Phi 1$ and $\mathfrak{C}_0$, where Φ is the base field of $\mathfrak{C}$ and $\mathfrak{C}_0$ is the subspace of elements orthogonal to 1. Special properties are obtained by specializing Φ. The following question is raised: Is the group of automorphisms of any Cayley division algebra over an algebraic number field Φ simple? It is known that this is not true over an arbitrary field. The answer is yes if Φ is the field of real numbers. To prove this the author proves a more general result which may be useful in answering the above question. *L. A. Kokoris* (Chicago, Ill.)

E04-14 (21# 7184)

Springer, T. A. On the equivalence of quadratic forms. Nederl. Akad. Wetensch. Proc. Ser. A **62**=Indag. Math. **21** (1959), 241–253.

The author describes the Hasse invariant of a quadratic form by a new homological-algebraic method. Let Q be a quadratic form over a field K. He shows first that there is a 1-1 correspondence between the set of equivalence classes, over K, of forms which become equivalent to Q in an extension field L/K, and the noncommutative 1-cohomology classes of the orthogonal group of Q (in L), over the Galois group of L/K. Using the Clifford algebra he derives from this the Hasse invariant.

By the same methods he handles nondefective quadratic forms over fields of characteristic 2, obtaining results of C. Arf [Rev. Fac. Sci. Univ. Istanbul Sér. A **8** (1943), 297–327; MR **7**, 359, 621].

G. Whaples (Bloomington, Ind.)

Citations: MR 7, 359a = E08-4.

E04-15 (22# 5612)

Malyšev, A. V. Quadratic forms in an arbitrary field. A generalization of Pall's theorem. Uspehi Mat. Nauk **15** (1960), no. 3 (93), 167–172. (Russian)

Let P be a field of characteristic different from 2, and let $f=f(x_1,\cdots,x_n)$ and $g=g(y_1,\cdots,y_m)$ be quadratic forms with matrices A and B, of ranks r and s respectively, and having entries in P. It is shown that there exists a rank q representation of g by f (i.e., a matrix T with entries in P and rank q, such that $T'AT=B$) if and only if the following conditions are satisfied: $s\leqq q\leqq m$ and there is a form $h=h(z_1,\cdots,z_l)$ such that f is equivalent over P to

$$g+\sum_{i\leqq(q-s)-(n-r)}2u_iv_i+h,$$

where it is supposed that the sets of variables $(y_1,\cdots,y_m)$, $(u_1,\cdots,u_k,v_1,\cdots,v_k)$ and $(z_1,\cdots,z_l)$ are disjoint. This theorem reduces to a result of G. Pall's [see Theorem 5, p. 11, of B. W. Jones' *Arithmetic theory of quadratic forms*, Math. Assoc. of America, Buffalo, N.Y., 1950; MR **12**, 244] in case $n=r$, $m=s=q$, and in case $q=m$, $s=0$ gives conditions in order that f be an m-zero form [loc. cit., p. 50, Theorem 18].

W. J. LeVeque (Ann Arbor, Mich.)

Citations: MR 12, 244a = E02-3.

E04-16 **(22# 8023)**

Nakamura, Yoshio. On Witt ring of quadratic forms. J. Math. Soc. Japan **12** (1960), 187–191.

Let k be a commutative field of characteristic $\neq 2$. If R is a vector space over k with a regular symmetric bilinear form, R permits direct decompositions $R = R_0 \oplus N_1 \oplus N_2 \oplus \cdots$ with the following properties: R_0 and the N_i are mutually orthogonal; the form is definite in R_0; each N_i is a two-space spanned by two isotropic vectors with the scalar product 1. The "kernel" R_0 of R is uniquely determined up to isomorphisms. A "type" over k is the set of all the vector spaces over k whose kernels are isomorphic to the same R_0. Define type R + type S = type $(R \oplus S)$; type $R \cdot$ type S = type of the Kronecker (= tensor) product of R and S. The types over k then form a commutative ring, the Witt ring over k; cf. E. Witt, J. Reine Angew. Math. **176** (1936), 31–44. The author determines the structure of this ring in the following cases: (i) k is finite; (ii) k is complete with respect to a discrete non-archimedian valuation whose residue class field is finite and has a characteristic $\neq 2$; (iii) k is algebraic over the rational field. *P. Scherk* (Toronto)

E04-17 **(25# 3942)**

Springer, T. A.
Note on quadratic forms in characteristic 2.
Nieuw Arch. Wisk. (3) **10** (1962), 1–10.

Let K be a commutative field with arbitrary characteristic and E a vector space over K of dimension $2m$. Generally, if $f(x, y)$ is a bilinear function on $E \times E$, then

$$\bar{f}(x_1 \wedge x_2, y_1 \wedge y_2) = f(x_1, y_1)f(x_2, y_2) - f(x_1, y_2)f(x_2, y_1)$$

determines a bilinear function on the space $F \times F$, where F is the space spanned by the bivectors $x \wedge y$ (the exterior product of x and y). Henceforth let f be a non-degenerate alternate form on E. There exists a unique element ω of F such that $f(x, y) = \bar{f}(x \wedge y, \omega)$. Furthermore, there are bilinear forms $g(x, y)$ on $E \times E$ such that $f(x, y) = g(x, y) - g(y, x)$. Put $\alpha(g) = \bar{g}(\omega, \omega)$. It is with the properties of this scalar that the present note is primarily concerned. For example, it is shown that if the matrices of f and g are A and B, respectively, then $\alpha(g) = \mathrm{tr}((BA^{-1})^{-2} - (BA^{-1})^3)$.

From now on assume that K is of characteristic 2. Let Q be a quadratic form and let $Q(x+y) - Q(x) - Q(y) = f(x, y)$. Choose a bilinear form $g(x, y)$ such that $g(x, x) = Q(x)$. Let (e_i) be a symplectic basis of E with respect to f, that is, $f(e_i, e_{m+j}) = 0$ if $|i-j| \neq m$, $f(e_i, e_{m+i}) = 1$ $(1 \leqq i \leqq m)$. It is shown that $\alpha(g) = \Delta(Q) + \wp(\lambda)$, where $\Delta(Q) = \sum_{i=1}^m Q(e_i)Q(e_{m+i})$, $\lambda = \sum_{i=1}^m g(e_i, e_{m+i})$ and $\wp(\lambda) = \lambda + \lambda$. This gives a new proof of the theorem of C. Arf [J. Reine Angew. Math. **183** (1941), 148–167; MR **4**, 237]. Further applications of the preceding results include a description of the Dickson invariant of an orthogonal transformation of Q [see J. Dieudonné, *La géométrie des groupes classiques*, Springer, Berlin, 1955; MR **17**, 236], and a new proof of a congruence relation for quadratic forms due to the reviewer [Comm. Math. Helv. **33** (1959), 34–37; MR **20** #6999]. *W. Ledermann* (Brighton)

Citations: MR 4, 237f = E04-1; MR 17, 236a = E56-8; MR 20# 6999 = E12-64.

E04-18 **(26# 175)**

Delzant, Antoine
Définition des classes de Stiefel-Whitney d'un module quadratique sur un corps de caractéristique différente de 2.
C. R. Acad. Sci. Paris **255** (1962), 1366–1368.

Let A be a field of characteristic not two. Then the set of equivalence classes of non-degenerate quadratic forms over A can be embedded in a ring Q (addition is direct sum and multiplication is tensor product of the vector spaces on which the forms are defined). The ring Q is generated by the multiplicative group D of one-dimensional forms. But D is also isomorphic to $H^1(G, Z/2Z)$, where G is the Galois group of the separable closure of A, acting trivially on $Z/2Z$, the integers mod 2. By a procedure of Grothendieck's, this induces mappings $w^i : Q \to H^i(G, Z/2Z)$ satisfying $w^n(q+q') = \sum_{i+j=n} w^i(q)w^j(q')$, where the product on the right is cup product. In particular, w^1 is the discriminant; w^2 is also described explicitly. By translating classical results, if A is a P-adic field, then a quadratic form is characterized by its rank and w^1 and w^2. Over the reals, a form is characterized its rank and the w^i. Hence the same will hold over an algebraic number field. *D. Zelinsky* (Evanston, Ill.)

E04-19 **(26# 3673)**

Kurepa, Svetozar
Note on quadratic forms.
Univ. Beograd. Publ. Elektrotehn. Fak. Ser. Mat. Fiz. No. 97–99 (1963), 7–12.

In this note the well-known Jacobi formulae are given for the reduction of a quadratic form over the field of reals or complex numbers to a diagonal form in terms of the principal minors on the assumption that none of these is zero. To do this, a scalar product with some claim to novelty is introduced.

Burton W. Jones (Boulder, Colo.)

E04-20 **(29# 73)**

Lenz, Hanfried
Einige Ungleichungen aus der Algebra der quadratischen Formen.
Arch. Math. **14** (1963), 373–382.

In this paper the author improves some inequalities of Tsuzuku [J. Math. Soc. Japan **6** (1954), 325–331; MR **16**, 669]. Let φ denote a quadratic form in n variables, of non-zero determinant over a non-formally real field K of characteristic different from 2. Let s denote the least number r such that -1 is the sum of r squares in K and t is determined by $2^t \leqq s < 2^{t+1}$. The author denotes by φ^k the k-fold direct sum of φ with itself, $E(\varphi)$ the vector space determined by φ and $G(\varphi)$ the set of forms φ for which $\varphi(x) \neq 0$ with x in $E(\varphi)$. $Q(\varphi)$ denotes the set of non-zero square classes represented by φ, $q(\varphi)$ is the weight of $Q(\varphi)$ and $G_k = ((1)^k)$.

Two of the theorems proved by the author are the following. Theorem 2: Let k be one of the numbers 1, 2, 4, 8 and $a \notin G_k$, $-a \in G_s$ and $s > k$. Then either $(1, a)^k$ is a null form or $q((1, a)^k) \geqq 4q_k$, where q_k is the weight of $Q((1)^k)$. Theorem 3: Let e be one of the numbers 0, 1, 2, 3, $f = 2^e$ and $a \in G_f$. Then $q(1, a) \geqq 2^{t-e}$.

Burton W. Jones (Boulder, Colo.)

Citations: MR 16, 669e = E04-10.
Referred to in E04-22.

E04-21 **(29# 3439)**

Pall, G.
Simultaneous representation by adjoint quadratic forms.
Acta Arith. **9** (1964), 271–284.

Let φ be an n-ary quadratic form with real coefficients and φ' its adjoint form, with matrices $A = (a_{ij})$ and $A' = (a_{ij}')$, respectively. Two real numbers m and m' are said to be simultaneously represented by φ and φ' if there exist integers x_i, z_i' $(i = 1, 2, \cdots, n)$ such that

$m = \sum a_{ij}x_ix_j, \qquad m' = \sum a_{ij}'z_i'z_j', \qquad 0 = \sum x_iz_i',$

where the sums are over all i and j. The pair of column vectors $x = (x_i)$ and $z' = (z_i')$ is called a simultaneous representation, and the representation is primitive if each vector is.

An algorithm is given which produces all the simultaneous representations of given m and m' by φ and φ', each set of primitive representations (a set being an aggregate Wx, and $W'z'$, W running over the unimodular automorphs of φ) being associated with a unique class of quadratic forms in $n-2$ variables and a certain set of solutions of certain quadratic congruences modulo m and m'. In particular there is Theorem 6. Every set of simultaneous and primitive representations of nonzero numbers m and m' by the real nonsingular n-ary quadratic form φ and its adjoint φ' is associated with a unique class of matrices G of order $n-2$ and, if we select a particular matrix G in this class, with a unique G-set. One such set of representations obtains for every matrix G and accompanying G-set for which a certain matrix B is equivalent to the matrix of φ. *Burton W. Jones* (San Jose)

E04-22 (32# 2408)

Pfister, Albrecht

Multiplikative quadratische Formen.

Arch. Math. **16** (1965), 363–370.

The author recently [J. London Math. Soc. **40** (1965), 159–165; MR **31** #169] obtained important results concerning the composition of sums of squares of elements in a given field F, showing, in particular, that the sums of $n = 2^m$ squares form a group. Now all quadratic forms φ are determined which allow composition. They are exactly all the null forms (i.e., forms which represent zero) and the forms equivalent to the Kronecker product $(1, a_1) \times \cdots \times (1, a_k)$, where $\varphi = (b_1, \cdots, b_n)$ denotes a form equivalent to the diagonal form $\sum b_ix_i^2$. Here $a_i \neq 0$; for $k=0$, the form is equivalent to (1). The latter forms are even strongly multiplicative, i.e., the composition is not only accomplished by rational functions, but even by polynomials linear in the components of one of the vectors. They include all the special null forms equivalent to $(1, -1)^i$, $i > 0$. Multiplicative forms are also characterized by the fact that the numbers $\neq 0$ represented by them, for all extension fields of F, form a group. The fact that the forms $(1)^{2^k}$ are multiplicative implies that in a not formally real field F the minimum number of terms in $\sum x_i^2 = -1$ is a power of 2. The author generalizes a result of Lenz [Arch. Math. **14** (1963), 373–382; MR **29** #73] concerning the Witt group of F. The proofs make use of generalizations of several results of Cassels [Acta Arith. **9** (1964), 79–82; MR **29** #95].

O. Taussky-Todd (Pasadena, Calif.)

Citations: MR 29# 73 = E04-20; MR 29# 95 = E24-98; MR 31# 169 = E24-101.

Referred to in E04-24, E04-25, E24-108.

E04-23 (33# 7304)

Lenz, Hanfried

Elementare Bemerkungen zur Beschreibung quadratischer Formen durch Invarianten.

Abh. Math. Sem. Univ. Hamburg **27** (1964), 39–43.

Two quadratic forms over a field k of characteristic $\neq 2$ are in the same Witt class if the metric space of one of them, plus finitely many isotopic planes, is isometric to that of the other [E. Witt, J. Reine Angew. Math. **176** (1936), 31–44]. The author defines an invariant of equivalence classes of quadratic forms over k in terms of Witt class and determinant, shows that the norm residue symbol can be expressed in terms of this invariant, and exhibits some of its conveniences. *G. Whaples* (Amherst, Mass.)

E04-24 (34# 169)

Pfister, Albrecht

Quadratische Formen in beliebigen Körpern.

Invent. Math. **1** (1966), 116–132.

Die Arbeit enthält interessante Sätze über die Struktur des Wittschen Ringes. Es sei W dieser Ring, k^* die multiplikative Gruppe des zugrunde liegenden kommutativen Körpers k (char$(k) \neq 2$), G_1 die Menge der Quadrate in k^*. Es gelten dann u.a. folgende Sätze: Räume ungerader Dimension (genauer, durch solche Räume bestimmte Ähnlichkeitsklassen) sind nie Nullteiler in W. W ist genau dann nullteilerfrei, wenn entweder $W \cong Z/2Z$ und $k^* = G_1$ (z.B. k der Körper der komplexen Zahlen) oder $W \cong Z$, $k^* = -G_1 \cup G_1$, $-G_1 \cap G_1 = \varnothing$ und k formal reell ist (z.B. der Körper der reellen Zahlen). Es sei M das Ideal von W definiert durch die Räume gerader Dimension; ist dann k nicht formal reell so gilt: M ist das Nilradikal von W; M ist das einzige Primideal von W; Ringelemente die nicht in M liegen (Räume ungerader Dimension) sind Einheiten von W. (Man kennt also sämtliche Nullteiler und Einheiten von W.) Ähnliche Resultate werden für den formal reellen Fall aufgestellt, wobei die Torsionselemente der abelschen Gruppe W^+ eine entscheidende Rolle spielen. Bedeutsam für sämtliche Untersuchungen sind die vom Autor studierten "stark multiplikativen" Formen [J. London Math. Soc. **40** (1965), 159–165; MR **31** #169; Arch. Math. **16** (1965), 363–370; MR **32** #2408]. *H. Gross* (Zürich)

Citations: MR 31# 169 = E24-101; MR 32# 2408 = E04-22.

Referred to in E04-25, E04-27, E04-36, E24-105, E24-125.

E04-25 (36# 110)

Pfister, Albrecht

Multiplikative quadratische Formen.

Algebraische Zahlentheorie (Ber. Tagung Math. Forschungsinst. Oberwolfach, 1964), pp. 229–238. Bibliographisches Institut Mannheim, Mannheim, 1967.

This is a report with proofs on the author's recent achievements concerning multiplicative quadratic forms (see the author's papers in J. London Math. Soc. **40** (1965), 159–165 [MR **31** #169]; Arch. Math. **16** (1965), 363–370 [MR **32** #2408] and, in the meantime, in Invent. Math. **1** (1966), 116–132 [MR **34** #169]) with their application to the minimum s for which $-1 = \sum_1^s x_i^2$, $x_i \in K$, K a given field, and to the composition of sums of 2^k squares. These results are based on generalizations of theorems by Cassels on sums of squares of rational functions.

O. Taussky-Todd (Pasadena, Calif.)

Citations: MR 31# 169 = E24-101; MR 32# 2408 = E04-22; MR 34# 169 = E04-24.

E04-26 (35# 5389)

Fröhlich, A.

Quadratic forms "à la" local theory.

Proc. Cambridge Philos. Soc. **63** (1967), 579–586.

The author defines a Hilbert field to be a field K with characteristic $\neq 2$ satisfying the conditions (a) $K^\times \neq K^{\times 2}$, and (b) for any quadratic extension L/K, the group index $[K^\times : \mathrm{Norm}_{L/K}(L^\times)] = 2$. A complete local field is a Hilbert field. But there are others, for instance the maximal algebraic extension of a finite algebraic number field which is contained in its $\mathfrak{p}$-adic completion for some prime ideal $\mathfrak{p}$. It is proved (by elementary means) that a Hilbert field always belongs to one of two types: (A) K is ordered, and the positive elements coincide with the squares, (B) there exists, up to isometry, exactly one quaternary anisotropic quadratic form with coefficients in K. Conversely, every field K satisfying either (A) or (B) is a Hilbert field. The proof of this theorem yields at the same time the classification of quadratic forms which is well known in the local case. In other words, the local classification theory is extended to Hilbert fields. *M. Eichler* (Basel)

Referred to in E08-40.

E04-27 (39# 2793)

Scharlau, Winfried

Zur Pfisterschen Theorie der quadratischen Formen.

Invent. Math. **6** (1969), 327–328.

Es wird ein neuer, kurzer und elementarer Beweis dafür gegeben, daß der Torsionsteil des Witt-Ringes $W(K)$ der nicht degenerierten quadratischen Formen eines Körpers K keine Elemente $\neq 0$ von ungerader Ordnung enthält [A. Pfister, Invent. Math. **1** (1966), 116–132; MR **34** #169]. *H. Gross* (Zürich)

Citations: MR 34# 169 = E04-24.

E04-28 (39# 6823)

Gross, Herbert

Der Euklidische Defekt bei quadratischen Räumen.

Math. Ann. **180** (1969), 95–137.

The author deals chiefly with symmetric forms over a commutative field: $\phi: E\times E\to k$. A space (E, ϕ) is called Euclidean if (E, ϕ) is semi-simple and is spanned by an orthogonal basis. For a given semi-simple space (E, ϕ), its Euclidean defect $d(E)$ is defined to be $\min\{\dim E/F: F\subset E, F \text{ Euclidean}\}$. A number of results are proved of which the following is typical: If (E, ϕ) is Euclidean and anisotropic, then E has no subspace F of dimension between 1 and $\aleph_0$, inclusive.

Applications are made to the isomorphism problem. Examples are given, as well as a list of open problems.

Burton W. Jones (Boulder, Colo.)

E04-29 (39# 6996)

Connors, Edward A.

The structure of O'/Ω over local fields of characteristic 2.

Proc. Amer. Math. Soc. **22** (1969), 596–599.

Let E be a nondefective quadratic space over a field of characteristic 2, $O(E)$ the orthogonal group of E, $O^+(E)$ the group of rotations, $\Omega(E)$ the commutator subgroup of $O(E)$, and $O'(E)$ the spinorial kernel. The author proves that $O'=\Omega$ if the underlying field is local. (This result is well known if E is isotropic.) *H. Gross* (Zürich)

E04-30 (39# 7493)

Schwabhäuser, Wolfram

The connection between two geometrical axioms of H. N. Gupta.

Proc. Amer. Math. Soc. **22** (1969), 233–234.

H. N. Gupta ["On some axioms in foundations of Cartesian spaces", Canad. Math. Bull., to appear]* raised a question which is equivalent to the following: In n-dimensional Cartesian space over an ordered field F, let (b) be the property: Every plane $(n-1)$-space through the origin intersects every sphere (with equation in F) about the origin. Does (b) involve that every positive element in F is a square? The author answers in the negative by showing that (b) holds if F is the field Q of rationals and $n\geqq 5$. This is a consequence of H. Hasse's theorem [J. Reine Angew. Math. **152** (1923), 129–148] that for $n\geqq 4$ every n-ary positive definite quadratic form over Q represents every positive rational number.

A. Heyting (Amsterdam)

E04-31 (41# 5465)

Milnor, John

Algebraic K-theory and quadratic forms.

Invent. Math. **9** (1969/70), 318–344.

The functors K_0, K_1, and K_2 of algebraic K-theory take the following values on a field F: $\dim: K_0F\cong \mathbf{Z}$; $\det: K_1F\cong \dot F$; and $K_2F=\dot F\otimes_{\mathbf{Z}}\dot F/R$, where R is the group generated by all $a\otimes b$ for which $a+b=1$. The first two results are trivial, but this elementary description of K_2F results from a difficult theorem of H. Matsumoto [Ann. Sci. École Norm. Sup. (4) **2** (1969), 1–62; MR **39** #1566].

The author observed that these groups reduced mod 2 are closely related to the Witt ring WF of quadratic forms over F (of characteristic $\neq 2$). More precisely, if I is the ideal of elements of even rank in WF, then $WF/I\cong \mathbf{Z}/2\mathbf{Z}\cong K_0F/2K_0F$; $I/I^2\cong \dot F/\dot F^2\cong K_1F/2K_1F$; and there is an isomorphism $I^2/I^3\cong K_2F/2K_2F$.

The present paper develops some elegant generalizations of the ideas underlying this observation.

To begin with, the author introduces the ring $K_*F=T(\dot F)/J=\bigoplus_{n\geq 0}K_nF$, where $T(\dot F)$ denotes the tensor algebra (over $\mathbf{Z}$) of $\dot F$ and where J is the (homogeneous) ideal generated by R. Despite its rather naive appearance this ring K_*F turns out to be a fairly tractable vehicle for some interesting arithmetic information about F.

Results of R. Steinberg, C. Moore and J. Tate on K_2 yield simple calculations of K_*F when F is finite, locally compact, and $\mathbf{Q}$, respectively.

Other general results include the following: (1) F is not formally real if and only if all elements of positive degree in K_*F are nilpotent. (2) If F has a discrete valuation with residue class field $\bar F$ there are canonical epimorphisms $\partial: K_nF\to K_{n-1}\bar F$. (3) Let t be an indeterminate, and for each monic irreducible polynomial π in $F[t]$, let $\partial_\pi: K_nF(t)\to K_{n-1}F[t]/(\pi)$ be as in (2). Then the sequence $0\to K_nF\to K_nF(t)\overset{(\partial_\pi)}{\to}\bigoplus_\pi K_{n-1}F[t]/(\pi)\to 0$; is split exact. The proof of this is a mild generalization of the case $n=2$ due to Tate.

Putting $k_nF=K_nF/2K_nF$ and $k_\pi F=\prod_{n\geq 0}k_nF$, the author next shows that Delzant's procedure for defining Stiefel-Whitney classes of quadratic modules works equally well in defining a homomorphism from WF to the group of units of $k_\pi F$. (We assume now that char $F\neq 2$.)

In connection with the observation discussed above, the author now constructs a canonical epimorphism $S: k_*F\to \operatorname{gr} WF=\bigoplus_{n\geq 0}I^n/I^{n+1}$. He poses the following conjectures: (I_n) S_n is an isomorphism; (II) $\bigcap_{n\geq 0}I^n=0$.

Using the Stiefel-Whitney invariant, he establishes (I_n) in case the map $k_nF\to k_tF$, $x\mapsto \varepsilon^{t-n}x$, is injective, where $t=2^{n-1}$ and where ε is the class of $-1\in\dot F$ in k_1F. This is automatic for $n=1, 2$ since $t=n$ in those cases.

Using a computation by Tate of k_*F for F a global field (a computation included as an appendix to the present paper), the conjectures are verified for global fields and their direct limits. They are also confirmed whenever Card $k_2F\leq 2$; this applies to finite and locally compact fields.

A computation of $WF(t)$ analogous to that (discussed above) of $K_*F(t)$ further yields the conjectures for $F(t)$ whenever they hold for F.

A final section of the paper constructs a homomorphism $k_*F\to H^*(G, \mathbf{Z}/2\mathbf{Z})$, where G is the Galois group of the separable closure of F. This is shown to be an isomorphism for fields including those of arithmetic (locally compact and global). The author remarks that no examples are known for which it is not an isomorphism. *H. Bass* (New York)

Citations: MR 39# 1566 = E60-33.

Referred to in E04-36, E04-37.

E04-32 **(42# 1851)**

Lorenz, F.; Leicht, J.
Die Primideale des Wittschen Ringes.
Invent. Math. **10** (1970), 82–88.

This is a contribution to the study of the structure of the Witt ring W_K of quadratic forms over a field K of characteristic not 2. The authors determine the prime ideals of W_K. It turns out that for K a real field the minimal prime ideals correspond in a one-to-one fashion to the orderings of which K is capable. The authors determine furthermore the zero divisors of W_K [cf. the first author's *Quadratische Formen über Körpern*, Springer, Berlin, 1970].

H. Gross (Zürich)

Referred to in E02-20.

E04-33 **(42# 3647)**

Kneser, Martin
Witts Satz über quadratische Formen und die Erzeugung orthogonaler Gruppen durch Spiegelungen.
Math.-Phys. Semesterber. **17** (1970), 33–45.

The theorem of Witt referred to may be described as follows: Let K be any field of characteristic $\neq 2$ and let (x, y) be a symmetric bilinear form in a finite-dimensional vector space E over K. A motion is a non-singular linear operator of E that preserves (x, y). A figure is a set $f_1, \cdots, f_m$ of linearly independent vectors; two figures $f_1, \cdots, f_m$ and $g_1, \cdots, g_m$ are congruent if $(f_i, f_k) = (g_i, g_k)$ $(i, k = 1, \cdots, m)$. Witt's theorem states that two congruent figures can be mapped one into the other by means of a motion. The theorem can be proved in such a way that the motion is seen to be a product of at most $n+1$ reflections, where n is the dimension of E.

The author generalizes this theorem to include the case of characteristic 2. Using quadratic forms over any field and carefully analysing the special cases that may arise, he establishes the analogous theorem. In a final section he extends the results to quadratic forms over local rings, and uses them for new proofs of some number-theoretic results.

F. A. Sherk (Toronto, Ont.)

E04-34 **(42# 4490)**

Savithri, K.
Units of certain quadratic forms.
Duke Math. J. **36** (1969), 425–430.

The author denotes by k a finite field of characteristic not 2, and $k(x) = K$ the field of rational functions in x over k. $K_{1/x}$ is the completion of K at $1/x$. S is a non-degenerate symmetric matrix of order m over $K_{1/x}$ and U is called a unit of S if $U'SU = S$ and U has elements in $k[x]$ and the group of units of S is denoted by $\Gamma(S)$.

The first part of the paper is expository and the second a summary of the author's Ph.D. thesis. One of her two principal results is that $\Gamma(S)$ is finitely generated. She proposes to apply her results to the proof of the main theorem of Siegel on the representation theory of quadratic forms.

Burton W. Jones (Boulder, Colo.)

E04-35 **(43# 7403)**

Ryškov, S. S.
On the reduction theory of positive quadratic forms. (Russian)
Dokl. Akad. Nauk SSSR **198** (1971), 1028–1031.

The author announces several results comparing reduction domains for definite quadratic forms in n variables obtained by the different methods of Minkowski, Hermite and Venkov. He shows that these are essentially identical for $n=5$, confirming a conjecture of Minkowski (who also conjectured its truth for $n=6$). This leads to a simple reduction algorithm for $n=5$.

On the other hand, the quadratic form

$$x_1^2 + \cdots + x_{10}^2 + 4/3x_{11}^2 + 49x_{12}^2 + \cdots + 49x_n^2 + (x_1 + x_2 + 1/3x_3 + 2/3x_4 + \cdots + 2/3x_9 + 1/3x_{10})x_{11}$$

is Minkowski-reduced, but not Hermite or Venkov reduced.

{This article has appeared in English translation [Soviet Math. Dokl. **12** (1971), 946–950].}

G. Maxwell (Vancouver, B.C.)

E04-36 **(44# 238)**

Elman, Richard; Lam, T. Y.
Pfister forms and K-theory of fields.
Bull. Amer. Math. Soc. **77** (1971), 971–974.

Let F be a field with characteristic not equal to two. J. Milnor [Invent. Math. **9** (1969/70), 318–344; MR **41** #5465] associated with F a graded ring $K_*F = (K_nF)_{n \geq 0}$ which is the quotient ring of the tensor algebra

$$(Z, K_1F, K_1F \otimes K_1F, K_1F \otimes K_1F \otimes K_1F, \cdots)$$

by the ideal generated by all expressions $l(a) \otimes l(1-a)$, with $a \neq 0, 1$; here l denotes the logarithmic isomorphism between the multiplicative group F^* and the additive group K_1F. If we factor out the principal ideal $2K_*F$, we obtain the reduced graded algebra k_*F over $Z/2Z$, with $k_1F \cong F^*/F^{*2}$. These reduced algebraic k_n-groups are deeply related to A. Pfister's theory of multiplicative and strongly multiplicative forms [ibid. **1** (1966), 116–132; MR **34** #169]. Call $l(a_1) \cdots l(a_n) \in k_nF$ the generators of k_nF, and call the 2^n-dimensional diagonal quadratic forms $\{a_1, \cdots, a_n\} = \bigotimes_{i=1}^n (1, a_i)$ the n-fold Pfister forms. Denote by I the ideal in the Witt ring $W(F)$ generated by the even dimensional forms. For any positive integer n, Milnor defined the (unique) epimorphism $s_n(l(a_1) \cdots l(a_n)) = \{-a_1, \cdots, -a_n\} \pmod{I^{n+1}}$ from k_nF onto I^n/I^{n+1}. Moreover, he also showed that s_1 and s_2 are always bijective, and then asked whether s_n is always bijective. In the present paper, the authors announce a series of interesting results about the n-fold Pfister forms, the most striking of which is that the creature $l(a_1) \cdots l(a_n) \in k_nF$ is a complete invariant for the isometry class of an n-fold Pfister form $\{-a_1, \cdots, -a_n\}$. While obtaining this result, they also observe that two n-fold Pfister forms are isometric if and only if they are "chain-p-equivalent" (p for Pfister, presumably), a notion that is analogous to the classical chain-equivalence of Witt; the authors thereby, in theory, reduce the classification problem of n-fold Pfister forms to 2-fold forms. They then apply the general results about Pfister forms to give partial affirmative answers to Milnor's problem. In particular, some "stable" results are achieved; for instance, s_m is bijective for each $m \geq n$ if either (i) every element of k_nF is equal to a generator (e.g., when $|k_2F| \leq 4$; also, $n=3$ if F is a global field), or (ii) every 2^n-dimensional form is universal (e.g., non-real fields).

{The details have appeared elsewhere [Proc. Amer. Math. Soc. **31** (1972), 427–428].} *J. S. Hsia* (Columbus, Ohio)

The reference cited in the last two lines is incorrect. Details of the article are to appear in the Journal of Algebra.

Citations: MR 34# 169 = E04-24; MR 41# 5465 = E04-31.

E04-37 **(44# 6792)**

Elman, Richard; Lam, T. Y.
Determination of k_n $(n \geq 3)$ for global fields.
Proc. Amer. Math. Soc. **31** (1972), 427–428.

In the algebraic K-theory of a field F, the reduced groups k_nF were first defined by J. Milnor [Invent. Math. **9** (1969/70), 318–344; MR **41** #5465]. In that paper, the following theorem (due to Tate) was proved by the use of idèle groups, Kummer theory and reciprocity laws. Theorem: If F is a global field and $\{F_v\}$ is the family of real completions of F, then, for $n \geq 3$, $k_nF \to \bigoplus_v k_nF_v$ is an isomorphism. In the present article, a simple proof is given, based on a straightforward application of the Hasse-Minkowski theorem (a deep result).

J. S. Hsia (Columbus, Ohio)

Citations: MR 41# 5465 = E04-31.

E04-38 **(44# 6809)**

Broué, Michel; Enguehard, Michel
Une famille infinie de formes quadratiques entières; leurs groupes d'automorphismes.
C. R. Acad. Sci. Paris Sér. A-B **274** (1972), A19–A22.

The authors define a remarkable series of positive-definite quadratic forms in 2^d variables having "large" groups of automorphisms whose construction and structure recall those of Conway's group. In fact they define a lattice $U(d)$ in $\mathbf{Q}^{2^d}$ by means of certain chains of vector subspaces of $\mathbf{F}_2^{2^d}$; if $G(d)$ is the group of automorphisms of $U(d)$, considered as a permutation group of the set of minimal vectors of $U(d)$, then, for $d \geq 4$, $G(d)/\{-1, +1\}$ is an extension of an elementary abelian group of order 2^{2d} by the simple Chevalley group of type $\mathbf{D}_d$ over the field $\mathbf{F}_2$.

J. A. Todd (Cambridge, England)

E08 QUADRATIC FORMS OVER LOCAL RINGS AND FIELDS

See also reviews E02-3, E02-4, E02-11, E04-26, E12-87, E12-100, E12-110, E12-116, E20-14, E20-15, R52-22, T15-45, Z02-73, Z10-6.

E08-1 **(3, 260e)**

Jones, Burton W. An extension of a theorem of Witt. Bull. Amer. Math. Soc. **48**, 133–142 (1942).

If $\mathfrak{u}_1, \cdots, \mathfrak{u}_n$ is a set of vectors such that $\mathfrak{u}_i\mathfrak{u}_j = \mathfrak{u}_j\mathfrak{u}_i = a_{ij}$ $(i, j = 1, 2, \cdots, n)$, where the a_{ij} are elements of a field K, then all linear combinations of these vectors with coefficients in K constitute a vector space $\mathfrak{S} = <\mathfrak{u}_1, \cdots, \mathfrak{u}_n>$ over K. We assume that $|a_{ij}| \neq 0$, and make a like assumption for all spaces considered. The vector space $\mathfrak{S}$ may be made into a metric space by defining the inner product of two vectors $\sum x_i\mathfrak{u}_i$ and $\sum y_i\mathfrak{u}_i$ to be $\sum a_{ij}x_iy_j$. If $\mathfrak{C}$ is a nonsingular matrix, with coefficients in K, such that $(\mathfrak{u}_1, \cdots, \mathfrak{u}_n)\mathfrak{C} = (\mathfrak{v}_1, \cdots, \mathfrak{v}_n)$, then the space $\mathfrak{S}'$ defined by $\mathfrak{v}_1, \cdots, \mathfrak{v}_n$ is equivalent to $\mathfrak{S}$; in symbols, $\mathfrak{S} \cong \mathfrak{S}'$. The notation $\mathfrak{S} = \mathfrak{S}_1 + \mathfrak{S}_2$ is used to indicate that $\mathfrak{S}_1$ and $\mathfrak{S}_2$ are complementary orthogonal subspaces of $\mathfrak{S}$.

E. Witt [J. Reine Angew. Math. **176**, 31–44 (1936)] has shown that, if $\mathfrak{S}_1$, $\mathfrak{S}_2$ and $\mathfrak{S}_3$ are vector spaces over a field K of characteristic other than 2 and $\mathfrak{S}_2$ and $\mathfrak{S}_3$ are orthogonal to $\mathfrak{S}_1$, then $\mathfrak{S}_1 + \mathfrak{S}_2 \cong \mathfrak{S}_1 + \mathfrak{S}_3$ implies that $\mathfrak{S}_2 \cong \mathfrak{S}_3$. The present paper shows that this result holds if the field K is replaced throughout by any ring of p-adic integers with p an odd prime. Witt's result, as well as this extension, may also be expressed in the language of equivalence of quadratic forms. *N. H. McCoy* (Northampton, Mass.).

E08-2 **(6, 114c)**

Durfee, William H. Congruence of quadratic forms over valuation rings. Duke Math. J. **11**, 687–697 (1944).

E. Witt [J. Reine Angew. Math. **176**, 31–44 (1936)] proved that if f, g and h are quadratic forms over a field of characteristic not 2, if g and h each have no variables in common with f, and if $f+g$ and $f+h$ are congruent and nonsingular, then g is congruent to h. The author proves that this is true over any complete valuation ring whose associated residue-class field has characteristic not 2. These results may be stated in terms of matrices. For some of the theorems the restriction "characteristic not 2" is not used but it is essential to the main theorem. *B. W. Jones.*

E08-3 **(7, 50e)**

Jones, Burton W. A canonical quadratic form for the ring of 2-adic integers. Duke Math. J. **11**, 715–727 (1944).

The author seeks an easily applicable criterion for rational equivalence of two quadratic forms. He observes that, since Siegel [Amer. J. Math. **63**, 658–680 (1941); these Rev. **3**, 163] has shown that two integral forms belong to the same genus if and only if they are equivalent in the real field and in every ring R_p of p-adic integers, it suffices to study equivalence of forms in R_p. The major part of the paper is devoted to the difficult case $p=2$. The author obtains a unique "canonical" representative for every set of forms equivalent in R_2. He shows that every symmetric matrix in R_2 is equivalent in R_2 to a matrix (1) $\mathfrak{A} = \{2^{t_1}\mathfrak{A}_1, \cdots, 2^{t_n}\mathfrak{A}_n\}$, where, for every i, $t_i < t_{i+1}$ and $|\mathfrak{A}_i|$ is a unit. Furthermore, every $\mathfrak{A}_i$ is either in the form $\sum_{k=1}^{n_i} a_kx_k^2$, where a_k are prescribed odd residues modulo 8, or in one of the forms $\{\mathfrak{T}, \cdots, \mathfrak{T}\}$ or $\{\mathfrak{T}, \cdots, \mathfrak{T}, \mathfrak{S}\}$, where $\mathfrak{T} = \binom{0\ 1}{1\ 0}$, $\mathfrak{S} = \binom{2\ 1}{1\ 2}$ and the following conditions are fulfilled. (a) If $\mathfrak{A}_{i+1}$ is properly primitive and $t_{i+1} = t_i + 1$, then $\mathfrak{A}_i = \{\mathfrak{T}, \cdots, \mathfrak{T}\}$ if $\mathfrak{A}_i$ is improperly primitive, while $\lambda(\mathfrak{A}_i) = 1 \equiv |\mathfrak{A}_i| \pmod 4$ if $\mathfrak{A}_i$ is properly primitive. (b) If $\mathfrak{A}_i$ is properly primitive and $x'\{2^{t_{i+1}-t_i}\mathfrak{A}_{i+1}, 2^{t_{i+2}-t_i}\mathfrak{A}_{i+2}\} \equiv 4 \pmod 8$ solvable, then $|\mathfrak{A}_i| \equiv \pm 1 \pmod 8$. (c) If the initial conditions for both (a) and (b) hold with $\mathfrak{A}_i$ properly primitive, then $|\mathfrak{A}_i| \equiv 1 \pmod 8$ and $\lambda(\mathfrak{A}_i) = 1$. Here $\lambda(\mathfrak{A}) = -c_2(\mathfrak{A})(-1 \,|\, |\mathfrak{A}|)$, where c_2 is Hasse's invariant. In view of the uniqueness of (1), the problem of rational equivalence of two forms is reduced to the determination of their canonical forms.

A. E. Ross (St. Louis, Mo.).

Citations: MR 3, 163b = E12-9.
Referred to in E08-7.

E08-4 **(7, 359a)**

Arf, Cahit. Untersuchungen über quadratische Formen in Körper der Charakteristik 2. II. Über aritmetische Aequivalenz quadratischer Formen in Potenzreihenkörpern über einem vollkommenen Körper der Charakteristik 2. Rev. Fac. Sci. Univ. Istanbul (A) **8**, 297–327 (1943). (German. Turkish summary)

[Part I appeared in J. Reine Angew. Math. **183**, 148–167 (1941); these Rev. **4**, 237.] Let $k = \Omega\{t\}$ be the field of power series in t with coefficients in the perfect field Ω of characteristic 2. Suppose that ω is the natural valuation of k with $\omega(t) = 1$, $\omega(\alpha) = 0$ for $\alpha \neq 0$ in Ω. Let g be the valuation ring of ω. Then two equivalent quadratic forms over k are called arithmetically equivalent if the associated transformation matrix has coefficients in g. The author considers binary and ternary forms and exhibits complete systems for arithmetical equivalence. Let $y/\wp$ be a solution of the equation $x^2 - x = y\varepsilon k$. Then the study of the effect of the transformations (with coefficients in g) on a completely regular binary form $f = ax^2 + bxy + cy^2$, $b \neq 0$, shows that the algebraic invariants (i) the field $K = k((ac/b^2)/\wp)$ and (ii) the algebra $C = (a, K)$ have to be supplemented by (i′) the order $\nu = -\omega(ac/b^2)$ and (iii) the multiplicative residue class $aE^2 \pmod{t^\mu}$, where E is the unit group of k, $\mu = \min[\omega(b/a), \omega(c/a)]$, and $\min[\omega(a), \omega(b), \omega(c)]$. Conversely, the data K, C, $aE^2 \pmod{t^\mu}$ with $C = (a, K)$, $\mu \equiv \nu \pmod 2$ for $\mu \leq \nu$ always serve as a complete system of invariants for a class of completely regular forms. The representation theory by forms is set up. Moreover, the results are extended to quasilinear forms ax^2+cy^2. In the latter case considerable simplifications are possible since k has only one inseparable quadratic extension. The theory of ternary forms is reduced to the discussion of binary forms by observing that a ternary form F can always be expressed as $(ax^2+bxy+cy^2)+dz^2 = f+dz^2$ after a suitable arithmetic equivalence transformation. An involved analysis leads to the following invariants for $F=f+z^2$: (iv) the multiplicative residue class $aE^2 \pmod{t^M}$, where $M=\min[\mu, v(a)-2\omega(a)]$ for $\omega(a)<0$, $M=0$ otherwise, with $v(a)$ the maximal x for which a is a quadratic residue mod t^x, μ for f as in (iii); (v) the additive residue class of ac/b^2 (mod $H(F)$), where

$$H(F)=\{a\lambda^2/b^2+c\kappa^2/b^2\} \pmod{\wp k}$$

for all κ, $\lambda \varepsilon g$ and ν for f as in (i'); (vi) the algebra C for f as in (ii). Conversely, each set of data (iv) to (vi) belongs to a suitable form. *O. F. G. Schilling* (Chicago, Ill.).

Citations: MR 4, 237f = E04-1.

Referred to in E04-14.

E08-5 (9, 561a)

Durfee, William H. Quadratic forms over fields with a valuation. Bull. Amer. Math. Soc. **54**, 338–351 (1948).

L'auteur généralise les résultats de Hasse sur l'équivalence des formes quadratiques à coefficients $\mathfrak{p}$-adiques au cas des formes à coefficients dans certains corps valués complets; une partie de ces résultats subsistent dans tous les corps valués complets dont le corps de restes n'est pas de caractéristique 2. Soient K un corps valué complet, T son domaine d'intégrité, U son groupe multiplicatif des unités, $K^{(2)}$ le groupe multiplicatif des carrés des éléments non-nuls de K, R (supposé de caractéristique non 2) son corps de restes, $\mathfrak{M}$ son module de valuation. Le reste d'un $a\varepsilon T$ suivant l'idéal premier de K sera noté $\bar{a}$. Des éléments a, $b\varepsilon K$ seront dits congrus (notation: $a\equiv b$) s'ils le sont suivant le groupe multiplicatif $UK^{(2)}$. Soit $f=\sum a_i x_i^2$ une forme quadratique à coefficients a_i dans K, mise sous une forme diagonale (ce qui est un problème banal). Donc $\bar{f}=\sum \bar{a}_i x_i^2$ $(a_i\varepsilon T)$ est dite le reste de f, et f est dite unitaire si tous les a_i sont des unités de K. Elle est dite une forme standartisée, si $f=\sum b_i f_i$, où les f_i sont des formes unitaires et où les b_i sont incongrus deux à deux. Chaque forme de K est équivalente à une forme standartisée. Si f représente 0 dans K ou dans T, f elle est dite nullique (zero form) dans K ou dans T; f est dite totalement nullique et est notée H_q si

$$f=(x_1^2-x_2^2)+(x_3^2-x_4^2)+\cdots+(x_{q-1}^2-x_q^2).$$

L'auteur montre que si $f=\sum b_i f_i$ est standartisée, elle est nullique dans K si, et seulement si, une des f_i l'est, et que, si $g=\sum c_i g_i$ est aussi standartisée, la question d'équivalence dans K des f, g se réduit à celle de certaines de leurs composantes f_i, g_j ou de leurs sommes avec des formes totalement nulliques convenables, donc à l'équivalence des formes unitaires. Ensuite, l'auteur prouve qu'une forme unitaire est nullique dans K ou deux formes unitaires f, g y sont équivalentes si, et seulement si cela a lieu pour ces formes dans T, et que cela a lieu dans T si, et seulement si cela a lieu dans R pour les restes de ces formes.

Soient $|f|$ le déterminant de f, $(a, b)[a, b\varepsilon K]$ le symbole égal à $+1$ ou -1 suivant que la forme ax^2+by^2 représente ou non 1 dans K, $c(f)=\prod_{i=1}^n(-d_{i-1}, d_i)$, où $d_0=1$, et où $d_i=a_1a_2\cdots a_i$. Sous les hypothèses simultanées suivantes: (1) K est discrètement valué [mais il me semble qu'il suffit de supposer $(\mathfrak{M}:2\mathfrak{M})=2$]; (2) $(R^*:R^{(2)})=2$ (où R^* est le groupe multiplicatif des éléments non nuls de R); (3) pour tous les α, $\beta\varepsilon R^*$, $(\alpha, \beta)=+1$, l'auteur démontre les résultats suivants, dus à Hasse dans le cas $\mathfrak{p}$-adique: f est nullique si, et seulement si $n=2$ et $-|f|\varepsilon K^{(2)}$, ou $n=3$ et $c(f)=1$, ou $n=4$ et $c(f)=1$ ou $-|f|\bar{\varepsilon}K^{(2)}$, ou $n\geqq 5$; deux formes non-singulières f, g d'un même nombre de variables sont équivalentes si, et seulement si $|f|\equiv|g|$ $(\mathrm{mod}^\times K^{(2)})$ et $c(f)=c(g)$. En particulier, si ν est une unité de K telle que $\bar{\nu}\not\equiv 1(\mathrm{mod}^\times R^{(2)})$, et si t est un élément de K dont l'ordre n'est pas dans $2\mathfrak{M}$, f équivaut toujours à une forme canonique $x_1^2+x_2^2+\cdots+x_{s-1}^2+ax_s^2+t(x_{s+1}^2+\cdots+x_{n-1}^2+bx_n^2)$, où $s\leqq n$ et où a, b peuvent prendre indépendamment les valeurs 1, ν. *M. Krasner* (Paris).

Referred to in E08-15.

E08-6 (9, 572a)

Moses, Irma. On the representation, in the ring of p-adic integers, of a quadratic form in n variables by one in m variables. Bull. Amer. Math. Soc. **54**, 159–166 (1948).

Let S and T be symmetric, nonsingular integral matrices of respective orders m and n. It is proved that if S represents T in the field of reals and integrally-p-adically for every prime p, then S represents T rationally without essential denominator (that is, the denominators in the rational representation may be taken prime to any preassigned integer). The principal new lemma used is the following. Let a prime p be given. Let S be integral and T in the ring J_p of p-adic integers. Let $B'SB=T$ with B in the field R_p of p-adic numbers, and $C'SC=T$ with C in J_p. Then there exists in J_p a matrix D such that $D'TD=T$, and $|B'SCD-T|\neq 0$.
G. Pall (Chicago, Ill.).

E08-7 (11, 164d)

Jones, Burton W., and Durfee, William H. A theorem on quadratic forms over the ring of 2-adic integers. Bull. Amer. Math. Soc. **55**, 758–762 (1949).

Two quadratic forms over the ring $R(p)$ of p-adic integers, p a prime, with symmetric matrices A and B, respectively, are said to be equivalent if there exists a matrix T, with elements in $R(p)$ and whose determinant is a unit of $R(p)$, such that $T'BT=A$. For $p\neq 2$, Witt's cancellation theorem holds, that is: if f, g and h are quadratic forms over $R(p)$ such that g and h have no variables in common with f, then the equivalence of $f+g$ and $f+h$ implies that of g and h. For $p=2$, this is no longer valid in general and the complete domain of its validity is not known. The theorem of the present paper has to do with a case in which the result holds. It follows from some results in an earlier paper by Jones [Duke Math. J. **11**, 715–727 (1944); these Rev. **7**, 50], but the proof here is independent of lengthy arguments there. *R. Hull* (Lafayette, Ind.).

Citations: MR 7, 50e = E08-3.

E08-8 (16, 450c)

O'Meara, O. T. Characterization of quadratic forms over local fields. Proc. Nat. Acad. Sci. U. S. A. **39**, 969–972 (1953).

Let F be a field complete with respect to a discrete valuation with finite residue class field. Let e be the ordinal of 2. The author gives a complete set of invariants for quadratic forms with integral coefficients in F under integral equivalence, in the cases $e=0$ and $e=1$. These invariants can be expressed in terms of the Hasse symbols and determinants of the principal minors of the matrix of the form. Certain semi-canonical forms, from which the invariants can be read off, are also described. In case $1<e<\infty$, the question of integral equivalence is shown to depend only on the residues of the coefficients mod π^{2e+m+1}, where m is the number of variables. Finally, if $e<\infty$, two forms of unit determinant are integrally equivalent if they are rationally equivalent and represent the same numbers mod π^{2e+1}.

J. Tate (Cambridge, Mass.).

E08-9 (16, 680d)

O'Meara, O. T. Quadratic forms over local fields. Amer. J. Math. **77**, 87–116 (1955).

The author is concerned with integral equivalence of quadratic forms over local fields F, that is, fields which are complete under a discrete non-Archimedean valuation and have a perfect residue class field. He defines $e=\text{ord}\ (2)$ to be the ramification index of F and denotes by $\mathfrak{o}$ the ring of integers in F. A lattice L is said to be integral if $N(L)\subseteq\mathfrak{o}$ and totally integral if an addition $X\cdot Y\in\mathfrak{o}$ for all X and Y in L. He proves the following cancellation theorem: If $e\leqq 1$ and L is a totally integral lattice having the two decompositions $L=L_0\oplus L_1=K_0\oplus K_1$ in which L_0 and K_0 are isometric and of unit determinant, then L_1 and K_1 are isometric provided that their norms are equal.

A complete set of invariants is found for L in the unramified case with 2 a prime in F. In the ramified case he proves that if L and K are totally integral lattices of unit determinant in the same metric space V, then L is isometric to K provided that L and K represent the same numbers. The problem remains of finding a complete set of invariants for forms of arbitrary determinant over a general local field.

B. W. Jones (Boulder, Colo.).

Referred to in E08-12, E08-14, E08-28.

E08-10 (17, 17a)

Springer, T. A. Quadratic forms over fields with a discrete valuation. I. Equivalence classes of definite forms. Nederl. Akad. Wetensch. Proc. Ser. A. **58**= Indag. Math. **17**, 352–362 (1955).

The author considers quadratic forms over a commutative field K which is complete for a non-Archimedian discrete valuation, $|\lambda|$, and E a vector space over K with finite dimension n. Since it has been shown by Witt that equivalence classes are determined by the equivalence classes of definite quadratic forms, the author considers only definite forms, that is those for which $f(x,x)\neq 0$ if $x\neq 0$. Let $\bar{K}$ be the residue class field A/P where A is the ring of integers of K (those elements of K whose values are not greater than 1) and P the principal ideal, (π), formed by the elements of K whose valuation is less than 1. If E has a basis e_i $(1\leq i\leq n)$, and $x=\sum_i \xi_i e_i$, define $\|x\|=\max(|\xi_i|)$ and M_i the set of vectors x in E such that $\|x\|\leq\pi^{\frac{1}{2}}$. Let $\bar{E}_i=M_{i-1}/M_i$. Denote by η the canonical homomorphism of A onto $\bar{K}$ and by φ_i $(i=1,2)$ the canonical homomorphism of M_{i-1} onto $\bar{E}_i$. The following two quadratic forms on $\bar{E}_i$ $(i=1,2)$ are called the residue class forms of f:

$$f_1(\varphi_1(x),\varphi_1(x))=\eta(f(x,x))\quad (x\in M_0),$$
$$f_2(\varphi_2(x),\varphi_2(x))=\eta(\pi^{-1}f(x,x))\ (x\in M_1).$$

The author proves: 1. Let f and f' be two definite quadratic forms on the vector spaces E and E' with the same dimension over K. Suppose that the residue class forms f_i and f_i' are equivalent for $i=1,2$. Then f and f' are equivalent. 2. Suppose that f_1 and f_2 are two definite quadratic forms over $\bar{K}$. Then there exists a quadratic form f over K whose residue class forms are equivalent to f_1 and f_2. 3. Two definite forms in 4 variables over a field K with finite residue class field are equivalent.

B. W. Jones (Boulder, Colo.).

The author, with the consent of the reviewer, wishes to make the following remarks. "The definition of M_i given by the reviewer (line 13 of the review) is not that given in the paper (p. 354, line 15 from the bottom). In the paper use is made of the function $\|x\|$ defined in prop. 1 (p. 354), the use of this function is essential. The function $\|x\|$ mentioned by the reviewer is of no use. Moreover in line 14 of the review the formula $\|x\|\leq\pi^{\frac{1}{2}}$ should read $\|x\|\leq|\pi|^{i/2}$. Finally the assertion 1 (line 21 of the review) is proved in the paper only for the case that the characteristic of the field $\bar{K}$ is $\neq 2$."

Referred to in D72-8, E02-20, E08-11, E08-43.

E08-11 (17, 945e)

Springer, T. A. Quadratic forms over fields with a discrete valuation. II. Norms. Nederl. Akad. Wetensch. Proc. Ser. A. **59**=Indag. Math. **18** (1956), 238–246.

This paper uses notations of a previous paper of the same title [same Proc. **58** (1955), 352–362; MR **17**, 17]. First we use this opportunity to correct errors made by the reviewer in reporting the previous paper. That paper treated definite quadratic forms and used as the norm of x, $\|x\|=|f(x,x)|^{\frac{1}{2}}$. There M_i is the set of vectors of $x\in E$ satisfying $\|x\|\leqq|\pi|^{\frac{i}{2}}$ and π is defined in the review cited above. With these corrected definitions the assertions given in the previous review are correct except that the characteristic of the field $\bar{K}$ is restricted to be different from 2.

In paper II the forms are merely restricted to be non-degenerate and, as before, are on E, a finite-dimensional vector space over a commutative field K which is complete under a discrete valuation. Here a more general norm is used in accordance with a general definition given in the previous paper, i.e. the norm on E of x is a function $x\to\|x\|$ of E into the non-negative real numbers such that

$$\|x\|=0 \text{ is equivalent to } x=0,$$
$$\|x+y\|\leqq\max(\|x\|,\|y\|),$$
$$\|\lambda x\|=|\lambda|\cdot\|x\|\ (x,y\in E,\lambda\in K).$$

Such a norm is called a majorant of f if

$$|f(x,x)|<\|x\|^2\ (x\in E).$$

A majorant will be called an f-norm if it is minimal in the following sense: if $x\to\|x\|'$ is a majorant of f with $\|x\|'\leqq\|x\|$ for all $x\in E$, then $\|x\|'=\|x\|$. This paper is concerned with f-norms.

The author proves that if $x\to\|x\|$ is a majorant of f on E, then it is an f-norm if and only if for every non-zero x in E, there is a y in E such that

$$\|y\|<\|x\|,\ |f(x+y,x+y)|=\|x+y\|^2.$$

He shows that an f-norm may be defined with reference to a direct sum $E=E_0+E_1+\cdots+E_p$ of orthogonal subspaces where f is definite on E_0 and E_i are two-dimensional. He also shows that if f is non-degenerate and, when the characteristic of K is 2, non-defective (that is, the bilinear form g associated with f is non-degenerate) and if $x\to\|x\|$ and $x\to\|x\|'$ are two f-norms on E, then there exists an orthogonal transformation u of f such that $\|x\|'=\|u(x)\|$. Conversely, if $x\to\|x\|$ is an f-norm and u an orthogonal transformation, then $x\to\|u(x)\|$ is an f-norm.

B. W. Jones (Boulder, Col.).

Citations: MR 17, 17a = E08-10.

Referred to in E08-43.

E08-12 (17, 716d)

O'Meara, O. T. Witt's theorem and the isometry of lattices. Proc. Amer. Math. Soc. **7** (1956), 9–22.

If $F+G$ and $F+H$ are equivalent quadratic forms in a field, Witt has shown that G and H are field equivalent. This is also true over any local field in which 2 is a unit. The author [Amer. J. Math. **77** (1955), 87–116; MR **16**,

680] has extended this to any local field in which 2 is a prime and also to the ramified case when F is restricted to be a form in only one variable. In this paper he removes this limitation on F. Also he shows that G and H are equivalent provided that F is the orthogonal sum of totally isotropic binary forms, that is, forms of the type

$$\begin{pmatrix} 0 & \pi^{\lambda(i)} \\ \pi^{\lambda(i)} & 0 \end{pmatrix}$$

where $\lambda(i)$ are arbitrary integers and π is a prime element in the field. *B. W. Jones* (Boulder, Colo.).

Citations: MR 16, 680d = E08-9.

E08-13 (18, 562a)

McCarthy, Paul J. Representation by quadratic forms in valuation rings. Portugal. Math. **15** (1956), 1–7.

Let K be a field which is complete with respect to a non-Archimedean valuation, and let R be the valuation ring of K with respect to this valuation. On the assumption that the residue class field of K is not of characteristic 2, the author uses results of the reviewer and W. H. Durfee to derive theorems on the representation of a form g in m variables by a form f in n variables, with $n \geqq m$. He shows that the classical results hold, that is: if f is a form of unit determinant in R, then f represents a number N in R if and only if it represents N in K. Also if f and g are two forms in R whose determinants are units in R, f represents g in R if and only if it represents g in K, for $n \geqq m$. *B. W. Jones* (Boulder, Colo.).

E08-14 (18, 562b)

O'Meara, O. T. Integral equivalence of quadratic forms in ramified local fields. Amer. J. Math. **79** (1957), 157–186.

The author considers the problem of finding a set of invariants of a quadratic form which completely characterizes an equivalence class. This has been accomplished by W. H. Durfee, B. W. Jones, and Gordon Pall over local fields in which 2 is a unit and over p-adic numbers. The author solved the problem for any local field in which 2 is a prime and for unitary forms in the ramified extensions of 2-adic numbers [same Amer. **77** (1955), 87–116; MR **16**, 680]. This paper considers the remaining case-fields where 2 is not a unit. Some simplifications of earlier proofs result. The invariants are too complex to give here.

B. W. Jones (Boulder, Colo.).

Citations: MR 16, 680d = E08-9.

E08-15 (18, 641g)

McCarthy, Paul J. The representation of one quadratic form by another in valuated fields. Portugal. Math. **14** (1955), 31–34.

Soit K un corps discrètement valué complet. Soit (α, β) où α, β sont ϵK le symbole égal à $+1$ ou à -1 selon que l'équation $\alpha x^2 + \beta y^2 = 1$ a ou n'a pas de solution dans K. Sous les hypothèses: A) la carcatéristique résiduelle p de K est $\neq 2$; B) si E est le groupe des unités de K et si $E^{(2)}$ est celui de leurs carrés, $(E : E^{(2)}) = 2$; C) si $\alpha, \beta \in E$, on a $(\alpha, \beta) = 1$ {remarque du référant; en vertu du lemme de Hensel, cette condition équivaut à la résolubilité, dans le corps résiduel R de K, de $\bar{\alpha}x^2 + \bar{\beta}y^2 = 1$ pour tous $\bar{\alpha}, \bar{\beta} \in R$}, Durfee a montré [Bull. Amer. Math. Soc. **54** (1948), 338–351; MR **9**, 561] que: 1) $(\alpha, \beta) = (\beta, \alpha)$; 2) $(\alpha, -\alpha) = 1$; 3) $(\alpha\gamma^2, \beta\gamma^2) = (\alpha, \beta)$; 4) $(\alpha, \beta)(\alpha, \gamma) = (\alpha, \beta\gamma)$; 5) $(\alpha\gamma, \beta\gamma) = (\alpha, \beta)(\gamma, -\alpha\beta)$. L'auteur démontre, sous les mêmes hypothèses, que si $\alpha = \alpha_1\pi^a$, $\beta = \beta_1\pi^b$, où (π) est l'idéal premier de K, on a

$$(\alpha, \beta)(-1|\pi)^{ab}(\alpha_1|\pi)^b(\beta_1|\pi)^a,$$

où $(\mu|\pi)$ est le symbole des restes quadratiques dans K. Il exprime, ensuite, la condition, nécéssaire et suffisante pour qu'une forme quadratique nondégénérée de $n > m$ variables représente une forme quadratique non-dégénérée donnée de m variables. *M. Krasner* (Paris).

Citations: MR 9, 561a = E08-5.

E08-16 (18, 786a)

Reiner, Irma. On the two-adic density of representations by quadratic forms. Pacific J. Math. **6** (1956), 753–762.

Using Siegel's notation, the author denotes by $A_q(S, T)$ the number of solutions of $X'SX \equiv T \pmod{q}$, where S and T are integral matrices of order m and n respectively, in integral matrices X. Now $A_q(S, T)$ has been determined by Siegel and others for q a power of an odd prime and is easily shown to depend on A_2 and A_8 for q a power of 2. The author gives expressions for $A_2(S, T)$ and $A_8(S, T)$ when the determinants of S and T are both odd. These are explicit for the former, and means of getting explicit expressions are given for the latter. *B. W. Jones.*

E08-17 (19, 732g)

O'Meara, O. T. Local characterization of integral quadratic forms by Gauss sums. Amer. J. Math. **79** (1957), 687–709.

This paper is concerned with the existence of a unimodular solution X to the n by n matrix equation $X^THX = G$, with H and G symmetric. The author deals with characterization of equivalence classes by means of Gaussian sums over local fields with a finite residue class field. He shows that Gaussian sums alone characterize the class of H when ord $2 = 0$, while one must include the type as an invariant in the unramified case. In the ramified theory further conditions must be imposed. If, however, H is unitary, the Gauss sums form a complete set of invariants. *B. W. Jones* (Boulder, Colo.).

E08-18 (20# 4526)

O'Meara, O. T. The integral representations of quadratic forms over local fields. Amer. J. Math. **80** (1958), 843–878.

The author finds necessary and sufficient conditions that will determine the integral representations of an arbitrary quadratic form over any local field in which 2 is either a unit or a prime. His criteria are in terms of the field representations of forms derived from certain canonical decompositions of the given forms. The exact criteria are stated in terms of the lattices associated with the forms, and the treatment is from this point of view. Since the notation is intricate, space does not permit giving the detailed conditions in this review.

B. W. Jones (Boulder, Colo.)

Referred to in E08-27.

E08-19 (21# 3380)

Cugiani, Marco. Forme quadratiche e cubiche binarie nei domini P-adici. Ist. Lombardo Accad. Sci. Lett. Rend. A **92** (1957/58), 307–320.

The author obtains necessary and sufficient conditions that a given binary quadratic form with p-adic integer coefficients should represent a given p-adic integer for p-adic integral values of the variables. He also obtains incomplete results for binary cubic forms. For earlier work of the author on special cases see Ann. Mat. Pura Appl. (4) **44** (1957), 1–22; Riv. Mat. Univ. Parma **8** (1957), 81–92 [MR **20** #1669, #7011].

J. W. S. Cassels (Cambridge, England)

Citations: MR 20# 1669 = E16-34; MR 20# 7011 = E76-21.

Referred to in E16-40, E76-25.

E08-20 **(22# 10954)**

Sah, Chih-Han. Quadratic forms over fields of characteristic 2. Amer. J. Math. **82** (1960), 812–830.

This paper gives a solution to the integral equivalence problem for quadratic forms in any finite number of variables over a local field of characteristic 2. Let Ω denote a finite field of characteristic 2, and k the formal power series field over Ω with uniformizer π; $\mathfrak{o}$ is the ring of integral power series. By a quadratic lattice, M, the author means a free module of finite type over $\mathfrak{o}$ together with a map $Q: M \to k$ such that $Q(ax) = a^2Q(x)$ for $a \in k$ and $x \in M$, and such that $\langle x, y\rangle = Q(x+y)+Q(x)+Q(y)$ is bilinear. A quadratic lattice M is called an i-modular lattice if, when $\{x\} \subseteq M$ is a pure subset, $\langle x, M\rangle = \pi^i\mathfrak{o}$. Also $s(M) = \{\langle x, y\rangle | x, y \in M\}$ is called the scale of M and $q(M) = \{Q(x)+s(M)| \; x \in M\}$ is called the norm group of M.

One of the author's principal results is the following theorem. Let M_1 and M_2 be i-modular lattices. Then, $M_1 \cong M_2$ if and only if $kM_1 \cong kM_2$ and $q(M_1) = q(M_2)$.

Conditions also are established for equivalence of lattices in general but they are too involved to give here.

B. W. Jones (Boulder, Colo.)

Referred to in E08-25.

E08-21 **(26# 2398)**

Cassels, J. W. S.

Über die Äquivalenz 2-adischer quadratischer Formen.

Comment. Math. Helv. **37** (1962/63), 61–64.

The author considers quadratic forms $f(x)$ in r variables over the ring of 2-adic integers, whose determinants are 2-adic units. Then there is a vector w in the ring which is uniquely determined modulo 2, for which

$$f(x) \equiv \sum_{i,j} f_{ij}x_iw_j \pmod 2$$

for all vectors x over the ring, where x_i and w_j are the components of x and w, respectively, and f_{ij} are the coefficients of f. The value of $f(w) \pmod{2^3}$ is independent of the choice of w.

The author proves the following. For quadratic forms described above, $\bar{c}_2(f) = (-1)^{e/4}$, where $\bar{c}_2(f)$ is the Minkowski-Hasse symbol and $e = f(w) + \det(f) - r - 1$. An immediate consequence of this is that the class of such a form is determined by its determinant $\pmod{2^3}$ and $f(w)$ $\pmod{2^3}$.

Burton W. Jones (Boulder, Colo.)

E08-22 **(27# 131)**

Jacobowitz, Ronald

Hermitian forms over local fields.

Amer. J. Math. **84** (1962), 441–465.

Es sei F ein nicht notwendig kommutativer Körper mit den folgenden Eigenschaften: (1) F besitzt eine von der Identität verschiedene Involution $a \to a^*$; (2) F ist lokal, d.h. F ist komplett mit endlichem Restklassenkörper in Bezug auf eine diskrete, nichtarchimedische Bewertung; (3) Wenn F nicht kommutativ ist, so ist F eine Quaternionenalgebra über einem kommutativen Teilkörper E, d.h. F besitzt eine E-Basis der Form $1, u, v, uv$ mit $u^2 = \theta$, $v^2 = \Delta$, $uv = -vu$, $\theta, \Delta \in E$; ausserdem soll die Involution * die Form

$$(\alpha + \beta u + \gamma v + \delta uv)^* = \alpha - \beta u - \gamma v - \delta uv$$

besitzen. Der Verfasser betrachtet hermitesche Formen über F, in Bezug auf die vorgegebene Involution. Es werden Invarianten für ganzzahlige Äquivalenz solcher Formen angegeben. Das entsprechende Problem für rationale Äquivalenz wurde von Jacobson behandelt [Bull. Amer. Math. Soc. **46** (1940), 264–268; MR **1**, 325]. Für quadratische Formen über einem kommutativen lokalen Körper vgl. auch O'Meara [*Introduction to quadratic forms*, Academic Press, New York, 1963; MR **27** #2485].

P. Roquette (Tübingen)

Citations: MR 27# 2485 = E02-11.

Referred to in E08-34.

E08-23 **(28# 5057)**

Riehm, Carl

On the integral representations of quadratic forms over local fields.

Amer. J. Math. **86** (1964), 25–62.

This is an extensive study of the integral representations of quadratic forms over 2-adic fields. Let F be a finite extension of the field of 2-adic numbers, $\mathfrak{o}$ the integers in F, V an n-dimensional vector space over F provided with a symmetric bilinear form $B: V \times V \to F$. A lattice L on V is a finitely generated $\mathfrak{o}$-module in V which contains n independent vectors over F; L admits an $\mathfrak{o}$-base $x_1, \cdots, x_n$. L is said to be unimodular if the matrix $(B(x_i, x_j))$ is unimodular and modular if $(aB(x_i, x_j))$ is unimodular for some $a \in F$. Let L, M be lattices on V. M is said to be represented by L (written $M \to L$) if there is an isometry s such that $s(M) \subseteq L$. The first main theorem gives necessary and sufficient conditions for $M \to L$ when L is unimodular and M is arbitrary. The second main theorem is a special case of the first one and gives a simple condition for L unimodular, M modular: $M \to L \Leftrightarrow B(M, M) \subseteq B(L, L) \subseteq B(M\#, M\#)$, here $M\# = \{x \in V, B(x, M) \subseteq \mathfrak{o}\}$. The author discusses also the representations of lattices on metric spaces with different dimensions by giving conditions when one of the two lattices is unimodular (the third main theorem) and concludes the paper with comments on arbitrary lattices.

T. Ono (Philadelphia, Pa.)

E08-24 **(30# 3923)**

O'Meara, O. T.; Pollak, Barth

Generation of local integral orthogonal groups.

Math. Z. **87** (1965), 385–400.

Il est connu que sur un corps K, tout groupe orthogonal est engendré par les symétries (par rapport aux hyperplans non singuliers) sauf pour $K = \mathbf{F}_2$, la dimension $n = 4$ et l'indice maximum (égal à 2). Les auteurs étudient le même problème lorsque K est remplacé par l'anneau des entiers d'un corps $\mathfrak{p}$-adique; lorsque la caractéristique résiduelle $p \neq 2$, le théorème est encore valable (M. Kneser); aussi les auteurs se bornent-ils au cas où $p = 2$ et où le corps $\mathfrak{p}$-adique K est non ramifié sur $\mathbf{Q}_2$. Ils montrent que si $K \neq \mathbf{Q}_2$, tout groupe orthogonal sur l'anneau des entiers de K est encore engendré par les symétries. Par contre, lorsque $K = \mathbf{Q}_2$, il y a 9 types exceptionnels de formes quadratiques sur l'anneau des entiers de K, pour lesquelles le théorème n'est plus valables (les dimensions correspondantes prenant l'une des valeurs 4, 5, 6). Dans ces cas exceptionnels, ils prouvent en outre que l'on engendre alors le groupe orthogonal à l'aide des symétries et des "doubles transvections" de Siegel-Eichler, $E_w{}^i(x) = x + B(x, i)w - B(x, w)i - \frac{1}{2}Q(w)B(x, i)i$, où i est un vecteur isotrope $\neq 0$, w un vecteur $\neq i$ et orthogonal à i. Les démonstrations reposent sur les méthodes développées dans le livre de O'Meara [*Introduction to quadratic forms*, Academic Press, New York, 1963; MR **27** #2485].

J. Dieudonné (Nice)

Citations: MR 27# 2485 = E02-11.

Referred to in E56-52.

E08-25 **(30# 4728)**

Riehm, C. R.

Integral representations of quadratic forms in characteristic 2.

Amer. J. Math. **87** (1965), 32–64.

Let F be the field of power series in one variable, over a

finite field of characteristic 2, and $\mathfrak{o}$ the order of integral power series. The author studies the integral representation of a quadratic form $q(x)$ by another form $Q(x)$. The local rational representation (i.e., with coefficients in F) has been studied by C. Arf [J. Reine Angew. Math. **183** (1941), 148–167; MR **4**, 237] and C. H. Sah [Amer. J. Math. **82** (1960), 812–830; MR **22** #10954]. These results are freely used. The concept of a lattice in the underlying vector space is employed throughout. An arithmetic invariant of a lattice L with respect to a quadratic form is the norm group, namely, the $\mathfrak{o}^2$-ideal generated by all $Q(x)$ with $x \in L$. The conditions for integral equivalence and of representability of forms are studied, under simplifying assumptions, but they still turn out to be rather involved, so that they cannot be reproduced here. The most effective simplification is that a lattice L be maximal, i.e., that L be a largest $\mathfrak{o}$-module of a given norm group. Two maximal lattices in the same space are isometric.
M. Eichler (Basel)

Citations: MR 4, 237f = E04-1; MR 22# 10954 = E08-20.

E08-26 (32# 2379)

James, D. G.
Integral invariants for vectors over local fields.
Pacific J. Math. **15** (1965), 905–916.

The author considers isometric invariants of vectors in lattices (quadratic forms) over the ring of integers in a local field for the prime 2. By extending the notion of order to vectors in the lattice, the author obtains a set of invariants which enables the general vector to be decomposed into a sum of simple vectors. The lengths of these simple vectors are invariant modulo certain powers of 2, and these lengths together with the original invariants form a complete set for the 2-adic integers. In the special case where there are no one-dimensional, orthogonal sublattices (improper quadratic forms), the invariants form a complete set for all local fields.
Burton W. Jones (Boulder, Colo.)

E08-27 (32# 2403)

Johnson, Arnold A.
Integral representations of Hermitian forms over local fields.
Bull. Amer. Math. Soc. **72** (1966), 118–121.

Let E be a local field (of characteristic $\neq 2$) with a non-trivial involution, F its fixed field, and V, V' finite-dimensional Hermitian spaces over E. Let $\mathfrak{O}$ be the ring of integers in E. A linear mapping of an $\mathfrak{O}$-lattice L in V into another $\mathfrak{O}$-lattice L' in V' is called a representation if it preserves the Hermitian forms. The author gives the conditions that L be represented by L', in terms of "Jordan splittings" of L, L'. When E/F is either unramified or ramified with E nondyadic, the problem of the above integral representation is reduced to the one of rational representations, which has already been solved by Jacobson [same Bull. **46** (1940), 264–268; MR **1**, 325] and O'Meara [Amer. J. Math. **80** (1958), 843–878; MR **20** #4526]. The remaining case, where E/F is ramified with E dyadic, is more complicated. Detailed proofs are not given.
T. Ono (Philadelphia, Pa.)

Citations: MR 20# 4526 = E08-18.

E08-28 (33# 7306)

Rosenzweig, Samson M.
On the number of inequivalent binary unimodular forms.
Proc. Amer. Math. Soc. **17** (1966), 948–952.

Let F be a dyadic local field of characteristic not 2, and let $\mathcal{O}$ denote the ring of integers of F; let $e = \text{ord}_\pi 2$, where π is any prime element of F, and let ν be an arbitrary rational integer satisfying $0 \leqq \nu \leqq e$. Using results obtained by O. T. O'Meara [Amer. J. Math. **77** (1955), 87–116; MR **16**, 680; *Introduction to quadratic forms*, Springer, Berlin, 1963; MR **27** #2485] on $\mathcal{O}$-equivalence of quadratic forms in F, the author shows that the number of $\mathcal{O}$-inequivalent forms of norm $\pi^\nu \mathcal{O}$ is precisely

$$4[(e-\nu+1)/2]q^{e-\nu-1}(q-1)+2q^{2[(e-\nu)/2]},$$

where [ ] denotes the greatest-integer function.
R. Jacobowitz (Lawrence, Kan.)

Citations: MR 16, 680d = E08-9; MR 27# 2485 = E02-11.

E08-29 (34# 2561)

Trojan, Allan
The integral extension of isometries of quadratic forms over local fields.
Canad. J. Math. **18** (1966), 920–942.

If x and y are vectors of the same length in a quadratic space over an arbitrary field, then by the Witt cancellation law, there exists an isometry of the space sending x to y. In the present paper the analogous problem, for a quadratic lattice over the integers of an unramified extension of the 2-adic numbers, is studied; necessary and sufficient conditions are determined, in terms of invariants associated with a Jordan splitting of the lattice, for existence of the isometry. The author states that the integral problem for non-dyadic local fields was solved by S. Rosenzweig ["Analogy of Witt's theorem for modules over the ring of p-adic integers", Ph.D. thesis, M.I.T., Cambridge, Mass., 1958], but remains unsolved for ramified extensions of the 2-adic numbers. *R. Jacobowitz* (Lawrence, Kan.)

Referred to in E08-32.

E08-30 (36# 1468)

Hsia, John S.
Integral equivalence of vectors over local modular lattices.
Pacific J. Math. **23** (1967), 527–542.

Let F be a local field with characteristic $\neq 2$, and in which the element 2 is not unitary. Let V be a regular quadratic space over F, L a lattice on V. The group of units of L is the subgroup $O(L) = \{\sigma \in O(V) : \sigma L = L\}$ of the orthogonal group $O(V)$. Two vectors u and v in L are defined to be integrally equivalent if there exists an isometry $\sigma \in O(L)$ mapping one onto the other. This paper gives necessary and sufficient conditions for integral equivalence of vectors when the underlying lattice L is modular.

For instance, the author proves the following. Let L be a unimodular lattice over a dyadic local field of characteristic zero, with dim $L \neq 4, 5, 6$. Then two maximal vectors u and v in L are integrally equivalent if and only if $Q(u) = Q(v)$ and $Q(\mathfrak{M}_u) = Q(\mathfrak{M}_v)$, where Q is the quadratic form of V over F, B its associated bilinear form and $\mathfrak{M}_x = \{z \in L : B(x, z) = 1\}$. *Burton W. Jones* (Boulder, Colo.)

Referred to in E08-36.

E08-31 (36# 3754)

James, D. G.; Rosenzweig, S. M.
Associated vectors in lattices over valuation rings.
Amer. J. Math. **90** (1968), 295–307.

Let F denote a field with non-archimedean valuation of rank 1 and R the ring of integers in F. Denote by $\nu(x)$ the order of x in F and assume that $\nu(2) = 0$. G is the value group of ν and L a free R-module with finite basis ξ_i, $1 \leqq i \leqq m$. Two vectors of the lattice L are said to be associated if there is an isometry of the lattice taking one into the other. The object of the paper is to find invariants in terms of which necessary and sufficient conditions for two vectors to be associated can be stated.

To this end, define $\nu_0(\alpha)=\min \nu(\alpha\cdot\xi_i)$ taken over the basis vectors ξ_i and $\nu_r(\alpha)=\min \nu(a_i\xi_i\cdot\alpha)$ over the basis of $L(r)=\{\alpha\in L|\nu_0(\alpha)\geqq r\}$. The authors call $r\in G$ a critical index of the vector α of L if (i) $r=0$ and $\nu_0(\alpha)<\nu_s(\alpha)$ for all $s>0$, and (ii) $r>0$, $\nu_r(\alpha)<\nu_{r+s}(\alpha)$ for all $s>0$, and there exists an $s<r$ with $\nu_s(\alpha)=\nu_r(\alpha)$. There are finitely many critical indices.

The authors prove: The vectors α and β in L are associated if and only if (i) $\alpha^2=\beta^2$, (ii) α and β have the same critical indices $r_1<r_2<r_3<\cdots<r_s$, (iii) $\nu_{r_i}(\alpha)=\nu_{r_i}(\beta)$, $1\leqq i\leqq s$, and (iv) $\nu(\sum_{i=1}^t x_i\lambda_i)^2-(\sum_{i=1}^t y_i\mu_i^2)\geqq \nu_{r_{t+1}}(\alpha)+\nu_{r_t}(\alpha)-r_t$. *Burton W. Jones* (Boulder, Colo.)

Referred to in E08-39.

E08-32 (36# 6377)

Hsia, John S.

Integral equivalence of vectors over depleted modular lattices on dyadic local fields.

Amer. J. Math. **90** (1968), 285–294.

This paper deals with the problem of extending an isometry of two vectors in a quadratic lattice L, over a dyadic local field F, to an isometry of L. The author solves the problem for modular lattices L having weight ideal $\mathfrak{w}L$ equal to twice the scale ideal $\mathfrak{s}L$. This is a partial generalization of the work of A. Trojan [Canad. J. Math. **18** (1966), 920–942; MR **34** #2561], who studied the problem in the special case in which F is unramified (where the condition $\mathfrak{w}L=2\mathfrak{s}L$ is automatic for modular L), but without the restriction that L be modular.

R. Jacobowitz (Lawrence, Kan.)

Citations: MR 34# 2561 = E08-29.

E08-33 (37# 1348)

Johnson, Arnold A. [Johnson, Arnold Arvid]

Integral representations of hermitian forms over local fields.

J. Reine Angew. Math. **229** (1968), 57–80.

Let $\mathfrak{o}$ denote the ring of integers of a local field, and let L and K be $\mathfrak{o}$-modules with an inner product; find invariants for the existence of an isometry (i.e., a product-preserving homomorphism) from L into K. In this paper, the author completely solves this problem in the case in which the inner product is hermitian. Only partial results, however, are known for quadratic forms, i.e., where the inner product is symmetric. *R. Jacobowitz* (Lawrence, Kan.)

E08-34 (37# 2723)

Jacobowitz, Ronald

Gauss sums and the local classification of hermitian forms.

Amer. J. Math. **90** (1968), 528–552.

In demselben J. **84** (1962), 441–465 [MR **27** #131] (Zitat [4]), hatte der Autor Invarianten für hermitesche Gitter über lokalen Körpern sowie über lokalen Quaternionenschiefkörpern bezüglich Standard-Involution angegeben. In der vorliegenden Arbeit werden einige (nur im Kommutativen wesentliche) dieser Invarianten durch Gauß'sche Summen ersetzt. Deshalb beschränkt sich Referent auf den kommutativen Fall. F sei ein vollständig diskret bewerteter Körper der Charakteristik $\neq 2$ mit endlichem Restklassenkörper und einer Involution $*\neq\mathrm{id}$, $\mathfrak{O}$ der Bewertungsring von F und L ein $\mathfrak{O}$-Gitter mit bezüglich $*$ hermiteschem Skalarprodukt (,). $\mathfrak{o}$ sei der Bewertungsring des Fixkörpers von $*$ in F, $\mathfrak{p}$ sein Primideal. Für einen komplexwertigen Charakter χ von $\mathfrak{o}$ mit Kern $\chi=\mathfrak{p}^m$ wird die Gauß'sche Summe

$$\chi(L) = \sum_{x\in L,\, x \bmod \mathfrak{p}^m L} \chi((x,x))$$

gesetzt. Ist $L=L_1\perp\cdots\perp L_t$ eine Jordan-Zerlegung von L, so sei X_L die Gruppe aller Charaktere von $\mathfrak{o}$, die auf $4\mathfrak{p}(L_t,L_t)\cap\mathfrak{o}$ trivial sind. Hauptergebnis der Arbeit ist: Der Typ der Jordan-Zerlegung, die in [4] definierten u-Invarianten und die $\chi(L)$ für alle $\chi\in X_L$ bilden zusammen ein vollständiges Invarianten-System (Theorem 5). Zum Beweise wird die Klassifikation aus [4] benutzt sowie ein Kriterium für das Verschwinden von Gauß'schen Summen (Theorem 4). Im unverzweigten Falle genügen Rang und Gauß'sche Summen, im nicht dyadischen Falle der Typ der Jordan-Zerlegung und Gauß'sche Summen zur Klassifizierung. *S. Böge* (Heidelberg)

Citations: MR 27# 131 = E08-22.

E08-35 (37# 6381)

Pollak, Barth

Generation of local integral orthogonal groups in characteristic 2.

Canad. J. Math. **20** (1968), 1178–1191.

L'auteur considère un corps local F de caractéristique 2, un espace vectoriel V de dimension n sur F, une forme quadratique Q non défective sur V (ce qui implique n pair), et un réseau $L\subset V$; il désigne par $\mathbf{O}(L)$ le sous-groupe du groupe orthogonal de la forme Q qui laisse invariant L. Il se propose d'examiner la possibilité d'engendrer $\mathbf{O}(L)$ par des transformations simples: en premier lieu les symétries hyperplanes (qui sont ici des transvections de vecteur non singulier); il désigne par $\mathbf{S}(L)$ le sous-groupe de $\mathbf{O}(L)$ qu'elles engendrent. Il introduit d'autre part des "doubles transvections" analogues aux transformations de Siegel-Eichler du cas classique, et prouve d'abord que $\mathbf{O}(L)$ est engendré par $\mathbf{S}(L)$ et certaines de ces doubles transvections. Il montre d'autre part que si le corps résiduel de F a plus de 2 éléments, on a toujours $\mathbf{S}(L)=\mathbf{O}(L)$. Au contraire, si le corps résiduel de F est $\mathbf{F}_2$, il y a deux cas exceptionnels, correspondant à des dimensions égales à 4 ou 6 et à des réseaux L d'un type particulier. La plus grande partie de l'article est consacrée à l'étude générale du cas $n=4$, et des deux cas exceptionnels. *J. Dieudonné* (Nice)

E08-36 (39# 2704)

Hsia, J. S.

A note on the integral equivalence of vectors in characteristic 2.

Math. Ann. **179** (1968), 63–69.

The author extends, to the characteristic 2 case, his earlier study [Pacific J. Math. **23** (1967), 527–542; MR **36** #1468] of the integral analogue of Witt's cancellation law: given a unimodular quadratic lattice L over a local field, when can an isometry between two vectors of L be extended to all of L? The principal result is that an extension exists if and only if certain subsets of L called "characteristic sets", associated with these two vectors, represent the same field elements. *R. Jacobowitz* (Lawrence, Kan.)

Citations: MR 36# 1468 = E08-30.

Referred to in E08-37.

E08-37 (40# 5540)

Hsia, John S.

One dimensional Witt's theorem over modular lattices.

Bull. Amer. Math. Soc. **76** (1970), 113–115.

In Math. Ann. **179** (1968), 63–69 [MR **39** #2704], the author showed that, over a local field of characteristic

2, two maximal vectors in a unimodular quadratic lattice (of dimension not 4 or 6) are integrally equivalent if and only if their so-called "characteristic sets" represent the same field elements. In the present paper, it is stated (only a sketch of the proof is given at this time) that the result holds also in characteristic 0, and that the restriction on dimension is unnecessary.

R. Jacobowitz (Lawrence, Kan.)

Citations: MR 39# 2704 = E08-36.

E08-38 (40# 4207)

Pfeuffer, Horst

Bemerkung zur Berechnung dyadischer Darstellungsdichten einer quadratischen Form über algebraischen Zahlkörpern.

J. Reine Angew. Math. **236** (1969), 219–220.

Using the classification of unimodular lattices on a quadratic space over a dyadic local field given in O. T. O'Meara's book, *Introduction to quadratic forms* [§ 93, Academic Press, New York, 1963; MR **27** #2485], the author gives a simpler proof, with a generalization, of the evaluation by K. Barner [J. Reine Angew. Math. **229** (1968), 194–208; MR **36** #5079] of the dyadic representation density of 1 as a sum of $4m$ squares.

E. S. Barnes (Adelaide)

Citations: MR 27# 2485 = E02-11; MR 36# 5079 = R26-37.

E08-39 (41# 1642)

Band, Melvin

On the integral extensions of quadratic forms over local fields.

Canad. J. Math. **22** (1970), 297–307.

Generalizing Witt's classical cancellation law to quadratic forms over rings—in particular, rings of integers in local or global fields—one considers the following problem: if L is a quadratic lattice over a ring R, and τ an isometry between sublattices W, W', when does there exist an extension of τ to all of L? D. G. James and S. M. Rosenzweig [Amer. J. Math. **90** (1968), 295–307; MR **36** #3754] have solved the problem in the special case for which R is the ring of integers of a non-dyadic local field and W and W' are lines. For such R, the author in the present paper shows how to express the solution for arbitrary W, W' in terms of this special one-dimensional case. Main result: the extension of τ exists if and only if for every vector x in W, each of the isometries $Rx \leftrightarrow R(\tau x)$ can be extended to L; and in fact only a finite number of computations must be made for a given $\{L, W, W', \tau\}$, so that the invariants are effective.

R. Jacobowitz (Tempe, Ariz.)

Citations: MR 36# 3754 = E08-31.

E08-40 (41# 1644)

Kaplansky, Irving

Fröhlich's local quadratic forms.

J. Reine Angew. Math. **239/240** (1969), 74–77.

A. Fröhlich [Proc. Cambridge Philos. Soc. **63** (1967), 579–586; MR **35** #5389] calls a field k a Hilbert field if for any element $d \neq 0$, -1 there exist exactly two classes of binary quadratic forms of discriminant d. The present author calls k a generalized Hilbert field if there exist at most two classes of such quadratic forms. The elements $a \in k^\times$ for which the following binary quadratic forms are equivalent: $(a, b) \sim (1, ab)$ for all $b \in k^\times$ form a subgroup $R \subseteq k^\times$, the "radical" of k. Theorem 1: The following statements are equivalent: (a) k is a generalized Hilbert field and $[k^\times : R] = 2$, (b) k is an ordered field and $(a, b) \sim (1, ab)$ for all positive a, b. Theorem 2: Let k be a generalized Hilbert field. If $[k^\times : R] > 2$, then there exist exactly two classes of quadratic forms in $n \geqq 3$ variables with discriminant d. All forms in $n \geqq 5$ variables are isotropic. Two forms are equivalent if and only if their discriminants and their Witt invariants coincide. These theorems can be extended to "abstract quadratic forms" introduced by the author and R. J. Shaker [Canad. J. Math. **21** (1969), 1218–1233; MR **40** #2701].

M. Eichler (Basil)

Citations: MR 35# 5389 = E04-26.

E08-41 (41# 1893)

Johnson, Robert Paul

Orthogonal groups of local anisotropic spaces.

Amer. J. Math. **91** (1969), 1077–1105.

Denote by $P\Omega_n$ the projective commutator group of the orthogonal group of an n-dimensional vector space V over a local field F for which the finite residue class field has characteristic $\neq 2$ and where V is endowed with an anisotropic non-degenerate quadratic form. For $n \geqq 5$, $P\Omega_n$ is simple since in this case V is isotropic, i.e., the quadratic form on V represents 0 non-trivially, cf. B. Pollak [same J. **88** (1966), 763–780; MR **34** #4369]. $P\Omega_2$ is always 1, according to Pollak. As one knows already from the case of an arbitrary field, orthogonal groups of an anisotropic quadratic form are not always simple for $n = 3$ and $n = 4$. Since Pollak has determined the normal subgroups of $P\Omega_3$ for the case under consideration, there did remain the problem to investigate the structure of $P\Omega_4$. The present author now gives a complete description of the normal subgroups of $P\Omega_4$. For a precise formulation of the result we refer to the paper.

The proofs depend strongly on the results and methods of Pollak and on the following well known facts which can be proved using the Clifford algebra: First, $P\Omega_4$ is a subgroup of index 1 or 2 in PO_4', where O_4' is the group of rotations of V with spinor norm 1, and second, $PO_4' = \Omega_3 \times \Omega_3$, where $\Omega_3 = P\Omega_3$ is just the group considered by Pollak.

W. Klingenberg (Bonn)

Citations: MR 34# 4369 = E56-43.

E08-42 (41# 3395)

Hsia, J. S.

Grothendieck groups of unimodular quadratic forms over local fields.

J. Algebra **15** (1970), 328–334.

Let F be a local field with $\mathrm{char}(F) \neq 2$, R the ring of integers in F, $\mathfrak{p}$ the maximal ideal of F. Let $\mathbf{Q}(R)$ and $\mathbf{Q}(F)$ be, respectively, the category of unimodular lattices over R and the category of non-degenerate quadratic vector spaces over F, $\mathbf{K}_0\mathbf{Q}(R)$ and $\mathbf{K}_0\mathbf{Q}(F)$ be their respective Grothendieck groups. The inclusion map $i: R \to F$ induces a functor $\mathbf{Q}(R) \to \mathbf{Q}(F)$ which, in turn, defines a group homomorphism $i_*: \mathbf{K}_0\mathbf{Q}(R) \to \mathbf{K}_0\mathbf{Q}(F)$, whose cokernel will be written as $\overline{\mathbf{K}}_0\mathbf{Q}(F)$. The canonical epimorphism $\mathbf{K}_0\mathbf{Q}(F) \to \overline{\mathbf{K}}_0\mathbf{Q}(F)$ is denoted by p_*.

Then, one obtains the following theorem: The following sequence is exact: $0 \to \mathbf{K}_0\mathbf{Q}(R) \xrightarrow{i_*} \mathbf{K}_0\mathbf{Q}(F) \xrightarrow{p_*} \overline{\mathbf{K}}_0\mathbf{Q}(F) \to 0$. The sequence admits a non-natural splitting except in the case where $\mathfrak{p}$ contains 2 and -1 is of quadratic defect $4R$.

Moreover, one has $\mathbf{K}_0\mathbf{Q}(R) = Z \oplus Z_2$ if $\mathfrak{p} \not\ni 2$, $\mathbf{K}_0\mathbf{Q}(R) = Z \oplus Z_2 \oplus \cdots \oplus Z_2$ ($n+2$ copies of Z_2) if $\mathfrak{p} \ni 2$ and -1 is either a square or of quadratic defect $4R$, $\mathbf{K}_0\mathbf{Q}(R) = Z \oplus Z_4 \oplus Z_2 \oplus \cdots \oplus Z_2$ (n copies of Z_2) otherwise, where $n = [F : \mathbf{Q}_2]$ ($\mathbf{Q}_2$ is the two-adic number field). Further, $\overline{\mathbf{K}}_0\mathbf{Q}(F) = Z_2 \oplus Z_2$ if $\mathfrak{p} \not\ni 2$ and -1 is a square, $\overline{\mathbf{K}}_0\mathbf{Q}(F) = Z_4$ if $\mathfrak{p} \not\ni 2$ and -1 is not a square, $\overline{\mathbf{K}}_0\mathbf{Q}(F) = Z_2$ if $\mathfrak{p} \ni 2$.

K. Iyanaga (Tokyo)

E08-43 **(41# 8473)**

Scharlau, Winfried

Klassifikation hermitescher Formen über lokalen Körpern.

Math. Ann. **186** (1970), 201–208.

Let K be a local field and D a finite-dimensional division algebra with centre K. Let J be an involution of D of the first or of the second kind (for the nomenclature, see Chapter X, in A. A. Albert's *Structure of algebras* [Amer. Math. Soc., New York, 1939; MR **1**, 99; revised printing, 1961; MR **23** #A912]).

The valuation on K has a unique extension to D and the corresponding residue class ring is a division algebra $\bar{D}$ say. Let V be a finite-dimensional (left) vector space over D and $h: V\times V\to D$ a hermitian form over (D, J). If h is anisotropic, then $\|x\|=\sqrt{|h(x,x)|}$ for all $x\in V$ defines a norm and $M_0=\{x\mid \|x\|\leqq 1\}$, $M_1=\{x\mid \|x\|<1\}$ are both modules over the valuation ring of D. $\bar{V}=M_0/M_1$ is a $\bar{D}$ vector space and h defines an anisotropic hermitian form $\bar{h}_1: \bar{V}\times\bar{V}\to\bar{D}$ over $(\bar{D}, \bar{J})$. If characteristic $k\neq 2$ and if there is a symmetrical uniformising $t\in D$, then th defines $\bar{h}_2$ ($\bar{J}$ has to be replaced in an appropriate way) and it is shown that two forms h are isometric if and only if the corresponding forms $\bar{h}$ are isometric. Necessary and sufficient conditions for the existence of t are established by a process of elimination. As the author states, his method is similar to the one used by T. A. Springer [Nederl. Akad. Wetensch. Proc. Ser. A **58** (1955), 352–362; MR **17**, 17, see also ibid. **59** (1956), 238–246; MR **17**, 945] and closely related to the work by F. Bruhat and J. Tits [Proc. Conf. Local Fields (Driebergen, 1966), pp. 23–36, Springer, Berlin, 1967; MR **37** #6396].

C. F. Moppert (Clayton)

Citations: MR 17, 17a = E08-10; MR 17, 945e = E08-11; MR 37# 6396 = E64-20.

E08-44 **(43# 246)**

Šapiro, A. P.

Characteristic polynomials of symmetric matrices of order four over the field of p-adic numbers. (Russian)

Dal'nevostoč. Gos. Univ. Učen. Zap. **16** (1968), 114–147.

Suppose that a polynomial $f(x)$ with rational coefficients has real roots alone. This article is related to the classical problem: under what conditions does $f(x)$ become the characteristic polynomial of a rational symmetric matrix. Let α be a root of $f(x)$ and let $\omega_1,\cdots,\omega_n$ be a basis of $k=Q(\alpha)$ over the rationals. It is known that the problem can be reduced to finding a number $\lambda\in k$ such that the quadratic form $\mathrm{Sp}\{\lambda(x_1\omega_1+\cdots+x_n\omega_n)^2\}$ is rationally equivalent to the form $x_1^2+\cdots+x_n^2$ [D. K. Faddeev, Dokl. Akad. Nauk SSSR **58** (1947), 753–754; MR **9**, 270]. In an earlier paper the author solved the case $n=3$ by making use of the well-known fact that two forms are rationally equivalent if and only if these are equivalent over all p-adic fields and over the real field [ibid. **119** (1958), 890–892; MR **20** #5785]. In the present article he considers the case $n=4$ and shows that any polynomial of fourth degree with p-adic coefficients becomes (up to a constant) the characteristic polynomial of a symmetric matrix with p-adic entries. *E. Inaba* (Tokyo)

Citations: MR 9, 270e = R26-3; MR 20# 5785 = C20-30.

E08-45 **(43# 6160)**

James, D. G.

On Witt's theorem for unimodular quadratic forms. II.

Pacific J. Math. **33** (1970), 645–652.

F sei ein lokaler Körper mit vollkommenem Restklassenkörper, in dem 2 prim ist, und $\mathfrak{o}$ der Ring der ganzen Zahlen in F. L sei ein $\mathfrak{o}$-Gitter mit einer unimodularen symmetrischen Bilinearform ϕ. Man setzt $\phi(\alpha,\alpha)=Q(\alpha)$. Für einen primitiven Vektor $\alpha\in L$ ist $Q(\alpha^\perp)\subset 2\mathfrak{o}$ gleichbedeutend mit $\phi(\alpha,\beta)^2Q(\gamma)\equiv\phi(\alpha,\gamma)^2Q(\beta) \bmod 2$ für alle β, $\gamma\in L$. Insbesondere ist die Restklasse $\phi(\alpha,\beta)^2/Q(\beta) \bmod 2$ von β unabhängig, wenn β alle Vektoren aus L mit $Q(\beta)\notin 2\mathfrak{o}$ durchläuft. Der Autor setzt dann für primitive $\alpha\in L$ $T(\alpha)=\phi(\alpha,\beta)^2/Q(\beta) \bmod 2$, falls $Q(\alpha^\perp)\subset 2\mathfrak{o}$ und $Q(\beta)\notin 2\mathfrak{o}$, $T(\alpha)=0 \bmod 2$, falls $Q(\alpha^\perp)\not\subset 2\mathfrak{o}$ oder $Q(L)\subset 2\mathfrak{o}$. Ist $\alpha=2^s\beta$ mit primitivem β, so wird $T(\alpha)=T(\beta)$ gesetzt. Dann wird der Satz bewiesen, daß eine Isometrie φ zwischen zwei primitiven Teilgittern J und K von L sich genau dann zu einer Isometrie von L fortsetzen läßt, wenn $T(\alpha)=T(\varphi\alpha)$ für alle $\alpha\in L$ ist.

{Part I appeared in same J. **26** (1968), 303–316 [MR **38** #3227].} *S. Böge* (Heidelberg)

Citations: MR 38# 3227 = E12-133.

E12 QUADRATIC FORMS OVER GLOBAL RINGS AND FIELDS

For forms of low dimensions, see **E16** and **E20**. For forms with specified numerical coefficients, see **E24** and **E28**.

See also reviews C20-23, C20-29, C20-48, D08-16, D08-20, D08-21, D08-23, E02-4, E02-6, E02-9, E02-11, E02-16, E04-33, E04-34, E08-6, E08-16, E16-10, E20-1, E20-15, E44-13, E56-58, E68-37, F02-7, F10-32, F10-38, F25-3, F40-2, F45-13, F50-2, F65-5, F65-9, J44-11, P08-47, P28-29, R26-3, R52-22, T15-17, T15-40, Z02-73, Z10-10.

E12-1 **(2, 36f)**

Braun, Hel. Geschlechter quadratischer Formen. J. Reine Angew. Math. **182**, 32–49 (1940).

In this paper the author gives the necessary and sufficient conditions, involving Gauss sums, for the existence of quadratic forms with integral coefficients possessing a given set of generic invariants. Here forms f are represented by their symmetric matrices $\mathfrak{S}$. Two symmetric matrices $\mathfrak{S}_1$ and $\mathfrak{S}_2$ are said to be equivalent if there exist integral matrices $\mathfrak{A}$, $\mathfrak{B}$ such that $\mathfrak{A}'\mathfrak{S}_1\mathfrak{A}=\mathfrak{S}_2$ and $\mathfrak{B}'\mathfrak{S}_2\mathfrak{B}=\mathfrak{S}_1$. Should $\mathfrak{A}'\mathfrak{S}_1\mathfrak{A}\equiv\mathfrak{S}_2$ and $\mathfrak{B}'\mathfrak{S}_2\mathfrak{B}\equiv\mathfrak{S}_1 \pmod q$, then $\mathfrak{S}_1$ and $\mathfrak{S}_2$ are equivalent modulo q. Matrices equivalent modulo any integer q and moreover equivalent in the field of real numbers form a genus. Two matrices $\mathfrak{S}_1$ and $\mathfrak{S}_2$ of order m belong to the same genus if and only if (i) they have the same index μ, (ii) the same absolute value D of the determinant and (iii) if they belong to the same class modulo q_0, where $q_0=8D^3$. [H. Minkowski, Gesammelte Abhandlungen, 1911, vol. 1, p. 158; C. L. Siegel, Ann. of Math. (2) **36**, 527–606 (1935); in particular, p. 548.] Employing the system (i)–(iii) of generic invariants, the author proves that the necessary and sufficient conditions for the existence of the genus with assigned invariants are: (1) $|\mathfrak{S}|=x^2(-1)^{m-\mu}D \pmod{q_0}$ has a solution x prime to q_0,

$$(2)\qquad \sum_{\mathfrak{r}(q_0)} e^{(2\pi i/q_0)\mathfrak{r}'\mathfrak{S}\mathfrak{r}}=e^{(\pi i/4)(2\mu-m)}(2q_0)^{m/2}D^{\frac{1}{2}}.$$

Here the elements $x_1,\cdots,x_n$ of the column vector $\mathfrak{r}$ in the Gauss sum in (2) run independently through a complete residue system modulo q_0. In the conclusion of the paper it is shown that these results yield a more direct proof of two important lemmas by Siegel [l.c., pp. 550 and 559].

A. E. Ross (St. Louis, Mo.).

Referred to in E12-103.

E12-2 (2, 147c)

Wenkov, B. Über die Reduction positiver quadratischer Formen. Bull. Acad. Sci. URSS. Sér. Math. [Izvestia Akad. Nauk SSSR] **4**, 37–52 (1940). (Russian. German summary)

The author introduces (after Minkowski) the space P of the coefficients a_{ij} ($i \leqq j$) of positive real quadratic forms $f=\sum_{i=1}^{n} a_{ij}x_ix_j$ and studies the problem of determination of the fundamental domains, with respect to P, of the group G_n of unimodular transformations of f. He considers the domain $V(\varphi)$ of points $f=(a_{11}, a_{12}, \cdots, a_{nn})$ defined by inequalities

$$(f, \Phi) \leqq (f, \mathfrak{G}'\Phi\mathfrak{G}) \quad \text{for every } \mathfrak{G} \text{ in } G_n,$$

where Φ is the adjoint of (the form) f and (f, Φ) is the scalar product of f and Φ. Employing results of Minkowski and Voronoi [H. Minkowski, Diskontinuitätsbereich für arithmetische Äquivalenz, Gesammelte Abhandlungen, Bd. II, 1911; G. Voronoi, J. Reine Angew. Math. **133** (1908)], the author shows that $V(\varphi)$ is a pyramid with a finite number of faces, and that should φ have no automorphs then $V(\varphi)$ is a fundamental domain of G_n. In conclusion, the author points out that with the help of this more general fundamental domain one can see that for $n>2$ a fundamental domain may be deformed continuously. This is unlike the case for $n=2$, where the boundary of this domain consists entirely of forms with automorphs. *A. E. Ross.*

Referred to in F45-17.

E12-3 (2, 148a)

Humbert, Pierre. Théorie de la réduction des formes quadratiques définies positives dans un corps algébrique K fini. Comment. Math. Helv. **12**, 263–306 (1940).

In this paper Minkowski's theory of the equivalence of positive definite quadratic forms with respect to transformations with integral coefficients (and determinant ± 1) is extended to transformations whose coefficients are integers in a finite algebraic field K and whose determinant is a unit in K. As it stands the group of such "unimodular" transformations is not properly discontinuous in the space of the coefficients of the form. The author therefore deals with a system S of forms consisting of a positive definite quadratic form with real coefficients for each real conjugate of K and a pair of conjugate imaginary Hermitian forms for each pair of conjugate imaginary conjugates of K. These forms in S are then simultaneously transformed by the transformations conjugate to the given unimodular transformation in K. In the space of the coefficients of S the group is then found to be properly discontinuous and results analogous to Minkowski's hold: There exists a fundamental domain formed by the union of several convex solid angles R_i each bounded by a finite number of hyperplanes; each R_i is in contact with a finite number of equivalent fundamental domains. In particular it follows that the unimodular group here considered has a finite number of generators, a fact that had been proved by Hurwitz [Gesammelte Werke, v. 2, p. 244].

The method used is essentially that of Minkowski and consists in finding a "reduced" system equivalent to S. The main modification is that the process of "reduction" is accomplished in two steps, this being made necessary by the fact that the class number of K may be greater than one. First a given system S is transformed by all non-singular transformations with integral coefficients. From the resulting family of systems, systems are then selected successively by minimum requirements similar to those used by Hermite and Minkowski. One or more systems S_1 thus result, each being obtained by transforming S by a transformation A_0 which will not usually be unimodular. It is shown, however, that the norm of the determinant of A_0 is bounded, and, as a consequence, that $A_0=UA_\nu$, where U is unimodular and A_ν belongs to a certain fixed set of non-singular matrices A_i ($i=1, 2, \cdots, N$). Transformation by A_ν^{-1} then yields a system S_2 equivalent to S and this is called a "reduced" system. To each matrix A_i corresponds a domain R_i of reduced systems and the union of these is the fundamental domain of the unimodular group. The fundamental domain thus found is then shown to have the properties stated above. Throughout these proofs the main tool employed is Minkowski's theorem on linear forms.

H. W. Brinkmann (Swarthmore, Pa.).

Referred to in E12-34, E12-115, H05-5.

E12-4 (2, 148b)

Siegel, Carl Ludwig. Einheiten quadratischer Formen. Abh. Math. Sem. Hansischen Univ. **13**, 209–239 (1940).

This paper contains an extended discussion of results presented in Hamburg in January, 1939. The first part of the paper is devoted to a simple development of Minkowski's theory of the reduction of positive quadratic forms [J. Reine Angew. Math. **129**, 220–274 (1905); Werke, Bd. 2, pp. 53–100. Cf. Bieberbach und Schur, S.-B. Preuss. Akad. Wiss., Phys.-Math. Kl. **1928**, 510–535] and of Hermite's theory of the reduction of indefinite quadratic forms [Hermite, J. Reine Angew. Math. **47**, 330–342 (1854); Oeuvres, T. 1, pp. 220–238; Stouff, Ann. École Norm. (3) **19**, 89–118 (1902)]. The second part contains the subject proper of this paper, that is, the study of the group Γ of integral automorphs of an indefinite quadratic form $\mathfrak{r}'\mathfrak{S}\mathfrak{r}$. Here the author proves that this group of automorphs has a finite number of generators (a deep and difficult theorem), thus generalizing the well-known result for indefinite binary quadratic forms. He also establishes the convergence of the integral

$$v(\mathfrak{S}) = D^{-n/2}\int_G |\mathfrak{T}|^{-m/2} d\mathfrak{Y}$$

(where G is the fundamental domain of Γ in a suitably chosen space $\mathfrak{Y}$), and employs it to define the mass $\mu(\mathfrak{S})$ of Γ. [Cf. Siegel, Math. Z. **44**, 398–426 (1939).] He next defines the mass (weight) of a genus as the sum $\mu(\mathfrak{S}_1)+\cdots+\mu(\mathfrak{S}_n)$, where $\mathfrak{S}_i$ are representatives of distinct classes of that genus and gives a formula for the weight of the genus of indefinite quadratic forms [cf. Siegel, Ann. of Math. (2) **37**, 230–263 (1936)]. *A. E. Ross* (St. Louis, Mo.).

Referred to in E12-27, E12-34, E12-41, E20-8, E60-5, F02-5, P28-29.

E12-5 (2, 251d)

Pall, Gordon. Simultaneous representation in a quadratic and linear form. Duke Math. J. **8**, 173–180 (1941).

The solvability in integers of the simultaneous equations

(1) $$c_1x_1^2+\cdots+c_sx_s^2=a, \quad c_1x_1+\cdots+c_sx_s=b$$

is considered. Put $t=c_1+\cdots+c_s$. The identity

(2) $$ta-b^2=\sum_{i<k} c_ic_k(x_i-x_k)^2$$

and the substitution $y_j=x_1-x_j$, $j=2, \cdots, s$ leads to a representation of $ta-b^2$ by a quadratic form in the $s-1$ y's. A study of this single form leads to criteria for the solvability of the system (1), including conditions for the existance of non-negative solutions. Various examples and a table of forms with $s=4$ are given. *M. Hall.*

Referred to in E12-109.

E12-6 **(2, 348e)**

Ko, Chao. On the Meyer's theorem and the decomposition of quadratic forms. J. Chinese Math. Soc. **2**, 209–224 (1940).

It is proved first that an n-ary form $f=\sum a_{ij}x_ix_j$ (a_{ij} integers) of determinant ± 1 has minimum not greater than 1, if $n\leqq 7$, and represents zero if its signature is 1. A proof of Meyer's theorem that indefinite forms in five or more variables represent zero is then obtained by imbedding a related form as a section of a form of determinant ± 1 in 7 variables. Similarly by imbedding an n-ary form in a form of determinant 1 in $n+3$ variables it is proved that every n-ary integral f can be expressed as an algebraic sum of $n+3$ squares of linear forms with integer coefficients. The proof uses the author's work [Acta Arith. **3**, 79–85 (1938)] on quadratic forms of determinant 1, and a theorem by Zilinskas [J. London Math. Soc. **13**, 225–240 (1938)] that every properly primitive indefinite quadratic form of determinant ± 1 is equivalent to a form $\sum x_i^2-\sum x_j^2$.

G. Pall (Montreal, Que.).

E12-7 **(3, 70i)**

Braun, Hel. Zur Theorie der hermitischen Formen. Abh. Math. Sem. Hansischen Univ. **14**, 61–150 (1941).

The author obtains for Hermitian forms results analogous to those of C. L. Siegel [Ann. of Math. (2) **36**, 527–606 (1935); **37**, 230–263 (1936); **38**, 212–291 (1937)] for quadratic forms. The coefficients of the Hermitian forms are algebraic integers in an arbitrary quadratic field K over the field of rational numbers. Siegel's methods appear to carry through to a large extent if every ideal in K is a principal ideal. For Hermitian forms over other quadratic fields it is not true, for instance, that every form is equivalent to one with a non-zero determinant. Here it is necessary to build on Siegel's results for quadratic forms with algebraic integers as coefficients and on methods of Humbert [C. R. Acad. Sci. Paris **169**, 309–316, 360–365, 407–414 (1919)].

An important result of Braun's which appears to have no analogue in Siegel's work is his theorem II: Given r, β, d, an r-rowed Hermitian matrix $\mathfrak{H}$ and the modulus q with $4\,Md^3\,|\,q$, where M is the absolute value of the fundamental number (Grundzahl) of the quadratic field K. Then there is a matrix $\mathfrak{H}_0\sim\mathfrak{H}$ (mod q) of rank r, index β and discriminant d (d is the greatest common ideal divisor of the r-rowed minors of $\mathfrak{H}_0$) if there is an integer x in K and an integral ideal α in K such that

$$(-1)^\beta dN(x)\equiv N(\alpha)\,|\mathfrak{H}|\pmod q,\quad (x,q)=1,\ (\alpha,q)=1.$$

Furthermore one can choose $\mathfrak{H}_0$ to be an $r+1$-rowed matrix such that

$$\mathfrak{H}_0\equiv\begin{pmatrix}\mathfrak{H} & \mathfrak{n}\\ \mathfrak{n}' & 0\end{pmatrix}\pmod q.$$

While the basis is laid for consideration of indefinite as well as positive Hermitian forms, the theory is carried through explicitly only for the latter. Here, the result analogous to Siegel's is

$$\frac{M(\mathfrak{H},\mathfrak{K})}{M(\mathfrak{H})}=\epsilon d^{-s}c^{r-s}\lambda\prod_{j=r-s+1}\frac{(2\pi)^j}{(j-1)!M^{j/2}},$$

where Hermitian forms $\mathfrak{H}$ and $\mathfrak{K}$ have ranks r and s and discriminants d and c, respectively, $r\geqq s$, $\epsilon=\frac{1}{2}$ or 1 according as $r=s$ or $r>s$, M is defined above,

$$\lambda=\lim_{q\to\infty}q^{s(s-2r)}A_q(\mathfrak{H},\mathfrak{K})$$

and the other terms are defined as in Siegel's work.

B. W. Jones (Ithaca, N. Y.).

Referred to in E12-103, E12-116, F55-2.

E12-8 **(3, 161f)**

Griffiths, L. W. Universal functions of extended polygonal numbers. Amer. J. Math. **63**, 726–728 (1941).

This paper supplements the results of a previous paper [Amer. J. Math. **55**, 102–110 (1933)] on the problem of determining which linear functions

$$a_1t_1+a_2t_2+\cdots+a_nt_n,\quad a_1+a_2+\cdots+a_n\leqq m;\ m>5,$$

represent every number when the t's range independently over all "extended" polygonal numbers $-x+m(x^2+x)/2$ ($x=-1, 0, 1, 2, \cdots$) of order m. Certain necessary conditions were found in the previous paper and in some cases these were found sufficient. It is now found that the possibly exceptional cases of the previous paper are also sufficient. The methods of proof, which appear to be complicated, are illustrated by considering the representation of all numbers lying between $151m-22$ and $153m-23$. *D. H. Lehmer.*

Referred to in E12-13.

E12-9 **(3, 163b)**

Siegel, Carl Ludwig. Equivalence of quadratic forms. Amer. J. Math. **63**, 658–680 (1941).

If R, R_p, R_∞ are the fields of rational, p-adic, real numbers, respectively, and J and J_p the rings of integral numbers and of p-adic integers, respectively, the main object of this paper can be stated in the two theorems: (I) If two quadratic forms with coefficients of R are equivalent in all R_p and in R_∞ then they are also equivalent in R. (II) If two quadratic forms with coefficients of J are equivalent in all J_p and in R_∞ then they are semiequivalent. Semiequivalence of two quadratic forms means that the transformation matrix can be chosen so as to have elements with denominators prime to a preassigned integer q. Theorem (I) was found by Minkowski and proved in detail first by Hasse. Theorem (II) was proved for three variables by Smith, stated in general by Minkowski, but not completely proved before this paper.

It is easily seen that only nondegenerate forms, and for (I) in particular only diagonal forms with integral coefficients, need to be considered. Instead of Dirichlet's theorem on the prime numbers in arithmetical progressions, which had been used in previous proofs, the author employs here the properties of theta-functions, which he considers the appropriate tools for the investigation of quadratic forms. To the indefinite form $S=\sum_{k=1}^m a_kx_k^2$ with integral coefficients Siegel associates the form $P=\sum_{k=1}^m|a_k|x_k^2$ and enumerates the solutions of $S=0$ by $A(\epsilon)=\sum_{s=0}\exp(-\pi\epsilon P)$, for an arbitrary $\epsilon>0$ and where $x_1, \cdots, x_m$ run over all solutions of $S=0$. Introducing

$$f(u)=\sum_x\exp(-\pi\epsilon P+2\pi iuS),$$

where the sum is extended over all integral values $x_1, \cdots, x_m$, we have clearly that $A(\epsilon)=\int_0^1 f(u)du$. On this equation Siegel applies the Hardy-Littlewood method of Farey arcs and studies in particular the emerging singular series in order to prove: (III) For $m>4$ we have $\lim_{\epsilon\to 0}\epsilon^{(m/2)-1}A(\epsilon)\to\omega\sigma>0$ with explicitly known constants ω and σ depending on the quadratic form S. (IV) If for $m=4$ the indefinite form S represents zero in all R_p and if its determinant is a square then $(\epsilon/|\log\epsilon|)A(\epsilon)$ tends to a positive limit with $\epsilon\to 0$. These theorems are quantitative refinements of theorems due to Legendre, H. Hasse and A. Mayer.

Theorem (I) requires an induction in the number of variables which is based on a theorem of E. Witt, here specialized to the lemma: If S and T are two quadratic forms in the variables $x_1, \cdots, x_m$ and with coefficients in one of the fields R, R_p, R_∞ and if ax_0^2+S and ax_0^2+T are equivalent in the field under consideration, then S and T are also equivalent in that field. Now in Theorem (I) two quadratic forms

$$S=\sum_{k=1}^{m} a_k x_k^2, \quad T=\sum_{k=1}^{m} b_k y_k^2$$

with integral coefficients are given which are equivalent in all R_p and in R_∞. Then the author considers the quadratic form $V=S-T$ in $2m$ variables $x_1, \cdots, x_m, y_1, \cdots, y_m$. On account of the equivalence of S and T in R_∞ the form V is indefinite and on account of the equivalence in all R_p the form V represents zero in all R_p. This makes it possible to apply Theorems (III) and (IV) to the proof of (I). Theorem (II) is derived from (I) by means of some additional algebraic considerations. *H. Rademacher* (Philadelphia, Pa.).

Referred to in E08-3.

E12-10 (3, 163d)

Witt, Ernst. Eine Identität zwischen Modulformen zweiten Grades. Abh. Math. Sem. Hansischen Univ. **14**, 323–337 (1941).

Let $(u_{k1}, \cdots, u_{km})$ $(k=1, \cdots, m)$ be a basis of the lattice of all vectors $(u_1, \cdots, u_m)$ satisfying the conditions $u_k\equiv 0$ (mod $\frac{1}{2}$), $u_k\equiv u_l$ (mod 1), $\sum_{k=1}^m u_k\equiv 0$ (mod 2), where m denotes a multiple of 8. Then

$$Q_m(x)=\sum_{l=1}^{m}(u_{1l}x_1+\cdots+u_{ml}x_m)^2$$

is an even positive quadratic form of determinant 1. For $m=16$, the genus of Q_m contains exactly two classes, namely, the class of $Q_{16}(x)$ and the class of $Q_8(x)+Q_8(y)$. The two non-equivalent quadratic forms $Q_{16}(x)$ and $Q_8(x)+Q_8(y)$ represent every binary quadratic form the same number of times. The proof uses the analytic theory of quadratic forms and the theory of modular forms of degree 2. The result can be expressed by the identity $(\sum|\mathfrak{A}\mathfrak{Z}+\mathfrak{B}|^{-4})^2=\sum|\mathfrak{A}\mathfrak{Z}+\mathfrak{B}|^{-8}$, where $\mathfrak{Z}$ is a symmetric matrix with two rows and positive imaginary part, and $\mathfrak{A}, \mathfrak{B}$ run over a complete system of non-associate coprime symmetric pairs of matrices with two rows. *C. L. Siegel.*

Referred to in E12-31, E12-124, F50-61.

E12-11 (3, 268c)

Griffiths, L. W. A note on representation by polygonal numbers. Bull. Amer. Math. Soc. **48**, 122–124 (1942).

The problem considered in this paper is the representation of all positive integers by the linear combination

$$(1) \qquad a_1f(x_1)+a_2f(x_2)+\cdots+a_nf(x_n),$$

where the a's are positive integers, the x's are nonnegative integers, and $f(x)=f_m(x)=x+m(x^2-x)/2$. For $m\geqq 3$, the least value N of n for which such a linear combination (1) exists is proved to be the greatest integer less than $\log_2(8m+8)$. Such a minimal combination exists uniquely (except for rearrangement of the terms) if and only if $m=3, 4, 2^{N-2}-2, 2^{N-2}-1$. *D. H. Lehmer.*

E12-12 (5, 141f)

Jones, Burton W. Related genera of quadratic forms. Duke Math. J. **9**, 723–756 (1942).

Employing the case $n=1$ of the Siegel formula for the weighted mean $A_0(\mathfrak{S}, \mathfrak{T})$ of the number of representations of a quadratic form $\mathfrak{T}$ in n variables by the genus of a quadratic form $\mathfrak{S}$ in m variables [Ann. of Math. (2) **36**, 527–606 (1935)], the author derives [§4] recurrence relations [(11) and (12), pp. 743–744] between the weighted mean $A_0(\mathfrak{S}, pt)$ of the number of representations of pt by the genus of $\mathfrak{S}$ and such weighted means of the numbers of representations of the divisor t of pt by each of the genera "related" [§3] to $\mathfrak{S}$. Sections 6–8 of this paper contain some interesting applications to forms in two, three and four variables. There, among other things, the author obtains for ternary forms $\mathfrak{S}$ a simple expression for $A_0(\mathfrak{S}, t)$ in terms of class number and illustrates the use of his above-mentioned recurrence formulae through the study of numerical examples, obtaining in passing a number of fundamental classical results on the number of representations of integers by certain ternary and quaternary forms. In applications the often troublesome question of the number of classes in a genus can, in some cases, be settled conclusively by means of the useful theorems 7 and 8. *A. E. Ross* (St. Louis, Mo.).

E12-13 (5, 199d)

Griffiths, L. W. Universal functions of polygonal numbers. II. Amer. J. Math. **66**, 97–100 (1944).

[The first part appeared in Ann. of Math. (2) **31**, 1–12 (1930).] This paper is a continuation of the author's study of those integer linear combinations

$$(1) \qquad a_1f(x_1)+a_2f(x_2)+\cdots+a_nf(x_n), \quad 1\leqq a_1\leqq\cdots\leqq a_n,$$

of $f(x_k)=x_k+m(x_k^2-x_k)/2$, which represent all integers greater than 0, in which case (1) is said to be universal. The cases in which the weight $w=a_1+\cdots+a_n$ is less than $m+3$ was treated in part I. The present paper deals with $w=m+3$. In this case for (1) to be universal the first four coefficients must be either (1,1,1,1), (1,1,1,2) or (1,1,2,2). In the first two cases certain necessary further conditions on the remaining a's are shown to be sufficient. In the third case the corresponding necessary conditions are perhaps insufficient since a finite number of integers may not be represented by (1). The paper concludes with a discussion of the cases in which the universality of (1) is not a trivial consequence of the universality of another form of lesser weight [see also the same J. **63**, 726–728 (1941); Amer. Math. Monthly **49**, 107–110 (1942); these Rev. **3**, 161, 268]. *D. H. Lehmer* (Berkeley, Calif.).

Citations: MR 3, 161f = E12-8; MR 3, 268b = P02-1.
Referred to in E12-21.

E12-14 (5, 200d)

Ko, Chao. On the decomposition of quadratic forms in seven variables. Acad. Sinica Science Record **1**, 30–33 (1942).

Let

$$f_n=\sum_{i=1}^{n} x_i^2+(\sum_i x_i)^2-2x_1x_2-2x_1x_n.$$

It is proved that every classic positive definite $f=\sum a_{ij}x_ix_j$ $(i, j=1, \cdots, 7)$, which can not be expressed as $f'(x_1, \cdots, x_7)+f''(x_1, \cdots, x_7)$, where f' and f'' are classic and represent no negative numbers, is equivalent to the form f_7 (of determinant 2). The proof starts with the observation that f must be represented by one of the two forms $y_1^2+\cdots+y_{10}^2$, $y_{10}^2+y_9^2+f_8(y_1, \cdots, y_8)$, and hence (if nondecomposable) by f_8. A detailed analysis of the representation of f by f_8 leads to the stated result. *G. Pall.*

E12-15 (5, 201a)

Ko, Chao. On the decomposition of quadratic forms in eight variables. Acad. Sinica Science Record **1**, 33–36 (1942).

It was previously proved [Ko, Sci. Rep. Tsing Hua Univ. **5**, nos. 4–6 (1941)] that every positive definite classic f in eight variables not equivalent to f_8 is decomposable [see the preceding review] as $f'+f''$. It is now shown that we can take f' to be a square of a linear form. Use is made of the representation of f by one of the two classes of forms of determinant 1 in eleven variables [Ko, Acta Arith. **3**, 79–85 (1938)]. *G. Pall* (Montreal, Que.).

Referred to in E12-16.

E12-16 **(10, 103c)**

Ko, Chao. On the decomposition of quadratic forms in eight variables. Sci. Rep. Nat. Tsing Hua Univ. **4**, 337–340 (1947).

This article apparently preceded one already reviewed [Acad. Sinica Science Record **1**, 33–36 (1942); these Rev. **5**, 201] but was delayed in publication. It modifies slightly the proof of the theorem given in the cited article.

G. Pall (Chicago, Ill.).

Citations: MR 5, 201a = E12-15.

E12-17 **(5, 254e)**

O'Connor, R. E. and Pall, G. The construction of integral quadratic forms of determinant 1. Duke Math. J. **11**, 319–331 (1944).

The authors prove that there exists a quadratic form in 24 variables with integer coefficients and determinant unity which does not represent 1 and 2. They also construct a form in 40 variables not representing 1, 2 and 3. The question whether there exist for every k forms with determinant unity and integer coefficients whose minimum is k is left open for $k>3$. *P. Erdös* (Lafayette, Ind.).

Referred to in E12-47.

E12-18 **(6, 38b)**

Siegel, Carl Ludwig. On the theory of indefinite quadratic forms. Ann. of Math. (2) **45**, 577–622 (1944).

Let $\mathfrak{S}$ be a nonsingular m-rowed symmetric matrix with integer elements and $\Gamma(\mathfrak{S})$ the group of all integral matrices $\mathfrak{U}$ satisfying the equation $\mathfrak{S}[\mathfrak{U}]=\mathfrak{S}$ (that is, $\mathfrak{U}'\mathfrak{S}\mathfrak{U}=\mathfrak{S}$). If $\mathfrak{X}$ and $\mathfrak{W}$ are m by m real nonsingular matrices and $\mathfrak{W}$ is symmetric, $\mathfrak{S}[\mathfrak{X}]=\mathfrak{W}$ defines an $\frac{1}{2}m(m-1)$ dimensional surface and $\rho(\mathfrak{S})$ is the volume of a fundamental domain on the surface $\mathfrak{S}[\mathfrak{X}]=\mathfrak{W}$ with respect to $\Gamma(\mathfrak{S})$ computed with a certain given volume element. Let $\mathfrak{G}$ be a given real matrix with m rows and n columns and of rank n, while $\Gamma(\mathfrak{S},\mathfrak{G})$ is the subgroup of $\Gamma(\mathfrak{S})$ defined by the condition $\mathfrak{U}\mathfrak{G}=\mathfrak{G}$. Moreover, $\mathfrak{G}_1$ and $\mathfrak{G}_2$ are said to be associate relative to $\Gamma(\mathfrak{S})$ if for some element $\mathfrak{U}$ of $\Gamma(\mathfrak{S})$ it is true that $\mathfrak{G}_2=\mathfrak{U}\mathfrak{G}_1$.

The author defines the "measure of the representations of $\mathfrak{T}$ by $\mathfrak{S}$" as

$$\mu(\mathfrak{S},\mathfrak{T})=\sum_{G}(\mathfrak{S},\mathfrak{G})/\rho(\mathfrak{S}),$$

where $\mathfrak{G}$ runs over a complete set of nonassociate integral solutions of $\mathfrak{S}[\mathfrak{G}]=\mathfrak{T}$ of rank n. Let $A_q(\mathfrak{S},\mathfrak{T})$ be the number of modulo q incongruent solutions $\mathfrak{G}$ of the congruence $\mathfrak{S}[\mathfrak{G}]\equiv\mathfrak{T}$ (mod q), where q is an arbitrary positive integer, and

$$\alpha_p(\mathfrak{S},\mathfrak{T})=\lim_{l\to\infty} q^{\frac{1}{2}n(n+1)-mn}A_q(\mathfrak{S},\mathfrak{T})$$

for $q=p^l$, p being a prime. The author's principal result is the following theorem. Let $r, m-r$ be the signature of $\mathfrak{S}$ and $n\leqq r$, $n\leqq m-r$, $2n+2<m$. Then

$$\mu(\mathfrak{S},\mathfrak{T})=\prod_{p}\alpha_p(\mathfrak{S},\mathfrak{T}),$$

where p runs over all primes. A corresponding result is proved for primitive solutions. This is a refinement of a result in a former paper [Ann. of Math. (2) **36**, 527–606 (1935); also (2) **37**, 230–263 (1936)], and consists chiefly in showing that all quadratic forms in the same genus have the same representation measures when the conditions of the theorem hold, whereas the former results were concerned with a sum over the classes of the genus. *B. W. Jones.*

Referred to in E12-34, E12-42, E12-94, E12-117.

E12-19 **(7, 50f)**

Pall, Gordon. The arithmetical invariants of quadratic forms. Bull. Amer. Math. Soc. **51**, 185–197 (1945).

This lecture is a survey of the recent developments in the study of the arithmetic invariants of quadratic forms with particular emphasis placed on the author's own contributions to the subject; a more detailed account is to appear in a forthcoming book. The major aim is the construction of a complete system of generic invariants which can be readily evaluated with the help of an easily computable canonical form. It is shown that, if p is a finite prime, then every integral $n$ary quadratic form f can be expressed (by means of a rational transformation which is integral modulo p and has determinant $+1$) in the form

$$p^{e_1}\phi_1+\cdots+p^{e_s}\phi_s, \qquad e_1<\cdots<e_s,$$

where each ϕ_i denotes a form with integral coefficients modulo p, the variables in different ϕ_i do not overlap, $|\phi_i|$ is prime to p $(i=1,\cdots,s)$ and the e_i are integers. Also, $e_1\geqq 0$, except that $e_1=-1$ if $p=2$ and f has any odd cross-product coefficient. If n_i denotes the number of variables in ϕ_i, $\sum n_i=n$ and $\sum e_in_i$ is the exponent to which p appears in f. The proof (which serves also as the method of reduction) amounts to little more than judiciously completing squares. A complete system of invariants is then defined in terms of the above canonical form and their use is illustrated by an example. A very neat and compact condition for the existence of a quadratic form in n variables with prescribed invariants is given. It consists of the equality $\prod_p c_p(f)=+1$ and the assumption that the product of all the characters modulo $p>2$ has the same value as $(d_1|p)$, where $d=p^ed_1$, $(d_1,p)=1$. Here $c_p(f)$ are generic invariants of f.

The author points out that although the ideas and methods employed are essentially those of Hensel [Zahlentheorie, Göschen, Berlin-Leipzig, 1913] and Hasse [J. Reine Angew. Math. **152**, 129–148, 205–224 (1923)] there are three aspects in which his treatment differs from theirs. First, in defining generic invariants he introduces a symbol which, although essentially equal to Hilbert's norm-residue symbol, is defined more simply and symmetrically. Second, he does not use p-adic numbers as such, but replaces them by rational congruences. Third, in deriving all of the results of this article, the author avoids the use of the deep result of Dirichlet on the existence of primes in an arithmetical progression and employs instead the essentially more elementary theorem of Gauss on the existence of a genus of binary quadratic forms. As an illustration of this approach he gives a very simple proof of Legendre's theorem that every positive integer not of the form $4^k(8n+7)$ is a sum of three squares. *A. E. Ross* (St. Louis, Mo.).

E12-20 **(7, 51a)**

Siegel, Carl Ludwig. The average measure of quadratic forms with given determinant and signature. Ann. of Math. (2) **45**, 667–685 (1944).

In the first part of this paper the author proves (in two ways) that

$$(1) \qquad \sum_{k\leqq N} h_{4k}\log\epsilon_{4k}\sim 4\pi^2N^{\frac{3}{2}}/(21\zeta(3)), \qquad N\to\infty.$$

This result is equivalent to a hitherto unproved assertion of Gauss that the mean value of the expression $h_{4k}\log\epsilon_{4k}$ is asymptotically equal to $2\pi^2k^{\frac{1}{2}}/(7\zeta(3))$. Here h_d is the number of classes of primitive binary quadratic forms $Q(x,y)=ax^2+bxy+cy^2$ of positive discriminant $d=b^2-4ac$; two forms belong to the same class if they can be transformed into one another by an integral transformation of determinant $+1$; if d is not a perfect square, $\epsilon_d=\frac{1}{2}(t+u\sqrt{d})$, where t, u are the smallest positive integral solutions of

$t^2-du^2=4$.

The author observes that both methods of proof can be used to determine the average of $h_d \log \epsilon_d$ in any class of residues $d\equiv d_0 \pmod m$. The first proof contains explicitly the results for $m=4$ and $d_0=0, 1$ and yields the formula

$$(2) \qquad \sum_{k\leqq N} h_k \log \epsilon_k = \pi^2 N^{\frac{3}{2}}/(18\zeta(3)) + O(N \log N).$$

It is pointed out that the first method applied to positive binary forms leads to the corresponding results

$$(1') \qquad \sum_{k\leqq N} h_{-4k} \sim 4\pi N^{\frac{3}{2}}/(21\zeta(3)),$$

$$(2') \qquad \sum_{k\leqq N} h_{-k} = \pi N^{\frac{3}{2}}/(18\zeta(3)) + O(N \log N).$$

Mertens [J. Reine Angew. Math. **77**, 289–339 (1874)] proved (1′) by direct computation of the lattice points in the three-dimensional domain $|b|<a<c$, $0<4ac-b^2<T$. Application of a corresponding idea in the case of indefinite forms serves as the basis for the second proof of (1).

The second part of the paper contains a geometric treatment of the analogous problem for quadratic forms $\mathfrak{S}[\mathfrak{x}]$ in m variables. It is shown that

$$(3) \qquad \sum_{S\leqq N} S\rho(\mathfrak{S}) \sim \tfrac{1}{2} N \prod_{k=2}^{m} \zeta(k), \qquad N\to\infty.$$

Here the summation is extended over a system of representatives $\mathfrak{S}$ of all classes of given signature $n, m-n$ whose determinants have the absolute value $S\leqq N$, and $\rho(\mathfrak{S})$ is defined as follows: let $\mathfrak{T}$ be a variable real symmetric matrix of signature $n, m-n$ which lies in a domain T, let Y be the domain in the space of all real m-rowed matrices $\mathfrak{Y}$ which is mapped into T by the condition $\mathfrak{S}[\mathfrak{Y}]=\mathfrak{T}$, and let Y_0 be a fundamental domain in Y with respect to the group of units of $\mathfrak{S}$. Then, if $v(Y_0)$ and $v(T)$ are the Euclidean volumes of Y_0 and T, where the m^2 elements of $\mathfrak{Y}$ and the $\frac{1}{2}m(m+1)$ independent elements of $\mathfrak{T}$ are taken as rectangular Cartesian coordinates, we have

$$\rho(\mathfrak{S}) = \lim_{T\to\mathfrak{S}} v(Y_0)/v(T)$$

if the limit exists, and $\rho(\mathfrak{S})=0$ otherwise. It is brought out by the author that in case $n=0$ or $n=m$ (3) follows from a result of Minkowski [J. Reine Angew. Math. **129**, 220–274 (1906)]. *A. E. Ross* (St. Louis, Mo.).

Referred to in M05-32.

E12-21 (7, 146d)

Griffiths, L. W. Universal functions of polygonal numbers. III. Amer. J. Math. **67**, 443–449 (1945).

The author continues the investigation of those quadratic forms

$$f=\sum_{i=1}^{n} a_i(x_i+mx_i(x_i-1)/2), \qquad m\geqq 3,$$

which represent all integers. The paper is devoted to the case in which the weight $w=\sum_{i=1}^{n} a_i$ has the value $m+4$. The case $w\leqq m+3$ was treated in part II [same J. **66**, 97–100 (1944); these Rev. **5**, 199]. The results are too complicated to be quoted here. *D. H. Lehmer.*

Citations: MR 5, 199d = E12-13.

E12-22 (7, 369a)

Eichler, Martin. Zur Theorie der quadratischen Formen gerader Variablenzahl. Festschrift zum 60. Geburtstag von Prof. Dr. Andreas Speiser, 34–46, Füssli, Zürich, 1945.

It has long been known that there exists a very close relationship between the arithmetic theory of binary quadratic forms and the arithmetic of quadratic fields. More recently Brandt has shown [Math. Ann. **99**, 1–29 (1928); **94**, 179–197 (1925)] that a similar connection exists between the ideal theory in quaternion algebras and the quaternary quadratic forms. Hecke's studies of the number of representations of integers by quadratic forms in $2n$ variables seemed to point to the existence of a generalization of these results [cf. Hecke's Lectures on Dirichlet Series, Institute for Advanced Study, Princeton, N. J., 1938]. The paper under review contains a condensed exposition of such a generalization for quadratic forms in $2n$ variables. Following Brandt [Jber. Deutsch. Math. Verein. **47**, 149–159 (1937)] the author studies "stem forms" (Stammformen), that is, integral forms of smallest discriminant into which an integral form may be transformed by a rational transformation and cancellation of the g.c.d. of the coefficients. He introduces a canonical form into which a stem may be transformed by an integral p-adic transformation and, employing suitable arithmetic invariants, classifies stem forms into orders and genera. Next, he considers the set $f_j=x'A_jx$ $(j=1, \cdots, h)$ of representatives of classes of stem forms of a given order and defines a "transformer" [cf. Brandt, loc. cit.] of norm t as a linear transformation T_{ik} for which $T_{ik}'A_iT_{ik}=tA_k$. The concept of the transformer is the pivotal concept of the theory. Multiplication of transformers and their decomposition into primes obey the same laws as the ideals of a simple algebra [cf. M. Eichler, S.-B. Math.-Nat. Abt. Bayer. Akad. Wiss. **1943**, 1–28].

In the concluding two sections the author employs his theory to give a new proof for certain forms in $2n$ variables of A. Meyer's theorem [Vierteljschr. Naturforsch. Ges. Zürich **36**, 241–250 (1891)] that in general two indefinite quadratic forms of the same genus are equivalent. To the best of the reviewer's knowledge this is the first essentially new approach to the problem posed by Meyer. It is the hope of the author that the restrictive hypotheses of his present proof will be removed in the near future. *A. E. Ross* (St. Louis, Mo.).

Referred to in E12-26, E12-28.

E12-23 (7, 414e)

de Bruijn, N. G. On the number of solutions of the system $x_1^2+x_2^2+x_3^2=n$, $x_1+x_2+x_3=m$. Nieuw Arch. Wiskunde (2) **22**, 53–56 (1943). (Dutch)

The author gives an elegant proof of the (known) theorem that this number of solutions is $\alpha_N F(N)$, where $N=\frac{1}{2}(3n-m^2)$, $\alpha_N=6$ or 3 according as $N\equiv 0$ or $\not\equiv 0 \pmod 3$, and where $F(N)$ is the sum $\sum(-3|d)$, summed over all divisors d of N. *H. D. Kloosterman* (Leiden).

E12-24 (8, 138a)

Brandt, H. Über quadratische Kern- und Stammformen. Festschrift zum 60. Geburtstag von Prof. Dr. Andreas Speiser, 87–104, Füssli, Zürich, 1945.

A Kernform is an integral quadratic form of nonzero determinant which cannot be derived from any other such form by an integral linear transformation of determinant greater than 1. If also no integer multiple of the form can be so derived it is called a Stammform. Necessary and sufficient conditions for a form to be either a Kernform or Stammform are obtained. One can confine attention to transformations of a prime determinant p, where p^2 divides the discriminant (for a Kernform) or p divides the discriminant (for a Stammform). A form f is not a Kernform with respect to a prime p, if and only if the congruence $f(x_1, \cdots, x_n)\equiv 0 \pmod{p^2}$ is solvable primitively with the n linear forms $\partial f/\partial x_i$ all divisible by p. Simple conditions in terms of the generic characters and the expressions of f in canonical forms mod p^2 or mod 8 are obtained. This investigation has useful applications. It arises from the study of families of forms suggested by the theory of quadratic forms in the field of rationals and was inspired by a letter to the author from A. Speiser. [See Brandt, Jber. Deutsch. Math.-Verein. **47**, Abt. 1, 149–159 (1937).] *G. Pall.*

Referred to in E12-28, E12-48.

E12-25 (9, 79e; 9, 79f)

Oppenheim, A. A positive definite quadratic form as the sum of two positive definite quadratic forms. I. J. London Math. Soc. **21** (1946), 252–257 (1947).

Oppenheim, A. A positive definite quadratic form as the sum of two positive definite quadratic forms. II. J. London Math. Soc. **21** (1946), 257–264 (1947).

If ϕ is a positive definite integral quadratic form in $x_1, \cdots, x_n$, the problem is to determine a decomposition $\phi=\phi_1+\phi_2$, where ϕ_1, ϕ_2 are also positive definite integral quadratic forms. Let $L(\phi)$ denote the minimum of ϕ for all integers $x_1, \cdots, x_n$, the set $0, \cdots, 0$ excepted. In (II) the author proves the following results. (1) There exists a least integer $K_n \geqq 2$ such that all positive definite classical integral forms ϕ with $L(\phi) \geqq K_n$ are decomposable. There exist indecomposable forms ϕ with $L(\phi)<K_n$. (2) There exists a corresponding integer $K_n{}^*$ for the case of positive definite integral forms (not necessarily classical). In (I) it is proved that (a) $K_2=3$, $K_3=3$, (b) $K_2{}^*=2$, $K_3{}^*=2$. [Actually the existence of K_n and $K_n{}^*$ follows immediately from a theorem of Bieberbach and Schur, S.-B. Preuss. Akad. Wiss., Phys.-Math. Kl. **1928**, 510–535.] *H. S. A. Potter* (Aberdeen).

E12-26 (9, 136a)

Eichler, Martin. Über gewisse Anzahlformeln in der Theorie der quadratischen Formen. S.-B. Math.-Nat. Abt. Bayer. Akad. Wiss. **1943**, 1–24 (1944).

Consider a set of integral quadratic forms in $2n$ variables, all of the same determinant, which can be carried into one another by a rational linear transformation and division by a rational number. Let $f_i=x'A_ix$ be a set of representatives of the different classes in this set and let T_{ik} be an integral matrix such that $T'_{ik}A_iT_{ik}=tA_k$. As in a later paper [Festschrift zum 60. Geburtstag von A. Speiser, pp. 34–46, Zürich, 1945; these Rev. **7**, 369] the author calls such a matrix a transformer of norm t belonging to A_i and A_k and discusses a correspondence between these transformers and ideals of a simple algebra. He studies the factorization properties of these transformers, establishes a relation between the number of transformers of a given norm and the number of representations of integers by quadratic forms, and obtains in a purely number-theoretic manner equations corresponding to the representation formulae first obtained by analytic methods by Hecke [Lectures on Dirichlet Series, Institute for Advanced Study, Princeton, N. J., 1938]. *A. E. Ross* (Notre Dame, Ind.).

Citations: MR 7, 369a = E12-22.
Referred to in E12-28.

E12-27 (9, 273c)

Siegel, Carl Ludwig. Indefinite quadratische Formen und Modulfunktionen. Studies and Essays Presented to R. Courant on his 60th Birthday, January 8, 1948, pp. 395–406. Interscience Publishers, Inc., New York, 1948. $5.50.

Let $\mathfrak{S}$ be the matrix of an even quadratic form $\mathfrak{S}[\mathfrak{x}]$ of signature (n, ν) in $m=n+\nu$ variables x_i and with determinant $|\mathfrak{S}|=S>0$ so that ν is even. Then $\mathfrak{S}[\mathfrak{x}]=r-\rho$, where $r=t_1^2+\cdots+t_n^2$, $\rho=\tau_1^2+\cdots+\tau_\nu^2$ and the t_i and τ_i are homogeneous linear functions in the x_i with real coefficients. If z and ζ are complex variables in the upper and lower half-plane, respectively, and $\mathfrak{H}[\mathfrak{x}]=r+\rho$ then the quadratic form $\mathfrak{R}[\mathfrak{x}]=zr-\zeta\rho$ has the matrix $\mathfrak{R}=\frac{1}{2}(z+\zeta)\mathfrak{S}+\frac{1}{2}(z-\zeta)\mathfrak{H}$ with a positive imaginary part. The author first proves by well-known methods that the function $f(z, \zeta)=\sum \exp \pi i\mathfrak{R}[\mathfrak{G}]$, where $\mathfrak{G}$ ranges over all integral vectors, satisfies

$$f(\hat{z}, \hat{\zeta})=\omega(cz+d)^{\frac{1}{2}n}(c\zeta+d)^{\frac{1}{2}\nu}f(z, \zeta)$$

if z and ζ are transformed by the simultaneous modular substitutions

$$z\rightarrow\hat{z}=(az+b)/(cz+d), \quad \zeta\rightarrow\hat{\zeta}=(a\zeta+b)/(c\zeta+d),$$

and $c\mathfrak{S}^{-1}$ is even. Here $\omega^4=1$.

The author then shows how a modular form $F(z)$ in one variable z can be attached to the form $\mathfrak{S}[\mathfrak{x}]$ if $\mathfrak{S}$ is indefinite (so that $n\nu>0$) (the two special cases (a) $m<4$, $\mathfrak{S}[\mathfrak{x}]$ is a zero form; (b) $m=4$, $\mathfrak{S}[\mathfrak{x}]$ is a zero form, S is a square, have to be excluded). This is achieved in the following way. All positive solutions of $\mathfrak{H}\mathfrak{S}^{-1}\mathfrak{H}=\mathfrak{S}$ constitute an $n\nu$-dimensional space H. If $\mathfrak{F}$ is a real automorph of $\mathfrak{S}[\mathfrak{x}]$ then H is mapped onto itself by the mapping $\mathfrak{H}\rightarrow\mathfrak{H}[\mathfrak{F}]$. The quadratic differential form $ds^2=\frac{1}{8}$ trace $(\mathfrak{H}^{-1}d\mathfrak{H}\ \mathfrak{H}^{-1}d\mathfrak{H})$ is invariant under the group Ω of all real automorphs $\mathfrak{F}$ and defines a Riemann metric in H. The subgroup $\Gamma(\mathfrak{S})$ of Ω consisting of all integral automorphs of $\mathfrak{S}$ has a fundamental domain $H(\mathfrak{S})$ in H. It has been proved by the author in an earlier paper [Abh. Math. Sem. Hansischen Univ. **13**, 209–239 (1940); these Rev. **2**, 148] that the volume V of $H(\mathfrak{S})$ is finite (unless $m=2$ and S is a square) and that the integral $J(f)=\int f dv$ over $H(\mathfrak{S})$ converges. The author now proves that

$$F(z)=\Gamma(\tfrac{1}{2}n)\Gamma^{-1}(\tfrac{1}{2}m)V^{-1}(z-\zeta)^{1-1/n}(\partial/\partial x)^{\frac{1}{2}\nu}\{(z-\zeta)^{\frac{1}{2}m-1}J(f)\}$$

is a function of z only and is a modular form satisfying

$$F(z+1)=F(z), \quad F((az+b)/(cz+d))=\omega(cz+d)^{\frac{1}{2}m}F(z),$$

if $c\mathfrak{S}^{-1}$ is even and $c>0$. *H. D. Kloosterman* (Leiden).

Citations: MR 2, 148b = E12-4.
Referred to in E12-120.

E12-28 (10, 102f; 10, 102g)

Eichler, Martin. Grundzüge einer Zahlentheorie der quadratischen Formen im rationalen Zahlkörper. I. Comment. Math. Helv. **20**, 9–60 (1947).

Eichler, Martin. Grundzüge einer Zahlentheorie der quadratischen Formen im rationalen Zahlkörper. II. Comment. Math. Helv. **21**, 1–28 (1948).

Brandt has pointed out, with many illustrations, the relative simplicity of the arithmetical theory of quadratic stem-forms, as compared with the usual theory which treats stem-forms and others alike, or in some cases excludes stem-forms by fixing attention on so-called classical forms. [I: Jber. Deutsch. Math. Verein. **47**, 149–159 (1937); II: Festschrift zum 60. Geburtstag von Prof. Dr. Andreas Speiser, 87–104, Füssli, Zurich, 1945; these Rev. **8**, 138.] In his studies of the arithmetic of quaternions [cf. III: Jber. Deutsch. Math. Verein. **53**, 23–57 (1943); these Rev. **8**, 198], Brandt has also considered simultaneously all ideals belonging to a quaternion order (integral set) and the corresponding system of quaternary quadratic forms. These are stem-forms when the order is maximal. Eichler develops here an arithmetical theory of quadratic forms, in any number of variables, in which stem-forms only are dealt with for the most part, and in which an appropriate system of forms is simultaneously studied. He has already initiated the theory, chiefly for an even number of variables, in two earlier papers [IV: S.-B. Math.-Nat. Abt. Bayer Akad. Wiss. **1943**, 1–24; V: same Festschrift as in II, 34–36; these Rev. **9**, 136; **7**, 369]. In particular he has introduced [V] the concept of a transformer, which is here expanded into an "ideal" theory, and by means of which a system of forms is effectively studied.

A fundamental basis for the theory is the work of Hasse on quadratic forms over a number field [cf. VI: J. Reine Angew. Math. **153**, 158–162 (1924)] and that of Witt on the same subject, which leads to a group of form types like Brauer's group of algebra classes [VII: J. Reine Angew. Math. **176**, 31–44 (1937)]. The recent analytical studies of quadratic forms by Hecke [cf. VIII: Danske Vid. Selsk. Math.-Fys. Medd. **17**, no. 12 (1940); these Rev. **2**, 251] and Siegel [cf. IX: Ann. of Math. (2) **36**, 527–606 (1935)] also indicate a certain parallelism between the theory of forms and algebras, from a different point of view, and provide one of Eichler's principal objectives for the application of his arithmetical theory. This is Hecke's theorem on matrices of representation numbers by members of a system of definite forms, called Hecke matrices by Brandt [cf. III for 2 and 4 variables]. A second principal objective is the generalization of Meyer's theorem on the equality of class-number and genus-number in the indefinite case.

The first chapter deals with the theory of types and genera. A quadratic form in n variables $f^{(n)}=f(x_1, \cdots, x_n)$ is written as a matrix product $f^{(n)}=\mathfrak{F}^{(n)}=\acute{x}\mathfrak{F}x$, $\mathfrak{F}=(f_{ij})$, $f_{ij}=f_{ji}$, and f_{ii} even if the form is integral. The discriminant [cf. I] is defined to be

$$D(\mathfrak{F})=D=(-1)^m|\mathfrak{F}^{(2m)}|=(-1)^m|f_{ij}|, \quad n=2m,$$
$$D(\mathfrak{F})=D=\tfrac{1}{2}(-1)^m|\mathfrak{F}^{(2m+1)}|=\tfrac{1}{2}(-1)^m|f_{ij}|, \quad n=2m+1.$$

The form $\mathfrak{F}_0^{(2m)}$, with the matrix consisting of 1's on the secondary diagonal and zeros elsewhere, is in the neutral element of Witt's group. Two forms $\mathfrak{F}_1^{(n_1)}$ and $\mathfrak{F}_2^{(n_2)}$ are of the same type if $n_1\equiv n_2 \pmod 2$ and

$$\mathfrak{F}(x_1, \cdots, x_{n_1})-\mathfrak{F}(x_{n_1+1}, \cdots, x_{n_1+n_2})$$

is in the same genus as $\mathfrak{F}_0^{(n_1+n_2)}$. Two forms F_1 and F_2 in the same number of variables are said to be in the same genus if there exists a nonsingular matrix S such that $F_1=\acute{S}F_2S$, and in the same class if such a relation holds with an integral S whose determinant is a unit. The author determines two sets of genus invariants, the second of which involves characters but is independent of order invariants ("order" in the usual form theory sense). The theory of genera is not restricted to stem-forms, but the chapter is concluded with a characterization of them in terms of discriminants and characters. The cases of an even and an odd number of variables exhibit nontrivial differences.

The second chapter deals with the ideal theory of form systems, where a system is the totality of stem-forms having the same number of variables, signature and discriminant. Representatives of the classes in a system are considered and transformers from one to another of these are studied. Some numbers of ideals of various prime power norms are computed for use in Chapters 3 and 4. Vectors in Witt's metric space [VII] associated with a genus of forms are also studied and various numbers of them are computed.

In the third chapter [part II], Eichler partly attains his first principal objective. By his new methods, he obtains a proof of some of Hecke's results [VIII] for an even number of variables, but he states that he has not been able so far to find the connection between his results and Hecke's in the case of primes for which $(D/p)=-1$. He also obtains a result of Siegel [IX] on representation weights.

In the fourth chapter Eichler attacks his second principal objective. He proves a theorem on the existence of principal transformers in an extension field, which is a generalization of a theorem of Wedderburn. He studies units of indefinite forms. He does not completely achieve his objective, but states that he has in mind a method to complete an induction proof if Meyer's method [Vierteljschr. Naturforsch. Ges. Zürich **36**, 241–250 (1891)], inaccessible to him at the time of writing, will not go through. *R. Hull.*

Citations: MR 2, 251f = F25-4; MR 7, 369a = E12-22; MR 8, 138a = E12-24; MR 8, 198b = R52-12; MR 9, 136a = E12-26.

Referred to in E12-38.

E12-29 (10, 103a)

Eichler, M. Zahlentheorie der quadratischen Formen. Ber. Math.-Tagung Tübingen 1946, pp. 63–64 (1947).

Cf. the preceding review.

E12-30 (10, 103b)

Ko, Chao, and Chu, Fu-Tsu. On the equivalence of positive definite quadratic and Hermitian forms. Acad. Sinica Science Record **2**, 148–155 (1948).

Let $f_n(x)=\sum_{i,j=1}^n a_{ij}\bar{x}_i x_j$, $a_{ij}=\bar{a}_{ji}$, be a quadratic or Hermitian form according as the coefficients and variables are real or complex. Let $x_i=\sum\alpha_{ij}y_j$ be a unimodular transformation with α_{ij} rational integers, or quadratic integers of the field $k(\theta)\subset F$. Two positive definite forms $f_n(x)=a\bar{x}_1x_1+f_{n-1}(x)$, $g_n(x)=a\bar{y}_1y_1+g_{n-1}(y)$ are equivalent if and only if $f_{n-1}(x)\sim g_{n-1}(y)$. If $A(x_1, \cdots, x_s)$, $B(x_{s+1}, \cdots, x_n)$, $C(y_1, \cdots, y_s)$, $D(y_{s+1}, \cdots, y_n)$ are positive definite forms with integral coefficients, either rational or in $k(\theta)$, and if $A\sim C$ and A is indecomposable, then $A+B\sim C+D$ if and only if $B\sim D$. *C. C. MacDuffee* (Madison, Wis.).

E12-31 (10, 182g)

Maass, H. Quadratische Formen über quadratischen Körpern. Math. Z. **51**, 233–254 (1948).

Let K be the real quadratic field $R(\sqrt{a})$, where a is a positive squarefree rational integer, and let I be the ring of integers of K. A quadratic form $\nu=\sum\alpha_{ik}\xi_i\xi_k$ $(\alpha_{ik}=\alpha_{ki}\subset I)$ is said to be an even positive form over K if, for all nontrivial sets $\xi\subset I$, $\nu\gg 0$ and $\nu\equiv 0 \pmod 2$. The author proves that there exists an even positive ν over K, whose determinant is a unit $\epsilon\subset I$, if and only if

$$\epsilon\gg 0, \quad n\equiv 0 \pmod 2, \quad (-1)^{n/2}\epsilon\equiv\alpha^2 \pmod 4, \quad \alpha\subset I.$$

These conditions lead to a method of constructing such forms, following Witt [Abh. Math. Sem. Hansischen Univ. **14**, 289–322, 323–337 (1941); these Rev. **3**, 100, 163], except for the case $a\equiv 1 \pmod 8$, which differs essentially from the others. The author carries out the constructions, studies vector diagrams whose groups of reflections lead easily to the groups of automorphisms of the associated forms, and obtains criteria for the equivalence of even positive ν over K. He has previously studied forms ν over $R(\sqrt{5})$ [Math. Ann. **118**, 65–84 (1941); these Rev. **3**, 272]. *R. Hull.*

Citations: MR 3, 163d = E12-10; MR 3, 272b = F40-2.

Referred to in E12-145.

E12-32 (11, 15d)

Jones, B. W. A theorem on integral symmetric matrices. Bull. Amer. Math. Soc. **55**, 620–622 (1949).

A proof is given of the following theorem. If A and B are integral, nonsingular symmetric matrices, of orders n and m $(n>m)$, and if S is a rational representation of B by A, then there exists a rational n by n matrix T, whose denominators contain at most prime factors which appear in the denominators of S, such that $|T|=1$ and T replaces A by a matrix A_0 which represents B integrally. The essential idea of the proof is a canonicization of S, rather than A or B. From Jones's theorem follows in particular a theorem of Siegel [Ann. of Math. (2) **36**, 527–606 (1935), lemma 24] that if a number or form is represented rationally, but with denominators prime to $2|A|$, by an integral matrix A, then that number or form is represented integrally by some form in the genus of A. Also, if a classic quadratic form f represents an integer or classic form g rationally, then some other classic form f' of the same determinant as f represents g integrally. *G. Pall* (Chicago, Ill.).

E12-33 (11, 85c)

van der Blij, F. On the theory of quadratic forms. Ann. of Math. (2) **50**, 875–883 (1949).

Let S and T be symmetric positive matrices with integer elements and of orders m and n, respectively, with $m \geqq n$. Let P be an m by n integral matrix the greatest common divisor of whose n-rowed minors is 1 and $A(S, T; P, \nu)$ the number of solutions of $X'SX=T$ with $X\equiv P \pmod{\nu}$, while a subscript q on A indicates that the equation is replaced by the congruence $X'SX\equiv T \pmod{q}$. The principal class $PC(S, \nu)$ of S consists of all matrices $U'SU$, where U is a unimodular matrix for which $U\equiv E \pmod{\nu}$. The matrix S_1 belongs to the principal genus $PG(S, \nu)$ of S if, for every q, there is a matrix U satisfying the conditions $(|U|, q)=1$, $U'SU\equiv S_1 \pmod{q}$, $U\equiv E \pmod{\nu}$. For $\nu>2$, by a result of Minkowski pointed out by C. L. Siegel, $M(S, \nu)$ reduces to the number of principal classes in the principal genus of S. Define $M(S, T; P, \nu)=\sum A(S_k, T; P, \nu)$, the sum being over all principal classes S_k in the principal genus of S and $A_0(S, T; P, \nu)=M(S, T; P, \nu)/M(S, \nu)$. The author proves

$$A_0(S, T; P, \nu)=\epsilon\delta_\nu\gamma_{mn}|S|^{-\frac{1}{2}n}|T|^{\frac{1}{2}(m-n-1)} \times\lim_{q\to\infty} A_q(S, T; P, \nu)/(\alpha q^{mn-\frac{1}{2}n(n+1)}),$$

where, if $m\neq n$, $\alpha=\delta_\nu=1$ while if $m=n$, $\alpha=2^{\omega(q)}$; $\omega(q)$ is the number of prime factors of q, ϵ and γ_{mn} are explicitly given in terms of m and n and δ_ν in terms of ν. A few consequences are noted. *B. W. Jones* (Boulder, Colo.).

Referred to in E12-79.

E12-34 (11, 164a)

Humbert, Pierre. Réduction de formes quadratiques dans un corps algébrique fini. Comment. Math. Helv. **23**, 50–63 (1949).

This posthumous paper is provided with an introduction by C. L. Siegel who summarizes some of the results of one of his own papers [Abh. Math. Sem. Hansischen Univ. **13**, 209–239 (1940); these Rev. **2**, 148] which Humbert here generalized, and indicates other results of the same and another paper of his [Ann. of Math. (2) **45**, 577–622 (1944); these Rev. **6**, 38] which Humbert proposed to extend but had only begun to treat. Let $\mathfrak{S}$ be the matrix of a quadratic form in m variables: $F=\mathfrak{x}'\mathfrak{S}\mathfrak{x}$, integral over an algebraic number field K of (absolute) degree k. When $k=1$, i.e., in Siegel's case, suppose F is equivalent under real transformations to a sum of n positive and $m-n$ negative squares. Then the set of positive definite real symmetric matrices $\mathfrak{H}$ such that $\mathfrak{S}\mathfrak{H}^{-1}\mathfrak{S}=\mathfrak{H}$ constitutes a subspace H of dimension $n(m-n)$ of the space P of dimension $m(m+1)/2$, of positive definite real symmetric matrices $\mathfrak{P}$. An indefinite form F is called reduced if the space H intersects the Minkowski reduced space R, of reduced positive definite forms. When $\mathfrak{U}$ ranges over all unimodular integral matrices the transforms of the space R defined by $\mathfrak{U}'\mathfrak{R}\mathfrak{U}$, $\mathfrak{R}$ in R, simply cover P. Since $\mathfrak{S}\mathfrak{H}^{-1}\mathfrak{S}=\mathfrak{H}$ implies $\mathfrak{U}'\mathfrak{S}\mathfrak{U}(\mathfrak{U}'\mathfrak{H}\mathfrak{U})^{-1}\mathfrak{U}'\mathfrak{S}\mathfrak{U}=\mathfrak{U}'\mathfrak{H}\mathfrak{U}$, it follows that there exists at least one reduced form equivalent to F. Other consequences of the properties of R are that the number of reduced forms equivalent to a given indefinite form is finite, that the class-number of indefinite forms of given determinant and variable-number m is finite, and that the group of units, i.e., automorphs, of F has a finite set of generators. It is these theorems which are extended to the general case $k>1$, and also to Hermitian forms when K is complex. Humbert's earlier extension of Minkowski's reduction theory for positive definite forms is employed [same Comment. **12**, 263–306 (1940); these Rev. **2**, 148]. In the Hermitian case the corresponding theorems are all valid only if the automorphism: $K\to\bar{K}$, elementwise, is permutable with the other automorphisms of the minimal normal extension of K. *R. Hull* (Lafayette, Ind.).

Citations: MR 2, 148a = E12-3; MR 2, 148b = E12-4; MR 6, 38b = E12-18.

Referred to in E12-41.

E12-35 (11, 368e)

Everett, C. J., and Ryser, H. J. Rational vector spaces. I. Duke Math. J. **16**, 553–570 (1949).

A detailed study is made of vector spaces over the field of rationals. First, some results on cardinal numbers of such spaces are obtained, culminating in the theorem that every two infinite-dimensional rational vector spaces of the same cardinal number are isomorphic. Here and elsewhere in the paper, the dominating idea is that of a Hamel basis of a rational vector space, together with certain spaces of rationally-valued functions. Next, a rationally-valued inner product is postulated, which permits the introduction of orthogonal bases, the Schmidt orthogonalization process, etc., for such "rational inner product spaces." In the finite-dimensional case, to which most of the remainder of the paper is devoted, the study of "equivalence" of two rational inner product spaces reduces to a study of the Minkowski-Hasse invariants of associated quadratic forms under rational transformations. Not all n-dimensional rational inner product spaces are equivalent, but each is equivalent to a space consisting of all polynomials over the rationals of degree not exceeding n with an inner product of the form $(f, g)=\int_0^\infty f(x)g(x)d\psi$. This result is proved by use of a classical theorem on moments of Stieltjes. The Minkowski-Hasse invariants of the direct sum and direct product of two finite-dimensional rational inner product spaces are computed in terms of their values for the spaces themselves. The paper closes with some theorems on infinite-dimensional inner product spaces which are either denumerable or separable. In particular it is shown that every infinite-dimensional denumerable space has an orthonormal basis, in contrast to the situation for a finite number of dimensions. *D. H. Hyers* (Los Angeles, Calif.).

Referred to in R10-1.

E12-36 (11, 643d)

Jones, Burton W. Representations by quadratic forms. Ann. of Math. (2) **50**, 884–899 (1949).

Capital letters will denote integral matrices, A and B, symmetric of orders n and m, and determinants d and q. If T_1 is a solution of $T_1^TAT_1=B$ (i.e., a representation of B by A), the representations PT_1 (where P ranges over the unimodular automorphs of A) form a set of "essentially equal" representations. If T_1 is primitive, T_2 can be chosen so that $T=(T_1\ T_2)$ is unimodular. The matrix $Q=T^TAT$ has B as leading minor. Completing squares with reference to B yields the matrix $E=qD-C^T(\operatorname{adj} B)C$ (where C is the minor of Q to the right of B). The class of C depends only on T_1, not on T_2. A certain set of possible matrices C is defined. With each of these, and with a set of "essentially equal" solutions of the congruence $X^T(\operatorname{adj} B)X\equiv -E \pmod{q}$, is associated, conversely, a set of primitive representations by a certain class of forms. The possible classes may be those of the same determinant as A, or if q is assumed prime to $2d$, those of the genus of A. The resulting equality is shown to be particularly simple if $m=n-1$, or if $m=1$ and q is prime to $2d$. The matrices E which can arise for a given genus of matrices A is explicitly described in the case $n=3$. This leads to the following particular case of the general theory. Let $h(\Delta)$ denote the number of classes of properly primitive binary quadratic forms of determinant Δ; let t denote the greatest common divisor of the second-order minor determinants of A, $\Delta=qd/t^2$, q prime to $2d$, $q\neq\pm1$; let $\mu(w)$ be the number of distinct odd prime factors of w. Then the number of sets of primitive representations of the number q by the genus of the ternary matrix A is $2^{-\mu(d/t^2)}h(\Delta)\rho$ or 0, where $\rho=\frac{1}{2}$ if $\Delta\equiv1$ or 2 (mod 4) or 4 (mod 8), $\rho=2$ if $\Delta\equiv7$ (mod 8) and t is odd, $\rho=1$ if $\Delta\equiv7$ (mod 8) and t is even; if $\Delta\equiv3$ (mod 8), $\rho=\frac{1}{3}$ unless one of the three cases ((i) $c_2(A)=(-1)^r$, where 2^r is the highest power of 2 in t, (ii) $\Delta=3$, (iii) $c_2(A)\neq(-1)^r$, $\Delta<0$, and vu is odd in the fundamental solution of $v^2+\Delta u^2=4$) holds, when $\rho=1$; $\rho=\frac{1}{4}$ if $\Delta\equiv0$ (mod 8); if $\Delta<0$ and $v\not\equiv\pm1$ (mod q) in the fundamental solution of $v^2+\Delta u^2=1$, the preceding value of ρ is to be divided by 2. The number of sets of representations of an odd number by $xy+xz+yz$ is considered as a further application. There is a close affinity between this article and one by the reviewer [see the following review]. *G. Pall* (Chicago, Ill.).

Referred to in E12-128.

E12-37 (11, 643e)

Pall, Gordon. Representation by quadratic forms. Canadian J. Math. **1**, 344–364 (1949).

Let A and B_1 be symmetric matrices of orders n and k, respectively, having real elements, $1\leqq k\leqq n$; T_1 is a matrix with integer elements for which $T_1AT_1^T=B_1$, T_1 being primitive, i.e., 1 being the g.c.d. of its k-rowed minors. There is a matrix T_2 with integer elements such that $T=(T_1\ T_2)$ is unimodular, that is, has determinant 1. Then

$$B=T^TAT=\begin{bmatrix}B_1 & K^T\\ K & B_2\end{bmatrix},\quad G+K(\operatorname{adj} B_1)K^T=B_1\,B_2$$

define matrices B, K, B_2, and G. A fundamental theorem is theorem 3. Let A, T_1, B_1, G, and K be defined as above. Let $\Gamma_1(A, T_1)$ denote the subgroup of unimodular automorphs W of A such that $WT_1=T_1$, and $\Gamma_2(G, K)$ the subgroup of unimodular automorphs U of G such that U^TK and K are congruent modulo B_1. The two subgroups are isomorphic.

The author derives various consequences of this result including the following which fills a gap in a proof of Linnik on the representations of large numbers by ternary quadratic forms. Consider a representative set of forms $f_1, \cdots, f_s$ with integral matrices of a given nonzero determinant d, and an integral binary quadratic form $\varphi=k\varphi_1$ (φ_1 properly or improperly primitive) of determinant $b_1=k^2\Delta$, where k is prime to d. Let h^2 denote the largest square factor common to k and Δ. Let ρ denote the number of sets of representations of φ by $f_1, \cdots, f_s$ such that the divisor of the representations is k. Then, for any positive ϵ, there exists a constant q, depending on ϵ and d, but independent of b_1 and φ, such that $\rho<qh(b_1)^\epsilon$.

Theorem 3 is very similar to a result of the reviewer [see the preceding review] appearing almost simultaneously and independently derived; but the applications are very different. *B. W. Jones* (Boulder, Colo.).

Referred to in P04-29.

E12-38 (12, 591d)

Eichler, Martin. Zur Algebra der orthogonalen Gruppen. Math. Z. **53**, 11–20 (1950).

The author first discusses briefly the similarities between the theory of simple algebras, the theory of algebraic number fields, and the theory of quadratic forms which he developed recently [Comment. Math. Helv. **20**, 9–60 (1947); **21**, 1–28 (1948); these Rev. **10**, 102], which have their basis in the rôles played in the theories by certain groups, for example, the orthogonal groups of the title in the theory of quadratic forms. He then proves theorems relating to quadratic forms which include a generalization and a specialization of theorems from the other theories. Let $\mathfrak{F}$ be the symmetric matrix, over a field k of characteristic not equal to 2, of a quadratic form $\frac{1}{2}\dot{x}\mathfrak{F}x$ [erroneously $\dot{x}\mathfrak{F}x$ in the review cited above] in n variables, which does not represent 0 properly in k [restriction erroneously omitted for certain conclusions in the second cited paper, §12]. A matrix $\mathfrak{J}$, over k or an extension field, is called $\mathfrak{F}$-orthogonal ($\mathfrak{F}$-o) if $\dot{\mathfrak{J}}\mathfrak{F}\mathfrak{J}=\mathfrak{F}$. The antiautomorphism ($\mathfrak{F}$): $\mathfrak{M}^{(\mathfrak{F})}=\mathfrak{F}^{-1}\dot{\mathfrak{M}}\mathfrak{F}$ of the ring (algebra over k) of all n by n matrices, is an automorphism of order 2 for certain commutative subrings R, called $\mathfrak{F}$-automorphic ($\mathfrak{F}$-a) rings, viz., such that both $\mathfrak{M}$ and $\mathfrak{M}^{(\mathfrak{F})}$ are in R. For example, $R=k\cdot\mathfrak{E}+k\cdot\mathfrak{J}+k\cdot\mathfrak{J}^2+\cdots$ is an $\mathfrak{F}$-a ring if $\mathfrak{J}$ is $\mathfrak{F}$-o. It is easily shown that any $\mathfrak{F}$-a ring is semisimple and can be imbedded in an $\mathfrak{F}$-a ring of rank n over k. Next, every $\mathfrak{F}$-o matrix $\mathfrak{J}$ of determinant 1 can be expressed in the form $\mathfrak{J}=(\mathfrak{M}^{(\mathfrak{F})})^{-1}\mathfrak{M}=\mathfrak{M}^{1-(\mathfrak{F})}$, where $\mathfrak{M}$ is a nonsingular element of an $\mathfrak{F}$-a ring. This follows from the fact that $\mathfrak{M}=\mathfrak{E}-(\mathfrak{E}+\mathfrak{J})^{-1}(\mathfrak{E}-\mathfrak{J})$ serves in case -1 is not an eigenvalue of $\mathfrak{J}$, together with a reduction of the other case to this by methods of the theory of matrices. A generalization of a theorem of Wedderburn is: If R_1 and R_2 are ($\mathfrak{F}$)-operator-isomorphic $\mathfrak{F}$-o rings over k, there exists an $\mathfrak{F}$-o matrix $\mathfrak{S}$, with elements in k or in an extension of k, such that $R_2=\mathfrak{S}^{-1}R_1\mathfrak{S}$ (understood elementwise). The proof is quite elementary. A specialization of the norm-theorem for quadratic extensions of number fields is: If R_1 and R_2 in the foregoing theorem are of rank n over k, and if k is an algebraic number field, then there exists a matrix $\mathfrak{S}$ as described, with elements in k, if and only if the same is true for every $\mathfrak{p}$-adic extension of k. The proof of this is less elementary. The author suggests that the conclusions of the last two theorems may be valid under broader conditions than those which the restriction on $\mathfrak{F}$ imposes. *R. Hull.*

Citations: MR 10, 102f = E12-28; MR 10, 102g = E12-28.

E12-39 (13, 324a)

Cassels, J. W. S. A remark on the class number of quadratic forms of given determinant. Proc. Cambridge Philos. Soc. **47**, 820 (1951).

It is proved by induction with respect to n that any quadratic form in n variables with integer coefficients and of a given determinant $D\neq0$, is equivalent to at least one of a finite set $\mathfrak{S}(n, D)$ of forms. The author points out that this is a very simple proof of the finiteness of the class number of such forms. *C. Arf* (Istanbul).

E12-40 (13, 443a)

Eichler, Martin. Arithmetics of orthogonal groups. Proceedings of the International Congress of Mathematicians, Cambridge, Mass., 1950, vol. 2, pp. 65–70. Amer. Math. Soc., Providence, R. I., 1952.

Let k be an algebraic number field, R be a vector space of finite rank n over k, where a norm $|\alpha|$ of $\alpha\epsilon R$ is defined by means of a quadratic form, and S_R be a group of similarities of R, i.e. of linear transformations ξ of R, which multiply the square $|\alpha|^2$ of the norm $|\alpha|$ of each $\alpha\epsilon R$ by a non-zero constant $n(\xi)$, depending only on ξ and called norm of ξ.

Let $\mathfrak{o}$ be the ring of all integers of k. An $\mathfrak{o}$-modulus $\mathfrak{J}$ of vectors $\alpha\epsilon R$ is called (by the author) a lattice if it contains n linearly independent vectors and is generated by a finite number of vectors. Norms $n(\mathfrak{J})$ and discriminants $\mathfrak{d}(\mathfrak{J})$ of lattices $\mathfrak{J}$ are defined, in a convenient way, as certain ideals of k. If $\mathfrak{J}$ and $\mathfrak{K}$ are two lattices, the author defines the ideal $\mathfrak{J}/\mathfrak{K}$ as the set of all the $\xi \varepsilon S_R$ such that $\xi\mathfrak{K} \subseteq \mathfrak{J}$. The multiplication of these ideals being defined as the multiplication of subsets of S_R, their divisibility theory appears to be quite analogous to that of ideals in a simple algebra. The part of right and left orders of an ideal of a simple algebra is played here by classes of equivalent lattices: two lattices $\mathfrak{J}$ and $\mathfrak{K}$ are called equivalent when there exists a $\xi \varepsilon S_R$ such that $\mathfrak{K} = \xi\mathfrak{J}$.

In the remaining part of his paper, the author makes the assumption that k is the rational number field and that the quadratic form defining the norm $|\alpha|$ in R is definite positive. Under this assumption, there exist only a finite number of units in S_R and only a finite number of classes of equivalent lattices of R. Certain matrices and representations are defined, which describe more precisely the divisibility properties of the set of ideals of S_R. If a lattice $\mathfrak{J}$ is chosen, a vector $\beta\varepsilon\mathfrak{J}$ is said to be divisible by an operator $\xi\varepsilon S_R$ if there exists a $\alpha\varepsilon\mathfrak{J}$ such that $\beta = \xi\alpha$. A function $\zeta(\mathfrak{J}; s)$ of s, depending on lattice $\mathfrak{J}$ as parameter, can be defined as $\sum_{\alpha\varepsilon\mathfrak{J}}([2n(\mathfrak{J})]^{-1}|\alpha|^2)^{-s} = \sum_{m=1}^{\infty}\delta(\mathfrak{J}; m)m^{-s}$, where $\delta(\mathfrak{J}; m)$ is the number of vectors $\alpha\varepsilon\mathfrak{J}$ such that $|\alpha|^2 = 2n(\mathfrak{J})m$. In fact, this function depends only on the equivalence class j of $\mathfrak{J}$, and can be written $\zeta(j; s)$ (and $\delta(\mathfrak{J}; m)$ can be written $\delta(j; m)$). The divisibility properties of vectors by operators permit one to define, starting from the previously mentioned representations, certain matricial functions $Z^{(r)}(m)$ of degree r, having the multiplicative property $Z^{(r)}(a)Z^{(r)}(b) = Z^{(r)}(ab)$ for a, b prime one to another, and these functions are linear functions of $\delta(j; m)$, where j ranges over all the equivalence classes of lattices: $Z^{(r)}(m) = \sum_j Z_j^{(r)}\delta(j; m)$. Each such function permits one to define a matricial ζ-function $\zeta^{(r)}(s) = \sum_{m=1}^{\infty} Z^{(r)}(m)m^{-s}$, and $\zeta^{(r)}(s)$ can be represented as an Euler product $\prod_p \zeta_p^{(r)}(s)$, where $\zeta_p^{(r)}(s) = \sum_{i=0}^{\infty} Z^{(r)}(p^i)p^{-is}$ is, for the prime p, the corresponding local ζ-function, obtained by means of $Z^{(r)}(m)$ if k is replaced in other definitions by its local field k_p. In certain cases these $\zeta^{(r)}(s)$ and their local factors are the same as in Hecke's theory, but, generally, they are only related in a more indirect manner to the objects of this last theory.

This paper being an address delivered at an international congress of mathematicians, no demonstrations are given. But a reader familiar enough with the topics considered is able to form a general idea about the author's methods.

M. Krasner (Notre Dame, Ind.).

E12-41 (13, 628b)

Ramanathan, K. G. The theory of units of quadratic and Hermitian forms. Amer. J. Math. **73**, 233–255 (1951).

Humbert recently extended Siegel's reduction theory to indefinite quadratic forms and hermitean forms whose coefficients are integers of an algebraic number field K [Comment. Math. Helv. **23**, 50–63 (1949); these Rev. **11**, 164]. The author starts from Humbert's theory and studies the groups of units of such forms, i.e., unimodular transformations which are integral in K and which leave a form invariant. For K totally real, he proves that the group of units of a quadratic form over K is always finitely generated; it is a finite group if and only if the form is totally definite, i.e., all its conjugates corresponding to the conjugates of K are positive definite. For K totally real, d totally positive in K, he proves similar results for hermitean forms over $K(\sqrt{d})$. The greater part of the paper is devoted to a generalization of Siegel's theorems on the measure of unit groups [Abh. Math. Sem. Hansischen Univ. **13**, 209–239 (1940); these Rev. **2**, 148]. In a suitable space, a unit group, modulo its center, is represented faithfully as a discontinuous group of non-euclidean motions which leave invariant an open subspace of a certain dimension depending on the signature of the form. In this space an invariant volume element is defined whose integral over a fundamental domain is proved to be finite, except in the case of a decomposable binary quadratic form. The author states that analogous results can be proved for quadratic forms over fields which are not necessarily totally real. He also remarks that some of his results could be obtained alternatively from topological considerations alone. *R. Hull* (Lafayette, Ind.).

Citations: MR 2, 148b = E12-4; MR 11, 164a = E12-34.
Referred to in E12-42.

E12-42 (14, 453b)

Ramanathan, K. G. Units of quadratic forms. Ann. of Math. (2) **56**, 1–10 (1952).

The notation and terminology employed are those of the author's earlier paper [Amer. J. Math. **73**, 233–255 (1951); these Rev. **13**, 628], and two papers of Siegel [(1) Ann. of Math. **44**, 674–689 (1943); (2) ibid. **45**, 577–622 (1944); these Rev. **5**, 228; **6**, 38]. If S is the matrix of a quadratic form with coefficients integral in an algebraic number field K, its group of units (automorphs) is $\Gamma(S)$, consisting of the matrices U, integral in K, such that $U'SU = S$. By way of preparation, it is shown that all compact subgroups of $G(m, c)$, the complex orthogonal group of order m, that is, of complex m-by-m matrices C such that $C'C = E$, are conjugates of $G(m, R)$, the real orthogonal group. Hence the coset space $G(m, c)/G(m, R)$ is homeomorphic to the algebraic manifold H of positive hermitean matrices Y which are orthogonal. Further, H is parametrized by $m(m-1)/2$ real variables whose domain is the bounded region: $E - Y^2 > 0$, on which $G(m, c)$ acts transitively. The euclidean volume of H is finite, but its volume for the invariant element $dV = |E - Y^2|^{(1-m)/2}\{dY\}$ is infinite. Similar preparatory results are obtained for the group $G(n, m-n)$ of real matrices C such that $C'DC = D$, where

$$D = \mathrm{diag}\,(1, \cdots, 1, -1, \cdots, -1),$$

n 1's and $m-n$ (-1)'s. Then with S is associated an algebraic manifold constructed out of the topological product of r_1 groups like $G(n, m-n)$, and r_2 groups like $G(m, c)$, as is H above from $G(m, c)$, where r_1 is the number of real conjugates of K, $2r_2$ the number of complex conjugates. This manifold reduces to a point if $r_2 = 0$ and S is totally definite. Some results are that $\Gamma(S)$ is finite if and only if $r_2 = 0$ and S is totally definite, or if $r_2 = 0$ and S is binary decomposable; in any case, $\Gamma(S)$ is finitely generated. Other results are obtained, extending those of Siegel for the rational case, relating to the properties of $\Gamma(S)$ from the standpoint of discontinuous groups [Siegel (1)], furnishing examples of discontinuous groups of the first kind with normal fundamental sets. *R. Hull* (Lafayette, Ind.).

Citations: MR 6, 38b = E12-18; MR 13, 628b = E12-41.

E12-43 (14, 22d)

Venkov, B. A. On indeterminate quadratic forms with integral coefficients. Trudy Mat. Inst. Steklov., v. 38, pp. 30–41. Izdat. Akad. Nauk SSSR, Moscow, 1951. (Russian) 20 rubles.

Let $f(X) = \sum_{i=1}^{n}\sum_{j=1}^{n} a_{ij}x_ix_j$ be an indefinite quadratic form with integral coefficients consisting of one positive square and $n-1$ negative ones. In n-dimensional X-space, denote by $\mathfrak{K}$ one of the two convex cones $f(X) \geqq 0$, by $\mathfrak{M}$ the set of all lattice points in the interior of $\mathfrak{K}$, and by Π the convex cover of $\mathfrak{M}$; this is an unbounded polyhedron. The author studies the fundamental regions of the group G of all automorphisms of f with integral coefficients and determinant ∓ 1, and the properties of Π with respect to this group; e.g., the $(n-1)$-dimensional sides of Π are equivalent to a finite number amongst them.

K. Mahler (Manchester).

E12-44 **(14, 252f)**

Ramanathan, K. G. Abelian quadratic forms. Canadian J. Math. **4**, 352–368 (1952).

The generalized symplectic (g.s.) group $G(n, K)$ over a field K is the set of all $2n\times 2n$ matrices $\mathfrak{M}$ with elements in K and such that $\mathfrak{M}'\mathfrak{J}\mathfrak{M}=k\mathfrak{J}$, where $\mathfrak{J}$ is the matrix $\begin{pmatrix}\mathfrak{O} & \mathfrak{E}\\ -\mathfrak{E} & \mathfrak{O}\end{pmatrix}$ ($\mathfrak{O}$ is the zero matrix and $\mathfrak{E}$ the unit matrix of order n; $\mathfrak{M}'$ is the transpose of $\mathfrak{M}$) and $k\neq 0$ is an element of K. It is called the kernel of $\mathfrak{M}$. If $k=1$, the matrix $\mathfrak{M}$ is symplectic (s.). A g.s. matrix $\mathfrak{S}$ is called abelian if it is symmetric. The quadratic form $\mathfrak{x}'\mathfrak{S}\mathfrak{x}$ is called abelian if its matrix $\mathfrak{S}$ is an abelian g.s. matrix. Then (A) $\mathfrak{S}=\begin{pmatrix}\mathfrak{A} & \mathfrak{B}\\ \mathfrak{B}' & \mathfrak{C}\end{pmatrix}$, where $\mathfrak{A}$, $\mathfrak{B}$, $\mathfrak{C}$ are $n\times n$ matrices such that $\mathfrak{A}=\mathfrak{A}'$, $\mathfrak{B}=\mathfrak{B}'$, $\mathfrak{A}\mathfrak{B}'=\mathfrak{B}\mathfrak{A}$, $\mathfrak{A}\mathfrak{C}-\mathfrak{B}^2=k\mathfrak{E}$. There exists a s. matrix $\mathfrak{P}$ such that $\mathfrak{P}'\mathfrak{S}\mathfrak{P}=\begin{pmatrix}\mathfrak{D} & \mathfrak{O}\\ \mathfrak{O} & k\mathfrak{D}^{-1}\end{pmatrix}$, where $\mathfrak{D}$ is a diagonal matrix with elements in K. The notions of abelian hermitian form and abelian hermitian matrix (over a field $K_0=K(\sqrt{d})$ which is a quadratic extension of a field K) can be defined accordingly. The determinant $|\mathfrak{S}|$ of an abelian (or hermitian) matrix $\mathfrak{S}$ is k^n. Two integral g.s. matrices $\mathfrak{M}_1$ and $\mathfrak{M}_2$ are called associated if an integral s. (modular) matrix $\mathfrak{P}$ exists such that $\mathfrak{M}_1=\mathfrak{M}_2\mathfrak{P}$. The number of classes of associate matrices with a given kernel is shown to be finite. The author develops a reduction theory for abelian forms. The analogy of the results with those of the theory of binary quadratic forms is striking: Two abelian matrices $\mathfrak{S}_1$ and $\mathfrak{S}_2$ are called s. equivalent if a modular matrix $\mathfrak{P}$ exists such that $\mathfrak{S}_2=\mathfrak{P}'\mathfrak{S}_1\mathfrak{P}$. A positive definite abelian form (A) is called reduced if (i) the determinant $|\mathfrak{A}|$ is minimal; (ii) $\mathfrak{A}$ is reduced in the sense of Minkowski; (iii) the elements of $\mathfrak{B}^{-1}\mathfrak{A}$ are in absolute value $\leqq\frac{1}{2}$. Then (generalization of the Gauss-Minkowski inequality): $|\mathfrak{A}|\cdot|\mathfrak{C}|\leqq a_1\cdots a_n c_1\cdots c_n\leqq\mu_n|\mathfrak{S}|$, where the a_i and c_i are the diagonal elements of the matrices $\mathfrak{A}$ and $\mathfrak{C}$ respectively and μ_n depends on n only. There is only a finite number of positive reduced forms with a given kernel. The author gives also a short discussion of the reduction of indefinite abelian forms and of abelian hermitian forms, and mentions some further generalizations.

H. D. Kloosterman (Leiden).

E12-45 **(14, 540c)**

Eichler, Martin. Die Ähnlichkeitsklassen indefiniter Gitter. Math. Z. **55**, 216–252 (1952).

In the first part of this paper the author proves two theorems. Theorem 2: If S is the set of all integral rational numbers, two spinor-related lattices of an indefinite space of dimension greater than 2 over the rational number field are similar. Theorem 3: Under the hypotheses of theorem 2, two arithmetic maximal lattices of the same genus are similar. For ternary forms there is the added restriction that the reduced determinant of the lattice have no square factor greater than 4 and is not divisible by 8. These results are related to those of Meyer on the number of classes in genera of indefinite ternary quadratic forms.

The second part is concerned with results of Siegel having to do with the identity of the Zeta functions of related indefinite forms. *B. W. Jones* (Boulder, Colo.).

Referred to in E12-57, E12-91.

E12-46 **(14, 954b; 14, 954c; 14, 954d)**

Voronoĭ, G. F. Notes on indeterminate quadratic forms. Ukrain. Mat. Žurnal **3**, 240–271 (1951). (Russian)

Voronoĭ, G. F. On indeterminate quadratic forms. Ukrain. Mat. Žurnal **3**, 272–278 (1951). (Russian)

Venkov, B. A. On the scientific diary of G. F. Voronoĭ. Ukrain. Mat. Žurnal **3**, 279–289 (1951). (Russian)

Voronoĭ, who died in 1908 at the age of 40, is best remembered by his classical work on positive definite quadratic forms [J. Reine Angew. Math. **133**, 97–178 (1908); **134**, 198–287 (1909)] which even today are not yet exhausted in their implications. Mathematicians will be grateful to Professor Venkov for preparing for print notes on indefinite quadratic forms taken from a diary kept by Voronoĭ shortly before his death.

The longer extract deals mainly with the decomposition of an indefinite quadratic form $f(x_1, \cdots, x_n)$ of characteristic (μ, ν), $\mu+\nu=n$, into a sum $\phi(u_1, \cdots, u_\mu)+\psi(v_1, \cdots, v_\nu)$ of a positive definite form ϕ and a negative definite form ψ; here $u_1, \cdots, u_\mu, v_1, \cdots, v_\nu$ are independent linear forms in $x_1, \cdots, x_n$. Such decompositions are studied from the algebraic and geometric standpoint, and they are connected by means of Hermite's method of continuous variables with the reduction theory of positive definite forms. The ternary case $(\mu=2, \nu=1)$ is considered in detail.

The second shorter extract from the diary consists of some inconclusive results on the example $f=x^2+y^2-3z^2-3t^2$. In the third paper, Venkov comments on the interest of these notes and places them in their historical position with regard to classical and modern work on quadratic forms.

K. Mahler (Manchester).

E12-47 **(16, 340f)**

Oppenheim, A. Least determinants of integral quadratic forms. Duke Math. J. **20**, 391–393 (1953).

Let g_m be an integral quadratic form in m variables with signature s and determinant $\Delta(g_m)$. The result of this paper is that

$$\Delta(g_m)\geqq 1/2^m \quad (s\equiv 0), \qquad \Delta(g_m)\geqq 2/2^m \quad (s\equiv\pm 1),$$
$$\Delta(g_m)\geqq 3/2^m \quad (s\equiv\pm 2), \qquad \Delta(g_m)\geqq 4/2^m \quad (s\equiv\pm 3, 4),$$

where all congruences are computed modulo 8. Forms are given for which the minima are attained. The problem is reduced by a series of unimodular transformations to the case where $m=s$, for which case the solution was given by O'Connor and Pall [same J. **11**, 319–331 (1944); these Rev. **5**, 254]. *D. Derry* (Vancouver, B. C.).

Citations: MR 5, 254e = E12-17.

E12-48 **(16, 680e)**

Žmud', È. M. On integer transformations of quadratic forms. Mat. Sb. N.S. **32(74)**, 287–344 (1953). (Russian)

The author says that the integral quadratic form f in n variables is m-derived from the integral form g if it arises from g by an integral transformation of determinant m. If f is not the m-derivative of any form it is m-simple. For prime m the author determines all the genera which can be m-derived from a given genus, and also gives a criterion for m-simplicity. Finally for m prime he gives a formula of the type $h(\mathfrak{G}')M(\mathfrak{G}')=\sum j(\mathfrak{G}, \mathfrak{G}')M(\mathfrak{G})$ for the mass of a genus $\mathfrak{G}'$ in terms of the masses of the genera $\mathfrak{G}$ from which it is m-derivable. Here $h(\mathfrak{G}')$ and $j(\mathfrak{G}, \mathfrak{G}')$ are integers which are given explicitly in terms of the invariants of $\mathfrak{G}'$ and $\mathfrak{G}$, $\mathfrak{G}'$ respectively. The work depends heavily on the results and techniques of Minkowski's Paris Prize Essay [Mém. Acad. Sci. Inst. France (2) **29**, no. 2 (1884)], which is the most modern reference cited (apart from the author's own dissertation and an elementary text). The author is apparently unaware of more recent relevant work: the series of papers by Meyer [J. Reine Angew. Math. **98**, 177–230 (1885); **103**, 98–117 (1888); **108**, 125–139 (1891); **112**, 87–88 (1893); **113**, 186–206 (1894); **114**, 233–254; **115**, 150–182 (1895); **116**, 307–325 (1896)]; the work of H. Brandt and his school [see, e.g., Brandt, Festschrift zum 60. Geburtstag von Prof. Dr. Andreas Speiser, Füssli, Zürich, 1945, pp. 87–104; MR **8**, 138] and of Eichler [Quadratische

Formen und orthogonale Gruppen, Springer, Berlin, 1952; MR 14, 540]. *J. W. S. Cassels* (Cambridge, England).

Citations: MR 8, 138a = E12-24; MR 14, 540a = E02-4.

E12-49 (16, 800a)

Siegel, Carl Ludwig. Indefinite quadratische Formen und Funktionentheorie. I. Math. Ann. **124**, 17–54 (1951).

Let $\mathfrak{S}[\mathfrak{x}]=\mathfrak{x}'\mathfrak{S}\mathfrak{x}=\sum_{k,l=1}^{n} s_{kl}x_kx_l$ be a quadratic form in m variables $x_1, x_2, \cdots, x_m$, where the matrix $\mathfrak{S}$ is supposed to be real, symmetric ($\mathfrak{S}'=\mathfrak{S}$) and non-singular. If its signature is $(n, m-n)$, there exists a real linear transformation $\mathfrak{x}=\mathfrak{C}\mathfrak{y}$, transforming $\mathfrak{S}[\mathfrak{x}]$ into $q-r$, where $q=y_1^2+\cdots+y_n^2$, $r=y^2_{n+1}+\cdots+y_m^2$. The positive definite quadratic form $\mathfrak{P}[\mathfrak{x}]$ defined by $\mathfrak{P}[\mathfrak{x}]=q+r$ (and whose matrix is $(\mathfrak{C}\mathfrak{C}')^{-1}$) is called a "majorant" of $\mathfrak{S}[\mathfrak{x}]$. All majorants of $\mathfrak{S}$ are exactly the solutions of $\mathfrak{P}\mathfrak{S}^{-1}\mathfrak{P}=\mathfrak{S}$, $\mathfrak{P}'=\mathfrak{P}>0$. A parametric representation of the set P of all majorants $\mathfrak{P}$ of S shows that P is in birational correspondence with those $(m-n-1)$-dimensional linear subspaces of $(m-1)$-dimensional projective space (in which the coordinates $x_1, x_2, \cdots, x_m$ are the components of the column vector x) in all points of which $\mathfrak{S}[\mathfrak{x}]$ is everywhere positive, so that P corresponds to the subset determined by $\mathfrak{S}[\mathfrak{x}]>0$ of the Grassmann variety of $n(m-n)$ dimensions. If Ω is the "orthogonal" group of $\mathfrak{S}$ (the group of all linear transformations which transform $\mathfrak{S}[\mathfrak{x}]$ into itself) then a transitive representation of Ω on P is obtained by considering the mappings $\mathfrak{P}\rightarrow\mathfrak{P}[\mathfrak{B}]=\mathfrak{B}'\mathfrak{P}\mathfrak{B}$ (where $\mathfrak{B}\in\Omega$), which map P into itself. A Riemannian metric on P, invariant under Ω, is then defined. If $\mathfrak{S}$ is supposed to be rational and Γ is the subgroup of Ω consisting of all "units" of $\mathfrak{S}$ (i.e. integral matrices $\mathfrak{B}$ satisfying $\mathfrak{S}[\mathfrak{B}]=\mathfrak{S}$) then Γ is discontinuous on P and the author shows by means of the reduction theory of quadratic forms that the volume of the fundamental domain F_0 of Γ on P is, with one trivial exception), always finite.

A quadratic equation with integral coefficients can be written in the form $\mathfrak{S}[\mathfrak{x}+\mathfrak{a}]=t$, where $\mathfrak{S}=(s_{kl})$ is a given symmetric matrix, $\mathfrak{a}$ a given vector and t a given number, and where s_{kk}, $2s_{kl}$, $2\mathfrak{S}\mathfrak{a}$, $\mathfrak{S}[\mathfrak{a}]-t$ are integral. If $\mathfrak{P}$ is a majorant of $\mathfrak{S}$, $z=x+iy$ a complex variable with $y>0$ and if $\mathfrak{R}=x\mathfrak{S}+iy\mathfrak{P}$, the author introduces the theta series

$$f(z)=f_{\mathfrak{a}}(z)=f_{\mathfrak{a}}(z,\mathfrak{P})=\sum_{\mathfrak{x}} e^{2\pi i\mathfrak{R}[\mathfrak{x}+\mathfrak{a}]},$$

where the summation extends over all integral vectors $\mathfrak{x}$. Since the imaginary part of $\mathfrak{R}$ is $y\mathfrak{P}$ and $y>0$ the series is convergent. The function $f(z)$ is not an analytic function of z. Under modular substitutions it shows a behaviour which is similar to that of the theta series for positive definite quadratic forms. All those automorphs $\mathfrak{U}$ of $\mathfrak{S}$ such that $\mathfrak{U}\mathfrak{a}-\mathfrak{a}$ is integral constitute a subgroup $\Gamma_{\mathfrak{a}}$ of Γ. The function $f_{\mathfrak{a}}(z,\mathfrak{P})$ remains unchanged if $\mathfrak{P}$ is replaced by $\mathfrak{P}[\mathfrak{U}]$. The author's principal result is the formula

$$\text{(I)}\qquad V^{-1}\int_F f_{\mathfrak{a}}(z,\mathfrak{P})dv=\gamma+\sum\gamma(r)(z-r)^{-\frac{1}{2}n}(\bar z-r)^{\frac{1}{2}(n-m)}.$$

Here the integration is extended over the fundamental domain F of $\Gamma_{\mathfrak{a}}$ and V is the volume of F which is shown to be finite by means of the Minkowski reduction theory of quadratic forms; $\gamma=1$ or 0 according as $\mathfrak{a}$ is integral or not; r runs through all rational numbers a/b (where $(a,b)=1$) and

$$\gamma(r)=e^{\frac{1}{4}\pi i(2n-m)}s^{-\frac{1}{2}}b^{-m}\sum_{\mathfrak{y}\bmod b} e^{2\pi ir\mathfrak{S}[\mathfrak{y}]};$$

s is the determinant of $2\mathfrak{S}$; $\mathfrak{y}$ runs through a complete set of residues mod b. It is supposed that $n(m-n)>0$, $n>3$ and for $m=4$ the zero forms $\mathfrak{S}[\mathfrak{x}]$ for which the determinant $|\mathfrak{S}|$ is a square, are excluded.

Since $\mathfrak{S}[\mathfrak{x}]$ is an indefinite form, the number of units is infinite. Therefore if one solution $\mathfrak{y}_1=\mathfrak{x}_1+\mathfrak{a}$ of the diophantine equation $\mathfrak{S}[\mathfrak{x}+\mathfrak{a}]=t$ exists, there is an infinity of associated solutions given by $\mathfrak{y}=\mathfrak{U}\mathfrak{y}_1$, where $\mathfrak{U}\in\Gamma_{\mathfrak{a}}$. However, the number of classes of associated solutions is finite. Every solution $\mathfrak{y}$ is provided with a mass $\mu(\mathfrak{S},\mathfrak{y})$ depending on its class only. The "Lösungsmass" ("number" of solutions) is defined as the sum

$$M(\mathfrak{S},\mathfrak{a},t)=\sum\mu(\mathfrak{S},\mathfrak{y})$$

extended over a complete set of solutions $\mathfrak{y}=\mathfrak{x}+\mathfrak{a}\neq0$ of $\mathfrak{S}[\mathfrak{y}]=t$ which are non-associated with respect to $\Gamma_{\mathfrak{a}}$. From the Fourier-series development of the Eisenstein series on the right-hand side of (I) the author obtains his second fundamental result:

$$M(\mathfrak{S},\mathfrak{a},t)=\mu_{\mathfrak{a}}(\mathfrak{S})\prod_p\delta_p(\mathfrak{S},\mathfrak{a},t),$$

where p runs through all primes; $\mu_{\mathfrak{a}}(\mathfrak{S})$ is the volume of the fundamental domain of $\Gamma_{\mathfrak{a}}$ on Ω, which is connected with the volume V on P by means of the formula

$$\mu_{\mathfrak{a}}(S)=\rho_n\rho_{m-n}S^{-\frac{1}{2}(m+1)}V;$$

S is the absolute value of the determinant of $\mathfrak{S}$ and

$$\rho_l=\prod_{k=1}^{l}\pi^{-\frac{1}{2}k}\Gamma^{-1}(\tfrac{1}{2}k).$$

The numbers $\delta_p(\mathfrak{S},\mathfrak{a},t)$ are the p-adic solution densities defined by

$$\delta_p(\mathfrak{S},\mathfrak{a},t)=\lim_{k\to\infty}\frac{A_q(\mathfrak{S},\mathfrak{a},t)}{q^{m-1}}\qquad(q=p^k),$$

where $A_q(\mathfrak{S},\mathfrak{a},t)$ is for any integer q the number of solutions $\mathfrak{x}$ of the congruence

$$\mathfrak{S}[\mathfrak{x}+\mathfrak{a}]\equiv t\pmod q.$$

H. D. Kloosterman (Leiden).

Referred to in E12-51, E12-72, E12-89, E12-91, E44-12, F15-36, P28-29.

E12-50 (16, 801a)

Siegel, Carl Ludwig. Indefinite quadratische Formen und Funktionentheorie. II. Math. Ann. **124**, 364–387 (1952).

The author shows that his results on indefinite quadratic forms [see the preceding review] with rational integral coefficients can be extended to the case of algebraic number fields and even to certain algebras of finite rank over the field of rational numbers. He develops in detail the case of the Gaussian field (of all numbers $a+ib$, where a and b are rational). In order to extend the notion of quadratic form to the case of an algebra A the existence of an involution $a\rightarrow a^*$ such that $a^{**}=a$, $(a+b)^*=a^*+b^*$, $(ab)^*=b^*a^*$ is supposed, in which case a quadratic form is defined by $\mathfrak{x}^*\mathfrak{S}\mathfrak{x}=\sum_{k,l=1}^{m}x_k^*s_{kl}x_l$, $s_{lk}=s^*_{kl}$. The algebra A is further supposed to be simple. *H. D. Kloosterman* (Leiden).

Referred to in E12-91, R54-24.

E12-51 (24# A79)

Watson, G. L.

Indefinite quadratic Diophantine equations.

Mathematika 8 (1961), 32–38.

A weaker form of a result of Siegel [Math. Ann. **124** (1951), 17–54; MR **16**, 800] is proved by elementary methods.

B. Stolt (Stockholm)

Citations: MR 16, 800a = E12-49.

E12-52 (17, 128d)

Watson, G. L. Representation of integers by indefinite quadratic forms. Mathematika **2** (1955), 32–38.

The author considers the Diophantine equation

$$\text{(1)}\qquad f(x_1, x_2, \cdots, x_k)=n\quad(n\neq0),$$

where f is a quadratic form with integer coefficients and where the solution is subject to the restriction

(2) $(x_1, x_2, \cdots, x_k) \equiv (t_1, t_2, \cdots, t_k) \pmod q$

for q positive, the t_i given and 1 the g.c.d. of the x_i. He proves the following theorem: If f is an indefinite form in four or more variables, $n \neq 0$, and the congruence $f \equiv n \pmod m$ has for every m a solution satisfying (2), then (1) has a solution satisfying (2). In particular, taking $q=1$, an indefinite form f in four or more variables represents properly every integer $n \neq 0$ for which the congruence $f \equiv n \pmod m$ is solvable for every m.

The author indicates that modifications of his method can be made for $k \geqq 5$ if $n=0$ or if n is replaced by a form g of non-zero determinant and having no more than $k-3$ variables. *B. W. Jones* (Boulder, Colo.).

Referred to in E12-61.

E12-53 (17, 587h)

Piehler, Joachim. Über die Charaktere quadratischer Formen. Wiss. Z. Martin-Luther-Univ. Halle-Wittenberg. Math.-Nat. Reihe **4** (1955), 1215–1224.

H. J. S. Smith, Minkowski, and, later, G. Pall developed the theory of orders of quadratic forms in n variables. Pall [Quart. J. Math. Oxford Ser. **6** (1935), 30–51] developed the order invariants systematically and introduced simplifications over the classical results. The author of this paper, using the notation of H. Brandt [Math. Ann. **124** (1952), 334–342; MR **14**, 454], gets Pall's results and goes on to define the generic characters of forms and their concomitants, f_ν, primitive forms the elements of whose matrices are, except for certain factors, the ν-rowed minors of the matrix of f for $\nu=1, 2, \cdots, n-1$. Certain so-called prime discriminant divisors (Primdiskriminanteneiler) are defined in terms of the order invariants and it is shown that the primitive forms f_ν possess all and only characters with respect to these prime discriminant divisors. Relationships among characters are found and simultaneous characters are defined. The Hasse and Hilbert symbols are not used. *B. W. Jones.*

Citations: MR 14, 454a = E20-36.

E12-54 (17, 1186a)

Venkov, B. A. On an integral invariant of the group of unimodular linear substitutions. Leningrad. Gos. Univ. Uč. Zap. **144.** Ser. Mat. Nauk **23** (1952), 3–25. (Russian)

For positive integral n, let $\mathfrak{R}$ be the $\nu=n(n+1)/2$ dimensional space of all real quadratic forms

$$f(X)=\sum_{p,q=1}^{n} a_{pq}x_px_q=X'AX, \quad X'=(x_1, \cdots, x_n),$$
$$A=(a_{pq})=A',$$

(the dash denotes the transposed matrix), and let $\mathfrak{P}$ be the cone of all positive-definite forms. Denote by Γ the group of all integral unimodular matrices S. Every transformation $X=SX_1$ changes f into an equivalent form f_1 of matrix $S'AS$. In each class of equivalent forms there is one and in general only one representative which is reduced in the sense of Hermite and Minkowski. Denote by $\mathfrak{G} \subset \mathfrak{R}$ the set of all such reduced points. Minkowski proved [J. Reine Angew. Math. **129** (1905), 220–274= Ges. Abh., Bd. II, Teubner, Leipzig-Berlin, 1911, pp. 53–100] that $\mathfrak{G}$ is a convex conical polyeder bounded by finitely many planes. If

$$dA=\prod_{1\leq p<q\leq n} da_{pq}$$

defines the volume element in $\mathfrak{R}$, Minkowski further showed that the volume v_n of the set of all reduced points of determinant $\det A \leqq 1$ equals

$$v_n=\frac{2}{n+1}\pi^{-n(n+1)/4}\Gamma\Big(\frac{1}{2}\Big)\Gamma\Big(\frac{2}{2}\Big)\cdots\Gamma\Big(\frac{n}{2}\Big)\zeta(2)\zeta(3)\cdots\zeta(n).$$

A second proof was given by C. L. Siegel [Trans. Amer. Math. Soc. **39** (1936), 209–218, pp. 210–211], who also obtained a third proof as a by-product in a more recent paper [Ann. of Math. (2) **46** (1945), 340–347; MR **6**, 257] which is not mentioned by the author. The author derives Minkowski's formula by the following analytical considerations.

For complex $s=\sigma+ti$, let

$$\Phi(s)=\pi^{-\frac{1}{2}ns-\frac{1}{4}n(n-1)}\Gamma\Big(\frac{s}{2}\Big)\Gamma\Big(\frac{s+1}{2}\Big)\cdots\Gamma\Big(\frac{s+n-1}{2}\Big).$$

If M is any integral matrix of determinant $\det M=\mp\Delta$, $\Delta\geqq 1$, and if $\sigma(M'AM)$ denotes the trace of $M'AM$, then

$$\Delta^{-(n+s-1)}\Phi(s)=\int_{\mathfrak{P}} e^{-\pi\sigma(M'AM)}(\det A)^{\frac{1}{2}s-1}dA.$$

Write now $\mathfrak{P}$ as the union of all polyhedra $\mathfrak{G}, \mathfrak{G}_1, \mathfrak{G}_2, \cdots$ equivalent to $\mathfrak{G}$ under Γ, and transform the respective integrals into such over $\mathfrak{G}$. Then

$$2\Delta^{-(n+s-1)}\Phi(s)=\int_{\mathfrak{G}}(\det A)^{\frac{1}{2}s-1}\sum_S e^{-\pi\sigma(M'S'ASM)}dA,$$

where S runs over the elements of Γ. On summing here first over all classes of matrices SM, $S \in \Gamma$, and then over the determinants $\Delta=1, 2, 3, \cdots$, one obtains the identity $2\Phi(s)\zeta(s)\zeta(s+1)\cdots\zeta(s+n-1)=$

$$\int_{\mathfrak{G}}(\det A)^{\frac{1}{2}s-1}\sum_{\det M\neq 0} e^{-\pi\sigma(M'AM)}dA.$$

The left-hand side has at $s=1$ the residue

$$r=2\pi^{-\frac{1}{4}n(n+1)}\Gamma\Big(\frac{1}{2}\Big)\Gamma\Big(\frac{2}{2}\Big)\cdots\Gamma\Big(\frac{n}{2}\Big)\zeta(2)\zeta(3)\cdots\zeta(n),$$

while the residue of the right-hand side is found to be $r=(n+1)v_n$. *K. Mahler* (Manchester).

Citations: MR 6, 257b = H25-2.

E12-55 (18, 273c)

Roelcke, W. Über die Verteilung der Klassen eigentlich assoziierter zweireihiger Matrizen, die sich durch eine positiv-definite Matrix darstellen lassen. Math. Ann. **131** (1956), 260–277.

Let Q be a m-rowed positive definite symmetric matrix with integer elements and with even diagonal element. Let $a(T)$ be the number of $m\times 2$ matrices G with integer elements such that $G'QG=T$, where $T=\begin{pmatrix} t_0 t_1 \\ t_1 t_2\end{pmatrix}$ is a two-rowed integer matrix with even t_0 and t_2 satisfying (*) $|2t_1|\leqq t_2 \leqq t_0$. Let $\varepsilon(T)$ be the number of unimodular matrix U such that $U'+U=T$. Let

$$T=u\begin{pmatrix}(x^2+y^2)y^{-1} & xy^{-1}\\ xy^{-1} & y^{-1}\end{pmatrix}$$

with $u=(\det T)^{\frac{1}{2}}$. The domain (*) is equivalent to $\mathfrak{F}$: $|2x|\leqq 1$, $x^2+y^2\geqq 1$, $y>0$. Let $\mathfrak{G}$ be subset of $\mathfrak{F}$. Then

$$\sum \frac{a(T)}{\varepsilon(T)} \sim \frac{3}{\pi}\,\mathrm{area}(\mathfrak{G})(4\pi q)^m/(12m\Gamma(m-1)),$$

where the sum runs through T with $u\leqq q$ and $(x, y)\in\mathfrak{G}$. The proof follows in principle the line of Hecke [Math. Z. **1** (1918), 357–376; **6** (1920), 11–51] with the aid of the properties of modular functions of the second degree. *L. K. Hua* (Peking).

Referred to in E12-68.

E12-56 **(18, 555h)**

Ramanathan, K. G. Quadratic forms over involutorial division algebras. J. Indian Math. Soc. (N.S.) 20 (1956), 227–257.

Let K be a field which is either an algebraic number field or an algebraic function field of one variable with finite constant field, and D be an involutorial non-commutative division algebra with K as center. The author considers quadratic forms over D. In the case where the involution of D leaves K fixed it is well known that D is a quaternion algebra over K. The author shows that in the function field case every quadratic form $f(x)$ in n variables is a universal form and is a null form if $n>1$. In the algebraic number field case he shows that the form $f(x)$ represents an element $b\neq 0$ of K if and only if this occurs in every completion of K. Also two nonsingular forms in n variables are equivalent in D if and only if they are equivalent in every completion. The author also makes a study of forms over involutorial algebras in which the involution moves the center and gives some results for skew forms. *A. A. Albert.*

Referred to in E12-81, E12-87.

E12-57 **(18, 562f)**

Kneser, Martin. Klassenzahlen indefiniter quadratischer Formen in drei oder mehr Veränderlichen. Arch. Math. 7 (1956), 323-332.

M. Eichler defined spinor genera and showed that a spinor genus of indefinite quadratic forms in more than two variables contains only one class [Quadratische Formen und orthogonale Gruppen, Springer, Berlin, 1952; Math. Z. 55 (1952), 216–252; MR 14, 540]. Using a slightly different definition of genus from the classical one, the author shows that the number of spinor genera in a genus can be written as a certain group index. Roughly speaking, if the reduced determinant D of the form has only a few prime divisors to high powers, the number of genera in a spinor genus is small — in particular it is 1 if D has no cubic factors. More generally (and more precisely) if R is an indefinite space of dimension greater than 2 over the field of rational numbers, if the reduced determinant of the lattice is equal to $\prod_p p^{s_p}$ with

$$s_2<\tfrac{1}{2}n(n-1)+[\tfrac{1}{2}(n+1)],\quad s_p<\tfrac{1}{2}n(n-1)$$

for odd p, the genus of K has but one class.

B. W. Jones (Boulder, Colo.).

Citations: MR 14, 540a = E02-4; MR 14, 540c = E12-45.

Referred to in E12-102, E68-5.

E12-58 **(18, 718k)**

Springer, T. A. Note on quadratic forms over algebraic number fields. Nederl. Akad. Wetensch. Proc. Ser. A. 60=Indag. Math. 19 (1957), 39–43.

In this paper a proof, which uses neither Dirichlet's theorem on the prime ideals in an arithmetical progression or quaternion algebras, is given of the following fundamental theorem of Hasse: If f is a quadratic form in n variables with coefficients in an algebraic number field K, then $f=0$ has a non-trivial solution in K if it has such a solution in all p-adic fields K_p corresponding to the finite or infinite places p of K. Standard results of class field theory are used. *B. W. Jones* (Boulder, Colo.).

E12-59 **(18, 719a)**

Carlitz, L. A note on representations of quadratic forms. Portugal. Math. 15 (1956), 79–81.

This paper gives an elementary simple proof of the following result. If I_k is the identity matrix with k rows, $N_{s-1}(m)$ is the number of solutions of $\sum_{i=1}^{s-1} u_i^2=m$ and B is the matrix $\begin{bmatrix} m & 0\\ 0 & I_r\end{bmatrix}$ of order $r+1$, then the number of solutions of $UI_sU'=B$ in s by r matrices U with integer elements is

$$2^r s(s-1)\cdots(s-r+1)N_{s-r}(m).$$

This is an extension of a result of Siegel for the case $s=5$, $r=1$. *B. W. Jones* (Boulder, Colo.).

Referred to in C20-53.

E12-60 **(19, 252a)**

Maass, Hans. Spherical functions and quadratic forms. J. Indian Math. Soc. (N.S.) 20 (1956), 117–162.

Let $x'Tx=T[x]$ and $x'Sx=S[x]$ be two positive quadratic forms of m and n variables, respectively, with $m>n$. Let B be a subset of all m by n matrices X such that $X\in B$ implies $XV\in B$ for all non-singular matrices V. Let C be a subset of the set of all reduced positive matrices in the sense of Minkowski such that $Y\in C$ implies $\lambda Y\in C$ for λ a positive scalar. Let $a_t(B, C)$ denote the number of integral matrices G such that $G'SG=S[G]=T$, $G\in B$, $T\in C$, $|T|=t$. The author remarks that in the field of reals and under certain measure conditions on B and C an asymptotic value can be found for $A_t(B, C)=t^{-1}\sum_{r\leq t} a_r(B, C)$. This paper is a contribution toward the analogous problem in algebraic number fields, based on the approximation of $\varphi(s; B, C)=\sum_{t=1}^{\infty} a_t(B, C)t^{-s}$ by a finite or infinite linear combination of certain zeta functions. Let $S=Q'Q$, $Q'=Q>0$; $f(X)=1$ or 0 according as $Q^{-1}X\in B$ or not, $g(Y)=1$ or 0 according as $Y[U]\in C$ for a unimodular U or not. It can be seen that

$$\varphi(s; B, C)=\sum_G f(QG)g(S[G])|S[G]|^{-s},$$

the summation being over a complete set of integral matrices $G=G^{(m,n)}$ of rank n such that no two differ by a unimodular right factor. The aim of the paper is to introduce a generalized class of spherical functions which are useful for the approximation of $f(X)$ for arbitrary n. These functions are too complex to be included here.

B. W. Jones (Boulder, Colo.).

Referred to in F65-13.

E12-61 **(19, 838b)**

Watson, G. L. The equivalence of quadratic forms. Canad. J. Math. 9 (1957), 526–548.

This is a sequel to a previous paper [Mathematika 2 (1955), 32–38; MR 17, 128], which dealt with ternary indefinite forms and in which some of the basic ideas and notations are introduced. The author here also uses Brandt's definition of the determinant d of the form; he lets Γ denote the set of all square-free integers under the operation $v_1\cdot v_2=v_1v_2(v_1, v_2)^{-2}$ and Γ_d the subgroup of Γ where $(v, d)=1$. Then groups $\Gamma(f)$ and $\Gamma^+(f)$ are defined for which the following theorem holds: Theorem 1: Let f be a non-degenerate quadratic form, with integral coefficients, in at least three variables. Then (i) the number of classes in the genus of f is not less than the order of the factor group $\Gamma_{d(f)}/\Gamma(f)$ or $\Gamma_{d(f)}/\Gamma^+(f)$, when improper equivalence is or is not, respectively, admitted; (ii) $\Gamma(f)=\Gamma^+(f)$ is a necessary condition for f to be improperly equivalent to itself; (iii) if f is indefinite, then there is equality in (i) and the necessary condition in (ii) is also sufficient.

The author also proves Theorem 4: Suppose that f is indefinite, k (the number of variables) not less than 3; let d_1 be the greatest integer whose $(k(k-1)/2)$th power divides d. Suppose also that $d_1=1$, 2, 4, p or $2p$; $p\equiv -1 \pmod 4$. Then the class-number of f, in the strict sense (determinant 1), is 1. *B. W. Jones.*

Citations: MR 17, 128d = E12-52.

E12-62 **(19, 838c)**

Kneser, Martin. Klassenzahlen definiter quadratischer Formen. Arch. Math. 8 (1957), 241–250.

The author considers positive definite quadratic forms

in n variables of determinant d, over the ring of rational numbers whose denominators are powers of 2. Using extensions of the reduction theory and other methods, he determines the class number for all $d \leqq 3$ with $n+d \leqq 17$. In particular, the class number is 1 for $n \leqq 6$ and $d=1$ or 2; for $d=1$ and $n=7$; for $d=3$ and $n=1$. *B. W. Jones.*

Referred to in E12-141, E24-115.

E12-63 (19, 942h)

Vartak, Manohar N. On the Hasse-Minkowski invariant of the Kronecker product of matrices. Canad. J. Math. **10** (1958), 66–72.

Let C_r denote the leading principal minor matrix of order r of a matrix C. Let A, B be square matrices of orders m, n respectively, and put $D=A\times B$ (the Kronecker product of A and B). Set $u=rn+s$, $0\leqq r<m$, $0\leqq s\leqq n$. The author proves that

(1) $\det D_u=(\det A_r)^{n-s}(\det A_{r+1})^s(\det B)^r\det B_s$

provided none of the determinants $\det A_r$ vanishes. If A, B are rational symmetric matrices having no zero leading principal minor determinant, the author deduces the following formula for the Hasse-Minkowski invariant of $A\times B$:

(2) $$C_p(A\times B)=(-1,-1)_p^{m+n-1}\{C_p(A)\}^n\{C_p(B)\}^m \times(\det A,-1)_p^{\frac12 n(n-1)}(\det B,-1)_p^{\frac12 m(m-1)} \times(\det A,\det B)_p^{mn-1}.$$

Here, p is a fixed prime and $(a,b)_p$ is the Hilbert norm residue symbol. Formula (2) is used to derive a result of Jones: $C_p(aB)=C_p(B)(a,-1)_p^{\frac12 n(n+1)}(a,\det B)_p^{n-1}$, where a is a non-zero rational; and a result of MacDuffee: $C_p(\Delta_m)=(-1,\ -1)_p^{m-1}\{C_p(B)\}^m(\det\ B,\ -1)_p^{\frac12 m(m-1)}$, where Δ_m is the direct sum of m B's.

M. Newman (Washington, D.C.).

E12-64 (20# 6999)

Ledermann, Walter. An arithmetical property of quadratic forms. Comment. Math. Helv. 33 (1959), 34–37.

Let $\mathfrak{Q}$ be the domain of rational numbers with odd denominators. For a in $\mathfrak{Q}$, $a\equiv 0$ (2^α) will mean that the numerator of a is divisible by 2^α. The author proves, by induction on n, the following theorem: Let f be a quadratic form of degree n with coefficients and variables in $\mathfrak{Q}$. If the determinant Δ of f is odd and if w is a vector such that $f(x,x)\equiv f(x,w)$ (mod 2) for all x, then $f(w,w)-\tau\equiv \Delta-\operatorname{sgn}\Delta$ (mod 4), where τ is the signature of f and $\operatorname{sgn}\Delta=+1$ or -1 according as $\Delta>0$ or $\Delta<0$.

A special case of the theorem where $\Delta=\pm 1$ was previously obtained as a corollary of topological investigations by Hirzebruch and Hopf.*

R. Ree (Vancouver, B.C.)

*MR **20** #7272

Referred to in E04-17, E12-69.

E12-65 (21# 3377)

Cassels, J. W. S. Note on quadratic forms over the rational field. Proc. Cambridge Philos. Soc. **55** (1959), 267–270.

The author considers the following theorem. Let $f(x)$ be a non-singular quadratic form in n variables with coefficients in R. Suppose that f represents 0 in R_p for every prime p and in R_∞. Then f represents 0 in R, the field of rational numbers. Except for $n=4$ the proof of this theorem requires no deep tools but for $n=4$ the truth of the theorem has been shown only by use of fairly deep results such as Dirichlet's theorem on primes in an arithmetic progression. The author gives a simple proof using nothing deeper than Minkowski's convex body theorem and Gauss's theorem on the existence of forms in genera.

B. W. Jones (Mayaguez, P.R.)

Referred to in E12-66.

E12-66 (23# A857)

Cassels, J. W. S.
Note on quadratic forms over the rational field. Addendum.
Proc. Cambridge Philos. Soc. **57** (1961), 697.

An addendum to the author's paper [same Proc. **55** (1959), 267–270; MR **21** #3377], in which the author points out that he had overlooked the work of M. Eichler [*Quadratische Formen und orthogonale Gruppen*, Springer, Berlin, 1952; MR **14**, 540], and that his own work seems to be somewhat simpler.

Citations: MR 14, 540a = E02-4; MR 21# 3377 = E12-65.

E12-67 (21# 4134)

Kneser, Martin. Klassenzahlen quadratischer Formen. Jber. Deutsch. Math. Verein. **61** (1958), Abt. 1, 76–88.

This is an expository paper which, after outlining the fundamental concepts for forms with coefficients over an integral domain of characteristic not 2, deals with the reduction theory, the Minkowski-Siegel-Maass formula and spinor genera. Except for the last topic, the emphasis is on positive forms. *B. W. Jones* (Mayaguez, P.R.)

E12-68 (21# 6359)

Maass, Hans. Über die Verteilung der zweidimensionalen Untergitter in einem euklidischen Gitter. Math. Ann. **137** (1959), 319–327.

Let $\mathfrak{T}$ be an n-dimensional lattice in Euclidean m-space and denote by $\mathfrak{L}(\mathfrak{T})$ the subspace determined by $\mathfrak{T}$, by $\langle\mathfrak{T}\rangle$ the class of lattices similar to $\mathfrak{T}$ and by $|\mathfrak{T}|$ the n-dimensional lattice volume of $\mathfrak{T}$. Let $\mathfrak{R}_0$ be the space of two-dimensional subspaces and $\mathfrak{G}_0$ the space of similarity classes of two-dimensional lattices. Measures (both denoted by I) are introduced in a natural way into $\mathfrak{R}_0$ and $\mathfrak{G}_0$. Let $\mathfrak{R}$ and $\mathfrak{G}$ be measurable sets in $\mathfrak{R}_0$ and $\mathfrak{G}_0$ respectively and denote by $\alpha_q(\mathfrak{S};\mathfrak{R},\mathfrak{G})$ the number of two-dimensional sublattices $\mathfrak{T}$ of the m-dimensional lattice $\mathfrak{S}$ satisfying $\mathfrak{L}(\mathfrak{T})\in\mathfrak{R}$, $\langle\mathfrak{T}\rangle\in\mathfrak{G}$ and $|\mathfrak{T}|\leqq q$. The author proves the asymptotic result

$$\alpha_q(\mathfrak{S};\mathfrak{R},\mathfrak{G})\sim\frac{I(\mathfrak{R})I(\mathfrak{G})}{I(\mathfrak{R}_0)I(\mathfrak{G}_0)}\,\frac{(2\pi q)^m}{24|\mathfrak{S}|^2 m\Gamma(m-1)}$$

for $q\to\infty$. For $\mathfrak{R}=\mathfrak{R}_0$ this result was established by W. Roelcke [same Ann. **131** (1956), 260–277; MR **18**, 273]. The present paper follows the same method of proof but utilizes in addition recent results of the author about zeta-functions [ibid. **134** (1957), 1–32; MR **19**, 838].

A. Dvoretzky (Jerusalem)

Citations: MR 18, 273c = E12-55; MR 19, 838g = F65-13.

Referred to in E12-72.

E12-69 (21# 7183)

van der Blij, F. An invariant of quadratic forms mod 8. Nederl. Akad. Wetensch. Proc. Ser. A **62** = Indag. Math. **21** (1959), 291–293.

Let $f(x,y)$ be an integral quadratic form in n variables with odd determinant D and signature τ. If the integral vector w satisfies the congruence $f(x,x)\equiv f(x,w)$ (mod 2) for all integral vectors x, then

(*) $$\exp\{\tfrac14\pi i(f(w,w)-\tau)\}=|D|^{1/2}G_0^{-1},$$

where $G_0 = \sum_{y \in M'/M} \exp 4\pi i\{f(y, y)\}$, M is the lattice of all integral vectors and M' is the dual lattice relative to f. This generalizes a formula due to the reviewer [Comment. Math. Helv. **33** (1959), 34–37; MR **20** #6999]. Furthermore, the author shows that the right-hand side of (*) can be expressed in terms of characters of the Witt group. For a unimodular form the formula reduces to $f(w, w) \equiv \tau$ (mod 8), a result which is related to recent topological work by Hirzebruch and H. Hopf [Math. Ann. **136** (1958), 156–172; MR **20** #7272]. *W. Ledermann* (Manchester)

Citations: MR 20# 6999 = E12-64.

E12-70 **(22# 705)**

Watson, G. L. Bounded representations of integers by quadratic forms. Mathematika **4** (1957), 17–24.

Es sei $f(x_1, \cdots, x_k)$ eine quadratische Form mit ganzzahligen Koeffizienten. Man nennt eine Lösung von (1) $n = f(x_1, \cdots, x_k)$ eine beschränkte Darstellung von n durch f, wenn (2) $\max(|x_1|, \cdots, |x_k|) \ll n^{1/2}$ ist. Dabei ist das Zeichen $\ll$ im Sinne von Vinogradov zu verstehen. (D. h. die Ungleichung gilt für eine nicht spezialisierte Konstante auf der rechten Seite.) Es fragt sich, ob man die Konstante unabhängig von n wählen kann. Folgt aus der Lösbarkeit von (1) für beliebiges n auch (2), so sagt man, f stellt ganze Zahlen beschränkt dar. Dies gilt insbesondere für definite Formen. — I. Stellt eine indefinite Form f die Null nicht trivial dar, dann stellt sie ganze Zahlen beschränkt dar, sofern $k \geqq 4$ ist. — II. Stellt eine indefinite Form f die Null nur trivial dar, dann stellt sie ganze Zahlen beschränkt dar. — Der Beweis von Satz II benützt die Theorie der Reduktion der positiv definiten Formen, während Satz I aus elementaren Kongruenzen und Ungleichungen folgt. Satz I gilt nicht für $k = 2$ und ob er für $k = 3$ gilt, ist derzeit noch ungewiß.

N. Hofreiter (Zbl **77**, 264)

E12-71 **(22# 10953)**

Lubelski, S. Unpublished results on number theory. I. Quadratic forms in a Euclidean ring. Edited by C. Schogt. Acta Arith. **6** (1960/61), 217–224.

This is the first of a sequence of notes giving original results contained in an unpublished manuscript of the Polish mathematician S. Lubelski who met his death in World War II.

Let $\mathfrak{R}$ be the ring of rational integers or the ring of integers in one of the complex quadratic fields with a euclidean algorithm. It is shown that the number of classes of quadratic forms with coefficients in $\mathfrak{R}$ and with a given non-zero determinant and with a given number of variables is finite. {The reviewer notes that the corresponding result when $\mathfrak{R}$ is the ring of integers of any algebraic number field is Hilfssatz 40 of C. L. Siegel, Ann. of Math. (2) **38** (1937), 212–291.} The proof here gives an explicit upper bound for the least non-zero number represented by the form.

J. W. S. Cassels (Cambridge, England)

Referred to in E16-48.

E12-72 **(22# 10981)**

Maass, Hans. Über die räumliche Verteilung der Punkte in Gittern mit indefiniter Metrik. Math. Ann. **138** (1959), 287–315.

The author studied the spatial distribution of the points and sub-lattices of lattices with indefinite metric. He [Math. Ann. **137** (1959), 319–327; MR **21** #6359] and others have considered similar questions for Euclidean lattices. Here, however, new tools are needed and these are provided by C. L. Siegel's theory of indefinite quadratic forms [ibid. **124** (1951), 17–54; MR **16**, 800]. The considerations are very involved and the results do not lend themselves to concise quotation. We therefore content ourselves with mentioning a special result about the ternary case. Let S be a rational symmetric matrix of signature (1, 2) and assume that the form $S[\mathfrak{x}]$ does not rationally represent 0. Let $\mathfrak{F}$ be a polygonal fundamental domain corresponding to a group of integral automorphisms of S of finite rank. Let $\mathfrak{B} \subset \mathfrak{F}$ be Riemann measurable and $\mathfrak{B}_0$ be the corresponding domain in $S[\mathfrak{x}] > 0$. Then we have for the number $\alpha_q(S, \mathfrak{B})$ of integral $\mathfrak{g} \in \mathfrak{B}_0$ satisfying $0 < S[\mathfrak{g}] \leqq q$ the asymptotic formula

$$\alpha_q(S, \mathfrak{B}) \sim \frac{2\pi}{3} \|S\|^{-1/2} V(\mathfrak{B}) q^{3/2}$$

as $q \to \infty$, where $V(\mathfrak{B})$ denotes the hyperbolic volume of $\mathfrak{B}$.

A. Dvoretzky (Jerusalem)

Citations: MR 16, 800a = E12-49; MR 21# 6359 = E12-68.

E12-73 **(23# A116)**

Ankeny, N. C.

Definite quadratic forms.

Proc. London Math. Soc. (3) **11** (1961), 353–384.

The purpose of this paper is to give a new proof of Siegel's genus representation formulas of integers, m, by quadratic forms F in n variables with integral coefficients; namely,

$$\sum N(F_j, m) N(F_j, F_j)^{-1} = K \prod M_q(F, m)\, M_q(F, F)^{-1},$$

$$\sum N(F_j, F_j)^{-1} = L \prod M_q(F, F)^{-1},$$

where the sums are over a set of inequivalent matrices in a genus, the products over all primes q, and K and L are explicitly given functions of n and the determinant of F. Here $N(F, m)$ is the number of integral representations of m by F, $N(F, F)$ the number of integral automorphisms of F, and the corresponding M_q are, except for a power of q, the number of representations and automorphisms mod q^c, independent of c for c sufficiently large.

While parts of Siegel's derivation were essentially analytic in character, this is algebraic, exploiting the methods of Eichler and the point of view of Artin in his *Geometric algebra* [Interscience, New York, 1957; MR **18**, 553]. Results of O'Meara are also found useful. Other applications of these methods are promised in a later paper. *B. W. Jones* (Boulder, Colo.)

E12-74 **(23# A119)**

Delone, B. N.

Reduction theory.

Kristallografija **5** (1960), 501–507 (*Russian*); *translated as Soviet Physics Cryst.* **5** (1961), 482–488.

A proof is first of all given for those reduction conditions that were introduced by Voronoĭ without proof. The region V determined by these conditions is a fundamental region. An investigation then follows into the division of the cone K of positive quadratic forms into regions equivalent to V. At the end of the paper, there is a table in which those parts of V which correspond to the different Bravais lattices are indicated. *Werner Nowacki* (Bern)

E12-75 **(23# A122)**

Pommerenke, C.

Über die Gleichverteilung von Gitterpunkten auf m-dimensionalen Ellipsoiden.

Acta Arith. **5** (1959), 227–257.

Let S be a positive definite symmetric $(m \times m)$-matrix with integral elements. Let H be the ellipsoid $x'Sx = 1$, where x is the column vector (x_i) $(i = 1, 2, \cdots, m)$ and x'

its transpose (row-)vector. Let Δ be a domain on H which is measurable in the Jordan sense with respect to the metric defined by the line element $ds^2=(dx)'S(dx)$. Let $r(\Delta, n)$ be the number of integral solutions y of $y'Sy=n$ with $y/\sqrt{n} \in \Delta$. The author proves for $m \geqq 5$ that

$$\frac{r(\Delta, n)}{r(n)} \to \frac{D}{E},$$

where D and E are the areas of Δ and H respectively. $r(n)=r(H, n)$ and where $n \to \infty$ through those n for which $r(n) \neq 0$. This remains true for $m=4$ if $r(n) \geqq cn$ for $r(n) \neq 0$.

H. D. Kloostermann (Leiden)

Referred to in E12-76, E12-80, E12-92.

E12-76 (26# 6126)

Pommerenke, C.

Berichtigung zu meiner Arbeit "Über die Gleichverteilung von Gitterpunkten auf m-dimensionalen Ellipsoiden".

Acta Arith. **7** (1961/62), 279.

Corrections to the author's earlier paper [same Acta **5** (1959), 227–257; MR **23** #A122].

Citations: MR 23# A122 = E12-75.

E12-77 (23# A136)

Raghavan, S.

Modular forms of degree n and representation by quadratic forms.

Ann. of Math. (2) **70** (1959), 446–477.

Let T and S be positive-definite and symmetric $(n \times n)$- and $(m \times m)$-matrices respectively with integral elements (integral matrices) and let $A(S, T)$ be the number of integral representations of T by S (i.e., the number of integral $(m \times n)$-matrices X satisfying $X'SX=T$). If S is the k-rowed identity matrix, then we have the well-known asymptotic formula

$$\text{(A)} \qquad A(S, t) = \frac{\pi^{k/2}t^{(k/2)-1}}{\Gamma(k/2)}\sigma(t)+O(t^{k/4}),$$

where $\sigma(t)$ is the "singular series". The author wants to prove a formula of the same type for arbitrary n and $m>2n+2$. He uses Siegel's theory of modular forms $f(Z)$ of degree n and introduces generalized Eisenstein series. As in Hecke's theory for $n=1$, an associated linear combination $\varphi(Z)$ of Eisenstein series is introduced. For $n=1$ the difference $f(Z)-\varphi(Z)$ is a cusp form; this, however, is not generally true for $n>1$. The author then uses Siegel's generalization of the "Farey dissection" to matrix spaces and obtains an estimate for the Fourier coefficients of $f(Z)-\varphi(Z)$. This method gives an analogue of (A) for $A(S, T)$ if the product of the minima of T and T^{-1} is bounded below, independently of T. By studying the singular series he gives some special cases in which the error term is of a strictly lower order than the principal term.

H. D. Kloosterman (Leiden)

Referred to in E12-78, E12-94.

E12-78 (24# A97)

Raghavan, S.

Modular forms of degree n and representation by quadratic forms.

Contributions to function theory (Internat. Colloq. Function Theory, Bombay, 1960), pp. 181–183. Tata Institute of Fundamental Research, Bombay, 1960.

A colloquium lecture, the substance of which has been previously published [Ann. of Math. (2) **70** (1959), 446–477; MR **23** #A136].

Citations: MR 23# A136 = E12-77.

E12-79 (23# A2381)

van der Blij, P.

Simultaneous representation of integers by a quadratic and a linear form.

Nieuw Arch. Wisk. (3) **7** (1959), 109–114.

The Siegel theory is carried over to the study of the number of solutions of the system $x'Sx=\alpha$, $x'a=\beta$, where $x'Sx$ is a positive definite quadratic form in $n>3$ variables with integral coefficients, and a is a primitive vector with integral entries. For the definition of classes and genera, the author uses unimodular transformations V with $V \equiv E \pmod{a'\bar{S}a}$ and $V'a=a$; here $\bar{S}$ is an integral matrix such that $S\bar{S}=\sigma E$ with the smallest possible integer $\sigma>0$. He conjectures that this congruence condition should be removable. The paper depends on an earlier one [Ann. of Math. (2) **50** (1949), 875–883; MR **11**, 85].

W. J. LeVeque (Ann Arbor, Mich.)

Citations: MR 11, 85c = E12-33.

E12-80 (23# A2382)

Malyšev, A. V.

The representation of integers by positive quadratic forms with four or more variables.

Dokl. Akad. Nauk SSSR **133** (1960), 1294–1297 (*Russian*); *translated as Soviet Math. Dokl.* **1** (1961), 975–978.

Various complicated asymptotic expressions are given for the number of integral points (or of primitive integral points) lying on an ellipsoid $f(x_1, \cdots, x_n)=m$ with $n \geqq 4$ and inside a cone emanating from the origin. Related results have been given by the author [same Dokl. **114** (1957), 25–28; MR **20** #1662; ibid. **133** (1960), 1017–1020; Izv. Akad. Nauk SSSR Ser. Mat. **23** (1959), 337–364] and by C. Pommerenke [Acta Arith. **5** (1959), 227–257; MR **23** #A122].

W. J. LeVeque (Ann Arbor, Mich.)

Citations: MR 20# 1662 = E24-70; MR 23# A122 = E12-75.

E12-81 (23# A3718)

Ramanathan, K. G.

Quadratic forms over involutorial division algebras. II.

Math. Ann. **143** (1961), 293–332.

[For Part I, see J. Indian Math. Soc. (N.S.) **20** (1956), 227–257; MR **18**, 555.] This highly technical paper deals with much of the elaborate spade work which the author needs for an analytic theory of quadratic forms $\tilde{x}Sx$ over a rational division algebra D. Here $a \to \tilde{a}$ is an involution of D, $S=(s_{kl})$ with $\tilde{S}=(\tilde{s}_{lk})=\varepsilon S$, $\varepsilon=\pm 1$ depending on the involution (Albert's classification is used) and $x'=(x_1, \cdots, x_n)$. Thus, building and extending the basic classical prototypes of Siegel in a by no means trivial manner, fundamental domains of the unit groups of the generalized quadratic forms ($\tilde{U}SU=S$, elements of U, U^{-1} in a given order of D) are constructed via the orthogonal groups of the given forms (extension by means of the reals for the former) according to the methods of Humbert and Siegel. It is shown that the unit groups are finitely generated. Furthermore, for the proper definition of theta series and the investigation of their convergence properties and integrals (connection with ζ-functions), a suitable new Siegel upper half-plane is defined which is homeomorphic to the symmetric representation space of the orthogonal group belonging to the $2n \times 2n$ matrix $\begin{pmatrix} 0 & E \\ -\varepsilon E & 0 \end{pmatrix}$, i.e., the symplectic group, ε as above. Dimensions of the various representation spaces consisting of matrices H which essentially satisfy $HS^{-1}\tilde{H}=S'$, $H'=H>0$, are determined by means of parametrizations, as was done by Siegel. Generalizations of Siegel's modular group and its relations to symmetric pairs of integral (in D) matrices ($C\tilde{D}=\varepsilon D\tilde{C}$)

are discussed; existence of fundamental domains and properties of their volumes are established. Finally, the author determines for special cases the structure of his generalized Siegel upper half-planes as products of certain symmetric spaces (types I to III occur).

O. F. G. Schilling (Lafayette, Ind.)

Citations: MR 18, 555h = E12-56.

E12-82 **(24# A78)**

Watson, G. L.

Quadratic Diophantine equations.

Philos. Trans. Roy. Soc. London Ser. A **253** (1960/61), 227–254.

Let $f=f(x_1, x_2, \cdots, x_n)$ be a positive definite quadratic form with integral coefficients, and N a positive integer. Suppose that f does not represent N, although the congruence $f\equiv N \pmod m$ is soluble for every modulus. Then Tartakowsky [Izv. Akad. Nauk SSSR **1929**, 111–122, 165–196] showed that for a given f with $n\geqq 5$ there are at most finitely many possibilities for N. Tartakowsky's argument does not lead to any estimate for N. In this paper the author gives such estimates for N in terms of the coefficients of the quadratic form. To simplify the argument and improve the estimates, the problem is slightly generalized by considering the equation

(1) $$f(x_1, x_2, \cdots, x_n)+b_1x_1+\cdots+b_nx_n = N,$$

where $b_1, b_2, \cdots, b_n$ are integers. Of interest in itself, and necessary for the proof, is the following theorem: Let f be a non-singular quadratic form with integral coefficients and discriminant $d\neq 0$. Then there exists a positive integer $m_0=m_0(f)$, depending only on f, with the following properties: The congruence $f+\sum_{i=1}^n b_ix_i\equiv 0 \pmod m$ is soluble in integers x_i, for every positive integer m, whenever b_i and N are integers such that the congruence is soluble with $m=m_0$. Further, if d' is the product of the distinct prime factors of d, then $m_0^{n-3}d'$ divides d.

The proof is very complicated, but in an introduction the author gives a short and valuable outline of the methods which are used. *W. Ljunggren* (Oslo)

E12-83 **(24# A717)**

Ramanathan, K. G.

Zeta functions of quadratic forms.

Acta Arith. **7** (1961/62), 39–69.

Let S be an m-rowed non-singular symmetric matrix whose elements are integers in an algebraic number-field K; this defines the quadratic form $\alpha'S\alpha$, where α is a column-vector and α' its transpose. It is assumed that this is not a zero-form in 2, 3 or 4 variables, and that it is indefinite (i.e., K has at least one imaginary prime spot at infinity, or one real prime spot at infinity where the form is indefinite). For each signature (assigning a sign to each real prime spot of K where the form is indefinite), and for each ideal $\mathfrak{a}\neq 0$, the author considers the zeta function

$$N\mathfrak{a}^{2s}\sum M(S, \mathfrak{a}, g)|Ng|^{-s};$$

here g runs over a complete set of representatives of the integers $g\neq 0$ in K with the given signature, with respect to the equivalence relation $g\sim g'=g\varepsilon^2$ (note the disturbing misprint $\varepsilon^2\bar{\varepsilon}$ for ε^2, which occurs on p. 39, line 3 from bottom, and again p. 54, line 7); and $M(S, \mathfrak{a}, g)$ is the "measure of representation" of g by the quadratic form $\alpha'S\alpha$ under the condition $\alpha\equiv 0 \bmod \mathfrak{a}$ (the definition, following the pattern which is familiar to all students of Siegel's work, is explained in § 5). The main result of the paper is the functional equation for these zeta functions, extending the classical result of Siegel (who treated only the case that K is the rational number-field). The final sections treat, by a somewhat different method, the parallel case of Hermitian forms over a quadratic extension of an algebraic number-field; after proving some basic lemmas, the author restricts himself to imaginary quadratic extensions of the rational number-field, while at the same time extending the scope of his investigations by including representations with congruence conditions.

A. Weil (Princeton, N.J.)

Referred to in E68-18.

E12-84 **(24# A1252)**

Malyšev, A. V.

On representations of integers by positive quadratic forms with four or more variables. I. (Russian)

Izv. Akad. Nauk SSSR Ser. Mat. **23** (1959), 337–364.

The author develops an asymptotic formula concerning the distribution of the integral points $(x_1, \cdots, x_s)$ on the surface of the ellipsoid $f=f(x_1, \cdots, x_s)=\sum_{i,j=1}^s a_{i,j}x_ix_j=m$, where m is a positive integer and f is a positive quadratic form with integral coefficients $a_{i,j}$. Let Ω be a convex region on the ellipsoid, ω the f-elliptical solid angle of Ω (i.e., the $(s-1)$-dimensional area of the region Ω', obtained from Ω with the help of a linear transformation which changes the form f into a sum of squares $x_1^2+x_2^2+\cdots+x_s^2$, divided by $m^{(s-1)/2}$). Further, let $q, g, b_1, \cdots, b_s$ be integers,

$$S_{g;b_1,\cdots,b_s}(f, q) = g^{-s}\sum_{x_1,\cdots,x_s=0}^{q-1} \exp(2\pi iq^{-1}f(gx_1+b_1, \cdots, gx_s+b_s))$$

(the Gaussian sums mod g),

$$H(f, g, b_1, \cdots, b_s; m) = H(f, g; m) = \sum_{q=1}^{\infty} q^{-s} \sum_{p \pmod q}' S_{g;b_1,\cdots,b_s}(pf, q)\exp(-2\pi iq^{-1}mp)$$

("singular" series, introduced by G. H. Hardy and J. E. Littlewood [Nachr. Gesellschaft Wiss. Göttingen, Math.-Phys. Kl. **1920**, 33–54]). The main result of the paper is the following theorem (which generalizes and strengthens a theorem of V. A. Tartakovskiĭ [Izv. Akad. Nauk SSSR Otd. Fiz.-Mat. **1929**, 111–122, 165–196]). Let $s\geqq 4$ and $\omega>0$, and denote by $b_1, \cdots, b_s$ the integers satisfying the congruence $f(b_1, \cdots, b_s)\equiv m \pmod g$, by Δ the discriminant of the quadratic form f, and by $r(f, \Omega, g; m)$ the number of all integral points $(x_1, \cdots, x_s)$ in the region Ω which are congruent to $(b_1, \cdots, b_s)$ mod g. Then, if $m\to\infty$,

$$r(f, \Omega, g; m) = \frac{\omega}{\omega_0}\frac{\pi^{s/2}}{\Delta^{1/2}\Gamma(s/2)} m^{s/2-1}H(f, g; m)+O(m^{s/2-1-(s-3)/(6s+2)+\varepsilon}),$$

where $\omega_0=2\pi^{s/2}/\Gamma(s/2)$ (the solid round angle in the s-dimensional space) and ε is an arbitrary positive real number. *J. W. Andrushkiw* (Newark, N.J.)

Referred to in E12-92, Z10-22.

E12-85 **(24# A1896)**

Nanava, Š. I.

On the representation of numbers by positive quadratic forms. (Russian)

Izv. Vysš. Učebn. Zaved. Matematika **1960**, *no.* 5 (18), 116–128.

Using the circle method, the author notes several new cases of interest where one obtains exact formulae for the number of representations of a number by a definite quadratic form. The number of variables is 5, 6, 7 or 8 and the variables themselves lie in suitably chosen arithmetic progressions with small common difference (2 or 4). *S. Chowla* (Boulder, Colo.)

E12-86 **(24# A1897)**

Nanava, Š. I.

The representation of numbers by positive quadratic forms (asymptotic formulas). (Russian)

Izv. Vysš. Učebn. Zaved. Matematika **1960**, *no.* 3 (16), 219–229.

The author obtains asymptotic formulae for the number of representations of a large number by a quadratic form (definite) in 5 or more variables when the variables lie in arithmetic progressions with the same common difference. As usual in applications of the Hardy-Littlewood method, the dominant term involves the so-called "singular series". *S. Chowla* (Boulder, Colo.)

E12-87 **(25# 127)**

Tsukamoto, Takashi

On the local theory of quaternionic anti-hermitian forms.

J. Math. Soc. Japan **13** (1961), 387–400.

L'auteur donne d'abord la classification des formes anti-hermitiennes Φ sur un corps de quaternions K ayant pour centre un corps $\mathfrak{p}$-adique k. Il montre (retrouvant des résultats de Ramanathan [J. Indian Math. Soc. (N.S.) **20** (1956), 227–257; MR **18**, 555] que ces formes sont déterminées, à une équivalence près, par la dimension et le discriminant (classe modulo les carrés dans k de la norme réduite de la matrice de la forme). Il étudie ensuite les similitudes pour une telle forme, en introduisant un "Gitter" (module sur l'ordre maximal du corps K, contenant une base de l'espace où est définie Φ) et le sous-groupe des similitudes laissant fixe ce "Gitter", qui est un sous-groupe compact maximal du groupe des similitudes. *J. Dieudonné* (Paris)

Citations: MR 18, 555h = E12-56.

Referred to in E12-100.

E12-88 **(25# 128)**

Satake, Ichiro

Some remarks to the preceding paper of Tsukamoto.

J. Math. Soc. Japan **13** (1961), 401–409.

L'auteur complète les résultats du travail précédent [#127] en considérant d'abord le groupe des automorphismes d'une forme anti-hermitienne sur un K-module libre, où cette fois K est une algèbre de quaternions sur un corps $\mathfrak{p}$-adique, qui n'est pas un corps; il montre que ce groupe est isomorphe à un groupe orthogonal sur le corps k. Utilisant ce résultat et les isomorphismes classiques des groupes orthogonaux de dimension $\leqq 6$, il montre que lorsque K est un corps, les groupes d'automorphismes d'une forme anti-hermitienne sur K, pour les dimensions 1, 2 et 3, peuvent aussi s'interpréter (à isogénie près) comme groupes multiplicatifs des éléments de norme 1 dans des corps gauches de rang 2, 8 ou 16 sur k. *J. Dieudonné* (Paris)

E12-89 **(25# 1134)**

Rao, V. Venugopal

Lattice points of indefinite quadratic forms with integral coefficients.

Proc. Indian Acad. Sci. Sect. A **54** (1961), 352–355.

Let S be a rational, symmetric, non-singular indefinite square matrix with $m>4$ rows. C. L. Siegel has defined a density $M(S, A, t)$ for the (infinite) number of column vectors X with ${}^tXSX=t$, $X\equiv A \bmod 1$, where t is a given integer [C. L. Siegel, Math. Ann. **124** (1951), 17–54; MR **16**, 800]. In this note it is proved that $\sum_{0<t\leqq x} M(S, A, t) = ax+O(1)$ (a suitable constant). The proof consists in a straightforward application of Siegel's explicit formula for $M(S, A, t)$. *T. A. Springer* (Utrecht)

Citations: MR 16, 800a = E12-49.

E12-90 **(25# 3906)**

Siegel, Carl Ludwig

Zur Reduktionstheorie quadratischer Formen.

Publications of the Mathematical Society of Japan, Vol. 5.

The Mathematical Society of Japan, Tokyo, 1959. ix+69 *pp.* $2.00.

Table of contents: (1) Normal coordinates; (2) Linear coordinates; (3) Compactification of the Minkowski domain; (4) The translation group; (5) Reduced boundary points; (6) Equivalence of boundary points; (7) The fundamental domain of the boundary points; (8) Geodesic lines; (9) Parabolic mappings; (10) Reduced distances; (11) Asymptotes; (12) Ideal points; (13) Action space (Wirkungsraum) of the orthogonal group; (14) Boundary points of the action space; (15) Asymptotes in the action space; (16) The automorphism group; (17) Representations of zero; (18) Finiteness of volume of the fundamental domain.

The first part of the book (§§ 1–12) is concerned with reduced positive quadratic forms of n variables with real coefficients. The author studies the geometric properties of the Hermite-Minkowski fundamental domain of the group of unimodular integral permutations in the coefficient space of quadratic forms. His main attention is focussed on properties of forms on the boundary of the fundamental domain. He develops far-reaching analogues to methods and results related with the fundamental domain of the elliptic modular group.

The second part of the book (§§ 13–18) is devoted to the theory of automorphisms of indefinite quadratic forms. In a specially constructed "action space" (Wirkungsraum) of the automorphism group of a given indefinite form, he forms a fundamental domain of the group of integral automorphisms of this form. The fundamental domain of the automorphism group is studied in the plane, in complete analogy to the Hermite-Minkowski domain in the first part of the book. In the very last chapter (§ 18) he gives a simple proof that the volume of the fundamental domain is finite. *A. V. Malyšev* (RŽMat **1961** 12A219)

Referred to in E12-115.

E12-91 **(25# 3907)**

Kneser, Martin

Darstellungsmasse indefiniter quadratischer Formen.

Math. Z. **77** (1961), 188–194.

The main result of this note is the following theorem. Let f be a quadratic form in n variables over the algebraic number field k, let $a\in k$. Assume $n\geqq 5$ or $n\geqq 4$ and $a\neq 0$. Consider a fixed genus of representations of a by f. The contribution of this genus to the measure of the representation of a by a given spinor genus of lattices is the same for all spinor genera of a genus. For indefinite f this implies previous results of Siegel [Math. Ann. **124** (1951), 17–54; MR **16**, 800; ibid. **124** (1952), 364–387; MR **16**, 801] and Eichler [Math. Z. **55** (1952), 216–252; MR **14**, 540]. The proof is purely arithmetical, using the adele language. It is a good example for showing the adequacy of the adeles for handling this kind of problem.

The author also gives results for the cases $n=4$, $a=0$ and $n=3$ (related to those of Jones and Watson [Canad.

J. Math. **8** (1956), 592–608; MR **18**, 467]).

T. A. Springer (Utrecht)

Citations: MR 14, 540c = E12-45; MR 16, 800a = E12-49; MR 16, 801a = E12-50; MR 18, 467c = E20-49.

Referred to in E12-117.

E12-92 (26# 80)

Malyšev, A. V.

On the representation of integers by positive quadratic forms. (Russian)

Trudy Mat. Inst. Steklov. **65** (1962), 212 *pp.*

Let

$$f = f(x_1, \cdots, x_n) = \sum_{\alpha,\beta=1}^{n} f_{\alpha,\beta} x_\alpha x_\beta$$

be a positive-definite quadratic form with rational integer coefficients $f_{\alpha,\beta}$. This monograph is primarily concerned with the distribution of the integer vectors $(x_1, \cdots, x_n)$ for which $f(x) = m$ (a given positive integer) on the surface of the ellipsoid $f(x) = m$ and between the different residue classes to a fixed integer g. It gives in full detail results published or announced by the author and by Linnik.

The situation is simplest when the number n of variables exceeds 3. Then the Hardy-Littlewood-Vinogradov method is applicable. The main result is as follows: Let d be the determinant of $f(x)$ and let g be an integer prime to $2dm$. Let Λ be a convex region on the surface $f(x) = m$ subtending an f-solid angle λ at the origin (the f-solid angle is the solid angle after an affine transformation which reduces f to $\sum_{\alpha=1}^{n} x_\alpha^2$) and let $\lambda_0 = 2\pi^{n/2}/\Gamma(n/2)$ be the total solid angle at the origin. Let $b_1, \cdots, b_n$ be integers such that g.c.d. $(b_1, \cdots, b_n, g) = 1$ and $f(b_1, \cdots, b_n) \equiv m \pmod{g}$. Then the number of primitive integral points in Λ which are congruent to $(b_1, \cdots, b_n) \bmod g$ is given by

$$\frac{\lambda}{\lambda_0} \frac{\pi^{n/2} m^{(n/2)-1}}{d^{1/2}\Gamma(n/2)} G_{g;b_1,\cdots,b_n}(f, m) + O(d^{n/4+5/2} g^{3n/2+7} m^{n/2-1-(n-3)/4(3n-2)+\varepsilon}),$$

where $G_{g;b_1,\cdots,b_n}(f, m)$ is the appropriate singular series. The singular series satisfies the inequality

$$G_{g;b_1,\cdots,b_n}(f, m) > \kappa_\varepsilon d^{-3(n-1)/2} g^{-2(n-1)} m^{-\varepsilon},$$

where κ_ε is a constant depending only on ε, so that there are certainly primitive integral points in Λ satisfying the congruence if

$$\lambda^{-1} = O(d^{-7n/4-3/2} g^{-7n/2-5} m^{(n-3)/4(3n-2)-\varepsilon}).$$

This result is a more precise version of those given by the author [Dokl. Akad. Nauk SSSR **114** (1957), 25–28; MR **20** #1662; Izv. Akad. Nauk SSSR Ser. Mat. **23** (1959), 337–364; MR **24** #A1252], these being improvements on results of Wright [Quart. J. Math. Oxford Ser. **4** (1933), 37–51, 228–232; ibid. **7** (1936), 230–240; Proc. London Math. Soc. (2) **42** (1937), 481–500] and Pommerenke [Acta Arith. **5** (1959), 227–257; MR **23** #A122]. There is also a version of this result in which Λ is not required to be convex, but is similar in shape for the different values of m, when the error term depends on the shape.

When $n = 3$ the results are less complete and require the use of the algebra of hermitians (generalized quaternions) as used for the same purpose by Linnik [see, e.g., Izv. Akad. Nauk SSSR Ser. Mat. **3** (1939), 87–108]. Here f is an integral primitive form with relatively prime odd invariants $[\Omega, \Delta]$. The author first proves a generalization of a result of Linnik according to which there exists a constant s_0 depending only on Ω and Δ such that if m is everywhere locally representable by f (i.e., satisfies the generic conditions for representability) and is divisible by the square of an integer $s > s_0$, then the number of representations $r(f: m)$ of m by f is at least $\kappa h(-m\Delta)$, where $h(-m\Delta)$ is, as usual, the number of classes of binary properly primitive, positive definite, quadratic forms with determinant $m\Delta$, and $\kappa > 0$ is a constant depending only on $\Omega\Delta$. The next result has the blemish that it depends on an auxiliary prime q not dividing 2Δ. The number m to be represented is required to satisfy the auxiliary condition $(-\Delta m/q) = +1$. Under these conditions the number of primitive integral points in a region Λ on $f(x) = m$ satisfying a congruence $x_j \equiv b_j \pmod{g}$ $(1 \leqq j \leqq n)$ lies, for sufficiently large m, between $\kappa h(-\Delta m)$ and $\kappa' h(-\Delta m)$, where $0 < \kappa < \kappa' < \infty$ are constants depending only on Ω, Δ, q, g, the shape of Λ and the f-solid angle subtended by Λ at the origin. It is also shown that the condition involving q could be dispensed with if a certain hypothesis about the zeros of L-functions is true. The results and methods for ternary forms so far discussed follow the author's series of articles [Vestnik Leningrad. Univ. **14** (1959), no. 7, 55–71; MR **21** #2622; ibid. **14** (1959), no. 13, 63–70; MR **22** #4676; ibid. **15** (1960), no. 1, 70–84; MR **22** #4677; ibid. **15** (1960), no. 7, 14–27; MR **22** #4678]. Finally, when $f = x_1^2 + x_2^2 + x_3^2$, or, more generally, is representable as the sum of the squares of three integral linear forms, more precise results are obtained [cf. the author, Izv. Akad. Nauk SSSR Ser. Mat. **21** (1957), 457–500; MR **21** #32]. Here, subject to an auxiliary condition $(-m/q) = +1$, the integral points on $f(x) = m$ for which $x_j \equiv b_j \pmod{g}$ tend to uniform distribution as $m \to \infty$. The greater precision in this case comes from the use of ordinary quaternions instead of hermitians and the fact that there is one class in the genus. The author does not expound the method of Linnik for getting similar results by the application of ergodic theory [Linnik, Mat. Sb. (N.S.) **43 (85)** (1957), 257–276; MR **20** #2328], nor does he more than mention Linnik's work on the similar problem for the indefinite quadratic form $x_2^2 - x_1 x_3$ [e.g., Vestnik Leningrad. Univ. **10** (1955), no. 2, 3–23; no. 5, 3–32; no. 8, 15–27; MR **18**, 193].

The analytical machinery required for forms in more than 3 variables is developed in considerable detail. The first chapter is devoted to evaluating and estimating sums of the type

$$g^{-n} \sum_{x_1,\cdots,x_n=0}^{q-1} e^{2\pi i\{f(gx_1+b_1,\cdots,gx_n+b_n)+l(gx_1+b_1,\cdots,gx_n+b_n)\}/q},$$

where $l(x_1, \cdots, x_n)$ is an integral linear form. The author remarks that the case $g > 1$ appears to be new and gives formulae reducing it to the case $g = 1$. In the case $g = 1$, he gives formulae reducing the general sum to the homogeneous case (i.e., $b_j = 0$ $(1 \leqq j \leqq n)$). Finally, in the homogeneous case, he gives explicit formulae for the sums, which, he states, are in essence due to Minkowski [*Gesammelte Abhandlungen*, I, pp. 3–144, Teubner, Leipzig, 1911], but have not been written down before. The second chapter is devoted to generalizations of Kloostermann sums and to estimates for them (using Weil's Riemann Hypothesis for function fields).

The work on ternary quadratics requires the arithmetical theory of hermitians, which is developed from scratch in Chapter 4, following Venkov [Izv. Akad. Nauk SSSR (6) **16** (1922), 205–220; ibid. **16** (1922), 221–246], Linnik [Mat. Sb. (N.S.) **5 (47)** (1939), 453–472; MR **2**, 36; Izv. Akad. Nauk SSSR Ser. Mat. **3** (1939), 87–108] and Pall [Trans. Amer. Math. Soc. **59** (1946), 280–332; MR **8**, 318].

The paper concludes with a discussion of possible future developments and a bibliography of 89 items.

J. W. S. Cassels (Cambridge, England)

Citations: MR 2, 36a = E20-4; MR 8, 318b = E20-16; MR 18, 193d = E16-25; MR 20# 1662 = E24-70; MR 20# 2328 = E24-55; MR 21# 32 = E20-53; MR 21# 2622 = E20-56; MR 22# 4676 = E20-57; MR 22# 4677 = E20-58; MR 22# 4678 = E20-59; MR 23# A122 = E12-75; MR 24# A1252 = E12-84.

Referred to in E12-118, E12-123, E12-126, E12-135.

E12-93 (26# 81)

Watson, G. L.

Transformations of a quadratic form which do not increase the class-number.

Proc. London Math. Soc. (3) **12** (1962), 577–587.

The author denotes by Λ_n a lattice in an n-dimensional vector space over the field of rational numbers, and f a quadratic form associated with this lattice. For a given positive integer m he defines an m-mapping as follows. Let Λ_m denote the set of all vectors $\mathbf{x}$ such that $f(\mathbf{x}+\mathbf{z})\equiv f(\mathbf{z}) \pmod m$, for all $\mathbf{z}$ in Λ_n. Let M be an n-by-n matrix whose column vectors form a basis of Λ_m and define $g(\mathbf{y})=m^{-1}f(M\mathbf{y})$. This defines a mapping, called an m-mapping, of the class of f onto the class of g. The author proves that under an m-mapping none of the following increase: the number of classes in the genus; the number of spinor genera in the genus; the number of classes in a spinor genus. The rank and signature are invariant. Other theorems are concerned with the changes in the other invariants of the form under such a mapping. The applications are mainly to positive forms, since for indefinite forms of three or more variables there is only one class in a spinor genus.

Burton W. Jones (Boulder, Colo.)

E12-94 (26# 1286)

Raghavan, S.

On representation by hermitian forms.

Acta Arith. **8** (1962/63), 33–96.

Let hermitian matrices S (of m rows and rank r) and T (of n rows and rank n) have elements in the ring of integers of an imaginary quadratic extension $k(\sqrt{d})$ of the rational number field k. The author studies, in this paper, the problem of integral representation of T by S when $r>2n$. He shows that the method adopted by Siegel [Ann. of Math. (2) **45** (1944), 577–622; MR **6**, 38] for indefinite quadratic forms over the rational number field can be applied to both definite and indefinite forms.

In the case of definite forms, he obtains an analogue of his earlier theorem on representation by quadratic forms [ibid. **70** (1959), 446–477; MR **23** #A136]. He proves that if $\min T>c_1|T|^{1/n}>c_2$, the number $A(S, T)$ of reduced integral representations of T by S is given by the asymptotic formula

$$(1)\quad A(S,T) = |T|^{r-n}\delta(S)^{-n}\prod_{j=r-n+1}^{r}\frac{(2\pi)^j|d|^{-j/2}}{\Gamma(j)}\prod_p \alpha_p(S,T) + O(|T|^{r-n-(r-2n)/2n}),$$

where $\prod_p \alpha_p(S, T)$ is the product of the p-adic densities of representations for all rational primes p, $\delta(S)$ denotes the discriminant of S, and the constant in the O-term involves c_1.

In the case of indefinite forms, let u, v be the signature of S. He proves analogously to the result of Siegel that if $u\geqq n$ and $v\geqq n$, then $M(S, T)$, the measure of representation of T by S, is given by

$$M(S,T) = \mu(S)\prod_p \alpha_p(S,T),$$

where $\mu(S)$ is the measure of the reduced unit group of S.

As an application of (1), the author proves that in case $r=m$ and $n=2$ (with c_2 depending also on S), S represents T integrally if and only if S represents T modulo $p^{6\lambda+8}$, for primes p and natural numbers λ satisfying

$$p^\lambda \mid |d|\,|S|,\ p^{\lambda+1}\nmid |d|\,|S|.$$

This generalizes a result of Tartakowsky [C. R. Acad. Sci. Paris **186** (1928), 1401–1403].

V. C. Nanda (Bombay)

Citations: MR 6, 38b = E12-18; MR 23# A136 = E12-77.

E12-95 (26# 3694)

Shimura, Goro

Arithmetic of alternating forms and quaternion hermitian forms.

J. Math. Soc. Japan **15** (1963), 33–65.

En vue de développer, dans un travail ultérieur, la théorie des fonctions zéta attachées aux groupes algébriques sur **Q**, l'auteur construit une théorie des réseaux sur une algèbre de quaternions (relatifs à un ordre maximal de cette algèbre), en relation avec une forme hermitienne non dégénérée sur cette algèbre, en la calquant sur la théorie analogue (développée notamment par M. Eichler et M. Kneser) des réseaux sur un anneau de Dedekind, en relation avec une forme quadratique non dégénérée. On part d'un anneau de Dedekind $\mathfrak{g}$, dont F est le corps des fractions, et d'une algèbre de quaternions A sur F; il y a deux cas à distinguer suivant que A est l'algèbre de matrices $M_2(F)$ ou un corps. Le premier cas est traité sans autre hypothèse sur $\mathfrak{g}$; en considérant la base matricielle de A sur F, l'auteur montre que l'étude des $\mathfrak{g}$-réseaux (dont l'ordre à gauche est un ordre maximal de A), engendrant un A-module à gauche V libre de dimension n, en relation avec une forme hermitienne f sur V, équivaut à l'étude des $\mathfrak{g}$-réseaux dans un espace vectoriel W de dimension $2n$ sur F, en relation avec une forme alternée non dégénérée g sur W. C'est donc à cette dernière théorie qu'est consacrée le § 1 du mémoire. L'auteur commence d'abord, généralisant un résultat classique de Frobenius, par montrer que si M est un $\mathfrak{g}$-réseau de W, il y a une base symplectique de W formée de $2n$ vecteurs y_i, z_i $(1\leqq i\leqq n)$ telle que M soit somme directe des $\mathfrak{g}$-modules $\mathfrak{g}y_i$ et $\mathfrak{a}_iz_i$ $(1\leqq i\leqq n)$ où les $\mathfrak{a}_i$ sont des idéaux fractionnaires de F tels que $\mathfrak{a}_i\supset\mathfrak{a}_{i+1}$ pour tout i (facteurs invariants de M); on dit que $\mathfrak{a}_1=N(M)$ est la norme de M par rapport à g, et que M est un réseau maximal s'il est maximal dans l'ensemble des réseaux de même norme; alors tous les $\mathfrak{a}_i$ sont égaux à $\mathfrak{a}_1=N(M)$, et réciproquement. Lorsqu'en outre $\mathfrak{g}$ est un anneau principal, il y a un théorème analogue décrivant la position respective de deux réseaux maximaux quelconques, L, M; il y a une base symplectique comme ci-dessus pour L, tous les $\mathfrak{a}_i$ étant égaux à un même idéal $\mathfrak{a}$, et M est somme directe des $\mathfrak{g}a_iy_i$ et des $\mathfrak{a}b_iz_i$ $(1\leqq i\leqq n)$ avec $a_ib_i=N(M)/N(L)$, et $\mathfrak{g}a_1\supset\cdots\supset\mathfrak{g}a_n\supset\mathfrak{g}b_n\supset\cdots\supset\mathfrak{g}b_1$. Le § 2 met en relation cette théorie avec celle des $\mathfrak{g}$-réseaux de V lorsque $A=M_2(F)$; il donne aussi des définitions générales sur les $\mathfrak{g}$-réseaux de V (sans distinguer les deux cas pour A); en fait, l'auteur se borne aux réseaux pour lesquels l'ordre à gauche $\mathfrak{o}$ est maximal dans A; pour un tel réseau L, la norme (relative à f) est le $\mathfrak{o}$-idéal bilatère (fractionnaire) $N(L)$ engendré par les $f(x,x)$ pour $x\in L$; un réseau est encore dit maximal s'il est maximal parmi les $\mathfrak{g}$-réseaux de même norme dans V. Au § 3, l'auteur se restreint au cas où $F=F_{\mathfrak{p}}$ est un corps $\mathfrak{p}$-adique, $\mathfrak{g}=\mathfrak{g}_{\mathfrak{p}}$ l'anneau des entiers $\mathfrak{p}$-adiques dans $F_{\mathfrak{p}}$; on sait alors que si $A=D_{\mathfrak{p}}$ est le corps des quaternions sur $F_{\mathfrak{p}}$ (unique à F-isomorphie près), ce corps a un seul ordre maximal $\mathfrak{o}_{\mathfrak{p}}$, formé des éléments x dont la norme (réduite) $N_{A/F}(x)$ appartient à $\mathfrak{g}_{\mathfrak{p}}$; dans $\mathfrak{o}_{\mathfrak{p}}$ tous les idéaux sont bilatères et principaux, et puissances de l'unique idéal maximal $\mathfrak{P}$ tel que $\mathfrak{P}^2=\mathfrak{p}\mathfrak{o}_{\mathfrak{p}}$; en outre, tout élément de $\mathfrak{g}_{\mathfrak{p}}$ est de la forme $N_{A/F}(x)$ avec $x\in\mathfrak{o}_{\mathfrak{p}}$. Ces particularités permettent alors de développer pour les réseaux maximaux de V une théorie analogue à celle déjà vue pour le cas $A=\mathrm{M}_2(F)$.

La partie la plus importante du mémoire est le § 4, où l'auteur prend maintenant pour F un corps de nombres algébriques, et se borne au cas où A est "indéfinie", c'est-à-dire, où il y a au moins une place à l'infini $\mathfrak{p}$ de F telle que $A_{\mathfrak{p}}=A\otimes_F F_{\mathfrak{p}}$ soit de la forme $\mathrm{M}_2(F_{\mathfrak{p}})$. On désigne par $G(V,f)$ le groupe des similitudes (pour f) dans V, par $G(V_{\mathfrak{p}},f)$ le groupe analogue dans $V_{\mathfrak{p}}=V\otimes_F F_{\mathfrak{p}}$ pour toute place $\mathfrak{p}$ de F. Pour un ordre maximal $\mathfrak{o}$ de A, on considère l'ensemble $\mathfrak{L}(\mathfrak{o})$ des $\mathfrak{g}$-réseaux maximaux de V ayant $\mathfrak{o}$ pour ordre à gauche; on dit que L et M sont de la même classe [du même genre] s'il existe un $\sigma\in G(V,f)$ transformant L en M [si, pour toute place $\mathfrak{p}$ de F, il existe un $\sigma_{\mathfrak{p}}\in G(V_{\mathfrak{p}},f)$ transformant $L_{\mathfrak{p}}$ en $M_{\mathfrak{p}}$]. Les places finies $\mathfrak{p}$ de F pour lesquelles $A_{\mathfrak{p}}$ est un corps sont en nombre fini, soient $\mathfrak{p}_i$ $(1\leqq i\leqq s)$, et soit $\mathfrak{P}_i$ l'idéal maximal de $\mathfrak{o}_{\mathfrak{p}_i}$; on peut écrire pour tout $L\in\mathfrak{L}(\mathfrak{o})$, $N(L)=\mathfrak{a}\prod_{i=1}^{s}\mathfrak{P}_i^{e_i}$ où $\mathfrak{a}$ est un idéal fractionnaire de F et $e_i=0$ ou 1; deux réseaux sont du même genre si et seulement si les e_i sont les mêmes pour ces deux réseaux, de sorte qu'il y a en tout 2^s genres dans $\mathfrak{L}(\mathfrak{o})$. Cela étant, le théorème principal (Théorème 2) s'énonce comme suit. On considère les places à l'infini $\mathfrak{q}_j$ de F où $A_{\mathfrak{q}_j}$ est un corps et où l'indice d'inertie de la forme f (considérée sur l'espace $V_{\mathfrak{q}_j}$) n'est pas $n/2$. On considère d'autre part un réseau maximal M de V, et un nombre fini de places finies $\mathfrak{p}_i$ de F; pour chaque i, on suppose donnée un $\sigma_i\in G(V_{\mathfrak{p}_i},f)$ laissant stable le réseau $M_{\mathfrak{p}_i}$, tous les σ_i ayant un même multiplicateur $\alpha\in F$ tel que α soit positif à toutes les places $\mathfrak{q}_j$. Alors, si on se donne arbitrairement un entier λ_i pour tout i, on peut trouver une transformation $\sigma\in G(V,f)$ de multiplicateur α, laissant stable M et telle que si l'on pose $\tau_i=\sigma-\sigma_i$, on ait $\tau_i(M_{\mathfrak{p}_i})\subset\mathfrak{p}_i^{\lambda_i}M_{\mathfrak{p}_i}$ pour tout i. Comme applications de ce résultat, l'auteur montre d'abord que le nombre de classes dans un genre est égal au nombre des classes d'idéaux "modulo le produit des $\mathfrak{q}_j$" (deux idéaux de $\mathfrak{g}$ étant dans la même classe si leur quotient est un idéal principal positif en chacune des places $\mathfrak{q}_j$). Une autre application concerne le groupe $\mathfrak{G}$ déduit de G par "adélisation". Si $\mathfrak{U}_L$ est le sous-groupe de $\mathfrak{G}$, produit des sous-groupes $\mathfrak{U}_{\mathfrak{p}}$ des $G_{\mathfrak{p}}=G(V_{\mathfrak{p}},f)$ laissant stables $L_{\mathfrak{p}}$, et des groupes $G(V_{\mathfrak{q}},f)$ pour toutes les places à l'infini $\mathfrak{q}$, et si l'on pose $\Gamma_L=\mathfrak{U}_L\cap G$, alors, pour tout couple de réseaux maximaux L, M d'un même genre et tout $\xi\in\mathfrak{G}$, on a $\mathfrak{U}_L\xi\mathfrak{U}_M=\mathfrak{U}_L\xi\Gamma_M=\Gamma_L\xi\mathfrak{U}_M$. *J. Dieudonné* (Paris)

Referred to in E12-102.

E12-96 (26# 6129)

Andrianov, A. N.

The analytic arithmetic of quadratic forms in an odd number of variables in connection with the theory of modular forms. (Russian)

Dokl. Akad. Nauk SSSR **145** (1962), 241–244.

The author proves the following result. Let $f(x_1,\cdots,x_m)=\sum_{1\leqq i\leqq j\leqq m}a_{ij}x_ix_j$ in integral coefficients and $m=2k+1$; let D be the discriminant and q be the "Stufe" of f and l be square-free. Let $r_f(n)$ be the number of representations of n by f and t_0 the minimum positive integer for which $r_f(lt_0^2)>0$; $q_1=4lt_0^2q$, $q_2=16l^3t_0^6q$, and let $\Gamma(N)$ be the subgroup of unimodular matrices of second order $M=\begin{vmatrix}\alpha&\beta\\ \gamma&\delta\end{vmatrix}$ such that $\gamma\equiv 0\pmod N$ (while $\Gamma(N,N_0)$ refers to the subgroup with the added condition $\beta\equiv 0\pmod{N_0}$ for $N\equiv 0\pmod{N_0}$). With (P/Q) the Jacobi symbol we define $g_l(t)=\sum_{d|t,(d,t_0)=1}d^{k-1}(2lD/d)r_f(lt^2/d^2)$. With τ a complex variable with Im $\tau>0$, define

$$G_l(\tau)=\sum_{t=1}^{\infty}g_l(t)\exp(2\pi i\tau t/t_0);$$

then the theorem states that $G_l(\tau)$ can be decomposed as C_l (constant) $+F_l(\tau)+\tilde F_l(\tau)$, where $F_l(M\tau)=(\gamma\tau+\delta)^{2k}F_l(\tau)$ for $M\in\Gamma(q_2,t_0)$, and $\tilde F_l(M\tau)=(2lD/\alpha)\times(\gamma\tau+\delta)^k\tilde F_l(\tau)$ for $M\in\Gamma(q_1)$.

This continues work of the author [same Dokl. **141** (1961), 9–12; MR **24** #A2560] and extends results of Hecke [Abh. Math. Sem. Univ. Hamburg **5** (1927), 199–224] and Eichler [Arch. Math. **5** (1954), 355–366; MR **16**, 116]. Using estimation formulas in the latter work, the author shows

$$r_f(lt^2)=C_{lf}\sum_{d|t}d\prod_{p|d}\left(1-\left(\frac{2lD}{p}\right)\frac{1}{p}\right)+\alpha_{lf}(t),$$

with $|\alpha_{lf}(t)|<C'_{lf}\tau^2(t)t^{1/2}$. Here f is ternary and $\tau(t)$ is the number of divisors of t. The result generalizes Gauss's well-known formula for the representations of lt^2 as the sum of three squares. *H. Cohn* (Tucson, Ariz.)

Citations: MR 16, 116d = G30-15; MR 24# A2560 = E20-65.

E12-97 (27# 107)

Watson, G. L.

The class-number of a positive quadratic form.

Proc. London Math. Soc. (3) **13** (1963), 549–576.

The main object of this paper is to prove the following result: For each positive integer n, let c_n denote the lower bound of the class number $c(f)$ of a quadratic form with integral coefficients, taken over all positive definite n-ary forms f. Then $c_n\geqq 2$ for $n=11$, 12, 14, 15, 16, $\geqq 3$ for $n=13$, $\geqq 4$ for $n\geqq 17$, and $\geqq c_{n-8}+2$ if $n\geqq 17$.

{The author announces that he is able to show that the equality holds for $11\leqq n\leqq 17$ [same Proc. (3) **13** (1963), 577–592].} Some related results are also proven.

Burton W. Jones (Boulder, Colo.)

Referred to in E12-101.

E12-98 (27# 3598)

Watson, G. L.

Positive quadratic forms with small class-numbers.

Proc. London Math. Soc. (3) **13** (1963), 577–592.

Let f be a non-singular quadratic form with integral coefficients, and denote by $c(f)$ the class number of f under arithmetical equivalence not restricted to be proper. For each positive integer n, denote by c_n the lower bound of $c(f)$ for positive-definite n-ary f. As a result of this paper and previous ones by the author and others the following results are established: $c_n=1$ if and only if $n\leqq 10$; $c_n=2$ if and only if $n=11$, 12, 14, 15, 16; $c_n=3$ if and only if $n=13$; $c_n=4$ if $n=17$. The author conjectures that c_n begins to increase rapidly from $n=18$ and that for greater n, all positive genera contain classes which are not "well-behaved". *Burton W. Jones* (Boulder, Colo.)

E12-99 (27# 1420)

Hijikata, Hiroaki

Hasse's principle on quaternionic anti-hermitian forms.

J. Math. Soc. Japan **15** (1963), 165–175.

Let k be an algebraic number field, let D be a quaternion division algebra over k, with standard involution $\lambda \to \bar{\lambda}$. Consider anti-hermitian forms over D, or, in matrix language, $n\times n$ matrices U with elements in D, such that ${}^t\bar{U} = -U$.

The author studies Hasse's principle for three kinds of equations in D: (I) ${}^t\bar{x}Ux=0$, where x is a column vector with elements in D; (II) ${}^t\bar{X}UX=U'$, where U and U' are given anti-hermitian $n\times n$ matrices and X is a non-singular $n\times n$ matrix; (III) ${}^t\bar{X}UX=\alpha U'$, where now X (non-singular) and $\alpha\in k^*$ are to be determined.

Hasse's principle (H.I) states that (I) is solvable with $x\neq 0$ in D if for each prime $\mathfrak{p}$ of k (finite or infinite) the equation (I) is solvable with an $x_{\mathfrak{p}}\neq 0$ with elements in $D_{\mathfrak{p}}=D\otimes_k k_{\mathfrak{p}}$. The Hasse principle (H.II) states that (II) is solvable with a non-singular matrix X having elements in D if for each $\mathfrak{p}$ there exists a non-singular matrix $X_{\mathfrak{p}}$ with elements in $D_{\mathfrak{p}}$ satisfying (II). Similarly for (H.III). The author proves (H.III) for $n=1$ and $n=3$. For $n=1$ this is easy; for $n=3$ he reduces the problem, using the well-known isogenies of low-dimensional orthogonal groups, to known results (for instance the (H.III) theorems for hermitian forms over a division algebra with an involution of the second kind, proved by Landherr [Abh. Math. Sem. Hansische Univ. **12** (1938), 200–241]).

He then claims to prove (H.I) for $n\geqq 3$. However, the Hasse principle (H.I) as stated above is not correct for $n\geqq 3$, as may be seen from counterexamples. The correct formulation of (H.I) is as follows: (I) is solvable with $x\neq 0$ in D if for each $\mathfrak{p}$ there exists an $x_{\mathfrak{p}}$ in $D_{\mathfrak{p}}$ such that ${}^t\bar{x}_{\mathfrak{p}}Ux_{\mathfrak{p}}=0$ and that at least one of its components is invertible in $D_{\mathfrak{p}}$ (the author implicitly uses this stronger condition in the proof of his lemma 3). However, the reviewer believes that slight modifications of the arguments of this paper will give a proof of the correct result {other proofs, which have not yet been published, have been given by M. Kneser and by the reviewer}.

The paper also contains a counterexample which shows that (H.I) is not true for $n=2$. By Witt's theorem this implies that (H.II) is false for all n.

T. A. Springer (Utrecht)

E12-100 (27# 4813)

Tsukamoto, Takashi

A few remarks on algebraic groups and quadratic forms. (Japanese)

Sûgaku **12** (1960/61), 226–231.

This paper, arranged by Satake and Hijikata, consists of the following three topics taken from the author's posthumous manuscripts: (I) A proof of Weil's results about the realization of the k-forms (k being of characteristic zero) of standard classical groups [cf. A. Weil, J. Indian Math. Soc. (N.S.) **24** (1960), 589–623; MR **25** #147]. (II) The invariance of the Witt-Dieudonné index of a quadratic form over any field under the field extension of odd degree. (III) A theory of the anti-hermitian forms over a $\mathfrak{p}$-adic quaternion algebra. The author determines the types (in the sense of Witt) of such forms, studies the maximal lattices and proves the Witt decomposition theorem for such lattices. A more detailed and complete version of (III) was given by the author [J. Math. Soc. Japan **13** (1961), 387–400; MR **25** #127].

T. Ono (Philadelphia, Pa.)

Citations: MR 25# 127 = E12-87.

E12-101 (28# 1172)

Watson, G. L.

One-class genera of positive quadratic forms.

J. London Math. Soc. **38** (1963), 387–392.

Let $c(f)$ be the class-number of the positive definite n-ary quadratic form f, i.e., the number of classes in the genus of f. The author has shown [Proc. London Math. Soc. (3) **13** (1963), 549–576; MR **27** #107] that $c(f)\geqq 2$ for $n\geqq 11$; also, it was previously known that for all $n\leqq 8$ there exists a genus with $c(f)=1$. Here the author completes the gap in these results by exhibiting forms in 9 and 10 variables with $c(f)=1$, namely $E+x_9^2$ and $E+x_9^2+x_9x_{10}+x_{10}^2$, where E is the absolutely extreme 8-variable form with discriminant 1.

E. S. Barnes (Adelaide)

Citations: MR 27# 107 = E12-97.

E12-102 (28# 2104)

Shimura, Goro

Arithmetic of unitary groups.

Ann. of Math. (2) **79** (1964), 369–409.

Let k be a finite algebraic number field and K either a quadratic extension or a quaternion algebra over k (the preliminary part deals with a more general situation). Let ρ be the non-identical automorphism [the canonical anti-automorphism] of K/k. Finally, let V be the n-dimensional (left) vector space over K and $\Phi(x,y)$ a non-degenerate Hermitian form in $V\times V$ with respect to ρ. The author studies the following four groups: $G(V,\Phi)=\{\alpha\mid\alpha\in GL(V,K),\ \Phi(x\alpha,y\alpha)=a\Phi(x,y),\ a\in K\}$, $H(V,\Phi)=\{\alpha\mid\alpha\in G(V,\Phi),\ a^{n/2}=\det(\alpha)$, defined only for even $n\}$, $U(V,\ \Phi)=\{\alpha\mid\alpha\in G(V,\ \Phi),\ a=1\}$, $SU(V,\ \Phi)=\{\alpha\mid\alpha\in G(V,\Phi),\ \det(\alpha)=1\}$. If K is the matrix algebra of degree 2, $SU(V,\Phi)$ is the symplectic group over k. A lattice in V is a finite module of rank n with respect to the [a] maximal order of integral elements of K. The norm of a lattice is the ideal generated by all $\Phi(x,x)$, $x\in L$. A lattice is called maximal if there does not exist a larger lattice with the same norm. Three principal theorems are proved under the common assumption that $n>1$ and $\Phi(x,y)$ is indefinite, the first of which serves as a tool for the proof of the others. Theorem 1 (approximation theorem): Let L be a lattice and P a finite set of prime ideals of k; furthermore, for each $\mathfrak{p}\in P$ let an element $\sigma_{\mathfrak{p}}\in SU(V_{\mathfrak{p}},\Phi)$ be given. Then there exists a $\sigma\in SU(V,\Phi)$ such that $L_{\mathfrak{p}}(\sigma-\sigma_{\mathfrak{p}})\subseteqq\mathfrak{p}^hL_{\mathfrak{p}}$ for all $\mathfrak{p}\in P$ and an arbitrary exponent h, and $L_{\mathfrak{q}}\sigma=L_{\mathfrak{q}}$ for all prime ideals $\mathfrak{q}\notin P$. Theorem 2: Two lattices L and M are said to belong to the same genus with respect to $SU(V,\Phi)$ if for each prime spot $\mathfrak{p}$ of K there exists a $\sigma_{\mathfrak{p}}\in SU(V,\Phi)$ such that $L_{\mathfrak{p}}\sigma_{\mathfrak{p}}=M_{\mathfrak{p}}$. A genus of lattices consists of only one class. When $SU(V,\Phi)$ is replaced by one of the other three groups, the class number in a genus is given in terms of class numbers of certain ideals in K. Theorem 3: For a pair L, M of maximal lattices a system $\{L,M\}$ of elementary divisors is introduced. Now let L, M, N be three maximal lattices, and let a $\sigma\in G(V,\Phi)$ be given such that $L\sigma=L$, $M\sigma=N$. Then the systems $\{L,M\}$ and $\{L,N\}$ of elementary divisors are equal. Conversely, if $\{L,M\}=\{L,N\}$, then there exists a $\sigma\in SU(V,\Phi)$ such that $L\sigma=L$, $M\sigma=N$. Here we define elementary divisors only under the restrictive assumption that K is the direct sum of two copies of k, the orthogonal idempotents being e_1 and e_2. If $\mathfrak{p}$ is a prime ideal of K, and L and M are two maximal lattices, there exists a basis u_i of V with respect to K having the following properties: (1) $\Phi(u_i,u_j)=\delta_{ij}$ (Kronecker's symbol). (2) A basis of $L_{\mathfrak{p}}$ with respect to the order $\mathfrak{o}_{\mathfrak{p}}$ of all integers of $k_{\mathfrak{p}}$ is $(\mathfrak{o}_{\mathfrak{p}}e_1+\mathfrak{a}_{\mathfrak{p}}e_2)$, where $\mathfrak{a}_{\mathfrak{p}}$ denotes an $\mathfrak{o}_{\mathfrak{p}}$-ideal. (3) A basis of $M_{\mathfrak{p}}$ with respect to $\mathfrak{o}_{\mathfrak{p}}$ is $(\mathfrak{o}_{\mathfrak{p}}a_ie_1+\mathfrak{a}_{\mathfrak{p}}b_ie_2)u_i$ with $a_1\mathfrak{o}_{\mathfrak{p}}\geqq a_2\mathfrak{o}_{\mathfrak{p}}\geqq\cdots$, $b_1\mathfrak{o}_{\mathfrak{p}}\leqq b_2\mathfrak{o}_{\mathfrak{p}}\leqq\cdots$, $a_ib_i=a_jb_j$. The system $\mathfrak{o}_{\mathfrak{p}}(a_ie_1+b_ie_2)$ is called the system of elementary divisors of the pair L, M. The paper supplements an earlier one of the author [J. Math. Soc. Japan **15** (1963), 33–65; MR **26** #3694]. Theorems 1 and 2 are modelled after corresponding theorems in the theory of quadratic forms (Meyer's theorem) [cf. the reviewer, Math. Z. **55** (1952), 216–252; MR **14**, 540] and M. Kneser [Arch. Math. **7** (1956), 323–332; MR **18**, 562]. An analogue of Theorem 3 is not known.

M. Eichler (Basel)

Citations: MR 14, 450c = A14-22; MR 18, 562f = E12-57; MR 26# 3694 = E12-95.

Referred to in E12-116, E12-141, E12-149, G15-27.

E12-103 (28# 5051)

Nanda, V. C.

On the genera of quadratic and hermitian forms over an algebraic number field.

Acta Arith. **8** (1962/63), 431–450.

Let K be an algebraic number field with an involution τ and let k be the fixed field of τ. One can naturally define the notions of hermitian forms of n variables with respect to K/k, class and genus of forms (in case $\tau=1$, "hermitian" is replaced by "quadratic"). The author proves that a genus can be defined by means of a finite set of invariants and also proves the existence of a genus with prescribed invariants (§ 4, Theorem), generalizing the results of Gauss ($\tau=1$, $k=\mathbf{Q}$, $n=2$), Minkowski ($\tau=1$, $k=\mathbf{Q}$), C. L. Siegel ($\tau=1$) and H. Braun ($k=\mathbf{Q}$, K/k: imaginary quadratic). In the proof, the methods of Braun are used [J. Reine Angew. Math. **182** (1940), 32–49; MR **2**, 36; Abh. Math. Sem. Hansischen Univ. **14** (1941), 61–150; MR **3**, 70].

T. Ono (Philadelphia, Pa.)

Citations: MR 2, 36f = E12-1; MR 3, 70i = E12-7.

E12-104 (29# 2324)

Weil, André

Sur certains groupes d'opérateurs unitaires.

Acta Math. **111** (1964), 143–211.

This is the first of two memoirs in which the author proposes to throw light on the role played by the symplectic group in the celebrated work of C. L. Siegel on quadratic forms. To a large extent the results of this installment may be formulated and proved as theorems about a certain group of unitary operators invariantly associated with a locally compact commutative group G. These general results are proved in Chapter I, which occupies slightly less than half of the paper. In Chapters II and III G is specialized to the local and adélic groups of modern number theory. The main result of Chapter II is a deduction of the quadratic reciprocity law from the theorems of Chapter I and the main result of the paper is proved in Chapter III. Chapters IV and V contain supplementary material of various kinds; in particular, a formulation of the main result of the projected second installment.

Let G be a commutative locally compact group and let G^* be its dual. For each $w=u$, $u^*\in G\times G^*$ let $U(w)$ be the unitary operator in $L^2(G)$ which maps ϕ into ϕ', where $\phi'(x)=\phi(x+u)\langle x, u^*\rangle$. Then $U(w_1)U(w_2)=F(w_1, w_2)\times U(w_1+w_2)$, where $F(u_1, u_1^*; u_2, u_2^*)=\langle u_1, u_2^*\rangle$, so that U is a projective representation of $G\times G^*$ with $1/F$ as multiplier. Let $\mathbf{A}(G)$ denote the group of all unitary operators in $L^2(G)$ of the form $tU(w)$, where t is a complex number of modulus one, and let $\mathbf{B}_0(G)$ denote the group of all unitary operators V in $L^2(G)$ such that $V\mathbf{A}(G)V^{-1}=\mathbf{A}(G)$. $\mathbf{A}(G)$ is clearly isomorphic to the group $A(G)$ of all pairs w, t, where $w\in G\times G^*$, t is as above and $(w_1, t_1)(w_2, t_2)=(w_1+w_2, F(w_1, w_2)t_1t_2)$. Thus each member of $\mathbf{B}_0(G)$ induces an automorphism of $A(G)$ which is readily seen to have the form $w, t\to(w)\sigma, tg(w)$, where σ is an automorphism of $G\times G^*$, g is a continuous function from $G\times G^*$ to the complex numbers of modulus one and g and σ are related by the following identity: $F((w_1)\sigma, (w_2)\sigma)=F(w_1, w_2)\times g(w_1+w_2)/g(w_1)g(w_2)$. Conversely, any pair σ, g with σ and g so related defines an automorphism of $A(G)$, and the group of all such is denoted by $B_0(G)$. Let π_0 denote the homomorphism of $\mathbf{B}_0(G)$ into $B_0(G)$ defined by the foregoing considerations. Theorem 1 asserts that π_0 is surjective and has the group of constant multiples of the identity as its kernel. {Reviewer's remark: The identity connecting g and σ says that $1/F$ and its transform by σ are equivalent multipliers in the sense of the theory of projective representations and that g defines the trivial multiplier which is their ratio. It is known that $G\times G^*$ has a unique irreducible $1/F$ representation and that U is irreducible. Thus for each pair σ, g in $B_0(G)$ the mapping $w\to g(w)U((w)\sigma)$ is an irreducible $1/F$ representation equivalent to U. Let $V_{\sigma,g}$ be any unitary operator setting up the equivalence. Then $V_{\sigma,g}$ is unique up to a multiplicative constant and $\sigma, g\to V_{\sigma,g}$ defines a projective representation of $B_0(G)$ whose range (choosing the constant in all possible ways) coincides with $\mathbf{B}_0(G)$. π_0 is then the inverse of this projective representation, that is, $\pi_0(V_{\sigma,g})=\sigma, g$.}

The author defines a continuous complex-valued function f on G to be a character of the second degree if its values lie on $|z|=1$ and $f(u_1+u_2)/f(u_1)f(u_2)$ is an ordinary character in u_1 for each fixed u_2. If f is any such, then there clearly exists a unique homomorphism ρ of G into G^* such that $\langle u_1, (u_2)\rho\rangle\equiv f(u_1+u_2)/f(u_1)f(u_2)$. When ρ is an isomorphism of G with G^*, then f is said to be non-degenerate. For each non-degenerate f let W_f be the unitary operator which carries ψ into ψ', where $\psi'(u)=cf(u)\psi^*((u)\rho)$. Here c is a positive real number chosen so as to make W_f unitary and ψ^* is the Fourier transform of ψ. Straightforward calculations show that $W_fU(u, u^*)W_f^{-1}=aU((u^*)\rho^{-1}, (-u)\rho-u^*)$, where $a=(-u, u^*)/f((u^*)\rho^{-1})$, and that $W_f^3U(u, u^*)W_f^{-3}=U(u, u^*)$. Thus $W_f\in\mathbf{B}_0(G)$, and W_f^3 is a constant multiple of the identity. This constant, which the author denotes by $\gamma(f)$, plays a central role in the proof of the quadratic reciprocity law given in Chapter II. A simple calculation shows that if we use ρ to identify G and G^*, then the Fourier transform of convolution by f is multiplication by b/f, where b is a constant and $b/|b|=\gamma(f)$. In other words, the (generalized) Fourier transform of f is a constant b times $1/f$ and $\gamma(f)$ is $b/|b|$. That $\gamma(f)$ may be so defined is the content of Theorem 2. ($|b|$ is 1 whenever ρ preserves Haar measure.) Theorem 3 presents still another interpretation of the important invariant $\gamma(f)$.

Now let Γ be a closed subgroup of G and let Γ^* be its annihilator in G^*. Let $B_0(G, \Gamma)$ be the subgroup of $B_0(G)$ consisting of all σ, g such that g is identically one on $\Gamma\times\Gamma^*$ and $(\Gamma\times\Gamma^*)\sigma=\Gamma\times\Gamma^*$. Let $H(G, \Gamma)$ be the Hilbert space of all locally integrable functions θ on $G\times G^*$ which satisfy the identity $\theta(u+\xi, u^*+\xi^*)=\theta(u, u^*)\langle\xi, -x^*\rangle$ for $\xi, \xi^*\in\Gamma\times\Gamma^*$ and are such that $\int_{G\times G^*/\Gamma\times\Gamma^*}|\theta(u, u^*)|^2<\infty$. The proofs of Theorems 4 and 5 are based on the observation that the $1/F$ representation U of $G\times G^*$ may be defined in a "natural" way in $H(G, \Gamma)$ and that this realization of U leads to a natural unitary representation of $B_0(G, \Gamma)$ which inverts π_0. Indeed, the mapping $\phi\to\theta$, where $\theta(u, u^*)=\int_\Gamma\phi(u)\langle\xi, u^*\rangle\,d\xi$ is defined for all continuous ϕ with compact support on G, has a unique continuous extension Z which is a unitary map of $L^2(G)$ on $H(G, \Gamma)$. Moreover, if $U^\Gamma(u, u^*)$ is the operator mapping θ into θ', where $\theta'(x, x^*)=\theta(x+u, x^*+u^*)F(x, x^*; u, u^*)$, then $Z^{-1}U^\Gamma(u, u^*)Z=U(u, u^*)$. For each σ, g in $B_0(G, \Gamma)$ let $r_\Gamma(\sigma, g)$ map θ into θ'', where $\theta''(x, x^*)=\theta((x, x^*)\sigma)g(x, x^*)$. One verifies at once that r_Γ is a homomorphism of $B_0(G, \Gamma)$ into the group of unitary operators in $H(G, \Gamma)$ and that $\pi_0(Z^{-1}r_\Gamma(\sigma, g)Z)=\sigma, g$. Now when ϕ is continuous with compact support, then $Z(\phi)(e, e)=\int_\Gamma\varphi(\xi)\,d\xi$. Since $\theta'(e, e)=\theta(e, e)$ whenever θ' is the transform by $r_\Gamma(\sigma, g)$ of θ and both θ and θ' are continuous at e, e, it follows that $\int_\Gamma\varphi(\xi)\,d\xi=\int_\Gamma s\varphi(\xi)\,d\xi$ whenever φ is suitably restricted

$s=\sigma$, $g \in B_0(G, \Gamma)$ and $s\varphi$ means the transform of φ by $Z^{-1}r_\Gamma(\sigma, g)Z$. Let $S(G)$ denote the Bruhat generalization (from R^n to G) of the space of all rapidly decreasing infinitely differentiable functions. The author shows that $S(G)$ is invariant under the operators $Z^{-1}r_\Gamma(s)Z$ and that the above cited identity $\int_\Gamma \varphi(\xi)\,d\xi = \int_\Gamma s\varphi(\xi)\,d\xi$ holds for φ in $S(G)$ and s in $B_0(J, \Gamma)$. This is Theorem 4. It reduces to the classical Poisson summation formula when s and Γ are suitably chosen. In addition, the author calls attention to the following corollary. For each $\phi \in S(G)$ the function $s \to \int_\Gamma s\varphi(\xi)\,d\xi$ defined for all $s \in \mathbf{B}_0(G)$ is constant on the right $\mathbf{B}_0(G, \Gamma)$ cosets. Here $\mathbf{B}_0(G, \Gamma)$ is $r_\Gamma(B_0(G, \Gamma))$. {Reviewer's remark: As shown by the reviewer [same Acta **99** (1958), 265–311; MR **20** #4789] the "inducing" construction allowing one to pass from an arbitrary unitary representation of a closed subgroup of a locally compact group to a well-defined representation of the whole group may be extended so as to apply to projective representations with a fixed multiplier. The multiplier $1/F$ is identically one on $\Gamma \times \Gamma^*$, and U^Γ is just the $1/F$ representation induced by the one-dimensional identity representation of $\Gamma \times \Gamma^*$. When $\Gamma = G$, U^Γ reduces to U. That these induced projective representations are all irreducible and mutually equivalent is a consequence of the general theory developed in the work cited above—at least when G is separable.}

Now let f be a non-degenerate character of the second degree on G which reduces to one on Γ and is such that $(\Gamma)\rho = \Gamma^*$. The formula for $W_f U(u, u^*) W_f^{-1}$ shows at once that $\pi_0(W_f) \in B_0(G, \Gamma)$ and that $r_\Gamma(\pi_0(W_f)) = ZW_fZ^{-1}$. It follows that W_f^3 is the identity, that is, that $\gamma(f) = 1$. This is Theorem 5.

The derivation of the quadratic reciprocity law in Chapter II is based upon the following considerations. (a) If χ is a character of the additive group of a finite-dimensional vector space X over a locally compact field k and f is a quadratic form on X, then $\chi \circ f$ is a character of the second degree on the additive group of X. (b) Let k be as in (a) but not discrete, not of characteristic two and not the complex field. Let a and b be non-zero members of k and let f be the quadratic form taking x, y, z, t into $x^2 - ay^2 - bz^2 + abt^2$. Then for any non-trivial χ we have $\gamma(\chi \circ f) = (a/b)$, where (a/b) is one if a is the norm of an element in $k(b^{1/2})$ and is minus one otherwise. (c) Applying (b) to the locally compact completions k_v of a suitable discrete field k, one can reduce the problem of showing that $\prod_v (a/b)_v = 1$ to showing that $\gamma(f) = 1$ for a certain character of the second degree on the appropriate adèle group. That $\gamma(f) = 1$ follows on applying Theorem 5 with G the adèle group, and Γ the subgroup of principal adèles.

The first half of Chapter III is concerned with the special case of the general theory of Chapter I in which the group G is a vector space X over a local field. In this special case it is possible to replace $B_0(X)$ and $\mathbf{B}_0(X)$ by closely related groups which may be topologized so as to be locally compact. For any field k let X be a finite-dimensional vector space over k and let $B(x_1, x_1^*, x_2, x_2^*) = [x_1, x_2^*]$, where x_1^* and x_2^* are in the dual of X. Using B instead of F, the author defines a group $\mathrm{Ps}(X)$ by analogy with the definition of $B_0(G)$. Now let k be local and let χ be a non-trivial character on its additive group. The vector space dual of X may be identified with the dual of its additive group by setting $\langle x, x^*\rangle = \chi([x, x^*])$. The mapping μ which takes σ, f into $\sigma, \chi \circ f$ is clearly a homomorphism of $\mathrm{Ps}(X)$ into $B_0(X)$. Consider the subgroup of $\mathrm{Ps}(X) \times B_0(X)$ consisting of all triples σ, f, V with $\mu(\sigma, f) = \pi_0(V)$. The author calls it the metaplectic group and denotes it by $\mathrm{Mp}(X)$. It is to the groups $\mathrm{Ps}(X)$ and $\mathrm{Mp}(X)$ that he gives locally compact topologies. The mapping μ is injective whenever k is not of characteristic 2, and then $\mathrm{Ps}(X)$ and $\mathrm{Mp}(X)$ may be identified with subgroups of $B_0(X)$ and $\mathbf{B}_0(X)$, respectively. In any case the mapping π which takes σ, f, V into σ, f is a surjective homomorphism of $\mathrm{Mp}(X)$ into $\mathrm{Ps}(X)$ whose kernel is isomorphic to the one-dimensional torus.

In the second half of the chapter analogues of $\mathrm{Ps}(X)$ and $\mathrm{Mp}(X)$ are defined with X the adèle group X_A of a finite-dimensional vector space X_k over a field k which is either an algebraic number field or an algebraic function field in one variable over a finite field. These groups are also given locally compact topologies. The chapter concludes with a discussion of the result of applying the corollary of Theorem 4 of Chapter I to the special case in which $G = X_A$ and $\Gamma = X_k$ (which, of course, has a natural imbedding in X_A). Replacing $\mathbf{B}_0(X_A)$ by $\mathrm{Mp}(X_A)$ and using a natural map of $\mathrm{Ps}(X_k)$ in $B_0(X_A, X_k)$, the author gives additional arguments to show that the functions on $\mathrm{Mp}(X_A)$, invariant under the action of $\mathrm{Ps}(X_k)$, provided by the corollary in question, are actually continuous with respect to the topology of $\mathrm{Mp}(X_A)$. This is Theorem 6. It is the main result of the paper and, according to the author, contains as a special case the classical construction of automorphic functions by means of theta series.

The homomorphism π described above shows that $\mathrm{Ps}(X)$ is an extension of $\mathrm{Mp}(X)$ by the group T of complex numbers of modulus one. In Chapter IV it is shown that this extension need not be trivial but can be reduced to an extension of $\mathrm{Mp}(X)$ by the two-element group. The situation is discussed in detail in the local case and sketched in the adélic case.

Let X be a finite-dimensional vector space over a field k which is also a left A module for a finite-dimensional associative algebra A over k. It is assumed that A has an identity e and comes equipped with the following further elements of structure: (a) an involutary anti-automorphism $t \to t^i$ which is the identity on ke, (b) a distinguished linear functional τ invariant under i such that $t, u \to \tau(tu)$ is a non-degenerate symmetric bilinear form. Under these circumstances X^* and $X \oplus X^*$ become left A modules in a natural way, and one obtains a subgroup $\mathrm{Ps}(X/A)$ of $\mathrm{Ps}(X)$ by considering the set of all σ, f such that (i) σ commutes with all left multiplications by members of A and (ii) f may be written in the form $f(x) = \tau(F(x, x))$, where F is a function from $X \times X$ to A which is linear in the first variable and i-linear in the second. The statement of the main theorem of the projected sequel to this paper concerns a group of the form $\mathrm{Ps}(X/A)$ and its subgroup $\mathrm{P}(X/A) = \mathrm{Ps}(X, A) \cap \mathrm{P}(X)$. Here $\mathrm{P}(X)$ is the set of all σ, f in $\mathrm{Ps}(X)$ with $(X^*)\sigma = X^*$. Chapter V is mainly concerned with the definition and formal properties of $\mathrm{Ps}(X/A)$ and $\mathrm{P}(X)$ and concludes with the following statement of the main theorem in question. Let k be an algebraic number field and let A be simple. Let G be the group of all elements a in A for which $aa^i = e$. Let G_A be the corresponding adèle group, and normalize Haar measure so that G_A/G has measure one. Let X_A be the adèle group corresponding to the left A module X and let ϕ be an element in $S(X_A)$. Then

$$\int_{G_A/G} \sum_{\xi \in X} \phi(a\xi)\,da = \sum_s r_k(s)\phi(0),$$

where r_k is the r_Γ of Theorem 4 of Chapter I adapted to the circumstances of Theorem 6 of Chapter III, Γ is the subgroup X of X_A and the summation is over a complete set of representatives of the left cosets of $\mathrm{P}(X/A)$ in $\mathrm{Ps}(X/A)$. The formula is valid whenever both members are absolutely convergent and the second member is absolutely convergent if and only if $\dim(X) > 4 \dim \mathrm{Q}(X/A)$. Here

$Q(X/A)$ is the vector space of all functions on X of the form $x \rightarrow \tau(F(x, x))$ as described under (ii) above, and it is assumed that no member of the center of A is invariant except members of ke.

G. W. Mackey (Cambridge, Mass.)

Referred to in E12-105, E12-106, E12-121, E56-56, E60-32, E68-31, F50-69, F70-19, G15-51.

E12-105 (36# 6421)

Weil, André

Sur la formule de Siegel dans la théorie des groupes classiques.

Acta Math. **113** (1965), 1–87.

The article is a direct continuation of a previous work by the author [same Acta **111** (1964), 143–211; MR **29** #2324] and is essentially based on the results of that work. The author's aim is the proof of a certain identity which generalizes a known result of C. L. Siegel concerning quadratic forms. One part of the identity represents the Eisenstein series corresponding to a semi-simple algebra $\mathfrak{A}$ over an arithmetical field k and to an $\mathfrak{A}$-module X. The second part is obtained from a certain theta-function, which depends on a parameter whose values are in the factor space G_a/G_k, by integrating with respect to this parameter. Here G is an algebraic group canonically connected with the algebra $\mathfrak{A}$, G_a is its adele group, and G_k is the set of points of G over k. As a consequence of this relation, the author computes the Tamagawa number of many classical groups and establishes the correctness of the so-called Hasse principle and an approximation theorem for these groups.

A. Kirillov (RŽMat **1967** #12 A343)

Citations: MR 29# 2324 = E12-104.

Referred to in E12-106, E12-117, E68-19, E68-23, E68-32, E68-37, F50-69.

E12-106 (33# 1311)

Weil, André

On the arithmetical theory of the classical groups.

Arithmetical Algebraic Geometry (Proc. Conf. Purdue Univ., 1963), *pp.* 1–3. *Harper & Row, New York*, 1965.

A summary of work which has appeared in Acta Math. **111** (1964), 143–211 [MR **29** #2324]; ibid. **113** (1965), 1–87.

Citations: MR 29# 2324 = E12-104; MR 36# 6421 = E12-105.

E12-107 (29# 3440)

Watson, G. L.

A problem of Dade on quadratic forms.

Mathematika **10** (1963), 101–106.

Let $f(x_1, \cdots, x_n)$, $n \geqq 3$, be a non-singular quadratic form with rational integer coefficients whose greatest common divisor is 1. The problem is that of finding an algebraic extension E of $\mathbf{Q}$ such that the equation $f(x_1, \cdots, x_n) = 1$ has a solution in integers $x_1, \cdots, x_n$ of E. Using theorems from the theory of integral quadratic forms, the author proves the following theorems, which give constructions for E as quadratic extensions of $\mathbf{Q}$. Theorem 1: Suppose $n \geqq 4$, then there exists a rational integer q such that $f(y_1 + z_1\sqrt{q}, \cdots, y_n + z_n\sqrt{q}) = 1$ has a solution in rational integers y_i, z_i $(1 \leqq i \leqq n)$. Theorem 2: Suppose that $n = 3$, then there exist rational integers q, r such that the equation $f(y_1 + z_1\sqrt{q} + w_1\sqrt{r}, \cdots, y_3 + z_3\sqrt{q} + w_3\sqrt{r}) = 1$ has a solution in rational integers y_i, z_i, w_i $(1 \leqq i \leqq 3)$.

J. V. Armitage (Durham)

E12-108 (29# 3441a; 29# 3441b)

Dade, E. C.

Algebraic integral representations by arbitrary forms.

Mathematika **10** (1963), 96–100.

Dade, E. C.

A correction.

Mathematika **11** (1964), 89–90.

Let $\mathfrak{O}$ be the integral closure of the rational integers in some algebraic closure K of the rationals, and let $f(X_1, \cdots, X_n)$ be a polynomial with relatively prime coefficients in $\mathfrak{O}$. The first of these papers generalizes the result of Watson [see #3440 above] as follows: For some $x_1, \cdots, x_n \in \mathfrak{O}$, $f(x_1, \cdots, x_n)$ is a unit. An immediate deduction from this is that if $f(X_1, \cdots, X_n)$ is homogeneous, then $f(x_1, \cdots, x_n) = 1$ for suitable $x_1, \cdots, x_n \in \mathfrak{O}$.

The proof depends on a theorem of Steinitz, which in turn requires that a certain determinant shall be divisible by ideals $\mathfrak{q}_1, \cdots, \mathfrak{q}_s$ of $\mathfrak{O}$. Siegel has pointed out that the proof of this last is incomplete at one point, and the author supplies a correct version in the second of these papers.

It should be noted that, whereas Watson's result [#3440] essentially gives the extension in which $x_1, \cdots, x_n$ lie in terms of the coefficients of the form, the present generalization is just an existence theorem.

J. V. Armitage (Durham)

E12-109 (29# 4732)

Muwafi, Amin

Simultaneous quadratic and linear Diophantine equations.

J. Natur. Sci. and Math. **4** (1964), *no.* 1, 163–165.

Theorem on a problem treated by L. E. Dickson and G. Pall [Pall, Duke Math. J. **8** (1941), 173–180; MR **2**, 251].

B. Stolt (Stockholm)

Citations: MR 2, 251d = E12-5.

E12-110 (30# 3883)

Dress, Andreas

Träge Formen über globalen Körpern.

J. Reine Angew. Math. **217** (1965), 133–142.

Si K est un corps, on appelle semi-ordre sur K un homomorphisme ω du groupe multiplicatif K^* dans $\{-1, +1\}$; l'indice relatif à ω d'une forme quadratique non dégénérée f sur un espace vectoriel sur K est le nombre d'éléments d'une base orthogonale pour f pour lesquels $\omega(f(x))$ est -1, lorsque ce nombre est indépendant de la base choisie (auquel cas on dit que la forme f est inerte). L'auteur détermine toutes les formes inertes f lorsque K est un corps p-adique ou un corps de nombres algébriques, le second cas étant ramené au premier par localisation.

J. Dieudonné (Paris)

E12-111 (31# 125)

Brauer, R.

On certain classes of positive definite quadratic forms.

Acta Arith. **9** (1964), 357–364.

Let $Q(\mathfrak{x}) = \sum_{i,j=1}^{n} c_{ij}x_ix_j$ be a positive definite quadratic form with integral coefficients. Assume that Q can be represented by the unit form in $m > n$ variables, so that there is an $m \times n$ matrix D with integral coefficients such that ${}^tD \cdot D = C = (c_{ij})$. The author proves results of the following kind. Let Δ be the largest elementary divisor of C and let $\mathfrak{r}$ be a fixed row of D. Then $\mathfrak{x} = \Delta\mathfrak{r}C^{-1}$ is a row with integral coefficients and $Q(\mathfrak{x}) \leqq \Delta^2$. Also, there exists a form Q^* equivalent to Q whose matrix (g_{ij}) satisfies $|g_{ij}| \leqq (3/2)^{i+j-2}\Delta^2$ for the coefficients. Applications are made to the estimation of bounds on the coefficients of Cartan matrices of blocks for representations of finite groups. *W. E. Jenner* (Chapel Hill, N.C.)

E12-112 (31# 2217)

Cohn, H.
On theta-functions for certain quadratic fields.
Acta Arith. **9** (1964), 53–66.

An invariant set (under a certain group of transformations) of conjugate theta-functions is constructed, corresponding to totally positive quadratic forms of determinant 1 whose coefficients are integers in certain quadratic fields and whose matrices are integral. The author is concerned with formulas for the number of representations of a number by such quaternary forms. The result for the form $x_1^2+x_2^2+2x_3^2+2(\sqrt{3})x_3x_4+2x_4^2$ is surprising, since the number of representations is given exactly by the "singular series", even though the genus of this form contains at least three classes.

Gordon Pall (Baton Rouge, La.)

E12-113 (31# 3386)

Pall, Gordon
The weight of a genus of positive n-ary quadratic forms.
Proc. Sympos. Pure Math., Vol. VIII, pp. 95–105. *Amer. Math. Soc., Providence, R.I.*, 1965.

Given an n-by-n symmetric matrix A, with integer elements, and a prime power p^r, the author studies the congruence $X^tAX \equiv A \pmod{p^r}$, where the superscript t denotes transposition, and $X=(x_{ij})$ is an n-by-n matrix whose elements are integers modulo p^r. It is known that for sufficiently large r, the congruence has $2p^{rn(n-1)/2}\alpha_p$ solutions, where $\alpha_p=\alpha_p(A)$ is independent of r and is called the p-adic density of the genus of the quadratic form with matrix A.

α_p occurs in formulae given by Siegel [Ann. of Math. (2) **36** (1935), 527–606] and others for the weight of a genus of positive forms. So the author seeks an expression for α_p in terms of certain p-adic invariants of A. This elementary (but exasperatingly complicated) problem was considered by Minkowski [Acta Math. **7** (1885), 201–258]. The author confirms Siegel's remark that there are some mistakes in Minkowski's work.

{The reviewer believes that the author's result for odd p would be correct if the third minus sign in his Formula (23), which is probably a misprint, were changed to $+$. The reviewer could not face the task of checking the calculations for $p=2$.} *G. L. Watson* (London)

E12-114 (32# 5600)

Knight, James T.
Quadratic forms over $R(t)$.
Proc. Cambridge Philos. Soc. **62** (1966), 197–205.

The author considers quadratic forms over $R(t)$, the field of rational functions with real coefficients. He denotes by $F_{\mathfrak{p}}$ the completion of $R(t)$ with respect to the valuation $\mathfrak{p}$ and calls it a series field. He finds a complete set of invariants for a regular quadratic space F over a real series field. Witt's theorem becomes: A non-singular quadratic form in three or more variables over $R(t)$ is isotropic if and only if the form is isotropic over R for all but a finite number of valuations in R. There is an analogue of the Hilbert reciprocity law. Integral equivalence over series fields is also considered, and other results proved.

Burton W. Jones (Boulder, Colo.)

E12-115 (32# 5601)

Spilker, Jürgen
Kompaktifizierung des Humbertschen Fundamentalbereichs.
Math. Ann. **161** (1965), 296–314.

This is a translation of an earlier work of C. L. Siegel [*Zur Reduktionstheorie Quadratischer Formen*, Math. Soc. of Japan, Tokyo, 1959; MR **25** #3906] into a more general and more abstract language, with the exception that Siegel also treats the unit groups of indefinite quadratic forms which are excluded here. Since Siegel's monograph has been reviewed but superficially, it is appropriate to give a more detailed report on this occasion. P. Humbert [Comment. Math. Helv. **12** (1940), 263–306; MR **2**, 148] considered the representation of the unimodular group Γ of a finite algebraic number field Ω in the space of definite Hermitean forms. Let Ω_ν $(\nu=1,\cdots,r)$ be all subfields of $\mathbf{C}$ isomorphic to Ω, while $\Omega_\nu \subset \mathbf{R}$ for $\nu=1,\cdots,r_1$. Take r_1 m-rowed positive definite real symmetric matrices and $r_2=r-r_1$ m-rowed positive definite complex Hermitean matrices H_ν. Their elements form a submanifold $\mathfrak{H}$ in an affine space of mn dimensions $(n=r_1+2r_2)$. Furthermore, take r nonsingular matrices M_ν in $\mathbf{R}$, or $\mathbf{C}$, particularly such M_ν originating from a matrix M in Ω by the isomorphism $\Omega \to \Omega_\nu$. Associate with the M_ν the affine transformations

$$(1) \qquad M: H_\nu \to M_\nu^* H_\nu M_\nu, \qquad M_\nu^* = \bar{M}_\nu^t.$$

Humbert showed that the group Γ of unimodular M in Ω, represented in this way, has a fundamental domain which is bounded by a finite number of $(mn-1)$-dimensional hyperplanes. Now $\mathfrak{H}$ has an invariant Riemann metric with the line element

$$ds^2 = \tfrac{1}{4}\sum_\nu \operatorname{trace}(H_\nu^{-1}\,dH_\nu)^2.$$

The problem is to compactify the quotient variety $\mathfrak{H}/\Gamma$. Siegel has treated the case $n=1$, which allows no essential simplifications.

Here $\mathfrak{H}$ is mapped by $H \to K=(H-E)(H+E)^{-1}$, with E = unit matrix, onto a bounded subset $\mathfrak{K}$ of $\mathfrak{H}$, the map being unique in each direction. The group of affine transformations (1) of $\mathfrak{H}$ is then represented by a group of fractional linear transformations of $\mathfrak{K}$, and there is a corresponding invariant line element in $\mathfrak{K}$. The topologies defined by this Riemann metric and by the Euclidean metric of $\mathfrak{K}$ are equivalent (limit points of $\mathfrak{K}$ which do not lie in $\mathfrak{K}$ excluded). In this transformation the author's solution of the problem differs from Siegel's. It has the advantage of directly visualizing the boundary of $\mathfrak{K}$ although, in the actual execution, it offers little help.

Adding all limit points of $\mathfrak{K}$, one gets a point set $\bar{\mathfrak{K}}$. The invariant distance between interior points and boundary points is, of course, infinite. Now one can also define a distance between two boundary points in an obvious way. The boundary is then divided into disjoint subsets $\partial\mathfrak{K}_i$ whose points have finite distances. Two boundary points can be transformed into each other by an affine transformation (1) if and only if their distance is finite.

In particular, the unimodular group Γ of Ω acts on each $\partial\mathfrak{K}_i$. It is discontinuous, and a fundamental domain is obtained from a fundamental domain in $\mathfrak{K}$ by forming the appropriate boundary points. Adding all these fundamental domains of Γ in each $\partial\mathfrak{K}_i$ to a fundamental domain of Γ in $\mathfrak{K}$, the author achieves the desired compactification. The quotient space $\mathfrak{K}/\Gamma$ is a Hausdorff space.

M. Eichler (Basel)

Citations: MR 2, 148a = E12-3; MR 25# 3906 = E12-90.

E12-116 **(32# 7509)**

Böge, Sigrid

Schiefhermitesche Formen über Zahlkörpern und Quaternionenschiefkörpern.

J. Reine Angew. Math. **221** (1966), 85–112.

Let D be a skew-field with anti-involution $\iota: \alpha \mapsto \bar{\alpha}$ and let D^* be the multiplicative group of D. Let V be an n-dimensional left vector space over D and let (x, y) be a non-degenerate skew-hermitian scalar product on V with respect to ι. Let U be the unitary group of V with respect to (x, y). The author studies local and global properties of U along the lines of the treatment of the orthogonal group given by O'Meara [*Introduction to quadratic forms*, Academic Press, New York, 1963; MR **27** #2485] and concludes with an analogue of Siegel's theorem on the number of representations of a quadratic form by a genus of forms and its relation to the calculation of the Tamagawa number of a hermitian vector space.

The group U is generated by reflections $S=(s;\sigma)$ such that $Sx = x-(x, s)\sigma^{-1}s$, where $s \in V$, $\sigma \in D^*$ and $\sigma - \bar{\sigma} = (s, s)$. Let S be the sub-set of D^* generated by those α for which $\alpha = \bar{\alpha}$ and let $D^{*\prime}$ be the commutator sub-group of D^*. Write $\mathfrak{R} = \mathfrak{S}D^{*\prime}$. The map $(s;\sigma) \mapsto \sigma\mathfrak{R}$ defines a homomorphism $\chi: U \to D^*/\mathfrak{R}$ analogous to the spinor norm in the case of quadratic forms. For $n \geqq 2$ and index $\geqq 1$ the sequence

$$1 \to U' \xrightarrow{\text{inj}} U \xrightarrow{\chi} D^*/\mathfrak{S}D^{*\prime} \to 1$$

is exact; thus the spinor kernel $U_1 \cong U'$, the commutator sub-group of U.

If the centre of D is a number field k, then (I) D is a quadratic extension of k, or (II) D is a quaternion skew-field and k consists of those elements of D fixed by ι, or (III) D is a quaternion skew-field in which the fixed elements form a three-dimensional vector space over k. Now let $\mathfrak{p}$ be a prime spot of k and let $k_\mathfrak{p}$ be the completion of k at $\mathfrak{p}$. The scalar product extends in a natural way to the (left) vector space $V_\mathfrak{p} = V \otimes_k k_\mathfrak{p}$ over $D_\mathfrak{p}$, where $D_\mathfrak{p} = D \otimes_k k_\mathfrak{p}$ (and, of course, the structure of $D_\mathfrak{p}$ depends on which one of the above cases holds). Let $U_\mathfrak{p}$ be the corresponding unitary group and let $U_\mathfrak{p}{}^0$ be the sub-group generated by proper reflections; that is, by reflections $x \mapsto x-(x, s)\sigma^{-1}s$ with $s \in V_\mathfrak{p}$, $\sigma - \bar{\sigma} = (s, s)$, $\sigma \in D_\mathfrak{p}{}^*$ and such that $(S-1)V_\mathfrak{p} = D_\mathfrak{p}s$. Then, in all three cases, $U_\mathfrak{p}$ is generated by $U_\mathfrak{p}{}^0$ and the group $U_\mathfrak{p}(D_\mathfrak{p}a)$, where $a \in V$ is fixed.

It is proved that the weak approximation theorem holds in U in cases (I) and (III), and in U' in cases (I), (III) and, for $n \geqq 2$, (II).

The definition of the spinor norm is extended to a homomorphism $\chi_\mathfrak{p}: U_\mathfrak{p}{}^0 \to D_\mathfrak{p}{}^*/\mathfrak{S}_\mathfrak{p}D_\mathfrak{p}{}^{*\prime}$ and $U_\mathfrak{p}{}' \subset U_{\mathfrak{p}1} = \operatorname{Ker}\chi_\mathfrak{p}$. The relation $U_\mathfrak{p}{}' = U_{\mathfrak{p}1}$ is discussed and it is shown that if $V_\mathfrak{p}$ contains a hyperbolic plane over $D_\mathfrak{p}$, then the sequence

$$1 \to U_\mathfrak{p}{}' \to U_\mathfrak{p} \to D_\mathfrak{p}{}^*/S_\mathfrak{p}D_\mathfrak{p}{}^{*\prime} \to 1$$

is exact. (The author poses the question: given a product of reflections $(s_i;\sigma_i)$, when is the product of the σ_i in $k_\mathfrak{p}{}^*D_\mathfrak{p}{}^{*\prime}$?)

Returning to global considerations, the author proves that the strong approximation theorem holds in U_1 if V is indefinite and if $\dim_D V \geqq 5$. It follows from the strong approximation theorem that the spinor genus consists of exactly one class and then, using the facts that $U_1 = U^+$ (the special unitary group) in case (I) and that $U_1 = U$ in (III), it follows that if V is indefinite and if $\dim_D V \geqq 5$, then a proper genus of lattices consists of only one class in case (I) and that, with the same hypotheses, in case (III) a genus consists of only one class [cf. G. Shimura, Ann. of Math. (2) **79** (1964), 369–409; MR **28** #2104].

A connection between the local and the global theories is provided by a theorem which asserts that an element of the unitary group belongs to the spinor kernel if this holds at every prime spot. It follows that in case (II) (the other cases are not interesting in this context) a similar result holds for the commutator sub-group.

The author now returns to the local unit groups in case (I). Let A be the adèle ring of k and use the sub-script A to distinguish algebraic sets defined over k in the adèle space. Let M be a lattice in V and denote by $U(M)_A$ the sub-group of U_A which is the automorphism group of $M_\mathfrak{p}$ at each prime spot $\mathfrak{p}$ of k. If $\mathfrak{p}$ does not split in D, then $D_\mathfrak{p}$ is a field and $M_\mathfrak{p}$ is a lattice for the order $O_\mathfrak{p}$ of integers of $D_\mathfrak{p}$. The author investigates the generating systems of $U_\mathfrak{p}(M_\mathfrak{p})$ under various hypotheses on $\mathfrak{p}$ and relates the range of values of det $U_\mathfrak{p}$ to the group $W_\mathfrak{p}$ of units of the ring of integers, α, of $D_\mathfrak{p}$ for which $N_{D_\mathfrak{p}|k_\mathfrak{p}}\alpha = 1$. As a consequence, he obtains an expression for the number of proper genera in the genus of M in terms of the number of ramified prime spots of k [cf. Shimura, loc. cit.].

In the final section of the paper, the author computes the Tamagawa number of the unitary group following Weil [*Adèles et groupes algébriques*, Secrétariat mathématique, Paris, 1959; MR **28** #1091; English translation, Princeton Univ. Press, Princeton, N.J., 1961], and shows that the independence of the Tamagawa number is equivalent to representation theorems of Braun [Abh. Math. Sem. Hansischen Univ. **14** (1941), 61–150; MR **3**, 70] and that a unification of the two points of view leads to an evaluation of $\tau(V)$ in terms of the number of representations of a lattice by a genus of lattices. *J. V. Armitage* (Durham)

Citations: MR 3, 70i = E12-7; MR 27# 2485 = E02-11; MR 28# 1091 = Z10-14; MR 28# 2104 = E12-102.

E12-117 **(32# 7511)**

Weil, André

Sur la théorie des formes quadratiques.

Colloq. Théorie des Groupes Algébriques (*Bruxelles*, 1962), *pp.* 9–22. *Librairie Universitaire, Louvain; Gauthier-Villars, Paris*, 1962.

This paper deals with a new proof and extension of Siegel's formula for the "number" of integral representations of one quadratic form by another. (For a simple formulation of this classical problem see C. L. Siegel [Ann. of Math. (2) **36** (1935), 527–606].) The author's approach is based on a detailed study of the Tamagawa numbers of orthogonal groups by means of adèles (see the author's Princeton lecture notes of 1961, *Adèles and algebraic groups* [Institute for Advanced Study, Princeton, N.J., 1961; see also Séminaire Bourbaki, 1958/59, Secrétariat mathématique, Paris, 1959; MR **28** #1091]). Suppose then that k is an algebraic number field, k_v a typical completion of k with respect to a valuation v of k (infinite or finite, for the latter the symbol p shall be used exclusively), k^m a fixed m-dimensional vector space over k, given by a basis; S and T denote m-by-m and n-by-n symmetric matrices with integral coefficients from k (used to describe quadratic forms relative to fixed bases); X is to denote generically integral m-by-n matrices for which ${}^tX \cdot S \cdot X = S[X] = T$. The symbol G shall stand for the orthogonal group of all matrices X of determinant 1 which satisfy $S[X] = S$ (unit group of S); similarly, G_k, G_v, G_p, G_A denote the corresponding groups with coefficients in k, k_v, k_v and A, the adèle ring of k, respectively. Each of these groups is to be considered as a topological group with respect to the natural topology of the underlying system of coefficients.

Suppose next that G_Ω is some open subgroup of G_A with a corresponding double coset decomposition $G_A = \bigcup_i G_\Omega U_i G_k$. The representatives U_i are termed the "classes" which make up the "orthogonal genus" which is defined by G and G_Ω; it will be indicated later how the author sets up the connection between these classes, which are defined by means of groups, and the classes which make up a genus of quadratic forms in the classical theory. Using class field theory, it follows that the factor commutator group G_A/G_A' has exponent 2. Next, finiteness of "the" Haar measure of G_A/G_k (this being the Tamagawa number of G for a suitably normalized measure [see the author's Princeton notes, loc. cit., and also Acta Math. **113** (1965), 1–87], and discreteness imply that $G_A/G_\Omega G_A' G_k$ is a finite group (of exponent 2) whose elements are called the "subgenera" of the genus which is determined by G and G_Ω. The author then notes that for indefinite S, classes and subgenera coincide. Next, the groups G_Ω are restricted to products $\prod_v G_\Omega^{(v)}$, where the groups $G_\Omega^{(v)}$ are to satisfy: (a) if v is infinite, then $G_\Omega^{(v)} = G_v$; (b) $G_\Omega^{(p)}$ is an open and compact subgroup of G_p; (c) for almost all p, the group $G_\Omega^{(p)}$ is the subgroup of G_p which has integral coefficients in k_p. Then $G_\Omega = G_\infty \times G_c$, where $G_\infty = \prod_v G_v$, for all infinite v, and G_c denotes the compact group $\prod_p G_\Omega^{(p)}$, the product being taken over all finite p. In order to prove the generalization of Siegel's formula, the author now makes use of the fact that G is an algebraic group of dimension $2\delta = m(m-1)$ and that as such it carries essentially one gauge (differential form) of degree 2δ which is right and left invariant and rational over k. This gauge then determines on each G_v a Haar measure m_v; furthermore, the product $\prod_p \mu(p)$ with $\mu(p) = m_p(G_\Omega^{(p)})$ is seen to be absolutely convergent. Whence it follows that the product $\prod_v m_v$ is a measure on G_Ω. It turns out that the particular Haar measure m of G_A which coincides on G_Ω with $|D|^{-\delta} \prod_v m_v$, D the discriminant of k, is independent of the choice of G_Ω, the particular gauge of G; it is the "Tamagawa measure" of G_A. It determines on the factor group G_A/G_k, G_k being a discrete subgroup of G_A, a measure which is again labelled m. Then $m(G_A/G_k)$ equals 2 as is shown in the author's Princeton notes ([loc. cit.]; for details see p. 107 et seq.). Now Siegel's formula for $S = T$ is proved in the general form

$$m(G_A/G_k) = \prod_p \mu(p) \sum_i m_\infty(G_\infty/U_i^{-1} G_\Omega U_i \cap G_k),$$

where m_∞ is the Haar measure on G_∞ which equals $|D|^{-\delta} \prod_v m_v$, v all infinite places of k. For the proof it is noted that the properties of the Tamagawa number imply that $m(F) = m(G_\Omega G_k/G_k)$ is finite and distinct from zero since G_Ω is open; F is a fundamental domain of G_k in $G_\Omega G_k$ which can be chosen as a fundamental domain of $G_\Omega \cap G_k = G_0$ in G_Ω; the author selects $F = F_0 \times G_c$, where F_0 is a fundamental domain of $\mathrm{proj}_{G_\infty} G_0$ in G_∞. Hence $m(F) = m_\infty(F_0) \prod_p \mu(p)$ and

$$m(G_\Omega G_k/G_k) = m_\infty(G_\infty/\mathrm{proj}_{G_\infty} G_\Omega \cap G_k) \prod_p \mu(p).$$

Replacement of $G_\Omega \cap G_k$ by $U^{-1}(G_\Omega \cap G_k)U$, $U \in G_A$, and summation over the representatives U_i then yields the above formula. Finally, the author tackles the general case of non-degenerate matrices for $1 \leqq n \leqq m-3$, which carries beyond Siegel's original result where the method necessitated the restriction $n \leqq \inf(p, m-p, (m-3)/2)$, where S determines a quadratic form which is equivalent over $\mathbf{R}$ to a sum of p "positive" squares [see C. L. Siegel, Ann. of Math. (2) **45** (1944), 577–622, Theorem 1 on p. 422 and the intricate Lemma 24 on p. 456; MR **6**, 38]. For this purpose the affine variety $H = \{X, S[X] = T\}$ of all $m \times n$ matrices X, assumed to contain at least one rational point over k, is introduced. An element M of H_k is picked; all $Y \in G$ satisfying $Y \cdot M = M$ make up a subgroup g of G. The columns $m_1, \cdots, m_n$ of M generate in k^m a subspace V such that T is the matrix, relative to the vectors m_i, which is induced on V by the quadratic form belonging to S in k^m.

If W is the orthogonal complement (with respect to S) of V in k^m, then S induces on W a non-degenerate quadratic form. The group g leaves fixed the vectors of V and can be identified with the orthogonal group of the above form in W. This fact implies in turn that H can be viewed as the homogeneous space G/g. Similarly, there are isomorphisms of G_k/g_k and H_k, G_v/g_v and H_v, and G_A/g_A and H_A (the mappings $Y \to Y \cdot M$ are open for G_A, G_v on H_A, H_v, respectively). The group-theoretic technique used for $S = T$ and the group G is now extended to the group g. For the technical details (and further extensions of Siegel's theorem), the author's paper must be consulted. The assumption $1 \leqq n \leqq m-3$ is used at a crucial step to identify the spinor norm with a quaternionic norm, because then g is large enough to contain a subgroup which is isomorphic to an orthogonal group of 3 variables. (The group-theoretical fact in question is $G_A = g_A G_\Omega G_A' G_k$.) In order to show the connection with the classical theory of classes in the genus of a symmetric matrix, a lattice R is selected in k^m, that is, a submodule of k^m, which is finitely generated over the integers of k, for which $R \otimes k = k^m$. Let R_p be the closure of R in $k_p{}^m$ for each finite p. Then let $G_\Omega = \prod G_\Omega^{(v)}$, where $G_\Omega^{(v)} = G_v$ for infinite v, and, for finite p, let $G_\Omega^{(p)}$ equal the group of elements in G_p which transform R_p into itself. Each element U_i^{-1}, U_i as above, transforms R_p into a lattice $R_p^{(i)}$ which is, for each p, the closure of a lattice $R^{(i)}$. These lattices $R^{(i)}$ of k^m, together with the quadratic form of S, then represent the classes of the genus of S in the classical sense. Furthermore, this construction shows that the author's subgenera represent the spinor genera. For $n = 1$, see also M. Kneser [Math. Z. **77** (1961), 188–194; MR **25** #3907]. *O. F. G. Schilling* (Lafayette, Ind.)

Citations: MR 6, 38b = E12-18; MR 25# 3907 = E12-91; MR 28# 1091 = Z10-14; MR 36# 6421 = E12-105.

E12-118 **(32# 7523)**

Beridze, R. I.

On the summation of the singular series of Hardy-Littlewood. (Russian. Georgian summary)

Soobšč. Akad. Nauk Gruzin. SSR **38** (1965), 529–534.

The Hardy-Littlewood singular series of a general integral positive-definite quadratic form in at least four variables (cf. A. V. Malyšev [Trudy Mat. Inst. Steklov. **65** (1962); MR **26** #80]) is expressed as the product of a finite expression and an L-function or the reciprocal of an L-function. The proof is said to use ideas of H. Streefkerk [*On the number of solutions of the Diophantine equation* $U = \sum_{i=1}^{s} (Ax_i^2 + Bx_i + C)$ (Dutch), Thesis, Free Univ., Amsterdam, 1943; MR **7**, 414] and G. A. Lomadze [Akad. Nauk Gruzin. SSR Trudy Tbiliss. Mat. Inst. Razmadze **17** (1949), 281–314; MR **12**, 805].

J. W. S. Cassels (Cambridge, England)

Citations: MR 7, 414d = P04-22; MR 12, 805b = E24-34; MR 26# 80 = E12-92.

E12-119 **(33# 103)**

Smirnov, G. P.

On the solution of certain diophantine equations with quadratic forms. (Russian)

Baškir. Gos. Univ. Učen. Zap. Vyp. 20 (1965), 11–15.

Let the coefficients a_{ij} $(=a_{ji})$ of the quadratic form (1) $A(x, x) = \sum_{i,j=1}^{n} a_{ij} x_i x_j$ be given integers and let

(2) $A(x, y) = \frac{1}{2}[A(x+y, x+y)-A(x, x)-A(y, y)] = \frac{1}{2}\sum_{i=1}^{n} A_{x_i}(x, x)y_i$

be its symmetric bilinear form ($A_{x_j}(x, x)=\partial A/\partial x_j$). The author proves two theorems, the first of which is as follows. All possible integer solutions of the equation (3) $A(x, x)=A(y, y)$, with $2n$ unknowns $x_1, x_2, \cdots, x_n, y_1, y_2, \cdots, y_n$, are given by the formulas

$$(4)\quad x = au+\frac{b}{2}KA_x(u, u), \qquad y = au-\frac{b}{2}KA_x(u, u),$$

where K denotes any square matrix of order n with integer elements $k_{ii}=0$, $k_{ji}=-k_{ij}$, u is an arbitrary vector with integer coordinates, and $A_x(u, u)$ is the vector with coordinates $A_{x_1}(u, u), \cdots, A_{x_n}(u, u)$, the derivatives of $A(x, x)$ at the point $x=u$; a and b are any integers so chosen that the greatest common divisor of the numbers (4) is equal to one. *Chr. Karanikolov* (Sofia)

E12-120 (33# 4017)

Maass, Hans

Modulformen zu indefiniten quadratischen Formen.

Math. Scand. **17** (1965), 41–55.

Aus der analytischen Theorie der indefiniten quadratischen Formen mit ganzen rationalen Koeffizienten ist bekannt, wie man diesen (nicht-analytische) Modulformen n-ten Grades zuordnen kann, so dass die zahlentheoretisch interessanten Grössen sinnvoll erfasst werden: Man geht aus von der zugehörigen Thetareihe und bildet den Integralmittelwert über den Majorantenraum der gegebenen quadratischen Form; entwickelt man diesen Mittelwert nach gewissen konfluenten hypergeometrischen Funktionen, so treten als Koeffizienten die Darstellungsmasse auf. Diese Integralmittelwerte haben ein übersichtliches Verhalten gegenüber Modulsubstitutionen n-ten Grades, sind aber nicht-analytisch bezüglich der komplexen Variablen Z im Siegelschen Halbraum, weil neben Z auch $\bar{Z}$ in den Reihengliedern auftritt. Siegel [*Studies and essays presented to R. Courant on his 60th birthday, January 8, 1948*, pp. 395–406, Interscience, New York, 1948; MR **9**, 273] zeigte für $n=1$, wie man durch Anwendung geeigneter Differentialoperatoren die Variable $\bar{Z}$ eliminieren kann, wenn die Determinante der gegebenen Form positiv ist. Man gelangt so zu analytischen Modulformen. Die Verallgemeinerung auf beliebiges n wurde vom Verfasser [Math. Ann. **126** (1953), 44–68; MR **16**, 449] begonnen durch das Auffinden gewisser Differentialoperatoren, welche der symplektischen Geometrie angemessen sind. Die damaligen Untersuchungen werden nun fortgeführt und es gelingt zunächst der Beweis der Transformationsformel für diese Operatoren gegenüber symplektischen Substitutionen. Die technisch komplizierte Handhabung jener Operatoren wird dabei erheblich vereinfacht durch Verwendung einer Verallgemeinerung der Capellischen Identität. Die Anwendung der Differentialoperatoren auf die Integralmittelwerte der Thetareihen wird so geführt, dass man auf Grund der genannten Entwicklungsmöglichkeit ihre Wirkungsweise auf die hypergeometrischen Funktionen untersucht. In voller Verallgemeinerung des Falles $n=1$ gelingt jetzt für beliebiges n und positive Determinante der gegebenen quadratischen Form die Elimination von $\bar{Z}$, so dass analytische Modulformen entstehen. Dieses schöne Resultat rechtfertigt den erheblichen technischen Aufwand. *H. Klingen* (Freiburg)

Citations: MR 9, 273c = E12-27; MR 16, 449c = F10-36.

E12-121 (33# 4605)

Cartier, P.

Über einige Integralformeln in der Theorie der quadratischen Formen.

Math. Z. **84** (1964), 93–100.

The author considerably improves certain aspects of a recent paper by Weil [Acta Math. **111** (1964), 143–211; MR **29** #2324]. Let G be a locally compact abelian group and G^* its dual group. A continuous function f from G into the complex numbers of modulus one is called a non-degenerate character of the second degree if there exists an isomorphism ρ_f of G onto G^* such that $f(x+y)=f(x)f(y)\langle x, \rho_f y\rangle$ for all $x, y \in G$. For a given pair of normalized Haar measures dx and dx^* on G and G^*, respectively, there exists a constant $|\rho_f|>0$ such that $\int_{G^*} F(x^*)\,dx^*=|\rho_f|\int_G F(\rho_f x)\,dx$ for any $F\in L^1(G^*)$. Let $d_f x=|\rho_f|^{1/2}\,dx$ and $(T_f u)(x)=\int_G u(y)\langle y, \rho_f x\rangle\,d_f y$ for any $u\in\Lambda(G)$, the set of continuous integrable functions on G whose Fourier transforms are also integrable. The author gives direct and very simple proofs to the following two theorems, which correspond, respectively, to Theorems 2 and 5 in Weil's paper. Theorem 1: If f is a non-degenerate character of the second degree on G, then there exists a complex constant $\gamma(f)$ of modulus one such that $\int_G f(x)(T_f u)(x)\,d_f x=\gamma(f)\int_G u(x)\overline{f(x)}\,d_f x$ for all $u\in\Lambda(G)$. Theorem 2: If a non-degenerate character of the second degree f reduces to 1 on a subgroup Γ of G, and Γ contains all $x\in G$ with $\langle\gamma, \rho_f x\rangle=1$ for all $\gamma\in\Gamma$, then $\gamma(f)=1$. To prove Theorem 1, he notes first that $f(x)(T_f u)(x)=|\rho_f|^{1/2}(f*v)(x)$ with $v(x)=u(-x)\overline{f(-x)}$. That $\gamma(f)$ is a constant then follows readily from commutativity of the convolution operation in $L^1(G)$, i.e., $v_0*(f*v)=v*(f*v_0)$. The fact $|\gamma(f)|=1$ is obtained by putting $u=\overline{T_f u_0}$ in the formula and using the Fourier inversion relation $T_f(\overline{T_f u_0})=\bar{u}_0$. To prove Theorem 2, let $\Lambda'(G)$ be the set of functions of the form $g*h$, where g and h are continuous functions on G having compact carriers. Now, Γ is the closed subgroup Δ of G consisting of all $x\in G$ with $\langle\gamma, \rho_f x\rangle=1$ for all $\gamma\in\Gamma$. The author first shows a general Poisson summation formula $\int_\Gamma v(\gamma)\,d\gamma=c\int_\Gamma (T_f v)(\gamma)\,d\gamma$ for all $v\in\Lambda'(G)$ with $c>0$. Let $u\in\Lambda'(G)$ be such that $\int_G u\bar{f}\,d_f x\neq 0$. Then the function v defined by $v(x)=f(a)\langle x-a, \rho_f a\rangle u(x-a)=\overline{f(x-a)}u(x-a)f(x)$ $(a\in G)$ is also in $\Lambda'(G)$ and $(T_f v)(\gamma)=f(\gamma+a)(T_f u)(\gamma+a)$ for all $\gamma\in\Gamma$. By the above formula,

$$\int_\Gamma \overline{f(\gamma-a)}u(\gamma-a)\,d\gamma = c\int_\Gamma f(\gamma+a)(T_f u)(\gamma+a)\,d\gamma$$

for any $a\in G$. Integrating both sides over G/Γ, one gets $\gamma(f)=c>0$ and thus $\gamma(f)=1$. This method of proof, combined with Chapter II of Weil's paper, gives a proof of the quadratic reciprocity law for arbitrary number fields, far simpler than Weil's.

The author also obtains the following extension of Theorem 2. Suppose that a non-degenerate character of the second degree f reduces to 1 on a closed subgroup Γ of G. Then $\Gamma\subset\Delta$ in the above notation, and so f defines a function g on the factor group $H=\Delta/\Gamma$ by $g(\delta+\Gamma)=f(\delta)$. Theorem 3: g is a non-degenerate character of the second degree on H and $\gamma(f)=\gamma(g)$. *M. Hasumi* (Mito)

Citations: MR 29# 2324 = E12-104.

E12-122 (34# 2531)

Smirnov, G. P.

On the representation of zero by quadratic forms. (Russian)

Baškir. Gos. Univ. Učen. Zap. Vyp. 20 (1965), *Ser. Mat. no.* 2, 109–113.

Let Q be the ring of rational integers and $x=(x_1, \cdots, x_n)$

a vector with coordinates in Q, and let X_n be the integral linear space whose elements are the vectors x and which has the usual operations of addition and multiplication by elements of Q. Let there be given in X_n the quadratic form $A(x, x) = \sum_{i,j=1}^{n} a_{ij}x_i x_j$ with coefficients $a_{ij} = a_{ji} \in Q$. $A(x, x)$ is said to represent zero in Q if there exists a vector x_0 with coefficients in Q, not all of whose coordinates are zero, such that $A(x_0, x_0) = 0$. The main result of this paper is the following theorem: The quadratic form $A(x, x)$ represents zero in Q if and only if the equation $\det[\lambda E - D(A)] = 0$ is solvable in integers, where $D(A) = KA$, A is the matrix of the form $A(x, x)$ and K is a skew-symmetric matrix with elements in Q. The author gives some numerical examples illustrating this theorem.
R. Finkelstein (Tucson, Ariz.)

E12-123 (34# 4212)

Malyšev, A. V.
On representing integers by indefinite quadratic forms. (Russian)
Volž. Mat. Sb. Vyp. 2 (1964), 91–95.

Let $p(x_1, \cdots, x_s) = \sum_{k=1}^{s} a_k x_k^2 + \sum_{k=1}^{s} b_k x_k + c$ be a non-singular integral quadratic polynomial, not necessarily positive definite, and let $\omega(x) = \sum \alpha_k x_k^2 + \sum \beta_k x_k + \gamma$ be a complex quadratic polynomial. Write $R(N) = \sum \exp(-\omega(x)/N)$, where the sum is taken over all integer points on $p(x) = 0$. The author announces that the methods of his monograph [Trudy Mat. Inst. Steklov. **65** (1962); MR **26** #80] may be applied to estimate $R(N)$ in certain circumstances (the conditions of his theorem take a very long time to state; in particular, $a_k + \mathrm{Re}(\alpha_k) > 0$ for $k = 1, \cdots, s$). Accordingly, one may obtain information about the distribution of integer points on unbounded quadrics, as well as on ellipsoids. *B. J. Birch* (Oxford)

Citations: MR 26# 80 = E12-92.

E12-124 (34# 5768)

Kneser, Martin
Lineare Relationen zwischen Darstellungsanzahlen quadratischer Formen.
Math. Ann. **168** (1967), 31–39.

Let V be the n-dimensional linear vector space over the rationals and (x, y) a definite scalar product. Call a finite submodule of V with integral $\frac{1}{2}(x, x)$ for all its vectors a lattice. To each lattice there corresponds an integral quadratic form F. Assume finitely many lattices L_i in V to be given and denote by $b_F(x)$ the number of these L_i which contain a given vector x and whose quadratic forms are equivalent to a given form F. If now, for a finite system of quadratic forms F and for all $x \in V$, a linear relation $\sum_F d_F b_F(x) = 0$ holds, then also $\sum_F d_F b_F(0) a_F(t) = 0$ for all t, where $b_F(0)$ is the number of all L_i and $a_F(t)$ the number of representations of t by F. The consequence of this theorem can as well be expressed as $\sum_F d_F b_F(0) \vartheta_F(\tau) = 0$, where $\vartheta_F(\tau)$ is the theta series with F. The proof requires but a few lines. The theorem can be extended to the representation of quadratic forms by quadratic forms in an obvious way. Some applications to simple theta series are given. E. Witt has shown [Abh. Math. Sem. Hansischen Univ. **14** (1941), 323–337; MR **3**, 163] that there exist two inequivalent integral definite quadratic forms F and G with determinant 1 which have the same theta series. Now this is proved by application of the above theorem and the same for the (Siegel) theta series expressing the representations of quadratic forms in two and three variables by F and G. In order to show that the assumptions of the theorem hold, two lemmas on the classification of a lattice by its minimal vectors are proved.
M. Eichler (Basel)

Citations: MR 3, 163d = E12-10.

E12-125 (35# 4190)

Nobusawa, Nobuo
On class numbers of lattices in isotropic spaces.
J. Reine Angew. Math. **227** (1967), 209–211.

If R is a regular quadratic space over an algebraic number field, it is known that the number $h(\mathfrak{a})$ of classes of integral lattices with volume $\mathfrak{a}$ is finite. Here a quantitative formulation of this result is given for the case of an isotropic R, namely that positive constants A, B exist for which $h(\mathfrak{a}) < A(N\mathfrak{a})^B$, where $N\mathfrak{a}$ is the absolute norm of $\mathfrak{a}$.
E. S. Barnes (Adelaide)

Referred to in E12-131.

E12-126 (36# 3723)

Malyšev, A. V.
Representation of integers by quadratic forms. (Russian)
Proc. Fourth All-Union Math. Congr. (Leningrad, 1961) (Russian), Vol. II, pp. 118–124. *Izdat. "Nauka", Leningrad,* 1964.

Author's summary: "A survey of investigations on the representation of numbers by means of positive quadratic forms is presented here [see the author, Trudy Mat. Inst. Steklov. **65** (1962); MR **26** #80]. New paths are indicated for transferring the results obtained to the case of indefinite quadratic forms." (RŽMat **1965** #7 A116)

Citations: MR 26# 80 = E12-92.

E12-127 (36# 6348)

Moroz, B. Z.
The distribution of integer points on multidimensional hyperboloids and cones. (Russian)
Zap. Naučn. Sem. Leningrad. Otdel. Mat. Inst. Steklov. (LOMI) **1** (1966), 84–113.

Let $s \geqq 4$, $\rho(\bar{x}) = \sum_{k=1}^{s} (a_k x_k^2 + b_k x_k) + C$. The problem of determining the integral solutions of $\rho(\bar{x}) = 0$ by an asymptotic formula was discussed by Hardy and Littlewood (for $s \geqq 5$) and Kloostermann ($s = 4$). More recently Linnik and Mal′cev (following Hecke's idea of studying the number of primes in a "Winkelraum" of an ellipse) studied the distribution of integer points on multi-dimensional ellipsoids intersected by cones.

The author obtains very general results, which are too complicated to quote here. These results generalize some of the work of Hardy, Littlewood, Kloostermann cited above. *S. Chowla* (University Park, Pa.)

Referred to in Z10-48.

E12-128 (36# 6351)

Gilman, S. J. F.
A bound on the number of representations of quadratic forms.
Acta Arith. **13** (1967/68), 363–374.

Let f and g be two integral quadratic forms with non-singular matrices A and B, respectively, in n and m variables with $m \leqq n$. Let $N(A, B)$ denote the number of essentially distinct primitive representations of B by A and $M(d, B) = \sum N(A_k, B)$, where the sum is over a representative set of classes of n-ary forms of determinant $d = |A|$; let $|B| = q$. The reviewer [Ann. of Math. (2) **50** (1949), 884–899; MR **11**, 643] defined a set $\mathfrak{G}$ of forms in $n - m$ variables, of determinant dq^{n-m-1}, characterized by the conditions: (1) no two forms of $\mathfrak{G}$ are in the same class, (2) if $E \in \mathfrak{G}$, there are matrices D and C such that $E = qD - C^T (\operatorname{adj} B)C$, and (3) the set is maximal. He proved that $M(d, B) = \sum P(d, B, E_i)$, where the sum is over all forms E in $\mathfrak{G}$ and $P(d, B, E)$ denotes the number of essentially distinct solutions C of $E \equiv -X^T(\operatorname{adj} B)X \pmod q$, if $q = \pm 1$, $P(d, B, E_i) = 1$. $M(d, B)$ has been evaluated for $n - m = 1$, $m = 1$, and, if $(q, 2d) = 1$ for $n = 3$, and $m=1$; also for $n=4$ and $m=2$ when B is primitive. Upper bounds have been found for $n=4, 5$.

The author gets upper bounds for $n-m=2, 3$ if B has a primitive adjoint. In the course of the proof he proves other theorems which are of independent interest.

Burton W. Jones (Boulder, Colo.)

Citations: MR 11, 643d = E12-36.

E12-129 (37# 152)

Lursmanašvili, A. P.

The representation of the natural numbers by quadratic forms with integral square-free variables. (Russian. Georgian summary)

Sakharth. SSR Mecn. Akad. Moambe **48** (1967), 7–12.

The author proves the following theorem. Let $Q(x_1, \cdots, x_k) = \sum_{\alpha,\beta=1}^{k} b_{\alpha\beta}x_\alpha x_\beta$ be a positive definite quadratic form with integer coefficients. Let D be the determinant of Q and $R_Q(n)$ the number of representations of a positive integer n by the form Q with square-free arguments. If $k\geqq 5$, then $R_Q(n)=\sigma(n, Q)n^{k/2-1}+O(n^{k/4+\varepsilon})$, where

$$\sigma(n, Q) = (\pi^{k/2}/D^{1/2}\Gamma(k/2)) \times \sum_{q=1}^{\infty} \sum_{h \bmod q}' (G(h, q)/q^k)e(-nh/q),$$

$$G(h, q) = \sum_{t_1,\cdots,t_k=1}^{\infty} (\mu(t_1)\cdots\mu(t_k)/t_1^{2}\cdots t_k^{2}) \times \sum_{l_1,\cdots,l_k=0}^{q-1} e((h/q)Q(t_1^{2}l_1, \cdots, t_k^{2}l_k)),$$

$e(z)=e^{2\pi iz}$, and $\mu(t)$ is the function of Möbius.

T. T. Tonkov (Leningrad)

Referred to in E12-147.

E12-130 (37# 1318)

Mattics, Leon E.

Quadratic spaces of countable dimension over algebraic number fields.

Comment. Math. Helv. **43** (1968), 31–40.

This paper adds a beautiful theorem to the algebraic theory of bilinear forms in infinite-dimensional spaces. Let K be an algebraic number field, E a vector space over K and $\Phi: E\times E\to K$ a nondegenerate symmetric bilinear form. For finite-dimensional E one has the classic result that the quadratic space (E, Φ) is characterized, up to orthogonal isomorphism, by the dimension of the space, the discriminant of the space, the Hasse symbols at all discrete spots, and the positive indices at all real spots. In this paper, the author establishes the corresponding result for quadratic spaces (E, Φ) of denumerably infinite dimension. Assume that K is formally real; thus K has $r\geqq 1$ distinct orderings. Furthermore E admits an orthogonal basis $\{e_i\}_{i\geqq 0}$ with respect to Φ. Fixing an ordering on K we sort out the e_i according as $\Phi(e_i, e_i)$ is positive or negative; we achieve an orthogonal decomposition $E=F\oplus G$ with Φ positive definite on F and Φ negative definite on G. We set $n=\dim F$, $n^-=\dim G$. The spaces F and G are not uniquely determined but their dimensions n and n^- are. Doing this for every ordering, we obtain a set of "indices" $n_1, n_2, \cdots, n_r$; $n_1^-, n_2^-, \cdots, n_r^-$. The author's theorem says that (E, Φ) is, up to metric orthogonal isomorphism, completely characterized by the invariants n_i, n_i^- $(1\leqq i\leqq r)$. The theorem also holds true in case of no orderings at all (i.e., K not formally real). In that case (E, Φ) admits an orthonormal basis. This special case was first established by I. Kaplansky [An. Acad. Brasil. Ci. **22** (1950), 1–17; MR **12**, 238].

H. Gross (Zürich)

E12-131 (37# 2689)

Nobusawa, Nobuo

A note on class numbers of lattices in quadratic spaces.

Arch. Math. (*Basel*) **18** (1967), 595–596.

Let V be a regular quadratic space over an algebraic number field F. For any integral ideal $\mathfrak{a}$ of F, let $h(\mathfrak{a})$ denote the number of classes of integral lattices on V with volume $\mathfrak{a}$, and let $N\mathfrak{a}$ denote the norm of $\mathfrak{a}$. The author shows that $h(\mathfrak{a})\leqq A(N\mathfrak{a})^B$ for some positive constants A and B. The author has already proved this result for the case when V is isotropic [J. Reine Angew. Math. **227** (1967), 209–211; MR **35** #4190]. For a proof that $h(\mathfrak{a})$ is finite, and also for auxiliary results used in this paper, see O. T. O'Meara [*Introduction to quadratic forms*, Springer, Berlin, 1963; MR **27** #2485].

J. Pitman (Adelaide)

Citations: MR 27# 2485 = E02-11; MR 35# 4190 = E12-125.

E12-132 (38# 116)

Fuchs, Peter

Ein Beitrag zum Problem der Darstellungsanzahlen von positiven ganzzahligen quadratischen Formen.

Studien zur Theorie der quadratischen Formen, pp. 199–223. *Birkhäuser, Basel,* 1968.

E. Hecke, in his theory of modular correspondences, discovered connections among the numbers of representations of integers by definite quadratic forms [*Mathematische Werke*, memoirs 35, 36, 41, Vandenhoeck & Ruprecht, Göttingen, 1959; MR **21** #3303]. The reviewer gave a purely arithmetical foundation for a part of these facts, which proved, however, technically complicated and unwieldy [*Quadratische Formen und orthogonale Gruppen*, Chapter IV, Springer, Berlin, 1952; MR **14**, 540]. The author of this paper explains the concepts and results of the theory from the beginning and applies them in sufficiently simple cases, especially under the assumption that the class number in the genus considered is 1.

M. Eichler (Basel)

Citations: MR 14, 540a = E02-4; MR 21# 3303 = Z25-14.

E12-133 (38# 3227)

James, D. G.

On Witt's theorem for unimodular quadratic forms.

Pacific J. Math. **26** (1968), 303–316.

L sei ein **Z**-Gitter vom Rang $r(L)$ mit einer symmetrischen, unimodularen Bilinearform ϕ der Signatur $s(L)$, J ein primitives Teilgitter von L, für welches $r(L)-|s(L)|\geqq 2(r(J)+1)$ ist. Unter diesen Voraussetzungen wird der folgende Satz vom Typ des Wittschen Isomorphiesatzes bewiesen: Eine Isometrie φ von J auf ein primitives Teilgitter K von L ist genau dann fortsetzbar zu einer Isometrie von L auf sich, wenn für jeden primitiven Vektor x von J die Bedingungen $(Q-\phi_x)(L)\equiv 0$ mod 2 und $(Q-\phi_{\varphi x})(L)\equiv 0$ mod 2 gleichbedeutend sind. Dabei ist $\phi_x(y)=\phi(x, y)$ und $Q(y)=\phi(y, y)$. Für $r(J)=1$ wurde dies von C. T. C. Wall [Math. Ann. **147** (1962), 328–338; MR **25** #2009] bewiesen. Es wird ein Beispiel dafür angegeben, daß der Satz falsch wird, wenn man die Ungleichung $r(L)-|s(L)|\geqq 2(r(J)+1)$ verletzt.

S. Böge (Heidelberg)

Referred to in E08-45.

E12-134 (38# 5820)

James, D. G.

Indefinite quadratic forms of determinant $\pm 2p$.

Proc. Amer. Math. Soc. **21** (1969), 214–218.

Es werden notwendige und hinreichende Bedingungen

angegeben dafür, daß zwei Vektoren α und β eines $\mathbf{Z}$-Gitters L mit nicht ausgearteter quadratischer Form Q sich durch eine orthogonale Transformation des Gitters ineinander überführen lassen. Von dem Gitter wird vorausgesetzt, daß es sich in der Form $U \perp \mathbf{Z}\eta$ schreiben lasse, wo U ungerade (d.h. $Q(U) \not\subset 2\mathbf{Z}$) und unimodular ist, der Witt-Index von U mindestens 2 und $Q(\eta) = \pm 2p$ mit einer ungeraden Primzahl p. Es wird gezeigt, daß insbesondere alle ungeraden Gitter L vom Witt-Index >2 und mit Diskriminante $\pm 2p$, wo p eine Primzahl $\equiv 3 \bmod 4$ ist, diese Voraussetzungen erfüllen; denn jedes indefinite, ungerade Gitter vom Rang $\geqq 3$ mit solcher Diskriminanten besitzt eine Orthogonalbasis $\{\xi_1, \cdots, \xi_{r-1}, \eta\}$ mit $Q(\xi_i) = \pm 1$ und $Q(\eta) = \pm 2p$. Die (offensichtlich notwendigen) Bedingungen lauten: (1) $Q(\alpha) = Q(\beta)$; (2) $\{d \in \mathbf{Z} \mid d\alpha \in L\} = \{d \in \mathbf{Z} \mid d\beta \in L\}$; (3) $(\alpha, L) = (\beta, L)$; (4) $Q(L \cap \alpha^\perp) \subset 2\mathbf{Z}$ if and only if $Q(L \cap \beta^\perp) \subset 2\mathbf{Z}$. *S. Böge* (Heidelberg)

E12-135 (39# 212)

Malyšev, A. V.

The distribution of integral points on surfaces of the second order. (Russian)

Kabardino-Balkarsk. Gos. Univ. Učen. Zap. No. 19 (1963), 195–196.

This is a brief summary of an address given by the author. Two theorems are stated without proof. The author indicates that the results are obtainable by the methods of his treatise [Trudy Mat. Inst. Steklov. **65** (1962); MR **26** #80] and that the first theorem is due to B. Z. Moroz.

Citations: MR 26# 80 = E12-92.

E12-136 (39# 1406)

Gerstein, Larry J.

Splitting quadratic forms over integers of global fields.

Amer. J. Math. **91** (1969), 106–134.

Let F be a global field and $\mathfrak{o}$ a Hasse domain of F, that is, a Dedekind domain which can be obtained as the intersection of almost all valuation rings on F. Let V be a regular quadratic space over F and L an $\mathfrak{o}$-lattice on V. For V indefinite over $\mathfrak{o}$, the author shows the existence of a constant $n_0 = n_0(\mathfrak{o})$ such that L has a non-trivial orthogonal splitting $L = L_1 \perp L_2$ whenever rank $L \geqq n_0$. (If V is definite, n_0 need not exist.) In particular, if F is an algebraic function field in one variable over a finite field of constants, $n_0 = 7$ always suffices. If F is an algebraic number field, there is no universal value for n_0; in fact, it is shown, for any natural number k, that there exist F, $\mathfrak{o}$, V and L with rank $L \geqq k$, V indefinite for $\mathfrak{o}$ and L indecomposible as an $\mathfrak{o}$-lattice. This paper generalizes results of G. L. Watson [*Integral quadratic forms*, Cambridge Univ. Press, New York, 1960; MR **22** #9475], who proved, for $\mathfrak{o}$ the rational integers, that $n_0(\mathbf{Z}) = 12$, and this is best possible.

{Reviewer's remark: In Theorem 6, the value of n_p should be 10; $A(0,0) \perp 2A(2,2) \perp \langle 2^5 \cdot 3 \rangle \perp \langle 2^{11} \cdot 7 \rangle \perp \langle 2^{16} \rangle \perp \langle 2^{20} \rangle \perp \langle 2^{24} \rangle$ is a lattice of rank 9 with no sq(4)-splitting over the ring of 2-adic integers.}

D. G. James (University Park, Pa.)

Citations: MR 22# 9475 = E02-9.

Referred to in E12-146.

E12-137 (39# 2703)

van der Blij, F.

Quelques remarques sur la théorie des formes quadratiques.

Bull. Soc. Math. Belg. **20** (1968), 205–212.

This article is a survey of some known results and numerical examples in the classification problem for quadratic forms. *R. Jacobowitz* (Lawrence, Kan.)

Referred to in E02-16.

E12-138 (39# 5476)

Kogan, L. A.

Theory of modular forms and the problem of finding formulas for the number of representations of numbers by positive quadratic forms.

Dokl. Akad. Nauk SSSR **182** (1968), 259–261 (*Russian*); *translated as Soviet Math. Dokl.* **9** (1968), 1130–1132.

The author calls a positive quadratic form $Q(x)$ in $2k$ variables with integral coefficients a form of Liouville type if the theta series of $Q(x)$ is the sum of an Eisenstein series and a cusp form which can be represented by special generalized theta series $\sum P(x_1, x_2) \exp(2\pi i \tau G(x_1, x_2))$ with suitable binary quadratic forms $G(x)$ and spherical harmonics $P(x)$. For such forms the remainder term of the number of representations $Q(x) = n$ satisfies the Ramanujan-Petersson conjecture. Without proof he states the following theorem: Let $\varepsilon > 0$ be a real number and l an integer satisfying the inequalities $(k-1)((4\sqrt{e})^{-1} + \varepsilon) - \frac{1}{2} < l \leqq k-1$. There exists a real number $C(\varepsilon)$ depending only on ε such that for every prime $q > C(\varepsilon)$ no form in $2k$ variables with determinant q^{2l+1} and with odd $k \geqq 3$ is of Liouville type. For the proof in the case $k > 3$ he seems to apply a hypothesis of Vinogradov on the least quadratic non-residue mod q. {The theorem seems inconsistent with another statement made by the author, that all $Q(x)$ in 6 variables are of Liouville type.} *M. Eichler* (Basel)

E12-139 (39# 6817)

Malyšev, A. V.

The weighted number of integer points lying on a surface of the second order. (Russian)

Zap. Naučn. Sem. Leningrad. Otdel. Mat. Inst. Steklov. (LOMI) **1** (1966), 6–83.

The author studies the number $R(p, \omega/N)$ of integral points on the surface $p(x_1, \cdots, x_s) = 0$ (p is an integer-valued second degree polynomial and $s \geqq 4$), taken with the weight $G(x_1, \cdots, x_s) = \exp\{N^{-1}[\omega(x_1, \cdots, x_s)]\}$ (ω is a second degree polynomial). Under certain assumptions about p and ω, the author establishes an asymptotic formula for $R(p, \omega/N)$ $(N \to \infty)$ with a lower power in the remainder term. As a corollary the author obtains the asymptotic number of integral points in De Lury regions [D. B. De Lury, *On the representation of numbers by the indefinite form* $ax^2 + by^2 + cz^2 + dt^2$, Univ. of Toronto Press, Toronto, Ont., 1938] on the surface $p(x_1, \cdots, x_s) = 0$.

E. Golubeva (RŽMat **1968** #4 A91)

E12-140 (40# 4203)

van der Waerden, B. L.

Das Minimum von $D/(f_{11} f_{22} \cdots f_{55})$ für reduzierte positive quinäre quadratische Formen.

Aequationes Math. **2** (1969), 233–247.

Let $f = \sum_{i=1}^{5} f_{ii} x_i^2 + \sum_{i<k\leq 5} f_{ik} x_i x_k$ be a positive definite quadratic form in five variables. Minkowski showed in his reduction theory that for reduced forms one has $D \geqq c f_{11} f_{22} f_{33} f_{44} f_{55}$, where D denotes the discriminant of f and c is a constant. In this paper, the author shows that the best possible value for c is $\frac{1}{8}$. This constant corresponds to the densest lattice arrangement of spheres in 5-dimensional space. The difficulty of the proof of this theorem is caused by the fact that the coefficient f_{55} of a reduced form is not necessarily the fifth successive minimum of f. It is shown that it is sufficient to consider only forms with equal successive minima. The result is then

obtained by a careful investigation of the domain of reduced forms in the coefficient space.

H. Groemer (Tucson, Ariz.)

E12-141 (40# 7201)

Iyanaga, Kenichi

Class numbers of definite Hermitian forms.

J. Math. Soc. Japan **21** (1969), 359–374.

An analogue of the method of M. Kneser [Arch. Math. **8** (1957), 241–250; MR **19**, 838] for determining class numbers for definite quadratic forms in a small number of variables and with simple discriminants is developed for certain definite modular Hermitian forms. This is then applied to the following special case. Let $v_1, \cdots, v_n$ be a basis of an n-dimensional vector space over $\mathbf{Q}(i)$ and H the Hermitian form determined by $H(v_j, v_k)=\delta_{jk}$. Let c_n denote the unitary class number and $c_n{}^1$ the special unitary class number of the lattice $\sum_{j=1}^{n}\mathbf{Z}[i]v_j$. Then $c_n \leqq c_n{}^1 \leqq (n, 4)c_n$. Furthermore, $c_1=c_2=c_3=c_4=1$, $c_5=2$, $c_6=3$ and $c_7=4$. For indefinite Hermitian forms it has been shown by G. Shimura [Ann. of Math. (2) **79** (1964), 369–409; MR **28** #2104] that every genus of lattices consists of only one class, that is, the special unitary class number is one.

D. G. James (Göttingen)

Citations: MR 19, 838c = E12-62; MR 28# 2104 = E12-102.

E12-142 (41# 151)

Estes, Dennis; Pall, Gordon

The definite octonary quadratic forms of determinant 1.

Illinois J. Math. **14** (1970), 159–163.

A direct, matrix-computational proof, where "the deepest thing used is the elementary theory of the Hasse symbol", is given of the fact that there are exactly two classes of 8-ary positive definite unimodular quadratic forms over the rational integers.

R. Jacobowitz (Lawrence, Kan.)

E12-143 (42# 199)

Kogan, L. A.

Liouville formulae and parabolic forms that are generated by generalized binary theta-series. (Russian. Lithuanian and German summaries)

Litovsk. Mat. Sb. **9** (1969), 519–533.

Let $Q(x_1, x_2, \cdots, x_{2k})$ be a positive definite quadratic form in $2k \geqq 2$ variables. For $k \geqq 2$ the associated theta-function $\theta(t, Q)=\sum_{x_1,x_2,\cdots,x_{2k}} e^{2\pi i \tau Q(x_1,\cdots,x_{2k})}$ can be expressed as $E(\tau)+\Theta(\tau)$, where $E(\tau)$ is an Eisenstein series and $\Theta(\tau)$ is a cuspform. $Q(x_1, x_2, \cdots, x_{2k})$ is called a Liouville quadratic form in the restricted sense, when k is odd and when $\Theta(\tau)$ can be expressed as a linear combination of series of the form (1) $\sum_{x_1,x_2=-\infty}^{\infty} P_{k-1}(x_1, x_2)e^{2\pi i \tau Q^*(x_1,x_2)}$, where P_{k-1} is a spherical harmonic polynomial of order $k-1$ and $2Q^*(x_1, x_2)=a_{11}x_1{}^2+a_{12}x_1x_2+a_{21}x_2x_1+a_{22}x_2{}^2$ ($a_{11}, a_{12}=a_{21}, a_{22}$ integral) is positive definite. For, in this case, formulae of Liouville type can be given for the number of representations of an integer n by the form Q.

The author is concerned with quadratic forms Q of discriminant $-q^{2l+1}$, where q is an odd prime, and of type $(-k, q, \chi)$, where k is odd, $k \geqq 3$ and $\chi(n)=(n/q)$ (generalised Jacobi symbol) [see E. Hecke, Danske Vid. Selsk. Math.-Fys. Medd. **17** (1940), no. 12; MR **2**, 251]. His object is to obtain restrictive conditions on the existence of Liouville forms of this type by showing that, for sufficiently large q, the cuspform $\Theta(\tau)$ will not belong to the space spanned by the series (1), and he notes the similarity of this situation with a problem studied by the reviewer [Amer. J. Math. **87** (1965), 857–860; MR **32** #5605]. To do this he chooses an nth power occurring in the series for $\theta(\tau)$ with a non-zero coefficient, which does not occur in any of the series (1). This happens, under certain conditions, when n is a quadratic non-residue modulo q, and the best results arise when n is as small as possible. If the Vinogradov conjecture $n=O(q^{\varepsilon})$ holds for the least positive non-residue n ($\varepsilon>0$ and arbitrary), his main result takes the following form: For arbitrary $\varepsilon>0$ there exists a positive integer $q_0(\varepsilon)$ such that there exist no Liouville quadratic forms in the restricted sense when $q>q_0$. If D. A. Burgess' estimate $n=O(q^{(1/4\sqrt{e})+\varepsilon})$ is used [Mathematika **4** (1957), 106–112; MR **20** #28] in place of the Vinogradov conjecture, the corresponding result is that no Liouville quadratic forms in the restricted sense with $(k-1)((4\sqrt{l})^{-1}+\varepsilon)-\frac{1}{2}<l\leqq k-1$ can exist for $q>q_0$. The author concludes by giving explicit examples for $q=23$, $k=3$ of quadratic forms where the series (1) do span the space (of dimension 3) containing the cuspforms $\Theta(\tau)$.

R. A. Rankin (Glasgow)

Citations: MR 2, 251f = F25-4; MR 20# 28 = N68-28; MR 32# 5605 = E24-103.

E12-144 (42# 388)

Pollak, Barth

Orthogonal groups over global fields of characteristic 2.

J. Algebra **15** (1970), 589–595.

L'auteur considère un corps "global" F de caractéristique 2 (corps de fonctions algébriques d'une variable sur un corps fini de caractéristique 2), une forme quadratique non défective sur un espace vectoriel V de dimension finie sur F, et le groupe orthogonal correspondant $O(V)$. Il se propose de prouver que le groupe spinoriel $O'(V)$ est égal au groupe des commutateurs $\Omega(V)$; comme on sait que l'espace V contient des droites isotropes si $\dim(V)>4$, le cas à élucider est celui où $\dim(V)=4$ et où V est anisotrope. Utilisant le fait que tout élément de $O'(V)$ est produit de 2 ou 4 transvections orthogonales, l'auteur se ramène à construire un plan contenu dans V et tel que la restriction de la forme quadratique à ce plan contienne quatre éléments de F de la forme 1, b_1, b_2 et b_1b_2. Cette construction assez subtile utilise le principe de passage du local au global (que l'auteur prouve en caractéristique 2) et la loi de réciprocité globale.

J. Dieudonné (Nice)

E12-145 (42# 3021)

Chang, Kwong-shin

Diskriminanten und Signaturen gerader quadratischer Formen.

Arch. Math. (*Basel*) **21** (1970), 59–65.

The author determines necessary and sufficient conditions, relating the dimension and local signatures of V and the discriminants of V and L, for the existence of an integral lattice L on a quadratic space V over an algebraic number field k. He then specializes to the cases $k=$ rationals and k real quadratic, the latter generalizing a similar result of H. Maass [Math. Z. **51** (1948), 233–254; MR **10**, 182] on the existence of positive definite even quadratic forms over such a field.

R. Jacobowitz (Tempe, Ariz.)

Citations: MR 10, 182g = E12-31.

E12-146 (42# 4487)

Gerstein, Larry J.

Integral decomposition of hermitian forms.

Amer. J. Math. **92** (1970), 398–418.

In an earlier paper [same J. **91** (1969), 106–134; MR **39** #1406], the author studied the existence of a positive integer n_0 such that any lattice of rank at least n_0 on a quadratic space over a global field F has a non-trivial orthogonal splitting, also whether an n_0 can be found that will work for an entire class of fields and lattices, e.g., all algebraic function fields (in one variable over a finite constant field) and lattices with respect to Hasse domains of these fields. In the present article, he considers the similar question for hermitian forms, where predictably sharper answers can usually be given. The principal result is as follows. Let K/F be a quadratic extension of algebraic number fields, V an indefinite hermitian space over K with respect to the natural involution of K/F, L a lattice on V; then (1) if dim V is at least 5, L has an orthogonal splitting into components of rank at most 4; and (2) given another lattice M in V of smaller rank than L, L has an orthogonal splitting with one component isometric to M if and only if the same is true for the localizations at all discrete spots on F.

R. Jacobowitz (Tempe, Ariz.)

Citations: MR 39# 1406 = E12-136.

E12-147 (42# 5907)

Lursmanašvili, A. P.

The representation of natural numbers by quadratic forms with integer square-free variables. (Russian. Georgian and English summaries)

Sakharth. SSR Mecn. Akad. Moambe **53** (1969), 281–284.

Let $R_f(n)=\sum_{f(r_1,\cdots,r_k)=n} 1$ denote the number of representations of the natural number n by a quadratic form with determinant D whose variables are square-free integers. Let $S(h,q)=\sum_{a \bmod q}\exp(2\pi i a^2 h/q)$,

$$S(f(t_1^2,\cdots,t_k^2);h,q)=\sum_{l_1,\cdots,l_k=0}^{q-1}\exp\{2\pi i h f(t_1^2 l_1,\cdots,t_k^2 l_k)/q\},$$

$$G(h,q)=\sum_{t_1,\cdots,t_k=1}^{\infty}(\mu(t_1)\cdots\mu(t_k)/(t_1^2\cdots t_k^2))S(f(t_1^2,\cdots,t_k^2);h_i q).$$

In his previous paper [Sakharth. SSR Mecn. Akad. Moambe **48** (1967), 7–12; MR **37** #152] the author proved that for $k\geqq 5$, $R_f(n)=(\pi^{k/2}/D^{1/2}\Gamma(k/2))\sigma(f,n)n^{k/2-1}+O(n^{k/4+\varepsilon})$, where

$$\sigma(f,n)=\sum_{q=1}^{\infty}\sum_{h \bmod q,(h,q)=1}(G(h,q)/q^k)\exp(-2\pi i h n/q).$$

In this paper it is proved that if for each odd prime divisor of discriminant d of the form f and for $p=2$, the congruences $f(m_1,m_2,\cdots,m_k)\equiv n \pmod{p^{M_p}}$ for some M_p are solvable in integers $m_1,\cdots,m_k$ which are not divisible by p^2, then $\sigma(f,n)>0$. In other cases $\sigma(f,n)=0$.

A. Rotkiewicz (Warsaw)

Citations: MR 37# 152 = E12-129.

E12-148 (43# 3209)

Böge, Sigrid

Spinorgeschlechter schiefhermitescher Formen.

Arch. Math. (Basel) **21** (1970), 172–184.

D sei ein Quaternionenschiefkörper mit dem algebraischen Zahlkörper k als Zentrum. V sei ein n-dimensionaler D-Linksvektorraum mit schiefhermitescher nichtausgearteter Form (,): $V\times V\to D$ bezüglich der Standardinvolution von D über k. O sei eine Maximalordnung in D. M sei ein O-Gitter in V mit $(M,M)\subset O$. In der vorliegenden Arbeit wird u.a. das folgende Theorem über die Anzahl der Spinorgeschlechter im Geschlecht eines Gitters M bewiesen. Satz: Ist $\dim_D V\geqq 4$, so ist die Anzahl $s(M)$ der Spinorgeschlechter im Geschlecht eines Gitters M bezüglich der speziellen unitären Gruppe eine Zweierpotenz, und zu jeder Zweierpotenz 2^t, $t\geqq 0$, gibt es ein Gitter M in V mit $s(M)=2^t$.

Da die Klassenzahl bezüglich U^+ im Spinorgeschlecht gleich 1 ist im Falle indefiniter Form (,), macht der genannte Satz eine Aussage über Klassenzahlen, wenn der unterliegende Vektorraum indefinit ist. Die vom Autor gegebenen Beweise geben zudem Aufschluß über die Erzeugung der lokalen Einheitengruppen eines Gitters durch spezielle Spiegelungen.

H. Gross (Zürich)

E12-149 (43# 7425)

Wall, C. T. C.

On the classification of hermitian forms. I. Rings of algebraic integers.

Compositio Math. **22** (1970), 425–451.

In an earlier paper [Proc. Cambridge Philos. Soc. **67** (1970), 243–250; MR **40** #4285], the author introduced his versions of "reflexive" and "quadratic" forms, both of which generalize the classical notion of hermitian forms. Here number-theoretic techniques are used to classify nonsingular "quadratic" forms on projective modules over rings of algebraic integers—with respect to some nontrivial involution of the base ring. The author mentions that, in large measure, the present paper closely parallels the paper by G. Shimura [Ann. of Math. (2) **79** (1964), 369–409; MR **28** #2104], but that different emphasis motivates and justifies his giving this new account (whereas Shimura develops the general theory and then specializes to maximal lattices, this paper deals exclusively with modular lattices). In particular, the local structures are carefully considered here and these will also be applied in a subsequent paper to orders in semisimple algebras over the rationals. The paper includes some interesting cancellation and stability theorems that parallel the corresponding results of Bass for projective modules. Moreover, the cancellation theorem here does not follow from results of A. Bak [*Algebraic K-theory and its geometric applications* (Conf., Hull, 1969), pp. 55–66, Springer, Berlin, 1969; MR **40** #5651], who needs another condition about the hyperbolic rank. Finally, some Witt groups are calculated.

J. S. Hsia (Columbus, Ohio)

Citations: MR 28# 2104 = E12-102.

E12-150 (44# 3955)

Maurer, Donald

AF-lattices on a regular quadratic space.

J. Number Theory **3** (1971), 347–363.

Let F be a field with a Dedekind set of spots S and let $\mathcal{O}$ be the integers of F determined by S. Let V be a regular quadratic space over F with associated bilinear form $B(x,y)$. The author finds necessary and sufficient conditions on the volume of a lattice L under which if $x,y\in L$, then $B(x,y)\in\mathcal{O}$ and L is maximal with respect to this condition. An application is made to the case in which V is an algebraic number field over the rational numbers and the bilinear form is given by $Tr(xy)$.

H. W. Brinkmann (Wallingford, Pa.)

E16 GENERAL BINARY QUADRATIC FORMS

See also Section D08.

See also reviews A52-42, A56-3, D12-60, D44-119, E02-3, E02-6, E08-4, E12-12, E20-17, E24-69, E28-5, E28-74, F15-34, H25-33, J44-45, L10-3, L10-4, L10-5, L10-10, L10-16, L25-26, N20-19, N20-20, N20-40, N32-30, N32-40, N32-41, N40-46, N56-3, N56-21, N56-23, N80-17, N80-41, P20-12, P20-19, P20-22, P20-31, P28-74, R10-2, R10-10, R12-18, R12-19, R22-35, R42-32, R42-49, R44-14, R52-16, T35-58, Z15-83.

E16-1 (2, 35g)

Hall, Newman A. The number of representations function for binary quadratic forms. Amer. J. Math. **62**, 589–598 (1940).

Explicit formulae are obtained for the number of representations of an arbitrary integer in a positive binary quadratic form, for all cases in which there is a genus of one class. *G. Pall* (Princeton, N. J.).

E16-2 (4, 240h)

Tchudakoff, N. On Siegel's theorem. Bull. Acad. Sci. URSS. Sér. Math. [Izvestia Akad. Nauk SSSR] **6**, 135–142 (1942). (Russian. English summary)

This paper gives a modification of Heilbronn's simplification [Quart. J. Math., Oxford Ser. **9**, 194–195 (1938)] of Siegel's proof that $hR\geqq k^{\frac{1}{2}-\epsilon}$ if $k\geqq k_0(\epsilon)$, where h is the number of binary quadratic classes of determinant $\pm k$ and R the regulator. Let $f(s)$ denote an analytic function defined by $\sum a_n n^{-s}$, convergent in a half-plane, such that $f(s)$ is meromorphic and $f(s)=O(|t|^\beta)$ uniformly over the half-plane $\sigma\geqq\frac{1}{2}$ excepting the poles, and such that for certain positive constants λ and A, and an integer q, $A^s\Gamma^q(\lambda s)f(s)=F(s)$ satisfies the functional equation $F(1-s)=F(s)$. If $F_0(s)$ is the rational function part of $F(s)$, containing all the poles, if $\mu=(q\lambda)^{-1}$, and Nx and Sx stand for $x_1\cdots x_q$ and $x_1+\cdots+x_q$, then

(1) $F(s)-F_0(s)=$

$$\sum_{n=1}^{\infty} a_n \int\cdots\int_{Nx\geqq 1} [(Nx)^{\lambda s-1}+(Nx)^{\gamma(1-s)-1}]e^{-A^{-\mu}n^{\mu}Sx}dx_1\cdots dx_q.$$

This is applied with $f(s)=\zeta(s)L(s, \chi)L(s, \chi_1)L(s, \chi_2)$, where the χ's are real characters for which the a_n turn out to be nonnegative, so that the inequality obtained by dropping all but the first term on the right of (1) suffices to prove $1-\rho>k^{-\epsilon}$ if $k\geqq k_0(\epsilon)$, where ρ is the largest real root of $L(s, \chi)$, χ being a character mod k. No use is made of algebraic numbers. *G. Pall* (Montreal, Que.).

E16-3 (5, 91f)

Gupta, Hansraj. On the class-numbers of binary quadratic forms. Univ. Nac. Tucumán. Revista A. **3**, 283–299 (1942).

This paper contains a 14 page table giving for each possible value of $d=4ac-b^2\leqq 12500$ the number $h'(d)$ of properly primitive classes of forms $ax^2+bxy+cy^2$ of determinant $-d$. The table is in two parts devoted, respectively, to the cases $d=4n$, $4n+3$. The total number $h(d)$ of classes can be found by summing the values of $h'(d/k^2)$ over all the square divisors k^2 of d. This is the most extensive table of its kind ever published and should be of considerable future use in investigating the properties of this interesting function. *D. H. Lehmer* (Berkeley, Calif.).

E16-4 (5, 254h)

Gage, Walter H. An arithmetical identity. Trans. Roy. Soc. Canada. Sect. III. **37**, 9–11 (1943).

A new arithmetical identity of a type similar to those obtained by Liouville is derived in this paper by the well-known method of symmetry. The identity is then applied to obtain various recursion formulas for the class-number functions $F(n)$, $G(n)$, $E(n)$. One such formula is the following: $F(m)-F(m-1^2)+22F(m-4^2)-F(m-3^2)+2F(m-8^2)-F(m-5^2)+\cdots=0$, where $F(n)$ is the number of uneven classes of quadratic forms of determinant $-n$ and $m\equiv 3$ (mod 8). *H. W. Brinkmann* (Swarthmore, Pa.).

E16-5 (5, 254i)

Walfisz, Arnold. On the class-number of binary quadratic forms. Trav. Inst. Math. Tbilissi [Trudy Tbiliss. Mat. Inst.] **11**, 57–71 (1942). (English. Russian summary)

The chief object of this paper is the proof of the following two results obtained from various class number relationships:

$$\limsup_{k\to\infty} \frac{L_k}{\log\log k}\geqq e^C$$

and

$$L_k^{-1}=\Omega(\log\log k)^{\frac{1}{2}},$$

where $L_k=\sum_{n=1}^{\infty}(-k|n)n^{-1}$, $(-k|n)$ being the Kronecker symbol of quadratic residuacity, C is Euler's constant and k is positive, square-free except perhaps for a factor 4 and identical to 3 (mod 4) or 4, 8 (mod 16). The symbol Ω apparently means that there is a constant A and an increasing sequence of positive integers k such that $L_k^{-1}\geqq A(\log\log k)^{\frac{1}{2}}$. The former of the two results was obtained under a certain assumption by Littlewood [Proc. London Math. Soc. (2) **27**, 358–372 (1927)]. A direct application to the class number function is provided by the relationship $h(k)=\sqrt{k}\,L_k/\pi$ if $k>4$, where $h(n)$ is, for $n>4$, the number of primitive classes of forms $ax^2+bxy+cy^2$ with $b^2-4ac=-n$. *B. W. Jones* (Ithaca, N. Y.).

Referred to in M20-4, M20-5, M55-40.

E16-6 (7, 369b)

Reiner, Irving. On genera of binary quadratic forms. Bull. Amer. Math. Soc. **51**, 909–912 (1945).

Employing Dirichlet's theorem on the infinity of primes in an arithmetic progression, the author proves two well-known theorems of Gauss [Disquisitiones Arithmeticae, arts. 234–265], one relating to the existence of genera of properly primitive binary quadratic forms and the other on the equality of the number of classes of such forms in different genera of the same determinant. The proof of the second theorem is made to depend upon the existence of a linear transformation of prime determinant p which carries forms β_1, β_2 of one genus into forms $p\phi_1$, $p\phi_2$, where ϕ_1, ϕ_2 belong to another preassigned genus and where the equivalence of ϕ_1 and ϕ_2 implies the equivalence of β_1 and β_2. *A. E. Ross.*

E16-7 (7, 418a)

Rédei, L. Zur Gaussischen Theorie der Reduktion binärer quadratischer Formen. Acta Univ. Szeged. Sect. Sci. Math. **10**, 134–140 (1941).

The author gives a simple proof of Gauss's theorem that equivalent reduced binary quadratic forms with positive determinant belong to the same period. The proof is by a method, not using continued fractions, somewhat similar to that of F. Mertens [J. Reine Angew. Math. **89**, 332–339 (1880)]. A method is deduced for finding the fundamental solution of Pell's equation $t^2-Du^2=1$ without using continued fractions. *H. S. A. Potter* (Aberdeen).

E16-8 (9, 336e)

Reuvecamp, W. J., Jr. Eichenberg's theorem. Nieuw Tijdschr. Wiskunde **35**, 202–207 (1947). (Dutch)

Translation of Epstein's exposition [Weber-Wellstein, Enzyklopädie der Elementarmath., 5th ed., Teubner, Leipzig-Berlin, 1934, p. 280]. *N. G. de Bruijn* (Delft).

E16-9 (10, 182f)

Swift, J. Dean. Note on discriminants of binary quadratic forms with a single class in each genus. Bull. Amer. Math. Soc. **54**, 560–561 (1948).

The author has verified that, beyond the largest known ($d=-3315$ if odd, $d=-4\cdot 1848$ if even), there are no negative discriminants with only one class of binary quadratic forms in each genus, at least up to $d=-10^7$. D. H. Lehmer's linear congruence machine was used. *G. Pall.*

E16-10 (10, 434a)

Pall, Gordon. Composition of binary quadratic forms. Bull. Amer. Math. Soc. **54**, 1171–1175 (1948).

A compound of binary quadratic forms is defined in a manner similar to that of Dirichlet [cf. L. E. Dickson, History of the Theory of Numbers, vol. 3, Carnegie Institution of Washington, 1923, p. 66]. It is shown that, if the divisors of the classes of two forms are coprime, then their compound defines a unique class. Gauss's criterion for the equivalence of two binary quadratic forms is generalised to forms in n variables. *H. S. A. Potter* (Aberdeen).

Referred to in E16-74.

E16-11 (10, 594e)

Reiner, Irving. A generalization of Meyer's theorem. Trans. Amer. Math. Soc. **65**, 170–186 (1949).

A classical theorem asserts that a binary quadratic form with integral coefficients, which represents at least one number of an arithmetic progression, represents an infinity of primes of this progression, provided that the progression contains at least two coprime numbers. The author generalises this theorem; instead of considering the representability of numbers by quadratic forms of discriminant D, he considers a more general division into classes. His formulation, which is too complicated to be given here in detail, could be considerably simplified in the language of quadratic fields. The proof proceeds along conventional lines, but in order to show that his L-series do not vanish at $s=1$, the author has to assume that $L'(s)$ is bounded for $s>1$.
H. A. Heilbronn (Bristol).

E16-12 (11, 233d)

Vinogradov, I. M. Improvement of the remainder term of some asymptotic formulas. Izvestiya Akad. Nauk SSSR. Ser. Mat. **13**, 97–110 (1949). (Russian)

Let $h(-t)$ be the class number of the binary quadratic forms with determinant $-t$. The author improves on previous work of Gauss and himself to obtain, for each $\epsilon>0$,

$$\sum_{t=1}^{N} h(-t)=4\pi\{21\zeta(3)\}^{-1}N^{\frac{3}{2}}-(2/\pi^2)N+O(N^{.7-\delta+\epsilon})$$

where $\delta=1/405$. A previous paper of the author [Bull. Acad. Sci. Petrograd [Izvestiya Akad. Nauk] (6) **11**, 1347–1378 (1917)] gave the error term $O(N^{5/6}\log^{\frac{2}{3}} N)$. The improved result depends on the sharpening of estimates of the number of lattice points in certain three-dimensional regions. This is accomplished by using results of the author and van der Corput on the estimation of exponential sums. The author states that his method enables him to show that the number of lattice points in the sphere of radius r and center at the origin is equal to its volume plus an error term not exceeding $r^{1.4-2\delta+\epsilon}$. *L. Schoenfeld* (Urbana, Ill.).

Referred to in E16-55, L15-15, P20-12, Z10-51.

E16-13 (11, 643c)

Jones, B. W. The composition of quadratic binary forms. Amer. Math. Monthly **56**, 380–391 (1949).

Let Δ be a nonsquare integer congruent to 0 or 1 (mod 4), and write $\sigma=\frac{1}{2}(\epsilon+\Delta^{\frac{1}{2}})$, where $\epsilon=0$ or 1 according as Δ is even or odd. The ring $J(\Delta)$ of numbers $a+b\sigma$ (with a and b any rational integers) is studied. In previous treatments [for example, Landau, Vorlesungen über Zahlentheorie, v. III, Hirzel, Leipzig, 1927, pp. 187–196], Δ was assumed to be divisible by no square s^2 such that Δ/s^2 is again a discriminant, and a correspondence was set up between classes of ideals in $J(\Delta)$ and classes of nonnegative primitive binary quadratic forms of discriminant Δ. In the more general case of this article there is similarly set up a correspondence between classes of ideals in $J(\Delta)$ and classes (not necessarily primitive) of binary quadratic forms of discriminant Δ. Composition of primitive classes is shown to map into the multiplication of the corresponding classes of ideals. Some consequences relating to composition of binary quadratic forms are deduced. *G. Pall* (Chicago, Ill.).

E16-14 (12, 595a)

Linnik, Yu. V. An elementary method for a problem of the theory of prime numbers. Uspehi Matem. Nauk (N.S.) **5**, no. 2(36), 198 (1950). (Russian)

The author suggests a possible method for proving elementarily Siegel's theorem on the class-number of positive definite binary quadratic forms [Acta Arith. **1**, 83–86 (1935)]. He has since constructed a proof on these lines [Izvestiya Akad. Nauk SSSR. Ser. Mat. **14**, 327–342 (1950); these Rev. **12**, 482]. *H. Davenport* (London).

Citations: MR 12, 482a = M20-14.

E16-15 (14, 358b)

Brandt, Heinrich. Binäre quadratische Formen im Gaussschen Zahlkörper. Math. Nachr. **7**, 151–158 (1952).

The author studies characters and genera of primitive quadratic forms $\varphi=\rho\xi^2+\sigma\xi\eta+\tau\eta^2$, where ρ, σ, τ are Gaussian integers [cf., H. J. S. Smith, Proc. Roy. Soc. London **13**, 278–298 (1864) = Collected math. papers, v. 1, Oxford, 1894, pp. 418–442]. His theory is based on the first of his two recent formulations of the quadratic reciprocity law for the Gaussian field [Comment. Math. Helv. **26**, 42–54 (1952); these Rev. **13**, 726], and it is much simpler than Smith's. He employs stem-discriminants (corresponding to field-discriminants for the rational base-field) and prime-discriminants (-4, 8, -8, $\pm p$, p prime, $\pm p\equiv 1$ (mod 4), in the rational case). In the Gaussian case, however, not all stem-discriminants are products of (proper) prime-discriminants. Improper prime-discriminants, which are not discriminants, but of which an even number may occur as factors of stem-discriminants, must also be considered. An effective summary of results of Smith stated for 31 cases (loc. cit., 420–423, and Table III) is the theorem that for every proper or improper prime-discriminant which divides $\Delta=\sigma^2-4\rho\tau$, there is a character of φ. The proof is relatively simple. The author's necessary and sufficient condition for the existence of a genus differs more essentially from Smith's. It is as follows. Let $\Delta=\theta^2\bar{\Delta}$, where θ^2 is the square discriminant factor of Δ of maximum norm. Then $\bar{\Delta}$ is a product $\bar{\Delta}=\delta_1\delta_2\cdots\delta_e$ of e distinct proper or improper prime-discriminants, and if χ_i is the character associated with δ_i, $i=1,\cdots,e$, and μ is an integer represented by φ and prime to Δ, then $\chi_1(\mu)\chi_2(\mu)\cdots\chi_e(\mu)=1$. *R. Hull* (Lafayette, Ind.).

Citations: MR 13, 726b = R40-8.

E16-16 (15, 856f)

Linnik, Yu. V. Some applications of Lobačevskiĭ's geometry to the theory of binary quadratic forms. Doklady Akad. Nauk SSSR (N.S.) **93**, 973–974 (1953). (Russian)

The author announces some results on the distribution of the reduced positive definite binary quadratic forms $a\xi^2+2b\xi\eta+c\eta^2$ of large determinant $b^2-ac=-D<0$. On putting $2x=c+a$, $y=b$, $2z=c-a$, the reduced forms are represented by points (x, y, z) on the hyperboloid $x^2-y^2-z^2=D>0$ with y integral and x and z halves of integers of the same parity, in the region A defined by $2|y| \leqq x-z \leqq x+z$. Results are given concerning the number of such points in certain sub-regions of A. The method of proof is said to be similar to that indicated in a previous paper [Linnik and Malyšev, same Doklady (N.S.) **89**, 209–211 (1953); these Rev. **15**, 406], but to depend on the existence, in certain algebras of generalized quaternions with indefinite norm, of a ring of integers with a Euclidean algorithm. One of the results stated is as follows. Suppose $q \geqq 3$ is a prime, and $(-D|q)=+1$. Then there exist forms (a, b, c) satisfying

$$\alpha_1 D^{\frac{1}{2}} < a < \alpha_2 D^{\frac{1}{2}}, \quad \alpha_3 D^{\frac{1}{2}} < b < \alpha_4 D^{\frac{1}{2}},$$

where $\alpha_1, \cdots, \alpha_4$ are constants consistent with the conditions of reduction, provided $D > D_0(q, \alpha_1, \alpha_2, \alpha_3, \alpha_4)$. Moreover, the number of such forms, divided by the total number $h(-D)$, is greater than a positive constant depending on $q, \alpha_1, \alpha_2, \alpha_3, \alpha_4$. *H. Davenport* (London).

Citations: MR 15, 406b = E20-41.
Referred to in E16-25.

E16-17 (15, 857a)

Goldberg, Karl, Newman, Morris, Straus, E. G., and Swift, J. D. The representation of integers by binary quadratic rational forms. Arch. Math. **5**, 12–18 (1954).

The authors consider the integers represented by

$$f(x, y) = (ax^2+bxy+cy^2)/(p+qxy),$$

where a, b, c, p, q are integers and without loss of generality $(p, q)=1$. They prove that (I) if there exist integers x_0, y_0 not both 0 such that $ax_0^2+bx_0y_0+cy_0^2=p+qx_0y_0=0$, $(ax_0, qy_0)|(c, qy_0)$ then $f(x, y)$ represents all the integers in some arithmetic progression, but (II) if $a|(b, q)$, $c|(b, q)$ then $f(x, y)$ represents only a finite number of integers with $xy \neq 0$. Here (I) results at once from the consideration of $f(x, y_0)$ and $f(x_0, y)$. The proof of (II) depends on the equivalence of $f(x, y)=m$ and $ax^2+Bxy+cy^2=mp$, $B=b-mq$, where $a|B$, $c|B$ by hypothesis. Hence the L.H.S. has the integral automorphs

$$x \to x, \quad y \to -\frac{B}{c}x - y$$

and

$$x \to -\frac{B}{a}y - x, \quad y \to y$$

whose product is of infinite order. Thus infinite descent applies (and the relevant Pellian equation has a solution which may easily be written down despite the authors' introduction). *J. W. S. Cassels* (Cambridge, England).

Referred to in D32-53.

E16-18 (16, 222e)

Chowla, S., and Briggs, W. E. On discriminants of binary quadratic forms with a single class in each genus. Canadian J. Math. **6**, 463–470 (1954).

It follows from Siegel's theorem on the asymptotic behaviour of $h(-\Delta)$, the number of classes of integral quadratic forms with discriminant $-\Delta$ ($-\Delta<0$ a fundamental discriminant) and from a crude bound for the number of genera that there are only a finite number of Δ with one class in each genus. A more refined analysis with the usual machinery shows that there is at most one $\Delta > 10^{60}$ with this property; and, further, that Δ cannot have the property if $\Delta > 10^{14}$, $L_\Delta(53/54) \geqq 0$, where $L_\Delta(s) = \sum (-\Delta/n)n^{-s}$. Reference should have been made to the recent work of Heegner on the special case of 1 genus [Math. Z. **56**, 227–253 (1952); these Rev. **14**, 725]. *J. W. S. Cassels.*

Citations: MR 14, 725j = R14-23.
Referred to in E16-56.

E16-19 (16, 222g)

Fogel', È. K. Finite proofs of some results of the analytic theory of numbers. Latvijas RSR Zinātņu Akad. Fiz. Inst. Raksti **3**, 49–63 (1952). (Russian. Latvian summary)

The paper begins with a general discussion of the nature of 'finite' proofs of arithmetical theorems. Reference is then made to Landau's remark [Vorlesungen über Zahlentheorie, Bd 1, Hirzel, Leipzig, 1927, pp. 128–129] that no one had given an elementary proof of the fact that, for a prime $p \equiv 3 \pmod 4$, the numbers $1^2, 2^2, \cdots, \{\frac{1}{2}(p-1)\}^2$ when divided by p leave more remainders in the range $0<r<\frac{1}{2}p$ than in the range $\frac{1}{2}p<r<p$. Without claiming to supply a short and simple proof such as Landau probably had in mind, the author announces his intention of giving a finite proof by casting into a finite form Dirichlet's proof of the underlying formula for the class number $h(-p)$. According to the author's rules such a proof should use only rational numbers with bounded denominators. But the reader who hopes for an explicit solution within this rigid framework will be disappointed. For after some introductory work on approximate substitutes for Rolle's theorem, the mean-value theorem, and $\log x$ (involving only rational numbers and polynomials with rational coefficients), the author lapses into 'semi-finite' analysis; and it is not easy to see from the indications given how this differs significantly from classical analysis. The semi-finite system seems to ban infinite series, but to admit other concepts traditionally based on the idea of limit, such as the derivative, and the definite integral over a finite interval (of functions like x, $\cos 2n\pi x$, $\sin 2n\pi x$, and their products). For a 'finite' (approximate) theory of the trigonometric functions reference is made to earlier work by the author on 'A finite theory of elementary functions'. The paper actually cited for this purpose (without page reference, and without the subtitle 'I. Logarithmic and exponential functions') [Latvijas PSR Zinātņu Akad. Vēstis **1951**, no. 5(46), 801–813; these Rev. **15**, 218] proves to be irrelevant, but the theory is sketched in another paper quoted later [ibid. **1950**, no. 9(38), 117–125]. There is, however, no clear explanation of the logical status of the unmodified cos, sin, π, or of differentiation and integration, in the 'semi-finite' argument of §5. Elucidation of these points is highly desirable if the merits claimed for this style of proof are to be understood and appreciated. Classical analysts ignorant of the rules of the game may be puzzled by eccentricities of technique for which they can see no motive, such as the needless complication (in conception and in execution) of the method used to replace a certain Fourier expansion by a finite summation with remainder (even after a basic formula has been stated without proof). [The paper contains a number of inaccuracies of detail, and a more substantial error. This is in Lemma 2, where it is proved (correctly) that $\{f(x)-f(a)\}/(x-a)$ is of fixed sign (and greater in absolute value than a positive constant $\frac{1}{2}c$) for $a-\delta \leqq x \leqq a+\delta$, $x \neq a$, and inferred (incorrectly) that $f(x)$ is monotonic in $[a-\delta, a+\delta]$. This could be corrected (in the 'finite' context), but it would suffice to restate the lemma with the weaker conclusion, since this is all that is used in the sequel.] *A. E. Ingham* (Cambridge, England).

Referred to in E16-20.

E16-20 (16, 450f)

Fogel' [Fogelis], È. K. A finite proof of the Gauss-Dirichlet formula. Latvijas PSR Zinātņu Akad. Vēstis **1950**, no. 9 (38), 117–125 (1950). (Russian. Latvian summary)

This is an alternative version of the author's "finite" proof of the well known (finite) formulae for the class number $h(d)$ of binary quadratic forms of negative discriminant d [cf. Latvijas PSR Zinātnu Akad. Fiz. Inst. Raksti **3**,

49–63 (1952); MR 16, 222]. The logical status of this proof is easier to understand, since it involves none of the "semi-finite" analysis of the other version. There is no differentiation or integration; $\cos x$, $\sin x$, π are replaced by rational approximations based on the power series for cos and sin; and classical Fourier analysis is approached by way of finite Fourier analysis of periodic functions of an integral variable.
A. E. Ingham (Cambridge, England).

Citations: MR 16, 222g = E16-19.

E16-21 (16, 674a)

Sanielevici, S. Sur les formes x^2+Ay^2. Acad Repub. Pop. Române. Bul. Şti. Secţ. Şti. Mat. Fiz. **5**, 337–347 (1953). (Romanian. Russian and French summaries)

The author employs an argument due to Hermite to show that if a solution of the congruence $z^2\equiv -A \pmod n$ is known the continued fraction for n/z yields a solution (x, y) of the diophantine equation $x^2+Ay^2=kn$ for some $k<A$. A study is made of various A's, especially $A=7$, 11, 19, 67, 163 for which it is shown that $4p=x^2+Ay^2$ for every prime p that has $-A$ for a quadratic residue. *D. H. Lehmer.*

E16-22 (17, 350d)

Byers, G. Cleaves. Class number relations for quadratic forms over GF $[q, x]$. Duke Math. J. **21** (1954), 445–461.

The author develops the general theory of binary quadratic forms with coefficients in GF$(q)[x]$. One of the main results is the following. Let $h(\Delta)$ denote the number of classes of equivalent binary quadratic forms of discriminant Δ. Then for any given element ∇ in GF$(q)[x]$ of degree $2m+1$ the relation $\sum_R h(R-\nabla)=2\sum_K q^k$ holds, where $\sum_R$ extends over all $R\in \mathrm{GF}(q)[x]$ with $\deg R\leqq m$ and $\sum_K$ extends over all primary factors K of ∇ with $k=\deg K>m$. *Y. Kawada* (Tokyo).

Referred to in E16-33.

E16-23 (17, 827d)

Cellitti, Carlo. Sopra una proprietà delle forme quadratiche binarie primitive di determinante $D\equiv 1 \pmod 4$. Boll. Un. Mat. Ital. (3) **10** (1955), 527–530.

The author proves the following results (which are essentially a part of one of the standard proofs of the relation between the class-numbers of properly primitive and improperly primitive classical integral binary quadratic forms of the same discriminant, and which is proved in the usual way): (I) Every class of properly primitive forms $ax^2+2bxy+cy^2$ of discriminant $D=b^2-ac\equiv 1$ (4) contains a form for which $a\equiv 0$ (4), $b\equiv c\equiv 1$ (2). (II) If $a_ix^2+2b_ixy+c_iy^2$ $(1\leqq i\leqq h)$ are a set of representatives of this type, one from each class then $\frac{1}{2}a_ix^2+2b_ixy+2c_iy^2$ are a complete set of representatives of the classes with respect to the modular group $\begin{pmatrix}\alpha & \beta\\ \gamma & \delta\end{pmatrix}$, $\beta\equiv 0$ (2) of improperly primitive forms having the last coefficient $\equiv 2$ (4).
J. W. S. Cassels (Cambridge, England).

Referred to in E16-29, E16-35.

E16-24 (17, 1140c)

Porter, R. J. On irregular negative determinants of exponent $9n$. Math. Tables Aids Comput. **10** (1956), 22–25.

The determinant $D=b^2-ac$ of the quadratic form $ax^2+2bxy+cy^2$ is called irregular if the principal genus is non-cyclic. The number of classes divided by the highest period is called the exponent of D. The first 58 values of $-D$ with exponents $9n$ are listed, giving the complete table up to 150,000. Tables are given which reveal special properties and a method for squaring a class of forms is outlined. The discriminant -3299 seems to play an exceptional role in various respects. *O. Taussky-Todd.*

E16-25 (18, 193d)

Linnik, Yu. V. The asymptotic distribution of reduced binary quadratic forms in relation to the geometries of Lobačevskiĭ. I, II, III. Vestnik Leningrad. Univ. **10** (1955), no. 2, 3–23; no. 5, 3–32; no. 8, 15–27. (Russian)

Let Δ consist of those points (a, b, c) in three-dimensional Euclidean space such that $|2b|<a<c$ or $0\leqq 2b<a=c$ or $0<2b=a\leqq c$. Let Σ be a convex cone with center at the origin lying entirely either in that portion of Δ for which $c\leqq Ka$ or in that portion for which $c\geqq Ka$, where K is a given positive number >1. Let $\Lambda(\Delta)$ be the volume of that portion of Δ lying inside the hyperboloid $ac-b^2=1$ and similarly for $\Lambda(\Sigma)$. (Thus if we regard the positive sheet of the hyperboloid $ac-b^2=1$ as a realization of the Lobatchevskian plane in the usual way, $\Lambda(\Sigma)$ is a constant times the Lobatchevskian area of that portion of the hyperboloid which lies in Σ.) If D is an odd positive integer let $h(-D)$ be the number of lattice points (a, b, c) on the hyperboloid $ac-b^2=D$ such that a, $2b$, and c have g.c.d. 1 and (a, b, c) lies in Δ, and let $h_\Sigma(-D)$ denote the number of these lattice points which also lie in Σ. Thus, if to each triple (a, b, c) we make correspond the binary quadratic form $ax^2+2bxy+cy^2$, then $h(-D)$ is the number of reduced properly primitive binary quadratic forms of determinant $-D$. (Still another interpretation is in terms of 2 by 2 matrices L such that $L^2=-DI$, where I is the 2 by 2 identity matrix.) By the Heilbronn-Siegel Theorem $h(-D)$ tends to infinity with D. The author proves that if D goes to infinity through the odd integers such that $(-D|p)=1$ for some fixed odd prime number p, then

$$\lim_{D\to\infty} h_\Sigma(-D)/h(-D)=\Lambda(\Sigma)/\Lambda(\Delta).$$

This is an improvement of a result announced earlier [Dokl. Akad. Nauk SSSR (N.S.) **93** (1953), 973; MR **15**, 856] to the effect that if K is sufficiently large, then $\liminf_{D\to\infty} h_\Sigma(-D)/h(-D)>0$ (with the same set of values for D). The arguments employed are related to those used in proving a similar result concerning the asymptotic distribution of lattice points on spheres [ibid. **96** (1954), 909–912; MR **16**, 451 . A certain generalized quaternion algebra is an important tool. {The reviewer believes that in § 43 there is a minor error in a volume calculation which the author makes in applying the main theorem to a special situation.} *P. T. Bateman.*

Citations: MR 15, 856f = E16-16; MR 16, 451c = E24-54.

Referred to in E12-92, E16-27, E16-30, E16-31, E28-29, R52-21.

E16-26 (18, 194a)

Linnik, Yu. V. An new arithmetic application of the geometry of Lobačevskiĭ. Dopovidi Akad. Nauk Ukrain. RSR **1955**, 112–114. (Ukrainian. Russian summary)

A summary of the paper reviewed above.
P. T. Bateman (Princeton, N.J.).

E16-27 (18, 467b)

Linnik, Yu. V. The asymptotic geometry of the Gaussian genera; an analogue of the ergodic theorem. Dokl. Akad. Nauk SSSR (N.S.) **108** (1956), 1018–1021. (Russian)

In a previous paper [Vestnik Leningrad. Univ. **10** (1955), no. 2, 3–23, no. 5, 3–32, no. 8, 15–27; MR **18**, 193] the author obtained results on the distribution, as $D\to\infty$, of the integers (a, b, c) which correspond to reduced positive definite forms $ax^2+2bxy+cy^2$ of odd determinant $-D$, $D=ac-b^2$. The present paper indicates how the method can be developed to give similar results concerning the forms in a particular genus (in the sense of Gauss). As previously, the result is imperfect to the extent that it involves a prime p for which $(-D/p)=1$, and consequently the uniformity of distribution (in the sense of Lobatchevsky area) follows at once only if $D\to\infty$ through values for which p remains bounded. The main result is as follows. Represent each form by the point $x_1=aD^{-1/2}$, $x_2=cD^{-1/2}$, $x_3=bD^{-1/2}$, lying on that portion, say Δ_0, of the hyperbolic surface $x_1x_2-x_3^2=1$ which is cut off by the inequalities defining reduction. Let Σ_0 be a simply connected region contained in Δ_0 and having a piece-wise smooth boundary. Let R be any one of the genera, the numbers of which is $2^{\beta(D)}$. Let $H_R(\Sigma_0, D)$ denote the the number of reduced forms of determinant $-D$ in the genus R with representative points in Σ_0. Then

$$H_R(\Sigma_0, D)=\frac{9}{2\pi}A(\Sigma_0)2^{-\beta(D)}h(-D)(1+\eta(p, D)),$$

where $A(\Sigma_0)$ is the area of Σ_0 in the sense of Lobatchevsky, $h(-D)$ is the total number of reduced forms of determinant $-D$, and $\eta(p, D)\to 0$ as $D\to\infty$ for fixed p. The detailed proof is not given, but it is indicated that it depends on an "ergodic theorem" to the effect that, for almost all forms $\varphi(x, y)$, the forms $\varphi^\nu(x, y)$ obtained by applying a particular linear transformation ν times, are uniformly distributed for a long sequence of ν, all this to be interpreted asymptotically as $D\to\infty$. *H. Davenport.*

Citations: MR 18, 193d = E16-25.

E16-28 (18, 561g)

Mouette, L. Sur la théorie des formes quadratiques binaires. Mathesis **65** (1956), 364–371.

The author gives the usual definitions of equivalence of binary quadratic forms and, using the theory of composition, points out certain obvious consequences of representations of numbers by forms of given determinant d. If $h(d)$ denotes the class number and

$$\mu'(d) \text{ or } \mu''(d) = h(d)/\sqrt{|d|}$$

according as d is negative or positive, he gives a table of values of these functions for square-free values of d from 2 to 57, 1001 to 1055. He tabulates $\sum\mu'$ and $\sum\mu''$ over the first 100 values of d, the second 100, up to the fourteenth 100 and observes that the respective mean values seem to approach .754 and .997. (These results seem to be allied to Merten's asymptotic value of $\sum h(d)$.) He lists the determinants of positive forms having one and two classes in a genus; and the number having three and four classes presumably up to the limits of his table.

B. W. Jones (Boulder, Colo.).

E16-29 (18, 641h)

Cellitti, Carlo. Sopra una costruzione di sistemi di rappresentanti di classi di forme quadratiche binarie, primitive di prima e di seconda specie rispettivamente, di determinante $D=1$ (mod. 8). Atti Accad. Naz. Lincei. Rend. Cl. Sci. Fis. Mat. Nat. (8) **21** (1956), 57–60.

The author continues his partial rediscovery of one of the standard proofs of the relationship between the class numbers of properly and improperly primitive binary quadratic forms [Boll. Un. Mat. Ital. (3) **10** (1955), 527–530; MR **17**, 827] by showing that they are equal when the discriminant is congruent to 1 modulo 8. As before, the latest reference to the literature is to a paper of 1840.

J. W. S. Cassels (Cambridge, England).

Citations: MR 17, 827d = E16-23.

Referred to in E16-35.

E16-30 (18, 719b)

Linnik, Y. V. An application of the theory of matrices and of Lobatschevskian geometry to the theory of Dirichlet's real characters. J. Indian Math. Soc. (N.S.) **20** (1956), 37–45.

This paper contains a brief exposition of the author's recent work [Vestnik Leningrad Univ. **10** (1955), no. 2, 3–23, no. 5, 3–32, no. 8, 15–27; MR **18**, 193] on the distribution of the reduced forms $ax^2+2bxy+cy^2$ with integral a, b, c and $ac-b^2=D>0$, as $D\to\infty$. The connection between this work and the problem of the existence of zeros of real Dirichlet L-functions near $s=1$ is indicated, and some new results are mentioned.

H. Davenport (London).

Citations: MR 18, 193d = E16-25.

E16-31 (18, 874e)

Linnik, Yu. V. More on the analogues of the ergodic theorems for the imaginary quadratic field. Dokl. Akad. Nauk SSSR (N.S.) **109** (1956), 694–696. (Russian)

Let $\mathfrak{H}$ be the group of properly primitive positive definite binary quadratic forms $(a, b, c)=ax^2+2bxy+cy^2$ of odd determinant $D=ac-b^2$. Each such form corresponds to a 'fundamental point' $\mathfrak{a}=(a_0, b_0, c_0)$ $(a_0=a/\sqrt{D}$, etc.) on the hyperboloid $a_0c_0-b_0^2=1$ $(a_0>0)$, and the reduced forms correspond to points inside a triangular region Δ_0 whose Lobatchesvkian area $\mu(\Delta_0)$ is taken to be 1. Let p be an odd prime such that $(-D/p)=1$ and let $\mathfrak{p}=(a_0', b_0', c_0')$ denote the fundamental point corresponding to either of the forms $(p, \pm\xi, n)$ of $\mathfrak{H}$. By Gaussian composition we obtain a third fundamental point $\mathfrak{a}\mathfrak{p}=(a_0'', b_0'', c_0'')$, and so a transformation $\mathfrak{T}$ is defined which transforms the class of forms $\mathfrak{a}$ into the class $\mathfrak{a}\mathfrak{p}$; powers of this transformation can then be defined Let Ω be a simply-connected subset of Δ_0 bounded by piece-wise smooth arcs and of Lobatchevskian area $\mu(\Omega)$ and let $f_\Omega(P)=1$ if $P\in\Omega$ and $f_\Omega(P)=0$ if $P\notin\Omega$. The author states, without proof, the following theorem concerning the behaviour of the ergodic mean value of $f_\Omega(\mathfrak{a}\mathfrak{T}^l)$:

$$\frac{1}{s}\{f_\Omega(\mathfrak{a})+f_\Omega(\mathfrak{a}\mathfrak{T})+\cdots f_\Omega(\mathfrak{a}\mathfrak{T}^{s-1})\}=\mu(\Omega)\{1+o(1)\},$$

for $s>c_0\log D$, as $D\to\infty$, for all classes $\mathfrak{a}$ with the possible exception of $o\{h(-D)\}$ classes. Here $h(-D)$ is the order of $\mathfrak{H}$. In this result $\mathfrak{T}$ can be replaced by $\mathfrak{T}^r$ and the positive constant c_0 will then depend on r. Various consequences of this theorem are stated. In particular, if $\mathfrak{G}$ is a subgroup of $\mathfrak{H}$ of bounded index g and r is chosen so that $\mathfrak{p}^r\in\mathfrak{G}$, then the number of points in any coset of $\mathfrak{G}$ which are mapped into Ω by the transformation $\mathfrak{T}^r$ is

$$\frac{h(-D)}{g}\mu(\Omega)\{1+o(1)\}$$

as $D\to\infty$. If $\mathfrak{G}=\mathfrak{H}$ this yields an earlier result of the author's [Vestnik Leningrad. Univ. **10** (1955), no. 2, 3–23, no. 5, 3–32, no. 8, 15–27; MR **18**, 193].

R. A. Rankin (Glasgow).

Citations: MR 18, 193d = E16-25.

E16-32 (19, 16a)

Noguera Barreneche, Rodrigo. Quadratic forms in identities. Stvdia. Rev. Univ. Atlantico **2** (1957), nos. 11–12, 127–132. (Spanish)

Various new theorems of the following type: if p is a prime of the form $sk+t$, then all integral solutions of $cx^2+dy^2=p$ are found from identities of the form

$f(a, b)=cx^2+dy^2$, where f is a quadratic polynomial in a and b, with coefficients depending on the given constants s, t, c, d.

E16-33 (19, 253a)

Carlitz, L. Class number formulas for quadratic forms over GF$[q, x]$. Duke Math. J. **23** (1956), 225–235.

Let q be a power of an odd prime and let GF$[q, x]$ be the ring of polynomials in the indeterminate x with coefficients in the Galois field of order q. G. C. Byers has studied binary quadratic forms over such rings, deriving relations between class numbers [same J. **21** (1954), 445–461; MR **17**, 350]. The author proves these results and generalizations of them by his method of singular series (Gauss sums). He concludes with a formula for the class number of GF$(q)(x)(\Delta^{\frac{1}{2}})$, for $\Delta \in$ GF$[q, x]$ and Δ not a square in the completion of this ring under the valuation with $|x|>1$. *G. Whaples* (Bloomington, Ind.).

Citations: MR 17, 350d = E16-22.

E16-34 (20# 1669)

Cugiani, Marco. Approssimazioni quadratiche nei domini P-adici. Ann. Mat. Pura Appl. (4) **44** (1957), 1–22.

Necessary and sufficient conditions for representation by $x^2-\alpha y^2$, where α is a given p-adic integer and x, y take p-adic integer values. Only the p-adic completions of the rationals are discussed.

J. W. S. Cassels (Cambridge, England)

Referred to in E08-19, E16-40, E76-21.

E16-35 (20# 3822)

Cellitti, Carlo. Sopra una costruzione di sistemi di rappresentanti di classi relative a G_2 di forme quadratiche binarie primitive di seconda specie di determinante $D>0$ e $\equiv 5$ (mod. 8). Atti Accad. Naz. Lincei. Rend. Cl. Sci. Fis. Mat. Nat. (8) **23** (1957), 15–21.

The author continues his painstaking rediscovery of one of the less ancient ways of relating the number of properly and improperly quadratic forms of given determinant [cf. Boll. Un. Mat. Ital. (3) **10** (1955), 527–530; same Atti (8) **21** (1956), 57–60; MR **17**, 827; **18**, 641].

J. W. S. Cassels (Cambridge, England)

Citations: MR 17, 827d = E16-23; MR 18, 641h = E16-29.

E16-36 (20# 5164)

Djerasimović, Božidar. Über die binären quadratischen Formen. Math. Z. **66** (1957), 328–340.

This is an exposition of known results on the connection between binary quadratic forms and continued fractions, with slight simplifications resulting from the author's notation for ordered sets of numbers, introduced in two previous papers [same Z. **62** (1955), 320–329; **66** (1956), 228–239; MR **17**, 255; **18**, 635].

H. Davenport (Cambridge, England)

Citations: MR 17, 255d = A54-22; MR 18, 635e = A56-32.

Referred to in A56-47.

E16-37 (21# 4147)

Schmidt, Hermann. Über spezielle mehrgradige Gleichungen und Quadratsummendarstellungen in imaginär quadratischen Körpern. Math. Nachr. **19** (1958), 323–330.

Let $L\geqq 1$, $Q\geqq 1$ be rational squarefree integers. It is proved that $-L$ can be represented as the sum of two squares of numbers in the imaginary quadratic field $P(\sqrt{-Q})$, except when (1) there exists a prime $p\equiv 3 \pmod 4$ such that $p|L$, $p\nmid Q$, $\left(\frac{Q}{p}\right)=-1$, or (2) L has an even number of prime divisors $\equiv 3 \pmod 4$. Two proofs are given. One depends on an elementary reduction of the problem to the non-trivial solvability of a certain diophantine equation

$$a_1x_1^2+a_2x_2^2+a_3x_3^2+a_4x_4^2 = 0,$$

for which classical results are available [e.g. L. E. Dickson, *Studies in the theory of numbers*, Univ. of Chicago Press, 1930, theorem 61; T. Skolem, *Diophantische Gleichungen*, Springer, Berlin, 1938, Ch. 3, Theorem 3; B. W. Jones, *The arithmetic theory of quadratic forms*, Math. Assoc. Amer., Buffalo, N.Y., 1950; MR **12**, 244; Corollary 27c]. The second proof depends on p-adic methods [see K. Hensel, *Zahlentheorie*, Göschen, Berlin-Leipzig, 1913; H. Hasse, *Vorlesungen über Zahlentheorie*, Springer, Berlin-Göttingen-Heidelberg, 1949; MR **14**, 534; § 26; J. Reine Angew. Math. **153** (1924), 113–130; theorem 5]. The note concludes with some examples. [See also I. Niven, Trans. Amer. Math. Soc. **48** (1940), 405–417; MR **2**, 147; and O. Hemer, Ark. Mat. **2** (1952), 57–82; MR **14**, 247]. *H. Halberstam* (London)

Citations: MR 2, 147b = E24-4; MR 12, 244a = E02-3; MR 14, 247d = E20-33; MR 14, 534b = Z02-23.

E16-38 (21# 7185)

Stuchlik, Franz. Beiträge zur Zahlentheorie Hermitescher Formen. I. Wiss. Z. Hochsch. Schwermaschinenbau Magdeburg **2** (1958), 11–14.

The author studies binary hermitian forms:

$$h = h(x, x'; y, y') = axx'+(b'/2)xy'+(b/2)x'y+cyy',$$

in which a and c are integers of the rational field k, and b, b', and the variables x, x' and y, y' are conjugate pairs of integers of $k(i)$. He calls the rational integer $bb'-4ac=D$ the discriminant of h, and calls D a "stem-discriminant" [cf. Brandt, Ber. Verh. Sächs. Akad. Wiss. Leipzig, Math.-Nat. Kl. **99** (1951), no. 1; MR **13**, 537] if there does not exist a linear transformation $x_1=\alpha x+\beta y$, etc., with integral α and β in $k(i)$, which yields h when applied to a form of smaller discriminant in absolute value than D. The author proves that all rational integers $\not\equiv 3 \pmod 4$ are discriminants of forms like h, while stem-discriminants are square-free, not divisible by primes $\equiv 1 \pmod 4$, have $D_1\equiv 3 \pmod 4$ if $D=2D_1$, and are products of prime stem-discriminants. His other results deal with the equivalence of forms and the existence of representations of rational integers by forms of a prescribed stem-discriminant. In the latter case, he employs the Dirichlet theorem on primes in arithmetical progression. For each of his results, the author states the analog for quadratic forms $ax^2+bxy+cy^2$, a, b, c, x and y integral in k. *R. Hull* (Santa Monica, Calif.)

Citations: MR 13, 537b = A14-20.

E16-39 (22# 693)

Touchard, Jacques. Sur quelques séries de Lambert et de Dirichlet. Canad. J. Math. **12** (1960), 1–19.

Let D be a squarefree positive integer, let $\chi(n)=(D/n)$ be the Jacobi symbol, and let 2ω be its period as a function of n. The author considers the expression $g\{\exp(2\pi in/2\omega)\}$, which is well known in the theory of the class number of binary quadratic forms with a given discriminant, and which can be considered as a generalized Ramanujan sum. He obtains analogies of Ramanujan's formula

$$\sum c_q(n)q^{-s} = n^{1-s}(\zeta(s))^{-1} \sum_{d|n} d^{s-1}.$$

The paper connects this matter with a general (but rather trivial) formula for sums of the form

$$\sum a_k x^k y^k/(1-x^k)(1-y^k).$$

N. G. de Bruijn (Amsterdam)

E16-40 (22# 1543)

Cugiani, Marco. I domini P-adici e le forme binarie. Rend. Sem. Mat. Fis. Milano **29** (1959), 198–220. (English summary)

Expository paper, with special reference to the author's papers [Ist. Lombardo Accad. Sci. Lett. Rend. A **92** (1957/58), 307–320; Ann. Mat. Pura Appl. (4) **44** (1957), 1–22; Riv. Mat. Univ. Parma **8** (1957), 81–92; MR **21** #3380; **20** #1669, 7011].

J. W. S. Cassels (Cambridge, England)

Citations: MR 20# 1669 = E16-34; MR 20# 7011 = E76-21; MR 21# 3380 = E08-19.

E16-41 (22# 2576)

Babaev, G. Distribution of integral points on certain surfaces defined by norms. Dokl. Akad. Nauk SSSR **134** (1960), 13–15 (Russian); translated as Soviet Math. Dokl. **1**, 992–995.

Theorems are proved concerning the asymptotic behavior of the distribution of integral points on certain ellipses, hyperbolas, and surfaces of the third order as these curves or surfaces tend to infinity.

It is proved, for example, that if $d=1, 2, 3, 7, 11, 19, 43, 67, 163$, if $\delta=1$ for $-d\equiv 2, 3 \bmod 4$ and $\delta=4$ for $-d\equiv 1 \bmod 4$, if the Legendre symbol $\left(\frac{-d}{p_i}\right)=1$ for the prime factors p_i $(i=1, \cdots, s)$ of the odd integer m, if r is the number of integral points on the ellipse $x^2+dy^2=\delta m$, and if T is the number of integral points on this ellipse contained between rays from the origin inclined at angles a and b to the x-axis, then if $\Delta=\sqrt{(\ln (p_1\cdots p_s)/\ln r)}\to 0$ for $m\to\infty$, it follows that

$$T = (r/2\pi)\{\operatorname{arc}\tan(d^{1/2}\tan b)-\operatorname{arc}\tan(d^{1/2}\tan a)\}+O(r).$$

F. Goodspeed (Quebec)

E16-42 (22# 3719)

Lavrik, A. F. On the problem of distribution of the values of class numbers of properly primitive quadratic forms with negative determinant. Izv. Akad. Nauk UzSSR. Ser. Fiz.-Mat. **1959**, no. 1, 81–90. (Russian. Uzbek summary)

Let $h(-\Delta)$ be the class number of the binary quadratic properly primitive forms of determinant $-\Delta$ where Δ is a positive integer. Denote by $Q\{\cdots\}$ the number of positive integers $\Delta\leqq N$ which satisfy the conditions inside the curly brackets. The main result of the author is that

$$\lim_{N\to\infty}\frac{1}{N}Q\{\alpha(x)\sqrt{\Delta} < h(-\Delta) < \beta(x)\sqrt{\Delta}\} > \frac{5x^2-1}{5x^2},$$

where $x>0$ is a constant and where $\alpha(x)=2\pi/7\zeta(3)-2x/\pi$, $\beta(x)=2\pi/7\zeta(3)+2x/\pi$. Hence, for sufficiently large N, $Q\{0.04\sqrt{\Delta}<h(-\Delta)<1.45\sqrt{\Delta}\}>0.83N$ and $Q\{h(-\Delta)< 8\sqrt{\Delta}\}>0.998N$. The proof is based on the asymptotic formulae

$$\sum_{\Delta\leqq N}\{h(-\Delta)\}^2 = \frac{36}{29\pi^2}N^2\sum_{n=1}^{\infty}\frac{\varphi(n)\tau(n^2)}{n^3}+O(N^{1.75+\varepsilon}),$$

$$\sum_{\Delta\leqq N}\{h(-\Delta)\}^3 = \frac{16}{5\pi^3}N^{5/2}\sum_{n=1,\,n\text{ odd}}^{\infty}\frac{\varphi(n)\tau_3(n^2)}{n^3}+O(N^{2.4+\varepsilon}),$$

where $\varphi(n)$ and $\tau(n)$ have their usual meanings, and $\tau_i(n)$ denotes the number of times n can be written as a product of i integral factors $\geqq 1$.

K. Mahler (Manchester)

Referred to in R14-47.

E16-43 (22# 6772)

Piehler, Joachim. Über Primzahldarstellungen durch binäre quadratische Formen. Math. Ann. **141** (1960), 239–241.

The author proves by elementary methods the following theorems about binary quadratic forms with rational integral coefficients: (1) If two forms with the same discriminant both represent some prime number, then they are properly or improperly equivalent; (2) If p_1 and p_2 are two positive prime integers, then a necessary and sufficient condition for the existence of a positive definite form of discriminant D which represents both of them is that $D=(k^2-4p_1p_2)/h^2$ for some integers $k=0, 1, \cdots, (2p_1p_2)^{1/2}$ and h. Thus there are only finitely many positive definite forms representing both p_1 and p_2.

G. Whaples (Bloomington, Ind.)

E16-44 (22# 7966)

Ferrier, A. Nombres idoines. Mathesis **69** (1960), 34–36.

A positive integer N is called idoneal if every odd number P which is representable uniquely in the form $P=a^2+Nb^2$ is necessarily a prime. These numbers were studied by Euler, who discovered a necessary and sufficient condition that a number be idoneal. He also found all idoneal numbers less than 10,000; there are 65 of them. This search was carried to 100,000 by Cullen and Cunningham who found no others. The present paper reports on a similar search up to 200,000. No additional idoneal numbers were found and it is natural to conjecture that there are no others. The author uses Euler's criterion and is able to eliminate many values of N by a systematic consideration of the last digit of N. He reports that it took him about 15 hours to complete the search.

H. W. Brinkmann (Swarthmore, Pa.)

E16-45 (23# A115)

Christilles, William Edward

An elementary analysis of an integral quadratic form.

Amer. Math. Monthly **68** (1961), 138–143.

The author associates with the quadratic form $x^2+hxy+ky^2$ with integral coefficients the matrix $(xI+yA)$, where A is the two-by-two matrix with trace h and determinant k. If A has no rational characteristic root, the set S of matrices $xI+yA$ for integer values of x and y forms an integral domain. The author finds a necessary condition that S have unique factorability, and a few auxiliary results are proved.

B. W. Jones (Boulder, Colo.)

E16-46 (23# A1606)

Mrowka, Erwin

Ambige Klassen und Kompositionen binärer quadratischer Formen.

Wiss. Z. Hochsch. Verkehrswes. Dresden **5** (1957), *no.* 2, 293–300.

The author calls a positive definite binary quadratic form $\varphi=ax^2+bxy+cy^2\equiv(a, b, c)$, and the class Φ to which it belongs, ambiguous if Φ is of order 2 with respect to Gauss' composition [Gauss, *Disquitiones arithmeticae*, J. Springer, Berlin, 1889; Articles 235–240]. The coefficients a, b, c are rational integers, $a>0$, and the discriminant $D=b^2-4ac$ is a negative integer $\equiv 0$ or $1 \pmod 4$. The first parts of the paper include enough about proper and improper equivalence, reduced forms, properties of ambiguous forms and Brandt's generalization of Gauss' composition theory [H.

Brandt, "Komposition der binaren quadratischen Formen relativ einer Grundform", Habilitationsschrift, Karlsruhe, 1917] to make it self-contained. Then the author easily obtains the following result for $D \equiv 1 \pmod 4$, and a corresponding result for $D \equiv 0 \pmod 4$. Every ambiguous class of discriminant $D \equiv 1 \pmod 4$ has one and only one representative in the set of forms $(P_1, P_1, (P_1+P_2)/4)$, where P_1 is a positive divisor of $-D$, $P_1>1$, $P_1P_2 = -D$, $P_1<P_2$. *R. Hull* (Santa Monica, Calif.)

E16-47 (23# A3118)

Mel'nikov, I. G.
La découverte des "nombres commodes" par L. Euler. (Russian)
Istor.-Mat. Issled. **13** (1960), 187–216.

A number $\alpha\beta$ is "suitable" ("idoneus" in the original Latin of Euler) if every positive integer representable in exactly one way by the binary form $\alpha\beta x^2+y^2$, with $(\alpha\beta x, y)=1$, is "prime", where Euler uses the word "prime" in his conventional sense of p, $2p$, p^2 or a power of 2, with p prime. Euler found 35 suitable numbers under 10,000 (the greatest being 1848) and conjectured that there are no others. The present essay reviews the previous history of criteria for primality which are related to Fermat's theorem for the binary form x^2+y^2, and discusses Euler's various theorems regarding suitable numbers. *S. H. Gould* (Providence, R.I.)

E16-48 (24# A90)

Lubelski, S.
Unpublished results on number theory. II. Composition theory of binary quadratic forms.
Edited by C. Schogt.
Acta Arith. **7** (1961/62), 9–17.

[For Part I see same Acta **6** (1960/61), 217–224; MR **22** #10953.]

From the introduction: "This second note gives an elementary exposition of the composition of binary quadratic forms. It is shown that the classical theory carries over to the case that the coefficients are taken from a (commutative) Euclidean ring." *J. W. S. Cassels* (Cambridge, England)

Citations: MR 22# 10953 = E12-71.

E16-49 (24# A2562)

Mordell, L. J.
On recurrence formulae for the number of classes of definite binary quadratic forms.
J. Indian Math. Soc. (*N.S.*) **24** (1960), 367–378 (1961).

The author denotes by $F(m)$, with m a non-negative integer, the number of classes of forms $AX^2+2BXY+CY^2$ with at least one of A and C odd and of determinant $-m=B^2-AC$, with the conventions that $F(0)=0$ and the class $(A, 0, A)$ is reckoned as $1/2$. Also $G(m)$ denotes the total number of classes of determinant $-m$ with the conventions that $G(0)=-1/12$ and that the class $(2A, A, 2A)$ is reckoned as $1/3$. Furthermore, d denotes a divisor of m and $d'=m/d$.

There are various class relation formulae, one of which is

$$\Sigma_{r^2\leq m}(-1)^r F(m-r^2) = \sum' d(-1)^{(1/2)(d+d')+1},$$

where the "dash" (i.e., prime) on the summation denotes that the weight $1/2$ applies to the term when $d=d'$, and the summation is over all $d\leqq d'$ such that d and d' are of the same parity.

Using theta functions the author derives various formulae including the following:

$$(27)\quad 8\sum_{r^2\leqq m} r^2G(m-r^2) = -2\sum'(-1)^{d+d'}d(d+d')^2 - \frac{4m}{3}[2+4(-1)^m]\sum d - 2\sum' d^3 + 2m\sum' d,$$

where the first and third summations on the right are over $d\leqq\sqrt{m}$, the second over odd d and the fourth over $d\geqq\sqrt{m}$.

$$(28)\quad 8\sum_{r^2\leqq m} r^2F(m-r^2) = -\sum'(-1)^{d+d'}d(d+d')^2 - 2m(-1)^m\sum d - \sum' d^3 + m\sum' d,$$

where the second summation on the right is over odd d and the other three over $d\leqq\sqrt{m}$.

The author remarks that since they are not easily deduced from the theta function expansions used for most of the other formulas, other expansions might be found from which these would come more directly. *Burton W. Jones* (Boulder, Colo.)

E16-50 (25# 53)

Zeckendorf, E.
Les diviseurs de $x^2 \pm N\cdot y^2$.
Bull. Soc. Roy. Sci. Liège **30** (1961), 480–488.

L'auteur donne une méthode pour déterminer les diviseurs de la forme quadratique binaire $x^2 \pm Ny^2$, $(x, y)=1$, N étant premier ou composé. Soit N un nombre premier, on groupe les nombres impairs a_k premiers à $4N$ et inférieurs à $4N$ en quadruplets a_k, $2N-a_k$, $2N+a_k$, $4N-a_k$, les nombres $4rN+a_k$ constituant une classe. On attribue à chacun des nombres un caractère grâce à la définition suivante: On appelle classe quadratique une classe de forme $(4s+1)$ comportant des carrés; c'est une classe de résidus à laquelle on donne le symbole $(+q)$, et l'on attribue le symbole $(-q)$ à la classe complémentaire $(4s+3)$; le symbole des classes $(4s+1)$ non-quadratiques sera $(+n)$, et celui des classes complémentaires $(4s+3)$ sera $(-n)$.

Au sujet de la forme x^2-Ny^2, pour $N\equiv 1 \pmod 4$, on trouve pour les divers quadruplets 4 groupes distincts de symboles renfermant les uns 2 fois $(+q)$ et 2 fois $(-q)$, et les autres 2 fois $(+n)$ et 2 fois $(-n)$, la position du premier caractère conditionnant celle des 3 autres. Pour $N\equiv 3 \pmod 4$, il y a encore 4 groupes distincts de symboles renfermant ici chacun les 4 caractères, la position du premier conditionnant encore celle des 3 autres. Les nombres correspondant à $(+q)$ et à $(-q)$ sont les diviseurs de x^2-Ny^2.

Quant à la forme x^2+Ny^2, pour $N\equiv 1 \pmod 4$, on trouve une caractérisation identique des quadruplets que pour x^2-Ny^2, de même pour $N\equiv 3 \pmod 4$. Mais ici, tant pour $N\equiv 1 \pmod 4$ que pour $N\equiv 3 \pmod 4$, les diviseurs de x^2+Ny^2 correspondent à $(+q)$ et à $(-n)$.

La démonstration des résultats précédents se base sur l'utilisation du symbole de Legendre.

L'auteur donne encore les facteurs 2 des deux formes envisagées. Ses résultats correspondant au facteur 2 de x^2-Ny^2 figurent, par exemple, dans P. Bachmann, Encyklopädie der mathematischen Wissenschaften, Bd. I, Teil II, Heft 5, pp. 556–581, p. 565, Teubner, Leipzig, 1900–04. *A. Gloden* (Luxembourg)

E16-51 (24# A2552)

Zeckendorf, E.
Les diviseurs de $x^2 \pm N\cdot y^2$. (Suite)
Bull. Soc. Roy. Sci. Liège **31** (1962), 51–61.

Pour I, voir le même Bull. **30** (1961), 480–488. L'auteur expose ici sa méthode pour déterminer les diviseurs premiers de la forme $x^2 \pm Ny^2$, N étant composé. La recherche des diviseurs peut être limitée au cas où N ne comporte que des facteurs premiers distincts. Soit N' un nombre "quadratfrei" composé de ν facteurs premiers distincts. Les classes se définissent comme pour N premier (l'auteur les appelle catégories). Pour ν facteurs premiers distincts, les classes s'associent en groupements de $2^{\nu+1}$ classes. Dans ce qui suit, N' sera toujours supposé "quadratfrei".

Si N' est composé exclusivement de facteurs premiers $(4s+1)$ et si l'on définit comme groupements $(\pm Q)$ ceux dont les nombres premiers sont non-résidus pour un nombre pair de facteurs p_k de N' et comme groupements $(\pm N)$ ceux dont les nombres premiers sont non-résidus pour un nombre impair de ces facteurs, on a, comme pour les N premiers, des groupements homogènes, soit de caractère $(\pm Q)$, soit de caractère $(\pm N)$. Les classes communes à un groupement comportent des nombres premiers diviseurs tous ensemble, ou bien non-diviseurs tous ensemble de $x^2-N'y^2$. Diviseurs de $x^2-N'y^2$, seuls les nombres premiers $(4s+1)$ divisent aussi $x^2+N'y^2$. Non-diviseurs de $x^2-N'y^2$, seuls les nombres premiers $(4s+1)$ ne divisent pas non plus $x^2+N'y^2$.

Si N' est composé exclusivement de facteurs premiers $(4s+3)$ et éventuellement d'un facteur 2, les classes de chaque groupement se répartissent également entre les 4 espèces $(+Q)$, $(+N)$, $(-Q)$ et $(-N)$. Après la désignation des classes $(+Q)$ congrues à 1 (mod 4) et quadratiques, celle des classes complémentaires $(-Q)$, des classes $(+N)$ congrues à 1 mais non-quadratiques et des classes $(-N)$ est fixée.

Si N' est composé de facteurs premiers $(4s+1)$ et $(4s+3)$, on construit, pour chacun des facteurs distincts, le tableau des classes; pour les facteurs $(4s+3)$, on distingue les nombres $(\pm q)$ des nombres $(\pm n)$. On construit ensuite le tableau par groupements pour N'. En se basant sur les tableaux particuliers aux facteurs $(4s+3)$, on établit, pour 2 et pour ces seuls facteurs, la qualité de nombres $(\pm Q)$ ou $(\pm N)$ des diverses classes: Toute classe $(\pm n)$ pour un nombre pair des tableaux particuliers envisagés est présumée $(\pm Q)$; est présumée $(\pm N)$ toute classe $(\pm n)$ pour un nombre impair de ces tableaux. Pour un seul nombre premier c de chaque groupement, on calcule la valeur du symbole $\left(\frac{N'}{c}\right)$. Si la valeur correspond au renseignement présumé, il y a confirmation des résultats obtenus. Si au contaire il y a contradiction, on doit permuter les diviseurs et les non-diviseurs du groupement dans la liste provisoire. *A. Gloden* (Luxembourg)

E16-52 (26# 1301)

Christofferson, Stig

On representation of integers by binary quadratic forms in algebraic number fields.

Inaugural dissertation, University of Uppsala.

Almqvist & Wiksells Boktryckeri AB, Uppsala, 1962. 43 *pp.*

The author extends and generalizes work of Nagell [Nova Acta Soc. Sci. Upsal. (4) **15** (1953), no. 11; MR **17**, 241; Ark. Mat. **4** (1961), 267–286; MR **24** #A713; ibid. **4** (1962), 467–478]. Among his results are the following. (I) Let $f(x, y)=\alpha x^2+\beta xy+\gamma y^2$ have coefficients in the algebraic number field Ω with $\delta=4\alpha\gamma-\beta^2\neq 0$. If $\omega=f(x, y)$ for some x, y in Ω, then ω has infinitely many such representations except when (i) $\Omega(\sqrt{-\delta})$ is the rational or the Gaussian field, or (ii) Ω is totally real and δ is totally positive. In these special cases no ω has an infinity of representations. (II) Let Ω be the Gaussian field and let $D=2, 3, 7, 11, 19, 43, 67, 163$, so that $\Omega(\sqrt{D})$ and $\Omega(\sqrt{-D})$ have class number 1. Necessary and sufficient conditions for ω to be represented by x^2+Dy^2 in Ω are given. A correction is given to Theorem 14 of the first reference given above [loc. cit.]. *D. J. Lewis* (Ann Arbor, Mich.)

Citations: MR 17, 241a = E24-61; MR 24# A713 = E24-87.

E16-53 (26# 4974)

Babaev, G.

Asymptotic-geometric properties of the set of integers on certain hyperbolas. (Russian)

Izv. Vysš. Učebn. Zaved. Matematika **1963**, *no.* 1 (32), 3–7.

Consider the integral points (x, y) on the right branch of the hyperbola $H_m: X^2-dY^2=m>0$, where $d>1$ is a square-free integer not congruent to 1 (mod 4). Let ε be the generator of the subgroup of units of norm $+1$ in the real quadratic field $Q(\sqrt{d})$ which satisfies $\varepsilon>1$. Then all the points (x', y') such that $x'+y'\sqrt{d}=\varepsilon^n(x+y\sqrt{d})$ also lie on the right branch of H_m. For a suitable unique n, the point (x', y') will be one of the $r(m)$ points on the intersection of H_m and the wedge: $0\leqq y'\leqq \phi\cdot x'$, where $\phi=(\varepsilon^2-1)/(\sqrt{d}(\varepsilon^2+1))$. The author finds an asymptotic formula for the number $T(m, a, b)$ of integral points on the intersection of H_m with the sub-wedge: $ax\leqq y\leqq bx$ (where $0<a<b<\phi$), as $m\to\infty$ in a suitable fashion.

Of course, the numbers $r(m)$ and $T(m, a, b)$ are closely connected with the factorization of m in $Q(\sqrt{d})$. So the author assumes (1) that the class number of $Q(\sqrt{d})$ is one, (2) that each of the distinct rational primes $p_1, \cdots, p_s$ dividing m is odd and splits in $Q(\sqrt{d})$ and, (3) that $m\to\infty$ in such a way that

$$\Delta = \log(\varepsilon^{3s}p_1\cdots p_s)/\log[r(m)(\varepsilon\log\varepsilon)^{-s}]\to 0.$$

Under these assumptions, he concludes that

$$\frac{T(m, a, b)}{r(m)} = \frac{1}{2\log\varepsilon}\cdot\log\left[\frac{1-a\sqrt{d}}{1+a\sqrt{d}}\cdot\frac{1+b\sqrt{d}}{1-b\sqrt{d}}\right]+O(\Delta^{1/2}).$$

An almost identical formula holds in the case $d\equiv 1$ (mod 4).

{Misprint: On page 4, the point B should be the intersection of the lines $w+v=\log m$ and $w=v-2\log\varepsilon$.}

E. C. Dade (Pasadena, Calif.)

E16-54 (27# 2478)

Yamamoto, Koichi

Decomposition fields of difference sets.

Pacific J. Math. **13** (1963), 337–352.

Among other things, the author proves three theorems on the solvability of the Diophantine equation $x^2+Dy^2=4n$ for certain D. *B. Stolt* (Stockholm)

Referred to in T15-59.

E16-55 (27# 2487)

Vinogradov, I. M.

On the number of integer points in a three-dimensional domain. (Russian)

Izv. Akad. Nauk SSSR Ser. Mat. **27** (1963), 3–8.

The author shows that $h(-t)$, the number of primitive quadratic forms of discriminant $-t\,(<0)$, satisfies the asymptotic formula $h(-1)+\cdots+h(-n)=4\pi n^{3/2}/21\zeta(3)-2n/\pi+O(n^{t+\varepsilon})$. The author had shown the error term can have $t=5/6$ [Izv. Rossiĭsk. Akad. Nauk (6) **11** (1917), 1347–1378], then $t=7/10-1/405$ [Izv. Akad. Nauk SSSR Ser. Mat. **13** (1949), 97–110; MR **11**, 233], then $t=11/16$ [ibid. **19** (1955), 3–10; MR **16**, 908], then $t=19/28$ [ibid. **24** (1960), 777–786; MR **23** #A860], and now $t=2/3$. The techniques continue to involve estimates of exponential sums of type $\sum \varphi(x) \exp 2\pi i f(x)$. *H. Cohn* (Tucson, Ariz.)

Citations: MR 11, 233d = E16-12; MR 16, 908b = P20-12; MR 23# A860 = P20-19.
Referred to in P20-27, R14-57.

E16-56 (28# 64)

Grosswald, E.
Negative discriminants of binary quadratic forms with one class in each genus.
Acta Arith. **8** (1962/63), 295–306.

The main result of this paper runs as follows. If $-k$ is a negative discriminant with one class in each genus, then either $-k$ is one of the classically known 101 discriminants [cf. L. E. Dickson, *Introduction to the theory of numbers*, 3rd ed., Univ. Chicago Press, Chicago, Ill., 1934], or $10^{9.12919} < k < 4.10^{10}$, provided the following conjecture is true: If $-k$ is a fundamental discriminant and $k > 10^{10}$, then $L(s, \chi) \neq 0$ for $s_0 < s < 1$, where $\chi(m) = (-k/m)$ and $s_0 = \mathrm{Max}\{1 - 2\log^{-1} k, 53/54\}$.

This result is an improvement of a theorem of Chowla and Briggs [Canad. J. Math. **6** (1954), 463–470; MR **16**, 222]. The proof follows the same lines, except that an ingenious descent is used for the treatment of relatively small k's. Besides, it is shown that the non-fundamental discriminants $-d < -960$ with one class per genus are exactly those of the form $d = 4k$, where $k \equiv 0 \pmod 8$ and $-k$ is a fundamental discriminant with one class per genus. {By an oversight, the condition $-d < -960$ is omitted from the enunciation of the theorem. Also, the auxiliary Theorem B (p. 298) is misquoted: the inequality $k > 315$ should be replaced there by $k > 960$.}
A. Schinzel (Warsaw)

Citations: MR 16, 222e = E16-18.

E16-57 (28# 1174)

Lippmann, R. A.
Note on irregular discriminants.
J. London Math. Soc. **38** (1963), 385–386.

Let $G(d)$ be the group of classes of binary quadratic forms of discriminant d in the principal genus. Let $e(d)$ be the order of $G(d)$ divided by the maximum of the orders of its elements. If $e(d) > 1$, d is called "irregular" following Gauss, who found numerous examples where $e(d) = 2$ or 3. Using an IBM 650, the author has calculated $e(d)$ for selected negative prime discriminants d and found that $e(-12451) = 5$, and $e(-63499) = 7$. Direct proofs not involving machine computation are also given.
B. Gordon (Los Angeles, Calif.)

E16-58 (28# 2093)

Hasse, Helmut; Hornfeck, Bernhard
Über den Wertevorrat quadratischer Formen.
Abh. Math. Sem. Univ. Hamburg **26** (1963/64), 230–233.

If a, b are fixed nonzero rational numbers, let $[a, b]$ denote the set of numbers u which can be expressed as $u = ax^2 + by^2$, with x and y rational. The authors prove the following theorem: $[a_1, b_1] \subset [a_2, b_2] \cup [a_3, b_3]$ if and only if $[a_1, b_1] \subset [a_2\ b_2]$ or $[a_1, b_1] \subset [a_3, b_3]$. This generalizes a result attributed to R. Lingenberg. A number of corollaries are derived. The proofs are elementary and make use of the Jacobi symbol. *D. J. Lewis* (Ann Arbor, Mich.)

E16-59 (28# 5032)

Rotkiewicz, André; Schinzel, André
Sur les nombres pseudopremiers de la forme $ax^2 + bxy + cy^2$.
C. R. Acad. Sci. Paris **258** (1964), 3617–3620.

The positive integer n is pseudoprime if n is composite and if n divides $2^n - 2$. One of the authors has shown that suitable arithmetic progressions contain infinitely many pseudoprimes [Rotkiewicz, same C. R. **257** (1963), 2601–2604]. Now it is shown that, in further imitation of the behavior of the primes, there are infinitely many pseudoprimes represented by a quadratic form $ax^2 + bxy + cy^2$ (with natural restrictions on a, b, and c). The authors employ a theorem of Zsigmondy on primitive prime factors of $a^n - b^n$ [Monatsh. Math. **3** (1892), 265–284] and a representation of cyclotomic polynomials given by Schinzel [Proc. Cambridge Philos. Soc. **58** (1962), 555–562; MR **26** #1280].

{Formula (7) should read: $p = ax^2 + bxy + cy^2 \equiv f \pmod{em}$.} *J. B. Kelly* (Tempe, Ariz.)

Citations: MR 26# 1280 = B40-36.

E16-60 (29# 72)

Mordell, L. J.
On Lerch's class number formulae for binary quadratic forms.
Ark. Mat. **5**, 97–100 (1964).

In this paper, the author gives new proofs of the following two theorems of Lerch. Theorem 1: Let $D > 0$ and $-\Delta < 0$ be two fundamental discriminants with $(D, \Delta) = 1$. Then

$$h(-\Delta D) = 2 \sum_{a=1}^{\Delta/2} \left(\frac{-\Delta}{a}\right) \sum_{n=1}^{aD/\Delta} \left(\frac{D}{n}\right),$$

$$-h(-\Delta D) = 2 \sum_{a=1}^{D/2} \left(\frac{D}{a}\right) \sum_{n=1}^{a\Delta/D} \left(\frac{-\Delta}{n}\right).$$

Theorem 2: Let $D_1, \cdots, D_r$ denote fundamental discriminants relatively prime in pairs with absolute values $\Delta_1, \cdots, \Delta_r$ and with $2s+1$ of the D negative. Then

$$h(D_1, \cdots, D_r) = (-1)^s \sum \left(\frac{D_1}{n_1}\right) \cdots \left(\frac{D_r}{n_r}\right) \left[\frac{n_1}{\Delta_1} + \cdots + \frac{n_r}{\Delta_r}\right],$$

where the square bracket denotes the integer part and the summation is taken over $0 < n_1 < \Delta_1, \cdots, 0 < n_r < \Delta_r$. The author's proof is very simple and elementary, being deduced from the well-known formula

$$h(-\Delta) = -\frac{1}{\Delta} \sum_{n=1}^{\Delta} \left(\frac{-\Delta}{n}\right) n,$$

where $-\Delta$ is a fundamental discriminant. He first gives a proof of Theorem 2; then Theorem 1 is deduced from Theorem 2 by using a simple transformation. One might object to his use of notation (for example, he writes $\prod (D_1/n_1)$ for $(D_1/n_1) \cdots (D_r/n_r)$); however, this hardly causes any confusion. *T. Tamagawa* (New Haven, Conn.)

E16-61 (29# 3437)

Christilles, William Edward
A result concerning integral binary quadratic forms.
Pacific J. Math. **14** (1964), 795–796.

Let M be properly represented by the integral positive definite form $ax^2 + bxy + cy^2$ of discriminant $-D = b^2 - 4ac$. It is well known that any factor of M is properly represented by some form of discriminant $-D$. Let $a_i x^2 + b_i xy + c_i y^2$ $(i = 1, \cdots, k)$ be the reduced primitive forms of discriminant $-D$. The author shows, by a simple elementary argument, that if $(M, D) = 1$ and $M \leqq 3D/16$, then, in any factorization $M_1 M_2$ of M, one of the factors is an a_i for some i.

{Reviewer's remark: The bound $3D/16$ may easily be improved to $D/4$, and the result is then best possible.}
E. S. Barnes (Adelaide)

E16-62 **(30# 1100)**

Meyer, C.

Über die Bildung von Klasseninvarianten binärer quadratischer Formen mittels Dedekindscher Summen.

Abh. Math. Sem. Univ. Hamburg **27** (1964), 206–230.

Denote by Z, Q the ring of rational integers and the rational number field, respectively. For two $a, c \neq 0$ in Z, we take the Dedekind sum to be

$$s(a, c) = \sum_{\mu \bmod c}' P_1\left(\frac{\mu a}{c}\right) P_1\left(\frac{\mu}{c}\right), \qquad (a, c) = 1,$$

where $P_1(x) = x - [x]$. Rademacher introduced the function Ψ on $SL(2, Z)$ such that

$$(1) \quad \Psi\begin{pmatrix} a & b \\ c & d \end{pmatrix} = \frac{a+d}{c} - 12 \operatorname{sgn} c \cdot s(a, c) - 3 \operatorname{sgn}(c(a+d)) \quad \text{if } c \neq 0,$$

$$= \frac{b}{d} \quad \text{if } c = 0 \text{ and } a = d = \pm 1.$$

He proved the formulas (i) $\Psi(L^{-1}ML) = \Psi(M)$ ($L, M \in SL(2, Z)$), (ii) $\Psi(M) = \Psi(-M)$, (iii) $\Psi(M^{-1}) = -\Psi(M)$, (iv) $\Psi(M^k) = k\Psi(M)$ if M is not an elliptic substitution ($k \in Z$) [Math. Z. **63** (1956), 445–463; MR **18**, 114]. Using these formulas, the author defines the class invariant of quadratic forms $Q(x, y)$ with coefficients in Z and given discriminant $\Delta = df^2$ (d denotes the discriminant of the quadratic field $Q(\sqrt{\Delta})$) such that

$$(2) \qquad \Psi_\varepsilon(Q) = \Psi(M_\varepsilon),$$

where M_ε denotes the orthogonal matrix of Q corresponding to a fixed ring unit $\varepsilon \bmod f$ in $Q(\sqrt{d})$. It is shown that when Δ and ε are given, (2) defines a class invariant of the quadratic forms, but not the converse, i.e., (2) does not always separate each class. And the author calculates the class invariant explicitly for positive definite forms and several indefinite forms. Examples are also given of classes not separated by (2). *S. Konno* (Osaka)

Citations: MR 18, 114d = F20-16.

E16-63 **(31# 2211)**

Pignataro, Salvatore

Sulla rappresentazione dei numeri dispari mediante forme canoniche binarie.

Ricerca (*Napoli*) (2) **9** (1958), *gennaio-giugno*, 11–31.

The author develops, without reference to the classical Gauss-Dirichlet theory of sets of representations of an integer by a binary quadratic form (under the group of unimodular automorphs of the form), linear relations between solutions of $ax^2 - by^2 = m$ or $-m$, which amount essentially to the composition of a given solution with solutions of $x^2 - aby^2 = \pm 1$. The "least" solutions for m and $-m$ are specifically connected, and occurrence in a set of certain parity properties is noted.

Gordon Pall (Baton Rouge, La.)

E16-64 **(33# 5566)**

Barban, M. B.; Gordover, G.

On moments of the number of classes of purely radical quadratic forms with negative determinant. (Russian)

Dokl. Akad. Nauk SSSR **167** (1966), 267–269.

The paper brings out an asymptotic formula for $\sum_{D \leq N} h^n(-D)$, where $h(-m)$ stands for the class-number of purely radical (i.e., Gaussian) quadratic forms with negative discriminant $-m$, and $n \geq 2$ is an integer. The result improves on a previous formula due to the first author [see Izv. Akad. Nauk SSSR Ser. Mat. **26** (1962), 573–580; MR **27** #1426]. The present (sketchy) proof rests upon an inequality, involving values of characters, due to A. I. Vinogradov [ibid. **29** (1965), 485–492; MR **31** #3395] and partly to Ju. V. Linnik [ibid. **24** (1960), 629–706; MR **23** #A130].

{This article has appeared in English translation [Soviet Math. Dokl. **7** (1966), 356–358].}

S. Knapowski (Coral Gables, Fla.)

Citations: MR 23# A130 = P36-26; MR 27# 1426 = R14-47; MR 31# 3395 = R42-32.

E16-65 **(33# 5569)**

Mordell, L. J.

Solvability of the equation $ax^2 + by^2 = p$.

J. London Math. Soc. **41** (1966), 517–522.

Let a, b and p denote rational integers, p a prime such that $(p, ab) = 1$. The author proves that there exists an integer solution x, y of $ax^2 + by^2 = Mp$ for some values of M satisfying $M < 2(ab)^{1/2}$ if $a > 0$, $b > 0$ and $M < |ab|^{1/2}$ if $ab < 0$. To find out if $M = 1$ is possible, he then shows how many of the values of M can be eliminated by congruence considerations. He states results for $a = 1$, $|b| < 20$, giving details for $b = 11$ and $b = -19$. The method of attack goes back to A. Thue. The same problem is dealt with in a similar way by T. Nagell [*Introduction to number theory*, Wiley, New York, 1951; MR **13**, 207].

W. Ljunggren (Oslo)

Citations: MR 13, 207b = Z01-13.

E16-66 **(33# 5570)**

Steinig, J.

On Euler's idoneal numbers.

Elem. Math. **21** (1966), 73–88.

Girard, Fermat, Frenicle und andere, vor allem aber Euler bemühten sich um Kriterien, wann aus der eindeutigen Darstellbarkeit von n in der Gestalt $n = ax^2 + by^2$ geschlossen werden kann, daß n eine Primzahl ist (so ist etwa ein ungerades $n > 1$, das auf genau eine Art als Summe zweier Quadrate dargestellt werden kann, eine Primzahl, wenn diese Quadrate teilerfremd sind).

Der Autor gibt einen ausführlichen, kritischen Überblick über diese Untersuchungen (aus der Zeit vor Gauß), insbesondere über Eulers "numeri idonei", formuliert die Ergebnisse korrekt und weist auf viele Stellen in der Literatur hin, wo diesbezügliche Ergebnisse fehlerhaft zitiert sind [so auch in L. E. Dickson's *History of the theory of numbers*, Vol. I, Seite 89, Stechert, New York, 1934].

W. Schwarz (Freiburg)

E16-67 **(34# 144)**

Knight, James T.

Binary integral quadratic forms over $R(t)$.

Proc. Cambridge Philos. Soc. **62** (1966), 433–440.

Two lattices K and L on a quadratic space over $R(t)$, the field of rational functions with real coefficients, and its Dedekind set are said to be in the same genus if, for all $\mathfrak{p} \in C$, the lattices $K_\mathfrak{p}$ and $L_\mathfrak{p}$ are in the same class. The author proves that the number of classes of lattices in a given genus over a binary space is either 1 or $2^{\aleph_0}$. Which it is depends largely on whether the degree of the determinant of the binary form is not greater than 2, or greater than 2.

Burton W. Jones (Boulder, Colo.)

E16-68 **(37# 173)**

Kusaba, Toshio

Remarque sur la distribution des nombres premiers.

C. R. Acad. Sci. Paris Sér. A-B **265** (1967), A405–A407.

Let $f(x, y) = ax^2 + bxy + cy^2$ be an integral quadratic form whose discriminant d is fundamental. Such a form is said to be of the first kind if the primes represented by f are precisely those in a set of arithmetic progressions. Let h

be the class number of $\mathbf{Q}(\sqrt{d})$, and t the number of different primes dividing d. The author proves that f is of the first kind if and only if (a) $h=2^{t-1}$ or (b) $h=2^t$ and $f(x, y)$ is inequivalent to $f(x, -y)$. The theorem follows from Hasse's theory of genera [H. Hasse, J. Math. Soc. Japan **3** (1951), 45–51; MR **13**, 324]. {Reviewer's remark: More generally, the primes represented by a set S of classes of forms are those in certain arithmetic progressions if and only if S is a union of genera. This consequence of Hasse's paper is pointed out on page 242 of the English version of Z. I. Borevič and I. R. Šafarevič's *Number theory* [Russian original, Izdat. "Nauka", Moscow, 1964; MR **30** #1080; English translation, Academic Press, New York, 1966; MR **33** #4001; German translation, Birkhäuser, Basel, 1966; MR **33** #4000; French translation, Gauthier-Villars, Paris, 1967; MR **34** #5734].

B. Gordon (Los Angeles, Calif.)

Citations: MR 13, 324e = R10-2; MR 30# 1080 = Z02-44; MR 33# 4000 = Z02-45; MR 33# 4001 = Z02-46; MR 34# 5734 = Z02-47.

E16-69 (37# 6260)

Hafner, P.
Automorphismen von binären quadratischen Formen.
Elem. Math. **23** (1968), 25–30.

The well-known connection between the automorphisms of binary quadratic forms and the solutions of the Pell equation is reconsidered at some length from the point of view of the arithmetic theory of quadratic number fields.

M. Eichler (Basel)

E16-70 (38# 2120)

Hardy, John
A note on the representability of binary quadratic forms with Gaussian integer coefficients as sums of squares of two linear forms.
Acta Arith. **15** (1968), 77–84.

The author presents necessary and sufficient conditions for the problem in the title. Particular reference is made to background work by I. Niven [Trans. Amer. Math. Soc. **48** (1940), 405–417; MR **2**, 147] and G. Pall [Duke Math. J. **18** (1951), 399–409; MR **12**, 676].

Harvey Cohn (Tucson, Ariz.)

Citations: MR 2, 147b = E24-4; MR 12, 676g = E24-33.

E16-71 (38# 2155)

Taussky, Olga
Automorphs and generalized automorphs of quadratic forms treated as characteristic value relations.
Linear Algebra and Appl. **1** (1968), 349–356.

In a recent paper by the reviewer and G. Pall [Acta Arith. **15** (1968), 23–44] the equation $T'AT=eB$ was studied, where A and B are matrices of integral binary quadratic forms, T is an integral 2×2 matrix, and e is an integer. The special case $A=B$ is given particular consideration, and for a fixed $A=B$ the set of T's and e's that can occur is of interest, as a generalization of the concept of automorphs of quadratic forms. If $\det A\neq 0$, it is clear that $e=\det T$ or $e=-\det T$; assuming that $\det A$ is not a square, it is shown that for each case ($\det T=\pm e$) the corresponding T's form a two-dimensional Z-module, Z the ring of rational integers. Section 2 of the present paper is devoted to giving a new interpretation of this result (considering the relation $T'AT=eA$ as a characteristic value problem), which sheds further light on the difference between the two cases. The author remarks that the method of Section 2 can be used for n-dimensional problems. In Section 3 the equation $T'AT=eA$ is obtained from a relation concerning elements in a quadratic field; this was done in the paper cited above and is reformulated here. The ideas developed in Section 2 are then translated into the point of view adopted in Section 3. Section 4 is devoted to the study of a generalized characteristic value problem, which may lead to further interesting generalizations.

H. S. Butts (Baton Rouge, La.)

Citations: MR 39# 6822 = E16-78.
Referred to in E24-131.

E16-72 (38# 3225)

Mrowka, Erwin
Reduktion von positiven binären quadratischen Formen modulo S.
Wiss. Z. Hochsch. Verkehrswesen "Friedrich List" Dresden **11** (1964), 135–138.

Two positive binary quadratic forms $\varphi_i(x, y)=a_ix^2+b_ixy+c_iy^2$ $(i=1, 2)$ are here defined to be equivalent modulo S if one may be transformed into the other by an integral unimodular transformation $T=\begin{pmatrix}\alpha & \beta\\ \gamma & \delta\end{pmatrix}$ with $\gamma\equiv 0 \pmod S$. The author investigates the problem of determining an upper bound (depending only on S and the discriminant d) for the minimum leading coefficient of a form in any equivalence class of integral forms.

E. S. Barnes (Adelaide)

E16-73 (38# 3228)

Kaplansky, Irving
Composition of binary quadratic forms.
Studia Math. **31** (1968), 523–530.

The author here extends the composition of binary quadratic forms to Bézout domains (integral domains where every finitely generated ideal is principal). Let K denote a field and L a separable quadratic extension of K. He considers pairs $[A, a]$, where A is an R-submodule of L, a is a non-zero element of K and R is an integral domain with quotient field K. A^* is the image of A under the automorphism of L over K, and D, the discriminant of the pair $[A, a]$, is defined by DA/a^2. The norm of the pair is defined by $N[A, a]=NA/a$. An order is a free 2-dimensional module which is a ring containing 1.

A sketch of the proof of the following theorem is given: Let R be a Bézout domain. Then (a) two orders are identical if and only if they have the same discriminant (up to the square of a unit in R), (b) a (free 2-dimensional) module A is an invertible ideal over the unique order P having the same discriminant as the pair $[A, NA]$, and $AA^*=N(A)P$, and (c) for any modules A and B, $N(AB)=N(A)N(B)$. The author shows that, wherever applicable, Dedekind's method of united forms gives the same composition.

Burton W. Jones (Boulder, Colo.)

E16-74 (38# 4503)

Butts, Hubert S.; Estes, Dennis
Modules and binary quadratic forms over integral domains.
Linear Algebra and Appl. **1** (1968), 153–180.

Gordon Pall defined composition of binary quadratic forms [Bull. Amer. Math. Soc. **54** (1948), 1171–1175; MR **10**, 434] in a manner similar to that of Dirichlet [cf. L. E. Dickson, *History of the theory of numbers*, Vol. 3, p. 66, Carnegie Institution of Washington, 1923].

In the present paper, the authors main purpose is to determine conditions on an integral domain D in order that composition of binary quadratic forms over D (or classes of such forms) can be defined, and to extend to such domains some of the applications of composition of forms over the rational integers.

A domain D in which $2\neq 0$ is called a C-domain provided (a) each nonzero element of D is contained in only a finite number of maximal ideals, and (b) $x^2 \equiv y^2 \bmod (4)$ implies $x \equiv y \bmod (2)$ in D. Several number theoretic conditions on a domain D are investigated, and various properties and examples of C-domains are obtained. If C_1 and C_2 are two classes of binary quadratic forms over a C-domain with coprime divisors and equal discriminants, then it is shown that a compound C_1C_2 can be defined by the use of "united forms" and the class group of primitive classes of fixed discriminant is obtained.

These results are applied to obtain the basic result (Theorem 4.2, too complicated to be reproduced here) which gives an algorithm whereby the transformations T of a primitive binary quadratic form f into a multiple eg of a primitive binary quadratic form g are uniquely related to representations of e by one of two specific forms.

The authors also consider quadratic extensions of a domain D and examine the connection between multiplication of modules and composition of forms.

L. M. Chawla (Lahore)

Citations: MR 10, 434a = E16-10.
Referred to in E24-131.

E16-75 (38# 4504)

Selenius, Clas-Olof
Quasireduzierte indefinite binäre quadratische Formen.
Acta Acad. Åbo. Ser. B **28**, *no.* 7, 11 *pp.* (1968).

The author first gives a brief exposition of the classical construction of a chain of reduced forms equivalent to a given indefinite binary quadratic form. He then sets up a new set of conditions for reduction, namely: $0 < \sqrt{d} - 2|a| < b < \sqrt{d} + 2|a|$, where the form is written $ax^2 + bxy + cy^2$ and $d = b^2 - 4ac$. The sequence of reduced equivalent forms is shorter for this definition. Other ramifications are discussed. *Burton W. Jones* (Boulder, Colo.)

E16-76 (39# 5472)

Anfert′eva, E. A.; Čudakov, N. G.
The minima of a normed function in imaginary quadratic fields. (Russian)
Dokl. Akad. Nauk SSSR **183** (1968), 255–256; *erratum, ibid.* **187** (1969), *no.* 1–3, vi.

Let (a_i, b_i, c_i), $i = 1, \cdots, h$, be the complete set of reduced binary quadratic forms of discriminant $-\Delta$ with $4a_ic_i - b_i^2 = \Delta > 0$. The authors are concerned with the maximum $a(\Delta) = \max a_i$. They sketch a proof of the inequality $a(\Delta) \geqq \Delta^{1/2}/(\log \Delta)^k$ $(\Delta > \Delta_0)$ for effectively computable constants k and Δ_0. This follows from results of A. Baker [Mathematika **13** (1966), 204–216; ibid. **14** (1967), 102–107; ibid. **14** (1967), 220–228; MR **36** #3732] and H. M. Stark [Acta Arith. **13** (1967/68), 123–129; MR **36** #5102].

{This article has appeared in English translation [Soviet Math. Dokl. **9** (1968), 1342–1344].}

D. H. Lehmer (Berkeley, Calif.)

Citations: MR 36# 3732 = J80-26; MR 36# 5102 = R14-62.

E16-77 (39# 5474)

Faĭnleĭb, A. S.
The limit theorem for the number of classes of primitive quadratic forms with negative determinant. (Russian)
Dokl. Akad. Nauk SSSR **184** (1969), 1048–1049.

Let $h(-\mathscr{D})$ be the class-number of primitive quadratic forms with negative discriminant $-\mathscr{D}$. M. B. Barban [Izv. Akad. Nauk SSSR Ser. Mat. **26** (1962), 573–580; MR **27** #1426; Uspehi Mat. Nauk **21** (1966), no. 1 (127), 51–102; MR **33** #7320] proved that the number of $\mathscr{D} \leqq N$ satisfying $h(-\mathscr{D}) \leqq 2\pi^{-1}(\mathscr{D}x)^{1/2}$ is $NF(\ln x) + o(N)$ as $N \to \infty$, where $F(u)$ is the distribution function with the characteristic function

$$\prod_{p>2} \{p^{-1} + \tfrac{1}{2}(1-p^{-1})((1-p^{-1})^{-i\xi} + (1+p^{-1})^{-i\xi})\}.$$

The author improves this result to

$$NF(\ln x) + O(N(\ln N)^{-1/2} \ln\ln N (\ln\ln\ln N)^{1/2}).$$

The proof is only sketched. It is based on E. Bombieri's results on the "large sieve" [Matematika **12** (1965), 201–225; MR **33** #5590] and a generalization of Esseen's inequality given by the author [Izv. Akad. Nauk SSSR Ser. Mat. **32** (1968), 859–879; MR **39** #146].

{This article has appeared in English translation [Soviet Math. Dokl. **10** (1969), 206–207].} *J. Kubilius* (Vilnius)

Citations: MR 27# 1426 = R14-47; MR 33# 5590 = M55-43; MR 33# 7320 = Z02-53; MR 39# 146 = N60-76.

E16-78 (39# 6822)

Butts, Hubert S.; Pall, Gordon
Modules and binary quadratic forms.
Acta Arith. **15** (1968), 23–44.

From the authors' introduction: "The basic result of this article is a theorem which gives an algorithm whereby the transformations T of a primitive binary quadratic form f into a multiple $e \cdot g$ of a primitive binary quadratic form g are uniquely related to representations of e by one of two specific forms according as $e(\det T)$ is positive or negative. Allowing e to vary, one deduces certain remarkable additive properties of the transformations of a binary quadratic form into an arbitrary multiple of another. These, it may be mentioned, are useful in a new theory of reduction of the quaternary quadratic forms which arise as norm forms of modules in quaternion rings."

The authors have written a highly interesting paper on the relationship between modules of quadratic fields and classes of binary quadratic forms. It is said that Emmy Noether and Brandt had repeatedly pointed out that one should concentrate on modules rather than ideals (as Dedekind had done). This is carried out beautifully in this article. *H. Gross* (Zürich)

Referred to in E16-71, E24-131.

E16-79 (39# 6841)

Haneke, W.
Darstellungen von Primzahlen durch quadratische Formen.
Math. Z. **110** (1969), 10–14.

Es sei d eine Fundamentaldiskriminante und $h(d)$ die zugehörige Klassenzahl der quadratischen Formen der Diskriminanten d. Ferner seien $Q(x, y) = x^2 + xy + (1-d)4^{-1}y^2$ wenn $d \equiv 1 \pmod 4$, $Q(x, y) = x^2 - d4^{-1}y^2$ wenn $d \equiv 0 \pmod 4$. Es wird gezeigt, dass es für $h(d) < c_1\sqrt{|d|}/\log^{c_2}|d|$ bei genügend grossem c_2 mindestens $c_3\sqrt{|d|}/\log^2|d|$ Primzahlen der Form $|Q(x, 2)|$ mit ganzem x, $|x| \leqq c_4\sqrt{|d|}$ gibt. Dabei sind die c_i absolut positive Konstanten, die sich numerisch angeben lassen.

H. Gross (Zürich)

E16-80 (40# 1335)

Pall, Gordon
Discriminantal divisors of binary quadratic forms.
J. Number Theory **1** (1969), 525–533.

The author deals with integral binary forms $[a, b, c] = ax^2 + bxy + cy^2$ for which $a|b$, that is, ambiguous forms, and the factors of the discriminant, $b^2 - 4ac = d$, which they represent for d positive. One theorem which he proves, using a method of Cantor, is the following: Let $h = -1$, 2 or -2, and let k be a positive integer. Then $[1, 0, -k]$

represents h if and only if there exists in the class of $[1, 0, -k]$ a form $[ha, 2b, a]$ with $(a, 2b) = 1$. For a prime $p \equiv 9 \pmod{16}$, he shows that $x^2 - 2py^2$ never represents 2, gives necessary and sufficient conditions that it represents -1, and sufficient conditions for representing -2. There are similar results for $p \equiv 1 \pmod{16}$.

Burton W. Jones (Boulder, Colo.)

E16-81 (40# 2606)

Pronin, L. N.

Integral binary Hermitian forms over the sfield of quaternions. (Russian)

Vestnik Har'kov. Gos. Univ. **1967**, *no.* 26, 27–41.

The theory of the cited forms is presented in connection with classical results and certain generalisations.

The forms $xa\bar{x} + xb\bar{y} + y\bar{b}\bar{x} + yc\bar{y}$, where x, y are quaternion arguments, a, c rational integers, b integer quaternions, are called Q-forms. Let $t(f)$ be the order of the group of the automorphisms of any Q-form f, $\nu_f(m)$ be the number of representations in integer quaternions x, y of the rational positive integer m by f, $m = f(x, y)$; $\nu_f'(m)$ the number in integer quaternions without left common divisor $\neq 1$, $(x, y)_l = 1$.

Let S be the set of all representatives of classes of equivalent positive definite Q-forms with given discriminant Δ.

Theorem 1: There exist only finitely many classes of equivalent Q-forms. Theorem 2: If $(M, 2\Delta) = 1$, then $\sum_{f \in S} \nu_f'(m)/t(f) = (m^3/24) \sum_{d|m} \mu(d)/d^2$, where μ is the Möbius function. Theorem 3: If $(m, 2\Delta) = 1$, then

$$\sum_{f \in S} \nu_f(m)/t(f) = (1/24) \sum_{d|m} d^3.$$

Theorems related to an arbitrary set of equivalent classes of Q-forms are proved by using geometrical methods. The author promises to publish a completely arithmetical proof. *T. T. Tonkov* (Sofia)

Referred to in E16-87.

E16-82 (40# 5543)

Wolke, Dieter

Moments of the number of classes of primitive quadratic forms with negative discriminant.

J. Number Theory **1** (1969), 502–511.

Let $h(-n)$ be the number of classes of primitive quadratic forms with negative discriminant $-n$. The sum

$$\sum_{n \leq x} h^k(-n)$$

was studied by I. M. Vinogradov [Soobšč. Har'kov. Mat. Obšč. (2) **16** (1918), 10–38] in the case $k = 1$, and by M. B. Barban [Izv. Akad. Nauk SSSR Ser. Mat. **26** (1962), 573–580; MR **27** #1426] for all integers $k \geqq 1$. Barban proved that

$$\sum_{n \leq x} h^k(-n) = (2^{k+1}/((k+2)\pi^k)) r(k) x^{(k+2)/2} + O(x^{(k+2)/2} \exp(-\ln^{1/2-\varepsilon} x)),$$

where $r(k) = \sum_{n=1, 2 \nmid n}^{\infty} \phi(n) \tau_k(n^2)/n^3$. Various other authors obtained improved estimates for special values of k. The author's method is based on the recent version of the "large sieve" due to K. F. Roth [Mathematika **12** (1965), 1–9; MR **33** #5589], E. Bombieri [ibid. **12** (1965), 201–225; MR **33** #5590], H. Davenport and H. Halberstam [ibid. **14** (1967), 229–232; MR **36** #2569], and P. X. Gallagher [ibid. **14** (1967), 14–20; MR **35** #5411] and, for $k \geqq 4$, he obtains improvements on all earlier results. His error term is $O(x^{(k+2)/2 - 1/k})$.

S. Chowla (University Park, Pa.)

Citations: MR 27# 1426 = R14-47; MR 33# 5589 = M55-42; MR 33# 5590 = M55-43; MR 35# 5411 = M55-52; MR 36# 2569 = M55-46.

E16-83 (41# 1640)

Gafurov, N.

A generalization of a theorem on the distribution of integral points on short arcs of an equilateral hyperbola. (Russian. Tajiki summary)

Dokl. Akad. Nauk Tadžik. SSR **11** (1968), *no.* 7, 11–15.

Let $p_1, \cdots, p_n$ be fixed distinct prime numbers, and let $m = p_1^{\alpha_1} \cdots p_n^{\alpha_n}$. For $\alpha_i \to \infty$ $(i = 1, \cdots, n)$, the author obtains an asymptotic formula for the distribution of integral points (x, y) on the hyperbola $xy = m$. The case $n = 2$ has been previously considered by G. Babaev [*Distribution of integral points on algebraic surfaces* (Russian), Tadžik. Gosudarstv. Univ., Dushanbe, 1966; MR **41** #3394]. *A. Malyšev* (RŽMat **1969** #6 A149)

Citations: MR 41# 3394 = E16-84.

E16-84 (41# 3394)

Бабаев, Г. [Babaev, G.]

Распределение целых точек на алгебраических поверхностях. (Russian) [Distribution of integral points on algebraic surfaces]

Tadžik. Gosudarstv. Univ., Dushanbe, 1966. 277 *pp.* (*errata insert*) 1.70 *r.*

This book develops in a connected form investigations of the author together with some classical material. Most of it is concerned with the representation of rational integers as norms of integers of an algebraic number-field of class-number 1.

§§ 1, 2 consider the distribution of integral points (x, y) on a hyperbola $xy = m$, especially when $m \to \infty$ through values with only two given prime factors p_1, p_2 and uses results of A. O. Gel'fond [*Transcendental and algebraic numbers* (Russian), GITTL, Moscow, 1952; MR **15**, 292; English translation, Dover, New York, 1960; MR **22** #2598] about the behaviour of the linear form $u \log p_1 + v \log p_2$. In § 3 the central limit theorem is applied to the more general case of many prime factors.

In § 4 it is shown, roughly speaking, that if there are many integral points (x, y) on a circle $x^2 + y^2 = m$, then they are uniformly distributed. The proof uses unique factorization in the Gaussian field together with Weyl's criterion for uniform distribution in a quantitative form due to I. M. Vinogradov. In § 5 much better estimates for the uniformity of the distribution are obtained when m contains only two fixed prime factors. In § 6 it is shown that $|x| > m^{(1/2)-\varepsilon}$, $|y| > m^{(1/2)-\varepsilon}$, when $x^2 + y^2 = m$ and $m \to \infty$ through values with only a fixed set of prime factors.

In §§ 7, 8 similar results to the foregoing are proved for ellipses and in §§ 9–13 they are extended to hyperbolae $x^2 - dy^2 = m$. Finally, §§ 14, 15 give generalizations to non-real cubic fields and §§ 16–25 consider yet more general number fields. A separate final chapter considers the distribution of integral points on the cone $x^2 + y^2 = z^2$ and more generally on $x^2 + y^2 = z^k$ $(k > 2)$.

In a somewhat hostile review A. I. Vinogradov [Mat. Zametki **1** (1967), 119–126] has shown how some of the results of this book can be improved by the use of the Hecke L-series "mit Grössencharakteren".

J. W. S. Cassels (Cambridge, England)

Citations: MR 15, 292e = J02-6; MR 22# 2598 = J02-7.

Referred to in E16-83, E16-89.

E16-85 (41# 6814)

Shanks, Daniel

On Gauss's class number problems.

Math. Comp. **23** (1969), 151–163.

Recently Stark showed that $\Delta = 163$ is the largest integer for which the algebraic field $R(\sqrt{-\Delta})$ has class number 1 ($-\Delta$ is the discriminant). This is equivalent to the statement that binary quadratic forms $Au^2+Buv+Cv^2$ with $\Delta=4AC-B^2$ will have more than one class if $\Delta>163$. The author uses Gauss' formulation, where the quadratic form is $Au^2+2Buv+Cv^2$ and $-D=AC-B^2$ is the corresponding determinant. (A determinant -163 means a discriminant -652.) He shows that if the class number h of the above quadratic form is of the form $6n\pm 1$, then the series of determinants corresponding to the same classification always terminates, and moreover all the determinants can be obtained constructively. The author further proves that for negative determinants the noncyclic group of order 25, 49 or 121 cannot occur as a composition group; that although most prime determinants $=n^2-8$ appear to have class number 1, there is a subclass that does not; and that there exists a positive irregular determinant with an odd "exponent of irregularity".

T. Lepistö (Tampere).

E16-86 (42# 1763)

Rice, Bart

Quaternions and binary quadratic forms.

Proc. Amer. Math. Soc. **27** (1971), 1–7.

Author's summary: "Methods are discussed for studying binary quadratic forms by use of quaternions derived from the ternary quadratic form $f=x^2-yz$. In particular, Gauss composition of binary quadratic forms may be achieved by factoring and multiplying quaternions in a natural way." *J. Knopfmacher* (Johannesburg)

E16-87 (43# 1923)

Pronin, L. N.

On a measure of the set of classes of integral quaternionic binary Hermitian forms with given determinant. (Russian)

Izv. Vysš. Učebn. Zaved. Matematika **1970**, *no.* 6 (97), 86–95.

Let Γ be a complete set of representatives of equivalence classes of binary integral quaternionic hermitian forms with a given determinant Δ and $t(f)$ the number of automorphisms of an element $f\in\Gamma$. The author gives an "elementary" derivation of the value of $\sum_{f\in\Gamma} 1/t(f)$, which he has already found by analytic methods [Vestnik Har′kov. Gos. Univ. **1967**, no. 26, 27–41; MR **40** #2606].

G. Maxwell (Vancouver, B.C.)

Citations: MR 40# 2606 = E16-81.

E16-88 (43# 6166)

Lavrik, A. F.

The moments of the number of classes of primitive quadratic forms of negative determinant. (Russian)

Dokl. Akad. Nauk SSSR **197** (1971), 32–35.

This very interesting paper contains a (completely elementary!) proof of the asymptotic relation

$$\sum_{1<D\leq N, D\equiv l(d)} h^k(-D) = c(k,d,l)N^{(k/2)+1}(1+O(N^{-1/4}\lg^{2+(k^2/2)}Nd^{(1/2)+\varepsilon}))$$

$(0<l\leq d,\ (l,d)=1)$ which holds, for any $\varepsilon>0$, uniformly with respect to N, l and d, where $h(-D)$ is the number of classes of primitive quadratic forms of negative determinant $-D$. (It is known that the Bombieri density hypothesis on the number of zeros of L-functions gives only $O(N^{(-1/5)+\varepsilon})$ in the case $d=1$.)

The proof (given very briefly) is based on the estimates of the double sum $\sum_{n\leq x, n\neq m^2, (n,2d)=1} |\sum_{1<D\leq N}\chi_D(n)|^2$. Further, the author states (without proof) that his methods (together with some results of A. I. Vinogradov) give some results on the above sum with D prime; e.g., for arbitrary c we have the relation $\sum_{p\leq N, p\equiv 3(4)} h^k(-p)=c(k)\pi(N)N^{k/2}\times(1+O(\lg^{-c}N))$.

{This article has appeared in English translation [Soviet Math. Dokl. **12** (1971), 399–403].} *B. Novák* (Prague)

E16-89 (44# 152)

Ismoilov, D.

The distribution of integral points on elliptic cones of higher order. (Russian. Tajiki summary)

Dokl. Akad. Nauk Tadžik. SSR **13** (1970), *no.* 7, 7–11.

Let A, B, C and k be integers, with $A>0$, g.c.d. $(A,B,C)=1$ and $k\geqq 2$. Let $-d=B^2-4AC<0$ coincide with the discriminant of the field $Q(\sqrt{-d})$. The author gives asymptotic formulae involving several main terms for the number of integral points (x,y,z) on the cones $Ax^2+Bxy+Cy^2=z^k$, $1\leqq z\leqq X$ for $X\to+\infty$.

The proof is based on a method explained in G. Babaev's monograph *Distribution of integral points on algebraic surfaces* [(Russian), Tadžik. Gos. Univ., Dushanbe, 1966; MR **41** #3394] and on a further elaboration of the author's method [Dokl. Akad. Nauk Tadžik. SSR **12** (1969), no. 9, 7–10; MR **42** #210] used for $k=2$.

B. Diviš (Columbus, Ohio)

Citations: MR 41# 3394 = E16-84; MR 42# 210 = E20-89.

E16-90 (44# 2703)

Brown, Ezra

Representations of discriminantal divisors by binary quadratic forms.

J. Number Theory **3** (1971), 213–225.

If $f=(a,b,c)$ is a binary quadratic form, then f is ancipital of type 1 if $b=0$ and ancipital of type 2 if $a=b$. If the first coefficient k of a primitive ancipital form of discriminant d satisfies $4k^2<d$ if the form is of type 1 or $k^2<d$ if the form is of type 2 then k is a discriminantal divisor.

Partial results on the representation of discriminantal divisors are obtained when $d=4^kpq$, $p\equiv q \pmod 4$ and the author's methods are sufficiently powerful to enable him to give a complete discussion of the discriminantal divisors represented by $(1,0,-pq)$ when $q=5$ or 13.

The author also obtains the complete parametric solution of the system of equations: $p=x_1^2+x_2^2=-x_3^2+qx_4^2=x_5^2+qx_5^2$, where p, q are primes such that p is represented by both $x_1^2+x_2^2$ and $x_5^2+qx_6^2$.

W. J. Ellison (Talence)

E20 GENERAL TERNARY AND QUATERNARY QUADRATIC FORMS

For forms with specified numerical coefficients, see **E24** and **E28**.

See also reviews C20-44, D08-9, D08-25, D08-46, D08-47, D16-37, D80-29, E02-3, E02-6, E04-6, E04-12, E08-4, E12-12, E12-36, E12-37, E12-91, E12-92, E12-96, E12-139, E16-16, E16-25, E16-27, E16-30, E16-31, E16-37, E16-41, E16-78, E16-84, E24-129, E28-76, F15-4, F30-41, G30-15, N40-32, P02-18, P20-33, P24-4, P24-9, P99-1, R42-32, R52-3, R52-12, R52-14, R52-16, T20-45, Z10-37.

E20-1 **(1, 68f)**

DeLury, D. B. On the representation of numbers by the indefinite form $ax^2+by^2+cz^2+dt^2$. University of Toronto Studies, Mathematical Series, no. 5. University of Toronto Press, Toronto, 1938. 17 pp.

The purpose of this paper is to establish an asymptotic formula, for large k, for $R(m, k)$, the number of integral solutions of

$$ax^2+by^2+cz^2-dt^2=m, \qquad ax^2+by^2+cz^2+dt^2\leqq k,$$

where a, b, c, d, k are positive integers and m is integral. When $m\neq 0$, $R(m, k)$ is found to be either zero or $\sim(\pi/(\Delta)^{\frac{1}{2}})S(m)k$ as $k\to 0$, where $\Delta=abcd$ and $S(m)$ is Hardy's singular series [see Kloosterman, Acta Math. **49**, 406–464 (1926)]. Necessary and sufficient conditions that $R(m, k)=0$ are found. The methods extend to all indefinite forms $ax^2+by^2+cz^2+dt^2$ for $m\neq 0$ and to forms without cross products in five or more variables for all m. The methods are those Kloosterman [ibid.] used for the corresponding positive form. *B. W. Jones* (Ithaca, N. Y.).

E20-2 **(1, 68g)**

Ross, Arnold E. A theorem on simultaneous representation of primes and its corollaries. Bull. Amer. Math. Soc. **45**, 899–906 (1939).

Necessary and sufficient conditions that a ternary quadratic form

$$f=ax^2+by^2+cz^2+2ryz+2sxz+2txy$$

should represent all integers were given by Dickson [Studies in the Theory of Numbers, Chicago, 1930, 21–22] for the case $r=s=t=0$, and by the present author [Quart. J. Math. **4**, 147–158 (1933)] for the general case. In this paper a theorem on the simultaneous representation of primes by a form f and its reciprocal F is established and used to obtain the necessary conditions in the general case directly from the conditions in the special case $r=s=t=0$.

R. D. James (Saskatoon, Sask.).

E20-3 **(1, 134g)**

Townes, S. B. Table of reduced positive quaternary quadratic forms. Ann. of Math. **41**, 57–58 (1940).

Employing conditions for a unique representative of each class of equivalent positive quaternary quadratic forms obtained in his dissertation [Chicago, 1936, unpublished. Cf. also B. W. Jones, Ann. of Math. **40**, 92–119 (1939)] by carrying through the Eisenstein method of reduction, the author computes a table of such representative forms for determinants 1 to 25. One would have liked to see included some indication of the method of construction used. The thesis indicates [p. 65] that the author is in possession of a table extending up to determinant 50.

A. E. Ross (St. Louis, Mo.).

Referred to in E20-12.

E20-4 **(2, 36a)**

Linnik, U. V. On certain results relating to positive ternary quadratic forms. Rec. Math. [Mat. Sbornik] N.S. **5** (47), 453–471 (1939). (English. Russian summary)

The author studies the problem of representation of integers m by a positive ternary quadratic form F. He associates a suitably chosen algebra of generalized quaternions with every such form F and expresses the diophantine equation $F=m$ as a quaternion equation. In the process of solution of this latter equation the author employs the automorphs of F expressed in terms of generalized quaternions and investigates in detail the related properties of binary quadratic forms of discriminant $-m$. The principal results are proven under certain restrictions on m for forms with the invariants $\Omega=p^s$, $\Delta=1$, where p is an odd prime, and enable one to study representation of integers by individual forms with such invariants, in a genus containing more than one class [cf., for similar results, B. W. Jones and G. Pall, Acta Math. **70**, 165–191 (1939)]. In the addendum the author states that by a combination of the algebraic results of this paper and an analytic method similar to Viggo Brun's sieve he has proven that every positive ternary quadratic form represents every sufficiently large integer satisfying its generic conditions and certain supplementary congruence conditions with respect to an arbitrary fixed system of a sufficiently large system of moduli. Such a theorem would be an important extension to ternary forms of the results of Tartakowsky [Bull. Acad. Sci. URSS [Izvestia Akad. Nauk SSSR] (7) **1929**, 111–122, 165–196] for quadratic forms in four or more variables.

A. E. Ross (St. Louis, Mo.).

Referred to in E12-92, E20-9, E20-16.

E20-5 **(2, 36b)**

Linnik, J. On the representation of large numbers by positive ternary quadratic forms. C. R. (Doklady) Acad. Sci. URSS (N.S.) **25**, 575–576 (1939).

In this note the author gives the following results: Let f be a positive ternary quadratic form of invariants $\Omega=p$ (p an odd prime), $\Delta=1$ and such that $(f|p)=(-1|p)$, $f\neq 8b+7$. Then f represents all the sufficiently large integers m not divisible by p and satisfying the last two conditions for f. Next let F be the reciprocal of the form f above. Then all sufficiently large integers m which are prime to p and for which $F=m$ (mod 8) is solvable, are represented by F. For the method of proof one is referred to a former note [C. R. (Doklady) Acad. Sci. URSS (N.S.) **24**, 211–212 (1939)]. These results are special cases of a general theorem stated at the conclusion of another paper [cf. the preceding review]. *A. E. Ross* (St. Louis, Mo.).

Referred to in E20-9.

E20-6 **(2, 36c)**

Linnik, U. V. Some new theorems on the representation of large numbers by separate positive ternary quadratic forms. C. R. (Doklady) Acad. Sci. URSS (N.S.) **24**, 211–212 (1939).

In this paper the author gives some results concerning the representation of large integers by positive ternary quadratic forms of order $[\Omega, 1]$ and generic invariants $f\not\equiv 7$ (mod 8) and $(f|\omega)=(-1|\omega)$ for all $\omega|\Omega$. Following some special representation theorems, the author observes (Th. III) that one can distribute all integers compatible with the above generic invariants into an infinite sequence of arithmetic progressions $\mathfrak{A}_i$ so that each form of the genus in question should represent all sufficiently large integers m ($m>c_i$) in each of these progressions. Here the lower bound c_i for such m depends on $\mathfrak{A}_i$. In a later note [see the preceding review] a stronger result is given, subject to the restriction that Ω be an odd prime. There is a brief outline of the methods employed. Complete proofs are promised in a forthcoming paper. *A. E. Ross* (St. Louis, Mo.).

Referred to in E20-9.

E20-7 **(2, 248a)**

Wahlgren, Agne. Sur l'équation $ax^2+bxy+cy^2=ez^2$. Ark. Mat. Astr. Fys. **27A**, no. 6, 26 pp. (1940).

Let $f(x, y)$ be a positive definite quadratic form of discriminant D with relatively prime integer coefficients. The author gives a method for solving the Diophantine equation $f(x, y)=ez^2$, using the composition of the representations of the powers of primes p by forms of discriminant D, where p is a divisor of D. [Cf. Dickson, History of the Theory of Numbers, vol. 2, 1934, pp. 404–407; Dickson, Introduction to the Theory of Numbers, pp. 44–48; E. T. Browne, Amer.

Math. Monthly **42**, 502–503 (1935).] *A. Brauer.*

E20-8 (2, 252b)

Sominski, I. S. Construction of the fundamental and basic domains of the arithmetic group of the automorphisms of an indefinite ternary quadratic form. Leningrad State Univ. Annals [Uchenye Zapiski] Math. Ser. **10**, 148–153 (1940). (Russian)

In this paper, making use of the ideas of Selling [J. Reine Angew. Math. **77**, 143–229 (1873)], the author gives a geometrical method for the construction of a fundamental domain in the interior of the asymptotic cone of the hyperboloid $f(x, y, z)=D$, of the group Γ of automorphs of an indefinite ternary quadratic form $f(x, y, z)$ of determinant $D>0$. The author shows that a fundamental domain H of Γ on this hyperboloid may be obtained by combining in a certain way a number of adjacent fields of Selling. Then, by drawing rays from the origin through points of H, he obtains a fundamental domain of Γ inside the asymptotic cone, or, as one may put it, a fundamental domain of Γ on every surface $f=k>0$. Each of the above fundamental domains on $f=D$ is bounded. They cover the whole surface without overlapping and are transformed into one another by the automorphs of f. Each domain has but a finite number of neighboring domains and the group Γ has but a finite number of generators. It is next shown that to every fundamental domain on $f=D$ one may assign a bounded domain (called "basic" by the author) on $f=-D$, which, although not a fundamental domain of Γ, contains at least one point equivalent to any given point on the surface. In this manner the author solves the problem of Markoff [Mém. Imp. Acad. Sci. St. Pétersbourg (8) **23**, no. 7 (1909)], that is, the problem concerning the existence of "reduced" solutions of a diophantine equation $f=m$, $m\leqq 0$. All of these results are obtained under the non-trivial restriction that f should not represent zero properly.

One should mention that in a very elegant development of the theory of quadratic forms [Abh. Math. Sem. Hansischen Univ. **13**, 209–239 (1940); these Rev. **2**, 148] Siegel obtained, without the above restriction, similar results for the automorphs of an indefinite quadratic form of index $(n, m-n)$, in any number m of variables. There a fundamental domain is constructed in a suitably chosen space H of $n(m-n)$ dimensions. It may be of interest to note that the specialization of these general results to the case of this paper permits of a geometric interpretation closely related to that given here. The author refers to another general study by Wenkov [Bull. Acad. Sci. USSR **1937**, 139–170]. *A. E. Ross* (St. Louis, Mo.).

Citations: MR 2, 148b = E12-4.

Referred to in E20-21.

E20-9 (2, 348f)

Linnik, U. Über die Darstellung grosser Zahlen durch positive ternäre quadratische Formen. Bull. Acad. Sci. URSS. Sér. Math. [Izvestia Akad. Nauk SSSR] **4**, 363–402 (1940). (Russian. German summary)

[In the title of the German summary the word "grosser" was incorrectly translated as "ganzer." For the author's previous work, cf. these Rev. **2**, 36.] The fundamental result concerns quaternions, an extension to generalized quaternions being sketched in the second part. Let p be an odd prime, m large, $m\neq 4k$ or $8k+7$, $(-m|p)=1$, $x_0^2\equiv -m \pmod{p}$; as x ranges over all proper, pure quaternions $i_1x_1+i_2x_2+i_3x_3$ of norm m, every quaternion of norm p occurs as a divisor of x_0+x. The proof is ingenious but has a serious error, which the reviewer has corrected only with considerable effort: Linnik uses the false result that the number of representations as a sum of three squares of a binary quadratic form of determinant D is $O(D^{\epsilon})$. The connection between classes of binary quadratic forms of determinant m and pairs (x, y) of vectors of norm m is used to count the number of such pairs in which x_0+x and x_0+y have conjugate divisors of norm p^s, where s is variable with m: $m^{\frac{1}{2}+\tau}\leqq p^s<pm^{\frac{1}{2}+\tau}$, $\tau=-\frac{1}{2}\log(1-p^{-1})/\log p$. Net result: the number is $O(m^{\frac{1}{2}+\epsilon})$. But the assumption that any divisor of norm p fails to occur makes the number of larger order than $m^{\frac{1}{2}+2\tau^2-\epsilon}$. Application: if f is a positive primitive ternary of invariants $[p, 1]$, such that $(f|p)=(-1|p)$ [whence, it might be remarked, f is derived from a sum of three squares by a transformation of determinant p], then (our above) m is represented by f. The extension involves any form of invariants $(\Omega, 1)$, where Ω is odd, and, for at least one prime p dividing Ω, $(f|p)=(-1|p)$; then every large m satisfying the generic conditions and prime to Ω is represented. The same error is made in the extension, but perhaps can be adjusted. *G. Pall* (Montreal, Que.).

Citations: MR 2, 36a = E20-4; MR 2, 36b = E20-5; MR 2, 36c = E20-6.

Referred to in E20-16, E20-40, E20-44, E20-45, E20-52, E20-56, E20-58, P04-18, P04-20, R52-4.

E20-10 (3, 70h)

Pall, Gordon. The construction of positive ternary quadratic forms. Bull. Amer. Math. Soc. **47**, 641–650 (1941).

A defect of earlier methods of constructing reduced positive ternary quadratic forms was that the construction would readily yield all reduced forms with determinant less than a given fixed value but was not adapted to the construction of forms with a specified determinant. The present method, utilizing in part the adjoint form, avoids this defect, and is also well adapted to the construction of a single genus. The method is quite simple and is illustrated with calculations for determinant 600 and for a genus of determinant 324. *M. Hall* (New Haven, Conn.).

E20-11 (3, 163c)

Hua, Loo-keng. A note on the class number of ternary quadratic forms. J. London Math. Soc. **16**, 82–83 (1941).

To prove that the number of classes of positive ternary quadratic forms of determinant d tends to infinity with d, Hua notes that the forms $x^2+f(y, z)$ are non-equivalent, where f ranges over the $h(d)$ binary forms of determinant d, and that $h(d)\rightarrow\infty$. The result follows, we may observe, somewhat more simply from the Eisenstein-Smith formula for the weight of a ternary genus. *G. Pall.*

E20-12 (5, 141g)

Ko, Chao and Wang, S. C. Table of primitive positive quaternary quadratic forms with determinants $\leqq 25$. Acad. Sinica Science Record **1**, 54–58 (1942).

The authors of this paper appear to be unaware of a similar table by S. B. Townes [Ann. of Math. (2) **41**, 57–58 (1940); these Rev. **1**, 134]. The present table differs from that of Townes by the choice of the cross-product coefficients in the representative (reduced) forms. Page 56 contains the following errata: $D=20$ has $(1, 1, 2, 20)$, should have $(1, 1, 2, 10)$; $D=21$ has $(1, 2, 3, 3, 0_4, -1, 0)$, should have $(1, 2, 3, 4, 0_4, -1, 0)$; in $D=24$, $(2, 2, 8, 3, -1, 0_3, -1, 0)$ should read $(2, 2, 3, 3, -1, 0_3, -1, 0)$. On page 58, the fourth determinant is 9 and not 8. In addition to these errata, we note that the entries $(2, 2, 3, 4, -1_2, 0_3, -1)$ for $D=16$ and $(2, 2, 3, 3, 0, -1_2, 0, -1_2)$ and $(2, 2, 3, 5, -1_2, 0_3, -1)$ for $D=24$ are incorrect, being actually of determinants 28, 11 and 36, respectively. A representative for one of the twenty-four classes of determinant 24 is missing, and the entry $(2, 3, 3, 3, -1, 0_2, -1, 0_2)$ of $D=25$, should read $(2, 2, 3, 3, -1, 0_2, -1, 0_2)$. To restore completeness of the table one may use the following reduced forms from Townes in place of the entries referred to above: the form

(2, 2, 3, 3, 1_2, 0, 1_3) for $D=16$, and the forms (2, 2, 3, 4, 1_2, 0, 1_3), (2, 3, 3, 3, -1_2, 1, 0, 1_2), and (1, 2, 4, 4, 0_5, 2) for $D=24$. The count of the number of classes yields 14 for $D=16$ and 24 for $D=24$. We have, in the above, used the well-known notation $(a, b, c, d, r, s, t, u, v, w)=ax_1^2+bx_2^2+cx_3^2+dx_4^2+2rx_2x_3+2sx_1x_3+2tx_1x_2+2ux_1x_4+2vx_2x_4+2wx_3x_4$. A run of K zeros is indicated by 0_k for brevity. One may note that the entry (1, 1, 4, 4, 0_5, 2) for $D=16$ in Townes' table should read (1, 1, 4, 5, 0_5, 2). *A. E. Ross.*

Citations: MR 1, 134g = E20-3.

E20-13 (7, 274g)

Ross, Arnold E. On a problem of Ramanujan. Amer. J. Math. **68**, 29–46 (1946).

The author considers the problem of determining the conditions under which general integral positive quaternary quadratic forms represent all except a finite number of integers. If the leading principal minors of the integral symmetric matrix $A=(a_{ij})$ of a quaternary quadratic form $f=\sum a_{ij}x_ix_j$ with determinant $|a_{ij}|=|A|$ are denoted by A_1 $(=a_{11})$, o_1A_2 $(=a_{11}a_{22}-a_{12}^2)$ and $o_1^2o_2A_3$ (where the o_μ are the Minkowski-Smith invariants) he proves that every properly primitive classic quaternary form is equivalent to a canonical form f, where A_μ or $\frac{1}{2}A_\mu$ is an odd prime not dividing $|a_{ij}|A_kA_l$ for $(\mu, k, l)=(1, 2, 3)$, $(2, 1, 3)$, $(3, 1, 2)$. Starting from a canonical form f, the form $A_3A_2A_1f$ is replaced by an equivalent form G without the cross products. If f represents an integer m, then G represents $A_1A_2A_3m$. If $(o_1o_2A_1, A_3)=(o_1, A_2)=1$, the converse is also true. For properly primitive canonical forms f of odd determinants the latter conditions are satisfied. The problem is thus reduced to the case of forms without the cross products. For this special case the problem has been solved (save for a finite number of exceptions) by the reviewer [Acta Math. **49**, 407–464 (1926)]. The author shows that the reviewer's conditions assuring representation of all large integers are restrictions upon the generic characters of f. Some of these conditions are also necessary. However, the failure of the remaining conditions merely implies that a form represents all large integers only if it represents all positive integers or all even positive integers. The author shows that the determinants of such forms do not exceed a fixed number. For universal quadratic forms the exact upper bound is 112. Thus there is only a finite number of classes of forms of odd determinants representing all large integers and not satisfying the above generic character conditions. Indeed, there are only three such classes representing all positive integers. These three classes are explicitly determined. Two of them are the only classes in their respective genera.

H. D. Kloosterman (Leiden).

Referred to in E20-19.

E20-14 (7, 275a)

Pall, Gordon. The completion of a problem of Kloosterman. Amer. J. Math. **68**, 47–58 (1946).

The problem of determining all forms $f=(a, b, c, d)=ax^2+by^2+cz^2+dt^2$ (where a, b, c, d are positive integers) which represent all but a finite number of positive integers was solved by the reviewer, except that he was unable to decide whether the four forms (1, 2, 11, 38), (1, 2, 17, 34), (1, 2, 19, 22), (1, 2, 19, 38) represent all large integers [Acta Math. **49**, 407–464 (1926)]. The author proves that these forms do in fact represent all large integers. He gives an elegant formulation of the reviewer's conditions [loc. cit., pp. 453–454] assuring representation of all large integers. If p is any prime, a form f is said to be p-adically universal when $f\equiv n \pmod{p^r}$ is solvable in integers x, y, z, t for every n and $r\geqq 0$. The form f is said to represent zero p-adically if the congruence $f\equiv 0 \pmod{p^r}$ is solvable for every positive integer r in integers x, y, z, t not all divisible by p. The author gives criteria for p-adic universality and criteria for p-adic representation of zero (the latter being essentially those of Hasse [J. Reine Angew. Math. **152**, 129–148 (1923)]). The following result is then obtained. If (a) f is p-adically universal for every p and (b) f represents zero p-adically for every p, then f represents all sufficiently large integers. This follows from the following theorem. Let n denote any integer such that $f\equiv n \pmod k$ is solvable for every modulus k. If for each prime p such that f fails to represent zero p-adically an upper bound is imposed to the power of p in n, then f represents every sufficiently large positive n thus restricted. This theorem follows from the reviewer's asymptotic formula for the number $f(n)$ of representations of n by f. It is clear that the condition (a) is also necessary for a form f to represent all large integers. There are, however, exactly 199 forms which fail to represent zero p-adically for some p and yet represent all large integers. *H. D. Kloosterman* (Leiden).

E20-15 (7, 275b)

Ross, Arnold E., and Pall, Gordon. An extension of a problem of Kloosterman. Amer. J. Math. **68**, 59–65 (1946).

The following theorem is proved. Let f be any positive m-ary quadratic form, $m\geqq 4$. Let n be such that $f(x_1, \cdots, x_m)\equiv n \pmod{p^r}$ is solvable for every p and r. For each prime p (if any) such that f fails to represent zero p-adically [see the preceding review] impose an upper bound to the power of p which may divide n. Then f represents every such n sufficiently large. The proof makes use of an extension to a general positive m-ary form $(m\geqq 4)$ of the asymptotic formula for the number of representations of n in f which the reviewer proved [Acta Math. **49**, 407–464 (1926)] for the special case of a quaternary form $ax^2+by^2+cz^2+dt^2$ without the cross products. This extension is, however, a corollary of a theorem which the reviewer proved [Abh. Math. Sem. Hamburgischen Univ. **5**, 337–352 (1927)]. The authors prove it by induction, starting from the special case without cross products. Conditions for p-adic universality and p-adic representation of zero for quaternary forms are given and the following theorem is proved. The number of classes of integral positive quaternary forms which represent all large integers and yet fail to represent zero p-adically for some prime p is finite. The authors give an upper bound for the determinants of such forms. This enables the determination of all positive quaternary quadratic forms which represent all large integers. *H. D. Kloosterman* (Leiden).

E20-16 (8, 318b)

Pall, Gordon. On generalized quaternions. Trans. Amer. Math. Soc. **59**, 280–332 (1946).

In this paper the author develops systematically the theory of the arithmetic of generalized quaternions as it arises out of the study of integral quadratic forms $f=x'Ax$, where $A=(a_{ij})$, adj $A=(A_{ij})$. He chooses the basal elements 1, i_1, i_2, i_3 so that $i_\alpha^2=-A_{\alpha\alpha}$, $i_2i_3=-A_{23}+\sum a_{1\alpha}i_\alpha$, $i_3i_2=-A_{32}-\sum a_{1\alpha}i_\alpha$, with i_3i_1, etc. obtained by the cyclic permutation of subscripts [cf. U. V. Linnik, Rec. Math. [Mat. Sbornik] N.S. **5**(47), 453–471 (1939); Bull. Acad. Sci. URSS. Sér. Math. [Izvestia Akad. Nauk SSSR] **4**, 363–402 (1940); these Rev. **2**, 36, 348]. Here multiplication of two quaternions ("Hermitions") corresponds to the composition of related automorphs of f. "Integral" quaternions are defined by a suitable choice of an integral basis. This set of integral elements has all the properties prescribed by L. E. Dickson except that the set is maximal if and only if adj f is fundamental, i.e., adj f cannot be obtained by an integral linear transformation of determinant greater than unity from an adjoint of an integral form. It is shown that if $(b_{\alpha\beta})=U'(a_{\alpha\beta})U$ then the basis $K=\{K_1K_2K_3\}$ associated with $(b_{\alpha\beta})$ is related to $i=\{i_1i_2i_3\}$ through $K=Ti$, where $(B_{\alpha\beta})=T'(A_{\alpha\beta})T$, $T'U=UT'=|U|I\neq 0$. If T is unimodular, integrality is preserved.

The author shows next that the factors with a given norm of a primitive quaternion are essentially unique and [theorem 3] that if $m|N(x)$, then, unless the genus of the norm-form F contains a class of forms which do not represent 1, there exists a right divisor t of a primitive quaternion x, of norm m. Here $F=x_0+\frac{1}{2}\epsilon_1x_1+\frac{1}{2}\epsilon_2x_2+\frac{1}{2}\epsilon_3x_3+\sum A_{\alpha\beta}x_\alpha x_\beta$, where $\epsilon_\alpha=0$ or 1 and all the coefficients are integral. Furthermore, using integral quaternions as defined above, he obtains the exact formula for the integral automorphs of adj f and the norm-form F in the case when this latter is fundamental. In conclusion, the author determines all the fundamental definite norm-forms F (5 in number) in whose arithmetics factorization is always possible in the sense of theorem 3 and determines all of the 39 classes of positive integral forms f for which the genus of the associated norm-form F contains only one class. *A. E. Ross.*

Citations: MR 2, 36a = E20-4; MR 2, 348f = E20-9.
Referred to in E12-92.

E20-17 (8, 318c)

Chu, Fu-Tsu. Determination of the class number of Hermitian forms with determinant ±1. Acad. Sinica Science Record **1**, 325–329 (1945).

This paper is a summary of results whose proofs "will appear elsewhere." The misprints are so numerous as to make the reviewer somewhat doubtful of the results quoted. The author appears to find the class number $h_{n,1}(m)$ of positive Hermitian forms of determinant one in n variables ($n=2, 3$) over some imaginary fields $k(\sqrt{(-m)})$, where k is the rational field and m is so chosen that the class number of the field is unity. Some of his results for positive forms may be summarized in the following table:

m	1	2	7	11	19	43	67	163
$h_{2,1}(m)$	1	2	1	2	2	4	6	14
$h_{3,1}(m)$	1	2	1	2				

Representative forms are exhibited for each class. Certain general results for definite and indefinite forms are stated depending on the character of m (mod 4).
B. W. Jones (Ithaca, N. Y.).

E20-18 (9, 270g)

Mahler, K. On the adjoint of a reduced positive definite ternary quadratic form. Acad. Sinica Science Record **2**, 21–31 (1947).

Let $a_1x_1^2+a_2x_2^2+a_3x_3^2+2b_1x_2x_3+2b_2x_3x_1+2b_3x_1x_2$ be a positive definite form reduced in the sense of Seeber and Minkowski. Let D be the discriminant of the form and $A_1, A_2, A_3, B_1, B_2, B_3$ be the coefficients of the adjoint form. The author proves the best possible inequality $A_1A_2A_3\leqq\frac{9}{4}D^2$ and states several others such as $D\leqq a_1a_2a_3-4b_1b_2b_3\leqq 2D$, $\frac{3}{4}a_2a_3\leqq A_1\leqq a_2a_3$, $A_2\geqq\frac{3}{4}A_3$, $|B_1|\leqq\frac{2}{3}A_2$. *H. S. A. Potter.*

E20-19 (9, 571e)

Willerding, Margaret F. Determination of all classes of positive quaternary quadratic forms which represent all (positive) integers. Bull. Amer. Math. Soc. **54**, 334–337 (1948).

Ramanujan found that there are exactly 54 forms $ax^2+by^2+cz^2+du^2$, where a, b, c, d are positive integers and $1\leqq a\leqq b\leqq c\leqq d$, which represent all positive integers for integral values of x, y, z, u [Proc. Cambridge Philos. Soc. **19**, 11–12 (1916)]. A. E. Ross [Amer. J. Math. **68**, 29–46 (1946); these Rev. **7**, 274] gave an upper limit to the determinant of any positive quaternary quadratic form with even cross-product coefficients, which represents all positive integers. The author has shown in her dissertation that there are exactly 178 such classes, and describes the methods of proof in this article. *G. Pall* (Chicago, Ill.).

Citations: MR 7, 274g = E20-13.

E20-20 (10, 15d)

Skolem, Th. A property of ternary quadratic forms and its connection with the quadratic reciprocity theorem. Norsk Mat. Tidsskr. **30**, 1–10 (1948). (Norwegian)

Let F be a homogeneous form with integral coefficients in the variables $x, y, z, \cdots$. The prime p is said to be a divisor of F if the congruence $F\equiv 0 \pmod{p^n}$ is solvable for all positive integers n in integral values of the variables not all divisible by p. Any other prime is a nondivisor of F. When $F=0$ is solvable in real numbers (not all zero) the symbolic "infinite" prime $p=p_\infty$ is said to be a divisor of the form. The following theorem holds. The number of the nondivisors of a ternary quadratic form is an even number. The author gives a new proof of this "nondivisor theorem" based upon the quadratic reciprocity theorem. Inversely he shows that the latter theorem can be derived from the following special cases of the nondivisor theorem: (1) if no odd nondivisor exists, the primes 2 and p_∞ are both divisors or they are both nondivisors; (2) if exactly one odd nondivisor exists, then either 2 is a divisor and p_∞ a nondivisor or inversely. This proof of the quadratic reciprocity theorem is in reality (expressed in another language) the same as the second demonstration of Gauss [Werke, v. 1, pp. 284–286].
T. Nagell (Uppsala).

E20-21 (10, 15e)

Sominsky, I. Sur les limites du domaine fondamental d'un groupe d'automorphismes d'une forme ternaire quadratique indéfinie. C. R. (Doklady) Acad. Sci. URSS (N.S.) **56**, 127–128 (1947).

Let $f(x, y, z)$ be a ternary indefinite quadratic form with integer coefficients of positive determinant and not representing zero. Let $\mathfrak{G}$ be the group of automorphisms of $f(x, y, z)$, Ω be a fundamental domain and $\gamma_1, \cdots, \gamma_k$ the boundaries of Ω, which separate Ω from its neighboring fundamental domains $\Omega_1, \cdots, \Omega_k$. In a preceding paper [Leningrad State Univ. Annals [Uchenye Zapiski] Math. Ser. **10**, 148–153 (1940); these Rev. **2**, 252] the author proved that γ_i is in general a quadratic surface. In this note he establishes that Ω can be deformed into another fundamental domain $\bar{\Omega}$ whose boundaries are planes.
L.-K. Hua (Urbana, Ill.).

Citations: MR 2, 252b = E20-8.

E20-22 (10, 15f)

Sominskiĭ, I. S. On the structure of the group of automorphisms of a ternary quadratic indefinite form. Doklady Akad. Nauk SSSR (N.S.) **56**, 241–243 (1947). (Russian)

Let $f(x, y, z)=ax^2+by^2+cz^2+2gyz+2hzx+2kxy$ be a ternary indefinite quadratic form with integer coefficients a, b, c, g, h, k of positive determinant and not representing zero. Let $\mathfrak{G}$ be the group of automorphisms of f, let Ω be a fundamental region of $\mathfrak{G}$ and let $\gamma_1, \cdots, \gamma_k$ be the boundaries of Ω, which separate Ω from its neighboring fundamental domains $\Omega_1, \cdots, \Omega_k$. Let $S_1, \cdots, S_k$ be the transformations carrying Ω into $\Omega_1, \cdots, \Omega_k$. The author proves that S is either of order two or of order infinity. The method based on the fact that the order of a modular transformation of finite order can only be 2, 3, 4 or 6. Then he works out the cases admitting automorphisms of order 3, 4 and 6. *L.-K. Hua* (Urbana, Ill.).

E20-23 **(10, 101h)**

Davenport, H., and Hall, Marshall. On the equation $ax^2+by^2+cz^2=0$. Quart. J. Math., Oxford Ser. **19**, 189–192 (1948).

Let a, b, c be integers, not all of the same sign, each pair of which is relatively prime. The paper gives a new proof of the classical result that the equation $ax^2+by^2+cz^2=0$ has an integral solution other than $x=0$, $y=0$, $z=0$ if the congruences, $A^2 \equiv -bc \pmod a$, $B^2 \equiv -ca \pmod b$, $C^2 \equiv -ab \pmod c$, are soluble. It is first shown that the result follows from the fact that a point (not 0) of a lattice of determinant 1 is always within the interior of the star body $|X^2+Y^2-Z^2| \leqq 1$. The proof of this is obtained by use of lattice point theorems for plane convex domains. *D. Derry.*

E20-24 **(10, 182e)**

Morrow, D. C. Universal quaternary quadratic forms. Bull. Amer. Math. Soc. **54**, 903–904 (1948).

A partial determination has been made of all positive quaternary quadratic forms $\sum c_{ij}x_ix_j$ (with integral coefficients c_{ii} and $2c_{ij}$) which represent all positive integers. Tables of the results so far obtained are being sent to the library of the American Mathematical Society.

G. Pall (Chicago, Ill.).

E20-25 **(10, 357f)**

Sominskiĭ, I. S. On the existence of automorphisms of the second order for certain ternary quadratic indefinite forms. Mat. Sbornik N.S. **23(65)**, 279–296 (1948). (Russian)

Let $f(x, y, z)=ax^2+by^2+cz^2+2gyz+2hzx+2kxy$ be an indefinite form with integer coefficients. The author attacks the problem of the existence of involutory automorphs of f. He obtains some partial results. (1) Every form where invariants are odd relatively prime numbers, possesses involutory automorphs; (2) every nonzero form whose determinant is a power of an odd prime possesses involutory automorphs.

It should be remarked that, on p. 284, he proves that a form which has an involutory automorph can be transformed by means of an unimodular integral substitution into one of the following:

$$(1)\qquad ax^2+by^2+cz^2+2gyz,$$
$$(2)\qquad 2a_1x^2+by^2+cz^2+2a_1xy+2gyz,$$
$$(3)\qquad 2a_1x^2+by^2+cz^2+2a_1xy+2a_1xz+2gyz;$$

but (2) and (3) are equivalent. In fact,

$$2a_1x^2+by^2+cz^2+2a_1xy+2a_1xz+2gyz=2a_1(x+z)^2 +b(y-z)^2+(-2a_1+b+c+2g)z^2+2a_1(x+z)(y-z) +2(b+g-a_1)(y-z)z.$$

L. K. Hua (Urbana, Ill.).

Referred to in Z10-51.

E20-26 **(11, 85b)**

Sominskiĭ, I. S. On the existence of automorphs of the second order for certain indefinite quadratic forms. Amer. Math. Soc. Translation no. **1**, 25 pp. (1949).

Translated from Mat. Sbornik N.S. **23(65)**, 279–296 (1948); these Rev. **10**, 357.

Referred to in Z10-51.

E20-27 **(11, 642h)**

Skolem, Th. On the Diophantine equation $ax^2+by^2+cz^2+du^2=0$. Norske Vid. Selsk. Forh., Trondheim **21**, no. 19, 76–79 (1949).

A new proof is given of the theorem that

$$f(x, y, z, u)=ax^2+by^2+cz^2+du^2=0$$

is solvable under the hypotheses that a, b, c, d are square-free and not all of the same sign, that $abcd$ contains no cube and not the factor 4, that $f\equiv 0 \pmod 8$ is solvable, and that $-ab$, $-ac$, $-ad$, $-bc$, $-bd$, $-cd$ are quadratic residues of (c, d), (b, d), (b, c), (a, d), (a, c), (a, b) respectively. The proof is a simplification of an earlier proof by the author [Diophantische Gleichungen, Springer, Berlin, 1938]. For example, no use is now made of Dirichlet's theorem on the existence of primes in an arithmetic progression. *I. Niven* (Eugene, Ore.).

E20-28 **(13, 437c)**

Skolem, Th. A simple proof for the solvability condition for the Diophantine equation $ax^2+by^2+cz^2=0$. Norsk Mat. Tidsskr. **33**, 105–112 (1951). (Norwegian)

A simplified proof for the congruence conditions for the solvability of the equation given in the title by means of Thue's congruence principle; the analogous conditions for solvability in polynomials is also derived. *O. Ore.*

E20-29 **(13, 534c)**

Mordell, L. J. On the equation $ax^2+by^2-cz^2=0$. Monatsh. Math. **55**, 323–327 (1951).

A short proof is given of Legendre's theorem that the equation $f(x, y, z)=ax^2+by^2-cz^2=0$, where a, b, c are positive square-free integers, relatively prime in pairs, has a solution other than (0, 0, 0) if, and only if, $-ab$ is a quadratic residue of c, bc of a and ca of b. Such a solution is an immediate consequence of the existence of a non-trivial solution of the congruence $f(x, y, z)\equiv 0 \pmod{4abc}$ with $|x| \leqq \sqrt{(2bc)}$, $|y| < \sqrt{(2ac)}$, $z < 2\sqrt{(ab)}$. A solution of this congruence is obtained with the use of the quadratic reciprocity law from the following elementary result. Let $L_1, L_2, \cdots, L_n$ be homogeneous linear forms with integer coefficients in x, y, z. Let $q_1, q_2, \cdots, q_n$ be positive integers, and r_1, r_2, r_3 positive numbers for which $r_1r_2r_3 \geqq q_1q_2\cdots q_n$. Then a solution of the congruences $L_1\equiv 0 \pmod{q_1}, \cdots, L_n\equiv 0 \pmod{q_n}$ exists other than (0, 0, 0) with $|x| \leqq r_1$, $|y| < r_2$, $|z| < r_3$. *D. Derry* (Vancouver, B. C.).

Referred to in E20-32, T35-58.

E20-30 **(13, 537a)**

Jones, Burton W. An extension of Meyer's theorem on indefinite ternary quadratic forms. Canadian J. Math. **4**, 120–128 (1952).

Let f, F, $d=|F|$, Ω, Δ be, respectively, an indefinite ternary quadratic form with integral coefficients of g.c.d. 1, its matrix, the determinant of this matrix, the g.c.d. of minors of F of order 2, the integer $\Delta=d/\Omega^2$. A form f^* is called reciprocal form of f, if its matrix F^* is the quotient by Ω of the adjoint matrix adj F of F. The family of forms f having a same pair Ω, Δ is called a genus of ternary quadratic forms. The paper gives certain sufficient conditions, generalizing that, given formerly by Meyer and Dickson, for the (arithmetical) equivalence of all the forms of some given genus, i.e. for the number of classes of this genus being 1.

Meyer and Dickson have proved that such is the case when the g.c.d. of Ω and Δ is 1 or 2, $\Omega\not\equiv 0 \pmod 4$ and $\Delta\not\equiv 0 \pmod 4$. The author, essentially, extends this theorem, under certain supplementary conditions, to the case where the g.d.c. of Ω and Δ has no square factors. The supplementary conditions are the following: If p is a common odd prime divisor of Ω and Δ, there exists an integer q such that: 1) $|q|$ is an odd prime or double of an odd prime; 2) let $f_p(x_1, x_2, x_3)$ be a form equivalent to f, which is congruent (mod p^3) to an expression $a_1x_1^2+p^2a_2x_2^2+pa_3x_3^2$ (it is always possible to find such an f_p); then $-q$ is representable by the form $g^*=[p^{-1}f_p(px_1, x_2, x_3)]^*$ reciprocal to the form $g=p^{-1}f_p(px_1, x_2, x_3)$; 3) every solution of the congruence $x^2-qy^2\equiv 1 \pmod p$ is congruent (mod p) to a solution of the Pell equation $x^2-qy^2=1$. To prove this result, the author proves that if p, but not p^2, divides both Ω and Δ, and if the conditions 1), 2), 3) are satisfied for this p, the genus of f_p has only one class if and only if the genus of $g=p^{-1}f_p(px_1, x_2, x_3)$ has only one. And, if Ω', Δ' is the genus of g, the g.c.d. of Ω', Δ' is equal to that of Ω, Δ divided by p.

In the last part of the paper, it is proved that the condition 2) is satisfied for given f, p, q if it is satisfied by replacing the ring R of rational integers by rings R_l of l-adic integers, where l ranges over all the prime divisors of $2\Delta/p$. Besides, the representability of $-q$ by g^* in R_l is equivalent to satisfying, by q, a certain congruence modulo a certain power of l. The author proves also that in certain particular cases, the condition 3) is satisfied. *M. Krasner.*

Referred to in E20-31.

E20-31 (14, 850c)

Jones, B. W. Correction to "An extension of Meyer's theorem on indefinite ternary quadratic forms". Canadian J. Math. **5**, 271–272 (1953).

G. L. Watson has shown by a counter-example that the results of the author's paper are not completely correct. This counter-example (indicated in the present paper and which seems not to have been published by G. L. Watson in any other place) is given by the form

$$f=2x^2+12y^2+byz+12z^2.$$

In order to make his results correct, the author adds to his Theorems 2, 4, 6 some supplementary conditions. After these modifications, the author's theorem appears as a generalization of that of Meyer (where the g.c.d. of Ω and Δ is 1 or 2), not to the case where the g.c.d. of Ω and Δ is free from square factors, but only to the case where this g.c.d. is prime (see the review of the author's paper [same J. **4**, 120–128 (1952)] in these Rev. **13**, 537).

M. Krasner (Paris).

Citations: MR 13, 537a = E20-30.

E20-32 (14, 136h)

Skolem, Th. A simple proof of the condition of solvability of the Diophantine equation

$$ax^2+by^2+cz^2=0.$$

Norske Vid. Selsk. Forh., Trondheim **24** (1951), 102–107 (1952).

The theorem proved is the well-known result of Legendre that if abc is square-free, necessary and sufficient conditions for the non-trivial solvability of (*) $ax^2+by^2+cz^2=0$ are that a, b, c are not of like sign and that $-bc$, $-ca$, $-ab$ are quadratic residues modulo a, b, c respectively. This latter condition is proved equivalent to the reducibility of $ax^2+by^2+cz^2 \pmod{abc}$ under the hypothesis that abc is square-free, and this enables the author to treat (*) by discussing bounds for the least nontrivial solution of a linear congruence. Thus a lemma is introduced which is a special case of a theorem on linear congruences of A. Brauer and R. L. Reynolds [Canadian J. Math. **3**, 367–374 (1951); these Rev. **14**, 21]. As a corollary the treatment yields bounds for the minimum solution of (*) which, however, are not quite as good as those of L. Holzer [ibid. **2**, 238–244 (1950); these Rev. **12**, 11]. Another simple proof of Legendre's theorem was given recently by L. J. Mordell [Monatsh. Math. **55**, 323–327 (1951); these Rev. **13**, 534], who also employs bounds for the solution of a congruence, a quadratic congruence however. *I. Niven.*

Citations: MR 12, 11b = D08-9; MR 13, 534c = E20-29; MR 14, 21a = A10-8.

Referred to in E20-43.

E20-33 (14, 247d)

Hemer, Ove. On the solvability of the Diophantine equation $ax^2+by^2+cz^2=0$ in imaginary Euclidean quadratic fields. Ark. Mat. **2**, 57–82 (1952).

The equation of the title, with abc square-free, is shown to be solvable non-trivially in the quadratic fields $R(\sqrt{-1})$, $R(\sqrt{-2})$, $R(\sqrt{-3})$, $R(\sqrt{-11})$ if and only if $-bc$, $-ca$, $-ab$ are quadratic residues of a, b, c respectively. This was shown earlier for $R(\sqrt{-1})$ and $R(\sqrt{-3})$ by Th. Skolem [Norsk Mat. Tidsskr. **10**, 50–62 (1928), pp. 50–54]. In the case of the other imaginary Euclidean quadratic field $R(\sqrt{-7})$, another condition is needed for solvability, which stems from the author's method, a reduction method similar to that commonly used for the equation in the case of rational integers. Say that the index of the equation is the middle value of the three norms, $N(ab)$, $N(ac)$, $N(bc)$. Then if the index is sufficiently large, a new equation of lower index can be obtained, and the two equations are solvable or not simultaneously. Thus the problem is reduced to solving certain special cases with small index. The special case $x^2+y^2+z^2=0$ is established as impossible in integers of $R(\sqrt{-7})$, and so are all equations which reduce to this. The author lists all equations of this type having index less than 22. The result mentioned in the first sentence of this review, then, holds for equations in $R(\sqrt{-7})$ except those which reduce to $x^2+y^2+z^2=0$. *I. Niven.*

Referred to in E16-37.

E20-34 (14, 354f)

Samet, P. A. An equation in Gaussian integers. Amer. Math. Monthly **59**, 448–452 (1952).

This paper is concerned with the following extension of Legendre's Theorem: A necessary and sufficient condition for the equation $ax^2+by^2+cz^2=0$ to be soluble in Gaussian integers, not all zero, if a, b, c are square-free Gaussian integers and are co-prime in pairs, is that bc, ca, and ab be quadratic residues of a, b, and c respectively. The main object is to show that the proof of Legendre's Theorem given in Dickson's "Modern elementary theory of numbers" [Univ. of Chicago Press, 1939, p. 155 ff.; these Rev. **1**, 65] can be adapted to the case where the coefficients and unknowns are Gaussian integers. *B. N. Moyls.*

Citations: MR 1, 65a = Z02-1.

E20-35 (14, 453c)

Brandt, Heinrich. Über das Mass positiver ternärer quadratischer Formen. Math. Nachr. **6**, 315–318 (1952).

The weight (Mass) of a genus G of positive definite ternary quadratic forms is, by Eisenstein's definition [J. Reine Angew. Math. **35**, 117–136 (1847)], the number $M=\sum 1/t$, summed over the classes in G, where t is the number of proper (i.e., of determinant 1) integral automorphs of a form in the class. Eisenstein gave without proof a formula for M in the case of properly primitive forms of odd determinant. Smith [Collected mathematical papers, v. I, Oxford, 1894, pp. 455–509] supplied a proof and also gave the corresponding formulas for all properly and improperly primitive cases. The formulas [loc. cit., p. 499] involve the invariants Ω and Δ of a form f of G, character-values of f and its adjoint, and a numerical factor ζ with values tabulated for 20 cases: type A (16 cases), types B and C (2 cases each). Brandt here considers ternary forms with odd as well as even coefficients of the product terms, that is, in terms of forms, he studies properly primitive ones and the halves of improperly primitive ones. He gives a formula for M which is simpler than Smith's in that ζ is replaced by a factor κ for which there are only 3 cases, viz., the "types" A, B, C, instead of 20. He does not derive his formulas directly by the usual transcendental means but verifies them using Smith's formulas. The relation between his formulas and Smith's is thus made clear. [The same considerations have advantages in the character-theory of ternary forms which the author has developed in the paper reviewed below.] *R. Hull* (Lafayette, Ind.).

Referred to in E20-37.

E20-36 (14, 454a)

Brandt, H. Zur Zahlentheorie der ternären quadratischen Formen. Math. Ann. **124**, 334–342 (1952).

The ternary quadratic form

$$f=a_1x_1^2+a_2x_2^2+a_3x_3^2+a_4x_2x_3+a_5x_1x_3+a_6x_1x_2,$$

with rational integral a's, may be written $f=tf_0$, where $t=\pm$(g. c. d. of the a's) and f has positive signature. With sign so chosen, t is called the coefficient-divisor of f and f is called primitive when t is $+1$. Write x for the row-matrix (x_1, x_2, x_3), or the set of variables, and let A be the symmetric 3-by-3 matrix of the a's such that $f=xAx'/2$. The elements of A have g. c. d. $2|t|$ or $|t|$, according as a_4, a_5, a_6 are all even or not, and f is called of the second or first kind in the respective cases. The discriminant of f is defined to be $-\frac{1}{2}|A|$. Let F be the primitive adjoint of a primitive f and hence of the same signature. The identities

$$(f_1y_1+f_2y_2+f_3y_3)^2-4f(x)f(y)=I_1F(s), \quad f_i=\partial f(x)/\partial x_i,$$
$$(F_1y_1+F_2y_2+F_3y_3)^2-4F(x)F(y)=I_2f(s), \quad F_i=\partial F(x)/\partial x_i,$$

where $s=(x_2y_3-x_3y_2, x_3y_1-x_1y_3, x_1y_2-x_2y_1)$, define the first and second invariants I_1 and I_2 of f, which are the second and first invariants of F. Also $I_1^2I_2=16d$ and $I_2^2I_1=16D$, and I_1, I_2, d, and D are all negative when f is positive definite and all positive when f is indefinite (of positive signature). Ternary forms fall into three types: (1) I_1 odd $16|I_2$; (2) $4|I_1$, $4|I_2$; (3) I_2 odd, $16|I_1$. Ternary prime-discriminants are $-4, 8, -8, -3, 5, -7, -11, 13, \cdots$. The paper is devoted chiefly to showing that all characters of f belong to the prime-discriminants into which I_1 factors, those of F similarly from I_2, provided that when I_1 and I_2 are not both divisible by 16, certain signs are taken into consideration. The claims of the author for the advantages of his notations and methods over those of Smith [Collected mathematical papers, v. I, Oxford, 1894, pp. 455–509] for Gaussian forms (a_4, a_5, a_6 all even) appear to be justified. [See also the preceding review.] *R. Hull.*

Referred to in E12-53, E20-37.

E20-37 (14, 730c)

Brandt, H. Über Stammfaktoren bei ternären quadratischen Formen. Ber. Verh. Sächs. Akad. Wiss. Leipzig. Math.-Nat. Kl. **100**, no. 1, 24 pp. (1952).

Let $f=a_1x_1^2+a_2x_2^2+a_3x_3^2+a_4x_2x_3+a_5x_1x_3+a_6x_1x_2$ be a ternary form with rational, or rational integral, coefficients a_i. The author points out that the arithmetical theory of such forms has been in an unsatisfactory state, requiring a distinction between properly and improperly primitive forms when the a_i are integral, and the consideration of numerous special cases, due to the nearly exclusive attention given to forms with even a_4, a_5, a_6, following Gauss. He avoids this restriction and suitably defines discriminant, coefficient-matrix, divisor of a form, adjoint form, primitive form, first and second invariants, etc., without it. [See his papers: (1) Math. Nachr. **6**, 315–318 (1952); (2) Math. Ann. **124**, 334–342 (1952); these Rev. **14**, 453, 454.] In particular, he defines the stem-factors (Stammfaktoren) of f as those primes common to the discriminants of all integral forms obtained from f by applying a non-singular rational transformation and multiplying by a rational factor. He proves that the stem-factors are the primes p for which, if f is integral, $f(x_1, x_2, x_3)\equiv 0 \pmod{p^n}$ has non-trivial solutions only for a finite number of exponents n. He has previously used them in studying the characters of f, obtaining much simpler results than those of Smith [see (2), above]. This paper is devoted chiefly to their determination, by means of values of Legendre symbols for odd primes, and by various criteria for the prime 2, with different cases according to the power of 2 dividing the invariants or their residues modulo 16. *R. Hull* (Lafayette, Ind.).

Citations: MR 14, 453c = E20-35; MR 14, 454a = E20-36.

E20-38 (15, 15a)

Brandt, Heinrich. Über die Reduktion der positiven ternären quadratischen Formen. Math. Nachr. **9**, 249–254 (1953).

Among the forms equivalent to a real positive definite ternary quadratic form

$$f=a_1x_1^2+a_2x_2^2+a_3x_3^2+a_{23}x_2x_3+a_{13}x_1x_3+a_{12}x_1x_2,$$

that is, forms obtained from f by integral unimodular transformations on the x's, of determinant 1, those for which

$$0<a_1\leqq a_2\leqq a_3, \quad |a_{12}|\leqq a_1, \quad |a_{13}|\leqq a_1, \quad |a_{23}|\leqq a_2,$$
$$|a_{23}|+|a_{13}|+|a_{12}|\leqq a_1+a_2$$

if $a_{23}a_{13}a_{12}\leqq 0$, are called semi-reduced. Among the semi-reduced forms equivalent to f, there are forms for which further $|a_{23}|$, $|a_{13}|$, $|a_{12}|$ have values m_1, m_2, m_3 in some order, where m_1 is an absolute minimum, m_2 is a minimum for the other two when one is m_1, and m_3 is a minimum for the other one when two of them are m_1 and m_2, resp. If two or more permutations of m_1, m_2, and m_3, occur, retain only the forms with lexicographic precedence. At most a change of sign of two of the variables will produce the further conditions $a_{23}\geqq 0$, $a_{13}\geqq 0$, $a_{12}\geqq 0$, unless all three are not 0. Then a unique reduced form is obtained except for the possibility of $a_{23}\lesseqgtr 0$, $a_{13}>0$, $a_{12}>0$. The foregoing conditions have recently been employed by O. Intrau [dissertation as yet unpublished] to construct tables of integral reduced forms, listed by genus and order, and to derive simple rules for determining the number of proper automorphs of such forms. *R. Hull* (Lafayette, Ind.).

E20-39 (15, 106d)

Jones, Burton W., and Hadlock, E. H Properly primitive ternary indefinite quadratic genera of more than one class. Proc. Amer. Math. Soc. **4**, 539–543 (1953).

L'auteur démontre que les genres d'un certain type de formes quadratiques ternaires indéfinies contiennent plus d'une classe. Il en donne, également, des exemples. Les démonstrations sont trop techniques pour pouvoir être résumées ici. *M. Krasner* (Paris).

Referred to in E20-50.

E20-40 (15, 406a)

Malyšev, A. V. On the representation of large numbers by positive ternary quadratic forms. Doklady Akad. Nauk SSSR (N.S.) **87**, 175–178 (1952). (Russian)

Suppose h is a given odd positive integer. The author sketches a proof of the existence of positive numbers m_0 and c depending only on h and having the following property: If $m\equiv 1, 2, 3, 5, 6 \pmod 8$, $(m, h)=1$, $(-m|p)=1$ for all primes p dividing h, and $m>m_0$, if l_0 is an integer such that $l_0^2\equiv -m \pmod h$, and if H is any (Lipschitz) integral quaternion of norm h, then among the $R(m)$ primitive lattice points (x, y, z) on the sphere $x^2+y^2+z^2=m$ there are more than $cR(m)$ for which $l_0+xi+yj+zk=HU$, where U is a (Lipschitz) integral quaternion. This result is a stronger form of a lemma used by Linnik in deriving theorems on the existence of representations of large natural numbers by positive ternary quadratic forms [Izvestiya Akad. Nauk SSSR. Ser. Mat. **4**, 363–402 (1940); these Rev. **2**, 348], and in fact the author states the corresponding stronger form of two of Linnik's theorems. However, no mention is made of the fact that a serious error in the proof of Linnik's lemma was discovered and corrected by G. Pall [Amer. J. Math. **64**, 503–513 (1942); these Rev. **4**, 34]. The reviewer was unable to tell from the sketch given whether or not a similar flaw occurs in the proof of the present author.

P. T. Bateman (Urbana, Ill.).

Citations: MR 2, 348f = E20-9; MR 4, 34d = R52-4.
Referred to in E20-45, E20-52.

E20-41 (15, 406b)

Linnik, Yu. V., and Malyšev, A. V. On integral points on a sphere. Doklady Akad. Nauk SSSR (N.S.) **89**, 209–211 (1953). (Russian)

Suppose q is a given odd prime number and λ is a given positive number less than unity. Using a result of E. M. Wright [Quart. J. Math., Oxford Ser. **7**, 230–240 (1936), Theorem 1] and the main result of the paper reviewed above, the authors prove that there exist positive numbers c and m_0, depending on q and λ, such that if $m\equiv 1, 2, 3, 5, 6 \pmod 8$, $(-m|q)=1$, and $m>m_0$, then on any segment of the sphere $x^2+y^2+z^2=m$ which has surface area greater than $\lambda 4\pi m$ there are more than $cR(m)$ primitive lattice points, where $R(m)$ is the total number of primitive lattice points on the sphere mentioned. This is related to another result of Wright [Proc. London Math. Soc. (2) **42**, 481–500 (1937), Theorem 2]. *P. T. Bateman* (Urbana, Ill.).

Referred to in E16-16, E20-45, E24-54.

E20-42 (15, 406c)

Malyšev, A. V. On the representation of numbers by positive ternary quadratic forms. Doklady Akad. Nauk SSSR (N.S.) **89**, 405–406 (1953). (Russian)

The author shows that the following theorem can be deduced rather easily from a theorem on the representations of large positive integers by sums of three squares which is stated in the paper reviewed second above. Let $f(x, y, z)$ be a positive ternary properly primitive quadratic form with invariants $[k, 1]$, where k is odd, suppose f belongs to the genus such that $(f|p)=(-1|p)$ for all primes p dividing k, and let g be an arbitrary odd positive integer. Suppose m, x_0, y_0, z_0 are integers satisfying the conditions: (i) $m\equiv 1, 2, 3, 5, 6 \pmod 8$; (ii) $(m, kg)=1$; (iii) $m\equiv f(x_0, y_0, z_0) \pmod{8kg}$; (iv) $(m|q)=(-1|q)$ for each prime q dividing g; (v) $m>m_0(k, g)$. Then there are more than $c(k, g)h(-m)$ primitive representations of the number m by the form $f(x, y, z)$ such that $x\equiv x_0$, $y\equiv y_0$, $z\equiv z_0 \pmod g$. Here $c(k, g)$ and $m_0(k, g)$ are positive numbers depending only on k and g, and $h(-m)$ is the number of primitive classes of binary quadratic forms $au^2+buv+cv^2$ (with integral coefficients) such that $b^2-4ac=-4m$.

P. T. Bateman (Urbana, Ill.).

E20-43 (15, 601i)

Skolem, Th. On the diophantine equation $ax^2+by^2+cz^2=0$. Univ. Roma. Ist. Naz. Alta Mat. Rend. Mat. e Appl. (5) **11**, 88–100 (1952).

The author repeats his proof [Norske Vid. Selsk. Forh., Trondheim **24**, 102–107 (1952); these Rev. **14**, 136] of Legendre's theorem and extends it to the case where $a=a(t)$, $b=b(t)$ and $c=c(t)$ are polynomials with integral coefficients, say of degrees n, $n-r$ and $n-s$. If r and s are not both even, non-trivial polynomial solutions $x(t)$, $y(t)$ and $z(t)$ exist if and only if $-b(t)c(t)$, $-c(t)a(t)$ and $-a(t)b(t)$ are quadratic residues modulo $a(t)$, $b(t)$ and $c(t)$ respectively in the ring of polynomials with rational coefficients. If r and s are both even, polynomial solutions exist if and only if these quadratic residue conditions are fulfilled and further a rational number t_0 exists such that $a(t_0)b(t_0)c(t_0)\neq 0$ and $a(t_0)x^2+b(t_0)y^2+c(t_0)z^2=0$ has a non-trivial solution in integers x, y, z. *I. Niven* (Eugene, Ore.).

Citations: MR 14, 136h = E20-32.

E20-44 (15, 936b)

Malyšev, A. V. An asymptotic law for the representation of numbers by some positive ternary quadratic forms. Doklady Akad. Nauk SSSR (N.S.) **93**, 771–774 (1953); erratum, **95**, 700 (1954). (Russian)

Let f be a positive, integral, properly primitive, ternary quadratic form of invariants $[r, 1]$, r odd, with characters $(b/p)=(-1)^{p-1}$ for all primes $p|r$. For any integer m prime to r, denote by $N(f, m)$ the number of primitive representations of m by f. Asymptotic formulas for $N(f, m)$ as $m\to\infty$ are obtained in terms of the prime divisors of r and the number of classes of positive properly primitive binary quadratic forms of determinant m. The proof, employing the arithmetic of quaternions, is related to work of Linnik [Izvestiya Akad. Nauk SSSR. Ser. Mat. **4**, 363–402 (1940); these Rev. **2**, 348]. *I. Niven* (Eugene, Ore.).

Citations: MR 2, 348f = E20-9.
Referred to in E24-54.

E20-45 (16, 450g)

Linnik, Yu. V., and Malyšev, A. V. Applications of the arithmetic of quaternions to the theory of ternary quadratic forms and to the decomposition of numbers into cubes. Uspehi Mat. Nauk (N.S.) **8**, no. 5(57), 3–71 (1953); corrections, **10**, no. 1 (63), 243–244 (1955). (Russian)

This is a semi-expository paper in which the authors give a connected presentation, with full details of proof, of results on positive ternary quadratic forms which they have published (mostly without complete proofs) during the last fifteen years [Izv. Akad. Nauk SSSR. Ser. Mat. **4**, 363–402 (1940); Dokl. Akad. Nauk SSSR (N.S.) **87**, 175–178 (1952); **89**, 209–211, 405–406 (1953); MR **2**, 348; **15**, 406]. The positive ternary quadratic forms studied are those properly primitive forms f with integral coefficients and invariants $[\Omega, \Delta]$ such that Ω is odd, $\Delta=1$, and $(f|p)=(-1)^{(p-1)/2}$ for each prime p dividing Ω. The reciprocal forms to these are also considered. Such forms are singled out because the representations of large positive integers by them can be studied by means of the arithmetic of quaternions, and also because they include important special cases, such as those used by Linnik in proving that every sufficiently large positive integer can be expressed as a sum of seven non-negative integral cubes [Mat. Sb. N.S. **12**(54), 218–224 (1943); MR **5**, 142]. The proof of this last fact is also given in full in the present paper, and apparently one of the purposes of the paper is to put this proof on a sound footing. Unfortunately, an error in Linnik's work which was pointed out by G. Pall [MR **2**, 348; Amer. J. Math. **64**, 503–513 (1942); MR **4**, 34] is perpetuated in the present paper; the correction straightens out the difficulty. However, G. L. Watson's proof of the same result [J. London Math. Soc. **26**, 153–156 (1951); MR **13**, 915] is much shorter and requires less preparation.

P. T. Bateman

Citations: MR 2, 348f = E20-9; MR 5, 142c = P04-20; MR 13, 915a = P04-29; MR 15, 406a = E20-40; MR 15, 406b = E20-41.
Referred to in E20-46, R52-20.

E20-46 **(17, 1056e)**

Linnik, Yu. V.; and Malyšev, A. V. Applications of the arithmetic of quaternions to the theory of ternary quadratic forms and to the decomposition of numbers into cubes. Amer. Math. Soc. Transl. (2) 3 (1956), 91–162.

Translated from Uspehi Mat. Nauk (N.S.) **8** (1953), no. 5(57), 3–71; **10** (1955), no. 1(63), 243–244; MR **16**, 450.

Citations: MR 16, 450g = E20-45.

E20-47 **(16, 680c)**

Watson, G. L. The representation of integers by positive ternary quadratic forms. Mathematika 1, 104–110 (1954).

Let f be a positive definite ternary quadratic form of determinant d and whose coefficients are integers with g.c.d. equal to 1. The author defines n to be an exceptional integer if $f \equiv n \pmod{m}$ is solvable for all integers m and $f=n$ is not solvable in integers. An exceptional integer is called primitively exceptional if it is not of the form $n_1^2 n_2$ with $n_1 > 1$ and n_2 exceptional. Let $E(f)$ and $E_0(f)$ be the number of exceptional and primitively exceptional, respectively, integers of f. The author proves: for any positive δ and sufficiently large d, $E_0(f) > d^{1-\delta}$. *B. W. Jones.*

E20-48 **(17, 128f)**

Jones, Burton W., and Marsh, Donald. A proof of a theorem of Meyer on indefinite ternary quadratic forms. Amer. J. Math. **77** (1955), 513–525.

A proof of Meyer's theorem that a very wide set of genera of indefinite ternary forms have only one class. The proof is on the same lines, but is claimed to be more perspicuous and accurate than Meyer's paper [J. Reine Angew. Math. **108** (1891), 125–139] or the versions of Bachmann [Die Arithmetik der quadratischen Formen, Abt. 1, Teubner, Leipzig, 1898, pp. 233–251] and Dickson [Studies in the theory of numbers, Univ. of Chicago Press, 1930, pp. 35–60].

J. W. S. Cassels (Cambridge, England).

E20-49 **(18, 467c)**

Jones, B. W.; and Watson, G. L. On indefinite ternary quadratic forms. Canad. J. Math. **8** (1956), 592–608.

For an indefinite ternary quadratic form f with determinant d the author defines a multiplicative group Γ_d of square free integers prime to d. Further, he shows that Γ_d has a subgroup $\gamma(f)$ consisting of all those elements of Γ_d which are the l.c.m. of the denominators of the elements of the matrices of the rational automorphs of f and proves that the number of classes in the genus of f is equal to the order of the factor group $\Gamma_d/\gamma(f)$. Moreover, if n is represented by at least one but not all of the classes of forms in the genus of f, then the number of classes in the genus that represent n is equal to the number of classes that do not. *W. H. Simons.*

Referred to in E12-91.

E20-50 **(18, 562d)**

McCarthy, Paul J. The existence of indefinite ternary genera of more than one class. Duke Math. J. **24** (1957), 19–24.

Let f be an indefinite ternary quadratic form whose matrix, A, has integral elements. In the classical notation, let Ω be the g.c.d. of the two-rowed minor determinants of A and Δ is defined by $|A| = \Omega^2\Delta$. The author proves the following generalization of results of the reviewer and Hadlock [Proc. Amer. Math. Soc. **4** (1953), 539–543; MR **15**, 106]. Theorem 1. Let $\Omega = 2^\omega \Omega_1^2 \pi$ and $\Delta = -2^\delta \Delta_1^2 \pi$, where Ω_1 and Δ_1 are odd and π is an odd prime. Let ω and δ be both even and $\omega+\delta \geqq 2$ if $\pi \equiv 5 \pmod 8$, and $\omega + \delta \geqq 4$ if $\pi \equiv 3 \pmod 4$. Then there are at least two properly primitive forms with properly primitive reciprocal forms, which have the given invariants and which are in the same genus but not the same class.

Using related forms the author proves the same result for the same conditions as given above except that $\Delta = -2^\delta \Delta_1^2$ with Δ_1 divisible by π. *B. W. Jones.*

Citations: MR 15, 106d = E20-39.

E20-51 **(19, 838d)**

McCarthy, Paul J. On indefinite ternary genera of one class. Math. Z. **68** (1957), 290–295.

The author gives a set of theorems stating sufficient conditions that an indefinite ternary form be in a genus of one class. Here J is the g.c.d. of the two-rowed minor determinants of the form and K is determined by the fact that J^2K is equal to the determinant. Two of the results are: A ternary indefinite quadratic form is in a genus of one class if 2 is the g.c.d. of J and K and if one of the following hold:

$$J \equiv 8 \pmod{16} \text{ and } K \equiv 2 \pmod 4,$$
$$J \equiv 2 \pmod 4 \text{ and } K \equiv 4 \pmod 8.$$

B. W. Jones (Boulder, Colo.).

E20-52 **(20# 3124)**

Malyšev, A. V. On integral points on ellipsoids. Vestnik Leningrad. Univ. **11** (1956), no. 19, 18–34. (Russian)

The author considers the question of representing numbers by ternary quadratic forms. The basic result is given by the following theorem.

Suppose that $f(x, y, z)$ is a positive ternary integral properly primitive quadratic form of invariants $[r, 1]$ (r odd) belonging to the genus $\Gamma_{[r,1]}$ with characters $(-f/p) = 1$ for all primes $p|r$; g is an odd number satisfying the condition $rg \neq 1$; Λ_λ is the circular-cone region with vertex at the coordinate-origin and solid angle $\lambda > 0$. Let us consider an integer m prime to rg and integers x_0, y_0, z_0 satisfying the following conditions:

$$f(x_0, y_0, z_0) \equiv m \pmod{8rg},$$
$$(x_0, y_0, z_0, 2) = 1, \quad (-m/q) = 1$$

for all primes $q|g$. By $\Pi_{f,m}$ let us denote the ellipsoid $f(x, y, z) = m$, and by $t(\Pi_{f,m} \cap \Lambda_\lambda;\ x_0, y_0, z_0, g)$ the set of integral points (x, y, z) of the ellipsoid $\Pi_{f,m}$ lying in the cone Λ_λ and congruent to $(x_0, y_0, z_0) \bmod g$. Then constants $\kappa > 0$, $\kappa' > 0$ and m_0, depending only on f, g and λ, are found such that for $m > m_0$

$$\kappa h(-m) \leqq t(\Pi_{f,m} \cap \Lambda_\lambda;\ x_0, y_0, z_0, g) \leqq \kappa' h(-m),$$

where $h(-m)$ is the set of classes of integral, properly primitive positive binary quadratic forms of determinant m.

The proof is based on the arithmetic of quaternions. Also formulated are the most important special cases of this theorem, some of which were obtained earlier [Yu. V. Linnik, Izv. Akad. Nauk SSSR **4** (1940), 363–402; MR **2**, 348; A. V. Malyšev, Dokl. Akad. Nauk SSSR (N.S.) **87** (1952), 175–178; MR **15**, 406].

From the above inequality an estimate is deduced for the number of integral points of the ellipsoid $f(x, y, z) = m$ lying in the cone Λ_λ. *G. A. Lomadze* (RŽMat **1957** #3734)

Citations: MR 2, 348f = E20-9; MR 15, 406a = E20-40.
Referred to in E20-56.

E20-53 **(21# 32)**

Malyšev, A. V. Asymptotic distribution of points with integral coordinates on certain ellipsoids. Izv. Akad. Nauk SSSR. Ser. Mat. **21** (1957), 457–500. (Russian)

The author considers the Diophantine equation

$$f(x, y, z) = m,$$

where f is a positive ternary quadratic form with integral coefficients and m is a large positive integer. It is supposed that the invariants Ω, Δ (in the classical notation) satisfy $\Delta=1$, Ω odd, and further that $(-f/p)=1$ for each prime factor p of Ω. (Thus f is rationally related to $x^2+y^2+z^2$.) Let $\mathscr{C}$ be a cone in x, y, z space, with vertex at the origin, and with solid angle λ in the space of X, Y, Z, where $f(x, y, z)=X^2+Y^2+Z^2$. Let g be an odd integer satisfying $\Omega g\neq 1$. Let $t(f, \mathscr{C}, g, m)$ denote the number of primitive representations of m by f which lie in $\mathscr{C}$ and for which x, y, z have fixed residues to the modulus g. Then, as $m\to\infty$,

$$t(f, \mathscr{C}, g, m) \sim (\lambda/4\pi)2^k\Omega^{-1}g^{-2}t(m) \prod_{p|\Omega g} (1+p^{-1})^{-1},$$

where $t(m)$ is the number of primitive representations of m as a sum of three squares. The proof makes use of the analytic arithmetic of quaternions, and is an extension and refinement of work by Linnik.

H. Davenport (Cambridge, England)

Referred to in E12-92.

E20-54 (21# 33)

Malyšev, A. V. Representation of large numbers by positive ternary quadratic forms of odd, relatively prime, invariants. Dokl. Akad. Nauk SSSR. (N.S.) **118** (1958), 1078–1080. (Russian)

The author announces without proof five theorems somewhat similar to the main theorem of his previous paper [reviewed above], but the restrictions on the form f are relaxed considerably. It is now supposed only that Ω, Δ are odd and relatively prime. Now, however, the asymptotic formula is replaced by estimates. The following (theorem 3) may be quoted as representative. Let q be a prime not dividing 2Δ, let g be relatively prime to $2\Omega\Delta$, and let $\mathscr{C}$ be a cone of solid angle λ as before. Let m be a large positive integer, relatively prime to $2\Omega\Delta qg$, such that the congruence $f(x_0, y_0, z_0)\equiv m \pmod{8\Omega\Delta g}$ is soluble and such that $(-\Delta m/q)=1$. Then, with $t(f, \mathscr{C}, g, m)$ as before, there exist m_0, $k>0$, $k'>0$, depending only on Ω, Δ, q, g, $\mathscr{C}$, such that

$$kh(-\Delta m) < t(f, \mathscr{C}, g, m) < k'h(-\Delta m)$$

for $m\geqq m_0$, where $h(-\Delta m)$ denotes the number of classes of positive, properly primitive, binary forms of determinant Δm.

H. Davenport (Cambridge, England)

Referred to in E20-55, E20-57, E20-58.

E20-55 (21# 658)

Malyšev, A. V. The relationship between the theory of the distribution of L-series zeroes and the arithmetic of ternary quadratic forms. Dokl. Akad. Nauk SSSR **122** (1958), 343–345. (Russian)

In an earlier paper [same Dokl. **118** (1958), 1078–1079; MR **21** #33] the author formulated a series of general theorems concerning the representation of a large integer m by positive ternary quadratic forms with odd prime invariants Ω, Δ. In certain of these theorems it was required that there exist an odd prime q such that $(-\Delta m/q)=1$. It is announced in the present paper that this condition can be dropped if the following weakening of the extended Riemann hypothesis holds: For sufficiently large m there is in the region $|s-1|<(\ln\ln m)^2\ln\ln\ln m/\ln^{1/2} m$ no zero of the L-function $L(s)=\sum_{n=1}^{\infty}\chi(n)n^{-s}$, where $\chi(n)=(-4\Omega^2\Delta m/n)$ is a character (mod $4\Omega^2\Delta m$). The proof of one of the modified theorems is outlined.

W. J. LeVeque (Ann Arbor, Mich.)

Citations: MR 21# 33 = E20-54.

Referred to in E20-59.

E20-56 (21# 2622)

Malyšev, A. V. Theory of ternary quadratic forms. I. Arithmetic of hermitions. Vestnik Leningrad. Univ. **14** (1959), no. 7, 55–71. (Russian. English summary)

This is the first of a series of papers which will give in detail proofs of generalisations of results of Linnik [Izv. Akad. Nauk SSSR. Ser. Mat. **4** (1940), 363–402; MR **2**, 348] on the representation of large integers by definite ternary quadratic forms, and of the results of Linnik and the author about their uniform distribution [cf. Malyšev, same Vestnik **11** (1956), no. 19, 18–34; MR **20** #3124]. This paper deals with the arithmetic of Hermitions; that is, the generalized quaternions $x_0+x_1\iota_1+x_2\iota_2+x_3\iota_3$ with norm-form $x_0{}^2+\Delta f(x_1, x_2, x_3)$, where f is a given ternary primitive positive-definite form of invariants $[\Delta, \Omega]$. An integral Hermition is one with integral coordinates $x_0, \cdots, x_3$.

In the first section (§§ 1–10) arithmetic and algebraic properties are developed from first principles without recourse to the general theory of algebras. A key result is that if M is a primitive integral Hermition (i.e. not divisible by a rational integer) whose norm is divisible by a rational integer r prime to $2\Delta\Omega$, and if R is a given primitive integral Hermition of norm r, then there exists an integral Hermition X_0 such that MX_0 is divisible by R on the right and such that $X_0\bar{R}$ is primitive (the bar denotes the anti-automorphism $\iota_j\to-\iota_j$ $(j=1, 2, 3)$). If, further, Norm $M=r$ and MX is divisible by R on the right, then $X\equiv uX_0$ (mod R on right) for some rational integer u. In the second section (§ 11) the author shows that results of his about the representation of numbers by quaternary forms [Izv. Akad. Nauk SSSR Ser. Mat. **23** (1959), 337–364; cf. Tartakowsky, Izv. Akad. Nauk SSSR. Otd. Fiz.-Mat. Nauk **1929**, 111–122, 165–196] ensure the existence of Hermitions with special properties. In the third section (§ 12) the author generalizes to Hermitions the work of Venkov [ibid. **16** (1922), 205–246], which relates the theory of ordinary quaternions to that of binary quadratic forms.

J. W. S. Cassels (Cambridge, England)

Citations: MR 2, 348f = E20-9; MR 20# 3124 = E20-52.

Referred to in E12-92, E20-57.

E20-57 (22# 4676)

Malyšev, A. V. A contribution to the theory of ternary quadratic forms. II. On the theorem of Linnik. Vestnik Leningrad. Univ. **14** (1959), no. 13, 63–70. (Russian. English summary)

The principal result in this paper has already been announced in Dokl. Akad. Nauk SSSR **118** (1958), 1078–1080 [MR **21** #33] and is as follows. Let $f(x, y, z)$ be an integral primitive ternary quadratic form with odd coprime invariants $[\Omega, \Delta]$. Let m be an integer prime to $2\Omega\Delta$ for which there is an integral solution of the congruence $f(x, y, z)\equiv m \pmod{8\Omega\Delta}$. Then there exists an s_0, depending only on Ω, Δ, such that if m is divisible by the square of an integer $s\geqq s_0$ then m is primitively representable by f. Indeed, the number of primitive representations exceeds $\kappa h(-\Delta m)$, where h is the class-number of primitive binary quadratic forms and κ depends only on Ω, Δ.

The basic idea of the proof is to note that m/s^2 is certainly representable by some form in the same genus as f. The detailed knowledge of the automorphs of the form obtained in the first part [same Vestnik **14** (1959), no. 7, 55–71; MR **21** #2622] allows the representations of m by f to be deduced.

J. W. S. Cassels (Cambridge, England)

Citations: MR 21# 33 = E20-54; MR 21# 2622 = E20-56.

Referred to in E12-92.

E20-58 **(22# 4677)**

Malyšev, A. V. On the theory of ternary quadratic forms. III. On the representation of large numbers by positive quadratic forms of odd coprime invariants. Vestnik Leningrad. Univ. **15** (1960), no. 1, 70–84. (Russian. English summary)

The principal results of this paper have already been announced in Dokl. Akad. Nauk SSSR **118** (1958), 1078–1080 [MR **21** #33]. The most general result is as follows. Let $f(x, y, z)$ be an integral, primitive, positive definite quadratic form with odd coprime invariants $[\Omega, \Delta]$. Let q be a prime not dividing 2Δ and let g be an integer prime to $2\Omega\Delta$. Let Λ be a conical point-set with vertex at the origin and subtending there an inner solid angle (in the sense of Jordan) $\lambda > 0$. Let m be prime to $2\Omega\Delta qg$ and such that $\left(-\frac{\Delta m}{q}\right) = 1$. Suppose that there exist integers (x_0, y_0, z_0) such that $f(x_0, y_0, z_0) \equiv m \pmod{8\Omega\Delta g}$. Then there exist constants κ, κ', m_0 depending only on Ω, Δ, q, g, Λ such that the number t of representations of m by f with $(x, y, z) \in \Lambda$, $(x, y, z) \equiv (x_0, y_0, z_0) \pmod g$ satisfies $\kappa h(-\Delta m) < t < \kappa' h(-\Delta m)$ provided that $m \geqq m_0$ (h is the class-number).

The author conjectures that the occurrence of q in these theorems is an accident caused by the method of proof. The method of proof using the generalized theory of quaternions goes back to B. A. Venkov [Izv. Akad. Nauk (6) **16** (1922), 205–246] and Yu. B. Linnik [Izv. Akad. Nauk. Ser. Mat. **4** (1940), 363–402; MR **2**, 348].

J. W. S. Cassels (Cambridge, England)

Citations: MR 2, 348f = E20-9; MR 21# 33 = E20-54.
Referred to in E12-92.

E20-59 **(22# 4678)**

Malyšev, A. V. On the theory of ternary quadratic forms. IV. On the connection with the Riemann hypothesis. Vestnik Leningrad. Univ. **15** (1960), no. 7, 14–27. (Russian. English summary)

The principal result of this paper has already been announced in Dokl. Akad. Nauk SSSR **122** (1958), 343–345 [MR **21** #658]. It is that the results of the previous instalment [see preceding review] can be freed of the auxiliary condition $\left(\frac{-\Delta m}{q}\right) = 1$ provided that the following weakened form of the generalized Riemann Hypothesis is true: For sufficiently large m there are no zeroes of

$$L(s) = \sum_{1 \leqq n < \infty} \frac{\chi(n)}{n^s}, \quad \chi(n) = \left(\frac{-4\Omega^2\Delta m}{n}\right)$$

in $|s-1| < (\log\log m)^2 \log\log\log m/\surd(\log m)$. The author deduces from this hypothesis that there exists a prime q with

$$\left(\frac{-\Delta m}{q}\right) = +1, \quad q \leqq \kappa \exp\left\{\frac{\mu\surd(\log m)}{\log\log m}\right\},$$

where κ, μ depend only on Ω, Δ. This is enough for the methods of the preceding instalment to go through with some modifications.

J. W. S. Cassels (Cambridge, England)

Citations: MR 21# 658 = E20-55.
Referred to in E12-92.

E20-60 **(21# 4938)**

Brandt, Heinrich; und Intrau, Oskar. Tabellen reduzierter positiver ternärer quadratischer Formen. Abh. Sächs. Akad. Wiss. Math.-Nat. Kl. **45** (1958), no. 4, 261 pp. DM 16.

The authors use the notation

$$f = a_1x_1^2 + a_2x_2^2 + a_3x_3^2 + a_4x_2x_3 + a_5x_3x_1 + a_6x_1x_2$$

for ternary quadratic forms, and

$$d = a_1a_4^2 + a_2a_5^2 + a_3a_6^2 - a_4a_5a_6 - 4a_1a_2a_3$$

is the formula for the discriminant. A form in which the a's are integers is called "primitive" if 1 is the g.c.d. of the a's. This table lists all reduced primitive positive ternary quadratic forms with integral coefficients with discriminants from -2 to -1000. There are over 36,000 forms listed. [Cf. the shorter tables of the reviewer, Nat. Res. Council Bull. no. 97 (1935)].

Two forms are of the same genus ("verwandt") if one may be taken into the other by a non-singular linear transformation with rational coefficients. The fundamental discriminant ("Stammdiskriminante") of a genus is the least discriminant among the forms of the genus with integral coefficients.

The adjugate form of f has the coefficients

$$a_4^2 - 4a_2a_3, \quad a_5^2 - 4a_3a_1, \quad a_6^2 - 4a_1a_2,$$
$$4a_1a_4 - 2a_5a_6, \quad 4a_2a_5 - 2a_4a_6, \quad 4a_3a_6 - 2a_4a_5.$$

The author denotes by I_1 the g.c.d. of these coefficients and defines I_2 by $I_1^2I_2 = 16d$. Two forms with the same invariants I_1, I_2 are said to be of the same order and I is defined by $I = I_1I_2/16$.

The basic conditions for a reduced form are

$$0 < a_1 \leqq a_2 \leqq a_3, \quad |a_6| \leqq a_1, \quad |a_5| \leqq a_1, \quad |a_4| \leqq a_2,$$

and, in case a_4, a_5, a_6 are all negative,

$$|a_4 + a_5 + a_6| \leqq a_1 + a_2.$$

These do not define in all cases a unique reduced form and the author merely sketches further considerations leading to unicity. He is not aware of or chooses to disregard the complete conditions obtained laboriously by L. E. Dickson [*Studies in the theory of numbers*, Chicago, 1930, Chap. IV].

In the table, forms for each discriminant are classified according to order and genus and the following invariants given: the number of automorphs, the number of forms in each genus, the prime factors of the discriminant, I_1, I_2, I and the related invariants of Minkowski, the fundamental discriminant and the characters.

This is a monumental piece of work and should be of great service to those working with quadratic forms.

B. W. Jones (Mayaguez, Puerto Rico)

E20-61 **(22# 7976)**

Bašmakov, M. I.; Faddeev, D. K. Simultaneous representation of zero by a pair of quadratic quaternary forms. Vestnik Leningrad. Univ. **14** (1959), no. 19, 43–46. (Russian. English summary)

The authors give necessary and sufficient conditions in order that a pair of quaternary quadratic forms over a field k of characteristic $\neq 2$ or 3 be simultaneously equal to zero, and give an interpretation of the result as a condition for the simultaneous existence of rational points on a pair of curves in projective space over the field k.

W. H. Simons (Vancouver, B.C.)

E20-62 **(22# 8035)**

Aeberli, G. Der Zusammenhang zwischen quaternären quadratischen Formen und Idealen in Quaternionenringen. Comment. Math. Helv. **33** (1959), 212–239.

Let $\mathfrak{A}$ be an algebra of quaternions over the field of rational numbers. As usual in the arithmetical theory of algebras, the author considers those ideals $\mathfrak{a}$ of $\mathfrak{A}$ whose right and left orders are maximal. Two such ideals $\mathfrak{a}$, $\mathfrak{b}$ are called equivalent (in the narrow sense), if $\mathfrak{a} = \rho\mathfrak{b}\sigma$ with $\rho, \sigma \in \mathfrak{A}$ and $\mathrm{Norm}(\rho\sigma) > 0$. There are finitely many corresponding ideals classes. They form under multiplication an algebraic structure which Brandt has called "groupoid".

The purpose of this paper is to show that this groupoid is isomorphic to another groupoid consisting of classes of quaternary quadratic forms. Let $\alpha=(\alpha_0\alpha_1\alpha_2\alpha_3)$ be a basis of the ideal $\mathfrak{a}$ over the rational integers. Put $\operatorname{Norm}(\sum_{i=0}^3 \alpha_i x_i)=\operatorname{Norm}(\mathfrak{a})\cdot F(x_0, x_1, x_2, x_3)$, where the norm of the ideal $\mathfrak{a}$ is taken to be a positive integer. Then F is the quadratic form corresponding to the ideal $\mathfrak{a}$. If certain conventions about the arrangement of the basis elements α_i are made (such that the determinant of the substitution from one basis into another is positive) then it can be shown that F is uniquely determined up to equivalence by the ideal class of $\mathfrak{a}$. Here two forms are said to be equivalent (in the narrow sense) if one can be transformed into the other by a linear substitution with integral coefficients and determinant $+1$. The correspondence $\mathfrak{a}\to F$ then gives the above-mentioned isomorphism of the groupoid of ideal classes of $\mathfrak{A}$ onto a groupoid of form classes. The multiplication of ideal classes corresponds to the so-called "composition" of forms, defined by bilinear transformations of the variables. The forms F corresponding to ideals $\mathfrak{a}$ of $\mathfrak{A}$ have the following properties: (1) The coefficients of F are rational integers with greatest common divisor 1 (i.e., F is integral and primitive); (2) F is a stem form (Stammform) in the following sense. The discriminant of F has minimal absolute value among the discriminants of those integral primitive forms G which can be transformed into a multiple of F by a linear substitution of the variables with rational coefficients. It is shown that all the forms F corresponding to ideals $\mathfrak{a}$ of $\mathfrak{A}$ have the same discriminant D, which is a square. Every form F satisfying (1) and (2) and having the discriminant D corresponds to an ideal of $\mathfrak{A}$. The result of this paper extends a similar theorem concerning the ideal classes of quadratic fields (instead of quaternion algebras) and their corresponding binary norm forms. [Literature: Deuring, *Algebren*, J. Springer, Berlin, 1935; and the papers of Brandt cited there.]

P. Roquette (Tübingen)

Referred to in Z10-45.

E20-63 (23# A858)

Gross, H.

Darstellungsanzahlen von quaternären quadratischen Stammformen mit quadratischer Diskriminante.

Comment. Math. Helv. **34** (1960), 198–221.

This paper treats the representation of rational integers by certain quadratic forms in four variables. These quadratic forms arise in a natural way from the theory of generalized quaternions. Let $\mathfrak{A}$ be a generalized quaternion algebra. Certain subsets of $\mathfrak{A}$ are called ideals. An ideal $\mathfrak{a}$ in $\mathfrak{A}$ has a basis a_1, a_2, a_3, a_4 in the sense that $a_i\in\mathfrak{a}$, $1\leqq i\leqq 4$, and every element of $\mathfrak{a}$ can be expressed uniquely in the form $\sum x_i a_i$, where the x_i are rational integers. The ideal $\mathfrak{a}$ has associated with it a left order $\mathfrak{o}_l$ and a right order $\mathfrak{o}_r$, which are subrings of $\mathfrak{A}$. If $n(\alpha)$ denotes the norm of α, we can write $n(\sum x_i a_i)=\lambda f(x)$, where $f(x)$ is a primitive integral quadratic form in four variables, and λ is rational. Let A denote the ideal class containing $\mathfrak{a}$ and let A^{-1} denote the inverse class. In the present paper it is shown that f represents the rational integer m if and only if A^{-1} contains an integral left $\mathfrak{o}_r$-ideal of norm m. If f is positive definite, then the number of representations of m by f is equal to the product of the number of units of $\mathfrak{o}_l$ by the number of integral left $\mathfrak{o}_r$-ideals of norm m in A^{-1}. If f is an indefinite form, then the number of essentially different representations of m by f is equal to the sum of those divisors of m that are relatively prime to the discriminant of a minimal basis of $\mathfrak{A}$.

W. H. Mills (New Haven, Conn.)

Referred to in Z10-45.

E20-64 (23# A1608)

Latimer, Claiborne

Indefinite ternary forms. (Romanian and Russian summaries)

An. Şti. Univ. "Al. I. Cuza" Iaşi Secţ. I (N.S.) **6** (1960), 21–28.

Let $f=\sum_{i,j=1}^n a_{ij}x_ix_j$ be an indefinite properly primitive ternary form with $a_{ij}=a_{ji}$ integers. Let $-\Omega$ be the g.c.d. of the 2-by-2 minor determinants of its matrix. The author shows that if $\Omega=-1$ and if f is in the principal genus, then there is just one class in the genus. This is included in Meyer's classical result if the determinant of the form is not divisible by 4, and closely related to other known results. The rational quaternion algebra is used in the proofs.

B. W. Jones (Boulder, Colo.)

E20-65 (24# A2560)

Andrianov, A. N.

Generalization of Eichler's theorem in the theory of quaternary quadratic forms. (Russian)

Dokl. Akad. Nauk SSSR **141** (1961), 9–12.

The author proves the following generalization of a theorem of Eichler [Arch. Math. **5** (1954), 355–366; MR **16**, 116] by a method stated to be a generalization of Eichler's. Let

$$F(x_1, \cdots, x_4) = \sum_{1\leqq i\leqq j\leqq 4} a_{ij}x_ix_j = \tfrac{1}{2}X'FX, \qquad (X' = (x_1, x_2, x_3, x_4))$$

be a positive definite quaternary form with integral coefficients a_{ij}, of Stufe q and determinant D. Let $\mathfrak{E}'=(e_1, \cdots, e_4)$ be any integral solution of $F\mathfrak{E}\equiv 0 \pmod q$ and let $t=\text{g.c.d.}\ (q, E'FE/2q)$. Put

$$\theta_F(\tau|\mathfrak{E}) = \sum_N \exp\{\pi i\tau(N'+q^{-1}\mathfrak{E}')F(N+q^{-1}\mathfrak{E})\} = \sum_{0\leqq n<\infty} a_F(n)\exp\left(\frac{2\pi i\tau tn}{q}\right),$$

where the summation is over all integral vectors $N'=(n_1, n_2, n_3, n_4)$, so that $a_F(n)$ is the number of integral solutions of the equation $2qtn=(qX'+\mathfrak{E}')F(qX+\mathfrak{E})$. By a result of Hecke [*Mathematische Werke*, pp. 461–486, Vandenhoeck & Ruprecht, Göttingen, 1959; MR **21** #3303] there is a decomposition $\theta_F(\tau|\mathfrak{E})=E_F(\tau|\mathfrak{E})+S_F(\tau|\mathfrak{E})$ where $E_F(\tau|\mathfrak{E})$ [respectively, $S_F(\tau|\mathfrak{E})$] is an Eisenstein [respectively, a parabolic] form. Let $d_F(n)$ be the coefficient of $\exp(2\pi i\tau tn/q)$ in $S_F(\tau|\mathfrak{E})$. Then there exists an integer Q (depending on F and $\mathfrak{E}$) and a number C_F (depending only on F) such that

$$|d_F(n)| \leqq c_F\tau(n)n^{1/2}$$

for all integers n prime to Q. Here $\tau(u)$ denotes the number of divisors of n.

J. W. S. Cassels (Cambridge, England)

Citations: MR 16, 116d = G30-15; MR 21# 3303 = Z25-14.

Referred to in E12-96, F30-41.

E20-66 (25# 1127)

Estermann, T.

A new application of the Hardy-Littlewood-Kloosterman method.

Proc. London Math. Soc. (3) **12** (1962), 425–444.

Let a_1, a_2, a_3, a_4 k be given non-zero integers such that the first four are neither all positive nor all negative. The author obtains an asymptotic formula for the number $\nu(n)$ of solutions of the equation

$$a_1h_1^2+\cdots+a_4h_4^2 = k$$

in positive constants h_1, h_2, h_3, h_4 such that $|a_jh_j^2|\leqq n$ $(j=1, 2, 3, 4)$. The result is of the form

$$|\nu(n) - K|a|^{-1/2}Dn| \leq Cn^{3/4+\varepsilon},$$

where $a = a_1a_2a_3a_4\varepsilon > 0$ and C is a positive number depending at most on a_1, a_2, a_3, a_4, k and ε. The definition of K and D is somewhat complicated.

L. Carlitz (Durham, N.C.)

E20-67 (25# 2037)

Weber, Oskar
Über die Reduktion und die Darstellungen positiver quaternärer quadratischer Formen.
Comment. Math. Helv. **36** (1961), 181–213.

The author considers quaternary quadratic forms

$$\sum_{i,j=1}^{k} g_{ik}x_ix_k, \quad g_{ik} = g_{ki},$$

with integer coefficients, that is, g_{ii} and $2g_{ij}$ are integers for $i \neq j$. He defines the discriminant of such a form to be $D = 16|G|$, where G is the matrix of coefficients of the form. The author specializes van der Waerden's reduction theory to quaternary forms and shows that in any four-dimensional lattice with discriminant greater than 4 every system of four successive minima forms a reduced lattice basis.

The rest of the paper is concerned with quaternary forms of discriminant 5. For this case he shows that there is a single two-sided class. (That is, every form may be taken into the reduced form by a unimodular transformation of determinant 1 or -1.) He then finds all the transformations which take reduced forms into reduced forms. He derives Eisenstein's and Liouville's formulas for the number of representations by such forms.

Burton W. Jones (Boulder, Colo.)

Referred to in Z10-45.

E20-68 (25# 3904)

Bambah, R. P.
A note on the equation $ax^2 - by^2 - cz^2 = 0$.
Indian J. Math. **4** (1962), 11–12.

Variant of a proof of Legendre's theorem obtained by Minikowski's theorem on linear forms. *B. Stolt* (Stockholm)

E20-69 (27# 5738)

Gongadze, R. Š.
Summation of a singular series related to certain quaternary quadratic forms. (Georgian. Russian summary)
Tbiliss. Gos. Univ. Trudy Ser. Meh.-Mat. Nauk **84** (1962), 239–260.

The following notation is used: M, a, d, n, q, r, λ, ω denote integers; b, m, u, v odd integers; l, χ, α, β, γ negative integers; h, j, k, x, y, z, t integers; ζ a complex number. Define $S(h, q) = \sum_{j \bmod q} \exp 2\pi i(hj^2/q)$ and

$$L(q, h) = \sum_{u=1}^{\infty} \left(\frac{h}{u}\right) u^{-q} = \prod_{p>2} \left\{1 - \left(\frac{h}{p}\right) p^{-q}\right\}^{-1} \quad (q > 1)$$

and

$$A(q) = q^{-4} \sum_{h \bmod q}' \exp 2\pi i \left(\frac{-hM}{4aq}\right) \tilde{S}(h, q),$$

where $\tilde{S}(h, q) = S(h, q)S(a_1h, q)S(a_2h, q)S(ah, q)$. The object of the paper seems to be to sum the series

$$\rho(M) = \frac{\pi^2 M}{4a\sqrt{(a_1a_2a)}} \sum_{q=1}^{\infty} A(q)$$

by applying results of H. D. Kloosterman [Proc. London Math. Soc. (2) **25** (1926), 143–173] and G. A. Lomadze [Trudy Tbiliss. Gos. Univ. **76** (1959), 107–159]. The result stated is

$$\rho(M) = \frac{2^{\alpha} v \pi^2}{\sqrt{(a_1a_2a)}}$$

$$\times \chi_2 \prod_{p|l} \chi_p \prod_{\substack{p>2 \\ p|r}} \left(1 - \left(\frac{\omega}{p}\right) p^{-2}\right)^{-1} L^{-1}(2, \omega) \sum_{d_1d_2=u} \left(\frac{a_1a_2u}{d_1}\right) d_2,$$

where $\chi_p = 1 + A(p) + A(p^2) + \cdots$.

A. J. Lohwater (Providence, R.I.)

Referred to in E28-62.

E20-70 (28# 63)

Timofeev, V. N.
On positive quadratic forms representing the same numbers. (Russian)
Uspehi Mat. Nauk **18** (1963), *no.* 4 (112), 191–193.

It was shown by Delaunay (B. N. Delone) [Zap. Rossiĭsk. Mineralog. Obšč. (1926), and Uspehi Mat. Nauk **4** (1938), 102–164] that if two inequivalent definite integral quadratic forms in two variables represent precisely the same set of integers for integer values of the variables, then they must be equivalent to $a(x^2 + xy + y^2)$ and $a(x^2 + 3y^2)$ for some integer a. By elementary means the author constructs sets of inequivalent definite ternary integral forms which represent precisely the same integers. One set contains four members.

J. W. S. Cassels (Cambridge, England)

E20-71 (30# 3071)

Uchiyama, Saburô
On the distribution of integers representable as a sum of two h-th powers.
J. Fac. Sci. Hokkaido Univ. Ser. I **18** (1964/65), 124–127.

The reviewer and S. Chowla [Proc. Nat. Inst. Sci. India **13** (1947), 101–103; MR **9**, 273] proved the following result: If $c > 2\sqrt{2}$, then for all large n, the inequalities

$$(*) \qquad n < x^2 + y^2 < n + cn^{1/4}$$

have a solution in integers x, y. Their proof also shows that if $c > 2\sqrt{2} + 1/n_0^{1/4}$, (*) have a solution with $xy \neq 0$ for all $n \geqq n_0$. The author shows that if $c = 2\sqrt{2}$, the inequalities (*) have a solution with $xy \neq 0$ for all $n \geqq 1$. His method (especially for the case $n = 2$) is similar to that of the reviewer and Chowla. He deduces from his proof that the integers n for which (*) have a solution for a given $c > 0$ have positive density.

He conjectures that if $c > 3 \cdot 2^{-1/4}$, (*) have a solution for all $n \geqq 1$ with $xy \neq 0$, and if $c > 2^{-1/2} \cdot 5^{3/4}$, (*) have a solution for all $n \geqq 1$. He generalizes his proofs and theorems to numbers of the type $x^h + y^h$.

The question of replacing $n^{1/4}$ in (*) by an n^k with $k < \frac{1}{4}$ is still open. It is not even known if for every $c > 0$, (*) have solutions for all large n.

R. P. Bambah (Columbus, Ohio)

Citations: MR 9, 273a = E24-29.
Referred to in P12-15.

E20-72 (31# 2210)

Germann, Kurt
Tabellen reduzierter, positiver quaternärer quadratischer Formen.
Comment. Math. Helv. **38** (1963), 56–83.

Extending an earlier table of S. B. Townes, the author constructs a table of all classes of positive quaternary quadratic forms up to discriminant 61. Beginning with reduced ternary forms he sets up necessary conditions on the remaining coefficients for inequivalence, and forms a preliminary table of quaternary forms. Then, by developing sufficient conditions he eliminates equivalent pairs from the preliminary table. Finally, he deals with proper and improper equivalence by means of ambiguous forms (forms improperly equivalent to themselves).

Burton W. Jones (Boulder, Colo.)

Referred to in Z10-45.

E20-73 **(31# 2212)**

Wolf, Adolf

Positive Formen der Gestalt $ax^2+by^2+cz^2+dt^2$ mit zwei und drei Ausnahmewerten.

Inaugural-Dissertation zur Erlangung des Grades eines Doktors der Naturwissenschaften der Mathematisch-naturwissenschaftlichen Fakultät der Eberhard-Karls-Universität zu Tübingen.

Dissertation, Tübingen, 1963. vi + 145 *pp.*

The author first surveys previous allied results about representations of integers by positive forms $ax^2+by^2+cz^2+dt^2$ with integer coefficients. In particular, he notes Dickson's determination of all such universal forms (that is, those which represent all positive integers), Halmos's results on forms universal with one exception, Ross and Pall's bounds for determinants of almost universal forms in more than four variables (those which represent all but a finite number of positive integers) and various other allied results.

He then proceeds to almost solve the problem of finding all such forms which are universal with two or three exceptions. He determines that there are 126 forms which are universal except for exactly two integers not represented, with doubt whether or not the form (1, 3, 5, 7) represents all integers except 2 and 22. He shows that there are 93 forms with exactly three exceptions, with doubt about the forms (1, 1, 11, 14), (1, 3, 5, 11), (1, 2, 12, 20) and (1, 2, 12, 22). He builds on results for ternary forms. The calculations are long and intricate.

Burton W. Jones (Boulder, Colo.)

E20-74 **(34# 4213)**

Mordell, L. J.

The representation of numbers by some quaternary quadratic forms.

Acta Arith. **12** (1966/67), 47–54.

This paper deals with the problem of representing the positive integer m by the quadratic form $f=x^2+bcy^2+caz^2+abw^2$, where a, b, c are given integers. Using the result of A. Korkine and G. Zolotarev [Math. Ann. **5** (1872), 581–583] on minima of positive definite quaternary forms, the author first proves the following lemma: If the congruence $cA^2+bB^2+a\equiv 0 \pmod{m}$ is solvable in integers A, B, then there is an integer M, with $|M|\leqq\sqrt{(2|abc|)}$, such that Mm is represented nontrivially by f. A number of examples are then given describing a general method, applicable in many cases, for obtaining a representation of m from one of Mm. *R. Jacobowitz* (Lawrence, Kan.)

E20-75 **(34# 5761)**

Konusbekov, K. K.

Application of the Dirichlet formula on representation of a number by the totality of binary quadratic forms to the study of quaternary forms. (Russian)

Taškent. Gos. Ped. Inst. Učen. Zap. **61** (1966), 20–25.

Let p be a prime; denote by Q the quadratic form $Q=x^2+y^2+p(z^2+t^2)$, x^2+y^2 odd, z^2+t^2 odd. Let $n=p^\beta m=2^\alpha p^\beta r$, with $(m,p)=(2p,r)=1$. The author derives a relation between the number N_1 of representations of $2n$ by Q and the number N_2 of representations of $2m$ by Q, namely: $N_1=(-1)^\beta(-1/p)^\beta N_2+8\sigma(r)(1-(-1)^{2^\alpha})(-1/p)\times(p+(-1/p))^{-1}$, where $\sigma(r)=\sum_{d|r}d$ and $(-1/p)$ denotes the Jacobi symbol. *W. Schwarz* (Freiburg)

E20-76 **(36# 1391)**

Muwafi, Amin

Two Diophantine equations associated with a ternary quadratic form.

J. Natur. Sci. and Math. **6** (1966), 235–236.

Let

$$d=\begin{vmatrix} a & 0 & r\\ 0 & b & r\\ 1 & r & c\end{vmatrix}$$

be the determinant associated with the integral ternary quadratic form $F=ax^2+by^2+cz^2+2ryz+2xz$. Then $d=a\Delta-b$, where $\Delta=bc-r^2$.

The author proves the following theorem: Given two integers a and d, there exist integers b, r and c such that the form F has a as its leading coefficient and d as its determinant. *L. M. Chawla* (Lahore)

E20-77 **(36# 2553)**

Linnik, Ju. V.; Malyšev, A. V.

An elementary proof of the Kloosterman-Tartakovskiĭ theorem on the representation of numbers by positive quaternary forms. (Russian)

Proc. Fourth All-Union Math. Congr. (*Leningrad*, 1961) (*Russian*), *Vol. II*, *pp.* 116–117. *Izdat. "Nauka", Leningrad*, 1964.

Authors' summary: "A short sketch of an elementary proof is given for the following problem of Kloosterman-Tartakovskiĭ. Let $f=f(x_1,x_2,x_3,x_4)$ be an integral positive quaternary quadratic form with determinant $d>0$, let m be a positive integral number for which the congruence $f(x_1,x_2,x_3,x_4)\equiv m \pmod{8dm}$ is solvable; further, $m=m_1m_2$, where m_1 and $2d$ are mutually prime, and $|m_2|\leqq C$. Then there exists an $m_0=m_0(d,c)$ such that for $m\geqq m_0$ the equation $f(x_1,x_2,x_3,x_4)=m$ is solvable in integers x_1, x_2, x_3, x_4." (RŽMat **1965** #7 A117)

E20-78 **(37# 6244)**

Höfliger, P.

Geschlechtereinteilung der reduzierten, positiven quaternären quadratischen Formen mit Diskriminante ≤ 64.

Studien zur Theorie der quadratischen Formen, *pp.* 156–164. *Birkhäuser, Basel*, 1968.

As the title suggests, the author lists all reduced positive-definite quaternary quadratic forms, over the rational integers, having determinant at most 64, classifying them according to genus and computing the Hasse symbols at relevant primes. A discussion is also given of the method by which this list was compiled.

R. Jacobowitz (Lawrence, Kan.)

E20-79 **(38# 117)**

Hadlock, E. H.; Muwafi, Amin

On the equivalence of a ternary quadratic form.

Proc. Amer. Math. Soc. **19** (1968), 1167–1168.

The authors prove that every primitive, positive or indefinite, ternary integral quadratic form is equivalent to a primitive form f where, $f=ax^2+by^2+cz^2+2ryz+2xz$. This extends a theorem of B. W. Jones [Trans. Amer. Math. Soc. **33** (1931), 111–124].

D. G. James (University Park, Pa.)

E20-80 **(38# 2087)**

Asadulla, Syed

Some results on ternary quadratic form.

J. Natur. Sci. and Math. **8** (1968), 53–65.

A ternary quadratic form $ax^2+by^2+cz^2+2ryz+2sxz+2txy$ is always equivalent to a form with the coefficient of xy zero. The determinant is then $d=abc-ar^2-bs^2$. For arbitrary positive integers d and a (with a minor restriction on a), formulae are given determining b, c, r and s for which the resulting forms have determinant d. Proofs and formulae are only given in some representative cases. (See also #2088 below.)

D. G. James (University Park, Pa.)

E20-81 (38# 2088)

Hadlock, E. H.; Muwafi, Amin

On the construction of a ternary quadratic form.

J. Natur. Sci. and Math. **7** (1967), 219–226.

Let $f=ax^2+by^2+cz^2+2ryz+2xz$ be an integral ternary quadratic form. For an arbitrary positive integer d and an almost arbitrary positive integer a, formulae are derived determining b, c and r for which the resulting form f has determinant d. The form can be made either positive or indefinite. $\{(D_1, \delta_2)=1$ in (11) does not follow unless further restrictions are imposed.$\}$

D. G. James (University Park, Pa.)

E20-82 (38# 2089)

Hadlock, E. H.

On the existence of a ternary quadratic form.

Univ. Nac. Tucumán Rev. Ser. A **17** (1967), 7–36.

Theorem: Let Ω^2 and Δ be divisors of a given positive integer d such that $d=\Omega^2\Delta$. Put $\Omega=2^{\varepsilon_1}\Omega_1$, $\Delta=2^{\varepsilon_2}\Delta_1$, $\alpha=2^{\varepsilon_1+\varepsilon_2}\Omega_1$ (Ω_1, Δ_1 odd). Let a be a given positive integer such that $a=\Delta_1^{\varepsilon_3}\cdot a_1$, $a_1=2^{\varepsilon_4}a_2$, $(a_2, 2\Omega_1\Delta_1)=1$; $\varepsilon_3, \varepsilon_4=0, 1$. There are integers b, s, r, c such that the form $f=ax^2+by^2+cz^2+2ryz+2sxz$ has determinant d. Under certain conditions, discussed in the paper, there exists a properly primitive such form f. *H. Gross* (Zürich)

Referred to in E28-66.

E20-83 (38# 2090)

Mennicke, J.

On the groups of units of ternary quadratic forms with rational coefficients.

Proc. Roy. Soc. Edinburgh Sect. A **67** (1966/67), 309–352 (1968).

Let f be an indefinite ternary quadratic form with rational integral coefficients. The author classifies the groups of units with rational integral elements, where a "unit" is a transformation taking the form into itself. The classification is according to the number of rotations of orders 2, 3, 4 and 6. He also considers the groups F of those units which, as hyperbolic motions, preserve orientation. He shows that with a finite number of exceptions they are all subgroups of one particular group of units belonging to the form $f=x^2-3y^2-3z^2$ and having the representation $\{A, B, S|A^6=B^4=S^2=ABS=1\}$. For this he uses some of the methods of the reviewer [*The arithmetic theory of quadratic forms*, Chapter 8, The Math. Assoc. of America, Buffalo, N.Y., 1950; MR **12**, 244].

Burton W. Jones (Boulder, Colo.)

Citations: MR 12, 244a = E02-3.

E20-84 (39# 4100)

Hadlock, E. H.

On the existence of a ternary quadratic form.

Univ. Nac. Tucumán Rev. Ser. A **18** (1968), 81–122.

In this paper, the author proves a theorem (the statement of which is too complicated to be reproduced here) which establishes the existence of a ternary quadratic form (*) $f=ax^2+by^2+cz^2+2ryz+2sxz$ associated with a given determinant of positive integral value d. The author defines Ω and Δ as any divisors of d such that $\Omega^2\Delta=d$ instead of taking Ω as the g.c.d. of the cofactors of the elements of d and then defining Δ by the above equality. However, the conventions of signs on d, Ω and Δ are retained as in L. E. Dickson's *Studies in the theory of numbers* [Univ. Chicago Press, Chicago, Ill., 1930; reprint, Chelsea, New York, 1957].

The author's method of construction is general and explicit and includes positive and indefinite forms. The theorem of the paper shows the existence of a ternary quadratic form (*) with a given determinant d (>0), chosen values of Ω and Δ such that $\Omega^2\Delta=d$, and leading coefficient $a=\alpha n+\beta$, $(\alpha, \beta)=1$, by giving formulas for its coefficients b, s, r, and c in that order.

In view of B. W. Jones' theorem [Trans. Amer. Math. Soc. **33** (1931), 92–110] that any form $ax^2+\cdots+2sxz+2txy$ is equivalent to one in which $t=0$, the form f(*) constructed in this paper is a general one.

L. M. Chawla (Lahore)

E20-85 (40# 2605)

Peters, M.

Ternäre und quaternäre quadratische Formen und Quaternionenalgebren.

Acta Arith. **15** (1968/69), 329–365.

The author studies the relations between quadratic forms with integral coefficients in an algebraic number field K and the orders in the second Clifford algebra attached to them by the reviewer [*Quadratische Formen und orthogonale Gruppen*, § 14, Springer, Berlin, 1952; MR **14**, 540]. But instead of quadratic forms he speaks of lattices in a metric space R over K. Two lattices $\mathfrak{J}$ and $\mathfrak{J}'$ belong to the same "ideal complex", if their p-adic extensions are $\mathfrak{J}_p'=\Sigma_p\mathfrak{J}_p$ with a similarity Σ_p of R_p which is almost always a unit of $\mathfrak{J}_p$. For odd dimension of R the number of genera in an ideal complex of lattices is equal to the ideal class number h_0 of K. For even dimension, and under the assumption that the discriminant Δ of R be not a square, this number of genera is equal to the number of ambiguous ideal classes of $K(\sqrt{\Delta})$, up to a power of 2. If the dimension of R is 3 or 4, more specific statements for the number of lattice classes are made.

First let the dimension of R be 3. The second Clifford algebra $C_2(R)$ is a quaternion algebra over K, and to a lattice $\mathfrak{J}\subset R$ there corresponds an order $\mathfrak{o}\subset C_2(R)$. Let $\mathfrak{o}^*$ be the Dedekind complement of $\mathfrak{o}$ with respect to the maximal order of K. Then $q(\mathfrak{o})=n_{C_2(R)}/K^{(\mathfrak{o}^*)^{-1}}$ is called the basic ideal (Grundideal) of $\mathfrak{o}$. The discriminant $D(\mathfrak{o})$ is the square of an ideal $d(\mathfrak{o})$ in K. A remarkable result of the paper is the following statement: an order $\mathfrak{o}\subset C_2(R)$ is attached to some lattice $\mathfrak{J}\subset R$ if and only if $q(\mathfrak{o})=d(\mathfrak{o})$. (The proof, though still not quite easy, is much shorter than an earlier one given by F. Sohn ["Beiträge zur Zahlentheorie der ternären quadratischen Formen und der Quaternionenalgebren", Ph.D. Thesis, Univ. of Münster, Münster, 1957].) The reduced determinant of such a lattice $\mathfrak{J}$ is then $2d(\mathfrak{o})$. The number of similarity classes of these $\mathfrak{J}$ in an ideal complex is equal to the ideal class number h_0 of K times the number m of types of orders with this basic ideal $q(\mathfrak{o})=d(\mathfrak{o})$.

Secondly, we assume the dimension of R to be 4, and the discriminant Δ of R not a square. Then the Clifford algebra is a quaternion algebra over $K(\sqrt{\Delta})$. Those lattices $\mathfrak{J}$ are of special interest for which the orders $\mathfrak{o}\subset C_2(R)$ attached to them contain the maximal order of $K(\sqrt{\Delta})$. Necessary and sufficient conditions for these cases are given. The number of similarity classes of such orders, subjected to certain further conditions, is equal to the number of types of orders $\mathfrak{o}$ with appropriate discriminant ideals.

Now the number of types of orders in a quaternion algebra remains to be determined. From now on the basic number field K is assumed to be totally real, and the space R totally definite. Under these conditions the number of types of orders $\mathfrak{o} \subset C_2(R)$ of a given local behaviour is expressed in terms of traces of "Anzahlmatrizen" for quaternion algebras which are given in the reviewer's paper [J. Reine Angew. Math. **195** (1955), 127–151 (1956); MR **18**, 297; correction, ibid. **197** (1957), 220; MR **19**, 17]. Two corrections of that paper are necessary in the cases that the order $\mathfrak{o}$ is not maximal, or that the class number of K is $h_0 > 1$.

Not only the number of similarity classes of lattices $\mathfrak{J} \subset R$, but also the traces of the Anzahlmatrizen for such lattices (introduced in the above quoted book of the reviewer [loc. cit., Chapter IV]) are expressed as sums over the traces of certain Anzahlmatrizen of quaternion algebras.

The theory leads in the end to numerical tables, but the general picture is rather complex because of many restricting conditions which are unfortunately inevitable.

M. Eichler (Basel)

Citations: MR 14, 540a = E02-4; MR 18, 297c = F15-3; MR 19, 17e = F15-7.

E20-86 (40# 7200)

Hadlock, E. H.; Moore, T. O.

A new definition of a reduced form.

Proc. Amer. Math. Soc. **25** (1970), 105–113.

The author shows that every integral ternary quadratic form (positive or indefinite) with determinant d ($\neq 0$) is equivalent to a unique reduced form $f = ax^2 + by^2 + cz^2 + 2ryz + 2sxz + 2txy$ with the coefficients satisfying the following conditions. a (or $-a$) is the minimum nonzero integer represented by $|f|$; $t|(a, d)$ and $s = 0$, or $t = 0$ and $s|(a, d)$; $|b|$, then $|c|$, then $|t|$ or $|s|$, are minimal subject to the prior restrictions. Conventions remove sign ambiguities, and determine whether s or t is to be zero when both possibilities occur. Three examples are given illustrating the reduction to the reduced form.

D. G. James (Göttingen)

E20-87 (41# 3396)

Ponomarev, Paul

Class numbers of positive definite quaternary forms.

Bull. Amer. Math. Soc. **76** (1970), 646–649.

From the author's introduction: "Let V be a (quaternary) vector space over the field of rational numbers Q. We assume that the associated quadratic form q is positive definite with square discriminant. Let M be a lattice in V which is maximal integral with respect to q. Denote by H the number of proper classes of maximal integral lattices. The purpose of this note is to announce a formula for H. The method we use is motivated by the successful use of the Selberg trace formula in the computation of ideal class numbers of quaternion algebras over Q." An outline of the proof for the main result is included.

J. S. Hsia (Columbus, Ohio)

E20-88 (41# 5295)

Golubeva, E. P.

The representation of large numbers by ternary quadratic forms. (Russian)

Dokl. Akad. Nauk SSSR **191** (1970), 519–521.

This paper contains conditional theorems of the uniform distribution of whole points on a surface $n = f(x_1, x_2, x_3)$, where $f(x_1, x_2, x_3)$ is a ternary diagonal wholly numerical quadratic form, coefficients of which are mutually simple in pairs and where one of them is positive. The author obtains these results using a combination of methods considered earlier by Ju. V. Linnik [*Ergodic properties of algebraic fields* (Russian), Izdat. Leningrad. Univ., Leningrad, 1967; MR **35** #5408; English translation, Ergeb. Math. Grenzgeb., Band 45, Springer, New York, 1968; MR **39** #165] and by A. I. Vinogradov [Mat. Zametki **1** (1967), 189–197; MR **34** #7485] and by making a certain assumption concerning zero free regions of Dirichlet L-functions with real characters.

In addition, this paper includes an unconditional theorem on the uniform distribution of whole points on the hyperboloid $f(x_1, x_2, x_3) = x_1^2 - x_2^2 + \mathscr{D}x_3^2$, where $\mathscr{D} \neq 0$ is an arbitrary whole number.

The theorem is based on methods used by C. Hooley [Math. Z. **69** (1958), 211–227; MR **20** #3107; errata, see MR **20**, p. 1372] and on results given by D. A. Burgess [Proc. London Math. Soc. (3) **12** (1962), 193–206; MR **24** #A2570].

{This article has appeared in English translation [Soviet Math. Dokl. **11** (1970), 394–396].}

L. A. Kogan (Tashkent)

Citations: MR 20# 3107 = N40-32; MR 24# A2570 = L25-17; MR 34# 7485 = P36-51; MR 35# 5408 = Z02-60; MR 39# 165 = Z02-61.

E20-89 (42# 210)

Ismoilov, D.

The distribution of integral points on an elliptic cone of order two. (Russian. Tajiki summary)

Dokl. Akad. Nauk Tadžik. SSR **12** (1969), *no.* 9, 7–10.

The author computes by standard methods the asymptotics of the number of integral points on a cone.

A. I. Vinogradov (Leningrad)

Referred to in E16-89.

E20-90 (42# 4488)

Intrau, Oskar

Kompositionstafeln quaternärer quadratischer Formen.

Abh. Sächs. Akad. Wiss. Leipzig Math.-Natur. Kl. **50**, *Heft* 2, xxiii + 121 *pp.* (1970).

The study of the composition of quaternary forms led successfully to the development of the groupoid concept by H. Brandt in a series of papers [Math. Ann. **88** (1923), 211–214; ibid. **91** (1924), 300–315; ibid. **94** (1925), 166–175; ibid. **94** (1925), 179–197; ibid. **96** (1926), 353–359; ibid. **99** (1928), 1–29; ibid. **96** (1926), 360–366]. The present work provides examples in seven tables: (I) Composable primitive forms of the first kind with D from 1 through 50; (II) Those of second kind with D from 2 through 100; (III) Composition tables for (I); (IV) Composition tables for (II); (V) The principal forms of fundamental genera with $D = p$ from 101 through 499; (VI) Those for $D = pqr$ from 102 through 994; (VII) The forms and composition tables of the first examples of $D = pqr$ with three ($D = 138$), four ($D = 165$), and five ($D = 273$) principal forms. Here D is the "Grundzahl", essentially the determinant. The calculation relies heavily on an earlier table of Brandt and the author of positive ternary quadratic forms [Abh. Sächs. Akad. Wiss. Math.-Natur. Kl. **45** (1958), no. 4; MR **21** #4983]. The tables (I) and (II) are complete in providing invariants and there it is also pointed out which sets of composable forms share the same groupoid structure.

Harvey Cohn (Tucson, Ariz.)

E20-91 (42# 7593)

Asadulla, Syed

On the existence of a primitive ternary quadratic form.

J. Natur. Sci. and Math. **9** (1969), 161–177.

In an earlier paper [same J. **8** (1968), 53–65; MR **38** #2087], the author constructed ternary quadratic forms with certain prescribed conditions on the coefficients. Here he investigates which of these forms are primitive (properly or improperly).

D. G. James (University Park, Pa.)

E20-92 **(43# 7407)**

Gafurov, N.
Distribution of integral points on the surface $xy=z^2+a$, $1\leq z\leq T$. (Russian. Tajiki summary)
Dokl. Akad. Nauk Tadžik. SSR **13** (1970), *no.* 7, 12–13.

Let $s(T, \alpha, \beta)$ denote the number of integral points (x, y, z) on the surface in the title, subject to the conditions $0<\alpha\leq\{z/y\}\leq\beta\leq 1$ and $1\leq y\leq(T^2+a)^{1/2}$, where α and β are given real numbers and $\{u\}$ means the fractional part of u. In a previous paper [same Dokl. **12** (1969), no. 10, 7–10; MR **44** #151] the author obtained the asymptotic formula $s(T, \alpha, \beta)=\frac{1}{2}(\beta-\alpha)A_2(a)T\lg T+O(T\lg^{1/2}T)$ for $T\to+\infty$, where $A_2(a)$ is a positive constant depending on a. In this paper he improves on that earlier result to $s(T, \alpha, \beta)=\frac{1}{2}(\beta-\alpha)A_2(a)T\lg T+C(a, \alpha, \beta)T+\frac{1}{2}[s(T, \alpha, \alpha)+s(T, \beta, \beta)]+O(T^{9/10+\varepsilon})$ for $T\to+\infty$, where $C(a, \alpha, \beta)$ is a constant depending on a, α and β and $\varepsilon>0$ is arbitrary. A sketch of the proof, based on C. Hooley's method of the estimates of the trigonometrical sums involved [Acta Math. **110** (1963), 97–114; MR **27** #3610], is given. *B. Diviš* (Columbus, Ohio)

Citations: MR 27# 3610 = N40-47; MR 44# 151 = E28-74.

E24 SUMS OF SQUARES

See also Sections D16, P20, R10.

See also reviews A10-8, A66-25, A99-3, C20-31, C20-58, C20-59, D04-46, D08-2, D08-4, D08-10, D08-24, D08-35, D08-42, D08-48, D12-73, D36-15, D48-36, D48-49, D48-73, D52-102, D56-11, D56-23, D56-24, D72-9, D80-50, E02-20, E04-2, E04-10, E04-22, E04-25, E08-38, E12-6, E12-10, E12-19, E12-92, E16-37, E16-70, E20-40, E20-41, E28-2, E28-6, E28-13, E28-14, E28-18, E28-64, E76-2, E76-3, E76-12, F02-23, F10-29, F25-7, F30-11, F35-4, F35-19, H02-4, K10-7, L10-3, L10-13, L99-12, M20-1, M40-35, N24-14, N28-29, N28-31, N28-33, N28-51, N28-54, N28-59, N28-66, N28-78, N36-25, N36-77, N36-86, N56-21, N60-76, P04-22, P04-26, P08-47, P16-12, P16-17, P16-26, P16-29, P20-16, P60-34, P72-29, Q05-46, Q20-1, R14-33, R18-76, R26-37, R28-14, R44-2, R44-3, R44-6, R44-36, R48-26, R48-31, R48-39, R52-4, R52-7, R52-9, R52-11, T35-5, T35-58, T45-4, T55-3, T55-4, T55-6, T55-9, T55-36, T55-46, Z02-4, Z15-5, Z15-41, Z15-70.

E24-1 **(2, 36d)**

Pall, Gordon. On the rational automorphs of $x_1^2+x_2^2+x_3^2$. Ann. of Math. (2) **41**, 754–766 (1940).

The automorphs are represented explicitly each as a matric function $A(t)$ of a quaternion t. This matric function has the multiplicative property $A(t)A(u)=A(tu)$. This leads to the factorization of automorphs of denominator $m=m_1m_2$ as a product of automorphs of denominators m_1 and m_2. Application is made to transforming integral solutions of $x_1^2+x_2^2+x_3^2=n$ into other integral solutions. Throughout the paper results are obtained with elegance and precision and with many details that cannot be indicated here. *M. Hall* (New Haven, Conn.).

Referred to in R52-4.

E24-2 **(2, 36e)**

Pall, Gordon. On the arithmetic of quaternions. Trans. Amer. Math. Soc. **47**, 487–500 (1940).

In this paper the author studies certain divisibility properties of the Lipschitz integral quaternions (that is, those with integral coordinates) and applies his results to the study of the connection between the congruence $v_1^2+v_2^2+v_3^2=0 \pmod m$ and the equation $t_0^2+t_1^2+t_2^2+t_3^2=m$, and to the derivation of known relations concerning binary quadratic class numbers and representation by the sum of three squares. *A. E. Ross* (St. Louis, Mo.).

Referred to in E24-5, R52-4, R52-6, R52-10, R52-18.

E24-3 **(2, 119f)**

Habicht, W. Über die Zerlegung strikte definiter Formen in Quadrate. Comment. Math. Helv. **12**, 317–322 (1940).

Let us denote by "form" a homogeneous polynomial with rational coefficients; the variables are supposed to run through all real values. A form that never assumes a negative value is called definite; a form that always assumes positive values, except of course at the point $(0, 0, \cdots, 0)$, is called strictly definite. Hilbert stated and proved for ternary forms, and Artin proved generally, the theorem that each definite form is the sum of the squares of certain homogeneous rational functions (not necessarily polynomials!) [see Abh. Math. Sem. Hansischen Univ. **5**, 100–115 (1926)]. The author proves the much more special theorem that results from the foregoing when "definite form" is replaced by "strictly definite form." His proof is essentially different from Artin's proof, more elementary and constructive, and reaches the conclusion in a few surprisingly simple steps, starting from a foregoing theorem of Pólya [Vierteljschr. Naturforsch. Ges. Zürich **73**, 141–145 (1928) or Hardy, Littlewood and Pólya, Inequalities, Cambridge, 1934, pp. 57–60]. *G. Pólya* (Providence, R. I.).

E24-4 **(2, 147b)**

Niven, Ivan. Integers of quadratic fields as sums of squares. Trans. Amer. Math. Soc. **48**, 405–417 (1940).

The author proves that in an imaginary quadratic field every integer of the form $a+2b\sqrt{-m}$ is expressible as a sum of three squares of integers of the form $x+y\sqrt{-m}$ (x, y rational integers). To do this he derives a condition that such an integer be expressible as a sum of two squares. Thus for the case of Gaussian integers ($m=-1$), an integer of the form $a+2bi$ is the sum of two squares if and only if not both $a/2$ and b are odd integers; the theorem about three squares follows immediately. In the case where $m\equiv 3 \pmod 4$, it readily follows as a corollary that every integer in the field is expressible as the sum of three such squares. The case of a real quadratic field is also briefly treated. The main tool used is a theorem of Mordell on expressing a quadratic form as the sum of two squares of linear forms with integral coefficients [Math. Z. **35**, 1–15 (1932)]. For example, in the Gaussian case, the author sets $a+2bi=(a+t)+2bi+ti^2$ and then tries to choose t so as to make this quadratic form in $1, i$ the sum of two squares. By Mordell's theorem this turns out to be possible if and only if a, b satisfy the conditions stated above. *H. W. Brinkmann* (Swarthmore, Pa.).

Referred to in E16-37, E16-70, E24-45, E24-61, E24-102, E24-109, E24-111, R48-3, T55-46.

E24-5 **(2, 348c)**

Olds, C. D. On the representations, $N_3(n^2)$. Bull. Amer. Math. Soc. **47**, 499–503 (1941).

Let any integer $n=2^kPQ$, where the prime factors (if any) of Q are of the form $4x+3$, while those of P are of the form $4x+1$. Let the actual factorization of Q be

$$Q=\prod_{\nu=1}^{s} q_\nu^{b_\nu}.$$

Then the number $N_3(n^2)$ of representations of n^2 as the sum of three squares (with the usual conventions as to their enumeration) is given by the formula

$$N_3(n^2)=6P\prod_{\nu=1}^{s}\left\{q_\nu^{b_\nu}+2\frac{q_\nu^{b_\nu}-1}{q_\nu-1}\right\}.$$

This formula is credited to Stieltjes, who used elliptic functions. A proof of it using integral quaternions has been given recently by Pall [Trans. Amer. Math. Soc. **47**, 487–500 (1940); cf. these Rev. **2**, 36]. A completely elementary arithmetical proof, based on the methods of Liouville, is given in the present paper. *D. H. Lehmer.*

Citations: MR 2, 36e = E24-2.
Referred to in E24-9.

E24-6 **(3, 65c)**

Richard, Ubaldo. Risoluzione elementare dell'equazione indeterminata $u^2+v^2=p$, essendo p un numero primo. Atti Accad. Sci. Torino. Cl. Sci. Fis. Mat. Nat. **75**, 268–273 (1940).

Well-known proof for the representation of the primes of form $4n+1$ as sums of two squares. *A. Brauer.*

E24-7 **(3, 65f)**

Skolem, Th. On orthogonally situated lattice-points on spheres. Norsk. Mat. Tidsskr. **23**, 54–61 (1941). (Norwegian)

Consider a sphere Σ of radius r about O. Two points P_i of Σ are called orthogonal lattice points if their coordinates are integers and if the vectors OP_i are orthogonal. For the existence of a mutually orthogonal triple it is necessary and sufficient that r be an integer. If r is odd, then any lattice point P on Σ belongs to an orthogonal triple. Among the other results of the paper we mention: Σ contains two orthogonal lattice points if and only if the Diophantine equation $u^2+v^2=n$, where $n=r^2$, has a solution (here r is not necessarily an integer). *W. Feller* (Providence, R. I.).

E24-8 **(3, 67d)**

Benneton, Gaston. Sur la représentation des nombres entiers par une somme de 2^m carrés et sa mise en facteurs. C. R. Acad. Sci. Paris **212**, 591–593, 637–639 (1941).

The author considers the representation of numbers as sums of 4 squares. An ordered set of four integers $[a, b, c, d]$ which are not necessarily positive such that $a^2+b^2+c^2+d^2=p$ is called a form of p and is denoted by P. Here p is any integer called the argument of P. If a, b, c and d are replaced by their absolutely least residues modulo m we obtain a new form R of argument less than m^2 called the remainder of P on division by m. The product of two forms $P=[a, b, c, d]$ and $Q=[x, y, z, t]$ is denoted by PQ and is defined as the form

$$PQ=[ax+by+cz+dt,\ -bx+ay-dz+ct,\ -cx+dy+az-bt,\ -dx-cy+bz+at],$$

so that the argument of a product of forms is the product of the arguments of these forms. Euler's simplification of a part of Lagrange's proof of the 4 square theorem is translated into the above theory to give a very simple proof of the fact that, if p is a prime and if pq is the sum of four squares, so also is p. The author proceeds to problems of which the following is the simplest. Let X be any primitive form (that is, one whose elements have no common factor) of argument x, and let e be any integer, to find the number of forms E of e for which the form EX is likewise primitive. The number depends not on X but only on e and x and is given by $8Ke\prod(1+1/p)$, where the product extends over all those primes p dividing e but not x. The constant $K=1$, 0 or $\frac{1}{3}$ in different cases. The problem of the number of decompositions of a given form into a product of k forms is considered also, especially for $k=2$ and 3. *D. H. Lehmer* (Berkeley, Calif.).

E24-9 **(3, 67e)**

Olds, C. D. On the representations, $N_7(m^2)$. Bull. Amer. Math. Soc. **47**, 624–628 (1941).

The author gives a purely arithmetical proof of the theorem that the number $N_7(m^2)$ of representations of $m^2=(p_1^{\alpha_1}p_2^{\alpha_2}\cdots p_s^{\alpha_s})^2$ as the sum of 7 squares is given by

$$N_7(m^2)=14\prod_{\nu=1}^{s}\{\sigma_5(p_\nu^{\alpha_\nu})-(-1)^{(p_\nu-1)/2}p_\nu\sigma_5(p_\nu^{\alpha_\nu-1})\}.$$

The method is similar to the one used in a recent paper [same vol., 499–503; these Rev. **2**, 348] to obtain $N_3(m^2)$. The scheme is based on the fact that the arguments of f in a typical sum $\sum_x f(n-kx^2)$ become factorable when n and k are squares, a fact first noted and used by Hurwitz in discussing $N_5(m^2)$. *D. H. Lehmer* (Berkeley, Calif.).

Citations: MR 2, 348c = E24-5.

E24-10 **(3, 162i)**

Chakrabarti, M. C. On the limit points of a function connected with the three-square problem. Bull. Calcutta Math. Soc. **32**, 1–6 (1940).

Let $c(x)$ denote the number of integers not greater than x which can be represented as a sum of at most three integral squares; let $\psi(x)=(c(x)-5x/6)/\log x$. It is known that $\psi(x)=O(1)$. In this paper it is proved that (a) $\underline{\lim}\,\psi(x)=0$; (b) $\overline{\lim}\,\psi(x)=1/\log 8$; (c) every point of the interval $(0, 1/\log 8)$ is a limit point of $\psi(x)$. The method of proof is to find a formula for $c(x)$ based on the representation of x in the scale of 2. *R. D. James* (Madison, Wis.).

Referred to in E24-12.

E24-11 **(3, 163a)**

Maass, Hans. Über die Darstellung total positiver Zahlen des Körpers $R(\sqrt{5})$ als Summe von drei Quadraten. Abh. Math. Sem. Hansischen Univ. **14**, 185–191 (1941).

It is known that the number of representations of a positive rational integer n as a sum of three integral squares is closely related to the number of classes of ideals in the quadratic field $R(\sqrt{-n})$. The author finds an analogous relationship connecting the number $a(\mu)$ of representations of a totally positive integer μ in the field $R(\sqrt{5})$ as a sum of three integral squares with the number of classes of ideals in the biquadratic field $R(\sqrt{5}, \sqrt{-\mu})$. He proves that there exists in $R(\sqrt{5})$ only one class of ternary quadratic forms with integral coefficients and determinant 1; consequently the theta series and the analytic genus invariant $\phi(\tau)$ belonging to the quadratic form $x_1^2+x_2^2+x_3^2$ are identical, and the theorem follows from the expression of $\phi(\tau)$ as a power series. Moreover, it is proved that $a(\mu)$ is always positive; hence every totally positive integer in $R(\sqrt{5})$ can be written as the sum of three integral squares. *C. L. Siegel* (Princeton, N. J.).

Referred to in E24-79.

E24-12 (4, 33d)

Gupta, Hansraj. On numbers of the form $4^a(8b+7)$. J. Indian Math. Soc. (N.S.) 5, 192–202 (1941).

This paper is concerned with the number $k(n)$ of integers not exceeding n which are not sums of less than 4 squares. By considering the digits of n when written to the base 4 it is readily shown that for $s\geqq 0$ and for each m such that $1\leqq m\leqq 4s$, there exists an n such that $4^{s-1}\leqq n<4^s$ for which $m=n-6k(n)$. From this result it follows that for the function $F(n)=(n/6-k(n))/\log n$, $\liminf F(n)=0$, $\limsup F(n)=1/\log 8$, and that every point between these limits is a limit point of $F(n)$. These three facts were proved previously by M. C. Chakrabarti [Bull. Calcutta Math. Soc. **32**, 1–6 (1940); these Rev. **3**, 162]. The rest of the paper considers the number $N(m, s)$ of values of $n<4^s$ for which $n-6k(n)=m$. In particular cases, such as $m=4s-1$, in which $N(4s-1, s)$ is the sth term of the Fibonacci series, explicit results are obtained. *D. H. Lehmer.*

Citations: MR 3, 162i = E24-10.

E24-13 (5, 33g)

Kloosterman, H. D. Simultane Darstellung zweier ganzen Zahlen als einer Summe von ganzen Zahlen und deren Quadratsumme. Math. Ann. **118**, 319–364 (1942).

The author studies the number $r_s(n, m)$ of solutions of the following system of Diophantine equations:

$$x_1^2+x_2^2+\cdots+x_s^2=n,\quad x_1+x_2+\cdots+x_s=m,$$

where n and m are positive integers. The Hardy-Littlewood methods easily apply to give approximations for $r_s(n, m)$ even when the sum of squares is replaced by any positive definite form with integral coefficients and the linear form by any linear form with integral coefficients; but the author's aim is to use these approximations to get exact results for certain special cases. Using methods based on those of Mordell and Hardy [L. J. Mordell, Quart. J. Math. **48**, 93–104 (1917); G. H. Hardy, Trans. Amer. Math. Soc. **21**, 255–284 (1920)] he proves certain results leading to the following three theorems. For $s=3, 5, 7$ it is true that $r_s(n, m)\neq 0$ only if $m^2\leqq sn$ and $m\equiv n \pmod 2$. In case $m^2=sn$, then $r_s(n, m)=1$. In case $m^2<sn$ and $m\equiv n\pmod 2$, then

$$r_3(n, m)=3\sum_{d|N}\left(\frac{d}{3}\right),$$

$$r_5(n, m)=5N\sum_{d|N}\left(\frac{d}{5}\right)\cdot\frac{1}{d},$$

$$r_7(n, m)=\frac{7N^2}{8}\sum_{d|N}\left(\frac{d}{7}\right)\cdot\frac{1}{d^2}$$

for $N\not\equiv 0\pmod s$ and

$$r_3(n, m)=6\sum_{d|N}\left(\frac{d}{3}\right),$$

$$r_5(n, m)=5N\left(1-\left(\frac{N_0}{5}\right)\cdot\frac{1}{5^\beta}\right)\sum_{d|N_0}\left(\frac{d}{5}\right)\cdot\frac{1}{d},$$

$$r_7(n, m)=\frac{7N^2}{8}\left(1-\left(\frac{N_0}{7}\right)\cdot\frac{1}{7^{2\beta}}\right)\sum_{d|N_0}\left(\frac{d}{7}\right)\cdot\frac{1}{d^2}$$

for $N\equiv 0\pmod s$, where β is the highest power of s dividing $N=\frac{1}{2}(sn-m^2)$ and $N=s^\beta N_0$, while the sums range over all positive divisors of N and N_0, respectively. By letting m vary, new formulas for the sum of 3, 5 and 7 squares are obtained. *B. W. Jones* (Ithaca, N. Y.).

Referred to in E24-39, E24-40, E24-48, E24-52, E24-53, E24-59, E24-92.

E24-14 (6, 37d)

Levi, B. Some elementary notions of the theory of numbers. Math. Notae **4**, 65–79 (1944). (Spanish)

An expository article on Gaussian complex integers and some related matters, written to prepare the reader for the paper reviewed below. *H. W. Brinkmann.*

E24-15 (6, 37e)

Uspensky, J. V. A new proof of Jacobi's theorem. Math. Notae **4**, 80–89 (1944). (Spanish)

It is known that the theorem of Jacobi on the number of representations of a positive integer n as a sum of four squares can be deduced from Eisenstein's formula for the number of primitive representations as the sum of four squares. It is Eisenstein's formula for an odd n that is derived in this paper. To do this, the author shows that all primitive solutions of the equation (1) $t^2=4x^2+4y^2+z^2$ with t odd are obtained by the formulas $x+yi=\alpha\bar{\beta}$, $t=\alpha\bar{\alpha}+\beta\bar{\beta}$, $z=\beta\bar{\beta}-\alpha\bar{\alpha}$, where α, β are relatively prime Gaussian complex integers; each solution of (1) occurs exactly four times. If we set $\alpha=a+bi$, $\beta=c+di$, we get $t=a^2+b^2+c^2+d^2$, where a, b, c, d are subject to the restriction that α, β are relatively prime. This restriction is removed by a simple device (although a, b, c, d continue to be relatively prime) and thus a relation is established between the number of primitive representations of t as a sum of four squares and the number of solutions of (1). It remains only to derive a formula for the number of solutions of (1); the author does this by using a theorem of Liouville which itself can be derived either by using an identity in the theory of elliptic functions or by the well-known elementary methods discovered by Liouville. *H. W. Brinkmann* (Swarthmore, Pa.).

Referred to in A44-2.

E24-16 (6, 58d)

Basoco, M. A. On certain arithmetical functions due to G. Humbert. Bull. Amer. Math. Soc. **50**, 547–555 (1944).

The functions in question are integral functions of z and satisfy functional equations of the form

$$h(z+\pi)=(-)^a h(z),\quad h(z+\pi\tau)=(-)^b h(z)+F_{ab}^{(\alpha)}(z),$$

where a, b are 0 or 1 and $F_{ab}^{(\alpha)}(z)$ is an expression which involves $\vartheta_\alpha(z)$. The solution $H_{ab}^{(\alpha)}(z)$ of the functional equations is uniquely determined except when $a=b=0$, when the additional condition $H_{00}^{(\alpha)}(0)=0$ makes the determination unique. The solutions are given in the form of Fourier series; for instance,

$$H_{00}^{(2)}(z)=4\sum_{n=1}^{\infty}(q^{n(n+1)}/(1-q^{2n}))\sin 2nz,$$

where $q=e^{i\pi\tau}$. The Fourier series can be converted into an "arithmetized form," for example,

$$H_{00}^{(2)}(z)=4\sum_{n=1}^{\infty}q^n\{\textstyle\sum'\sin 2\delta z\},$$

where $\sum'$ refers to the summation over the conjugate divisors (d, δ) of n such that $\delta<d$ and $\delta-d\equiv 1\pmod 2$. The comparison of the arithmetized series with the trigonometric developments for certain theta quotients leads to identities between $H_{ab}^{(\alpha)}(z)$ and theta functions. These identities may be paraphrased into arithmetical relations of which a sample is

$$\sum f(x_1)=2\sum(t+\tau-4h)f(\tau+2h),$$

where $f(x)$ is an arbitrary even function, β is a positive integer of the form $4k+3$ partitioned as follows:

$$\beta = x_1^2+x_2^2+x_3^2+w_1^2+w_2^2=4h^2+tz, \qquad \tau<t,$$

and the summation extends over all partitions. The paraphrased formulae with $f(x)=1$ yield enumerations relative to the number of representations of a number as a sum of five squares. There are also applications to relations between the greatest integer function and certain incomplete numerical functions of the divisors of an integer.

A. Erdélyi (Edinburgh).

E24-17 (9, 412g)

Basoco, M. A. On certain arithmetical functions due to M. Georges Humbert. J. Math. Pures Appl. (9) **26** (1947), 237–250 (1948).

Humbert's functions are entire functions which are related to the theta functions by the functional equations which determine them. The author displays these functions along with their functional equations. He also obtains identities involving these functions and theta functions from which he is able to find formulas connected with the representation of an integer as a sum of five squares.

H. S. Zuckerman (Seattle, Wash.).

E24-18 (6, 259d)

Rankin, R. A. On the representations of a number as a sum of squares and certain related identities. Proc. Cambridge Philos. Soc. **41**, 1–11 (1945).

Define $s_r=\sum_{i=1}^4 x_i^r$ and $t_1=s_1$, $t_2=s_2$, $t_3=s_3-\frac{3}{4}s_2s_1+\frac{1}{8}s_1^3$, $t_4=s_4-s_3s_1$. If G is any function of t_1, t_2, t_4, and an odd function of t_3, and if n is any positive even integer, then $\sum G(t_1, t_2, t_3, t_4)=0$, the sum being over all x_1, x_2, x_3, x_4 which are solutions of $\sum_{i=1}^4 x_i^2=n$. The x_i may be positive, negative, or zero. This is a typical one of several identities proved. Whereas this one involves a Diophantine equation with a sum of four squares, other identities involve eight squares and, more generally, $4c$ squares. Some identities are summations over those particular solutions of the Diophantine equation which satisfy $x_i\equiv 1 \pmod 4$ for all i. The results are obtained by elementary methods, and it is shown that they may also be derived by equating coefficients in elliptic function expansions.

I. Niven.

E24-19 (7, 50b)

Banerjee, D. P. On the application of the congruence property of Ramanujan's function to certain quaternary form. Bull. Calcutta Math. Soc. **37**, 24–26 (1945).

The author considers the number $N_k(n)$ of solutions $(r_1, \cdots, r_k)$ of

$$kn=\sum_{i=1}^{k}(2r_i+1)^2, \qquad k=2, 4, 8,$$

where n is a given odd integer, and notes that

$$N_4(n)\equiv N_8(n)\equiv \tau(n) \pmod 2,$$
$$N_2(n)\equiv \tau(n) \pmod 4,$$

where $\tau(n)$ is Ramanujan's function. [The author's remarks on the number of solutions of

$$4n=a_1^2+a_2^2+a_3^2+a_4^2+du^2$$

appear to be erroneous.]

D. H. Lehmer.

E24-20 (7, 146e)

Pry, G., et Prigogine, I. Rayons et nombres de coordination de quelques réseaux simples. Acad. Roy. Belgique. Bull. Cl. Sci. (5) **28**, 866–873 (1942).

Suppose that a lattice contains N_k points at distance R_k from the origin, for $k=1, 2, \cdots$. In the case of the simple cubic lattice we have $N_k=\nu_k$, the number of ways of expressing k as a sum of three integral squares; for example, $\nu_{14}=48$ from the permutations of $(\pm1)^2+(\pm2)^2+(\pm3)^2$. Here $R_k^2=k$ (and $R_1^2=1$). In the case of the body-centered cubic lattice, the N's are the nonvanishing terms of the sequence μ_3, μ_4, $\cdots$, where μ_q is the number of ways of expressing q as a sum of three squares all of the same parity as q itself; thus $\mu_{4n}=\nu_n$, $\mu_{8n+3}=\nu_{8n+3}$, but every other $\mu_q=0$. Here $R_k^2=q$ and $R_1^2=3$, so $R_k^2/R_1^2=q/3$. Finally, in the case of the face-centered (or close packed) cubic lattice we have $N_k=\nu_{2k}$, $R_k^2=2k$, $R_1^2=2$, $R_k^2/R_1^2=k$. The authors tabulate these sequences up to $k=25$, without mentioning their interdependence. They give the correct value $N_7=\nu_{14}=48$ for the close packed lattice, but the incorrect value 24 for ν_{14} and μ_{56} (cited as $R_k^2/R_1^2=18\frac{2}{3}$) in connection with the other two lattices.

H. S. M. Coxeter.

E24-21 (7, 242h)

Drach, Jules. Sur quelques points de théorie des nombres et sur la théorie générale des courbes algébriques. C. R. Acad. Sci. Paris **221**, 729–732 (1945).

The author gives, by the method of descent, proofs of well-known theorems on the numbers represented by the sums of two, three and four squares and by the sum of three triangular numbers. He also gives a means of classification of algebraic curves with certain specified types of singularities. There seems to be little connection between the two parts of the paper.

B. W. Jones (Ithaca, N. Y.).

E24-22 (7, 415d)

Reitan, L. On solutions of the number theoretical equation $x^2+y^2+z^2+v^2=t$ for a given t. Norsk Mat. Tidsskr. **28**, 21–23 (1946). (Norwegian)

E24-23 (7, 507d)

Marengoni, A. Sulla scomponibilità di un intero nella somma di due quadrati. Period. Mat. (4) **22**, 182–185 (1942).

E24-24 (8, 7e)

Skolem, Th. A relation between the congruence $x^2+y^2+z^2+u^2\equiv 0$ (mod. m) and the equation $x^2+y^2+z^2+u^2=m$. Norsk. Mat. Tidsskr. **25**, 76–87 (1943). (Norwegian)

The author gives a new proof of the theorem of Jacobi on the number of representations of a positive integer m as a sum of four squares. A proof by Hurwitz [Nachr. Ges. Wiss. Göttingen. Math. Phys. Kl. **1896**, 314–340] is based on the theory of quaternions. The author's proof, which is much simpler, also uses the arithmetic of quaternions, but only its elements. It makes evident the relation between the equation $x^2+y^2+z^2+u^2=m$ and the congruence $x^2+y^2+z^2+u^2\equiv 0 \pmod m$.

T. Nagell.

Referred to in E24-32.

E24-25 (8, 11a)

Barbilian, D. Modernisierung des Beweises des Dirichlet-Jacobischen Satzes. Mathematica, Timişoara **22**, 159–169 (1946).

The modernization begins with the use of the Wedderburn theorem that every finite skew field is commutative, instead of the more old fashioned result that $x^2+y^2+1\equiv 0 \pmod p$ is solvable for every prime p. From this the author proves that every integer is representable as a sum of four squares (a result first proved by Lagrange). He does not prove the theorems of Jacobi and Dirichlet on the number of representations but, using the arithmetic of integral quaternions, he derives related theorems on the enumeration of right ideals of odd square-free norm.

M. Hall.

E24-26 (8, 502a)

van der Blij, F. On the theory of simultaneous linear and quadratic representation. I, II, III. Nederl. Akad. Wetensch., Proc. **50**, 31–40, 41–48, 166–172 = Indagationes Math. **9**, 16–25, 26–33, 129–135 (1947).

The author determines the numbers of solutions of the following pairs of simultaneous Diophantine equations: (1) $x_1^2+x_2^2+\cdots+x_r^2=n$, $x_1+x_2+\cdots+x_r=m$ in the cases $r=3, 4, 5, 8$; (2) $s_1x_1^2+s_2x_2^2+s_3x_3^2=n$, $s_1x_1+s_2x_2+s_3x_3=m$ in the cases (a) $s_1=s_2=1$, $s_3=2$, (b) $s_1=s_2=1$, $s_3=3$, (c) $s_1=1$, $s_2=s_3=2$, (d) $s_1=1$, $s_2=s_3=3$, (e) $s_1=3$, $s_2=2$, $s_3=1$; (3) $9x_1^2+x_2^2+x_3^2+x_4^2=n$, $9x_1+x_2+x_3+x_4=m$.
T. Estermann (London).

Referred to in E24-48, E24-52, E24-59, E24-92.

E24-27 (8, 502b)

van der Blij, F. On the theory of simultaneous linear and quadratic representation. IV, V. Nederl. Akad. Wetensch., Proc. **50**, 298–306, 390–396 = Indagationes Math. **9**, 188–196, 248–254 (1947).

[Cf. the preceding review.] The author determines the number of solutions of the simultaneous Diophantine equations $x_1^2+x_2^2+\cdots+x_r^2=n$, $x_1+x_2+\cdots+x_r=m$, for $r=5$, 6 and 7, and shows that the analogous result for $r=9$ is not true. He also obtains formulae for the number of representations of a number as the sum of (i) three octagonal numbers, (ii) three pentagonal numbers, (iii) four triangular numbers. He determines the numbers of solutions of certain cubic Diophantine equations, e.g., $x^3+y^3+z^3-3xyz=N$.
T. Estermann (London).

Referred to in E24-52, E24-92.

E24-28 (8, 566f)

Gupta, Hansraj. A table of values of $N_3(t)$. Proc. Nat. Inst. Sci. India **13**, 35–63 (1947).

The main table of this paper gives the number $n_3(k)$ of sets (x, y, z) of nonnegative integers for which $x^2+y^2+z^2=k$ for $k=1(1)10000$. These values are subtotalled at intervals of 8, thus giving values of the sum function $N_3(t)=\sum_{k=0}^{t}n_3(k)$ for $t=8m-1$, $m=1(1)1250$. There is a short table, based on the main table, giving data on the lattice points inside circles and spheres. Let $C(r)$ and $S(r)$ denote the number of points with integer coordinates inside or on the circle and sphere, respectively, of radius r about the origin. The table gives these functions for $r=1(1)100$ together with $N_3(r^2)$ and $N_2(r^2)$ (the number of pairs (x, y) of nonnegative integers for which $x^2+y^2\leqq r^2$). For comparison with $S(r)$, the nearest integer to the volume of a sphere of radius r is also given. *D. H. Lehmer* (Berkeley, Calif.).

Referred to in E24-38.

E24-29 (9, 273a)

Bambah, R. P., and Chowla, S. On numbers which can be expressed as a sum of two squares. Proc. Nat. Inst. Sci. India **13**, 101–103 (1947).

By a straightforward elementary construction the authors prove the existence of a constant C such that for $x>0$ there is at least one integer between x and $x+Cx^{\frac{1}{4}}$ which can be expressed as a sum of two squares. They remark that this is obviously very far from the probable truth.
P. T. Bateman (New Haven, Conn.).

Referred to in E20-71, E76-12, P12-15, P12-21.

E24-30 (10, 182c)

Lehmer, D. H. On the partition of numbers into squares. Amer. Math. Monthly **55**, 476–481 (1948).

Let $P_k(n)$ denote the number of partitions of n into k squares, i.e., the number of sets of integers $(x_1, \cdots, x_k)$ such that $0\leqq x_1\leqq\cdots\leqq x_k$ and $x_1^2+\cdots+x_k^2=n$. For every positive integer k except 3, the author determines all positive integers n for which $P_k(n)=1$. In the case $k=3$, since $P_3(4n)=P_3(n)$, it is sufficient to consider numbers n not divisible by 4. The author determines all such numbers n for which $P_3(n)=1$ up to 427, and shows that there are no more up to 10 000, and that there cannot be infinitely many. His list is therefore probably complete. *T. Estermann.*

Referred to in D52-102.

E24-31 (10, 283d)

Sprague, R. Über Zerlegungen in ungleiche Quadratzahlen. Math. Z. **51**, 289–290 (1948).

The author shows in a quite elementary way that every positive integer greater than 128 is the sum of distinct squares. The proof depends on showing with a small list of such representations that the integers between 129 and 256 are sums of distinct squares not exceeding 100. There are exactly 32 integers 2, 3, 6, 7, 8, 11, $\cdots$, 128 which are not the sum of distinct squares. *D. H. Lehmer.*

Referred to in A46-7, A46-8, D52-40, P99-3.

E24-32 (11, 582d)

Skolem, Th. Remarks on the representation of natural numbers as sums of three or four squares. Norske Vid. Selsk. Forh., Trondheim **21**, no. 39, 172–175 (1949).

New proofs are given of the following two theorems, the first being used to prove the second. If the positive integer m is a divisor of the norm $N(A)$ of a Lipschitz integral quaternion A, then there exists an integral quaternion B of norm m such that m is a divisor of $A'B$, where A' denotes the conjugate of A. (Proof is given for m odd.) If an integer m is a sum of three rational squares, it is a sum of three integral squares. The proof of the first theorem is based on previous work of the author [Norsk Mat. Tidsskr. **25**, 76–87 (1943); these Rev. **8**, 7] on the arithmetic of quaternions.
I. Niven (Eugene, Ore.).

Citations: MR 8, 7e = E24-24.

E24-33 (12, 676g)

Pall, Gordon. Sums of two squares in a quadratic field. Duke Math. J. **18**, 399–409 (1951).

The author uses $r_2(d)$ to denote the number of representations of d as the sum of the squares of two rational integers. He proves: a quadratic form f can be expressed as the sum of squares of two linear forms with integral coefficients if and only if $f=d_1f_1$, where f_1 is primitive, positive definite or semidefinite, and of a square determinant m^2, and d_1 is a positive integer such that no prime of the form $4n+3$ divides d_1 to an odd exponent. If $m^2\neq 0$, the number of representations is $2r_2(d_1)$; if $m^2=0$, the number is $r_2(d_1)$. These results are applied to find the number of representations of $a+2k\rho$ in the ring $R(\rho)$ of quadratic integers specifically for $\rho^2=-1$, 2 or $\rho^2+\rho+1=0$. Investigation of other cases by students of the author is promised. Reference is made to the allied work of Hel Braun [J. Reine Angew. Math. **178**, 34–64 (1937)] and Mordell [Math. Z. **35**, 1–15 (1932)].
B. W. Jones (Boulder, Colo.).

Referred to in E16-70, E24-110, E24-111, E24-126.

E24-34 (12, 805b)

Lomadze, G. A. On the representation of numbers by sums of an odd number of squares. Akad. Nauk Gruzin. SSR. Trudy Tbiliss. Mat. Inst. Razmadze **17**, 281–314 (1949). (Georgian. Russian summary)

In an earlier paper [same Trudy **16**, 231–275 (1948)] the author obtained explicit formulae for the number $r_s(n)$ of representations of n as the sum of s squares, where s is odd and $9\leqq s\leqq 23$. These formulae involve infinite products of the type

$$\prod_{p\nmid n}\left\{1-\left(\frac{\pm n}{p}\right)p^{-\sigma}\right\}^{-1}, \qquad \sigma=\frac{s-1}{2},$$

where $\left(\frac{a}{b}\right)$ denotes Jacobi's symbol. The object of the present paper is to replace these products by finite expressions. If $n=l^2t$, where t is squarefree, it is easily seen that the problem reduces to that of expressing the series

$$L(\sigma, \pm t)=\sum_{u=1}^{\infty}\left(\frac{\pm t}{u}\right)u^{-\sigma}$$

in finite form. The method, though elementary, involves a considerable amount of computation, and since the full statement of results proved in the paper takes up some 13 pages it is impossible to quote them here in detail. As an example we may, however, mention the identity

$$r_{13}(n)=\frac{3932160}{691}\pi^{-6}n^{11/2}\chi_2(n)T_6(n)L(6,t)+\frac{6968}{691}\sum(x_1^4-3x_1^2x_2^2);$$

here the summation on the right ranges over sets of integers $x_1, \cdots, x_5$ satisfying $x_1^2+\cdots+x_5^2=n$; $\chi_2(n)$ depends on the residues (mod 8) of γ and m, where $n=2^\gamma m$, and m is odd; $T_6(n)$ is a rather complicated finite product, and $L(6, t)$ can be expressed, in each of the cases that may arise, as a finite sum. For instance, when $t>1$, $t\equiv1$ (mod 4), we have

$$L(6,t)=-2\pi^6t^{-\frac{1}{2}}\sum_{0<h\leqq\frac{1}{2}t}\left(\frac{h}{t}\right)\left\{\frac{h^2}{2^4\cdot3\cdot t^2}-\frac{h^4}{2^2\cdot3\cdot t^4}+\frac{h^5}{3\cdot5\cdot t^5}\right\}.$$

L. Mirsky (Bristol).

Referred to in E12-118, E24-58.

E24-35 (13, 111i)

Bateman, Paul T. On the representations of a number as the sum of three squares. Trans. Amer. Math. Soc. **71**, 70–101 (1951).

The problem of representation of integers as sums of squares has received a great deal of attention [see, for instance, the bibliography at the end of the paper under review]. In particular it was proved by G. H. Hardy that, for $5\leqq s\leqq8$, the number $r_s(n)$ of representations of n as the sum of s squares is given by

$$(*)\qquad r_s(n)=\rho_s(n),$$

where

$$\rho_s(n)=\frac{\pi^{\frac{1}{2}s}}{\Gamma(\frac{1}{2}s)}n^{\frac{1}{2}s-1}\mathfrak{S}_s(n)$$

and

$$\mathfrak{S}_s(n)=\sum_{k=1}^{\infty}k^{-\frac{1}{2}s}\sum_h\{\eta(h,k)\}^se^{-\pi ihn/k};$$

here h ranges over a complete system of residues mod $2k$, whilst $\eta(h, k)$ is defined as 0 when $(h, k)>1$ and as

$$\tfrac{1}{2}k^{-\frac{1}{2}}\sum_j e^{\pi ihj^2/k}$$

when $(h, k)=1$, with j ranging over a complete system of residues mod $2k$. Hardy obtained his result by demonstrating, with the aid of the theory of modular functions, the identity of the functions

$$\Psi_s(\tau)=1+\sum_{n=1}^{\infty}\rho_s(n)e^{\pi i\tau n}$$

and

$$\{\vartheta_3(0|\tau)\}^s=1+\sum_{n=1}^{\infty}r_s(n)e^{\pi i\tau n}=\left\{\sum_{n=-\infty}^{\infty}e^{\pi i\tau n^2}\right\}^s$$

in the half-plane $\mathfrak{J}(\tau)>0$. He also noted that (*) is still valid for $s=3$ and $s=4$ but that his proof is then no longer applicable owing to difficulties arising in connexion with the convergence of series involved in the argument.

In the present paper these two exceptional cases are considered. For $s=4$ the difficulty can be overcome fairly easily by the device (due to L. J. Mordell) of restoring absolute convergence to the series in question by grouping together suitable pairs of terms. For $s=3$, however, a much more drastic modification of the argument is needed and the resulting treatment involves a considerable amount of technical detail. The author succeeds in showing that (*) continues to hold for $s=3$ by combining the ideas of Hardy and Mordell with a limiting process of a type used by E. Hecke. He begins by establishing the convergence of the "singular series" $\mathfrak{S}_3(n)$ and hence deducing the convergence, for $\mathfrak{J}(\tau)>0$, of the series defining $\Psi_3(\tau)$. It is precisely the properties of $\Psi_3(\tau)$ that are essential in the discussion of $r_3(n)$. They do not, however, appear to be amenable to direct study, and the crucial idea of the paper consists in the introduction of the auxiliary function

$$\Psi_{3,\sigma}(\tau)=1+\sum_{k=1}^{\infty}\sum_{h=-\infty}^{\infty}\frac{\{\eta(h,k)\}^3}{(hi-ki\tau)^{\frac{3}{2}}|hi-ki\tau|^\sigma}$$

which is shown to be defined for $\sigma>0$. The author then proves that

$$(**)\qquad \lim_{\sigma\to0}\Psi_{3,\sigma}(\tau)=\Psi_3(\tau)$$

and thereby reduces the study of the required properties of $\Psi_3(\tau)$ to that of the corresponding properties of the more manageable function $\Psi_{3,\sigma}(\tau)$. It is now shown that

$$\Psi_{3,\sigma}(-1/\tau)=(-i\tau)^{\frac{3}{2}}|-i\tau|^\sigma\Psi_{3,\sigma}(\tau);$$

in view of (**) this implies

$$\Psi_3(-1/\tau)=(-i\tau)^{\frac{3}{2}}\Psi_3(\tau).$$

The limit, as $\tau\to i\infty$, of $\Psi_{3,\sigma}(1-1/\tau)$ is evaluated next and as a consequence $\lim_{\tau\to i\infty}\Psi_3(1-1/\tau)$ is obtained. From this point onward it is possible to proceed as in Hardy's treatment of the cases $s=5, \cdots, 8$; and a comparison of the functions $\Psi_3(\tau)$ and $\{\vartheta_3(0|\tau)\}^3$ leads to the conclusion that they are identically equal. Hence (*) is valid for $s=3$.

By summing the singular series the author also obtains a formula for $r_3(n)$ which exhibits the fluctuations of $r_3(n)$ due to the arithmetical structure of n. We content ourselves with quoting one special case of this formula. If $n\equiv3$ (mod 8) and n is not divisible by the fourth power of any prime, then

$$r_3(n)=\frac{16}{\pi}n^{\frac{1}{2}}K(-4n)\prod_{p^2|n}\left\{1+\left(p-\left(\frac{-p^{-2}n}{p}\right)\right)^{-1}\right\}$$

where

$$K(-4n)=\sum_{m=1}^{\infty}\left(\frac{-4n}{m}\right)\frac{1}{m}.$$

As an incidental result of the investigation the author also obtains expressions for the number of primitive representations of n as the sum of three squares and for the number of representations of n as the sum of three or of four triangular numbers. *L. Mirsky* (Bristol).

Referred to in E24-54, E24-71, E24-81, E28-54, F10-84.

E24-36 (13, 914b)

Eljoseph, Nathan. Notes on a theorem of Lagrange. Riveon Lematematika **5**, 74–79 (1952). (Hebrew. English summary)

The main theorem proved in this paper is as follows: A necessary and sufficient condition that it be possible to represent a Gaussian integer $a+bi$ as a sum of squares of Gaussian integers is that b be even. In the latter case $a+bi$ may be always represented as the sum of two such squares, except in the case where both a and b are twice odd numbers. In any case any number $a+2ci$ may be represented in an infinite number of ways as the sum of three Gaussian integers. When a Gaussian integer can be represented as the sum of two squares, the number of representations is finite and can be easily counted. The fundamental theorem of arithmetic for Gaussian integers is used for that purpose. (Author's summary.) *E. G. Straus* (Los Angeles, Calif.).

E24-37 (14, 249d)

Ankeny, N. C. Representations of primes by quadratic forms. Amer. J. Math. **74**, 913–919 (1952).

Hecke proved that there are infinitely many primes $g=a^2+b^2$, $b^2=o(g)$. The author proves, by assuming the extended Riemann hypothesis on certain series introduced by Hecke, that there are infinitely many primes $g=a^2+b^2$, $b=O(\log g)$. The proof makes use of several results of A. Selberg on Dirichlet series. *P. Erdös.*

Referred to in R44-6.

E24-38 (14, 450i)

Gupta, Hansraj A table of values of $N_2(t)$. Res. Bull. East Panjab Univ. **1952**, no. 20, 13–93 (1952).

The function $N_2(t)$ is defined by $N_2(t)=\sum_{j\leq t}n_2(j)$ in which $n_2(j)$ is the number of non-negative solutions (x, y) of (*) $x^2+y^2=j$, the solution (x, y) being considered as different from (y, x) in case $x\neq y$. The table gives for each possible $j<20000$ all solutions (x, y) of (*) in which $0\leqq x\leqq y$, together with the accumulated score $N_2(t)$. As a check, we have

$$N_2(t)=\sum[(t-j^2)^{\frac{1}{2}}]+[t^{\frac{1}{2}}]+1,$$

the sum extending over integers j for which $0\leqq j\leqq t^{\frac{1}{2}}$. The table was of use in preparing two previous papers [Proc. Indian Acad. Sci., Sect. A. **13**, 519–520 (1941); Proc. Nat. Inst. Sci. India **13**, 35–63 (1947); these Rev. **3**, 65; **8**, 566]. *D. H. Lehmer* (Los Angeles, Calif.).

Citations: MR 3, 65h = E28-2; MR 8, 566f = E24-28.

E24-39 (14, 622a)

Lomadze, G. A. On the simultaneous representation of two whole numbers by sums of whole numbers and their squares. Akad. Nauk Gruzin. SSR. Trudy Mat. Inst. Razmadze **18**, 153–181 (1951). (Russian. Georgian summary)

Let $r_s(n, m)$ denote the number of solutions of the simultaneous equations $x_1^2+\cdots+x_s^2=n$, $x_1+\cdots+x_s=m$ in integers $x_1, \cdots, x_s$. Precise formulae for $r_s(n, m)$ were obtained by H. D. Kloosterman for $s=5, 7$ [Math. Ann. **118**, 319–364 (1942); these Rev. **5**, 33; **9**, 735] and by P. Bronkhorst for $s=6, 8$ [Thesis, Groningen, 1943]. Both these writers used the theory of modular functions to establish their results. In the paper under review the author obtains all these formulae for $r_s(n, m)$ by relying solely on elementary results in the theory of functions of a complex variable and generalizing a method due to T. Estermann which is contained in a book as yet unpublished. Moreover, all infinite series occurring in the formulae of Kloosterman and Bronkhorst are now replaced by finite expressions. *L. Mirsky* (Sheffield).

Citations: MR 5, 33g = E24-13.
Referred to in E24-59.

E24-40 (14, 1063e)

Bronkhorst, Pieter. Over het aantal oplossingen van het stelsel diophantische vergelijkingen:

$$\left.\begin{matrix}x_1^2+x_2^2+\cdots x_s^2=n\\ x_1+x_2+\cdots x_s=m\end{matrix}\right\}\text{ voor } s=6 \text{ en } s=8.$$

[On the number of solutions of the system of Diophantine equations:

$$\left.\begin{matrix}x_1^2+x_2^2+\cdots x_s^2=n\\ x_1+x_2+\cdots x_s=m\end{matrix}\right\}\text{ for } s=6 \text{ and } s=8.]$$

Thesis, University of Groningen, 1943. North Holland Publishing Co., Amsterdam, 1943. i+68 pp.

Let s be a fixed positive integer; let $n>0$ and m be variable integers, and let $r(n, m)$ denote the number of integral solutions of

$$x_1^2+x_2^2+\cdots+x_s^2=n,\quad x_1+x_2+\cdots+x_s=m.$$

The function $r(n, m)$ has been investigated by H. D. Kloosterman [Math. Ann. **118**, 319–364 (1942); these Rev. **5**, 33; **9**, 735] for odd squarefree s, and he gave explicit expressions for $r(n, m)$ when $s=3$, 5, or 7. In this thesis, the author obtains such explicit equations in the even cases $s=6$ and $s=8$. *K. Mahler* (Manchester).

Citations: MR 5, 33g = E24-13.
Referred to in E24-52, E24-59, E24-92.

E24-41 (15, 103b)

Kubilyus, I. P., and Linnik, Yu. V On the decomposition of the product of three numbers into the sum of two squares. Trudy Mat. Inst. Steklov., v. 38, pp. 170–172. Izdat. Akad. Nauk SSSR, Moscow, 1951. (Russian) 20 rubles.

The authors prove that there are infinitely many positive integers w such that (1) w is the product of three prime numbers of the form $4n+1$, (2) $w=k^2+l^2$, where k and l are integers and $|l|\leqq\exp(\ln w)^{4/5}$. This is a corollary of a more inclusive theorem derived in this paper from certain results in Vinogradov's monograph [Trav. Inst. Math. Stekloff **23** (1947); these Rev. **10**, 599]. *P. T. Bateman.*

Citations: MR 10, 599a = L02-2.
Referred to in L25-9, R44-6.

E24-42 (15, 103d)

Lomadze, G. A. On the representation of numbers by sums of squares. Akad. Nauk Gruzin. SSR. Trudy Tbiliss. Mat. Inst. Razmadze **16**, 231–275 (1948). (Russian. Georgian summary)

This is a readable, semi-expository paper in which the author works out in detail the explicit formulas for $r_s(n)$, the number of representations of a positive integer n as a sum of s squares, when $9\leqq s\leqq 24$. The method is based on the rudiments of the theory of modular functions and stems from the classical papers of Mordell [Quart. J. Pure Appl. Math. **48**, 93–104 (1917); Trans. Cambridge Philos. Soc. **22**, 361–372 (1919)] and Hardy [Trans. Amer. Math. Soc. **21**, 255–284 (1920)]. [See also Dickson, Studies in the theory of numbers, Chicago, 1930, Chap. 13, and Hardy, Ramanujan . . . , Cambridge, 1940, Chap. 9; these Rev. **3**, 71.] Actually the author follows a variant of the Hardy-Mordell method given by Estermann [Acta Arith. **2**, 47–79 (1936)] which avoids the use of the theory of modular functions as such. The basic result is that if $s\geqq 5$, then in the upper half of the τ-plane

$$\sum_{n=1}^{\infty}r_s(n)e^{\pi i\tau n}=\sum_{n=1}^{\infty}\rho_s(n)e^{\pi i\tau n}+\sum_{v=1}^{l}\alpha_s^{(v)}\vartheta_3(0\,|\,\tau)^{s-8v}\vartheta_0(0\,|\,\tau)^{4v}\vartheta_2(0\,|\,\tau)^{4v}$$

where $\rho_s(n)$ is Hardy's approximation to $r_s(n)$, $l=[(s-1)/8]$, and the $\alpha_s^{(v)}$ are certain constants. From this the detailed results for each s from 9 to 24 are derived by evaluating the $\alpha_s^{(v)}$ numerically and using Hardy's formulas for $\rho_s(n)$. *P. T. Bateman* (Urbana, Ill.).

Citations: MR 3, 71d = Z20-4.
Referred to in E24-58.

E24-43 (15, 288g)

Sandham, H. F. A square as the sum of 7 squares. Quart. J. Math., Oxford Ser. (2) **4**, 230–236 (1953).

Let $r_a(n)$ be the number of representations of n as a sum of a squares, $(n|4)=(-1)^{(n-1)/4}$ for n odd, $=0$ for n even. A. Hurwitz [Math. Werke, Bd. II, Birkhäuser, Basel, 1933, p. 751] has given formulas for $r_3(m^2)$, $r_5(m^2)$ in terms of sums involving σ_1, σ_3 respectively. The author proves

$$r_7(m^2)=14\sum_{r\,\mathrm{odd}}\left\{\sigma_5\left(\frac{m}{r}\right)+8\sigma_5\left(\frac{m}{2r}\right)\right\}r^2(r|4)\mu(r),$$

where $\sigma_5(x)=0$ if $x\neq$integer. The proof is based on the following elementary theorem: If $N(pn)=N(p)N(n)-f(p)N(n/p)$ for p prime, with $f(rs)=f(r)f(s)$, and if $N(0)=0$ or $N(p)=1+f(p)$, then the coefficient of q^{m^2} in

$$(1+2q^{1^2}+2q^{2^2}+2q^{3^2}+\cdots)(N(0)+N(1)q+N(2)q^2+\cdots)$$

is equal to $\sum_r M(2m/r)f(r)\mu(r)$, where

$$\{\sum_{k\geqq 0}N(k)q^{k^2}\}^2=\sum_{n\geqq 0}M(n)q^n.$$

This theorem is applied to identities derived from elliptic functions. [For $N(x)$, $M(x)$, the convention is the same as for $\sigma_5(x)$.] *N. J. Fine* (Princeton, N. J.).

Referred to in E24-72.

E24-44 (15, 289a)

Sandham, H. F. A square as the sum of 9, 11 and 13 squares. J. London Math. Soc. **29**, 31–38 (1954).

[For definitions, see the preceding review.] The author gives formulas for $r_9(m^2)$, $r_{11}(m^2)$, $r_{13}(m^2)$ in terms of divisor sums and arithmetical functions of the type studied by Glaisher and Ramanujan. The method is similar to that used in the preceding paper, but uses an extension of the elementary theorem given there. *N. J. Fine.*

Referred to in A30-31.

E24-45 (15, 401d)

Eljoseph, Nathan. On the representation of a number as a sum of squares. Riveon Lematematika **7**, 38–43 (1954). (Hebrew. English summary)

In the first part of this paper the author points out an error in the proofs of Theorems 4 and 10 of I. Niven's paper, Trans. Amer. Math. Soc. **48**, 405–417 (1940) [these Rev. **2**, 147]. He points out that instead of proving that every number $a+2b\sqrt{-m}$ (a, b, m rational integers, $m\geqq 2$, square free) is the sum of squares of three integers in $R(\sqrt{-m})$, all that Niven's argument for Theorem 4 proves is: Either $a+2b\sqrt{-m}=\alpha^2+\beta^2+\gamma^2$ or $a+2b\sqrt{-m}=\alpha^2-\beta^2-\gamma^2$ where α, β, γ are integers in $R(\sqrt{-m})$. The author gives a valid counterexample to Theorem 10 and an invalid counterexample to Theorem 4. However Theorem 4 was disproved by C. L. Siegel [Ann. of Math. (2) **46**, 313–339 (1945); these Rev. **7**, 49], who gives an infinite number of imaginary quadratic fields, including $R(\sqrt{-7})$, in which 7 is not the sum of three squares.

In the second part the author investigates the possibility of expressing positive rational integers as sums of squares of numbers $a+b\sqrt{D}$ (a, b, D integers, $D\neq$square). He proves: Every positive rational integer n is the sum of (1) two squares, if and only if $D=-1$; (2) three squares, if $D=2, 3, 5, 6$ but not if $D\geqq 8$ ($n=7$ is the common counterexample. This leaves the case $D=7$ open).

E. G. Straus (Los Angeles, Calif.).

Citations: MR 2, 147b = E24-4; MR 7, 49b = R48-5.

E24-46 (15, 602g)

Ser, J. La disposition des restes dans les deux classes de nombres premiers. Mathesis **63**, 18–20 (1954).

E24-47 (15, 935a)

van der Pol, Balth. The representation of numbers as sums of eight, sixteen and twenty-four squares. Nederl. Akad. Wetensch. Proc. Ser. A. **57** = Indagationes Math. **16**, 349–361 (1954).

Ramanujan's formulas for $r_8(n)$, $r_{16}(n)$, $r_{24}(n)$ are derived in a relatively simple way. The author [same Proc. **54** = Indagationes Math. **13**, 261–271, 272–284 (1951); these Rev. **13**, 135] has already obtained the principal relations and the derivations depend on the skillful choice of certain modular transforms. The $r_{8k}(n)$ are the coefficients in the power series development of θ_3^{8k}. Some simplicity and symmetry is gained by considering θ_2^{8k}, θ_0^{8k}, θ_3^{8k} together. Formulas for the coefficients of θ_2^{8k} and θ_0^{8k} are also obtained for $k=1, 2, 3$. *H. S. Zuckerman* (Seattle, Wash.).

Citations: MR 13, 135a = F30-11.
Referred to in E24-60.

E24-48 (15, 936a)

Val'fiš, A. Z. On the representation of numbers by sums of squares. Asymptotic formulas. Uspehi Matem. Nauk (N.S.) **7**, no. 6(52), 97–178 (1952). (Russian)

This paper is a very readable survey of the field in question. The author has taken great pains to give all the proofs in full detail and to make his treatment as self-contained as possible, with the result that it can be read by anyone who knows elementary number theory and the rudiments of analysis and algebra. The paper is divided into two main parts. The first is devoted to a very thorough treatment of the asymptotic formula for the number $r_k(n)$ of representations of a positive integer n as a sum of k squares ($k\geqq 5$), namely

$$r_k(n)=\frac{\pi^{k/2}}{\Gamma(k/2)}n^{k/2-1}\mathfrak{S}_k(n)+O(n^{k/4}),$$

where $\mathfrak{S}_k(n)$, the so-called singular series, is a bounded function of n given by a certain infinite series involving Gaussian sums. This result is the simplest application of the circle method of Hardy, Littlewood, and Ramanujan and as such has much didactic value in addition to its intrinsic interest. It was stated without proof by Hardy and by Ramanujan, but was first proved explicitly (in more general form) by Walfisz himself [Math. Z. **19**, 300–307 (1924)]. The second and larger part of the paper is devoted to a similarly thorough treatment of the analogous asymptotic formula for the number $r_k(m, n)$ of solutions in integers of the pair of simultaneous equations

$$x_1+\cdots+x_k=m,\quad x_1^2+\cdots+x_k^2=n,$$

where k is a given integer greater than 7 and m and n are integers such that $m\equiv n \pmod 2$ and $kn-m^2>0$. The formula in this case is

$$r_k(m, n)=\frac{\pi^{(k-1)/2}}{k^{\frac{1}{2}k-1}\Gamma(\frac{1}{2}(k-1))}(kn-m^2)^{(k-3)/2}\mathfrak{S}_k(m, n)+O(n^{\frac{1}{4}k-2}\log n),$$

where $\mathfrak{S}_k(m, n)$ is somewhat similar to $\mathfrak{S}_k(n)$ above. The material discussed in this second part of the paper stems mostly from a paper of Kloosterman [Math. Ann. **118**, 319–364 (1942); these Rev. **5**, 33; **9**, 735], a paper of van der Blij [Nederl. Akad. Wetensch., Proc. **50**, 31–40, 41–48 = Indagationes Math. **9**, 16–25, 26–33 (1947); these Rev. **8**, 502], and a paper by the author [Akad. Nauk Gruzin. SSR. Trudy Tbiliss. Mat. Inst. Razmadze **19**, 33–59 (1953)] and one by G. A. Lomadze [ibid. **19**, 61–77 (1953)]. In both parts of the paper the singular series is discussed in great detail, but no exact results are proved for either $r_k(n)$ or $r_k(m, n)$. *P. T. Bateman* (Urbana, Ill.).

Citations: MR 5, 33g = E24-13; MR 8, 502a = E24-26.
Referred to in E24-49, E24-52, E24-59.

E24-49 (17, 1057a)

Val'fiš, A. Z. On the representation of numbers by sum of squares. Asymptotic formulas. Amer. Math. Soc. Transl. (2) 3 (1956), 163–248.
Translated from Uspehi Mat. Nauk (N.S.) 7 (1952), no. 6(52), 97–178; MR **15**, 936.

Citations: MR 15, 936a = E24-48.

E24-50 (16, 17c)

Ananda-Rau, K. On the representation of a number as the sum of an even number of squares. J. Madras Univ. Sect. B. **24**, 61–89 (1954).

Certain arithmetical formulae for expressing the number of representations of n as a sum of an even number of squares were enunciated by Ramanujan (without proof) in the form of analytical identities involving elliptic theta-functions and series of the Lambert type [Collected papers of Srinivasa Ramanujan, Cambridge, 1927, paper no. 18, pp. 136–162]. Mordell later proved Ramanujan's formulae [Quart. J. Pure Appl. Math. **48**, 93–104 (1918)], by applying the theory of modular invariants. In this paper the author employs the theory of elliptic functions to give new proofs of these identities, and asserts that his methods lead to other interesting formulas which he hopes to consider in a future paper. *T. M. Apostol* (Pasadena, Calif.).

Referred to in E24-123.

E24-51 (16, 117a)

Lenz, Hanfried. Zur Quadratsummendarstellung in relativquadratischen Zahlkörpern. S.-B. Math.-Nat. Kl. Bayer. Akad. Wiss. **1953**, 283–288 (1954).

The following theorem is proved. Let G denote an algebraic number field, K a quadratic extension of G, and γ any totally positive number of K. Then γ can be given in the form $\gamma=\alpha^2+a_1^2+\cdots+a_m^2$, where α belongs to K and $a_1, \cdots, a_m$ belong to G. The proof of the theorem is elementary. Using Siegel's theorem that every totally positive number of G can be given as a sum of four squares of numbers of G, however, the author can prove that $m=4$.
H. Bergström (Göteborg).

E24-52 (16, 448b)

Val'fiš, A. Z. The additive theory of numbers. XI. Akad. Nauk Gruzin. SSR. Trudy Tbiliss. Mat. Inst. Razmadze **19**, 33–59 (1953). (Russian. Georgian summary)

Suppose $r_k(m, n)$ is the number of solutions in integers $x_1, \cdots, x_k$ of the pair of simultaneous diophantine equations $x_1+\cdots+x_k=m$, $x_1^2+\cdots+x_k^2=n$, where m and n are integers such that $m\equiv n \pmod 2$ and $kn-m^2\geqq 0$. It is known that if $5\leqq k\leqq 8$, then $r_k(m, n)=R_k(m, n)$, where

$$R_k(m, n)=\pi^{\frac{1}{2}k-\frac{1}{2}}k^{1-\frac{1}{2}k}\Gamma(\tfrac{1}{2}k-\tfrac{1}{2})^{-1}(kn-m^2)^{\frac{1}{2}k-\frac{3}{2}}\mathfrak{S}_k(m, n),$$

$\mathfrak{S}_k(m, n)$ being the singular series defined in the paper reviewed below [Kloosterman, Math. Ann. **118**, 319–364 (1942); MR **5**, 33; **9**, 735; Bronkhorst, Dissertation, Univ. of Groningen, 1943; MR **14**, 1063; van der Blij, Nederl. Akad. Wetensch., Proc. **50**, 31–40, 41–48, 166–172, 298–306, 390–396 = Indag. Math. **9**, 16–25, 26–33, 129–135, 188–196, 248–254 (1947); MR **8**, 502]. If $k>8$, the equality $r_k(m, n)=R_k(m, n)$ is no longer generally true, but the present author proves that the weaker result

$$r_k(m, n)=R_k(m, n)+O((n+1)^{\frac{1}{4}k-2}\cdot\log(n+2))$$

still holds. The proof is by induction on k, starting from the case $k=8$. The step from k to $k+1$ is not difficult, and actually most of the paper is devoted to discussing the case $k=8$ in order that the induction can be started. The author seems to feel that Bronkhorst's proof of the equality $r_8(m, n)=R_8(m, n)$ is too complicated and so gives a proof himself on the following lines: (i) He uses an identity of van der Blij in order to express $r_8(m, n)$ in terms of $r_7(\Delta)$, $r_7(\Delta/4)$, and $r_7(\Delta/16)$, where $\Delta=8n-m^2$ and $r_7(u)$ is the number of solutions of $u=y_1^2+\cdots+y_7^2$ in integers $y_1, \cdots, y_7$. (ii) Following van der Blij again, he substitutes the Hardy-Stanley formula [Stanley, J. London Math. Soc. **2**, 91–96 (1927)] for $r_7(u)$ into the results of (i) in order to get a formula for $r_8(m, n)$. (iii) He sums the series $\mathfrak{S}_8(m, n)$ in a more elementary way than Bronkhorst and compares the resulting expression for $R_8(m, n)$ with the result obtained for $r_8(m, n)$ in (ii). Most of the material in this paper is also presented in an expository paper of the author [Uspehi Mat. Nauk (N.S.) **7**, no. 6(52), 97–178 (1952); MR **15**, 936].
P. T. Bateman (Urbana, Ill.).

Citations: MR 5, 33g = E24-13; MR 8, 502a = E24-26; MR 8, 502b = E24-27; MR 14, 1063e = E24-40; MR 15, 936a = E24-48.
Referred to in E24-59.

E24-53 (16, 448c)

Lomadze, G. A. On the summation of a singular series. I. Akad. Nauk Gruzin. SSR. Trudy Tbiliss. Mat. Inst. Razmadze **19**, 61–77 (1953). (Russian. Georgian summary)

The singular series occurring in the paper reviewed above is defined as follows

$$\mathfrak{S}_k(m, n)=\sum_{q=1}^{\infty}\sum_{r\mid q}\sum_{a \bmod q}{}'\sum_{b \bmod r}{}'\left(\frac{S(a, q; b, r)}{qr}\right)^k \times\exp 2\pi i\left(-\frac{na}{q}-\frac{mb}{r}\right),$$

where the prime denotes summation over a reduced residue system and

$$S(a, q; b, r)=\sum_{h \bmod qr}\exp 2\pi i\left(\frac{ah^2}{q}+\frac{bh}{r}\right).$$

Kloosterman [Math. Ann. **118**, 319–364 (1942); MR **5**, 33; **9**, 735] has summed this series for all odd squarefree k greater than unity. Using Kloosterman's method, the present author does the same thing for all odd k greater than unity and obtains results similar to those of Kloosterman.
P. T. Bateman (Urbana, Ill.).

Citations: MR 5, 33g = E24-13.
Referred to in E24-59.

E24-54 (16, 451c)

Linnik, Yu. V. The asymptotic distribution of lattice points on a sphere. Dokl. Akad. Nauk SSSR (N.S.) **96**, 909–912 (1954). (Russian)

Let Γ be a convex cone with center at the origin in three-dimensional Euclidean space and suppose that the part of the unit-sphere which is contained in Γ has area $4\pi\lambda$. If m is a positive integer greater than unity, let $R(m)$ denote the number of primitive lattice points (x, y, z) on the sphere $x^2+y^2+z^2=m$ and let $R_\Gamma(m)$ denote the number of these lattice points which also lie in Γ. It is known that $R(m)=0$ if $m\equiv 0, 4, 7 \pmod 8$, $R(m)=8h(-m)$ if $m\equiv 3 \pmod 8$, and $R(m)=12h(-m)$ if $m\equiv 1, 2, 5, 6 \pmod 8$, where $h(-m)$ is the number of primitive classes of binary quadratic forms $au^2+buv+cv^2$ (with integral coefficients) such that $b^2-4ac=-4m$ [see, e.g., p. 99 of a paper of the reviewer, Trans. Amer. Math. Soc. **71**, 70–101 (1951) [MR **13**, 111] in connection with pp. 127 and 152 of Landau's Vorlesungen über Zahlentheorie, vol. 1, Hirzel, Leipzig, 1927]. Thus by the Heilbronn-Siegel theorem $R(m)$ tends to infinity if m goes to infinity through the integers con-

gruent to 1, 2, 3, 5, or 6 modulo 8. The author sketches a proof that if, in addition to satisfying the restriction $m \equiv 1, 2, 3, 5, 6 \pmod 8$, m is required to be a quadratic residue of some fixed odd prime number q, then $\lim_{m\to\infty} R_\Gamma(m)/R(m) = \lambda$. This is an improvement of an earlier result of Linnik and Malyšev [Dokl. Akad. Nauk SSSR (N.S.) **89**, 209–211 (1953); MR **15**, 406] to the effect that $\liminf_{m\to\infty} R_\Gamma(m)/R(m) > 0$ under the same restrictions on m. The proof uses methods from a paper of Malyšev [ibid. **93**, 771–774 (1953); **95**, 700 (1954); MR **15**, 936], elementary considerations from probability theory, and a geometrical lemma ascribed to V. A. Zalgaller.
P. T. Bateman (Urbana, Ill.).

Citations: MR 13, 111i = E24-35; MR 15, 406b = E20-41; MR 15, 936b = E20-44.

Referred to in E16-25, E24-55, E24-122.

E24-55 (20# 2328)

Linnik, Yu. V. Asymptotic-geometric and ergodic properties of sets of lattice points on a sphere. Mat. Sb. N.S. **43(85)** (1957), 257–276. (Russian)

A detailed proof of the results about the uniform distribution of integral points on the surfaces of spheres enunciated in Dokl. Akad. Nauk SSSR (N.S.) **96** (1954), 909–912 [MR **16**, 451]. The proof is on similar lines to that there adumbrated but is considerably simplified by using ergodic theory. *J. W. S. Cassels* (Cambridge, England)

Citations: MR 16, 451c = E24-54.

Referred to in E12-92, E24-56, E24-122, E28-28, E28-29.

E24-56 (22# 3731)

Linnik, Yu. V. Asymptotic-geometric and ergodic properties of sets of lattice points on a sphere. Amer. Math. Soc. Transl. (2) **13** (1960), 9–27.

The original Russian version [Mat. Sb. (N.S.) **43 (85)** (1957), 257–276] has already been reviewed [MR **20** #2328].

Citations: MR 20# 2328 = E24-55.

E24-57 (16, 674h)

Sanielevici, S. La décomposition d'un nombre entier en une somme de deux carrés. Acad. Repub. Pop. Romîne. Bul. Şti. Secţ. Şti. Mat. Fiz. **5**, 5–18 (1953). (Romanian. Russian and French summaries)

The author traces the well known connection between the representation $m = a^2 + b^2$ of a number m dividing $1 + c^2$ and the continued fraction for m/c. This result is used to study quadratic equations whose roots have periodic continued fractions with "metasymmetric" partial quotients. The connection with the Pell equation $x^2 - Dy^2 = \pm 4$ is noted.
D. H. Lehmer (Berkeley, Calif.).

E24-58 (16, 905b)

Lomadze, G. A. On the representation of numbers by sums of squares. Akad. Nauk Gruzin. SSR. Trudy Tbiliss. Mat. Inst. Razmadze **20**, 47–87 (1954). (Russian)

If s and n are positive integers, let $r_s(n)$ denote the number of solutions of the equation $m_1^2 + \cdots + m_s^2 = n$ in integers $m_1, \cdots, m_s$. Using the Hardy-Mordell method [cf. Hardy, Ramanujan . . . , Cambridge, 1940, Chap. 9; MR **3**, 71] the author has previously worked out in full detail the exact formulas for $r_s(n)$ when $9 \leqq s \leqq 24$ [same Trudy **16**, 231–275 (1948); **17**, 281–314 (1949); MR **15**, 103; **12**, 805]. Here he does the same thing for $25 \leqq s \leqq 32$. This involves a tremendous amount of calculation. *P. T. Bateman.*

Citations: MR 3, 71d = Z20-4; MR 12, 805b = E24-34; MR 15, 103d = E24-42.

E24-59 (16, 905c)

Lomadze, G. A. On the summation of a singular series. II. Akad. Nauk Gruzin. SSR. Trudy Tbiliss. Mat. Inst. Razmadze **20**, 21–45 (1954). (Russian)

[For Part I see same Trudy **19**, 61–77 (1953); MR **16**, 448].Suppose s is a fixed integer and n and m are integers with $\Delta = sn - m^2 > 0$. Let $r_s(n, m)$ be the number of solutions of the pair of equations $m_1^2 + \cdots + m_s^2 = n$, $m_1 + \cdots + m_s = m$ in integers $m_1, \cdots, m_s$. Let

$$\rho_s(n, m) = \pi^{(s-1)/2}\Delta^{(s-3)/2}\mathfrak{S}_s(n, m)/s^{(s/2)-1}\Gamma((s-1)/2),$$

where $\mathfrak{S}_s(n, m)$ is the sum of the appropriate singular series, the full definition of which may be found in the review of Part I. From the work of Kloosterman [Math. Ann. **118**, 319–364 (1942); MR **5**, 33; **9**, 735], Bronkhorst [Dissertation, Groningen, 1943; MR **14**, 1063], and Lomadze [Akad. Nauk Gruzin. SSR. Trudy Mat. Inst. Razmadze **18**, 153–181 (1951); MR **14**, 622] it is known that $r_s(n, m) = \rho_s(n, m)$ for $s = 3, 5, 6, 7, 8$. From the work of Val'fiš [Uspehi Mat. Nauk (N.S.) **7**, no. 6(52), 97–178 (1952); Akad. Nauk Gruzin. SSR. Trudy Tbiliss. Mat. Inst. Razmadze **19**, 33–59 (1953); MR **15**, 936; **16**, 448] it is known that $r_s(n, m) = \rho_s(n, m) + O((n+1)^{(s/2)-2}\log(n+2))$ if $s > 8$. In Part I the author obtained formulas for $\mathfrak{S}_s(n, m)$ for all odd $s \geqq 3$. In the present paper he does the same for all even $s \geqq 4$. The methods used stem from Kloosterman and Bronkhorst. In the special case $s = 4$ his result, in conjunction with an exact formula for $r_4(n, m)$ given by van der Blij [Nederl. Akad. Wetensch., Proc. **50**, 41–48 = Indag. Math. **9**, 26–33 (1947); MR **8**, 502], shows that $r_4(n, m) = \rho_4(n, m)$.
P. T. Bateman (Urbana, Ill.).

Citations: MR 5, 33g = E24-13; MR 8, 502a = E24-26; MR 14, 622a = E24-39; MR 14, 1063e = E24-40; MR 15, 936a = E24-48; MR 16, 448b = E24-52; MR 16, 448c = E24-53.

Referred to in E24-92.

E24-60 (17, 240b)

Carlitz, L. On the representation of an integer as the sum of twenty-four squares. Nederl. Akad. Wetensch. Proc. Ser. A. **58** = Indag. Math. **17** (1955), 504–506.

Let $r_s(n)$ be the number of representations of an integer n as the sum of s squares. The author derives Ramanujan's formula for $r_{24}(n)$, and several related formulae, in very simple fashion by equating the coefficients of two series, each an ingenious combination of elliptic theta functions. The formula was proved by Hardy using modular functions [see "Ramanujan", Cambridge, 1940, Chap. 9; MR **3**, 71], and the theory of elliptic functions was applied with success, somewhat in the manner of the present paper, by Bulygin to the more general problem of determining $r_{2s}(n)$ [Izv. Imp. Akad. Nauk (6) **8** (1914), 389–404]. There is a recent evaluation or $r_{24}(n)$ by van der Pol [Nederl. Akad. Wetensch. Proc. Ser. A. **57** = Indag. Math. **16** (1954), 349–361; MR **15**, 935]. *H. Halberstam.*

Citations: MR 3, 71d = Z20-4; MR 15, 935a = E24-47.

E24-61 (17, 241a)

Nagell, Trygve. On the representations of integers as the sum of two integral squares in algebraic, mainly quadratic fields. Nova Acta Soc. Sci. Upsal. (4) **15** (1953), no. 11, 73 pp.

Let α be a non-zero integer in the algebraic field Ω. If α is representable as the sum of two integral squares in Ω, α is said to be an A-number in Ω. The representation $\alpha = \xi^2 + \eta^2$, where ξ, η are integers in Ω is said to be "primitive" if the principal ideals (ξ) and (η) are relatively prime. Ω is called "simple" when the number of its ideal classes is 1.

The present paper contains an exhaustive account of A-numbers in various algebraic fields. In §§2–10 the author determines all the A-numbers in the sixteen quadratic fields $K(\sqrt{D})$ for $D=\pm 2, \pm 3, \pm 7, \pm 11, \pm 19, \pm 43, \pm 67$ and ± 163 [the case $D=-1$ was dealt with by I. Niven, Trans. Amer. Math. Soc. **48** (1940), 405–417; MR **2**, 147, and is discussed again here]. These values of D have the property, shared by at most one other value of $|D|$, that $K(\sqrt{D})$ and $K(\sqrt{-D})$ are both simple [see H. Heilbronn and E. H. Linfoot, Quart. J. Math. Oxford Ser. **5** (1934), 293–301], and it follows from a general theorem of Dirichlet [Werke, Bd. I, Reimer, Berlin, 1889, pp. 578–588] that the Dirichlet field $K(\sqrt{D}, \sqrt{-D})$ of the fourth degree is also simple; the author makes frequent use of this result. He announces that in a future paper he will deal also with the quadratic fields $K(\sqrt{D})$ where $D=\pm 5, \pm 13$ or ± 37.

The number of representations of an A-number in Ω is discussed in § 11; in § 12 the author uses a result of H. Weber [Math. Ann. **20** (1882), 301–329] on the representation of primes by a quadratic form, to obtain results about the existence of A-primes in a given quadratic field, and in § 13 are determined those A-numbers in the quadratic fields discussed in §§ 2–9 which have at least one primitive representation.

The proofs are given in detail, and depend mostly on arguments in terms of congruences and quadratic residue theory. *H. Halberstam* (Providence, R.I.).

Citations: MR 2, 147b = E24-4.

Referred to in E16-52, E24-87, E24-93.

E24-62 (17, 460f)

Carlitz, L. Some partition formulas related to sums of squares. Nieuw Arch. Wisk. (3) 3 (1955), 129–133.

Let $\vartheta_4(q)=\sum_{n=-\infty}^{\infty}(-1)^n q^{n^2}$. Extending the method of his earlier paper [Quart. J. Math. Oxford Ser. (2) **4** (1953), 168–172; MR **15**, 201] the author shows that identities such as

$$(*)\qquad 1+16\sum_{n=1}^{\infty}\frac{n^3q^n}{1-(-1)^nq^n}=\vartheta_4^{8}(q)$$

can be obtained from the familiar formula $\wp'(u)=-\sigma(2u)/\sigma^4(u)$, when the $\wp$-function is replaced by its Fourier series. Evidently (*) yields the well-known formula for the number of representations of an integer as the sum of 8 squares. *A. L. Whiteman* (Los Angeles, Calif.).

Citations: MR 15, 201b = P60-18.

Referred to in E24-66.

E24-63 (17, 945f)

Ebel, Ilse. Analytische Bestimmung der Darstellungsanzahlen natürlicher Zahlen durch spezielle ternäre quadratische Formen mit Kongruenzbedingungen. Math. Z. **64** (1956), 217–228.

Let

$$A\left(n\,\middle|\,\begin{matrix}a_1 & a_2 & a_3\\ k_1 & k_2 & k_3\end{matrix}\right)$$

denote the number of solutions of the equation $n=n_1^2+n_2^2+n_3^2$ subject to the congruence conditions $n_i\equiv a_i \pmod{k_i}$ $(i=1, 2, 3)$. The author determines explicit formulas for

$$A\left(n\,\middle|\,\begin{matrix}0 & 0 & 1\\ 4 & 4 & 4\end{matrix}\right)\text{ and }A\left(n\,\middle|\,\begin{matrix}1 & 2 & 2\\ 4 & 4 & 4\end{matrix}\right).$$

As usual, this is done by equating coefficients in an appropriate identity involving modular forms. The identities are gotten by the methods of H. Petersson [Abh. Math. Sem. Hamburg Univ. **8** (1930), 215–242]. The equation $n=3n_1^2+n_2^2+n_3^2$ (subject to similar congruence relations) is also discussed for the triple $(k_1, k_2, k_3)=(2, 6, 6)$.

T. M. Apostol (Pasadena, Calif.).

E24-64 (17, 1055b)

Kubilyus, I. P.; and Linnik, Yu. V. An elementary theorem on the theory of prime numbers. Uspehi Mat. Nauk (N.S.) **11** (1956), no. 2(68), 191–192. (Russian)

On the extended Riemann Conjecture for the Hecke ζ-function of the Gaussian field it is true that there exists an infinite number of primes p representable as k^2+l^2, where k and l are integers such that $l=O(\ln p)$. In contrast the authors give a completely elementary and exceedingly simple proof of the weaker result that there exist infinitely many pairs of primes p_1, p_2 such that $p_1p_2=k^2+l^2$ with k and l integral and $l=O(\ln p_1p_2)$. The argument amounts to little more than the application of Dirichlet's 'Schubfachprinzip' to a suitable division of a circle in the complex plane into equal sectors. *H. Halberstam.*

E24-65 (18, 468c)

Postnikov, A. G. Additive problems with a growing number of terms. Dokl. Akad. Nauk SSSR (N.S.) **108** (1956), 392. (Russian)

Asymptotic expressions are stated for the numbers of solutions of the diophantine equations

$$(1)\qquad x_1+x_2+\cdots+x_n=N,$$

$$(2)\qquad x_1^2+x_2^2+\cdots+x_n^2=N,$$

obtained by considering the addition of independent random variables, applying the local limit theorem of probability theory and estimating certain resulting trigonometric sums. *W. H. Simons* (Vancouver, B.C.).

E24-66 (18, 874c)

Carlitz, L. Note on sums of four and six squares. Proc. Amer. Math. Soc. **8** (1957), 120–124.

Using the formula $\wp'(u)=-\sigma(2u)/\sigma^4(u)$ and the elementary methods of a previous note [Nieuw Arch. Wisk. (3) 3 (1955), 129–133; MR **17**, 460] the author gives short proofs of familiar formulas for the number of representations of an integer as a sum of four and six squares, also of the formula $\theta_3^4(g)=\theta_0^4(g)+\theta_2^4(g)$. *N. J. Fine.*

Citations: MR 17, 460f = E24-62.

E24-67 (19, 15d)

Ankeny, N. C. Sums of three squares. Proc. Amer. Math. Soc. **8** (1957), 316–319.

The author gives a proof of Legendre's theorem that every positive integer m which is not of the form $4^a(8n+7)$ is representable as a sum of three integral squares; this proof uses only Minkowski's theorem on the existence of an integer point in a convex body, Dirichlet's theorem on the existence of primes in an arithmetic progression, and simple facts on quadratic reciprocity and on representation by two squares. The details are given for $m\equiv 3 \pmod 8$ and square-free, the modifications for other cases being briefly indicated. The essential idea is to represent m as

$$R^2+2(qx^2+bxy+hy^2),$$

where R is a linear form in x, y, z, and q, b, h are suitable integers satisfying $b^2-4qh=-m$. The construction of these is such as to permit a proof that $qx^2+bxy+hy^2$ has no prime factor $\equiv 3 \pmod 4$ dividing it to an odd power exactly, whence it follows that $2(qx^2+bxy+hy^2)$ is a sum of two squares. *H. Davenport* (London).

Referred to in E24-84.

E24-68 **(19, 943e)**

Val'fiš, A. Z. Additive number theory. XII. Akad. Nauk Gruzin. SSR. Trudy Tbiliss. Mat. Inst. Razmadze **22** (1956), 3–31. (Russian)

Referred to in P32-71.

E24-69 **(19, 1161b)**

Pall, G.; and Taussky, O. Application of quaternions to the representations of a binary quadratic form as a sum of four squares. Proc. Roy. Irish Acad. Sect. A. **58** (1957), 23–28.

Let $\varphi_1=e\varphi_l$, $\varphi_l=ax^2+2t_0xy+by^2$, where e, a, t_0, b are integers and l is the g.c.d. of a, t_0, and b. Let $r_s(n)$ denote the number of representations of the integer n as a sum of s squares of integers, and let $r_s(\varphi)$ denote the number of representations of φ as the sum of s squares of linear forms with integral coefficients. The authors derive the formula

$$r_4(\varphi)=\sum r_4(kh)r_3(e^2d;h),$$

where k is the g.c.d. of the coefficients of φ_l, h ranges over the positive divisors of s and $r_3(e^2d;h)$ denotes the number of solutions of

$$e^2d=t_1^2+t_2^2+t_3^2,\ (t_1, t_2, t_3, e)=h.$$

They also show that the function $f(e)=r_4(\varphi)/r_4(\varphi_l)$ is multiplicative in the restricted sense and from this fact derive a formula for $f(e)$ in terms of the prime power factors of e. *B. W. Jones* (Boulder, Colo.).

E24-70 **(20# 1662)**

Malyshev, A. V. The distribution of integer points on a four-dimensional sphere. Dokl. Akad. Nauk SSSR (N.S.) **114** (1957), 25–28. (Russian)

The following theorem is stated, and a proof of it is lightly sketched: Let Ω be a 4-dimensional convex conical region with vertex at the origin and with vertex solid angle $\omega>0$. Let n be an odd positive integer, and let $r(\omega, n)$ be the number of integral points on the sphere $x_1^2+x_2^2+x_3^2+x_4^2=n$ and lying in Ω. Then for fixed ω,

$$r(\omega, n)=(2\pi^2)^{-1}\omega r(n)(1+O(n^{-1/18+\varepsilon}))\text{ as }n\to\infty,$$

where $r(n)$ is the total number of integral points on the sphere. Similar results are stated concerning the number of primitive points in Ω, and the number of points in Ω whose coordinates lie in specified residue classes. *W. J. LeVeque* (Göttingen)

Referred to in E12-80, E12-92.

E24-71 **(20# 3837)**

Carlitz, L. The singular series for a single square. Portugal. Math. **16** (1957), 7–10.

In the problem of representation of integers as the sum of s squares, the singular series plays a dominant role [for the bibliography, see, for instance, P. T. Bateman, Trans. Amer. Math. Soc. **71** (1951), 70–101; MR **13**, 111]. The author considers the singular series for $s=1$, which turns out to be a very special case of Siegel's main theorem on positive quadratic forms [Ann. of Math. (2) **36** (1935), 527–606; theorem 2]. *S. Ikehara* (Tokyo)

Citations: MR 13, 111i = E24-35.

E24-72 **(20# 4528)**

van Lint, J. H. Über einige Dirichletsche Reihen. Nederl. Akad. Wetensch. Proc. Ser. A **61**=Indag. Math. **20** (1958), 56–60.

Sandham [Quart. J. Math. Oxford Ser. (2) **4** (1953), 230–236; MR **15**, 288] has given Euler product expansions for the Dirichlet series $\sum_m r_a(m^2)m^{-s}$, where $r_a(m^2)$ is the number of representations of m^2 as a sum of a squares, for $a=3, 5, 7$. For a odd >8, such simple formulas do not exist, since the genus of the quadratic form $\sum_{i=1}^a x_i^2$ contains more than one class. The author replaces $r_a(m^2)$ by $R_a(m^2)$, a weighted mean of the representations of m^2 in the genus of the form, and sums over odd m only. The resulting Dirichlet series then has a very simple form, of which Sandham's formulas are special cases. It is stated that a generalization to determinant $D>1$ can be given, in which the summation is over those m prime to $2D$. *N. J. Fine* (Princeton, N.J.)

Citations: MR 15, 288g = E24-43.

E24-73 **(21# 3376)**

Grosswald, E.; Calloway, A.; and Calloway, J. The representation of integers by three positive squares. Proc. Amer. Math. Soc. **10** (1959), 451–455.

Theorem: There exists a finite set S of numbers with the following property. If $n>0$ is not divisible by 4, not $\equiv -1 \pmod 8$ and not in S, then n is the sum of three strictly positive squares. The authors conjecture that S can be taken to consist of 1, 2, 5, 10, 13, 25, 37, 58, 85, 130 only. The proof, which is short, depends on Siegel's estimate for $L(1, \chi)$. The authors also give an asymptotic formula for the number of integers less than x which are the sum of three strictly positive squares, but this formula depends on the set S. There is a review of earlier work on the analogous problem for s squares ($s\geqq 4$). *J. W. S. Cassels* (Cambridge, England)

Referred to in E24-76, E24-96.

E24-74 **(21# 6352)**

Cohn, Harvey. Numerical study of the representation of a totally positive quadratic integer as the sum of quadratic integral squares. Numer. Math. **1** (1959), 121–134.

This paper describes almost 200,000 experiments in representing real quadratic integers as sums of squares of integers in the same quadratic field. For such a representation to be possible the number being represented must be totally positive. Results indicate that if such a number is not the sum of 5 or fewer squares then it is not the sum of any number of squares. (The smallest totally positive quadratic integer which is not a sum of squares in its own field is $6+\sqrt{6}$.)

To give further details, let m be a positive square-free rational integer and let $f=2$ or 1 according as $m\equiv 1 \pmod 4$ or not. The numbers $\alpha=(fa+2b\sqrt{m})/f^2$, where a and b are rational integers such that $a\equiv b \pmod f$, $a>0$, $b\geqq 0$, $fa>2b\sqrt{m}$, are the only integers in $K(\sqrt{m})$ that have a chance to be sums of squares in $K(\sqrt{m})$. For a given m a large number of suitable pairs $[a, b]$ were selected and the corresponding α's represented by the sum of the least number Q of squares. Tallies were kept of the numbers Q and the results tabulated for each m. The most popular number in almost all cases was $Q=3$. The 50 numbers m considered include all the square-free integers $\leqq 41$, three triples 86, 87, 89; 173, 174, 177; 255, 257, 258; two larger numbers 1487, 3467 and thirteen small integers with square factors. The calculations were done by GEORGE, the Argonne Laboratory's computer, by a typically elaborate program complicated by the fact that in $K(\sqrt{m})$ there are infinitely many units. The reader must consult the paper for further details. *D. H. Lehmer* (Berkeley, Calif.)

E24-75 **(22# 27)**

Barrucand, Pierre. Sur certaines fonctions à caractère arithmétique. C. R. Acad. Sci. Paris **249** (1959), 2146–2148.

Let $r_s(n)$ be the number of representations of n as a sum of s squares. By adroit manipulation of the formula

$$\sum_{n=0}^{\infty} r_s(n)\frac{t^n}{n!}=\frac{1}{2\pi i}\int e^{tx}\Big(\sum_{k=-\infty}^{\infty} x^{-k^2}\Big)^s\frac{dx}{x},$$

in which the contour of integration is a circle $|x|=a>1$

in the complex plane, the author derives a number of interesting relations, among them

$$r_s(m) = \pi \sum_{n=0}^{\infty} r_s(n) J_{s/2-1}(\pi m, \pi n, \pi/2)$$

in which

$$J_\nu(t, k, \varphi) = \frac{1}{2\pi i} \int_{e^{-i\phi}}^{e^{i\phi}} \exp(tx - k/x) x^{-\nu-1} dx,$$

and the path of integration passes to the right of the origin. The last integral represents a kind of incomplete Bessel function. *A. Erdélyi* (Pasadena, Calif.)

E24-76 (22# 2590)

Schinzel, A. Sur les sommes de trois carrés. Bull. Acad. Polon. Sci. Sér. Sci. Math. Astr. Phys. **7** (1959), 307–310. (Russian summary, unbound insert)

This paper concerns the problem of the decomposition of a natural integer into a sum of three squares. One of the results proved is the following. A necessary and sufficient condition that a number n admits a decomposition $n = x^2 + y^2 + z^2$ when $x, y, z > 0$ and $(x, y, z) = 1$ is that n has the two properties (i) $n \not\equiv 0, 4, 7 \pmod 8$ and (ii) n has a divisor of the form $4K-1$, or else is not a "numerus idoneus" [Dickson, *History of the theory of numbers*, Vol. 1, Stechert, New York, 1934; p. 360]. Various corollaries are given, one of which is that "the only natural integers $n < 101{,}200$ with $n \not\equiv 0, 4, 7 \pmod 8$ which are not representable as a sum of three positive squares are 1, 2, 5, 10, 13, 25, 37, 58, 85, 130. The author conjectures that the restriction $n < 101{,}200$ may be dropped. {The subject was considered earlier by Grosswald, Calloway, and Calloway [Proc. Amer. Math. Soc. **10** (1959), 451–455; MR **21** #3376].} *I. A. Barnett* (Cincinnati, Ohio)

Citations: MR 21# 3376 = E24-73.

Referred to in P12-12.

E24-77 (22# 3718)

Dzewas, Jürgen. Quadratsummen in reellquadratischen Zahlkörpern. Math. Nachr. **21** (1960), 233–284.

The author considers the following two related problems. (A) The determination of all real-quadratic number fields in which the genus of the form $x'E_q x = x_1^2 + \cdots + x_q^2$ $(q \geqq 2)$ contains only one class. He shows that for $q \geqq 9$ there are no such forms. For $q = 8$ only the rational field has this property. For $q \geqq 4$ there is only a finite number of totally real number fields with this property; they are of at most the 11th degree, and have a discriminant not greater than 62,122,500. For $q = 2, 3$ there is, for any given degree, only a finite number of totally real fields with this property. More detailed results are given for $q = 2$. (B) The determination of the number of representations of a number of one of these fields as a sum of q squares of integers. This is solved for the above-mentioned fields. *B. W. Jones* (Boulder, Colorado)

Referred to in R26-37.

E24-78 (22# 4686)

Cohn, Harvey. Decomposition into four integral squares in the fields of $2^{1/2}$ and $3^{1/2}$. Amer. J. Math. **82** (1960), 301–322.

Recent experiments by the author [Numer. Math. **1** (1959), 121–134] indicated that every totally positive integer, $\mu = a + b\sqrt{2}$, is the sum of four squares in the field of $\sqrt{2}$ when b is even (a necessary condition). This fact is proved in the present paper by the forthright method of actually giving a formula for the number of representations of such a number as the sum of 4 squares, like that of Jacobi for rational integers and that of Götzky [Math. Ann. **100** (1928), 411–437] for the field of $\sqrt{5}$.

Let G and H denote the sum of the norms of the divisors of μ that have odd norms and even norms respectively. Then the number of representations of μ as the sum of 4 squares is given by $8G$, $32G$, or $48G + 6H$ according as the norm of μ is odd, four times an odd number or a multiple of 8.

The method uses Götzky's procedure in that it employs the appropriate theta functions of two complex variables and the fourth power of such series is matched by an Eisenstein series having the same modular transformation group.

For the field of $\sqrt{3}$ the same formulas fail to give the exact number of representations of $a + b\sqrt{3}$ as a sum of 4 squares, there being an additional non-zero error function $E(\mu)$ which, being of lower order than G, permits the conclusion that for all μ of sufficiently large norm 4 squares suffice.

It is conjectured that 3 squares suffice in both fields. *D. H. Lehmer* (Berkeley, Calif.)

Referred to in E24-79, F40-26, R48-26.

E24-79 (24# A110)

Cohn, Harvey
Calculation of class numbers by decomposition into three integral squares in the fields of $2^{1/2}$ and $3^{1/2}$.
Amer. J. Math. **83** (1961), 33–56.

Humbert [J. Math. Pures Appl. (6) **2** (1906), 329–355] observes that the discriminants $D = 5, 8$ and 12 (to which we may add trivially $D = 1$) play a special role in the theory of theta functions. This fact is illustrated once more by the present paper, which is a continuation of the author's previous one [Amer. J. Math. **82** (1960), 301–322; MR **22** #4686] quoted in what follows as (I). The discriminants above mentioned correspond to the quadratic fields $R(5^{1/2})$, $R(2^{1/2})$ and $R(3^{1/2})$ (besides the rational one), in all of which the euclidean algorithm is valid; hence their class number is $h = 1$. However, let μ be a totally positive (for simplicity, square-free) integer of $R(D^{1/2})$. Then the class number $H = H(D^{1/2}, (-\mu)^{1/2})$ of the field $R(D^{1/2}, (-\mu)^{1/2})$ is closely connected with the number $A_3 = A_3(\nu)$ of representations of ν as a sum of three squares, $\nu = \sum_{i=1}^{3} \xi_i^2$, where ν and ξ_i are integers of $R(D^{1/2})$ and, in general, $\nu = \mu$; in case $\nu \neq a + bD^{1/2}$ (a, b rational integers), then $\nu = 2\mu$ if $D = 8$ and $\nu = (1 + 3^{1/2})^2 \mu$ if $D = 12$. The factor (*) $G = A_3/H$ depends on the prime-ideal factorization of (2) in $R(D^{1/2}, (-\mu)^{1/2})$. The case $D = 1$ is classical (Gauss; see also Maass [Abh. Math. Sem. Hansischer Univ. **14** (1941), 185–191; MR **3**, 163]); the case $D = 5$ has been studied by Götzky [Math. Ann. **100** (1928), 411–437], and by Maass [Abh. Math. Sem. Hansischer Univ. **12** (1938), 133–162]. The cases $D = 8$ and $D = 12$ are discussed in (I) and the present paper. In (I) the number of representations of a totally positive integer as a sum of four squares in $R(D^{1/2})$ is determined, using essentially Götzky's method of modular functions of two complex variables. A similar approach works in the present paper for representations by sums of three squares. A Θ series is set up, such that $A_3(\nu)$ is the coefficient of $e^{\pi i(\nu\tau - \nu'\tau')D^{-1/2}}$ in the Fourier series of Θ^3 (convergence enforced by Hecke's method). Next, a "singular series" Ψ is computed. It is shown that: (i) Θ^3 and Ψ satisfy the same functional equation; (ii) the first coefficient in the Fourier series of Ψ is GH; (iii) $\Theta^3 - \Psi$ is a cusp form, identically zero if $D = 8$, but $\not\equiv 0$ if $D = 12$. Hence, comparison of coefficients proves (*) for $D = 8$ and shows that (*) holds only "approximately" in case $D = 12$. Numerical evidence suggests that also in this case (i.e., in $R(3^{1/2})$) every totally positive integer has a representation as a sum of three squares and that, at least for $\mu \in R$, $(\mu, 6) = 1$, (*) actually holds. *E. Grosswald* (Philadelphia, Pa.)

Citations: MR 3, 163a = E24-11; MR 22# 4686 = E24-78.

Referred to in F40-26.

E24-80 **(22# 4687)**

Schinzel, A. On a certain conjecture concerning partitions into sums of three squares. Wiadom. Mat. (2) **1** (1955/56), 205. (Polish)

G. Pall [Amer. Math. Monthly **40** (1933), 10–18] conjectured that every integer of the form $2(8n+1)$, $n \geqq 1$, is the sum of three squares of natural numbers. The author disproves this conjecture by pointing out that it is false for $130 = 2(8 \cdot 8 + 1)$. *H. Halberstam* (London)

E24-81 **(22# 4688)**

Estermann, T. On the representations of a number as a sum of three squares. Proc. London Math. Soc. (3) **9** (1959), 575–594.

The author achieves a proof of the important formula for the number of representations of n as a sum of 3 squares by the Hardy-Littlewood method, which had failed hitherto owing to the fact that the double series which occurs in the "singular series" is not absolutely convergent. He overcomes this difficult problem by dealing directly with the double series involved. Previous authors, Maass [Abh. Math. Sem. Univ. Hamburg **12** (1938), 133–162], Streefkerk [Thesis, Free Univ. of Amsterdam, 1943; MR **7**, 414] and P. T. Bateman [Trans. Amer. Math. Soc. **71** (1951), 70–101; MR **13**, 111], also made the evaluation of the representation function by modifications of Hardy's method, based on ideas of Hecke.

S. Chowla (Notre Dame, Ind.)

Citations: MR 7, 414d = P04-22; MR 13, 111i = E24-35.

E24-82 **(22# 5616)**

Subba Rao, M. V. On representation of numbers as sum of two squares. Math. Student **26** (1958), 161–163.

The author proves the classical formula $r_2(n) = 4\{d_1(n) - d_3(n)\}$, where $r_2(n)$ is the number of representations of n as the sum of two squares, and $d_1(n)$, $d_3(n)$ are the sums of the divisors of n of the forms $4x+1$, $4x+3$ respectively, by observing that $r_2(n)/4$ and $d_1(n) - d_3(n)$ are both multiplicative functions of n which agree when n is a prime power. The crucial point, that primes of the form $4x+1$ have essentially one representation as the sum of two squares while primes of the form $4x+3$ have no representations as the sum of two squares, is stated as a "well-known result", and the proof depends on this. *M. Newman* (Washington, D.C.)

E24-83 **(22# 10975)**

Newman, Morris. Subgroups of the modular group and sums of squares. Amer. J. Math. **82** (1960), 761–778.

Put $(\sum_{n=-\infty}^{\infty} q^{n^2})^s = \sum_{n=0}^{\infty} r_s(n) q^n$; also define $r_s(x) = 0$ for $x \neq 0, 1, 2, \cdots$. The paper is concerned with relationships of the following kind:

$$r_3(np^2) - r_3(n) = (p - (-n/p))(r_3(n) - r_3(n/p^2)),$$

where p is an odd prime, n an arbitrary integer and $(-n/p)$ the Legendre symbol. The principal purpose of the paper is to prove that formulas of this type exist for all positive integers s and all odd primes p; the number of terms in these formulas depends only on s and p. The method employed is the "subgroup" method which is concerned with functions invariant with respect to a suitable subgroup of the modular group. The reviewer notes that the group-theoretic preliminaries of the paper are developed in greater detail than is required for the present paper; also several theorems concerning the structure of modular subgroups are proved that are not needed in the remainder of the paper. The main results of the paper are too complicated for a brief statement. However we note the following special results:

$$r_s(np^2) = \{1 + p^{s-2} - (-1)^{(s-1)(p-1)/4} p^{(s-3)/2}(n/p)\} r_s(n) - p^{s-2} r_s(n/p^2) \qquad (s = 1, 3, 5, 7),$$

$$r_s(np^2) = \{1 + p^{s-2} - (-1)^{(s-1)(p-1)/4} p^{(s-2)/2}(n/p)^2\} r_s(n) - p^{s-2} r_s(n/p^2) \qquad (s = 2, 4, 6, 8).$$

L. Carlitz (Durham, N.C.)

E24-84 **(23# A117)**

Mordell, L. J.

On the representation of a number as a sum of three squares.

Rev. Math. Pures Appl. **3** (1958), 25–27.

This paper considers the proof of the "Three Square Theorem" [see Ankeny, Proc. Amer. Math. Soc. **8** (1957), 316–319; MR **19**, 15], and shows a simplification which shortens the proof. The simplification is in dealing with equivalent quadratic forms, instead of reducing the representation by three squares to that of two squares. Also, Hermite's inequality on quadratic forms, instead of Minkowski's, is shown to be sufficient for the proof.

N. C. Ankeny (Cambridge, Mass.)

Citations: MR 19, 15d = E24-67.

E24-85 **(23# A2374)**

Sierpiński, W.

Sur les nombres impairs admettant une seule décomposition en une somme de deux carrés de nombres naturels premiers entre eux.

Elem. Math. **16** (1961), 27–30.

The author proves that the necessary and sufficient condition that the equation $n = x^2 + y^2$ ($n \equiv 1 \pmod 2$, $0 < x < y$, $(x, y) = 1$) should have a unique solution is that $n = p^k$ ($k > 0$), $p \equiv 1 \pmod 4$. *P. Erdös* (Budapest)

Referred to in D32-71.

E24-86 **(24# A109)**

Krätzel, Ekkehard

Über die Anzahl der Darstellungen von natürlichen Zahlen als Summe von $4k$ Quadraten.

Wiss. Z. Friedrich-Schiller-Univ. Jena **10** (1960/61), 33–37.

The author derives a general formula for the number of ways of representing a natural number as the sum of $4k$ squares. He does this by the classical method of using theta functions. It turns out that the second derivatives of the logarithms of the classical theta functions are related in a sufficiently simple way so that he can actually express his results in terms of the arithmetic function $\sigma(n)$, as is required. The results check with those obtained by Mordell for the problem of $2k$ squares [L. J. Mordell, Quart. J. Math. **48** (1917), 93–104].

H. W. Brinkmann (Swarthmore, Pa.)

Referred to in E24-90.

E24-87 **(24# A713)**

Nagell, Trygve

On the sum of two integral squares in certain quadratic fields.

Ark. Mat. **4** (1961), 267–286.

Für einen algebraischen Zahlkörper K wird die diophantische Gleichung $\xi^2+\eta^2=\alpha$ studiert. Im Falle der absolut-quadratischen Zahlkörper $K=P(\surd\pm 5)$ und $K=P(\surd\pm 13)$ werden notwendige und hinreichende Bedingungen für die Lösbarkeit gegeben (Theorem 3 und Theorem 5). Die Beweise sind elementar und benutzen frühere Ergebnisse des Autors [Nova Acta Soc. Sci. Upsal. (4) **15** (1953); MR **17**, 241]. *G. J. Rieger* (Munich)

Citations: MR 17, 241a = E24-61.
Referred to in E16-52.

E24-88 (26# 94)

Rankin, R. A.
Representations of a number as the sum of a large number of squares.
Proc. Roy. Soc. Edinburgh Sect. A **65**, 318–331 (1960/61).

Let N, s denote positive integers, P a positive real number, $r=r(s, P; N)$ the number of representations of N as a sum of s non-negative squares, where each square does not exceed P^2, and let

$$\rho = \rho(s, P; N) = \left(\frac{45}{8\pi s}\right)^{1/2} P^{s-2} \exp\left\{-\frac{45}{8sP^4}\left(N-\frac{s}{3}P^2\right)^2\right\}.$$

By an application of the Hardy-Littlewood method the author obtains the estimate $|r-\rho|<5P^{s-2}/s$ whenever $P\geqq 10^{12}$ and $100\leqq s\leqq \frac{1}{3}P^{2/3}$. When s is large and N is near enough to $\frac{1}{3}sP^2$, the error $|r-\rho|$ is of smaller order than ρ. More precisely, if $P\geqq 10^{12}$, $|N-\frac{1}{3}sP^2|\leqq cP^2s^{1/2}$ and $100e^{45c^2/4}\leqq s\leqq \frac{1}{3}P^{2/3}$, then $\frac{3}{5}\rho\leqq r\leqq \frac{7}{5}\rho$. The proof makes use of a number of lemmas for estimating certain exponential sums related to Gauss sums. {In Lemma 2, s_n should be S_n.} *T. M. Apostol* (Pasadena, Calif.)

Referred to in B24-18.

E24-89 (26# 96)

Rankin, R. A.
On the representation of a number as the sum of any number of squares, and in particular of twenty.
Acta Arith. **7** (1961/62), 399–407.

Let $r_s(n)$ be the number of solutions of the equation $x_1^2+x_2^2+\cdots+x_s^2=n$ in integers x_i: positive, negative or zero. The author uses theta functions to explain how to express $r_s(n)$ in the form $r_s(n)=\rho_s(n)+R_s(n)$, where $\rho_s(n)$ can be expressed as a "singular series" or as a summation over divisors of n of various forms. His main concern is the calculation of the "error term" $R_s(n)$. This is expressed in terms of the coefficients of the expansions of so-called cusp forms, and the problem is to find the forms most suitable for this purpose. For purposes of calculation it seems best to use cusp forms whose coefficients have multiplicative properties; this was done by Glaisher in his treatment for even $s\leqq 18$ [Proc. London Math. Soc. (2) **5** (1907), 479–490]. For the case $s=20$ the author has discovered a set of two exceptionally simple cusp forms. These enable him to write $R_{20}(n)=(16/93)[155\psi_1(n)+76\psi_1^*(n)]$ where both $\psi_1(n)$ and $\psi_1^*(n)$ have the multiplicative property $\psi(m\cdot n)=\psi(m)\cdot\psi(n)$ whenever $(m, n)=1$. Further, for any odd prime p and positive integer k the equation $\psi(p^{k+1})=\psi(p)\psi(p^k)-p^9\psi(p^{k-1})$ holds for each function and, finally, $\psi_1(2^k)=0$, $\psi_1^*(2^k)=3\cdot 16^k$ $(k>0)$. He also points out that

$$\rho_{20}(n) = \frac{8}{31}\Big[\sum_{\substack{d|n\\ n/d\text{ odd}}} d^9 - \sum_{\substack{d|n\\ n/d\text{ even}}} (-1)^d d^9\Big],$$

so that a complete expression for $r_{20}(n)$ is available.
H. W. Brinkmann (Swarthmore, Pa.)

E24-90 (26# 1296)

Krätzel, Ekkehard
Über die Anzahl der Darstellungen von natürlichen Zahlen als Summe von $4k+2$ Quadraten.
Wiss. Z. Friedrich-Schiller-Univ. Jena **11** (1962/63), 115–120.

Let $r_{2k}(n)$ denote the number of representations of the positive integer n as a sum of $2k$ squares. In a previous paper [same Z. **10** (1960/61), 33–37; MR **24** #A109] the author showed how $r_{4k}(n)$ can be obtained recursively starting with $r_4(n)$. The object of the present paper is to do the same thing for $r_{4k+2}(n)$ starting now with $r_2(n)$. Put

$$\Theta_3 = \Theta_3(v,\tau) = \sum_{-\infty}^{\infty} q^{n^2}e^{2\pi inv} \qquad (q=e^{\pi i\tau}),$$

$$\Theta_0(v,\tau) = \Theta_3(v+\tfrac{1}{2},\tau),$$

$$\Theta_2(v,\tau) = e^{\pi i(v+\tau/4)}\Theta_3(v+\tfrac{1}{2}\tau,\tau);$$

also put

$$\Theta_3^{4k+2} = 1+\sum_{n=1}^{\infty}\gamma_{4k+2}(n)q^n,$$

$$\Theta_0^{4k+2} = 1+\sum_{n=1}^{\infty}s_{4k+2}(n)q^n,$$

$$\Theta_2^{4k+2} = 1+\sum_{n=1}^{\infty}t_{4k+2}(n)q^n,$$

$$\rho_k(n) = \sum_{\substack{t|n\\ t\equiv 1(4)}} t^k - \sum_{\substack{t|n\\ t\equiv 3(4)}} t^k,$$

$$\delta_k(n) = \sum_{\substack{t|n\\ n/t\equiv 1(4)}} t^k - \sum_{\substack{t|n\\ n/t\equiv 3(4)}} t^k.$$

Then $r_2(n)=4\rho_0(n)$, $s_2(n)=4(-1)^n\rho_0(n)$, $t_2(n)=4\delta_0(2n-1)$,

$$\tfrac{1}{4}E_{2k}\gamma_{4k+2}(n) = \rho_{2k}(n)+(-1)^k\delta_{2k}(2n)+K_{4k+2},$$

$$\tfrac{1}{4}(-1)^{n-1}E_{2k}s_{4k+2}(n) = \rho_{2k}(n)+(-1)^k\delta_{2k}(2n)+K'_{4k+2},$$

$$\tfrac{1}{4}E_{2k}t_{4k+2}(n) = \rho_{2k}(2n-1)+(-1)^k\delta_{2k}(2n-1)+K''_{4k+2},$$

where the E_{2k} are Euler numbers and K_{4k+2}, K'_{4k+2}, K''_{4k+2} are defined as the coefficients in certain q-products. For example, K_{10} is equal to the coefficient of q^n in $8f^{14}(q^2)f^{-4}(-1)$, where $f(q)=q^{1/24}\prod_1^{\infty}(1-q^n)$. The paper concludes with the formula

$$(-1)^n 2^{2k-2}\rho_{2k}(2n-1) =$$

$$\sum_{t=1}^{k}\sum_{d=1}^{2n-1}\binom{2k-1}{2t-2}(-1)^d\rho_{2t-2}(4n-2d-1)\sigma_{2k-2r+1}(2d-1).$$

L. Carlitz (Durham, N.C.)

Citations: MR 24# A109 = E24-86.

E24-91 (26# 3687)

Kiselev, A. A.; Slavutskiĭ, I. S.
Some congruences for the number of representations as sums of an odd number of squares. (Russian)
Dokl. Akad. Nauk SSSR **143** (1962), 272–274.

Let, for s odd, $r_s(n)$ denote the number of representations of n as a sum of s squares. Write $r_s(n)=\rho_s(n)+e_s(n)$, where $\rho_s(n)$ is the "dominant" term represented as the "singular" series (with a trivial factor) in the Hardy-Littlewood method, and $e_s(n)$ is the "error" term. Write $s=2\sigma+1$ $(\sigma\geqq 1)$. The authors introduce a function $T_\sigma(n)$, roughly of the form

$$\prod_{p|n}\{1+(n/p)g(p^\sigma)\},$$

where $g(x)$ is a simple rational function of x, and (n/p) is Legendre's symbol.

Typical of the congruences announced by the author is

$$\frac{1}{T_3(n)}\rho_7(n) \equiv \frac{1}{3T_5(n)}\rho_{11}(n) \quad (\text{mod } 3),$$

where $(3, n) = 1$ and n is also subject to a further condition (whose full description would be too long for this review). Another announcement of interest is

$$(1) \qquad H(12n)U_1 \equiv 2T_1\frac{r_3(n)}{3} \quad (\text{mod } 3),$$

where $n \equiv 1$ (mod 4) and $(3, n) = 1$. (Here the letters have their usual significance, H is the class-number of a certain imaginary quadratic field while T_1, U_1 relate to the fundamental unit of a certain real quadratic field.)

The authors also announce similar congruences modulo 5, 7, 9, 19 and 27. They refer to previous literature on this and related topics (Bateman, Carlitz, Kiselev, Leopoldt). The reviewer notes that Ankeny, Artin and Chowla [Ann. of Math. (2) **56** (1952), 479–493; MR **14**, 251] proved the congruence

$$(2) \qquad h \equiv \frac{u}{t}H \ (\text{mod } 3),$$

where h, t, u relate to the class-number and fundamental of a certain real quadratic field, while H is the class-number of a certain imaginary quadratic field. There is some similarity between (1) and (2), in view of the connection between H and $r_3(n)$. *S. Chowla* (Boulder, Colo.)

Citations: MR 14, 251h = R14-19.

E24-92 **(26# 6142)**

Seshu, Lily

On the simultaneous representation of a given pair of integers as the sum respectively of four integers and their squares. I, II.

Nederl. Akad. Wetensch. Proc. Ser. A **64** = *Indag. Math.* **23** (1961), 64–79, 80–88.

From the author's introduction (with references added from the Bibliography): "In this paper an expression is obtained for the arithmetic function $r_s(n, m)$ which represents the number of solutions of the diophantine equations:

$$x_1^2 + x_2^2 + \cdots + x_s^2 = n, \quad x_1 + x_2 + \cdots + x_s = m,$$

when the value of s is four. H. D. Kloosterman used the circle method of Hardy and Littlewood to obtain heuristically a function $\rho_s(n, m)$ which approximates $r_s(n, m)$. When $3 \leqq s \leqq 8$, it turns out that $\rho_s(n, m) = r_s(n, m)$. Kloosterman himself [Math. Ann. **118** (1942), 319–364; MR **5**, 33; erratum, MR **9**, 735] showed this for $s = 3, 5, 7$ and P. Bronkhorst [Thesis, Univ. of Groningen, 1943, North Holland, Amsterdam, 1943; MR **14**, 1063] did the same for $s = 6, 8$. F. van der Blij [Nederl. Akad. Wetensch. Proc. **50** (1947), 31–40, 41–48, 166–172; MR **8**, 502; ibid. **50** (1947), 298–306, 390–396; MR **8**, 502] used an algebraic method to obtain an exact formula for $r_4(n, m)$. G. A. Lomadze [Akad. Nauk Gruzin. SSR Trudy Tbiliss. Mat. Inst. Razmadze **20** (1954), 21–45; MR **16**, 905] on the other hand summed the singular series to obtain a closed expression for $\rho_s(n, m)$ for $s \geqq 3$. His results together with those of van der Blij indicate that $r_4(n, m) = \rho_4(n, m)$. In this paper the same result is proved directly, utilizing the techniques of Bronkhorst and Kloosterman. A convergence problem arises in the process similar to that encountered by several other authors in the solution of problems of a similar nature. . . . The technique used to overcome the difficulty, namely the introduction of a convergence-producing factor into the terms of a formal series, goes back to E. Hecke [Abh. Math. Sem. Hamburg Univ. **1** (1922), 102–126; ibid. **3** (1924), 213–236]."

A. Sklar (Chicago, Ill.)

Citations: MR 5, 33g = E24-13; MR 8, 502a = E24-26; MR 8, 502b = E24-27; MR 14, 1063e = E24-40; MR 16, 905c = E24-59.

E24-93 **(27# 128)**

Nagell, Trygve

On the number of representations of an A-number in an algebraic field.

Ark. Mat. **4**, 467–478 (1962).

An algebraic integer α in an algebraic number field Ω is said to be an A-number in Ω if α is representable as the sum of the squares of two algebraic integers in Ω. In counting the number of representations of α, the representations $\alpha = x^2 + y^2$ with $x = \pm\xi$, $y = \pm\eta$ and $x = \pm\eta$, $y = \pm\xi$ are counted as one representation.

It is proved that if the number 1 has only the representation $1 = 1^2 + 0^2$, then there is exactly one representation of every A-number which generates a prime ideal in Ω, and the number of representations of every A-number is finite. Otherwise, there is an infinity of representations of every A-number. It is also shown that every A-number in Ω has an infinity of representations except when Ω is the Gaussian field or when Ω is totally real. The equation $\xi^2 + \eta^2 = 1$ in a quadratic field is considered in moderate detail.

{Several misprints in a previous paper by the author [Nova Acta Soc. Sci. Upsal. (4) **15** (1953), no. 11; MR **17**, 241] are noted and corrected; Theorem 2 of that paper is modified slightly.} *J. K. Goldhaber* (College Park, Md.)

Citations: MR 17, 241a = E24-61.

E24-94 **(27# 5749)**

Nagell, Trygve

On the A-numbers in the quadratic fields $K(\sqrt{\pm 37})$.

Ark. Mat. **4**, 511–521 (1963).

An algebraic integer α in an algebraic number field Ω is said to be an A-number in Ω if α is representable as the sum of the squares of two algebraic integers in Ω. This paper addresses itself to the problem of determining the A-numbers of the field $K(\sqrt{37})$ and of the field $K(\sqrt{-37})$. Necessary and sufficient conditions for a prime in $K(\sqrt{37})$ to be an A-number are given; from these, a complete determination of the A-numbers in $K(\sqrt{37})$ is obtained. There are too many details in this result for it to be quoted here. For the field $K(\sqrt{-37})$, necessary and sufficient conditions for a prime to be an A-number are derived, and it is indicated how one should proceed in order to determine all the A-numbers of this field.

J. K. Goldhaber (College Park, Md.)

E24-95 **(27# 2495)**

Davenport, H.

A problematic identity.

Mathematika **10** (1963), 10–12.

An ingenious proof that there do not exist rational functions F_1, F_2, F_3 of the variables x_1, x_2, x_3, x_4 with real coefficients such that

$$x_1^2 + x_2^2 + x_3^2 + x_4^2 = F_1^2 + F_2^2 + F_3^2.$$

(Problem proposed by N. J. Fine.) This is a special case of a general result subsequently proved by the reviewer [to appear in Acta Arith.].

J. W. S. Cassels (Cambridge, England)

E24-96 (28# 1162)

Mordell, L. J.
The representation of integers by three positive squares.
Michigan Math. J. **7** (1960), 289–290.

The problem is studied by other authors in a recent paper of the same title [see E. Grosswald, A. and J. Calloway, Proc. Amer. Math. Soc. **10** (1959), 451–455; MR **21** #3376]. It is there proved that every integer $n \neq 4^a(8m+7)$ is a sum of three positive squares, unless $n = 4^a m$, $m \in S$, where the exceptional set S consists of a finite number of integers m. Every integer $m \in S$, except 25, satisfies the following conditions: (a) m is square-free, (b) $m \equiv 1, 2, 5 \pmod 8$, (c) m has no prime factor $\equiv 3 \pmod 4$. In this paper the author proves that a necessary and sufficient condition for a number m, satisfying (a), (b), (c), to belong to S is that the only non-negative integer solutions of: $xy+xz+yz=m$ are those for which $xyz=0$, or also (in the case $m \equiv 1 \pmod 4$)) those for which $(x-y)(x-z)(y-z)=0$.
M. Cugiani (Zbl **97**, 31)

Citations: MR 21# 3376 = E24-73.

E24-97 (29# 51)

Dixon, John D.
Another proof of Lagrange's four square theorem.
Amer. Math. Monthly **71** (1964), 286–288.

A short new proof is given of the famous theorem that every positive integer can be written as the sum of four squares. *W. H. Mills* (Princeton, N.J.)

E24-98 (29# 95)

Cassels, J. W. S.
On the representation of rational functions as sums of squares.
Acta Arith. **9** (1964), 79–82.

The author proves the following theorems. Theorem 1: Let k be any field and denote by $k(x)$ and $k[x]$, respectively, the field of rational functions and the ring of polynomials in a single variable x having coefficients in k. Then any $f \in k[x]$ which is the sum of squares of elements of $k(x)$ is the sum of the same number of squares of elements of $k[x]$. The new part of the theorem is the statement that the same number of squares suffices. Theorem 2: Let $d \in k$ and suppose that the characteristic of k is not 2. A necessary and sufficient condition that x^2+d be the sum of $n>1$ squares in $k(x)$ is either that -1 is the sum of $n-1$ squares of k or that d is the sum of $n-1$ squares of k. Theorem 3: Let R denote the field of real numbers and let $x_1, x_2, \cdots, x_n$ be independent variables over R. Then $x_1^2+\cdots+x_n^2$ is not the sum of $n-1$ squares of elements of $R(x_1, \cdots, x_n)$. *J. W. Andrushkiw* (S. Orange, N.J.)

Referred to in E04-22, E24-101, E24-105, E24-108, Z10-36.

E24-99 (29# 4726)

Spira, Robert
Polynomial representations of sums of two squares.
Amer. Math. Monthly **71** (1964), 760–766.

Let $P_0, \cdots, P_k$ be primes congruent to 1 modulo 4, expressed as sums of squares $P_i = a_i^2 + b_i^2$. The author obtains polynomials in the a's and b's, which give all the expressions of $P_0^{j_0} \cdots P_k^{j_k}$ as a sum of two squares.
B. J. Birch (Manchester)

E24-100 (29# 5794)

Gupta, H.; Vaidya, A. M.
The number of representations of a number as a sum of two squares.
Amer. Math. Monthly **70** (1963), 1081–1082.

The authors obtain what they call an apparently new expression for $r_2(n)$ (the number of representations of n as sum of two squares) in the form

$$r_2(n) = 4\prod\left\{\left[\frac{\alpha+2}{2}\right]+(-1)^{[p/2]}\left[\frac{\alpha+1}{2}\right]\right\},$$

where $n = 2^\beta \prod p^\alpha$ is the canonical factorization of n. {Reviewer's remark: This is the same as (16.9.5) in Hardy and Wright's *An introduction to the theory of numbers* [fourth edition, Clarendon, Oxford, 1960].}
M. V. Subbarao (Edmonton, Alta.)

E24-101 (31# 169)

Pfister, Albrecht
Zur Darstellung von -1 als Summe von Quadraten in einem Körper.
J. London Math. Soc. **40** (1965), 159–165.

If a field F is not formally real, then there exists a smallest number $s = s(F)$ such that -1 is a sum of s squares in F. Van der Waerden pointed out [Jber. Deutsch. Math.-Verein. **42** (1932), 71] that not every number can occur as an $s(F)$. For further results see H. Kneser [ibid. **44** (1934), 143–146], who showed that $s(F)$ can only be 1, 2, 4, 8, $16m$; however, only fields with 1, 2, 4 were known. It is now shown that s is a power of 2. Further, for every 2^m a class of fields F with $s(F) = 2^m$ is constructed, generalizing another result of Kneser. For $n = 2^m$ the set $G_n = G_n(F)$ of elements in F which are sums of n squares in F form a group. Since Hurwitz's result concerning the composition of sums of squares is so well known, this is of particular interest. For these groups $G_m G_n = G_{m \circ n}$, where $m \circ n$ is the smallest integer k such that for all fields the relation $G_m G_n \subset G_k$ holds. This $m \circ n$, $m \leqq n$, can be found by induction and satisfies $m \circ n \leqq m+n-1$. The proofs use very recent results of Cassels [Acta Arith. **9** (1964), 79–82; MR **29** #95], one of which the author generalizes from the reals to formally real fields.
O. Taussky-Todd (Pasadena, Calif.)

Citations: MR 29# 95 = E24-98.
Referred to in E04-22, E04-24, E04-25, E24-105, E24-108, E24-124.

E24-102 (31# 5860)

Leahey, William J.
A note on a theorem of I. Niven.
Proc. Amer. Math. Soc. **16** (1965), 1130–1131.

The author gives a simpler proof of the following result due to the reviewer [Trans. Amer. Math. Soc. **48** (1940), 405–417; MR **2**, 147]. A Gaussian integer $a+2bi$ (b an integer) is a sum of two squares of Gaussian integers if and only if not both $a/2$ and b are integral and odd. Explicit formulations of the sums of squares are given in the sufficiency part of the proof. *I. Niven* (Eugene, Ore.)

Citations: MR 2, 147b = E24-4.
Referred to in E24-111.

E24-103 (32# 5605)

Rankin, R. A.
Sums of squares and cusp forms.
Amer. J. Math. **87** (1965), 857–860.

If $r_s(n)$ is the number of representations of n as the sum of s squares, one has (1) $r_s(n) = \rho_s(n) + R_s(n)$, where $\rho_s(n)$ is a "divisor function" and $R_s(n)$ is the nth Fourier coefficient of a cusp modular form. Going to the generating functions, one has (2) $\vartheta_3^s(z) = E_s(z) + f_s(z)$, where E_s is an Eisenstein series, f_s is a cusp form. Whereas (1) is defined only for integral s, (2) makes sense for arbitrary real positive s. It is known that $f_s(z) \equiv 0$ for $s = 5, 6, 7, 8$. The author proves that $f_s(z) \not\equiv 0$ for real $s > 8$. Thus $r_s(n)$ cannot be represented exactly by a divisor function for $s > 8$, a fact well known for special values of s.

The author's method is very simple, relying in particular on the known representation of the Fourier coefficients of the Eisenstein series. *J. Lehner* (College Park, Md.)

Referred to in E12-143.

E24-104 **(33# 4002)**

Carlitz, L.

A short proof of Jacobi's four square theorem.

Proc. Amer. Math. Soc. **17** (1966), 768–769.

Let $\theta_0(q)=1+2\sum_{n=1}^{\infty}(-1)^n q^{n^2}$, $\theta_2(q)=2\sum_{n=0}^{\infty}q^{(2n+1)^2/4}$, and $\theta_3(q)=1+2\sum_{n=1}^{\infty}q^{n^2}$. By logarithmic differentiation of the product representations for $\theta_2{}^4/\theta_3{}^4$ and $\theta_0{}^4/\theta_3{}^4$, the author deduces power series expansions for $\theta_2{}^4$ and $\theta_3{}^4$ that lead at once to Jacobi's four square theorem. There is a misprint in the last displayed formula on each page.
T. M. Apostol (Pasadena, Calif.)

E24-105 **(34# 4210)**

Cassels, J. W. S.

Représentations comme somme de carrés.

Les Tendances Géom. en Algèbre et Théorie des Nombres, pp. 55–65. *Éditions du Centre National de la Recherche Scientifique, Paris,* 1966.

Let R be the real field and let $x_1, \cdots, x_n$ be independent indeterminates; the author has proved [Acta Arith. **9** (1964), 79–82; MR **29** #95] that $x_1{}^2+\cdots+x_n{}^2$ is not the sum of $n-1$ squares of $R(x_1, \cdots, x_n)$. A related theorem of A. Pfister [J. London Math. Soc. **40** (1965), 159–165; MR **31** #169] asserts that if k is any field, and $G(n)$ is the set of non-zero elements of k which are sums of at most n squares, then $G(2^m)$ is always a group. In this exposé, the author discusses these and related theorems; for further developments, see Pfister [Invent. Math. **1** (1966), 116–132; MR **34** #169]. *B. J. Birch* (Oxford)

Citations: MR 29# 95 = E24-98; MR 31# 169 = E24-101; MR 34# 169 = E04-24.

E24-106 **(35# 2845)**

Pumplün, Dieter

Über Darstellungsanzahlen von quadratfreien Zahlen durch Quadratsummen.

Math. Ann. **170** (1967), 253–264.

This paper contains several congruences satisfied by the numbers $e_{2l+1}^*(f)$ for various l, these numbers being related to the number of representations of the odd square-free number f as the sum of $2l+1$ squares. The work thus extends that of H. Petersson [Math. Nachr. **14** (1956), 361–375; MR **18**, 867], who considered some cases when f is prime, and uses the author's earlier work [J. Reine Angew. Math. **213** (1963/64), 200–220; MR **30** #1118] on the factorization of the cyclotomic polynomial.
H. J. Godwin (Swansea)

Citations: MR 18, 867i = R14-33; MR 30# 1118 = C15-29.

E24-107 **(35# 4147)**

Bergquist, J. W.; Foster, Lorraine L.

Infinite classes of harmonic integers.

Math. Mag. **40** (1967), 128–132.

The authors combine the ideas of cross-ratio of a harmonic set and the representation of integers as the sum of four squares, and make the following definitions, in which all numbers referred to are natural numbers. Let H_n be the set of $N=a^2+b^2+c^2+d^2$ for which $(d^2-a^2)(c^2-b^2)=-n\times(d^2-b^2)(c^2-a^2)$, $H_n{}'$ the subset of H_n for which $abcd\neq 0$ and $H_n{}''$ the subset for which $a=0$.

Several results are obtained, including that $H_n{}'$ and $H_n{}''$ are nonempty and that $H_1{}'$, $H_1{}''$, $H_2{}'$, $H_2{}''$ contain infinitely many distinct integers with, moreover, $(a, b, c, d)=1$. *H. J. Godwin* (Swansea)

E24-108 **(36# 5095)**

Pfister, Albrecht

Zur Darstellung definiter Funktionen als Summe von Quadraten.

Invent. Math. **4** (1967), 229–237.

The author proves the following quantitative version of Hilbert's seventeenth problem: Let R be a real closed field and let f be a definite rational function in $R(X_1, \cdots, X_n)$ (i.e., $f(a_1, \cdots, a_n)\geqq 0$ for all a_i in R for which $f(a_1, \cdots, a_n)$ is defined). Then f is expressible as the sum of 2^n squares of rational functions in $R(X_1, \cdots, X_n)$. D. Hilbert showed that definite polynomials could not be expressed as sum of squares of polynomials [Math. Ann. **32** (1888), 342–350], but that the above result held if $n=2$ [Acta Math. **17** (1893), 169–197], and listed as his seventeenth problem the task of showing that a definite function could be expressed as the sum of squares. That problem was resolved by E. Artin [Abh. Math. Sem. Univ. Hamburg **5** (1926), 100–115 (1927)]. J. Ax ["On ternary definite rational functions" to appear in Proc. London Math. Soc.] showed that the above quantitative version was implied by Artin's result and by the condition (A): -1 is expressible as a sum of squares in each nonreal algebraic extension L of $R(X_1, \cdots, X_n)$. Ax went on to show, using cohomological dimension arguments, that the condition (A) held if $n=3$. In this paper, the author shows, by extending the ideas and methods regarding sums of squares of himself [J. London Math. Soc. **40** (1965), 159–165; MR **31** #169; Arch. Math. **16** (1965), 363–370; MR **32** #2408] and J. W. S. Cassels [Acta Arith. **9** (1964), 79–82; MR **29** #95]: If L is nonreal and $L(i)$ has the property (B): Every quadratic form over $L(i)$ in more than 2^n variables has a nontrivial zero in $L(i)$, then -1 is a sum of squares in L. Now the theorem of Tsen [see S. Lang, Ann. of Math. (2) **55** (1952), 373–390; MR **13**, 726] assures us that every extension E of an algebraically closed field C of transcendency degree n over C has the property: Every quadratic form over E in more than 2^n variables has a nontrivial zero in E. It follows that if L is a nonreal extension of $R(X_1, \cdots, X_n)$, then $L(i)$ has property (B); whence L has property (A), and the theorem follows from that of Ax. The proof of each of these steps is elegant and entails only elementary ideas and concepts, giving us a most elegant and understandable proof.
D. J. Lewis (Ann Arbor, Mich.)

Citations: MR 13, 726d = D72-6; MR 29# 95 = E24-98; MR 31# 169 = E24-101; MR 32# 2408 = E04-22.

Referred to in E24-124.

E24-109 **(37# 138)**

Williams, Kenneth S.

On a theorem of Niven.

Canad. Math. Bull. **10** (1967), 573–578.

It has been proved by the reviewer [Trans. Amer. Math. Soc. **48** (1940), 405–417; MR **2**, 147] that $x+iy$ is a sum of two squares of gaussian integers if and only if y is even and not both of $x/2$ and $y/2$ are odd. The author determines the number of representations of $x+iy$ as a sum of two squares in terms of the factorization of $x+iy$ into gaussian primes. *I. Niven* (Eugene, Ore.)

Citations: MR 2, 147b = E24-4.

Referred to in E24-110.

E24-110 **(37# 5152)**

Williams, Kenneth S.

Addendum: "On a theorem of Niven".

Canad. Math. Bull. **11** (1968), 145.

The author reports that his results [same Bull. **10** (1967), 573–578; MR **37** #138] on the number of representations of a Gaussian integer as a sum of two squares of Gaussian integers were established earlier by G. Pall [Duke Math. J. **18** (1951), 399–409; MR **12**, 676]. Although the results by Pall were formulated differently, the author shows the equivalence. *I. Niven* (Eugene, Ore.)

Citations: MR 12, 676g = E24-33; MR 37# 138 = E24-109.

E24-111 (37# 5181)

Hardy, J.

Sums of two squares in a quadratic ring.

Acta Arith. **14** (1967/68), 357–369.

Let $D \neq 0$, 1 denote a positive or negative squarefree integer, and let $\Delta = D$ if $D \equiv 1 \pmod 4$, and $\Delta = 4D$ if $D \not\equiv 1 \pmod 4$. Then Δ is a non-square and $\Delta \equiv 0$ or $1 \pmod 4$. We write $\Delta = -4k+j$, where $j=0$ or 1, $\theta = \frac{1}{2}(-j+\sqrt{\Delta})$, so that $R = \{x_0 + x_1\theta \mid x_0, x_1 \in Z\}$ is a quadratic domain over Z of discriminant Δ. The author considers the problem of representing elements of R as sums of two squares in R. This problem was considered by I. Niven [Trans. Amer Math. Soc. **48** (1940), 405–417; MR **2**, 147] when $D=-1$, $\Delta=-4$; $D=2$, $\Delta=8$ and $D=5$, $\Delta=5$. For example, he showed (using a theorem of Mordell giving necessary and sufficient conditions for a positive binary quadratic form with integral coefficients to be expressible as a sum of the squares of two linear forms with integral coefficients) that $c_0 + c_1\sqrt{-1}$ is the sum of two squares of gaussian integers if and only if c_1 is even and not both of $\frac{1}{2}c_0$ and $\frac{1}{2}c_1$ are odd integers. W. J. Leahey [Proc. Amer. Math. Soc. **16** (1965), 1130–1131; MR **31** #5860] gave a simple proof of this result, which did not require Mordell's theorem. G. Pall [Duke Math. J. **18** (1951), 399–409; MR **12**, 676] pointed out that the number of representations of an element of R as the sum of two squares in R is obviously finite if $D>0$. When $D<0$ he proved that if the number of representations is not zero, it is infinite, except in the special case $D=-1$ when it is finite. Pall gave formulae for the number of representations in the three cases $D=-1$, $D=2$, $D=5$. He suggested that by defining sets of representations appropriately one could find similar formulae for the number of sets of such representations when $D<-1$. In this paper the author does precisely this. He extends Pall's method to the cases $D=3$, 7, 13, 37, $-p$ (p (prime) $\geqq 2$), pointing out the limitations of the method. An example of the type of theorem proved is the following. To find the number ν of integral solutions of $c_0 + 2c_1\sqrt{3} = (a_0 + a_1\sqrt{3})^2 + (b_0 + b_1\sqrt{3})^2$, where $c_0 > 0$, we may set $c_0^2 - 12c_1^2 = 2^{2\alpha}3^{2\sigma} \prod p_i^{2\gamma_i+\delta_i} \prod q_i^{2\beta_i} \prod r_i^{2\varepsilon_i}$, where the p_i denote primes of the form $12n+1$ and γ_i is the exponent to which p_i occurs in (c_0, c_1), the q_i are primes of the form $12n \pm 5$, and the r_i are primes of the form $12n+11$. In order that ν shall not be zero, it is necessary that the exponents of the primes 2, 3, q_i and r_i be even, as indicated, and that the r_i shall occur in (c_0, c_1) to even exponents $\geqq 0$. With these conditions holding, $\nu = 4\varepsilon_\alpha \prod (1+\gamma_i)(1+\gamma_i+\delta_i) \prod (1+\beta_i)$, where $\varepsilon_\alpha = 1$ if $\alpha = 0$ or 1, and $\varepsilon_\alpha = 3$ if $\alpha \geqq 2$. *K. S. Williams* (Ottawa, Ont.)

Citations: MR 2, 147b = E24-4; MR 12, 676g = E24-33; MR 31# 5860 = E24-102.

E24-112 (39# 152)

Chowla, Paromita

On the representation of -1 as a sum of squares in a cyclotomic field.

J. Number Theory **1** (1969), 208–210.

The main theorem states: Let $n \equiv 3 \pmod 8$, $K = Q(\exp 2\pi i/n)$; then $-1 = \alpha^2 + \beta^2$, $\alpha, \beta \in K$. The author shows that for $n>0$, $n \equiv 3 \pmod 8$ $i\sqrt{n} \in K$ (applying a result about Gaussian sums) and makes use of the fact that there are rational integers x, y, z such that $n = x^2 + y^2 + z^2$. Otherwise, all proofs are elementary. *W. G. H. Schaal* (E. Lansing, Mich.)

E24-113 (40# 2607)

Whitehead, Earl Glen, Jr.

The cross ratio on the real line.

Math. Mag. **42** (1969), 193–195.

The author proves the following two theorems: (1) If $l = a^2 + b^2 + c^2 + d^2$, where $a>b>c>d$ and cross ratio $\mathrm{CR}(a, c, b, d) = -1$, then there are integers e, f such that $l = e^2 + 3f^2$, where $a+b+c+d = e+3f$ and l is a quadratic residue modulo 6. (2) There are an infinite number of integers l satisfying the conditions of the first theorem.

By writing an IBM 7094 program, the author reports that he has found all integers l of the second theorem between 1 and 1000. He gives the 12 values of l between 1 and 100. The number of l's in the 10 ranges of hundreds, as also given by him, shows preference for 18 that appears in 4 ranges, the rest being all different but between 15 and 20 besides 12. *S. R. Mandan* (Kharagpur)

E24-114 (40# 4235)

Chowla, Paromita

On the representation of -1 as a sum of two squares of cyclotomic integers.

Norske Vid. Selsk. Forh. (*Trondheim*) **42** (1969), 51–52.

The author proves that if A is the ring of integers in $K = Q(e^{2\pi i/p})$, where p is a prime $\geqq 3$, then there exist α and β in K such that $-1 = \alpha^2 + \beta^2$ if $2|f$, where f is the least positive integer such that $2^f \equiv 1 \pmod p$. She conjectures that the condition $2|f$ is necessary.

E24-115 (40# 5542)

Salamon, Reinhild

Die Klassen in Geschlecht von $x_1^2 + x_2^2 + x_3^2$ und $x_1^2 + x_2^2 + x_3^2 + x_4^2$ über $\mathbf{Z}[\sqrt{3}]$.

Arch. Math. (*Basel*) **20** (1969), 523–530.

Using the method developed by M. Kneser [same Arch. **8** (1957), 241–250; MR **19**, 838] of neighbors of quadratic forms, the author shows that the genus of the quadratic form $x_1^2 + x_2^2 + x_3^2 + x_4^2$ over $\mathbf{Z}[\sqrt{3}]$ has exactly three classes and that representations of the other two classes are $x_1^2 + x_2^2 + 2x_3^2 + 2(\sqrt{3})x_3x_4 + 2x_4^2$ and $3(x_2^2 + x_3^2 + x_4^2) + 2(x_1^2 + x_1x_2 + x_1x_3 - (\sqrt{3})x_1x_4 + (1+\sqrt{3})x_2x_3 + (1-\sqrt{3})x_2x_4)$. It then follows that the genus of $x_1^2 + x_2^2 + x_3^2$ over $\mathbf{Z}[\sqrt{3}]$ contains exactly two classes. *D. G. James* (Göttingen)

Citations: MR 19, 838c = E12-62.

E24-116 (41# 184)

Manin, Ju. I.

On Hilbert's seventeenth problem. (Russian)

Hilbert's problems (*Russian*), *pp.* 196–199. *Izdat. "Nauka", Moscow,* 1969.

A brief exposition of Hilbert's seventeenth problem and its proof by Artin. [E. Artin and O. Schreier, Abh. Math. Sem. Univ. Hamburg **5** (1926), 85–99; Artin, ibid. **5** (1926), 100–115 (1927)]. *E. Inaba* (Tokyo)

E24-117 (41# 1637)

Đerasimović, Božidar

A Fermat theorem. (Serbo-Croatian. French summary)

Mat. Vesnik **6** (**21**) (1969), 423–424.

This is a rediscovery of the ingenious proof of H. J. Smith [J. Reine Angew. Math. **50** (1855), 91–92; cf. L. E. Dickson, *History of the theory of numbers, Vol. II: Diophantine analysis,* Chapter 6, Carnegie Inst. of

Washington, Washington, D.C., 1920; reprint, Chelsea, New York, 1966; MR **39** #6807b] that every prime of the form $4n+1$ is a sum of two squares.

I. Danicic (Aberystwyth)

Citations: MR 39# 6807b = Z15-88.

E24-118 **(41# 5315)**

Kano, Takeshi

On the number of integers representable as the sum of two squares.

J. Fac. Sci. Shinshu Univ. **4** (1969), 57–65.

Let $C(x)$ be the number of integers $\leqq x$ which are representable as the sum of two squares of coprime natural numbers, let $P(x)$ be the number of integers $\leqq x$ with precisely one such primitive representation, let $R(x)$ be the number of integers $\leqq x$ with precisely one representation as a sum of two integer squares, and let $D(x)$ be the number of integers $\leqq x$ with no representation as a sum of two integer squares. Let $b_0=2^{-1/2}\prod_r(1-r^{-2})^{-1/2}$, where r ranges over all primes $\equiv 3 \pmod 4$. It is shown that $C(x)\sim 3x/(8b_0\sqrt{\log x})$, $P(x)\sim 3x/(4\log x)$, $R(x)\sim c_1x/\log x + c_2x/\log^2 x+\cdots$, and

$$D(x) = 4b_0x/(\pi\sqrt{\log x})+O(x\log^{-3/2}x).$$

The constant b_0 was introduced by E. Landau [Arch. Math. Phys. (3) **13** (1908), 305–312].

B. Garrison (San Diego, Calif.)

E24-119 **(41# 6774)**

Niven, Ivan; Zuckerman, Herbert S.

Variations on sums of squares.

Pi Mu Epsilon J. **4** (1968), 407–410.

It is a well known theorem of Lagrange that every positive integer is a sum of four squares of integers. However, these integers need not all be different from zero. The author here proves two elementary theorems, the first of which asserts that every integer $\geqq 170$ is a sum of five squares of nonzero integers, while the second states that every sufficiently large positive integer is a sum of three nonzero integral squares and a nonzero kth power provided $k=2$, 4 or 6 or any odd positive integer. The assertions are shown to be false if 5 is replaced by four in the former and in the latter k is an even integer $\geqq 8$. The proofs are elementary. For instance, the first assertion follows from Lagrange's theorem and the fact that $169=13^2=12^2+5^2=12^2+4^2+3^2=10^2+8^2+2^2+1^2$.

K. G. Ramanathan (Bombay)

E24-120 **(42# 3020)**

Taussky, Olga

Sums of squares.

Amer. Math. Monthly **77** (1970), 805–830.

This article is a wide ranging survey in which the topic of the title is approached from many different points of view. The paper is divided into ten chapters, each of which has a substantial bibliography. The following is a list of the chapter titles with an indication of a portion of the contents of some of the chapters: (1) Introduction. (2) Pythagorean triangles and Fermat's last theorem. Here, among other facts, we find the classic formulas for the integral solutions of $a^2+b^2=c^2$ obtained first by elementary trigonometry, second by an application of Hilbert's Theorem 90. (3) Sums of squares in number theory. Much of this chapter discusses the eigenvalues of integral and rational symmetric matrices. (4) Positive definite matrices. This chapter is partly analytic and partly number theoretic and among many topics touches upon stability theory, factorizations of matrices, and congruence classes of integral definite matrices. (5) Formally real fields. Results of Pfister are mentioned here, as is a matrix commutator theorem of the reviewer. (6) Composition of sums of squares, anticommuting matrices, composition algebras. (7) Division algebras over the reals, n-dimensional spheres, n-dimensional Laplace equations. (8) Positive definite polynomials. This is a summary of old and new facts about expressing a polynomial or rational function as a sum of squares. (9) Sums of squares in number theory. This chapter is a discussion of normal fields for which the Galois group is a cyclic group of order four or the quaternion group. (10) Rational arc tangents (this chapter was written by John Todd). This chapter discusses identities for the arc tangent function of the type appearing in the calculation of π, and in particular discusses when arc tan m (for fixed integral m) can be expressed as an integral linear combination of arc tangents of other integers. This depends on the prime factors of $1+m^2$.

In addition to the topics mentioned in the above chapter descriptions, there are many other topics discussed, far too many to list in a review. Those interested in algebra, number theory, analysis, or topology will all find something worthwhile in this interesting article.

R. C. Thompson (Santa Barbara, Calif.)

E24-121 **(42# 4484)**

Chowla, S.

An idea of Tate-Dwork for the "Hasse invariant" applied to a classical theorem of Fermat.

J. Number Theory **2** (1970), 423–424.

For any prime $p\equiv 1 \pmod 4$ write $p=a^2+b^2$, with integers a and b chosen so that $a\equiv 1 \pmod 4$. It is proved that $a\equiv \pm\frac{1}{2}F_n(\frac{1}{2},\frac{1}{2},1;-1) \pmod p$, where $n=(p+1)/2$ and $F_n(\alpha,\beta,\gamma;x)$ denotes the sum of the first n terms of the hypergeometric series $F(\alpha,\beta,\gamma;x)$. A sketch of the proof is given.

I. Niven (Eugene, Ore.)

E24-122 **(42# 5933)**

Linnik, Yu. V. [Linnik, Ju. V.]

Application of the method of D. Burgess to the investigation of integer points on large spheres.

Symposia Mathematica, Vol. IV (INDAM, Rome, 1968/69), pp. 99–112. Academic Press, London, 1970.

This paper is concerned with integer points on 2-spheres $x^2+y^2+z^2=m$; such a sphere is denoted by Sph(m). Let Γ_0 be a closed convex domain on Sph(1) and Γ its central projection on Sph(m). Let $H_0(\Gamma)$ be the number of primitive integer points on Sph(m) inside Γ and $H_0(m)$ the total number of primitive integer points on Sph(m). The author shows that for $(-m/q)=+1$, q an odd prime and $m\not\equiv 0$, 4, 7 (mod 8), $H_0(\Gamma)=\frac{1}{4}\omega(\Gamma)\pi^{-1}H_0(\Gamma)(1+x_0(\Gamma_0,q,m))$ ($\omega(\Gamma)$ being the solid angle subtended by Γ), where $x_0(\Gamma_0,q,m)$ tends to 0 for fixed Γ_0, q. On the assumption of a small zero free region near $s=1$ of real L-series, the dependence on q is eliminated. {Earlier papers by the same author appeared in Dokl. Akad. Nauk SSSR **96** (1954), 909–912 [MR **16**, 451]; Mat. Sb. (N.S.) **43** (**85**) (1957), 257–267 [MR **20** #2328].}

R. Spira (E. Lansing, Mich.)

Citations: MR 16, 451c = E24-54; MR 20# 2328 = E24-55.

E24-123 **(42# 5934)**

Bhaskaran, M.

A plausible reconstruction of Ramanujan's proof of his formulae for $\theta^{4s}(q)$.

Publ. Ramanujan Inst. No. 1 (1968/69), 25–33.

Let $\vartheta(q)=1+2\sum_{v=1}^{\infty}q^{v^2}(|q|<1)$. Then for any positive integer s, $\vartheta^{4s}(q)=1+\sum_{n=1}^{\infty}r(n)q^n$, where $r(n)$ is the number of representations of n as a sum of $4s$ integer squares. S. Ramanujan [*Collected papers of Srinivasa Ramanujan*, Cambridge Univ. Press, London, 1927] has stated without proof certain other formulae for $\vartheta^{4s}(q)$ in terms of powers of q, thus making it possible to calculate the $r(n)$. L. J. Mordell [Quart. J. Pure Appl. Math. **48** (1917/18), 93–96; ibid. **48** (1917/18), 97–104] and K. Ananda-Rau [J. Madras Univ. Sect. B **24** (1954), 61–89; MR **16**, 17] have obtained proofs for these formulae. In this paper new proofs are obtained which might also have been obtained by Ramanujan. *B. Garrison* (San Diego, Calif.)

Citations: MR 16, 17c = E24-50.

E24-124 (42# 7630)

Moser, Claude

Représentation de -1 par une somme de carrés dans certains corps locaux et globaux, et dans certains anneaux d'entiers algébriques.

C. R. Acad. Sci. Paris Sér. A-B **271** (1970), A1200–A1203.

The problem of representing negative one as a sum of squares in an algebraic number field goes back to Hilbert. A. Pfister [J. London Math. Soc. **40** (1965), 159–165; MR **31** #169; Invent. Math. **4** (1967), 229–237; MR **36** #5095] has proved that the smallest number $s(K)$ necessary to represent negative one as a sum of squares in an algebraic number field K is a power of 2. In the present paper $s(K)$ is determined for the following systems: abelian extensions of rational p-adic fields; cyclotomic extensions of the field of rationals; quadratic imaginary extensions of the field of rationals; the ring of integers of quadratic imaginary fields. The elegant proofs are generally borrowed from algebraic number theory; use is made of the Minkowski-Hasse theorem on the form $X_1^2+\cdots+X_n^2$. The following almost conventional notations are used: Q_p stands for the p-adic rational field, p a prime; $Q^{(k)}=Q(e^{2\pi i/k})$ is the cyclotomic field with rational integer $k\geqq 3$; $Q(\sqrt{-m})$ is the field generated by $\sqrt{-m}$ over the rationals, m a square-free natural; A_m is the ring of integers in $Q(\sqrt{-m})$; L_m and E_m stand for the real quadratic field $Q(\sqrt{m})$ and the biquadratic field $Q(\sqrt{-m},\sqrt{m})$, respectively; e_m denotes the fundamental unit of L_m and w_m the rational part of e_m^3; $N(e_m)$ is the norm of e_m. The following theorems are proved. Theorem 1: Let K be an abelian extension of Q_2; then $s(K)=4$ if n is odd, and $s(K)=2$ if n is even; moreover, $s(K)=1$ if $i\in K$. Theorem 1a: Let K be an abelian extension of Q_p (p odd) and let F_q denote the residue field of K; then $s(K)=1$ if $q\equiv 1$ (4), and $s(K)=2$ if $q\equiv 3$ (4). Theorem 2: Let $k>1$ be an odd rational integer and let 2 belong to f modulo k; then $s(Q^{(k)})=2$ if f is even, and $s(Q^{(k)})=4$ if f is odd. Corollary: Let p be an odd prime; then $s(Q^{(p)})=2$ if $p\equiv 3$ or 5 (mod 8), and $s(Q^{(p)})=4$ if $p\equiv 7$ (mod 8). Theorem 3: If $m=1$, $s(Q\sqrt{-m})=1$; if $m\equiv 7$ (mod 8), $s(Q\sqrt{-m})=4$; otherwise $s(Q\sqrt{-m})=2$. Theorem 4: If $m\equiv 7$ (mod 8), $s(A_m)=4$. Theorem 5: If $m\not\equiv 7$ (mod 8), $s(A_m)=3$. Theorem 6: If $N_{L_m/Q}(e_m)=-1$, then $s(A_m)=2$. Theorem 7: If $N_{L_m/Q}(e_m)=+1$ and $m\equiv 1$ or 2 (mod 4), then $s(A_m)=3$. Theorem 8: If $m\equiv 3$ (mod 8) the following statements are equivalent: (a) $s(A_m)=2$; (b) the diophantine equation $x^2-my^2=-2$ has a solution in rational integers x, y; (c) the number w_m-1 is a square in Z. *L. Bernstein* (Chicago, Ill.)

Citations: MR 31# 169 = E24-101; MR 36# 5095 = E24-108.

E24-125 (43# 245)

Revoy, Ph.

Formes quadratiques et représentation de -1 comme somme de carrés dans un corps.

Mélanges d'Algèbre Pure et Appliquée, pp. 27–41. *Université de Montpellier, Montpellier*, 1970.

The author reproduces some recent results on the algebra of quadratic forms, quoting the sources. The main results of the author's exposition are due to A. Pfister [Invent. Math. **1** (1966), 116–132; MR **34** #169]. *H. Lenz* (Berlin)

Citations: MR 34# 169 = E04-24.

E24-126 (43# 3229)

Williams, Kenneth S.

Note on a theorem of Pall.

Proc. Amer. Math. Soc. **28** (1971), 315–316.

As a special case of a more general result G. Pall [Duke Math. J. **18** (1951), 399–409; MR **12**, 676] has calculated the number of representations of any Gaussian integer as the sum of two squares of Gaussian integers. The present author gives a very simple proof of this result. *R. Tijdeman* (Leiden)

Citations: MR 12, 676g = E24-33.

E24-127 (43# 4794)

Thérond, Jean-Daniel

Détermination effective de certaines décompositions en somme de deux carrés.

Thèse présentée à la Faculté des Sciences de Montpellier pour obtenir le grade de Docteur de Spécialité-Mathématiques. Secrétariat des Mathématiques de la Faculté des Sciences de Montpellier, 1969–1970, Publication No. 91.

Université de Montpellier, Montpellier, 1970. i+41 *pp. n.p.*

Let N be the set of natural numbers and let $m, n, u, v\in N$. Using only elementary number-theoretic techniques and by working in the ring of Gaussian integers, the author develops a new simple procedure for determining when $n=u^2+v^2$. The procedure yields all the representations of n as the sum of two squares. The author then uses the same techniques to develop a procedure for determining when, for a given integer m, $m^{-1}=u^{-2}+v^{-2}$. In this case also the procedure yields all the representations of m satisfying $m^{-1}=u^{-2}+v^{-2}$. In the last chapter of this thesis, the author investigates the question of when $n=u^2+v^2$ with n, u, v being rational numbers.

The author writes a FORTRAN program for the IBM 1130 which determines all $m, u, v\in N$, $m<2^{15}$, such that $m^{-1}=u^{-2}+v^{-2}$. The program and a table of m, u, v satisfying $m^{-1}=u^{-2}+v^{-2}$ is in the appendix.

The bibliography contains two references which are very old, to Simon Stevin and A. Legendre. *H. London* (Montreal, Que.)

E24-128 (43# 6944)

Wong, Yung-chow; Young, Samuel S. H.

On the lengths and the numbers of congruence classes of closed geodesics in Grassmann manifolds.

Tôhoku Math. J. (2) **22** (1970), 604–612.

The authors amplify known results in number theory to find (1) the possible lengths of closed geodesics in Grassmann manifolds and (2) a partial answer to how many congruence classes of closed geodesics there are for a given length. In order to answer the second question completely one needs to know how many ways a given positive integer can be represented as the sum of squares of a non-decreasing sequence of r nonnegative relatively prime integers. The partial results give a complete answer for $r=1$ or 2 and an enumeration ($r\neq 3$) or characterization ($r=3$) of those integers for which the number of these representations is one. *R. L. Bishop* (Urbana, Ill.)

E24-129 **(44# 150)**

Fricker, François
Eine Beziehung zwischen der hyperbolischen Geometrie und der Zahlentheorie.
Math. Ann. **191** (1971), 293–312.

Es sei $\mathfrak{H}$ das Poincaré-Modell der dreidimensionalen hyperbolischen Geometrie, Γ eine diskrete Untergruppe von SL(2, **C**), die als diskontinuierliche Bewegungsgruppe von $\mathfrak{H}$ gedeutet ist und einen kompakten, meßbaren Fundamentalbereich $\mathfrak{F}(\Gamma)$ mit Volumen $|\mathfrak{F}(\Gamma)|$ besitzen soll. Für $T=\begin{pmatrix}\alpha & \beta\\ \gamma & \delta\end{pmatrix}$ bedeute $\|T\|=\sqrt{(|\alpha|^2+|\beta|^2+|\gamma|^2+|\delta|^2)}$. Dann gilt (Satz 1): Für $x\to+\infty$ folgt $\sum_{T\in\Gamma,\|T\|\leq x}1\sim(\pi/(2|\mathfrak{F}(\Gamma)|))x^4$. Satz 2 lautet folgendermaßen: Es sei $p\equiv -1 \bmod 8$ eine Primzahl; $A(k,p)$ bezeichne für natürliches k die Lösungszahl des diophantischen Gleichungssystems $c_1^2+c_2^2+c_3^2+c_4^2=k$, $d_1^2+d_2^2+d_3^2+d_4^2=pk+1$, $c_1d_1+c_2d_2+c_3d_3+c_4d_4=0$; dann gilt

$$\sum_{k\leq x}A(k,p)\sim(8\pi\sqrt{(p)}x^2)/\sum_{l=0}^{\infty}x(l)/(2l+1)$$

für $x\to+\infty$, wobei $x(l)=1$ für $l=0$, $=0$ für $2l+1\equiv 0 \bmod p$ und $=(-p)/(2l+1)$ sonst. *V. Havel* (Brno)

E24-130 **(44# 3954)**

Nagell, Trygve
Sur une catégorie d'équations diophantiennes insolubles dans un corps réel. (English summary)
Norske Vid. Selsk. Skr. (Trondheim) **1971**, *no.* 4, 5 *pp.*

Let K be the imaginary quadratic field generated by $\sqrt{-\Delta}$, where Δ is a positive square-free integer. If $\Delta\equiv -1 \pmod 8$, then the equation $x^2+y^2+z^2+w^2=0$ has only the trivial solution $x=y=z=w=0$ in K. If the equation $x^4+y^4+z^4=0$ has a non-trivial solution in K, then $\Delta\equiv 3 \pmod 8$. If $x^6+y^6+z^6=0$ has a non-trivial solution in K, then $\Delta\equiv 1 \pmod 4$. These last two results imply that $x^{12}+y^{12}+z^{12}=0$ has only the trivial solution in K. *W. H. Mills* (Princeton, N.J.)

E24-131 **(44# 5278)**

Waid, Carter
Generalized automorphs of the sum of four squares.
J. Number Theory **3** (1971), 468–473.

A generalized automorph of a quadratic form is an integral linear transformation which carries the form into an integral multiple of itself. This term was adopted by O. Taussky Todd in a paper in which she investigated the generalized automorphs of binary quadratic forms, giving a new interpretation of some results in papers by the reviewer and G. Pall and by the reviewer and D. Estes [O. Taussky, Linear Algebra and Appl. **1** (1968), 349–356; MR **38** #2155; the reviewer and Pall, Acta Arith. **15** (1968), 23–44; MR **39** #6822; the reviewer and Estes, Linear Algebra and Appl. **1** (1968), 153–180; MR **38** #4503]. The purpose of this paper is to characterize the generalized automorphs of the sum of four squares, and the following theorem is the main result (where L denotes the Lipschitz ring of integral quaternions in the Hamiltonian quaternion algebra). If g is a generalized automorph of the sum of four squares, then there exist a primitive quaternion q of odd norm, a quaternion b in L and an automorphism f of L such that $g(x)=qf(x)b$ for $\det f>0$ and $g(x)=qf(\bar{x})b$ for $\det f<0$; moreover, if q', f', b' satisfy the same conditions as q, f, b respectively, then there is a unit h of L such that $q'=qh^{-1}$, $b'=hb$, and $f'(x)=hf(x)h^{-1}$. This yields a unique factorization theorem for 4×4 integral matrices T satisfying $T'T=mI$, where m is a positive integer and I is the identity matrix. *H. S. Butts* (Baton Rouge, La.)

Citations: MR 38# 2155 = E16-71; MR 38# 4503 = E16-74; MR 39# 6822 = E16-78.

E24-132 **(44# 6632)**

Pourchet, Y.
Sur la représentation en somme de carrés des polynômes à une indéterminée sur un corps de nombres algébriques.
Acta Arith. **19** (1971), 89–104.

Let K be an algebraic number field and x an indeterminate. The author's main theorem (which is a little more general than the following) implies that every f in $K[x]$ that is positive-definite (i.e., f considered as a function on K takes on only non-negative values with respect to all possible orderings of K) is a sum of five squares of elements of $K[x]$.

In the case $K=Q$ (the field of rational numbers) this result is best possible as far as the number of squares needed for such representations is concerned. Later the author gives a precise characterization of all elements of $Q[x]$ that are sums of four squares in $Q[x]$. Finally these general results are applied to the cyclotomic polynomials of degree >1. For each of them (each being a sum of squares in $Q[x]$) the exact number of squares is determined. The proof of the main theorem mentioned above rests on the Hasse-Minkowski theorem for quadratic forms and on properties of quaternion forms. It is remarked that the main theorem can be extended to arbitrary global arithmetic fields of characteristic $\neq 2$. *O. H. Körner* (Ulm)

E28 OTHER PARTICULAR QUADRATIC FORMS

See also Section P24.

See also reviews E12-46, E12-112, E16-86, E20-14, E20-75, E24-20, E24-63, E24-115, F10-73, M20-1, N32-62.

E28-1 **(1, 292e)**

Pall, Gordon. An almost universal form. Bull. Amer. Math. Soc. **46**, 291 (1940).

The author studies the form $h=(1, 2, 7, 13)$ and shows that it represents all positive integers with the exception of 5. This completes the count (88 in all) of all positive quaternary forms without cross products which represent all integers with but one exception, carried out by P. R. Halmos [Bull. Amer. Math. Soc. **44**, 141–144 (1938)]. *A. E. Ross* (St. Louis, Mo.).

Referred to in A38-6.

E28-2 **(3, 65h)**

Gupta, Hansraj. Some idiosyncratic numbers of Ramanujan. Proc. Indian Acad. Sci., Sect. A. **13**, 519–520 (1941).

The author lists all odd numbers not greater than 20000 not of the form $x^2+y^2+10z^2$ as follows: 3, 7, 21, 31, 33, 43, 67, 79, 87, 133, 217, 219, 223, 253, 307, 391, 679, 2719. All but the last two numbers were given by Ramanujan, who remarked that these numbers obey no obvious law. There is also given a table of the number $N_2(x)$ of non-negative integers not greater than x which are sums of two non-negative squares, for $x=4$, 100 and $1000k$, $k=1, 2, 3, \cdots, 20$. These values are compared with an empirical formula

$$N_2(x)=\frac{.764x}{(\log x)^{\frac{1}{2}}}+\frac{.52x^{31/40}}{(\log x)^{\frac{1}{2}}}+212\left\{1-\cos\frac{\pi x}{9.104}\right\},$$

in which the first term is asymptotically correct [see these Rev. 1, 201]. *D. H. Lehmer* (Berkeley, Calif.).

Citations: MR 1, 201a = Z30-2.
Referred to in E24-38.

E28-3 (3, 68f)

Walfisz, Arnold. Zur additiven Zahlentheorie. VIII. Trav. Inst. Math. Tbilissi [Trudy Tbiliss. Mat. Inst.] **8**, 69–107 (1940). (German. Russian summary)

This paper is a continuation of VI in the same series [Trav. Inst. Math. Tbilissi **5**, 197–253 (1938)]. It deals with the representation of integers by certain quaternary quadratic forms, nineteen in all, such as $x^2+y^2+z^2+3t^2$. The number of representations is given in terms of divisor functions. Some of the results have been stated without proof by Liouville, Jacobi and others, but here they are gathered together systematically in one paper.

R. D. James (Saskatoon, Sask.).

Referred to in E28-57, P32-2.

E28-4 (4, 132a)

Walfisz, Arnold. Zur additiven Zahlentheorie. IX. Trav. Inst. Math. Tbilissi [Trudy Tbiliss. Mat. Inst.] **9**, 75–96 (1941). (German. Russian summary)

This paper is a continuation of (VI) and (VII) of the same series [Trav. Inst. Math. Tbilissi **5**, 197–253 (1938); **8**, 69–107 (1940); these Rev. **3**, 68]. In (VI) the representation of integers by thirty-two quaternary quadratic forms was discussed; in (VII) nineteen more forms were considered. In the present paper formulas are established for the number of representations of integers by twenty-two more forms. The formulas all involve one or more of the number-theoretic functions

$$\tau(u)=\sum_{mn=u} n(3|m), \qquad 3\nmid u,$$

$$\zeta(u)=\sum_{s^2+3t^2=4u} s(-1)^{(s-1)/2},$$

$$\eta(u)=\sum_{s^2+3t^2=4u} t(-1)^{(s-1)/2}.$$

R. D. James (Saskatoon, Sask.).

Citations: MR 3, 68e = P32-2.
Referred to in E28-49, E28-57, E76-5, P20-14.

E28-5 (4, 188b)

Gage, Walter H. An arithmetical identity for the form $ab-c^2$. Bull. Amer. Math. Soc. **48**, 898–900 (1942).

An identity of the Liouville type is obtained involving sums over the integral solutions a, b, c of the equation $ab-c^2=n$. Certain of these solutions are then related in the familiar manner to the class number $G(n)$ of the binary quadratic forms of determinant $-n$. Since, by setting $a=x+z$, $b=y+z$, $c=z$, $ab-c^2$ becomes $xy+yz+zx$, it is then possible to derive a formula for the number N of representations of n by the form $xy+yz+zx$ with positive integers x, y, z. The result is $N=3(G(n)-\frac{1}{2}\zeta(n))$, where $\zeta(n)$ is the number of divisors of n. The forms $xy+yz+2zx$ and $xy+2yz+2zx$ are handled in a similar manner.

H. W. Brinkmann (Swarthmore, Pa.).

E28-6 (5, 91c)

Aigner, Alexander and Reichardt, Hans. Stufenreihen im Potenzrestcharakter. J. Reine Angew. Math. **184**, 158–160 (1942).

Let p be a prime of the form $4n+1$, so that it can be represented by x^2+4u^2. It is possible to distinguish between the cases $u=t$ (odd), $u=2t$, $u=4t$, $u=8t$, according to the character of -2 modulo a prime ideal factor $\mathfrak{p}$ of p in the field $R(\zeta)$, where ζ is a primitive 8th root of unity. In fact, the cases mentioned correspond, respectively, to -2 being a quadratic nonresidue, quadratic residue, quartic residue, octic residue, modulo $\mathfrak{p}$. In the present paper the authors start with a prime of the form $8n+1$ which can be always represented by x^2+16u^2. Here $u=t$, $2t$, $4t$, $8t$ according as the number $4+3\sqrt{2}$ (which is in $R(\zeta)$) is a quadratic nonresidue, quadratic residue, quartic residue, octic residue, modulo $\mathfrak{p}$. Such a prime can also be represented by x^2+8u^2 and here the number $2+2\sqrt{2}$ serves to distinguish the four cases mentioned in exactly the same way.

H. W. Brinkmann (Swarthmore, Pa.).

E28-7 (7, 243g)

Chowla, S. A formula similar to Jacobsthal's for the explicit value of x in $p=x^2+y^2$ where p is a prime of the form $4k+1$. Proc. Lahore Philos. Soc. **7**, 2 pp. (1945).

For any prime p of the form $3k+1$, the Diophantine equation $4p=x^2+27y^2$ has a unique solution in x and y except for signs. Choose the sign of x so that $x\equiv 1 \pmod 3$. It is proved that

$$x=1+\sum_{m=1}^{p}\left(\frac{m}{p}\right)\left(\frac{m^3-4}{p}\right),$$

where $(\frac{m}{p})$ is Legendre's symbol. [Presumably the author intended the summation to extend only to $m=p-1$.]

I. Niven (West Lafayette, Ind.).

Referred to in L10-3.

E28-8 (7, 243h)

Chowla, S. The cubic character of 2 (mod p). Proc. Lahore Philos. Soc. **7**, 1 p. (1945).

On the basis of a previous result [see the preceding review] a new proof is given of the theorem that $u^3\equiv 2 \pmod p$ is solvable if and only if x is even. *I. Niven.*

E28-9 (9, 332e; 9, 332f)

Kadian, Sher Singh. Numbers representable by a ternary quadratic form. I. Math. Student **14**, 22–23 (1946).

Chowla, S., and Nazir, Abdur Rahman. Numbers representable by a ternary quadratic form. II. Math. Student **14**, 23 (1946).

The conjecture is made [first note] that positive numbers prime to 11 and congruent to 1 mod 4 are represented by $x^2+y^2+11z^2$. This conjecture is true and was proved in an unpublished manuscript by the reviewer. A similar conjecture [second note] that $x^2+y^2+13z^2$ represents every positive integer congruent to 1 mod 52 will be, in the reviewer's opinion, more difficult to prove. *G. Pall* (Chicago, Ill.).

E28-10 (9, 412e)

Bell, E. T. The problem of Liouville's theorems on arithmetical quadratic forms. Scripta Math. **13**, 177–185 (1947).

E28-11 **(10, 15b)**

Gage, Walter H. Proof of a formula of Liouville. Bull. Amer. Math. Soc. **54**, 581–586 (1948).

The author asserts that this is the first elementary proof of formula (Q) of Liouville's set of general formulas in the theory of numbers. It is accomplished by the ingenious use of the usual methods and employs only elementary operations. However, at one point it involves the formal manipulation of a series which appears to be infinite and perhaps not even convergent. *H. S. Zuckerman* (Seattle, Wash.).

E28-12 **(11, 332d)**

Whiteman, Albert Leon. Theorems on quadratic partitions. Proc. Nat. Acad. Sci. U. S. A. **36**, 60–65 (1950).

Let $f(k)$ and $F(k)$ represent the number of distinct solutions of $x^2+x\equiv k \pmod p$ and $x^3+x^2\equiv k \pmod p$, respectively. Let g be a primitive root of a prime p. In case $p=3f+1$, the unique solution with $a\equiv 1 \pmod 3$ and $b\equiv 0 \pmod 3$ of $4p=a^2+3b^2$ is given by $a=-p+\sum_{s=0}^{p-1}f(s^3)$ and $3b=\sum_{s=0}^{p-1}\{f(gs^3)-f(g^2s^3)\}$. In case $p=7f+1$, the unique solution of $4p=a^2+7b^2$ with $a\equiv 5 \pmod 7$ is given by $a=-p+\sum_{s=0}^{p-1}F(s^7)$ and $7b=\sum_{s=0}^{p-1}\{F(gs^7)-F(g^6s^7)\}$. Problems of this kind were previously treated by the author in terms of Jacobsthal sums [Duke Math. J. **16**, 619–626 (1949); these Rev. **11**, 230] but those methods seem to be inapplicable to the case $p=7f+1$. *I. Niven.*

Citations: MR 11, 230b = L10-3.

E28-13 **(12, 676a)**

v. Vlaardingen, M. On a formula of Eisenstein. Simon Stevin **28**, 55–59 (1951). (Dutch)

The author gives a short elementary proof of a formula of Eisenstein. From it can be deduced the representation of a prime $4n+1$ as a sum of two squares, and the representation of a prime $3n+1$ in the form x^2-xy+y^2.

W. J. LeVeque (Manchester).

Referred to in E28-14.

E28-14 **(14, 22g)**

van de Vooren-van Veen, J. F. On prime numbers and prime ideals. Simon Stevin **29**, 13–20 (1952). (Dutch)

The author gives proofs of the following theorems, the proofs being very similar to those given in Hardy and Wright [An introduction to the theory of numbers, Oxford, 1938, pp. 218–221] except that a and b are determined explicitly, using Fermat's theorem: every prime $p\equiv 1 \pmod 4$ is of the form a^2+b^2; every $p\equiv 1 \pmod 6$ is of the form a^2-ab+b^2; the primes of $k(i)$ are the associates of $1+i$, $a+bi$ where $p=4n+1=a^2+b^2$, and $p=4n+3$; the primes of $k(\rho)$ are the associates of $1-\rho$, $a+b\rho$ where $p=6n+1=a^2-ab+b^2$, and $p=3n+2$. The constructive proof of the representability of the primes in question is shorter, but more sophisticated, than that contained in a recent paper by M. v. Vlaardingen [Simon Stevin **28**, 55–59 (1951); these Rev. **12**, 676]. *W. J. LeVeque.*

Citations: MR 12, 676a = E28-13.

E28-15 **(14, 137c)**

Palamà, Giuseppe. Numeri primi e composti contenuti nella forma $1848x^2+y^2$ dell'intervallo 11 000 000–11 100 000. Boll. Un. Mat. Ital. (3) **7**, 168–171 (1952).

The author lists the 202 prime, and the 121 composite, numbers of the idoneal form $1848x^2+y^2$ among the first 100000 numbers of the 12th million. In the case of the primes, the values of x and y are also given.

D. H. Lehmer (Los Angeles, Calif.).

E28-16 **(14, 623d)**

van der Blij, F. Binary quadratic forms of discriminant −23. Nederl. Akad. Wetensch. Proc. Ser. A. **55** = Indagationes Math. **14**, 498–503 (1952).

Let $F_1=x^2+xy+6y^2$, $F_2=2x^2+xy+3y^2$, $F_3=2x^2-xy+3y^2$ be the reduced binary forms of discriminant -23 and $a(n, F_i)$ denote the number of representations of n by F_i. The author proves

$$a(n, F_1)=(2/3)\sum_{d|n}(d123)+4t(n)/3,$$

$$a(n, F_2)=a(n, F_3)=a(n, F_1)-2t(n),$$

where $t(n)$ are given by

$$\sum t(n)x^n=x\prod_1^\infty(1-x^k)(1-x^{23k}).$$

The function $t(n)$ is shown to be multiplicative and imply certain congruential properties of Ramanujan's function $\tau(n)$. *B. W. Jones* (Boulder, Colo.).

Referred to in E28-30, F10-97.

E28-17 **(17, 827b)**

Rusu, Eugen. Des nombres représentables par la forme $F=a^2+kb^2$, $(a, b)=1$. Acad. Repub. Pop. Romîne. Bul. Şti. Secţ. Şti. Mat. Fiz. **7** (1955), 273–286. (Romanian. Russian and French summaries)

Let p be any possible prime divisor of the quadratic form $F=a^2+kb^2$, $(a, b)=1$. In general, p itself need not be representable by F (e.g., for $k=11$, $p=5$ is a divisor of $2^2+11\times 1^2$, but $5\neq a^2+11b^2$ for any rational integral a,b). For specific numerical values of k, the author proves that either p, or some specified multiple of p is representable by F. The following is a characteristic result: For $k=47$, any prime divisor of a quadratic form $F=a^2+47b^2$ is such that either p, or $3p$, or $9p$ are representable by F, the alternatives being mutually exclusive. Hence, all prime divisors of this form F are divided into three classes. The product of two primes belonging to the same class is representable by F, the product of primes belonging to different classes is not. If $3p=F$, then also $16p=F$ and conversely; if $9p=F$, then also $8p=F$ and conversely. If p is any divisor of this F, then p^5 is representable by F. Twelve other results, of the same kind are proven. The proofs use elementary divisibility arguments and quadratic residues. *E. Grosswald.*

E28-18 **(18, 476c)**

Heegner, Kurt. Reduzierbare Abelsche Integrale und transformierbare automorphe Funktionen. Math. Ann. **131** (1956), 87–140.

In dieser Arbeit wird die Beziehung zwischen die Theorie der Reduktion Abelscher Integrale und die Lösung diophantischer Fragestellungen betrachtet. Die transcendente Theorie der einfachen Reduzierbarkeit der Abelschen Integrale wird dabei auf die Aufgabe der Darstellung einer positiven natürlichen ganzen Zahl durch eine ternäre Hermitische Form

$$H=u\bar{v}+\bar{u}v+w\bar{w}=H(u, v, w)$$

zurückgeführt. Die Auffindung der unimodularen Transformationen des Periodenschemas wird auf die der Automorphismen der Hermiteschen Form H zurückgeführt. Es ergibt sich dabei dass die Automorphismengruppe von H vollständig erzeugt wird durch die drei Substitutionen V_1, $V_2(1)$ und $V_3(i+1)$ wo:

$$V_1: u=v',\ v=u',\quad V_2(m): u=u'+imv \ (m \text{ ganz rational}),$$

$$V_3(c)\begin{cases} u=u'-\tfrac{1}{2}c\bar{c}v'-\bar{c}w', \\ v=v', \\ w=cv'+w'. \end{cases}$$

Insbesondere wird gezeigt, dass die Anzahl der reduzierten Darstellungen von $-m$ durch H endlich ist. Die Darstellungstheorie ganzer Zahlen durch H findet dadurch ihren Abschluss, dass auch die Darstellung binärer Hermitescher Formen durch H in Betracht gezogen wird. Es ergibt sich u.a.:

Die indefinite Hermitesche Form $(1, 0, -n)$ hat nur eine Darstellung durch H. Sämtliche Darstellungen einer positiven ganzen Zahl $n \equiv 0, 2, 3 \pmod 4$ durch H sind einander äquivalent.

Bei den binären Hermiteschen Formen von der Determinante $D=-2$ und dem Teiler $(1+i)$ ist die reproduzierende Gruppe oktaedrisch. Die orthogonale Hermitesche Form zeigt sich äquivalent mit

$$H_2=(1+i)x\bar{y}+(1-i)\bar{x}y+z\bar{z}.$$

Die Gruppe von H_2 wird in den Variabeln von H durch $V_2(2)$, (6), (8) vollständig erzeugt und die Transformationsgruppe modulo $(1+i)$ als Untergruppe der unimodularen Substitutionen durch V_0, V_1, $V_2(2)$, (8).

S. C. van Veen (Delft).

E28-19 (21# 7193)

Lomadse, G. Über die Darstellung der Zahlen durch einige quaternäre quadratische Formen. Acta Arith. **5** (1959), 125–170.

The author considers the number $r(n)$ of representations of a positive integer n in the form $a(x_1^2+x_2^2)+a'(x_3^2+x_4^2)$, where a, a' are fixed positive integers with $(a, a')=1$ and x_1, x_2, x_3, x_4 are any integers. Then $r(n)$ is the Fourier coefficient in the expansion of a product of theta-functions

$$F(\tau) = \vartheta_{00}{}^2(\tau; 0, 2a)\vartheta_{00}{}^2(\tau; 0, 2a')$$

which is a modular form of dimension -2 belonging to the principal congruence group $\Gamma(4aa')$. As in the classical investigations of Hardy, Littlewood and Mordell, the form of this function at rational points τ is investigated and yields a singular series $\Theta(\tau; aa')$, which is itself a modular form of dimension -2 for $\Gamma(4aa')$; $\Theta(\tau; aa')$ is, of course, a combination of Eisenstein series which behaves similarly to $F(\tau)$ at the parabolic cusps of the fundamental region and the difference $F(\tau)-\Theta(\tau; aa')$ is a cusp form which is found explicitly in the cases

$$a = 1, a' = 5, 6, 7, 9, 10; \quad a = 2, a' = 5.$$

This yields formulae for $r(n)$. For example, when $a=1$, $a'=5$, the cusp form is $\frac{8}{3}\vartheta_{21}{}^2(\tau; 0, 10)\,\vartheta_{61}{}^2(\tau; 0, 10)$, while, when $a=2$, $a'=5$, it is a linear combination of three such products of theta-functions.

The details of the analysis are very complicated and employ methods and results due to Kloostermann, Streefkerk and the author. See, in particular, H. Streefkerk, Thesis, Free Univ. of Amsterdam, 1943 [MR **7**, 414] and G. A. Lomadze [Akad. Nauk Gruzin. SSR. Trudy Tbiliss. Mat. Inst. Razmadze **22** (1956), 77–102; MR **19**, 942].

When $a=1$, $a'=5$, 6, 7, 9 the results agree with those stated by Kloostermann and Liouville.

R. A. Rankin (Glasgow)

Citations: MR 7, 414d = P04-22; MR 19, 942e = P04-41.

Referred to in E28-44, E28-47.

E28-20 (22# 697)

Zeckendorf, E. Familles de nombres premiers. Bull. Soc. Roy. Sci. Liège **29** (1960), 15–27.

With reservation for the primes 2 and 3, the author proposes to partition the prime numbers in the following three families: (1) the prime numbers $P\equiv 1 \pmod 4$, which can be expressed, as well as their products, by a sum (a^2+b^2) of terms relatively prime on the condition that no prime factor $P'\equiv -1 \pmod 4$ is included; (2) the prime numbers $P\equiv 1 \pmod 6$, which can be expressed, as well as their products, by a sum $(3a^2+b^2)$ of terms relatively prime on the condition that no prime factor $P'\equiv -1 \pmod 6$ is included; and (3) the prime numbers $P\equiv \pm 1 \pmod{12}$. Since the case (1) is known, the case (2) is mainly treated, and the case (3) will be discussed later.

S. Ikehara (Tokyo)

Referred to in E28-21.

E28-21 (22# 5617)

Zeckendorf, E. Familles de nombres premiers. Bull. Soc. Roy. Sci. Liège **29** (1960), 62–73.

This paper treats the prime numbers $P\equiv \pm 1 \pmod{12}$, which may be expressed as a difference $|3a^2-b^2|$ of terms relatively prime, and whose products are also of the above form when no prime factor $P'\equiv \pm 5 \pmod{12}$ is included. The integral values of a and b are obtained by solving equations of the type $b^2-3a^2=k$, where a and b are terms of certain recurring series. Tables are given for the numbers $|3a^2-b^2|$, $|b^2-3|$, and $|3a^2-1|$. Only some of the author's papers are given for references [same Bull. **26** (1957), 112–122; **27** (1958), 28–40, 68–73, 128–141; **29** (1960), 15–27; MR **19**, 730; **20** #1660, 4524a, 4524b; **22** #697].

S. Ikehara (Tokyo)

Citations: MR 19, 730b = B36-22; MR 20# 1660 = D12-39; MR 20# 4524a = B36-24; MR 20# 4524b = B36-24; MR 22# 697 = E28-20.

E28-22 (22# 10942)

Miller, J. C. P. (Editor). Representations of primes by quadratic forms: displaying solutions of the Diophantine equation $kp=a^2+Db^2$. Part I: $D=5$, 6, 10, and 13. Royal Society Mathematical Tables, Vol. 5. Prepared by Hansraj Gupta, M. S. Cheema, A. Mehta and O. P. Gupta. Cambridge University Press, New York, 1960. xxiv+135 pp. $8.50.

The forms considered in this volume are: a^2+Db^2 ($D=5$, 6, 10, 13). The primes are those less than 10^5. Primes p of the forms:

$$\begin{aligned} p &= 20m+1, 9 && \text{if } D = 5,\\ p &= 24m+1, 7 && \text{if } D = 6,\\ p &= 40m+1, 9, 11, 19 && \text{if } D = 10,\\ p &= 52m+1, 9, 17, 25, 29, 49 && \text{if } D = 13\end{aligned}$$

can be uniquely represented by a^2+Db^2 and so there exists positive integers k, n such that $kp=n^2+D$. The tables give a, b, k, n. The doubles of primes p of the forms

$$\begin{aligned} p &= 20m+3, 7 && \text{if } D = 5,\\ p &= 24m+5, 11 && \text{if } D = 6,\\ p &= 40m+7, 13, 23, 37 && \text{if } D = 10,\\ p &= 52m+7, 11, 15, 19, 31, 47 && \text{if } D = 13\end{aligned}$$

can be represented by a^2+Db^2 and in these cases the tables give a, b, k, n in $2p=a^2+Db^2$ and $2kp=n^2+D$. These tables greatly extend the data about these forms in Cunningham, *Quadratic partitions*, F. Hodgson, London, 1904.

An elaborate introduction of 22 pages gives the underlying theory of quadratic fields and their ideals. There is no mention of applications of the table to such things as cyclotomy or power residues.

The tables were prepared by hand and then punched on cards for verifying and printing. The tables are beautifully printed.

D. H. Lehmer (Berkeley, Calif.)

E28-23 **(22# 10966)**

Lomadse, G. Über die Darstellung der Zahlen durch einige ternäre quadratische Formen. Acta Arith. **6** (1960/61), 225–275.

Exact formulae are obtained, by means of theta functions, for the number of representations of any positive integer in the form $x^2+y^2+7z^2$, $x^2+y^2+10z^2$ and $2x^2+2y^2+5z^2$, where x, y, z are integers.

T. Estermann (London)

Referred to in E28-54.

E28-24 **(23# A2383)**

Ananda-Rau, K.

Application of modular equations to some quadratic forms.

J. Indian Math. Soc. (*N.S.*) **24** (1960), 77–130 (1961).

The author considers forms $f=x_1^2+x_2^2+cx_3^2+cx_4^2$, where c is a prime or double a prime. Let $r(n)$ denote the number of integral solutions of $f=n$, and $q=e^{i\pi\tau}$. Following Kloosterman,

$$1+\sum_{n=1}^{\infty} r(n)q^n = \theta_3{}^2(0|\tau)\theta_3{}^2(0|c\tau) = W(q)+Z(q),$$

where $\theta_3(0|\tau)=1+2\sum_{n=1}^{\infty} q^{n^2}$, $W(q)=1+\sum_{n=1}^{\infty}\rho(n)q^n$ and $\rho(n)=\pi^2 nS(n)/c$ with $S(n)$ the sum of the appropriate singular series. The author calls $W(q)$ the dominant function and derives four main identities for the squares of the dominant functions. He shows that the resulting exact forms obtained for $r(n)$ check with those of Liouville and Kloosterman for $c=3, 5, 6, 7$ and goes on to similar formulas for $c=11$ and 23. Results for further values of c are discussed. He also remarks in a note added in proof that it is possible to express the dominant function associated with $a(x_1^2+x_2^2)+b(x_3^2+x_4^2)$ in terms of series of the Lambert type if a and b are relatively prime and square-free.

B. W. Jones (Boulder, Colo.)

Referred to in E28-40.

E28-25 **(23# A2390)**

Ananda-Rau, K.

On the summation of singular series associated with certain quadratic forms. I.

J. Indian Math. Soc. (*N.S.*) **23** (1959), 65–96 (1960).

The quadratic forms which are mainly considered in this paper are

(1) $$a(x^2+y^2)+c(z^2+t^2),$$

(2) $$a(x^2+y^2)+2c(z^2+t^2),$$

where x, y, z, t are integer variables and the constant coefficients a, c are unequal odd positive primes. Kloosterman [Proc. London Math. Soc. (2) **25** (1926), 143–173] has evaluated the singular series that arises in connection with the problem of finding the number of representations of a given positive integer n by one or the other of these forms. In the present paper the author gives an alternative method of summation along substantially different lines. The basic feature of the procedure may be described as follows. For positive integers h, k, let the Gauss sum $S(h, k)$ be defined by $S(h, k)=\sum_{n=1}^{k}\exp(2\pi ihn^2/k)$. In the singular series associated with the forms (1) and (2) the terms involve $S^2(ah, k)S^2(ch, k)$ and $S^2(ah, k)S^2(2ch, k)$, respectively. The author shows that the values of these products are entirely independent of h. It is this circumstance that contributes to the effectiveness of his technique for summing the singular series. A further point of interest is that his method leads to properties of certain infinite series whose terms involve Ramanujan sums and which appear to have a natural place in the theory.

A. L. Whiteman (Los Angeles, Calif.)

Referred to in E28-26, E28-39.

E28-26 **(26# 2397)**

Ananda-Rau, K.

On the summation of singular series associated with certain quadratic forms. II.

J. Indian Math. Soc. (*N.S.*) **25** (1961), 173–195 (1962).

In Part I [same J. (N.S.) **23** (1959), 65–96; MR **23** #A2390] the author developed a method for evaluating the singular series associated with the representation of a positive integer n in one or the other of the forms

$$a(x^2+y^2)+c(z^2+t^2),\ a(x^2+y^2)+2c(z^2+t^2),$$

where a is either 1 or an odd prime, c is either 1 or an odd prime and $(a, c)=1$. The present paper contains a more elaborate treatment of this method. The author now shows how to sum the singular series in all cases in which a, c are relatively prime square-free odd integers (the number 1 being included among square-free integers). His final results are incorporated in Theorems 1 and 2 which express the sum related to each of the forms in terms of the divisors of n. It is not feasible to summarize the rather lengthy statements of these theorems here. In conclusion, the author states that it is unlikely that Theorems 1 and 2 can be deduced from the standard method of summing the singular series as developed by Kloosterman [Proc. London Math. Soc. (2) **25** (1926), 143–173].

A. L. Whiteman (Los Angeles, Calif.)

Citations: MR 23# A2390 = E28-25.

Referred to in E28-68.

E28-27 **(25# 1137)**

Gongadze, R.

On the representation of numbers by certain quadratic forms of four variables. **(Russian)**

Soobšč. Akad. Nauk Gruzin. SSR **28** (1962), 385–392.

The author obtains exact formulas for the number of representations of integer $n>0$ by a quadratic form $x^2+a_1y^2+a_2z^2+at^2$ in the cases: $a_1=3$, $a_2=2$, $a=6$; $a_1=5$, $a_2=2$, $a=10$; $a_1=2$, $a_2=6$, $a=6$.

S. Knapowski (Poznań)

E28-28 **(26# 3697)**

Babaev, G.

Asymptotic-geometric properties of the set of integral points on a circle and on certain ellipses. **(Russian)**

Izv. Vysš. Učebn. Zaved. Matematika **1962**, *no.* 6 (31), 14–18.

Analogously with results of Linnik for the sphere [Mat. Sb. (N.S.) **43 (85)** (1957), 257–276; MR **20** #2328], the author considers the distribution of the $r(m)$ solutions (x, y) in integers of $m=x^2+dy^2$ for several values of d, where the class number for $(-d)^{1/2}$ is unity. On each ellipse, uniform distribution is shown to occur with regard to the "angle" $2\pi\alpha=\arctan(d^{1/2}y/x)$ under the special assumptions that $m=p_1^{\beta_1}\cdots p_s^{\beta_s}$, where the p_i are splitting primes for $(-d)^{1/2}$ and are sufficiently few that $\Delta=[\log(p_1\cdots p_s)/\log r(m)]^{1/2}\to 0$. Then the number of solutions in the angular sector $(2\pi A, 2\pi B)$ is $r(m)(B-A)$ to within an error of order $r(m)\Delta$.

The method is the Vinogradov technique of trigonometric sums. We consider $s^{(k)}{}_m=\sum\exp 2\pi ik\alpha_j$ summed over the $r(m)$ solutions (x_j, y_j) for m; such sums are estimated by $\min[r(m), 4(p_1\cdots p_s)^{k/2}]$. We then let $\psi(u)$ denote a function which is "almost" the characteristic function for the interval $A\leqq u\leqq B$ except that it goes linearly from 0 to 1 in intervals of Δ at each end. Thus the constant term in $\psi(u)$ is $B-A+\Delta$ and the remaining terms can be estimated directly, yielding $\sum_{j=1}^{r(m)}\psi(\alpha_j)=(B-A)r(m)+\text{error}$.

H. Cohn (Tucson, Ariz.)

Citations: MR 20# 2328 = E24-55.

E28-29 **(27# 1421)**

Skubenko, B. F.

The asymptotic distribution of integers on a hyperboloid of one sheet and ergodic theorems. (Russian)

Izv. Akad. Nauk SSSR Ser. Mat. **26** (1962), 721–752.

The author extends the results of Ju. V. Linnik [Vestnik Leningrad. Univ. **10** (1955), no. 2, 3–23; ibid. **10** (1955), no. 5, 3–32; MR **18**, 193; ibid. **10** (1955), no. 8, 15–27; MR **18**, 193; Mat. Sb. (N.S.) **43** (**85**) (1957), 257–276; MR **20** #2328] on the asymptotic distribution of integer points on a hyperboloid of two sheets and a sphere to the case of a hyperboloid of one sheet $H: b^2-ac=\mathscr{D}$, where $\mathscr{D}$ is supposed to be an odd positive integer and not an exact square. Let Δ be a classical region of reducibility on the surface $H: 0<b<\mathscr{D}^{1/2}, \mathscr{D}^{1/2}-b<|a|<\mathscr{D}^{1/2}+b$. Let $\Delta_1\subset\Delta$ be a finitely connected domain with piecewise smooth contour, $V(\Delta_1)$ be the volume of the cone with basis Δ_1 and vertex at the origin, $A(\Delta_1)$ be a solid hyperbolic angle $A(\Delta_1)=V(\Delta_1)\mathscr{D}^{-3/2}$, $T(\Delta_1)$ be the number of integer points on Δ_1 for which g.c.d. $(a, 2b, c)=1$, and p be a prime such that $(\mathscr{D}/p)=1$. Then

$$T(\Delta_1) = T(\Delta)(1+\eta(p,\mathscr{D}))A(\Delta_1)/A(\Delta),$$

where $\eta(p,\mathscr{D})\to 0$ as $\mathscr{D}\to\infty$ and p, $A(\Delta_1)$ are fixed.

The author proves also two ergodic theorems, which are analogous to those of Linnik. Because of the complexity of their formulation they are not reproduced here.

J. Kubilius (Vilnius)

Citations: MR 18, 193d = E16-25; MR 20# 2328 = E24-55.

E28-30 **(27# 2486)**

Lomadze, G.A.

On the representation of numbers by binary quadratic forms. (Russian. Georgian summary)

Tbiliss. Gos. Univ. Trudy Ser. Meh.-Mat. Nauk **84** (1962), 285–290.

Let $r(n; a_1, a_2)$ be the number of representations of the positive integer n by the quadratic form $Q=a_1x_1{}^2+a_2x_2{}^2$. The author studies $r(n; a_1, a_2)$ in cases where the genus of Q contains more than one class, and as examples of his method obtains expressions for $r(n; 1, 11)$, $r(n; 1, 17)$, and $r(n; 4, 5)$ involving the coefficients of certain modular functions. For example, the formula for $r(n; 1, 11)$ (simplifying the author's notation) is as follows. Let

$$x\prod_{m=1}^{\infty}(1-x^{2m})(1-x^{22m}) = \sum_{n=1}^{\infty}c_nx^n.$$

Let $n=2^\alpha 11^\beta k$, where $(k, 22)=1$. Put

$$f(n) = (1+(k/11))\sum_{d|n}(d/11).$$

Then

$$\begin{aligned} r(n;1,11) &= \tfrac{1}{3}(f(n)+4c_n) && \text{for } \alpha = 0\\ &= f(n) && \text{for even } \alpha>0\\ &= 0 && \text{for odd } \alpha. \end{aligned}$$

This result is of the same type as that of van der Blij [Nederl. Akad. Wetensch. Proc. Ser. A **55** (1952), 498–503; MR **14**, 623]. *B. Gordon* (Los Angeles, Calif.)

Citations: MR 14, 623d = E28-16.

Referred to in E28-42.

E28-31 **(28# 1173)**

Kogan, L. A.

On the representation of numbers by certain quadratic forms in three variables. (Russian. Uzbek summary)

Izv. Akad. Nauk UzSSR Ser. Fiz.-Mat. Nauk **1963**, *no.* 4, 13–22.

The author gives, by means of theta functions, exact formulae for the number of representations of any positive integers in the form $x^2+y^2+\alpha z^2$ $(\alpha=2, 4)$, $x^2+\beta(y^2+z^2)$ $(\beta=2, 4, 8, 16)$, $x^2+4y^2+16z^2$ and of positive integers $4m+1$ in the form $x^2+y^2+16z^2$, where x, y, z are integers.

J. Kubilius (Vilnius)

Referred to in E28-54.

E28-32 **(28# 3979)**

Kogan, L. A.

On the number of representations of an integer by the quadratic forms $x^2+y^2+z^2+pt^2$, $x^2+p(y^2+z^2+t^2)$. (Russian. Uzbek summary)

Izv. Akad. Nauk UzSSR Ser. Fiz.-Mat. **1960**, *no.* 6, 24–33.

J. Liouville gave without proof explicit formulae for the number of representations of an integer n by the quadratic forms $x^2+y^2+z^2+5t^2$, $x^2+5(y^2+z^2+t^2)$, $x^2+y^2+2z^2+2zt+3t^2$, $5(x^2+y^2)+2z^2+2zt+3t^2$. Later writers supplied proofs involving the theory of elliptic functions. The present author gives a simpler proof.

{Reviewer's remark: In formula (14) x^2 in the exponent should be replaced by $2x^2$.} *S. Knapowski* (Poznań)

E28-33 **(30# 1982)**

Konusbekov, K. K.

On some quaternary quadratic forms. (Russian. Uzbek summary)

Izv. Akad. Nauk UzSSR Ser. Fiz.-Mat. Nauk **1964**, *no.* 5, 18–23.

The author gives exact formulae for the number of representations of positive integers by the forms $m(x^2+y^2)+z^2+3t^2$ $(m=2, 4, 6)$ and $2(x^2+3y^2)+z^2+3t^2$, where z and t are odd. He proves also some relations among the numbers of representations of positive integers by the following forms: $x^2+y^2+3(z^2+t^2)$, $5(x^2+y^2)+2(z^2+5t^2)$, $10(x^2+y^2)+z^2+5t^2$, $4(x^2+y^2)+z^2+mt^2$ $(m=7, 9)$, $x^2+my^2+z^2+zt+2t^2$ $(m=1, 7)$, $2(x^2+y^2)+2z^2+2zt+5t^2$, $4(x^2+3y^2)+z^2+3t^2$, $x^2+3y^2+z^2+zt+t^2$, $x^2+5y^2+2(z^2+5t^2)$, $4(x^2+4y^2)+z^2+7t^2$, $2(x^2+9y^2)+2z^2+2zt+5t^2$, $4(x^2+9y^2)+z^2+9t^2$. *J. Kubilius* (Vilnius)

E28-34 **(30# 3066)**

Kogan, L. A.

Exact formulae for representations of numbers by certain quadratic forms. (Russian. Uzbek summary)

Izv. Akad. Nauk UzSSR Ser. Fiz.-Mat. Nauk **1964**, *no.* 5, 12–17.

The author obtains exact formulae for the number of representations of integers by the forms $x^2+y^2+2^m(z^2+t^2)$ $(m\geqq 3)$. *J. Kubilius* (Vilnius)

E28-35 **(31# 3376)**

Andrianov, A. N.

The representation of numbers by certain quadratic forms in connection with the theory of elliptic curves. (Russian)

Izv. Akad. Nauk SSSR Ser. Mat. **29** (1965), 227–238.

The author justifies the title by, for example, proving the following formula. Let $r_f(p)$ denote the number of representations of the prime p by the quadratic form $f=x^2+y^2+9(z^2+t^2)$. Then if $(p, 6)=1$, one has

$$r_f(p) = \frac{4}{3}(p+1)-\frac{8}{3}\sum_{x=0}^{p-1}\left(\frac{x^3+1}{p}\right),$$

where the summand is the Legendre symbol. This is certainly an elegant formula, which the author generalizes to $r_f(p^n)$.

Let p be a prime $\equiv 5 \pmod 6$. In Lemma 2 the author asserts that $S=\sum_{x=0}^{p-1}((x^3+a)/p)=0$. This he deduces from (i) $|S|<2\sqrt{p}$, and (ii) $S\equiv 0 \pmod p$. But it is simpler to prove that $S=0$ from the observation that for primes $p=6k+5$ $(k\geqq 0)$, the numbers x^3 $(0\leqq x\leqq p-1)$ run over a complete set of residues (mod p) as x runs over a similar set. {Regarding Lemma 1, a reference to Jacobsthal's Berlin dissertation (1906) seems proper. See also a note by the reviewer [Proc. Nat. Acad. Sci. U.S.A. **35** (1949), 244–246; MR **10**, 592].}

S. Chowla (University Park, Pa.)

Citations: MR 10, 592f = L10-2.

Referred to in E28-73, Z10-43.

E28-36 (31# 3385)

Beridze, R. I.

The representation of numbers by certain quadratic forms in four variables. (Georgian. Russian summary)

Tbiliss. Gos. Univ. Trudy Ser. Meh.-Mat. Nauk **102** (1964), 221–233.

Author's summary: "Let $r(n; a, a')$ denote the number of representations of a natural number n by a quadratic form $f=a(x_1^2+x_2^2+x_3^2)+a'x_4^2$, where a and a' are prescribed numbers. Precise formulas are obtained for the number of representations of n by the forms

$$f = 6(x_1^2+x_2^2+x_3^2)+x_4^2,\ 2(x_1^2+x_2^2+x_3^2)+3x_4^2,$$
$$3(x_1^2+x_2^2+x_3^2)+2x_4^2,\ 7(x_1^2+x_2^2+x_3^2)+x_4^2."$$

E28-37 (32# 1171)

Rusu, Eugen

Numbers of the form A^2+AB+B^2 (A, B integers). (Romanian. Russian and French summaries)

Acad. R. P. Romîne Fil. Cluj Stud. Cerc. Mat. **14** (1963), 157–164.

L'auteur considère l'anneau des nombres $a+bj$, a et b étant des entiers rationnels, $j=1/2+i(\sqrt{3})/2$. Il démontre le théorème suivant: Si le nombre $N=A^2+AB+B^2$ (la norme du nombre $A+Bj$) est divisible par le nombre premier $p=a^2+ab+b^2>3$ sans que A et B soient divisibles par p, alors $A+Bj$ est divisible, soit par $a+bj$, soit par le conjugué de ce nombre. L'auteur démontre en outre l'unicité de la décomposition en facteurs premiers dans l'anneau envisagé, d'une façon directe (sans faire appel à l'algorithme d'Euclide) et il décrit le procédé de décomposition.

Concurremment, il démontre que tout nombre premier de la forme $p=6k+1$ s'écrit d'une seule façon sous la forme $p=a^2+ab+b^2$ avec $a>b>0$, et qu'un nombre N admettant m facteurs premiers de la forme $6k+1$, chacun à une puissance quelconque, s'écrit de 2^{n-1} manières sous la forme a^2+ab+b^2, avec $a>b>0$.

A. Gloden (Luxembourg)

E28-38 (32# 7510)

Kogan, L. A.

On the representation of numbers by certain quadratic forms in four variables. III. (Russian. Uzbek summary)

Izv. Akad. Nauk UzSSR Ser. Fiz.-Mat. Nauk **9** (1965), *no.* 2, 5–10.

The author uses an elementary method of Jacobi to determine the number of representations of natural n by some quadratic forms of the type $x^2+2^by^2+2^cz^2+2^dt^2$.

{Part II appeared in Taškent. Gos. Univ. Naučn. Trudy Vyp. 245 (1964), 23–27.}*

S. Knapowski (Coral Gables, Fla.)

*MR 37 #2688 = E28-57

Citations: MR 37# 2688 = E28-57.

Referred to in E28-57.

E28-39 (32# 7524)

Bhaskaran, M.

On the summation of singular series associated with the quadratic form $\sum_{r=1}^{2s} a_r(x_r^2+y_r^2)$.

J. Indian Math. Soc. (N.S.) **27** (1963), 135–144 (1964).

The singular series which occurs in the asymptotic formula for the number of representations $r_s(n)$ of a positive integer n as a quadratic form $\sum_{i=1}^{s} a_ix_i^2$, where the coefficients a_i are given positive integers, has been studied by Kloosterman. The case $s\geqq 5$ was treated in his dissertation [Groningen, 1924] and the case $s=4$ in a later paper [Proc. London Math. Soc. (2) **25** (1926), 143–173]. An alternative method for summing the singular series for certain special quadratic forms in four variables was also given by K. Ananda-Rau [J. Indian Math. Soc. (N.S.) **23** (1959), 65–96 (1960); MR **23** #A2390]. The present paper extends the methods of Ananda-Rau to the quadratic form $\sum_{r=1}^{2s} a_r(x_r^2+y_r^2)$, where $s\geqq 1$ and the a_r are positive odd integers, coprime in pairs.

T. M. Apostol (Pasadena, Calif.)

Citations: MR 23# A2390 = E28-25.

E28-40 (32# 7525)

Bhaskaran, M.

On the quadratic form $\sum_{r=1}^{2s} a_r(x_r^2+y_r^2)$.

J. Indian Math. Soc. (N.S.) **27** (1963), 145–161 (1964).

The sum of the singular series connected with the quadratic form $\sum_{r=1}^{2s} a_r(x_r^2+y_r^2)$ discussed in the foregoing review [#7524] is expressed in terms of the divisor functions $\sigma_{2s-1}(n/d)$, where d runs through the divisors of $\Delta=a_1a_2\cdots a_{2s}$. The resulting formula shows that $r_s(n)$ is of order n^{2s-1} if $s>1$ and $(n,\Delta)=1$. The method extends that of K. Ananda-Rau [same J. **24** (1960), 77–130 (1961); MR **23** #A2383], who discussed the case $s=2$. The dominant function associated with the given quadratic form is expressed in terms of series of Lambert type.

T. M. Apostol (Pasadena, Calif.)

Citations: MR 23# A2383 = E28-24.

E28-41 (33# 99)

Vephvadze, T. V.

On certain Liouville formulae. (Russian. Georgian summary)

Soobšč. Akad. Nauk Gruzin. SSR **40** (1965), 279–286.

Let $r(n; a_1, a_2, a_3)$ be the number of integer-valued solutions $x_1, x_2, \cdots, x_6$ of the equation $n=a_1(x_1^2+x_2^2)+a_2(x_3^2+x_4^2)+a_3(x_5^2+x_6^2)$, where a_1, a_2, a_3, n are given natural numbers. The author finds expressions for $r(n; 1, 1, 4)$, $r(n; 1, 4, 4)$ and $r(n; 1, 2, 4)$, for $n=2^\alpha m$, $(m, 2)=1$, $\alpha\equiv 1 \pmod 2$.

E28-42 (33# 2601)

Lomadze, G. A.

On the representation of numbers by positive binary diagonal quadratic forms. (Russian)

Mat. Sb. (N.S.) **68 (110)** (1965), 282–312.

Let $r(n; a_1, a_2)$ be the number of representations of n by the quadratic form $f=a_1x_1^2+a_2x_2^2$, where a_1, a_2 are positive integers. In a previous paper [Tbiliss. Gos. Univ. Trudy Ser. Meh.-Mat. Nauk **84** (1962), 285–290; MR **27** #2486], the author sketched a method for expressing $r(n; a_1, a_2)$ in terms of the coefficients of certain modular forms, when the genus of f contains more than one class. As examples, he gave explicit formulas for $r(n; 1, 11)$, $r(n; 1, 17)$ and $r(n; 4, 5)$. In the present paper, detailed proofs of these results are given, and a formula for $r(n; 1, 20)$ is obtained. *B. Gordon* (Los Angeles, Calif.)

Citations: MR 27# 2486 = E28-30.

Referred to in E28-44, E28-67, E28-71, E28-72.

E28-43 (33# 4003)

Davis, Constance

A group of binary substitutions transitive on integral solutions of $px^2-y^2-z^2=0$.

Scripta Math. **27**, 331–337 (1966).

Let p be a prime and suppose that $p\equiv 1 \pmod 4$. Put $x=(1/2\sqrt{p})(\zeta_1{}^2+\zeta_2{}^2)$, $y=\zeta_1\zeta_2$, $z=\frac{1}{2}(\zeta_1{}^2-\zeta_2{}^2)$. Using an idea of Fricke and Klein [*Vorlesungen über die Theorie der automorphen Funktionen*, Teubner, Leipzig, 1926], the author constructs a group of linear substitutions on ζ_1, ζ_2 that induces a group of homogeneous linear substitutions with integral coefficients mapping the form $px^2-y^2-z^2$ onto itself. This latter group acts transitively on the relatively prime integral solutions of $px^2-y^2-z^2=0$. A corresponding result for the form $x^2-y^2-z^2$ was obtained by Mariani [Amer. Math. Monthly **69** (1962), 125–128; MR **24** #A2549]. *J. B. Kelly* (Tempe, Ariz.)

Citations: MR 24# A2549 = D16-28.

E28-44 (33# 4013)

Lomadze, G. A.

On the arithmetic meaning of certain coefficients. (Russian. Georgian summary)

Soobšč. Akad. Nauk Gruzin. SSR **41** (1966), 257–263.

The Fourier coefficients $\nu(n)$ of the expansions of certain products of theta-functions are investigated. It is known [H. D. Kloosterman, Proc. London Math. Soc. (2) **25** (1926), 143–173; the author, Acta Arith. **5** (1959), 125–170; MR **21** #7193; Trudy Tbiliss. Gos. Univ. **76** (1959), 107–159; Mat. Sb. (N.S.) **68** (**110**) (1965), 282–312; MR **33** #2601] that $\nu(n)$ occurs in formulas giving the number of representations of n by either of the quadratic forms $x^2+y^2+7z^2+7t^2$, $x^2+y^2+z^2+7t^2$, x^2+11y^2. The author considers in each case a certain convolution $\nu^*(n)$ of $\nu(n)$ and proves formulas which exhibit the arithmetic meaning of $\nu^*(n)$. *H.-E. Richert* (Marburg)

Citations: MR 21# 7193 = E28-19; MR 33# 2601 = E28-42.

E28-45 (33# 5567)

Kogan, L. A.; Fedorova, T. V.

Representation of numbers by certain quadratic forms in six variables. (Russian)

Taškent. Politehn. Inst. Naučn. Trudy (N.S.) No. 29 (1965), 23–38.

Using identities of theta-function type, the authors give formulae for the number of representations of an integer by a dozen quadratic forms in six variables, which are in diagonal form and have 1, 2 or 4 along the diagonal. They similarly give the number of representations by $x^2+y^2+2^a(z^2+t^2+u^2+v^2)$, where a is any integer not less than 3. *J. W. S. Cassels* (Cambridge, England)

E28-46 (33# 5568)

Kogan, L. A.

An elementary method of Jacobi-Ramanujan-Hardy-Wright-Val'fiš and its applications. (Russian)

Taškent. Politehn. Inst. Naučn. Trudy (N.S.) No. 29 (1965), 39–57.

A survey of results about the numbers of representations of integers by definite quadratic forms which have been obtained by the manipulation of theta-function and related identities. More than a hundred quadratic forms are mentioned, mainly (but not entirely) quaternary diagonal ones. There are many references, including eleven of the author's earlier papers.

J. W. S. Cassels (Cambridge, England)

E28-47 (34# 1272)

Beridze, R. I.

On the representation of numbers by certain quadratic forms with eight variables. (Russian. Georgian summary)

Thbilis. Sahelmc. Univ. Šrom. Mekh.-Math. Mecn. Ser. **110** (1965), 303–322.

The author finds explicit formulae for the number of representations of a natural number n by certain quadratic forms with eight variables. He uses the method of theta-functions, initiated by H. D. Kloosterman [Abh. Math. Sem. Hamburg Univ. **6** (1928), 163–188] and developed by G. Lomadze [Acta Arith. **5** (1959), 125–170; MR **21** #7193]. *S. Knapowski* (Coral Gables, Fla.)

Citations: MR 21# 7193 = E28-19.

Referred to in E28-50.

E28-48 (34# 1274)

Lomadze, G. A.

On the representation of numbers by certain quaternary quadratic forms. (Russian. Georgian summary)

Thbilis. Sahelmc. Univ. Šrom. Mekh.-Math. Mecn. Ser. **110** (1965), 163–180.

The author finds explicit formulae for the number of representations of natural n by forms $x_1{}^2+x_2{}^2+12(x_3{}^2+x_4{}^2)$ or $3(x_1{}^2+x_2{}^2)+4(x_3{}^2+x_4{}^2)$. Following the idea of H. D. Kloosterman [Proc. London Math. Soc. (2) **25** (1926), 143–173], he works with the theta-functions.

S. Knapowski (Coral Gables, Fla.)

E28-49 (34# 5762)

Konusbekov, K. K.

Certain exact formulae for quaternary quadratic forms. (Russian)

Taškent. Gos. Ped. Inst. Učen. Zap. **61** (1966), 26–32.

Using results of P. S. Nazimov ["Application of the theory of elliptic functions to number theory" (Russian), Ph.D. Dissertation, Moscow Univ., Moscow, 1885], and A. Z. Val'fiš [Trudy Tbiliss. Mat. Inst. **9** (1941), 75–96; MR **4**, 132], the author deduces an exact formula for the number $N_1(n)$ of representations of n by the form $f_1=4x^2+16y^2+z^2+3t^2$ (z, t odd); namely, if $n=2^\alpha 3^\beta r$, where $(r, 6)=1$, then

$$N_1(n) = 2^{\alpha-2}(3^{\beta+1}-(-1)^{\alpha+\beta}(r/3))r\sum_{d|r}(3/d)\cdot d^{-1}$$

for $\alpha\geqq 3$; for $\alpha=2$, there is an additional term $R=2\sum_{n=u^2+3v^2}(-1)^{(u-1)/2}v=O(n^{1/2+\varepsilon})$; for $\alpha=0$, 1 one has $N_1=0$.

Results for other forms are given without proof. Some asymptotic formulae of M. M. E. Eichler [Arch. Math. **5** (1954), 355–366; MR **16**, 116] are contained in the results of the author. *W. Schwarz* (Freiburg)

Citations: MR 4, 132a = E28-4; MR 16, 116d = G30-15.

E28-50 (34# 7459)

Beridze, R. I.

Representation of numbers by certain quadratic forms in eight variables. II. (Russian. Georgian summary)

Thbilis. Sahelmc. Univ. Šrom. Mekh.-Math. Mecn. Ser. **117** (1966), 77–101.

The author finds explicit formulas for the number of representations of a natural number n by quadratic forms $f=a_1(x_1{}^2+x_2{}^2+x_3{}^2+x_4{}^2+x_5{}^2+x_6{}^2)+a_2(x_7{}^2+x_8{}^2)$, where $a_1=1$, $a_2=2$, 3, 4, 5; $a_1=2$, 3, 4, 5, $a_2=1$.

{Part I appeared in same Šrom. **110** (1965), 303–322 [MR **34** #1272].} *S. Knapowski* (Coral Gables, Fla.)

Citations: MR 34# 1272 = E28-47.

E28-51 **(34# 7460)**

Lomadze, G. A.

Representation of numbers by certain quadratic forms in six variables. I. (Russian. Georgian summary)

Thbilis. Sahelmc. Univ. Šrom. Mekh.-Math. Mecn. Ser. **117** (1966), 7–43.

The author finds explicit formulas for the number of representations of a natural number n by quadratic forms $f=a_1(x_1^2+x_2^2)+a_2(x_3^2+x_4^2)+a_3(x_5^2+x_6^2)$, where $a_1=a_2=1$, $a_3=3, 5, 6$; $a_1=1$, $a_2=a_3=3, 5, 6$.

S. Knapowski (Coral Gables, Fla.)

Referred to in E28-65.

E28-52 **(35# 4157)**

Vephvadze, T. V.

On a formula of Ja. V. Uspenskiĭ. (Russian. Georgian summary)

Sakharth. SSR Mecn. Akad. Moambe **46** (1967), 301–308.

Let $r(n; a, a')$ denote the number of solutions (in integers X_i) of the equation $n=a(x_1^2+x_2^2+x_3^2)+a'(x_4^2+x_5^2+x_6^2)$, where a and a' are fixed natural numbers. The author proves that

$$r(n; 1, 3) = (3^{2\beta+1}-(u/3)) \textstyle\sum_{d_1 d_2=u} (d_1/3)\, d_2^2 + 4\sum(-1)^{(xy-1)/2}xy$$

(the last sum being over all x, y such that $4n=x^2+3y^2$, $2\nmid x$, $2\nmid y$, $x>0$, $y>0$) for $\alpha=0$, where $n=2^\alpha 3^\beta u$, $(u, 6)=1$; if $\alpha>0$ then $r(n; 1, 3)=$

$$(3/5)(2^{2\alpha+1}+(-1)^\alpha 3)(3^{2\beta+1}-(-1)^\alpha(\tfrac{1}{3}u)) \textstyle\sum_{d_1 d_2=u} (\tfrac{1}{3}d_1)\, d_2^2.$$

S. Chowla (University Park, Pa.)

E28-53 **(35# 6640)**

Gongadze, R. Š.

Representation of numbers by the forms $x^2+3y^2+4z^2+12t^2$ and $x^2+2y^2+32z^2+32t^2$. (Russian. Georgian summary)

Sakharth. SSR Mecn. Akad. Moambe **46** (1967), 33–40.

For a positive integer n, write $r(n; 3, 4)$ for the number of solutions x, y, z, t of $n=x^2+3y^2+4z^2+12t^2$. Write $Q=\exp(2\pi i\tau)$. The "singular series" gives an explicit approximation $\rho(n; 3, 4)$ to $r(n; 3, 4)$. The generating function $1+\sum r(n; 3, 4)Q^n$ is a product of theta functions; the author notes that it is a modular form of dimension -2 on $\Gamma_0(48)$; he deduces an identity giving $\sum[r(n; 3, 4)-\rho(n; 3, 4)]Q^n$ in terms of cusp forms which are again products of theta functions. His identity gives $r(n; 3, 4)$ as a main term, plus the coefficients of two cusp forms, which may be made rather explicit.

Similar arguments apply to $r(n; 2, 32)$, the number of solutions of $n=x^2+2y^2+32z^2+32t^2$; this time one has a modular form on $\Gamma_0(128)$. *B. J. Birch* (Oxford)

Referred to in E28-62.

E28-54 **(36# 1390)**

Kogan, L. A.

Representation of numbers by certain ternary quadratic forms. (Russian)

Taškent. Gos. Ped. Inst. Učen. Zap. **61** (1966), 10–19.

In the present paper the author states without proof some results of representation of integers by ternary quadratic forms, which were derived by the elementary method of Jacobi, Ramanujan, Hardy, Wright and Walfish. Most of these formulas were derived by the author in some of his previous works [see, e.g., same Zap. **38** (1963), 29–44; Izv. Akad. Nauk UzSSR Ser. Fiz.-Mat. Nauk **1963**, no. 4, 13–22; MR **28** #1173; Dokl. Akad. Nauk UzSSR **1964**, no. 12, 5–8].

Using some of his formulas, the author brings to light some reasons for the inapplicability of the asymptotic method of Hardy, Littlewood and Kloosterman to the derivation of asymptotic formulas for the number of representations of an integer by positive ternary quadratic forms.

Finally, the author modifies some results of P. T. Bateman [Trans. Amer. Math. Soc. **71** (1951), 70–101; MR **13**, 111] and G. A. Lomadze [Acta Arith. **6** (1960/61), 225–275; MR **22** #10966] to derive results concerning the singular series of Hardy. *R. Finkelstein* (Tempe, Ariz.)

Citations: MR 13, 111i = E24-35; MR 22# 10966 = E28-23; MR 28# 1173 = E28-31.

E28-55 **(37# 1317)**

Gogišvili, G. P.

The representation of numbers by quaternary quadratic forms with coefficients equal to 1 and 11. (Russian. Georgian summary)

Sakharth. SSR Mecn. Akad. Moambe **49** (1968), 9–12.

A formula is obtained for the number of representations of the natural number n by each of the quadratic forms $x_1^2+x_2^2+x_3^2+11x_4^2$, $x_1^2+x_2^2+11(x_3^2+x_4^2)$, $x_1^2+11(x_2^2+x_3^2+x_4^2)$. *R. A. Good* (College Park, Md.)

E28-56 **(37# 2687)**

Kogan, L. A.

On the representation of numbers by certain quadratic forms in four variables. I. (Russian)

Taškent. Gos. Univ. Naučn. Trudy Vyp. 228 (1963), 49–55.

See the review of Part II below [#2688].

E28-57 **(37# 2688)**

Kogan, L. A.

On the representation of numbers by certain quadratic forms in four variables. II. (Russian)

Taškent. Gos. Univ. Naučn. Trudy Vyp. 245 (1964), 23–27.

This is a continuation of the first part [#2687 above], inaccessible to the reviewer, and as it makes frequent reference to equations in the first part, it is pretty unintelligible without it. According to the review of the first part in RŽMat **1964** #10A 113, it treated the integral diophantine equation $x^2+4y^2+16z^2+16t^2=n$ by a method of Jacobi as elaborated by A. Z. Val'fiš [Akad. Nauk Gruzin. SSR Trudy Tbiliss. Mat. Inst. Razmadze **5** (1938), 197–254; ibid. **8** (1940), 69–107; MR **3**, 68; ibid. **9** (1941), 75–96; MR **4**, 132]. The present paper uses the same methods to discuss representations by 14 forms $ax^2+by^2+cz^2+dt^2$, where a, b, c, d are powers of 2 and $abcd$ is a square. It is claimed that the method extends to some other such forms.

{Part III appeared in Izv. Akad. Nauk UzSSR Ser. Fiz.-Mat. Nauk **9** (1965), no. 2, 5–10 [MR **32** #7510].}

J. W. S. Cassels (Cambridge, England)

Citations: MR 3, 68f = E28-3; MR 4, 132a = E28-4; MR 32# 7510 = E28-38.

Referred to in E28-38.

E28-58 **(37# 4008)**

Beridze, R. I.

The representation of numbers by certain quadratic forms in four variables. (Russian. Georgian summary)

Sakharth. SSR Mecn. Akad. Moambe **50** (1968), 267–272.

The author investigates formulas for the number of representations of numbers by forms in the form

$$a(x_1^2+x_2^2+x_3^2)+a'x_4^2$$

for $a=6$, $a'=1$; $a=2$, $a'=3$; $a=3$, $a'=2$; $a=7$, $a'=1$.
T. T. Tonkov (Leningrad)

E28-59 **(37# 4009)**

Lomadze, G. A.
The number of representations of numbers by certain quadratic forms in four variables. (Russian. Georgian summary)
Sakharth. SSR Mecn. Akad. Moambe **50** (1968), 295–300.

The author investigates the representations of numbers by forms $a(x_1^2+x_2^2+x_3^2)+a'x_4^2$ for $a=1$, $a'=6$; $a=1$, $a'=7$; $a=1$, $a'=32$. *T. T. Tonkov* (Leningrad)

Referred to in E28-70.

E28-60 **(37# 5150)**

Benz, Eduard
Über die Anzahl Darstellungen einer Zahl n durch gewisse quaternäre quadratische Formen: Beweise, welche auf Identitäten aus dem Gebiete der Thetafunktionen basieren.
Studien zur Theorie der quadratischen Formen, pp. 165–198. *Birkhäuser, Basel*, 1968.

Mit Hilfe von Identitäten zwischen verschiedenen Thetareihen werden Darstellungszahlen durch gewisse quaternäre quadratische Formen berechnet, und zwar zunächst gleichzeitig für die beiden Formen $f_1=x^2+y^2+z^2+2t^2$ und $f_2=x^2+2y^2+2z^2+2t^2$. Es ergibt sich für die Anzahl N_i der Darstellungen von $n=2^a n'$, n' ungerade, $N_i=2\left\{2^{a+i}\left(\frac{2}{n'}\right)-1\right\}\sum_{m|n'} m\left(\frac{2}{m}\right)$ für $i=1, 2$. Im nächsten Abschnitt werden simultan die Formen $x^2+y^2+z^2+3t^2$, $x^2+y^2+2z^2+6t^2$, $x^2+3y^2+3z^2+3t^2$ und $2x^2+3y^2+3z^2+6t^2$ behandelt. Das Resultat ist ein ähnlich gebauter Ausdruck, in dem $\sum_{m|n'} m\left(\frac{3}{m}\right)$ vorkommt, wenn $n=2^a3^bn'$ mit $(n', 6)=1$ ist. Damit läßt sich die Anzahl der Darstellungen durch jede positive Form der Diskriminanten 12 (es gibt davon 2 Klassen) auf elementare Weise berechnen. Zum Schluß werden die positiven Formen der Diskriminanten 48 behandelt, deren 9 Klassen sich auf 8 Geschlechter verteilen. Für die einklassigen Geschlechter ergeben sich wieder explizite Darstellungszahlen; für die beiden Klassen, die in ein Geschlecht fallen, muß eine unbewiesene Formel von Liouville benutzt werden.
S. Böge (Heidelberg)

E28-61 **(38# 115)**

Demuth, Peter
Die Zahl der Darstellungen einer natürlichen Zahl durch spezielle quaternäre quadratische Formen aufgrund der Siegelschen Massformel.
Studien zur Theorie der quadratischen Formen, pp. 224–254. *Birkhäuser, Basel*, 1968.

For special quaternary positive definite quadratic forms f the number $A(f, N)$ of representations of a natural number N by f has been obtained as an explicit expression in N by Jacobi, Hurwitz and others. For this they used various methods, e.g., the theory of theta-functions and the theory of quaternions. In the present paper all these known formulae and formulae for three new special f are derived by one method, namely, by means of C. L. Siegel's formula for the weight of representations [Ann. of Math. **36** (1935), 527–606]. This method was already known to Eisenstein, Smith and Minkowski. The evaluation of Siegel's formula amounts to the computation of certain p-adic representation numbers. The author confines his general considerations essentially to forms f for which genus and class coincide and for which $A(f, 1)>0$.
O. H. Körner (Marburg)

E28-62 **(39# 4098)**

Gongadze, R. Š.
The representation of numbers by certain forms of the type $x^2+2^{2k+1}y^2+32z^2+32t^2$. (Russian. Georgian summary)
Sakharth. SSR Mecn. Akad. Moambe **50** (1968), 519–524.

Let $r(n; a_1, a_2)$ be the number of representations of a positive integer n in the form $x^2+a_1y^2+a_2z^2+at^2$, where $a=[a_1, a_2]$. Using methods and results from previous papers [Tbiliss. Gos. Univ. Trudy Ser. Meh.-Mat. Nauk **84** (1962), 239–260; MR **27** #5738; Sakharth. SSR Mecn. Akad. Moambe **46** (1967), 33–40; MR **35**#6640], the author obtains expressions for $r(n; a_1, a_2)$ in cases when $n=2^\alpha u$, $2\nmid u$ and (a) $a_1=2$, $a_2=32$, (b) $a_1=8$, $a_2=32$, and (c) $a_1=32$, $a_2=32$. *W. H. Simons* (Corvallis, Ore.)

Citations: MR 27# 5738 = E20-69; MR 35# 6640 = E28-53.

E28-63 **(40# 4206)**

Lomadze, G. A.
The number of representations of numbers by the forms $x_1^2+3x_2^2+36x_3^2$ and $x_1^2+12x_2^2+36x_3^2$. (Russian. Georgian summary)
Sakharth. SSR Mecn. Akad. Moambe **51** (1968), 25–30.

E28-64 **(40# 5541)**

Fedorova, T. V.
The representation of numbers by certain quadratic forms with eight variables. (Russian)
Taškent Gos. Univ. Naučn. Trudy Vyp. 292 (1967), 44–60.

The author gives exact formulae for the number of representations of the numbers by 20 special quadratic forms with 8 arguments and with coefficients equal to 1, 2 or 4.

One of the proved theorems is the following: The number of representations of the numbers n, $n=2^\alpha m$, $(m, 2)=1$, by the form $k^2+l^2+x^2+y^2+z^2+t^2+u^2+v^2$ is equal to $(-1)^n\cdot 16((2^{3\alpha+3}-15)/7)\sum_{d|n} d^3$. *T. T. Tonkov* (Sofia)

E28-65 **(40# 7202)**

Lomadze, G. A.
Representation of numbers by certain quadratic forms in six variables. II. (Russian. Georgian summary)
Thbilis. Saḫelmç. Univ. Šrom. Mekh.-Math. Mecn. Ser. **129** (1968), 275–297.

The author obtains explicit formulas for the number of representations of a natural number n by the forms $f=a_1(x_1^2+x_2^2)+a_2(x_3^2+x_4^2)+a_3(x_5^2+x_6^2)$, where $a_1=1$, $a_2=2$, $a_3=6, 8$; $a_1=a_2=1$, $a_3=8, 9$; $a_1=1$, $a_2=a_3=8, 9$; $a_1=1$, $a_2=3$, $a_3=6$; $a_1=1$, $a_2=4$, $a_3=8$. {Part I appeared in same Šrom. **117** (1966), 7–43 [MR **34** #7460].}
S. E. Schuur (E. Lansing, Mich.)

Citations: MR 34# 7460 = E28-51.

E28-66 **(41# 150)**

Beverage, David G.
On Ramanujan's form $x^2+y^2+10z^2$.
Univ. Nac. Tucumán Rev. Ser. A **19** (1969), 195–199.

Using a construction of E. H. Hadlock [same Rev. **17** (1967), 7–36; MR **38** #2089], the author determines classes of integers represented by the form $x^2+y^2+10z^2$ but not by the other class in its genus.
Burton W. Jones (Boulder, Colo.)

Citations: MR 38# 2089 = E20-82.

E28-67 **(41# 8340)**

Beridze, R. I.

The representation of numbers by certain pairs of binary quadratic forms. (Russian)

V. I. Lenin. Sakharth. Politekh. Inst. Šrom. **1968**, *no.* 2 (122), 7–15.

G. A. Lomadze [Mat. Sb. (N.S.) **68** (**110**) (1965), 282–312; MR **33** #2601] has given a method for expressing the number $r(n)=r(n, a_1, a_2)$ of representations of n by the form $a_1x^2+a_2y^2$ as the coefficient in the Fourier expansion of a certain modular form. In certain cases $r(n)$ can be given as a sum of Jacobi symbols over some of the divisors of n.

Using the same approach, the author solves the problem of finding $r(n, 1, 14)+r(n, 2, 7)$ and $r(n, 1, 34)+r(n, 2, 17)$. For example, the latter sum is given by

$$\tfrac{1}{2}\{1+(-2/u)\}\{1+(u/17)\}\sum(-34/d),$$

where u is the largest divisor of n prime to 34 and d ranges over the divisors of u. *D. H. Lehmer* (Berkeley, Calif.)

Citations: MR 33# 2601 = E28-42.

E28-68 **(42# 1788)**

Ananda-Rau, K.

Application of a theorem of I. M. Vinogradov to the summation of certain singular series.

Publ. Ramanujan Inst. No. 1 (1968/69), 11–23. (1 *plate*)

The singular series considered in this paper are the ones related to the quadratic forms $a(x^2+y^2)+c(z^2+t^2)$, $a(x^2+y^2)+2c(z^2+t^2)$, in which x, y, z, t are integer variables, and the coefficients a, c are positive, odd, square-free integers, prime to each other. Let n be a positive integer whose representations by the above forms are being considered. Let v denote a typical positive divisor of $2ac$, and let $\Delta_v(n)$ denote the sum of the positive divisors of n whose conjugates are prime to v. In a previous paper [J. Indian Math. Soc. (N.S.) **25** (1961), 173–195; MR **26** #2397] it was shown by the author that the sums of the singular series associated with the above forms can be expressed linearly in terms of the arithmetical functions $\Delta_v(n)$, the coefficients in the linear expressions depending only on the divisors of v and not on n. The results obtained in the earlier paper were in the nature of existence theorems, and it was not there possible to find explicitly the coefficients in the linear expressions. The purpose of the present paper is to evaluate the coefficients, and thus complete the solution of the problem of the summation of the singular series. This is done by applying a simple but very effective theorem given by I. M. Vinogradov [English translation, *Elements of number theory*, pp. 25, 26, Dover, New York, 1954; MR **15**, 933; seventh Russian edition, Izdat. "Nauka", Moscow, 1965; MR **32** #7472]. The complete expressions for the sums of the singular series are too involved to be summarized in this review.

A. L. Whiteman (Los Angeles, Calif.)

Citations: MR 15, 933c = Z01-6; MR 26# 2397 = E28-26; MR 32# 7472 = Z01-9.

E28-69 **(42# 4486)**

Fedorova, T. V.

Certain quadratic forms with six and eight variables. (Russian. Uzbek summary)

Dokl. Akad. Nauk UzSSR **1966**, *no.* 3, 3–5.

The author obtains, by a method that goes back to the work of Jacobi, Ramanujan, Hardy, Wright and A. Z. Val'fiš [Akad. Nauk SSSR Gruzin. Filial. Trudy Tbiliss. Mat. Inst. **5** (1938), 197–254 (1939); ibid. **8** (1940), 69–108], exact formulae for the number of representations of numbers by all quadratic forms of the type $\sum_{i=1}^{k} a_ix_i^2$, $a_i=2^{\alpha_i}$, α_i integers, $0\leq\alpha_i\leq 2$, $k=6$ or 8.

Part of the author's results involving quadratic forms with six variables were published without proofs by Liouville, and subsequently certain of Liouville's results were proved by Ja. V. Uspenskiĭ [Soobšč. Har'kov. Mat. Obšč. (2) **15** (1916), 81–147] (by Liouville's arithmetical method), P. S. Nazimov ["Application of the theory of elliptic functions to number theory" (Russian), Doctoral Dissertation, Moscow Univ., Moscow, 1885] (by means of elliptic functions), T. V. Vephvadze (by means of a method based on the theory of modular forms). Certain of the author's results, involving quadratic forms with eight variables, were obtained earlier by Jacobi (by means of elliptic functions) and R. I. Beridze (by means of a method based on the theory of modular forms).

L. Kogan (RŽMat **1966** #12 A113)

E28-70 **(42# 5906)**

Gogišvili, G. P.

The number of representations of numbers by certain quaternary quadratic forms. (Russian. Georgian and English summaries)

Sakharth. SSR Mecn. Akad. Moambe **56** (1969), 525–528.

The author derives explicit formulas for $r(n; a_1, a_2, a_3, a_4)$, the number of representations $n=a_1x_1^2+\cdots+a_4x_4^2$, for $(a_1, a_2, a_3, a_4)=(4, 9, 12, 36)$ and $(3, 4, 9, 36)$. The method is to expand $1+\sum_{n=1}^{\infty} r(n; a_1, a_2, a_3, a_4)Q^n=\prod_1^4 \theta_{00}(\tau, 2a_k)$, where

$$Q = \exp 2\pi i\tau,\ \theta_{gh}(z|\tau, N) = \sum_{m=-\infty}^{\infty}(-1)^{hm}Q^{(2Nm+g)^2/8N}\exp \pi iz(2Nm+g)$$

and $\theta_{gh}(\tau, N)=\theta_{gh}(0|\tau, N)$; $\theta_{gh}'(\tau, N)=(\partial/\partial z)\theta_{gh}(0|\tau, N)$. If $\theta(\tau; a_1, a_2, a_3, a_4)$ is the singular-series approximation to $\prod_1^4 \theta_{00}$, then (with suitable indices and coefficients) $\prod_1^4 \theta_{00}=\theta(\tau; a_1, a_2, a_3, a_4)+$terms in θ_{gh} times $\theta'_{g'h'}$. Thus, $\prod_1^4 \theta_{00}$ could be calculated explicitly. This is done by looking at both members as modular forms of dimension -2 in $\Gamma_0(144)$ and comparing terms up to Q^{48}. The actual evaluation is essentially in terms of Jacobi character sums. Reference is made to the paper of G. A. Lomadze [Sakharth. SSR Mecn. Akad. Moambe **50** (1968), 295–300; MR **37** #4009]. *Harvey Cohn* (Princeton, N.J.)

Citations: MR 37# 4009 = E28-59.

E28-71 **(42# 5908)**

Vephvadze, T. V.

The representation of numbers by positive binary quadratic forms with odd discriminant. (Russian. Georgian and English summaries)

Sakharth. SSR Mecn. Akad. Moambe **58** (1970), 29–32.

The author formulates three theorems and describes the proofs.

He applies a method of G. A. Lomadze [Mat. Sb. (N.S.) **68** (**110**) (1965), 282–312; MR **33** #2601]. Exact formulae for representation of numbers by forms (3, 3, 4), (2, 1, 4) and (2, 1, 6) are given. *T. T. Tonkov* (Sofia)

Citations: MR 33# 2601 = E28-42.

E28-72 **(42# 7594)**

Vephvadze, T. V.

The representation of numbers by positive Gaussian binary quadratic forms. (Russian. Georgian and English summaries)

Sakharth. SSR Mecn. Akad. Moambe **56** (1969), 277–280.

The author, using G. A. Lomadze's method [Mat. Sb. (N.S.) **68** (**110**) (1965), 282–312; MR **33** #2601] based on the modular form theory, derives formulas for the number of representations of a positive integer by the quadratic forms (1) $4x^2+2xy+9y^2$, $3x^2+2xy+15y^2$, $5y^2+4xy+9y^2$ (these quadratic forms belong to polyclass genera).

In formulas by T. V. Vephvadze the number of representations of each of the forms (1) is introduced as a sum $\rho(n)+\nu(n)$, where $\rho(n)$ is a simple numerical function dependent on divisors of the integer represented, and $\nu(n)$ is a Fourier coefficient of a finite linear combination of products of some theta functions with characteristics.

L. A. Kogan (Tashkent)

Citations: MR 33# 2601 = E28-42.

E28-73 (43# 6159)

Fomenko, O. M.

An application of Eichler's reduction formula to the representation of numbers by certain quaternary quadratic forms. (Russian)

Mat. Zametki **9** (1971), 71–76.

The author obtains the exact formulas for the numbers of solutions $r_f(n)$ of the Diophantine equations

$$f(x_1, x_2, x_3, x_4) = n,$$

where f is a positive-definite quadratic form with integral coefficients of level $N=N(f)=11, 19, 20, 22$. The proofs are based on the Eichler congruence-relations for the Hecke operators [M. M. Eichler, Arch. Math. **5** (1954), 355–366; MR **16**, 116] and the results of J. Igusa [Amer. J. Math. **81** (1959), 561–577; MR **21** #7214]. A typical result is as follows: Let $f=x_1^2+x_2^2+5(x_3^2+x_4^2)(N(f)=20)$ and let p be a prime number, $p\neq 2, 35$; then $r_f(p)=(4/3)(p+1)-(8/3)\sum_{x=0}^{p-1}((x^3+11x/3+74/24)/p)$, where (/p) is the Legendre symbol. Similar formulas for $N=27, 32, 36$ were obtained earlier by the reviewer in another manner [Izv. Akad. Nauk SSSR Ser. Mat. **29** (1965), 227–238; MR **31** #3376].

{This article has appeared in English translation [Math. Notes **9** (1971), 41–44].} *A. N. Andrianov* (Leningrad)

Citations: MR 16, 116d = G30-15; MR 21# 7214 = F10-61; MR 31# 3376 = E28-35.

E28-74 (44# 151)

Gafurov, N.

The distribution of integral points on the surface $xy=z^2+a$, $1\leqq z\leqq T$. (Russian. Tajiki summary)

Dokl. Akad. Nauk Tadžik. SSR **12** (1969), *no.* 10, 7–10.

Let us consider the surface: (1) $xy=z^2+a$, $x\geqslant 1$, $y\geqslant 1$, $1\leqq z\leqq T$, and let $S(T,\alpha,\beta)$ be the set of all integral points (x,y,z) on the surface (1) such that $0<\alpha\leqq\{x/z\}\leqq\beta\leqq 1$ and $1\leqq y\leqq\sqrt{(T^2+a)}$ (α,β, real numbers), where $\{x/z\}$ is the fractional part of x/z. Then, for $T\to\infty$ one has $S(T,\alpha,\beta)=\frac{1}{2}(\beta-\alpha)A_2(a)T\log T+O(T(\log)^{1/2})$, where $A_2(a)$ is a real constant that depends on a. *N. Popescu* (Bucharest)

Referred to in E20-92.

E28-75 (44# 153)

Lomadze, G. A.

The representation of numbers by certain binary quadratic forms.

Izv. Vysš. Učebn. Zaved. Matematika **1970**, *no.* 11 (102), 71–75.

The author establishes the formulae for the numbers of integral representations by the quadratic forms $x_1^2+19x_2^2$, $x_1^2+23x_2^2$, $x_1^2+27x_2^2$, $x_1^2+32x_2^2$. The proofs are based on relations between corresponding theta-series.

A. N. Andrianov (Leningrad)

E28-76 (44# 169)

Gogišvili, G. P.

The summation of a singular series that is connected with diagonal quadratic forms with four variables. (Russian. Georgian summary)

Sakharth. SSR Mecn. Akad. Math. Inst. Šrom. **38** (1970), 5–30.

In der Arbeit werden Formeln für die Auswertung von Summen der den Formen $f=a_1x_1^2+a_2x_2^2+a_3x_3^2+a_4x_4^2$, $(a_1,a_2,a_3,a_4)=1$, entsprechenden singulären Reihen $\rho(n)=(\pi^2/\Delta^{1/2})n\sum_{q=1}^{\infty}A_q(n)$ abgeleitet. Dabei ist $\Delta=\prod_{k=1}^4 a_k$, $A_q(n)=q^{-4}\sum'_{h \bmod q}C(-hn/q)\prod_{k=1}^4 S(a_kh,q)$, $C(u)=\exp 2\pi iu$. Das Symbol $\sum'_{h \bmod q}$ bedeutet, daß h alle Zahlen des reduzierten Restsystems mod q durchläuft. Weiter ist $S(h,q)=\sum_{j=0}^{q-1}C(hj^2/q)$.

Vom methodologischen Standpunkt knüpft die Arbeit eng an die früheren Arbeiten von H. D. Kloosterman [Proc. London Math. Soc. (2) **25** (1926), 143–173] und G. A. Lomadze [Trudy Tbilis. Gos. Univ. **76** (1959), 107–159] an.

T. Šalát (Bratislava)

E32 REDUCTION THEORY OF QUADRATIC FORMS

See reviews E02-6, E02-15, E04-35, E08-3, E12-2, E12-3, E12-4, E12-19, E12-34, E12-39, E12-44, E12-54, E12-67, E12-74, E12-90, E12-115, E12-140, E16-7, E16-72, E16-75, E16-76, E20-3, E20-8, E20-10, E20-18, E20-21, E20-38, E20-60, E20-67, E20-72, E20-78, E20-86, E60-5, E68-15, E99-5, F45-2, F45-3, F45-13, F50-2, F50-51, H02-1, H05-3, H05-5, H05-6, H25-2, J32-3, J44-4.

E36 DISTRIBUTION OF LATTICE POINTS ON QUADRICS

See reviews D16-29, D16-37, D56-36, E12-75, E12-80, E12-84, E12-92, E12-123, E12-127, E12-135, E12-139, E16-16, E16-25, E16-27, E16-30, E16-31, E16-41, E16-53, E16-83, E16-84, E16-89, E20-40, E20-41, E20-52, E20-53, E20-56, E20-88, E20-89, E20-92, E24-37, E24-41, E24-54, E24-64, E24-70, E24-122, E28-28, E28-29, E28-74, N80-41, P28-54, P28-60, P28-67, P36-48, R52-20, Z02-60, Z10-48.

E40 CLASS NUMBERS OF QUADRATIC FORMS

See also Section R14.

See reviews B68-76, E12-20, E12-34, E12-39, E12-44, E12-57, E12-61, E12-62, E12-67, E12-71, E12-93, E12-97, E12-101, E12-103, E12-125, E12-131, E12-141, E12-142, E16-2, E16-3, E16-4, E16-5, E16-12, E16-14, E16-18, E16-19, E16-22, E16-23, E16-28, E16-29, E16-33, E16-39, E16-42, E16-49, E16-55, E16-60, E16-64, E16-77, E16-82, E16-85, E16-88, E20-11, E20-49, E20-87, E24-11, E24-54, F15-34, F45-13, H02-1, P20-12, P20-19, P20-22, P20-31, P20-33, Z02-53, -.

E44 EPSTEIN ZETA-FUNCTIONS

See also reviews F30-1, F30-4, M25-4, M30-48, M40-11, M40-19, M40-37, M40-46, M40-59, N36-77, P20-4, P28-11, P28-17, R42-20, R42-45, Z30-54.

E44-1 (2, 190e)

Taylor, P. R. The functional equation for Epstein's zeta-function. Quart. J. Math., Oxford Ser. **11**, 177–182 (1940).

A proof of the functional equation for Epstein's zeta-function

$$f(s, A, B, C) = \sum_{m,n=-\infty}^{\infty}{}' \frac{1}{(Am^2+Bmn+Cn^2)^s},$$

is given in the special case where the quadratic form is positive definite. This proof depends on the functional equation for Riemann's zeta-function and some properties of hypergeometric functions, and it uses Mellin's inversion formula. A result, due to Kober, that expresses $f(s, A, B, C)$ as a double series involving Bessel functions is also given under the same restriction. The author implies that his proof can be extended beyond the special case considered.

H. S. Zuckerman (Seattle, Wash.).

E44-2 (9, 272a)

Chowla, S. On an unsuspected real zero of Epstein's zeta function. Proc. Nat. Inst. Sci. India **13**, no. 4, 1 p. (1947).

Let the Epstein ζ-function be defined by

$$\zeta(s, Q) = \sum_{x,y=-\infty}^{\infty}{}' Q(x, y)^{-s},$$

where $Q(x, y) = ax^2+bxy+cy^2$ is a positive definite form with integral coefficients and the fundamental discriminant b^2-4ac; here the prime on the summation indicates that $(x, y) \neq (0, 0)$. Davenport and Heilbronn [J. London Math. Soc. **11**, 181–185 (1936)] showed that this ζ-function has an infinity of zeros with $\Re(s) > 1$. The author considers the special case $Q(x, y) = x^2+dy^2$ for arbitrary d and indicates a proof of the result that there exists a d_0 such that corresponding to each $d > d_0$ there is a real zero $s(d)$ of this ζ-function such that $s(d) \sim 1-3/(\pi d^{\frac{1}{2}})$ as $d \to \infty$. Thus for large d, $\frac{1}{2} < s(d) < 1$, so that the analogue of the Riemann hypothesis is false. The proof is said to be similar to that used previously by the author [Quart. J. Math., Oxford Ser. **5**, 302–303 (1934)]. However, in that paper the author was able to show that $s(d) > 1-c/\log d$, for some c, by assuming the existence of infinitely many imaginary quadratic fields with the class number one; it is not clear how he will establish this inequality in the present case. For $d=5$, Potter and Titchmarsh [Proc. London Math. Soc. (2) **39**, 372–384 (1935)] had already suspected that the seventh and eighth zeros were off the line $\Re(s) = \frac{1}{2}$.

L. Schoenfeld (Cambridge, Mass.).

E44-3 (10, 431h)

Bochner, S., and Chandrasekharan, K. Summations over lattice points in κ-space. Quart. J. Math., Oxford Ser. **19**, 238–248 (1948).

This paper generalizes results of Dixon and Ferrar [Quart. J. Math., Oxford Ser. **5**, 48–63, 172–185 (1934)]. Let $P(n, n)$ be a positive definite quadratic form in the κ variables $n_1, \cdots, n_\kappa$; $0 < \lambda_1 < \lambda_2 < \cdots$ are the values of $P(n, n)$ for integral vectors n; $h_1, \cdots, h_\kappa$ are real numbers; $\tau_\kappa^P(\lambda_m, h) = \sum \exp\{2\pi i(n_1h_1+\cdots+n_\kappa h_\kappa)\}$, with summation extended over all lattice points (n) which satisfy $P(n, n) = \lambda_m$. The real number ξ satisfies $\xi^2 \neq Q(h+n, h+n)$ for all lattice points (n); here Q is the inverse of P. It is proved that the series

$$\sum_m \tau_\kappa^P(\lambda_m, h) \exp(2\pi i\xi\lambda_m^{\frac{1}{2}})\lambda_m^{-s}$$

is summable by Riesz's typical means of order γ if $\gamma > \frac{1}{2}(\kappa-1)$, $s > \frac{1}{2}\kappa - \frac{1}{2} - \frac{1}{2}\gamma$. The restriction $\gamma > \frac{1}{2}(\kappa-1)$ can be replaced by $\gamma \geqq 0$ if P is integer-valued. The results are obtained from results for Bessel series of the form

$$\sum_m \tau_\kappa^P(\lambda_m, h) J_\mu(2\pi\xi\lambda_m^{\frac{1}{2}})\lambda_m^{-s+\frac{1}{4}} \qquad (\mu > -1).$$

Some special cases are indicated where the sum of the latter series is zero for all admissible values of ξ.

N. G. de Bruijn (Delft).

Referred to in E44-4, P20-8.

E44-4 (11, 646c)

Bochner, S., and Chandrasekharan, K. Summations over lattice points in κ-space. (A supplementary note.) Quart. J. Math., Oxford Ser. (2) **1**, 80 (1950).

Corrections of some errors and misprints occurring in a previous paper with the same title [Quart. J. Math., Oxford Ser. (1) **19**, 238–248 (1948); these Rev. **10**, 431].

N. G. de Bruijn (Delft).

Citations: MR 10, 431h = E44-3.

E44-5 (11, 84d)

Chowla, S., and Selberg, A. On Epstein's zeta function. I. Proc. Nat. Acad. Sci. U. S. A. **35**, 371–374 (1949).

Without detailed proofs the following results are announced. (1) $\sum_{n=1}^{\infty}(-p/n)n^{-s} > 0$ for $s > 0$, $p = 43$, 67 or 163. (2) Let K and K' have the usual meaning in the theory of elliptic functions and let $d < 0$ be the discriminant of a quadratic field of class-number h, containing w roots of unity. Then if iK/K' belongs to the field, the number

$$K\pi^{-\frac{1}{2}}\left\{\prod_{m=1}^{|d|-1} \Gamma(m/|d|)^{(d/m)}\right\}^{-\frac{1}{4}w/h}$$

is algebraic. (3) The function $\sum'(x^2+y^2+dz^2)^{-s}$ has a real zero which tends to 0 as $d \to \infty$.

H. Heilbronn.

Referred to in E44-17, E44-23, E44-25, E44-26, G15-26, M20-10, M20-25, M40-59.

E44-6 **(11, 162g)**

Emersleben, Otto. Einige Identitäten für Epsteinsche Zetafunktionen 2. Ordnung. Math. Ann. **121**, 103–106 (1949).

For the particular Epstein zeta function

$$Z(s;h_1,h_2)=Z\left|h_1^0h_2^0\right|(s)_\delta=\sum{}'\frac{\exp(2\pi i(h_1m_1+h_2m_2))}{(m_1^2+m_2^2)^{s/2}},$$

where $\sum'$ denotes a sum extending over all lattice points (m_1, m_2) except the origin, the author proves that

$$Z(2,\tfrac12,\tfrac12)=-\pi\log 2,\quad Z(2,0,\tfrac12)=-\tfrac12\pi\log 2,$$
$$Z(2,\tfrac14,\tfrac14)=-\tfrac14\pi\log 2.$$

Alternative proofs can be obtained easily by the following observations: $Z(s;0,0)=4L(s/2)\zeta(s/2)$, where

$$L(s)=\sum_{n=1}^{\infty}\chi(n)n^{-s}$$

and $\chi(n)=0$ for even n and $\chi(n)=(-1)^{\frac12(n-1)}$ for odd n, and

$$Z(s;\tfrac12,\tfrac12)=\sum{}'(-1)^{m_1+m_2}(m_1^2+m_2^2)^{-s/2}=4\sum_{l=1}^{\infty}(-1)^l l^{s/2}\sum_{d\mid l}\chi(d)$$
$$=4\sum_{d=1}^{\infty}\chi(d)d^{-s/2}\sum_{n=1}^{\infty}(-1)^n n^{-s/2}=4(2^{1-s/2}-1)L(s/2)\zeta(s/2);$$

since $i^{m_1+m_2}=-i^{-m_1+m_2}$ for odd m_1, we have

$$Z(s;\tfrac14,\tfrac14)=\sum_{2\mid(m_1,m_2)}{}'\frac{i^{m_1+m_2}}{(m_1^2+m_2^2)^{s/2}}=2^{-s}Z(s;\tfrac12,\tfrac12)$$

and

$$2Z(s;0,\tfrac12)=Z(s;0,\tfrac12)+Z(s;\tfrac12,0)$$
$$=\sum{}'\frac{(1+(-1)^{m_1})(1+(-1)^{m_2})}{(m_1^2+m_2^2)^{s/2}}-\sum{}'\frac{1}{(m_1^2+m_2^2)^{s/2}}$$
$$-\sum{}'\frac{(-1)^{m_1+m_2}}{(m_1^2+m_2^2)^{s/2}}$$
$$=4\cdot 2^{-s}Z(s;0,0)-Z(s;0,0)-Z(s;\tfrac12,\tfrac12)$$
$$=2^{3-s/2}(2^{1-s/2}-1)L(s/2)\zeta(s/2).$$

Also, $L(1)=\pi/4$.

L. K. Hua (Peking).

E44-7 **(13, 328c)**

Emersleben Otto. Über die Konvergenz der Reihen Epsteinscher Zetafunktionen. Math. Nachr. **4**, 468–480 (1951).

The author discusses the convergence of the Epstein zeta function

$$\sum_{k_1,\cdots,k_p=-\infty}^{\infty}{}'\frac{e^{2\pi i(k_1h_1+\cdots+k_ph_p)}}{(k_1^2+\cdots+k_p^2)^{s/2}}$$

where the numbers h_r are real and the prime indicates that all the summation indices cannot simultaneously be zero. The author quotes known results of Walfisz, Landau and Hua on exponential sums and the number of lattice points on a p-dimensional sphere to give trivial proofs of a number of results of which the following are typical. Let α be the abscissa of convergence of the above Dirichlet series and let β be the abscissa of absolute convergence. (i) If all h_r are rational and not all are integral, then $\beta-2\leqq\alpha\leqq p-2$ if $p\geqq 4$. (ii) If all h_r are arbitrary real numbers then $\beta-2\leqq\alpha\leqq p-2+2/(p+1)$ if $p\geqq 2$. *L. Schoenfeld.*

E44-8 **(15, 507c)**

Rankin, R. A. A minimum problem for the Epstein zeta-function. Proc. Glasgow Math. Assoc. **1**, 149–158 (1953).

Let $Z_h(s)=\sum_{m,n=-\infty}^{\infty}{}'h(m,n)^{-s}$, where

$$h(m,n)=am^2+2dmn+bn^2,$$

a positive definite quadratic form of determinant unity, and $Z_Q(s)=6(\frac12\sqrt{3})^s\zeta(s)L(s)$. The author proves that for all $s\geqq 1.035$, the inequality $Z_h(s)\geqq Z_Q(s)$ holds, with equality only when h and Q are equivalent forms. The Epstein zeta-function $Z_h(s)$ is a constant multiple of the mean value of the variance of the number of lattice points in a random circle [see D. G. Kendall and R. A. Rankin, Quart. J. Math., Oxford Ser. (2) **4**, 178–189 (1953); these Rev. **15**, 237]. The result above asserts that the minimum variance is associated with a hexagonal lattice. *R. Bellman.*

Citations: MR 15, 237g = P24-7.

Referred to in E44-15, E44-20, E44-23, E44-25.

E44-9 **(16, 1106a)**

Emersleben, Otto. Über Summen Epsteinscher Zetafunktionen regelmässig verteilter "unterer" Parameter. Math. Nachr. **13**, 59–72 (1955).

Proof of

$$Z\begin{vmatrix}0&0\\x&y\end{vmatrix}(s)+Z\begin{vmatrix}0&0\\\frac12-x&\frac12-y\end{vmatrix}(s)=2^{1-\frac12 s}Z\begin{vmatrix}0&0\\x+y&x-y\end{vmatrix}(s)$$

and of

$$\sum_{m_1=1}^{n}\cdots\sum_{m_p=1}^{n}Z\begin{vmatrix}0&\cdots&0\\\cdot&\cdots&\cdot\\h_1+m_1/n&\cdots&h_p+m_p/n\end{vmatrix}(s)$$
$$=n^{p-s}Z\begin{vmatrix}0&\cdots&0\\\cdot&\cdots&\cdot\\nh_1&\cdots&nh_p\end{vmatrix}(s)$$

with examples of such transformations. *A. Erdélyi.*

E44-10 **(17, 968e)**

van der Blij, F. The value of a certain Epstein zeta function. Nieuw Arch. Wisk. (3) **4** (1956), 13–14.

Let $r_k(n)$ denote the number of representations of n as a sum of k squares of integers, and define the entire function $\xi_k^*(s)$ by the Dirichlet series

$$\xi_k^*(s)=\sum_{n=1}^{\infty}\frac{(-1)^n}{n^s}r_k(n).$$

The author proves that

$$\xi_6^*(3)=-\frac{\pi^3}{2}\log 2+\frac{3\pi}{4}\xi(3),$$

where $\xi(s)$ is Riemann's zeta function.

A. Erdélyi (Pasadena, Calif.).

E44-11 **(17, 1056h)**

van der Blij, F. Quadratic forms and Euler products. Nederl. Akad. Wetensch. Proc. Ser. A. **59**=Indag. Math. **18** (1956), 229–237.

The zeta-functions associated with the representations of a number by a quadratic form in an even number of variables do not, in general, have Euler products. This remains true if one takes means over all classes of a fixed genus or over all genera with a fixed discriminant. However, by taking linear combinations of Dirichlet series with different discriminants one can obtain Euler products, and this the author does in various cases. *R. A. Rankin.*

E44-12 **(18, 873e)**

Siegel, Carl Ludwig. A generalization of the Epstein zeta function. J. Indian Math. Soc. (N.S.) **20** (1956), 1–10.

Let $\mathfrak{x}'\mathfrak{S}\mathfrak{x}=\mathfrak{S}[\mathfrak{x}]$ be an even quadratic form of m variables, with signature n, r $(n+r=m)$. Let $\mathfrak{a}$ be a vector such that $\mathfrak{S}\mathfrak{a}$ is integral, and $d=(-1)^r|\det\mathfrak{S}|$. The Gaussian sum $g_{\rho\mathfrak{a}}$ is defined by

$$g_{\rho\mathfrak{a}}=\sum_{\mathfrak{x}\bmod\gamma}\exp(\pi i\rho\mathfrak{S}[\mathfrak{x}+\mathfrak{a}]),$$

if α and γ are integers, $(\alpha,\gamma)=1$, $\gamma>0$, $\rho=\alpha/\gamma$. Furthermore, the number g_a is defined as 1 if a is an integral vector, and 0 otherwise. The author introduces the function

$\varphi_a(s)=$

$$g_a+e^{\frac{1}{4}\pi i(n-r)}d^{-\frac{1}{2}}\sum_\rho g_{\rho a}\gamma^{-1-s}(z-\rho)^{\frac{1}{2}(r-1-s)}(\bar{z}-\rho)^{\frac{1}{2}(n-1-s)},$$

where ρ runs through all rational numbers; $z=\xi+i\eta$ and $s=\sigma+it$ are complex numbers, with $\eta>0$, $\sigma>1+\frac{1}{2}m$. The author proves that $\varphi_a(s)$ is (by analytic continuation) a meromorphic function of s. And, if $\mathfrak{S}$ is a stem-form, it satisfies the functional equation $\varphi_a(s)=\eta^{\frac{1}{2}m-s}q(s)\varphi_a(m-s)$, where $q(s)=$

$$\pi d^{-\frac{1}{2}}2^{1-s+\frac{1}{2}m}\Gamma(s-\tfrac{1}{2}m)\Gamma^{-1}(\tfrac{1}{2}(s+1-n))\Gamma^{-1}(\tfrac{1}{2}(s+1-r))f(s),$$

$f(s)=\sum g_{\rho 0}\gamma^{-1-s}$

(ρ runs through the rationals in $0\leqq\rho<1$) in a function of the singular series type.

In the proof, the author uses the transformation formula (under modular substitutions of z) of the theta series

$$f_a(z,\mathfrak{w})=\sum_{\mathfrak{x}}\exp(\pi i\mathfrak{R}[\mathfrak{x}+a]+2i\mathfrak{w}'(\mathfrak{x}+a)).$$

Here $\mathfrak{w}$ is a real vector, $\mathfrak{x}$ runs through all integral vectors, $\mathfrak{P}$ is a majorant of $\mathfrak{S}$ (i.e. $\mathfrak{P}\mathfrak{S}^{-1}\mathfrak{P}=\mathfrak{P}$, $\mathfrak{P}=\mathfrak{P}'>0$), and $\mathfrak{R}=\xi\mathfrak{S}+i\eta\mathfrak{P}$. The special case $\mathfrak{w}=0$ occurs in a previous paper [Math. Ann. **124** (1951), 17–54; MR **16**, 800]. A theta series vector is considered: if a runs through a complete set of representatives $a_1, \cdots, a_l$ (mod 1) (all satisfying $\mathfrak{S}a\equiv 0$ (mod 1)), then $f_a(z,\mathfrak{w})$ describes a column vector of length l. Under modular substitutions of z this column is multiplied on the left by an $l\times l$ matrix. The coefficients of this matrix are closely related to the function $\varphi_a(s)$. *N. G. de Bruijn* (Amsterdam).

Citations: MR 16, 800a = E12-49.

E44-13 (19, 943f)

Val'fiš, A. Z. Convergence abscissae of certain Dirichlet series. Akad. Nauk Gruzin. SSR. Trudy Tbiliss. Mat. Inst. Razmadze 22 (1956), 33–75. (Russian)

E44-14 (20# 1429)

Emersleben, Otto. Werte einer Zetafunktion 2. Ordnung mit Argument $s=2$, der Grundfunktion der doppelperiodischen Parallelströmung zäher Flüssigkeiten. Anwendungen der Mathematik. Reihe: Funktionstabulierungen. Universität Greifswald, Greifswald, 1956. 13 pp. (1 insert)

This gives, on a single, multiply-folded, sheet, a table of the Epstein Zeta-function

$$Z\begin{vmatrix}0 & 0\\ x & y\end{vmatrix}(2)_\delta=\sum_{k=-\infty}^{\infty}\sum_{l=-\infty}^{\infty}{}'\frac{\exp\{2\pi i(kx+ly)\}}{k^2+l^2}$$

$k=l=0$ being excluded. Values are to 6 decimals generally, with 7 or 8 in a few places, for $y=0(.01).5$, $x=y(.01).5$. The values for $(x,y)=(\frac{1}{2},\frac{1}{2})$, $(0,\frac{1}{2})$, $(\frac{1}{4},\frac{1}{4})$ which are respectively $-\pi\ln 2$, $-\frac{1}{2}\pi\ln 2$ and $-\frac{1}{4}\pi\ln 2$ are given to 25 decimals.

The insert lists a number of errata.

J. C. P. Miller (Cambridge, England)

E44-15 (22# 7975)

Cassels, J. W. S. On a problem of Rankin about the Epstein zeta-function. Proc. Glasgow Math. Assoc. **4**, 73–80 (1959).

Let $h(m,n)=am^2+2bmn+cn^2$ be a positive definite quadratic form with determinant $ac-b^2=1$. A special form of this kind is $Q(m,n)=2\cdot 3^{-1/2}(m^2+mn+n^2)$. The author considers the Epstein zeta-function $Z_h(s)=\sum'\{h(m,n)\}^{-s}$ $(s>1)$, in which summation m, n assume all integral values and the prime indicates that the term with $m=n=0$ is excluded from the summation. For $s>1.035$, Rankin [same Proc. **1** (1953), 149–158; MR **15**, 507] proved that

$$(1)\qquad Z_h(s)-Z_Q(s)\geqq 0$$

and that the sign of equality is needed only when h is equivalent to Q. Rankin asked if (1) is true for $s\geqq 1$. (The function $Z_h(s)$ may be analytically continued over the whole plane, and its only singularity is at $s=1$.) The author proves that (1) holds for all $s\geqq 0$.

S. Chowla (Boulder, Colo.)

Citations: MR 15, 507c = E44-8.

Referred to in E44-16, E44-20, E44-21.

E44-16 (27# 4803)

Cassels, J. W. S.

Corrigendum to the paper "On a problem of Rankin about the Epstein zeta-function".

Proc. Glasgow Math. Assoc. **6**, 116 (1963).

The author points out that his asserted inequality between the second and third lines of p. 77 of his earlier paper [same Proc. **4** (1959), 73–80; MR **22** #7975] does not follow from the inequality for d_0x at the bottom of p. 76, thus compromising the entire argument.

Citations: MR 22# 7975 = E44-15.

E44-17 (23# A3724)

Anfert'eva, E. A.

On an identity of Chowla and Selberg. (Russian)

Izv. Vysš. Učebn. Zaved. Matematika **1959**, *no.* 3 (10), 13–21.

The author gives a proof of the following identity [announced by S. Chowla and A. Selberg, Proc. Nat. Acad. Sci. U.S.A. **35** (1949), 371–374; MR **11**, 84]:

$$\zeta_Q(s)=2a^{-s}\zeta(2s)+\frac{\zeta(2s-1)2^{2s}a^{s-1}\pi^{1/2}\Gamma(s-\frac{1}{2})}{\Delta^{s-1/2}\Gamma(s)}$$

$$+\sum_{n=1}^{\infty}\sigma_{1-2s}(n)\frac{2^{s+3/2}n^{s-1/2}\pi^s\cos(n\pi b/a)}{a^{1/2}\Gamma(s)(\Delta^{1/2})^{s-1/2}}$$

$$\times\int_0^\infty v^{s-3/2}\exp\left(\frac{-\pi n\Delta^{1/2}}{2a}(v+v^{-1})\right)dv,$$

where $\zeta_Q(s)$ is Epstein's zeta function associated with the definite quadratic form $Q(x,y)=ax^2+bxy+cy^2$ $(a>0)$, and $\sigma_m(n)$ denotes the sum of the mth powers of the divisors of n. *S. Chowla* (Boulder, Colo.)

Citations: MR 11, 84d = E44-5.

E44-18 (25# 3017)

Val'fiš, Anna [Walfisz, A.]

On the theory of a class of Dirichlet series. (Russian)

Soobšč. Akad. Nauk Gruzin. SSR **27** (1961), 9–16.

Let $Z(s)=\sum_{n=1}^\infty c_nl_n^{-s}$ $(0<l_1<l_2<\cdots)$ be a Dirichlet series; the paper is concerned with the expression of the sum $\sum_{l_n\leq x}c_n$ in terms of the residues of $x^sZ(s)/s$ and a certain infinite series. The precise definitions and conditions of validity are too complicated to be repeated in this review; one condition is that $Z(s)$ should satisfy a functional equation of the type satisfied by $Z_Q(s)$, the Epstein zeta-function for a positive quadratic form Q. The general conditions are similar to those of the author's previous paper in same Soobšč. **26** (1961), 9–16. From the main theorem there is deduced a new result for binary forms with arbitrary real coefficients; the theorem also includes various previously known results, such as that of Hardy in the case where $l_n=n$ and c_n is the number of representations of n as the sum of two squares. Proofs are given in outline only. *J. H. Williamson* (Cambridge, England)

Referred to in P28-64.

E44-19 **(27# 2660)**

Emersleben, Otto

Auswertung von Beziehungen zwischen elliptischen Funktionen und einer Epsteinschen Zetafunktion zweiter Ordnung.

Math. Nachr. **25** (1963), 232–254.

The Epstein Zeta-function $Z\begin{vmatrix}0 & 0\\ x & y\end{vmatrix}(s)$ $(s=\sigma+it)$ corresponding to the quadratic form $\delta(k,l)=k^2+l^2$ is defined [see P. Epstein, Math. Ann. **56** (1903), 615–644; ibid. **63** (1907), 205–216] for $\sigma>2$ by the absolutely convergent double series

$$\sum_{k=-\infty}^{\infty}\sum_{l=-\infty}^{\infty}\frac{\cos 2\pi(kx+ly)}{(k^2+l^2)^{s/2}}$$

(omit the term $k=l=0$), otherwise by analytic continuation. This function is clearly periodic (period one), even in the variables x and y. It may be shown that for $s=0$, $Z\begin{vmatrix}0 & 0\\ x & y\end{vmatrix}(0)=-1$ identically in x and y, but for $s\neq 0$ the periodicity in x and y is non-trivial. For $s=2$, $f(x,y)=Z\begin{vmatrix}0 & 0\\ x & y\end{vmatrix}(2)$ is a solution of Poisson's equation $\Delta f=4\pi^2$ and in this connection $f(x,y)$ had been studied previously by the author [Diss., Göttingen, 1922; Physik. Z. **24** (1923), 73–80; ibid. **26** (1925), 601–610]. $f(x,y)$ has simple relations to the Weierstrass functions, namely

$$f(x,y)-\pi^2(x^2+y^2) = -2\pi\Re\ln\sigma(z)+c_0 \quad (c_0 \text{ a constant}).$$

$$2\pi\{-\zeta(z\mid 1,i)+\pi z\} = \frac{\partial f}{\partial x}-i\left\{\frac{\partial f}{\partial y}-4\pi^2 y\right\},$$

$$2\pi(\wp(z\mid 1,i)+\pi) = \frac{\partial^2 f}{\partial x^2}-i\frac{\partial^2 f}{\partial x\,\partial y}.$$

The main purpose of the present paper seems to be the use of these relations for the computation (with errors of the order of 10^{-20}) of the coefficients in the expansions of $f(x,y)$ around the lattice points and around the centers of the squares of periods. If $\wp(z;g_2,0)=z^{-2}+\sum_{n=1}^{\infty}a_n g_2^{\,n}z^{4n-2}$, then [see Halphen, *Traité des fonctions elliptiques et de leurs applications*, Gauthier-Villars, Paris, 1886] $a_n=3(2n-3)^{-1}(4n+1)^{-1}(a_1a_{n-1}+\cdots+a_{n-1}a_1)$. The author shows that $f(x,y)=-\pi\ln(x^2+y^2)+c_0+\pi^2(x^2+y^2)+\sum_{n=1}^{\infty}c_{4n}\Re(x+iy)^{4n}$, where $c_{4n}=(\pi/2n(4n-1))a_n g_2^{\,n}$ $(n\geqq 1)$. Also, $f(x-\frac{1}{2},y-\frac{1}{2})=\bar{c}_0+\pi^2(x^2+y^2)+\sum_{n=1}^{\infty}\bar{c}_{4n}\Re(x+iy)^{4n}$ with $\bar{c}_0=-\pi\ln 2$ and $\bar{c}_{4n}=(-1)^n(4^n-(-1)^n)c_{4n}$. The constant $c_0=\lim_{(x,y)\to(0,0)}\{f(x,y)+\pi\ln(x^2+y^2)\}$ requires separate consideration, and at least three methods are indicated for its computation with 21 significant figures. For some rational arguments, $f(x,y)$ is given in closed form, e.g., $f(\frac{1}{2},\frac{1}{2})=-\pi\ln 2$.

E. Grosswald (Philadelphia, Pa.)

E44-20 **(29# 5797)**

Ennola, Veikko

On a problem about the Epstein zeta-function.

Proc. Cambridge Philos. Soc. **60** (1964), 855–875.

Let $h(m,n)=\alpha m^2+2\delta mn+\beta n^2$, where $\alpha\beta-\delta^2=1$, and write $Q(m,n)=2\cdot 3^{-1/2}(m^2+mn+n^2)$ and

$$Z_h(s) = \sum\sum\{h(m,n)\}^{-s},$$

the summation being over all integers m,n with the exception of $m=n=0$. The series converges for $\operatorname{Re}s>1$. The reviewer [Proc. Glasgow Math. Assoc. **1** (1953), 149–158; MR **15**, 507], Cassels [ibid. **4** (1959), 73–80; MR **22** #7975], the author [#5798a below] and Diananda [#5798b below] proved that $Z_h(s)\geqq Z_Q(s)$ for real $s>0$, where the sign of equality is needed only if h is equivalent to Q. The author considers the three-dimensional analogue of this problem and makes the conjecture that, for $s>0$, $Z_f(s)\geqq Z_R(s)$, strict inequality holding except when f is equivalent to R. Here

$$f(m,n,p) = am^2+bn^2+cp^2+2rnp+2spm+2tmn,$$

the determinant being $\frac{1}{2}$, and

$$R(m,n,p) = m^2+n^2+p^2+mp+np.$$

The zeta-functions $Z_f(s)$ and $Z_R(s)$ are defined similarly by infinite series that are absolutely convergent for $\operatorname{Re}s>\frac{3}{2}$. This conjecture he is unable to prove, but by very complicated analysis he shows that the form R gives a local minimum for $Z_f(s)$.

R. A. Rankin (Glasgow)

Citations: MR 15, 507c = E44-8; MR 22# 7975 = E44-15.

E44-21 **(29# 5798a; 29# 5798b)**

Ennola, Veikko

A lemma about the Epstein zeta-function.

Proc. Glasgow Math. Assoc. **6**, 198–201 (1964).

Diananda, P. H.

Notes on two lemmas concerning the Epstein zeta-function.

Proc. Glasgow Math. Assoc. **6**, 202–204 (1964).

The reviewer's paper [same Proc. **4** (1959), 73–80; MR **22** #7975] contained a silly blunder which apparently vitiated the whole argument. Ennola notes the blunder and shows that it can be rectified by a more elaborate argument on the same general lines as the original one. Diananda shows that the proof of the reviewer's results can be considerably simplified.

J. W. S. Cassels (Cambridge, England)

Citations: MR 22# 7975 = E44-15.

E44-22 **(30# 67)**

Kalnin', I. M.

An estimate for the Epstein zeta function on the line $\sigma=\frac{1}{2}$ by the method of trigonometric sums of van der Corput. (Russian. Latvian and English summaries)

Latvijas PSR Zinātņu Akad. Vēstis Fiz. Tehn. Zinātņu Sēr. **1964**, *no.* 4, 63–70.

Let $f(n,m)$ denote the quadratic form $an^2+bmn+cm^2$, where a,b,c are fixed real numbers and $a>0$, $D=4ac-b^2>0$. Define

$$Z(s) = \sum_{n,m}{}'\,[f(n,m)]^{-s},$$

where $s=\sigma+it$ $(\sigma>1)$ and the prime means that the term $m=n=0$ is omitted from the summation (n,m vary over all integers). The function $(s-1)Z(s)$ can be continued over the whole s-plane and is analytic there. Potter and Titchmarsh [Proc. London Math. Soc. (2) **39** (1935), 372–384] obtained the estimate

$$Z(\tfrac{1}{2}+it) = O(|t|^{1/2+\varepsilon}) \quad \text{as } |t|\to\infty.$$

The author uses van der Corput's methods to obtain the sharper estimate

$$Z(\tfrac{1}{2}+it) = O(|t|^{3/7}\log|t|).$$

{The reviewer remarks that in special cases, e.g., when the class number of binary quadratic forms of discriminant $-D$ is 1 (when $D=+3,+4,+7,+8,+11,+19,+43,+67,+163$ and, perhaps, one more case), the function $Z(s)$ splits into the product $\zeta(s)L(s)$, where $L(s)$ is a Dirichlet L-series. In these cases known results permit us to replace the exponent $\frac{3}{7}$ of the author by an exponent $<\frac{1}{3}$ (however, the author is in a much more general case since his a, b, c are any real numbers subject to $a>0$, $D>0$).} *S. Chowla* (University Park, Pa.)

Referred to in R44-34.

E44-23 (31# 3392)

Bateman, P. T.; Grosswald, E.
On Epstein's zeta function.
Acta Arith. **9** (1964), 365–373.

In their introduction the authors say "The purpose of this paper is to give detailed proofs of two theorems on the Epstein zeta function which were announced without proof by S. Chowla and A. Selberg about 15 years ago [Proc. Nat. Acad. Sci. U.S.A. **35** (1949), 371–374; MR **11**, 84]. The two results which they announced are our Theorem 1 and a slightly weaker form of our Theorem 3. Our Theorem 2 was not stated explicitly by Chowla and Selberg in their paper, but they did indicate that they were in possession of a result of the same nature as our Theorem 2, that is, one giving a good approximation to the Epstein zeta function in the critical strip, particularly on or near the real line." The authors have made a thorough study of the Epstein zeta function, culminating in the three theorems below.

Let a, b, c denote real numbers with $a>0$ and $d=b^2-4ac<0$. Define

$$Z(s) = \tfrac{1}{2}\sum{}' (am^2+bmn+cn^2)^{-s},$$

where the real part of s exceeds 1; the summation is for all pairs (m, n) of integers, except $(0, 0)$. Define the positive number k by $k^2=|d|/(4a^2)=(4ac-b^2)/(4a^2)$. The Bessel function (for arbitrary ν and $|\arg z|<\pi/2$) is

$$K_\nu(z) = \int_0^\infty e^{-z\cosh t}\cosh \nu t\, dt.$$

Theorem 1: When $\mathrm{Re}(s)>1$,

$$(3)\qquad a^sZ(s) = \zeta(2s)+k^{1-2s}\zeta(2s-1)\,\frac{\Gamma(s-\frac{1}{2})\Gamma(\frac{1}{2})}{\Gamma(s)} + \frac{\pi^s}{\Gamma(s)}k^{-s+1/2}H(s),$$

where

$$(4)\quad H(s) = 4\sum_1^\infty n^{s-1/2}\sigma_{1-2s}(n)\cos\left(\frac{n\pi b}{a}\right)K_{s-1/2}(2\pi kn).$$

Here $\sigma_\nu(n)=\sum_{d|n} d^\nu$. Further, $H(s)$ is an entire function of s and $H(s)=H(1-s)$.

Theorem 2: If $\frac{1}{2}\leqq \mathrm{Re}(s)=\sigma\leqq 1$,

$$(7)\qquad H(s) = 4\cos(\pi b/a)K_{s-1/2}(2\pi k) + \theta\frac{2\Gamma(\sigma)}{k^{1/2}|\Gamma(s)|}\sum_2^\infty \sigma_{-1}(n)e^{-2\pi kn},$$

where $|\theta|\leqq 1$, or, more crudely,

$$(8)\qquad |H(s)| < \frac{\Gamma(\sigma)}{|\Gamma(s)|}\left\{\frac{2e^{-2\pi k}}{k^{1/2}}+\frac{3e^{-4\pi k}}{k^{1/2}(1-e^{-2\pi k})^2}\right\}.$$

Theorem 3: If $k\geqq\frac{1}{2}\sqrt{3}$, then

$$(9)\qquad a^{1/2}Z(\tfrac{1}{2}) = \gamma+\log k-\log 4\pi+2\theta k^{-1/2}e^{-2\pi k},$$

where γ is Euler's constant and $-1<\theta<1$. Thus (10) $Z(\frac{1}{2})>0$ if $k\geqq 7.0556$, (11) $Z(\frac{1}{2})<0$ if $\frac{1}{2}\sqrt{3}\leqq k\leqq 7.0554$. Finally, some interesting information from a post-script to the paper, dated Sept. 1, 1964, will be mentioned. R. A. Rankin informed the authors that he, too, proved Theorem 1, in Proc. Glasgow Math. Assoc. **1** (1953), 149–158 [MR 15, 507]. It is also stated that in a forthcoming paper, Marc E. Low has proved that $Z(s)$ is negative for $0<s<1$, when $k\leqq 7.0554$.
S. Chowla (University Park, Pa.)

Citations: MR 11, 84d = E44-5; MR 15, 507c = E44-8.
Referred to in E44-25, E44-26.

E44-24 (33# 4023)

Kalnin', I. M. [Kalniņš, I.]
On the Epstein zeta-function. (Russian. Latvian and English summaries)
Latvijas PSR Zinātņu Akad. Vēstis Fiz. Tehn. Zinātņu Sēr. **1965**, *no.* 5, 66–75.

Let a, b, c be rational integers such that $a>0$ and $D=b^2-4ac$ is a positive fundamental discriminant. Further, let T, U denote the least positive solution of the Pell equation $t^2-Du^2=4$, and let R be the region of points (x, y) with $2ax+by\geqq yT/U$, $y\geqq 0$. Using van der Corput's method, the author proves the estimate $Z(\frac{1}{2}+it)\ll t^{5/12}\log t$ $(t>2)$ for the function $Z(s)$ $(s=\sigma+it)$ which in the half-plane $\sigma>1$ is defined by the series $\sum(an^2+bnm+cm^2)^{-s}$, the summation being over all lattice points $(n, m)\in R$. The proof rests on the approximate functional equation proved by Fischer [Math. Z. **57** (1952), 94–115; MR **15**, 606] for the zeta-function $\zeta(s, \mathbf{C})$ of a class of ideals in a real quadratic field. Applying the methods of I. M. Vinogradov and Kubilius [see Kubilius, Mat. Sb. (N.S.) **31** (**73**) (1952), 507–542; MR **14**, 847], the author gets the estimate

$$(*)\qquad Z(\sigma+it) \ll \exp\{c_1(\log t)^{1/4}(\log\log t)^{5/4}\}$$

in the region $1-c_2(\log t)^{-1/2}(\log\log t)^{1/2}\leqq\sigma\leqq 2$ $(t>t_0>10$; c_1, c_2 appropriate positive constants). Some parts of the latter proof are merely outlined.

{Reviewer's remarks: In fact, the author supposes that D is any positive discriminant. Yet, this is not a sufficient restriction as long as his proof rests on Fischer's theorem as it stands. On p. 71, using $Y\ll 1$ in that theorem, the author derives an equation for $\zeta(s, \mathbf{C})$, from which the proof of (*) begins. However, $Y\ll 1$ contradicts Fischer's restriction $c_1<X/Y<c_2$. The estimate of the sum S_1 on p. 71 is needlessly complicated; one can get the result very simply by observing that $S_1\ll\sum_{1\leqq n\leqq N_0} n^{1-2\sigma}$. The reader has to guess that by $7/6\sigma$, $1/\kappa m$, $\cdots$, the author actually means $(7/6)\sigma$, $(1/\kappa)m$, etc. On p. 72 (line 16), $T^{2(1-\sigma)}$ should be replaced by $T^{1-2\sigma}$.} *E. Fogels* (Riga)

Citations: MR 14, 847f = R44-3; MR 15, 606e = R42-13.

E44-25 (35# 6632)

Selberg, Atle; Chowla, S.
On Epstein's zeta-function.
J. Reine Angew. Math. **227** (1967), 86–110.

In 1949 a note by the authors (referred to hereafter by (P)) on the Epstein zeta function $Z(s)$ appeared in the Proc. Nat. Acad. Sci. U.S.A. **35** (1949), 371–374 [MR **11**, 84]. It contained a representation theorem for $Z(s)$ (sharpening considerably a similar result of M. Deuring [Math. Z. **37** (1933), 405–415]), from which several consequences were derived, concerning, besides $Z(s)$, also Dirichlet's functions $L_p(s)$ $(=\sum_{n=1}^\infty(n/p)n^{-s})$ and the complete elliptic integrals $K=\int_0^{\pi/2}(1-k^2\sin^2\varphi)^{-1/2}\,d\varphi$ and $K'=\int_0^{\pi/2}(1-k'^2\sin^2\varphi)^{-1/2}\,d\varphi$, $k^2+k'^2=1$. The results are stated rather fully, but without proofs, yet with the promise that the complete paper would follow. This promise has now been fulfilled by the authors—some 18 years later. It was inevitable that during this long interval, others would work on the same and related topics. A list of four such papers (by Rosser, Anferteva, Bateman and the reviewer and Ramachandra) appears in a recently added introduction to the present work; however, except for this introduction, the paper seems to be the unretouched text of the original manuscript, completed, as the authors state, in the spring of 1949. To the authors' list of related papers, one may well add also the following: R. A. Rankin [Proc. Glasgow Math. Assoc. **1** (1953), 149–158; MR **15**, 507]; M. E. Low (to appear in Acta Arith.; see also the review of the paper by P. T. Bateman and the reviewer in Acta Arith. **9** (1964), 365–373 [MR **31** #3392]); H. Stark [#6633 below; Michigan Math. J. **14** (1967), 1–27]. In comparing the results of the present and of Deuring's paper with those of the papers by Bateman and the reviewer and by Stark, one has to take into account that in the former, $Z(s)$ is defined by $\sum' q(m,n)^{-s}$, $q(m,n)=am^2+bmn+cn^2$ (with summation over all integers m, n except $m=n=0$, $s=\sigma+it$, $\sigma>1$), while in the latter ones $Z(s)$ is defined to mean one half of this value.

Most of the results of the paper are obtained from the following representation: (*) $Z(s)=2\zeta(2s)a^{-s}+2^{2s}a^{s-1}\times\pi^{1/2}(\Gamma(s))^{-1}\Delta^{1/2-s}\zeta(2s-1)\Gamma(s-\frac{1}{2})+Q(s)$, where

$$Q(s) = 4\pi^s 2^{s-1/2}a^{-1/2}\Gamma(s)^{-1} \times \Delta^{1/4-s/2}\sum_{n=1}^{\infty} n^{s-1/2}\sigma_{1-2s}(n)\cos(n\pi b/a)I_n,$$

$I_n=\int_0^\infty y^{s-3/2}e^{-n(y+y^{-1})\Delta^{1/2}\pi/2a}\,dy$ and $\Delta=4ac-b^2>0$. Two proofs are given for (*); the first one uses the transformation formula of theta functions

$$\sum_{-\infty}^{\infty}\exp(-(n+\alpha)^2\pi x) = x^{-1/2}\sum_{-\infty}^{\infty}\exp(2\pi in\alpha-\pi n^2/x),$$

while the second one is based (essentially as per Bateman and the reviewer) on the Fourier expansion of $a^sZ(s)-2\zeta(2s)$, considered as a function of b/a (the $Q(s)$ occurring in this second proof has no connection with the $Q(s)$ of (*)). The representation (*) is used in the first place to compute $Z(\frac{1}{2})=a^{-1/2}\{2\gamma+\log(\Delta/64\pi^2a^2)+4\sum_{n=1}^{\infty}d(n)\cos(n\pi b/a)I_c\}$ with $I_c=\int_0^\infty e^{-c(x+x^{-1})}x^{-1}\,dx$ and $c=c(n)=\pi n\Delta^{1/2}/2a$ ($\gamma=$ Euler constant, $d(n)=\sum_{d|n}1$). Although it is clear that the integral I_n of (*) equals $2K_{s-1/2}(\pi n\Delta^{1/2}a^{-1})$ and, in particular, $I_c=2K_0(2c)$, the well-known Bessel functions, the authors develop ab ovo the estimates and asymptotic series needed, without reference to classical results (e.g., G. N. Watson's *A treatise on the theory of Bessel functions*, Section 7.23 [Cambridge Univ. Press, Cambridge, 1944; MR **6**, 64]). For $\Delta^{1/2}a^{-1}$ large, the "error term" $Q(s)$ in (*) is very small and permits an accurate estimate of $Z(s)$. In particular, if $h(-\Delta)$ is the number of classes of binary quadratic forms of fundamental discriminant $-\Delta$, if $\Delta=p>7$ and $h(-p)=1$, then $Z(s)=2\zeta(s)L_p(s)$. It then follows from (*) and the estimate for $|Q(s)|$ that $L_p(\frac{1}{2})>0$ for $p=43$ and 163 (this follows also for $p=67$, as was actually stated explicitly in (P), but is not restated in the present paper). {Reviewer's remark: From these considerations it does not seem to follow that $L_p(s)\neq 0$ for $0<s<1$, and the respective primes p, because $L_p(s)$ may have an even number of real zeros on $1/2<s<1$; the result, however, is true, as shown by Rosser, in the paper quoted by the authors in the introduction.} Next, the well-known functional equation for $Z(s)$ is obtained from (*), by showing that the infinite series in $Q(s)$ remains invariant when s is replaced by $1-s$. Furthermore, by fairly straightforward computations, Kronecker's Grenzformel is obtained in the form

$$(**)\quad Z(1+\theta) = 2\pi\Delta^{-1/2}\{\theta^{-1}+2\gamma+\log(a/\Delta) + \pi\Delta^{1/2}a^{-1}/6+4\sum_1^\infty\sigma_{-1}(n)\cos(n\pi b/a)e^{-\pi n\Delta^{1/2}/a}\}+O(\theta),$$

for $\theta\to 0$. By similar techniques, the following result is obtained: $\sum'(x^2+y^2+dz^2)^{-s}$ converges in $\sigma>3/2$ and represents there a holomorphic function $H_d(s)$. It is shown that $H_d(s)=4\zeta(s)\eta(s)+(2\pi/(s-1))\,d^{1-s}\zeta(2s-2)+R(s)$, where $\eta(s)=\sum_{n=1}^{\infty}(-1)^n(2n+1)^{-s}$ and $R(s)$ (represented again by a series depending on Bessel functions) is small for large d; also that $H_d(s)=2\pi d^{-1/2}/(s-3/2)+A+O(s-3/2)$, with computable constant A (this is, therefore, a result of the Kronecker Grenzformel type). It is proven that for $d\to\infty$, there exists a real $\rho_d\neq 0$, $\rho_d\to 0$, such that $H(\rho_d)=0$. Other results have to do with the theory of elliptic functions. It is shown that K may be computed in finite terms if $K'/K=n^{1/2}$ and $h(-n)$ is small (this result was known only for $n=1, 2, 3$). In particular, if $n=p$ and $h(-p)=1$, one obtains

$$2K = (2kk')^{-1/6}(\pi/p)^{1/2} \times\{\textstyle\prod_{(\alpha/p)=+1}\Gamma(\alpha/p)/\prod_{(\beta/p)=-1}\Gamma(\beta/p)\}^{w/4}$$

($0<\alpha$, $\beta<p$; $w=2$ for $p>3$, $w=6$ for $p=3$). The proof is based on $\sum'(x^2+xy+\frac{1}{4}(p+1)y^2)^{-s}=w\zeta(s)L_p(s)$ and classical formulae of elliptic function theory, together with (**) and with Kronecker's series for $\log\Gamma(x)$.

In particular, for $p=3$ and $p=7$, one obtains the nice results $K=2^{2/3}3^{1/4}\Gamma^3(1/3)/8\pi$ and

$$K = (\pi/14)^{1/2}\{\Gamma(1/7)\Gamma(2/7)\Gamma(4/7)/\Gamma(3/7)\Gamma(5/7)\Gamma(6/7)\}^{1/2},$$

respectively (the latter already given in (P)). The method works in principle (with more computations) also if $h(-n)=2$. The case $n=4p$, $p=5$, $K'/K=5^{1/2}$ is worked out in detail. Finally, the general case (h arbitrary) is discussed and it is shown how K may be evaluated in finite terms, provided that iK'/K belongs to certain imaginary quadratic fields. A paragraph with speculations concerning the existence of "the tenth" imaginary quadratic field of class-number one (it is shown that its existence would disprove the generalized Riemann hypothesis) has lost its relevance, in view of Stark's last mentioned paper. *E. Grosswald* (Philadelphia, Pa.)

Citations: MR 11, 84d = E44-5; MR 15, 507c = E44-8; MR 31# 3392 = E44-23.

Referred to in E44-34, E44-35, M40-59.

E44-26 (35# 6633)

Stark, H. M.

On the zeros of Epstein's zeta function.

Mathematika **14** (1967), 47–55.

Let $Q(x,y)=ax^2+bxy+cy^2$ be a positive definite quadratic form with discriminant $d=b^2-4ac$. The Epstein zeta function associated with Q is $\zeta(s,Q)=\frac{1}{2}\sum_{x,y}'(Q(x,y))^{-s}$, $\sigma>1$, where the sum is over all pairs of integers x, y not both zero. Except for a first-order pole at $s=1$, $\zeta(s,Q)$ can be continued throughout the complex plane. H. S. A. Potter and E. C. Titchmarsh [Proc. London Math. Soc. (2) **39** (1935), 372–384] showed that $\zeta(s,Q)$ has an infinity of zeros on the line $\sigma=\frac{1}{2}$. The existence of a real zero s with $\frac{1}{2}<s<1$ in the case when $a=1$, $b=0$ and c is large enough, was pointed out by the reviewer and A. Selberg [Proc. Nat. Acad. Sci. U.S.A. **35** (1949), 371–374; MR **11**, 84]. P. T. Bateman and E. Grosswald [Acta Arith. **9** (1964), 365–373; MR **31** #3392] sharpened this by showing that $\zeta(s,Q)$ has a real zero between $\frac{1}{2}$ and 1 if $k=(\sqrt{|d|})/2a>7.0556$. In the case where a, b, c are integers, d is a fundamental discriminant and the class number $h(d)>1$, H. Davenport and H. Heilbronn [J. London Math. Soc. **11** (1936), 181–185; ibid. **11** (1936), 307–312] had previously shown that $\zeta(s,Q)$ has an infinity of zeros in the half-plane $\sigma>1$ arbitrarily close to the line $\sigma=1$. The author proves the following two striking theorems which are complements to the above results. Theorem 1: There exists a number K such that if $k>K$, then all the zeros of $\zeta(s, Q)$ in the region $-1<\sigma<2$, $-2k \leqq t \leqq 2k$ are simple zeros; with the exception of two real zeros between 0 and 1, all are on the line $\sigma=\frac{1}{2}$. Theorem 2: Let $N(T, Q)$ denote the number of zeros of $\zeta(s, Q)$ in the region $-1<\sigma<2$, $0 \leqq t \leqq T$. If $k>K$ and $0<T \leqq 2k$, then $N(T, Q)=(T/\pi)\log(kT/\pi e)+O(h(T+3))$, where $h(x)=\log^{1/3} \times (\log\log x)^{1/6}$ and the constant implied by "O" is independent of k. *S. Chowla* (University Park, Pa.)

Citations: MR 11, 84d = E44-5; MR 31# 3392 = E44-23.

E44-27 (36# 3728)

Delone, B. N.; Ryškov, S. S.

A contribution to the theory of the extrema of a multidimensional ζ-function.

Dokl. Akad. Nauk SSSR **173** (1967), 991–994 (*Russian*); *translated as Soviet Math. Dokl.* **8** (1967), 499–503.

Let Γ be an n-dimensional lattice, and $m>n/2$ a positive integer. Define $\zeta(m, \Gamma)=\zeta(m, f)=\sum 1/r^{2m}=\sum_\Gamma 1/f$, where the first sum is over the distances from the origin to all other points of Γ, $f=\sum a_{i\gamma}x_i x_\gamma$ is the quadratic form corresponding to the lattice, and the second sum is over all n-dimensional vectors with integer components excepting $(0, \cdots, 0)$.

The problem of finding for a given m, among all lattices with determinant Δ, that which minimizes the value of $\zeta(m, \Gamma)$ is simply solved by using Lagrange multipliers. (The problem is said to arise from work of Sobolev on multidimensional integrals.) Such lattices are called critical. A lattice is defined to be strongly critical if it is critical for some infinite sequence of integers m. It turns out that a strongly critical lattice is critical for all $m>n/2$, and most of the rest of the paper is devoted to a study, usually with no or only skeleton proofs, of strongly critical lattices. In particular, strongly critical lattices are interpreted geometrically, and it is claimed that there are only finitely many strongly critical n-dimensional lattices. {"ζ-finally extreme" lattices are also studied, but although ζ-finally extreme is defined as being ζ-extreme for all sufficiently large m, the reviewer could find no definition of ζ-extreme.} *S. L. Segal* (Rochester, N.Y.)

E44-28 (36# 5091)

Sandakova, N. N.

On the theory of ζ-functions of three variables. (Russian)

Dokl. Akad. Nauk SSSR **175** (1967), 535–538.

The following theorem is proved [cf. B. N. Delone, the author and S. S. Ryškov, same Dokl. **162** (1965), 1230–1233; MR **31** #3933]: The positive definite quadratic form $f_0=x^2+y^2+z^2+xy+yz+zx$ gives a local minimum of the function $\zeta(A, m)=\sum f^{-m}(x_i)$ with $m \geqq n$, where the summation extends over all integer points and A is the matrix of the positive definite quadratic form f.

{This article has appeared in English translation [Soviet Math. Dokl. **8** (1967), 893–896].}

H. A. Lauwerier (Amsterdam)

E44-29 (37# 2707)

Stark, H. M.

L-functions and character sums for quadratic forms. I.

Acta Arith. **14** (1967/68), 35–50.

Let $Q(x)$ be a positive definite quadratic form in n variables $x=(x_1, x_2, \cdots, x_n)$ with rational integral coefficients, and let χ be a character mod k. A generalized Epstein zeta function is then defined by $L(s, \chi, Q)=\frac{1}{2}\sum_{x\neq 0}\chi(Q(x))Q(x)^{-s}$. The main aim of this paper is to show that $L(s, \chi, Q)$ is, under some conditions, continued to an entire function of s satisfying a functional equation. The result is based upon an identity between certain character sums, and forms a part of the construction of a general theory which covers the basic part of the previous work of the author on the class number of imaginary quadratic fields [Michigan Math. J. **14** (1967), 1–27; MR **36** #5102].

T. Kubota (Nagoya)

Citations: MR 36# 5102 = R14-62.

Referred to in E44-31, E44-33, E44-39, E44-41, E44-44.

E44-30 (37# 5163)

Chowla, S.

Stark's series expressed by theta-functions.

Norske Vid. Selsk. Forh. (*Trondheim*) **40** (1967), 31–33.

In solving the 10th discriminant problem Stark introduced [H. M. Stark, Michigan Math. J. **14** (1967), 1–27; MR **36** #5102] the generalized Epstein series

$$\sum \chi(Q(x, y))/(Q(x, y)^s)$$

the summation being over all integers $x, y \neq 0, 0$, χ a non-principal character mod k and $Q(x, y)=Ax^2+Bxy+Cy^2$ a definite form with $A>0$. He requires an evaluation at $s=1$.

The object of this note is to express the value of the above series at $s=1$ in terms of elliptic functions with the help of the Kronecker limit formula.

R. Ayoub (University Park, Pa.)

Citations: MR 36# 5102 = R14-62.

E44-31 (38# 2101)

Chowla, S.; Smith, R. A.

On certain functional equations.

Norske Vid. Selsk. Forh. (*Trondheim*) **40** (1967), 43–47 (1968).

An elementary proof of a special case of the functional equation satisfied by the L-series of quadratic forms introduced by H. M. Stark [Michigan Math. J. **14** (1967), 1–27; MR **36** #5102]. A proof in the general case has since been given by Stark in his paper on L-series and character sums for quadratic forms [Acta Arith. **14** (1967/68), 35–50; MR **37** #2707]. *A. Brumer* (New York)

Citations: MR 36# 5102 = R14-62; MR 37# 2707 = E44-29.

E44-32 (38# 3243)

Motohashi, Yoichi

A new proof of the limit formula of Kronecker.

Proc. Japan Acad. **44** (1968), 614–616.

Starting with Poisson's summation formula and using Mellin's transform, the author gives a modified proof of the Kronecker limit formula for the Epstein-zeta function.

K. Thanigasalam (University Park, Pa.)

E44-33 (39# 4101)

Stark, H. M.

L-functions and character sums for quadratic forms. II.

Acta Arith. **15** (1968/69), 307–317.

This paper is devoted to the study of a special and particularly useful case of the function introduced in the first part of the work [same Acta **14** (1967/68), 35–50; MR **37** #2707]. For a positive definite quadratic form $Q(x, y)=ax^2+bxy+cy^2$ with $a, b, c \in \mathbf{Z}$ and $d=b^2-4ac<0$, the author observes the function

$$L(s, \chi, Q) = \tfrac{1}{2}\sum \chi(Q(x, y))Q(x, y)^{-s} \qquad (x, y \neq 0, 0),$$

where χ is a congruence character, and he presents as the main result an expansion of $L(s, \chi, Q)$ into an infinite series which contains among others the modified Bessel function K, and which converges very rapidly in a neighborhood of $s=1$. At the same time, the functional equation for $L(s, \chi, Q)$ is derived. *T. Kubota* (Nagoya)

Citations: MR 37# 2707 = E44-29.
Referred to in E44-44, R14-79, R14-89.

E44-34 (39# 5488)

Barrucand, Pierre
Sur une formule de Selberg et Chowla.
C. R. Acad. Sci. Paris Sér. A-B **268** (1969), A1398–A1401.

The author announces a class of formulas generalizing a representation of Epstein's zeta function given by A. Selberg and S. Chowla [J. Reine Angew. Math. **227** (1967), 86–110; MR **35** #6632]. Detailed proofs will presumably be published elsewhere.
T. M. Apostol (Pasadena, Calif.)

Citations: MR 35# 6632 = E44-25.

E44-35 (40# 101)

Barrucand, Pierre
Sur certaines séries de Dirichlet.
C. R. Acad. Sci. Paris Sér. A-B **269** (1969), A294–A296.

A. Selberg and the reviewer [J. Reine Angew. Math. **227** (1967), 86–110; MR **35** #6632] obtained a formula for the Epstein zeta function. The author obtains similar and more general formulae involving the confluent hypergeometric functions Ψ of A. Erdélyi, W. Magnus, F. Oberhettinger and F. Tricomi [*Higher transcendental functions*, Vol. I, p. 248 ff., especially p. 255, McGraw-Hill, New York, 1953; MR **15**, 419; Russian translation, Izdat. "Nauka", Moscow, 1969].

Let $\Phi(s)=\sum_1^\infty a(n)n^{-s}$ be a Dirichlet series satisfying the functional equation

$$(1) \qquad \Phi(1-s) = A^{-s+(1/2)}(\Gamma(s)/\Gamma(1-s))\Phi(s)$$

(A real >0).

For the moment suppose $\Phi(s)$ is an entire function; set (2) $A=\alpha\beta$, $R(\alpha)>0$. Then (3) $\beta^{s-(1/2)}\Gamma(1-s)\Phi(1-s)=\alpha^{(1/2)-s}\Gamma(s)\Phi(s)$. Set $B(x)=\sum_1^\infty a(n)e^{-nx}$; then

$$(4) \qquad \int_0^\infty B(\alpha x)x^{s-1}\,dx = \alpha^{-s}\Gamma(s)\Phi(s),$$

the integral converging for all s, whence (5) $(\sqrt{\alpha})B(\alpha x)=(\sqrt{\beta})x^{-1}B(\beta/x)$ and $B(x)$ is a modular function. From (4), (5),

$$\alpha^{-s}\Gamma(s)\Phi(s)=\sum_1^\infty a(n)\int_1^\infty e^{-n\alpha x}x^{s-1}\,dx + \sum_1^\infty a(n)\sqrt{(\beta/\alpha)}\int_0^1 e^{-n\beta/x}x^{s-1}\,dx,$$

$$(6) \quad \alpha^{-s}\Gamma(s)\Phi(s) = \sum_1^\infty a(n)e^{-n\alpha}\int_0^\infty e^{-n\alpha x}(1+x)^{s-1}\,dx + \sum_1^\infty a(n)\sqrt{(\beta/\alpha)}e^{-n\beta}\int_0^\infty e^{-n\beta x}(1+x)^{-s}\,dx.$$

Thus, using the notations of Erdélyi,

$$(7) \quad \alpha^{-s}\Gamma(s)\Phi(s) = \sum_1^\infty a(n)e^{-n\alpha}\Psi(1, 1+s, n\alpha) + \sum_1^\infty a(n)\sqrt{(\beta/\alpha)}e^{-n\beta}\Psi(1, 2-s, n\beta).$$

These series converge rapidly. We proceed similarly when $\Phi(s)$ is meromorphic with a pole at $s=1$. The author points out some advantages of using the functions Ψ.
S. Chowla (University Park, Pa.)

Citations: MR 35# 6632 = E44-25.

E44-36 (41# 1643)

Emersleben, Otto
Summen reziproker Abstandsquadrate von Gitterpunkten.
Wiss. Z. Ernst-Moritz-Arndt-Univ. Greifswald Math.-Natur. Reihe **17** (1968), 169–181.

Asymptotic expansions for sums of type

$$\sum_{k=-K}^{K}\sum_{l=-L}^{\prime L} f(k, l)^{-1}$$

are given for $K\to\infty$ and $L\to\infty$. Here $f(x, y)$ denotes a binary quadratic form of the shape x^2+xy+y^2 or ax^2+by^2 with positive constants a and b. $\sum'$ means that the pair k, l with $f(k, l)=0$ is to be excluded. Also, some other ranges of summation are considered. The asymptotic evaluations are obtained mainly by means of Euler's summation formula. Applications of the results to crystallography are pointed out. *O. H. Körner* (Marburg)

E44-37 (41# 3411)

Udrescu, Valeriu Şt.
On the zeta function of a totally positive definite quadratic form.
Rev. Roumaine Math. Pures Appl. **14** (1969), 1629–1632.

The author defines the zeta-function $Z(S; \mathfrak{A}_1, \cdots, \mathfrak{A}_m; Q) =\sum_{(\alpha_1, \cdots, \alpha_m)} N(Q(\alpha_1, \cdots, \alpha_m))^{-S}$, where S is a complex number, $\operatorname{Re} S>1$; Q is a totally positive definite symmetric quadratic form with real coefficients; $\mathfrak{A}_1, \cdots, \mathfrak{A}_m$ are m distant integral ideals in a totally real algebraic number field k; and the summation is extended over all non-associated m-tuples $\{\alpha_i, \cdots, \alpha_m\}\neq\{0, \cdots, 0\}$, $\alpha_i\in\mathfrak{A}_i$, $i=1, \cdots, m$ (two m-tuples $\{\alpha_1, \cdots, \alpha_m\}$ and $\{\alpha_1', \cdots, \alpha_m'\}$ are associated if there is a unit μ in k with $\alpha_i'=\alpha_i\mu$ all $i=1, \cdots, m$).

It is shown that the series so defined is absolutely convergent for $\operatorname{Re} S>m/2$.
S. L. Segal (Rochester, N.Y.)

E44-38 (42# 5929)

Glaeske, Hans-Jürgen
Eine Integrofunktionalgleichung verallgemeinerter Gitterfunktionen.
Math. Nachr. **45** (1970), 283–293.

From the author's introduction: "Im § 1 werden bzgl. einem komplexen variablen s meromorphe Hilfsfunktionen $Q_{\lambda\mu}(\omega; s)$ (called generalized Gitterfunction), $U_{\lambda\mu}(\omega; s)$ (expressed in terms of $Q_{\lambda\mu}$, gamma and zeta functions) untersucht und festgestellt, daß sie für alle werte von s einen endlichen Funktionswert besitzen. Im § 2 wird eine einfache Folgerung aus dem Cauchyschen Integralsatz angegeben und durch Anwendung auf unsere Hilfsfunktionen die eingangs erwähnte Integrofunktionalgleichung für $U_{\lambda\mu}$ hergeleitet." *Pl. Kannappan* (Waterloo, Ont.)

E44-39 (43# 1929)

Berndt, Bruce C.
The functional equation of some Dirichlet series.
Proc. Amer. Math. Soc. **29** (1971), 457–460.

The author derives functional equations for two classes of functions generalizing the Epstein zeta functions and Dirichlet L-functions. One class also generalizes some functions studied by H. M. Stark [Acta Arith. **14** (1967/68), 35–50; MR **37** #2707]. *T. M. Apostol* (Pasadena, Calif.)

Citations: MR 37# 2707 = E44-29.
Referred to in E44-40.

E44-40 (44# 2718)

Berndt, Bruce C.
The functional equation of some Dirichlet series. II.
Proc. Amer. Math. Soc. **31** (1972), 24–26.

For real h, g and $\sigma=\Re(s)>1$, the Epstein zeta function is given by $Z(s; g, h)=\sum_n e^{2\pi ihn}|n+g|^{-s}$. The author considers the sums $Z_h(s)=\sum_{r=1}^k e^{4\pi irh/k}Z^2(s; r/k, h)$ and $Z_h{}^*(s) =\sum_{r=1}^k Z(s; (r+h)/k, 0)Z(s; (k-r+h)/k, 0)$, and shows that there is a functional equation relating $Z_h(s)$ and

$Z_h{}^*(1-s)$.

{Part I has appeared in same Proc. **29** (1971), 457–460 [MR **43** #1929].} *T. M. Apostol* (Pasadena, Calif.)

Citations: MR 43# 1929 = E44-39.

E44-41 (43# 4778)

Kitaoka, Yoshiyuki

A simple proof of the functional equation of a certain L-function.

J. Number Theory **3** (1971), 155–158.

Author's summary: "By using character sums, H. M. Stark proved in 1968 [Acta Arith. **14** (1967/68), 35–50; MR **37** #2707] the functional equation of the Epstein zeta function with a character. Using a method due to A. Weil [Math. Ann. **168** (1967), 149–156; MR **34** #7473], we give a simple proof which shows that the proof reduces to the case in which the character is trivial."

K. Thanigasalam (Monaca, Pa.)

Citations: MR 34# 7473 = F65-21; MR 37# 2707 = E44-29.

E44-42 (44# 3970)

Terras, Audrey

A generalization of Epstein's zeta function.

Nagoya Math. J. **42** (1971), 173–188.

M. Koecher [J. Reine Angew. Math. **192** (1953), 1–23; MR **15**, 290] introduced a generalization of Epstein's zeta function suggested by C. L. Siegel's work on quadratic forms. This was also generalized by A. Selberg [Rep. Inst. Theory of Numbers (Univ. Colorado, Boulder, Colo., 1959), pp. 207–210, Amer. Math. Soc., Providence, R.I., 1959] who defined a zeta function $\zeta_{(n)}(S, \rho)$ associated with a positive matrix S and $n-1$ complex variables $\rho=(\rho_1, \rho_2, \cdots, \rho_{n-1})$. He proved that $\zeta_{(n)}(S, \rho)$ satisfies $n!$ functional equations and can be continued to a meromorphic function in C^{n-1}. The author considers a common generalization which relates Koecher's and Selberg's functions and fills a gap in one of Koecher's proofs. It is also shown that $n-1$ of Selberg's functional equations generate the rest. *T. M. Apostol* (Pasadena, Calif.)

Citations: MR 15, 290a = F65-9.

E44-43 (44# 6621)

Terras, Audrey A.

Functional equations of generalized Epstein zeta functions in several complex variables.

Nagoya Math. J. **44** (1971), 89–95.

The author's previous generalized Epstein zeta functions $\zeta_{(n)}(S, \rho)$ associated with a positive matrix S and $n-1$ complex variables $\rho=(\rho_1, \cdots, \rho_{n-1})$ [same J. **42** (1971), 173–188; MR **44** #3970] are generalized even further and shown to satisfy functional equations.

T. M. Apostol (Pasadena, Calif.)

Citations: MR 44# 3970 = E44-42.

E44-44 (44# 5283)

Takeuchi, Mamoru

A generalization of Stark's formula.

Bull. Fac. Sci. Ibaraki Univ. Ser. A No. 3, 39–46 (1971).

H. M. Stark [Acta Arith. **14** (1967/68), 35–50; MR **37** #2707] considered the L-function $L(s,\chi,Q)=\frac{1}{2}\sum_{x\neq 0}\chi(Q(x))Q(x)^{-s}$, where $Q(x)$ is a positive definite quadratic form in n variables $x=(x_1, \cdots, x_n)$ with integer coefficients, and χ is a character mod k. For the case $n=2$ Stark obtained a rapidly converging series for $L(s, \chi, Q)$ in the neighborhood of $s=1$ [ibid. **15** (1968/69), 307–317; MR **39** #4101]. This paper gives an extension for general n, subject to the restriction that either n is even or k is odd.

T. M. Apostol (Pasadena, Calif.)

Citations: MR 37# 2707 = E44-29; MR 39# 4101 = E44-33.

E44-45 (44# 6620)

Stark, H. M.

Values of L-functions at $s=1$. I. L-functions for quadratic forms.

Advances in Math. **7**, 301–343 (1971).

For a positive-definite binary quadratic form $q(x, y)=ax^2+bxy+cy^2$ with integral coefficients a, b, c and discriminant $d=b^2-4ac$ and for a primitive real character X (mod k) given by the Kronecker symbol $X(n)=(k/n)$, consider the L-series $L(s, X, q)=\frac{1}{2}\sum_{m,n} X(q(m, n))/q(m, n)^s$ where the summation is extended over all pairs m, n of integers different from 0, 0. The two main results of this paper are Theorem I: Under the assumptions that $q(x, y)$ is a primitive quadratic form, $d<-4$, and $(k, d)=1$, we have (1) $L(1, X, q)=(\pi/(12|k|\sqrt{|d|}))\log\varepsilon$, where ε is a unit in some algebraic number field. Theorem II: The unit ε of Theorem I is in $\mathrm{Re}\{Q(\sqrt{d}, \sqrt{k}, j((b+d)/2a))\}$, a field that is of degree $2h(d)$ over the field Q of rational numbers and independent of the primitive form q. Here $h(d)$ denotes the class number of all primitive positive-definite binary quadratic forms of discriminant d and $j(z)$ is the fundamental j-function of the theory of modular functions, normalized as usual so that its Fourier expansion starts with $e^{-2\pi iz}+744+\cdots$ Theorem 1 is proved by splitting the form q into several forms q_i of discriminant dk^2 (in the terminology of ideals that means splitting one class of ideals into several ring classes). This enables one to express $L(s, X, q)$ linearly in terms of the corresponding L-series $L(s, X_0, q_i)$ with the principal character X_0. Applying Kronecker's first limit formula to each of the $L(s, X_0, q_i)$ as $s\to 1+0$ yields for $L(1, X, q)$ a linear combination of logarithms of singular values of Dedekind's η-function. By the theory of complex multiplication it is shown that this linear combination equals the value on the right hand side of (1). The proof of Theorem II consists of a closer study of this value, again by using the theory of complex multiplication. It is remarked that Theorem I and a slightly weaker statement than Theorem II could be deduced almost immediately from results of K. Ramachandra [Ann. of Math. (2) **80** (1964), 104–148; MR **29** #2241]. *O. H. Körner* (Ulm)

Citations: MR 29# 2241 = G15-26.

E48 QUADRATIC FORMS AND AUTOMORPHIC FUNCTIONS

See also Sections E24, E28.

See reviews E02-4, E02-7, E02-12, E12-9, E12-27, E12-49, E12-55, E12-77, E12-90, E12-96, E12-120, E12-124, E12-138, E12-143, E16-49, E20-65, E24-50, E24-60, E24-83, E24-86, E24-90, E24-103, E24-104, E28-69, F35-29, P28-29.

E52 HERMITIAN FORMS

See reviews D08-18, E08-22, E08-27, E08-33, E08-34, E08-43, E12-7, E12-30, E12-41, E12-42, E12-44, E12-56, E12-81, E12-83, E12-87, E12-94, E12-95, E12-99, E12-102, E12-103, E12-115, E12-116, E12-141, E12-146, E12-148, E12-149, E16-38, E16-81, E16-87, E20-17, E28-18, E56-4, E60-8, F45-3, F55-2, H05-5, J32-3.

E56 CLASSICAL GROUPS

This section covers papers concerned with arithmetic properties and the algebraic structure of the classical groups, excluding SL(2). For the action of such a group on a space (fundamental domain, fixpoints, etc.), see **F45**; for linear representations, see **F70**. For the 2 × 2 unimodular groups, see **F05** and **F15**.

See also reviews B36-70, C20-11, C20-38, C20-44, C20-55, D16-28, D16-32, D76-27, E12-38, E12-40, E12-41, E12-44, E12-100, E12-102, E12-104, E12-116, E60-9, E60-11, E60-13, E60-14, E60-28, E60-32, E60-37, E60-38, E60-39, E68-32, F02-5, F02-17, F15-37, F40-55, F45-8, F45-18, F45-19, F45-20, F45-22, F45-26, F45-28, F45-31, F45-32, F50-24, F50-55, F55-18, F55-21, F70-3, F70-18, F99-3, G10-45, H25-4, R52-24, T35-24, T35-30, T35-61, Z05-6, Z10-14.

E56-1 **(5, 228b)**

Brenner, Joel. The linear homogeneous group. II. Ann. of Math. (2) **45**, 100–109 (1944).

The linear homogeneous group $\mathfrak{G}_{p,n,r}$ may be represented by $n\times n$ matrices M whose elements are residue classes mod p^r and whose determinants are not equal to 0 (mod p). In an earlier paper [Ann. of Math. (2) **39**, 472–493 (1938)] the author found the normal subgroups of $\mathfrak{G}_{p,n,r}$. In this paper the known results are recast in a different group-theoretic form and further results about normal and characteristic subgroups are obtained. The underlying vector space is an additive Abelian group $\mathfrak{A}$ of type $(p^r, p^r, \cdots, p^r)$ and the group $\mathfrak{G}_{p,n,r}$ is thought of as the group of autmomorphisms of $\mathfrak{A}$ and may be represented by the matrices M described above. If E is the unit matrix and $a\neq 0 (\mathrm{mod}\ p)$, then the matrices of the form $aE+p^sM$ $(0\leqq s\leqq r)$ form a normal subgroup $\mathfrak{N}_s{}^*$ and the matrices of the form $E+p^sM$ having unit determinant (mod p^r) form a normal subgroup $\mathfrak{N}_s$. In particular, $\mathfrak{N}_0{}^*=\mathfrak{G}$ and $\mathfrak{N}_r=E$. Every normal subgroup of $\mathfrak{G}$ lies between $\mathfrak{N}_s$ and $\mathfrak{N}_s{}^*$ for some s. The author states 22 theorems concerned with the relationships between the various normal subgroups and exhibits by diagrams the relationships of inclusion among the normal subgroups for the cases $n=2$, $p^r=27$; $n=5$, $p^r=9$; $n>2$, $p^r=8$; $n=p=2$, $r\geqq 3$. This latter is the most difficult case to describe. Among the typical theorems are the following [Theorems 13 and 14]. For $p>2$, $n>1$, the normal subgroups $\mathfrak{N}_s{}^*$ and $\mathfrak{N}_s$ are all characteristic.

J. S. Frame (East Lansing, Mich.).

Referred to in E56-19.

E56-2 **(10, 684d)**

Hua, L. K., and Reiner, I. On the generators of the symplectic modular group. Trans. Amer. Math. Soc. **65**, 415–426 (1949).

Every unimodular matrix of order $n\geqq 2$ with rational integral elements is here proved to be a product of the matrices U_1, U_2, U_3, and their inverses, where

$$xU_1=(x_2, x_3, \cdots, x_n, x_1),\quad xU_2=(x_1, x_1+x_2, x_3, \cdots, x_n),$$

and

$$xU_3=(-x_1, x_2, \cdots, x_n).$$

This is accomplished by using a known result and showing that U_4, where $xU_4=(x_2, x_1, x_3, \cdots, x_n)$, is a product of the U_1, U_2, U_3 and their inverses. With the aid of this theorem it is then proved that the symplectic modular group (factor group with respect to its centrum of the group of the skew-symmetric bilinear form $(x_1y_{n+1}-x_{n+1}y_1)+\cdots$ in $2n$ pairs of indeterminates) over the rational integers is generated by exactly four independent generators when $n>1$ and by two when $n=1$. The four matrices are $\mathfrak{T}_0$, $\mathfrak{R}_1$, $\mathfrak{R}_2$ and $\mathfrak{S}_0$, where

$$(x, y)\mathfrak{T}_0=(x_1, \cdots, x_n, x_1+y_1, y_2, \cdots, y_n),$$

$(x, y)\mathfrak{R}_i=(xU_i, yU_i'^{-1})$ for $i=1, 2$, and

$$(x, y)\mathfrak{S}_0=(-y_1, x_2, x_3, \cdots, x_n, x_1, y_2, y_3, \cdots, y_n).$$

It is remarked that the method can be extended to any Euclidean ring and some details are given for an analogous group over the Gaussian integers. Two lemmas employed are as follows. (1) Let m be a nonzero integer, and let T be an n-rowed symmetric matrix at least one of whose elements is not divisible by m. There exists a symmetric matrix S with integral elements such that

$$0<|\det (T-mS)|<|m|^n.$$

(2) Let A and B satisfy $AB'=BA'$ and let $\det A\neq 0$. There exists a symmetric matrix S such that either $B-AS=0$ or $0<|\det (B-AS)|<|\det A|$. *W. Givens.*

Referred to in E56-3, E56-11, E56-14, E56-23, E56-27, E56-31.

E56-3 **(13, 328f)**

Hua, L. K., and Reiner, I. Automorphisms of the unimodular group. Trans. Amer. Math. Soc. **71**, 331–348 (1951).

Let $\mathfrak{M}_n$ denote the unimodular group of order n (elements are the $n\times n$ matrices of determinant ± 1) and let $\mathfrak{A}_n$ be the group of its automorphisms. Let $\mathfrak{M}_n{}^+$ and $\mathfrak{M}_n{}^-$ stand for the subsets of $\mathfrak{M}_n$ with determinants $+1$ and -1, respectively; let $\mathfrak{R}_n$ be the commutator subgroup of $\mathfrak{M}_n$, $I^{(n)}$ the identity matrix of order n and X' the transpose of X. The authors determine the generators of $\mathfrak{A}_n$ explicitly, by proving: (1) For $n>2$, $\mathfrak{R}_n=\mathfrak{M}_n{}^+$; for $n=2$, $\mathfrak{R}_n$ is of index 2 in $\mathfrak{M}_n{}^+$. Corollary: Under any automorphism of $\mathfrak{M}_n$, $\mathfrak{M}_n{}^+\rightarrow\mathfrak{M}_n{}^+$. (2) The automorphism group of $\mathfrak{M}_2{}^+$ is generated by the set of "inner" automorphisms $X\rightarrow AXA^{-1}$ $(A\epsilon\mathfrak{M}_2)$ and $X\rightarrow\epsilon(X)\cdot X$ $(\epsilon(X)=\pm 1)$. (3) For $n>2$ the group of automorphisms of $\mathfrak{M}_n{}^+$ induced by automorphisms of $\mathfrak{M}_n$ is generated by the set of "inner" automorphisms $X\rightarrow AXA^{-1}$ $(A\epsilon\mathfrak{M}_n)$ and the automorphism $X\rightarrow X'^{-1}$. (4) The generators of $\mathfrak{A}_n$ are (i) the inner automorphisms $X\rightarrow AXA^{-1}$ $(A\epsilon\mathfrak{M}_n)$; (ii) $X\rightarrow X'^{-1}$; (iii) for even n only, $X\rightarrow(\det X)\cdot X$; (iv) for $n=2$ only, the automorphism $X\rightarrow\epsilon(X)\cdot X$, if $X\epsilon\mathfrak{M}_2{}^+$, or $X\rightarrow\epsilon(JX)\cdot X$, if $X\epsilon\mathfrak{M}_2{}^-$, with $J=\left(\begin{smallmatrix}1&0\\0&-1\end{smallmatrix}\right)$. The proof of (1) is comparatively simple and uses a previous result of the same authors [Trans. Amer. Math. Soc. **65**, 415–426 (1949); these Rev. **10**, 684]. (2) follows by establishing it first directly for the two generators of $\mathfrak{M}_2{}^+$. (4) follows easily from (2), (3) and the corollary. The real difficulty lies in the proof of (3). This consists of two parts. First, a direct proof for the case $n=3$ is given; then the proof is completed by induction on n, using two lemmas of some independent interest.

E. Grosswald (Princeton, N. J.).

Citations: MR 10, 684d = E56-2.

Referred to in E56-14, E56-20, E56-45.

E56-4 **(13, 531c; 13, 531d)**

Dieudonné, Jean. On the orthogonal groups over the rational field. Ann. of Math. (2) **54**, 85–93 (1951).

Dieudonné, Jean. Orthogonal and unitary groups over the rational field. Amer. J. Math. **73**, 940–948 (1951).

Let E be an n-dimensional space over the field Q of rational numbers and let f be a non-degenerate symmetric bilinear form defined on E with $g(x)=f(x,x)$ the corresponding quadratic form. The index of f is denoted by ν. [Cf. Dieudonné, Sur les groupes classiques, Actualités Sci. Ind., no. 1040, Hermann, Paris, 1948; these Rev. **9**, 494]. The corresponding orthogonal group is denoted by $O_n(Q,f)$ and its subgroup of rotations by $O_n^+(Q,f)$. The commutator subgroup of $O_n(Q,f)$ is denoted by $\Omega_n(Q,f)$ and the corresponding projective group by $P\Omega_n(Q,f)$. From a previous result of the author [loc. cit., p. 29], in case $n\geqq 5$ and $\nu\geqq 1$ the group $P\Omega_n(Q,f)$ is simple. By a theorem of A. Meyer [Vierteljschr. Naturforsch. Ges. Zürich **29**, 209–222 (1884)], if g is indefinite and $n\geqq 5$, then $\nu\geqq 1$. The main result in the first of the papers being reviewed here is that $P\Omega_n(Q,f)$ is also simple for any positive definite g and $n\geqq 6$. (The case $n=6$ is dealt with in the second paper.) The following automorphism theorems, which supplement results obtained by the author in the paper reviewed below*, are consequences of the above theorem: For $n\geqq 8$ and $\nu=0$, every automorphism of $O_n(Q,f)$ is of the form $u\to\chi(u)huh^{-1}$, where χ is a representation of $O_n(Q,f)$ in $\{-1,+1\}$ and h is a linear mapping of E onto E such that $g(h(x))=\lambda g(x)$; every automorphism of $PO_n(Q,f)$ is induced by an automorphism of $O_n(Q,f)$. For n even $\geqq 10$ and $\nu=0$, every automorphism on $O_n^+(Q,f)$ is induced by an automorphism of $O_n(Q,f)$; every automorphism of $PO_n^+(Q,f)$ is induced by an automorphism of $O_n^+(Q,f)$; every automorphism of $P\Omega_n(Q,f)$ is induced by an automorphism of $O_n(Q,f)$. It is also shown that the group $O_n(Q,f)/\Omega_n(Q,f)$ is infinite for any f and $n\geqq 2$. The automorphism result for the orthogonal groups has also been established by the reviewer, using very different methods, for arbitrary fields and dimensions (even infinite) $n\geqq 5$, if $\nu\neq 0$, and $n\geqq 3$, if $\nu=0$.

In the second paper, the author considers any quadratic extension K_1 of Q, an n-dimensional space E_1 over K_1 and a non-degenerate Hermitian form f on E_1. He then proves that the commutator subgroup of the projective unitary group $PU_n^+(K_1,f_1)$ is always simple for $n\geqq 5$. In view of results obtained in the author's monograph on the classical groups cited above [p. 70], the only case that required proof here was that in which K_1 is an imaginary quadratic field and f_1 is positive definite. *C. E. Rickart.*

*Not included here.

Referred to in E56-5.

E56-5 (13, 820d)

Dieudonné, Jean. On the orthogonal groups over an algebraic number field. Proc. London Math. Soc. (3) **2**, 245–256 (1952).

Let E be an n-dimensional vector space over a field K, f a non-degenerate symmetric bilinear form on E, and let $O_n(K,f)$ denote the corresponding orthogonal group over E and $\Omega_n(K,f)$ the commutator subgroup of $O_n(K,f)$. In the present paper, the author considers the group $O_n(K,f)$ over a finite algebraic number field K and gives generalizations of the results in his previous papers, where $K=Q$ was the rational field [cf. Ann. of Math. **54**, 85–93 (1951); Amer. J. Math. **73**, 940–948 (1951); these Rev. **13**, 531]. In particular, it is proved that, if K has $r_1\geqq 1$ real conjugates and the index ν of f is 0, then the projective group $P\Omega_n(K,f)$ is simple for $n\geqq 3\cdot 2^{r_1}$. Note that any form f over a purely imaginary field K has an index $\nu\geqq 1$ and that, whatever the field K is and $n\geqq 5$, $P\Omega_n(K,f)$ is always simple when f has an index $\nu\geqq 1$ [cf. the author's book, Sur les groupes classiques, Hermann, Paris, 1948, p. 29; these Rev. **9**, 494].

The proof of the above theorem is based upon the following proposition: If the space E contains a subspace F of dimension $\geqq 6$, such that $f(x,x)$ is totally positive for every $x\neq 0$ in F, then $P\Omega_n(K,f)$ is simple. It is also proved that $O_n(K,f)/\Omega_n(K,f)$ is an infinite group for any algebraic number field K, any form f and $n\geqq 2$, and that, if ρ is a totally positive number in K and f_1 a totally positive hermitean form in an n-dimensional space E_1 over $K_1=K(\sqrt{-\rho})$, then the commutator subgroup of the projective unitary group $PU_n(K_1,f_1)$ over E_1 is simple for $n\geqq 5$.

K. Iwasawa (Cambridge, Mass.).

Citations: MR 13, 531c = E56-4.
Referred to in E56-12.

E56-6 (16, 666e)

Reiner, Irving. Symplectic modular complements. Trans. Amer. Math. Soc. **77**, 498–505 (1954).

The problem solved in the paper is the following: Find a necessary and sufficient condition under which a matrix with rational integral elements can be completed to be a symplectic modular matrix, and if the condition is satisfied, find all possible complements. *L. K. Hua* (Peking).

E56-7 (16, 1087a)

Ono, Takashi. Arithmetic of orthogonal groups. J. Math. Soc. Japan **7**, 79–91 (1955).

Let K be a field of characteristic $\neq 2$ and let V be an n-dimensional vector space over K. The group of automorphisms of V over K is denoted by $\mathrm{GL}(V)$. Let f be a non-degenerate, symmetric bilinear form on V. For any $\sigma\in\mathrm{GL}(V)$ let $f^\sigma(x,y)=f(\sigma x,\sigma y)$, $x,y\in V$. Two forms f, g are said to be congruent, written $f\sim g$, if $g=f^\sigma$ for some $\sigma\in\mathrm{GL}(V)$ and are said to be similar in K, written $f\backsim g$, if $g\backsim af$ for some non-zero $a\in K$. The set of all $\sigma\in\mathrm{GL}(V)$ such that $f^\sigma=f$ is called the orthogonal group corresponding to f and is denoted by $O(V,f)$. If f, g are two forms on V, then $O(V,f)$ and $O(V,g)$ are conjugate in $\mathrm{GL}(V)$ if, and only if, $f\backsim g$ in K. Now let K be either a field of algebraic numbers or a field of algebraic functions of one variable over a finite field of characteristic $\neq 2$. Let K_p be a p-adic completion of K with respect to a place p in K. Denote by V_p the scalar extension of V with respect to K_p. If f is a form on V, then f may be considered as a form on V_p and $O(V,f)$ may be regarded as a subgroup of $O(V_p,f)$. The main results of the paper are contained in the following theorems which are examples of what the author calls the "Hasse principle." 1. $f\backsim g$ in K if and only if $f\backsim g$ in K_p for every place p in K. 2. $O(V,f)$ and $O(V,g)$ are conjugate in $\mathrm{GL}(V)$ if and only if $O(V_p,f)$ and $O(V_p,g)$ are conjugate in $\mathrm{GL}(V_p)$ for every place p in K. 3. If $O(V_p,f)$ and $O(V_{p,q})$ are isomorphic for every place p in K, then $O(V,f)$ and $O(V,g)$ are conjugate in $\mathrm{GL}(V)$. *C. E. Rickart.*

Referred to in E56-9.

E56-8 (17, 236a)

Dieudonné, Jean. La géométrie des groupes classiques. Ergebnisse der Mathematik und ihrer Grenzgebiete (N.F.), Heft 5. Springer-Verlag, Berlin-Göttingen-Heidelberg, 1955. vii+115 pp. DM 19.60.

This volume brings together most of the modern results concerning the so-called elementary theory of the classical groups. Here the term "classical group" is used as in the author's monograph, Sur les groupes classiques [Hermann, Paris, 1948; MR **9**, 494] and the "elementary theory" refers roughly to results which involve subgroup and homomorphisms as opposed to results concerned for example with topology, differential geometry, etc. The approach is, of course, algebraic but, as is characteristic of the author's work in this field, is strongly influenced by geometrical notions. Although many mathematicians have contributed to the subject, the bulk of the results presented here are due to the author, the main references being the monograph cited above and his paper, On the automorphisms of the classical group [Mem. Amer. Math. Soc. no. **2** (1951); MR **13**, 531]. The book contains, incidentally, an excellent bibliography. The material covered falls into four chapters: Ch. I on collineations and correlations, Ch. II on the structure of the classical groups, Ch. III on geometric characterizations of the classical groups and Ch. IV on automorphisms and isomorphisms of the classical groups. Ch. I contains most of the introductory material needed for reading the book. Although detailed proofs are usually not included, the author as a rule is able to indicate the main ideas and the principles involved, so the material is quite readable. The main complication, which seems to be characteristic of the subject, is the great multiplicity of cases which apparently need to be considered in many of the proofs.

The author has communicated the following list of corrections: On page 13 replace lines 13–15 from the bottom by the sentence: Un sous-espace V de E qui n'est pas isotrope est caractérisé par le propriété que le sous-espace orthogonal V^0 est supplémentaire de V; mais un tel sous-espace peut contenir des droites isotropes. On dit que V est anisotrope s'il ne contient pas de droites isotropes; un tel espace est évidemment non isotrope. On page 37 replace lines 5–8 from the bottom by the sentence: Si $A=(a_{ij})$ et si $a_{i1}\neq 0$, en retranchant des lignes de A d'indice $\neq i$ des multiples à gauche de la i-ème ligne, on obtient une matrice B dont la première colonne n'a que a_{i1} comme terme $\neq 0$; on pose alors

$$\det(A)=\psi((-1)^{i+1}a_{i1})\det(B_{i1}),$$

en désignant par B_{i1} la matrice obtenue en supprimant dans B la première colonne et la i-ème ligne. On page 107, line 16 from the bottom, read $m=n=1$ instead of $m=n=2$. On page 111 insert in the Bibliography the item: ABE, M.:[1] Projective transformation groups over non-commutative fields, Sijo-Sûgaku-Danwakai, 240 (1942). On page 114, line 13 from the top, read J. reine angew. Math, 196, instead of: Math. Zeitschrift.

C. E. Rickart (New Haven, Conn.).

Referred to in E04-17, E56-12.

E56-9 (17, 582b)

Ono, Takashi. Arithmetic of orthogonal groups. II. Nagoya Math. J. **9** (1955), 129–146.

This paper represents an extension of results, called theorems of Hasse type, obtained by the author in a previous paper [J. Math. Soc. Japan **7** (1955), 79–91; MR **16**, 1087]. Let K be a field with characteristic $\neq 2$, V a finite-dimensional vector space over K and f a (non-degenerate, symmetric, bilinear) form on V. Denote by $\Gamma(V,f)$ any one of the following three linear groups on V: the orthogonal group $O(V,f)$, the rotation group $O^+(V,f)$ or the commutator subgroup $\Omega(V,f)$ of $O(V,f)$. Now consider a second vector space W over K and g a form on W. Let Θ be a semi-linear injection (1-1 into) of W into V, with associated automorphism θ of K, such that $g=\lambda\Theta f$ where $\lambda\in K$ and $(\Theta f)(x,y)=f(\Theta x,\Theta y)^{\theta^{-1}}$. Let f_1 be the form f restricted to $\Theta(W)$ and for $\sigma\in O(\Theta(W),f_1)$, define $\Theta\sigma=\Theta^{-1}\sigma\Theta$. Then $\sigma\to\Theta\sigma$ is a group isomorphism, $\Theta(\Gamma(\Theta(W),f_1))=\Gamma(W,g)$ and the group $\Gamma(W,g)$ is said to be "semi-linearly embedded" in $\Gamma(V,f)$. If Θ is linear, the embedding is called linear instead of semi-linear. The form f is said to represent semi-similarly the form g. The author studies this relationship between forms in general and, when K is either a field of algebraic numbers or a field of algebraic functions of one variable over a finite field of characteristic $\neq 2$, obtains theorems of Hasse type. Let $K_\mathfrak{p}$ be the p-adic completion of K with respect to a place $\mathfrak{p}$ in K and denote by $V_\mathfrak{p}$ the scalar extension of V with respect to $K_\mathfrak{p}$. The following two results indicate the type of theorem obtained: $\Gamma(W,g)$ is linearly embedded in $\Gamma(V,f)$ if and only if $\Gamma(W_\mathfrak{p},g)$ is linearly embedded in $\Gamma(V_\mathfrak{p},f)$ for every place $\mathfrak{p}$ in K. (2) If $\Gamma(W_\mathfrak{p},g)$ is semi-linearly embedded in $\Gamma(V_\mathfrak{p},f)$ for every place $\mathfrak{p}$ in K, then $\Gamma(W,g)$ is linearly embedded in $\Gamma(V,f)$.

C. E. Rickart (New Haven, Conn.).

Citations: MR 16, 1087a = E56-7.

Referred to in E56-13.

E56-10 (17, 710c)

Reiner, Irving. Real linear characters of the symplectic modular group. Proc. Amer. Math. Soc. **6** (1955), 987–990.

Let Γ_{2n} denote the symplectic modular group of $2n\times 2n$ matrices with integer elements. Let K_{2n} denote the commutator subgroup of Γ_{2n}. It is proved by the author that $K_{2n}=\Gamma_{2n}$ for $n>2$; $\Gamma_4:K_4=2$ and $\Gamma_2:K_2=12$, and the factor groups $\Gamma_4:K_4$ and $\Gamma_2:K_2$ have been determined.

L. K. Hua (Peking).

Referred to in E56-33.

E56-11 (18, 191e)

Klingen, Helmut. Über die Erzeugenden gewisser Modulgruppen. Nachr. Akad. Wiss. Göttingen. Math.-Phys. Kl. IIa. **1956**, 173–185.

Let K be an algebraic field of degree s. Let $U_K{}^n$ be the group of n rowed matrices over K with determinant which is a unit in K. It was proved by A. Hurwitz [same Nachr. **1895**, 332–356] that $U_K{}^n$ has a finite set of generators. The author proves a similar result for the symplectic modular group over K. By symplectic modular group $M_n(K)$ we mean the group formed by $2n$ rowed matrices $\mathfrak{M}$ with integer elements of K and satisfying $\mathfrak{M}'\mathfrak{F}\mathfrak{M}=\mathfrak{F}$, where $\mathfrak{F}=\begin{pmatrix}0 & I^{(n)}\\ -I^{(n)} & 0\end{pmatrix}$. Similar result for rational field was proved previously by Hua and Reiner [Trans. Amer. Math. Soc. **65** (1949), 415–426; MR **10**, 684].

Let Σ be an imaginary quadratic field. He proves that the group formed by $2n$ rowed matrices $\mathfrak{M}$ with integer elements over Σ and satisfying $\overline{\mathfrak{M}}'\mathfrak{F}\mathfrak{M}=\mathfrak{F}$ has also a finite set of generators.

L. K. Hua (Peking).

Citations: MR 10, 684d = E56-2.

Referred to in E56-18, E56-23.

E56-12 (18, 192a)

Kneser, Martin. Orthogonale Gruppen über algebraischen Zahlkörpern. J. Reine Angew. Math. **196** (1956), 213–220.

Improving considerably on previous results of the reviewer [Proc. London Math. Soc. (3) **2** (1952), 245–256; MR **13**, 820], the author almost brings to a close the question of the structure of the orthogonal and unitary groups over algebraic number fields K. He namely proves the following three theorems (and indicates without proof how corresponding results may be obtained for unitary groups): (A) [Notations are those of the reviewer's book "La géométrie des groupes classiques" [Springer, Berlin, 1955; MR **17**, 236].] For $n\geqq 3$, the factor group $O_n{}^+(K,f)/O_n{}'(K,f)$ is isomorphic to $K^*(f)/K^{*2}$, where $K^*(f)$ is the group of elements $\neq 0$ of K which are positive for all places at infinity $\mathfrak{p}_k$, where f is a definite quadratic form. (B) For $n\neq 4$, $O_n{}'(K,f)=\Omega_n(K,f)$. (C) For $n\geqq 5$, the group $\Omega_n/(\Omega_n Z_n)$ is simple. The only questions left open concern the orthogonal groups for $n=3$ and $n=4$, and the unitary groups for $n\leqq 4$. The methods of proof are of the same "geometrical" kind as those of the reviewer, but with many original and skillful details, and above all they use three new ideas, which make the progress possible. The first one consists in applying the Hasse theorems on representations of quadratic forms by other quadratic forms (whilst the reviewer only used the theorems on representation of numbers by quadratic forms), and using systematically the spinor norm. The other two are: 1) an approximation theorem for orthogonal transformations, similar to the classical theorem enabling one to approximate at once finitely many elements, each in a different local field $K_{\mathfrak{p}_i}$, by a single element of K; 2) the remark that in a local field $K_{\mathfrak{p}}$, two quadratic forms, whose corresponding coefficients differ by a sufficiently small quantity, are equivalent. For the details of the very concise proofs, we must refer to the paper itself.

J. Dieudonné (Evanston, Ill.).

Citations: MR 13, 820d = E56-5; MR 17, 236a = E56-8.
Referred to in E56-26, E56-28.

E56-13 **(20# 72)**

Ramanathan, K. G. On orthogonal groups. Nachr. Akad. Wiss. Göttingen. Math.-Phys. Kl. IIa. **1957**, 113–121.

The author gives a criterion (described below) for two classical groups of like type and dimension to be conjugate within the full linear group. As an application, he obtains generalizations of some 'local-global' theorems of T. Ono on the conjugacy of orthogonal groups over finite algebraic number fields [Nagoya Math. J. **9** (1955), 129–146; MR **17**, 582].

The author states his criterion in terms of simple algebras. Let F be a field of characteristic $\neq 2$, A a central simple algebra of finite rank over F. Then A is a total matrix algebra of, say, m-rowed matrices over a division algebra D. Let A have an involution $x \to x^*$ and suppose that, if the involution leaves every element of F fixed, then D is either F or a quaternion algebra over F. Denote by $G = G_m(D)$ the group of the non-singular elements of A. If $\alpha \in G$, denote by $O(\alpha)$ the subgroup of all $v \in G$ such that $v^*\alpha v = \alpha$. Call elements α, β of G multiplicatively equivalent if $v^*\alpha v = t\beta$ for some $v \in G$ and $t \in F$. The author's criterion is that if $\alpha, \beta \in G$ and $\alpha^* = \varepsilon\alpha$, $\beta^* = \varepsilon\beta$ ($\varepsilon \neq 1$), then $O(\alpha)$, $O(\beta)$ are conjugate subgroups of G if, and only if, α, β are multiplicatively equivalent. The proof is quite short, the general case being deduced from the cases $m = 1, 2$. A similar criterion is also proved for a given $O(\alpha) \subseteq G_m(D)$ to be 'conjugate' (in a natural sense) to a subgroup of a given $O(\beta) \subseteq G_n(D)$ ($m < n$).

G. E. Wall (Sydney)

Citations: MR 17, 582b = E56-9.

E56-14 **(20# 907)**

Yien, Sze-chien. A system of relations of unimodular matrices and automorphisms of unimodular group. Sci. Record (N.S.) **1** (1957), no. 1, 13–17.

This paper reports and sketches proofs of satisfactorily complete relations among systems of generators of the $n \times n$ unimodular group $\mathfrak{M}_n$ (with integral entries) and of the proper subgroup $\mathfrak{M}_n^+$. Absolute completeness is not claimed. The relations obtained are enough to show that any automorphism of $\mathfrak{M}_n^+$ is composed of $X \to PXP^{-1}$ and $X \to X'^{-1}$, $P \in \mathfrak{M}_n$. For an automorphism of $\mathfrak{M}_n$ (n even) the additional (outer) automorphism $X \to (\det. X) \cdot X$ is needed. The computations cannot be conveniently abstracted. The related work is Hua and Reiner, Trans. Amer. Math. Soc. **71** (1951), 331–348; **65** (1949), 415–426 [MR 13, 328; **10**, 684]. A simplified unpublished discussion of the generators of $\mathfrak{M}_n$ is attributed to Wan.

J. L. Brenner (Palo Alto, Calif.)

Citations: MR 10, 684d = E56-2; MR 13, 328f = E56-3.

E56-15 **(20# 909)**

Wan, Cheh-hsian. On the automorphisms of linear groups over a non-commutative Euclidean ring of characteristic $\neq 2$. Sci. Record (N.S.) **1** (1957), no. 1, 5–8.

Let R be a non-commutative Euclidean ring of characteristic $\neq 2$; $GL_n[R]$ is the group of invertible $n \times n$ matrices with entries from R; $SL_n[R]$ is the group generated by the matrices $I + re_{ij}$ (transvections).

An outer automorphism of $SL_n[R]$ ($n \geq 3$) is represented either by $X \to X^\sigma$ or $X \to (S^\tau)^{-1}$, where σ is an automorphism, τ an antiautomorphism of R, or by transformation under $GL_n[R]$, or by the composition of the latter with one of the former.

The automorphisms of $GL_n[R]$ follow immediately; the Dieudonné determinant is involved in these.

Certain other principal ideal domains can be treated by the same method. However, when $n = 2$ there is an example attributed to Hua of an automorphism $X \to AXA^{-1}$, which is not of the above types. In this example $R = \{a + b\sqrt{-5},\ a, b \text{ integers}\}$; $A \notin GL_2[R]$;

$$A = \begin{pmatrix} 2, & 1+\sqrt{-5} \\ 1-\sqrt{-5}, & 2 \end{pmatrix}.$$

The methods of the paper extend to symplectic groups.

J. L. Brenner (Palo Alto, Calif.)

E56-16 **(20# 6464)**

Gutnik, L. A. On the extension of integral subgroups of some groups. Vestnik Leningrad. Univ. Ser. Mat. Meh. Astr. **12** (1957), no. 19, 47–78. (Russian. English summary)

Let Q_n ($n \geqq 2$) be the real unimodular group. If $n = 2p$ is even and M is a non-singular skew-symmetric n-rowed matrix, then the matrices α of Q_n satisfying $\alpha M \alpha' = M$ form a group denoted by $S(M)$; the subgroup consisting of matrices with integer coefficients is denoted by $S^*(M)$. In the special case where $M = \begin{pmatrix} 0 & I \\ -I & 0 \end{pmatrix}$, $S(M)$ is the symplectic group and $S^*(M)$ is the modular group. In general M may be taken to be of the form $D = \begin{pmatrix} 0 & D_1 \\ -D_1 & 0 \end{pmatrix}$, where D_1 is the diagonal matrix diag $\{d_1, d_2, \cdots, d_p\}$ with $d_1 = 1$, $d_i | d_{i+1}$ ($1 \leqq i \leqq p-1$). The author proves (i) Q_n^* is a maximal discrete subgroup of Q_n [this was proved by Hecke for $n = 2$, cf. Petersen, Abh. Math. Sem. Univ. Hamburg **12** (1938), 180–199], (ii) if $S^*(D)$ (where D is in the normal form given above) is a maximal discrete subgroup of $S(D)$, then the non-zero elements of D are square-free, (iii) if the nonzero elements of D are square-free, then there is a unique maximal discrete subgroup $S^{**}(D)$ of $S(D)$ containing $S^*(D)$, and $S^{**}(D)$ consists of all $\alpha \in S(D)$ with $\alpha S^*(D) \alpha = S^*(D)$. In case p is odd, $S^{**}(D) = S^*(D)$, while if p is even, $p = 2s$ say, the index $[S^{**}(D) : S^*(D)]$ equals 2^k, where k is the number of different prime divisors of d_{s+1}/d_s. In particular, for $D_1 = I$ this shows that the Siegel modular group is maximal in the symplectic group. The proofs (involving elementary transformations, partitioned matrices and the common measure of a set of commensurable numbers) are essentially computational, and enable the subgroup $S^{**}(D)$ to be constructed explicitly.

P. M. Cohn (Manchester)

Referred to in F55-29.

E56-17 **(21# 2012)**

Landin, Joseph; and Reiner, Irving. Automorphisms of the Gaussian unimodular group. Trans. Amer. Math. Soc. **87** (1958), 76–89.

Let G be the ring of Gaussian integers and G_n the group of $n \times n$ unimodular matrices over G. Denote the transpose of X by X' and the conjugate by $\bar{X}$. In the case $n = 2$, let

$$T_0 = \begin{pmatrix} 1 & 1 \\ 0 & 1 \end{pmatrix}, \quad S_0 = \begin{pmatrix} 0 & 1 \\ -1 & 0 \end{pmatrix}, \quad P_0 = \begin{pmatrix} i & 0 \\ 0 & 1 \end{pmatrix}.$$

Then the elements T_0, S_0, and P_0 generate the group G_2. The authors obtain a system of generators for the auto-

morphism group $\mathfrak{A}_n$ of the group G_n. Their main theorem asserts that $\mathfrak{A}_n$ is generated by: 1. $X \to AXA^{-1}$, $A \in \underline{G_n}$; 2. $X \to X'^{-1}$ (may be omitted when $n=2$); 3. $X \to \bar{X}$; 4. $X \to (\det X)^k X$, where $k=1$ if n is even and $k=2$ if n is odd; 5. For $n=2$ only, $(P_0, S_0, T_0) \to (P_0, -S_0, -T_0)$.
C. E. Rickart (New Haven, Conn.)

E56-18 (21# 4189)

Klingen, Helmut. Bemerkung über Kongruenzuntergruppen der Modulgruppe n-ten Grades. Arch. Math. **10** (1959), 113–122.

Denote by Γ the modular group of matrices $\begin{pmatrix} ab \\ cd \end{pmatrix}$ with rational integral entries and $ad-bc=1$. If ρ is an arbitrary integer, then $\Gamma_0(\rho)$, $\Gamma^0(\rho)$, $\Gamma_0{}^0(\rho)$ and $\Gamma(\rho)$ stand for the subgroups of Γ whose elements satisfy (mod ρ) the conditions $c\equiv 0$; $b\equiv 0$; $c\equiv b\equiv 0$; and $b\equiv c\equiv 0$, $a\equiv d\equiv 1$, respectively. The algebraic structure of Γ has been determined by F. Klein [*Gesammelte mathematische Abhandlungen*, v. 3, Springer, Berlin, 1923]. For ρ a rational prime, the corresponding problem for $\Gamma_0(\rho)$ (hence, also for $\Gamma^0(\rho)$, its conjugate) has been solved by H. Rademacher [Abh. Math. Sem. Univ. Hamburg **7** (1929), 134–148]; for $\Gamma(\rho)$ by H. Frasch [Math. Ann. **108** (1933), 229–252] and for $\Gamma_0{}^0(\rho)$ by the reviewer [Amer. J. Math. **72** (1950), 809–834; MR **12**, 591]. The situation can be generalized as follows. Let the field K be a finite algebraic extension over the rationals, denote by S_n the symplectic group of square matrices of order $2n$ and let ρ be an integral ideal in K. Then $\mathfrak{M}_n$, the modular group of degree n in K, consists of the matrices $M \in S_n$, $M=\begin{pmatrix} AB \\ CD \end{pmatrix}$, where A, B, C, D are square matrices of order n with elements in K. If E stands for the unit matrix, define $\mathfrak{M}_n(\rho)$, the principal congruence subgroup mod ρ, by the condition $M\equiv E$ (mod ρ), and, similarly, the congruence subgroup $\mathfrak{G}_n(\rho)$ by $C\equiv 0$ (mod ρ). These congruence subgroups have been considered by M. Koecher [Math. Z. **59** (1954), 399–416; MR **15**, 603], and the present author has determined a system of generators for $\mathfrak{M}_n$ [Nachr. Akad. Wiss. Göttingen, Math.-Phys. Kl. IIa **1956**, 173–185; MR **18**, 191]. In the present paper he solves the corresponding problem for $\mathfrak{M}_n(\rho)$ and $\mathfrak{G}_n(\rho)$; in addition, he also determines the indices of these subgroups in $\mathfrak{M}_n$ and obtains a necessary and sufficient condition for a $2n$ by m ($m\leqq n$) matrix to permit its completion to an element of either $\mathfrak{M}_n(\rho)$ or $\mathfrak{G}_n(\rho)$. The method used is mainly induction on n, starting from the (classical) case $n=1$. The (finite) sets of generators of $\mathfrak{M}_n(\rho)$ and $\mathfrak{G}_n(\rho)$ obtained are too complicated for quotation here; the index $[\mathfrak{M}_n:\mathfrak{M}_n(\rho)]=\mathfrak{N}(\rho)^{n(2n+1)}\prod_{\pi|\rho}\prod_{\nu=1}^{n}(1-1/\mathfrak{N}(\pi^{2\nu}))$ ($\mathfrak{N}(\rho)$=norm of ρ, π=prime ideal) and a similar formula holds for $[\mathfrak{M}_n:\mathfrak{G}_n(\rho)]$. *E. Grosswald* (Princeton, N.J.)

Citations: MR 12, 591c = F05-2; MR 15, 603e = F50-5; MR 18, 191e = E56-11.

E56-19 (22# 1622)

Brenner, J. L. The linear homogeneous group. III. Ann. of Math. (2) **71** (1960), 210–223.

[For part II see same Ann. (2) **45** (1944), 100–109; MR **5**, 228.]

Let $\mathrm{GL}_n(R)$ be the group of $n\times n$ invertible matrices with elements in a commutative ring R with unity, and set

$$\mathrm{GL}_n{}^+(R) = \{X \in \mathrm{GL}_n(R): \det X = 1\}.$$

The author obtains an assortment of theorems about these groups, mostly for the special cases where $R=Z$ (rational integers) or $R=Z_t$ $(=Z/(t))$, $t>0$.

Let $Q_{m,n}(R)$ be the normal subgroup of $\mathrm{GL}_n(R)$ generated by $I+me_{12}$, where e_{ij} denotes a matrix with 1 in position (i,j) and zeroes elsewhere, and let $Q^+_{m,n}$ be the analogously defined normal subgroup of $\mathrm{GL}_n{}^+$. Set

$$N^*_{m,n} = \{X \in \mathrm{GL}_n(R): X \equiv \text{scalar matrix } (\mathrm{mod}\ m)\},$$

$$N_{m,n} = \{X \in \mathrm{GL}_n{}^+(R): X \equiv I\ (\mathrm{mod}\ m)\}.$$

Typical results are as follows. (1) For $n>2$, every normal subgroup N of $\mathrm{GL}_n(Z)$ satisfies $Q_{m,n}\subset N\subset N^*_{m,n}$ for some m. (2) When $R=Z_t$, $Q_{m,n}=N_{m,n}$ for all n. (3) When $R=Z$, $Q^+_{m,2}=N_{m,2}$ for $m=1, 2, 3, 4, 5$. {The author conjectures that (3) holds for all m, or that at least for each m, $Q^+_{m,2}$ contains $N_{mk,2}$ for some k. Both conjectures have recently been disproved by the reviewer in a note "Normal subgroups of the unimodular group" to appear in Proc. Amer. Math. Soc. The corresponding conjectures for $n>2$ are still unsettled.} (4) For $R=Z[i]$, $Q^+_{1,n}=N_{1,n}=\mathrm{GL}_n{}^+$ when $n>2$, but $Q^+_{1,2}$ is a proper subgroup of $\mathrm{GL}_2{}^+$. (5) The groups $Q_{m,n}$ and $N^*_{m,n}$ are characteristic in $\mathrm{GL}_n(Z)$. (6) Let $\mathrm{SL}_2(R)$ be the subgroup of $\mathrm{GL}_2(R)$ generated by the transvections $\{I+\alpha e_{ij}: \alpha\in R, i\neq j\}$. If 6 is a unit in R, then $\mathrm{SL}_2(R)$ coincides with its commutator subgroup. *I. Reiner* (Urbana, Ill.)

Citations: MR 5, 228b = E56-1.

Referred to in E56-34, E60-14, F05-18, F05-22.

E56-20 (23# A943)

Wan, Cheh-hsian
Automorphisms of the modular group. (Chinese. English summary)
Advancement in Math. **3** (1957), 216–233.

Let $\mathfrak{M}_n$ be the group of all integral $n\times n$ matrices of determinant ± 1 and $\mathfrak{M}_n{}^+$ the subgroup of the matrices in $\mathfrak{M}_n$ of determinant $+1$. L. K. Hua and I. Reiner [Trans. Amer. Math. Soc. **71** (1951), 331–348; MR **13**, 328] determined the groups of automorphisms of $\mathfrak{M}_n$ for $n\geqq 2$ and of $\mathfrak{M}_2{}^+$ and $\mathfrak{M}_3{}^+$; they further mentioned that for odd n the automorphisms of $\mathfrak{M}_n{}^+$ are induced by automorphisms of $\mathfrak{M}_n$. For even $n\geqq 4$ the author shows now that all automorphisms of $\mathfrak{M}_n{}^+$ are either of the form $X\to AXA^{-1}$ or $X\to AX'^{-1}A^{-1}$, where in both cases $A\in\mathfrak{M}_n$.
K. Mahler (Manchester)

Citations: MR 13, 328f = E56-3.

E56-21 (23# A944)

Ying, Mei-chie
Automorphisms of the projective unimodular group. (Chinese. English summary)
Acta Math. Sinica **10** (1960), 55–65.

Let $\mathfrak{M}_n$ and $\mathfrak{M}_n{}^+$ be as in #A943; let further $\mathfrak{P}_n$ and $\mathfrak{P}_n{}^+$ denote the factor groups of $\mathfrak{M}_n$ and $\mathfrak{M}_n{}^+$ by their centrums, respectively. The author proves that if $n\geqq 6$ is even, the mappings $\bar{X}\to\bar{A}\bar{X}\bar{A}^{-1}$, $\bar{A}\in\mathfrak{P}_n$, and $\bar{X}\to\bar{A}\bar{X}'^{-1}\bar{A}^{-1}$, $\bar{A}\in\mathfrak{P}_n$, from $\mathfrak{P}_n{}^+$ onto itself are automorphisms of $\mathfrak{P}_n{}^+$, and that all automorphisms of $\mathfrak{P}_n{}^+$ are of one of these two forms. For the case of odd n this problem had already been solved by Hua and Reiner [cf. #A943 for reference].
K. Mahler (Manchester)

E56-22 (23# A1724)

Klingenberg, Wilhelm
Lineare Gruppen über lokalen Ringen.
Amer. J. Math. **83** (1961), 137–153.

Soient L un anneau local commutatif, I son idéal maximal, V un L-module libre de rang n; l'auteur se propose d'étudier les sous-groupes distingués du groupe linéaire $\mathrm{GL}(n, L)$ des automorphismes de V. Pour tout idéal $J\subset I$

de L, on a un homomorphisme naturel h_J: $\mathrm{GL}(n, L) \to \mathrm{GL}(n, L/J)$. L'image réciproque par h_J du centre de $\mathrm{GL}(n, L/J)$ est un sous-groupe distingué $\mathrm{GC}(n, L, J)$ de $\mathrm{GL}(n, L)$; il en est de même du sous-groupe $\mathrm{SC}(n, L, J)$ de $\mathrm{GC}(n, L, J)$ formé des automorphismes de déterminant 1 et dont l'image par h_J est l'identité; l'auteur montre que si $L/I \neq F_2$, $\mathrm{SC}(n, L, J) = [\mathrm{GL}(n, L), \mathrm{GC}(n, L, J)]$; $\mathrm{GC}(n, L, J)/\mathrm{SC}(n, L, J)$ est isomorphe au sous-groupe de $L^* \times (L/J)^*$ formé des couples (a, b) tels que l'image de a dans L/J soit b^n; si $\mathrm{SL}(n, L)$ désigne le sous-groupe de $\mathrm{GL}(n, L)$ formé des automorphismes de déterminant 1, et $\mathrm{HC}(n, L, J) = \mathrm{GC}(n, L, J) \cap \mathrm{SL}(n, L)$, $\mathrm{HC}(n, L, J)/\mathrm{SC}(n, L, J)$ est isomorphe au groupe des racines n-ièmes de l'unité dans L/J. Enfin, pour tout sous-groupe distingué N de $\mathrm{GL}(n, L)$, il existe un unique idéal J de L tel que $\mathrm{SC}(n, L, J) \subset N \subset \mathrm{GC}(n, L, J)$ (exception faite du cas où $n=2$ et où on a, soit $L/I = F_3$, soit L/I de caractéristique 2). Les démonstrations suivent la marche usuelle pour les théorèmes correspondants sur les groupes linéaires sur un corps, utilisant notamment les transvections: il faut prendre garde, pour définir ces dernières, de ne considérer que les transformations laissant invariants les points d'un "hyperplan" au sens de l'auteur, c'est-à-dire, un sous-L-module de V admettant un supplémentaire isomorphe à L. Cela complique naturellement quelque peu les raisonnements.

J. Dieudonné (Paris)

Referred to in E56-32, E60-9, E60-43.

E56-23 (24# A3137)

Klingen, Helmut

Charakterisierung der Siegelschen Modulgruppe durch ein endliches System definierender Relationen.

Math. Ann. **144** (1961), 64–82.

Let E be the $n \times n$ unit matrix and set $I = \begin{pmatrix} 0 & E \\ -E & 0 \end{pmatrix}$; then the (Siegel) modular group of degree n is defined by $\Gamma_n = \{M \mid M'IM = I\}$, where the M are square matrices of order $2n$ with rational integral entries and the dash stands for transposition. Hua and Reiner [Trans. Amer. Math. Soc. **65** (1949), 415–426; MR **10**, 684; see also Klingen, Nachr. Akad. Wiss. Göttingen Math.-Phys. Kl. IIa **1956**, 173–185; MR **18**, 191] determined a system of generators for Γ_n; but a characterization of Γ_n by its defining relations was known only for $n=2$ [Gottschling, Math. Ann. **138** (1959), 103–124; MR **21** #5748; ibid. **143** (1961), 111–149; MR **23** #A357]. In the present paper a complete, finite set of defining relations for Γ_n $(n \geq 2)$ is determined. The method consists in representing each $M \in \Gamma_n$ as a product of $n+3$ matrices, each belonging to a certain subgroup of Γ_n. The defining relations of these subgroups are partially known [see Magnus, Acta Math. **64** (1935), 353–367, and Gottschling's quoted papers], and are partially easily established. Jointly they form a complete set of defining relations for Γ_n, as is proven by induction on n.

E. Grosswald (Philadelphia, Pa.)

Citations: MR 10, 684d = E56-2; MR 18, 191e = E56-11; MR 21# 5748 = F45-9; MR 23# A357 = F45-11.

Referred to in E56-59.

E56-24 (25# 2009)

Wall, C. T. C.

On the orthogonal groups of unimodular quadratic forms.

Math. Ann. **147** (1962), 328–338.

The object of this paper is to study the extent to which the orthogonal group of a unimodular quadratic form is transitive on vectors. To this end the author considers a lattice L and a symmetric bilinear map φ of $L \times L$ to the integers, such that the matrix of values for a basis of L has determinant ± 1. Then $\varphi(x, x)$ is called the norm of a vector of L and the vector x is called primitive if xa^{-1} for an integer a is in L only if $a = \pm 1$. The type of L is 1 if every vector has even norm, otherwise 0. The orthogonal group $O(L)$ is the group of those automorphisms A of L which satisfy $\varphi(xA, yA) = \varphi(x, y)$ for all vectors x, y in L. T is the lattice with basis x and $\varphi(x, x) = 1$ and $\bar{T}$ the same lattice associated with $-\varphi$.

After showing the transitivity of certain groups with given generators, he goes on to show that for a certain lattice S of type 0, the group $O(S)$ is transitive on primitive vectors of given norm and type. He then shows that if L is the orthogonal direct sum of k copies of T and l copies of $\bar{T}$ and if k and l are at least 2, then the orthogonal group $O(L)$ is transitive on primitive vectors of given norm and type. The norm of a characteristic vector is congruent to $k-l$ (mod 8). He also shows Milnor's result that indefinite lattices with unimodular forms of the same rank, signature and type are equivalent provided the absolute value of the signature is not greater than $r-4$, where r is the rank of the form. Except for the proof of one lemma the methods are elementary.

Burton W. Jones (Boulder, Colo.)

Referred to in E56-25.

E56-25 (27# 5732)

Wall, C. T. C.

On the orthogonal groups of unimodular quadratic forms. II.

J. Reine Angew. Math. **213** (1963/64), 122–136.

Part I appeared in Math. Ann. **147** (1962), 328–338 [MR **25** #2009]. This paper analyzes the structure of orthogonal groups $\mathfrak{D}(X)$ of certain unimodular forms associated with lattices X over the integers and of determinant ± 1. A lattice X is called even if the square of each element is even; otherwise odd. The author denotes by I^+ and I^-, respectively, lattices of rank 1 with respective bases u and v, where $u^2 = 1$ and $v^2 = -1$; by U the lattice of rank 2 with basis x, y, where $x^2 = y^2 = 0$ and $xy = 1$; by V the even positive definite lattice of rank 8. An indefinite form is called near-definite if its index or the index of its negative is 1; otherwise, it is called strongly indefinite. He denotes by $\mathfrak{R}(X)$ the subgroup of $\mathfrak{D}(X)$ generated by reflections and $m(X)$ the index of $\mathfrak{R}(X)$ in $\mathfrak{D}(X)$.

He proves the following. Suppose X is an odd lattice with the properties: (1) It is a direct sum of copies of I^+ and I^-; (2) If it is near-definite, its rank does not exceed 10. Then $m(X) = 4$ if X is one of $I^+ + I^-$, $2I^+ + I^-$, $3I^+ + 2I^-$, $3I^+ + 3I^-$; $m(x) = 4$ or 8 if X is $2I^+ + 2I^-$; otherwise $m(X) = 2$.

If X is an even lattice which is strongly indefinite or one of V, U, $V+U$, then $m(X) = 1$ except for $m(2U) = 2$.

The author denotes by $\mathfrak{E}$ the subgroup of the orthogonal group of an isotropic form defined by the automorphs $E_\omega{}^1$ and $E_\omega{}^2$ of Eichler. He writes that "X has (R)" if for all $\xi \in X$ and nonzero integers a, we can find $\omega \in X$ with ω^2 even and either $\xi + a\omega = 0$ or $0 < |(\xi + a\omega)^2| < 2a^2$. He explores what this property means for certain lattices and proves that if X has (R) and either X is even with $m(X) = 1$ or X is odd with $m(X) = 2$, then $\mathfrak{E}(X)$ contains all elements of $\mathfrak{D}(X+U)$ of determinant and spinor norm 1.

Burton W. Jones (Boulder, Colo.)

Citations: MR 25# 2009 = E56-24.

E56-26 (25# 4004)

Pollak, Barth

On the commutator subgroup of the orthogonal group over the 2-adic numbers.

Proc. Amer. Math. Soc. **13** (1962), 736–738.

Let V be an n-dimensional vector space over a field k of

characteristic $\neq 2$, ϕ a non-singular quadratic form on V of Witt index ν. Let O denote the orthogonal group of ϕ, O' the subgroup formed by the rotations of spinor norm 1 and Ω the commutator group of O. It is known that $O'=\Omega$ if $n \leqq 3$ or $\nu > 0$. The author considers the relation between O' and Ω when k is a local field, i.e., field complete with respect to a discrete non-archimedean valuation and with a finite residue class field $\bar{k}$. Since $\nu > 0$ when $n > 4$, only the case $n=4$, $\nu=0$ has to be considered. Here it is proved that (a) $(O':\Omega)=2$ when the characteristic of $\bar{k} \neq 2$ and (b) $O'=\Omega$ when k is the field of 2-adic numbers. A related paper is that of M. Kneser [J. Reine Angew. Math. **196** (1956), 213–220; MR **18**, 192].
G. E. Wall (Sydney)

Citations: MR 18, 192a = E56-12.

E56-27 (25# 5113)

Trott, Stanton M.
A pair of generators for the unimodular group.
Canad. Math. Bull. **5** (1962), 245–252.

The unimodular group M_n is the multiplicative group of all $n \times n$ matrices with rational integral entries and determinant ± 1. The author shows that M_n can be generated by the matrices

$$\begin{bmatrix} 1 & 0 & 0 & \cdots & 0 \\ 1 & 1 & 0 & \cdots & 0 \\ 0 & 0 & 1 & \cdots & 0 \\ \cdot & \cdot & \cdot & \cdots & \cdot \\ 0 & 0 & 0 & \cdots & 1 \end{bmatrix}, \quad \begin{bmatrix} 0 & 1 & 0 & \cdots & 0 \\ 0 & 0 & 1 & \cdots & 0 \\ \cdot & \cdot & \cdot & \cdots & \cdot \\ 0 & 0 & 0 & \cdots & 1 \\ (-1)^n & 0 & 0 & \cdots & 0 \end{bmatrix}.$$

The basic identity needed in the proof is a variation of one given by L. K. Hua and the reviewer [Trans. Amer. Math. Soc. **65** (1949), 415–426; MR **10**, 684]. *I. Reiner* (Paris)

Citations: MR 10, 684d = E56-2.

E56-28 (26# 5071)

Pollak, Barth
4-dimensional orthogonal groups over algebraic number fields.
J. Reine Angew. Math. **211** (1962), 176–178.

Soit K un corps $\mathfrak{p}$-adique, V un espace vectoriel sur K de dimension 4, muni d'une forme quadratique non dégénérée d'indice 0. M. Kneser [même J. **196** (1956), 213–220; MR **18**, 192] a affirmé sans démonstration que dans ces conditions on a toujours $\Omega(V) \neq O'(V)$ dans le groupe orthogonal de V. L'auteur montre que ce n'est exact que lorsque la caractéristique p du corps résiduel de K est $\neq 2$, et on a en outre alors $(O'(V):\Omega(V))=2$. Il donne en outre des démonstrations pour deux autres résultats énoncés par Kneser [loc. cit.]: il s'agit cette fois d'un corps de nombres algébriques K, V étant toujours anisotrope et de dimension 4. Alors pour que $\sigma \in \Omega(V)$ il faut et il suffit que $\sigma \in \Omega(V_{\mathfrak{p}})$ pour toute place $\mathfrak{p}$ de K, et l'on a en outre $O'(V)/\Omega(V)$ isomorphe au produit des $O'(V_{\mathfrak{p}})/\Omega(V_{\mathfrak{p}})$.
J. Dieudonné (Paris)

Citations: MR 18, 192a = E56-12.

E56-29 (27# 211)

Pollak, Barth
Transitivity in the spinorial kernel and the commutator subgroup of the orthogonal group.
Amer. J. Math. **85** (1963), 36–46.

Soient V un espace vectoriel de dimension finie sur un corps commutatif K de caractéristique $\neq 2$, $O(V)$ le groupe orthogonal pour une forme quadratique non dégénérée f sur V, $O'(V)$ le noyau de la norme spinorielle. Etant donné un vecteur $a \neq 0$ de V, et désignant par Q_a la "quadrique" formée des vecteurs transformés de a par $O(V)$ (autrement dit, les $x \in V$ tels que $f(x)=f(a)$), l'auteur se propose de calculer le nombre des classes d'intransitivité du groupe $O'(V)$ opérant dans Q_a. Il obtient une expression générale de ce nombre faisant intervenir la norme spinorielle; puis il le calcule explicitement lorsque K est un corps fini, ou le corps des nombres réels, ou un corps local, ou un corps de nombres algébriques.
J. Dieudonné (Paris)

E56-30 (27# 2557)

Newman, M.
Normal congruence subgroups of the $t \times t$ modular group.
Bull. Amer. Math. Soc. **69** (1963), 719–720.

Let Γ denote the group of rational integral $t \times t$ matrices of determinant 1. If n is a positive integer, $\Gamma(n)$ denotes the principal congruence subgroup of Γ of level n, consisting of all elements of Γ congruent modulo n to a scalar matrix. A subgroup of Γ which contains a principal congruence subgroup $\Gamma(n)$ is called a congruence subgroup, and is said to be of level n if n is the least such integer. The author outlines a proof of the following theorem, which depends on a result of Dickson: If $t > 2$, every normal congruence subgroup of Γ of odd level is a principal congruence subgroup. *I. Reiner* (Urbana, Ill.)

E56-31 (27# 3709)

Stanek, Peter
Concerning a theorem of L. K. Hua and I. Reiner.
Proc. Amer. Math. Soc. **14** (1963), 751–753.

Improving a theorem of Hua and Reiner [Trans. Amer. Math. Soc. **65** (1949), 415–426; MR **10**, 684], the author proves that the symplectic modular group $Sp(2n)$ is generated for $n=2, 3$ by the three matrices R_{21}, T_1, D; for $n > 3$ by the two matrices $R_{21}T_n$ and D, where

$$R_{21} = \begin{pmatrix} I+E_{21} & O \\ O & I-E_{12} \end{pmatrix}, \quad T_i = \begin{pmatrix} I & E_{ii} \\ O & I \end{pmatrix}, \quad D = \begin{pmatrix} P & -E_{n1} \\ E_{n1} & P \end{pmatrix},$$

and
$$P = \sum_{i=1}^{n-1} E_{i,i+1}.$$

H. Schwerdtfeger (Montreal, Que.)

Citations: MR 10, 684d = E56-2.

E56-32 (27# 3710)

Klingenberg, Wilhelm
Symplectic groups over local rings.
Amer. J. Math. **85** (1963), 232–240.

Soient L un anneau local commutatif, I son idéal maximal, V un L-module libre de dimension $n=2m$, Φ une forme bilinéaire alternée non dégénérée sur $V \times V$. $Sp(V)$, dit groupe symplectique sur V, le groupe des automorphismes de Φ. L'auteur montre d'abord que toutes les formes alternées non dégénérés sur $V \times V$ sont équivalentes (ce qui justifie la notation $Sp(V)$). Supposant que le corps L/I n'est pas de caractéristique 2 et a au moins 5 éléments, il détermine ensuite les sous-groupes distingués de $Sp(V)$ en prouvant que ce sont les images réciproques de l'unité et du centre de $Sp(V/JV)$ pour tout idéal J de L. La méthode de démonstration est voisine de celle utilisée dans le cas où L est un corps: l'auteur introduit comme générateurs de $Sp(V)$ les transvections symplectiques et utilise ses propres résultats sur le groupe unimodulaire $SL(2, L)$ [même J. **83** (1961), 137–153; MR **23** #A1724] pour déterminer le sous-groupe distingué engendré par une transvection symplectique. Il prouve aussi que le centre de $Sp(V)$ est réduit aux deux éléments ± 1. *J. Dieudonné* (Paris)

Citations: MR 23# A1724 = E56-22.
Referred to in E56-35, E60-13.

E56-33 **(29# 5917)**

Maass, Hans

Die Multiplikatorsysteme zur Siegelschen Modulgruppe.
Nachr. Akad. Wiss. Göttingen Math.-Phys. Kl. II **1964**, 125–135.

Let Γ_n be the modular group of degree $n > 1$. A multiplier system on Γ_n of integral dimension (the only dimensions of interest when $n > 1$) is a character v of Γ_n of absolute value 1. The author proves that

$$(\Gamma_n : \Gamma_n') = 2, \quad n = 2,$$
$$= 1, \quad n > 2.$$

Since v is identically 1 on Γ_n', there is a nontrivial multiplier system only for Γ_2. The author characterizes Γ_2' by means of congruences and exhibits the unique character v on Γ_2 by its action on the generators.

In a note added in proof the author remarks that, unknown to him, the results of this paper had already been obtained by I. Reiner [Proc. Amer. Math. Soc. **6** (1955), 987–990; MR **17**, 710]. The reader should note that the author writes Γ_n for the modular group of degree n whereas Reiner writes Γ_{2n}. *J. Lehner* (College Park, Md.)

Citations: MR 17, 710c = E56-10.

E56-34 **(30# 2083)**

Mennicke, Jens L.

Finite factor groups of the unimodular group.
Ann. of Math. (2) **81** (1965), 31–37.

The group of the title is the group of $n \times n$ matrices $\mathrm{SL}(n, Z)$ with rational integral coefficients and determinant 1. For integral $m > 0$, let $N_{n,m}^*$ be the (normal) subgroup of all matrices congruent mod m to a scalar matrix; let $N_{n,m}$ be the (normal) subgroup of those congruent to I mod m; let $Q_{n,m}$ be the least normal subgroup containing $I + me_{21}$.

For every normal subgroup N, the reviewer established [same Ann. (2) **71** (1960), 210–223; MR **22** #1622] that $Q_{n,m} \subset N \subset N_{n,m}^*$ for some m, and conjectured $Q_{n,m} = N_{n,m}$. The author establishes this conjecture for $n \geqq 3$, so that in this case, Theorem 1 holds: Every normal subgroup of $\mathrm{SL}(n, Z)$ contains a full congruence subgroup. The conjecture is true for $n = 2$, $m < 6$, false for $n = 2$, $m > 5$. (The author asserts that he can establish similar results for the symplectic group $\mathrm{Sp}(2n, Z)$.) Thus for $n > 2$, any factor group of $\mathrm{SL}(n, Z)$ with respect to a noncentral normal subgroup is finite. For $n > 3$, the following stronger assertion is made: In $\mathrm{SL}(n, \mathfrak{o}(k))$, every subgroup of finite index contains a full congruence subgroup. Here k is an arbitrary field of algebraic numbers, and $\mathfrak{o}(k)$ is the set of algebraic integers in k. Results related to those of the present paper appear in H. Bass, M. Lazard and J.-P. Serre [Bull. Amer. Math. Soc. **70** (1964), 385–392; MR **28** #5117]. *J. L. Brenner* (Palo Alto, Calif.)

Citations: MR 22# 1622 = E56-19; MR 28# 5117 = E60-11.

Referred to in E56-37, E60-14, E60-33, E60-37, E60-39.

E56-35 **(31# 2335)**

Riehm, Carl R.

Symplectic groups over discrete valuation rings.
Bull. Amer. Math. Soc. **71** (1965), 388–392.

Let $\mathfrak{o}$ be a local ring, L a lattice over $\mathfrak{o}$ endowed with a nondegenerate alternating form $f: L \times L \to \mathfrak{o}$ and $S_p(L)$ the symplectic group of f. W. Klingenberg [Amer. J. Math. **85** (1963), 232–240; MR **27** #3710] showed that, with some exceptions, every normal subgroup of $S_p(L)$ is a congruence group provided that the discriminant of f is a unit. In this paper, the author drops this restriction on the discriminant and gives a generalization of Klingenberg's result, but this time $\mathfrak{o}$ is restricted to a discrete valuation ring (where 2 is a unit and the residue field $\neq F_3$). In this situation, ordinary congruence modulo one ideal is not enough to describe all normal subgroups, and the author proceeds as follows. Starting with the canonical splitting $L = L_1 \perp \cdots \perp L_t$ determined by the Frobenius basis of L, he attaches to a normal subgroup G a tableau $\{\mathfrak{g}_j^i\}$ $(1 \leqq i, j \leqq t)$, where each $\mathfrak{g}_j^i$ is an ideal of $\mathfrak{o}$. The matrix $\sigma = (s_{\mu\nu})$ with respect to the basis breaks up into t^2 blocks B_j^i. He writes $\sigma \equiv \rho = (r_{\mu\nu}) \bmod \{\mathfrak{g}_j^i\}$, if $s_{\mu\nu} \equiv r_{\mu\nu} \bmod \mathfrak{g}_j^i$ when $s_{\mu\nu}$ belongs to the block B_j^i. Then, he gets

$$G = \{\sigma \in S_p(L);\ \sigma \equiv \gamma \bmod \{\mathfrak{g}_j^i\} \quad \text{for some } \gamma \in \Gamma\},$$

where Γ is an abelian subgroup of $S_p(L)$ of type $(2, \cdots, 2)$. Detailed proofs are not given. *T. Ono* (Philadelphia, Pa.)

Citations: MR 27# 3710 = E56-32.

E56-36 **(31# 3513)**

O'Meara, O. T.

On the finite generation of linear groups over Hasse domains.
J. Reine Angew. Math. **217** (1965), 79–108.

Let F be a global field, i.e., a field which is either an algebraic number field or an algebraic function field in one variable over a finite constant field, let $\mathfrak{o}$ be a Hasse domain in F, i.e., a Dedekind domain which can be obtained as the intersection of almost all valuation rings of F, and let M be a lattice with respect to $\mathfrak{o}$ in an n-dimensional vector space V over F. There is a basis (x_i) of V in which $M = \sum \mathfrak{a}_i x_i$ for some fractional ideals $\mathfrak{a}_i$, $1 \leqq i \leqq n$. Put $\mathrm{GL}_n(M) = \{s \in \mathrm{GL}_n(V); sM = M\}$, $\mathrm{SL}_n(M) = \mathrm{GL}_n(M) \cap \mathrm{SL}_n(V)$. An element $t \in \mathrm{SL}_n(V)$ $(n \geqq 2)$ is called a transvection if $t(x) = t_{a,r}(x) = x + (rx)a$, with $a \in V$ and $r \in V'$ (the dual of V) such that $ra = 0$. A transvection t is called an elementary transvection with respect to the basis (x_i) if $t = t_{cx_i, x_j'}$ $(i \neq j)$, where $c \in F$ and (x_j') is the dual basis of (x_i). The author denotes by $\mathrm{TL}_n(M)$ [$\mathrm{EL}_n(M)$] the subgroup of $\mathrm{SL}_n(M)$ generated by all transvections [elementary transvections with respect to (x_i)] in $\mathrm{SL}_n(M)$. (If $n \geqq 3$, $\mathrm{EL}_n(M) = \mathrm{TL}_n(M)$ (13.4 Theorem).) Thus

$$(*) \qquad \mathrm{EL}_n(M) \subsetneqq \mathrm{TL}_n(M) \subsetneqq \mathrm{SL}_n(M) \subsetneqq \mathrm{GL}_n(M).$$

The main result is that all groups in (*) are finitely generated, with the following possible exception: the characteristic of F is positive, the Hasse domain $\mathfrak{o}$ is the intersection of all but exactly one of the valuation rings of F, and $n = 2$. In the exceptional case, the author shows that $\mathrm{EL}_2(M)$ is not finitely generated, by following partly the method of Nagao [J. Inst. Polytech. Osaka City Univ. Ser. A **10** (1959), 117–121; MR **22** #5684], and that his result generalizes Nagao's result that $\mathrm{SL}_2(k[x])$ is not finitely generated when k is finite.
T. Ono (Philadelphia, Pa.)

Referred to in E56-49, E56-50.

E56-37 **(32# 5739)**

O'Meara, O. T.

Finiteness of $\mathrm{SL}_n/\mathrm{TL}_n$ over Hasse domains for $n \geqq 4$.
Math. Z. **86** (1964), 273–284.

Let O be a "Hasse domain" in a global field F. (We follow the author's terminology [*Introduction to quadratic forms*, Springer, Berlin, 1963; MR **27** #2485].) If M is an O-lattice of rank n, write $\mathrm{SL}_n(M)$ for the O-automorphisms of determinant 1, and $\mathrm{TL}_n(M)$ for the subgroup generated by transvections. The author shows that $\mathrm{SL}_n(M)/\mathrm{TL}_n(M)$ is finite for $n \geqq 4$. This had been proved earlier by the reviewer for all "sufficiently large" n. The author makes heavy use of the number theory in F, in addition to the basic idea in the reviewer's proof. Recent work of Mennicke [Ann. of Math. (2) **81** (1965), 31–37; MR **30** #2083] has made it clear how to prove the result for $n \geqq 3$. In a forthcoming paper of the reviewer with J. Milnor it is even proved that $\mathrm{SL}_n = \mathrm{TL}_n$ for all $n \geqq 3$, at least for free lattices, and a similar result holds for the symplectic groups over O. *H. Bass* (New York)

Citations: MR 27# 2485 = E02-11; MR 30# 2083 = E56-34.

E56-38 (33# 4018)

Solomon, Louis
An action of the symplectic modular group.
Nagoya Math. J. **27** (1966), 65–69.

Es sei V ein freier **Z**-Modul vom Range $2n$, ferner $G = \mathbf{Sp}(2n, \mathbf{Z})$ die symplektische Modulgruppe und ϕ die nichtsinguläre alternierende Bilinearform auf V, die bei G invariant bleibt. Für eine Primzahl $p \in \mathbf{Z}$ sei X die Menge aller Endomorphismen ξ von V mit der Eigenschaft $\phi(\xi x, \xi y) = p\phi(x, y)$ für alle $x, y \in V$. Vermöge der Linksmultiplikation operiert die Gruppe G in natürlicher Weise auf X. In der vorliegenden Arbeit beweist der Verfasser, daß die Anzahl der G-Orbiten von X gleich dem Produkt $\prod_{i=1}^{n} (1 + p^i)$ ist. Für den Beweis wird die Reduktion mod p benutzt, indem nämlich V/pV als Vektorraum über $\mathbf{Z}/p\mathbf{Z}$ aufgefaßt wird. *E. Gottschling* (Berlin)

E56-39 (33# 4151)

Suprunenko, D. A.
Minkowski's homomorphism. (Russian)
In Memoriam: N. G. Čebotarev (Russian), pp. 89–92. Izdat. Kazan. Univ., Kazan, 1964.

Let R be an associative ring with unity, R_n the ring of all matrices of order n over R, and $\mathrm{GL}(n, R)$ the group of all invertible elements of R_n. If N is a two sided ideal of the ring R and f_N the canonical homomorphism of R to R/N, then f_N can be extended to a homomorphism of the ring R_n to the ring $\bar{R}_n = R_n/N$ if one assumes $g_N(a) = \bar{a} = \|\bar{a}_{ij}\|$, where $\|a_{ij}\| = a \in R_n$, $\bar{a}_{ij} = f_N(a_{ij})$. The map g_N defines a homomorphism, called Minkowski's homomorphism, of the group $\mathrm{GL}(n, R)$ into the group $\mathrm{GL}(n, \bar{R})$ if one sets $\psi_N(x) = g_N(x)$ for all x in $\mathrm{GL}(n, R)$. Let H be a subgroup of $\mathrm{GL}(n, R)$ and $\mathfrak{n}$ a set of two sided ideals of R. The problem arises as to which properties of the group $\psi_N(H)$, where N runs over the set $\mathfrak{n}$, carry over to the group H. Minkowski proved [*Gesammelte Abhandlungen*, Band I, Teubner, Leipzig, 1911] that if R is the ring of rational integers Z and N is a prime ideal in Z, q an odd rational prime, $N = (q)$, then the kernel of ψ_q is a torsion-free group.

In the present paper it is shown that (i) for any finite subgroup H of the group $\mathrm{GL}(n, Z)$ and any odd prime q, H is isomorphic to $\psi_q(H)$, and (ii) if a subgroup H of $\mathrm{GL}(n, Z)$ is nilpotent and q is any odd prime, then H is isomorphic to $\psi_q(H)$. The theorem of Minkowski is also extended to the case of Gaussian and Dedekind rings.

R. Finkelstein (Tucson, Ariz.)

E56-40 (33# 7427)

O'Meara, O. T.
The automorphisms of the linear groups over any integral domain.
J. Reine Angew. Math. **223** (1966), 56–100.

Let R be a commutative integral domain distinct from its quotient field F. Let V be an n-dimensional vector space over F, and M a free R-module on n generators contained in V. As usual, $\mathrm{GL}(V)$ denotes the group of F-automorphisms of V. Now define $\mathrm{GL}(M) = \{x \in \mathrm{GL}(V) : xM \subset M\}$, $\mathrm{SL}(M) = \{x \in \mathrm{GL}(M) : \det x = 1\}$, and let $\mathrm{TL}(M)$ be the subgroup of $\mathrm{SL}(M)$ generated by those elements of $\mathrm{SL}(M)$ which are transvections in $\mathrm{GL}(V)$. Let G be any one of the groups $\mathrm{GL}(M)$, $\mathrm{SL}(M)$, $\mathrm{TL}(M)$. Various authors have determined all automorphisms of G, for suitably restricted domains R. The present paper is the first to treat the general case, and the author succeeds in finding all automorphisms of G, provided only that $n \geqq 3$.

The main result obtained here is that G has only the "expected" kinds of automorphisms. Specifically, let $P(\rho)$ be an automorphism of the form $x \to \rho(x)x$ $(x \in G)$, where ρ is some homomorphism of G into its center. Let $\Phi(g)$ be an automorphism of the form $x \to g \times g^{-1}$ $(x \in G)$, where g is some semi-linear automorphism of V. Finally, let $V' = \mathrm{Hom}(V, F)$ be the dual of V. For $x \in \mathrm{GL}(V)$, let x^* denote its contragredient, so that (relative to suitable bases) the matrix of x^* is the transpose of the inverse of the matrix of x. Now let $\Psi(h)$ be an automorphism of G of the form $x \to h^{-1}x^*h$ $(x \in G)$, where h is some semi-linear isomorphism of V onto V'.

Main theorem: Every automorphism of G is uniquely expressible in exactly one of the forms $P(\rho) \circ \Phi(g)$ or $P(\rho) \circ \Psi(h)$.

For an arbitrary semi-linear automorphism g of V, the map $\Phi(g)$ is, of course, an automorphism of $\mathrm{GL}(V)$, but it may fail to give an automorphism of G. To complement the above result, the author proves that $\Phi(g)$ is an automorphism of G if and only if $g(M)$ has the form AM, where A is some fractional ideal of F. (In this context, a fractional ideal A is a nonzero R-submodule of F, for which there exists a nonzero $r \in R$ such that $rA \subset R$.) Likewise, if $h: V \to V'$ is a semi-linear isomorphism with associated field automorphism μ, then $\Psi(h)$ is an automorphism of G if and only if $\mu(R) = R$, and $h(M) = A\tilde{M}$ for some fractional ideal A of F. Here, $\tilde{M} = \{u \in V' : u(M) \subset R\}$.

In order to state the key lemma used in the proof of the main theorem, we introduce some notation. Let $u \in V'$, $a \in V$ be such that $u(a) = 0$, and denote by $T(a, u)$ the transvection $x \to x + u(x)a$ $(x \in V)$. Basic lemma: For each automorphism Γ of G, and each transvection $T(a, u)$, there exists a nonzero $k \in R$ such that all of the following are transvections lying in G: $\Gamma \cdot T(rka, u)$, $T(rka, u)$, $\Gamma^{-1} \cdot T(rka, u)$, $r \in R$. The proof of this lemma is extremely complicated, and depends on a detailed study of involutions in G, and their centralizers.

The paper concludes with a discussion of the case where R is a Dedekind ring, and where now M is any R-torsion-free finitely generated R-module. It is shown that all of the preceding theorems remain valid in this case.

I. Reiner (Urbana, Ill.)

E56-41 (34# 2712)

Riehm, Carl R.
Orthogonal groups over the integers of a local field. I.
Amer. J. Math. **88** (1966), 553–561.

From the author's introduction: "Let o be the ring of integers in a non-dyadic local field. Let L be a finitely generated free o-module endowed with a symmetric non-degenerate bilinear form; here non-degenerate means non-zero discriminant. The orthogonal group $O(L)$ is the group of isometries of L. The structure of $O(L)$ has been studied by Klingenberg [same J. **83** (1961), 281–320; MR **23** #A1726] when L is unimodular (discriminant a unit), and when the ring o is, more generally, a local ring. His results are very similar to those in the case of a field. The present paper gives initial results on the structure of $O(L)$ in the local integral case without the restriction of unimodularity on L, and is independent of Klingenberg's paper.

"Let $\Omega(L)$ be the commutator subgroup of $O(L)$. The main concern of this paper is to describe the groups contained between $O(L)$ and $\Omega(L)$ and the corresponding factor groups, to give generators for these groups and to determine their centers, and finally to give alternate characterizations of $\Omega(L)$.

"The results depend on a technique of 'reduction mod $\mathfrak{p}$' which makes it possible to 'lift' properties of the orthogonal group over finite fields. Partly for this reason, the theory is radically different from the field and local ring theory. For example, the 'spinor group' $O'(L)$ is always equal to the commutator subgroup."

W. Klingenberg (Bonn)

Referred to in E56-44, E56-46.

E56-42 **(34# 4264)**

Kubota, Tomio

Topological covering of SL(2) over a local field.

J. Math. Soc. Japan **19** (1967), 114–121.

Let F be the completion, by a finite or infinite place, of an algebraic number field of finite degree, and let $G = SL(2, F)$ be the corresponding topological group of all 2×2 matrices over F, with determinant unity. Suppose that F contains the mth roots of unity and is not the field of complex numbers. For non-zero elements α, β of F, let (α, β) denote the Hilbert symbol of degree m. If $\sigma \in G$ let $x(\sigma)$ be the first non-zero element in the second row of σ. Write $a(\sigma, \tau) = (x(\sigma), x(\tau))(-x(\sigma)^{-1}x(\tau), x(\sigma\tau))$ for $\sigma, \tau \in G$. The author shows that this satisfies the conditions for a factor set on G, namely $a(\sigma, \tau)a(\sigma\tau, \rho) = a(\sigma, \tau\rho)a(\tau, \rho)$, and determines a non-trivial m-fold topological covering of G.

H. K. Farahat (Sheffield)

Referred to in E68-31, R40-28.

E56-43 **(34# 4369)**

Pollak, Barth

On the structure of local orthogonal groups.

Amer. J. Math. **88** (1966), 763–780.

Le rapporteur a montré en 1951 que les groupes orthogonaux à 3 et 4 variables sur un corps local F, relativement à une forme quadratique anisotrope, admettent une suite infinie décroissante de sous-groupes distingués, ayant pour intersection l'élément neutre. L'auteur complète ce résultat lorsque F est un corps local non dyadique. Soit V un espace vectoriel anisotrope de dimension 3 sur F; soient $\mathfrak{p}$ l'idéal maximal de F, $O(V)$ le groupe orthogonal de V, $\Omega(V)$ son groupe des commutateurs; on pose $\Lambda_0(V) = \Omega(V)$ et pour tout entier $n > 0$, $\Lambda_{2n}(V)$ est le groupe des matrices de $O(V)$ (nécessairement à éléments entiers) dont la réduction mod $\mathfrak{p}^n$ est l'unité. On a $\Lambda_{2n}(V) \subset \Omega(V)$ et $\operatorname{Tr} \sigma \equiv 3 \pmod{\mathfrak{p}^{2n}}$ pour $\sigma \in \Lambda_{2n}(V)$. L'auteur introduit les sous-groupes $\Lambda_1(V)$ formé des $\sigma \in O(V)$ pour lesquels $\operatorname{Tr} \sigma \equiv 3 \pmod{\mathfrak{p}}$ et $\Lambda_{2n+1}(V)$ formé des $\sigma \in \Lambda_{2n}(V)$ pour lesquels $\operatorname{Tr} \sigma \equiv 3 \pmod{\mathfrak{p}^{2n+1}}$. Son résultat principal est que tout sous-groupe distingué Γ de $\Omega(V)$ est tel que $\Lambda_{2n+1}(V) \subset \Gamma \subset \Lambda_{2n}(V)$, sauf lorsque le corps résiduel de F a 3 éléments, auquel cas on a $\Lambda_{2n}(V) \subset \Gamma \subset \Lambda_{2n-1}(V)$. L'outil essentiel de sa démonstration est formé par les résultats qu'il a obtenus sur les éléments conjugués dans une algèbre de quaternions [Duke Math. J. **27** (1960), 261–271; MR **22** #4740; Illinois J. Math. **8** (1964), 5–13; MR **28** #2159].

J. Dieudonné (Nice)

Citations: MR 22# 4740 = R52-22.
Referred to in E08-41.

E56-44 **(34# 5941)**

James, D. G.

On the orthogonal groups of lattices over local fields.

J. Reine Angew. Math. **225** (1967), 116–119.

Let K be a local field, R its ring of integers, and F its residue class field. Assume char F odd or 2 a unit in K. Let L be a lattice over R with a quadratic form. Then $O(L, R)$ denotes the associated orthogonal group. Let $L = \bigoplus_i L_i$ be a Jordan splitting of L. Let $\Omega(L, R)$ and $Z(L, R)$ be the commutator subgroup and the center of $O(L, R)$. For each i, there is derived from the Jordan splitting of L an orthogonal group $O(U_i, F)$ in $n_i = \dim L_i$ variables. The author shows the following.

(A) $O(L, R)/\Omega(L, R) \cong \prod_i O(U_i, F)/\Omega(U_i, F)$.

(B) $\Omega(L, R)$ contains a normal subgroup $N(L, R)$ such that $\Omega(L, R)/N(L, R) \cong \prod_i \Omega(U_i, F)$. (C) $Z(L, R)$ $(= (\pm I))$ is contained in $\Omega(L, R)$ if and only if $n_i \equiv 0 \bmod 2$ and $\det L_i \in K^2$, for all i. The paper concludes with the observation that all the non-commutative factors for the composition series are removed in $\Omega(L, R)/N(L, R)$.

{Reviewer's remark: Except for the result C, there seems to be no overlap with the paper by C. R. Riehm [Amer. J. Math. **88** (1966), 553–561; MR **34** #2712], the latter paper being concerned mainly with the problem of how to generate O and Ω and related groups by reflections.}

W. Klingenberg (Bonn)

Citations: MR 34# 2712 = E56-41.

E56-45 **(34# 7670)**

Cohn, P. M.

On the structure of the GL_2 of a ring.

Inst. Hautes Études Sci. Publ. Math. No. 30 (1966), 5–53.

This well-written article encompasses a wealth of information about general linear groups over certain classes of rings. The author generalizes many earlier results about such groups, and gives a number of new and striking results.

We proceed to describe some of the main theorems. Assume throughout that the underlying ring R has a unity element and is associative, though not necessarily commutative. Denote by $U(R)$ its groups of units.

(1) Let $GL_n(R)$ be the group of $n \times n$ invertible matrices over R, and $D_n(R)$ its subgroup of diagonal matrices. Let $E_n(R)$ be the group generated by the set of transvections $\{I + ae_{ij} : a \in R, 1 \leq i, j \leq n, i \neq j\}$, where $\{e_{ij}\}$ is a set of matrix units. Define $GE_n(R) = D_n(R) \cdot E_n(R)$, the subgroup of $GL_n(R)$ generated by elementary matrices. Of course, $E_n(R) \Delta GE_n(R)$. The author calls R a generalized Euclidean ring (GE-ring) if $GL_n(R) = GE_n(R)$ for all n. As is well-known, classical Euclidean rings are of this type. In particular, GE_2-rings are those for which $GL_2(R) = GE_2(R)$. For an arbitrary ring R, set $E(a) = \begin{pmatrix} a & 1 \\ -1 & 0 \end{pmatrix}$, $a \in R$. These matrices, together with those in $D_2(R)$, generate the group $GE_2(R)$. The author gives a set of relations connecting these generators, namely, (i) $E(x)E(0)E(y) = -E(x+y)$, $E(\alpha)E(\alpha^{-1})E(\alpha) = -\operatorname{diag}(\alpha, \alpha^{-1})$, $E(x) \cdot \operatorname{diag}(\alpha, \beta) = \operatorname{diag}(\beta, \alpha) \cdot E(\beta^{-1}x\alpha)$, where $x, y \in R$, and $\alpha, \beta \in U(R)$. Other relations may possibly hold as well. Call the ring R universal for GE_2 if the above relations, together with those relations valid in $D_2(R)$, are a full set of defining relations for $GE_2(R)$. For arbitrary R, relations (1) already imply that $E_2(R) \Delta GE_2(R)$, and that every element of $GE_2(R)$ is expressible in a certain standard form (ii) $\operatorname{diag}(\alpha, \beta) \cdot E(a_1) \cdots E(a_r)$, where $\alpha, \beta \in U(R)$, $a_1, \cdots, a_r \in R$, and some minor restrictions are satisfied. If each element of $GE_2(R)$ has a unique standard form, it follows easily that R is universal for GE_2. The converse is false, as is shown by example. Indeed, there is even an intermediate class of rings, namely those for which no non-trivial standard form (ii) can be equal to the identity matrix; the author calls such rings quasi-free for GE_2.

(2) The property of being a GE-ring is preserved under direct sums, but not under direct products. In order to discuss free products, some auxiliary definitions are required. (a) Let K be a skewfield. Call R a K-ring if there is a canonical injection of K into R. (b) A semifir (semi-free-ideal-ring) is an integral domain R, not necessarily commutative, such that every finitely generated right ideal of R is free, and such that any two bases of a free R-module have the same cardinality. These rings were previously studied by the author [J. Algebra **1** (1964), 47–69; MR **28** #5095], where they were called "local firs". (c) A strong GE-ring is a semifir which is a GE-ring. It is shown that R is a strong GE-ring if and only if for each $n \geqq 1$, and each relation $\sum_{i=1}^{n} a_i b_i = 0$, $a_i, b_i \in R$, with $b_1, \cdots, b_n$ not all zero, there exists a matrix $C \in E_n(R)$ such that $(a_1, \cdots, a_n)C$ has at least one zero entry. Rings satisfying this condition had been called "generalized Euclidean" by H. Bass [ibid. **1** (1964), 367–373; MR **31** #2290]. By slightly modifying the arguments in his above-mentioned work, the author proves the following theorem: Let K be a skewfield, $\{R_\lambda\}$ a family of K-rings each of which is a strong GE-ring; then the free product of the $\{R_\lambda\}$ over K is again a strong GE-ring. A special case of this theorem is as follows: The group algebra (over a field) of a free group is a GE-semifir. The same holds for the semigroup algebra of a free semigroup. W. Klingenberg [Arch. Math. **13** (1962), 73–81; MR **26** #1367] proved that a local ring R (not necessarily commutative) is a GE-ring. The author shows that R is universal for GE_2. Further, if R is local but not a skewfield, then there is no unique standard form (2) for the elements of $GE_2(R)$; indeed, in this case R is not even quasi-free for GE_2.

(3) Call R a discretely normed ring if there is a real-valued norm $|\ |$ on R satisfying $|0|=0$, $|x| \geqq 1$ for $x \in R$, $x \neq 0$; $|xy| = |x|\,|y|$, $|x+y| \leqq |x| + |y|$, and in addition there is no $x \in R$ for which $1 < |x| < 2$. Basic lemma: Let $r > 1$, and let $a_1, \cdots, a_r$ be nonzero elements of the discretely normed ring R such that none of $a_2, \cdots, a_r$ is a unit; then the norm of the (1, 1)-entry of $E(a_1)E(a_2) \cdots E(a_r)$ cannot be less than the norm of its (1, 2)-entry. (Conditions for equality are given, under further hypotheses.) This lemma implies that every discretely normed ring is quasi-free, and hence universal for GE_2. For such a ring R, every involution ($\neq \pm I$) in $GE_2(R)$ is conjugate therein to a matrix $\pm \begin{pmatrix} 1 & 0 \\ h & -1 \end{pmatrix}$, with suitably restricted $h \in R$. This implies that a 2-torsion-free discretely normed Dedekind ring which is a GE_2-ring must in fact be a principal ideal domain. (a) The ring R_d of all algebraic integers in $Q(\sqrt{-d})$ is discretely normed. Here, d is a square-free positive integer, $d \neq 1, 2, 3, 7, 11$. (For these exceptional values, R_d is already known to be Euclidean with respect to the usual norm.) (b) Rings with degree functions, such as $K[X_1, X_2, \cdots, X_n]$ (K = field), are discretely normed.

(4) The reviewer and others have asked whether every principal ideal domain must be a GE-ring. The author gives a negative answer. In terms of the notation in (3a) above, it turns out that R_{19} (which is known to be a principal ideal domain) is not a GE_2-ring. Analogous results are obtained for function fields. For rings with a degree function, it is shown that each element of $GE_2(R)$ has a unique standard form. Not every such ring is a GE_2-ring, however. Thus, $K[X_1, \cdots, X_n]$ is a GE-ring if and only if $n = 1$. Instead of taking R to be discretely normed, much the same purpose is achieved by assuming R to be a totally ordered ring satisfying some additional restrictions. Such rings are universal for GE_2. It is shown that $Z[X_1, \cdots, X_n]$ ($n > 0$) cannot be a GE_2-ring, although it is universal for GE_2.

(5) For any group G, let G' denote its commutator subgroup, and set $G^a = G/G'$. The author proves that $GE_2(R)/E_2(R) \cong U(R)^a$ if R is universal for GE_2. Further, $E_2(R) = GE_2(R)'$ whenever there exist $\alpha, \beta \in U(R)$ with $\alpha + \beta = 1$. Specific formulas are obtained for $E_2(R)^a$, under various hypotheses on R. For example, if R is a discretely normed ring whose only units are ± 1, then $E_2(R)^a \cong R/M$, where M is the additive subgroup generated by 12. To quote another result of this nature: Let R be any ring which is quasi-free for GE_2, and let N be the ideal of R generated by $\{\alpha - 1 : \alpha \in U(R)\}$; then $E_2(R)/GE_2(R)' \cong R/N$. When $R = Z$, this yields the isomorphism $SL_2(Z)/GL_2(Z)' \cong Z/(2)$, a result due to L. K. Hua and the reviewer [Trans. Amer. Math. Soc. **71** (1951), 331–348; MR **13**, 328].

(6) The author proves that if $U(R)$ is finitely generated (f.g.), and if R is a f.g. $U(R)$-bimodule, then $GE_2(R)$ is also f.g. Conversely, if R is quasi-free for GE_2, and $GE_2(R)$ is f.g., then $U(R)^a$ is f.g., and R is f.g. as $U(R)$-bimodule. This generalizes the result due to H. Nagao [J. Inst. Polytech. Osaka City Univ. Ser. A **10** (1959), 117–121; MR **22** #5684] that if K is a field, and X an indeterminate, then $GL_2(K[X])$ is not f.g.

(7) For $m \in Z$, $m \geqq 2$, it is known that the matrices $\begin{pmatrix} 1 & m \\ 0 & 1 \end{pmatrix}$, $\begin{pmatrix} 1 & 0 \\ m & 1 \end{pmatrix}$ generate a free group. Generalizing this, the author proves: Let R be quasi-free for GE_2, and let A, B be additive subgroups of R which contain no units; then the group generated by

$$\left\{\begin{pmatrix} 1 & a \\ 0 & 1 \end{pmatrix} : a \in A\right\} \cup \left\{\begin{pmatrix} 1 & 0 \\ b & 1 \end{pmatrix} : b \in B\right\}$$

is the free product of the group generated by the first set with that generated by the second set.

(8) Consider next the question of homomorphisms between linear groups. By a U-homomorphism φ of the ring R into the ring S is meant an additive homomorphism $x \to x'$ such that $1' = 1$, and $(\alpha a \beta)' = \alpha' a' \beta'$, $a \in R$, $\alpha, \beta \in U(R)$. For a U-antihomomorphism ψ, replace the last condition by $(\alpha a \beta)' = \beta' a' \alpha'$. The form of the set of relations (i) then implies: If R is universal for GE_2, then any U-homomorphism $\varphi: R \to S$ induces a homomorphism $\varphi^*: GE_2(R) \to GE_2(S)$, by letting $E(x) \to E(x')$, $\mathrm{diag}(\alpha, \beta) \to \mathrm{diag}(\alpha', \beta')$. Likewise, a U-antihomomorphism $\psi: R \to S$ induces a homomorphism $\psi^*: GE_2(R) \to GE_2(S)$ by letting $E(x) \to E(x')^{-1}$, $\mathrm{diag}(\alpha, \beta) \to \mathrm{diag}(\alpha', \beta')^{-1}$. These results generalize those of the reviewer for the case where $R = K[X]$, K a field [see Proc. Amer. Math. Soc. **8** (1957), 1111–1113; MR **20** #2358; Ann. of Math. (2) **66** (1957), 461–466; MR **20** #2380].

(9) The author takes up finally the problem of determining all isomorphisms $GL_n(R) \cong GL_n(S)$, and as usual, the case $n = 2$ presents the greatest difficulty. The results obtained here generalize theorems of Schreier–van der Waerden, Dieudonné, Hua, and the reviewer.

A central homothety is an endomorphism of $GL_n(R)$ given by $A \to \sigma(A)A$, where σ is a homomorphism of $GL_n(R)$ into the group of central units of R. The major result for $n = 2$ is as follows: Let R be a K-ring, S a K'-ring, both with a degree function, where K and K' are skewfields of the same characteristic, and where S is a GE_2-ring; then every isomorphism $GL_2(R) \cong GL_2(S)$ is gotten by taking either φ^* or ψ^* ($\varphi = U$-isomorphism, $\psi = U$-anti-isomorphism), followed by a central homothety and an inner automorphism. The author uses this to handle the case $n > 2$, and proves the following. Let R be a K-ring, S a K'-ring, where K and K' are skewfields of characteristic $\neq 2$. Assume that both R and S have a degree function, and that every f.g. projective S-module is free. Then every isomorphism $\mathrm{GL}_n(R) \cong \mathrm{GL}_n(S)$ for $n \geqq 3$ is obtained by taking either φ^* or ψ^* (where now $\varphi: R \to S$ is a ring isomorphism, and $\psi: R \to S$ a ring anti-isomorphism), followed by a central homothety and an inner automorphism. *I. Reiner* (Urbana, Ill.)

Citations: MR 13, 328f = E56-3.
Referred to in E56-51.

E56-46 (35# 6765)

Riehm, Carl R.
Orthogonal groups over the integers of a local field. II.
Amer. J. Math. **89** (1967), 549–577.

Soient $\mathfrak{o}$ un anneau commutatif avec unité, $\mathfrak{g} = (\mathfrak{g}_{ij})$ une matrice carrée d'ordre n dont les éléments sont des idéaux de $\mathfrak{o}$, G un sous-groupe de $\mathrm{GL}(n, \mathfrak{o})$; pour deux matrices $s = (s_{ij})$, $t = (t_{ij})$ de G, on écrit $s \equiv t \bmod \mathfrak{g}$ si $s_{ij} \equiv t_{ij} \bmod \mathfrak{g}_{ij}$ pour tous les couples d'indices. Soit alors Γ un sous-groupe de G, et soit $G(\Gamma, \mathfrak{g})$ l'ensemble des $s \in G$ tels qu'il existe $\gamma \in \Gamma$ pour lequel $s \equiv \gamma \bmod \mathfrak{g}$. Moyennant des conditions assez simples sur les $\mathfrak{g}_{ij}$, on montre que $G(\Gamma, \mathfrak{g})$ est un sous-groupe distingué de G. Cette notion généralise la notion classique de sous-groupe de congruence. Supposons alors que $\mathfrak{o}$ soit un anneau de valuation discrète complet, dont le corps résiduel est fini, de caractéristique $\neq 2$ et a au moins 5 éléments. L'auteur se propose d'étudier les sous-groupe distingués du groupe des commutateurs Ω du groupe orthogonal sur $\mathfrak{o}$ correspondant à une forme quadratique non-dégénérée Q sur $\mathfrak{o}^n$; cette étude a déjà été faite par W. Klingenberg [même J. **83** (1961), 281–320; MR **23** #A1726] lorsque le discriminant de Q est inversible, et il a montré que pour $n \geqq 3$, les sous-groupes cherchés sont de la forme $G(\Gamma, \mathfrak{g})$, où les $\mathfrak{g}_{ij}$ sont nuls pour $i \neq j$, égaux à un même idéal $\mathfrak{a}$ pour $i = j$, et Γ est réduit à la matrice unité I ou à $\pm I$. L'auteur montre que ce résultat se généralise lorsqu'on ne suppose plus le discriminant de Q inversible, en remplaçant $\mathfrak{g}$ par une matrice $(\mathfrak{g}_{ij})$ convenable et Γ par un groupe de matrices diagonales avec ± 1 pour éléments. Il lui faut toutefois faire une hypothèse supplémentaire relative aux "décompositions de Jordan" de $\mathfrak{o}^n$ pour la forme Q: on dit qu'un sous-module libre L de $\mathfrak{o}^n$ est modulaire s'il a une base orthogonale (a_i) telle que si $\mathfrak{b}_i$ est l'idéal engendré par les $B(a_i, x)$ pour $x \in L$ (B forme bilinéaire associée à Q), tous les $\mathfrak{b}_i$ sont égaux. On montre que $\mathfrak{o}^n$ a une décomposition en somme de sous-modules modulaires L_i deux à deux orthogonaux, tels que si $\mathfrak{s}_i$ est l'idéal engendré par les $B(x, y)$ pour x, y dans L_i, $\mathfrak{s}_i$ soit contenu dans $\mathfrak{s}_{i+1}$ et distinct de ce dernier; dans cette "décomposition de Jordan" les dimensions n_i des L_i et les idéaux $\mathfrak{s}_i$ sont bien déterminés. Il faut alors supposer que $n_i \geqq 3$ pour tout i et que si $n_i = 4$, L_i n'est pas somme de deux plans hyperboliques orthogonaux (ces restrictions sont nécessaires en vertu du comportement exceptionnel des groupes orthogonaux de dimension 2 ou 4 sur un corps). Les démonstrations sont très techniques; l'outil principal est fourni par les "doubles transvections" de Siegel-Eichler (que l'auteur appelle "quasi-transvections").

{Part I appeared ibid. **88** (1966), 553–561; MR **34** #2712].} *J. Dieudonné* (Nice)

Citations: MR 34# 2712 = E56-41.

E56-47 (36# 6352)

Kodama, Tetsuo
On the law of product in the Hecke ring for the symplectic group.
Mem. Fac. Sci. Kyushu Univ. Ser. A **21** (1967), 108–121.

The Hecke ring, in the sense considered here, is constructed from the double cosets of the modular symplectic group with respect to subgroups of level m. The author is concerned with the multiplication in this ring. {The paper is badly written and consists of masses of formidable computations whose utility is unlikely. No indication of applications is given.} *W. E. Jenner* (Chapel Hill, N.C.)

E56-48 (37# 1485)

Mennicke, J.
On Ihara's modular group.
Invent. Math. **4** (1967), 202–228.

Consider the ring $Z^{(p)} = \{x/p^t | t, x \in Z\}$ and the group $G = \mathrm{SL}(2, Z^{(p)})$, where Z is the ring of rational integers and p is a fixed prime number. The author proves the following theorems. Theorem 1: For each $m \not\equiv 0 \pmod p$, let $N_m = \{X \in G | X \equiv 1 \pmod m\}$ be the full congruence subgroup of G modulo m, and let Q_m be the normal closure of the element $\begin{pmatrix} 1 & 0 \\ m & 1 \end{pmatrix}$. Then $N_m = Q_m$. As an immediate consequence of this, he obtains the corollary. The group G has the congruence subgroup property; i.e., every subgroup of G with finite index contains N_m for some m. He also proves Theorem 2: The normal subgroups of G of infinite indices are contained in the center $\{\pm 1\}$ of G.

As is well-known today, the congruence subgroup property had been established for various groups, e.g., for $\mathrm{SL}(n, Z)$ ($n \geqq 3$), $\mathrm{Sp}(2n, Z)$ ($n \geqq 2$), by the author; H. Bass, M. Lazard and J. P. Serre; H. Matsumoto; H. Bass, J. Milnor and J. P. Serre, etc. But as for SL(2) over arithmetic rings R, this is not true if $R = Z$ (well-known) or if R is the ring of integers of totally imaginary number fields (T. Kubota); and the above corollary is the first affirmative result for SL(2). (This was a conjecture made by the reviewer in connection with some problems on algebraic curves modulo p.) From the author's note: "After a preliminary version of this paper (which contained a proof of $N_m = Q_m$ for $p = 2$) had been circulated, Serre found that one can obtain, by combining methods of C. Moore and R. Steinberg, and the author, strikingly general results on the congruence subgroup property for SL(2) over arithmetic rings R." J. P. Serre's result will appear in a forthcoming paper ("Le problème des groupes de congruence pour SL_2"). It covers the case $R = Z^{(p)}$ and hence the author's corollary; however, the author's theorem $N_m = Q_m$ is sharper than Serre's for $R = Z^{(p)}$.

The proof depends more on arithmetic properties of the ring $Z^{(p)}$ than on the linear algebraic structure of SL(2), and one can find considerable number theoretic elegance in the proofs. To prove Theorem 1, the author first proves that if $p^2 - 1 | m | (p^2 - 1)^t$ for some t, then N_m/Q_m lies in the center of G/Q_m. The method is arithmetic (uses the Dirichlet theorem on the primes in arithmetical progressions). Then he deduces $N_m = Q_m$ for such m by making use of the triviality of the Schur multiplier of $G/N_m = \mathrm{SL}(2, Z/mZ)$ (a fact essentially known, but an independent proof is given in the text). Finally, he generalizes this relation to the case of the general modulus m. Theorem 2 is an easy consequence of Theorem 1 (not of its corollary). *Y. Ihara* (Tokyo)

Referred to in E60-47.

E56-49 (37# 4175)

Rege, Neela S.
On certain classical groups over Hasse domains.
Math. Z. **102** (1967), 120–157.

The author proves that certain integral generalizations of the unitary, symplectic and orthogonal groups are finitely generated. Let K be a global field with characteristic $\neq 2$, let $\sigma: a \to \bar{a}$ be an involutory automorphism of K and let F be the fixed field of σ. A Hasse domain $\mathfrak{o}$ in

F is a Dedekind domain which can be obtained as the intersection of almost all valuation rings of F. The integral closure $\mathfrak{o}^*$ of $\mathfrak{o}$ in K is again a Hasse domain. Let S be a nonsingular $2n \times 2n$ matrix and denote by $\Gamma_s(2n, \mathfrak{o}^*)$ the group of matrices M with elements in $\mathfrak{o}^*$ such that $\bar{M}'SM = S$. The author proves $\Gamma_s(2n, \mathfrak{o}^*)$, $n \geqq 1$ is finitely generated when S is hermitian, i.e., $\bar{S}' = S$ and $\sigma \neq 1$, or S is skew-symmetric (and $\sigma = 1$), with the following possible exception: $n = 1$, K is an algebraic function field and the Hasse domain $\mathfrak{o}$ is the intersection of all but exactly one of the valuation rings of F. If S is symmetric and has maximal index (and $\sigma = 1$) the orthogonal group $\Gamma_s(2n, \mathfrak{o})$, $n \geqq 1$, is again finitely generated, except when $n = 2$ with K and $\mathfrak{o}$ as above. In the exceptional cases the groups are, in general, not finitely generated. The method of proof reduces the generators of these groups to systems depending on the generators of the special linear group SL(2, $\mathfrak{o}$). The results of O. T. O'Meara [J. Reine Angew. Math. **217** (1965), 79–108; MR **31** #3513] are then used.
D. G. James (University Park, Pa.)

Citations: MR 31# 3513 = E56-36.

E56-50 (37# 5186)

Rege, Neela S.
On the finite generation of orthogonal groups over Hasse domains.
Nederl. Akad. Wetensch. Proc. Ser. A **71** = *Indag. Math.* **30** (1968), 101–116.

Let K be an algebraic function field in one variable over a finite field of constants of characteristic $\neq 2$. Let S be a finite set of places of K. Denote by G the orthogonal group of a g-dimensional nondegenerate quadratic form f over K, of index n. Then $g = 2n + t$, where $0 \leqq t \leqq 4$. Let Γ be the subgroup of G whose elements, in a given matrix realization of G, have entries which are integral at all places outside S.

The author proves that Γ is finitely generated in the following cases: (i) $n = 0$; (ii) $g \leqq 4$, $n \geqq 1$ and S contains at least two primes if $g = 3, 4$; (iii) $g \geqq 5$ and $t \leqq 2$.

A basic tool is a result, due to O. T. O'Meara [J. Reine Angew. Math. **217** (1965), 79–108; MR **31** #3513], which states that the corresponding result for $G = \mathrm{SL}(2, K)$ is true if S contains at least two places. If S consists of only one place, Γ need no longer be finitely generated.

{Reviewer's remark: Quite recently, results for general semisimple algebraic groups over function fields have been obtained independently by A. Borel, H. Behr and G. Harder.}
T. A. Springer (Utrecht)

Citations: MR 31# 3513 = E56-36.

E56-51 (38# 4568)

Cohn, P. M.
A presentation of SL_2 for Euclidean imaginary quadratic number fields.
Mathematika **15** (1968), 156–163.

Let R be the ring of algebraic integers in the field $Q(\sqrt{-d})$, where $d = 1, 2, 3, 7$ or 11; these are precisely the values of d for which R is euclidean. Let $GL_2(R)$ be the group of invertible 2×2 matrices over R, and $SL_2(R)$ its subgroup of matrices of determinant $+1$. Let G^a denote G/G', for any group G. The author determines explicitly the structure of $GL_2(R)^a$ and $SL_2(R)^a$. This is done by using presentations of $GL_2(R)$ and $SL_2(R)$ in terms of generators and relations.

While it is an easy matter to give generators for these groups, the determination of a full set of defining relations is considerably more difficult. Such a full set is given by means of certain "universal" relations, together with others which depend on the specific properties of the rings R under consideration. The present work extends earlier results of the author [Inst. Hautes Études Sci. Publ. Math. No. 30 (1966), 5–53; MR **34** #7670], and corrects a minor oversight therein.
I. Reiner (Urbana, Ill.)

Citations: MR 34# 7670 = E56-45.

E56-52 (39# 2728)

Hayakawa, Keizô
Generation of local integral unitary groups over an unramified dyadic local field.
J. Fac. Sci. Univ. Tokyo Sect. I **15** (1968), 1–11.

In analogy with the results of O. T. O'Meara and B. Pollak [Math. Z. **87** (1965), 385–400; MR **30** #3923] for orthogonal groups, the author studies the group of units of a hermitian lattice with respect to the natural involution associated with a ramified quadratic extension of a base field F which is itself an unramified extension of the 2-adic numbers Q_2. As in the orthogonal case, the units are generated by the symmetries if F is a proper extension of Q_2, whereas exceptional cases arise when $F = Q_2$.
R. Jacobowitz (Lawrence, Kan.)

Citations: MR 30# 3923 = E08-24.

E56-53 (39# 5711)

Cohn, P. M.
Automorphisms of two-dimensional linear groups over Euclidean domains.
J. London Math. Soc. (2) **1** (1969), 279–292.

The Euclidean domains for which the author is able to establish his results in sharpest form are those rings of integers of imaginary quadratic fields admitting a Euclidean algorithm, that is, the rings I_d of integers of $\mathbf{Q}(\sqrt{-d})$, $d = 1, 2, 3, 7, 11$. Although many of the steps leading to these results are taken under hypotheses considerably more general, no attempt is made in this review to specify such hypotheses. The cases $d = 2, 7, 11$ seem to be new, the remaining two cases being subsumed under hypotheses utilized by J. Landin and I. Reiner [Proc. Amer. Math. Soc. **9** (1958), 209–216; MR **21** #2013]. The "small automorphism group" of $GL_2(R)$, or of $SL_2(R)$, R a commutative ring, is the subgroup of the automorphism group generated by (i) conjugations by elements of $GL_2(R)$; (ii) homotheties $X \to \varphi(X)X$, φ a homomorphism of the group into the group of units of R; (iii) automorphisms induced by automorphisms of R. The main result: For $R = I_d$ as above, all automorphisms of $GL_2(R)$ or of $SL_2(R)$ are small. General analysis of the structure of the small group and arithmetical considerations enable the author to give explicit descriptions for the "automorphism class group" Aut(G)/Inn(G) in these cases. One of several interesting ideas in the paper is the group-theoretical characterization of non-scalar matrices in G with a single eigenvalue ("generalized transvections"), as those elements with (abelian) centralizers of maximal rank. This enables one to characterize transvections in $GL_2(R)$ (as generalized transvections which are products of two involutions). In $SL_2(R)$, the result gives a group-theoretical characterization of the set of transvections and negatives of transvections.
G. B. Seligman (London)

E56-54 (40# 4380)

O'Meara, O. T.
The automorphisms of the orthogonal groups and their congruence subgroups over arithmetic domains.
J. Reine Angew. Math. **238** (1969), 169–206.

Es werden unter geeigneten Voraussetzungen (im Wesentlichen, daß der Witt-Index an wenigstens einer Ausnahmestelle groß genug ist) alle Automorphismen von gewissen durch drei Axiome gekennzeichneten Untergruppen Δ der orthogonalen Gruppe $O_n(V)$ eines n-dimensionalen Vektorraumes V über einem globalen Körper F bestimmt, zu denen insbesondere die Automorphismengruppe $O_n(M)$ für jedes $\mathfrak{o}$-Gitter M ($\mathfrak{o}$ ein Hassering in F) und deren Kongruenzuntergruppen $\pm O_n{}^+(M, \mathfrak{a})$ gehören. Sie sind alle von der aus der Situation über Körpern bekannten Form $P_\chi \circ \Phi_g|_\Delta$, wo χ ein Homomorphismus von Δ in das Zentrum $\{\pm 1\}$ von $O_n(V)$, g eine Semiähnlichkeitstransformation von V, $\Phi_g(\varphi) = g\varphi g^{-1} \in \pm\Delta$ für alle $\varphi \in \Delta$ und $P_\chi(\varphi) = \chi(\varphi)\varphi$ für $\varphi \in \Delta$ ist. Ein analoges Resultat wird für lokale Ringe erzielt. An einem lokalen, dyadischen Beispiel wird gezeigt, daß der Homomorphismus χ sich nicht auf $O_n(V)$ fortsetzen zu lassen braucht.

Wegen des möglichen Mangels an Spiegelungen ist die von Körpern bekannte Beweismethode nicht anwendbar. Statt dessen werden Aussagen über Dimension und Regularität der Räume $(\varphi - 1)V$ für $\varphi \in \Delta$ als Eigenschaften von gewissen Zentralisatoren und mehrfach derivierten Untergruppen gewonnen. Dadurch kann gezeigt werden, daß jeder Automorphismus von Δ eine Permutation der Menge aller Ebenen Π induziert, für die es unendlich viele $\varphi \in \Delta$ gibt mit $(\varphi - 1)V = \Pi$. Diese Permutation liefert die gesuchte Semiähnlichkeitstransformation g. *S. Böge* (Heidelberg)

E56-55 **(40# 7268)**

Kneser, Martin

Normal subgroups of integral orthogonal groups.

Algebraic K-Theory and its Geometric Applications (Conf., Hull, 1969), *pp.* 67–71. *Springer, Berlin,* 1969.

Let K be an algebraic number field, S a finite set of places of K containing all infinite places, and I the subring of K of all S-integral elements. For an algebraic group $G \subset GL_n$, defined over K, and for a subring A of K, denote by G_A the subgroup of G of matrices $x = (x_{ij})$ such that $x_{ij} \in A$ and $\det x \in A^x$, invertible elements of A. A subgroup of G_I is called an S-congruence subgroup if it contains the group $\{x \in G_I, x \equiv 1 \bmod \mathfrak{a}\}$ for some non-zero ideal $\mathfrak{a}$ of I. On G_K, consider the following two topologies: the topology with the S-congruence subgroups as basis of neighborhoods of 1, and the topology with the subgroups of G_I of finite index as basis. Let $\bar{G}_K$ [$\hat{G}_K$] be the completion of G_K in these topologies. Then the identity mapping of G_K induces a surjective homomorphism $\hat{G}_K \to \bar{G}_K$ with the kernel $C^S(G)$. Obviously, $C^S(G) = \{1\}$ if and only if every subgroup of G_I of finite index is an S-congruence subgroup. In this note, the author considers as G the spin group of the quadratic space (X, q) defined over K with the Witt index $i(X)$. He first proves that $C^S(G)$ is contained in the center of $\hat{G}_K$, if $\dim X \geqq 8$, $i_S(X) = \sum_{v \in S} i(X \otimes K_v) \geqq 2$. Using this, he determines $C^S(G)$ completely when $i(X) \geqq 2$ (incompletely when $i(X) = 1$) and thus contributes towards the problem of the congruence subgroups for twisted algebraic groups. *T. Ono* (Baltimore, Md.)

E56-56 **(41# 152)**

Kubota, Tomio

On automorphic functions and the reciprocity law in a number field.

Lectures in Mathematics, Department of Mathematics, Kyoto University, No. 2.

Kinokuniya Book-Store Co., Ltd., Tokyo, 1969. iii + 65 *pp.* 500 *yen*; $1.50.

Let k be a totally imaginary number field, σ its ring of integers. These notes deal with results concerning GL(2, k). The results are a generalization of the well-known relationship between automorphic forms and reciprocity laws. The abstract background of this relationship, as it is to be found in E. Hecke's book on algebraic numbers [*Vorlesungen über die Theorie der algebraischen Zahlen*, Akad. Verlagsgesselsch., Leipzig, 1923; second edition, Akad. Verlagsgesselsch. Geest & Portig, 1954; MR **16**, 571], was given by A. Weil [Acta Math. **111** (1964), 143–211; MR **29** #2324]. In this paper, the construction of the metaplectic group plays an important role. If k contains all the nth roots of unity, the author constructs an n-fold covering $\tilde{G}_A$ over the adèle group G_A belonging to GL(2, k). This group $\tilde{G}_A$ is the generalization of the metaplectic group. There is a connection between the existence of non-trivial covering groups of G_A and the existence of non-congruence subgroups of finite index of certain arithmetical discontinuous groups [cf. H. Bass, J. Milnor and J.-P. Serre, Inst. Hautes Études Sci. Publ. Math. No. 33 (1967), 59–137; MR **39** #5574].

In the first part, the author gives a summary of the construction of the Hecke ring on a locally compact unimodular group. Several facts concerning constructions and special properties of the Hecke ring are mentioned in detail. These facts are then applied in the special case of the group $\tilde{G}_A$. The covering group is explicitly constructed using cocycles defined with the Hilbert-Hasse norm residue symbol. Details concerning commutativity of the Hecke ring are deduced in the frame of the general theory of automorphic functions.

In the fifth part, Eisenstein series belonging to certain congruence subgroups of GL(2, σ) are defined. Fourier expansions of these series are studied. Since there is in this context no need for the functional equation of the Eisenstein series, the author does not make use of R. P. Langlands' general theory [*Algebraic groups and discontinuous subgroups* (Proc. Sympos. Pure Math., Vol. IX, Boulder, Colo., 1965), pp. 235–252, Amer. Math. Soc., Providence, R.I., 1966; MR **40** #2784]. Using the Eisenstein series, the author constructs a unitary representation of $\tilde{G}_A$ in a Hilbert space of automorphic forms and he deduces a decomposition into a sum of finite irreducible representations. A remarkable fact is that the corresponding zonal spherical functions are of a simple arithmetical structure. This is a generalization of the classical fact that arithmetical functions, such as the sum of the divisors of an integer, are connected with the eigenvalues of Hecke operators applied to classical Eisenstein series. Not all the specific properties between Eisenstein series and theta functions, between the Dirichlet series occurring in this theory and the Hecke L-series could be carried over from the case $n = 2$ (Weil's metaplectic group) to the general case $n > 2$. It seems to be possible to obtain very interesting explicit arithmetical results from the results of the author.

F. van der Blij (Bilthoven)

Citations: MR 16, 571b = R02-14; MR 29# 2324 = E12-104; MR 39# 5574 = E60-37; MR 40# 2784 = F60-10.

Referred to in Z10-69.

E56-57 **(41# 6781)**

Takeuchi, Kisao

On some discrete subgroups of $SL_2(R)$.

J. Fac. Sci. Univ. Tokyo Sect. I **16** (1969), 97–100.

To each indefinite quaternion algebra over Q there is associated a Fuchsian group Γ of the "first kind" (i.e., the orbit space of Γ has finite measure). The author asks: when is such a Γ derivable from a quaternion algebra. The answer is, as he proves: when and only when the trace of every element of Γ is a rational integer. Corollary: If $\Gamma \subset SL(2, Q)$ is of the first kind, Γ is commensurable with the modular group SL(2, Z) if and only if the traces satisfy the above condition. *J. Lehner* (Washington, D.C.)

E56-58 **(43# 3210)**

James, D. G.

Witt's theorem for symplectic modular forms.

J. Austral. Math. Soc. **9** (1969), 409–414.

Let L be a free Z-module of rank $2n$ and $\Phi: L \times L \to Z$ a non-singular unimodular alternating bilinear form into the rational integers. A vector $\alpha \in L$ is said to be imprimitive if it can be written in the form $d\beta$ with $\beta \in L$ and d not a unit in Z; otherwise α is primitive. The maximal such d is called the divisor of α. The following Witt-type theorem is proved. Theorem: A bijective linear transformation $\Theta: J_1 \to J_2$ between two sublattices J_1 and J_2 of L extends to an isometry in $\mathrm{Sp}(2n, Z)$ (the symplectic modular group) if and only if (i) it preserves the symplectic form Φ and (ii) it preserves the divisor of each vector in J_1.

H. Gross (Zürich)

E56-59 **(43# 6325)**

Birman, Joan S.

On Siegel's modular group.

Math. Ann. **191** (1971), 59–68.

The primary purpose of this paper is to give an abstract definition of Siegel's modular group of genus g by a finite set of generators and defining relations. In same Ann. **144** (1961), 64–82 [MR **24** #A3137] the reviewer has given a procedure by which the general case is reduced to the case of genus 2. In an unpublished voluminous paper P. Gold has given an abstract definition of Siegel's modular group of genus 2. From these two sources the author computes a rather reasonable finite set of defining relations explicitly. Applications are concerned with the characterization of the kernel of the natural homomorphism from the mapping class group of a sphere with g handles to Siegel's modular group of genus g. *H. Klingen* (Freiburg)

Citations: MR 24# A3137 = E56-23.

E60 ARITHMETIC SUBGROUPS OF LINEAR ALGEBRAIC GROUPS

See also reviews E02-13, E02-15, E56-16, E56-48, E56-55, E56-56, E64-28, E68-15, E68-17, F02-8, F02-20, F50-30, F50-38, G15-52, G30-31, S45-7.

E60-1 **(25# 5067)**

Borel, Armand; Harish-Chandra

Arithmetic subgroups of algebraic groups.

Bull. Amer. Math. Soc. **67** (1961), 579–583.

The authors bring to light all the basic qualitative theorems on the arithmetic of algebraic groups which stimulate and support further quantitative investigations. These theorems cover the qualitative results of Siegel, Ramanathan and Weil for classical groups and that of the reviewer for solvable groups. Actually, these known ideas or results, in particular, the notion of Siegel domains, are used and generalized by the techniques of the Lie theory, e.g., Iwasawa's KAN-decomposition of a reductive group compatible with a Cartan involution. Let G be a connected complex algebraic group defined over $\mathbf{Q}$. For a subring B of $\mathbf{C}$, one denotes by G_B the subgroup of elements of G which have coefficients in B, and whose determinant is a unit of B. One calls an open subset U of $G_{\mathbf{R}}$ fundamental if: (i) $G_{\mathbf{R}} = UG_{\mathbf{Z}}$; (ii) $KU = U$ for suitable maximal compact subgroup K of $G_{\mathbf{R}}$; (iii) $U^{-1}U \cap xG_{\mathbf{Z}}y$ is finite for any $x, y \in G_{\mathbf{Q}}$. Theorem 1 states the existence of such U. The construction of U is a generalization of Hermite's procedure in the case of indefinite quadratic forms, thereby a lemma on the rational representation of reductive groups (Lemma 2) is crucial. (iii) implies the finite generation of $G_{\mathbf{Z}}$. Theorem 2, which the reviewer will not state explicitly, is a generalization of the classical fact that the number of classes of integral forms with a given non-zero determinant is finite. Theorem 3 gives a criterion for the compactness of the homogeneous space $G_{\mathbf{R}}/G_{\mathbf{Z}}$: $G_{\mathbf{R}}/G_{\mathbf{Z}}$ is compact if and only if the identity component of G has no nontrivial characters defined over $\mathbf{Q}$ and every unipotent element of $G_{\mathbf{Q}}$ belongs to the radical of $G_{\mathbf{Q}}$ [see also Mostow and Tamagawa, #5069]. The details of this paper have been published in Ann. of Math. (2) **75** (1962), 485–535. *T. Ono* (Vancouver, B.C.)

Citations: MR 25# 5069 = E60-3.

Referred to in E60-2, E60-5.

E60-2 **(25# 5068)**

Borel, Armand

Some properties of adele groups attached to algebraic groups.

Bull. Amer. Math. Soc. **67** (1961), 583–585.

This is the adelized version of the theorems reviewed above [#5067]. Let G be a connected algebraic group defined over $\mathbf{Q}$ and denote by G_A the adelization of G. Using the terminologies introduced by the reviewer [Ann. of Math. (2) **70** (1959), 266–290; MR **22** #5635], the author proves that: (i) G is of type (F) and of type (M); (ii) G is of type (C) if and only if every unipotent element of $G_{\mathbf{Q}}$ belongs to the radical of $G_{\mathbf{Q}}$; (iii) $G_A/G_{\mathbf{Q}}$ is compact if and only if G is of type (C) and $X_{\mathbf{Q}}(G) = 1$ (Theorem 1). Theorem 2 is the adelization of Theorem 2 in the paper reviewed above [loc. cit.]: Assuming G reductive, let $\pi: G \to \mathrm{GL}(m, \mathbf{C})$ be a rational representation, defined over $\mathbf{Q}$, and $v \in \mathbf{Q}^m$ a point whose orbit is closed. Then $v\pi_A(G_A) \cap \mathbf{Q}^m$ is the union of a finite number of orbits of $G_{\mathbf{Q}}$. Theorem 2 implies the following Theorem 3: Assuming G reductive, the principal homogeneous spaces over $\mathbf{Q}$ which have rational points in all $\mathbf{Q}_p$ (including $p = \infty$) form a finite number of isomorphism classes. Details of proofs of these theorems are not given. *T. Ono* (Vancouver, B.C.)

Citations: MR 22# 5635 = E68-2; MR 25# 5067 = E60-1.

E60-3 **(25# 5069)**

Mostow, G. D.; Tamagawa, T.

On the compactness of arithmetically defined homogeneous spaces.

Ann. of Math. (2) **76** (1962), 446–463.

Let G be an algebraic matric group defined over $\mathbf{Q}$. Denote by $G_{\mathbf{R}}$ the subgroup of G formed by real matrices and by $G_{\mathbf{Z}}$ the subgroup of $G_{\mathbf{R}}$ formed by unimodular matrices. In Chapter I, the authors consider the homogeneous space $G_{\mathbf{R}}/G_{\mathbf{Z}}$ and prove the following. Theorem: $G_{\mathbf{R}}/G_{\mathbf{Z}}$ is compact if and only if (i) G has no non-trivial character defined over $\mathbf{Q}$ and (ii) every unipotent matrix of $G_{\mathbf{Q}}$ is contained in the radical of $G_{\mathbf{Q}}$. {A minor remark by the reviewer: When G is not connected, the above statement is incorrect because there is a G without unipotent matrix $\neq 1$ which has no non-trivial character and $G_{\mathbf{R}}/G_{\mathbf{Z}}$ is not compact, e.g., $G = \left\{\begin{pmatrix} x & 0 \\ 0 & x^{-1}\end{pmatrix}, \begin{pmatrix} 0 & 1 \\ 1 & 0\end{pmatrix}\right\}$. The same remark will be applied to Theorem$_A$ below.} The proof based on the lemmas by Mahler and Minkowski on the manifold of lattices is ingenious and elegant. The same result has been obtained by Borel and Harish-Chandra [same Ann. (2) **75** (1962), 485–535, Th. 11.8]. Chapter II is the adele version of Chapter I. Denote by G_A the adelized group and $G_A{}^1$ a certain subgroup of G_A defined in connection with the characters of G defined over $\mathbf{Q}$. Then one has the following. Theorem$_A$: $G_A{}^1/G_{\mathbf{Q}}$ is compact if and only if every unipotent matrix of $G_{\mathbf{Q}}$ is contained in the radical of $G_{\mathbf{Q}}$. The proofs in I and II are "parallel but independent". Theorem$_A$ is a generalization of a statement conjectured by Godement [see also A. Borel, #5068].

T. Ono (Vancouver, B.C.)

Referred to in E02-15, E60-1, E60-5, E68-15.

E60-4 (26# 255)

Saito, Masahiko
Sous-groupes discrets des groupes resolubles.
Amer. J. Math. **83** (1961), 369–392.

Soit G un groupe de Lie résoluble connexe et soit D un sous-groupe discret de G. L'auteur donne des relations entre les longueurs des séries des commutateurs de G et de D valables lorsque G/D est compact et démontre des résultats énoncés [C. R. Acad. Sci. Paris **248** (1959), 1909–1911; MR **21** #3507] qui concernant le cas où D est commutatif. Dans la suite, G désigne un sous-groupe résoluble algébrique de $\mathrm{Gl}(n, \mathbf{R})$ et $\mathfrak{n}$ le plus grand idéal nilpotent de l'algèbre de Lie de G. Si $\mathscr{B}$ est une base de $\mathfrak{n}$, on note $G^{\mathscr{B}}$ le sous-groupe des éléments $s \in G$ tels que la matrice par rapport à $\mathscr{B}$ de la restriction de $\mathrm{ad}(s)$ à $\mathfrak{n}$ ait des coefficients entiers et un déterminant $= \pm 1$. L'auteur démontre le théorème: pour qu'il existe un sous-groupe discret D de G tel que G/D soit compact, il faut et il suffit qu'il existe une base $\mathscr{B}$ de $\mathfrak{n}$ telle que (1) $G/G^{\mathscr{B}}$ soit compact, (2) les constantes de structure de $\mathfrak{n}$ soient rationnelles, (3) $\mathscr{B}$ contienne une base de l'algèbre de Lie du facteur compact du sous-groupe de G engendré par $\mathfrak{n}$. Soit $G^{\mathbf{Z}}$ le sous-groupe des éléments de $G \subset \mathrm{Gl}(n, \mathbf{R})$ dont les coefficients sont entiers et le determinant est ± 1. Comme conséquence de résultats de T. Ono [Ann. of Math. (2) **70** (1959), 266–290; MR **22** #5635] l'auteur montre que, si G est irréductible et défini sur le corps des rationnels, la non-compacité de $G/G^{\mathbf{Z}}$ est mesurée par le rang du groupe des caractères rationnels de G.

J. L. Koszul (Strasbourg)

Citations: MR 22# 5635 = E68-2.

E60-5 (26# 5081)

Borel, Armand; Harish-Chandra
Arithmetic subgroups of algebraic groups.
Ann. of Math. (2) **75** (1962), 485–535.

Let G be a group of $m \times m$ matrices with complex entries, defined as the set of common zeroes of a set of polynomials in m^2 variables with rational coefficients. By G_R, G_Q and G_Z are meant respectively the subgroups of G consisting of the matrices with real, rational, integral entries; then G_R is a real Lie group and G_Z a discrete subgroup of G_R. In numerous special instances, it was known that G_R/G_Z has finite invariant measure (this is due chiefly to Siegel; see for example Abh. Math. Sem. Hansischen Univ. **13** (1940), 209–239 [MR **2**, 148]). Here, the authors prove similar statements quite generally and by a uniform method. An outline of the main results follows (see also an abstract by the authors [Bull. Amer. Math. Soc. **67** (1961), 579–583; MR **25** #5067]).

Assume G is reductive and acts transitively on an algebraic variety V in affine space; assume also that V is defined by equations with integral coefficients, and that the action of G on V can be defined by polynomials with integral coefficients; therefore, the set V_Z of points in V with integral coordinates is acted on by G_Z and there are only a finite number of orbits of G_Z in V_Z. As a corollary, the subgroup G_Z of G is defined up to commensurability by the structure of G as an algebraic group over the field Q of rationals.

By a rational character of G, we mean a homomorphism χ of G into the multiplicative group C^* of complex numbers, where $\chi(g)$ is a polynomial with rational coefficients in the entries of $g \in G$. There exists therefore a homogeneous symmetric space P for G_R, defined by a suitable maximal compact subgroup of G_R, and a suitable open set U_0 in P, whose transforms by G_Z cover P; moreover, U_0 meets only a finite number of its transforms by G_Z, from which it follows that G_Z is finitely generated. If G has no rational character except 1, the set U_0 is of finite invariant measure.

Finally, the homogeneous space G_R/G_Z is compact if and only if G has no rational character (except 1) and every unipotent matrix in G_Q is contained in the maximal solvable invariant subgroup of G.

The method of proof relies on the classical results for the reduction of quadratic forms, on a theorem by Mostow about self-adjoint matric groups, and the equivalence "H reductive$\Leftrightarrow G/H$ is an affine variety" for the algebraic subgroups H of G.

{The reviewer wants to add here some historical remarks. The criterion of compactness of G_R/G_Z was conjectured by R. Godement, and has since been proved very simply by G. D. Mostow and T. Tamagawa [Ann. of Math. (2) **76** (1962), 446–463; MR **25** #5069]. The main results have been used by Borel himself to prove statements concerning the adèle group attached to G. Recently, R. Godement and A. Weil, by improving on the method of Mostow and Tamagawa, have been able to derive directly the results on adèle groups, and thus to recover the case of G_R/G_Z; the needed tools are simpler than those of the authors [see a report by R. Godement in the Seminar Bourbaki, May, 1963].}

P. Cartier (Strasbourg)

Citations: MR 2, 148b = E12-4; MR 25# 5067 = E60-1; MR 25# 5069 = E60-3.

Referred to in E02-15, E60-6, E60-20, E60-41, E68-15, E68-17.

E60-6 (26# 6173)

Borel, Armand
Ensembles fondamentaux pour les groupes arithmétiques.
Colloq. Théorie des Groupes Algébriques (Bruxelles, 1962), *pp.* 23–40. *Librairie Universitaire, Louvain; Gauthier-Villars, Paris;* 1962.

Let G be an algebraic linear semi-simple group defined over $\mathbf{Q}$; G being identified to a group of matrices, let $G_{\mathbf{R}}$, $G_{\mathbf{Q}}$, $G_{\mathbf{Z}}$ denote the groups consisting of matrices whose entries are in $\mathbf{R}$, $\mathbf{Q}$, $\mathbf{Z}$, respectively, and have a determinant which is invertible in $\mathbf{R}$, $\mathbf{Q}$, $\mathbf{Z}$, respectively. An arithmetic subgroup Γ of G is a subgroup of $G_{\mathbf{Q}}$ commensurable with $G_{\mathbf{Z}}$; the notion is independent of the particular way of writing G as a group of matrices. If K is a maximal compact subgroup of $G_{\mathbf{R}}$, a subset Ω of $G_{\mathbf{R}}$ is said to be fundamental for Γ if $K \cdot \Omega = \Omega$, $\Omega \cdot \Gamma = G_{\mathbf{R}}$ and if for every translate $\Omega \cdot a$ of Ω by an $a \in G_{\mathbf{R}}$, there are only finitely many translates $\Omega \cdot x$ by elements $x \in \Gamma$ which meet $\Omega \cdot a$. In a previous paper [Ann. of Math. (2) **75** (1962), 485–535; MR **26** #5081] the author and Harish-Chandra have proved the existence of fundamental sets of finite Haar measure. In this paper, the author gives a much more precise description of some fundamental sets (distinct from those of the previous paper). He starts from "generalized Siegel sets" $\mathfrak{S}_{t,\eta,\omega}$ which are defined by using a torus T in G, defined over $\mathbf{Q}$, decomposed over $\mathbf{Q}$ and maximal for these two properties, t is real, η and ω are suitably compact sets in $G_{\mathbf{R}}$; the precise description of $\mathfrak{S}_{t,\eta,\omega}$ is too long to be given here. In general $\mathfrak{S}_{t,\eta,\omega}$ is not relatively compact, it has one part extending to infinity which is called a "vertex" ("pointe"). The main theorem (Theorem 4) describes fundamental sets obtained from $\mathfrak{S}_{t,\eta,\omega}$: a parabolic subgroup H of G is defined as being such that G/H is a complete algebraic variety. Choose a parabolic subgroup H containing T, defined over $\mathbf{Q}$ and minimal for these properties. Then (G being supposed to be connected), a finite union of translates $\mathfrak{S}_{t,\eta,\omega}\cdot x_i$ (with $x_i \in G_{\mathbf{Q}}$) is a fundamental set for large enough t, η, ω, if and only if the set of x_i's contains a set of representatives of the double classes $H_{\mathbf{Q}}\backslash G_{\mathbf{R}}/\Gamma$. As there always exist fundamental sets obtained in this way (Theorem 2), this shows that these double classes are finite in number, that number being the minimal number of "vertices" in a fundamental set of the preceding type. In the course of the proof the author obtains valuable information on the compactification of D/Γ (where $D=K\backslash G_{\mathbf{R}}$) in the sense of Satake, and he has to use in an essential way Satake's theory. *J. Dieudonné* (Paris)

Citations: MR 26# 5081 = E60-5.

Referred to in E02-15, E68-15, F45-24.

E60-7 (27# 2533)

van der Blij, F.; Springer, T. A.
The arithmetics of octaves and of the group G_2.
Nederl. Akad. Wetensch. Proc. Ser. A **62** = *Indag. Math.* **21** (1959), 406–418.

Let A be a Cayley algebra over a field K which is either complete under a discrete valuation or the field $\mathbf{Q}$ of rationals, let Q be the norm form in A and let (,) denote the associate bilinear form. An element a in A is "integral" if $Q(a)\in\mathbf{Z}$ and $(a, e)\in\mathbf{Z}$. An octave-ring is an 8-dimensional lattice in A which consists only of integral elements, is a ring, and is maximal with these two properties. The main result of the paper is that two octave-rings in A are isomorphic; this implies the finiteness of the class number for the exceptional group G_2 (it has been shown later by A. Borel [Inst. Hautes Études Sci. Publ. Math. No. 16 (1963), 5–30] that the same holds for any algebraic matrix group). The proof for the global case ($K=\mathbf{Q}$) is especially interesting; it is based first on a localisation argument, then on the consideration of the units in an octave-ring: they are 240, their vector structure is that of the roots of the exceptional Lie algebra E_8, and the authors determine their multiplication table by means of a reduction mod 2 (where the structure of the Cayley algebra over $\mathbf{F}_2$ is used). The paper starts with a clear and concise survey of the theory of algebras with multiplicative quadratic forms (including the often left-over characteristic 2 case). *J. L. Tits* (Brussels)

Citations: MR 34# 2578 = E68-17.

Referred to in R54-37, R54-50.

E60-8 (28# 2112)

Ramanathan, K. G.
Discontinuous groups.
Nachr. Akad. Wiss. Göttingen Math.-Phys. Kl. II **1963**, 293–323.

Es sei $\mathfrak{D}$ eine involutorische Divisionsalgebra von endlichem Rang über dem Körper der rationalen Zahlen Q und $\mathfrak{A}=\mathfrak{M}_n(\mathfrak{D})$ die Matrixalgebra n-ten Grades über $\mathfrak{D}$. Zu gegebener Ordnung $\mathfrak{O}$ in $\mathfrak{D}$ sei $\Gamma(S)$ die Einheitengruppe einer quadratischen oder bilinearen Form $S\in\mathfrak{A}$, welche aus allen $V\in\mathfrak{O}$ mit $\tilde{V}SV=S$ besteht. "$\sim$" bedeutet die von $\mathfrak{D}$ auf $\mathfrak{A}$ übertragene Involution, $\tilde{V}=\widetilde{(v_{kl})}=(\tilde{v}_{lk})$. Die Gruppenalgebra einer Untergruppe H von $GL(n, \mathfrak{D})$ besteht aus den endlichen Summen $\sum a_jH_j$, $a_j\in Q$, $H_j\in H$. Verfasser verwendet Sätze von Selberg und Borel über die Gruppenalgebra diskontinuierlicher Gruppen sowie arithmetische Eigenschaften der Einheitengruppen, um folgendes Resultat zu bekommen: Die Gruppenalgebra einer beliebigen Untergruppe von $\Gamma(S)$ ($S=\pm\tilde{S}$, indefinit) von endlichem Index stimmt mit $\mathfrak{A}$ überein, wenn man von einigen angebbaren Fällen absieht.

Dieses Ergebnis wird benutzt zur Untersuchung der Kommensurabilität von Einheitengruppen. $\Gamma(S)$ und $\Gamma_1(T)$ heissen kommensurabel, wenn Untergruppen von endlichem Index existieren, die in einem naheliegenden Sinne konjugiert sind. Als notwendige Bedingung für Kommensurabilität bekommt man so zunächst, dass die Zentren beider Algebren $\mathfrak{D}$ und $\mathfrak{D}_1$ gleich, beide Algebren äquivalent über ihrem Zentrum und beide Involutionen von gleicher Art sind. Die getrennte Behandlung der Involutionen erster und zweiter Art führt zu wesentlich schärferen Kriterien, welche es gestatten, unendlich viele inkommensurable diskrete Gruppen erster Art in orthogonalen Gruppen von quadratischen oder bilinearen Formen zu konstruieren. Sie enthalten als Spezialfälle die von Siegel [Amer. J. Math. **65** (1943), 1–86; MR **4**, 242] angegebenen Kommensurabilitätskriterien für Einheitengruppen Hermitescher Formen in imaginär-quadratischen Erweiterungen von total-reelen Zahlkörpern, es wird das Kommensurabilitätsproblem gelöst für die Einheitengruppen gewisser quinärer quadratischer Formen, die zu diskontinuierlichen Gruppen in dem Siegelschen Halbraum zweiten Grades führen, sowie für die Modulgruppen zu Riemannschen Matrizen. *H. Klingen* (Freiburg)

Citations: MR 4, 242b = F50-2.

Referred to in F55-18.

E60-9 (28# 4035)

Bass, Hyman
The stable structure of quite general linear groups.
Bull. Amer. Math. Soc. **70** (1964), 429–433.

Generalizing a classical result of Dieudonné, the reviewer recently showed [Amer. J. Math. **83** (1961), 137–153; MR **23** #A1724] that, for A any local ring, the normal subgroups of $GL(n, A)$, $n\geqq 3$, are essentially the congruence subgroups with respect to the ideals of A. In the present paper, the author describes the beginnings of a global theory pertaining to the structure of $GL(n, A)$ for a quite general ring A. As is to be expected, the results are effective only if n is sufficiently large compared with the dimension of the space X of maximal ideals in A, i.e., only if n is in the stable range. Put, for an ideal $\mathfrak{a}$ of A, $GL(n, A, \mathfrak{a})=\ker(GL(n, A)\rightarrow GL(n, A/\mathfrak{a}))$. Let $E(n, A)$ be the subgroup of $GL(n, A)$ generated by the elementary matrices and let $E(n, A, \mathfrak{a})$ be the normal subgroup of $E(n, A)$ generated by the elementary matrices in $GL(n, A, \mathfrak{a})$. From the obvious inclusion $GL(n, A)\rightarrow GL(n+1, A)$, we have the inductive limits of these groups which will be denoted by $GL(A)$, $E(A)$, etc. The first theorem states that

$$E(A, \mathfrak{a}) = [E(A), E(A, \mathfrak{a})] = [GL(A), GL(A, \mathfrak{a})].$$

Moreover, if $H\subset GL(A)$ is normalized by $E(A)$, then, for a unique ideal $\mathfrak{a}$, $E(A, \mathfrak{a})\subset H\subset GL(A, \mathfrak{a})$, and H is normal in $GL(A)$. Hence, the knowledge of the normal subgroups of $GL(A)$ is equivalent to a determination of the abelian groups $K^1(A, \mathfrak{a})=GL(A, \mathfrak{a})/E(A, \mathfrak{a})$. When $\mathfrak{a}=A$, we write $K^1(A)$ instead; this is just the commutator quotient of $GL(A)$.

The second theorem gives information on the stable range whenever A is an algebra, finitely generated as a module, over a commutative ring whose maximal ideal spectrum is a Noetherian space of dimension d. In particular, for $n>d+1$, the homomorphism

$$f_n: GL(n, A, \mathfrak{a})/E(n, A, \mathfrak{a}) \rightarrow GL(n+1, A, \mathfrak{a})/E(n+1, A, \mathfrak{a}),$$

induced by the inclusion, is surjective. Topological considerations suggest that, for $n>d+2$, f_n is also injective. An affirmation of this conjecture which would have a number of important applications, constitutes, when A is a division algebra, the essential part of Dieudonné's theory of noncommutative determinants. Next follow finiteness theorems. E.g., let Σ be a semisimple, finite-dimensional algebra over $\mathbf{Q}$, and let A be an order in Σ and $\mathfrak{a}$ an ideal in A. Then $\ker(K^1(A, \mathfrak{a}) \to K^1(\Sigma))$ is finite and $K^1(A, \mathfrak{a})$ is finitely generated. If, in addition, Σ is simple, then center $E(n, A)$ = center $SL(n, A)$ ($SL(n, A)$ is the group of elements of reduced norm one in $GL(n, A)$). Moreover, for $n \geqq 3$, a normal subgroup of $E(n, A)$ is either finite and central or of finite index and, for all sufficiently large n, the same is true for $SL(n, A)$. Here the author remarks that these results, combined with a rather formidable cohomological calculation, form the basis of the proof of the fact that every subgroup of finite index in $SL(n, \mathbf{Z})$, $n \geqq 3$, contains a congruence subgroup (cf. the author, M. Lazard and J.-P. Serre [Bull. Amer. Math. Soc. **70** (1964), 385–392]). In the next paragraph the author announces results of a joint paper with A. Heller and R. Swan (to appear) on the structure of the homomorphisms $K^1(A) \to K^1(A[t])$ and $K^1(A) \to K^1(A[t, t^{-1}])$, t an indeterminate. Concerning the latter, Atiyah has pointed out that the results form an analogue of Bott periodicity for the unitary group. In the final section, it is shown that the previous results yield information on J. H. C. Whitehead's groups of simple homotopy types, results which extend some earlier work of G. Higman [Proc. London Math. Soc. (2) **46** (1940), 231–248; MR **2**, 5]: Let π be a finite group and put $K^1(Z\pi)/\pm\pi = Wh(\pi)$, where $\pm\pi$ denotes the image of $\pm\pi \subset GL(1, Z\pi)$ in $GL(Z\pi)$. Assume that π has q irreducible rational representations and r irreducible real representations. Then $Wh(\pi)$ is finitely generated of rank $r-q$. In particular, if π is free abelian, then $Wh(\pi) = 0$.

W. Klingenberg (Mainz)

Citations: MR 23# A1724 = E56-22; MR 28# 5117 = E60-11.

Referred to in E60-38.

E60-10 (28# 5067)

Kneser, Martin

Erzeugende und Relationen verallgemeinerter Einheitengruppen.

J. Reine Angew. Math. **214/215** (1964), 345–349.

Soit G un groupe algébrique de matrices à coefficients dans un corps de nombres algébriques k et soit S un ensemble fini d'idéaux premiers de k. Pour que le groupe $G_{0(S)}$ des matrices de G dont les éléments n'ont pas de dénominateur en dehors de S soit à engendrement fini, il faut et il suffit que le groupe $G_{k_\mathfrak{p}}$ soit engendré par une partie compacte pour tout $\mathfrak{p}$ dans S. Enoncé analogue pour les relations entre les générateurs. La démonstration s'appuie sur les résultats de Borel [Inst. Hautes Études Sci. Publ. Math. No. 16 (1963), 5–30]; MR **34** #2578].

P. Cartier (Strasbourg)

Citations: MR 34# 2578 = E68-17.

Referred to in E60-41.

E60-11 (28# 5117)

Bass, H.; Lazard, M.; Serre, J.-P.

Sous-groupes d'indice fini dans SL(*n*, Z).

Bull. Amer. Math. Soc. **70** (1964), 385–392.

Les auteurs prouvent que tout sous-groupe d'indice fini de $G(n) = \mathbf{SL}(n, \mathbf{Z})$ est un groupe de congruence pour $n \geqq 3$, c'est-à-dire contient le noyau $G_q(n)$ d'un des homomorphismes canoniques $\mathbf{SL}(n, \mathbf{Z}) \to \mathbf{SL}(n, \mathbf{Z}/q\mathbf{Z})$ pour un entier $q \geqq 1$ convenable (il est classique que le résultat correspondant pour $n=2$ est faux). La méthode consiste à comparer les complétés $\hat{G}(n)$ et $A(n)$ de $G(n)$ pour la topologie des sous-groupes d'indice fini et la topologie des sous-groupes de congruence; on a une suite exacte

$$1 \to C(n) \to \hat{G}(n) \to A(n) \to 1$$

et il s'agit de prouver que le noyau $C(n) = 1$. On introduit pour tout entier $q \geqq 1$ le sous-groupe $E_q(n)$ de $G_q(n)$ engendré par les matrices de la forme $1 + aE_{ij}$ $(i \neq j)$ où $a \in q\mathbf{Z}$; on prouve que pour $n \geqq 3$, on a $C(n) = \lim_{\overleftarrow{q}} G_q(n)/E_q(n)$, $G_q(n) = E_q(n)G_q(n-1)$ et $(G(n), G_q(n)) \subset E_q(n)$ ((H, H') désignant le groupe engendré par les commutateurs $s^{-1}t^{-1}st$ où $s \in H$, $t \in H'$). De là on déduit d'abord que pour $n \geqq 3$, l'homomorphisme $S: C(n-1) \to C(n)$ est surjectif et que $C(n)$ est contenu dans le centre de $\hat{G}(n)$; il suffit donc de prouver que $C(3) = 1$, et cela résultera de ce que le sous-groupe $(S(\hat{G}(2)), C(3))$ est dense dans le sous-groupe fermé $C(3)$ de $\hat{G}(3)$. Par dualité, cela revient à prouver que $H^1(C(2), I)^{A(2)} = 0$, où $I = \mathbf{Q}/\mathbf{Z}$. Or, on a la suite exacte de Hochschild-Serre

$$0 \to H^1(A(2), I) \to H^1(\hat{G}(2), I) \to H^1(C(2), I)^{A(2)} \to H^2(A(2), I)$$

et le reste de la démonstration consiste à prouver que: (1) $H^2(A(2), I) = 0$; (2) les deux groupes $H^1(A(2), I)$ et $H^1(\hat{G}(2), I)$ sont des groupes cycliques isomorphes, d'ordre 12. Le second point est assez facile. Pour prouver le premier, on utilise le fait que $A(2)$ est isomorphe au produit des groupes p-adiques $G_p = \mathbf{SL}(2, \mathbf{Z}_p)$; on est ramené à montrer que pour chaque p, on a $H^2(U_p, I_p) = 0$, où U_p est un p-groupe de Sylow du groupe des commutateurs de G_p, et $I_p = \mathbf{Q}_p/\mathbf{Z}_p$. Cela résulte de profonds résultats de M. Lazard sur les "pro-p-groupes", non encore publiés.

J. Dieudonné (Paris)

Referred to in E56-34, E60-9, E60-14, E60-33, E60-37, E60-39.

E60-12 (31# 177)

Borel, Armand

Arithmetic properties of linear algebraic groups.

Proc. Internat. Congr. Mathematicians (Stockholm, 1962), *pp.* 10–22. *Inst. Mittag-Leffler, Djursholm*, 1963.

An exposition of recent developments in the arithmetic theory of algebraic groups.

Referred to in E72-5.

E60-13 (31# 275)

Jehne, Wolfram

Die Struktur der symplektischen Gruppe über lokalen und dedekindschen Ringen.

S.-B. Heidelberger Akad. Wiss. Math.-Natur. Kl. **1962/64**, 187–235.

One goal of this study is the result that symplectic groups over local rings have only congruence subgroups as normal subgroups. As he states in proof, the author has been anticipated here by Klingenberg [Amer. J. Math. **85** (1963), 232–240; MR **27** #3710], but the present paper goes farther in several ways, which one can only highlight here.

First, there are more results on symplectic groups over local rings: their p-Sylow subgroups are found and while doing this the author gives a nice generalization of the Schur extension splitting theorem. A formula is given for the indices of the congruence subgroups in terms of the Hilbert-Samuel function. Second, there are global results: a congruence topology is introduced in symplectic groups over Dedekind rings (in which 2 is a unit and all residue class fields have more than three elements), in terms of which the only closed normal subgroups are the congruence subgroups. Third, over a commutative ring in which 2 is a unit, the symplectic Lie algebras are relatively simple; their only ideals come from ideals of the base ring. Over local rings the $\mathfrak{M}$-adic filtration of the symplectic group yields a graded Lie algebra (via the Magnus-Lazard rule) and this turns out to be isomorphic to the associated graded Lie algebra of the corresponding symplectic Lie algebra.

The paper ends by investigating the idèle groups of the symplectic groups and by applying the results to the Siegel modular group. *G. Leger* (Medford, Mass.)

Citations: MR 27# 3710 = E56-32.

E60-14 (31# 5903)

Mennicke, J.

Zur Theorie der Siegelschen Modulgruppe.

Math. Ann. **159** (1965), 115–129.

Es sei Sp$(2n, Z)$ die Siegelsche Modulgruppe und $n>1$. Verfasser zeigt das wichtige Resultat: Jeder nicht im Zentrum gelegene Normalteiler von Sp$(2n, Z)$ enthält eine Hauptkongruenzuntergruppe geeigneter Stufe; eine Untergruppe von Sp$(2n, Z)$ ist genau dann Kongruenzuntergruppe, wenn sie endlichen Index besitzt. Dieser Sachverhalt ist bekanntlich falsch für $n=1$. Zum Beweise wird bei gewisser Normierung von Sp$(2n, Z)$ gezeigt: (i) jeder solche Normalteiler enthält ein Element $I+me_{12}$ (I Einheitsmatrix, e_{12} hat das Element 1 an der Stelle (1, 2) und sonst nur Elemente 0) für geeignetes ganzes $m\neq 0$; (ii) der kleinste Normalteiler, der $I+me_{12}$ enthält, ist die Hauptkongruenzuntergruppe der Stufe m. Beide Schritte werden bewiesen unter Verwendung expliziter Matrizenrechnung in Anlehnung an entsprechende Resultate für SL(n, Z) bei J. L. Brenner [Ann. of Math. (2) **71** (1960), 210–223; MR **22** #1622] und dem Verfasser [ibid. (2) **81** (1965), 31–37; MR **30** #2083]; vgl. auch H. Bass, M. Lazard, J.-P. Serre [Bull. Amer. Math. Soc. **70** (1964), 385–392; MR **28** #5117]. Verfasser kündigt die interessante Verallgemeinerung auf arithmetische Untergruppen einer grossen Klasse von linearen algebraischen Gruppen an. Nach Kenntnis des Referenten wurde dieses Programm (noch unveröffentlicht) inzwischen von H. Matsumoto und Verfasser unabhängig voneinander durchgeführt.

H. Klingen (Freiburg)

Citations: MR 22# 1622 = E56-19; MR 28# 5117 = E60-11; MR 30# 2083 = E56-34.

Referred to in E60-33, E60-39.

E60-15 (32# 5657)

Abe, Eiichi

Generation of some discrete subgroups of simple algebraic groups.

Tôhoku Math. J. (2) **17** (1965), 178–184.

Let G be a simple, simply connected, algebraic group split over the rational field and G_Z the subgroup of integral points relative to some Z-structure on G. The author shows that in case G is of type A_n or of rank greater than three, then G_Z is generated by two elements, and that in any case G_Z is generated by three elements. If G is adjoint instead of simply connected, a similar result holds. The development parallels to some extent that of the reviewer's paper [Canad. J. Math. **14** (1962), 277–283; MR **26** #1351], in which the problem with a finite field in place of Z was treated, but is too technical to be described here.

R. Steinberg (Los Angeles, Calif.)

E60-16 (34# 1330)

Voskresenskiĭ, V. E.

On decomposition of the genus into classes in uniform spaces. (Russian)

Volž. Mat. Sb. Vyp. 2 (1964), 21–25.

Sei $G\subset \mathrm{GL}(n, k)$ eine algebraische Gruppe über einem algebraischen Zahlkörper k, $X=\mathrm{Spec}(I)$ das Spektrum des Ringes I der ganzen Elemente von k, V ein endlichdimensionaler Vektorraum über k, auf dem G operiert, und L ein Gitter von V. In L wird zu $v\in L$ die Klasse $C(v)$, das rationale Geschlecht $Y(v)$ und das Geschlecht $\overline{Y}(v)$ von v definiert. Es gilt $C(v)\subset Y(v)\subset \overline{Y}(v)$, und $\overline{Y}(v)$ besteht aus endlich vielen Klassen. Der Autor nennt eine hinreichende Bedingung dafür, dass $\overline{Y}(v)=Y(v)$ ist. Ferner gibt er für den Fall, dass die erste Kohomologiemenge $H^1(X, E(G))$ der Garbe der lokal ganzen Untergruppen von G über X gleich Eins ist, eine Bijektion zwischen der Menge der Klassen, aus denen $Y(v)$ besteht, und $H^1(X, E(U))$ an, wobei U die stationäre Untergruppe von G in v ist [vgl. der Verfasser, Dokl. Akad. Nauk SSSR **150** (1963), 459–462; MR **27** #150]. Beide Aussagen zusammen ermöglichen in einem Spezialfall einen Überblick über die Zerlegung des Geschlechts in Klassen. Als Anwendung ergeben sich neue Beweise für bekannte Tatsachen aus der algebraischen Zahlentheorie bzw. algebraischen Geometrie. *H. G. Zimmer* (Tübingen)

Citations: MR 27# 150 = E68-6.

E60-17 (34# 4373)

Matsumoto, H. [Matsumoto, Hideya]

Subgroups of finite index in certain arithmetic groups.

Algebraic Groups and Discontinuous Subgroups (*Proc. Sympos. Pure Math., Boulder, Colo.*, 1965), *pp.* 99–103. *Amer. Math. Soc., Providence, R.I.*, 1966.

Let G be a connected, simply connected, simple linear algebraic group, split over $\mathbf{Q}$, and of rank $\geqq 2$. A congruence subgroup of $G_{\mathbf{Z}}$ is a subgroup containing $\ker(G_{\mathbf{Z}}\to G_{\mathbf{Z}/q\mathbf{Z}})$ for some $q\neq 0$. Evidently it has finite index in $G_{\mathbf{Z}}$. The author here outlines a proof of the converse: Every subgroup of finite index in $G_{\mathbf{Z}}$ is a congruence subgroup.

This result was known for SL_n ($n\geqq 3$) and Sp_{2n} ($n\geqq 2$). The author deduces the general case from the two special cases of SL_3 and Sp_4. Moreover, his reduction to these cases is carried out for an arbitrary number field in place of $\mathbf{Q}$, replacing $\mathbf{Z}$ by its ring of algebraic integers.

However, the analogue of the theorem is now known to be false for the groups SL_n and Sp_{2n} in totally imaginary number fields (forthcoming paper of J. Milnor, J.-P. Serre and the reviewer, in Ann. of Math.). It would therefore be of interest to have a more detailed exposition of the author's reduction method in order to analyze precisely what occurs in these fields for more general groups G.

H. Bass (New York)

E60-18 (34# 5822)

Allan, Nelo D.

The problem of the maximality of arithmetic groups.

Algebraic Groups and Discontinuous Subgroups (*Proc. Sympos. Pure Math., Boulder, Colo.*, 1965), *pp.* 104–109. *Amer. Math. Soc., Providence, R.I.*, 1966.

This is a survey of known results (mostly due to the author, and taken from his forthcoming thesis at the University of Chicago) on the maximality of arithmetic groups in a connected, semisimple linear algebraic group G defined over an algebraic number field k; say $G\subseteq \mathrm{SL}(n, \mathbf{C})$.

A subgroup Δ of G is called arithmetic if Δ is commensurable with G_O, where O is the set of all algebraic integers in k. (For a subring S of $\mathbf{C}$, G_S denotes the group of elements in G whose entries are in S; two subgroups H_1 and H_2 of a group G are said to be commensurable if $H_1\cap H_2$ is of finite index in both H_1 and H_2.) Among the results discussed are the following. Assuming that G_O is Zariski dense in G, there are only finitely many maximal arithmetic groups containing a given arithmetic group Δ. If Δ is maximal in G_k, then the normalizer $N(\Delta)$ of Δ in G is the unique maximal arithmetic group containing Δ. The author also discusses conditions under which local maximality at all finite spots implies global maximality; the maximality of G_0 for some special groups, from which some conjectures are derived; some applications to bounded domains. *Rimhak Ree* (Vancouver, B.C.)

Referred to in E60-49.

E60-19 (34# 5824)

Borel, Armand

Density and maximality of arithmetic subgroups.

J. Reine Angew. Math. **224** (1966), 78–89.

G sei eine Gruppe von $m \times m$-Matrizen mit komplexen Koeffizienten, welche die Nullstellenmenge von endlich vielen Polynomen in m^2 Unbestimmten mit Koeffizienten aus Q ist; G ist also eine über Q definierte lineare algebraische Gruppe. Weiter soll G zusammenhängend und halbeinfach sein. G_R bzw. G_Q bzw. G_Z bedeuten diejenigen Untergruppen von G, welche aus allen Matrizen von G mit Koeffizienten aus R bzw. Q bzw. Z bestehen. H sei eine diskrete Untergruppe von G_Z von endlichem Index. (H ist dann eine arithmetische Untergruppe von G.) Der Autor beweist u.a. folgendes: (1) Besitzt G keine normale zusammenhängende Q-Untergruppe $N \neq \{e\}$, so dass N_R kompakt ist, so ist H hinsichtlich der Zariski-Topologie dicht in G. (Dieser Satz findet sich schon in einer vorangehenden Arbeit des Autors [Ann. of Math. (2) **72** (1960), 179–188; MR **23** #A964].) (2) Die Gruppe $C(H)=\{g \in G_C: gHg^{-1}$ kommensurabel mit $H\}$ wird beschrieben. Es ist $C(H)=G_Q$, wenn G keine normale Q-Untergruppe $N \neq \{e\}$ besitzt, für welche N_R kompakt ist. (3) Hat G keine normale Q-Untergruppe $N \neq \{e\}$, so dass N_R kompakt ist, so gibt es in G_C nur endlich viele Untergruppen, welche H als Untergruppe von endlichem Index enthalten. Weiter ist H sogar maximal in G, wenn G über Q zerfällt und H eine spezielle arithmetische Untergruppe ist. Zu bemerken bleibt noch, dass in der Arbeit die angeführten Resultate zum Teil für einen beliebigen Zahlkörper bewiesen werden. *H. Popp* (Lafayette, Ind.)

Referred to in E60-22.

E60-20 (34# 7667)

Vinberg, È. B.

Discrete groups generated by reflections in Lobačevskiĭ spaces. (Russian)

Mat. Sb. (N.S.) **72 (114)** (1967), 471–488; *correction, ibid.* **73 (115)** (1967), 303.

Let S denote the euclidean space E^n or the Lobačevskiĭ space Λ^n. Reflections are considered with respect to hyperplanes in S; these divide the space into two half-spaces. An intersection of a finite number of half-spaces defines a convex polytope in S. Let Γ be a discrete group of motions of S, generated by a finite number of reflections. The mirror-hyperplanes of the reflections in Γ cause a decomposition of S into congruent convex polytopes P, called Γ-cells, each of which is a fundamental domain of Γ. The reflections in the hyperplanes H_i bounding a Γ-cell P generate Γ. For the description of P one uses the unit vectors e_i, perpendicular to H_i in outside direction with respect to P. Let $A=(a_{ij})$, $a_{ij}=(e_i, e_j)$ be the Gram matrix of P. Then P is called a C-polytope if all the angles between the H_i are $\leqq 90°$ and if P does not contain a straight line: $a_{ii}=1$, $a_{ij} \leqq 0$ $(i \neq j)$. In the case $S=E^n$, H. S. M. Coxeter [Ann. of Math. (2) **35** (1934), 588–621] has shown that there are two types of C-matrices of rank n which are not decomposable into direct sums: C^+-matrices, each associated with a unique simplicial angle; C^0-matrices, of order $n+1$ and associated with a simplex, unique up to similarity. All their principal submatrices are positive and a linear dependence between the rows of A has positive coefficients.

Let $E^{n,1}$ be an $(n+1)$-dimensional vector space with a non-degenerate scalar product of negative index of inertia; let $V=\{x \in E^{n,1}: (x, x)<0\}$; this is a set of two connected components V_+, V_-. The rays from O in V_+ represent the points in Λ^n. The automorphisms of $E^{n,1}$ preserving Λ^n are the motions in Λ^n. A subspace of $E^{n,1}$ is called hyperbolic [elliptic, parabolic] if the scalar product induced on it is non-degenerate indefinite [positive, degenerate]. To every s-dimensional plane $\Pi \subset \Lambda^n$ corresponds an $(s+1)$-dimensional hyperbolic subspace $\hat{\Pi}$ in $E^{n,1}$. To every half-space in Λ^n corresponds a half-space in $E^{n,1}$ bounded by a hyperbolic hyper-subspace. A convex polytope $P \subset \Lambda^n$ corresponds to a set $\hat{P} \subset E^{n,1}$: a many-sided angle with vertex in O. P is uniquely defined by $\hat{P}$ as the set of all rays in $\hat{P} \cap V_+$ and $\hat{P}$ can be defined by the inequalities $(e_i, x) \leqq 0$, none of which is satisfied as an equality everywhere on P. Between the e_i there cannot exist linear dependencies with non-negative coefficients.

A convex polytope P in Λ^n is called a C^--polytope if it has finite volume and all the angles between its bounding hyperplanes are $\leqq 90°$. The Gram matrix A of P is not decomposable. Conversely: A symmetric matrix A is the Gram matrix of a C-polytope in Λ^n if and only if (1) rank $A=n+1$ and the index of inertia of A is -1, (2) $a_{ii}=1$, $a_{ij} \leqq 0$ $(i \neq j)$, (3) A is indecomposable, (4) A has at least one principal submatrix which is either a C^+-matrix of rank n or a C^0-matrix of rank $n-1$ (these are called "nodal submatrices"), and (5) for every nodal submatrix B_1 and each of its submatrices B of rank $n-1$, there is a nodal submatrix $B_2 \neq B_1$ containing B.

For the enumeration of all the groups Γ in E^n one has to choose among all C-matrices those where (*) $a_{ij}=-\cos(\pi/m_{ij})$ $(m_{ij}=2, 3, \cdots, \infty)$. This has been carried out by Coxeter [loc. cit.]; in order to describe these matrices graphically, he has invented the well-known scheme of linked dots. In order to enumerate the groups Γ of Λ^n with finite fundamental domain, one has to select from all C^--matrices those for which, apart from (*), one has the possibility $a_{ij}<-1$. The nodal matrices are of the Coxeter type. To cover the case $a_{ij}<-1$ in the schemes the corresponding mirrors may be linked by a dotted line.

The second (algebraic) part of the paper begins with a description (in suitable form) of the method of A. Borel and Harish-Chandra [ibid. (2) **75** (1962), 485–535; MR **26** #5081] to construct the discrete subgroups Γ of a semi-simple Lie group $\mathscr{G}$ if the volume of the factor space $\mathscr{G}/\Gamma$ is finite. Let $\mathscr{G}^0$ be the connected component of the unit, a direct product of non-compact simple Lie groups without center, and G an irreducible algebraic group over a totally real field K of algebraic numbers; let G_R be locally isomorphic to $\mathscr{G}$, and for a non-identity morphism $\sigma: K \to R$, let the group $(G^\sigma)_R$ (i.e., the algebraic group over K^σ obtained from G by applying σ to the coefficients of G) be compact. Also, let $G_I=\{g \in G_R: \rho(g)_{ij} \in I\}$, where ρ is a faithful matrix representation of G and I is the ring of the integral elements of K. Let $\mathscr{A}(G, K)$ be the class of all subgroups of $\mathscr{G}$ generated by the subgroups of the form $\varphi(G_I)$, where φ is a homomorphism of $(G_R)^0$ onto $\mathscr{G}^0$, and by all commensurable subgroups. The subgroups $\Gamma \subset \mathscr{G}$ in $\bigcup_{G,K} \mathscr{A}(G, K)$ are said to be arithmetic; they are discrete and, as shown by Borel and Harish-Chandra [loc. cit.], $\mathscr{G}/\Gamma$ has finite volume. Subgroups of $\Gamma \subset \mathscr{G}$ where $\mathscr{G}/\Gamma$ is of finite volume and a subgroup of finite index in Γ is contained in $\varphi(G_K)$ (with a suitable homomorphism φ onto $\mathscr{G}^0$) are said to be quasi-arithmetic groups. The following theorem is proved. Let Γ be a discrete group of motions of Λ^n generated by a finite number of reflections and having as fundamental domain a polytope P of finite volume with Gram matrix $A=(a_{ij})$. Let $\tilde{K}$ be the field generated by the

a_{ij} and K generated by the numbers

$$(**) \qquad 2^m a_{i_1 i_2} a_{i_2 i_3} \cdots a_{i_{m-1} i_m} a_{i_m i_1}.$$

Then Γ is quasi-arithmetic if and only if $\tilde{K}$ is totally real and for each morphism $\sigma: \tilde{K} \to R$ (not identity in $\tilde{K}$) the matrix $A^\sigma = (a_{ij}{}^\sigma)$ is non-negative. Γ is arithmetic if and only if, moreover, the algebraic numbers (**) are integral. If the fundamental polytope P of Γ is non-compact, then these conditions can be simplified: The numbers (**) have to be rational and integral-rational, respectively. If, in the Coxeter scheme of a quasi-arithmetic Γ, dotted links do not occur, then Γ is arithmetic.

In the third part of the paper, the author enumerates the groups Γ whose fundamental polytopes are simplexes, reproduces the schemes of arithmetic groups, of the Makarov groups [cf. V. S. Makarov, Dokl. Akad. Nauk SSSR **167** (1966), 30–33; MR **34** #244], of two non-arithmetic groups in Λ^4 and gives an example of a group which is quasi-arithmetic, but not arithmetic, with unbounded fundamental domain. *H. Schwerdtfeger* (Montreal, Que.)

Citations: MR 26# 5081 = E60-5.

E60-21 **(35# 261)**

Gutnik, L. A.; Pjateckiĭ-Šapiro, I. I.

Maximal discrete subgroups of a unimodular group. (Russian)

Trudy Moskov. Mat. Obšč. **15** (1966), 279–295.

Let Ω_n be the group of real $n \times n$ matrices of determinant ± 1. A congruence subgroup Γ of Ω_n is one containing the group $U_n(m)$ of matrices $\equiv I \pmod m$ for some integer $m \geqq 1$. The following characterization of all maximal discrete congruence subgroups Γ of Ω_n is obtained. If φ and φ_p are the natural maps $\mathrm{GL}_n(\mathbf{R}) \to \mathrm{PGL}_n(\mathbf{R})$ and $\mathrm{GL}_n(\mathbf{Q}_p) \to \mathrm{PGL}_n(\mathbf{Q}_p)$ (where $\mathbf{Q}_p$ is the p-adic field), then $\varphi(\Gamma) \subseteq \mathrm{PGL}_n(\mathbf{Q})$. Moreover, for any prime p, the closure Γ_p of $\varphi_p(\Gamma)$ in $\mathrm{PGL}_n(\mathbf{Q}_p)$ (which makes sense by the previous sentence) is a maximal compact subgroup of $\mathrm{PGL}_n(\mathbf{Q}_p)$, and for all but a finite number of p, $\Gamma_p = \varphi_p(\mathfrak{A}_n)$, where $\mathfrak{A}_n$ is the group of matrices in $\mathrm{GL}_n(\mathbf{Q}_p)$ whose determinants are p-adic units. Next, the authors show that up to conjugacy, there are exactly $\tau(n)$ (the divisor function) maximal compact subgroups of $\mathrm{PGL}_n(\mathbf{Q}_p)$, which they determine explicitly. These results lead to an explicit construction, up to conjugacy, of all the maximal discrete congruence subgroups $\Gamma \subset \Omega_n$. A number of interesting facts concerning their structure are deduced. For example, among all such Γ, the group $\mathrm{U}_n(1)$ has a fundamental domain of least volume. *B. Gordon* (Los Angeles, Calif.)

E60-22 **(35# 2896)**

Allan, Nelo D.

Maximality of some arithmetic groups.

An. Acad. Brasil. Ci. **38** (1966), 223–227.

Let K be an algebraic number field of finite degree over the field Q of rational numbers and $\mathfrak{o}$ the ring of integers of K. Let G be a semi-simple linear algebraic group of n-rowed matrices defined over K. Let G_K be the group of K-rational elements of G and G_0 the group of elements in G_K with entries from $\mathfrak{o}$. A subgroup Γ of G is said to be arithmetic if it is commensurable with G_0, that is, if $\Gamma \cap G_0$ is of finite index in Γ as well as G_0. Γ is a discrete subgroup of G. The problem of maximality consists in determining, in case G is non-compact, all and therefore the maximal discrete subgroups of G which contain Γ. In a number of cases with G a classical group it was shown by the reviewer [Nachr. Akad. Wiss. Göttingen Math.-Phys. Kl. II **1964**, 145–164; MR **30** #2008] that there exist only finitely many such discrete groups containing Γ. In the general case this has been established recently by A. Borel [J. Reine Angew. Math. **224** (1966), 78–89; MR **34** #5824].

In the first part of the paper under review, the author proves that if Γ is maximal in G_K, that is, if there exists no discrete subgroup of G contained in G_K and containing Γ properly, then the normalizer $N(\Gamma)$ of Γ in G is the maximal discrete subgroup of G containing Γ, and $N(\Gamma)/\Gamma$ is finite. The proof, as did those of the reviewer and A. Borel, depends on the fact that the ring generated by Γ is an order in the complete matrix algebra $\mathfrak{M}_n(K)$ of n-rowed matrices over K. A bound, depending on the class number of $\mathfrak{o}$, number of generators of the unit group of $\mathfrak{o}$ and on the order determined by Γ, is also given for the order of $N(\Gamma)/\Gamma$.

In the second part of the paper the author considers four interesting examples and determines explicitly, under suitable restrictions, all the maximal discrete groups containing G_0.

{See also #2897 below.} *K. G. Ramanathan* (Bombay)

Citations: MR 30# 2008 = F55-18; MR 34# 5824 = E60-19.

E60-23 **(35# 2897)**

Allan, Nelo D.

A note on the arithmetic of the orthogonal group.

An. Acad. Brasil. Ci. **38** (1966), 243–244.

This note deals, in a more detailed manner, with one of the examples given in the paper reviewed above [#2896]. Let

$$H = \begin{pmatrix} 0 & 0 & E_p \\ 0 & V & 0 \\ E_p & 0 & 0 \end{pmatrix},$$

where E_p is the unit matrix of order $p \geqq 1$, and $V = \begin{pmatrix} E_m & 0 \\ 0 & V_1 \end{pmatrix}$, where V_1 is the matrix of a positive even quadratic form of unit determinant and $m \geqq 0$. Let H have n rows and signature $(q+\mu, q)$ with $n = 2q + \mu \geqq \mu + 6 \geqq 10$. Let $G = \mathrm{SO}(H)$ and $G_Z = G \cap \mathrm{SL}(n, Z)$. The author then proves that (i) $N(G_Z) = G_Z$, (ii) if m is not an odd multiple of 4 then G_Z is maximal in G, and (iii) if $m = 4$ then G_Z is not maximal in G. The proofs are elementary.

K. G. Ramanathan (Bombay)

E60-24 **(35# 4226)**

Langlands, R. P.

The volume of the fundamental domain for some arithmetical subgroups of Chevalley groups.

Algebraic Groups and Discontinuous Subgroups (*Proc. Sympos. Pure Math., Boulder, Colo.*, 1965), *pp.* 143–148. *Amer. Math. Soc., Providence, R.I.*, 1966.

Let G be the Chevalley group, i.e., the identity component of the group of automorphisms of a complex semi-simple Lie algebra $\mathfrak{g}$. With respect to a Chevalley basis of $\mathfrak{g}$ [cf. C. Chevalley, Tôhoku Math. J. (2) **7** (1955), 14–66, Theorem 1; MR **17**, 457] G becomes an algebraic matrix group defined over $\mathbf{Q}$. Let ω be an algebraic left invariant form on G of the highest degree defined over $\mathbf{Q}$ which is obtained by taking the wedge product of 1-forms dual to vectors in the Chevalley basis. Let $G_{\mathbf{R}}$, $G_{\mathbf{Z}}$ be the subgroups of G whose coordinates are in $\mathbf{R}$, $\mathbf{Z}$, respectively, and let $\omega_{\mathbf{R}}$ be the Haar measure on $G_{\mathbf{R}}$ derived from ω. As an application of his theory of Eisenstein series [*Algebraic groups and discontinuous subgroups* (Proc. Sympos. Pure Math., Boulder, Colo., 1965), pp. 235–252, Amer. Math. Soc., Providence, R.I., 1966], the author proves the following remarkable equality: $\int_{G_{\mathbf{Z}} \backslash G_{\mathbf{R}}} \omega_{\mathbf{R}} = c \prod_{i=1}^{p} \zeta(a_i)$, where c is the order of the fundamental group of G, $\zeta(s)$ is the Riemann zeta function and $\prod_{i=1}^{p} (t^{2a_i - 1} + 1)$ is the Poincaré polynomial of G.

{Reviewer's remark: Combining this result with a formula of the reviewer [Bull. Amer. Math. Soc. **71** (1965), 345–348, p. 347, line 1; MR **31** #1254] and his determination of the relative Tamagawa number [Ann. of Math. (2) **82** (1965), 88–111; MR **31** #2249], one settles the conjecture of Weil ($\tau(\tilde{G})=1$) for the universal covering group $\tilde{G}$ of the Chevalley group, although the method does not quite satisfy adelized geometers.}

T. Ono (Philadelphia, Pa.)

Citations: MR 31# 1254 = E68-11; MR 31# 2249 = E68-12; MR 40# 2784 = F60-10.

E60-25 (37# 2898)

Raghunathan, M. S.

Cohomology of arithmetic subgroups of algebraic groups. I, II.

Ann. of Math. (2) **86** (1967), 409–424; *ibid.* (2) **87** (1968), 279–304.

Let G be an algebraic group over **Q** which is **Q**-simple, let Γ be an arithmetic subgroup of G and ρ a rational representation of G. The aim of these papers is to prove, under suitable hypotheses, that one has $H^1(\Gamma, \rho)=0$. For the case that ρ is the adjoint representation, the vanishing of $H^1(\Gamma, \rho)$ implies a "rigidity theorem": Every injection $\Gamma \to G$ which is "sufficiently close" to the canonical one can be obtained by an inner conjugation. Let $G_{\mathbf{R}}$ denote the group of real points of G. For the case that $G_{\mathbf{R}}/\Gamma$ is compact, the problem was solved by A. Weil [same Ann. (2) **75** (1962), 578–602; MR **25** #1242]. In these papers the author deals with the case of a non-compact quotient. Part I treats the case that the **Q**-rank of G is at least 2, Part II the case **Q**-rank 1. The methods in these two cases are quite different.

In Part I it is assumed that G is connected, simply connected and of **Q**-rank at least 2. Then the vanishing theorem obtained is that $H^1(\Gamma, \rho)=0$ for any rational representation of G which does not contain the trivial one (so that, in particular, $H^1(\Gamma, \mathrm{Ad})=0$). Using the interpretation of the elements of H^1 as extension classes, this is obtained as an easy consequence of the following main result. Denote by $E(\Gamma)$ the subgroup of Γ generated by its unipotent elements. Then given any finite-dimensional representation ρ of Γ, there exists a subgroup Γ' of finite index in Γ, such that the restriction of ρ to $E(\Gamma')$ can be extended to a rational representation of G. An essential step in the proof is the following lemma. Let U be a unipotent algebraic group over **R**, let Γ be a discrete subgroup of $U_{\mathbf{R}}$ such that $U_{\mathbf{R}}/\Gamma$ is compact. Then any finite-dimensional representation of Γ by unipotent matrices can be extended to a unique rational representation of U. From this lemma the theorem is deduced by invoking the algebraic and arithmetic theory of semisimple groups over **Q**.

In Part II it is assumed that the **Q**-rank of G equals 1. The main vanishing theorems obtained here are as follows: (a) If $G_{\mathbf{R}}$ is not locally isomorphic to SL(2, **C**) (as a real Lie group) and does not have components locally isomorphic to SL(2, **R**), then $H^1(\Gamma, \mathrm{Ad})=0$; (b) If G has no components locally isomorphic to some SL(n, **C**) and if $G_{\mathbf{R}}$ has no components locally isomorphic to some $SO_0(n, 1)$, then $H^1(\Gamma, \rho)=0$ for any rational representation ρ which is irreducible and nontrivial. For the proof the author uses analytic tools.

Let X be the symmetric space associated to $G_{\mathbf{R}}$. One identifies $H^p(\Gamma, \rho)$ with the cohomology of a complex $A^{\cdot}(\Gamma, X, \rho)$ of C^∞ forms on X/Γ with values in a vector bundle $E(\rho)$. By a method of Andreotti and Vesentini (for which the author refers to the literature), it is established that if $E(\rho)$ satisfies a suitable ellipticity condition, any square integrable closed form of the complex is exact. The ellipticity is translated into positivity conditions of a quadratic form, which can be dealt with (for the H^1-case, see the author [Amer. J. Math. **87** (1965), 103–139; MR **30** #3940]).

The main burden of the paper is then to show that in favorable cases, any closed form in $A^{\cdot}(\Gamma, X, \rho)$ is cohomologous to a square integrable one. For this, one first invokes reduction theory, which in the rank 1 case gives a good description of the "ends" of X/Γ. Then results of W. T. van Est [Nederl. Akad. Wetensch. Proc. Ser. A **61** (1958), 399–413; MR **21** #2236] and B. Kostant [Ann. of Math. (2) **74** (1961), 329–387; MR **26** #265] allow the author to get such good control of the behaviour at infinity that he can prove that under certain conditions (involving the highest weight of ρ) indeed any closed form can be represented by a square integrable one. He then gets conditions on G and ρ for $H^p(\Gamma, \rho)$ to be 0, which are sufficient to establish (a) and (b).

T. A. Springer (Utrecht)

Referred to in E60-26, E60-40.

E60-26 (37# 4084)

Garland, H.; Hsiang, W. C.

A square integrability criterion for the cohomology of arithmetic groups.

Proc. Nat. Acad. Sci. U.S.A. **59** (1968), 354–360.

Let **G** be a connected semisimple algebraic group, defined over **Q**. Let $G=\mathbf{G}(\mathbf{R})$ be the group of real points of **G**, let Γ be an arithmetic subgroup of G. Let ρ be an irreducible rational representation of **G** in a complex vector space V, with highest weight λ (relative to a fixed maximal torus **T** of **G** and a fixed order on the character group of **T**). The authors consider a (familiar) cochain complex $\mathcal{E}^{\cdot}=\mathcal{E}^{\cdot}(G, \Gamma, \rho)$ of V-valued, C^∞-differential forms on G. They define a hermitian metric on this complex, using integration over G/Γ. The main result announced in this note is that, under suitable positivity conditions on the highest weight λ, any closed form in $\mathcal{E}^i$ is cohomologous to a square-integrable one. For the case that **G** has **Q**-rank 1, this was proved by M. S. Raghunathan [Ann. of Math. (2) **86** (1967), 409–424; ibid. (2) **87** (1968), 279–304; MR **37** #2898]. As a consequence, the authors obtain another proof of the following known "vanishing theorem" for $\rho=\mathrm{Ad}$, the adjoint representation; one has $H^1(\Gamma, \mathrm{Ad})=0$ if **G** is **Q**-simple, all absolutely simple factors of **G** have rank $\geqq 2$ and **G** is not **Q**-isomorphic to the split $\mathbf{SL}_3$ (first proved by Raghunathan [loc. cit.]).

T. A. Springer (Utrecht)

Citations: MR 37# 2898 = E60-25.

E60-27 (37# 5894)

Raghunathan, M. S.

A note on quotients of real algebraic groups by arithmetic subgroups.

Invent. Math. **4** (1967/68), 318–335.

Let **R**, **Q** denote the fields of real and rational numbers, respectively, and let $\mathbf{R}^+$ denote the positive real numbers. Let $G_{\mathbf{R}}$ denote the **R**-rational points of a connected, semisimple algebraic group defined over **Q**. The author then proves the following theorem: Let $\Gamma \subset G_{\mathbf{R}}$ be an arithmetic subgroup. There exists a C^∞ function $f: G_{\mathbf{R}}/\Gamma \to \mathbf{R}^+$ such that (i) $f^{-1}(0, r]$ is compact for all $r>0$, (ii) there exists $r_0>0$ such that f has no critical points outside $f^{-1}(0, r_0]$, and (iii) f is invariant under the left action of some maximal compact subgroup $K \subset G_{\mathbf{R}}$.

This theorem, together with elementary facts from Morse theory, implies $G_{\mathbf{R}}/\Gamma$ is homeomorphic to the interior of a smooth compact manifold with boundary. Moreover, the same is true for the locally symmetric space $K \backslash G/\Gamma$, provided Γ has no elements of finite order. From this fact, the author obtains, as an immediate corollary, that the functor $M \to H^*(\Gamma, M)$ from the category of Γ-modules ($H^*(\Gamma, M)$ denotes the Eilenberg-MacLane cohomology of Γ, with respect to the module M) commutes with the formation of inductive limits. This gives an affirmative answer to a question raised by Godement, and has implications in the theory of "parabolic cohomology" (unpublished results of Borel and Godement).

The main task in this paper is to construct the Morse function f. This is quite complicated and quite a feat. The proof uses results from Borel's reduction theory and delicate arguments involving partitions of unity. The author also uses his methods to obtain a new proof for a result in reduction theory which asserts, roughly speaking, that a transformation at ∞ must lie in an appropriate parabolic group. *H. Garland* (New Haven, Conn.)

Referred to in E60-40.

E60-28 (37# 6379)

Allan, Nelo D.

Arithmetic subgroups of some classical groups.

An. Acad. Brasil. Ci. **39** (1967), 15–18.

Let **O** be a Dedekind domain and **K** its quotient field. Further, let Ω be a universal domain containing **K** and let G be either $\mathrm{Sl}_n(\Omega)$ or $\mathrm{Sp}_n(\Omega)$. The author determines all arithmetic subgroups Δ of $G_{\mathbf{K}}$ and the normalizer $N(\Delta)$ of Δ in G. *W. H. Simons* (Corvallis, Ore.)

E60-29 (38# 4482)

Allan, Nelo D.

Some non-maximal arithmetic groups.

Rev. Colombiana Mat. **2** (1968), 21–28.

Let $\mathfrak{o}$ be a Dedekind domain and let its quotient field k be infinite such that $\mathfrak{o}/(2)$ is finite. Let H be a nonsingular symmetric n-rowed matrix with elements in $\mathfrak{o}$ and G the group of n-rowed matrices V with elements in k such that $V'HV = H$, V' denoting the transpose of V. Let G_0 be the corresponding group with elements in $\mathfrak{o}$. G_0 is said to be maximal in G if every subgroup Δ of G containing G_0, with the index $(\Delta : G_0)$ finite, coincides with G. The author gives a condition under which G_0 is not maximal.

Let $\mathfrak{p}$ be a prime ideal such that $\mathfrak{p}^\alpha|2$. H is said to be $\mathfrak{p}^\alpha$-even if all its diagonal elements are divisible by $\mathfrak{p}^\alpha$. The main theorem proved is: Let H be $\mathfrak{p}^\alpha$-even and let $\mathfrak{p}^\alpha \nmid a$. Suppose that there exists in $\mathfrak{o}$ a unit η and an element b such that $ba/2$ is in $\mathfrak{p}^{-1}$ but not in $\mathfrak{o}$ and such that $\eta^2 + b\eta = 1$. Then G_0 is not maximal in G. Two simple applications of the theorem are given. *K. G. Ramanathan* (Bombay)

Referred to in E60-30.

E60-30 (39# 2766)

Allan, Nelo D.

A correction on the paper "Some non maxima arithmetic groups".

Rev. Colombiana Mat. **3** (1969), 22.

The author remarks that Theorem 3 of his paper in same Rev. **2** (1968), 21–28 [MR **38** #4482] is not valid unless $\alpha = \beta + 1$, and that the proof of Lemma 3 is incorrect.

Citations: MR 38# 4482 = E60-29.

E60-31 (39# 213)

Behr, Helmut

Endliche Erzeugbarkeit arithmetischer Gruppen über Funktionenkörpern.

Invent. Math. **7** (1969), 1–32.

Let k be a field of algebraic functions of one variable over a finite constant field, and G be a linear algebraic group defined over k. Furthermore, let S be a finite set of prime divisors of k, and let $\mathfrak{o}_S$ be the set of elements in k which lie in the valuation ring of all $\mathfrak{p}$ except $\mathfrak{p} \in S$. The group $G(\mathfrak{o}_S)$ consisting of all matrices in G whose components are in $\mathfrak{o}_S$ is called then the group of S-units, and a fundamental problem is to examine if $\mathfrak{o}_S$ is finitely generated. While the corresponding problem is solved for algebraic groups defined over an algebraic number field, the condition for the finite generatedness of $\mathfrak{o}_S$ in the function field case becomes rather complicated. In the work reviewed here, the author makes precise and wide investigations for general algebraic groups, and obtains several main theorems which cover essentially all possible cases, apart from some restriction on the characteristic of k caused by a technical reason concerning the method of construction of a fundamental domain in the adèle group with respect to $G(\mathfrak{o}_S)$. One of the main results is the following: If G is reductive over k, and the characteristic of k is not 2, 3, or 5, then $G(\mathfrak{o}_S)$ is finitely generated, whenever either the semi-simple part G' of G is of rank 0 over k, or S contains at least two prime divisors. *T. Kubota* (Nagoya)

E60-32 (39# 1565)

Bass, H.

The congruence subgroup problem.

Proc. Conf. Local Fields (Driebergen, 1966), pp. 16–22. *Springer, Berlin,* 1967.

A sketch of the recent results on the congruence subgroup problem for the special linear and symplectic groups, stating the results of J. Milnor, J.-P. Serre and the author which have since appeared in more detail [Inst. Hautes Études Sci. Publ. Math. No. 33 (1967), 59–137]. The last section is a discussion of the relationship with recent work of Calvin Moore on the cohomology of locally compact groups and the "metaplectic conjecture", generalizing results of A. Weil [Acta Math. **111** (1964), 143–211; MR **29** #2324]. *G. B. Seligman* (New Haven, Conn.)

Citations: MR 29# 2324 = E12-104; MR 39# 5574 = E60-37.

E60-33 (39# 1566)

Matsumoto, Hideya

Sur les sous-groupes arithmétiques des groupes semi-simples déployés.

Ann. Sci. École Norm. Sup. (4) **2** (1969), 1–62.

The author solves the congruence subgroup problem for connected linear algebraic groups G defined over a number field k which are simple, simply connected, split over k and of rank $\geqq 2$. This extends previous solutions for $\mathrm{SL}_n (n \geqq 3)$ and $\mathrm{Sp}_{2n} (n \geqq 2)$, where $k = Q$ [J. Mennicke, Ann. of Math. (2) **81** (1965), 31–37; MR **30** #2083; Math. Ann. **159** (1965), 115–129; MR **31** #5903; H. Bass, M. Lazard and J.-P. Serre, Bull. Amer. Math. Soc. **70** (1964), 385–392; MR **28** #5117], the same groups for any number field k [H. Bass, J. Milnor and J.-P. Serre, Inst. Hautes Études Sci. Publ. Math. No. 33 (1968), 59–137], and recent results of Serre for SL_2.

Let $\mathfrak{o}$ be the ring of integers in k, G_k the rational points of G, G_0 the integral points (relative to an embedding of G in a general linear group). A subgroup Γ' of G_k is called arithmetic if $\Gamma' \cap G_0$ is of finite index in Γ' and in G_0. If $\mathfrak{q}$ is a $\neq 0$ ideal of $\mathfrak{o}$, $\Gamma_\mathfrak{q}$ is the set of elements g in G_0 such that $g \equiv 1 \pmod{\mathfrak{q}}$. An arithmetic subgroup Γ' is called a congruence subgroup if $\Gamma' \supset \Gamma_\mathfrak{q}$ for some non-zero $\mathfrak{q}$. The congruence subgroup problem is whether or not every arithmetic subgroup is a congruence subgroup.

The paper comes in three chapters. The first studies some exact sequences of locally compact groups. Take G simple, simply connected and split over k. Let $\hat{G}_k$ and $\bar{G}_k$ be the respective completions of G_k using arithmetic subgroups (respectively, congruence subgroups) as neighborhoods of 1, π the canonical morphism of $\hat{G}_k$ on $\bar{G}_k$, $C(G_k)$

the kernel of π. Then the congruence subgroup problem is whether or not $C(G_k)=1$. One identifies $\bar{G}_k$ with the adelic group $G_{A_k{}^f}$, where $A_k{}^f$ is the adele ring using only the finite places of k. The extension $\hat{G}_k$ of $G_{A_k{}^f}$ is trivial over G_k, regarded as a discrete group. For G_0, the author proves a reduction theorem on the rank of G analogous to H. Bass' stability theorem for $\mathrm{SL}_n(\mathfrak{o})$ [ibid. No. 22 (1964), 5–60; MR **30** #4805], from which he concludes that if rank $G\geqq 2$, then $C(G_k)$ is central in $\hat{G}_k$, and $\hat{G}_k$ can be universally characterized among all central extensions of $G_{A_k{}^f}$.

Chapter II treats central extensions of G_{k_t}, k_t an infinite topological field, G simple, simply connected and split over k. If A is an abelian topological group, $H^2(G_{k_t}, A)$ are the central extensions of G_k by A under Baer multiplication. This is studied by means of the Steinberg cocycles [R. Steinberg, Colloq. Théorie des Groupes Algébriques (Bruxelles, 1962), pp. 113–127, Librairie Universitaire, Louvain, 1962; MR **27** #3638; C. Moore, Inst. Hautes Études Sci. Publ. Math. No. 35 (1968), 157–222] and the Bruhat decomposition of G_{k_t}. Let $S(k_t{}^*, A)$ be the group of Steinberg cocycles on $k_t{}^*$ with values in A, and $S^0(k_t{}^*, A)$ be those which are bilinear on $k_t{}^* \times k_t{}^*$. Then the author proves that $H^2(G_{k_t}, A)\cong S(k_t{}^*, A)$ or $S^0(k_t{}^*, A)$ depending on whether or not G is isomorphic to a symplectic group. For $G=\mathrm{SL}_2$, this result is also obtainable from C. Moore [loc. cit.].

In Chapter III, the author puts together the results of Chapter II, notions of universal covering and fundamental group for central extensions of locally compact groups, and results of C. Moore [loc. cit.] on the determination of the Steinberg cocycles for a local field and on the uniqueness of the reciprocity formulas in a global field. The two key results are as follows. If k_v is an ultrametric local field or the reals, then there is an extension of G_{k_v}, corresponding to a suitable canonical Steinberg cocycle, which is a universal covering of G_{k_v}. If k is a global field, A_k the adele ring of k, then the relative fundamental group of the adelic group G_{A_k} with respect to G_k is isomorphic to the group μ_k of roots of unity contained in k. These two results had been previously obtained for SL_n and Sp_{2n} by various authors.

From all this, the following solution to the congruence subgroup problem arises for G simple, simply connected, of rank $\geqq 2$ split over an algebraic number field k: $C(G_k)\cong \mu_k$ if k is totally imaginary, and otherwise $C(G_k)=1$. In particular, if k possesses a real conjugate, then every arithmetic subgroup of G_k is a congruence subgroup. The author also notes that any arithmetic subgroup of G_k contains a subgroup of finite index generated by unipotent elements. *E. J. Taft* (New Brunswick, N.J.)

Citations: MR 28# 5117 = E60-11; MR 30# 2083 = E56-34; MR 31# 5903 = E60-14; MR 39# 5574 = E60-37; MR 39# 5575 = E68-31.

Referred to in E04-31, E60-37, E60-43, E60-47, E68-31, R38-55.

E60-34 (39# 2769)

Serre, Jean-Pierre

Cohomologie des groupes discrets.

C. R. Acad. Sci. Paris Sér. A-B **268** (1969), A268–A271.

Si k est un corps local, $G=\mathbf{PGL}_2(k)$, Y. Ihara a prouvé [J. Math. Soc. Japan **18** (1966), 219–235; MR **36** #6511] qu'un sous-groupe discret sans torsion de G est libre. L'auteur montre que ce résultat est un cas particulier d'un théorème limitant la dimension cohomologique $\mathrm{cd}(\Gamma)$ (si $\mathrm{cd}(\Gamma)=1$, Γ est libre par le théorème de Stallings-Swan). On considère des groupes G qui sont produits finis de groupes G_α, égaux soit à un groupe de Lie réel ayant un nombre fini de composantes connexes, soit au groupe des k_α-points d'un groupe algébrique réductif L_α sur un corps local k_α; $d(G_\alpha)$ est dans le premier cas la dimension du quotient de G_α par un sous-groupe compact maximal, dans le second le rang de L_α sur k_α au sens de Borel-Tits, et $d(G)=\sum_\alpha d(G_\alpha)$. L'inégalité prouvée par l'auteur est alors $\mathrm{cd}(\Gamma)\leqq d(G)$, sous les hypothèses que Γ est sans torsion et que toute partie bornée de Γ est finie. La méthode (esquissée sans démonstration) consiste à faire opérer Γ sur un produit d'"immeubles" de Bruhat-Tits, qui forment des CW-complexes acycliques, et à utiliser un résultat de Quillen qui majore $\mathrm{cd}(\Gamma)$ en fonction des $\mathrm{cd}(\Gamma_\sigma)$, où Γ_σ est le stabilisateur d'une cellule σ du complexe. Le théorème s'applique en particulier aux sous-groupes dits "S-arithmétiques" d'un groupe algébrique réductif L sur un corps de nombres algébriques k. L'auteur en déduit par exemple que tout sous-groupe sans torsion de type fini de $\mathbf{GL}_n(\mathbf{Q})$ est de dimension cohomologique finie. Il y a encore bien d'autres choses dans cette note très riche en résultats, et qu'on ne pourrait résumer qu'en la reproduisant intégralement. *J. Dieudonné* (Nice)

Citations: MR 36# 6511 = E64-19.

E60-35 (39# 4102)

Baily, Walter L., Jr.

An exceptional arithmetic group and its Eisenstein series.

Bull. Amer. Math. Soc. **75** (1969), 402–406.

From the author's introduction: "Let G_R be the simply connected, real Lie group of type E_7 which is isogenous to the full group of holomorphic automorphisms of a bounded symmetric domain in $\mathbf{C}^{27}$. It is the purpose of this note to announce results on a certain arithmetic subgroup Γ of G_R and its automorphic forms; in particular, we have proved that the automorphic forms for Γ given by Eisenstein series have Fourier coefficients which are rational numbers with a certain Euler product expansion. Because the proofs are too long to give here, they will be presented elsewhere."

The sketch of the proof begins with a detailed description of the groups G_R and Γ. Both have common features with $\mathrm{Sp}(n, \mathbf{R})$ and $\mathrm{Sp}(n, \mathbf{Z})$; in particular, they contain an inversion $Z\to -Z^{-1}$ (the "variable"), translations $Z\to Z+A$, and parabolic subgroups $G_{R,0}$ and $\Gamma_0=G_{R,0}\cap\Gamma$. For an element $g\in G_R$ define $j(Z, g)$ as the Jacobian $|\partial g(Z)/\partial Z|$. The Eisenstein series are then

$$E_k(Z) = \sum_{\gamma\in\Gamma/\Gamma_0} j(Z,\gamma)^{-k}.$$

They have Fourier expansions whose coefficients are rational numbers. The idea of the proof is that used by C. L. Siegel [Math. Ann. **116** (1939), 617–657; MR **1**, 203]. Namely, the coefficients are expressed as sums over certain Gauss sums, and these turn out to be (up to a trivial factor) certain products $\prod \zeta(2r)$ with integral r, where $\zeta(s)$ is the Riemann zeta-function. *M. Eichler* (Basel)

Citations: MR 1, 203f = F50-1.

E60-36 (39# 4288)

Každan, D. A.

Construction of Γ-rational groups for certain discrete subgroups Γ of the group SL(2, R). (Russian)

Funkcional. Anal. i Priložen. **2** (1968), *no.* 1, 36–39.

Let N be a given group and Γ a subgroup of N. Consider the set of elements n of N such that the subgroup $\Gamma\cap n\Gamma^{-1}n$ has finite index in Γ and in $n\Gamma^{-1}n$. These elements form a subgroup $\bar{\Gamma}$ of N called a Γ-rational group. The author proves the following theorem which is a partial converse of a theorem of I. I. Pjateckiĭ-Šapiro and I. R. Šafarevič [Izv. Akad. Nauk SSSR Ser. Mat. **30** (1966), 671–704; MR **34** #2581]. Theorem: Let Γ be a discrete subgroup in $\mathrm{SL}(2, R)$ such that (a) the factor space

$SL(2, R)/\Gamma$ has finite volume, but is not compact; (b) the group Γ consists of matrices whose elements are algebraic integers. Then the group $\bar{\Gamma}$ is either discrete or is conjugate to a subgroup in $SL(2, Z)$.

W. H. Simons (Corvallis, Ore.)

Citations: MR 34# 2581 = F99-4.

E60-37 (39# 5574)

Bass, H.; Milnor, J.; Serre, J.-P.

Solution of the congruence subgroup problem for SL_n ($n \geqq 3$) and Sp_{2n} ($n \geqq 2$).

Inst. Hautes Études Sci. Publ. Math. No. 33 (1967), 59–137.

Let G be one of the above groups, k an algebraic number field (finite over the rationals), and θ the ring of integers in k. Let Γ be the group of elements of G with coordinates in θ, and for any nonzero ideal q in θ let Γ_q be the kernel of reduction mod q. Any subgroup of Γ containing some Γ_q is called a congruence subgroup; such a group is necessarily of finite index since θ/q is finite. The problem now is to answer the question: (*) conversely, is every subgroup of Γ of finite index a congruence subgroup? The principal result of the present paper is that if k has a real imbedding (the special case in which k is the rational field had been proved earlier by the first author, M. Lazard and the third author [Bull. Amer. Math. Soc. **70** (1964), 385–392; MR **28** #5117] and by J. L. Mennicke [Ann. of Math. (2) **81** (1965), 31–37; MR **30** #2083] independently), then the answer is "yes", while if k has not, then the answer is "no" (in a rather precise sense (see (**) below)) but becomes "yes" if we adjoin to θ any other element of k. The authors also answer the analogous question for the other global fields, the function fields in one variable over finite constant fields, in the affirmative. To discuss the results further we assume that $G = SL_n$ ($n \geqq 3$), that Γ_q is as above, that E denotes the subgroup of Γ generated by its elementary matrices (those agreeing with the identity except possibly in one off-diagonal position) and E_q the normal subgroup of E generated by the elementary matrices of Γ_q. Then "by fairly elementary methods one can show": (0) E_q is a normal subgroup of Γ_q. (1) Every subgroup of Γ of finite index contains some E_q and each E_q is of finite index. (2) E_q is a congruence subgroup if and only if it equals Γ_q. (3) Γ_q is generated by E_q and $\Gamma_q \cap SL_2(\theta)$, with $SL_2(\theta)$ imbedded in the upper left-hand corner of $\Gamma = SL_n(\theta)$. Let $\Gamma_q/E_q = C_q$. By (1) and (2) the vanishing of all C_q is equivalent to a "yes" answer to (*), and in any case these groups provide a quantitative measure of the answer if it is "no". The authors continue as follows. Let W_q consist of all (a, b) in θ^2 congruent to $(1, 0)$ mod q and such that $a\theta + b\theta = \theta$. Given (a, b) in W_q one can find α in $\Gamma_q \cap SL_2(\theta)$ (see (3) above) and then project into C_q. The result turns out to depend only on (a, b), not on α, hence defines a map $(a, b) \to \begin{bmatrix} b \\ a \end{bmatrix}$ from W_q to C_q, which is surjective by (3). It (a result due to Mennicke) can be shown that $\begin{bmatrix} b+ta \\ a \end{bmatrix} = \begin{bmatrix} b \\ a \end{bmatrix}$ for t in q, $\begin{bmatrix} b \\ a+tb \end{bmatrix} = \begin{bmatrix} b \\ a \end{bmatrix}$ for t in θ, and $\begin{bmatrix} b \\ a \end{bmatrix}$ is multiplicative in b. Let D_q be the abstract group generated by symbols [ ] subject to these relations and f the natural homomorphism of D_q onto C_q. The authors prove that (4) f is in fact an isomorphism. It should be mentioned that the results (0) to (4) are made to depend on auxiliary results that hold for more general types of rings than θ and lead to calculations of Whitehead groups, theorems on finite generation (e.g., $SL_n(Z[t_1, t_2, \cdots, t_m])$ is finitely generated if the t's are indeterminates and $n \geqq m+4$), and other applications. The authors complete the main development by determining the groups D_q: (**) If k is not totally imaginary, then D_q is trivial for every ideal q, while if k is so, then D_q is isomorphic to an explicitly determined subgroup of μ, the group of roots of 1 of k, a finite cyclic group, and the projective limit of the D_q's is isomorphic to μ itself, which is therefore the final measure for the failure of an affirmative answer to (*) in this case. Using Dirichlet's theorem on primes in arithmetic progressions and the relations in D_q in essentially the way that Mennicke did in his paper, and also the reciprocity laws of algebraic number theory, the authors limit the possibilities for D_q as in (**), and then they use the symbols occurring in the statements of these laws to construct models for D_q that show no further limitation is possible. It turns out at an early stage (as it did in the two earlier papers) that Γ/E_q is always a central extension of Γ/Γ_q. This in combination with (**) yields, in terms of the completions of Γ with first the E_q's and then the Γ_q's forming a system of neighborhoods of the identity, a result closely related to one of C. Moore [see #5575 below] in his work on the covering groups of adelic semisimple groups. Further details on this interesting connection may be found in § 15 of the paper. The authors conjecture that their results so far discussed are true for arbitrary split simply connected simple groups of rank at least 2, not just those of the title. H. Matsumoto [Ann. Sci. École Norm. Sup. (4) **2** (1969), 1–62; MR **39** #1566] has shown this to be true. In their final section the authors show that if G is a simply connected semisimple algebraic group defined over Q and Γ is an arithmetic subgroup of G_Q, then under certain conditions, which in particular hold for the groups of the title by (**), every (abstract) homomorphism $\Gamma \to GL_n(Q)$ agrees on a subgroup of finite index of Γ with a homomorphism $G \to GL_n$ of algebraic groups defined over Q. From this it follows that every finite-dimensional $Q[\Gamma]$-module fixes some lattice and is completely reducible, and that every homomorphism $G_Q \to GL_n(Q)$ (hence every automorphism of G_Q) is algebraic.

R. Steinberg (Los Angeles, Calif.)

Citations: MR 28# 5117 = E60-11; MR 30# 2083 = E56-34; MR 39# 1566 = E60-33; MR 39# 5575 = E68-31.

Referred to in E56-56, E60-32, E60-33, E60-38, E60-42, E60-43, E60-47, Z10-69.

E60-38 (40# 210)

Vaserštein, L. N.

K_1-theory and the congruence problem. (Russian)

Mat. Zametki **5** (1969), 233–244.

Let L be an associative ring with unit, and J a two-sided ideal in L. $GL(n, L)$ and $GL(n, J)$ are the groups of invertible elements in $1_n + M_n(L)$ and $1_n + M_n(J)$, respectively; $M_n(\cdot)$ denotes the set of $n \times n$-matrices with coefficients in $\cdot$. $E(n, L)$ and $E(n, J)$ are the subgroups generated by the $1_n + ye_{i,j}$, $y \in L$, and $1_n + xe_{i,j}$, $x \in J$, respectively, where $1 \leqq i \neq j \leqq n$; $GL(L)$, $GL(J)$, $E(L)$, $E(L, J)$ the direct limits of these groups as $n \to \infty$. $K_1(L, J) = GL(J)/E(L, J)$ is the Whitehead group of the pair L, J. A column vector $b = (b_i)_{1 \leqq i \leqq n}$ with $b_i = \delta_i{}^1 + v_i$ ($v_i \in J$, $\delta_i{}^j$ = Kronecker symbol) is said to be J-unimodular if there is a row vector $a = (a^i) = \delta_1{}^i + w^i$, $w^i \in J$, such that $ab = 1$. The stable rank of J is said to be $\leqq m$ if for any $n > m$ and any J-unimodular $b = (b_i)_{1 \leqq i \leqq n}$, there is a $d = (d_i)_{1 \leqq i \leqq n-1}$, $d_i \in J$, such that $(b_i + d_i b_n)_{1 \leqq i \leqq n-1}$ is J-unimodular. Theorem: If the stable rank of $J \leqq m$ and $n \geqq m+1$, then $GL(n, J)/E(n, L, J) = K_1(L, J)$.

Let l be a (skew)field of finite rank over the rationals, L an order in l, $SL(n, J) = GL(n, J) \cap E(n, l)$, $n > 1$. Further, let $SL(n, L)$ be the completion of $SL(n, L)$ with respect to the finite index topology, and $SL(n, {}^\wedge L)$ the completion of $SL(n, L)$ with respect to its congruence subgroups

$\overline{SL(n, J)}$, $J \neq 0$. $C_n(L)$ denotes the kernel of the map $\overline{SL(n, L)} \to SL(n, L)$, and $C(L) = \lim C_n(L)$.

Theorem: If $n \geq 3$ then $C_n(L) = C(L)$; $C_n(L)$ is finite. Further, the finite index topology in $SL(n, L)$ is generated by any of the following four systems of subgroups: (a) $E(n, L, J)$, $J \neq 0$ (or $E(n, L, mL) m \neq 0$), (b) $[SL(n, mL), SL(n, mL)]$, (c) $[GL(n, L), GL(n, J)]$, $J \neq 0$, (d) normal subgroups in $SL(n, L)$ with infinitely many elements. The paper is related to previous work of H. Bass and others [cf. H. Bass, Inst. Hautes Études Sci. Publ. Math. No. 22 (1964), 5–60; MR **30** #4805; H. Bass, J. Milnor and J.-P. Serre, ibid. No. 33 (1967), 59–137; MR **39** #5574; H. Bass, Bull. Amer. Math. Soc. **70** (1964), 429–433; MR **28** #4035].

W. T. van Est (Leiden)

Citations: MR 28# 4035 = E60-9; MR 39# 5574 = E60-37.

E60-39 (40# 245)

Newman, Morris

Subgroups of SL(t, Z).

J. Res. Nat. Bur. Standards Sect. B **73B** (1969), 143–144.

It is shown that, in sharp contrast to the case of $SL_2(Z)$, no normal subgroup, or subgroup of finite index, in either $SL_t(Z)$ for $t \geq 3$ or $Sp_{2t}(Z)$ for $t \geq 2$, is a free group. Results of H. Bass, M. Lazard and J.-P. Serre [Bull. Amer. Math. Soc. **70** (1964), 385–392; MR **28** #5117] and of J. L. Mennicke [Ann. of Math. (2) **81** (1965), 31–37; MR **30** #2083; Math. Ann. **159** (1965), 115–129; MR **31** #5903] reduce the problem to that for congruence subgroups. In congruence subgroups one finds two commuting transvections that are not powers of a common element.

R. C. Lyndon (Ann Arbor, Mich.)

Citations: MR 28# 5117 = E60-11; MR 30# 2083 = E56-34; MR 31# 5903 = E60-14.

E60-40 (40# 269)

Garland, Howard

The spectrum of noncompact G/Γ and the cohomology of arithmetic groups.

Bull. Amer. Math. Soc. **75** (1969), 807–811.

In this note a theorem is announced about some well defined spaces of square summable harmonic forms on noncompact locally symmetric spaces associated with Q-rank one arithmetic groups—i.e., those spaces are found to be finite dimensional.

Upper bounds are then indicated for some Betti numbers—in an interesting extension of works of Y. Matsushima [Osaka J. Math. **14** (1962), 1–20; MR **25** #4549] and M. S. Raghunathan [Ann. of Math. (2) **86** (1967), 409–424; ibid. (2) **87** (1968), 279–304; MR **37** #2898; Invent. Math. **4** (1967/68), 318–335; MR **37** #5894]. Details will appear later.

A. Evyatar (*Gutwirth*) (Haifa)

Citations: MR 37# 2898 = E60-25; MR 37# 5894 = E60-27.

E60-41 (40# 2682)

Behr, Helmut

Über die endliche Definierbarkeit verallgemeinerter Einheitengruppen. II.

Invent. Math. **4** (1967), 265–274.

Let k be an algebraic number field, S a finite set of finite places of k and $o(S)$ the ring of those elements of k which are p-integral for all $p \notin S$. Let G be a reductive algebraic group defined over k and $G_{o(S)}$ the group of S-units of G, i.e., the subgroup of G consisting of X such that all components of X and X^{-1} belong to $o(S)$. By making use of results of M. Kneser [J. Reine Angew. Math. **214/215** (1964), 345–349; MR **28** #5067], A. Borel and J. Tits [Inst. Hautes Études Sci. Publ. Math. **27** (1965), 55–152; MR **34** #7527], F. Bruhat and J. Tits [C. R. Acad. Sci. Paris Sér. A-B **263** (1966), A598–A601; MR **39** #4160; ibid. **263** (1966), A766–A768; MR **39** #4161; ibid. **263** (1966), A822–A825; MR **39** #4162; ibid. **263** (1966), A867–A869; MR **39** #4163] the author proves that the group $G_{o(S)}$ is finitely generated and finitely presented. When S is empty, the result was obtained by A. Borel and Harish-Chandra [Ann. of Math. (2) **75** (1962), 485–535; MR **26** #5081].

T. Ono (Baltimore, Md.)

Citations: MR 26# 5081 = E60-5; MR 28# 5067 = E60-10; MR 39# 4160 = E64-23; MR 39# 4161 = E64-24; MR 39# 4162 = E64-25; MR 39# 4163 = E64-26.

E60-42 (41# 1894)

Vaseršteĭn, L. N.

The congruence problem for the classical groups. (Russian)

Funkcional. Anal. i Priložen. **3** (1969), *no.* 3, 88–89.

In this paper the author demonstrates some results concerning the "congruence subgroup problem" in the case of classical groups. Let G be a linear algebraic group defined over the field of rational numbers Q and let $G(Z) = G(Q) \cap GL(N, Z)$ be the group of matrices with integer entries in a matrix representation of $G \subset GL(N)$. The (full) congruence subgroups are $G(I) = G(Z) \cap GL(N, I)$, where $I = mZ$ is a non zero ideal of the ring Z. "The congruence subgroup problem" in the sense of J. P. Serre is the following: Does every subgroup of finite index in $G(Z)$ comprise a congruence subgroup, or in an equivalent formulation: Are the congruence subgroups a base of neighborhoods of the unit element in the Krull topology of $G(Z)$?

Let $G^f(Q)$ be the completion of the group $G(Q)$ in the topology for which the base of neighborhoods of the unit element is formed by the subgroups of finite index in $G(Z)$. There is a canonical homomorphism $G^f(Q) \to G(Q^f) = \Pi_p G(Q_p)$, where $Q^f = \Pi_p Q_p$ is the completion of the field Q in the topology of the non-zero ideals in the Z-product of the p-adic number fields Q_p. The kernel of this homomorphism is $C(G(Z))$; $C(G(Z)) = 1$ is equivalent to an affirmative answer for the congruence subgroup problem. There are four theorems which are concerned with the computation possibilities of $C(G(Z))$ in certain cases and the results are compared with the results of J. P. Serre, J. Milnor and H. Bass [e.g., Inst. Hautes Études Sci. Publ. Math. No. 33 (1967), 59–137; MR **39** #5574]. There are no proofs, but further details can be found in the author's earlier papers [e.g., Mat. Sb. (N.S.) **75** (**117**) (1968), 178–184; MR **37** #1475; ibid. (N.S.) **76** (**118**) (1968), 362–367; MR **37** #5301].

G. Pic (Cluj)

Citations: MR 39# 5574 = E60-37.

E60-43 (41# 3483)

Abe, Eiichi

Chevalley groups over local rings.

Tôhoku Math. J. (2) **21** (1969), 474–494.

Let G be a semisimple algebraic group, defined and split over Z as in the paper by C. Chevalley [Séminaire Bourbaki: 1960/61, Fasc. 3, Exp. 219, Secrétariat mathématique, Paris, 1961; see MR **27** #1339; facsimile reprint, Benjamin, New York, 1966; see MR **33** #5420a]. If R is a ring (commutative with 1), let $G(R)$ denote the group of points of G with coordinates in R. If A is an ideal in R, let $G(R, A)$ $[G^*(R, A)]$ denote the inverse image in $G(R)$, under reduction mod A, of 1 [the center], $E(R)$ the group generated by the one-parameter unipotent subgroups corresponding to a splitting of G, and $E(R, A)$ the normal subgroup of $E(R)$ generated by the intersections of those subgroups with $G(R, A)$. The author proves the following "congruence subgroup theorem". If G is simple and simply connected, and if R is a local ring, then $G(R, A)=E(R, A)$ for all ideals A in R. If further the characteristic of R is not the ratio of the squares of lengths of roots of G, then for every normal subgroup N of $G(R)$ there exists a unique ideal A in R such that $G(R, A)\subseteq N\subseteq G^*(R, A)$. The author in fact proves a more complicated result in which G need not be simply connected. Previously W. Klingenberg [Amer. J. Math. **83** (1961), 137–153; MR **23** #A1724] obtained these results for the groups SL_n and Sp_n. Analogous results over more general rings have been obtained by H. Bass, J. Milnor and J.-P. Serre [Inst. Hautes Études Sci. Publ. Math. No. 33 (1967), 59–137; MR **39** #5574] (for SL_n and Sp_n) and by H. Matsumoto [Ann. Sci. École Norm. Sup. (4) **2** (1969), 1–62; MR **39** #1566] (the general case). The author's proofs are computational, relying on the interrelationships of the basic unipotent generators of $G(R)$.

R. Steinberg (Los Angeles, Calif.)

Citations: MR 23# A1724 = E56-22; MR 39# 1566 = E60-33; MR 39# 5574 = E60-37.

E60-44 (41# 7153)

Borel, Armand

Pseudo-concavité et groupes arithmétiques.

Essays on Topology and Related Topics (Mémoires dédiés à Georges de Rham), pp. 70–84. Springer, New York, 1970.

Let G be an algebraic connected semisimple group defined over $\mathbf{Q}$, $K\subset G_{\mathbf{R}}$ a maximal compact subgroup, $X=K\backslash G_{\mathbf{R}}\subset \mathbf{C}^n$ a bounded symmetric domain, and $\Gamma\subset G$ an arithmetic subgroup. It is known [W. Baily and the author, Ann. of Math. (2) **84** (1966), 442–528; MR **35** #6870] that $V=X/\Gamma$ has a normal projective-algebraic compactification V^* such that $V^*\text{-}V$ is an algebraic subvariety. If G has no distinguished subgroup defined over $\mathbf{Q}$ and locally isomorphic to $SL(2, \mathbf{C})$, then $V^*\text{-}V$ has codimension $\geqq 2$ in V^*. A trivial consequence is that in this case V is pseudo-concave in the weak sense of A. Andreotti and H. Grauert [Nachr. Akad. Wiss. Göttingen Math.-Phys. Kl. II **1961**, 39–48; MR **24** #A2057] and Andreotti [Bull. Soc. Math. France **91** (1963), 1–38; MR **27** #2649].

The author gives a direct proof for the pseudo-concavity of V, not using the compactification V^*. He constructs a continuous proper map $q\colon V\to[0, \infty)$ such that for large $r\in\mathbf{R}$ through every $y\in q^{-1}(r)$ there passes a locally analytic subset $\alpha(D)$, $D\subset\mathbf{C}^2$ a neighborhood of the origin, $\alpha\colon D\to V$ holomorphic with $\alpha(0)=y$. Further, $q\circ\alpha$ is smooth enough and has a negative definite Levi-form at 0. This is more than the pseudo-concavity above, but less than strong $(n-1)$-pseudo-concavity in the sense of Andreotti and Grauert [ibid. **90** (1962), 193–259; MR **27** #343]. The proof uses many details of Baily and the author [loc. cit.] and the author [*Introduction aux groupes arithmétiques*, Actualités Sci. Indust., No. 1341, Hermann, Paris, 1969; MR **39** #5577]. Most important are the "rational boundary components" for X of maximal and minimal dimension.

W. Barth (Münster)

Citations: MR 24# A2057 = F40-23; MR 35# 6870 = F50-31; MR 39# 5577 = E02-15.

E60-45 (42# 3090)

Riehm, Carl

The congruence subgroup problem over local fields.

Amer. J. Math. **92** (1970), 771–778.

Let k be a field which is complete under a non-trivial absolute value. If G is an algebraic group over k, the group $G(k)$ of rational points of G in k inherits a topology from k. An open subgroup U of $G(k)$ is said to have the congruence subgroup property if every non-central normal subgroup of U is open.

Assume that G is semi-simple and almost k-simple. Then one or the other of the following conditions is necessary and sufficient for every open subgroup of $G(k)$ to have the congruence subgroup property: (1) k is perfect; (2) if $\tilde{G}$ is the simply connected covering group of G over k, then any covering isogeny $\pi\colon\tilde{G}\to G$ over k is separable. If neither of these conditions is fulfilled, then no open subgroup of $G(k)$ has the congruence subgroup property.

This generalizes a result of Borel for characteristic zero.

M. J. Greenberg (Santa Cruz, Calif.)

E60-46 (42# 5997)

Borel, Armand; Serre, Jean-Pierre

Adjonction de coins aux espaces symétriques; applications à la cohomologie des groupes arithmétiques.

C. R. Acad. Sci. Paris Sér. A-B **271** (1970), A1156–A1158.

Let G be a connected reductive linear algebraic group over $\mathbf{Q}$ with no nontrivial characters. The authors sketch briefly how to make the quotient X of $G(\mathbf{R})$ by a maximal compact subgroup into the interior of a manifold with corners $\bar{X}$. The construction is a gluing of certain open submanifolds of $\bar{X}$ associated with the elements of P, the set of parabolic subgroups of G defined over $\mathbf{Q}$. The space $\bar{X}$ is contractible. Its boundary $\partial\bar{X}$ has the homotopy type of the Tits building $T(P)$, which, by a theorem of Solomon-Tits, is that of a bouquet of $(l-1)$-spheres, where l is the $\mathbf{Q}$-rank of G. Putting $d=\dim X$ it follows that $H_c{}^q(\bar{X}, \mathbf{Z})=0$ for $q\neq d-l$ (cohomology with compact supports) and that $I=H_c{}^{d-l}(\bar{X}, \mathbf{Z})$ is a free $\mathbf{Z}$-module. The action of $G(\mathbf{Q})$ on $\bar{X}$ affords one on I which the authors observe to be analogous to the Steinberg representation of a finite group equipped with a Tits system (BN-pair).

If Γ is an arithmetic subgroup of $G(\mathbf{Q})$, the authors deduce from reduction theory that Γ acts properly on $\bar{X}$ with compact quotient. When Γ is torsion free and hence acts freely on $\bar{X}$, it follows that $H^q(\Gamma, M)\cong H_{d-l-q}(\Gamma, I\otimes M)$ for all Γ-modules M. In particular, $\mathrm{cd}(\Gamma)=d-l$. Moreover, $H^q(\Gamma, \mathbf{Z}[\Gamma])=0$ for $q\neq d-l$ and $H^{d-l}(\Gamma, \mathbf{Z}[\Gamma])=I$.

H. Bass (New York)

Referred to in E60-48.

E60-47 (42# 7671)

Serre, Jean-Pierre

Le problème des groupes de congruence pour $\mathbf{SL}_2$.

Ann. of Math. (2) **92** (1970), 489–527.

Let K be a global field (number field or function field in one variable over a finite field), S a finite nonempty set of places of K including the archimedean ones, $A=A_S$ the ring of S-integers of K, U the group of units in A (which is finite if and only if $\mathrm{Card}(S)=1$). The author gives a complete solution of the congruence subgroup problem for $G=\mathbf{SL}_2(K)$, supplementing the known results in rank >1 due to H. Bass, J. Milnor and the author [Inst. Hautes Études Sci. Publ. Math. No. 33 (1967), 59–137; MR **39** #5574] and H. Matsumoto [Ann. Sci. École Norm. Sup. (4) **2** (1969), 1–62; MR **39** #1566]. The special case $K=\mathbf{Q}$, $S=\{p, \infty\}$ was already worked out by J. Mennicke [Invent. Math. **4** (1967), 202–228; MR **37** #1485], some of whose methods are used here. As in the author's Bourbaki talk [*Séminaire Bourbaki, Vol. 1966/67*, Exposé 330, Benjamin, New York, 1968; see MR **37** #10], the problem leads to an exact sequence $1\to C(G)\to\hat{G}\to\bar{G}\to 1$, where $\hat{G}$ and $\bar{G}$ are the respective completions of G for the topologies of arithmetic and congruence subgroups. If Card $(S)\geqq 2$, then $C(G)$ is trivial unless S consists of imaginary places, in which case $C(G)$ is the finite group of roots of unity in K. (This result holds for rank >1 even when Card(S) = 1.) If Card(S) = 1, then $C(G)$ is infinite, a result due essentially to F. Klein when $K = \mathbf{Q}$.

First let Card(S) $\geqq 2$. By purely algebraic and number-theoretic arguments, involving comparison of elementary and congruence subgroups, the author shows that $C(G)$ is central in $\hat{G}$. This sets the stage for application of C. Moore's theory of central extensions [Inst. Hautes Études Sci. Publ. Math. No. 35 (1968), 157–222; MR **39** #5575], which yields the main theorem. As a byproduct, every normal subgroup of an S-arithmetic group N not contained in $\{\pm 1\}$ is shown to have finite index in N; in particular, $N^{ab} = N/(N, N)$ is finite. This is further used to investigate representations $\rho: N \to \mathbf{GL}_n(k)$. If char $k \neq$ char K, then $\rho(N)$ is finite. If char k = char $K = 0$, then ρ is "algebraic" on a subgroup of finite index in N; this implies that ρ is completely reducible, whence a vanishing theorem for H^1 of N. (The case char k = char $K > 0$ is not settled.)

Next let Card(S) = 1. There are only three possibilities for K, called by the author the rational, imaginary quadratic, and characteristic p cases. Let Γ be an S-arithmetic subgroup of G; Γ may be replaced by a "net" subgroup of finite index (no element having as eigenvalue a root of unity $\neq 1$). In contrast to the first case, the author proves that Γ^{ab} is infinite, which implies quickly that $C(G)$ is infinite (by considering $H^1(\Gamma, \mathbf{Z})$ or using cardinality arguments in characteristic p), and also that S-arithmetic groups are not finitely-generated in characteristic p. The proof that Γ^{ab} is infinite in the rational case is familiar: Γ acts freely on the Poincaré upper half-plane $\mathbf{X} = \mathbf{SL}_2(\mathbf{R})/\mathbf{SO}_2(\mathbf{R})$, with non-compact quotient, so Γ is a nonabelian free group. The other cases are obtained from a careful study of the kernel and cokernel of $\alpha: U(\Gamma) \to \Gamma^{ab}$, where $U(\Gamma)$ is direct sum of certain abelian unipotent subgroups of Γ stabilizing lines in K^2. For the imaginary quadratic case the author studies α by comparing the homology of Γ with that of a compactification (described in an Appendix) of $\mathbf{X} = \mathbf{SL}_2(\mathbf{C})/\mathbf{SU}_2(\mathbf{C})$. In characteristic p, the Bruhat-Tits "building" $\mathbf{X}$ (here a tree) is used for this purpose; for some omitted details the author refers to his book (*Arbres, amalgames et* $\mathbf{SL}_2$ (Springer, to appear)).

The paper includes many other interesting sidelights and refinements, e.g., a close study of $\mathbf{SL}_2(A)^{ab}$ in the imaginary quadratic case. *J. E. Humphreys* (New York)

Citations: MR 37# 1485 = E56-48; MR 39# 1566 = E60-33; MR 39# 5574 = E60-37; MR 39# 5575 = E68-31.

E60-48 (43# 221)

Borel, Armand; Serre, Jean-Pierre

Cohomologie à supports compacts des immeubles de Bruhat-Tits; applications à la cohomologie des groupes S-arithmétiques.

C. R. Acad. Sci. Paris Sér. A-B **272** (1971), A110–A113.

Let G be a semi-simple algebraic group over a locally compact field K. When $K = \mathbf{R}$ the authors, in a preceding note [same C. R. **271** (1970), A1156–A1158; MR **42** #5997], exhibited a compactification of the symmetric space of $G(K)$ and used this to obtain information about cohomology of arithmetic groups. Here they carry out a similar program when K is non-archimedean. Combined with the earlier results this yields an extension of their theorems to the cohomology of S-arithmetic groups.

There are two ways to construct Tits systems in $G(K)$, the first à la Borel-Tits [the first author and J. Tits, Inst. Hautes Études Sci. Publ. Math. No. 27 (1965), 55–150; MR **34** #7527] and the second à la Bruhat-Tits [F. Bruhat and Tits, Proc. Conf. Local Fields (Driebergen, 1966), pp. 23–36, Springer, Berlin, 1967; MR **37** #6396] since K is a local field. Denote the corresponding buildings by Y and X, respectively. They are simplicial complexes of dimensions $l-1$, respectively, l, where l is the K-rank of G. A mixed K-manifold-and-real topology is put on Y to define Y^{top}. Then X is compactified by $\bar{X} = X \cup Y^{top}$. Both X and $\bar{X}$ are contractible, so the cohomology with compact supports $H_c^i(X, \mathbf{Z})$ can be computed from the cohomology of Y^{top}. The authors exhibit an explicit complex with which to compute the latter. The upshot is: $H_c^i(X, \mathbf{Z}) = 0$ for $i \neq l$, and $I = H_c^l(X, \mathbf{Z})$ is isomorphic to the (free abelian) group of locally constant $\mathbf{Z}$-valued functions with compact support on B/T. Here $(G(K), B, N, S)$ is a Tits system of Borel-Tits, and $T = B \cap N$.

Now let G be defined over a number field k. Let S_∞ denote the set of archimedean places, and S a finite set of places containing S_∞. Let k_v denote the completion of k at v. Let Γ be an S-arithmetic subgroup of $G(k)$; it is discrete in $G_S = \prod_{v \in S} G(k_v)$. Let X_∞ denote the symmetric space of maximal compact subgroups of G_{S_∞} and let $\bar{X}_\infty$ denote the compactification of X_∞ constructed in the preceding note for the algebraic group over $\mathbf{Q}$ obtained from G by restriction of scalars. Let X_v denote the Bruhat-Tits building of G over k_v for $v \notin S_\infty$. Put $X_S = \bar{X}_\infty \times \prod_{v \in S - S_\infty} X_v$. Then $G(k)$ acts on X_S, and the authors prove that Γ acts properly and X_S/Γ is compact.

Denote the rank of G over k $[k_v]$ by l $[l_v]$. Put $d = \dim X_\infty$ and $m = \dim X_S - l = (d - l) + \sum_{v \in S - S_\infty} l_v$. The results of this and the preceding note then yield: $H_c^i(X_S, \mathbf{Z}) = 0$ for $i \neq m$ and $I_S = H_c^m(X_S, \mathbf{Z})$ is a free $\mathbf{Z}$-module. These results imply when Γ is torsion free, that for all Γ-modules M and all integers q one has an isomorphism $H^q(\Gamma, M) \simeq H_{m-q}(\Gamma, I_S \otimes M)$. Consequently $\mathrm{cd}(\Gamma) = m$. Moreover, $H^q(\Gamma, Z[\Gamma]) = 0$ for $q \neq m$ and $H^m(\Gamma, Z[\Gamma]) \simeq I_S$.

Suppose L is a product of a Lie group with finitely many components with finitely many groups like $G(K)$ above. For discrete subgroups Γ of L with L/Γ compact, the authors obtain results on cohomology similar in appearance to those above for S-arithmetic groups.

H. Bass (New York)

Citations: MR 37# 6396 = E64-20; MR 42# 5997 = E60-46.

E60-49 (43# 1994)

Allan, Nelo

Maximality of some arithmetic group.

Revista Colombiana de Matemáticas, Monografias Matemáticas, 7.

Departamento de Matemáticas y Estadística, Universidad Nacional de Colombia; Sociedad Colombiana de Matemáticas, Bogota, 1970. iv + 57 *pp.* \$2.00.

Let k be a number field, $\mathcal{O}$ the ring of integers of k and G a connected semisimple linear algebraic group over k. An arithmetic subgroup Γ of G is one for which $\Gamma \cap G_{\mathcal{O}}$ has finite index in Γ and in $G_{\mathcal{O}}$. The problem of maximality of arithmetic subgroups of G is twofold: (1) determine the maximal arithmetic subgroups Δ of G containing a fixed maximal arithmetic subgroup Γ of G_k, and (2) determine the maximal arithmetic sugroups Γ of G_k. As to the first part, the author shows that if $G \subset \mathbf{SL}(n, \mathbf{C})$ is an irreducible group of non-compact type over k, then $\Delta = N_G(\Gamma)$, the normalizer of Γ in G, and Δ/Γ is abelian with $g^n \in \Gamma$ for all $g \in \Delta$. He also gives an analysis of the structure of Δ/Γ in terms of ideal classes and units.

The solution of (2) is harder, and the author's results are less complete. First, let $H = \begin{pmatrix} 0 & D \\ -D & 0 \end{pmatrix}$ and $D = \mathrm{diag}(1, d_2, \cdots, d_p)$, where $d_i | d_{i+1}$, and let G be either $\mathbf{SU}$(H) or $\mathbf{Sp}(H)$. The author shows that $G_{\mathcal{O}}$ is maximal in G_k if d_p is "square-free" (i.e., if $\mathfrak{a}$ is an ideal of k dividing

d_p, then $\mathfrak{a} = \bar{\mathfrak{a}}$ and $\mathfrak{a}^2$ does not divide d_p). Secondly, let

$$H = \begin{pmatrix} 0 & 0 & E_p \\ 0 & V & 0 \\ E_p & 0 & 0 \end{pmatrix}$$

and let E_p be the $p \times p$ identity matrix, where V is a positive-definite symmetric matrix in $M(r, \mathcal{O})$, and let G be either $\mathbf{SO}(H)$ or $\mathbf{SU}(H)$. In the former case $k = k_0$ is real and in the latter k is an imaginary quadratic extension of a real field k_0. Let $\mathfrak{t} = \mathrm{Tr}_{k/k_0}(\mathcal{O})$, and let $V = (v_{ij})$ and $V^{-1} = (w_{ij})$. The author proves that, if $G = \mathbf{SO}(H)$, then $G_{\mathcal{O}}$ is maximal in G_k if r is odd or if $V = E_r$ with $r/2$ odd. He shows that, if $G = \mathbf{SU}(H)$, then $G_{\mathcal{O}}$ is maximal in G_k if $1 \in \mathfrak{t}$ and $p > 1$ (if $p = 1$ assume that there is an $\alpha \in k$ with $(2, \alpha) = (v_{ii}, \alpha) = 1$ for some $i < r$), or if $\mathfrak{t}$ divides v_{ii} and w_{jj} for all $i, j < r$, and $p > 1$. Whenever $G_{\mathcal{O}}$ is maximal in G_k, $N_G(G_{\mathcal{O}})$ consists of matrices with integral entries.

Finally, the author proves certain results on the maximality of arithmetic groups related to division algebras. If $\mathbf{D}$ is an involutorial quaternion algebra over k, generated by $1, w, w', ww'$, $w^2 = a$ and $w'^2 = b$, with $a, b \in \mathcal{O}$ and 2, a and b divisible only by principal primes, let $\mathbf{O}$ be any maximal $\mathbf{O}$-order in $\mathbf{D}$ containing w and w'. Then $G_{\mathbf{O}}$ is maximal in $G_{\mathbf{D}}$.

It is worth noting that the author's own summary of these and earlier results appears in *Algebraic groups and discontinuous subgroups* [(Proc. Sympos. Pure Math., Vol. IX, Boulder, Colo., 1965), pp. 104–109, Amer. Math. Soc., Providence, R.I., 1966; MR **34** #5822].

J. C. Fogarty (Philadelphia, Pa.)

Citations: MR 34# 5822 = E60-18.

E60-50 (43# 4827)

Chen, Su-shing

A dimension formula relating to algebraic groups.

Bull. Austral. Math. Soc. **4** (1971), 241–245.

Author's summary: "An upper bound is given of the dimension of certain spaces of cusp harmonic forms of arithmetic subgroups Γ of semisimple algebraic groups G in terms of the multiplicities of corresponding irreducible unitary representations of the group G_R of real rational points of G in the space ${}^0L^2(G_R/\Gamma)$ of cusp forms."

E60-51 (44# 4009)

Platonov, V. P.

The congruence problem for solvable integral groups. (Russian)

Dokl. Akad. Nauk BSSR **15** (1971), 869–872.

If Γ is any subgroup of $\mathrm{GL}(n, \mathbf{Z})$, let $c(\Gamma)$ be the kernel of the canonical map $\hat{\Gamma} \to \bar{\Gamma}$ ($\hat{\Gamma}$ and $\bar{\Gamma}$ are the respective completions of Γ in the topologies of subgroups of finite index and of congruence subgroups). Theorem 1: If Γ is solvable, then $c(\Gamma) = 1$. Theorem 2: Let G be an algebraic $\mathbf{Q}$-group, S a maximal semisimple $\mathbf{Q}$-subgroup; then $c(G_{\mathbf{Z}}) = 1$ if and only if $c(S_{\mathbf{Z}}) = 1$. The proof of Theorem 2 is based on lemmas about semidirect and almost-direct products, along with known results for tori and unipotent groups. When Γ is arithmetic, i.e., Γ is of finite index in $H_{\mathbf{Z}}$ (H its Zariski closure in $\mathrm{GL}(n, \mathbf{C})$), Theorem 1 follows directly from Theorem 2. In general, Γ is polycyclic (Mal'cev), from which the author deduces that $c(\Gamma) \subset c(H_{\mathbf{Z}})$. Finally, the author sketches a method for constructing solvable subgroups of $\mathrm{GL}(7, \mathbf{Z})$ not isomorphic to any arithmetic group {however, the reviewer finds this brief sketch to be inexact at several key points}. *J. E. Humphreys* (New York)

E64 *p*-ADIC LINEAR GROUPS

See also reviews E02-14, E56-7, E56-9, E56-22, E56-35, E56-41, E56-42, E56-43, E56-44, E56-46, E56-52, E60-13, E60-21, E68-30, E68-31, F50-72, G30-49, Z10-59.

E64-1 (19, 767h)

Rosenlicht, Maxwell. Some rationality questions on algebraic groups. Ann. Mat. Pura Appl. (4) **43** (1957), 25–50.

The main result contained in this paper is the following. Let G be a connected linear algebraic group defined over a perfect field k. Then the field $k(G)$ of rational functions on G defined over k is isomorphic to a subfield of a purely transcendental extension of k; this implies that, if k is infinite, then the set of points of G which are rational over k is dense in G. It is shown by examples that none of the assumptions in the statement of the theorem (connectedness of G, linearity of G, perfect character of k) may be dropped without the conclusion becoming false. It is also proved that, if G is a connected nilpotent linear algebraic group defined over an arbitrary field k, then the maximal torus of G is defined over k; however, an example shows that the group G_u of unipotent elements of G need not be defined over k, even if G is commutative. Finally, it is shown that, if G is a connected algebraic group defined over a field k, then the maximal connected linear subgroup of G may not be defined over k.

C. Chevalley (Paris).

E64-2 (20# 82)

Mautner, F. I. Spherical functions over 𝔓-adic fields. I. Amer. J. Math. **80** (1958), 441–457.

Let Ω be a field, complete under a discrete valuation such that the residue field $\mathfrak{O}/(\pi)$ is a finite field with q elements ($\mathfrak{O}$ = the valuation ring, (π) = the prime ideal of $\mathfrak{O}$ with generator π). As usual, let $G = \mathrm{PGL}(2, \Omega)$ denote the factor group of $\mathrm{GL}(2, \Omega)$ modulo its center and let K and A be the canonical images in G of the subgroup $\mathrm{GL}(2, \mathfrak{O})$ of $\mathrm{GL}(2, \Omega)$ and of the subgroup of all diagonal matrices in $\mathrm{GL}(2, \Omega)$, respectively. A complex-valued function f on G is called a spherical function if f is constant on every double coset of G mod K. Following the analogy of classical (complex) semi-simple Lie groups, the author studies the properties of such spherical functions on G.

Let S be the space of all spherical functions on G, S^0 the subspace of all spherical functions of compact support and S^p ($p \geqq 1$) the intersection of S with the L^p-space on G relative to Haar measure. For any complex number s, let α_s denote the character of A such that $\alpha_s(A \cap K) = 1$, $\alpha_s(y) = q^{s-1}$, where y is the element of G determined by the diagonal matrix with diagonal elements $1, \pi$. Then each α_s defines a representation, $g \to T_s(g)$, of G on a Hilbert space which corresponds to representations of the principal series in the classical case. For f in S^0, let $F(s)$ be the Fourier transform of f, namely, the trace of the operator $\int_G f(g) T_s(g) dg$. Then the author proves that the mapping $f \to F$ gives an isomorphism of the algebra S^0 onto the algebra of all even Fourier polynomials of the form $\sum c_n(q^{n(s-\frac{1}{2})} + q^{-n(s-\frac{1}{2})})$ and that, in general, the Fourier transform $F(s)$ of any f in S^1 is a regular analytic function of s on $0 < \mathrm{R}(s) < 1$ satisfying the functional equation $F(s) = F(1-s)$. Furthermore, all maximal ideals of S^1 are determined and the Plancherel formula for S^2 is also established. *K. Iwasawa* (Cambridge, Mass.)

Referred to in E64-3, F25-30.

E64-3 **(27# 3640)**

Satake, Ichiro

On spherical functions over $\mathfrak{p}$-adic fields.

Proc. Japan Acad. **38** (1962), 422–425.

This is an outline of the author's work on $\mathfrak{p}$-adic spherical functions generalizing the works of Mautner and Tamagawa [cf. F. I. Mautner, Amer. J. Math. **80** (1958), 441–457; MR **20** #82; T. Tamagawa, Ann. of Math. (2) **77** (1963), 387–405; MR **26** #2468]. Let G be a $\mathfrak{p}$-adic algebraic group. The main theorems (Theorem 1 and Theorem 2) say that the ring of all complex-valued continuous functions with compact carriers on G which are bi-automorphic with respect to the unit group U of G is an affine ring whose dimension over $\mathbf{C}$ is equal to the dimension ν of maximal tori of G, and that the space of all zonal spherical functions on G with respect to U is analytically isomorphic to the quotient space $W\backslash(\mathbf{C}^*)^\nu$, where W is the $\mathfrak{p}$-adic analogue of the Weyl group. He imposes on G two conditions which are satisfied by almost all classical groups. An outline of the proof is given. The paper concludes with some comments and announcements.

T. Ono (Philadelphia, Pa.)

Citations: MR 20# 82 = E64-2; MR 26# 2468 = R54-33.

E64-4 **(27# 3641)**

Satake, Ichiro

On maximal compact subgroups of $\mathfrak{p}$-adic algebraic groups. (Japanese)

Sûgaku **14** (1962/63), 36–39.

Let k be a $\mathfrak{p}$-adic field and let G, G' be semi-simple algebraic groups defined over k. We denote by G_k the group of rational points over k. The author considers the following conjectures and verifies their validity for groups of classical type: (1) G_k has a maximal compact subgroup (in the sense of $\mathfrak{p}$-adic topology), and the number of conjugate classes of maximal compact groups is finite, (2) a maximal compact subgroup coincides with its normalizer in G_k, (3) if $f: G\to G'$ is a k-isogeny, then, for a given maximal compact subgroup U of G, there exists a unique maximal compact subgroup U' of G' such that $f(U)\subset U'$.

T. Ono (Philadelphia, Pa.)

E64-5 **(29# 108)**

Satake, Ichirô

Algebraic groups over p-adic number fields. (Japanese)

Sûgaku **12** (1960/61), 195–202.

This is a survey of the theory of algebraic groups defined over perfect fields, especially p-adic fields. In § 1–§ 3, a proof of A. Borel's theorem on conjugacy of maximal trigonalizable subgroups is given. In § 4, the author shows that if the ground field is a p-adic field, the homogeneous space of an algebraic group modulo a maximal trigonalizable subgroup is compact. In § 5, the author gives a few remarks on maximal compact subgroups of G_k where k is a p-adic field. In § 6, groups of compact type, i.e., groups with trivial maximal trigonalizable subgroups, are discussed. The last section is a brief summary of the author's work on spherical functions on p-adic algebraic group. The details of the theory are given in the author's paper [Inst. Hautes Études Sci. Publ. Math. No. 18 (1963), 5–69]. Because of the age of this paper, many results on p-adic algebraic groups have been obtained by several researchers in the past few years which are not covered here.

T. Tamagawa (Evanston, Ill.)

Citations: MR 33# 4059 = E64-10.

E64-6 **(30# 201)**

Veĭsfeĭler, B. Ju.

The classification of semi-simple Lie algebras over a $\mathfrak{p}$-adic field. (Russian)

Dokl. Akad. Nauk SSSR **158** (1964), 258–260.

In this paper a Lie algebra $\mathfrak{G}$ means one taken over the universal domain. If $\mathfrak{G}$ is defined over a field k, the set $\mathfrak{G}_k$ of k-rational points of $\mathfrak{G}$ is a Lie algebra over k in the classical sense. A Lie algebra defined over k is called a k-form. If $\mathfrak{G}$ contains no non-trivial ideal defined over k, then $\mathfrak{G}$ is called k-simple. If $\mathfrak{G}$ is L-simple for any extension L of k, then $\mathfrak{G}$ is called absolutely simple. For any k-simple Lie algebra $\mathfrak{G}$, there exists a finite separable extension K of k and an absolutely simple Lie algebra $\mathfrak{G}'$ defined over K such that $\mathfrak{G}$ is obtained from $\mathfrak{G}'$ by restricting the field of definition. Notation: $\mathfrak{G}=R_{K/k}\mathfrak{G}'$. Now let k be a $\mathfrak{p}$-adic field and $\mathfrak{G}$ be an absolutely simple Lie algebra defined over k. Theorem 1: There exists a maximal subalgebra of $\mathfrak{G}$, consisting of nilpotent elements, which is defined over an unramified extension $\mathfrak{K}$ of k. Using Theorem 1 and some results of I. Satake [J. Math. Soc. Japan **15** (1963), 210–235; MR **27** #1438], the author finds a normal splitting field K of $\mathfrak{G}$ containing the above $\mathfrak{K}$. (a) If $\mathfrak{G}$ is of type B_n, C_n, E_7, E_8, F_4 or G_2, then $K=\mathfrak{K}$; (b) if $\mathfrak{G}$ is of type A_n, D_n ($n\neq 4$), or E_6, then the Galois group $\Gamma(K/k)$ is abelian and the index of $\Gamma(\mathfrak{K}/k)$ in $\Gamma(K/k)$ is either 1 or 2; (c) if $\mathfrak{G}$ is of type D_4, then $\Gamma(K/k)$ is one of $\{1\}$, Z_2, Z_3 or S_3 (symmetric group of three letters).

If the Lie algebra $\mathfrak{G}_k$ of k-rational points contains no nilpotent element, then the algebra $\mathfrak{G}$ is called k-compact. Let $\mathfrak{A}$ be an associative algebra over k, then $\mathfrak{A}$ turns into a Lie algebra $\mathfrak{B}$ with the bracket product $[x,y]=xy-yx$. The factor algebra $\mathfrak{B}/\mathfrak{Z}$ is denoted by $\mathfrak{G}(\mathfrak{A})$, where $\mathfrak{Z}$ is the centre of $\mathfrak{A}$. If $\mathfrak{D}$ is a division algebra, then $\mathfrak{G}(\mathfrak{D})$ is a k-compact Lie algebra. Theorem 2: Let $\mathfrak{G}$ be a k-compact, k-simple Lie algebra, then there exist a finite extension L of k and a division algebra $\mathfrak{D}$ over L such that $\mathfrak{G}=R_{L/k}\mathfrak{G}(\mathfrak{D})$. By a theorem of I. Satake [op. cit.], a k-form of a semisimple Lie algebra $\mathfrak{G}$ is completely determined by its normal splitting field L, $\Gamma(L/k)$-fundamental system Δ of roots, the operation of $\Gamma(L/k)$ on Δ and the k-compact k-form corresponding to the $\Gamma(L/k)$-subsystem $\Delta_0=\{\alpha\in\Delta;\ \sum_{\sigma\in\Gamma}\sigma\alpha=0\}$. Using this theorem of Satake and the above Theorem 2, the author obtains the classification of absolutely simple Lie algebras over a $\mathfrak{p}$-adic field k. The result is given in a table which contains the Galois group $\Gamma(K/k)$ of the splitting field K over k, the ramification exponent e and the relative degree f of K/k, the Satake diagram indicating Δ, Δ_0 and the operation of $\Gamma(K/k)$ on Δ. The k-compact k-form corresponding to Δ_0 is given also. Two different fields K, K' with the same invariants e,f and Γ correspond to different k-forms, and any field K with the invariants e,f and Γ given in the table corresponds to a k-form. This paper contains, moreover, a theorem on quasi-compactness of a Lie algebra over an algebraic number field. No proofs are given.

M. Sugiura (Osaka)

Referred to in E72-8.

E64-7 **(31# 2351)**

Bruhat, François

Sous-groupes compacts maximaux des groupes semi-simples $\mathfrak{p}$-adiques.

Séminaire Bourbaki, 16e année; 1963/64, *Fasc.* 3, *Exposé* 271, 11 *pp. Secrétariat mathématique, Paris,* 1964.

This exposé discusses p-adic analogues of some of the main structure theorems which relate real semi-simple Lie groups G with their maximal compact subgroups K. One of the main theorems (due to Langlands) is the existence of maximal compact subgroups. Various open questions are discussed, such as the analogues of the Iwasawa and Cartan decompositions $G = KAK = KAN$ which have been proved by the author for the classical groups [Amer. J. Math. **83** (1961), 321–338; 343–368; MR **23** #A3184] and by Iwahori and Matsumoto for p-adic Chevalley groups [Inst. Hautes Études Sci. Publ. Math. No. 25 (1965), 5–48], and the classification of maximal compact subgroups.

F. I. Mautner (Princeton, N.J.)

Citations: MR 32# 2486 = E64-9.
Referred to in E64-18.

E64-8 **(31# 2352)**

Bruhat, François

Sur les sous-groupes compacts maximaux des groupes semi-simples $\mathfrak{p}$-adiques.

Colloq. Théorie des Groupes Algébriques (Bruxelles, 1962), pp. 69–76. *Librairie Universitaire, Louvain; Gauthier-Villars, Paris;* 1962.

The author discusses the existence of maximal compact subgroups of semisimple algebraic matrix groups over $\mathfrak{p}$-adic fields, and considers some of the classical groups in detail. In a more recent lecture [Summer Institute on Algebraic Groups and Discontinuous Subgroups (Boulder, Colorado 1965), Proc. Sympos. Pure Math., Vol. 9, Amer. Math. Soc., Providence, R.I., to appear] the author presented a complete proof of the existence of maximal compact subgroups of semisimple $\mathfrak{p}$-adic groups, which he said was due to Langlands, and mentioned another proof due to Tamagawa.

F. I. Mautner (Princeton, N.J.)

Citations: MR 35# 4220 = E64-14.
Referred to in E64-15.

E64-9 **(32# 2486)**

Iwahori, N.; Matsumoto, H.

On some Bruhat decomposition and the structure of the Hecke rings of $\mathfrak{p}$-adic Chevalley groups.

Inst. Hautes Études Sci. Publ. Math. No. 25 (1965), 5–48.

Let G be a Chevalley group over a $\mathfrak{p}$-adic field K. In this paper, the authors study certain triples of subgroups of G which satisfy the conditions of Tits [C. R. Acad. Sci. Paris **254** (1962), 2910–2912; MR **25** #2149] and the Bruhat decomposition arising from them. The subgroups of G used arise mostly from the $\mathfrak{p}$-adicity of K.

The group that plays the role of the Weyl group here is the infinite group generated by the reflections with respect to the walls of a fundamental cell. Nearly half of the paper is devoted to a detailed study of this group; most of the results are classical. The Poincaré polynomial of this group is also given.

In the formation of the triples mentioned above, the most important is the group B, the full inverse image of a Borel subgroup of the group obtained by reduction (mod $\mathfrak{P}$) of G. As a consequence of the consideration of Tits triples and the resulting Bruhat decompositions, the number of conjugacy classes of maximal subgroups of G containing B is obtained.

In the last section, assuming that the residue-class field of K is finite, and using the properties of G obtained above, the authors give an explicit description of the Hecke ring $\mathscr{H}(G, B)$ defined earlier by the first author [J. Fac. Sci. Univ. Tokyo Sect. I **10**, 215–236 (1964); MR **29** #2307].

Rimhak Ree (Vancouver, B.C.)

Referred to in E64-7, E64-14, E64-15, E64-16, E64-20.

E64-10 **(33# 4059)**

Satake, Ichiro

Theory of spherical functions on reductive algebraic groups over $\mathfrak{p}$-adic fields.

Inst. Hautes Études Sci. Publ. Math. No. 18 (1963), 5–69.

Let k be a $\mathfrak{p}$-adic number field and G an algebraic group in $GL(n, k)$. In G, there are two topologies, $\mathfrak{p}$-adic and Zariski; the author invents the convention that the words "closed", "connected" are used exclusively in the sense of Zariski, while "open", "compact" are used only in the $\mathfrak{p}$-adic sense. The main purpose of the paper is to translate a result of Harish-Chandra on the identification of the totality of zonal spherical functions on a semi-simple Lie group with a complex vector space modulo the restricted Weyl group. The author makes two assumptions (I), (II) on G which are actually conjectures, and he proves, in Chapter III, that these are satisfied by all known examples of classical groups. (I) says that "there exist in G an open compact subgroup U, a connected reductive closed subgroup H consisting only of semi-simple elements and a unipotent subgroup N normalized by H such that $G = UHN = UHU$ and $U \supset H^u$, where H^u denotes the unique maximal compact subgroup of H" (it follows that U is a maximal compact subgroup of G and that G is reductive). Let $X(H)$ be the character module of H, and let $\hat{X}(H) = \mathrm{Hom}(X(H), \mathbf{Z})$. Denote by M the image in $\hat{X}(H)$ of the homomorphism $h \to l_h$ $(h \in H)$ given by $l_h(\chi) = \mathrm{ord}_{\mathfrak{p}}\, \chi(h)$, $\chi \in X(H)$. For $s \in N(H)$, the normalizer of H, call w_s the automorphism of $X(H)$ given by $(w_s\chi)(shs^{-1}) = \chi(h)$, $h \in H$, $\chi \in X(H)$. The group W_H formed of all w_s $(s \in N(H))$ is called the restricted Weyl group of G relative to H. W_H acts also on $\hat{X}(H)$ in a natural way and it leaves $M \subset \hat{X}(H)$ invariant. In this situation, (II) says that "there exist a subgroup W of W_H such that every $w \in W$ can be written as $w = w_u$ with $u \in N(H) \cap U$, and a linear order in M satisfying the following property: if $\pi^m N \cap U\pi^r U \neq \varnothing$ with $m \in M$, $r \in \Lambda$, we have $m \leqq r$, where $\Lambda = \{m \in M : wm \leqq m$ for all $w \in W\}$, π is a prime element in k and π^m is a 'diagonal' element of H determined by π and $m \in M$." Now, under these assumptions (plus the connectedness of G), let $L = L(G, U)$ be the algebra over $\mathbf{C}$ of all $\mathbf{C}$-valued continuous functions φ on G with compact carrier such that $\varphi(ugu') = \varphi(g)$ for all $g \in G$, $u, u' \in U$, where the product in L is the convolution $*$. A $\mathbf{C}$-valued continuous function ω on G is called a zonal spherical function on G relative to U, if (i) $\omega(ugu') = \omega(g)$, (ii) $\omega(1) = 1$, and (iii) for every $\varphi \in L$, $\varphi * \omega = \lambda_\varphi \omega$ with $\lambda_\varphi \in \mathbf{C}$. The main theorem (Theorem 3 in § 6) asserts that the Fourier transformation $\varphi \to \hat{\varphi}$ gives an isomorphism of $L(G, U)$ with the algebra of all W-invariant polynomial functions (allowing negative powers) on $\mathrm{Hom}(M, \mathbf{C}^*) \approx \mathbf{C}^\nu$, ν being the rank of $X(H)$. From this follows the analogue of the theorem of Harish-Chandra (Theorem 2 in § 5) asserting that the totality of zonal spherical functions on G relative to U is isomorphic to the quotient space $X(H) \otimes \mathbf{C}/W(c\hat{M})$ $(c = (2\pi i)/\log q$, q being the number of elements in the residue field of $k)$, where $\hat{M} = \{s \in X(H) \otimes \mathbf{C} : ms \in \mathbf{Z}$ for all $m \in M\}$, $W(c\hat{M})$ is the group of affine transformations of $X(H) \otimes \mathbf{C}$ generated by W and by the group of translations defined by $c\hat{M}$. In Chapter III, it is shown that if G is a simple classical group without center and U is a maximal compact subgroup of G defined by a maximal lattice, then the algebra $L(G, U)$ is actually a polynomial algebra of ν variables over $\mathbf{C}$ and, more precisely, the Hecke ring $L(G, U)_{\mathbf{Z}}$ (all $\mathbf{Z}$-valued functions in L) is a polynomial ring of ν variables over $\mathbf{Z}$. The paper contains two appendices: (I) Calculation of some (local) Hecke series and ζ-functions attached to classical groups; (II) Determination of zonal spherical functions of positive type on PL(2, $\mathfrak{K}$).

T. Ono (Philadelphia, Pa.)

Referred to in E64-5, E64-17, F50-65, F50-72.

E64-11 **(33# 4060)**

Tamagawa, Tsuneo

On discrete subgroups of p-adic algebraic groups.

Arithmetical Algebraic Geometry (Proc. Conf. Purdue Univ., 1963), *pp.* 11–17. *Harper & Row, New York*, 1965.

Let G be a p-adic algebraic group, i.e., the group of all $\mathbf{Q}_p$-rational points on a (linear) algebraic group defined over $\mathbf{Q}_p$. G is a locally compact topological group with respect to its natural p-adic topology. It is proved that, if there exists a discrete subgroup Γ of G such that the factor space G/Γ is of finite volume, then G/Γ is actually compact, and G is reductive. Some basic properties of such discrete subgroups Γ of G are given, together with an existence proof of Γ by arithmetical construction.

I. Satake (Chicago, Ill.)

E64-12 **(34# 5777)**

Ihara, Yasutaka

Discrete subgroups of PL(2, $k_{\mathfrak{p}}$).

Algebraic Groups and Discontinuous Subgroups (Proc. Sympos. Pure Math., Boulder, Colo., 1965), *pp.* 272–278. *Amer. Math. Soc., Providence, R.I.*, 1966.

Let K be a field, complete with respect to a discrete valuation and with a finite residue field of q elements. Furthermore, let $G=\mathrm{PL}(2, K)$ and $U=\mathrm{PL}(2, O)$, where O is the order of integral elements in K. The author states the following theorem: A torsion-free discrete subgroup $\Gamma\subseteq G$ with compact quotient space is isomorphic to a free group of $(q-1)h/2+1$ generators, where $h=$ number of elements of $U\backslash G/\Gamma$. (A certain generalization requires some lengthy explanations.) By virtue of the theorem, the centralizer of any $\gamma\in\Gamma$ is a cyclic group. Take a representative $\gamma_1\in \mathrm{GL}(2, K)$ of γ and form the eigenvalues λ_γ, λ_γ' of γ_1. They are elements of K. Now put deg $\gamma=$ order of $\lambda_\gamma'\lambda_\gamma^{-1}$ in the sense of the valuation. With this convention a zeta function of Γ is defined as the infinite product $Z_\Gamma(u)= \prod (1-u^{|\deg \gamma|})^{-1}$ extended over all $\gamma\in\Gamma$ such that γ generates its centralizer. $Z_\Gamma(u)$ is always a rational function with $2h-2$ poles at $u=\eta_i$, η_i^* with $\eta_i\eta_i^*=q^{-1}$. Examples are given when $|\eta_i|=|\eta_i^*|=q^{-1/2}$ and when some $|\eta_i|\neq q^{-1/2}$. Both are formed by application of quaternion algebras and theta functions, and the former make use of the Riemann hypothesis for function fields.

M. Eichler (Basel)

E64-13 **(34# 5817)**

Ihara, Yasutaka

Algebraic curves mod $\mathfrak{p}$ **and arithmetic groups.**

Algebraic Groups and Discontinuous Subgroups (Proc. Sympos. Pure Math., Boulder, Colo., 1965), *pp.* 265–271. *Amer. Math. Soc., Providence, R.I.*, 1966.

From the author's summary: "Let $\Gamma=\mathrm{SL}(2, Z^{(p)})/\pm 1$, where $Z^{(p)}$ denotes the ring of all rational numbers whose denominators are powers of p. Γ is a discrete subgroup of $G=\{\mathrm{SL}(2, R)\times \mathrm{SL}(2, Q_p)\}/\pm 1$. Thus our problem is to consider Γ as a dense subgroup of the Galois group of a certain infinite Galois extension K over $k=F_{p^2}(j)$ such that elliptic curves with moduli j have no points of order p, where F_{p^2} is a finite field such that the rational j-curve over F_{p^2} with three ramifications satisfies the conditions of decomposition at all such primes (j). (Such j are called supersingular.) Then, the Frobenius substitution of prime divisors of k in K/k determines a conjugacy class of Γ which vanishes if and only if the prime divisor is supersingular. This connects the set of all non-supersingular prime divisors of k and the set of all primitive and elliptic conjugacy classes of Γ in a one-to-one manner. This holds also for finite subextensions k' of k in K and corresponding subgroups Γ' of Γ, which implies the coincidence of congruence $\mathscr{G}$-functions of k' with $\mathscr{G}$-functions of Selberg's type for discrete subgroups Γ' of G (surely they are not precisely equal because of supersingular primes). These considerations lead us to the study of $\mathscr{G}$-functions of arbitrary discrete subgroups of G whose quotient spaces have finite volumes. Our interest lies in calculating the number which in our previous special case of Γ was the number of supersingular primes. By using this result, we can prove that all supersingular primes are actually decomposed completely in the field K constructed in § 1. Proofs are omitted, and will be published elsewhere."

P. Abellanas (Madrid)

E64-14 **(35# 4220)**

Bruhat, François

$\mathfrak{p}$-adic groups.

Algebraic Groups and Discontinuous Subgroups (Proc. Sympos. Pure Math., Boulder, Colo., 1965), *pp.* 63–70. *Amer. Math. Soc., Providence, R.I.*, 1966.

On the basis of theorems on connected real Lie groups G ((i) a compact subgroup of G is contained in a maximal compact subgroup of G, and (ii) maximal compact subgroups are conjugate by an inner automorphism), the author formulates a conjecture concerning maximal bounded subgroups of (linear) p-adic groups (Iwasawa and Cartan decompositions). He proves Langland's theorem that a compact subgroup of the group of P-rational elements of a reductive group over a locally compact field P is contained in a maximal compact subgroup of the former. Analogues of (ii) are discussed for a number of examples. A second conjecture concerns the Tits system of a simply connected group. In this connection see N. Iwahori and H. Matsumoto [Inst. Hautes Études Sci. Publ. Math. No. 25 (1965), 5–48; MR **32** #2486] and J. Tits [*Algebraic groups and discontinuous subgroups* (Proc. Sympos. Pure Math., Boulder, Colo., 1965), pp. 33–62, Amer. Math. Soc., Providence, R.I., 1966]. The author reports that he and J. Tits are preparing affirmative solutions to some of the questions raised in this note.

O. F. G. Schilling (Lafayette, Ind.)

Citations: MR 32# 2486 = E64-9.

Referred to in E64-8.

E64-15 **(35# 5448)**

Bruhat, François

Sous-groupes compacts maximaux des groupes semi-simples $\mathfrak{p}$-adiques. (With discussion)

Les Tendances Géom. en Algèbre et Théorie des Nombres, pp. 43–53. *Éditions du Centre National de la Recherche Scientifique, Paris*, 1966.

This is a summary of recent results (as of about the summer of 1965) on maximal compact subgroups in a $\mathfrak{p}$-adic semi-simple group. Let P be a field with a (non-trivial) discrete valuation (not necessarily complete), and let G_P be the group of P-rational points on a connected semisimple algebraic group G defined over P. The author raises the following three fundamental questions concerning maximal bounded subgroups in G_P: (a) existence; (b) classification up to inner automorphisms; (c) existence of at least one "good" class (having certain favorable properties such as the analogue of the Iwasawa decomposition and the elementary divisor decomposition). A proof for (a) (by Langlands) in the case of a locally compact field is given, as well as a solution of (c) under the completeness assumption for the case of classical groups (by several authors) and for the case of Chevalley groups (by the author [Colloq. Théorie des Groupes Algébriques (Bruxelles, 1962), pp. 69–76, Librairie Univ., Louvain, 1962; MR **31** #2352; Inst. Hautes Études Sci. Publ. Math. No. 23 (1964), 45–74; MR **31** #3546]). As for problem (b), a sketch is given for the result of Hijikata (unpublished) for the case of classical groups, and for the result of N. Iwahori and H. Matsumoto [ibid. No. 25 (1965), 5–48; MR **32** #2486] for the case of Chevalley groups, which solves the problem for that case modulo one conjecture on the "parahoric subgroups". {A more complete answer for the general case has since been obtained by joint work of the author and J. Tits, including an affirmation of the above conjecture when P is complete [C. R. Acad. Sci. Paris Sér. A-B **263** (1966), A598–A601; ibid. **263** (1966), A766–A768; ibid. **263** (1966), A822–A825; ibid. **263** (1966), A867–A869].} *I. Satake* (Chicago, Ill.)

Citations: MR 31# 2352 = E64-8; MR 32# 2486 = E64-9; MR 39# 4160 = E64-23; MR 39# 4161 = E64-24; MR 39# 4162 = E64-25; MR 39# 4163 = E64-26.

E64-16 (35# 6693)

Iwahori, Nagayoshi

Generalized Tits system (Bruhat decomposition) on p-adic semisimple groups.

Algebraic Groups and Discontinuous Subgroups (*Proc. Sympos. Pure Math., Boulder, Colo.,* 1965), *pp.* 71–83. *Amer. Math. Soc., Providence, R.I.,* 1966.

This paper is primarily expository.

Let k be a local field with ring of integers $\mathfrak{O}$ and residue class field $\mathfrak{k}$. Let G be a Chevalley group over k, A a maximal k-split torus of G, $G_{\mathfrak{O}}$ the group of integral points of G relative to an $\mathfrak{O}$-structure of G determined by a Chevalley basis of Lie(G) associated to A.

The author describes, using the notion of generalized Tits system, material in his joint paper with H. Matsumoto [Inst. Hautes Études Sci. Publ. Math. No. 25 (1965), 5–48; MR **32** #2486]. In particular, he discusses the generalized Tits system (G_k, B, N_k), where N is the normalizer of A, and B is the inverse image of a Borel subgroup of $G_{\mathfrak{k}}$ under the reduction homomorphism from $G_{\mathfrak{O}}$ to $G_{\mathfrak{k}}$, and recalls that $G_k = G_{\mathfrak{O}} A_k G_{\mathfrak{O}}$.

He further notes that, as shown by Matsumoto, $G_k = G_{\mathfrak{O}} A_k G_{\mathfrak{O}}$ holds when $\mathfrak{O}$ is replaced by any principal ideal domain and k by the quotient field of $\mathfrak{O}$.

Sylow type theorems for pro-p-subgroups of G_k are stated. For G simply connected, B is characterized up to conjugacy, following Matsumoto, as the normalizer of a maximal pro-p-subgroup of G_k.

Conjectures concerning the determination of the maximal compact subgroups of G_k and the homogeneous space G_k/B are given. {Reviewer's remark: Conjecture 1 of page 77 has since been solved and generalized by F. Bruhat and J. Tits. For the simply connected case, see proposition 6 of their paper [C. R. Acad. Sci. Paris Sér. A-B **263** (1966), A822–A825].}

Following Tits, it is proved that if (G, B, N) is an arbitrary Tits system with G finite, and if k is an arbitrary algebraically closed field whose characteristic does not divide the order of G, then the Hecke algebra $H(G, B) \otimes_{\mathbf{Z}} k$ is isomorphic to the group algebra $k[W]$, where $W = N/B \cap N$. *D. J. Winter* (Bonn)

Citations: MR 32# 2486 = E64-9; MR 39# 4162 = E64-25.

E64-17 (36# 5141)

Macdonald, I. G.

Spherical functions on a $\mathfrak{p}$-adic Chevalley group.

Bull. Amer. Math. Soc. **74** (1968), 520–525.

A general theory of zonal spherical functions on a reductive linear algebraic group over a $\mathfrak{p}$-adic field K has been set up by I. Satake [cf. Inst. Hautes Études Sci. Publ. Math. No. 18 (1963), 5–69; MR **33** #4059]. In this note, the author determines an explicit form for the spherical functions and Plancherel measure in the case of a Chevalley group. Let $\mathfrak{O}$ be the ring of integers of K, $\mathfrak{p}$ the maximal ideal of $\mathfrak{O}$, π a generator of $\mathfrak{p}$. Let G be a Chevalley group over K associated with a complex semi-simple Lie algebra $\mathfrak{g}$; let U be the stabilizer in G of a Chevalley lattice $\mathfrak{g}_{\mathfrak{O}}$, which is a maximal compact subgroup of G, H [N] a Cartan subgroup [maximal unipotent subgroup] of G. Let $\mathfrak{h}$ be the corresponding Cartan subalgebra of $\mathfrak{g}$, V the vector space dual of $\mathfrak{h}$, R^* the set of all co-weights of $\mathfrak{g}$, $\alpha^* \in R^*$ the co-weight corresponding to the root α of $\mathfrak{g}$. For $\lambda \in R^*$, let $\pi^\lambda = h(\chi)$ be an element of H such that $\chi(\alpha) = \pi^{(\lambda,\alpha)}$; then G is the disjoint union of the double cosets $U\pi^\lambda N$ $(\lambda \in R^*)$ (Iwasawa decomposition). Taking $s \in V$ as parameters for it, each zonal spherical function ω is expressed by $\omega_s(x) = \int_U q^{(\mu(x^{-1}u),\sigma - s)}\,du$, where μ is the projection of G on $R^* = U\backslash G/N$, $x = uhn \in G$, $u \in U$, $h \in R^*$, $n \in N$, $\sigma = \frac{1}{2}$ (sum of positive roots), q the number of elements in the residue field of $\mathfrak{O}$, du a normalized Haar measure of the compact group U. Then the author has the formula $\omega_s(\pi^\lambda) = (1/P(q^{-1})) \sum_{w \in W} q^{(\lambda, ws - \sigma)} c(ws)$, where $P(t)$ is the Poincaré polynomial and

$$c(s) = \prod_{\alpha > 0} (1 - q^{-1-(\alpha^*, s)})/(1 - q^{-(\alpha^*, s)}).$$

For this purpose, using the Iwahori-decomposition of U, he computes the above integral. From this he also gives explicitly an isomorphism of the ring $L(G, U)$ of all complex-valued continuous functions on G which have compact support and which are bi-invariant with respect to U onto the subalgebra $C[R^*]^W$ of W-invariant elements of the group algebra $C[R^*]$. Finally, he gives an explicit form of the Plancherel measure on the space of all zonal spherical functions on G relative to U by means of the function $c(s)$. No detailed proof is given. *E. Abe* (Tokyo)

Citations: MR 33# 4059 = E64-10.

Referred to in F50-72.

E64-18 (36# 5143)

Platonov, V. P.

Maximal bounded subgroups of $\mathfrak{P}$-adic groups. (Russian)

Dokl. Akad. Nauk BSSR **11** (1967), 201–203.

Let Γ be a connected reductive algebraic group over a complete discrete evaluation field Φ with nontrivial norm ν, and let Γ_Φ denote the subgroup of Φ-rational points. A subgroup R of Γ_Φ is said to be bounded if there is a rational representation ϕ of Γ_Φ with finite kernel such that $\phi(R)$ is bounded in the norm ν. The author proves that every bounded subgroup of Γ_Φ is contained in a maximal bounded subgroup. This generalizes a theorem of Langlands; see F. Bruhat [Séminaire Bourbaki: 1963/64, Exposé 271, Secrétariat mathématique, Paris, 1964; MR **31** #2351; facsimile reproduction, Benjamin, New York, 1966; see MR **33** #5420k]. *K. A. Ross* (Seattle, Wash.)

Citations: MR 31# 2351 = E64-7.

E64-19 (36# 6511)

Ihara, Yasutaka

On discrete subgroups of the two by two projective linear group over $\mathfrak{p}$-adic fields.

J. Math. Soc. Japan **18** (1966), 219–235.

Let $\mathfrak{k}$ be a locally compact field under a discrete valuation, $\mathfrak{O}$ the ring of integers and $\mathfrak{P}$ the maximal ideal in $\mathfrak{O}$. The author constructs all torsion-free, discrete subgroups Γ of $G = \mathrm{GL}(2, \mathfrak{k})/\mathfrak{k}^*$. They are free groups (of at most countable rank) and a generating set is given explicitly. If G/Γ

is compact, Γ is finitely generated, and a formula is given for its rank (analogous to the formula relating the rank and index of a subgroup of a free group).

It is shown that these properties are true for subgroups Γ of a class of groups G, which behave nicely with respect to a length function $l(x)$. For example, G could be a free group, and $l(x)$ the usual length. In the case $G = \mathrm{GL}(2, k)/k^*$, $l(x)$ is defined as follows: Choose a representative (a_{ij}) for x, modulo k^*, so that $a_{ij} \in \mathfrak{O}$ and $\sum_{i,j=1}^{2} a_{ij}\mathfrak{O} = \mathfrak{O}$. Then put $\det(a_{ij})\mathfrak{O} = \mathfrak{P}^{l(x)}$.

An analogue of Selberg's ζ function for discrete groups is defined as follows. For $\gamma \in \Gamma$, let $\{\gamma\}$ denote its conjugacy class in Γ, and $\deg\{\gamma\} = \min_{x\in G} l(x^{-1}\gamma x)$. Let $Z_\Gamma(u) = \prod_P (1 - u^{\deg P})^{-1}$, where P runs over all conjugacy classes of primitive elements in Γ. It is shown that $Z_\Gamma(u)$ is an explicit rational function.

The author also proves that all torsion-free, discrete subgroups Γ (with compact factor space G/Γ) have nontrivial deformations. *L. Greenberg* (College Park, Md.)

Referred to in E60-34.

E64-20 (37# 6396)

Bruhat, F.; Tits, J.

Groupes algébriques simples sur un corps local.

Proc. Conf. Local Fields (Driebergen, 1966), pp. 23–36. Springer, Berlin, 1967.

This is a survey of the theory of simple algebraic groups over local fields developed by the authors. It yields notably a description of the maximal compact subgroups when the ground field is locally compact, which generalizes the results of N. Iwahori and H. Matsumoto [Inst. Hautes Études Sci. Publ. Math. No. 25 (1965), 5–48; MR **32** #2486], and an extension of the results of M. Kneser [Math. Z. **89** (1965), 250–272; MR **32** #5658] on Galois cohomology and classification. The main results have been announced in four Comptes Rendus Notes [the authors, C. R. Acad. Sci. Paris Sér. A-B **263** (1966), A598–A601; ibid. **263** (1966), A766–A768; ibid. **263** (1966), A822–A825; ibid. **263** (1966), A867–A869].

A. Borel (Princeton, N.J.)

Citations: MR 32# 2486 = E64-9; MR 32# 5658 = E72-7; MR 39# 4160 = E64-23; MR 39# 4161 = E64-24; MR 39# 4162 = E64-25; MR 39# 4163 = E64-26.

Referred to in E08-43, E60-48.

E64-21 (38# 5988)

Silberger, Allan J.

All algebras of spherical functions defined on the two-by-two general linear group with entries in a locally compact p-adic field are commutative.

Proc. Amer. Math. Soc. **21** (1969), 437–440.

The author proves the result described in the title when $p \neq 2$. More precisely, let $G = \mathrm{GL}(2, \Omega)$, $K = \mathrm{GL}(2, \vartheta)$, where Ω is a locally compact p-adic field, ϑ its ring of integers. For any irreducible representation u of K on a vector space V_u, let S_u' be the (convolution) algebra of functions f on G with values in the endomorphism algebra of V_u, which satisfy $f(kgk') = u(k)f(g)u(k')$, $g \in G$, $k, k' \in K$. The author proves that S_u' is commutative. It follows that K is a large compact subgroup of G in Mackey's sense and that G is type I. *R. A. Gangolli* (Seattle, Wash.)

E64-22 (38# 5994)

Sally, P. J., Jr.; Shalika, J. A.

Characters of the discrete series of representations of SL(2) over a local field.

Proc. Nat. Acad. Sci. U.S.A. **61** (1968), 1231–1237.

From the authors' introduction: "In this note, we give explicit formulas for the characters of the square integrable, irreducible unitary representations of $G = \mathrm{SL}(2, k)$, where k is a nonarchimedean local field whose residual characteristic is not 2. Our basic approach is to use the construction of the discrete series of representations of G as representations induced from a maximal compact subgroup. The results of this note may be regarded as a first step in a proof of the Plancherel formula for G by methods similar to those used by Harish-Chandra for $\mathrm{SL}(2, R)$ (cf. I. M. Gel'fand, M. I. Graev and I. I. Pjateckiĭ-Šapiro [*Generalized functions, No. 6: Theory of representations and automorphic functions* (Russian), Izdat. "Nauka", Moscow, 1966; MR **36** #3725; English translation, Saunders, Philadelphia, Pa., 1969; MR **38** #2093])."

A. Dress (Princeton, N.J.)

Citations: MR 36# 3725 = F02-18; MR 38# 2093 = F02-19.

E64-23 (39# 4160)

Bruhat, François; Tits, Jacques

BN-paires de type affine et données radicielles.

C. R. Acad. Sci. Paris Sér. A-B **263** (1966), A598–A601.

In dieser Note werden BN-Paare [siehe den zweiten Verfasser, Ann. of Math. (2) **80** (1964), 313–329; MR **29** #2259] (G, B) mit einer irreduziblen affinen Weylgruppe betrachtet. Die Weylgruppe $W = N(H)/H$ heißt irreduzibel affin, wenn sie durch Spiegelungen an Hyperebenen des l-dimensionalen affinen euklidischen Raums erzeugt wird und wenn sie keinen echten affinen Teilraum dieses Raums festläßt. Die zu der Gruppe B konjugierten Untergruppen von G heißen Iwahoriuntergruppen. Eine echte Untergruppe von G, die eine Iwahoriuntergruppe enthält, heißt Parahoriuntergruppe.

Dem BN-Paar (G, B) wird ein simplizialer Komplex J zugeordnet. Die Ecken dieses Komplexes sind die maximalen Parahoriuntergruppen. Endlich viele maximale Parahoriuntergruppen $P_{i_1} \cdots P_{i_s}$ bilden genau dann die Eckpunkte eines $(s-1)$-dimensionalen Simplex, wenn ihr Durchschnitt eine Parahoriuntergruppe ist. Dieser Komplex wird das Gebäude (immeuble) des BN-Paares genannt. Auf J läßt sich auf natürliche Weise eine Metrik einführen, so daß J zu einem vollständigen metrischen Raum wird. Der folgende Fixpunktsatz ist für diese und die späteren Noten entscheidend: Sei $\Omega \subset J$ abgeschlossen, beschränkt und konvex, und Γ sei eine Gruppe von Automorphismen des Raumes J, die Ω invariant läßt. Dann besitzt Γ einen Fixpunkt in Ω. Hieraus folgt Théorème 1: Sei Γ eine Gruppe von Automorphismen von G, die die Klasse der Iwahorigruppen invariant lasse. Die Menge ΓB ist genau dann beschränkt (d. h. in endlich vielen Doppelklassen BNB enthalten) wenn Γ eine Parahoriuntergruppe invariant läßt.

Im Anschluß an diese Überlegungen definieren die Autoren den Begriff des Wurzeldatums zu einer affinen irreduziblen Weylgruppe W auf einer Gruppe G. Sie zeigen (Théorème 2), daß ein solches Wurzeldatum auf natürliche Weise zu einer BN-Struktur auf G führt, die W als Weylgruppe besitzt. Das Théorème 3 liefert eine Aussage darüber, unter welchen Umständen die Fixgruppe unter einer endlichen Gruppe Γ von Automorphismen von G wieder ein Wurzeldatum besitzt. *G. Harder* (Bonn)

Referred to in E60-41, E64-15, E64-20.

E64-24 (39# 4161)

Bruhat, François; Tits, Jacques

Groupes simples résiduellement déployés sur un corps local.

C. R. Acad. Sci. Paris Sér. A-B **263** (1966), A766–A768.

Sei K ein nicht trivial diskret bewerteter Körper, sei G/K eine einfach zusammenhängende Chevalleygruppe. Die

Verfasser zeigen, daß es auf der Gruppe $G(K)$ der Punkte von G mit Werten in K eine natürliche BN-Struktur mit irreduzibler affiner Weylgruppe gibt und daß die durch diese BN-Struktur definierten beschränkten Mengen gerade mit den durch die Bewertung definierten beschränkten Mengen übereinstimmen. Dies Ergebnis geht auf Iwahori und Matsumoto zurück. Die Verfasser führen daran anschließend aus, wie man für quasizerfallende Gruppen G/K, die residuell zerfallen, eine BN-Struktur auf $G(K)$ erhält. Das ergibt sich aus den Theoremen 2, 3 der vorangehenden Note [#4160]. Jeder residuell zerfallenden Gruppe wird ein residuelles Dynkinschema zugeordnet. *G. Harder* (Bonn)

Referred to in E60-41, E64-15, E64-20.

E64-25 (39# 4162)

Bruhat, François; Tits, Jacques

Groupes algébriques simples sur un corps local.

C. R. Acad. Sci. Paris Sér. A-B **263** (1966), A822–A825.

Sei G/K wieder eine einfach zusammenhängende Gruppe über einem diskret vollständig bewerteten Körper K. Sei $\mathfrak{O}$ der Ring der ganzen Elemente von K, der Restklassenkörper $\mathfrak{O}/\mathfrak{P}=k$ sei perfekt. Es wird von gewissen beschränkten Untergruppen P_Ω von $G(K)$ gezeigt, daß es glatte Gruppenschemata $G_\Omega/\mathfrak{O}$ gibt, deren allgemeine Faser G/K ist, so daß $G_\Omega(\mathfrak{O})=P_\Omega$. Über die Struktur dieser Gruppenschemata werden einige interessante Aussagen gemacht (Théorème 1). Insbesondere kann dieser Prozeß für Parahoriuntergruppen durchgeführt werden. Anschließend werden die gleichen Überlegungen auch auf den Fall angewendet, wo G/K quasizerfallend und residuell zerfallend ist (Théorème 2).

Sei nun G/K irgendeine einfach zusammenhängende halbeinfache algebraische Gruppe. Über der maximal unverzweigten Erweiterung $\tilde{K}/K$ ist $\tilde{G}/\tilde{K}$ residuell zerfallend und quasizerfallend, und die bisherigen Überlegungen lassen sich auf $\tilde{G}$ anwenden. Sei $\Gamma=\mathrm{Gal}(\tilde{K}/K)$. Eine Parahoriuntergruppe $\tilde{P}\subset G(\tilde{K})$ heißt definiert über k, falls sie unter der Operation von Γ invariant ist. Der Fixpunktsatz aus der ersten Note [#4160] liefert die Existenz einer solchen Parahoriuntergruppe $\tilde{P}$. Ist G/K anisotrop, so ist die Konjugationsklasse dieser Untergruppe $\tilde{P}$ eindeutig bestimmt, und es ist $\tilde{P}\supset G(K)$. Ist G/K nicht anisotrop, so liefern die Ergebnisse aus den vorangegangenen Noten [#4160, #4161] eine nicht triviale affine BN-Struktur auf $G(K)$ (Théorème 1, Abschnitt 4). Hieraus folgt insbesondere, daß jede beschränkte Untergruppe von $G(K)$ in einer maximal beschränkten Untergruppe liegt und daß die Anzahl der Konjugationsklassen maximal beschränkter Untergruppen gleich $\mathrm{Rang}_K\, G+1$ ist. *G. Harder* (Bonn)

Referred to in E60-41, E64-15, E64-16, E64-20.

E64-26 (39# 4163)

Bruhat, François; Tits, Jacques

Groupes algébriques simples sur un corps local: Cohomologie galoisienne, décompositions d'Iwasawa et de Cartan.

C. R. Acad. Sci. Paris Sér. A-B **263** (1966), A867–A869.

Hier werden einige Anwendungen der in den vorangehenden drei Noten [#4160–#4162] formulierten Resultate gegeben. Sei K wieder vollständig mit perfektem Restklassenkörper. Man nennt G/K residuell quasizerfallend, wenn es in $G(K)$ eine über k definierte Iwahoriuntergruppe gibt. Corollaire 1: Ist Γ kommutativ und G/K residuell quasizerfallend und anisotrop, so ist G/K eine innere Form der A_n. Proposition 2: Ist die kohomologische Dimension von $k\leqq 1$, so ist G/K residuell quasizerfallend. Außerdem ist dann $H^1(K,G)=0$ (Corollaire 2). Schließlich wird noch eine Iwasawa- und eine Cartanzerlegung für $G(K)$ angegeben. Ist K lokal kompakt, so betrachtet man die unter einer maximalen Parahoriuntergruppe $P\subset G(K)$ biinvarianten Funktionen. Diese bilden unter der Faltungsoperation eine Algebra, und die zuletzt genannten Resultate implizieren, daß diese Algebra kommutativ ist.

{Anmerkung des Referenten: Nach mündlicher Mitteilung eines der Verfasser an den Referenten ist die Proposition 3 auf S. 868 wahrscheinlich nicht richtig, und zwar müssen die Worte "et à K-isomorphisme près un seul" gestrichen werden.} *G. Harder* (Bonn)

Referred to in E60-41, E64-15, E64-20.

E64-27 (42# 1935)

Kiršteĭn, B. H.; Pjateckiĭ-Šapiro, I. I.

Invariant subrings of induced rings. (Russian)

Izv. Akad. Nauk SSSR Ser. Mat. **34** (1970), 83–89.

Let $\mathscr{G}$ be a topological group, $\mathscr{B}$ a closed subgroup of $\mathscr{G}$ and let there be given a continuous homomorphism χ of the group $\mathscr{B}$ into the group $\mathrm{Aut}(K)$ of automorphisms of a certain topological ring K. The ring of all continuous functions on $\mathscr{G}$ with values in K that satisfy the condition $f(bg)=f(g)^{\chi b}$ for all $b\in\mathscr{B}$ and $g\in\mathscr{G}$ (here a^σ is the image of $a\in K$ under the action of $\sigma\in\mathrm{Aut}(K)$) is called by the authors the induced ring. We denote it by $K(\mathscr{G})$. Each element $g_0\in\mathscr{G}$ gives an automorphism of this ring, which takes the element $f(g)\in K(\mathscr{G})$ into $f\circ g=f(gg_0)\in K(\mathscr{G})$. Subrings of the ring $K(\mathscr{G})$ that map into themselves under the action of all automorphisms belonging to the group $\mathscr{G}$ are called invariant. It is obvious that if A is a subring of the ring K that is invariant with respect to $\chi(\mathscr{B})$, then $A(\mathscr{G})$ is an invariant subring in $K(\mathscr{G})$. How are all the invariant subrings arranged in $K(\mathscr{G})$? The authors consider this question under the following hypotheses: $\mathscr{G}=\mathrm{GL}_2(k_\mathfrak{p})$ is the group of all nondegenerate matrices of order two over the p-adic number field $k_\mathfrak{p}$, $\mathscr{B}$ is the subgroup of lower triangular matrices, and $\mathfrak{v}$, $\mathfrak{p}$ and π are the ring of integers, a prime ideal and a generating element of the prime ideal, respectively, in the field $k_\mathfrak{p}$. K is a perfect field of characteristic q equal to the characteristic of the field $\mathfrak{v}/\mathfrak{p}$. The topology on K is assumed to be discrete. We select an integer $l\neq 0$ and a continuous homomorphism $\tau: k_\mathfrak{p}^*\to\mathrm{Aut}(K)$ such that $x^{\tau(\pi)}=x^{q^l}$ for all $x\in K$. Finally, let $b=\begin{pmatrix} b_{11} & 0\\ b_{21} & b_{22}\end{pmatrix}\in\mathscr{B}$, $b_{ii}=\pi^{k_i}\varepsilon_i$ $(i=1,2)$, where ε_i are units of the ring $\mathfrak{v}$. Then we define χ by the equality $\chi(b)=\tau(\pi^{k_1\lambda_1+k_2\lambda_1}\varepsilon_1\varepsilon_2)$, $\lambda_1,\lambda_2\in\mathbf{Z}$, $\lambda_1{}^2+\lambda_2{}^2\neq 0$. By means of the Iwasawa decomposition $\mathscr{G}=\mathscr{B}\mathscr{K}$, where $\mathscr{K}=\mathrm{SL}_2(\mathfrak{v})$, it is easy to prove that for any $a\in A$ there exists a unique function $f(g)\in K(\mathscr{G})$ equal to a on $\mathscr{K}$. Now let A be a certain subring in K. We denote by $R(A)$ the ring of all functions $f(g)\in K(\mathscr{G})$ that are equal to $a\in A$ on $\mathscr{K}$. The main result of the paper consists of the following: Every invariant subring of the ring $K(\mathscr{G})$ has the form: $R(A,S)=R(A)+S(\mathscr{G})$, where (1) The rings A and S are invariant with respect to all automorphisms belonging to $\tau(k_\mathfrak{p}{}^*)$; (2) S is an ideal in A; (3) $a^{q^{\lambda_1 l}}-a^{q^{\lambda_2 l}}\in S$ for any $a\in A$. Conversely, every ring $R(A,S)$, where A and S satisfy conditions (1), (2) and (3), is an invariant subring of the ring $K(\mathscr{G})$.

Example: We denote by R the set of all meromorphic functions on the upper halfplane of the complex variable z that are representable in the form $\varphi(j((q^kz+a)/q^l))/\psi(j)$, where the numerator is an arbitrary polynomial in $j((q^kz+a)/q^l)$, $k,l=0,1,\cdots$, $a\in\mathbf{Z}$, and the denominator is a polynomial in j with integral coëfficients and with the highest coefficient relatively prime to q; j is a modular invariant. Let I be the ideal of all $f\in R$ such that f^n is divisible by q for some natural number n; in this case $R/I=K(\mathscr{G})$, where $K=F_q(t,t^{1/q},\cdots)$ (F_q is the prime field of characteristic q), $\mathscr{G}=\mathrm{GL}_2(Q_q)$, $\lambda_1=-\lambda_2=1$, $l=1$, $\tau(\varepsilon)=1$ if ε is a unit of $\mathfrak{v}$. We denote by $\tilde{R}$ the subring of the

ring R that consists of all polynomials with q-integral coefficients in $j((q^kz+a)/q^l)$, $k, l=0, 1, \cdots, a \in \mathbf{Z}$. The above description of the invariant subrings of the ring $K(\mathscr{G})$ permits one to find what the ring $\tilde{R}$ reduces to, i.e., to compute the ring $\tilde{R}/I \cap \tilde{R}$. Since $\tilde{R}$ is the minimal invariant subring of the ring R that contains the polynomials in j with q-integral coefficients, the ring $\tilde{R}/I \cap \tilde{R}$ is the minimal invariant subring of the ring $K(\mathscr{G})$ that contains the ring $R(F_q[t])$. It is easy to verify that such a ring has the form $R(A, S)$, where $A=F_q[t, t^{1/q}, \cdots]$ and S is the ideal in A generated by $(t^q-t^{1/q})$, $(t^q-t^{1/q})^{1/q}, \cdots$.
D. Každan (RŽMat **1970** #7 A409)

E64-28 **(44# 6706)**

Ihara, Yasutaka

On congruence monodromy problems. Vol. 1.
Lecture Notes, No. 1.
Department of Mathematics, University of Tokyo, Tokyo, 1968. i+206 *pp.*

This book contains many very interesting and important new results of the author. The central notion is that of a $G_{\mathfrak{P}}$ field, where $G_{\mathfrak{P}}=\mathrm{PGL}(2, k_{\mathfrak{P}})$ and $k_{\mathfrak{P}}$ is a non-Archimedean local field of characteristic zero. A field L over k is called a $G_{\mathfrak{P}}$-field over k if (1) the transcendence degree L over k equals one, (2) $G_{\mathfrak{P}}$ acts effectively on L as automorphisms, (3) the fixed field of $G_{\mathfrak{P}}$ in L is k, (4) for each open compact subgroup $V \subset G_{\mathfrak{P}}$ its fixed field L_V is of finite type over k and L is a normal extension of L_V, and the Galois group $G(L/L_V)$ is canonically isomorphic to V, and (5) almost all prime divisors of L_V over k are unramified in L.

The author establishes a one-to-one correspondence between $G_{\mathfrak{P}}$-fields over $\mathbf{C}$ and subgroups Γ of $G=G_{\mathbf{R}} \times G_{\mathfrak{P}}$ such that $V(\Gamma\backslash G)<\infty$ and the projections $\Gamma_{\mathbf{R}}$ and $\Gamma_{\mathfrak{P}}$ are dense in $G_{\mathbf{R}}$ and $G_{\mathfrak{P}}$, respectively. Denote by Γ_n the subgroup of Γ that consists of all elements $\gamma \in \Gamma$ whose projection on $G_{\mathfrak{P}}$ belong to the principal congruence subgroup U_n of $G_{\mathfrak{P}}$. The projection of Γ_n to $G_{\mathbf{R}}$ is a discrete subgroup and hence it can be considered as a discrete subgroup of fractional-linear mappings of the upper half-plane. Denote by P_n the corresponding field of automorphic functions. The author proves that the union P of all the P_n is a $G_{\mathfrak{P}}$-field over $\mathbf{C}$ and that any $G_{\mathfrak{P}}$ field over $\mathbf{C}$ can be obtained in such a way. He also proves that any $G_{\mathfrak{P}}$ field over $\mathbf{C}$ can be defined over a number field.

General properties of such discrete subgroups of $G=G_{\mathbf{R}} \times G_{\mathfrak{P}}$ are considered in Chapter 1. The reviewer would like to mention as a very interesting notion the zeta-function that corresponds to such discrete subgroups of G. In Chapter 3 the author proves that if G/Γ is compact then Γ has no nontrivial deformation.

In Chapter 4 the author considers some examples of Γ. They are obtained by using the well-known Shimura construction of automorphic functions which corresponds to quaternion algebras over a totally real number field. It is plausible that there exist no other examples of a $G_{\mathfrak{P}}$ field over $\mathbf{C}$.

In Chapter 5 the author considers elliptic modular functions from an absolutely new point of view. The main result of this chapter is as follows: There is a one-to-one correspondence between nonexceptional divisors of the field $K=\mathbf{F}_p(j)$ and classes of primitive elliptic elements of $\Gamma^*=\{x \in \mathrm{GL}(2, \mathbf{Z}^{(p)}), \det x \in \Pi\}/\pm\Pi$, where $\Pi=\{p^n, n \in \mathbf{Z}\}$.
I. I. Pjateckiĭ-Šapiro (Moscow)

E64-29 **(44# 6707)**

Ihara, Yasutaka

On congruence monodromy problems. Vol. 2.
Lecture Notes, No. 2.
Department of Mathematics, University of Tokyo, Tokyo, 1969. i+204 *pp.*

Chapter 1 of this book contains a generalization of the calculation of $\mathfrak{S}_\Gamma$ (which was given in Chapter 1 of the first volume for the case G/Γ compact and Γ torsion-free) to the case in which the quotient G/Γ is not necessarily compact (only of finite measure) and Γ may contain nontrivial elements of finite order. In order to do it the author gives a detailed study of elements of Γ with parabolic and elliptic real parts. It is very interesting that the formula for $\mathfrak{S}_\Gamma(u)$ obtained by the author is similar to the well-known formula for the zeta-function of a curve over a finite field.

In Chapter 2 the author considers a differential equation that is similar to the classical equation connected with the problem of uniformization. The author proves that in the arithmetic case this equation can be uniquely characterized algebraically. He gives a generalization of these constructions to the case of "arithmetic" fields (including $G_{\mathfrak{P}}$-fields) over any field of characteristic zero.

The last chapter is a continuation of the last chapter of the first volume [see #6706 above]. It contains non-abelian class field theory—for one particular case. (The general conjectures were given in the introduction to the first volume.) In the last chapter the author considers the case that corresponds to the field of elliptic modular functions. The reviewer would like to emphasize the absolutely new approach to all the problems that are considered in this book.
I. I. Pjateckiĭ-Šapiro (Moscow)

E68 ADÈLE METHODS IN ARITHMETIC GROUPS

See also reviews E02-8, E02-14, E12-91, E12-95, E12-104, E12-116, E12-117, E56-56, E60-2, F25-18, F55-25, F60-4, G35-51, R54-53, Z10-14.

E68-1 **(20# 880)**

Ono, Takashi. Sur une propriété arithmétique des groupes algébriques commutatifs. Bull. Soc. Math. France **85** (1957), 307–323.

Soient k un corps de nombres algébriques, $k_\mathfrak{p}$ le complété de k pour un diviseur premier $\mathfrak{p}$ de k, $\mathscr{A}$ (resp. $\mathscr{A}_\infty$) l'anneau des familles $(x_\mathfrak{p})$ avec $x_\mathfrak{p} \in k_\mathfrak{p}$ pour tout diviseur premier $\mathfrak{p}$ de k, et où $x_\mathfrak{p}$ est entier pour presque tout $\mathfrak{p}$ fini (resp. pour tout $\mathfrak{p}$ fini). On a $k \subset \mathscr{A}$ et $\mathscr{A}_\infty \subset \mathscr{A}$. Si alors G est un sous-groupe du groupe $\mathrm{Gl}(n, k)$ des matrices $n \times n$ inversibles à coefficients dans k, défini par des équations polynomiales $f_\alpha(\cdots, u_{ij}, \cdots)=0$, ces mêmes équations définissent des sous-groupes J et J_∞ de $\mathrm{Gl}(n, \mathscr{A})$ et $\mathrm{Gl}(n, \mathscr{A}_\infty)$ respectivement, et l'on a $G \subset J$ et $J_\infty \subset J$. Lorsque G est défini par la représentation régulière d'un surcorps K de k de degré n, J est le groupe des idèles du corps K; on sait alors que $J/G\cdot J_\infty$ est fini. De là et du th. de Dirichlet sur les unités, on déduit que si G est commutatif, et si la représentation linéaire de G dans k^n est simple, puis semi-simple, alors $J/G\cdot J_\infty$ est fini. Si G est commutatif et unipotent, il est isomorphe comme groupe algébrique à k^r pour un entier r, et de la compacité de $\mathscr{A}/k$, on déduit la finitude de $J/G\cdot J_\infty$. De là, on déduit que si le groupe G est commutatif, le groupe $J/G\cdot J_\infty$ est fini, en utilisant le th. de structure de Kolchin-Borel; c'est le résultat central de cet article. On notera que si G est le groupe d'une forme quadratique, la finitude du nombre des doubles classes de J modulo G et J_∞ équivaut à la finitude du nombre de classes dans un genre de formes quadratiques; cette dernière a été démontré par C. L. Siegel. Lorsque $G=\mathrm{Sl}(n, k)$, la théorie des diviseurs élémentaires sur un anneau Dedekind prouve que $J=G\cdot J_\infty$.
P. Cartier (Princeton, N.J.)

Referred to in E68-2.

E68-2 **(22# 5635)**

Ono, Takashi. On some arithmetic properties of linear algebraic groups. Ann. of Math. (2) **70** (1959), 266–290.

In § 1, some lemmas are proved concerning toruses (in the sense of the theory of algebraic groups, cf. A. Borel, same Ann. **64** (1956), 20–82 [MR **19**, 1195]). Some essential concepts are then introduced concerning the arithmetic theory of an algebraic group G, defined over the rational number-field $\mathbf{Q}$, and isomorphic to a subgroup of a linear group. Let G_A be the adèle-group for G (here called the group of G-idèles, and denoted by $J(G)$; for the definition, cf. T. Ono, Bull. Soc. Math. France **85** (1957), 307–323 [MR **20** #880]). Let $G_A{}^1$ be the subgroup of G_A consisting of the elements $x \in G_A$ such that $|\chi(x)|=1$ for every rational character χ of G (i.e., every rational representation, defined over $\mathbf{Q}$, of G into the multiplicative group G_m in one variable; $|\ |$ is the idèle-module). Let $G_\mathbf{Q}$ be the group of elements of G with coordinates in $\mathbf{Q}$. For a given representation of G as a subgroup of a linear group, let $G_A{}^\infty$ be the subgroup of G_A consisting of the elements of G_A whose p-adic components are all units (i.e., matrices with coefficients in the ring of p-adic integers, with a determinant equal to a p-adic unit). The author says that G is of type (F) if G_A consists of finitely many double cosets $G_\mathbf{Q}\backslash G_A/G_A{}^\infty$ with respect to $G_\mathbf{Q}$ and $G_A{}^\infty$; of type (C) if $G_A{}^1/G_\mathbf{Q}$ is compact; of type (M) if it is of finite measure for the Haar measure on $G_A{}^1$ (this being shown to be both right and left invariant). It is shown that, if G is of type (C), it is of type (F) (obviously, it is of type (M)), and that its group of units, $G_\mathbf{Q} \cap G_A{}^\infty$, is finitely generated. If G is a semidirect product of two connected (i.e., irreducible) groups G', G'' (G' normal, $G''=G/G'$), and if G' has no rational characters and is of type (C), then G is of type (C), respectively (F), respectively (M), whenever G'' is so. The main theorems of the paper are then Theorem 3, stating that every connected solvable group is of type (C), and Theorem 5, which gives the rank of the group of units of all such groups (the latter is a wide generalization of the Dirichlet unit-theorem). The paper also includes a few results on non-connected algebraic groups. *A. Weil* (Princeton, N.J.)

Citations: MR 20# 880 = E68-1.

Referred to in E60-2, E60-4, E68-3, E68-33.

E68-3 **(25# 81)**

Ono, Takashi

On the arithmetic theory of algebraic groups. (Japanese)

Sûgaku **11** (1959/60), 65–75.

The results of this paper in Japanese are also published in Ann. of Math. (2) **70** (1959), 266–290 [MR **22** #5635].

K. Iwasawa (Cambridge, Mass.)

Citations: MR 22# 5635 = E68-2.

E68-4 **(23# A1640)**

Ono, Takashi

Arithmetic of algebraic tori.

Ann. of Math. (2) **74** (1961), 101–139.

The arithmetic of an algebraic torus T over a finite algebraic number field, or an algebraic function field of one variable over a finite constant field, is studied, and in particular its Tamagawa number $\tau(T)$ is defined and investigated. Thus, the ground field k being first assumed to be general, T is shown to be determined by the $\mathfrak{g}(K/k)(=\mathfrak{g})$-module structure of the character group $\hat{T}$, where K is a Galois splitting field of T, and Artin's [J. Reine Angew. Math. **164** (1931), 1–11] theorem is applied to the representation of $\mathfrak{g}$ defined by $\hat{T}$ in order to prove an isogeny ($\rightleftarrows$) relation

$$T^n \times \prod_\lambda (R_{k_\lambda/k}(G_m))^{n_\lambda} \rightleftarrows \prod_\lambda (R_{k_\lambda/k}(G_m))^{m_\lambda},$$

where G_m denotes the multiplicative group of the universal domain, k_λ are (representatives of) subfields of K/k such that K/k_λ are cyclic, and $R_{k_\lambda/k}(V)$, with a variety V over k_λ, is a variety over k defined by a certain universal mapping property. In the case of the arithmetic ground field k as above, a canonical Haar measure of the adelization T_A of T is defined as the product of component measures induced by an invariant differential form of highest degree on T, with correction by a certain factor defined in connection with the (Artin) L-function corresponding to the representation of $\mathfrak{g}$ by $\hat{T}$; the convergence of the product is shown by a result of Weil [Lectures, Princeton, N.J., 1959–1960] and a result on local reduction derived by means of the reviewer [Ann. of Math. (2) **65** (1957), 255–267; MR **19**, 841] cohomological lemma. Then the Tamagawa number $\tau(T)$ is defined, roughly speaking, as the volume of the maximal compact subgroup of T_A/T_k divided by the "quasi-residue" of the L-function, and has functorial properties similar to those of L-functions. Also, for a (separable) k-isogeny $\alpha: T \to T'$ a number $\tau(\alpha)$ is defined in terms of the canonical Haar measures of the adelizations of the tori T, T', and is shown by explicit computation to be a rational number. Combined with the above isogeny relation (and the functorial properties of τ as well as the equation $\tau(G_m)=1$), this leads to the main theorem of the paper that a certain power of $\tau(T)$ is a rational number. *T. Nakayama* (Nagoya)

Citations: MR 19, 841b = R38-25.

Referred to in E68-7, E68-14, E68-33, E72-1, E72-16.

E68-5 **(25# 3094)**

Kneser, Martin

Approximationssätze für algebraische Gruppen.

J. Reine Angew. Math. **209** (1962), 96–97.

Let G be a linear algebraic group defined over $\mathbf{Q}$. For a field $K \supset \mathbf{Q}$, G_K denotes the group of K-rational points. Fixing a matric representation over $\mathbf{Q}$ of G, the author calls G an A-group when G has the following properties: Given any prime numbers p_i $(i=1, \cdots, n)$, exponents t_i and elements $g_i \in G_{\mathbf{Q}_{p_i}}$, there exists an element $g \in G_\mathbf{Q}$ such that $g \equiv g_i \bmod p_i{}^{t_i}$ and g is p-unimodular for all $p \neq p_i$. E.g., the group G_a (additive group), the group of reduced norm 1 of a simple algebra over $\mathbf{Q}$ are A-groups. The author states that if $G(\neq e)$ is an A-group, it is simply connected (in the algebraic sense) and $G_\mathbf{R}$ is non-compact. Using the above examples and known isomorphisms among classical groups, he can prove that the unitary groups and spin groups are A-groups, provided $G_\mathbf{R}$ is non-compact. Thus, he reproduces his "Approximationssatz" for the group of spinor norm 1 [Arch. Math. **7** (1956), 323–332; MR **18**, 562]. *T. Ono* (Vancouver, B.C.)

Citations: MR 18, 562f = E12-57.

E68-6 **(27# 150)**

Voskresenskiĭ, V. E.

Factor spaces of the idèle of an algebraic group and the cohomology of bundles. (Russian)

Dokl. Akad. Nauk SSSR **150** (1963), 459–462.

Let G be a linear algebraic group over an algebraic number field k, with idèle group $J(G)$, and unit idèle group $J_0(G)$. The author shows that the quotient space of double cosets $G \backslash J(G)/J_0(G)$ is in one-to-one correspondence with the cohomology set $H^1(X, E(G))$ of the sheaf of locally integral subgroups of G over the spectrum of the ring of integers in k. He uses this correspondence to show how cohomological techniques can be used to prove some of the basic facts about $G\backslash J(G)/J_0(G)$.

{Several of the proofs seem sketchy and unconvincing. E.g., Theorem 1 (a "Chinese Remainder Theorem" for the embeddings of G in its $\mathfrak{p}$-adic completions) seems "easy" only if the function field of G is a purely transcendental extension of k, which does not always happen [C. Chevalley, J. Math. Soc. Japan **6** (1954), 303–324; MR **16**, 672]. The reviewer also questions Proposition 1 (Why should $A/E(G, m)$ be flabby?) and Theorem 4 (Why is ϕ_1 onto?). On the other hand, the results in this paper, if they could be proven correctly, would be quite illuminating and useful.}

E. C. Dade (Pasadena, Calif.)

Referred to in E60-16.

E68-7 (28# 94)

Ono, Takashi

On the Tamagawa number of algebraic tori.

Ann. of Math. (2) **78** (1963), 47–73.

Let T be an algebraic torus defined over a number field or function field with finite constant field, k. This paper continues a previous paper of the author [same Ann. (2) **74** (1961), 101–139; MR **23** #A1640], and is devoted to establishing the following relation, which connects three basic invariants of the torus:

$$(*) \qquad \tau(T)i(T) = h(T).$$

Here $\tau(T)$ is the Tamagawa number of T. To define the other two numbers, let K be a Galois extension of k, Galois group $\mathfrak{g}=\mathfrak{g}(K/k)$, which splits T. Let $\hat{T}$ be the group of rational characters of T, $C_k(T)$ the group of adele classes of T over k. Then $h(T)=[H^1(\mathfrak{g}, \hat{T})]$. One has a natural map $\alpha: C_k(T)\to C_K(T)^{\mathfrak{g}}$, and $i(T)=[\text{Coker }\alpha]$.

The author proves first the finiteness of $i(T)$ by the Nakayama duality theorem [ibid. (2) **65** (1957), 255–267; MR **19**, 841], which says that the pairing $H^{2-r}(\mathfrak{g}, \hat{T})\times H^r(\mathfrak{g}, C_K(T))\to H^2(\mathfrak{g}, C_K)$ is exact, $r \in \mathbf{Z}$.

The essential part of the proof of (*) is to establish a weaker relation (**) $\tau(E)i(E)=h(E)$, where E denotes a short exact sequence $0\to T'\to T\to T''\to 0$ and where $\tau(E)=\tau(T')\tau(T'')\tau(T)^{-1}$, etc. This part is done by more or less explicit computation of $\tau(E)$, combined with the Nakayama duality above. The passage from (**) to (*) is effected by defining $\phi(T)=\tau(T)i(T)h(T)^{-1}$; the result (**) shows that $\phi(T)$ is defined on the Grothendieck group of the category of tori defined over k and split by K; then a theorem of Swan shows that $\phi(T)=\phi(T')$ for isogenous tori T and T', from which $\phi=1$ follows easily by using the naturality properties of the three invariants.

In conclusion, a torus T is constructed for which $\tau(T)$ is not an integer, and from this a semi-simple group G is given for which $\tau(T)$ is not integral.

A. Mattuck (Cambridge, Mass.)

Citations: MR 19, 841b = R38-25; MR 23# A1640 = E68-4.

Referred to in E68-14, E68-20, E72-1, E72-3, G35-50.

E68-8 (28# 99)

Ono, Takashi

On the relative theory of Tamagawa numbers.

Bull. Amer. Math. Soc. **70** (1964), 325–326.

Let G be a connected semisimple algebraic group, defined over an algebraic number-field k; it has a uniquely defined simply connected covering $\tilde{G}$, with a projection π onto G, $\tilde{G}$ and π being also defined over k. Let N be the kernel of π; this is a finite subgroup of the center of $\tilde{G}$ and may be considered as a $\mathfrak{g}$-module if $\mathfrak{g}$ is the Galois group over k of the algebraic closure $\bar{k}$ of k. The author expresses the ratio $\tau(G)/\tau(\tilde{G})$ of the "Tamagawa numbers" of G and of $\tilde{G}$ in terms of some simple cohomological invariants of the $\mathfrak{g}$-module N, under the assumption that $\tilde{G}$ itself satisfies a certain condition (KS) of cohomological nature (the "Kneser-Serre conjecture"). The latter is known to be fulfilled by many of the classical groups; as many of those groups are also known to have the property $\tau(\tilde{G})=1$, this result represents a significant step forward in our knowledge of Tamagawa numbers. The proof is merely outlined.

A. Weil (Princeton, N.J.)

Referred to in E68-14.

E68-9 (29# 2237)

Gel'fand, I. M.; Graev, M. I.; Pjateckiĭ-Šapiro, I. I.

Representations of adèle groups. (Russian)

Dokl. Akad. Nauk SSSR **156** (1964), 487–490.

Es sei G die Gruppe der unimodularen Matrizen 2-ten Grades mit Koeffizienten aus dem rationalen Zahlkörper Q. Man denke sich G eingebettet in die zugehörige "Adelgruppe" G_A im Sinne von A. Weil [Séminaire Bourbaki, 1958/59, Exp. 186, Secrétariat mathématique, Paris, 1959; MR **28** #1091]. G_A wird folgendermassen konstruiert: Für jede Primstelle p von Q (einschliesslich der unendlichen Stelle) sei G_p die Gruppe der unimodularen Matrizen 2-ten Grades über der p-adischen Komplettierung Q_p von Q; wenn p endlich ist, bedeute U_p diejenige Untergruppe von G_p, die aus allen Matrizen mit p-adisch ganzen Koeffizienten besteht. Dann besteht G_A aus allen formalen Produkten $g=\prod_p g_p$, wobei $g_p \in G_p$ und $g_p \in U_p$ für alle bis auf endlich viele p. Für eine endliche Menge S von Primstellen p, welche die unendliche Primstelle enthält, wird $G_A{}^S=\prod_{p\in S} G_p\cdot\prod_{p\notin S} U_p$ gesetzt; G_A ist die Vereinigung aller dieser Untergruppen $G_A{}^S$. Die Topologie von G_A wird so definiert, dass die $G_A{}^S$ (versehen mit der Produkt-Topologie) als offene, topologische Untergruppen von G_A erscheinen. G_A ist lokal-kompakt, und G ist diskret in G_A [Weil, loc. cit.]. In der vorliegenden Arbeit wird die Darstellung untersucht, die von G_A im Raum $L_2(G_A/G)$ der quadratisch-integrierbaren Funktionen auf dem homogenen Raum G_A/G vermittelt wird. Und zwar handelt es sich um die Zerlegung dieser Darstellung in irreduzible Komponenten. Es sei Z die Untergruppe der Matrizen der Form $\begin{pmatrix}1 & 0\\ z & 1\end{pmatrix}$ und D die Untergruppe der Diagonalmatrizen aus G; sei $X=G_A/Z_AD$. Die Darstellung von G_A im Raume $L_2(X)$ zerlegt sich in irreduzible Darstellungen T_π, wobei π die Charaktere von Λ_A/Λ durchläuft und Λ die multiplikative Gruppe von Q bezeichnet. Der Darstellungsraum von T_π wird dabei gebildet durch diejenigen Funktionen $f_\pi(x)$ auf X, welche der Relation genügen: $f_\pi(\lambda x)=\pi(\lambda)|\lambda|^{-1}\cdot f_\pi(x)$, $\lambda\in\Lambda$, $|\lambda|=\prod_p|\lambda_p|_p$, und für welche $\|f_\pi\|^2=\int|f_\pi(x)|^2\,d\omega<+\infty$, wobei das Integral erstreckt wird über die Fläche Ω: $|x_p|_p=1$ und $d\omega$ das natürliche Mass auf Ω bezeichnet. Die Darstellungen T_{π_1} und T_{π_2} sind äquivalent wenn und nur wenn $\pi_1=\pi_2$ oder $\pi_1=\pi_2{}^{-1}$. Eines der Hauptergebnisse der Verfasser besagt, dass diese Darstellungen T_π auch in einer gewissen Teildarstellung der Darstellung von G_A in $L_2(G_A/G)$ vorkommen, und zwar mit der Multiplizität 1. π kann als Grössencharakter im Sinne von Hecke angesehen werden; zu ihm gehört ein Charakter χ der multiplikativen Gruppe χ von Q mit endlichem Führer. Die Funktionalgleichung der Dirichletschen L-Funktion $L(s, \chi)$ ist damit gleichbedeutend, dass T_π in der in Rede stehenden Teildarstellung nur einfach vorkommt. Ein Teil de- Resultate der Verfasser bezieht sich auf allgemeine algebraische Gruppen über einem beliebigen algebraischen Zahlkörper. Beweise werden nicht gegeben.

{Literatur: [1] A. Weil, Adèles and algebraic groups, [Lecture notes, Princeton, 1961], [2] A. Borel [Inst. Hautes Études Sci. Publ. Math. No. 16 (1963), 5–30],

[3] I. M. Gel'fand and I. I. Pjateckiĭ-Šapiro [Trudy Moskov. Mat. Obšč. **12** (1963), 389–412; MR **28** #3115].}

P. Roquette (Tübingen)

Citations: MR 28# 1091 = Z10-14.

E68-10 (31# 172)

Kneser, Martin

Einfach zusammenhängende algebraische Gruppen in der Arithmetik.

Proc. Internat. Congr. Mathematicians (Stockholm, 1962), pp. 260–263. *Inst. Mittag-Leffler, Djursholm,* 1963.

The groups mentioned in the title are those algebraic groups G which are connected in the Zariski topology and for which there is no surjective homomorphism $H \to G$ of a connected algebraic group H with finite nontrivial kernel. In this expository paper the author indicates the role of this notion in approximation theorems in p-adic fields, and in arithmetic properties of homogeneous spaces.

Referred to in F50-55.

E68-11 (31# 1254)

Ono, Takashi

The Gauss-Bonnet theorem and the Tamagawa number.

Bull. Amer. Math. Soc. **71** (1965), 345–348.

Let G_0 be a connected semisimple real Lie group without compact factor and center, $\mathfrak{g}_0$ its Lie algebra, and put $\mathfrak{g} = \mathfrak{g}_0 \otimes \mathbf{C}$. Let K be a maximal compact subgroup of G_0 and $\mathfrak{k}$ its Lie algebra. Let $\mathfrak{g}_0 = \mathfrak{k} + \mathfrak{p}$ be the Cartan decomposition and let $\check{\mathfrak{u}} = \mathfrak{k} + (-1)^{1/2}\mathfrak{p}$. Denote by U the compact form of G, i.e., the connected compact group whose Lie algebra is $\check{\mathfrak{u}}$. Let $m = \dim(G_0/K)$. Let Γ be a discrete subgroup of G_0 such that $\int_{\Gamma\backslash G_0} dG_0 < \infty$, and define the "Euler-Poincaré characteristic" of $\Gamma\backslash G_0/K$ by

$$\chi(\Gamma\backslash G_0/K) = \frac{2\kappa(G_0/K)}{A_m} \int_{\Gamma\backslash G_0/K} d(G_0/K),$$

where $\kappa(G_0/K)$ is the Gaussian curvature of G_0/K, and A_m the surface area of the unit m-sphere.

If now G is a Chevalley group, i.e., the identity component of the group of automorphisms of a complex semisimple Lie algebra $\mathfrak{g}$, then G is an algebraic subgroup of $\mathrm{GL}(n)$ defined over $\mathbf{Q}$, with respect to a Chevalley basis, where $n = \dim \mathfrak{g}$. Let G_0 be the identity component of $G_{\mathbf{R}}$. Choose a maximal compact subgroup K of G_0, let U be the corresponding compact form, T a maximal torus of U, and let $\Gamma = G_{\mathbf{Z}} \cap G_0$. Let l be the rank of $\mathfrak{g}$, and let the Poincaré polynomial of U be $\prod_{i=1}^{l} (t^{2a_i - 1} + 1)$. Using the Gauss-Bonnet theorem and the results of Iwahori and Matsumoto [Inst. Hautes Études Sci. Publ. Math. No. 25 (1965), 5–48], the author derives a formula relating the Tamagawa number $\tau(G)$ with $\chi(\Gamma\backslash G_0/K)$ when all a_i are even:

$$\tau(G) = \frac{(-1)^{(l+N)/2} 2^l N! [W]}{(2N)!} \prod_{i=1}^{l} a_i! B_{a_i/2}^{-1} \times \prod_{r>0} \langle r, r \rangle \frac{\chi(\Gamma\backslash G_0/K)}{\chi(U/K)\kappa(U/T)},$$

where N is the number of positive roots of $\mathfrak{g}$, $[W]$ is the order of the Weyl group W of $\mathfrak{g}$, $B_{a_i/2}$ are Bernoulli numbers, $\langle r, r \rangle$ is the inner product defined by the Killing form on $\mathfrak{g}$, $\chi(U/K)$ is the Euler-Poincaré characteristic of U/K, and $\kappa(U/T)$ is the Gaussian curvature of U/T.

E. T. Kobayashi (Evanston, Ill.)

Referred to in E60-24.

E68-12 (31# 2249)

Ono, Takashi

On the relative theory of Tamagawa numbers.

Ann. of Math. (2) **82** (1965), 88–111.

Let G be a connected semisimple algebraic group over an algebraic number-field k; let $\tau(G)$ be its Tamagawa number. The main purpose of this paper is to determine $\tau(G)/\tau(G')$ for two isogenous groups G, G' (this turns out to be rational). It is of course enough to consider the case where G' is the universal covering group $\tilde{G}$ of G, with the canonical homomorphism f onto G; the kernel of f is a subgroup of the (finite) center of $\tilde{G}$, rational over k. The case where G has a factor of type E_8 may be excluded without loss of generality, since E_8 has no center. The paper contains the complete determination of $\tau(G)/\tau(\tilde{G})$ in terms of certain invariants of the kernel M; as stated, this still depends on some conjectural statements in the arithmetic theory of semisimple groups, but these statements have been proved since (with the possible exception of E_8), so that the results of the paper are valid without exception. The proofs depend essentially on the method of "crossed diagrams" (which had been previously applied to special cases of the same problem) and on the solution of the similar problem for toruses, previously obtained by the author [same Ann. (2) **78** (1963), 47–73; MR **28** #94]. A final section gives some results on the two integers which occur as numerator and denominator of the formula for $\tau(G)/\tau(\tilde{G})$, including their complete determination in various special cases. For instance, $\tau(G)/\tau(\tilde{G})$ turns out to be equal to the number of elements of M (i.e., to the order of the "algebraic fundamental group" of G) whenever that number is 2, and also whenever G is "of Chevalley type".

A. Weil (Princeton, N.J.)

Referred to in E60-24, E68-14, E68-20, F70-18.

E68-13 (32# 2416)

Kneser, Martin

Starke Approximation in algebraischen Gruppen. I.

J. Reine Angew. Math. **218** (1965), 190–203.

Let k be an algebraic number field. Let S denote a finite set of places of k. Let G be a linear algebraic group defined over k, G_A the adèle group of G over k, let $G_S = \prod_{v \in S} G_{k_v}$ (the S-component of G_A), and let G_k be the subgroup of k-rational points of G. The author says that (G, S) admits the strong approximation if $G_S G_k$ is dense in G_A. Necessary conditions for strong approximation for $G \neq \{1\}$ are (1) G is simply connected, and (2) G_S is not compact (Satz 1). In particular, it follows that the radical R of G is unipotent, or equivalently, $\hat{G} = \mathrm{Hom}(G, G_m) = \{0\}$, and that G/R is a direct product of k-simple groups, each of which admits strong approximation with respect to S. Conversely, the main theorem (Satz 2) says that if G is a simply connected k-simple classical group such that G_S is not compact, then (G, S) admits strong approximation.

{After this work, the author found a unified approach which reduces the whole problem to the Hasse principle on the Galois cohomology of simply connected semisimple groups; in view of this, the above main theorem holds not only for classical groups but for all simply connected k-simple algebraic groups except possibly those of type E_8 [cf. the author, "Strong approximation", Summer Institute on Algebraic Groups and Discontinuous Subgroups, Boulder, Colorado, 1965] *.} *T. Ono* (Philadelphia, Pa.)

*See MR **35** #4225 = E68-22.

Citations: MR 35# 4225 = E68-22.

Referred to in E68-22, E68-24.

E68-14 (32# 7561)

Ono, Takashi

On Tamagawa numbers. (Japanese)

Sûgaku **15** (1963), 72–81.

This is a report on the state of affairs, up to the date of publication, of the theory of Tamagawa numbers (τ-theory), by the author who has been the principal force in developing this theory. In § 1 and § 2 some discussion is given, leading to the definition of the Tamagawa number $\tau_k(G)$ of an algebraic group G defined over a number field k. In § 3 the τ-theory of a torus is summarized, covering the main content of the author's two papers [Ann. of Math. (2) **74** (1961), 101–139; MR **23** #A1640; ibid. (2) **78** (1963), 47–73; MR **28** #94]. In § 4 it is interesting to see that half of the content of the author's later paper [ibid. (2) **82** (1965), 88–111; MR **31** #2249; also, Bull. Amer. Math. Soc. **70** (1964), 325–326; MR **28** #99] on "relative" τ-theory is already summarized here, ending with

$$\tau(f) = \tau(G)/\tau(\tilde{G}) = [\hat{M}^g]/i(T)r(H),$$

formula (2.1.5) of the 1965 Annals paper. From this formula, the author deduces, in the later paper, more conclusive results by introducing Kneser's conjecture on connected simply connected semi-simple algebraic groups.

E. T. Kobayashi (Evanston, Ill.)

Citations: MR 23# A1640 = E68-4; MR 28# 94 = E68-7; MR 28# 99 = E68-8; MR 31# 2249 = E68-12.

E68-15 (33# 126)

Godement, Roger

Domaines fondamentaux des groupes arithmétiques.

Séminaire Bourbaki, 1962/63. *Fasc.* 3, *No.* 257, 25 *pp.* *Secrétariat mathématique, Paris*, 1964.

Let G be a linear algebraic group defined over $\mathbf{Q}$, G_A the corresponding adèle group, and let $G_A{}^0 = \{g \in G_A;\ |\chi(g)| = 1$ for all $\chi \in (\hat{G})_{\mathbf{Q}}\}$, where $(\hat{G})_{\mathbf{Q}}$ is the set of $\mathbf{Q}$-rational characters of G and $|a|$ is the module of an idèle a. The group $G_{\mathbf{Q}}$ of $\mathbf{Q}$-rational points of G is a discrete subgroup of $G_A{}^0$. Borel and Harish-Chandra have proved that $G_A{}^0/G_{\mathbf{Q}}$ is of finite volume when G is connected and that, when G is connected reductive, $G_A{}^0/G_{\mathbf{Q}}$ is compact if and only if G is anisotropic over $\mathbf{Q}$ ($G_{\mathbf{Q}}$ has no unipotent element $\neq 1$) (cf. Borel and Harish-Chandra [Ann. of Math. (2) **75** (1962), 485–535; MR **26** #5081], and Borel [Inst. Hautes Études Sci. Publ. Math. No. 16 (1963), 5–30]). This compactness criterion (Godement's conjecture) was proved also by Mostow and Tamagawa [Ann. of Math. (2) **76** (1962), 446–463; MR **25** #5069] by methods entirely different from those of Borel and Harish-Chandra. In this exposé, the author and Weil show that one can extend the method of Mostow and Tamagawa to get the Minkowski reduction theory of reductive groups and thus obtain a new and simpler proof of theorems of Borel and Harish-Chandra. The author begins with "Mahler's criterion" (Theorem 1). Let G be an algebraic group over $\mathbf{Q}$ in GL(V), V being a vector space variety over $\mathbf{Q}$. Then a set $M \subset G_A{}^0$ is relatively compact mod $G_{\mathbf{Q}}$ if and only if $m_n(\xi_n) \to 0$ in V_A ($m_n \in M$, $\xi_n \in V_{\mathbf{Q}}$) implies $\xi_n = 0$ for large n. Theorem 1 is ingeniously used to prove the compactness of $G_A{}^0/G_{\mathbf{Q}}$ when G is solvable (Theorem 2), to prove Godement's conjecture (Theorem 4) and to prove Theorem 7, which implies immediately the finiteness of the volume of $G_A{}^0/G_{\mathbf{Q}}$ when G is connected. Theorem 7 is "Minkowski's inequalities" [cf. Borel, Colloq. Théorie des Groupes Algébriques (Bruxelles, 1962), pp. 23–40, Librairie Universitaire, Louvain, 1962; MR **26** #6173], and is stated as follows. Assuming G connected reductive of rank $r \geq 1$ over $\mathbf{Q}$ (note that $r = 0 \Leftrightarrow G$ anisotropic), let T be a maximal $\mathbf{Q}$-split torus and P a minimal parabolic subgroup of G determined by T. Choose a compact set $M \subset G_A$ such that $G_A = MP_A$, and an open relatively compact set $F \subset P_A{}^0$ such that $P_A{}^0 = FP_{\mathbf{Q}}$; for $c > 0$, put $T_A(c) = \{t \in T_A;\ |\alpha_i(t)| < c\}$, where α_i ($1 \leq i \leq r$) are simple roots of G with respect to T, and put $\Omega(c) = MT_A(c)F$. Then $G_A = \Omega(c)G_{\mathbf{Q}}$ for large c. The last third of the paper is devoted mainly to the construction of a fundamental open set, i.e., an open set $\mathfrak{S}$ of G_A such that $G_A = \mathfrak{S}G_{\mathbf{Q}}$ and $\{\gamma \in G_{\mathbf{Q}};\ \mathfrak{S}\gamma \cap \mathfrak{S} \neq \varnothing\}$ is finite. (The $\Omega(c)$ in Theorem 7 does not have this second property, in general.) Such an $\mathfrak{S}$ is obtained as $\mathfrak{S} = MT_{\mathbf{R}}{}^+(c)F$ with large c, where F, M are as above, the $\mathbf{R}$-component $M_{\mathbf{R}}$ of M is chosen so that $M_{\mathbf{R}}$ is a maximal compact subgroup of $G_{\mathbf{R}}$ compatible with $T_{\mathbf{R}}$, and $T_{\mathbf{R}}{}^+(c) = \{t \in T_{\mathbf{R}}{}^+$ (the identity component of topological group $T_{\mathbf{R}}$); $\alpha_i(t) < c\}$. This paper also contains the proof of various finiteness theorems, e.g., finiteness of the class number (Theorem 5), of minimal parabolic subgroups modulo conjugation by the group of units, and of points mod $G_{\mathbf{Q}}$ of $G_A\xi \cap V_{\mathbf{Q}}$ ($\xi \in V_{\mathbf{Q}}$) when the orbit $G\xi$ is Zariski-closed (Theorem 10).

T. Ono (Philadelphia, Pa.)

Citations: MR 25# 5069 = E60-3; MR 26# 5081 = E60-5; MR 26# 6173 = E60-6; MR 34# 2578 = E68-17.

Referred to in E02-15.

E68-16 (33# 7342)

Ono, Takashi

On algebraic groups and discontinuous groups.

Nagoya Math. J. **27** (1966), 279–322.

Let G be a connected, semi-simple, algebraic group over the rational number field $\mathbf{Q}$. The group $G_{\mathbf{R}}$ of real points on G is then a topological group; let G_0 be its connected component of the identity. It is easy to see that G_0 is a semi-simple Lie group. If K is a maximal compact subgroup of G_0, if $X = G_0/K$ is the associated symmetric space, and if X_u is the compact form of X, the author demands that the Gaussian curvature of X not vanish, or, equivalently, that $E(X_u)$ be strictly positive (here $E(X_u)$ is the Euler number of X_u). When these conditions are met, the author terms G "a group of type (P)"; it is groups of type (P) that are investigated in the present work.

The investigation proceeds along two fronts: algebraic and differential-geometric, and the main results come from comparing the results of one method with those of the other. As for the algebraic investigations, one may as well suppose that G is simple over $\mathbf{Q}$. If k is the smallest field of definition for an absolutely simple factor $\tilde{G}$ of G, then G is $\mathbf{Q}$-isogenous to $\mathbf{N}_{k/\mathbf{Q}}\tilde{G}$, where $\mathbf{N}_{k/\mathbf{Q}}$ is the operation introduced by Weil [Séminaire Bourbaki, 1958/59, Fasc. 3, Exp. 186, deuxième édition, Secrétariat mathématique, Paris, 1959; MR **28** #1091], and later refined by Grothendieck [ibid. 1960/61, Fasc. 3, Exp. 221, deuxième édition, Secrétariat mathématique, Paris, 1961; MR **27** #1339]. To such a G the author associates a Galois extension $\mathcal{N}_{G/k}$ of k, which he calls the "nuclear field" of G. The construction is technical, but the main points are as follows. (a) The Galois group of $\mathcal{N}_{G/k}$ over k is embedded in the group of automorphisms of the Dynkin diagram of $\tilde{G}$. (b) $\mathcal{N}_{G/k}$ respects isogeny. (c) $\mathcal{N}_{G/k}$ is contained in any field K over which G becomes isomorphic to a Chevalley group. (d) For almost all primes $\mathfrak{p}$ of k, the residue field of $\mathcal{N}_{G/k}$ at $\mathfrak{P}$ (lying above $\mathfrak{p}$) is the nuclear field of the group $G^{(\mathfrak{p})}$ obtained by reducing G mod $\mathfrak{p}$. (e) When k is finite, $\mathcal{N}_{G/k}$ is the unique smallest splitting field for G (i.e., field as in property (c)).

Properties (d) and (e) allow the author to interpret the order of the finite group $G_{\tilde{k}_{\mathfrak{p}}}{}^{(\mathfrak{p})}$ in terms of the decomposition law of $\mathfrak{p}$ in $\mathcal{N}_{G/k}$, hence, to associate with G (over k) a finite number of L-functions from $\mathcal{N}_{G/k}$. If G is of type (P), the author proves that k is totally real and $\mathcal{N}_{G/k}$ is either totally real or totally imaginary.

The differential-geometric investigations proceed briefly

as follows. Let U be the compact form of G_0 (so that $X_u = U/K$), and let T be a maximal torus of U. Let $V = U/T$. Then there are natural invariant measures on all the spaces which occur, and one has $\int_U dU = \int_{X_u} dX_u \int_K dK = \int_V dV \int_T dT$. Under hypothesis (P), one finds that dim $X =$ dim $X_u = m = 2m_0$, and that the Euler number of X_u is $[W(U)]/[W(K)]$, where $W(*)$ means the Weyl group of $(*)$ and $[*]$ is the cardinality of $(*)$. The space V is of dimension $2N$, and $E(V) = [W(U)]$. From the Gauss-Bonnet theorem one obtains the formulae $2\kappa(X_u)A_m^{-1}\int_{X_u} dX_u = [W(U)]/[W(K)]$, and $2\kappa(V)A_{2N}^{-1}\int_V dV = [W(U)]$, where A_r is the area of the unit r-sphere.

If Γ is a discrete subgroup of G_0, then Γ acts on X properly discontinuously. The author assumes $\int_{\Gamma/G_0} dG_0$ is finite and that Γ acts on X without fixed points. Another application of the Gauss-Bonnet theorem yields $E(\Gamma\backslash X) = 2\kappa(X)A_m^{-1}\int_{\Gamma\backslash X} dX$, and so

$$\int_{\Gamma\backslash G_0} dG_0 = (-1)^{m_0}E(\Gamma\backslash X)[W(K)][W(U)]^{-1}\int_U dU.$$

A computation of the volume of U in terms of the roots of the complexified Lie algebra of G_0 finally yields $(*)$ $\int_{\Gamma\backslash G_0} dG_0 \sim \pi^{l+N}|q^{(G)}|^{1/2}E(\Gamma\backslash X)$, where $\sim$ means mod $\mathbf{Q}^*$ and $q^{(G)}$ is a complicated expression in terms of the roots.

For the application to Tamagawa numbers, the author takes Γ to be an arithmetic group and uses Weil's result $\tau(SU(r)) = 1$ to show that the transcendental factors in $(*)$ and in the L-functions arising from G exactly cancel. He thus obtains his main theorem: $\tau(G) \sim E(\Gamma\backslash X)$ when G is of type (P) and is not one of a set of technically exceptional groups (like D_4). In particular, $\tau(G)$ is rational if $G_{\mathbf{Z}}\backslash G_{\mathbf{R}}$ is compact. *S. S. Shatz* (Philadelphia, Pa.)

Citations: MR 28# 1091 = Z10-14.

E68-17 **(34# 2578)**

Borel, Armand

Some finiteness properties of adele groups over number fields.

Inst. Hautes Études Sci. Publ. Math. No. 16 (1963), 5–30.

Let k be an algebraic number field of finite degree over $\mathbf{Q}$, $\mathfrak{o}$ the ring of integers of k, V the set of (equivalence classes of) valuations of k, $P \subset V$ the set of finite primes of k, k_v the completion of k with respect to v, $\mathfrak{o}_\mathfrak{p}$ ($\mathfrak{p} \in P$) the ring of $\mathfrak{p}$-adic integers of $k_\mathfrak{p}$, and I_k the group of ideles of k. Let G be an algebraic matric group defined over k, G^0 its identity component and, for a subring B of an overfield of k, G_B the group of elements of G with coefficients in B and determinant invertible in B. The adele group of G will be denoted by G_A. The group G_k is imbedded in G_A as a discrete subgroup. Put $G_A^\infty = \prod_{v\in V-P} G_{k_v} \times \prod_{\mathfrak{p}\in P} G_{\mathfrak{o}_\mathfrak{p}}$. The cardinality of the double coset space $G_A^\infty\backslash G_A/G_k$ will be denoted by $c(G)$. Let $X_k(G)$ be the module of rational characters of G defined over k. Each $\chi \in X_k(G)$ defines a homomorphism $\chi_A: G_A \to I_k$. Let $m_k: I_k \to \mathbf{R}^+$ be the homomorphism which associates to an idele its idele-module. To each character χ corresponds a homomorphism $m_k \circ \chi_A: G_A \to \mathbf{R}^+$; put ${}_mG_A = \bigcap_{\chi\in X_k(G)} \operatorname{Ker}(m_k \circ \chi_A)$, this contains G_k by the product formula of k.

The basic finiteness theorems for the pair (G_A, G_k) are proved in § 5. Theorem 5.1 (finiteness of the class number): $c(G)$ is finite. Theorem 5.4 (finiteness of orbits): Let G be reductive, H an algebraic subgroup over k of G, and σ the natural projection of G onto $X = G/H$. Assume that H is reductive or, equivalently, that X is an affine algebraic set. Then $\sigma_A(G_A) \cap X_k$ is the union of finitely many orbits of G_k. Theorem 5.6 (finiteness of volume): (i) G_A/G_k carries an invariant measure and has a finite volume for that measure if and only if $X_k(G^0) = 1$; (ii) G_A/G_k is compact if and only if $X_k(G^0) = 1$ and every unipotent element of G_k belongs to the radical of G_k. Theorem 5.8 (generalization of Theorem 5.6 for G connected): The space ${}_mG_A/G_k$ has a finite invariant measure, and it is compact if and only if every unipotent element of G_k belongs to the radical of G_k. §§ 6, 7 contain applications of § 5. Theorem 6.8: Let G be reductive and connected. Then the number of isomorphism classes over k of principal homogeneous spaces over k for G which split locally everywhere is finite. Theorem 7.3: Let G be connected and H be a parabolic subgroup, defined over k. Then $(G/H)_k$ is the union of finitely many orbits of $G_\mathfrak{o}$.

By the use of the technique of restriction of the ground field, the general case of a number field can be reduced to the case where $k = \mathbf{Q}$. When $k = \mathbf{Q}$, the pair $(G_A, G_\mathbf{Q})$ can be viewed as the global counterpart of the pair $(G_\mathbf{R}, G_\mathbf{Z})$, which was the main object of the paper (BH) by the author and Harish-Chandra [Ann. of Math. (2) **75** (1962), 485–535; MR **26** #5081]. The present paper depends essentially on (BH); § 3 reviews, reformulates in part, and strengthens slightly some results of (BH), and in § 4 one constructs, in much the same way as in (BH), "fundamental sets" for G_k in G_A. Because of this, the methods of this paper do not apply for the function field case, in view of the lack of archimedean valuations. The paper ends with a paragraph (§ 8) on a generalization to the group of S-units of the results of (BH) and of §§ 4, 5 in this paper.

T. Ono (Philadelphia, Pa.)

Citations: MR 26# 5081 = E60-5.

Referred to in E60-7, E60-10, E68-15.

E68-18 **(34# 5831)**

Raghavan, S.; Rangachari, S. S.

On zeta functions of quadratic forms.

Ann. of Math. (2) **85** (1967), 46–57.

In 1950 Iwasawa and Tate had expressed the zeta function of an algebraic number field by means of an integral over the idèle group, and in 1958 G. Fujisaki [J. Fac. Sci. Univ. Tokyo Sect. I **7** (1958), 567–604; MR **20** #2367] extended this method to simple algebras over the rational field. Next, A. Weil [*Adeles and algebraic groups*, Mimeographed lecture notes, Institute for Advanced Study, Princeton Univ., Princeton, N.J., 1961] defined zeta functions for the classical groups by this method. While these functions coincide with the familiar zeta functions (with a gamma factor) in the case of the general linear group, they were not explicitly known for the other classical groups. On the other hand, the zeta function of a quadratic form in an algebraic number field was previously defined and investigated by K. G. Ramanathan [Acta Arith. **7** (1961/62), 39–69; MR **24** #A717], following Siegel's well-known lines. Now the authors of this paper treat Weil's zeta function in the case of the orthogonal group with respect to a quadratic form $f(x)$ in an algebraic number field, and show that it is a finite sum extended over the genus of $f(x)$, the summands of which are in principle triple products of Ramanathan's zeta functions, gamma functions and hypergeometric functions. For this they choose the auxiliary definite quadratic form, entering in Weil's function, suitably. *M. Eichler* (Basel)

Citations: MR 20# 2367 = R54-27; MR 24# A717 = E12-83.

E68-19 **(35# 190a; 35# 190b)**

Mars, J. G. M.
The Siegel formula for orthogonal groups. I.
Algebraic Groups and Discontinuous Subgroups (*Proc. Sympos. Pure Math., Boulder, Colo.*, 1965), *pp.* 133–137. *Amer. Math. Soc., Providence, R.I.*, 1966.

Mars, J. G. M.
The Siegel formula for orthogonal groups. II.
Algebraic Groups and Discontinuous Subgroups (*Proc. Sympos. Pure Math., Boulder, Colo.*, 1965), *pp.* 138–142. *Amer. Math. Soc., Providence, R.I.*, 1966.

These two notes are essentially a report on the results on Tamagawa numbers of classical groups, which are obtained in A. Weil's paper [Acta Math. **113** (1965), 1–87]. The author restricts himself to the case of orthogonal groups. The first note gives an outline of a proof of the fact that the Tamagawa number of an orthogonal group is 2 (which is essentially Siegel's classical measure formula). The proof is based on Weil's ideas, but is slightly different in the details.

The second note gives a survey of Weil's procedure. It ends with an appendix giving, for all types of classical groups over number fields, the precise results about Tamagawa numbers and the Hasse principle, which are obtained in Weil's paper. *T. A. Springer* (Utrecht)

Citations: MR 36# 6421 = E12-105.

E68-20 **(35# 191)**

Ono, Takashi
On Tamagawa numbers.
Algebraic Groups and Discontinuous Subgroups (*Proc. Sympos. Pure Math., Boulder, Colo.*, 1965), *pp.* 122–132. *Amer. Math. Soc., Providence, R.I.*, 1966.

This is a very readable report on the author's work on the Tamagawa numbers of tori and on the "relative" theory of Tamagawa numbers, i.e., the relation between the Tamagawa numbers of a connected semisimple algebraic group (defined over an algebraic number field) and of its universal covering group [Ann. of Math. (2) **78** (1963), 47–73; MR **28** #94; ibid. (2) **82** (1965), 88–111; MR **31** #2249].

The proofs of the main results are given in outline. *T. A. Springer* (Utrecht)

Citations: MR 28# 94 = E68-7; MR 31# 2249 = E68-12.

E68-21 **(35# 2900)**

Tamagawa, Tsuneo
Adèles.
Algebraic Groups and Discontinuous Subgroups (*Proc. Sympos. Pure Math., Boulder, Colo.*, 1965), *pp.* 113–121. *Amer. Math. Soc., Providence, R.I.*, 1966.

This is an exposition of the Tamagawa number, introduced by the author. A connection between that number and Siegel's theorem on quadratic forms is explained. Mainly, following A. Weil's lecture notes ["Adèles and algebraic groups", mimeographed lectures, Inst. Advanced Study, Princeton Univ., Princeton, N.J., 1961], the author discusses the following: valuations, definition of adèle ring, adèlized variety, adèlized group, certain homogeneous spaces, restriction of the ground field, measure on V_{A_k}, and the connection between Siegel's theory and $\tau(O^+(n, S)) = 2$. *T. Ono* (Philadelphia, Pa.)

E68-22 **(35# 4225)**

Kneser, Martin
Strong approximation.
Algebraic Groups and Discontinuous Subgroups (*Proc. Sympos. Pure Math., Boulder, Colo.*, 1965), *pp.* 187–196. *Amer. Math. Soc., Providence, R.I.*, 1966.

Let k be an algebraic number field, let S be a finite set of places of k and denote by ∞ the set of infinite places of k. Let G be a linear algebraic group defined over k, let G_A be the adèle group, let $G_S = \prod_{v \in S} G_{k_v}$ be the S-component of G_A and let G_k ($\subset G_A$) be the k-rational points of G. The problem of strong approximation is the following: under what conditions (on G and S) is $G_S G_k$ dense in G_A. Necessary conditions ($G \neq \{1\}$) are: (1) G_S is not compact; (2) G is simply connected. (See the author's paper in J. Reine Angew. Math. **218** (1965), 190–203 [MR **32** #2416].) As noted at the end of the review of that paper, the author has found a unified approach to the problem which yields the following main theorem. Let G be simply connected and absolutely almost simple, and let G_S be not compact. Then if the Hasse principle holds for all k-forms of G (i.e., if the canonical mapping $H^1(k, G) \to \prod_{v \in \infty} H^1(k_v, G)$ is injective) then (G, S) has strong approximation. Now the Hasse principle holds for all such G except possibly those of type E_8 [see the author's lecture on the Hasse principle in *Algebraic groups and discontinuous subgroups* (Proc. Sympos. Pure Math., Boulder, Colo., 1965), pp. 159–163, Amer. Math. Soc., Providence, R.I., 1966], so also the main theorem. The paper contains a sketch of the proof of the main theorem (in parts too sketchy for the reviewer), together with examples of the application of strong approximation to the calculation of class numbers. *J. V. Armitage* (Durham)

Citations: MR 32# 2416 = E68-13; MR 36# 3788 = E72-13.

Referred to in E68-13, E68-24, E68-34, E68-36.

E68-23 **(35# 4227)**

Mars, J. G. M.
Les nombres de Tamagawa de certains groupes exceptionnels.
Bull. Soc. Math. France **94** (1966), 97–140.

Soit G un groupe algébrique linéaire, connexe et semi-simple, défini sur un corps de nombres algébriques k. Soit G_A le groupe adélique correspondant. C'est un groupe localement compact, qui contient le groupe G_k des points k-rationnels de G comme sous-groupe discret. L'espace homogène G_A/G_k possède une mesure invariante canonique, dite mesure de Tamagawa. Le volume de G_A/G_k, qui est fini, est le nombre de Tamagawa $\tau(G)$ de G. D'après la "conjecture de Weil" on devrait avoir $\tau(G) = 1$, lorsque G est en outre simplement connexe. Ceci a été établi pour la plupart des groupes dits "classiques". Dans le présent travail, la conjecture est démontrée pour les groupes de type F_4 et pour certaines formes des groupes de type E_6. La méthode est une adaptation de celle d'un travail récent de A. Weil [Acta Math. **113** (1965), 1–87]; MR **36** #6421].

Cette méthode utilise une représentation rationnelle de G sur k, dans un k-espace vectoriel X. Soit X_A [X_k] l'espace adélique attaché à X [le groupe des points k-rationnels de X]. Avec une fonction convenable Φ sur X_A on forme l'intégrale $I(\Phi) = \int_{G_A/G_k} \sum_{\xi \in X_k} \Phi(g\xi) |dg|_A$, où $|dg|_A$ est la mesure de Tamagawa (des intégrales similaires ont été introduits dans la théorie des formes quadratiques par Siegel).

Dans les cas étudiés par A. Weil [loc. cit.] G est un groupe classique, et la représentation dans X est le plus souvent la représentation de la plus basse dimension, ou une somme directe de telles représentations. Dans le présent travail, G est de type E_6 et dim $X=27$. On identifie X à une algèbre de Jordan exceptionnelle sur k, et G au groupe qui laisse invariante la norme générique N de X. N est une forme cubique irréducible, d'une forme très particulière (et le travail montre que ces formes cubiques ont une bonne théorie arithmétique).

Un premier point non-trivial est la démonstration de la convergence de l'intégrale $I(\Phi)$. L'auteur la démontre, lorsque Φ est une fonction de Schwartz-Bruhat sur X_A. Identifiant X_A à son dual et désignant par $\hat{\Phi}$ la transformée de Fourier de Φ, on déduit de la formule de Poisson l'égalité $I(\Phi)=I(\hat{\Phi})$.

Pour transformer $I(\Phi)$, on a besoin d'une connaissance détaillée des orbites de G_A dans X_A. D'abord, l'auteur détermine les orbites, et les sous-groupes de stabilité correspondants, de G_k dans X_k lorsque k est un corps parfait (de caractéristique $\neq 2, 3$). Les orbites sont les suivantes: (a) L'ensemble des $x\in X_k$ avec $N(x)=i$, pour $i\in k^*$. On dénote par $U(i)$ l'hypersurface correspondante. Les groupes d'isotropie sont des groupes semi-simples de type F_4. (b) L'ensemble des $x\in X_k$, avec $N(x)=0$, tels que x soit un point non-singulier de l'hypersurface correspondant. Soit $U(0)$ la variété algébrique correspondante. Les groupes d'isotropie sont extensions d'une forme de Spin (9) par un groupe unipotent connexe. (c) Soit V la variété des points singuliers de l'hypersurface $N=0$. L'orbite est $V_k-\{0\}$. (d) $x=0$. L'auteur déduit ces renseignements de résultats connus. En désignant par $|\Theta_i|_A$ et $|\omega|_A$ des mesures sur $U(i)_A$ $(i\in k)$ et V_A, on a, lorsque Φ est une fonction de Schwartz-Bruhat sur X_A, une formule (*) $I(\Phi)=\sum_{i\in k^*}\int_{U(i)_A}\varepsilon\Phi|\Theta_i|_A+\int_{U(0)_A}\Phi|\Theta_0|_A+\int_{V_A}\Phi|\omega|_A+\tau(G)\Phi(0)$, où ε est une fonction qui dépend des nombres de Tamagawa des groupes d'isotropie du cas (a). Du fait que le nombre des groupes de type F_4 sur un corps de nombres est fini, on conclut que ε est une fonction qui ne prend qu'un nombre fini de valeurs. On a utilisé ici le fait que le nombre de Tamagawa d'un groupe Spin (9) est 1; ceci entraîne que le deuxième terme du second membre a coefficient 1.

Maintenant l'auteur introduit un paramètre. Soit Γ le groupe des transformations linéaires non-singulières de X qui laissent invariante la forme N à un facteur près. Lorsque $g\in\Gamma_A$, $x\in X_A$, on a $N(gx)=\nu(g)N(x)$, où $\nu(g)$ est un idèle.

On remplace Φ par $\Phi_g: x\mapsto\Phi(gx)$ dans l'égalité $I(\Phi)=I(\hat{\Phi})$ et on applique (*). Une étude du comportement asymptotique pour $|\nu(g)|\to\infty$ des deux membres de cette égalité démontre que $\tau(G)$ est égal au nombre de Tamagawa de tout groupe de stabilité du cas (a) et de plus que ces nombres sont tous égaux à 1.

Dans cette étude, la formule suivante, qui est une conséquence de certains résultats de Weil [loc. cit.] est importante: $\sum_{i\in K}\int_{U(i)_A}\Phi|\Theta_i|_A=\sum_{i\in k}\int_{X_A}\Phi(x)\chi(iN(x))|dx|_A$ (χ est un caractère convenable du groupe des adèles). On en déduit une "formule de Siegel":

$$I(\Phi) = \textstyle\sum_{i\in k}\int_{X_A}\Phi(x)\chi(iN(x))|dx|_A+\int_{V_A}\Phi|\omega|_A+\Phi(0).$$

Pour les détails analytiques l'auteur a besoin de renseignements précis sur certains intégrales. Comme exemple, mentionnons le résultat suivant: Soit v une place de k, X_v la complétion correspondante de X, χ_v un caractère convenable sur k_v. Soit Φ une fonction de Schwartz-Bruhat sur X_v. Alors il existe deux nombres réels positifs α, c, avec $\alpha>2$, tels qu'on ait, pour $i\in k_v$,

$$\left|\textstyle\int_{X_v}\Phi(x)\chi_v(iN(x))|dx|_v\right| \leqq c\min(1, |i|^{-\alpha}).$$

L'étude de ces intégrales est ici nettement plus compliquée que dans le cas d'une forme quadratique N.

Dans un appendice, l'auteur définit, dans la situation du travail, une fonction zêta, et il démontre la continuation analytique et l'équation fonctionnelle.

T. A. Springer (Utrecht)

Citations: MR 36# 6421 = E12-105.

E68-24 (36# 6419)

Behr, Helmut

Zur starken Approximation in algebraischen Gruppen über globalen Körpern.

J. Reine Angew. Math. **229** (1968), 107–116.

Let k be a global field, k_v the completion of k with respect to a place v of k, O_v the ring of integers of k_v, S a finite set of places of k, A the adele ring of k. Let G be a smooth affine algebraic group over the field k, $G(X)$ the group consisting of the points of G with values in the k-algebra X and let G_S denote $\prod_{v\in S}G(k_v)$. A pair (G, S) is said to have strong approximation if $G_SG(k)$ is dense in $G(A)$. When k is a number field, M. Kneser has shown that if (G, S) $(G\neq\{1\})$ has strong approximation then (1) G_S is not compact and (2) G is simply connected. (If G is absolutely almost simple, the converse is also true except for the group of type E_8; cf. M. Kneser [same J. **218** (1965), 190–203; MR **32** #2416; *Algebraic groups and discontinuous subgroups* (Proc. Sympos. Pure Math., Boulder, Colo., 1965), pp. 187–196, Amer. Math. Soc., Providence, R.I., 1966; MR **35** #4225].) In this note, the author shows that, in the case of a global field of prime characteristic, the conditions (1) and (2) are also necessary for a pair (G, S) to have strong approximation. Here, a smooth affine algebraic group G over a field k is said to be simply connected if it is connected and has no proper covering over $\bar{k}$, where a proper covering is an isogeny between connected smooth affine groups whose kernel E is of multiplicative type and $E(X)\neq 1$ for some k-algebra X. For this purpose, he proves two propositions which are analogous to those in the case of a number field. Namely, let λ be an isogeny of the algebraic group F into G defined over the ring $O(S)=\bigcap_{v\notin S}(O_v\cap k)$, S being the set of infinite places. First, if $F\otimes_{O(S)}k$ and $G\otimes_{O(S)}k$ are smooth and if the kernel E of λ is of multiplicative type, then the index $\{G[O(S)]:\lambda(F[O(S)])\}$ is finite. This is proved by making use of the Amitsur-Grothendieck cohomology theory. Second, if F and G are affine and connected, $F\otimes_{O(S)}k$ is smooth, E is of multiplicative type and $E(X)\neq 1$ for some k-algebra X, then $\lambda[F(O_v)]\neq G(O_v)$ for infinitely many places v. The theorem is deduced from these propositions, together with a characterization of the simply connected groups.

E. Abe (Tokyo)

Citations: MR 32# 2416 = E68-13; MR 35# 4225 = E68-22.

E68-25 (37# 6286)

Ono, Takashi

A mean value theorem in adele geometry.

J. Math. Soc. Japan **20** (1968), 275–288.

Let G be a connected linear algebraic group defined over Q, $G=UTS$ be a Levi-Chevalley decomposition over Q, where U is the unipotent radical of G, $R=UT$ is the radical of G, S is a semi-simple sub-group of G, and T, S are uniquely determined up to isomorphisms over Q. Then G is said to be special if $T=1$. The author also gives some equivalent conditions for G to be special. Further, let (G, X) be a homogeneous space defined over Q, i.e., X is an algebraic variety on which G acts transitively and Q is the field of definition for G, X and the action. For $\xi\in X$, denote by G_ξ the isotropy group of ξ. Then (G, X) is said to be special if X_Q is non-empty, and G and G_ξ, for some $\xi\in X_Q$, are both special algebraic groups. Let (G, X) be special, dG_A, dX_A be the canonical measures of the adèle group G_A and the space X_A, respectively. Then the

Tamagawa number $\tau(G) = \int_{G_A/G_Q} dG_A$ is well defined and (G, X) is said to be uniform if there is a constant $\tau(G, X)$ such that

$$\int_{G_A X_Q} f(x)\, dX_A = \tau(G, X)\tau(G)^{-1} \int_{G_A/G_Q} \left(\sum_{\xi\in X_Q} f(g\xi)\right) dG_A$$

for all R-valued continuous functions f with compact support. $\tau(G, X)$ is called the Tamagawa number of (G, X) and if, in particular, $\tau(G, X) = 1$, (G, X) is said to have the mean value property. Further, (G, X) is said to be of type (H) if any two points of X_Q are globally equivalent if and only if they are locally equivalent, where two points ξ, η of X_Q are said to be globally [locally] equivalent if $\eta = g\xi$ for some $g \in G_Q$ $[G_A]$. Now, let (G, X) be special, of type (H) and suppose that Weil's conjecture holds for the universal covering groups of G and G_ξ for any $\xi \in X_Q$, i.e., if $\pi_1(K_C) = 1$ then $\tau(K) = 1$ for $K = G$ and G_ξ, $\xi \in X_Q$. The author shows that if $\pi_1(X_C) = \pi_2(X_C) = 0$, then $\tau(G, X) = 1$, i.e., (G, X) has the mean value property. If in particular $X = G$, the space (G, G) is of type (H) and $\pi_2(G_C) = 0$, hence the result is regarded as a direct extension of Weil's conjecture for the case of special homogeneous spaces. *E. Abe* (Tokyo)

Referred to in E68-26.

E68-26 **(38# 1096)**

Ono, Takashi

On Tamagawa numbers.

Proc. Internat. Congr. Math. (*Moscow*, 1966), *pp.* 509–512. *Izdat. "Mir", Moscow*, 1968.

The details of this paper have been published in J. Math. Soc. Japan **20** (1968), 275–288 [MR **37** #6286].

Citations: MR 37# 6286 = E68-25.

E68-27 **(38# 1073)**

Mautner, F. I.

The trace of Hecke operators.

Monatsh. Math. **72** (1968), 137–143.

Let Γ be an algebraic matrix group over an algebraic number field Ω. For each prime p of Ω, let G_p be the p-adic completion of Γ. Taking a group K_p of integral matrices suitably contained in G_p for each p, we obtain the adelized Γ, the group G of ideles over Γ, which is the restricted direct product of G_p with respect to K_p. We consider Γ a discrete subgroup of G.

Let $G_\infty = \prod_{p\in\infty} G_p$ and let G_0 be the restricted product of G_p for all finite primes p. $K_0 = \prod_{p\notin\infty} K_p$ is an open compact subgroup of G_0. Then $\mathbf{L}^0(K_0\backslash G_0/K_0)$ is the "space of K_0-spherical functions" on G_0. A linear transformation $\mathbf{F}_0$ is defined by $(\mathbf{F}_0\psi)(g) = \int_{G_0} f_0(g_0)\psi(g_0^{-1}g)\, dg_0$ for any $f_0 \in \mathbf{L}^0(K_0\backslash G_0/K_0)$, where ψ is a complex-valued function on G right invariant under Γ. The space of double cosets $K_0G_\infty\backslash G/\Gamma$ is finite and we have the "Hecke operators". Then the author computes the trace of these Hecke operators in terms of Tamagawa numbers and generalized Minkowski-Siegel-Tamagawa-Weil "alphas" [cf. A. Weil, "Adèles and algebraic groups", mimeographed lecture notes, Inst. Advanced Study, Princeton Univ., Princeton, N.J., 1961] and obtains a generalization [cf. A. Selberg, J. Indian Math. Soc. **20** (1956), 47–87; MR **19**, 531] of some of the classical class number relations to higher dimensions. The basic fact is the following equality: $\sum_{\{\gamma\}} m(G(\gamma)/\Gamma(\gamma)) \sum \alpha(M_\gamma', W_\gamma) = \int_G f(g)\, dg$. *K. Masuda* (Nagoya)

Citations: MR 19, 531g = F60-2.

E68-28 **(38# 2144)**

Tasaka, Takashi

On the quasi-split simple algebraic groups defined over an algebraic number field.

J. Fac. Sci. Univ. Tokyo Sect. I **15** (1968), 147–168.

The author proves, for G a k-quasi-split almost simple algebraic group defined over a number field k, that G_kG_A' is closed in G_A and G_A/G_kG_A' is a totally disconnected compact group, where G_A is the adele group of G over k and G_k is the group of k-rational points of G (imbedded in G_A as usual). Here G_A' denotes the commutator subgroup of G_A.

We quote from the author's introduction on material leading to the proof. "We assume that G is a quasi-split simple algebraic group over a perfect field k. In this introduction, for simplicity of explanation, we assume that k has more than three elements and the splitting field of G is a quadratic extension of k. Let A be a maximal k-trivial torus of G. We put $T = Z(A)$. Then one can easily see that T is a maximal torus of G defined over k. Let $\tilde G$ be the universal covering group of G defined over k and let π be the covering isogeny of $\tilde G$ onto G defined over k. If we denote by $\tilde T$ a maximal torus of $\tilde G$ defined over k corresponding to T, we can show that $G_k/G_k' = T_k/T_k^1$, where G_k' is the commutator subgroup of G_k and $T_k^1 = \pi(\tilde T_k)$ (see Theorem 1). If k is a local field, it is easily seen that G_k' is closed in G_k and T_k^1 is closed in T_k.

"If G is a quasi-split simple algebraic group over an algebraic number field k, we show that G_A' is closed in G_A and that we have an isomorphism of G_A/G_A' onto T_A/T_A^1, where $T_A^1 = \pi(\tilde T_A)$. One can easily verify that T_A^1 is closed in T_A. For $A_k(G)$ $(= G_A/G_kG_A')$, we have the following isomorphism: $A_k(G) = T_A/T_kT_A^1$. To determine the structure of $T_A/T_kT_A^1$, we consider the following case. Let $\tilde T$ and T be two tori defined over k which split over a quadratic extension K of k and let f be an isogeny of $\tilde T$ onto T defined over k. Putting $T_A^1 = f(\tilde T_A)$, we can show that $T_kT_A^1$ is closed in T_A and that T_A/T_kT_A' is a totally disconnected compact group. Using these facts, we can conclude that G_kG_A' is closed in G_A and $G_A/G_kG_A' = A_k(G)$ is a totally disconnected compact group."

The paper contains, in addition to this and material on quasi-split almost simple groups over local fields, a description of the class number of a lattice in the underlying k-vector space of a k-quasi-split almost simple algebraic linear group G defined over a number field k.

D. J. Winter (Ann Arbor, Mich.)

E68-29 **(39# 2767)**

Harder, Günter

Eine Bemerkung zum schwachen Approximationssatz.

Arch. Math. (*Basel*) **19** (1968), 465–471.

Let K be a field, S a finite set of non-trivial inequivalent rank one valuations v of K, and K_v the completion of K under v with the topology induced by the valuation. Moreover, let G be a semisimple linear algebraic group over K, $i: G(K) \to \prod_{v\in S} G(K_v)$ the diagonal embedding. The main result states that the closure of $i(G(K))$ in $\prod_{v\in S} G(K_v)$ contains an open normal subgroup of $\prod_{v\in S} G(K_v)$. As a consequence, $i(G(K))$ is dense in $\prod_{v\in S} G(K_v)$ (i.e., the weak approximation theorem holds for G, S) whenever either G splits over K_v for every $v \in S$, or G is simply connected and, for every $v \in S$, contains a Borel subgroup defined over K_v. *Martin Kneser* (Göttingen)

E68-30 **(39# 5530)**

Mautner, F. I.

On the zeros of certain L-polynomials.

Monatsh. Math. **73** (1969), 238–249.

Let Ω be a non-archimedean locally compact field; denote by $\mathfrak{O}$ its ring of integral elements and by $\mathfrak{U}$ the group of units of $\mathfrak{O}$. The author considers representation of $G = \mathrm{PG}(2, \Omega)$ $(= \mathrm{GL}(2, \Omega)$ mod its center), and of $K = \mathrm{PG}(2, \mathfrak{O})$. More specifically, he regards representations M_α in the principal series of representations of G as induced from characters α on Ω^x; these characters determine characters χ on $\mathfrak{U}$ and in turn induce representations u_χ on k. If α takes on a complex value on $\mathfrak{U}$, then M_α restricted to $\mathfrak{U}$ contains exactly one copy of u_χ when u_χ and u_α are equivalent in $\mathfrak{U}$, and none otherwise.

Suppose $\alpha_s(x)=\|x\|^s$, $\mathrm{Re}(s)=\frac{1}{2}$; the spherical functions on G with respect to K are the functions on G constant on double cosets KgK. The author shows that in a certain representation of an adelic group, the operators corresponding to some of these spherical functions are (essentially) the Hecke operators. The spherical functions with compact support turn out to correspond (via a map involving the representations M_{α_s}) to the even Fourier polynomials. As a result, it is easy to determine the maximal ideals of the algebra of spherical functions; thus one can derive a condition for when the analogue of the Ramanujan conjecture holds. One can make similar constructions for an arbitrary M_α, u_χ; "the spherical functions" are functions f from G to the operators on $H(u_\chi)$ such that $f(kgk')=u_\chi(k)f(g)u_\chi(k')$.

In the case where α is complex-valued, the author is able to prove the result analogous to Ramanujan's conjecture: the zeroes of the characteristic polynomials of representations of the functions F lie on the line $\mathrm{Re}\, s=\frac{1}{2}$. In a number of specific cases, these characteristic polynomials are known to have arithmetic interest; it would be interesting, as the author notes, to find an arithmetic interpretation for them in general.

Prospective readers should be warned that the paper is rather tersely written; the proofs of many results are only sketched. *L. Corwin* (Cambridge, Mass.)

E68-31 (39# 5575)

Moore, Calvin C.

Group extensions of p-adic and adelic linear groups.

Inst. Hautes Études Sci. Publ. Math. No. 35 (1968), 157–222.

This important paper exhibits and explores a striking arithmetic phenomenon in the theory of semi-simple algebraic groups. Starting from basic questions about central extensions of such groups over local fields and adèle rings, the author is led quite naturally to the fundamental objects of class field theory—norm residue symbols and reciprocity laws. This review attempts to describe roughly how this happens.

Recall that the universal covering $\tilde{G}$ of a connected topological group G forms part of a group extension $1\to\pi_1(G)\to\tilde{G}\xrightarrow{p}G\to 1$ in which $\pi_1(G)$, being discrete and normal in the connected group $\tilde{G}$, is central. In a similar fashion, if G is a connected semi-simple algebraic group over a field k, one can define $\tilde{G}$ by requiring that p be universal among surjective morphisms with zero dimensional (and hence finite) kernel. Then $\pi_1(G)$ is a finite algebraic group in the center of $\tilde{G}$. If $k=\mathbf{C}$, then $(\tilde{G})_{\mathbf{C}}$ coincides with the topological universal cover of the Lie group $G_{\mathbf{C}}$. The simply connected algebraic group $G=\mathrm{SL}_n$ shows that the analogous statement for $k=\mathbf{R}$ is false.

It was discovered long ago by Schur that, with the connectivity notions suitably defined, there is a "good" theory of covering groups, and the attendant π_1, in abstract group theory. To describe this situation the author proposes (approximately) the following terminology: Let G be a group. Put $\pi_0(G)=G/(G,G)$, and call G "connected" (or "homologically connected" when there is a possibility of confusion) if $\pi_0(G)=0$. Call a homomorphism $p: E\to G$ a "covering" (of G) if G and E are connected and if p is surjective and central (i.e., $\mathrm{Ker}(p)\subset$ center(E)). Schur's theory then asserts that the coverings of a connected group G have the desired properties. In particular, there is a well-defined "universal covering" p which defines a "universal central extension" $1\to\pi_1(G)\to\tilde{G}\xrightarrow{p}G\to 1$.

Homologically, $\pi_0(G)=H_1(G,\mathbf{Z})$ and, when $\pi_0(G)=0$, $\pi_1(G)=H_2(G,\mathbf{Z})$. In the latter case, therefore, the central extensions of G by an abelian group A are classified by $H^2(G,A)=\mathrm{Hom}(\pi_1(G),A)$.

The author begins by extending this theory to the case of topological central extensions $1\to A\to E\to G\to 1$, where all the intervening groups are locally compact. These extensions are classified by $H^2_{\mathrm{top}}(G,A)$, where the groups $H^n_{\mathrm{top}}(G,A)$ denote the cohomology defined for locally compact groups by the author [Trans. Amer. Math. Soc. **113** (1964), 40–63; ibid. **113** (1964), 64–86; MR **30** #2106].

One here calls G "(homologically) connected" if $H^1_{\mathrm{top}}(G,A)$ $(=\mathrm{Hom}_{\mathrm{top}}(G,A))=0$ for all A, i.e., if (G,G) is dense in G. In this case many of the uniqueness properties of coverings survive, but a universal covering, and hence the fundamental group $\pi_1{}^{\mathrm{top}}(G)$, do not always exist. If $\pi_1{}^{\mathrm{top}}(G)$ exists, and if $G=(G,G)$, so that $\pi_1(G)$ (attached to G as a discrete group) also exists then, for formal reasons, $\pi_1{}^{\mathrm{top}}(G)$ is a quotient of $\pi_1(G)$. In case G is a semi-simple and (topologically) connected Lie group with $G=(G,G)$, then the author asserts that $\pi_1{}^{\mathrm{top}}(G)$ exists and coincides with the usual fundamental group.

One now poses the following general question: Let G be a connected semi-simple and simply connected algebraic group over a field k. Is G_k then (homologically) simply connected as an abstract group, and, if not, what is $\pi_1(G_k)$? (The condition, $G_k=(G_k,G_k)$, for $\pi_1(G_k)$ to be defined holds in most cases of interest.) If, moreover, k is a locally compact field, what is $\pi_1{}^{\mathrm{top}}(G_k)$?

The author treats these and related questions when G is simple and split (i.e., a "Chevalley group"), an assumption we now fix.

The starting point is R. Steinberg's explicit construction, by generators and relations, of the covering group $\tilde{G}_k$ in $1\to\pi_1(G_k)\to\tilde{G}_k\xrightarrow{p}G_k\to 1$ [*Colloque théorie des groupes algébriques* (Bruxelles, 1962), pp. 113–127, Librairie Universitaire, Louvain, 1962; MR **27** #3638]. Steinberg "lifts" to $\tilde{G}_k$ the Bruhat decomposition in G_k (relative to some split torus H and ordering of the root system). Once Weyl group representatives in $\tilde{G}_k$ are chosen, one can thus define a canonical section s of p. (The "nice" behavior of s on each Bruhat cell of G_k is important in the discussion of topological extensions when k is locally compact.) One of the major facts implicit in Steinberg's work is that the 2-cocycle c resulting from s is determined by its restriction to the torus H_k, and even to a one parameter subgroup $H_k{}^\alpha=\{h_\alpha(t)\,|\,t\in k^*\}$ of H_k corresponding to a long root α. The restriction of c to $H_k{}^\alpha$ can be identified with a normalized 2-cocycle $c_\alpha: k^*\times k^*\to\pi_1(G_k)$ which turns out to be essentially independent of α.

The remarks above imply that the elements $c_\alpha(x,y)$ $(x,y\in k^*)$ generate $\pi_1(G_k)$. One asks now for the relations between these generators. Alternatively, if A is an abelian group, what relations must a function $b: k^*\times k^*\to A$ satisfy in order that it be the pullback under $h_\alpha: k^*\to G_k$ of a 2-cocycle obtained, as above, from a central extension $1\to A\to E\to G_k\to 1$?

Steinberg already observed enough such relations to conclude that $\pi_1(G_k)=0$ when k is a finite field [op. cit.]. The author here tabulates the following list of identities in the general case: (1) $b(s,tr)b(t,r)=b(st,r)b(s,t)$, $b(1,s)=b(s,1)=1$ (b is a normalized 2-cocycle), (2) $b(s,t)=b(t^{-1},s)$, (3) $b(s,t)=b(s,-st)$, (4) $b(s,t)=b(s,(1-s)t)$ $(s\neq 1)$, (5) if G is not symplectic (type C_n), then b is bilinear.

The functions $b: k^*\times k^*\to A$ satisfying (1)–(5) are christened Steinberg cocycles (of type G): they form a group, denoted $S^G(k,A)$. The author now summarizes the above theory by a natural monomorphism $\varphi: H^2(G_k, A) \to S^G(k, A)$. He similarly constructs, when k and A are locally compact, a monomorphism $\varphi_{\text{top}}: H^2_{\text{top}}(G_k, A) \to S^G_{\text{top}}(k, A)$, where the latter group consists of those $b \in S^G(k, A)$ which are continuous functions $k^* \times k^* \to A$. A fundamental result of the paper is that φ, and φ_{top} in the locally compact case, are isomorphisms if $G = \mathrm{SL}_2$. The author suggests, moreover, that this should be true for all simply connected Chevalley groups. This has since been proved in the thesis of H. Matsumoto [Ann. Sci. École Norm. Sup. (4) **2** (1969), 1–62; MR **39** #1566].

The most remarkable feature of these results is that $S^G(k, A)$ $(= \mathrm{Hom}(\pi_1(G_k), A))$ is almost independent of G; only in condition (5) does G intervene, and there only to distinguish symplectic groups from all others. Thus $\pi_1(G_k)$ reflects primarily the arithmetic of k. It will be interesting to see to what extent this situation prevails for general (non-split) semi-simple groups.

The above theory also suggests strongly that Steinberg cocycles should "exist in nature". While this is indeed the case, it appears almost miraculous (to the reviewer) that nature provided the first (and "only" classical) examples in the guise of norm residue symbols on local (=locally compact non-discrete) fields. If k is a local field with roots of unity μ_k, then the norm residue symbol $\nu_k: k^* \times k^* \to \mu_k$ is easily seen to be a continuous bilinear Steinberg cocycle. That it is essentially the only one is expressed by the author's fundamental local theorem: If k is a non-archimedean local field, then, for any locally compact abelian group A, $\mathrm{Hom}(\mu_k, A) \to S^G_{\text{top}}(k, A)$, $f \mapsto f \circ \nu_k$, is an isomorphism. Hence $\pi_1^{\text{top}}(G_k)$ exists and is isomorphic to μ_k.

Similar results for $G = \mathrm{SL}_2$ were independently obtained by T. Kubota [J. Math. Soc. Japan **19** (1967), 114–121; MR **34** #4264]. $\pi_1^{\text{top}}(G_k)$ exists also in the archimedean case, and is trivial if $k = \mathbf{C}$. If $k = \mathbf{R}$ and if G is non-symplectic, the conclusion of the local theorem remains valid: $\pi_1(G_{\mathbf{R}}) \cong \{\pm 1\}$. If G is symplectic then $\pi_1(G_{\mathbf{R}}) \cong \mathbf{Z}$, and a universal continuous Steinberg cocycle $b: \mathbf{R}^* \times \mathbf{R}^* \to \mathbf{Z}$ is defined by $b(x, y) = 1$ if $x, y < 0$, and $b(x, y) = 0$ otherwise.

The author next considers the adèle ring A of a global field k (=a number field or a function field in one variable over a finite field). A general result on H^2_{top} of restricted products, together with the local theorem, implies that $\pi_1^{\text{top}}(G_A)$ exists and is naturally isomorphic to $\coprod \pi_1^{\text{top}}(G_v)$, where v ranges over all places of k and where $G_v = G_{k_v}$.

Let C be an abelian group. A homomorphism $\pi_1^{\text{top}}(G_A) \to C$ which is trivial on the image of $\pi_1(G_k) \to \pi_1^{\text{top}}(G_A)$ is equivalent to a collection of homomorphisms $f_v: \mu_v \to C$ (v non-complex, $\mu_v = \mu_{k_v}$) such that, for all $x, y \in k^*$, $\prod_{v\,\text{non-complex}} f_v(\nu_v(x, y)) = 1$. An example of this is the explicit Artin reciprocity law: Take $C = \mu_k$ and put $f_v(t) = t^{m_v/m}$, where $m = \mathrm{Card}\,\mu_k$ and $m_v = \mathrm{Card}\,\mu_v$. Let $\nu: \pi_1^{\text{top}}(G_A) \to \mu_k$ be the corresponding homomorphism. The essential uniqueness of Artin's reciprocity law is expressed by the author's fundamental global theorem: The sequence $\pi_1(G_k) \to \pi_1^{\text{top}}(G_A) \xrightarrow{\nu} \mu_k \to 1$ is exact.

Actually, the author proves the corresponding statement about continuous Steinberg cocycles. The equivalence of that with the above formulation follows, for $G = \mathrm{SL}_2$, from the author's results and, in general, from Matsumoto's thesis [loc. cit.].

The global theorem classifies topological central extensions of G_A which split over the subgroup G_k. Such a 2-sheeted covering for symplectic G was first discovered by A. Weil [Acta Math. **111** (1964), 143–211; MR **29** #2324].

The paper concludes with a brief discussion of the connection (discovered by J.-P. Serre [see the reviewer, J. Milnor and J.-P. Serre; #5574 above]) between the global theorem and the congruence subgroup problem for G.

H. Bass (Bombay)

Citations: MR 29# 2324 = E12-104; MR 34# 4264 = E56-42; MR 39# 1566 = E60-33.

Referred to in E60-33, E60-37, E60-47, R38-55.

E68-32 (39# 5579)

Mars, Jean-Gérard

Solutions d'un problème posé par A. Weil.

C. R. Acad. Sci. Paris Sér. A-B **266** (1968), A484–A486.

Let l be an algebraic number field, D_k a central division algebra over l with an involution $x \mapsto \bar{x}$ of the second kind, i.e., l is a quadratic extension of the fixed field $k = \{x : x \in l, x = \bar{x}\}$. Let X_k be a right vector space over D_k of finite rank, and $F: X_k \times X_k \to D_k$ a non-degenerate hermitian form. Let D [X] be an algebraic variety over k, defined by the k-vector space D_k [X_k] and let G be the group of all the D-linear transformations of X which keep F invariant. G is a reductive algebraic group defined over k, its derived group G^1 is semi-simple and simply connected. The author proves the following theorem: The Tamagawa number $\tau(G^1)$ of G^1 is 1. A. Weil's conjecture is that the Tamagawa number of a simply connected group is 1. It was settled by Weil [Acta Math. **113** (1965), 1–87; MR **36** #6421] for any classical group other than the type G^1 above. It is now settled for any classical group.

Let $\tau_\lambda(G)$ be the measure of the adele group G_A modulo G_k under the Haar measure $|\lambda\, du|_A$ obtained from a gauge form du on G and a system of convergent factor λ. For a given D, by Weil [loc. cit.], $\tau_\lambda(G)$ does not depend on either the rank of X or F. The author actually computed $\tau_\lambda(G)$ to be $2c_l c_k^{-1}$, in the special case that $X_k = D_k^2$, $F(x, y) = \bar{y}_2 x_1 + \bar{y}_1 x_2$, where c_l [c_k] is the residue at 1 of the ζ-function of l [k]. Then, using the Hasse principle on $H^1(k, G^1)$, the theorem $\tau(G^1) = 1$ can be deduced.

H. Hijikata (Kyoto)

Citations: MR 36# 6421 = E12-105.

Referred to in E68-37.

E68-33 (39# 5580)

Weisman, Carl S.

On the connected identity component of the adèle-class group of an algebraic torus.

Proc. Amer. Math. Soc. **21** (1969), 155–160.

Let T be an algebraic torus defined over a number field k, T_k the group of points of T rational over k, T_A the adele group and $C_k(T) = T_A/T_k$, the adele class group. The author shows that the Artin method [E. Artin and J. Tate, "Class field theory", Chapter 9, mimeographed lecture notes, Princeton Univ., Princeton, N.J., 1961; abridged edition, Benjamin, New York, 1968; MR **36** #6383] of determining the connected identity component of the idele class group $C_k(G_m)$ can be generalized line-by-line to obtain that component of $C_k(T)$ by using results of the reviewer [Ann. of Math. (2) **70** (1959), 266–290; MR **22** #5635; ibid. (2) **74** (1961), 101–139; MR **23** #A1640].

T. Ono (Baltimore, Md.)

Citations: MR 22# 5635 = E68-2; MR 23# A1640 = E68-4; MR 36# 6383 = R02-53.

E68-34 (41# 3485)

Platonov, V. P.

The problem of strong approximation and the Kneser-Tits hypothesis for algebraic groups. (Russian)

Izv. Akad. Nauk SSSR Ser. Mat. **33** (1969), 1211–1219.

The paper contains a proof of the strong approximation theorem for algebraic groups: If G is a simple and simply connected algebraic group over an algebraic number field k and if for a finite set S of places of k the group $G_S = \prod_{v\in S} G_{k_v}$ is not compact, then $G_S G_k$ is dense in the adèle group G_A [cf. the paper of M. Kneser, *Algebraic groups and discontinuous subgroups* (Proc. Sympos. Pure Math. Vol. IX, Boulder, Colo., 1965), pp. 187–196, Amer. Math. Soc., Providence, R.I., 1966; MR **35** #4225]. The proof of this theorem is based on the following result: If a simple and simply connected group G defined over a field k_v is isotropic over k_v, then the group $G_{k_v}/Z(G_{k_v})$ is simple as an abstract group. Here $Z(G)$ denotes the center of G. This last result is proved by separate discussion of simple algebraic groups of different types.

J. Browkin (Warsaw)

Citations: MR 35# 4225 = E68-22.
Referred to in E68-35.

E68-35 (42# 7670)

Platonov, V. P.

A supplement to the paper "The problem of strong approximation and the Kneser-Tits hypothesis for algebraic groups". (Russian)

Izv. Akad. Nauk SSSR Ser. Mat. **34** (1970), 775–777.

The paper contains some remarks and corrections of the previous paper of the author [same Izv. **33** (1969), 1211–1219; MR **41** #3485]. *J. Browkin* (Warsaw)

Citations: MR 41# 3485 = E68-34.

E68-36 (41# 5379)

Platonov, V. P.

Strong approximation in algebraic groups, and the Kneser-Tits hypothesis. (Russian)

Dokl. Akad. Nauk BSSR **13** (1969), 585–587.

Soient k un corps de nombres, S un ensemble fini de places de k contenant toutes les places à l'infini, G un groupe algébrique défini sur k, G_A le groupe des adèles de G, G_k le groupe des adèles principaux de G, G_S le sous-groupe de G_A formé des éléments dont toutes les v-composantes, pour $v \notin S$, sont égales à 1. L'auteur démontre le théorème d'approximation forte: Pour qu'on ait $\overline{G_S G_k} = G_A$ (l'adhérence étant prise dans la topologie adélique), il faut et il suffit que G vérifie les deux conditions suivantes: (1) G est un groupe algébrique simplement connexe, (2) le groupe G_S n'est pas compact. Ce résultat était déjà connu pour tout groupe algébrique simple sauf E_8 [M. Kneser, *Algebraic groups and discontinuous subgroups* (Proc. Sympos. Pure Math., Vol. IX, Boulder, Colo., 1965), pp. 187–196, Amer. Math. Soc., Providence, R.I., 1966; MR **35** #4225]. L'auteur annonce la démonstration de la conjecture de Kneser-Tits: si v est une place de k et k_v le corps k_v-adique, si G est un groupe simple, simplement connexe et k_v-isotrope, alors G_{k_v} est engendré par des éléments unipotents.

J.-E. Bertin (Caen)

Citations: MR 35# 4225 = E68-22.

E68-37 (41# 8427)

Mars, J. G. M.

The Tamagawa number of ${}^2A_n$.

Ann. of Math. (2) **89** (1969), 557–574.

Let K be a quadratic extension of an algebraic number field k, D_k a central divison algebra over K with an involution of the second kind, F a non-degenerate hermitian form over a right vector space X_k over D_k and G the group of all D-linear transformations of X which leave F invariant, where D [X] denotes the algebraic variety defined over k determined by D_k [X_k]. G is a reductive algebraic group defined over k, the center Z of G is an anisotropic torus of dimension 1 and the kernel G^1 of the reduced norm map $G \to Z$ is a semi-simple and simply connected algebraic group. Let $\tau(G^1)$ be the Tamagawa number of G^1. The paper contains the proof of $\tau(G^1) = 1$ which was sketched by the author [C. R. Acad. Sci. Paris Sér. A-B **266** (1968), A484–A486; MR **39** #5579]. This result, together with those contained in A. Weil's paper [Acta Math. **113** (1965), 1–87; MR **36** #6421], makes up the complete solution of the problem of the determination of the Tamagawa number of all "classical groups". *T. Ono* (Baltimore, Md.)

Citations: MR 36# 6421 = E12-105; MR 39# 5579 = E68-32.

E68-38 (42# 5913)

Weil, André

On the analogue of the modular group in characteristic p.

Functional Analysis and Related Fields (Proc. Conf. for M. Stone, Univ. Chicago, Chicago, Ill., 1968), pp. 211–223. Springer, New York, 1970.

Let K be either a number field or a field of algebraic functions in one variable over a finite field of constants; let $G = \mathrm{GL}(2)$. There is a general notion of modular forms over k, expressed in the adèle language as functions on G_A, invariant under left translations by elements of G_k, behaving in a prescribed manner under right translations by elements of the center of G_A and of the usual maximal compact subgroup K of G_A (or at any rate of an open subgroup, e.g., a congruence subgroup, of K), and satisfying suitable harmonicity conditions at the infinite primes (in the number field case). In the classical case $k = \mathbf{Q}$, one can dispense with the adèle language by pushing everything onto the infinite prime, obtaining the usual description of modular forms as functions on the upper half plane, satisfying certain conditions. The same is true for the other extreme case, namely, $K = \mathbf{F}_q(t)$ is a rational function field over a finite field, as the author shows by an elementary treatment of the following problem.

In the classical case, and in the classical language [Math. Ann. **168** (1967), 149–156; MR **34** #7473], the author showed that modular forms for Hecke's group $\Gamma_0(N) = \left\{\begin{pmatrix} ab \\ cd \end{pmatrix} \in \mathrm{SL}(2, \mathbf{Z}): c \equiv 0 \pmod{N}\right\}$ are characterized by functional equations for many associated Dirichlet series $L_\chi(S)$. The author generalized this work to arbitrary k, in the adèle language [*Algebraic geometry* (Internat. Colloq., Tata Inst. Fund. Res., Bombay, 1968), pp. 409–426, Oxford Univ. Press, London, 1969; MR **41** #6857; *Dirichlet series and automorphic forms*, Springer, Berlin, 1971]. In the present article he treats the case of a rational function field. As the author notes, there are some interesting open questions remaining, especially concerning the role of the Hecke operators; in the classical case no assumption was made that the associated Dirichlet series $L(s)$ should have an Euler product, while in other cases the result has been proved only by making an eulerian assumption at almost all primes. *A. P. Ogg* (Berkeley, Calif.)

Citations: MR 34# 7473 = F65-21; MR 41# 6857 = F65-28.

E68-39 (42# 6158)

Jacquet, Hervé

Fonctions de Whittaker associées aux groupes de Chevalley.

Bull. Soc. Math. France **95** (1967), 243–309.

Let K be an algebraic number field. For each place p of K, let K_p denote the completion of K with respect to $\mathfrak{O}_p$, the ring of integers in K_p (whenever p is finite), and for $x \in K_p$, let $|x|_p$ denote the normalised absolute value of x with respect to p. Let $\mathbf{A}$ be the ring of adeles associated to K. For an idele $a = (a_p) \in A$, let $|a| = \prod |a_p|_p$. Let G be a semisimple algebraic group defined and split over K. For a subgroup H of G defined over K, let $H(K)$ [$H(K_p)$, $H(\mathbf{A})$]

denote the group of K-rational points of H [K_p-rational points of H, the adele group associated to H]. $G(K_p)_K$ and $G(\mathbf{A})$ are locally compact groups. Let $\mathfrak{g}$ be the K-Lie algebra determined by G. Let A be a maximal split torus of G and $\{e_i|i \in I\}$ a Chevalley basis for $\mathfrak{g}$ consisting of eigenvectors for A. Let L be the $\mathbf{Z}$ span of $\{e_i|i \in I\}$, and for each finite place p, let M_p be the subgroup of $G(K_p)$ which leaves the lattice $L \otimes \mathfrak{O}_p \subset \mathfrak{g} \otimes K_p$ stable. For p infinite, fix a maximal compact subgroup M_p of $G(K_p)$ compatible with A. Let $M = \prod M_p$. Let B be a Borel subgroup of G containing A and defined over k. Let N be the unipotent radical of B. Then, as is well known, $G(K_p) = M_p \cdot A(K_p) \cdot N(K_p)$ for all places p and $G(\mathbf{A}) = M \cdot A(\mathbf{A}) \cdot N(\mathbf{A})$. Let $X^*(A)$ be the group of rational characters on A and $F = \mathbf{C} \otimes_{\mathbf{Z}} X^*(A)$. Let R denote the set of roots of G with respect to A. Let W be the Weyl group of G with respect to A. For $\alpha \in R$, let N_α denote the one-parameter unipotent group associated to α. Let $R_+ = \{\alpha \in R | N_\alpha \subset N\}$. Let N^- be the subgroup G generated by N_α, $\alpha \in R_- = \{\alpha \in R | -\alpha \in R_+\}$. A subset $\Phi \subset R_+$ is parabolic if the following two conditions are satisfied: (i) if $\alpha, \beta \in \Phi$, $\alpha + \beta \in R$, then $\alpha + \beta \in \Phi$ and (ii) the group P generated by $\{N_\alpha | \alpha \in \Phi\}$ is a parabolic subgroup of G. A subset $\Psi \subset R$ is horocyclic if $R - \Psi$ is parabolic. Finally, a set $\Phi \subset R_-$ is hemicyclic if $\Phi = R_- \cap \Psi$, where Ψ is horocyclic. For a hemicyclic $\Phi \subset R_-$, let N_Φ denote the unipotent subgroup generated by $\{N_\alpha | \alpha \in \Phi\}$. Such a group is called a hemicycle. For each finite place p, an element $\lambda \in F$ defines a continuous homomorphism $A(K_p) \to \mathbf{C}^*$ as follows: if $\lambda = \sum s_i \otimes \lambda_i$, $\langle \lambda, a \rangle = \prod |\lambda_i(a)|_p{}^{s_i}$; and hence also a continuous homomorphism $A(\mathbf{A}) \to \mathbf{C}^*$: $\langle \lambda, a \rangle = \prod |\lambda_i(a)|^{s_i}$. Let D [D_p] be a unitary representation of M [M_p] on a finite-dimensional vector space W [W_p] (over $\mathbf{C}$). Let χ_p [χ] be a unitary character on $A(K_p)$ [$A(\mathbf{A})$, which is trivial on $A(K)$]. Let $W_{\chi_p} = \{w \in W_p | D_p(a)w = \chi_p(a)w$ for $a \in M_p \cap A(K_p)\}$ [$W_\chi = \{w \in W | D(a)w = \chi(a)w$ for $a \in M \cap A(\mathbf{A})\}$]. Finally, let V be a hemicycle and μ_p [μ] a unitary character on $V(K_p)$ [on $V(\mathbf{A})$, which is trivial on $V(K)$]. For $g \in G(K_p)$ [$G(\mathbf{A})$], a function $L_p(g, D_p, \chi_p, \lambda)$ [$L(g, D, \chi, \lambda)$] is defined as follows: For $g \in G(K_p)$ [$G(\mathbf{A})$], $g = man$, where $m \in M_p$ [M], $a \in A(K_p)$ [$A(\mathbf{A})$] and $n \in N(K_p)$ [$N(\mathbf{A})$]; then $L_p(g, D_p, \chi_p, \lambda) = D_p(n)\chi_p(a) \cdot \langle \lambda, a \rangle P(D_p, \chi_p)$ [$L(g, D, \chi, \lambda) = D(m)\chi(a)\langle \lambda, a \rangle P(D, \chi)$], where $P(D, \chi)$ [$P(D_p, \chi_p)$] is the orthogonal projection of W on W_χ [W_p on W_{χ_p}]. The author considers for each place p the integral $E_V(g, D_p, \chi_p, \lambda, \mu_p) = \int_{V(K_p)} L(gv, D_p, \chi_p, \lambda + \rho)\mu_p(v)\, dv$, where dv is a Haar measure on $V(K_p)$ and ρ is half the sum of the positive roots, $\rho = \frac{1}{2} \sum_{\alpha \in R_+} \alpha$, as well as the integral $E_V(g, D, \chi, \lambda, \mu) = \int_{V(\mathbf{A})} L(gv, D, \chi, \lambda + \rho)\mu(v)\, dv$, dv now denoting a Haar measure on $V(\mathbf{A})$. In the case of the local fields K_p, the author obtains the following results. Let (,) denote a W-invariant positive definite symmetric scalar product on $F_{\mathbf{R}} = \mathbf{R} \otimes_{\mathbf{Z}} X^*(A)$. Let Φ be the hemicyclic subset of R to which V is associated. Let $B(V) = \{\lambda \in F | (\mathscr{R}\lambda, \alpha) > 0$ for $-\alpha \in \Phi\}$, where $\mathscr{R}\lambda$ denotes the real part of λ. Then the integral $E_V(g, D_p, \chi_p, \lambda, \mu_p)$ converges absolutely for $\lambda \in B(V)$. Let Ω_G [Ω_F] be a compact subset of $G(K_p)$ [of F_R contained in $\{\lambda \in F_R | (\lambda, \alpha) > 0$ for $-\alpha \in \Phi\}$], then the convergence is normal for $g \in \Omega_G$ and $\mathscr{R}\lambda \in \Omega_F$. In particular, $E_V(g, D, \chi_p, \lambda, \mu_p)$ is a continuous function in g and λ, holomorphic in λ in the domain $G(K_p) \times B(V)$. The author also obtains an analogue in the global case. Let $B'(V) = \{\lambda \in F | (\mathscr{R}\lambda, \alpha) > 1$ for $-\alpha \in \Phi\}$. Then $E_V(g, D, \chi, \lambda, \mu)$ is absolutely convergent for $B'(V)$. Also, the convergence is normal for $g \in \Omega_G$, $\mathscr{R}\lambda \in \Omega_F$, where Ω_G [Ω_F] is a compact subset of $G(\mathbf{A})$ [F_R contained $\{\lambda | (\lambda, \alpha) > 1\}$], so that $E_V(g, D, \chi, \lambda, \mu)$ is continuous in (g, λ) and holomorphic in λ on $G(\mathbf{A}) \times B'(V)$.

The author has further results on the analytic continuation of these functions. To state these we need some further notation. Let Δ be the set of simple roots in R_+. For $\lambda \in F$, $\alpha \in \Delta$, define $s_\alpha \in \mathbf{C}$ by setting $\lambda = \sum s_\alpha \cdot \alpha$. For the character χ, let $\theta = \theta_\chi$ be the set $\{\alpha \in \Delta | -\alpha \in \theta$ and χ is nontrivial on $N_{-\alpha}\}$. Let W' be the subgroup generated by the symmetries $\{w_\alpha | \alpha \in \theta\}$. Also, for $\alpha \in \Delta$, let $G^{(\alpha)}$ be the subgroup generated by N_α and $N_{-\alpha}$. Let G be simply connected and ξ_α: SL(2, $\;$) $\to G^{(\alpha)}$ an isomorphism defined over K taking diagonal matrices [upper triangular unipotent matrices] into A [N]. Let τ_p be an isomorphism of K_p on its Pontrjagin dual. We identify diagonal matrices in SL(2, K_p) with $K_p{}^*$ and upper triangular unipotents in SL(2, K_p) with K_p in the obvious way. Thus $\chi_p{}^\alpha = \chi_p \circ \xi_\alpha$ will be regarded as a character on $K_p{}^*$, while $\mu_p{}^\alpha = \mu_p \circ \xi_\alpha$ as a character on K_p. Also, let $\gamma_p{}^\alpha = \tau_p{}^{-1}(\mu_p{}^\alpha)$. With this notation the author proves the following: $E_V(g, D_p, \chi_p, \lambda, \mu_p)$ can be analytically continued to a holomorphic function of λ on the convex envelope D of the set $\bigcup_{w \in W} w(B(V))$. Moreover, for $\lambda \in D$ and $\alpha \in \theta$ we have a functional equation of the form $E_V(g, D_p, \chi_p, \lambda, \mu_p) = \chi_p{}^\alpha(\gamma_p{}^\alpha) \cdot |\gamma_p{}^\alpha|_p{}^{s_\alpha} \cdot E_V(g, D, w_\alpha\chi, w_\alpha\lambda, \mu)\Theta_\alpha(D_p, \chi_p{}^\alpha, s_\alpha)$, where $\Theta_\alpha(D_p, \chi_p, s_\alpha)$ is a meromorphic function in s_α on the whole of C with values in the space $H(D_p)$ of endomorphisms of D_p; this last function is holomorphic for $\mathscr{R}(s_\alpha) < 1$.

The results in the local case are once again pieced up to obtain global versions of the above results. In the global version, however, one has to modify the function E_V by multiplying it by a meromorphic function which involves the Hecke zeta-functions to obtain analytic continuation properties as well as the functional equation.

These integrals arise naturally in the spectral analysis of $L^2(G(\mathbf{A})/G(K))$ of arithmetically defined homogeneous spaces, $G(\mathbf{A})/G(K)$. The integrals E_V for certain V in fact appear as "Fourier coefficients at a cusp" of suitable Eisenstein series.

The results are first established for the case $G = \mathrm{SL}(2)$, where explicit calculations are made for the local fields. These results are pieced up to obtain the global theorem for SL(2). The case of general G and special hemicycles, viz., N_α for some $-\alpha \in \Delta$, are next considered. Using these special cases the general theorem is deduced. The explicit computations in the case of SL(2, $\mathbf{R}$) show that the function E_V defined here is expressible in terms of the Γ-function and the Whittaker functions. The proof for the case of SL(2) is achieved by showing the existence of a "privileged" Schwarz-Bruhat function φ on $K_p{}^2$ (for every place) and introducing certain integrals $E_\varphi(D, \chi, \lambda, \mu)$ depending on φ generalising the functions E_V introduced above. *M. S. Raghunathan* (Bombay)

E68-40 **(44# 2705)**

Raghavan, S.; Rangachari, S. S.

On the Siegel formula for ternary skew-hermitian forms. *Acta Arith.* **16** (1969/70), 327–345.

Let A be an algebra of m-rowed matrices over a division-algebra R. The involutions i of the latter define the involutions of the algebra A. Let X be the left A-module of rank n, G the group of $u \in A$ such that $u \cdot u = 1$ and δ, δ' the dimensions over the center of the space R and the set $\{\xi \in R$: $\xi^i = \pm \xi\}$. If $m > 2n + 4\varepsilon - 2$, $\varepsilon = \delta'/\delta$, then according to A. Weil ["Adeles and algebraic groups", mimeographed lecture notes, Princeton Univ., Princeton, N.J., 1961; Russian translation in *Matematika. A collection of translations of foreign articles* (Russian), Vol. 8, No. 4, pp. 3–74, Izdat. "Mir", Moscow, 1964] there are two distributions on the adele space X_A of the module X, one defined by the Eisenstein-Siegel series and the other by the theta-series of the group G. In the paper under review the authors consider the case when $m = 3$ and R is an undetermined quaternion division-algebra whose center is equal to Q. They present a new definition of the Eisenstein-Siegel series for this case. (The series constructed by Weil under these conditions do not converge absolutely.) At the same time the construction of the theta-series is transferred to this case. The main result of the paper is the coincidence of the distributions defined by these series. *A. Paršin* (RŽMat **1970** #12 A350)

E72 GALOIS COHOMOLOGY OF LINEAR ALGEBRAIC GROUPS

See also Sections G25, G35, R34, S25.

See also reviews E02-14, E04-31, E64-26, F70-18, F99-4, G10-42, G25-6, G35-51, R38-55.

E72-1 (29# 4761)

Harder, Günter

Über die Galois-Kohomologie der Tori.

Dissertation zur Erlangung des Doktorgrades der Mathematisch-Naturwissenschaftlichen Fakultät der Universität Hamburg, Hamburg, 1963. iii + 71 *pp*.

Let k be a global field, i.e., either a finite algebraic number field or an algebraic function field of one variable over a finite constant field. Let T be an algebraic torus defined over k, i.e., an algebraic group defined over k which is isomorphic over the algebraic closure of k with the product $G_m \times \cdots \times G_m$, G_m being the multiplicative group of the universal domain. Viewing G_m as a trivial torus defined over k, it is natural to ask to what extent the arithmetical properties of G_m can be generalized for an arbitrary torus T defined over k. In this paper the author considers the Hasse principles. A torus T defined over k is said to be split by a finite Galois extension K of k if there exists an isomorphism $T = G_m \times \cdots \times G_m$ defined over K. The author says that the Hasse principle holds for T if the map φ: $H^1(K/k, T) \to H^1(K/k, T_A)$ is injective; here $T_A = T_{A_K}$ means the adelization. The main results are the following: the kernel of φ is always finite (§ 7, Satz 3), and the Hasse principle holds if every Sylow subgroup of the Galois group of K/k is cyclic (§ 6, Satz 8). This paper begins with careful preparations (§ 1–§ 5) which make it self-contained. [Cf. the reviewer's works, Ann. of Math. (2) **74** (1961), 101–139; MR **23** #A1640; ibid. (2) **78** (1963), 47–73; MR **28** #94.] *T. Ono* (Philadelphia, Pa.)

Citations: MR 23# A1640 = E68-4; MR 28# 94 = E68-7.

E72-2 (29# 4763)

Voskresenskiĭ, V. E.

The behaviour of semi-simple algebraic groups under extension of the ground field. (Russian)

Dokl. Akad. Nauk SSSR **158** (1964), 767–769.

Suppose G is a connected semi-simple algebraic group defined over an algebraic number field k. The author asks which G satisfy: (A) G splits (i.e., has a splitting maximal torus) over almost all $\mathfrak{p}$-adic extensions $k_\mathfrak{p}$ of k. The question is answered completely by cohomology. G corresponds to an element h of $H^1(k, A_{\bar{k}})$, where $A_{\bar{k}}$ is the automorphism group (over the algebraic closure $\bar{k}$ of k) of the Lie algebra of G. Let $\beta(h)$ be the natural image of h in $H^1(k, W)$, where W is the quotient of $A_{\bar{k}}$ by its maximal connected subgroup. Then G satisfies (A) if and only if $\beta(h) = 0$. *E. C. Dade* (Pasadena, Calif.)

E72-3 (30# 3097)

Voskresenskiĭ, V. E.

On two-dimensional algebraic tori. (Russian)

Izv. Akad. Nauk SSSR Ser. Mat. **29** (1965), 239–244.

The two-dimensional algebraic tori over a field k are in one-to-one correspondence with the elements of $H^1(k, \mathrm{GL}(2, Z))$ [J.-P. Serre, "Leçons sur la cohomologie galoisienne", Collège de France, Paris, 1963*]. These, in turn, correspond to equivalence classes of continuous homomorphisms of the Galois group G of k into $\mathrm{GL}(2, Z)$. The image of G must be a finite subgroup of $\mathrm{GL}(2, Z)$. Using the known classification of such subgroups and their embeddings, the author gives a complete list of all such tori in terms of finite extension fields of k having Galois groups (over k) isomorphic to subgroups of $\mathrm{GL}(2, Z)$. Combining this classification with results of Ono [Ann. of Math. (2) **78** (1963), 47–73; MR **28** #94], the author proves that every two-dimensional algebraic torus T over an algebraic number field k satisfies the following Hasse principle: If V is a principal homogeneous space for T defined over k and having a rational point in each completion k_p of k, then V has a rational point in k. *E. C. Dade* (Pasadena, Calif.)

*See MR **31** #4785 = R02-39.

Citations: MR 28# 94 = E68-7; MR 31# 4785 = R02-39.

E72-4 (30# 4760)

Kneser, Martin

Galois-Kohomologie halbeinfacher algebraischer Gruppen über $\mathfrak{p}$-adischen Körpern. I.

Math. Z. **88** (1965), 40–47.

The term "p-adic field" will refer to a field of characteristic 0 which is complete relative to a discrete valuation and which has a finite residue class field. The author aims at proving the following theorem: (1) If k is a p-adic field and if G is a semi-simple simply connected algebraic group defined over k, then $H^1(k, G) = 0$. In this part, I, only the classical simple types (with the triality types of D_4 excluded) are considered. Here the author presents a simple version of results which have been well known for some time. The key property of p-adic fields, for which a proof is included, is (2): If k is as above, then any non-singular quadratic, Hermitian, or quaternionic Hermitian form over k represents all values of k, provided the dimension exceeds a certain, explicitly given, number. Consider now the case of (1) in which $G = \mathrm{SU}_n$, the special unitary group corresponding to a Hermitian form h over k. If $n = 2$, then G is the group of elements of norm 1 in a quaternion algebra over k, and (1) easily follows in this case. Assume $n \geqq 3$. Let t be a point such that $h(t) = c \neq 0$, and let SU_{n-1} be the subgroup of G fixing t. Then $\mathrm{SU}_n/\mathrm{SU}_{n-1} \cong T$, the "sphere" $h(x) = c$. Now if $a: k \to G = \mathrm{SU}_n$ is a cocycle, it follows from (2) that the twisted version ${}_aT$ of T has a rational point over k, hence that a is equivalent to a cocycle with values in SU_{n-1}, from which (1) follows by induction. For the other classes of classical groups the proof of (1) is similar. *R. Steinberg* (Los Angeles, Calif.)

Referred to in E72-7, E72-11, Z10-36.

E72-5 (31# 5870)

Borel, A.; Serre, J.-P.

Théorèmes de finitude en cohomologie galoisienne.

Comment. Math. Helv. **39** (1964), 111–164.

Let k be a perfect field, $\bar{k}$ the algebraic closure and $\mathfrak{g}$ the Galois group of $\bar{k}/k$ with the usual topology. A discrete group Γ is called a $\mathfrak{g}$-group if $\mathfrak{g}$ acts continuously on it.

A $\mathfrak{g}$-group Γ is called an arithmetic $\mathfrak{g}$-group if (i) there is an imbedding f of Γ into the group $G_{\mathbf{Q}}$ of $\mathbf{Q}$-rational points of a linear algebraic group G over $\mathbf{Q}$ such that $f(\Gamma)$ is commensurable with the group $G_{\mathbf{Z}}$ of units, and (ii) there is a continuous homomorphism of $\mathfrak{g}$ into the discrete group Aut $G(\mathbf{Q})$, the group of $\mathbf{Q}$-automorphisms of G, such that f is compatible with the $\mathfrak{g}$-group structures of Γ and $G_{\mathbf{Q}}$. E.g., a finite $\mathfrak{g}$-group, Aut T (T: a torus over k) and Aut $C(\bar{k})$ (C: an abelian variety over k) are arithmetic $\mathfrak{g}$-groups. A group scheme A over k is called a local algebraic group over k if the underlying scheme is a union of open and closed sub-schemes which are algebraic varieties. Finally, a local algebraic group A over k is called a k-group of type (ALA) if it is an extension of an arithmetic $\mathfrak{g}$-group by a linear algebraic group over k. This is the class of groups for which the main theorems of this paper are stated. This class of groups contains linear algebraic groups, groups of automorphisms of abelian varieties and groups of automorphisms of linear algebraic groups in characteristic zero; the last fact is the only theorem throughout §§ 1–5. Main results are given in § 6 (local fields) and § 7 (number fields). The following two theorems are basic. Theorem 6.2: Let k be a perfect field which has only a finite number of extensions of a given degree. Then $H^1(k, A)$ is finite for any k-group A of type (ALA). Theorem 7.1: Let k be a number field, S a finite set of places of k, and A a k-group of type (ALA). Then the map $H^1(k, A) \to \prod_{v\notin S} H^1(k_v, A)$ is proper, i.e., the inverse image of any point is finite. The proof of the latter uses the finiteness of the number of conjugate classes of finite subgroups of arithmetic groups and the special case of that theorem where G is connected reductive, all these depending essentially upon the results of Borel and Harish-Chandra [see, e.g., the first author, Proc. Internat. Congr. Mathematicians (Stockholm, 1962), pp. 10–12, § 5, § 9, Inst. Mittag-Leffler, Djurholm, 1963; MR **31** #177]. Since the classes of principal homogeneous spaces over a field k [or of k-forms] of an algebraic group G over k correspond to elements of $H^1(k, G)$ [or $H^1(k, \text{Aut } G)$], the above two theorems imply the following: (*) the finiteness of the number of classes of principal homogeneous spaces over k of G [of the number of k-forms of G] when k is a p-adic field and G is linear [G is linear or an abelian variety]; (**) the finiteness of the number of classes of principal homogeneous spaces over k of G [of the number of k-forms of G] which are isomorphic to a given principal homogeneous space [isomorphic to G] locally everywhere, when k is a number field and G is linear [G is linear or an abelian variety]. § 6 and § 7 contain also applications to the problems of the conjugateness of maximal tori, Cartan subgroups, the classification of $\mathbf{R}$-forms, and the finiteness of orbits in algebraic transformation spaces.

T. Ono (Philadelphia, Pa.)

Citations: MR 31# 177 = E60-12.

Referred to in E72-11.

E72-6 (32# 4177)

Serre, Jean-Pierre

Cohomologie galoisienne des groupes algébriques linéaires.

Colloq. Théorie des Groupes Algébriques (Bruxelles, 1962), *pp.* 53–68. *Librairie Universitaire, Louvain; Gauthier-Villars, Paris,* 1962.

Some important conjectures are stated, most of which have since been resolved. See the author's treatise [*Cohomologie galoisienne*, Lecture Notes in Mathematics 5, Suppléments, Springer, Berlin, 1964; MR **31** #4785].

M. J. Greenberg (Boston, Mass.)

Citations: MR 31# 4785 = R02-39.

E72-7 (32# 5658)

Kneser, Martin

Galois-Kohomologie halbeinfacher algebraischer Gruppen über $\mathfrak{p}$-adischen Körpern. II.

Math. Z. **89** (1965), 250–272.

The author completes the proof of the following theorem: If k is a field of characteristic 0 which is complete relative to a discrete valuation and which has a finite residue field, and if G is a semisimple simply connected algebraic group defined over k, then $H^1(k, G) = 0$. He then derives the classification of semisimple groups over k and shows, in particular, that G can be anisotropic (with no nontrivial torus split over k) only if it is a product of groups of type A_n, in fact, a product of norm-one groups of skew fields over k. In Part I [same Z. **88** (1965), 40–47; MR **30** #4760] the author proved the above theorem for the classical groups, and in this part, II, he treats the exceptional groups. By a result of the reviewer (if k is a perfect field and G is a connected linear algebraic group defined over k which contains a Borel subgroup defined over k, then for every α in $H^1(k, G)$ there exists a torus T defined over k such that α is in the image of $H^1(k, T) \to H^1(k, G)$), the theorem can, for most exceptional groups, be reduced to the following result: If k and G are as in the theorem and T is a torus defined over k, then the image of $H^1(k, T) \to H^1(k, G)$ vanishes. To prove this, the author shows that each element of $H^1(k, T)$ can be reduced to some $H^1(k, T')$, T' being a torus in some proper semisimple subgroup of G, all defined over k, and then he uses induction on the dimension of G. This involves a detailed study of the lattice of weights and many separate, case by case, reductions which cannot be gone into here.

R. Steinberg (Los Angeles, Calif.)

Citations: MR 30# 4760 = E72-4.

Referred to in E64-20, E72-8, E72-11, F70-18, Z10-36.

E72-8 (32# 7677)

Harder, Günter

Über die Galoiskohomologie halbeinfacher Matrizengruppen. I.

Math. Z. **90** (1965), 404–428.

The author's main concern is the following theorem. (1) Let k be an algebraic number field and G a simply connected simple group defined over k. Let k_p denote the completion of k relative to the valuation p. Then the natural map $H^1(k, G) \to \prod H^1(k_p, G)$ is bijective, the product being over all completions. Because of a result of M. Kneser [same Z. **89** (1965), 250–272; MR **32** #5658], $H^1(k, G) = 0$ if p is not Archimedean. Thus the product need be taken only over the real completions. The most important special case of (1) is as follows. (2) If k is totally imaginary in (1), then $H^1(k, G) = 0$. {These results are known for the classical groups and for the groups of type G_2 and F_4, although, unfortunately, proofs do not yet exist in the literature, but the reviewer understands that an account is being prepared by Kneser.} This leaves the groups of type D_4 (trialitarian), E_6, E_7, and E_8. For the first three types the present author proves (1), but he is unable to handle E_8. In this Part I he proves (2) for these groups. (It should be remarked that B. Veĭsfeĭler [Dokl. Akad. Nauk SSSR **158** (1964), 258–260; MR **30** #201] has announced results analogous to (1) for Lie algebras which, in particular, imply (1) for groups of type E_8, but here also proofs are lacking.) The proof proceeds as follows: given an element x of $H^1(k, G)$, the author first constructs a certain k-subgroup H to which x can be reduced, and then by analyzing how H is imbedded in G and by using a suitable induction, he shows that

$x=0$. The success of this method depends on the construction of k-subgroups which can be effectively used. This involves many case-by-case considerations which cannot be gone into here. To indicate some of the ideas involved, a brief discussion of the group of type E_8 follows.

Assume in (2) that G is of type E_8. In this case $H^1(k, G)$ classifies the k-forms of G; so the problem is to show there is only one, i.e., G splits over k. As a first step the author shows that G splits over the field obtained by adjoining to k all 30^nth roots of 1 for some n. Thus it remains to show: if K/k is an extension of degree 2, 3, or 5, and if G splits over K, then G splits over k. Assume K/k is of degree 2. Relative to a splitting K-torus, there exists a standard parabolic K-subgroup P whose semisimple part is of type E_7, thus whose codimension in G is 57. The intersection of P and its conjugate is then a k-subgroup of codimension at most 114, hence of dimension at least 134. With this subgroup as a starting point, and a good deal of further argument, it can then be shown that G splits over k. If K/k is of degree 3, the above construction yields a subgroup of dimension at least 77 which can be successfully used. However, if K/k is of degree 5, the construction fails, and this is the case left open by the author. *R. Steinberg* (Los Angeles, Calif.)

Citations: MR 30# 201 = E64-6; MR 32# 5658 = E72-7.
Referred to in E72-9, E72-13, Z10-36.

E72-9 (34# 2777)

Harder, Günter
Über die Galoiskohomologie halbeinfacher Matrizengruppen. II.
Math. Z. **92** (1966), 396–415.

We continue with the notations of the review of Part I [same Z. **90** (1965), 404–428; MR **32** #7677]. In Part II the author completes the proof of the main theorem (1), for groups of type D_4 (trialitarian form), E_6, and E_7, thus leaving E_8 as the only unsettled case (our previous remark about B. Veĭsfeĭler's announcement has to be discounted since, according to a footnote in the paper under review, Veĭsfeĭler has informed the author that there is a gap in his work on algebras of type E_8). The difficult part of (1) is the proof of injectivity: If $\alpha \in H^1(k, G)$ and $\alpha_p=0$ for every $p \in S$, the set of real completions of k, then $\alpha=0$. This is done in two steps. First, by a series of reductions, it is shown that α can be reduced to a maximal k-torus T so that $(\alpha|_T)_p=0$ for every $p \in S$. Then it is shown that this condition implies $\alpha=0$. Both steps are proved by case-by-case considerations which need not be gone into here. The proof of surjectivity, on the other hand, is quite general, and works, in fact, when G is any connected linear algebraic group defined over k. The paper closes with an appendix in which a number of needed results from cohomology theory and the theory of algebraic groups are discussed. *R. Steinberg* (Los Angeles, Calif.)

Citations: MR 32# 7677 = E72-8.
Referred to in E72-11, E72-13.

E72-10 (35# 195)

Springer, T. A.
Nonabelian H^2 in Galois cohomology.
Algebraic Groups and Discontinuous Subgroups (*Proc. Sympos. Pure Math., Boulder, Colo.*, 1965), *pp.* 164–182. *Amer. Math. Soc., Providence, R.I.*, 1966.

In this note, the author gives a definition and basic properties of non-abelian relative H^1 and H^2 in group cohomology. (Though the definition of H^2 here is independent of those of Dedecker and Giraud, it seems to be essentially equivalent.) Let $\mathscr{G}$ be a topological group. A $\mathscr{G}$-set is a discrete topological space on which $\mathscr{G}$ operates continuously on the left. Let A be a $\mathscr{G}$-group, B any subgroup of A. The relative 1-cohomology set $H^1(\mathscr{G}, A, B)$ of A with respect to B is the set of isomorphism classes of homogeneous spaces of A which have B as the isotropy subgroup of one of its points. There is a bijection between $H^1(\mathscr{G}, A, B)$ and the set of equivalence classes of 1-cocycles of A relative to B. Let κ be a $\mathscr{G}$-kernel in A, i.e., a continuous homomorphism of $\mathscr{G}$ into the group $E(A)$ of outer automorphisms of A. $H^2(\mathscr{G}, A, \kappa)$ is the set of isomorphy classes of the group extensions E of $\mathscr{G}$ by A which have a continuous section $\sigma: \mathscr{G} \to E$ and whose associated kernel is κ. The author develops to some extent the machinery of exact sequences for the relative H^1 and H^2. He then gives some applications to Galois cohomology of algebraic groups. Namely, the main result of the paper is the following: Let k be a perfect field of dim $\leqq 1$, $\mathscr{G}(\bar{k}/k)$ the Galois group of $\bar{k}$ over k, A an algebraic group defined over $\bar{k}$; then any $\mathscr{G}(\bar{k}/k)$-kernel κ in A is trivial and $H^2(\mathscr{G}(\bar{k}/k), A, \kappa)=0$. Further, he gives some applications to homogeneous spaces. Finally, he gives some finiteness theorems for relative H^1. Let A be a linear algebraic group defined over k, B a subgroup of A defined over $\bar{k}$. If k is a locally compact field of characteristic 0, then $H^1(\mathscr{G}(\bar{k}/k), A, B)$ is finite. If k is an algebraic number field, for any place v of k, let k_v be the corresponding completion and $\bar{k}_v$ an algebraic closure of k_v containing $\bar{k}$. Then

$$w: H^1(\mathscr{G}(\bar{k}/k), A, B) \to \textstyle\prod_v H^1(\mathscr{G}(k_v/k_v), A, B)$$

is proper. *E. Abe* (Tokyo)

E72-11 (35# 1600)

Springer, T. A.
Galois cohomology of linear algebraic groups.
Algebraic Groups and Discontinuous Subgroups (*Proc. Sympos. Pure Math., Boulder, Colo.*, 1965), *pp.* 149–158. *Amer. Math. Soc., Providence, R.I.*, 1966.

In this note, the author gives a brief introduction to the notions and results of Galois cohomology of linear algebraic groups. Let G be a linear algebraic group defined over a field k. $H^1(k, G)$ is, by definition, the set of k-isomorphism classes of principal homogeneous spaces of G. Similarly, if k is perfect and K is a Galois extension of k with the Galois group Γ, $H^1(K/k, G)$ is the set of k-isomorphism classes of principal homogeneous spaces of G which have a K-rational point. There exists a natural one-to-one correspondence between $H^1(K/k, G)$ and the set of equivalence classes of 1-cocycles of Γ into G. If G is not abelian, no canonical group structure exists on the set. However, it has a privileged point which corresponds to the trivial principal homogeneous space of G, and if one defines $H^0(K/k, G)$ the set of Γ-invariant K-rational points of G, as in the commutative case, one has some exact sequences of the cohomology sets. The author first shows some examples of 1-cohomology sets related to the forms of algebras or algebraic groups. He then mentions a number of recent results on the Galois cohomology of linear algebraic groups over special ground fields (and gives a brief sketch of the proofs). Namely, let k be a perfect field of dimension $\leqq 1$. If G is connected, then $H^1(k, G)=0$ [R. Steinberg, Inst. Hautes Études Sci. Publ. Math. No. 25 (1965), 49–80; MR **31** #4788]. Let k be a local field of characteristic 0. Then $H^1(k, G)$ is finite [A. Borel and J.-P. Serre, Comment. Math. Helv. **39** (1964), 111–164; MR **31** #5870], and if G is connected semi-simple and simply connected, then $H^1(k, G)=0$ [M. Kneser, Math. Z. **88** (1965), 40–47; MR **30** #4760; ibid. **89** (1965), 250–272; MR **32** #5658]. Let k be an algebraic number field, v a valuation on k, k_v the completion of k at v. Then the mapping $\phi: H^1(k, G) \to \prod_v H^1(k_v, G)$ is proper [Borel and Serre, loc. cit.]. It is stated as a conjecture that if G is connected, semi-simple and simply connected, then ϕ is injective. This has been solved affirmatively provided that G has no simple factor of type E_8 [G. Harder, Math. Z. **92** (1966), 396–415; MR **34** #2777].

E. Abe (Tokyo)

Citations: MR 30# 4760 = E72-4; MR 31# 5870 = E72-5; MR 32# 5658 = E72-7; MR 34# 2777 = E72-9.

E72-12 (36# 1454)

Voskresenskiĭ, V. E.

Sheaves of local units of algebraic groups. (Russian)

Certain Problems in the Theory of Fields (Russian), pp. 16–31. *Izdat. Saratov. Univ., Saratov*, 1964.

Let $G \subseteq \mathrm{GL}(n, K)$ be an algebraic group over an algebraic number field K. K. Iwasawa [Ann. of Math. (2) **69** (1959), 408–413; MR **23** #A1632] applied sheaf theory to the study of algebraic number fields. The author generalizes the results of Iwasawa and constructs the sheaves of local units of certain algebraic groups G. He also studies sub-sheaves, sheaves that are locally isomorphic, and he establishes relations among their cohomologies. Other results: For $G \subseteq \mathrm{GL}(n, K)$ a unipotent algebraic group, the cohomology group $H^1(X, E(G))$ is trivial, and for any algebraic group G, $H^1(X, E(G))$ is finite, where X is the space of simple divisors of the algebraic number field K.

R. E. Peinado (Mayaguez, Puerto Rico)

Citations: MR 23# A1632 = R30-17.

E72-13 (36# 3788)

Kneser, Martin

Hasse principle for H^1 of simply connected groups.

Algebraic Groups and Discontinuous Subgroups (Proc. Sympos. Pure Math., Boulder, Colo., 1965), *pp.* 159–163. *Amer. Math. Soc., Providence, R.I.*, 1966.

Let G be a simply connected algebraic group defined over the number field k. It has been stated as a conjecture that the canonical mapping $H^1(k, G) \to \prod_{v \in \infty} H^1(k_v, G)$ is bijective (Hasse principle; the finite places can be omitted from the product because in that case $H^1(k_v, G) = 0$). The proof of the conjecture is easily reduced to the absolutely almost simple case and this has been solved in all cases except E_8. In this note, the author sketches some of these proofs. He first deals with the case of inner and exterior forms of type A_n. The groups of types B_n, C_n and D_n (except the trialitarian D_4) can be handled using isomorphisms with groups of type A_n in low dimensions, and also the known version of the Hasse principle for quadratic forms, hermitian forms, etc. Secondly, he takes up the case of groups of types D_4, E_6 and E_7. The proofs are based on papers of G. Harder [Math. Z. **90** (1965), 404–428; MR **32** #7677; ibid. **92** (1966), 396–415; MR **34** #2777] and parts of them are also valid for E_8. The proofs for F_4 and G_2 are comparatively easy. Let G be absolutely almost simple. Suppose that G is obtained from the quasi-split group G_1 by means of an inner twist $G = {}_aG_1$ with $a \in H^1(k, \mathrm{Ad}\, G_1)$. The proof consists in taking a series of extensions $k = k_0 \subset k_1 \subset \cdots \subset k_n$ such that each extension is cyclic of degree 2 or 3 and such that given $b \in H^1(k, G)$ which splits locally at each place and a split over k_n. Then one works down from k_n to k_0 one step at a time, showing at each stage that b still splits, thus finally achieving $b = 0$ over k.

E. Abe (Tokyo)

Citations: MR 32# 7677 = E72-8; MR 34# 2777 = E72-9.

Referred to in E68-22.

E72-14 (36# 6420)

Ishida, Makoto

On rational points of homogeneous spaces over finite fields.

J. Math. Soc. Japan **20** (1968), 122–129.

Let G be a connected algebraic group and V a homogeneous space for G defined over a finite field k. Let G_k and V_k be the set of rational points of G and V over k, respectively. Assume that there is a point P_0 in V_k having the following property: if H is the isotropy group of P_0 and if H_0 is the connected component of H containing the identity element of H, H has a representative system modulo H_0 consisting of k-rational points. Under this assumption the author calculated the number of G_k-orbits in V_k and the number of points in each G_k-orbit as follows: (i) The number of G_k-orbits in V_k is equal to that of the conjugates classes of the quotient group H/H_0. (ii) In general the number of points of each G_k-orbit in V_k is not necessarily the same (e.g., G is $\mathrm{GL}(3, \Omega)$ and V is the quotient space G/H, where H is a subgroup of G isomorphic to the symmetric group S_3 of three letters); however each G_k-orbit consists of the same number $[G_k : H_k]$ of points in the case where V is complete. Moreover, in this case it is shown that H/H_0 is commutative and hence the number of G_k-orbits is equal to the index $[H : H_0]$. (iii) If $\mathfrak{g}$ is a finite subgroup of G_k, the number of k-rational points in the quotient variety $V/\mathfrak{g}$ is equal to the number of k-rational points in V.

H. Yanagihara (Hiroshima)

E72-15 (39# 4165)

Harder, Günter

Bericht über neuere Resultate der Galoiskohomologie halbeinfacher Gruppen.

Jber. Deutsch. Math.-Verein. **70** (1967/68), *Heft* 4, *Abt.* 1, 182–216.

This is a well-organized exposition of basic concepts and recent results on algebraic groups. The main topics are the general structure theory of C. Chevalley and of M. Demazure and A. Grothendieck, basic facts on k-forms and Galois cohomology including a theorem due to R. Steinberg, and the Hasse principle of groups over number fields due to M. Kneser and the author.

T. Ono (Philadelphia, Pa.)

E72-16 (40# 1371)

Amano, Kazuo

A note on Galois cohomology groups of algebraic tori.

Nagoya Math. J. **34** (1969), 121–127.

Let k be a local field of characteristic zero with $\mathfrak{o}_k \subset k$ its valuation ring. Consider an algebraic torus T defined over k, and call K a finite Galois extension of k in which T splits. Let $\mathfrak{o}_K$ denote the valuation ring of K and G the Galois group of K/k. Then G operates naturally upon $T(\mathfrak{o}_K) =$ the $\mathfrak{o}_K$-valued points of T. In this set-up, the author obtains generalizations of several standard facts in the Galois cohomology theory of local fields. (The latter then become the special cases in which $T = \mathbf{G}_m$.) Principally, the generalizations are as follows: Theorem 1: If K/k is unramified, then $T(\mathfrak{o}_k)/\mathrm{Norm}_{K/k}(T(\mathfrak{o}_K))$ is isomorphic to the corresponding factor group attached to the reduction of T with respect to the valuation. Theorem 2: If K/k is cyclic, then $\hat{H}^n(G, T(\mathfrak{o}_K))$ have the same order for all n. (In spirit, Theorem 2 is a generalization of M. Rosen's result [Proc. Amer. Math. Soc. **17** (1966), 1183–1185; MR **34** #2568]. Compare also H. Yokoi's paper [Proc. Japan Acad. **40** (1964), 245–246; MR **29** #2239].) The proofs appear to be rather straightforward adaptations of those for the case $T = \mathbf{G}_m$, once the groups of points of T having

"values (or coordinates) in the groups $u_K^{(r)}$, $u_k^{(r)}$ of principal units" are properly defined and studied. This is done following T. Ono [Ann. of Math. (2) **74** (1961), 101–139; MR **23** #A1640]. In this connection, it is to be pointed out that Lemma 1 (p. 122) is false, as seen easily by taking an anisotropic torus T over k. The error invalidates Lemma 5 (p. 126) and, consequently, Theorem 3 (p. 126). {The author has communicated to the reviewer that both Lemma 5 and Theorem 3 can be saved by introducing an additional assumption that T be not anisotropic over k.}
T. Kambayashi (DeKalb, Ill.)

Citations: MR 23# A1640 = E68-4; MR 29# 2239 = R34-9; MR 34# 2568 = R34-20.

E76 FORMS OF DEGREE HIGHER THAN TWO

See also Sections D72, J52.

See also reviews A60-11, C05-25, D04-65, D24-24, D60-5, D72-1, D72-8, D72-9, E08-19, E20-45, E20-71, G05-96, J52-10, J84-14, M40-61, N32-1, N32-64, P04-48, P04-51, P04-54, P04-55, P08-47, P12-15, P12-16, P12-21, P20-4, R02-3, R10-4, R16-49, R42-32, T25-3, T55-19, Z10-35.

E76-1 (1, 42c)

Erdös, P. On the integers of the form x^k+y^k. J. London Math. Soc. **14**, 250–254 (1939).

The object of this paper is to give an elementary proof of the following theorem: If k is odd and not less than 3, the number of integers not exceeding n of the form x^k+y^k, where x and y are relatively prime and positive, is greater than $C\cdot n^{2/k}$, C being positive and independent of n. This is a very special case of a theorem proved by the author and K. Mahler in a less elementary way [J. London Math. Soc. **13**, 134–139 (1938)]. The proof as it stands is defective since one of the lemmas used (Lemma 3) is incorrect. It is possible, however, to fix up the proof by correcting this lemma and modifying the subsequent argument appropriately. *H. W. Brinkmann* (Swarthmore, Pa.).

Referred to in P04-51.

E76-2 (1, 201e)

Tricomi, Francesco. Sulla frequenza dei numeri interi decomponibili nella somma di due potenze k-esime. Atti Accad. Sci. Torino **74**, 369–380 (1939).

The author develops an approximate formula for the number $N_k(x)$ of numbers not greater than x which are sums of two positive kth powers. The method is based on probability considerations, the independence of certain probabilities being assumed. The general result obtained is

$$N_k(x)=x-\int_0^x \exp(-A_k t^{(2-k)/k})dt,$$

where

$$A_k=\frac{\Gamma^2(k^{-1})}{2k^2\Gamma(2k^{-1})}.$$

For $k=2$, we obtain $N_2(x)=(1-e^{-\pi/8})x=.32477x$, whereas it is known that $N_2(x)=.764x/\log x$. For $k=3$, the result is

$$(1)\quad N_3(x)=x(1-e^{-X})+\tfrac{1}{2}A_3x^{\frac{1}{3}}(1-X)e^{-X}-\tfrac{1}{2}A_3{}^3Ei(-X),$$

where $X=A_3x^{-\frac{1}{3}}$. Graphs are given comparing the actual step-functions $N_2(x)$ and $N_3(x)$ with their approximations for $x\leqq 1000$ and $x\leqq 2000$, respectively. At $x=1000$, $N_2(x)=307$ is decidedly below its approximation 324.8. For $x\leqq 2000$, the deviation of $N_3(x)$ from its approximation (1) is much less (not exceeding 3) and the agreement is described as "straordinariamente soddisfacente." Incidentally, the reviewer notes that $N_3(39050)=495$, whereas (1) gives 504.01. *D. H. Lehmer* (Bethlehem, Pa.).

E76-3 (1, 201f)

Lévy, Paul. Observations sur le mémoire de M. F. Tricomi: "Sulla frequenza dei numeri interi decomponibili nella somma di due potenze k-esime." Atti Accad. Sci. Torino **75**, 177–183 (1939).

In the paper reviewed above Tricomi has obtained by a simple heuristic argument, based on probability, the approximate result $N_2(x)=(1-e^{-\pi/8})x$, a result at variance with Landau's asymptotic formula:

$$(1)\qquad N_2(x)\sim\frac{bx}{(\log x)^{\frac{1}{2}}},$$

where the constant b is given by the product

$$b=\frac{1}{\sqrt{2}}\prod_{p\equiv 3(\mathrm{mod}\ 4)}(1-p^{-2})^{-\frac{1}{2}}.$$

In the present note the author derives (1) by a more elaborate probability argument, admittedly heuristic. The constant b is not determined, however. He also suggests that the probability, for a random x, that $N(x)=\nu$ is given by

$$\frac{b\theta^\nu}{e^\theta\nu!(\log x)^{\frac{1}{2}}},\quad\text{where}\quad \theta=\frac{\pi(\log x)^{\frac{1}{2}}}{8b}.$$

D. H. Lehmer (Bethlehem, Pa.).

Referred to in N28-31.

E76-4 (5, 141e)

Bell, E. T. A type of universal arithmetical forms. Proc. Nat. Acad. Sci. U. S. A. **29**, 375–378 (1943).

Let $\nu_1, \nu_2, \cdots, \nu_k$ be a set of k positive integers all different and let $I^{-1}[\nu_1, \nu_2, \cdots, \nu_k]$ be the set of all nonzero integers which may be represented in the form $x_1^{\nu_1}x_2^{\nu_2}\cdots x_k^{\nu_k}$, where the x_i are integers. A polynomial form $F(u_1, u_2, \cdot\cdot, u_n)$ is said to be universal for the set $[\nu_1, \nu_2, \cdots, \nu_k]$ if all the numbers in $I^{-1}[\nu_1, \nu_2, \cdots, \nu_k]$ may be represented by F with no u_i equal to zero. The theorem of this paper states that a form F of such a type may be written

$$\sum_{i=1}^{s} d_iu_1^{\alpha_i}u_2^{\beta_i}\cdots u_n^{\gamma_i},\qquad d_i\neq 0,$$

$\alpha_i, \beta_i, \cdots, \gamma_i$ integers not less than zero, where at least one of the α_i is zero, at least one of the β_i is zero, $\cdots$, at least one of the γ_i is zero. Also considered in this paper is the number of representations of an integer n by such forms. Some specific instances of the theorem are given for forms containing three terms. *I. A. Barnett* (Cincinnati, Ohio).

E76-5 (5, 255a)

Walfisz, Arnold. On the additive theory of numbers. X. Trav. Inst. Math. Tbilissi [Trudy Tbiliss. Mat. Inst.] **11**, 173–186 (1942). (English. Russian summary)

[For the last paper of the series, cf. the same Trav. **9**, 75–96 (1941); these Rev. **4**, 132.] von Sterneck's table giving the decomposition of integers $n\leqq 40{,}000$ into cubes was used by Dickson to show the universality of certain cubic forms. In order to show that the form $20x_1^3+x_2^3+\cdots+x_9^3$ is universal it is necessary to know that all integers n such that $40{,}000<n\leqq 61{,}496$ are sums of six cubes. This is beyond von Sterneck's table. It is the main

object of this paper to show that the form $20x_1^3+x_2^3+\cdots+x_9^3$ is universal using Dase's table published by Jacobi [J. Reine Angew. Math. **42**, 41–69 (1851)] giving the decomposition of integers $n\leqq 12{,}000$ into cubes. It is also shown that to prove that all integers are sums of nine cubes it is only necessary to have a table for $n\leqq 3{,}000$. Finally, some exceptions are noted to Dickson's statement [Bull. Amer. Math. Soc. **39**, 701–727 (1933)] that each of the forms $x_1^3+x_2^3+x_3^3+2x_4^3+2x_5^3$, $x_1^3+x_2^3+2x_3^3+2x_4^3+2x_5^3$ represents all integers $n\leqq 40{,}000$. *R. D. James.*

Citations: MR 4, 132a = E28-4.

E76-6 (6, 199g)

MacDuffee, C. C. On the composition of algebraic forms of higher degree. Bull. Amer. Math. Soc. **51**, 198–211 (1945).

[Lecture before the American Mathematical Society.] If f, g and h are homogeneous forms of degree k with coefficients in a commutative ring $\mathfrak{R}$ with unit element, such that $f(x)=g(y)\cdot h(z)$ is an identity in virtue of

$$x_k=\sum_{i,j} c_{ijk}y_iz_j,\quad i, j, k=1, 2, \cdots, n,$$

then $f(x)$ is composite and g and h are composable. The theory of composition is discussed only for principal ideal rings $\mathfrak{R}$. This lecture reviews previous results of the author [Amer. J. Math. **64**, 646–652 (1942); these Rev. **4**, 70], notably the following: if $\mathfrak{a}$ and $\mathfrak{b}$ are ideals of an integral domain of a finite algebra over the quotient field of $\mathfrak{R}$, then $n^b(\mathfrak{a})\cdot n(\mathfrak{b})=n(\mathfrak{c})$, where $n^b(\mathfrak{a})$ is the absolute value of the determinant of the matrix which corresponds to the class of $\mathfrak{b}$ and $\mathfrak{a}\times\mathfrak{b}=\mathfrak{c}$. This result applies directly to give a composition of the type described above. When $\mathfrak{R}$ is the ring of rational integers, these results connect with the Dedekind-Weber theorem. Also, the methods are applied to a non-commutative ring $\mathfrak{R}$ to produce a somewhat unorthodox composition. *B. W. Jones* (Ithaca, N. Y.).

E76-7 (7, 146c)

Bell, E. T. A representation of certain integer powers. Nat. Math. Mag. **20**, 3–4 (1945).

The author proves the following theorem and other results related to it. If a and b are coprime positive integers and n is a positive integer, a positive integer s and positive integers ξ, η, ζ may be found such that $x=\xi$, $y=\eta$, $z=\zeta$ is a solution of $n^{as}=F_{3a+2b,3a+b}(x,y,z)/F_{b,3a+2b}(x,y,z)$, where $F_{r,t}(x,y,z)$ denotes the ternary form $x^ry^t+y^rz^t+z^rx^t$. *B. W. Jones* (Ithaca, N. Y.).

E76-8 (7, 415f)

Suryanarayana Rao, B. On numbers which are the sum or difference of two cubes. Math. Student **13**, 57–58 (1945).

The author gives a parametric representation of the integers which are the sum of two cubes. *A. Brauer.*

E76-9 (8, 499e)

Richardson, A. R. The composition of cubic forms. Duke Math. J. **14**, 27–30 (1947).

The author indicates a method for studying the composition of n-ary cubic forms which is related to his study of the class-rings in multiplicative systems [Ann. of Math. (2) **44**, 21–39 (1943); these Rev. **4**, 185]. Applying the method in the binary case, he proves that every binary cubic form, over a commutative and associative ring R having a modulus 1, which represents 1 over R, arises by triplication. *R. Hull* (Seattle, Wash.).

Referred to in E76-15.

E76-10 (9, 10c)

Hoheisel, G. Über Diophantische Gleichungen. Ber. Math.-Tagung Tübingen 1946, pp. 81–84 (1947).

Let $F(x)=F(x_1,\cdots,x_n)$ be a homogeneous polynomial with integral coefficients, K an algebraic number field of degree n. Say that a rational integer h is representable by F if there exist integers $x_1,\cdots,x_n$ in K such that $F(x)=h$. Under eight hypotheses (which are not reproduced here) imposed on F, it is shown that, for all but a finite number of primes p, if gp is representable for some g it is representable with g less than a constant dependent on n. *I. Niven* (Eugene, Ore.).

E76-11 (9, 170c)

Segre, Beniamino. Equivalenza ed automorfismi delle forme binarie in un dato anello o campo numerico. Univ. Nac. Tucumán. Revista A. **5**, 7–68 (1946).

The author has previously [Proc. Cambridge Philos. Soc. **41**, 187–209 (1945); these Rev. **7**, 169] given necessary and sufficient conditions that two binary n-ics f and f_1, with nonvanishing discriminants, are equivalent over the complex field C; that is, that there exist complex numbers α, β, γ, δ such that $f_1(x,y)=f(\alpha x+\beta y, \gamma x+\delta y)$. In the first part of the present paper he shows how these conditions can be applied to determine the equivalence of binary forms over subfields or subrings R of C, and applies them to the cases $n=3$ and 4, R being a real field. For $n=2$ a criterion is given which holds for any field of characteristic different from 2.

The rest of the paper is devoted to the automorphisms of a binary n-ic over the rational field. The form f is weakly automorphic if there exist α, β, γ, δ other than α, 0, 0, 0 such that $f(\alpha x+\beta y, \gamma x+\delta y)=\epsilon f(x,y)$, $\epsilon\neq 0$; f is strongly automorphic if $\epsilon=1$. The automorphisms of a given n-ic, $n>2$, constitute a finite group; the author's first step is to determine all finite groups of rational one-dimensional projectivities, $x_1=(\alpha x+\beta)/(\alpha x+\delta)$ and of rational two-dimensional substitutions $x_1=\alpha x+\beta y$, $y_1=\gamma x+\delta y$. Excluding a few trivial cases there exist eight of each of these, cyclic groups of orders 2, 3, 4, and 6, and dihedral groups of orders 4, 6, 8, and 12. The structure of a binary n-ic invariant under each of these groups is then determined and the cases $n=2$, 3 and 4 are investigated in detail. *R. J. Walker.*

E76-12 (12, 318e)

Majumdar, Kulendra N. On numbers which can be expressed by a given form. Proc. Nat. Inst. Sci. India **16**, 99–100 (1950).

The author proves that for every k and for every sufficiently large x there is at least one integer between x and $x+Cx^{(1-k^{-1})^k}$ which is the sum of k positive integral kth powers. For $k=2$ this becomes a theorem of Bambah and Chowla [same Proc. **13**, 101–103 (1947); these Rev. **9**, 273]. This is a special case of a general theorem about integers of the form $\sum_{r=1}^k \alpha_r x_r^{n_r}$, the proof of which is presented. For the case $k=2$ the author states that for all $x\geqq 0$ there is always a sum of two squares between x and $x+(64x)^{\frac{1}{4}}+1$. *D. H. Lehmer* (Berkeley, Calif.).

Citations: MR 9, 273a = E24-29.

E76-13 (13, 323e)

Davenport, H. On the class-number of binary cubic forms. I. J. London Math. Soc. **26**, 183–192 (1951).

An estimate is obtained for the number of classes of properly equivalent irreducible binary cubic forms with integral coefficients and discriminant D satisfying $0<D\leqq X$. The essential idea is to use Hermite's definition of a reduced cubic form to obtain an approximate one-to-one correspondence between these classes of cubic forms and the points

with integral coordinates in a certain four-dimensional region R. The number of such points in R is then estimated by means of the result of the paper reviewed above.* In this way it is shown that the number of such classes is $KX+O(X^{15/16})$ as $X\to\infty$, where K is an absolute constant, in fact the volume of a certain four-dimensional region. This constant K is then computed. In formula (22) on page 188, X should be replaced by $3X$. This seems to mean that K should be $\pi^2/36$ instead of $\pi^2/108$. *W. H. Mills.*

*See MR 13, 323d = P28-14.

Citations: MR 13, 323d = P28-14.

Referred to in R16-49.

E76-14 (13, 323f)

Davenport, H. On the class-number of binary cubic forms. II. J. London Math. Soc. **26**, 192–198 (1951).

By methods similar to those used in the preceding paper the corresponding result for cubic forms of negative discriminant is obtained. If $h(D)$ is the number of classes of properly equivalent irreducible binary cubic forms with integral coefficients and discriminant D, then

$$\sum_{\Delta=1}^{X} h(-\Delta)=\frac{\pi^2}{12}X+O(X^{15/16})$$

as $X\to\infty$. *W. H. Mills* (New Haven, Conn.).

Referred to in R16-49.

E76-15 (13, 617d)

Richardson, A. R. Compositions involving ternary cubics. Duke Math. J. **18**, 595–598 (1951).

Let (α), (β), (x) denote the row-matrices $(\alpha_1, \alpha_2, \alpha_3)$, $(\beta_1, \beta_2, \beta_3)$, (x, y, z), respectively. Let $\mathbf{A}(\alpha)$, $\mathbf{B}(\beta)$, $\mathbf{F}(x)$ denote 3-by-3 matrices whose elements are linear in the α's, β's, and x, y, z, respectively, with coefficients in a commutative and associative ring having a modulus. The author has proved that, if $(x)\mathbf{A}(\alpha)=(\alpha)\mathbf{F}(x)$ and if $(x)=(\beta)\mathbf{A}^*(\alpha)$, where $\mathbf{A}^*$ denotes the adjoint matrix, then $f(x, y, z)=a(\alpha)\varphi(\beta, \alpha)$, where $f(x, y, z)=\det \mathbf{F}(x)$, $a(\alpha)=\det \mathbf{A}(\alpha)$, and $\varphi(\beta, \alpha)$ is a polynomial in the α's and β's [same J. **14**, 27–30 (1947); these Rev. **8**, 499]. In general, $\varphi(\beta, \alpha)$ is very complicated. It is given explicitly here in two special cases, in the second of which $f(x, y, z)=x^3+y^3+z^3$. The author's identities B for this case would yield several infinite sets of rational solutions of $x^3+y^3+z^2=uv$, but he says that it seems improbable that all rational solutions arise thus. *R. Hull.*

Citations: MR 8, 499e = E76-9.

E76-16 (17, 578f)

Dem'yanov, V. B. On representation of elements of a complete discrete normed field by forms over this field. Dokl. Akad. Nauk SSSR (N.S.) **105** (1955), 401–404. (Russian)

For characteristic $\neq 2$ it is well-known that a quadratic form which represents 0 also represents every element in the field. The author first notes that this result can be salvaged for characteristic 2 by assuming that the form can be anulled without annulling all the partial derivatives. This leads him to formulate an analogous theorem for forms of higher degree that can be proved for a field K complete in a discrete valuation. One assumes that s given forms in $x_1, \cdots, x_m$ can be annulled so as to make the matrix $\partial f_j/\partial x_i$ have rank s; the conclusion is that the forms can assume any s values $c_1, \cdots, c_s$ in K. For a single form which is a linear combination of nth powers, with n not divisible by the characteristic of K, it is noted that the extra condition is superfluous. *I. Kaplansky.*

E76-17 (17, 945b)

Grebenyuk, D. G. On the representation of certain types of integers in the form of a sum of a definite number of cubes. Dokl. Akad. Nauk Uzbek. SSR. **1953**, no. 2, 3–6. (Russian. Uzbek summary)

The author notes that if the numbers $d_1, \cdots, d_m, \delta_1, \cdots, \delta_m, d, \delta$ satisfy the equations: (1) $\delta_1-d_1=\delta-d$, (2) $\delta_{i+1}-d_{i+1}=d_i+\delta_i$, (3) $d_m+\delta_m=d+\delta$, then (4) $d\delta=\sum d_i\delta_i$.

For fixed m, n he attempts to solve the diophantine equation (5) $n=\sum A_i^3$ by putting (6) $n=d\delta$, $A_i^3=d_i\delta_i$. On eliminating d, δ from (1), (3), (6) we have

$$4n=(d_m+\delta_m)^2-(\delta_1-d_1)^2.$$

Also from (6) we have

$$\text{(8)}\qquad \begin{aligned} A_i&=l_i'''l_i^{\text{iv}}(\Delta_i)^2\varepsilon_i'\varepsilon_i''\\ \delta_i&=(l_i''')^2l_i^{\text{iv}}(\varepsilon_i')^3\Delta_i^3\\ d_i&=l_i'''(l_i^{\text{iv}})^2(\varepsilon_i'')^3\Delta_i^3\end{aligned}$$

(in the author's notation) for integers l_i''', l_i^{IV}, ε_i', ε_i'', Δ_i. If these integers can be found such that (8) satisfies (2), then we have a representation (5) of the number n given by (7).

The only special case discussed is $l_{i+1}'''=l_i'''+a$ $(1\leq i<m)$ $l_i^{\text{iv}}=a$, $\varepsilon_i'=\varepsilon_i''=\Delta_i=1$ which, effectively, gives the sum of the series

$$(l_1''')^3+(l_1'''+a)^3+\cdots+(l_1'''+(m-1)a)^3.$$

J. W. S. Cassels (Cambridge, England).

E76-18 (18, 562c)

Piehler, Joachim. Zur Theorie der binären kubischen Formen. Math. Ann. **132** (1956), 177–179.

The author considers the primitive cubic form

$$f=ax^3+bx^2y+cxy^2+dy^3$$

with integer coefficients whose g.c.d. is 1. He denotes by T the g.c.d. of the coefficients of its Hessian covariant form. For a prime p of the form $3n+1$ and K the multiplicative group of cubic residues mod p, the factor group R_p/K is of order 3. When all numbers prime to p represented by f lie in the same residue class of R_p/K, f is said to have a character (mod p). The author proves that f has a character (mod p) for p of the form $3n+1$ if and only if p is a divisor of T. *B. W. Jones.*

E76-19 (20# 837)

Fišman, K. M. The geometry of a binary form of fourth order. Černivec. Derž. Univ. Nauk. Zap. Ser. Fiz.-Mat. **19** (1956), no. 4, 75–82. (Ukrainian. Russian summary)

E76-20 (20# 6392)

Ugrin-Šparac, Dimitrije. Some properties of ternary cubic forms $x^3+my^3+m^2z^3-3mxyz$. Glasnik Mat.-Fiz. Astr. Društvo Mat. Fiz. Hrvatske Ser. II. **12** (1957), 23–29. (Serbo-Croatian summary)

Let $F_m(x, y, z)=x^3+my^3+m^2z^3-3mxyz$. It is shown that every positive prime $p\neq 3$ can be represented by F_1. If $p\equiv -1 \pmod 3$ the representation is unique and if $p\equiv 1 \pmod 3$ there are two representations, disregarding distinction between x, y and z. If $m\not\equiv\pm 1 \pmod 7$, the integers $7^n a$ with $n\not\equiv 0 \pmod 3$ and $(a, 7)=1$ are not representable by F_m. Some further results on the form F_m lead to a proof that the field $k(2^{\frac{1}{3}})$ is Euclidean.

L. Moser (Edmonton, Alta.)

Citations: MR 20# 1669 = E16-34.

Referred to in E08-19, E16-40, E76-25.

E76-21 **(20# 7011)**

Cugiani, Marco. Forme cubiche nei domini P-adici. Riv. Mat. Univ. Parma **8** (1957), 81-92.

Let α be a p-adic integer (p a rational prime). The author finds necessary and sufficient conditions that a given p-adic integer β can be represented in the form $x^3-\alpha y^3=\beta$, where x and y are integers. In particular, if $p\neq 3,7$, then a necessary and sufficient condition that $x^3-\alpha y^3$ represent all integers β is that α be the cube of a unit. The proof, which is entirely from first principles, is similar to that which he has already given in the quadratic case [Ann. Mat. Pura Appl. (4) **44** (1957), 1–22; MR 20 #1669]. *J. W. S. Cassels* (Cambridge, England)

E76-22 **(21# 3382)**

Podsypanin, V. D. On representation of numbers by binary forms of fourth degree. Mat. Sb. N.S. **42 (84)** (1957), 523–532. (Russian)

E76-23 **(21# 4137)**

Rubinstein, Elchanan. On binary forms of degree n, $n\geqq 3$. Riveon Lematematika **12** (1958), 41–72. (Hebrew. English summary)

Let (I) $F(x, y)=m$ be a representation of the integer m by a binary form of degree n. By considering transformations of the form: (II) $x=m_1^\nu u+ry$, where $m_1|m$ and $0\leqq r<m_1^\nu$, ν an arbitrary integer, the author obtains (as for quadratic forms) a classification of all solutions of (I) depending on the solutions of the congruence: (III) $F(r, 1)\equiv 0 \pmod{m_1}$. Two solutions, (x, y), (x_1, y_1) belong to the same class (are homologous) if and only if $xy_1-yx_1\equiv 0 \pmod{m_1^\nu}$, and each class determines a unique solution $(\mathrm{mod}\ m_1^\nu)$ of (III). Elementary bounds are given for the numbers of homologous classes of solutions. Furthermore, it is shown that if $m=m_1^{\nu_1}m_2$, where $\nu>\nu_1\geqq 1$ and $(m_1, m_2)=1$, can be represented by $F(x, y)$ only a finite number of times, then applying transformations (II) one obtains a finite number of binary forms of the same degree and of discriminant $D'=m_1^{(n-1)(n\nu-2\nu_1)}D$ (D = discriminant of $F(x, y)$) which represent m_2 only once or twice. The latter happens only if the degree of F is even, and the two representations of m_2 are given by (x, y) and $(-x, -y)$. *S. A. Amitsur* (New Haven, Conn.)

E76-24 **(25# 46)**

Brauer, Alfred; Shockley, James E.

On Diophantine equations of the form $x^n+y^n=hp^m$.

Proc. Amer. Math. Soc. **12** (1961), 951–953.

The authors prove effectively that if n and h are given positive integers and n is not a power of 2, then there are only finitely many coprime pairs of positive integers x, y such that $(x^n+y^n)/h$ is a power of a prime. This is an elementary deduction from the following known lemma: let q be an odd prime and $g(x, y)=(x^q+y^q)/(x+y)$; then for coprime x, y we have g.c.d. $[(x+y), g(x, y)]=1$ or q and $q^2\nmid g(x, y)$. *B. J. Birch* (Cambridge, England)

E76-25 **(26# 4970)**

Rodriquez, Gaetano

Forme cubiche nel dominio degli interi 3-adici.

Atti Sem. Mat. Fis. Univ. Modena **11** (1961/62), 95–109.

Let D_p be the domain of the integer elements in the p-adic number field and denote by $f(xy)=ax^3+bx^2y+cxy^2+dy^3$ a cubic form whose coefficients belong to D_p; we can suppose that a is a unit of D_p. The discriminant Δ_f of the form is assumed to be a square of D_p.

The reviewer established the conditions for solvability of the equation (*) $f(xy)=m$ in p-adic integers x, y, in the case $p\neq 3$ [Riv. Mat. Univ. Parma **8** (1957), 81–92; MR **20** #7011; Ist. Lombardo Accad. Sci. Lett. Rend. A **92** (1957/58), 307–320; MR **21** #3380].

The author now states the necessary and sufficient conditions for solvability of (*) in the case $p=3$. In particular, the form f is universal (i.e., the equation (*) is solvable for every m) when b is a unit of D_p and $3^8\,|\,\Delta_f$. *M. Cugiani* (Milan)

Citations: MR 20# 7011 = E76-21; MR 21# 3380 = E08-19.

E76-26 **(27# 3680)**

Jacobson, Nathan

Generic norm of an algebra.

Osaka Math. J. **15** (1963), 25–50.

In a previous paper [J. Reine Angew. Math. **201** (1959), 178–195; MR **21** #5666] the author introduced the notions of generic minimal polynomial and generic norm of a finite-dimensional, strictly power associative algebra A. The study of these is continued here.

First the following is proved: If M is a (suitably normalized) irreducible factor of the generic norm N of such an algebra A, then $M(ab)=M(a)M(b)$ if a and b are contained in an associative subalgebra. In the paper cited above a weaker result was proved. Then it is shown that this multiplicative property characterizes products of irreducible factors of the generic norm N (if the base field is big enough).

In the rest of the paper A is assumed to be a Jordan algebra. The author proves for this case similar multiplicative properties for the ternary product $\{abc\}=(ab)c+(bc)a-(ac)b$. One has $M(\{aba\})=M(a)^2M(b)$ for all $a, b\in A$, if M is as before. Moreover, this characterizes again the products of irreducible factors of the generic norm of A (if the base field is big enough).

It is also proved that the generic norm of a simple Jordan algebra over an arbitrary field is irreducible.

The author then investigates to what extent the generic norm of a Jordan algebra A characterizes A. His results imply the following "associative" result: two separable simple associative algebras A and B (over a field which is subject to some mild restrictions) have norms which are equivalent up to a non-zero scalar factor if and only if A and B are either isomorphic or anti-isomorphic. From this one can get examples of cubic forms over the rationals which are equivalent in all local fields but which are not rationally equivalent. *T. A. Springer* (Utrecht)

Referred to in T30-34.

E76-27 **(29# 71)**

Hooley, Christopher

On the representation of a number as the sum of two h-th powers.

Math. Z. **84** (1964), 126–136.

For any positive integer n let $r_h(n)$ denote the number of solutions of $n=x^h+y^h$ in non-negative integers x and y, where the order of the terms is relevant; put

$$N_h(x) = \sum_{\substack{r_h(n)>0\\ n\leq x}} 1.$$

If h is any prime $\geqq 7$, the author proves that

$$\sum_{n\leq x} r_h(n)^2 = \frac{1}{h}\frac{\Gamma(1/h)^2}{\Gamma(2/h)}x^{2/h}+O\left(\frac{x^{2/h}\log\log x}{(\log x)^{\Delta_h}}\right),$$

where $\Delta_h=1-2(h-1)^{-1/2}$, and

$$N_h(x) = \frac{1}{4h}\frac{\Gamma(1/h)^2}{\Gamma(2/h)}x^{2/h}+O\left(\frac{x^{2/h}\log\log x}{(\log x)^{\Delta_h}}\right).$$

The same formulae hold also for $h=3$ and $h=5$ with Δ_h replaced by $2-2(h-1)^{-1/2}$, and they have been proved for $h=3$ by the author [same Z. **82** (1963), 259–266; MR **27** #5742], and follow by the same method also for $h=5$.

K. Mahler (Canberra)

Citations: MR 27# 5742 = P04-51.

Referred to in P04-54.

E76-28 (30# 3876)

Rodriquez, Gaetano

Forme cubiche binarie nei domini di integrità P-adici.

Atti Sem. Mat. Fis. Univ. Modena **13** (1964), 165–186.

In this paper the author continues his work on the solvability of special diophantine equations in two variables with coefficients in a discrete rank-one valuation ring [Ist. Lombardo Accad. Sci. Lett. Rend. A **97** (1963), 811–893]. He considers primitive binary cubics $x^3+\gamma xy^2+\delta y^3=g(x,y)$, and asks for conditions insuring the solvability of $\mu=g(x,y)$ for given integral μ. The conditions are stated in terms of inequalities for the p-adic orders of γ, δ, μ (always $p\neq 2,3$), the solvability of reduced equations such as $x^3+\gamma_r xy^2+\delta_s y^3-\mu_t=0$, where $\gamma=\sum_{i=r}^{\infty}\gamma_i\pi^i$, $\delta=\sum_{i=s}^{\infty}\delta_i\pi^i$, $\mu=\sum_{i=t}^{\infty}\mu_i\pi^i$, π a prime element, and the discriminant of $g(x,y)$. The author's method consists in setting up suitable p-adic approximations. Solution of the reduced equations is, of course, always possible if the (finite) residue class field has at least 17 elements (reduction to the estimate for the number of rational points of an elliptic cubic). *O. F. G. Schilling* (Lafayette, Ind.)

E76-29 (35# 4163)

Hooley, Christopher

On binary cubic forms.

J. Reine Angew. Math. **226** (1967), 30–87.

In this memoir the author derives results on the number of representations of rational integers by binary cubic forms. Let $Y(n)$ be the number of positive integers not exceeding n that are representable by f, f a binary cubic form of determinant not of the form $-3\Delta^2$. Assuming that f is irreducible over the field of rationals, the main result states that $Y(n)\sim E(f)n^{2/3}$ as $n\to\infty$, the constant $E(f)$ depending only on f. The reducible case is easily reduced to earlier results by the author on the representation of a number as the sum of two cubes [Math. Z. **82** (1963), 259–266; MR **27** #5742]. Furthermore, almost all numbers that are represented by the form have only one representation. For forms with determinant of the form $-3\Delta^2$, a proof of the corresponding facts has yet to be found.

H. Gross(Zürich)

Citations: MR 27# 5742 = P04-51.

E76-30 (37# 2710)

Berlowitz, Bernard

On a method of Davenport.

Amer. J. Math. **90** (1968), 145–162.

In H. Davenport's adaption [Philos. Trans. Roy. Soc. London Ser. A **251** (1959), 193–232; MR **21** #4136] of the Hardy-Littlewood circle method to cubic forms in many variables, estimations of exponential sums of cubic forms and algebraic results on the Hessian of a cubic form are essential. The author is concerned with a closer study of these exponential sums and Hessians. Most of his results are of a rather technical nature, too complicated to be stated here, but they are important for possible extensions of Davenport's method. An interesting simple result of his is the following: Cubic forms without non-trivial zeros always have non-degenerate Hessians. This is proved for arbitrary coefficient fields with a suitable restriction on their characteristic. *O. H. Körner* (Marburg)

Citations: MR 21# 4136 = D72-19.

E99 NONE OF THE ABOVE, BUT IN THIS CHAPTER

See also review Z15-63.

E99-1 (9, 270f)

Rados, Gustav. Über die Elementarteiler der adjungirten Formen einer bilinearen Form mit ganzen Coefficienten. Math. Naturwiss. Anz. Ungar. Akad. Wiss. **60**, 333–351 (1941). (Hungarian. German summary)

Suppose that $B=\sum_{i=1}^{n}\sum_{j=1}^{n}b_{ij}x_iy_j$ is a bilinear form whose coefficients are rational integers and that $1\leqq k\leqq n$. Any two combinations $\lambda=(i_1,\cdots,i_k)$ and $\mu=(j_1,\cdots,j_k)$ of the integers $(1,\cdots,n)$ taken k at a time determine a minor $B_{\lambda\mu}^{(k)}$ of B; the adjoint forms of B are defined by $\mathrm{Adj}^{(k)}(B)=\sum_\lambda\sum_\mu B_{\lambda\mu}^{(k)}x_\lambda y_\mu$. If $(e_1,\cdots,e_n)$ is any set of numbers and $\mu=(i_1,\cdots,i_k)$ is a combination of the integers $(1,\cdots,n)$ taken k at a time, a combinatorial product $E_\mu^{(k)}$ is defined by $E_\mu^{(k)}=\prod_{j=1}^{k}e_{i_j}$. The author's principal result is the assertion that if the determinant of B does not vanish, and if the elementary divisors of B are $e_1,\cdots,e_n$, then there exist two unimodular forms P and Q such that

$$\mathrm{Adj}^{(k)}(PBQ)=\mathrm{Adj}^{(k)}(P)\,\mathrm{Adj}^{(k)}(B)\,\mathrm{Adj}^{(k)}(Q)=\sum_\mu E_\mu^{(k)}x_\mu y_\mu.$$

The elementary divisors of $\mathrm{Adj}^{(k)}(B)$ are then easily calculable from the combinatorial products $E_\mu^{(k)}$. Certain special cases and certain numerical examples are also studied. With minor modifications the results extend to the case in which the determinant of B vanishes. *P. R. Halmos.*

E99-2 (13, 538f)

Basoco, M. A. On a certain arithmetical identity related to the doubly periodic functions of the second and third kinds. Gaz. Mat., Lisboa **12**, no. 50, 11–13 (1951).

For every integer n consider the partitions (a) $n=i^2+2d\delta$, $i\gtreqless 0$, $\delta>0$, $d>0$; (b) $n=h^2+\Delta\Delta'$, $h\gtreqless 0$, $0<\Delta<\Delta'$, $\Delta\equiv\Delta'$ (mod 2); (c) let $\epsilon(n)=1$ if $n=s^2$, $\epsilon(n)=0$ otherwise; (d) let $\lambda(n)=1$ if $n=r^2+t^2$, $r>0$, $t>0$, $\lambda(n)=0$ otherwise. Then the following identity holds:

$$4\sum_{n=1}^{\infty}q^n\Big\{\sum_{(a)}\sin 2[(\delta+i)x+(\delta-d+i)y+iz]\Big\}$$
$$=4\sum_{n=1}^{\infty}q^n\Big\{\sum_{(b)}\sin[(\Delta+\Delta')x+(\Delta'-\Delta)y+2(\Delta-h)z]$$
$$-\sum_{(b)}\sin[-2hx+(\Delta'-\Delta)y+2(\Delta-h)z]\Big\}$$
$$+\cot(x+y)\sum_{n=1}^{\infty}q^n\epsilon(n)[\cos 2sz-\cos 2s(x+y+z)]$$
$$-\cot y\sum_{n=1}^{\infty}q^n\epsilon(n)[\cos 2s(x+z)-\cos 2s(x+y+z)]$$
$$+2\sum_{n=1}^{\infty}q^n\lambda(n)\Big\{\sum_{(d)}[\cos 2rz\sin 2t(x+z)-\cos 2r(x+z)\sin stz]\Big\}.$$

Here the summations (a), (b), (d) range over all corresponding partitions of n. The proof uses properties of the theta functions and Cauchy's residue theorem. The right hand side can be transformed so as to contain only terms of the form $\sin(\alpha x+\beta y+\gamma z)$, with α, β, γ integers. Identities of the same kind are indicated for single-valued functions of integral arguments and subject to certain parity conditions. As a particular case the author obtains two formulas due to Uspensky [Bull. Acad. Sci. URSS (6) **1926**, 547–566; Bull. Amer. Math. Soc. **36**, 743–754 (1930)]. *E. Grosswald.*

E99-3 (20# 40)

Lawton, B. Bounded representations of the positive values of an indefinite quadratic form. Proc. Cambridge Philos. Soc. **54** (1958), 14–17.

Theorem. If

$$f(x_1, \cdots, x_n) = \sum_i \sum_j f_{ij} x_i x_j$$

is a proper indefinite quadratic form with integral coefficients in the n variables $x_1, \cdots, x_n$ and $F = \max |f_{ij}|$, then $f(x) > 0$ is always soluble in integers $x_1, \cdots, x_n$ satisfying

$$\max_i |x_i| < c_n F^{n/2},$$

where c_n depends only on n.

A counter-example shows that the exponent $n/2$ cannot be improved in general, and a stronger result is indicated when f has more than one positive eigenvalue.

The hypothesis that the coefficients of f should be integers is not used in the extremely simple proof.

J. W. S. Cassels (Cambridge, England)

E99-4 (21# 7194)

O'Meara, O. T. Infinite dimensional quadratic forms over algebraic number fields. Proc. Amer. Math. Soc. **10** (1959), 55–58.

The author proves that nondegenerate quadratic forms in a countably infinite number of variables are equivalent over an algebraic number field F if and only if they are equivalent over all real completions of F. Main tools: The "weak approximation theorem" of product formula fields, and Witt's theory of finite-dimensional quadratic forms.

G. Whaples (Bloomington, Ind.)

E99-5 (32# 2427)

Venkatachaliengar, K.

The congruent reduction of a pencil of two skew symmetric matrices over a commutative field of characteristic 2, and the criteria for congruence of two such given pencils.

Math. Student **33** (1965), 33–35.

This is a sketch of some problems and results on the subject indicated in the title.

Burton W. Jones (Boulder, Colo.)

F. DISCONTINUOUS GROUPS AND AUTOMORPHIC FORMS

For complex multiplication, see **G15**.

F02 BOOKS AND SURVEYS

See also reviews C20-35, E02-12, E64-28, F10-16, F10-34, F10-89, F30-49, F35-29, F35-39, F35-46, F35-48, F40-34, F50-3, F50-39, F50-48, F50-69, F55-12, F55-19, F55-20, F60-7, F60-9, J02-8, R02-35, Z02-42, Z02-67, Z02-73.

F02-1 **(1, 136b)**

Rademacher, Hans. Fourier expansions of modular forms and problems of partition. Bull. Amer. Math. Soc. **46**, 59–73 (1940).

This paper consists of the address delivered by the author before the American Mathematical Society, December, 1938. It is an expository paper and, aside from a brief history of the problem of partitions, it is concerned mainly with the work that has recently been done on modular forms of positive dimension and the resulting formulas for partition functions. The theory of modular forms of positive dimension has not been as well developed as that for negative dimension. Some points in which this theory is not yet complete are mentioned as well as some other related unsolved problems. A large part of the recent developments were initiated by the author's solution of the problem of unrestricted partitions and many of the results are due either to him or to his direct inspiration. Numerous references to the relevant literature are given.

H. S. Zuckerman (Seattle, Wash.).

F02-2 **(11, 95d)**

Petersson, Hans. Elliptische Modulfunktionen und automorphe Funktionen. Naturforschung und Medizin in Deutschland 1939–1946, Band 1, pp. 243–275. Dieterich'sche Verlagsbuchhandlung, Wiesbaden, 1948. DM 10 = \$2.40.

F02-3 **(11, 651c)**

Siegel, Carl L. Analytic Functions of Several Complex Variables. Notes by P. T. Bateman. Institute for Advanced Study, Princeton, N. J., 1950. ii+200 pp. \$2.50.

Ces leçons sont essentiellement consacrées à une exposition d'ensemble de la théorie des fonctions automorphes de plusieurs variables complexes, théorie qui est due, pour une part, à Siegel lui-même. Voici le plan du livre. Les notions générales sur les fonctions analytiques de plusieurs variables, indispensables pour la suite, font l'objet des 3 premiers chapîtres. Les chapîtres IV à IX sont consacrés aux fonctions abéliennes et aux fonctions thêta. Au chapître X, on donne une théorie générale des fonctions automorphes attachées à un domaine borné D et à un groupe discontinu Γ d'automorphismes de D, tel que l'espace quotient D/Γ soit compact. Quant aux 2 derniers chapîtres XI et XII, disons, en gros, qu'on y étudie des exemples de domaines bornés D dont le groupe d'automorphismes Ω est transitif, et des sous-groupes discrets Γ de Ω, pour lesquels l'espace quotient D/Γ n'est plus nécessairement compact.

Voici une analyse plus détaillée de l'ouvrage: Chap. I. Étude de la divisibilité dans l'anneau des fonctions holomorphes à l'origine (dans l'espace de n variables complexes); cet anneau est à factorisation unique. Chap. II. On passe des propriétés de divisibilité locale (chap. I) aux propriétés de divisibilité globale dans un domaine: problèmes de Cousin. Les théorèmes de Cousin sont énoncés sans démonstration. Chap. III. Deux lemmes techniques. Chap. IV et V. On y montre essentiellement qu'une fonction abélienne (i.e., méromorphe de n variables complexes, admettant $2n$ périodes indépendantes) est quotient de 2 fonctions de Jacobi (i.e., fonction holomorphe $h(z)$ telle que, pour chaque période u, $h(z+u)=h(z)e^{L_u(z)}$, où $L_u(z)$ est linéaire-complexe en z). Chap. VI et VII. Consacrés aux relations (de Frobenius) nécessaires et suffisantes entre les périodes d'une fonction abélienne, et aux théorèmes d'existence des fonctions de Jacobi par les séries thêta. Chap. VIII. Structure algébrique du corps des fonctions abéliennes dans le cas "non dégénéré" (où il existe une fonction abélienne qui ne soit pas fonction de $n-1$ variables au plus). Démonstration des 2 théorèmes fondamentaux: (1) il existe n fonctions abéliennes analytiquement indépendantes (n translatées d'une même fonction); (2) si $f_1, \cdots, f_n$ sont algébriquement indépendantes, toute autre f abélienne satisfait à une équation $P(f, f_1, \cdots, f_n)=0$, où le degré en f du polynome P est borné. Dans le "cas dégénéré," le corps des fonctions abéliennes a la structure d'un corps de fonctions abéliennes, non dégénéré, à $r<n$ variables. Exemple d'un cas où $r=0$ (toutes les fonctions abéliennes sont constantes).

Chap. IX. Questions diverses en relation avec les fonctions abéliennes: problèmes (non résolus) concernant le corps des fonctions méromorphes sur une variété analytique (complexe) compacte; cas d'une variété algébrique, condition pour que son corps de fonctions soit isomorphe à un corps de fonctions abéliennes; démonstration topologique (de Lefschetz) des relations de Frobenius entre les périodes d'une fonction abélienne, etc. Chap. X. Cas d'un domaine borné D et d'un groupe discontinu Γ d'automorphismes de D: les séries de Poincaré; formes automorphes de poids $m\geqq 2$. Dans le reste du chapître, on suppose que l'espace quotient D/Γ est compact; D est alors nécessairement un domaine d'holomorphie. Théorèmes fondamentaux d'existence des fonctions automorphes: analogues aux 2 théorèmes fondamentaux du chapître VIII. Pour la démonstration du second, l'auteur utilise un théorème de H. Cartan sur les idéaux de fonctions holomorphes. Les 2 théorèmes fondamentaux entraînent l'existence d'un système de $n+2$ formes automorphes (de poids convenable) telle que toute fonction automorphe soit le quotient de 2 polynomes isobares par rapport à ces $n+2$ formes, lesquelles sont liées par une relation dont le premier membre est un polynome isobare [ce dernier point a aussi été prouvé par Hervé, par une autre méthode; voir C. R. Acad. Sci. Paris **226**, 462–464 (1948); ces Rev. **9**, 343].

Chap. XI. On considère désormais des domaines bornés D dont le groupe d'automorphismes Ω est transitif; ce sont donc des espaces homogènes de groupes de Lie, et É. Cartan a déterminé tous ceux qui sont en outre "symétriques" (on ignore s'il y en a d'autres). L'auteur donne un exposé détaillé des 4 grandes classes de domaines bornés homogènes indiquées par É. Cartan, et en donne aussi des formes équivalentes, non bornées. Il démontre explicitement, dans le cas d'une de ces classes, que l'espace homogène est le quotient du groupe Ω par un sous-groupe compact maximal. Le chapître contient aussi une méthode pour construire des sous-groupes discontinus Γ du groupe des automorphismes de la boule ouverte B, tels que B/Γ soit compact. Chap. XII. Consacré au "groupe modulaire de degré p." Il opère dans le "demi-plan généralisé" et a été étudié par l'auteur [Amer. J. Math. **65**, 1–86 (1943); ces Rev. **4**, 242]. Le demi-plan généralisé est l'espace homogène quotient du groupe symplectique à $2p$ variables (réelles) par le groupe unitaire à p variables (complexes); c'est un domaine de l'espace de $n=\frac{1}{2}p(p+1)$ variables complexes. Le "groupe modulaire" est le sous-groupe du groupe symplectique, défini par des matrices à coefficients entiers. Siegel donne une méthode de construction d'autres sous-groupes discrets Γ du groupe symplectique Ω (sous-groupes qui sont donc discontinus dans le demi-plan généralisé D), tels que D/Γ soit compact. Mais, si Γ est le groupe modulaire, D/Γ n'est pas compact. Les liens entre la théorie des fonctions abéliennes et celle des fonctions automorphes du groupe modulaire sont mis en évidence. Pour terminer, on donne la construction d'un domaine fondamental (non compact) du groupe modulaire, et une théorie abrégée des formes modulaires et des fonctions modulaires.

H. Cartan (Paris).

Citations: MR 4, 242b = F50-2.
Referred to in F02-8, F02-10, F50-10.

F02-4 **(14, 859g)**

Conforto, Fabio. Funzioni abeliane modulari. Vol. 1. Preliminari e parte gruppale. Geometria simplettica. Lezioni raccolte dal dott. Mario Rosati. Edizioni Universitarie "Docet", Roma, 1952. 454 pp. Lire 3900.

This is the first volume of what is to be a comprehensive account of the theory of abelian functions and their relation to the theory of generalized modular functions. The author prefaces his study of abelian functions proper with a brief discussion of elliptic functions in order to explain in this relatively simple and more familiar setting the plan of procedure and type of problem he envisages for the general case. Thus the following three aspects are emphasized. (A) The classification of elliptic fields under the identification of elliptic fields K, K' if their functions considered as dependent on the integrals of the first kind u, u' are identifiable by the relation $u'=au+b$ $(a\neq 0)$. The corresponding relations between the matrices of periods are stressed. (B) The classification of all possible sets of periods of distinct elliptic fields, that is, the construction of the fundamental domain of the restricted modular group, and the field of all modular functions. (C) The study of birational transformations on elliptic curves, the problem of division, and the function fields belonging to subgroups of the modular group. The following brief description indicates to what extent this program of generalization is carried out.

In chapter I a short account of the theory of abelian functions is presented, based upon the author's former book "Funzioni abeliane e matrici di Riemann" [Parte 1, Univ. di Roma, 1942; these Rev. **10**, 29]. It contains the classification of Riemann matrices with respect to isomorphism and the significance of the latter for the attached Picard varieties (as rational transforms). References to the work of Hurwitz, Scorza, and Albert on the existence of complex multiplications are made. In chapter II the customary concept of equivalence of Riemann matrices is modified, and it is shown how it leads to a natural (from the view point of abelian functions) introduction of symplectic groups (with elements $\binom{D\ B}{C\ A}$). Thus, if $\omega=|\Delta^{-1}\Omega|$, Δ the matrix of elementary divisors of the given Riemann matrix, with the imaginary part of Ω being positive symmetric, the mappings $\Omega\rightarrow\Delta^{-1}(\Omega C+\Delta^{-1}D)^{-1}(\Omega A+\Delta^{-1}B)$ with the defining relations

$$B\Delta D'-D\Delta B'=C\Delta A'-A\Delta C'=0$$

and

$$D\Delta A'-B\Delta C'=A\Delta D'-C\Delta B'=\Delta,$$

the modular group for the "level" Δ, are discussed; and it is shown that the symplectic groups do not depend, except for isomorphisms, on Δ. Next the work of Siegel on the geometry of the symplectic group is taken for a model. The symplectic cross-ratio is introduced in the space of Ω's and symplectic geometry is described in detail with the major portions of the corresponding infinitesimal geometry. Parametric representations of symplectic matrices are also studied. Siegel's theorem on the symplectic nature of the analytic transformations of the space of Ω's is presented. Chapter III is devoted to the problem of equivalence of Riemann matrices and the construction of a fundamental domain for the modular group of level Δ. The connections with the theory of quadratic forms and Eisenstein series with the prerequisite arithmetic study of matrices of integers are set forth clearly. It is to be noted that the author develops the equivalence theory of Riemann matrices for arbitrary Δ and brings out the distinction between the customary concept of equivalence. Equivalence for the level Δ requires $\omega'=\rho\omega T$ for Riemann matrices of genus p, where ρ is a nonsingular complex $p\times p$ matrix and T is unimodular and satisfies $TMT'=M$ with $M=\begin{vmatrix}0 & \Delta\\ -\Delta & 0\end{vmatrix}$. It is pointed out that this distinction is especially significant for the examination of singular abelian functions.

O. F. G. Schilling.

F02-5 **(21# 2750)**

Séminaire Henri Cartan; 10e année: 1957/1958. Fonctions Automorphes. 2 vols. Secrétariat mathématique, 11 rue Pierre Curie, Paris, 1958. ii+214+ii+152 pp. (mimeographed)

This tenth year of the Cartan seminar notes contains, as one has come to expect with this series, the exposition of a considerable amount of recent and interesting mathematics. The unifying theme for the 1957/58 year of the seminar was automorphic functions on the Siegel pattern; the five variations on this theme corresponding more or less to the various lecturers participating are, briefly and in the order of their appearance, as follows.

(A) Discrete subgroups of some classical groups and their fundamental domains (2 lectures by A. Weil).
(B) A review of some of Siegel's work as background for the remainder of the seminar (2 lectures by H. Cartan).
(C) The Siegel modular forms examined and generalized from the point of view of harmonic analysis and group representations (6 lectures by R. Godement).
(D) The compactification of the Siegel quotient spaces (7 lectures by H. Cartan and I. Satake).
(E) A connection between modular functions and the moduli of abelian varieties (3 lectures by G. Shimura).

These sections will next be reviewed separately in somewhat more detail.

(A) Weil's lectures. The first lecture is a review of work of Minkowski and Siegel on the reduction of quadratic forms under arithmetic equivalence [cf. C. L. Siegel, Abh. Math. Sem. Hamburg Univ. **13** (1940), 209–239; MR **2**, 148]. This can be considered as a case of the following general problem: to find a decent fundamental domain for a discrete subgroup Γ of a semi-simple Lie group G, in terms either of the group G itself or of the symmetric space G/K, where K is a maximal compact subgroup of G. In this case G is the projective linear group (the quotient of $\mathrm{GL}(n, R)$ by its center), Γ is the image in G of the subgroup of integer matrices in $\mathrm{GL}(n, R)$, and K is the image in G of the orthogonal subgroup $\mathrm{O}(n, R) \subset \mathrm{GL}(n, R)$; the homogeneous space $\mathrm{GL}(n, R)/\mathrm{O}(n, R)$ can be identified with the cone P of positive definite symmetric matrices A (or positive definite quadratic forms) under the group action $A \to {}^tXAX$ for $X \in \mathrm{GL}(n, R)$, and G/K is the image of the cone P in projective space. The work of Minkowski furnishes an explicit fundamental domain for the action of Γ on G/K. The work of Siegel demonstrates that Γ is what Weil terms Minkowskian in G: that is, there is an open subset $U \subset G$ of finite measure such that $KU = U$, that $U\Gamma = G$, and that for any $x \in G$ for which $x\Gamma x^{-1} \cap \Gamma$ has finite index both in $x\Gamma x^{-1}$ and in Γ there are only finitely many $\gamma \in \Gamma$ for which $Ux\gamma \cap U \neq \emptyset$.

In the second lecture two further cases of the above general problem are discussed. The first is that in which G is the orthogonal group of a non-singular indefinite quadratic form F, and Γ is the group of integer matrices in G when G is expressed in a matrix form; the second is the corresponding problem for a non-singular skew-symmetric form F. In both it can be shown that Γ is Minkowskian, by identifying the homogeneous space G/K with a submanifold of the cone P of positive definite symmetric matrices and using the results discussed in the first lecture. The proof is carried out in some detail for the first case; the connection between the second case and the Siegel spaces is also discussed in some detail. {The general problem has subsequently been treated more fully in mimeographed lecture notes by Weil [*Discontinuous subgroups of classical groups*, Univ. of Chicago, 1958].}

(B) Cartan's lectures. These two lectures form a review of background material required for the remaining lectures, taken principally from the two fundamental papers of Siegel on automorphic functions [Math. Ann. **116** (1939), 617–657; Amer. J. Math. **65** (1943), 1–86; MR **1**, 203; **4**, 242]; for the present purpose these two lectures need only be discussed to establish notation. The Siegel space S_n is the space of symmetric complex matrices z with positive definite imaginary parts ($\mathrm{Im}\ z \gg 0$). This is a homogeneous space under the symplectic group $\mathrm{Sp}(n, R)$, the group of real $2n \times 2n$ matrices $M = \begin{pmatrix} a & b \\ c & d \end{pmatrix}$ such that ${}^tMJM = J$ where $J = \begin{pmatrix} 0 & 1 \\ -1 & 0 \end{pmatrix}$; the group action is defined by M: $z \to (az+b)(cz+d)^{-1}$. The most important discontinuous subgroup of $\mathrm{Sp}(n, R)$ for the present purpose is the symplectic modular group $\Gamma = \Gamma_n$ consisting of the integral symplectic matrices; another discontinuous subgroup of some interest is the paramodular group Γ_δ associated to a diagonal integral matrix δ, consisting of those symplectic matrices for which a, $b\delta^{-1}$, δc, $\delta d\delta^{-1}$ are integral. Siegel's explicit form for the fundamental domain of Γ in S_n is described, thus completing the previous lecture by showing that Γ and Γ_δ are Minkowskian in $\mathrm{Sp}(n, R)$. A factor of automorphy $R(M, z)$ for Γ is a mapping from $\Gamma \times S_n$ into the complex Lie group of automorphisms of a complex vector space F, which is analytic in z and which satisfies the functional equation

$$R(M_1M_2, z) = R(M_1, M_2z)R(M_2, z);$$

to any complex analytic representation ρ of $\mathrm{GL}(n, C)$ in the vector space F is associated a factor of automorphy $J_\rho(M, z) = \rho(cz+d)$. A modular form (or automorphic form) for this factor of automorphy is an analytic mapping $f(z)$ of S_n into F such that $f(Mz) = J_\rho(M, z)f(z)$ for all $M \in \Gamma$. An analysis of the Fourier expansion of a modular form shows that there is a canonical linear transformation $\Phi_{n,r}$ from the space of modular forms for Γ_n on S_n into the space of modular forms for Γ_r on S_r, $r \leqq n$.

(C) Godement's lectures. Lecture 5 and the initial part of lecture 6 are devoted to two essential preliminaries. First is a brief yet lucid discussion of the irreducible representations ρ of the group $\mathrm{GL}_+(n, R)$ (real $n \times n$ matrices of positive determinant) in a finite-dimensional complex vector space F_ρ; the concept of the highest weight of the representation is the central theme of this discussion, from which only the notation α_n, for the power to which the determinant occurs in the highest weight, will be needed in this review. If α_n is real, as will be assumed henceforth, there is a positive definite Hermitian inner product $\langle a, b \rangle$ on F_ρ such that $\rho({}^tg) = \rho(g)^*$ for all $g \in \mathrm{GL}_+(n, R)$, where $\rho(g)^*$ is the adjoint of $\rho(g) \in F_\rho$ in this Hermitian structure; the norm on F_ρ associated to this inner product is $\|a\| = \langle a, a \rangle^{1/2}$. If α_n is an integer the representation ρ extends to a complex analytic representation of $\mathrm{GL}(n, C)$, to which is associated a factor of automorphy $J_\rho(M, z)$ as above. Second is the discussion of convergence conditions for certain integrals which will arise later; these are of the form

$$(1) \qquad \int_Y \|\rho(y^{1/2})a\|^\sigma \exp(-\pi \operatorname{Tr}(sy)) (\det y)^{-n-1}\, dy,$$

where Y is the space of real symmetric positive definite matrices y, for which of course $y^{1/2}$ is well-defined, $a \in F_\rho$ is arbitrary, $\sigma \geqq 1$, s is a real symmetric matrix, and dy is the usual Euclidean measure. For one-dimensional representations these integrals have been investigated by Siegel [Ann. of Math. (2) **36** (1935), 527–606]. It is proved that the integral (1) converges if and only if s is positive definite and $\alpha_n > 2n/\sigma$; the second condition is needed only to ensure the convergence of that part of the integral extended over the set of matrices y with $\det y \leqq c$ for any $c > 0$. In the proof Y is considered as a homogeneous space of the group $\mathrm{GL}_+(n, R)$ and the integral is rewritten as an integral over the group, in the study of which the work lies; an appendix to lecture 5 contains a general discussion of integrals and invariant measures on groups and homogeneous spaces, including especially such relations as arise in this proof and again later in lecture 10. As a first application of these convergence conditions it is noted that the integral

$$H_\rho(s) = \int_Y \rho(y) \exp(-\pi \operatorname{Tr}(sy)) (\det y)^{-n-1} dy$$

converges whenever s is positive definite and $\alpha_n > n$, and is then a positive definite Hermitian operator on F_ρ; the evaluation of this integral is simplified by observing that

$$H_\rho(s) = (\det s)^{(n+1)/2} \rho(s^{1/2}) H_\rho(1) \rho(s^{1/2}),$$

but an explicit value for $H_\rho(1)$ is given only for one-dimensional representations ρ, in which case it was determined by Siegel [loc. cit.].

The remainder of lecture 6 is devoted to a study of the space $H^2(\rho)$ of holomorphic functions $f(z)$ on the Siegel space S_n with values in F_ρ for which

$$(2) \qquad \|f\|_2 = \left(\int_{S_n} \|\rho(y^{1/2}) f(z)\|^2 dz \right)^{1/2} < +\infty,$$

where dz is the group-invariant measure on S_n and $y = \mathrm{Im}(z)$; this is a Hilbert space with the inner product corresponding to (2). The two central themes of this study are the Fourier transform and the reproducing kernel. The set of the real parts x of matrices $z \in S_n$ is the entire Euclidean space of real symmetric matrices; by using the analyticity of a function $f(z) \in H^2(\rho)$ its Fourier transform with respect to x can eventually be written in the form

(3) $$\hat{f}(s) = \int f(z) \exp(-2\pi i \operatorname{Tr}(sz))dx,$$

where s is a real symmetric matrix and the integral, not being absolutely convergent, is interpreted in an L^2-sense. The Plancherel formula and the convergence conditions obtained earlier for the integral (1) show that $H^2(\rho) \neq 0$ if and only if $\alpha_n > n$, and that $\hat{f}(s) \neq 0$ only when $s \gg 0$; indeed the Fourier transform (3) is an isomorphism of $H^2(\rho)$ onto the Hilbert space of those measurable functions $\hat{f}(s)$ of positive definite symmetric matrices s for which

$$\int_{s \gg 0} \|H_\rho(4s)^{1/2}\hat{f}(s)\|^2 ds < +\infty,$$

and in the inverse isomorphism

(4) $$\hat{f}(s) \to f(z) = \int_{s \gg 0} \hat{f}(s) \exp(2\pi i \operatorname{Tr}(sz))ds$$

the integral is absolutely convergent for all $z \in S_n$. If the Hilbert space $H^2(\rho)$ is non-empty ($\alpha_n > n$) it must have a Bergmann kernel function $K_\rho(z_1, z_2)$, that is, a linear operator on F_ρ holomorphic in z_1 and $\bar{z}_2$ with the property that

(5) $$f(z_1) = \int_{S_n} K_\rho(z_1, z_2)\rho(y_2)f(z_2)dz_2$$

for all $f(z) \in H^2(\rho)$, the integral being absolutely convergent. By considering the unitary representation $L_\rho(M^{-1})$: $f(z) \to J_\rho(M, z)^{-1}f(Mz)$ of $\operatorname{Sp}(n, R)$ on $H^2(\rho)$ a functional equation is derived for the kernel function which shows that it must indeed have the form

(6) $$K_\rho(z_1, z_2) = c(\rho)\rho\left(\frac{z_1 - \bar{z}_2}{2i}\right)^{-1}$$

for some constant $c(\rho)$; the introduction of the factor of automorphy $J_\rho(M, z)$ of course limits the discussion to representations ρ with integral α_n, although the modifications necessary to cover the case of arbitrary real α_n are briefly sketched.

Lecture 7 begins the study of generalized modular forms proper; it and the two following lectures are quite independent of all of lectures 5 and 6 except the initial discussion of the representation ρ. For the definition of the generalized modular forms consider in addition to the representation ρ (with α_n integral) a linear representation μ of the symplectic modular group Γ in a finite-dimensional complex vector space F_μ; it will be assumed throughout that the kernel of μ is of finite index in Γ, so that a Hermitian inner product can be put on F_μ in terms of which μ is a unitary representation. A modular form (or automorphic form) of type (ρ, μ) is then a holomorphic function $f(z)$ on the Siegel space S_n with values in the complex vector space $F = \operatorname{Hom}(F_\mu, F_\rho)$ such that

(7) $$f(Mz) = J_\rho(M, z)f(z)\mu(M^{-1})$$

for all $M \in \Gamma$. Many of the results in these lectures are derived for more general discontinuous subgroups of $\operatorname{Sp}(n, R)$ than Γ, but for brevity such extensions will not be noted in this review. As in the case of the classical modular forms the first step is to obtain a Fourier series expansion for these generalized modular forms, which is of the type

(8) $$f(z) = \sum_s \hat{f}(s) \exp(2\pi i \operatorname{Tr}(sz)),$$

where the summation is extended over some set of rational symmetric matrices s; in particular if μ is trivial only semi-integral matrices s appear. The functional equation (7) applied to this Fourier expansion leads to the Koecher theorem that $\hat{f}(s) = 0$ unless s is positive semi-definite; in addition the Fourier coefficients $\hat{f}(s)$ for positive semi-definite matrices of rank $< n$ are subject to some further restrictions, the investigation of which (at the end of lecture 7 and the beginning of lecture 8) is necessary in order to extend the operators $\Phi_{n,r}$ to these generalized modular forms. A modular form is called a cusp form (Spitzenform) if $\hat{f}(s) = 0$ unless s is positive definite.

The fundamental tool for the remainder of lectures 7, 8, and 9 is the inner product for modular forms of type (ρ, μ) generalizing that introduced and exploited so successfully in one complex variable by Petersson [probably most readily accessible in: Jber. Deutsch. Math. Verein. **49** (1939), 49–75]. The space $F = \operatorname{Hom}(F_\mu, F_\rho)$ has a natural Hermitian inner product $\langle a, b \rangle$ induced by the inner products on F_μ and F_ρ, and an associated norm $\|a\| = \langle a, a \rangle^{1/2}$; the inner product of two generalized modular forms $f(z)$ and $g(z)$ is then defined by

(9) $$\langle f, g \rangle_\Gamma = \int_{S_n/\Gamma} \langle \rho(y^{1/2})f(z), \rho(y^{1/2})g(z) \rangle dz$$

whenever the integral converges, where dz is the group-invariant measure on S_n as before. To simplify questions of the convergence of this inner product introduce the spaces $H^p{}_\Gamma(\rho, \mu)$ of those modular forms $f(z)$ for which

$$\int_{S_n/\Gamma} \|\rho(y^{1/2})f(z)\|^p dz < +\infty \quad (p = 1, 2, \cdots),$$

and the space $H^\infty{}_\Gamma(\rho, \mu)$ of those modular forms for which $\|\rho(y^{1/2})f(z)\|$ is bounded on S_n. These are Banach spaces with the obvious norms, $H^\infty{}_\Gamma(\rho, \mu) \subset H^p{}_\Gamma(\rho, \mu) \subset H^1{}_\Gamma(\rho, \mu)$, and the inner product (9) is of course a (finite) duality between $H^p{}_\Gamma(\rho, \mu)$ and $H^q{}_\Gamma(\rho, \mu)$ whenever $1/p + 1/q = 1$; in particular $H^2{}_\Gamma(\rho, \mu)$ is a Hilbert space with the inner product (9). As for the significance of these spaces in the study of modular forms, note that the inner product (9) is always convergent if one of the two forms is a cusp form; indeed the cusp forms are contained in all of the spaces $H^p{}_\Gamma(\rho, \mu)$ $(1 \leq p \leq \infty)$. If $\alpha_n \neq 0$ the space $H^\infty{}_\Gamma(\rho, \mu)$ is precisely the space of cusp forms; in an appendix to lecture 9 Satake proves, using results to be discussed in part (D), that $H^p{}_\Gamma(\rho, \mu)$ is also precisely the space of cusp forms if $p\alpha_n > 2n$. The first application of this inner product is in the Hilbert space structure of $H^2{}_\Gamma(\rho, \mu)$. This Hilbert space, or indeed any closed subspace $H \subset H^2{}_\Gamma(\rho, \mu)$, must possess a Bergmann kernel function $K_H(z_1, z_2)$ just as the space $H^2(\rho)$ considered earlier; if the subspace H lies in $H^\infty{}_\Gamma(\rho, \mu)$ as well, then its kernel function $K_H(z_1, z_2)$ is of Hilbert-Schmidt type, which leads to the conclusion that H is finite-dimensional. In particular therefore the space of cusp forms is finite-dimensional; and an inductive use of the operator $\Phi_{n,n-1}$ shows that the space of all modular forms is itself finite-dimensional. Two most interesting digressions, or rather amplifications, are inserted at this point in lecture 8. The first presents the last argument above in a more general setting; the second recalls some of the fascinating questions arising in a study of functions similar to modular forms but which, rather than being complex analytic, are other eigenfunctions of invariant differential operators on Lie groups. This range of problems will doubtless soon be the focus of even more interest, following the suggestive work of Maass [Math. Ann. **121** (1949), 141–183; J. Indian Math. Soc. (N.S.) **20** (1956), 117–162; MR **11**, 163; **19**, 252], Harish-Chandra [Trans. Amer. Math. Soc. **70** (1951), 28–96; MR **13**, 428; etc.], and Selberg [J. Indian Math.

Soc. (N.S.) **20** (1956), 47–88; MR **19**, 531]. To return to course again, the second application of the inner product is in the study of Eisenstein series, which is the topic of lecture 9; the method is a direct extension of Petersson's technique [loc. cit.]. It should perhaps be noted that Petersson and most others have called such series Poincaré series. Consider a positive definite real symmetric matrix s and an element $\omega \in F$ such that

$$\omega\mu(n) = \exp(-2\pi i \operatorname{Tr}(sn))\omega$$

for all translations $z \to z+n$ in Γ, that is, for all symmetric integral matrices n; the Eisenstein series to be considered are of the form

$$(10) \quad E_{s;\omega}(z) = \sum_M \exp(2\pi i \operatorname{Tr}(s\cdot Mz))J_\rho(M,z)^{-1}\omega\mu(M),$$

where the summation is extended over a set $\{M\}$ of left coset representatives of Γ modulo the subgroup of translations. If μ is trivial then $E_{s;\omega}(z) = E_s(z)\omega$ where

$$(11) \quad E_s(z) = \sum_M \exp(2\pi i \operatorname{Tr}(s\cdot Mz))J_\rho(M,z)^{-1}.$$

The series (10) converges to a cusp form of type (ρ, μ) whenever $\alpha_n > 2n$; and if $f(z)$ is any other cusp form of the same type with the Fourier expansion (8) then $\langle f, E_{s;\omega}\rangle = \operatorname{Tr}(\omega^* H_\rho(4s)\hat{f}(s))$, which leads to the conclusion that every cusp form can be expressed as a linear combination of these Eisenstein series. Godement also derives formulas for the Fourier coefficients of the Eisenstein series expressed in terms of some generalized Bessel functions

$$J_\rho(s) = \int \exp(-2\pi i \operatorname{Tr}(sz+sz^{-1}))\rho(z)^{-1}dx;$$

these reduce to Petersson's formulas for the Fourier coefficients in terms of the classical Bessel functions in one complex variable [Acta Math. **58** (1932), 169–215]. Series similar to (10) can be associated to matrices s which are only positive semi-definite; convergence conditions for such series are investigated, the situation being rather more complicated than in the positive definite case.

The first half of lecture 10 is a continuation of the investigations in lectures 5 and 6 of spaces of holomorphic integrable functions on the Siegel space S_n; the earlier results are extended by considering two other representations for these function spaces. First to any function $f(z)$ of $z \in S_n$ associate the function $f(M)$ of $M \in G = \operatorname{Sp}(n, R)$ defined by

$$(12) \quad f(M) = J_\rho(M^{-1}, i)^{-1}f(M^{-1}i),$$

where i stands for the matrix $iI \in S_n$ which is fixed under the subgroup $K \subset G$, $K \cong U(n)$; this establishes a one-to-one correspondence between the set of all functions on S_n and the set of those functions on the group G for which

$$(13) \quad f(WM) = \rho(W)f(M)$$

whenever $W \in K$ and $M \in G$. In this representation of the function space the norm (2) becomes

$$\|f\|_2 = \left\{\int_G \|f(M)\|^2 dM\right\}^{1/2},$$

where dM is the group-invariant measure on G; and if $K_\rho(M)$ is the function on G associated to the Bergmann kernel function $K_\rho(z, i)$ of $H^2(\rho)$ then (5) becomes

$$(14) \quad f(M_1) = \int_G K_\rho(M_1M_2^{-1})f(M_2)dM_2 = (K_\rho * f)(M_1),$$

with the usual notation for the convolution on G. One can of course also introduce the Banach spaces $L^p(\rho)$ of measurable functions on G satisfying (13) and

$$\|f\|_p = \left\{\int_G \|f(M)\|^p dM\right\}^{1/p} < +\infty;$$

and the Banach subspaces $H^p(\rho) \subset L^p(\rho)$ consisting of those functions on G which are associated to holomorphic functions on S_n through the correspondence (12). A further digression at this point is devoted to Harish-Chandra's direct characterization of the subspaces $H^p(\rho)$ as the spaces of solutions of certain invariant differential equations on the group. The second representation for these function spaces simply involves the bounded homogeneous domain equivalent to the Siegel space; as is well known this domain is the generalized unit disc consisting of the complex symmetric matrices ζ for which $I - \zeta\bar{\zeta}$ is positive definite. In this representation it is proved that for $\alpha_n > 2n$ every function $f(\zeta)$ holomorphic and bounded in the generalized unit disc lies in $H^p(\rho)$ for all p; in particular the polynomials in ζ form an everywhere dense linear subspace of $H^p(\rho)$. These two representations are now used to extend the main results of lectures 5 and 6, those involving the reproducing kernel and the Fourier transform, from the space $H^2(\rho)$ to the space $H^1(\rho)$. Thus it is proved that if $\alpha_n > 2n$ then (14) holds for every $f(M) \in H^1(\rho)$, which in turn leads to the conclusion that $H^1(\rho) \subset H^2(\rho)$; therefore the Fourier transform defined in $H^2(\rho)$ can be applied to any function in $H^1(\rho)$. Moreover the Fourier transform of a function $f(z) \in H^1(\rho)$ is equal almost everywhere to a continuous function $\hat{f}(s)$ which vanishes outside the set of positive definite matrices and which satisfies an inequality of the form

$$\|\hat{f}(s)\| \leqq \gamma(\rho)\|f\|_1(\det s)^{-(n+1)/2}\|\rho(s^{1/2})\|,$$

for a constant $\gamma(\rho)$ independent of $f(z)$; this inequality can be used to justify an application of the Poisson summation formula, leading to the result that for $\alpha_n > 2n$ and $f(z) \in H^1(\rho)$

$$(15) \quad \sum_{\substack{n={}^t n \\ (n \text{ integral})}} f(z+n) = \sum_{\substack{s={}^t s \gg 0 \\ (s \text{ half-integral})}} \hat{f}(s)\exp(2\pi i \operatorname{Tr}(sz)),$$

both sides being continuously convergent on the Siegel space S_n.

All of the results discussed in the last paragraph are valid for analytic functions with values in $F = \operatorname{Hom}(F_\mu, F_\rho)$ just as for the analytic functions with values in F_ρ, indeed with the same notation. Now considering the functions on G induced by (12), the generalized modular forms of type (ρ, μ) are characterized as the invariants of the linear representation $L_{\rho,\mu}$ of Γ defined by

$$L_{\rho,\mu}(M_0): f(M) \to f(MM_0)\mu(M_0^{-1}), \quad (M \in G,\ M_0 \in \Gamma),$$

while the spaces $H^p{}_\Gamma(\rho, \mu)$ discussed in lectures 7, 8, 9 are characterized as the spaces of those modular forms for which $\int_{G/\Gamma} \|f(M)\|^p dM < -\infty$. After these observations the second half of lecture 10 contains a discussion of the application of the results obtained in the first half of the lecture to modular forms, thus bringing together the two separate branches of Godement's lectures. The first application is to the representation of modular forms by Poincaré series. For every function $f(M) \in H^1(\rho)$ the series $f^\Gamma(M) = \sum_{M_0 \in \Gamma} f(MM_0^{-1})\mu(M_0)$ converges continuously and represents a modular form $f^\Gamma(M) \in H^1{}_\Gamma(\rho, \mu)$. The resulting linear map from $H^1(\rho)$ to $H^1{}_\Gamma(\rho, \mu)$ is continuous, and since $H^1{}_\Gamma(\rho, \mu)$ is finite-dimensional the image is the same as the image of any everywhere dense linear subspace of $H^1(\rho)$; for the particular subspace consisting of the polynomials in the representation of S_n as a bounded homogeneous domain, these series are called Poincaré series. The final result is that for $\alpha_n > 2n$ every cusp form (or equivalently every modular form in $H^1{}_\Gamma(\rho, \mu)$) is a Poincaré series and conversely. The second application is to an explicit representation of the Bergmann kernel function $K_\rho{}^\Gamma(M_1, M_2)$ of the subspace

$$H^\infty{}_\Gamma(\rho, \mu) \subset H^2{}_\Gamma(\rho, \mu);$$

to simplify these considerations Godement henceforth assumes that μ is trivial. If $\alpha_n > 2n$ the kernel function $K_\rho{}^\Gamma(M_1, M_2)$ can be expressed in terms of the kernel function $K_\rho(M)$ of $H^2(\rho)$ by

$$(16) \qquad K_\rho{}^\Gamma(M_1, M_2) = \sum_{M \in \Gamma} K_\rho(M_1 M M_2{}^{-1}).$$

The integral operator defined by this kernel function is really an orthogonal projection onto $H^\infty{}_\Gamma(\rho, \mu)$, hence the dimension of $H^\infty{}_\Gamma(\rho, \mu)$ is the trace of this operator; and it eventually follows as a corollary of (16) that

$$\dim_C H^\infty{}_\Gamma(\rho, \mu) = \int_{G/\Gamma} \sum_{M_0 \in \Gamma} \operatorname{Tr}(K_\rho(M M_0 M^{-1}))dM.$$

This is a version of the Selberg trace-formula [Selberg, loc. cit.]. The third application is to the relationship between the two explicit representations of modular forms which have been considered, that by Eisenstein series and that by Poincaré series. By use of (15) it is proved that if $\alpha_n > 2n$, $f(z) \in H^1(\rho)$, μ is again trivial, and if in addition

$$\sum_{\substack{s \gg 0 \\ (s \text{ half-integral})}} \|\rho(s^{1/2})\hat{f}(s)\| (\det s)^{(n+1)/2} < +\infty,$$

then

$$f^\Gamma(z) = \sum_{\substack{s \gg 0 \\ (s \text{ half-integral})}} E_s(z)\hat{f}(s),$$

where $E_s(z)$ was defined in (11), the series being continuously convergent for $z \in S_n$. Moreover by using the explicit formulas (6) and (16) for the kernel function it follows that

$$K_\rho{}^\Gamma(z_1, z_2) = \sum_{\substack{s \gg 0 \\ (s \text{ half-integral})}} E_s(z_1) H_\rho(4s)^{-1} \exp(-2\pi i \operatorname{Tr}(s\bar{z}_2)).$$

(D) Cartan's and Satake's lectures. After a brief survey of the necessary background in complex analytic spaces (cf. Séminaire H. Cartan 1953/54 [MR **19**, 577], where such spaces are called "espaces analytiques généraux"), lecture 11 (by Cartan) is devoted to the following problem concerning the analytic continuation of these spaces: if X is a locally compact space and V is an everywhere-dense open subset which has the structure of a normal complex analytic space, when is X itself a normal complex analytic space, compatible with V? The last restriction means that the local ring A_x of holomorphic functions at any point $x \in X$ must be the local ring of those continuous functions at x which are holomorphic on V. The fundamental result is that X is such a space, and that $X - V$ is an analytic subvariety, if the following conditions are fulfilled: (i) each point $x \in X - V$ has arbitrarily small open neighborhoods U such that $U \cap V$ is an irreducible analytic space; (ii) the local rings A_x induce the structure of an analytic space (of lower dimension than V) on the set $X - V$; (iii) each point $x \in X - V$ has an open neighborhood U such that the continuous functions on U which are holomorphic on V separate points in $U \cap V$. This result was first proved, though with stronger hypotheses, by Baily [Amer. J. Math. **80** (1958), 348–364; MR **20** #5890].

The next lectures turn to the central topic of this portion of the seminar: the analytic compactification of S_n/Γ_n, the quotient of the Siegel space S_n by the symplectic modular group Γ_n; this is a problem first discussed by Siegel [Comm. Pure Appl. Math. **8** (1955), 677–681; MR **17**, 602], and treated in more detail by Satake [J. Indian Math. Soc. (N.S.) **20** (1956), 259–281; MR **18**, 934]. Roughly speaking the compactification is of the form

$$(S_n/\Gamma_n)^* = (S_n/\Gamma_n) \cup (S_{n-1}/\Gamma_{n-1}) \cup \cdots \cup (S_0/\Gamma_0),$$

with a suitable topological and analytical structure. Lecture 12 is devoted to the construction of this compactification as a compact topological space containing S_n/Γ_n as an everywhere-dense open subset; indeed two versions of this construction are discussed, one by Satake and the other by Cartan. Both proceed by considering an auxiliary space $S_n{}^*$ on which Γ_n acts so that $S_n{}^*/\Gamma_n$ is the desired compactification; Satake constructs $S_n{}^*$ abstractly, while Cartan obtains $S_n{}^*$ from the closure of S_n (in the representation of S_n as a bounded domain). In lecture 13 Satake extends his presentation to cover the corresponding problem for discrete subgroups of the symplectic group commensurable with the modular group Γ_n. The next step is the introduction of a complex structure on the compactification. In preparation for this Satake introduces in lecture 14 an extension of the operator $\Phi_{n,r}$ mentioned earlier to local modular forms, that is, to modular forms defined only on Γ_n-invariant open subsets of S_n. By use of this operator and the theory of continuation of complex analytic spaces developed in lecture 11, Cartan and Satake prove in lecture 15 that $(S_n/\Gamma_n)^*$ is a normal complex analytic space, containing $(S_n/\Gamma_n)^* - (S_n/\Gamma_n)$ as a complex analytic subvariety of lower dimension; the corresponding result is also proved for groups commensurable with Γ_n. The final step is the projective imbedding of $(S_n/\Gamma_n)^*$. Again in preparation Satake discusses in lecture 16 conditions under which the mapping $\Phi_{n,r}$ is onto; this is a question originally investigated by Maass [Math. Ann. **123** (1951), 125–151; MR **13**, 210]. Finally in lecture 17 Cartan proves that the ordinary scalar modular forms of sufficiently high weight yield an imbedding of $(S_n/\Gamma_n)^*$ as a normal algebraic subvariety of a projective space, with $(S_n/\Gamma_n) \subset (S_n/\Gamma_n)^*$ a Zariski-open subset; this result is also proved for groups commensurable with Γ_n.

(E) Shimura's lectures. Lecture 18 is devoted to a review of some algebraic-geometric properties of abelian varieties, in particular those related to the notions of a polarized abelian variety, of a projective family of projective varieties, of the field of moduli of a polarized abelian variety, and of Kummer varieties; the references given for other discussions of these concepts are to Matsusaka [Amer. J. Math. **80** (1958), 45–82; MR **20** #878] and Weil [Proc. Internat. Sympos. Algebraic Number Theory, Tokyo and Nikko, 1955, pp. 9–22, Science Council of Japan, Tokyo, 1956; MR **18**, 673]. After a preliminary discussion of the concept of a generic point for holomorphic functions, lecture 19 is concerned with analytic systems of algebraic varieties. To define such a system suppose that $f_i(u, s)$ $(0 \leq i \leq N)$ are holomorphic functions on a product domain $U \times S \subset C_n \times C_m$ such that: (i) the $(n+1) \times (N+1)$ matrix, whose ith column consists of the function $f_i(u, s)$ and its n first order partial derivatives $\partial f_i/\partial u_j$, has rank $n+1$ everywhere on $U \times S$; (ii) for each $s \in S$ the point set

$$\{(f_0(u, s), \cdots, f_N(u, s)) | u \in U\},$$

considered as lying in a projective space P_N, is a Zariski-open subset of an algebraic variety $V(s) \subset P_N$; (iii) the degree of $V(s)$ is independent of s. The varieties $\{V(s)\}$ then compose an analytic system of algebraic varieties. The principal result is that there are meromorphic functions $\psi_1(s), \cdots, \psi_k(s)$ on S such that $(1, \psi_1(s), \cdots, \psi_k(s))$ is the Chow point of $V(s)$ whenever the functions $\psi_i(s)$ are defined. This is applied to abelian varieties in lecture 20.

If δ is a diagonal matrix with entries $\delta_1 = 1$, $\delta_i | \delta_{i+1}$ $(i = 1, \cdots, n-1)$, and z is any point of the Siegel space S_n, the columns of the matrix (z, δ) generate a lattice $D_\delta(z)$ in C_n such that the quotient space $C_n/D_\delta(z)$ is an abelian variety with a canonical polarization associated to the Riemann form $E = \begin{pmatrix} 0 & -\delta \\ \delta & 0 \end{pmatrix}$. By explicitly constructing a family of theta functions satisfying the three conditions listed above these abelian varieties are associated to an analytic system $A_\delta(z)$ of projective abelian varieties. Rather than these varieties, however, consider the projective family $F_\delta(z)$ associated to each $A_\delta(z)$. It is proved that the $F_\delta(z)$ also form an analytic system of algebraic varieties for all $z \in S_n - Y$, where Y is an analytic sub-variety of codimension 1; thus the Chow point of $F_\delta(z)$ can be given in the form $(1, \chi_1(z), \cdots, \chi_\lambda(z))$ for some meromorphic functions $\chi_i(z)$ on S_n. It is then demonstrated that $F_\delta(z) = F_\delta(z^1)$ if and only if $z^1 = Mz$ for some symplectic transformation M in the paramodular group Γ_δ; consequently the functions $\chi_i(z)$ are invariant under the paramodular group. If K_δ denotes the field of moduli and M_δ the field of invariant meromorphic functions under the paramodular group, then also $M_\delta = C \cdot K_\delta$. Somewhat similar results are derived for the Kummer varieties. *R. C. Gunning* (Princeton, N.J.)

Citations: MR 2, 148b = E12-4.

Referred to in F02-8, F40-17, F45-5, F50-21, F50-30, F50-31, F50-49, F50-53, F55-14, F55-20, F60-6, G15-22, G15-34.

F02-6 (23# A2556)

Bellman, Richard

A brief introduction to theta functions.

Athena Series: Selected Topics in Mathematics.

Holt, Rinehart and Winston, New York, 1961. x+78 *pp.* \$2.50.

This is an unorthodox book; perhaps its character is best described in the author's own words. "Despite our unqualified title, our aim is not so ambitious as to present any complete, or even partially complete theory of theta functions. . . . Instead, we wish to use three principal results in the theory of elliptic functions, all expressible in terms of theta functions, as a stage upon which to parade some of the general factota of analysis, and as an excuse to discuss some intimately related results of great mathematical elegance. Our aim is to indicate the applicability and versatility of analytic techniques that should be part of the hope chest of every young mathematician." The three results are the transformation formula for $\theta_3(z, t)$, the infinite product expansion of $\theta_4(z)$, and the determination of theta functions, as entire functions, by their functional equations. The surrounding material is a loosely-woven account of some of the diverse domains of analysis and number theory on which theta functions impinge, together with the derivation of many of the elementary identities involving theta functions. No mention is made of the connection between elliptic functions and quotients of theta functions, however. There are many references to the literature.

{Even if one grants that the author did not have in mind a systematic treatise, it remains disappointing that he made no attempt to lay a foundation for his subject; the four theta functions are defined on page 2 by their rather complicated Fourier series, with no comment as to their genesis and no hint as to why there are exactly four of them.} *W. J. LeVeque* (Ann Arbor, Mich.)

F02-7 (24# A2664)

Gunning, R. C.

Lectures on modular forms.

Notes by Armand Brumer. Annals of Mathematics Studies, No. 48.

Princeton University Press, Princeton, N.J., 1962. iv+86 *pp.* \$2.75.

In this thin (86 pp.) booklet, the author succeeds in bringing the most important parts of the theory of modular forms (as developed since Poincaré, Klein and Fricke, especially by Hecke and Petersson) within easy reach of the non-specialist. To this reviewer it seems of particular interest that important, and otherwise not very easily accessible, results of Petersson, could be presented so clearly in less than 20 pages. The book is essentially self-contained, as almost all non-elementary theorems used are proven (most notable exception: the Riemann-Roch theorem). The price that had to be paid for such a broad survey of the subject matter in so few pages is (a) the elimination of most generalizations (no mention of the Siegel or Hilbert modular groups, no multipliers $v(M) \not\equiv 1$, etc.); and (b) a certain terseness that may make the reading at times difficult (the presence of certain printing errors does not help either). This, however, is indeed a small price to pay for a lucid and concise presentation of the following topics. Chapter 1: Linear fractional transformations, the modular group, homogeneous and inhomogeneous (Γ) and its fundamental domain $D = H/\Gamma$ (H = upper half-plane); the Riemann surface $\overline{H/\Gamma}$; congruence (and other) subgroups Γ_q of Γ, their index in Γ and the computation of the genus of the corresponding Riemann surface. Chapter 2: An unrestricted modular form f of weight k for a group G is defined by the property

$$f(Tz) = (cz+d)^{2k} f(z) \quad (Tz = (az+b)/(cz+d),\ T \in G);$$

f is called simply a modular form, if in addition it is also holomorphic in H and at the parabolic vertices of G. Next, k-differentials on a Riemann surface are introduced and a few definitions are given in order to make the statement of the Riemann-Roch theorem intelligible. This is used only once, in the determination of the dimension of the space of modular forms; hence the author's decision to state, but not prove, the Riemann-Roch theorem appears well justified. Chapter 3: Poincaré series of weight k and character ν for a group G are defined by $\varphi_\nu(z) = \sum \exp(2\pi i \nu T(z) q^{-1}) J_T(z)^k$ (here $J_T(z) = dT/dz$ for every $T \in G$; the summation is taken over $T \in R$, where R is a complete set of coset representatives of G mod G_0, $G_0 = \{T \in G | \mu_T(z) \equiv 1\}$). It is shown that for $k > 1$, $\nu \geqq 0$, $\varphi_\nu(z)$ converges absolutely and uniformly on all compact subsets of H and represents there an unrestricted modular form of weight k for G. Furthermore, if $G \subset \Gamma$, $\varphi_0(z) = 0$ at finite parabolic vertices, $\varphi_0(i\infty) = 1$; for $\nu \geqq 1$, $\varphi_\nu(z) = 0$ at all parabolic vertices, i.e., $\varphi_\nu(z)$ $(\nu \geqq 1)$ is a cusp form. The Petersson inner product of modular forms is defined by $(f, g) = \int_D f \cdot \bar{g} y^{2(k-1)} d\mu(z)$ $(d\mu = \frac{1}{2} i dz \wedge \overline{dz})$, and it is shown that the space of cusp forms of weight k is a finite-dimensional Hilbert space with this inner product (f, g). The completeness of the Poincaré series is proven (every cusp form f is of the form $f = \sum_{\nu \geqq 1} c_\nu \varphi_\nu$), and the Fourier coefficients of the cusp forms are studied. Chapter 4: Eisenstein series (primitive and imprimitive, respectively; restricted and unrestricted, respectively) of weight k for Γ_q are defined by

$$G_k(z;\gamma,\delta;q) = \sum_{\substack{\{c,d\}\equiv\{\gamma,\delta\}\ (q)\\ \{c,d\}\neq\{0,0\}}} (cz+d)^{-2k}$$

(with, respectively, without the condition $(\gamma,\delta,q)=1$; with, respectively, without $(c,d)=1$), and it is shown that these series are modular forms of weight k for Γ_q. It follows that every modular form can be written as a sum of Eisenstein series $G_k(z)$ and Poincaré series φ_ν ($\nu\geqq 1$). The Fourier coefficients of $G_k(z;\gamma,\delta;q)$ are indicated, the proof (using Lipschitz' formula) is given only for $q=1$, when

$$E_k(z) = (2\zeta(2k))^{-1}G_k(z) = 1+(-1)^k B_k^{-1}(4k)\sum_{n=1}^{\infty}\sigma_{2k-1}(n)e^{2\pi i n z}$$

(B_k = Bernoulli number, $\sigma_r(n)=\sum_{d\mid n} d^r$). Numerous beautiful number-theoretic corollaries are now obtained with hardly any effort, e.g., Ramanujan's formula

$$\sum_{m=0}^{n}\sigma_{2k-1}(m)\sigma_{2l-1}(n-m) = \frac{\Gamma(2k)\Gamma(2l)}{\Gamma(2k+2l)}\frac{\zeta(2k)\zeta(2l)}{\zeta(2k+2l)}\sigma_{2k+2l-1}(n)+O(n^{k+l}).$$

The chapter ends with a proof of the theorem stating that all modular forms for Γ are polynomials in $E_2(z)$ and $E_3(z)$. Chapter 5 presents the theory of the Hecke operators T_n. Let $H_n=\left\{\begin{pmatrix}ab\\cd\end{pmatrix}, ad-bc=n\right\}$; then $M'=\left\{\begin{pmatrix}ab\\0d\end{pmatrix}, ad=n, d>0, b \bmod d\right\}$ form a complete set of right coset representatives of $H_n \bmod \Gamma$, and $f\circ T_n$ is defined as $\sum f|_k M_i$ ($M_i\in M'$), where $(f|_k M)(z)=J_M(z)^k f(Mz)$. The operators T_n on the space of modular forms f of weight k for G form an algebra $\mathscr{T}$ and satisfy $T_mT_n=\sum_{d\mid(m,n)} dT_s$ ($s=mn/d^2$). In particular, if $G=\Gamma$, $k>1$, $\varphi_\nu\circ T_n= n^k\sum_{d\mid(n,\nu)} d^{1-2k}\varphi_{\nu n/d^2}$, $\varphi_0\circ T_n=n^{1-k}\sigma_{2k-1}(n)\varphi_0$ (i.e., φ_0 is an eigenfunction), $\varphi_1\circ T_n=n^k\varphi_n$, $n^{-k}\varphi_\nu\circ T_n=\nu^{-k}\varphi_n\circ T_\nu$ (symmetry in n and ν). A study of the Fourier coefficients of $\varphi_\nu(z)$ and $n^{-k}\varphi_\nu\circ T_n$ follows. If (f,g) stands for the Petersson inner product, then $(\varphi_\nu\circ T_n,\varphi_\mu)=(\varphi_\nu,\varphi_\mu\circ T_n)$, so that the T_n are Hermitian. If $\mathbf{f}=\{f_1,f_2,\cdots,f_r\}$ is an orthogonal basis for the Hilbert space of cusp forms, then there exist matrices $\Lambda(n)$ such that $\mathbf{f}\circ T_n=\mathbf{f}\Lambda(n)$. Selecting properly the elements of $\mathbf{f}$, the matrices $\Lambda(n)$ can be taken in diagonal form. The Fourier coefficients of the (so normalized) basis functions $f(z)=\sum_{n=1}^{\infty}a_n e^{2\pi i n z}$ satisfy the remarkable multiplicative relation $a_na_m=\sum_{d\mid(n,m)}d^{2k-1}a_s$ ($s=mn/d^2$) and

$$\varphi(s) = \sum_{n=1}^{\infty} a_n n^{-s} = \prod_p (1-a_p p^{-s}+p^{2k-1-2s})^{-1}$$

(Euler product). Chapter 6 discusses quadratic forms, multiple theta series, Gaussian sums and representations by sums of squares. Poisson's formula is used in the proof of Jacobi's (generalized) inversion formula

$$\theta_A(z;X) = \sum_N \exp(\pi i z A[N+X]) = ((-iz)^r \det A)^{-1/2}\sum_M \exp\{-\pi i z^{-1}A^{-1}[M]+2\pi i X\cdot M\},$$

where $A[X]=X\cdot AX$ (A matrix, X, N, M vectors, N, M run through all integral r-vectors). In particular, $\theta_A(z)=\{(-iz)^r\det A\}^{-1/2}\theta_{A^{-1}}(-z^{-1})$. The case $A=I$ leads to representations by sums of squares. The Gaussian sum $G(a,c)=\sum_{N \bmod c}\exp(\pi i a c^{-1}A[N])$ is introduced and the reciprocity law $(-1)^k G(a,c)c^{-2k}(\det A)^{-1/2}=G(b,d)d^{-2k}$ is proven; also that $G(b,d)=G(1,d)$ and is rational. The chapter ends with some results on the number of representations of the integer n, by an even integral, positive definite, symmetric quadratic form A of odd order.

E. Grosswald (Philadelphia, Pa.)

Referred to in F30-41, F30-51.

F02-8 **(24# A3312)**

Pjateckiĭ-Šapiro, I. I.

Theory of modular functions and related problems in the theory of discrete groups. (Russian)

Uspehi Mat. Nauk **15** (1960), *no.* 1 (91), 99–136; *translated as Russian Math. Surveys* **15** (1960), 97–128.

This paper is a brief expository treatment of some aspects of the theory of automorphic functions of several complex variables, and is divided into four rather independent parts. The first section contains a sketch of the theory of Siegel's modular functions, the automorphic functions for the symplectic modular group acting on the Siegel generalized upper half-plane. This includes, in addition to the relevant definitions, Koecher's theorem, the theorems that modular functions separate points and furnish local coordinates at the regular points of the quotient space, and the theorem that the modular functions form an algebraic function field. The proofs are indicated, with reference for details to Siegel's papers [especially *Analytic functions of several complex variables*, Institute for Advanced Study, Princeton, N.J., 1950; MR **11**, 651], and some generalizations are mentioned. There is also a short discussion of the connection between modular functions or forms and Siegel's analytic theory of quadratic forms. The second section is a survey of those of the author's own works in which he has given a general construction of discontinuous transformation groups related to the moduli of fields of abelian functions; the original sources mentioned are a series of notes [Dokl. Akad. Nauk SSSR **95** (1954), 221–224; MR **16**, 338; ibid. **96** (1954), 917–920; MR **16**, 953; ibid. **106** (1956), 973–976; MR **18**, 19; ibid. **110** (1956), 19–22; MR **18**, 378; ibid. **113** (1957), 980–983; MR **20** #5888; ibid. **116** (1957), 181–184; MR **23** #A475], and a longer paper [Izv. Akad. Nauk SSSR Ser. Mat. **20** (1956), 53–98; MR **20** #991a]. This construction is based on the algebras of complex multiplication associated with the Riemann matrices (period matrices) of fields of abelian functions. The underlying spaces on which the transformation groups act, all of which spaces turn out to be "classical" bounded homogeneous symmetric domains, are derived from the set of all Riemann matrices which admit a given complex multiplication algebra, suitably reduced; the transformation groups then arise, roughly speaking, by identifying the Riemann matrices generically leading to isomorphic fields of abelian functions. The survey given in the paper is quite clear, so no further details will be presented here beyond the remark that the author gives, as examples of the general construction, the Siegel modular group discussed in the first section, the Hilbert modular group, and a quaternion group investigated by Eichler [J. Indian Math. Soc. (N.S.) **20** (1956), 163–206; MR **19**, 18]. The third section is a discussion of the analytic completion (continuation or compactification) of quotient spaces of the classical bounded homogeneous symmetric domains by discontinuous groups of transformations. The relevant work of Baily and Satake in the case of the Siegel modular group is mentioned [Satake, ibid. **20** (1956), 259–281; MR **18**, 934; Baily, Amer. J. Math. **80** (1958), 348–364; MR **20** #5890; 10e année: 1957/58, Secrétariat mathématique, Paris, 1958; MR **21** #2750]. There is also an outline of the author's treatment of the general case, and the prerequisite closer analysis of the boundaries of the classical domains; a detailed treatment of this material is now available in the author's recent book *Geometry of classical domains and theory of automorphic functions* (Russian) [Fizmatgiz, Moscow, 1961; MR **25** #231]. The fourth and final section is a most interesting discussion of some unsolved problems in the theory of automorphic functions of several complex variables, involving generalizations of the Hecke operators, discrete subgroups of Lie groups, and some other arithmetic questions; these have been and no doubt will prove to be areas of considerable mathematical activity. *R. C. Gunning* (Princeton, N.J.)

Citations: MR 11, 651c = F02-3; MR 16, 338a = F50-6; MR 18, 19c = F50-10; MR 18, 934c = F45-4; MR 19, 18a = F15-10; MR 20# 991a = F50-16; MR 20# 5890 = F45-5; MR 21# 2750 = F02-5; MR 25# 231 = F02-10.

F02-9 (24# A3313)

Peatețki-Şapiro, I. I.

Theory of modular functions and associated problems from the theory of discrete groups. (Romanian)

Acad. R. P. Romîne An. Romîno-Soviet. Ser. Mat.-Fiz. (3) **14** (1960), *no.* 4 (35), 11–48.

This paper is a literal translation from the author's Russian article reviewed above [#A3312].

E. Grosswald (Philadelphia, Pa.)

F02-10 (25# 231)

Pjateckiĭ-Šapiro, I. I. [Пятецкий-Шапиро, И. И.]

Geometry of classical domains and theory of automorphic functions [Геометрия классических областей и теория автоморфных функций].

Sovremennye Problemy Matematiki.

Gosudarstv. Izdat. Fiz.-Mat. Lit., Moscow, 1961. 191 *pp.* 0.66 *r.*

The introduction, and indeed each chapter of this fundamental work, if they appeared as individual works, would probably receive a longer review than the present one. Without attempting to do justice to the work, the reviewer notes that the introduction sets up the problem of the book. It is one of generalizing the famous result in one variable due to Klein, Poincaré, Koebe, etc., that for a given discrete group Γ there exist functions f_0 and f_1 (algebraically related) so that the arbitrary automorphic function on Γ is precisely the arbitrary rational function of these.

The work of C. L. Siegel [see *Analytic functions of several complex variables*, Institute for Advanced Study, Princeton, N.J., 1950; MR **11**, 651], set the course for the later development of the subject matter (see also the survey of I. M. Gel'fand and the author in Uspehi Mat. Nauk **14** (1959), no. 2 (86), 172–194 [MR **22** #2912]). Siegel's major theorem was that the totality of automorphic functions belonging to a given discrete group forms a field of algebraic functions of $f_0(z), \cdots, f_n(z)$ (which are connected by an algebraic relation). An important problem then consists of discovering such relations methodically, which Siegel had done when D/Γ is compact, where D, the region of existence of the functions, is bounded. In non-compact factor spaces, the proof of these results is considerably more involved. The author introduces normal discrete groups for this purpose.

The author describes these classical discrete groups and proves theorems on algebraic dependence by a detailed study of the geometry of such domains. He notes the difficulty that the boundary of a domain can be inhomogeneous, it can have components of different dimension; thus the region $|z_1|<1$, $|z_2|<1$ has such boundary components as $(1, z_2)$, where $|z_2|<1$ and $(1, 1)$, as well as $(1-|z_1|)(1-|z_2|)=0$, the three-dimensional boundary component. The author shows for É. Cartan's classical domains [Abh. Math. Sem. Hamburg Univ. **11** (1935), 116–162] that each component can be mapped onto a classical domain of minimal dimension, and the structure of the boundary closely depends on the structure of the set of unitary representations of the group consisting of analytical automorphisms [M. Graev, Trudy Moskov. Mat. Obšč. **7** (1958), 335–389; MR **21** #3510].

The author considers the "unit circle" type of classical domain as one for which the automorphisms are linear mappings. One can apply the theory in one variable to unbounded regions like the upper half-plane, where such transformations are again linear. Analogously, if D is a classical domain and F a component of its boundary, with z_0 a point on F, then there exists an analytic mapping of D into some unbounded region S such that all transformations of the region D keeping z_0 fixed transform a linear transformation of the domain S, and all mappings of the domain D transforming the component F into itself transform into mappings "analogous" to linear mappings. Such analogues of the upper half-plane are called Siegel domains, and they are the principal topic of the book.

Chapters: (I) Siegel domains; (II) Geometry of classical domains; (III) Normal discrete groups of analytic automorphisms of classical groups; (IV) Automorphic forms; (V) Bounded transitive domains. Reference is made to the following non-Russian work among others: S. Kobayashi, Trans. Amer. Math. Soc. **92** (1959), 267–290 [MR **22** #3017], J. L. Koszul, Canad. J. Math. **7** (1955), 562–576 [MR **17**, 1109], A. Selberg, J. Indian Math. Soc. (N.S.) **20** (1956), 47–87 [MR **19**, 531], I. Satake, ibid. **20** (1956), 259–281 [MR **18**, 934], M. Koecher, Amer. J. Math. **79** (1957), 575–596 [MR **19**, 867], and less specifically, to S. Bergmann and A. Weil. *H. Cohn* (Tucson, Ariz.)

Citations: MR 11, 651c = F02-3; MR 18, 934c = F45-4; MR 19, 531g = F60-2.

Referred to in F02-8, F02-11, F45-24, F50-30, F50-51, F55-28.

F02-11 (33# 5949)

Piatetsky-Chapiro, I. I. [Pjateckiĭ-Šapiro, I. I.]

Géométrie des domaines classiques et théorie des fonctions automorphes.

Traduit du Russe par A. W. Golovanoff. Travaux et Recherches Mathématiques, No. 12.

Dunod, Paris, 1966. iv + 160 *pp.* 46 *F.*

French translation of *Geometry of classical domains and theory of automorphic functions* (Russian) [Fizmatgiz, Moscow, 1961; MR **25** #231].

Citations: MR 25# 231 = F02-10.

Referred to in F50-51, F55-28.

F02-12 (29# 1332)

Lehner, Joseph

Discontinuous groups and automorphic functions.

Mathematical Surveys, No. VIII.

American Mathematical Society, Providence, R.I., 1964. xi + 425 *pp.* $12.60.

In view of the importance of the subject and the amount of work published in the last thirty years on automorphic functions and their groups, it is surprising that no comprehensive treatise in any language has appeared since the books by L. R. Ford [*Automorphic functions*, McGraw-Hill, New York, 1929] and P. Fatou [*Fonctions automorphes* (in *Théorie des fonctions algébriques d'une variable*, Tome II, deuxième édition, par P. Appell et É. Goursat), Gauthier-Villars, Paris, 1930] in 1929 and 1930, respectively. Despite the excellence of these works and of their eminent precursor, namely, the treatise of R. Fricke and F. Klein [*Vorlesungen über die Theorie der automorphen Funktionen*, Band 1, Teubner, Leipzig, 1897; Band 2, 1912], there has been for many years a great need for a book dealing with the subject in a modern way, using modern algebraic and topological concepts, particularly where Riemann surfaces and vector spaces are involved. In addition, the inclusion in book form of a concise and fairly comprehensive account of the important new ideas and techniques introduced in the last three decades by H. Petersson and others has for long been overdue. This book fills these gaps in an excellent manner and will be indispensable to the student of the subject and provide the basis from which he can begin his study of the extensive literature. It is also valuable since it provides proofs of many "known" facts which cannot, or only with difficulty, be found in the published literature. Although the scope of the book is wide, it naturally reflects the author's own special interests and there are several areas that are scarcely touched; this is particularly the case with regard to some parts of elliptic modular function theory.

In his first chapter the author gives a general historical account of the whole subject from its origin as an offshoot of elliptic function theory to the present day. The motivational advantage of such an introduction is considerable, and it is a feature that might well be copied more generally. Chapter II contains a survey of those parts of topology, Hilbert space theory, group theory, analytic function theory and hyperbolic geometry that are used in the sequel. The various types of bilinear transformations are discussed, and Ford's isometric circle is introduced. In Chapter III, discontinuous, properly discontinuous, and discrete groups of bilinear transformations are discussed and their properties are compared. In Chapter IV fundamental regions are introduced and a close study of their vertices and sides is made. {The sentence beginning at the bottom of p. 111 should be omitted as it adds nothing to the definition previously given, nor does the preceding sentence appear to amplify the one before it.} Principal circle groups are treated by the method of isometric circles and by hyperbolic geometry. Automorphic forms are defined in Chapter V, and the existence of such forms is proved by constructing Poincaré series and investigating their properties. At this stage the dimension $-k$ is assumed to be an even integer and the multipliers take the value 1. The valence of an automorphic function is defined to be the number of times it assumes any given value in a fundamental region, and does not depend upon the value chosen. The existence of an algebraic relation connecting any two automorphic functions is proved and various consequences are deduced. After a brief summary of the properties of Riemann surfaces, including the Riemann-Roch theorem, Chapter VI continues with a detailed study of the quotient space $\Gamma\backslash\mathscr{D}^+$, where Γ is a discontinuous group with domain of existence $\mathscr{D}$, and $\mathscr{D}^+$ is the union of $\mathscr{D}$ and its parabolic vertices. A full proof of the fact that $\Gamma\backslash\mathscr{D}^+$ can be given an analytic structure making it a Riemann surface is given, and the circumstances in which this surface is compact are studied. As he defines a topology on $\mathscr{D}^+$, instead of confining his attention to $\Gamma\backslash\mathscr{D}$, the author departs from the usual practice, with considerable advantage. The Riemann-Roch theorem is applied to find the dimension of certain subspaces of regular automorphic forms of even integral dimension when the Riemann surface is compact. Chapter VII begins with Poincaré's theorem that every polygon satisfying certain conditions determines a fundamental region of a horocyclic group, and an application to triangle groups is made. Relations holding between the generating transformations are discussed, the signature of a group is defined and a canonical polygon is constructed. Automorphic forms with general multipliers are introduced in Chapter VIII, the first example being the Dedekind-Hermite η-function. Poincaré series of integral dimension $-r$ ($r>2$) and cusp forms are defined. Petersson's scalar product of two cusp forms is introduced and the properties of the Hilbert space of cusp forms of a given dimension are obtained and the Fourier coefficients of such forms are studied and explicitly evaluated in certain cases. Chapter IX is devoted to the work of Rademacher and his school on forms of positive and zero dimension and their Fourier coefficients. Chapter X is concerned with transitivity. Roughly speaking, a circle orthogonal to the principal circle of a group having a fundamental region F with a finite number of sides is said to be transitive if the images of the circle are dense in F. In Chapter XI the modular group Γ and modular forms of arbitrary real dimension are studied. The multipliers of the η-function are obtained and Klein's absolute invariant $j(\tau)$ is introduced. Applications to number-theoretical results connected with partition theory and representations by sums of squares are briefly given. Formulae for the index and genus of the principal congruence group $\Gamma(n)$ and other subgroups of Γ are given. The final chapter contains a sketch of the theory of automorphic functions of several variables, their associated groups and fundamental regions. There are ten pages of notes amplifying the material of the text and a certain number of exercises for the student scattered throughout the text. The quality of reproduction of some of the figures does not come up to the high standard of the printing. In the text the chapter number occurs only on the first page of each chapter; since the index lists entries by chapter and section and not by page, this makes cross-reference unnecessarily difficult.

R. A. Rankin (Glasgow)

Referred to in F02-15, F02-17, F02-22, F30-44, F30-59.

F02-13 **(32# 164)**

Godement, Roger

La formule des traces de Selberg considérée comme source de problèmes mathématiques.

Séminaire Bourbaki, 1962/63. *Fasc.* 1, *No.* 244, 10 *pp.* *Secrétariat mathématique, Paris*, 1964.

The author's paper is that rarest of all objects in the mathematical literature: an expository article that places current research in perspective and suggests explicitly further areas for study. The author has taken as his central theme the trace formula of Selberg (see, e.g., J. Indian Math. Soc. **20** (1956), 47–87 [MR **19**, 531]). He first gives an account of this formula. Next, he shows how this result may be used to suggest reasonable problems in various branches of mathematics. *L. Auslander* (New York)

Citations: MR 19, 531g = F60-2.

F02-14 **(32# 1348)**

Fricke, Robert; Klein, Felix

Vorlesungen über die Theorie der automorphen Funktionen. Band 1: Die gruppentheoretischen Grundlagen. Band II: Die funktionentheoretischen Ausführungen und die Anwendungen.

Bibliotheca Mathematica Teubneriana, Bände 3, 4. *Johnson Reprint Corp., New York; B. G. Teubner Verlagsgesellschaft, Stuttgart*, 1965. *Band I:* xiv + 634 *pp.*; *Band II:* xiv + 668 *pp.* $27.50.

Volume I was first published by Teubner, Stuttgart, in 1897, and Volume II in 1912.

Referred to in F02-17.

F02-15 **(34# 1519)**

Lehner, Joseph

A short course in automorphic functions.

Holt, Rinehart and Winston, New York-Toronto, Ont.-London, 1966. vii + 144 *pp.* $5.00.

This 144-page book may be used as a text for a one-semester course on the theory of discontinuous groups and automorphic functions, and as an introduction to the more monumental work of the author [*Discontinuous groups and automorphic functions*, Amer. Math. Soc., Providence, R.I., 1964; MR **29** #1332]. As the following paragraphs will show, the work is essentially restricted to the classical case of a single complex variable.

Chapter I is devoted to the study of discontinuous groups. It starts with general properties of fractional linear transformations and their classification. The interest is then restricted to real linear transformations in the upper half plane. For real discontinuous groups, limit sets and sets of ordinary points are thoroughly studied; properties of discrete groups are discussed (including Lauritsen's theorem). The concept of a fundamental region is introduced and the necessary hyperbolic geometry is provided. A rather complete description of the boundary of a normal polygon is given: conjugate sides, incidence patterns and cycles are discussed. Some properties of the hyperbolic area of the fundamental region are exhibited. Fundamental polygons are actually constructed for the modular group, the principal congruence subgroups of level n ($n=2$ is taken as an example). Poincaré's method for determining a set of defining relations for a discrete group is touched upon in an end-of-chapter note.

Chapter II, on automorphic functions and forms, begins with a systematic study of the Poincaré series. They are used to prove the existence of nonconstant automorphic forms for all even dimensions on a real discrete horocyclic group possessing translations. For groups that have normal polygons with a finite number of sides, divisors and degrees are carefully described for both functions and forms with consequences as to the valence, number of zeros and number of poles. The Hilbert space of cusp forms is then introduced. The scalar product formula is used to study the identical vanishing of Poincaré series, and to give a Hilbert space characterization of the Poincaré series. It is shown that for a group of genus zero, one can pick up a basis consisting of Poincaré series. Remarks on the zeta function, Dirichlet series, Hecke operators and Petersson's Hilbert space of cusp forms are given as notes at the end of the chapter.

Chapter III on Riemann surfaces assumes some previous knowledge of the subject. If Γ is a real discrete group, P the set of its parabolic vertices and H^+ the union of the (open) upper half plane and P, it is shown in detail that $S=\Gamma/H^+$ can be endowed with a conformal structure which makes it a Riemann surface. The compact and noncompact case are examined. The genus is computed from the normal polygon of Γ. The remaining part of the chapter defines functions and differentials on S and discusses their relationship to automorphic functions and forms on Γ in H^+ (S is assumed to be compact). Riemann's inequality and the Riemann-Roch theorems are stated with some of their immediate consequences. The field of meromorphic functions on S and the field of automorphic functions on Γ are then shown to be isomorphic; a similar theorem is valid for the vector space of meromorphic differentials of weight m on S and the vector space of automorphic forms on Γ of dimension-$2m$. The Riemann-Roch theorem is then used for computing the dimension of the vector space of everywhere regular automorphic forms of dimension-$2m$ for horocyclic groups. The results are applied to the modular group M. Some introduction to the theory of conformal equivalence of Riemann surfaces is given in the notes to Chapter 3, which ends with a statement of Hurwitz's theorem on the group of self conformal homeomorphisms of a compact Riemann surface of genus $g>1$ (with a sketch of the proof).

A complete glossary of symbols is a welcome feature of the book. Many exercises, of various degrees of difficulty, are provided. *G. G. Weill* (New York)

Citations: MR 29# 1332 = F02-12.

Referred to in F02-22, Z02-75.

F02-16 **(35# 2862)**

Shimura, Gorô

Automorphic functions and number theory. II. (Japanese)

Sûgaku **13** (1961/62), 65–80.

This work contains the author's views on the future development of number theory based on various important modern and classical facts concerning automorphic forms, families of abelian varieties, construction of class fields, etc. This paper can be regarded as a preliminary announcement of the author's research plan, which has actually been carried out during the last few years. Many papers on these results have already been published, mostly in recent volumes of Ann. of Math.

{Part I appeared in Sûgaku **11** (1959/60), 193–205 [MR **24** #A3136].} *T. Kubota* (Nagoya)

Citations: MR 24# A3136 = G15-20.

F02-17 **(36# 1392)**

Maass, Hans

Lectures on modular functions of one complex variable.

Notes by Sunder Lal. Tata Institute of Fundamental Research Lectures on Mathematics, No. 29.

Tata Institute of Fundamental Research, Bombay, 1964. v + 269 + ii *pp.* $2.00.

The title as well as the chapter headings naturally call to mind the classical work of Fricke and Klein, as well as more recent books like those of L. R. Ford, Sr. [*Automorphic functions*, McGraw-Hill, New York, 1929; second edition, Chelsea, 1951] and J. Lehner [*Discontinuous groups and automorphic functions*, Amer. Math. Soc., Providence, R.I., 1964; MR **29** #1332]. The present book has indeed a non-empty intersection with the quoted ones, but does not come close to any of them. Roughly speaking, the first two chapters cover classical material, part of which could be found until a few years ago only in R. Fricke and F. Klein's *Vorlesungen über die Theorie der automorphen Funktionen* [Band I, Teubner, Stuttgart, 1897; Band II, 1912; reprint of Bands I and II, Johnson Reprint, New York, 1965; MR **32** #1348] (and the task of locating there a specific result was not always an easy one), the third chapter leads to the work of contemporary mathematicians (mainly Petersson; also Gundlach, Lehner, Rankin), while the material of the last two chapters is largely due to the author himself (almost entirely in Chapter IV, generalizations to non-analytic automorphic functions of Hecke's results for analytic ones in Chapter V).

The first chapter presents the general properties of horocyclic groups (Poincaré model of the hyperbolic plane, discontinuous groups of motions, fundamental domain, Riemann surfaces, meromorphic functions and differentials). This material is, of course, classical, but the very elegant and concise presentation (following, as the author states, Siegel's approach) does not lack in originality. Throughout this chapter, only the most elementary knowledge of geometry, group theory and the theory of functions of a complex variable is assumed, except, perhaps, for the concept of topological genus and the formula for the Euler-Poincaré characteristic. It is proved that for a horocyclic group, the area $\mathscr{I}(\mathscr{F})$ of a fundamental domain cannot be less than $\pi/21$; the fact that one actually has equality for a specific group is quoted from Fricke and Klein. The concepts of branch point, local uniformizing parameter, divisor and differential are carefully defined. The chapter concludes with a definition of automorphic forms and cusp forms (of dimension -2).

The second chapter discusses the modular group Γ and its subgroups, some elements of function theory and elliptic modular functions. General congruence subgroups, principal ones $\Gamma[N]$ and the commutator subgroup of Γ are investigated. The proofs given are complete and very carefully arranged. The long (two and a half pages) and beautifully precise proof of Theorem 9 (determination of the largest principal congruence subgroup, contained in a given congruence subgroup) may be quoted as characteristic. Other results (e.g., Petersson's theorem about the existence of infinitely many cycloid subgroups, of which exactly 1667868 are congruence subgroups) are quoted without proof. All congruence subgroups of level 2 are determined explicitly, with some stress on the theta group $\Gamma[2]+\Gamma[2]\begin{pmatrix} 0 & 1 \\ -1 & 0 \end{pmatrix}$. The existence of infinitely many subgroups of finite index in Γ which are not congruence subgroups is proven by direct construction (thus obviating the need to use the previously quoted result of Petersson, from which the statement follows trivially). After a short review of meromorphic functions and differentials on a Riemann surface (zeros, poles, residues, etc.) there follows a thorough discussion of the elliptic modular functions. Meromorphic and integral modular forms of dimension $-k$ $(0<k\in \mathbf{Z})$ are defined, the theory of the Weierstrass $\wp$-function is assumed, that of the discriminant $\Delta_0=g_2{}^3-27g_3{}^2$ of $4t^3-g_2t-g_3$ $(g_2=60G_{-4}(\omega,\omega')$, $g_3=140G_{-6}(\omega,\omega')$,

$$G_{-k}(\omega,\omega') = \textstyle\sum_{(m,n)\neq(0,0)}(m\omega'+n\omega)^{-k} = \omega^{-k}G_{-k}(\tau),$$

$\tau=x+iy=\omega'/\omega)$ and of the Eisenstein series G_{-k} is developed. On the way, the reader learns about the Riemann zeta function and about Bernoulli numbers. There follows a study of $J(\tau)=g_2{}^3/(g_2{}^3-27g_3{}^2)$, the theorem that any meromorphic modular function $f(\tau)$ is a rational function of $J(\tau)$ (a polynomial in J if f is holomorphic in the upper half-plane). The rank of the linear spaces $[\Gamma,-k]$ of modular functions of dimension $-k$ $(0<k\in\mathbf{Z})$ is determined and a basis (namely, $G_{-4}{}^p(\tau)G_{-6}{}^q(\tau)$, $0\leqq p,q\in\mathbf{Z}$, $4p+6q=k$) is explicitly obtained. The chapter concludes with a study (following Hecke) of $G_{-2}(\tau)$, based on the analytic continuation of $G_{-2}(\tau,s)$ $(=\sum_{(m,n)\neq(0,0)}(m\tau+n)^{-2}|m\tau+n|^{-s}$ for Re $s>0)$, and the remark that $G_{-2}(\tau)=G_{-2}(\tau,0)$.

Chapter III on modular forms of real dimension contains material that cannot be considered "classical" in the same sense as that of Chapters I and II, being due to a considerable extent to contemporary mathematicians. The transition is made in the first section (modular forms and partial fractions series), which contains the transformation of the theta series, the definition of multiplier systems (emphasis on even, abelian characters) and that of automorphic forms $f(\tau)\in[\Gamma,-r,v(S)]$ of (real) dimension $-r$ for a horocyclic group Γ and multiplier system $v(S)$. There follows the proof that each automorphic form can be decomposed into a cusp form and a "partial fractions series" (essentially an Eisenstein series), a study of some linear spaces of automorphic forms and the proof that for the modular group there exist exactly six multiplier systems for every real dimension $-r$. Section 2 discusses Poincaré and Eisenstein series of dimension $-r$ $(r>2)$ and the rank of the space $[\Gamma,-r,v]$ for Γ the modular group.

Section 3 consists mainly of a presentation of Petersson's results (scalar product of an automorphic and a cusp form, orthogonality, metrization theorem, completeness theorem, basis for the space $[\Gamma,-r,v]$) with an application to $\Delta(\tau)=\sum_{n=1}^{\infty}\tau(n)e^{2\pi i\tau}$ $(\in[\Gamma,-12,1])$, where $\tau(n)$ is Ramanujan's function. Finally, the last section contains results of Lehner, Petersson and Rankin on the Fourier coefficients of integral modular forms (with mention of an improvement by Gundlach valid for certain cusp forms).

Chapter IV contains the author's theory of non-analytic modular forms. The first section ("The invariant differential equation") consists largely of a study of the commutation and invariance properties of various differential operators. The problem of finding a differential equation that admits

$$G = G(\tau,\bar\tau,\alpha,\beta) = \textstyle\sum_{(c,d)\neq(0,0)}(c\tau+d)^{-\alpha}(c\bar\tau+d)^{-\beta}$$

$(\mathrm{Re}(\alpha+\beta)>2)$ as a solution is reduced (following a method of Selberg) to a problem of eigenvalues of a Laplace type differential operator Δ in the space $R=\{(\tau,t),\ \tau=x+iy,\ y>0,\ t \text{ real}\}$ equipped with the metric

$$ds^2 = y^{-2}(dx^2+dy^2)+(dt-(2y)^{-1}\,dx)^2,$$

which is invariant under the group of transformations $\hat\Omega=\{R_a\colon R_a(\tau,t)=(R\langle\tau\rangle, t+\arg(c\tau+d)+2\pi a),\ R=\begin{pmatrix} * & * \\ c & d\end{pmatrix},\ |R|=1,\ a \text{ real}\}$. By successive transformations it is found that G is a solution of (*) $\Omega_{\alpha\beta}G=0$, where the operator $\Omega_{\alpha\beta}$ has the invariance property

$$\Omega_{\alpha\beta}f(\tau,\bar\tau)|S_{\alpha,\beta} = (\Omega_{\alpha\beta}f(\tau,\bar\tau))|S_{\alpha,\beta}$$

$(|S|=1,\ S_{\alpha,\beta}$ defined by

$$f(\tau,\bar\tau)|S_{\alpha,\beta} = (c\tau+d)^{-\alpha}(c\bar\tau+d)^{-\beta}f(S\langle\tau\rangle,S\langle\bar\tau\rangle)).$$

The space of all solutions of (*) is denoted by $\{\alpha,\beta\}$. The action of several operators upon this space is studied. The second section, on non-analytic forms, starts by determining the periodic functions in $\{\alpha,\beta\}$. The relevance of Whittaker's differential equation and of the Whittaker functions is put in evidence; the action of the previously defined operators upon the Whittaker (and upon closely related) functions is investigated, by making full use of the theory of Whittaker functions, which is assumed known. The (non-analytic) automorphic forms of type $\{\Gamma,\alpha,\beta,v\}$ are defined by the properties: $f(\tau,\bar\tau)$ is real analytic in the upper halfplane, where it satisfies (*), $f|S=v(S)f$ for $S\in\Gamma$ and, if $A^{-1}\langle\infty\rangle$ is a parabolic cusp of Γ, then $f|A^{-1}=O(y^k)$ for $y\to\infty$, uniformly in x, for some constant k. The Fourier series of such a function $f(\tau,\bar\tau)$ at parabolic cusps $A^{-1}\langle\infty\rangle$ is determined, as well as properties of the corresponding function spaces $[\Gamma,\alpha,\beta,v]$. By restricting the group to be a subgroup Γ_0 of the modular group Γ, more precise results are obtained. In particular, it is shown (following a method of Siegel) that in this case $\alpha-\beta$ real and $\mathrm{Re}(\alpha+\beta)\geqq 0$ imply that $[\Gamma_0,\alpha,\beta,v]$ is of finite rank over the complex field C. This proof (almost five pages long), as well as most others, is very carefully laid out, but nevertheless these two last chapters are far more difficult than the previous three. The last section deals with Eisenstein series. Two different adjoint spaces of $[\Gamma,\alpha,\beta,v]$ are defined. From here on, the consideration is essentially restricted to non-analytic modular (rather than more general automorphic) functions. Under certain conditions the rank of the respective spaces is determined and the cusp forms are defined in the expected way. The theorem that for $f\in[\Gamma_0,\alpha,\beta,v]$ one can determine a linear combination $G=G(\tau,\bar\tau)$ of Eisenstein series so that $f-G$ is a cusp form holds also in the non-analytic case. If Re $\alpha>0$,

Re $\beta > 0$, then the Eisenstein series generate the whole space $[\Gamma_0, \alpha, \beta, v]$. Other conditions that insure the identical vanishing of cusp forms are also indicated, the Fourier coefficients of Eisenstein series for the modular group are found (for $\alpha-\beta$ an even integer and $v=1$) and the linear space $[\Gamma, \alpha, \alpha, 1]$ (Γ the modular group) is shown to be of rank 1 over $\mathbf{C}$, if $\alpha \geqq 0$, being generated by $G^*(\tau, \bar{\tau}, \alpha, \alpha)$ (=the Fourier series of $G(\tau, \bar{\tau}, \alpha, \alpha)$).

The fifth and last chapter starts out with an introductory section on a generalized gamma function $\Gamma(s; \alpha, \beta)$, defined essentially as the Mellin transform of a Whittaker function. Next, determinants formed with these generalized functions $\Gamma(s; \alpha, \beta)$ are considered, leading to the result that $\Gamma(s; \alpha, \beta) = 2^{r/2}(\Gamma(s)\Gamma(s+1-q)/\Gamma(s+1-\alpha)) \times F(\beta, 1-\alpha; s+1-\alpha; \frac{1}{2})$ ($\alpha-\beta=r$, $\alpha+\beta=q$, F the hypergeometric function). The Mellin transform of an infinite series of Whittaker functions is computed and the inversion of the Mellin transforms is shown to be valid. In the second section, on automorphic forms and Dirichlet series, one finds a generalization of Hecke's theory [E. Hecke, Math. Ann. **112** (1936), 664–699; *Mathematische Werke*, pp. 591–626, Vandenhoeck and Ruprecht, Göttingen, 1959; see MR **21** #3303] relating functions of signature $\{\lambda, k, \gamma\}$ to certain functions automorphic under the Hecke groups, but the main result of this section (Theorem 35) is too long (one and a half pages) for verbatim quotation. The functions

$$\varphi(s) = \textstyle\sum_{n+k>0} a_{n+k}(n+k)^s, \quad \psi(s) = \sum_{n+k<0} a_{n+k}|n+k|^{-s}$$

that satisfy the corresponding functional equations are investigated and it is shown that $(s-1)(s-q)\varphi(s)$ and $(s-1)(s-q)\psi(s)$ are entire functions of finite genus. Hecke's results on analytic modular forms are included in the present ones for $\beta=0$, $\psi=0$. Several other particular cases are also considered. The last section contains the generalization of the Hecke operators T_n to the present case and the investigation of the multiplicative properties of the Fourier coefficients of non-analytic modular forms and that of Euler products of the corresponding Dirichlet series. Let $O_n = \left\{\begin{pmatrix} a & b \\ c & d \end{pmatrix}, a, b, c, d \in \mathbf{Z}, ad-bc=n\right\}$, Γ be the modular group, V_n stand for a system of left residue classes of O_n by Γ; then T_n is defined on $[\Gamma, \alpha, \beta, 1]$ by $f|T_n = n^{q-1}\sum_{S\in V_n} f|S$ ($q=\alpha+\beta$). T_n maps $[\Gamma, \alpha, \beta, 1]$ into itself, the T_n commute with each other and $T_nT_m = \sum_{d|(m,n)} T(mn/d^2)d^{q-1}$ ($d>0$). Furthermore, the Eisenstein series $G^*(\tau, \bar{\tau}; \alpha, \beta)$ of Chapter IV are eigenfunctions of all operators T_n and, specifically, $G^*|T_n = d_{q-1}(n)G^*$ ($d_k(n) = \sum_{d|n} d^k$). The operators T_n are hermitian for all cusp forms in $[\Gamma, \alpha, \beta, 1]$. These properties imply that the Dirichlet series corresponding to (normed) Eisenstein series have Euler products, i.e.,

$$\textstyle\sum_{n=1}^{\infty} d_{q-1}(n)n^{-s} = \prod_p (1-d_{q-1}(p)p^{-s} + p^{q-1-2s})^{-1} = \zeta(s)\zeta(s+1-q)$$

and a similar result holds for the Dirichlet series corresponding to the bases of certain linear function spaces $\mathscr{L}_{\alpha\beta}^{(\varepsilon)}(\varepsilon^2=1)$, which it would be too long to define.

Practically everything covered in this book was available (in some form) before and some of the most important even among the modern results (Petersson's metrization and completeness theorems, the author's theory of non-analytic automorphic forms, generalized Hecke operators, etc.) were published quite some time ago; however, this seems to be the first (and still only) publication where one can find a systematic presentation of all this material, which, until now, had to be searched for in a large number of papers, by many different authors. This should prove to be an invaluable help to those who want to learn about this field, while the experts will appreciate the esthetically satisfying organization of such a large amount of important material. The reviewer would not be surprised if this book were to become (and stay for many years) *the* reference for automorphic functions (especially in the non-analytic case)—this, in spite of its rather inconvenient presentation as bulky, often difficult to read (and with often poor drawings) lecture notes. As the author observes, these notes were carefully prepared by Sunder Lal; however, even the most painstaking efforts cannot overcome all drawbacks inherent to lecture notes. There is an "Errata" of three and a half pages, which lists and corrects many typographical errors (mostly minor); there are many others (and not only minor ones) that were overlooked.

Summarizing: a beautiful work. The book is dedicated to Professor Petersson on his sixtieth birthday.

E. Grosswald (Philadelphia, Pa.)

Citations: MR 21# 3303 = Z25-14; MR 29# 1332 = F02-12; MR 32# 1348 = F02-14.

F02-18 (36# 3725)

Gel'fand, I. M. [Гельфанд, И. М.]; Graev, M. I. [Граев, М. И.]; Pjateckiĭ-Šapiro, I. I. [Пятецкий-Шапиро, И. И.]

Theory of representations and automorphic functions [Теория представлений и автоморфные функции].

Generalized functions, No. 6.

Izdat. "Nauka", Moscow, 1966. 512 *pp.* 1.77 *r.*

The theory of automorphic functions is of interest as the most likely approach to a proof of the Riemann hypothesis. The present treatment of the theory depends on recent results in the representation theory of locally compact groups. Automorphic functions are studied on the space of left cosets of a locally compact group G modulo a discrete group H. In addition, an invariant metric is required for the construction of fundamental regions. The construction of automorphic functions is made through the decomposition theory of unitary representations instead of by the usual Poincaré series. Automorphic functions enter in the representation theory as a device for computing the multiplicity of representations. Of fundamental importance is V. Bargmann's determination [Ann. of Math (2) **48** (1947), 568–640; MR **9**, 133] of the unitary representations of the group of 2×2-matrices having real entries and determinant one. It is a remarkable fact that analytic function theory is not necessary for the modern theory of automorphic functions. Indeed, it is not necessary for the underlying group G to have a differentiable structure. Thus it can be the group of 2×2-matrices with entries in a locally compact field and the whole theory is preserved intact. This generalization is of particular interest in the case of adèle groups. Such groups appear, for example, in the computation of the character group of the rationals considered without topology. They are used to study Dirichlet series having functional identities and factorization properties similar to those for the Riemann zeta function.

L. de Branges (Zbl **138**, 72)

Referred to in E64-22, F02-19, F70-19.

F02-19 (38# 2093)

Gel'fand, I. M.; Graev, M. I.; Pyatetskii-Shapiro, I. I. [Pjateckiĭ-Šapiro, I. I.]

Representation theory and automorphic functions.

Translated from the Russian by K. A. Hirsch.

W. B. Saunders Co., Philadelphia, Pa.-London-Toronto, Ont., 1969. xvi+426 *pp.* $18.00.

The Russian original has been reviewed [Izdat. "Nauka", Moscow, 1966; MR **36** #3725].

Citations: MR 36# 3725 = F02-18.

Referred to in E64-22.

F02-20 **(38# 5719)**

Pjateckiĭ-Šapiro, I. I.

Automorphic functions and arithmetic groups. (Russian)

Proc. Internat. Congr. Math. (*Moscow*, 1966), *pp.* 232–247. *Izdat. "Mir", Moscow*, 1968.

Verfasser gibt eine Übersicht über eine Reihe von Problemen in der Theorie der automorphen Funktionen von mehreren Variablen und der arithmetischen Gruppen. Die englischen Fassung [Amer. Math. Soc. Transl. (2) **70** (1968), 185–201; see MR **37** #1213] hat offenbar ein abgeändertes russisches Manuskript zugrunde gelegen. § 1 befaßt sich mit den Definitionsgebieten der automorphen Funktionen. Verfasser weist insbesondere darauf hin, daß die beschränkten homogenen nicht-symmetrischen Gebiete keine diskreten Gruppen von Automorphismen mit endlichem Inhalt des Fundamentalbereiches haben, was ihre Bedeutung für die Theorie der automorphen Funktionen stark einschränkt. Er vermutet aber, daß es möglich ist, Beispiele nicht-homogener Gebiete zu konstruieren, die solche diskreten Gruppen von Automorphismen besitzen. § 2 befaßt sich mit den Funktionenkörpern. Verfasser vermutet, daß mindestens für die beschränkten symmetrischen Gebiete der Körper der automorphen Funktionen zu einer diskreten Gruppe genau dann ein algebraischer Funktionenkörper ist, wenn der Fundamentalbereich der Gruppe endlichen Inhalt hat. § 3 befaßt sich mit Selberg's Vermutung, daß mit wenigen Ausnahmen diskrete Untergruppen halbeinfacher Lie-Gruppen mit endlichem Inhalt des Quotientenraumes arithmetische Gruppen sind. Verfasser hat gezeigt, daß jede diskrete Untergruppe vom Heckeschen Typ einer einfachen reellen auflösbaren Lie-Gruppe eine arithmetische Gruppe ist. Die Angaben zur Definition der Gruppen vom Heckeschen Typ und zur Beweismethode fehlen in der englischen Fassung. § 4 befaßt sich mit Beispielen nicht-arithmetischer diskreter Gruppen. § 5 befaßt sich mit Aussagen über den Funktionenkörper für arithmetische Gruppen, insbesondere im Zusammenhang mit der Kompaktifizierung des Quotientenraumes. Die englische Fassung enthält zusätzlich einige Angaben über Fälle, in denen der Funktionenkörper kein rationaler Funktionenkörper ist. § 6 befaßt sich mit Darstellungen diskreter Gruppen über dem Raum der quadratischen integrierbaren Funktionen des Quotientenraumes. Die englische Fassung ist ausführlicher als die russische. § 7 enthält Bemerkungen über maximale diskrete Untergruppen, § 8 über diskrete Gruppen, bei denen jede Untergruppe mit endlichem Index Kongruenzuntergruppe ist. § 9 befaßt sich mit einer Arbeit des Verfassers zusammen mit I. R. Šafarevič [Izv. Akad. Nauk SSSR Ser. Mat. **30** (1966), 671–704; MR **34** #2581]. § 10 und § 11 befassen sich mit diskreten Untergruppen von Lie-Gruppen bzw. von direkten Produkten von Lie-Gruppen, insbesondere mit der Frage der Existenz solcher Untergruppen mit einem nicht-kompakten Quotientenraum mit endlichem Inhalt und mit der Frage, ob diskrete Untergruppen gewisser direkter Produkte mit endlichem Inhalt des Quotientenraumes arithmetische Gruppen sind.

K.-B. Gundlach (Münster)

Citations: MR 34# 2581 = F99-4.

F02-21 **(40# 1254a; 40# 1254b)**

Klein, Felix

Vorlesungen über die Theorie der elliptischen Modulfunktionen. Band I: Grundlegung der Theorie.

Ausgearbeitet und vervollständigt von Robert Fricke. Nachdruck der ersten Auflage. Bibliotheca Mathematica Teubneriana, Band 10.

Johnson Reprint Corp., New York; B. G. Teubner Verlagsgesellschaft, Stuttgart, 1966. *Vol. I:* xix + 764 *pp.* $35.00 *the set.*

Klein, Felix

Vorlesungen über die Theorie der elliptischen Modulfunktionen. Band II: Fortbildung und Anwendung der Theorie.

Ausgearbeitet und vervollständigt von Robert Fricke. Nachdruck der ersten Auflage. Bibliotheca Mathematica Teubneriana, Band 11.

Johnson Reprint Corp., New York; B. G. Teubner Verlagsgesellschaft, Stuttgart, 1966. *Vol. II:* iv + 712 *pp.* $35.00 *the set.*

These two volumes reproduce the first edition of this work [Vol. I, Teubner, Leipzig, 1890; Vol. II, 1892].

F02-22 **(41# 8666)**

Lehner, Joseph

Lectures on modular forms.

National Bureau of Standards, Applied Mathematics Series, 61.

Superintendent of Documents, U.S. Government Printing Office, Washington, D.C., 1969. iv + 73 *pp.* $.70.

These lectures are concerned with some aspects of the theory of modular forms in one complex variable. The first chapter contains standard material on the modular group Γ and its subgroups of finite index: fundamental domains, invariant metric, Riemann surfaces, Poincaré- and Eisenstein-series, Θ-functions, rank of the space of cusp-forms, Fourier expansions together with well known applications to number-theory. The second chapter deals with the Hecke-Petersson theory of the operators T_n for the modular group. Special attention should be paid to the content of the third chapter, in which Hecke's theory is developed for the group $\Gamma_0(q)=\left\{\begin{pmatrix} a & b \\ c & d \end{pmatrix} \in \Gamma \mid c\equiv 0 \bmod q\right\}$ following the ideas of a recent joint paper of the author and A. O. L. Atkin [Math. Ann. **185** (1970), 134–160]. In this book q is assumed to be a prime. The main point is the modification of the Hecke operator with index q. Chapter 4 is devoted to the group of automorphisms of a compact Riemann surface of genus $g>1$. First Hurwitz' theory of these groups is discussed and its connection to the modular group. Then all Hurwitz groups among the groups $SL(2, k)$, where k is a finite field, as determined following A. M. Macbeath. The final two chapters are concerned with congruences for the Fourier coefficients of the absolute modular invariant with respect to the moduli $q=2, 3, 5, 7$ and 13. These moduli are distinguished by the fact that $\Gamma_0(q)$ is of genus 0 exactly for these five primes. The text is not completely self-contained; references for detailed proofs are mainly made to the author's two former books [*Discontinuous groups and automorphic functions*, Amer. Math. Soc., Providence, R.I., 1964; MR **29** #1332; *A short course in automorphic functions*, Holt, Reinhardt and Winston, New York, 1966; MR **34** #1519].

H. Klingen (Freiburg)

Citations: MR 29# 1332 = F02-12; MR 34# 1519 = F02-15; MR 42# 3022 = F25-27.

F02-23 **(42# 198)**

Knopp, Marvin I.

Modular functions in analytic number theory.

Markham Publishing Co., Chicago, Ill., 1970. x + 150 *pp.* $11.50.

As stated in the author's preface, "an accurate (though uninspiring) title for this book would have been 'Applications of the theory of the modular forms $\eta(\tau)$ and $\vartheta(\tau)$ to the number-theoretic functions $p(n)$ and $r_s(n)$, respectively'". The first two chapters present the general theory of modular functions and forms; in the other six chapters, however, the author discusses only the four mentioned functions. Among the topics covered are the following:

Chapter 1 (The modular group and certain subgroups): Definitions, fundamental region, subgroups of the modular group, some Hecke groups (not identified as such). Chapter 2 (Modular functions and forms): Multiplier systems, parabolic points, Fourier expansions, definitions of modular functions and forms, sufficient conditions for a modular function to reduce to a constant, or to vanish identically, Fourier expansions at cusps, cusp forms. Chapter 3 (The modular forms $\eta(\tau)$ and $\vartheta(\tau)$): The partition function $p(n)$, its generating function and the latter's relation to Dedekind's η-function, many classical identities due to Jacobi and to Euler (including the "pentagonal number theorem", not identified by this name), transformation formulae for theta-functions and for $\eta(\tau)$ (by use of Poisson's summation formula), modular properties of $\eta(\tau)$, definition of $\vartheta(\tau)$, $\{\vartheta(\tau)\}^s$ as a generating function of $r_s(n)$ (=number of representations of n as a sum of s squares), representation of $\vartheta(\tau)$ by $\eta(\tau)$, transformation formula for $\vartheta(\tau)$. Chapter 4 (The multiplier systems v_η and v_ϑ): Short historic sketch, elementary number theory (Legendre and Jacobi symbols, quadratic reciprocity), statement and verification of the theorems concerning v_η and v_ϑ. Chapter 5 (Sums of squares): Classical (Hardy and Littlewood) definitions and theorems for $s\geqq 5$ (in particular, for $5\leqq s\leqq 8$), with a short statement of P. T. Bateman's results for $s=3$ and $s=4$, Lipschitz' summation formula, Eisenstein series (carefully handled, but not identified as such). Chapter 6 (The order of magnitude of $p(n)$): A (fairly elementary) proof that $\log p(n)<\pi\nu\sqrt{n}$, followed by a proof (using the "circle method") that $p(n)=(4\sqrt{3})^{-1}(e^{\pi\nu m}/m^2)(1-(\pi\nu m)^{-1})+O(e^{\pi\nu m/2})$ $(\nu=\sqrt{(2/3)}$, $m^2=n-1/24)$. Chapter 7 (The Ramanujan congruences for $p(n)$): Statement of the congruences, bibliography of pertinent papers, definitions and study of $\Phi_{p,r}(\tau)=\{\eta(p\tau)/\eta(\tau)\}^r$, $h_p(\tau)=\eta(p^2\tau)/\eta(\tau)$, and

$$S_{p,r}(\tau) = \sum_{k=0}^{p-1} h_p{}^r(W^{-pk}\tau)(W\tau=\tau/(\tau+1));$$

Gaussian sums, modular equations; also Newman's proof that $p(11m+6)\equiv 0 \pmod{11}$. Chapter 8 (Proof of Ramanujan's conjectures for powers of 5 and 7): Atkin's version of Watson's proof of Ramanujan's quoted conjectures and some identities of Ramanujan.

It may be legitimate to ask the question: How many people are interested in just the four functions $\eta(\tau)$, $\vartheta(\tau)$, $p(n)$ and $r_s(n)$? One also can make the point that much of the theory of modular functions (but not all of it!) can be discussed with only moderate extra effort in the broader context of automorphic functions. On the other hand, if one accepts the self-imposed limitations of the author, one can enjoy a beautiful presentation of the topics considered.

The book is short (less than 150 pages) and fairly self-contained. It is accessible to readers familiar with real and complex variables as usually presented in first year graduate courses and appears suitable as a text for either a one, or (according to the mathematical maturity of the audience) a two-semester course in analytic number theory; however, it should be mentioned that it contains no problems, or exercises.

The author makes no claims to originality and, in fact, the book contains little that is new. Yet, many classical results are presented in an original setting and some fairly recent results are included. This is also, presumably, the first book, where the term "degree (of a form)" is used instead of the classical term "dimension". As an example of a new presentation (amounting, in fact, to an original contribution) one may quote Theorem 2 of Chapter 1, which gives a unified treatment of the Hecke groups $\tau'=\tau+\lambda$, $\tau'=-\tau^{-1}$ for $\lambda=\sqrt{n}$ $(1\leqq n\leqq 4,\ n\in\mathbf{Z})$. As an example of recent work included, one may quote Atkin's work concerning the Ramanujan conjectures in Chapter 8. The main merit of the book, however, is to be found neither in the originality of the material, nor in that of the presentation, but rather in the fact that here one finds a systematic, self-contained and very well written exposition of a beautiful chapter of analytic number theory, covering a material that until now had to be gleaned from a large number of different books and research papers. Theorems too far removed from the central theme of the book (e.g., the quadratic reciprocity law, or Lebesgue's dominated convergence theorem) are only stated (with precise references where proofs may be found); all other statements are very carefully proven. The printing is good, and no really annoying typographical errors seem to occur. This reviewer will abstain from making extensive critical remarks, because most would be very minor and would refer mainly to matters of taste (such as selection of material, topics omitted, the choice of one proof, rather than another, occasional omissions from the index, occasional paucity of historic remarks (Dedekind's name is never associated with Dedekind's η-function, or Hecke's with Hecke groups), etc.), or to unimportant imperfections (e.g., the inverted z^m, which does not belong there, on p. 39, right over the title to Section 3). All told, this is a very pleasing addition to the bookshelf of a number theorist.

E. Grosswald (Philadelphia, Pa.)

F05 THE MODULAR GROUP SL(2, Z) AND ITS SUBGROUPS: STRUCTURE, AND ACTION ON THE UPPER HALF-PLANE

For the unimodular group over algebraic number fields, etc., see **F15**. For SL(n, Z) and other linear algebraic groups, see **E56** ***ff.*** and **F45** ***ff.***

See also reviews E24-83, E56-48, E60-51, F10-70, F10-120, F70-3, F70-17, J02-8, J04-14, J04-29, J28-15, J28-27, J56-23, J64-2.

F05-1 **(12, 160a)**

Nielsen, Jakob. A study concerning the congruence subgroups of the modular group. Danske Vid. Selsk. Mat.-Fys. Medd. **25**, no. 18, 32 pp. (1950).

The author presents a method of determining a system of generators and relations for the principal congruence subgroup modulo q of the full modular group. Here q is a prime >5 subject to the restriction that $r=\frac{1}{2}(q-1)$ is the least positive exponent for which $2^r\equiv\pm 1 \pmod q$. His method is based on the fact that the fundamental region of a subgroup of the modular group (of finite index) is a polygon bounded by straight lines and circular arcs which are pairwise congruent under certain substitutions of the subgroup; these substitutions constitute a system of generators.

The author starts with a set of $r(q+1)$ q-sided polygons, which he combines into a two-dimensional closed orientable manifold Φ by introducing certain identifications of the sides based on the arithmetic of the moduli q and r. He then finds a set of generators and relations for the fundamental group G of Φ. Now let F be the abstract group on the letters S, T with the relations (1) $S^q=1$, $T^2=1$, $(ST)^3=1$, and H the normal subgroup generated by certain elements $\{k\}$ of F. Then H is shown to be isomorphic to G, and a system of generators of H is obtained from those of G. The isomorphism is demonstrated by realizing H as a group of non-Euclidean motions in the plane which generate the universal covering surface of Φ. The final step is to identify S with $\begin{pmatrix}1 & 1\\ 0 & 1\end{pmatrix}$, T with $\begin{pmatrix}0 & -1\\ 1 & 0\end{pmatrix}$, and consider the elements of the matrices modulo q. The set of matrices $\begin{pmatrix}a & b\\ c & d\end{pmatrix}\equiv\begin{pmatrix}\pm 1 & 0\\ 0 & \pm 1\end{pmatrix}$ (mod q) is by definition C, the principal congruence subgroup modulo q. The author now translates the abstract groups F, H, F/H into groups of matrices through the above identifications and, by using elementary group-theoretic devices, arrives at the following result. The set of matrices $\{mS^q m^{-1}\}$ and $\{k\}$ constitute a system of generators for C, where m runs over a finite set of mutually incongruent matrices modulo q, and $\{k\}$ are the generators of H expressed as matrices. The relations among the generators are obtained from (1) and the relations among the $\{k\}$ in H, and this system of relations is capable of further reduction which, however, the author does not attempt. The author points out that most of his results were obtained previously by Frasch [Math. Ann. **108**, 229–252 (1933)], who used the group-theoretic method of Reidemeister and Schreier. *J. Lehner* (Philadelphia, Pa.).

F05-2 (12, 591c)

Grosswald, Emil. On the structure of some subgroups of the modular group. Amer. J. Math. **72**, 809–834 (1950).

In the group of modular substitutions under consideration the elements are square matrices of 4 elements of determinant unity. The subgroups are defined by imposing suitable supplementary conditions on the above 4 elements. These supplementary conditions are: 1 element zero, 2 elements zero, 2 elements zero and at the same time the other elements unity. Thus 4 subgroups are arrived at which it is the purpose of this paper to study. The main results of the paper are: The subgroups mentioned in the second place are generated by a number of independent generators of which the explicit form is found. A number of properties of these generators are given. If the modulus is 2, both independent generators are parabolic. If the modulus is 3 or more, 3 of the independent generators are parabolic. If the modulus is 2 or more, the genus of a fundamental region corresponding to the subgroups is zero. If the modulus is more than 3 the genus of the fundamental region is given by a simple equation. Finally, some relations between the principal subgroup and the above subgroups are stated.

M. J. O. Strutt (Zurich).

Referred to in E56-18.

F05-3 (14, 250c)

Grosswald, Emil. On the genus of the fundamental region. of some subgroups of the modular group. Amer. J. Math. **74**, 86–88 (1952).

Let Γ be the group of modular transformations. Each element corresponds to matrices $M=\pm\left(\begin{smallmatrix}a & b\\ c & d\end{smallmatrix}\right)$, where a, b, c, and d are integers satisfying $ad-bc=1$. Let p be a prime >3. Let $\Gamma_0(p)$ be the subgroup of Γ satisfying $c\equiv 0$ (mod p); and $\Gamma_0{}^0(p)$ be the subgroup of $\Gamma_0(p)$ with $b\equiv 0$ (mod p) and $\Gamma(p)$ be the subgroup of $\Gamma_0{}^0(p)$ with $a\equiv d\equiv 1$ (mod p). The author proves by a uniformizing method that the genera of $\Gamma_0(p)$, $\Gamma_0{}^0(p)$, and $\Gamma(p)$ are $[p/12]-\frac{1}{4}\{(-1/p)+(-3/p)\}$,

$$[(p+2)(p-1)/12]-1-\tfrac{1}{4}\{(-1/p)+(-3/p)\},$$

and $(p^2-1)(p-6)/24+1$, respectively. The method depends essentially on the existence of a fundamental region corresponding to the generators used, but the author does not explain this fact clearly. *L. K. Hua* (Peking).

F05-4 (14, 250d)

Grosswald, Emil. On the parabolic generators of the principal congruence subgroups of the modular group. Amer. J. Math. **74**, 435–443 (1952).

Frasch [Math. Ann. **108**, 229–252 (1933)] has shown that the congruence modular group $\Gamma(p)$, where p is a prime, is generated by $\tau'=\tau+p$ and $(p-1)p(p+1)/12$ other generators. The author proves that, except $\tau'=\tau+p$, the other generators can be so chosen that none of them is parabolic, for p being a prime satisfying a certain condition. The condition is related to the primitive roots of p. It is conjectured by the author that the condition is always true, but the best known result due to Hua [Bull. Amer. Math. Soc. **48**, 726–730 (1942); these Rev. **4**, 130] is not enough for the present purpose. *L. K. Hua* (Peking).

Citations: MR 4, 130d = N76-1.

F05-5 (15, 291a)

Petersson, Hans. Über einen einfachen Typus von Untergruppen der Modulgruppe. Arch. Math. **4**, 308–315 (1953).

Associated with the fundamental region of any sub-group Γ' of the modular group Γ are certain invariants: the genus p, the number σ of non-equivalent parabolic fixed-points, and the numbers e_2 and e_3 which count the number of non-equivalent elliptic fixed-points of orders 2 and 3, respectively. These integers are related to the index of Γ' relative to Γ by the formula $\mu=12(p-1)+6\sigma+3e_2+4e_3$. The sub-groups mentioned in the title of this paper are those with $\sigma=1$ and these the author calls cycloidal sub-groups of Γ. The usual congruence sub-groups employed in the theory of elliptic modular functions have $\sigma\geqq 2$ and are therefore not cycloidal. A theorem of Walburga Rohde is quoted to the effect that when the genus $p=0$, then for every integer $\mu\geqq 1$ there exist several pair-wise non-isomorphic cycloidal sub-groups of Γ which have the same index μ. The author exhibits three cycloidal sub-groups of index $\mu=6$ which are pair-wise non-isomorphic and which correspond to the following values of the invariants: $p=e_2=0$, $e_3=3$; $p=e_3=0$, $e_2=4$; $p=1$, $e_2=e_3=0$. The construction of cycloidal sub-groups is discussed and the following theorem is proved: If Z and Z' are cycloidal sub-groups of Γ with relatively prime indices μ and μ', then $Z\cap Z'$ is a cycloidal sub-group of Γ with index $\mu\mu'$. *T. M. Apostol* (Pasadena, Calif.).

Referred to in F05-49.

F05-6 (15, 863h)

Rankin, R. A. On horocyclic groups. Proc. London Math. Soc. (3) **4**, 219–234 (1954).

Let $\bar{\Gamma}$ be a group of 2×2 matrices $T=\begin{pmatrix}a & b\\ c & d\end{pmatrix}$ with complex coefficients satisfying $ad-bc=1$, let Γ denote the corresponding inhomogeneous group; in particular, let $\Gamma(1)$ stand for the full modular group and $\Gamma(N)$ for the principal congruence subgroup (mod N). If $\bar{\Gamma}$ is properly discontinuous and leaves some circle $\mathfrak{S}$ invariant, $\bar{\Gamma}$ (or Γ) is called Fuchsian. If $\mathfrak{S}$ is identical with the set of limit points of the centers of the isometric circles, the Fuchsian group Γ is said to be of the first kind, otherwise of the second kind; the author uses the term "horocyclic" for Fuchsian groups of the first kind. In the particular case when Γ contains parabolic substitutions there is no loss in generality in taking ∞ as a parabolic point and $\mathfrak{S}$ as the real axis. Such a group is called zonal horocyclic; it has (some of its) fundamental regions $D(\Gamma)$ bounded by two vertical semi-infinite bounding lines and a (finite, or infinite) number of bounding arcs. The non-Euclidean area of $D(\Gamma)$ is defined by $J(\Gamma)=\iint_{D(\Gamma)}y^{-2}dxdy$; $J(\Gamma)$ is an invariant of the group and is finite if and only if $D(\Gamma)$ is bounded by a finite number N of bounding arcs [see Tsuji, Jap. J. Math. **21**, 1–27 (1952); these Rev. **14**, 968]. If N_1 is the number of cusps and N_2 the number of vertices of $D(\Gamma)$, then $N=N_1+N_2$. Using Ford's method of isometric circles [Automorphic functions, McGraw-Hill, New York, 1929] and results of Petersson [Math. Ann. **115**, 23–67 (1937)] and Poincaré [Acta Math. **3**, 49–92 (1893)], the author proves the identity of the horocyclic groups with the "Grenzkreisgruppen", as defined by Petersson [loc. cit.]. Furthermore, if Γ^* is Fuchsian and Γ is a subgroup of finite index μ of Γ^*, then Γ is Fuchsian and of the same kind as Γ^*. If Γ^* is a zonal horocyclic group, then $D(\Gamma)$ has a finite, or infinite number of sides, according as $D(\Gamma^*)$ has. The inequalities $N\pi \geqq J(\Gamma) \geqq N_1\pi + N_2\pi/3 \geqq (N_1+N_2)\pi/3 = N\pi/3$ are established and used to prove that

$$\mu\pi^{-1}J(\Gamma^*) \leqq N \leqq 3\mu\pi^{-1}J(\Gamma^*) \leqq 3\mu N^*,$$

where N^* and N are the number of arcs of isometric circles bounding $D(\Gamma^*)$ and $D(\Gamma)$, respectively. In particular, if $\Gamma^* = \Gamma(1)$, then $J(\Gamma^*) = \pi/3$ and $\mu/3 \leqq N \leqq \mu$; if $\Gamma^* \neq \Gamma(1)$, $J(\Gamma^*) > \pi/3$. An upper bound is established for the radii of the isometric circles bounding $D(\Gamma)$, where Γ is a subgroup of $\Gamma(1)$; for $\Gamma = \Gamma(N)$ the bound takes the simple form $|c| \leqq N^3(N+1)^{\frac{1}{2}}(N+2)^2/8$. *E. Grosswald.*

Referred to in F05-51.

F05-7 (16, 678a)

Rankin, R. A. Chebyshev polynomials and the modulary group of level p. Math. Scand. **2**, 315–326 (1954).

Define

$$T_n(x) = \cosh n\theta, \quad F_n(x) = \sinh n\theta/\sinh\theta,$$

where $x = \cosh\theta$. For p an odd prime let $\bar{G}(p)$ denote the group $\bar{\Gamma}(1)/\bar{\Gamma}(n)$, where $\bar{\Gamma}(1)$ is the full inhomogeneous modular group and $\bar{\Gamma}(n)$ is the inhomogeneous principal congruence group of level n, where n is a positive integer. Put $q = \frac{1}{2}(p-1)$, $r = \frac{1}{2}(p+1)$. Then the order of every element of $\bar{G}(p)$ other than the identity is either p or a divisor of q or r. The subgroups of order p or q are easily described. The main purpose of the present paper is to discuss the subgroups of order r by means of properties of $T_n(x)$ and $F_n(x)$. At the same time a number of congruence properties of these polynomials are obtained. If x is an integer, define the order n_x as the least positive n such that $F_n(x) \equiv 0 \pmod p$. It is proved that for any x, exactly one of the congruences $F_p(x) \equiv 0$, $F_q(x) \equiv 0$, $F_r(x) \equiv 0 \pmod p$ holds; the corresponding classes of residues are denoted by C_p, C_q, C_r, respectively. Then, for example, x is a generator of C_t, $t > 1$, if and only if it is of order t and $T_t(x) \equiv -1$; also if x is a generator of C_t, $t > 1$, then $T_{t+n}(x) \equiv -T_n(x)$, $F_{t\pm n}(x) \equiv \pm F_n(x)$. It is also proved that if $\xi \in \bar{G}(p)$, $p \neq 2$, $\xi \neq$ identity, and S is any matrix representing ξ, then the order of ξ is the same as the order of x, where $2x = \operatorname{tr} S$.

L. Carlitz (Durham, N. C.).

F05-8 (16, 801f)

Newman, Morris. Structure theorems for modular subgroups. Duke Math. J. **22**, 25–32 (1955).

Let $G_0(n)$ (for any positive integer n) be the group of all modular matrices $\begin{pmatrix}\alpha & \beta\\ \gamma & \delta\end{pmatrix}$ (where α, β, γ, δ are integers, $\alpha\delta - \beta\gamma = 1$) such that $\gamma \equiv 0 \pmod n$. The author shows that any subgroup of $G_0(n)$ which contains $G_0(mn)$ is a group $G_0(dn)$, where d divides m. He also proves: Let G_1 and G_2 be groups of modular matrices, $G_1 \subset G_2$ of finite index, and let F_1 and F_2 be the corresponding fields of modular functions. Suppose that G_2 is of genus zero so that F_2 is a simple transcendental extension $C(a)$ of the field of complex numbers. Then if b is an element of F_1 which is not invariant under any larger subgroup than G_1, we have $F_1 = F_2(b) = C(a, b)$. From these theorems he derives a number of special results of which the following is typical: If $J(\tau)$ is the modular invariant, the field of modular functions belonging to $G_0(n)$ is generated by $J(\tau)$ and $J(n\tau)$ over C.

H. D. Kloosterman (Leiden).

Referred to in F15-8, F15-9.

F05-9 (17, 824f)

Brenner, Joël Lee. Quelques groupes libres de matrices. C. R. Acad. Sci. Paris **241** (1955), 1689–1691.

The author proves that the group generated by the two matrices

$$A = \begin{pmatrix}1 & m\\ 0 & 1\end{pmatrix} \text{ and } B = \begin{pmatrix}1 & 0\\ m & 1\end{pmatrix}$$

is a free group for all real $m \geqq 2$. The elements of the group are, of course, of the form

$$M = \begin{pmatrix}1+k_{11}m^2 & k_{12}m\\ k_{21}m & 1+k_{22}m^2\end{pmatrix} = \begin{pmatrix}a_{11} & a_{12}\\ a_{21} & a_{22}\end{pmatrix}$$

with integers k_{ij} and determinant 1. The case when $m = 2$ has been treated by Sanov [Doklady Akad. Nauk SSSR (N.S.) **57** (1947), 657–659; MR **9**, 224] who showed that, conversely, every matrix of the form M belongs to the group. In the general case this is no longer true. The additional condition to be satisfied by a matrix M to belong to the group is that the ratio $|a_{11}/a_{12}|$ should not lie between the roots of the equation $x^2 - mx + 1 = 0$. For $m = 1$ the group in question is the full unimodular group with integer coefficients and is, therefore, not free. There is an infinity of values m between 0 and 2 for which the group is not free. The interesting question arises, therefore, whether there is an algebraic number m, $0 < m < 2$, for which the group turns out to be free. *K. A. Hirsch.*

F05-10 (17, 845j)

Szász, Pál. On the geometrical interpretation of the modular group. Magyar Tud. Akad. Mat. Fiz. Oszt. Közl. **5** (1955), 1–12. (Hungarian)

The author gives an original geometrical construction for the modular dissection of the upper half-plane [cf. E. T. Copson, Theory of functions of a complex variable, Oxford, 1935, Ch. 15]. Starting with two circles touching each other and the real axis, a construction is given for two more circles to touch the first two and the real axis, and so on; the semi-circles joining the points of contact on the real axis give a network of curvilinear triangles, of which we are to consider the "altitudes". Next studied is the interpretation of a modular substitution, put into continued-fraction form, in terms of this diagram, enabling the author to give an elementary proof that regions congruent to a fundamental region fill the half-plane. *F. V. Atkinson* (Canberra).

F05-11 (18, 11c)

Newman, Morris. The normalizer of certain modular subgroups. Canad. J. Math. **8** (1956), 29–31.

Let G be the modular group (of all matrices $\begin{pmatrix}a & b\\ c & d\end{pmatrix}$ with integers a, b, c, d such that $ad - bc = 1$) and $G_0(n)$ its subgroup characterized by $c \equiv 0 \pmod n$, where n is a positive integer. Writing $n = 2^\alpha 3^\beta n_0$, where $(n_0, 6) = 1$, the author proves that the normalizer of $G_0(n)$ in G is $G_0(n/2^u 3^v)$, where

$$u = \min(3, [\tfrac{1}{2}\alpha]), \quad v = \min(1, [\tfrac{1}{2}\beta]).$$

{The author's proof of this elementary theorem can be considerably simplified.} *H. D. Kloosterman* (Leiden).

F05-12 (18, 11d)

Newman, Morris. An alternative proof of a theorem on unimodular groups. Proc. Amer. Math. Soc. **6** (1955), 998–1000.

The theorem in question is: Let G be the full modular group (of matrices $\begin{pmatrix}a & b\\ c & d\end{pmatrix}$ with integers a, b, c, d such that $ad - bc = 1$) and $G_0(n)$ its subgroup characterized by

$c \equiv 0 \pmod n$, where n is a positive integer. Then any subgroup H of G containing $G_0(n)$ is of type $H = G_0(m)$, where $m|n$. *H. D. Kloosterman* (Leiden).

F05-13 **(19, 123b)**

Goldberg, Karl. Unimodular matrices of order 2 that commute. J. Washington Acad. Sci. **46** (1956), 337–338.

It is proved that every abelian subgroup of the modular group is cyclic. The method of proof consists in transforming the unimodular 2×2 matrices of rational integers to canonical form by a similarity. The eigenvalues of such matrices are units in quadratic fields and the known structure of the group of units in such fields yields the result. [For other proofs and generalizations see the paper reviewed below.] *O. Taussky-Todd.*

Referred to in F05-16.

F05-14 **(19, 123c)**

Taussky, Olga; and Todd, John. Commuting bilinear transformations and matrices. J. Washington Acad. Sci. **46** (1956), 373–375 (1957).

Another proof is given of the following theorem, proved in the paper reviewed above. A necessary and sufficient condition that two transformations of the type

$$w = (az+b)/(cz+d),$$

a, b, c, d rational integers, $ad-bc=1$, commute is that each is the iterate of the same transformation of this type. This theorem is extended to cover the case in which a, b, c, d are integers in a complex quadratic field F with determinant equal to a unit in F. This generalization is not immediate and in fact is subject to the following two provisos. The matrices of neither of the two transformations may be similar to $\zeta\begin{pmatrix}1 & 1\\ 0 & 1\end{pmatrix}$, where ζ is a root of unity in F, and the characteristic roots of neither matrix may be in the cyclotomic field generated by a primitive 8th or 12th root of unity. For example, the two matrices with Gaussian integer elements

$$\begin{pmatrix}0 & 1\\ 1 & -i\end{pmatrix} \text{ and } \begin{pmatrix}2+i & 2\\ 2 & 2-i\end{pmatrix}$$

commute and yet they are not powers of the same matrix. *D. H. Lehmer* (Berkeley, Calif.).

Referred to in F05-16.

F05-15 **(20# 2379)**

Reiner, Irving. Normal subgroups of the unimodular group. Illinois J. Math. **2** (1958), 142–144.

Let Γ be the proper unimodular group of 2×2 matrices (with rational integral entries). The author finds a large number of normal subgroups $\Omega(s, p)$ of Γ which have finite index, yet which contain no congruence subgroup $\Gamma(m) \equiv \{A \mid A \equiv I \bmod m\}$. Let f be the natural mapping of $\Gamma(p)$ onto $\Delta(p) = \Gamma(p)/\Gamma'(p)$. Set $\Delta^s(p) \equiv \{X^s \mid X \in \Delta(p)\}$. Then $\Omega(s, p)$ is $f^{-1}\{\Delta^s(p)\}$. Fricke [Math. Ann. **28** (1887), 99–118] and Pick [ibid. 119–124] defined $\Omega(2, p)$. *J. L. Brenner* (Palo Alto, Calif.)

Referred to in F05-32, F05-43.

F05-16 **(20# 5238)**

Coxeter, H. S. M. On subgroups of the modular group. J. Math. Pures Appl. (9) **37** (1958), 317–319.

The theorem due to K. Goldberg [J. Washington Acad. Sci. **46** (1956), 337–338; MR **19**, 123] that every abelian subgroup of the modular group is cyclic is reproved here by geometric arguments, namely by representing the displacements in the hyperbolic plane by elements of the modular group. {Another proof of the same theorem using abstract group theory appeared in the meantime [see A. Karrass and D. Solitar, Proc. Amer. Math. Soc. **9** (1958), 217–221; MR **20** #2373]. For generalizations see O. Taussky and J. Todd [J. Washington Acad. Sci. **46** (1956), 373–375; MR **19**, 123] and E. C. Dade [Illinois J. Math. **3** (1959), 11–27; MR **20** #6463].} *O. Taussky-Todd* (Pasadena, Calif.)

Citations: MR 19, 123b = F05-13; MR 19, 123c = F05-14; MR 20# 6463 = F15-13.

F05-17 **(21# 1350)**

Wohlfahrt, Klaus. Über Dedekindsche Summen und Untergruppen der Modulgruppe. Abh. Math. Sem. Univ. Hamburg **23** (1959), 5–10.

In this paper the author constructs subgroups of the modular group of finite index which are not congruence groups.

Let $\Gamma_0(n)$ be the subgroup of the full modular group Γ for which $\gamma \equiv 0 \pmod n$. With the help of Dedekind's multiplicator system for the modular group, the author defines a character χ on $\Gamma_0(n)$. If $L = \begin{pmatrix}\alpha & \beta\\ \gamma & \delta\end{pmatrix}$, then using the reciprocity law for Dedekind Sums, he deduces

$$\chi(L) = \exp\frac{\pi i r}{6}\cdot\frac{(n-1)(\beta+\gamma n^{-1})+2\{\gamma n^{-1}, \delta\}-2\{\gamma, \delta\}}{\delta},$$

where $\{j, h\} = 6|h|s(j, h)$, and r is arbitrary. He then proves the following theorem: The kernel Δ of χ with n a prime p, $r = 12/q$ (q a prime), $p^2 \not\equiv 0,1 \pmod q$) is not a congruence subgroup of the modular group. *R. Ayoub* (State College, Pa.)

F05-18 **(22# 11042)**

Reiner, Irving. Subgroups of the unimodular group. Proc. Amer. Math. Soc. **12** (1961), 173–174.

The congruence group $\Gamma(m)$ (for the modulus m) is the set of all 2×2 properly unimodular matrices which are congruent to the identity modulo m; $\Gamma(m)$ is a normal subgroup of $\Gamma \equiv \Gamma(1)$. It is known that Γ contains normal subgroups which do not contain any congruence group. The author proves, in particular, that the least normal subgroup of Γ which contains $\begin{bmatrix}1 & 6\\ 0 & 1\end{bmatrix}$ contains no congruence group; the same conclusion is valid if 6 is replaced by any integer which is not a prime power. The cases 2, 3, 4, 5 are special, as shown by the reviewer [Ann. of Math. (2) **71** (1960), 210–223; MR **22** #1622]. *J. L. Brenner* (Pala Alto, Calif.)

Citations: MR 22# 1622 = E56-19.

Referred to in F05-22.

F05-19 **(23# A3121)**

Roelcke, Walter

Über die Verteilung der zweiten Zeilen der Matrizen gewisser Grenzkreisgruppen.

Math. Ann. **141** (1960), 367–376.

Let Γ be a horocyclic group of the first kind containing the negative unit matrix $-I$ and possessing a Lebesgue-measurable fundamental region $\mathfrak{F}$ in the upper half-plane with finite hyperbolic area $F > 0$. Let A and B be real 2×2 matrices of determinant 1 such that $A^{-1}\infty$ is a parabolic cusp of Γ, and denote by $\mathfrak{G}(A, \Gamma, B)$ the set of second rows of matrices in $A\Gamma B$. Each such second row determines a vector $\mathfrak{a} \in R^2$, which is metrised by a positive definite quadratic form Q of determinant 1. $\mathfrak{E}_Q$ is the set of vectors $\mathfrak{a} \in R^2$ that have length 1 and determines an ellipse centred at the origin. A permissible angle space $\mathfrak{R}$ in R^2 is a set of non-zero vectors $\mathfrak{a} \in \mathfrak{R}$ such that $t\mathfrak{a} \in \mathfrak{R}$ for all $t > 0$ and such that $\mathfrak{E}_Q \cap \mathfrak{R}$ is Riemann-measurable; its measure is denoted by $\mu_Q(\mathfrak{R})$. For any $X \geqq 0$, $N(X)$ is the number of $\mathfrak{a} \in \mathfrak{G}(A, \Gamma, B) \cap \mathfrak{R}$ with $\mathfrak{a}Q\mathfrak{a}' \leqq X^2$. It is proved that

$$N(X) \sim \frac{\mu_Q(\mathfrak{R})}{\pi F} X^2$$

as $X \to \infty$, and a second result of a similar kind is deduced.

R. A. Rankin (Glasgow)

F05-20 (25# 4001)

Newman, Morris

The structure of some subgroups of the modular group.

Illinois J. Math. **6** (1962), 480–487.

Let Γ be the 2×2 modular group and let Δ be a subgroup of Γ. If the exponents of

$$\begin{pmatrix}1 & 1\\ 0 & 1\end{pmatrix} \text{ and } \begin{pmatrix}1 & 0\\ 1 & 1\end{pmatrix}$$

modulo Δ are r and s, respectively, then Δ is of type (r, s). If Δ is of finite index in Γ, then $rs \neq 0$; moreover, $\Delta \supset \Gamma^m$, the fully invariant subgroup of Γ generated by the mth powers of the elements of Γ, for some positive integer m. The question is raised whether Δ is of finite index if it contains such a subgroup. It suffices to consider only $\Delta = \Gamma^m$. It is proved that the answer is negative; the proof makes use of recent results of Novikov [Dokl. Akad. Nauk SSSR **127** (1959), 749–752; MR **21** #5680] on the Burnside problem.

Let Γ^1 denote the commutator subgroup of Γ. It is proved that

$$\Gamma^1 = \Gamma^2 \cap \Gamma^3.$$

The groups Γ^{6m} are free groups. The group Γ^6 is just $\Gamma^1(6, 6)$, so that Γ^6 is of index 216 in Γ and is the free group on 37 generators. *L. Carlitz* (Durham, N.C.)

Referred to in F05-24.

F05-21 (25# 5041)

McQuillan, Donald L.

A generalization of a theorem of Hecke.

Amer. J. Math. **84** (1962), 306–316.

The author generalizes a formula of Hecke [Abh. Math. Sem. Univ. Hamburg **6** (1928), 235–257; ibid. **8** (1930), 271–281] on characters of the modulary group of prime level p, $p \equiv 3 \pmod 4$ to modulary groups of level n, where $-n$ is an odd fundamental discriminant. The case $-n$ of an even fundamental discriminant is treated in his dissertation [Ph.D. thesis, Johns Hopkins University, Baltimore, Md., 1961]. The method of proof is algebraic, depending on the Riemann-Roch theorem. In the case of prime level p the character decomposes into two simple complex conjugate characters the difference of whose multiplicities is $h(-p)$, the class number of $R(\sqrt{-p})$. In the generalization proved by the author a certain alternating sum of multiplicities of simple characters equals $2^{t-1}h(-n)$, t the number of primes dividing n.

{One remark: The author's Lemma 1 proved for n odd and square-free has the following easy generalization. The number of sets of integers a, b, c, d modulo n such that $ad - bc \equiv 1 \pmod n$ and $(c, n) = r$ is just $n^2\varphi(r)\varphi(n/r)/r$.}

M. Newman (Washington, D.C.)

F05-22 (26# 230)

Knopp, Marvin Isadore

A note on subgroups of the modular group.

Proc. Amer. Math. Soc. **14** (1963), 95–97.

Let Γ be the modular group and denote by $\Gamma(m)$ the principal congruence subgroup of level m, i.e., the set of matrices $\begin{pmatrix}a & b\\ c & d\end{pmatrix}$, with rational integral entries satisfying $ad - bc = 1$, $a \equiv d \equiv \pm 1 \pmod m$, $b \equiv c \equiv 0 \pmod m$. Set $T_m = \begin{pmatrix}1 & m\\ 0 & 1\end{pmatrix}$ and denote by $\Delta(m)$ the smallest normal subgroup of Γ containing T_m. Then $\Delta(m) \subset \Gamma(m)$ and, for small m, $\Delta(m) = \Gamma(m)$. Brenner [Ann. of Math. (2) **71** (1960), 210–223; MR **22** #1622] asked and Reiner [Proc. Amer. Math. Soc. **12** (1961), 173–174; MR **22** #11042] answered negatively the questions: (a) Does $\Delta(m) = \Gamma(m)$ hold for all m? and (b) Given m, can one always find an integer k such that $\Delta(m) \supset \Gamma(mk)$? The present paper proves the stronger theorem: $\Delta(m) = \Gamma(m)$ for $1 \leqq m \leqq 5$, while for $m \geqq 6$, $\Delta(m)$ is of infinite index in $\Gamma(m)$ (and hence contains no principal congruence subgroup whatsoever, because these are of finite index in Γ). The theorem follows immediately from two results of Klein and Fricke [*Vorlesungen über die Theorie der elliptischen Modulfunktionen*, Bd. 1, Teubner, Leipzig, 1890–92] and the remark that $\Delta(m)$ is generated by $X^{-1}T_mX$ ($X \in \Gamma$). The paper concludes with a somewhat longer, but particularly elegant, independent proof of the theorem, based on some of the author's previous results [Pacific J. Math. **11** (1961), 661–678; MR **24** #A96], the fact (cf. Klein and Fricke [op. cit.]) that the fundamental region of $\Gamma(m)$ has genus zero if and only if $1 \leqq m \leqq 5$, and the Riemann-Roch theorem. *E. Grosswald* (Philadelphia, Pa.)

Citations: MR 22# 1622 = E56-19; MR 22# 11042 = F05-18; MR 24# A96 = F10-76.

Referred to in F05-32.

F05-23 (26# 231)

Newman, Morris

A note on modular groups.

Proc. Amer. Math. Soc. **14** (1963), 124–125.

Let Γ, $\Gamma(m)$, $\Delta(m)$, G, G' be defined as in the preceding review [#230]. From the paper reviewed above it follows that $m = 6$ is the first integer for which $\Delta(m) \neq \Gamma(m)$. In the present paper it is shown that $\Delta(6)$ is an interesting group; in particular, $\Delta(6) = \Gamma''$, the second commutator subgroup of Γ. The proof is short and is based on two lemmas: (1) If the group G is generated by two elements α, β and if N is any normal subgroup containing $\alpha\beta\alpha^{-1}\beta^{-1}$, then $G' \subset N$; (2) Γ' is a free group of rank 2, generated by $\alpha = \begin{pmatrix}2 & 1\\ 1 & 1\end{pmatrix}$, $\beta = \begin{pmatrix}2 & -1\\ -1 & 1\end{pmatrix}$ with $\alpha\beta\alpha^{-1}\beta^{-1} = \begin{pmatrix}1 & 6\\ 0 & 1\end{pmatrix}$. *E. Grosswald* (Philadelphia, Pa.)

F05-24 (26# 1366)

Newman, M.; Smart, J. R.

Note on a subgroup of the modular group.

Proc. Amer. Math. Soc. **14** (1963), 102–104.

Let Γ be the modular group, and let $\Gamma(n)$ be the principal congruence subgroup of Γ of level n, i.e., the set of matrices $\begin{pmatrix}a & b\\ c & d\end{pmatrix}$ with a, b, c, d rational integers satisfying $ad - bc = 1$, $b \equiv c \equiv 0 \pmod n$, $a \equiv d \equiv \pm 1 \pmod n$. Denote by Γ^n the subgroup of Γ generated by the nth powers of the elements of Γ, by G any subgroup of Γ, and by G' the commutator subgroup of G. It is known [Smart, Thesis, Michigan State Univ., East Lansing, Mich., 1961] that $(\Gamma^2)' \supset \Gamma(6)$, and one may similarly show that $(\Gamma^3)' \supset \Gamma(6)$; hence, $(\Gamma^2)' \cap (\Gamma^3)' \supset \Gamma(6)$. In the present paper the authors prove that one actually has $(\Gamma^2)' \cap (\Gamma^3)' = \Gamma(6)$. The proof uses results of Nielsen [Mat. Tidsskr. B **1948**, 49–56; MR **10**, 590], Schreier [Abh. Math. Sem. Hamburg Univ. **5** (1926/27), 161–183] and of the first author [Illinois J. Math. **6** (1962), 480–487; MR **25** #4001], together with the classical isomorphism theorems.

E. Grosswald (Philadelphia, Pa.)

Citations: MR 25# 4001 = F05-20.

F05-25 **(26# 6233)**

Suprunenko, D. A.

On the order of an element of a group of integral matrices. **(Russian)**

Dokl. Akad. Nauk BSSR **7** (1963), 221–223.

Es sei k eine natürliche Zahl mit der kanonischen Zerlegung $k=q_1^{\alpha_1}q_2^{\alpha_2}\cdots q_s^{\alpha_s}$. Gilt für $j=1, \cdots, s$ die Ungleichung $q_j^{\alpha_j}>2$, so werde $\rho(k)=\sum_{j=1}^{s}\varphi(q_j^{\alpha_j})$ gesetzt, wobei φ die Eulersche Funktion bedeutet. Ist dagegen $q_1^{\alpha_1}=2$, so sei $\rho(k)=\sum_{j=2}^{s}\varphi(q_j^{\alpha_j})$. Mit Γ_n wird die Gruppe aller (n, n)-Matrizen aus ganzen rationalen Zahlen mit den Determinanten ± 1 bezeichnet. Es wird bewiesen: Dann und nur dann enthält Γ_n ein Element der endlichen Ordnung k, wenn $\rho(k)\leqq n$. Daraus ergibt sich insbesondere das bekannte Resultat, daß in Γ_3 nur die endlichen Ordnungszahlen 1, 2, 3, 4, 6 vorkommen. Ferner gilt stets die (grobe) Abschätzung $k<e^n$. *R. Kochendörffer* (Rostock)

F05-26 **(26# 6264)**

Fell, Harriet; Newman, Morris; Ordman, Edward

Tables of genera of groups of linear fractional transformations.

J. Res. Nat. Bur. Standards Sect. B **67B** (1963), 61–68.

Let Γ be the modular group of 2×2 matrices $A=\begin{pmatrix} a & b\\ c & d\end{pmatrix}$, a, b, c, d rational integers, $ad-bc=1$. Define $\Gamma_0(n)=\{A\in\Gamma \mid c\equiv 0 \pmod n\}$ and $\Gamma^*(n)$ as the smallest group containing $\Gamma_0(n)$ and the matrix $\begin{pmatrix} 0 & -1\\ n & 0\end{pmatrix}$. The upper half-plane taken modulo $\Gamma_0(n)$, or $\Gamma^*(n)$, is called a fundamental region R of the corresponding group; it is possible to take R simply connected. By identification of sides of R one obtains the Riemann surface of functions automorphic under the respective group. The topological genera $g_0(n)$ [or $g^*(n)$, respectively] of these Riemann surfaces may be computed by simple, classical formulae [F. Klein, *Gesammelte mathematische Abhandlungen*, Bd. 3, J. Springer, Berlin, 1923]. The values of $g_0(n)$ and $g^*(n)$, as well as some other characteristic elements of an arithmetic nature of these groups have been tabulated up to $n=1000$, with the help of the IBM 7090 of the NBS.

E. Grosswald (Philadelphia, Pa.)

F05-27 **(27# 210)**

Lehner, Joseph

On the generation of discontinuous groups.

Pacific J. Math. **13** (1963), 169–170.

Generalizing a result of Knopp [same J. **11** (1961), 661–678; MR **24** #A96] the author proves the following theorem: Let Γ be a horocyclic group of genus g. Then Γ possesses a system of generators consisting entirely of parabolic and elliptic elements if and only if $g=0$. The proof that $g=0$ implies the existence of the system of generators without hyperbolic elements is simple, because a classical theorem [Fricke and Klein, *Vorlesungen über die Theorie der automorphen Functionen*, Bd. 1, p. 182, Teubner, Leipzig, 1897] states the existence of a system of generators with exactly $2g$ hyperbolic ones. For the converse, the author shows that if there exists a system of generators without hyperbolic substitutions, then there are no non-trivial abelian differentials of the first kind, so that $g=0$. In the particular case of the principal congruence subgroups of the modular group, Knopp [op. cit.] has shown that they can be generated by parabolic substitutions alone; this is not possible in the general case of horocyclic groups, as the author shows by a counter-example, credited to M. Newman.

E. Grosswald (Philadelphia, Pa.)

Citations: MR 24# A96 = F10-76.

F05-28 **(28# 3081)**

Newman, Morris

Free subgroups and normal subgroups of the modular group.

Illinois J. Math. **8** (1964), 262–265.

The main results of this paper are the following. Theorem 1: Let H be a nontrivial normal subgroup of the modular group Γ and let H be different from Γ, Γ^2, Γ^3. Then H is a free group. Lemma 1: A nontrivial subgroup of Γ is free if and only if it contains no elements of finite period.

These theorems are "easy consequences of the Kuroš subgroup theorem", which states that a nontrivial subgroup H of a free product G is itself a free product; each free factor is either a free group or a conjugate of a subgroup of one of the free factors of G. The modular group is the free product of a cyclic group of order two by one of order three. It is astonishing that these consequences have apparently not been noticed until now. The date of the Kuroš theorem is 1934.

In the remainder of the paper the author develops criteria for the freedom of $\Gamma_0(n)$ defined by $c\equiv 0 \pmod n$ in the matrices $(ab|cd)$ of Γ and of $\Gamma(m, n)$ defined by $b\equiv 0 \pmod m$, $c\equiv 0 \pmod n$. In particular, $\Gamma_0(n)$ is free when $n=12t-1$.

{Reviewer's remark: The results of this paper extend in an obvious way to a subclass of the class of F-groups; these are the finitely presented groups that admit faithful representations as discontinuous (finitely generated) Fuchsian groups. Because of the importance of these results, the desirability of obtaining a simplified proof of the Kuroš theorem is underlined in the case of free products with a finite number of factors.}

J. Lehner (College Park, Md.)

F05-29 **(29# 167)**

Newman, Morris

Normal congruence subgroups of the modular group.

Amer. J. Math. **85** (1963), 419–427; *errata, ibid.* **85** (1963), 753; *addendum, ibid.* **86** (1964), 465.

Let Γ be the inhomogeneous 2×2 modular group, the quotient group $SL(2, \mathbf{Z})/(\pm I)$; and let $\Gamma(n)$ be the subgroup of Γ consisting of all elements of Γ congruent to a scalar matrix modulo n. The principal theorem of the paper is the following: If G is a normal subgroup of Γ such that $\Gamma(mn)\subset G\subset\Gamma(n)$, where $(m, 6)=1$, then $G=\Gamma(nd)$ for some divisor d of m. Calling a subgroup $G\subset\Gamma$ a "congruence subgroup of level m" if m is the least integer such that $\Gamma(m)\subset G$, a corollary of the above theorem is that for $(m, 6)=1$, $\Gamma(m)$ is the only normal congruence subgroup of level m. The restriction $(m, 6)=1$ is essential, as the author shows by examples.

R. C. Gunning (Princeton, N.J.)

Referred to in F05-35.

F05-30 **(29# 1265)**

Newman, Morris

A complete description of the normal subgroups of genus one of the modular group.

Amer. J. Math. **86** (1964), 17–24.

Die Modulgruppe Γ besteht aus allen linear-gebrochenen Abbildungen der oberen Halbebene H mit ganzen Koeffizienten und der Determinante 1 und ist freies Produkt der zyklischen Gruppen $\{x\}$, $\{y\}$,

$$x:\tau\to-\frac{1}{\tau}\qquad y:\tau\to\frac{-1}{\tau+1}.$$

Das Geschlecht eines Normalteilers G von endlichem Index ist das topologische Geschlecht des kompaktifizierten Quotientenraumes H modulo G. Verfasser stellt gruppentheoretische Untersuchungen für die Normalteiler G vom

Geschlecht eins an. Unter Verwendung eines Satzes von Nielsen wird zunächst $\Gamma' \supseteq G \supset \Gamma''$ gezeigt, wobei Γ' bzw. Γ'' die erste bzw. zweite Kommutatorgruppe von Γ bedeutet. Als Hauptergebnis bekommt der Verfasser eine eineindeutige Zuordnung zwischen diesen Gruppen G und drei ganzzahligen Parametern p, m, d mit $p>0$, $0 \leqq m \leqq d-1$, $m^2+m+1 \equiv 0 \pmod d$. Diese Zuordnung wird explizit gegeben durch die Restklassenzerlegung

$$G = \sum A^k B^1 \Gamma'', \quad A = a^{pb^{mp}}, \quad B = b^{dp},$$

$$a = xyxy^2, \quad b = xy^2xy.$$

Der Index $[\Gamma : G]$ ergibt sich zu $6dp^2$, und es wird eine explizite Formel in diesen Parametern für die Anzahl der Normalteiler von Γ von gegebenem Index und Geschlecht eins angegeben. Da Γ' eine freie Gruppe vom Rang 2 und $[\Gamma : \Gamma'] = G$ ist, folgt nach Nielsen-Schreier, dass G frei und vom Rang $1+dp^2$ ist. *H. Klingen* (Freiburg)

Referred to in F05-33, F05-43.

F05-31 (29# 3546)

White, George K.

On generators and defining relations for the unimodular group $\mathfrak{M}_2$.

Amer. Math. Monthly **71** (1964), 743–748.

The unimodular group $\mathfrak{M}_2$ consists of all 2×2 matrices with rational integral entries and determinant ± 1. The author gives defining relations for $\mathfrak{M}_2$ as an abstract group on two generators, and briefly discusses various simple relations satisfied by these generators.

I. Reiner (Urbana, Ill.)

F05-32 (29# 4805)

Wohlfahrt, Klaus

An extension of F. Klein's level concept.

Illinois J. Math. **8** (1964), 529–535.

Let Γ be the modular group, the group of all 2×2 matrices with rational integral elements and determinant 1; let $\Gamma(n)$ be the principal congruence subgroup of level n, the group of all matrices in Γ that are congruent to ± 1 modulo n. F. Klein defined a subgroup G of Γ to be of level ("Stufe") n provided n is the smallest positive integer for which $\Gamma(n) \subset G \subset \Gamma$. Then G is called a congruence subgroup.

The author extends the level concept as follows. Every parabolic matrix P in Γ is conjugate over Γ to a translation by an integer m; $|m|$ is called the amplitude of P. Let $G \subset \Gamma$; then the level of G is defined to be the least common multiple of the amplitudes of all parabolic elements in G. When G is a congruence subgroup, the Klein level agrees with the level thus defined. The new definition has already demonstrated its importance in (as yet unpublished) research.

Using the new definition, the author proves a number of theorems. Let $\Delta(m)$ be the normal closure in $\Gamma(m)$ of $\begin{pmatrix} 1 & m \\ 0 & 1 \end{pmatrix}$. It is known that $\Delta(m) = \Gamma(m)$ if $1 \leqq m \leqq 5$; otherwise $\Delta(m)$ is of infinite index in $\Gamma(m)$ [cf. M. I. Knopp, Proc. Amer. Math. Soc. **14** (1963), 95–97; MR **26** #230]. The author reproves this theorem. He then constructs an infinite set of normal subgroups of Γ of level $m \geqq 6$ which, however, are not congruence subgroups in the sense of Klein and so contain no principal congruence subgroup. These are different from the groups of I. Reiner [Illinois J. Math. **2** (1958), 142–144; MR **20** #2379].

Next, by means of a theorem of Fricke, the author proves an arithmetic characterization of Γ^6. Finally, he shows that every subgroup of Γ of index $\leqq 6$ is a congruence subgroup. *J. Lehner* (College Park, Md.)

Citations: MR 20# 2379 = F05-15; MR 26# 230 = F05-22.

Referred to in F05-33, F05-42.

F05-33 (31# 5846)

Newman, Morris

Normal subgroups of the modular group which are not congruence subgroups.

Proc. Amer. Math. Soc. **16** (1965), 831–832.

Diese Note schliesst an die Arbeit [Amer. J. Math. **86** (1964), 17–24; MR **29** #1265] des Verfassers an. Dort wurden alle Normalteiler vom Geschlecht eins der elliptischen Modulgruppe mittels dreier ganzzahliger Parameter (p, m, d) beschrieben, welche $p>0$, $0 \leqq m \leqq d-1$, $m^2+m+1 \equiv 0 \pmod d$ genügen. In der vorliegenden Arbeit wird unter Verwendung des Stufenbegriffs von K. Wohlfahrt [Illinois J. Math. **8** (1964), 529–535; MR **29** #4805] gezeigt, dass genau die vier Gruppen (1, 0, 1), (1, 1, 3), (2, 0, 1), (2, 1, 3) Kongruenzgruppen sind. Die übrigen bilden eine neue Klasse von Normalteilern von endlichem Index, die keine Kongruenzuntergruppen sind.

H. Klingen (Freiburg)

Citations: MR 29# 1265 = F05-30; MR 29# 4805 = F05-32.

F05-34 (31# 5902)

Knopp, M. I.; Newman, M.

Congruence subgroups of positive genus of the modular group.

Illinois J. Math. **9** (1965), 577–583.

A subgroup G of finite index of the modular group Γ is said to be a congruence subgroup if it contains some principal congruence subgroup

$$\Gamma(n) = \left\{ \begin{pmatrix} a & b \\ c & d \end{pmatrix} \in \Gamma, \begin{pmatrix} a & b \\ c & d \end{pmatrix} \equiv \begin{pmatrix} 1 & 0 \\ 0 & 1 \end{pmatrix} \pmod n \right\}.$$

It is known that there exist subgroups of genus zero, and yet of arbitrarily high index, in Γ. On the other hand, Rademacher conjectured that there exists only a finite number of congruence subgroups of genus zero. The main result of the present paper consists in the proof of a particular case of that conjecture. The full conjecture remains an open problem. Specifically, the authors show that if $P = 2 \cdot 3 \cdot 5 \cdot 7 \cdot 13$ and if G is a free congruence subgroup of Γ of level n, with $(n, P) = 1$, then G cannot be of genus zero. The proof makes use of a decomposition modulo $\Gamma(n)$ of the group generated by $\Gamma(n)$ and $\begin{pmatrix} 1 & 1 \\ 0 & 1 \end{pmatrix}$, of the relation $g = 1 + \mu/12 - \frac{1}{2}t$ between the genus g, the index $\mu = (\Gamma : G)$ and the number t of parabolic classes of the free subgroup G of Γ, of a formula for the number of parabolic classes of a subgroup H, normal in G, and of the formula giving the genus g_p of $\Gamma_0(p) = \left\{ \begin{pmatrix} a & b \\ c & d \end{pmatrix} \in \Gamma, c \equiv 0 \pmod p \right\}$. The somewhat surprising fact that 11 is not a factor of P is due precisely to a peculiarity of g_p for $p \equiv -1 \pmod{12}$.

E. Grosswald (Philadelphia, Pa.)

Referred to in F05-39.

F05-35 (32# 2484)

McQuillan, Donald L.

Classification of normal congruence subgroups of the modular group.

Amer. J. Math. **87** (1965), 285–296.

In this interesting and significant paper, the author gives a complete classification of all normal congruence subgroups of the modular group (equivalently, of all normal subgroups of LF(2, n)). The case $(n, 6) = 1$ has been treated previously by the reviewer [same J. **85** (1963), 419–427; errata, ibid. **85** (1963), 753; addendum, ibid. **86** (1964), 465; MR **29** #167], but the extension to all n requires not only a detailed study of the normal subgroups of LF(2, 2^k) and LF(2, 3^k), but also some general theorems giving the structure of the normal subgroups of LF(2, n) in terms of direct products of normal subgroups of LF(2, p^k), where p^k runs over the prime powers dividing n.

Morris Newman (Washington, D.C.)

Citations: MR 29# 167 = F05-29.

F05-36 **(32# 2485)**

Petersson, Hans

Über die Kongruenzgruppen der Stufe 4.

J. Reine Angew. Math. **212** (1963), 63–72.

The author gives a complete tabulation of all congruence subgroups of the modular group Γ of level 4 (that is, the subgroups of Γ containing the principal congruence subgroup Γ(4)). Perhaps the most striking item is a diagram showing on horizontal levels the subgroups of a specified index (which is a divisor of 24), with diagonal lines indicating the chains of subgroups. There are 30 such groups in all, including Γ and Γ(4).

Morris Newman (Washington, D.C.)

F05-37 **(33# 133)**

Ochoa, J.

Matrices of second order with integer elements. (Spanish)

Fourth Annual Meeting Spanish Mathematicians (Spanish), *pp.* 65–78. *Univ. Salamanca, Salamanca*, 1965.

Author's summary: "The group of second-order matrices with integral elements and determinant one is studied. The classification which the inner automorphisms of the group induce on the set of these matrices determines the number of classes of matrices which, as is known, coincides with the number of classes of divisors of a certain quadratic field. For matrices with positive elements the number of matrices which belong to the same class as a given one is found, as well as the necessary and sufficient condition that two matrices belong to the same class. It is shown that there exists an isomorphism between the set of matrices of determinant d and the set of matrices of determinant one which commute with them. Finally, corresponding to definite quadratic fields, families of prime numbers are defined."

R. F. Rinehart (Monterey, Calif.)

F05-38 **(33# 7423)**

Greenberg, L.

Note on normal subgroups of the modular group.

Proc. Amer. Math. Soc. **17** (1966), 1195–1198.

Let Γ denote the modular group, defined by generators X, Y and relations $X^2 = Y^3 = 1$. Let $Z = XY$. All parabolic elements of Γ are conjugate to Z. If N is a normal subgroup of finite index in Γ, the parabolic class number of N is defined to be the number of distinct N-conjugacy classes contained in the Γ-conjugacy class of Z^n, n being the smallest positive integer such that $Z^n \in N$. The following results are obtained. Theorem 1: Let N be a normal subgroup of Γ with t parabolic classes and index μ. Then $\mu \leqq 6t^4$. It follows that there are at most a finite number of subgroups of Γ with given parabolic class number t. Theorem 2: Let p be a prime with $p \equiv -1$ (mod 3). Then there is no normal subgroup of finite index in Γ with p parabolic classes.

A. M. Macbeath (Pasadena, Calif.)

Referred to in F05-48, F05-57.

F05-39 **(34# 1402)**

McQuillan, Donald L.

On the genus of fields of elliptic modular functions.

Illinois J. Math. **10** (1966), 479–487.

The author extends some results of M. Knopp and the reviewer [same J. **9** (1965), 577–583; MR **31** #5902] and proves, among other things, that a congruence subgroup of the modular group Γ of level n, where the smallest prime factor of n exceeds 13, is of positive genus. He also proves that only finitely many congruence subgroups of prime level are of genus 0, and determines these completely. In addition, he gives a formula for the genus of any congruence subgroup of Γ and uses this to determine the genus of all congruence subgroups of Γ of prime level, using results of J. Gierster [Math. Ann. **18** (1881), 319–365].

Morris Newman (Washington, D.C.)

Citations: MR 31# 5902 = F05-34.

F05-40 **(34# 1416)**

Rankin, R. A.

Isomorphic congruence groups and Hecke operators.

Proc. Glasgow Math. Assoc. **7**, 168 (1966).

Let H be a subgroup of a group K, containing a normal subgroup G of K, and let θ be the natural homomorphism of K onto K/G; then an isomorphism Φ of H onto $H\Phi \subset K$ is an extension of an isomorphism of $H\theta$ onto $H\Phi\theta$ if $\Phi\theta = \theta\phi$ on H. If such an extension Φ is an inner automorphism of K restricted to H, then ϕ is an inner automorphism of K/G restricted to H/G. This result is applied to isomorphisms of congruence groups occurring in the theory of Hecke T_n-operators.

J. A. H. Shepperd (Manchester)

F05-41 **(34# 4217)**

Newman, Morris

Classification of normal subgroups of the modular group.

Trans. Amer. Math. Soc. **126** (1967), 267–277.

Let Γ be the modular group, Γ^μ the subgroup of Γ generated by the μth powers of the elements of Γ; let $M(\mu)$ be the number of subgroups G of Γ of (finite) index μ, and $N(\mu)$ the number of normal subgroups of index μ in Γ. The values of $M(\mu)$ are essentially (namely, recursively) known [see I. Dey, Proc. Glasgow Math. Assoc. **7**, 61–79 (1965); MR **32** #5718]. Concerning $N(\mu)$, it is known that for $\mu = 1, 2, 3$, $N(\mu) = 1$, with Γ^μ the only normal subgroup of index μ, and that for $\mu \geqq 4$, $N(\mu) \equiv 0$ (mod 6).

Let p, q stand for odd primes and (q/p) for the Legendre symbol; then the main results of the present paper are: (i) $N(6q) = 1 + (q/3)$ (this formula, claimed only for $q \geqq 5$, actually holds also for $q = 3$, because $N(18) = 1$; see the table (9)); (ii) if $q > 11$, $N(12q) = 0$ (the result holds also for $q = 3$, but not for $q = 5$, as $N(60) = 1$; for $q = 7$ and $q = 11$, $N(84)$ and $N(132)$ do not seem to be known); (iii) $N(\mu)$ becomes arbitrarily large ($(q/3) = 1$ implies $N(6q^{2r}) \geqq 2r - 1$). Finally, for $\mu \leqq 66$, all normal subgroups of index μ are explicitly listed. The proofs rely heavily on the genus formula for $G: g = 1 + \mu/12 - t/2 = 1 + \mu(n-6)/12n$ (t = number of parabolic classes, n = level of G) and the Sylow theorems.

E. Grosswald (Philadelphia, Pa.)

F05-42 **(35# 5518)**

Rankin, R. A.

Lattice subgroups of free congruence groups.

Invent. Math. **2** (1967), 215–221.

Let F_n be a free group of rank n with generators $x_1, \cdots, x_n$. For each $w \in F_n$ let $\sigma_j(w)$ be the exponent sum of w with respect to the generator x_j ($j = 1, \cdots, n$). The mapping $\sigma(w) = (\sigma_1(w), \cdots, \sigma_n(w))$ is a homomorphism of F_n onto Z^n, the cartesian product of the set of integers with itself

n times. Let Λ be a subgroup of Z^n, Z^n regarded as a free abelian group. The subgroup $\sigma^{-1}(\Lambda)$ is called a lattice subgroup of F_n.

The author considers the case when $F_n = \Gamma$ is a subgroup of the modular group $\Gamma(1)$. Let $\Gamma(N)$ denote the principal congruence subgroup of $\Gamma(1)$ of level N. In particular, the author classifies the groups Γ with $\Gamma(6) < \Gamma < \Gamma'(1)$ (the commutator subgroup of $\Gamma(1)$) as lattice subgroups; a subgroup with $\Gamma(N^2) < \Gamma < \Gamma(N)$ is also a lattice subgroup. He applies his results to lattice subgroups of $\Gamma(2)$ and he obtains a new proof for the fact that certain normal subgroups of finite index in $\Gamma(2)$ are not congruence groups. The main device is to consider the level (as defined by K. Wohlfahrt [Illinois J. Math. **8** (1964), 529–535; MR **29** #4805]) $N(\Lambda)$ of $\Gamma(\Lambda)$ as a lattice subgroup of $\Gamma(N)$. There is an open problem with regard to the relation between N and $N(\Lambda)$. *J. R. Smart* (Madison, Wis.)

Citations: MR 29# 4805 = F05-32.
Referred to in F05-56.

F05-43 (36# 2554)

Wohlfahrt, Klaus

Zur Struktur der rationalen Modulgruppe.

Math. Ann. **174** (1967), 79–99.

M. Newman [Amer. J. Math. **86** (1964), 17–24; MR **29** #1265] and I. Reiner [Illinois J. Math. **2** (1958), 142–144; MR **20** #2379] were the first to study the normal subgroups of the elliptic modular group Γ by purely algebraic means. It has been known since W. Fricke's paper [Math. Ann. **30** (1887), 100–118] that there exist such subgroups that are not congruence subgroups. Fricke used function theoretical methods. The present author shows that Fricke's subgroups are connected with a certain type of representations of Γ introduced by E. Hecke [ibid. **116** (1939), 469–510]. Let $D(M)$ be a representation of the elements $M \in \Gamma$ which maps Γ on the finite group $D(\Gamma)$ and $\mathscr{D}(M) = \begin{pmatrix} D(M) & d(M) \\ 0 & 1 \end{pmatrix}$ another representation, where $d(M)$ is a column vector satisfying $d(MN) = D(M)\,d(N) + d(M)$; thus $d(M)$ is a cocycle. $\mathscr{D}(\Gamma)$ is a homomorphic image of Γ and is easier to handle than Γ, even if $\mathscr{D}(\Gamma)$ is not finite. The images of Fricke's subgroups can be described in such $\mathscr{D}(\Gamma)$ for which $D(\Gamma)$ is a one-rowed matrix. The author develops a general method, which cannot easily be sketched here, of finding subgroups, especially of normal subgroups of $\mathscr{D}(\Gamma)$. Apart from Fricke's subgroups he gives some other explicit examples. *M. Eichler* (Basel)

Citations: MR 20# 2379 = F05-15; MR 29# 1265 = F05-30.

F05-44 (37# 1392)

Gale, Gene B.

Factorization of 2×2 integral matrices with determinant ± 1.

Fibonacci Quart. **6** (1968), 3–21.

An algorithm is given for expressing each matrix of the title as a product of powers of the matrices A and $B = AT$, where

$$A = \begin{pmatrix} 1 & 1 \\ 0 & 1 \end{pmatrix}, \quad T = \begin{pmatrix} 0 & 1 \\ 1 & 0 \end{pmatrix}, \quad TAT = \begin{pmatrix} 1 & 0 \\ 1 & 1 \end{pmatrix}.$$

{Since every such matrix which is elementary is a power of A, T or TAT, the usual algorithm for factorization into elementary matrices also yields the desired result.}

M. F. Smiley (Albany, N.Y.)

F05-45 (38# 3230)

Takeuchi, Kisao

On a Fuchsian group commensurable with the unimodular group.

J. Fac. Sci. Univ. Tokyo Sect. I **15** (1968), 107–109.

Let Γ be a finitely generated Fuchsian group of the first kind, where every element of Γ, regarded as an element of SL(2, R) has rational entries. The author gives necessary and sufficient conditions for Γ to be commensurable with the unimodular group. There is no statement as to the independence of these conditions. The author assumes that all Fuchsian groups are finitely generated. {In equation (6), replace n by 2.} *B. Maskit* (Cambridge, Mass.)

F05-46 (38# 5717)

Lehner, Joseph

On the multipliers of the Dedekind modular function.

J. Res. Nat. Bur. Standards Sect. B **72B** (1968), 253–261.

Die Dedekindsche Modulfunktion

$$\eta(\tau) = e^{\pi i\tau/12} \prod_{m=1}^{\infty} (1 - e^{2\pi i m\tau})$$

ist eine Modulform der Dimension $-\frac{1}{2}$ mit nichttrivialem Multiplikatorsystem. Die Multiplikatoren $v(A)$ sind 24-te Einheitswurzeln. Sie hängen in komplizierter Weise von den Modulmatrizen $A \in \Gamma$ ab. Verfasser studiert durch explizite Rechnung diese Abhängigkeit und beweist: Die Menge $G = \{A \in \Gamma : v(A) = 1\}$ liegt in der Kommutatorgruppe von Γ, und jede Untergruppe von Γ, welche in G liegt, ist zyklisch. *J. Spilker* (Freiburg)

F05-47 (39# 5477)

Millington, M. H.

Subgroups of the classical modular group.

J. London Math. Soc. (2) **1** (1969), 351–357.

A subgroup of finite index in the classical modular group is defined to have type $(\mu\colon g, t, e_2, e_3)$ if μ is the index, g the genus of the compactified quotient space, t the number of inequivalent parabolic vertices, e_2 the number of inequivalent vertices with stabilizer of order 2, and e_3 the number of inequivalent vertices with stabilizer of order 3. The main result is that there is at least one subgroup of every type satisfying the relations $12(g-1) = \mu - 6t - 6e_2 - 4e_3$, $\mu > 0$, $t > 0$, $e_2 \geqq 0$, $e_3 \geqq 0$, $g \geqq 0$. In the course of the proof a more refined classification of the subgroups, in terms of their cusp split, is introduced. It is shown, however, that certain arithmetically possible combinations of type and cusp split do not occur for any subgroup.

A. M. Macbeath (Birmingham)

F05-48 (39# 7100)

Mason, A. W.

On a theorem by Leon Greenberg.

Proc. Amer. Math. Soc. **23** (1969), 18–23.

Let Γ be the inhomogeneous modular group and let G be a normal subgroup of (finite) index μ and level N. Then $\mu = Nt$, where t is the parabolic class number. Leon Greenberg has shown that $N \leqq 6t^3$ [same Proc. **17** (1966), 1195–1198; MR **33** #7423]. The author shows that if $t > 1$, there exists an integer k such that $1 < k \leqq t$, $k|N$, and $N|kt$. It follows that $N \leqq t^2$ when $t > 1$. The same inequality was obtained by R. D. M. Accola using different methods [Trans. Amer. Math. Soc. **131** (1968), 398–408; MR **36** #5333]. The reader should note that the amplitude of a parabolic transformation is not well-defined in general, although the sign of the amplitude is well-defined. Of course, a parabolic transformation in Γ does have a well-defined amplitude since it is conjugate in Γ to a power of the translation $z \to z + 1$. *C. Earle* (Ithaca, N.Y.)

Citations: MR 33# 7423 = F05-38.

F05-49 (40# 1484)

Millington, M. H.

On cycloidal subgroups of the modular group.

Proc. London Math. Soc. (3) **19** (1969), 164–176.

Let G be a subgroup of the modular group Γ. Suppose that G has index μ, genus g, t inequivalent parabolic cusps, and

e_ν inequivalent elliptic fixed points of order ν (where $\nu=2, 3$). The area formula implies that (1) $g=1+\frac{1}{2}(\mu/6-t-e_2/2-2e_3/3)$. The author investigates the question of whether a group G exists, having preassigned data g, μ, t, e_2, e_3, satisfying (1). She answers the question affirmatively, in the case of cycloidal groups ($t=1$). The method, in essence, involves the construction of homomorphisms of Γ into permutation groups.

The following result is also proved. Theorem: Let Γ_i ($i=1, 2$) be cycloidal groups, with data $\{\mu_i, e_2^{(i)}, e_3^{(i)}\}$, such that $(\mu_1, \mu_2)=1$. Then $\Gamma_1 \cap \Gamma_2$ is cycloidal, with data $(\mu_1\mu_2, e_2^{(1)}e_2^{(2)}, e_3^{(1)}e_3^{(2)})$.

This extends a result of H. Petersson [Arch. Math. **4** (1953), 308–315; MR **15**, 291], that $\Gamma_1 \cap \Gamma_2$ is cycloidal of index $\mu_1\mu_2$.

The author also investigates inclusion relations among cycloidal groups, especially for a class of such groups constructed by H. Petersson.

L. Greenberg (College Park, Md.)

Citations: MR 15, 291a = F05-5.
Referred to in F05-54.

F05-50 (40# 1485)

Newman, Morris

Maximal normal subgroups of the modular group.
Proc. Amer. Math. Soc. **19** (1968), 1138–1144.

By a maximal normal subgroup G of the modular group Γ, the author means a normal subgroup such that Γ/G is simple. The main result is the following. Theorem: For each prime $p \geqq 37$, there is a maximal normal subgroup of Γ of index $\frac{1}{2}p(p^2-1)$ which is not a congruence group, and therefore there are infinitely many maximal, normal subgroups of Γ of finite index, which are not congruence groups.

The maximal normal subgroups G which are found have the property that $\Gamma/G \approx \mathrm{LF}(2, p)$, although $G \neq \Gamma(p)$. The method involves computations with finite fields and the group $\mathrm{LF}(2, p)$. The following two results illustrate the author's considerations, and are interesting in their own right.

Theorem 1: Let C be any element in $\mathrm{LF}(2, q)$ other than the identity. Then C may be written as $C=AB$, where $A, B \in \mathrm{LF}(2, q)$, A is of period 2, B of period 3.

Theorem 2: Suppose that the positive integer n satisfies (1) $n=p$ (prime) or $n|(p\pm 1)/2$, (2) $(n, 6)=1$, (3) $n>5$.

Then there are elements $A, B \in \mathrm{LF}(2, p)$ such that A is of period 2, B is of period 3, AB is of period n and $\mathrm{LF}(2, p)$ is generated by A and B.

L. Greenberg (College Park, Md.)

F05-51 (41# 1650)

Newman, Morris

Isometric circles of congruence groups.
Amer. J. Math. **91** (1969), 648–656.

Sei $\Gamma(n)$ die Hauptkongruenzuntergruppe der Stufe n der Modulgruppe und $r=r(\Gamma(n))$ die kleinste natürliche Zahl, so daß die reelle Achse vom Inneren aller isometrischen Kreise mit Radius $\geqq 1/r$ überdeckt wird. R. A. Rankin hat $r \leqq n^{11/2}$ gezeigt [Proc. London Math. Soc. (3) **4** (1954), 219–234; MR **15**, 863]. Verfasser beweist $cn^2 < r(\Gamma(n)) < n^{2+\varepsilon}$ für jedes $\varepsilon>0$ und ein geeignetes $c>0$. Diese Abschätzung hat Konsequenzen (1) für die Radien der isometrischen Kreise, welche den Fordschen Fundamentalbereich beranden, (2) für die Approximation irrationaler reeller Zahlen durch rationale Zahlen mit Teilerbedingungen und Nennerbeschränkung. *J. Spilker* (Freiburg)

Citations: MR 15, 863h = F05-6.

F05-52 (42# 200)

Rankin, Robert A.

The modular group and its subgroups.
The Ramanujan Institute, Madras, 1969. iii+85 *pp.* \$2.00.

Author's preface: "This short course of lectures was given at the Ramanujan Institute for Advanced Study in Mathematics, in the University of Madras, in September 1968. The object of the course was to study the modular group and some of its subgroups, with help of algebraic rather than analytic or topological methods. Most of the work covered is known and has appeared in literature. In some cases, however, the proofs that are given are believed to be new. Contents: (1) Introduction and notation. (2) The modular group. (3) The subgroups. (4) Normal and commutator subgroups. (5) The level of a subgroup; congruence groups. (6) Lattice subgroups of free subgroups of the modular group. (7) Subgroups of small index. These lecture notes contain especially rich material on free subgroups, lattice subgroups, and non-congruence subgroups of the modular group, chiefly due to R. Fricke, M. Newman, R. A. Rankin and K. Wohlfahrt. This is treated in a self-contained way." *M. Eichler* (Basel)

F05-53 (42# 386)

Greenberg, Leon; Newman, Morris

Normal subgroups of the modular group.
J. Res. Nat. Bur. Standards Sect. B **74B** (1970), 121–123.

Ankündigung neuer Resultate ohne Beweis über Normalteiler H der elliptischen Modulgruppe Γ. Zwei typische Resultate sind: (1) Von 4 Ausnahmen abgesehen ist jeder Normalteiler G von quadratfreiem Index μ vom Geschlecht 1, und es gilt $\mu \equiv 0 \bmod 6$ und $\mu/6 \equiv 1 \bmod 3$. (2) Setzt man $f(\mu)=1$ falls ein Normalteiler G vom Index μ in Γ mit auflösbarem Quotienten Γ/G existiert und sonst $=0$, dann gilt $\lim_{x\to\infty} x^{-1}\sum_{\mu\leq x} f(\mu)=0$. Weitere Resultate betreffen Existenz von Normalteilern bei vorgegebenem Geschlecht, Index oder Anzahl parabolischer Klassen.

J. Spilker (Freiburg)

F05-54 (42# 7788)

Wohlfahrt, Klaus

On some representations of $\mathrm{SL}(2, Z)$.
Illinois J. Math. **15** (1971), 144–149.

A connection between cycloidal subgroups of index n in the modular group and permutation representations of degree n is studied. The results bear a strong similarity to those of M. H. Millington [Proc. London Math. Soc. (3) **19** (1969), 164–176; MR **40** #1484]. Particular cases of index 7 and 9, which yield homomorphic maps of the modular group on $\mathrm{PSL}(2, 7)$ and $\mathrm{PSL}(2, 8)$, respectively, are studied in detail. *A. M. Macbeath* (Birmingham)

Citations: MR 40# 1484 = F05-49.

F05-55 (42# 7791)

Tahara, Ken-ichi

On the finite subgroups of $\mathrm{GL}(3, Z)$.
Nagoya Math. J. **41** (1971), 169–209.

This paper contains a complete list of all conjugate classes of finite subgroups of $\mathrm{GL}(3, Z)$ and $\mathrm{SL}(3, Z)$. There are 24 such classes in $\mathrm{SL}(3, Z)$ and 74 in $\mathrm{GL}(3, Z)$. Representatives of all their classes are explicitly given. In an appendix the author uses these results to find all groups of fixed point free rational automorphisms of tori of dimensions at most 3. He also conjectures that in characteristic 2 a group of fixed point free automorphisms of a 4-dimensional

torus is cyclic. This conjecture appears to be false since the quaternion group Q of order 8 is a subgroup of GL(4, Z) and some power of any nonidentity element of Q is -1.
W. Feit (New Haven, Conn.)

F05-56 **(43# 2112)**

Mason, A. W.
Lattice subgroups of free congruence groups.
Glasgow Math. J. **10** (1969), 106–115.

The author gives a solution of a problem posed by R. A. Rankin [Invent. Math. **2** (1967), 215–221; MR **35** #5518]. Let $\Gamma(1)$ be the inhomogeneous modular group (i.e., the group of 2×2 integral matrices of determinant 1 in which a matrix is identified with its negative); and let $\Gamma(n)$ be the principal congruence subgroup of level n (i.e., the subgroup of $\Gamma(1)$ consisting of all $M\in\Gamma(1)$ for which $M\equiv \pm I \pmod n$). It is well known that a subgroup G of $\Gamma(1)$ is said to be a congruence group of level n if G contains $\Gamma(n)$ and n is the least such integer. In the paper quoted above Rankin considers lattice subgroups F_n of rank n of $\Gamma(1)$ (i.e., a subgroup of F_n which contains the commutator group F_n'). Rankin shows in particular that if G is a lattice congruence subgroup of F_n of level qr (r = the largest divisor of qr prime to n) then n divides q and r divides 12; he poses also the problem of finding an upper bound for the factor q. In the present paper the author finds such an upper bound for q, and also considers bounds for r.
M. Rosati (Padova)

Citations: MR 35# 5518 = F05-42.

F05-57 **(44# 4103)**

Newman, Morris
2-generator groups and parabolic class numbers.
Proc. Amer. Math. Soc. **31** (1972), 51–53.

Sei G eine Gruppe der Ordnung μ mit 2 Erzeugenden x und y und $x^p=y^q=1$ (p, q teilerfremd). Der Verfasser beweist für die Ordnung n von xy und $t:=\mu/n$ die Abschätzungen $n\leqq pqt^p$ und $\mu\leqq pqt^{p+1}$. Dies ist eine Verallgemeinerung und Verbesserung eines Satzes von L. Greenberg [dieselben Proc. **17** (1966), 1195–1198; MR **33** #7423]. Sei H Normalteiler mit Index μ und Stufe n in der Modulgruppe und $t=\mu/n$ die Anzahl von Klassen parabolischer Elemente. Dann gilt $n\leqq 6t^3$ und $\mu\leqq 6t^4$. Speziell hat die Modulgruppe nur endlich viele Normalteiler vom endlichen Index und fester Zahl t. Der Beweis beruht auf einfachen gruppentheoretischen Methoden von R. Accola [Trans. Amer. Math. Soc. **131** (1968), 398–408; MR **36** #5333].
J. Spilker (Freiburg)

Citations: MR 33# 7423 = F05-38.

F05-58 **(44# 6953)**

Larcher, H.
Weierstrass points at the cusps of $\Gamma_0(16p)$ and hyperellipticity of $\Gamma_0(n)$.
Canad. J. Math. **23** (1971), 960–968.

Let n be a fixed positive integer and $\Gamma_0(n)$ the subgroup of the modular group $\Gamma(1)$ consisting of all linear fractional transformations $z\to(az+b)/(cz+d)$, $ad-bc=1$, $c\equiv 0 \pmod n$. If H is the upper half ($z>0$) of the complex plane then $S_0(n)=H/\Gamma_0(n)$ properly compactified is a compact Riemann surface of genus $g(n)$. A point P of $S_0(n)$ is called a Weierstrass point if there exists a function f analytic on $S_0(n)$ except for a pole of order $\alpha\leqq g$ at P. It is shown that if the prime p is not smaller than 3 then all cusps of $\Gamma_0(16p)$ are Weierstrass points. Also, for all sufficiently large positive integers n, $\Gamma_0(n)$ is not hyperelliptic.
G. G. Weill (Brooklyn, N.Y.)

F10 THE MODULAR GROUP SL(2, Z) AND ITS SUBGROUPS: AUTOMORPHIC FORMS

See also Section P72.

See also reviews A56-64, E24-16, E64-27, E64-28, F05-46, F05-58, F15-31, F40-35, G05-80, G05-90, G05-98, G15-39, G20-30, M10-7, M10-8, P60-1, P60-5, P60-15, P60-45, P80-1, Q05-83, R14-71, R14-82, R14-93, R14-94, R32-66, R40-28, R52-19, S99-12, Z02-73.

F10-1 **(1, 214c)**

Zuckerman, Herbert S. On the expansions of certain modular forms of positive dimension. Amer. J. Math. **62**, 127–152 (1940).

Hardy and Ramanujan have expanded modular forms of positive dimension which have a finite number of poles in the fundamental region, but are regular at $i\infty$ [Proc. Roy. Soc. London. Ser. A. **95**, 144–155 (1919); also S. Ramanujan's Collected Papers, pp. 310–321]. The author combines their method with that developed by Rademacher and Zuckerman [Ann. of Math. **39**, 433–462 (1938)] in order to treat the general case of a meromorphic modular form $F(\tau)$ of positive dimension, admitting a pole at $i\infty$. The transformation equations of $F(\tau)$ are given as

$$F\left(\frac{a\tau+b}{c\tau+d}\right)=\epsilon(a,b,c,d)\cdot(-i(c\tau+d))^{-r}F(\tau),\quad c>0,$$

$$F(\tau+1)=e^{2\pi i\alpha}F(\tau),\qquad 0\leqq\alpha<1.$$

The function $F(\tau)$ is supposed to have only a finite number of poles in the fundamental region. For $\Im(\tau)>A$, it is regular and admits there of a Fourier expansion

$$(*)\qquad f(e^{2\pi i\tau})=e^{-2\pi i\alpha\tau}F(\tau)=\sum_{n=-\mu}^{\infty}a_ne^{2\pi in\tau}.$$

As Hardy and Ramanujan, the author starts with

$$\frac{1}{2\pi i}\int_{C_N}\frac{f(x)}{x-y}dx=f(y)+R(N),$$

where y is a point of regularity and $R(N)$ represents the sum of the residues arising from the poles inside C_N. The path of integration C_N requires some attention. The author does not take that one employed by Hardy and Ramanujan. He chooses a geometrically simpler path, which can best be described in the variable τ after the substitution $x=\exp(2\pi i\tau)$. In the upper τ-halfplane the author considers first the semicircles which are the image of $\Re(\tau)=0$ by all the modular transformations

$$\tau'=\frac{h\tau+h'}{k\tau+k'},$$

where h'/k' and h/k are two adjacent fractions of the Farey series of order N, $0\leqq h'/k'<h/k\leqq 1$. These semicircles form a continuous chain from 0 to 1. Whereas in the Hardy-Ramanujan paper quoted above the integration can be extended into the cusps h/k of the path, here the cusps have to be cut off by horizontal segments $\Im(\tau)=B_N$, since in the rational points $F(\tau)$ becomes infinite. The constant B_N does not need to be precisely fixed, but $B_N<1/2N^2$ is necessary in order that all semicircles are hit by $\Im(\tau)=B_N$. Moreover

B_N is chosen as so small that the triangular pieces cut off by it contain no poles in the interior. (The author, incidentally, writes simply B instead of B_N.) On this path of integration only those parts yield essential contributions which consist of a horizontal piece and pieces of the semicircles in the neighborhood, that is, only the parts of the path close to the rational points h/k. This decomposition replaces here the customary "Farey-dissection." On each piece of the path of integration the transformation equation is applied. This provides an approximation to $F(\tau)$ in the neighborhood of each rational point. After the necessary estimations and after the passage to the limit $N\to\infty$, the result is

$$f(y)=2\pi\sum_{k=1}^{\infty}\frac{1}{k}\sum_{\nu=1}^{\mu}a_{-\nu}\sum_{n=0}^{\infty}A_{k,\nu}(n)\left(\frac{\nu-\alpha}{n+\alpha}\right)^{(r+1)/2}$$
$$\times I_{r+1}\left(\frac{4\pi}{k}((\nu-\alpha)(n+\alpha))^{\frac{1}{2}}\right)y^n-R(\infty),$$

where $A_{k,\nu}(n)$ are certain arithmetical sums, the $a_{-\nu}$ stem from the "principal part" of the Fourier series (*), and $R(\infty)$ stands for $\lim_{N\to\infty}R(N)$. The sum of residues $R(\infty)$ is then fully discussed in the case that the fundamental region besides the pole at $i\infty$ contains only one pole σ in its interior. It is interesting to note that the expression shows a modular form in the parameter σ of the negative dimension $-r-2$, appearing as a Poincaré series of the generalized type studied by Petersson.

In a further paragraph the class of all functions which satisfy the conditions of the main theorem is characterized in terms of $g_2(1,\tau)$, $g_3(1,\tau)$, $\eta(\tau)$, and $J(\tau)$. This parametrization of all those functions furnishes the particularly interesting example

$$F_r(\tau)=\frac{1}{1728}\eta(\tau)^{-24}(J(\tau)-J(\sigma))^{-1}$$

as covered by the main theorem. For $0<r\leqq 12$ the expansion is very simple and can be completely given. A comparison of leading terms yields the formula

$$1728\,\eta(\sigma)^{24}J'(\sigma)=-\frac{3\cdot 13!}{2^{11}\pi^{13}}i\sum_{p=-\infty}^{+\infty}\sum_{q=-\infty}^{+\infty}(p\sigma+q)^{-14},$$

where a special Eisenstein series appears on the right-hand side.

The author finally discusses briefly also the above-mentioned $F_r(\tau)$ for $12<r\leqq 24$. *H. Rademacher*.

Referred to in F10-15, F10-77.

F10-2 (2, 37a)

Behrens, Ernst-August. Bestimmung der Stufe für die aus binären Thetareihen erzeugten Modulformen. Math. Z. **46**, 350–374 (1940).

The theta series $\vartheta(\tau;\rho,\mathfrak{a},Q\sqrt{D})$ were discussed by E. Hecke [Math. Ann. **97**, 210–242 (1926)], who showed that they remain invariant under the principal congruence subgroup $\Gamma(Q|D|)$ of Stufe $Q|D|$. In this paper it is shown that, for the case $Q=1$ and a fixed D, there is no linear combination of the theta series which remains invariant under a principal congruence subgroup $\Gamma(R)$ with $|D|=pR$ and p a prime. From this it follows that the functions $\vartheta(\tau;\rho,\mathfrak{a},\sqrt{D})$ and their linear combinations are modular forms of the exact Stufe D, the discriminant of the quadratic field used in defining them. *H. S. Zuckerman* (Seattle, Wash.).

F10-3 (2, 87e)

Petersson, Hans. Über eine Metrisierung der automorphen Formen und die Theorie der Poincaréschen Reihen. Math. Ann. **117**, 453–537 (1940).

Let Γ be a group of linear substitutions

$$\tau\to\frac{\alpha\tau+\beta}{\gamma\tau+\delta}=M\tau$$

with real coefficients α, β, γ, δ and $\alpha\delta-\beta\gamma=1$, which has a finite number of generators and contains parabolic substitutions. Let F be a fundamental domain of Γ in the upper half-plane $\mathfrak{J}(\tau)\geqq 0$. A function $\phi(\tau)$ is called an automorphic form of the class $\{\Gamma,-r,v\}$ if it has the following two properties: (1) in any point of F, the function $\phi(\tau)$ is meromorphic with respect to the uniformizing local variable; (2) for any substitution M of Γ, the functional equation $\phi(M\tau)=v(M)(\gamma\tau+\delta)^r\phi(\tau)$ holds, where r is a constant and the multiplicator $v(M)$ depends only upon M. Suppose moreover that $r>2$ and $|v(M)|=1$. Generalizing the Eisenstein series from the theory of elliptic modular functions, Poincaré found a method of representing certain automorphic forms by an infinite series of elementary functions. Later Poincaré, Ritter and Fricke proved that any automorphic form can be expressed as a linear combination of Poincaré series; but their proof was not constructive.

The author obtains a new proof of this theorem, which is more satisfactory also from the practical point of view. He defines the scalar product (ϕ,ψ) of two automorphic forms $\phi(\tau)$ and $\psi(\tau)$ of the same class by the formula

$$(\phi,\psi)=\int\int_F\phi(\tau)\overline{\psi(\tau)}y^r\frac{dxdy}{y^2},\qquad \tau=x+iy.$$

Using the invariance of the hyperbolic measure in the group Γ, he calculates this scalar product if ϕ is an integral automorphic form vanishing in all the parabolic vertices of F and ψ a Poincaré series. The result gives a new independent definition of the Poincaré series, by their inner properties, and an explicit basis for all automorphic forms of the class $\{\Gamma,-r,v\}$. In particular, if Γ is a congruence-subgroup of the modular group, the theory still holds in the limiting case $r=2$, $v(M)=1$; but the proofs are more difficult. In this case, $\phi(\tau)d\tau$ becomes an Abelian differential on the Riemann surface F and (ϕ,ψ) is a bilinear form of the periods of Abelian integrals, closely connected to a well-known relationship from Riemann's work on Abelian functions.

Since the results contain a considerable simplification of the former theory of automorphic functions, they will be important for further research. *C. L. Siegel.*

Referred to in F10-92, F25-5, M10-7.

F10-4 (2, 114j)

Geppert, Harald. Wie Gauss zur elliptischen Modulfunktion kam. Deutsche Math. **5**, 158–175 (1940).

The paper is an address delivered before the second German Camp of Mathematicians and gives an account of the investigations of Gauss concerning the elliptic modular function. Gauss did not publish anything about these researches which anticipate a considerable part of the later work of Abel and Jacobi. The results found in his notebooks after his death were edited and discussed in the Collected Works of Gauss by Schering, Klein, Fricke and Schlesinger. The author makes some further suggestions on the ideas which led Gauss to his discoveries.

C. L. Siegel (Princeton, N. J.).

F10-5 (2, 276e)

Selberg, Atle. Beweis eines Darstellungssatzes aus der Theorie der ganzen Modulformen. Arch. Math. Naturvid. **44**, 33–44 (1941).

A new proof is given that every cusp-form of negative dimension $-k$ belonging to the principal congruence subgroup modulo Q can be expressed as a linear combination of Petersson functions

$$\sum (c\tau+d)^{-k}e^{2\pi i(\nu/Q)M\tau}$$

[cf. Petersson, Jber. Deutsch. Math. Verein. **49**, 49–75 (1939)]. Although the proof is carried out only for k an integer greater than 2, it will clearly go through for any real $k>2$. A further result is that, if $f(\tau)=\sum \alpha_\nu e^{2\pi i(\nu/Q)\tau}$ and $\varphi(\tau)=\sum \beta_\nu e^{2\pi i(\nu/Q)\tau}$ are two cusp forms of type $(-k, Q)$, then

$$\lim_{h\to 0} h \sum_{\nu=1}^{\infty} (\alpha_\nu\bar{\beta}_\nu/\nu^{k-1})e^{-2\pi(\nu/Q)h}$$

exists. The author defines the scalar product of f and φ to be this limit and notes that it differs from Petersson's scalar product only by a constant factor.

H. S. Zuckerman (Seattle, Wash.).

F10-6 (2, 358f)

Wintner, Aurel. On Riemann's fragment concerning elliptic modular functions. Amer. J. Math. **63**, 628–634 (1941).

In the first part of his posthumous fragment on the limiting values of the elliptic modular functions [B. Riemann, Mathematische Werke, 2nd ed., pp. 455–461], Riemann gives some examples of functions which are represented by trigonometric series but are discontinuous everywhere dense. It seems that Riemann did not prove the convergence of his series, and until now no proof of the validity of his formulae had been published. The author shows that Riemann's statements are simple consequences from known results in the modern theory of Fourier series.

C. L. Siegel (Princeton, N. J.).

F10-7 (3, 70b)

Zassenhaus, Hans. Tabelle der Absolutglieder der Eisensteinreihen $E_2(\tau)$ für die ersten Primzahlen und Dimensionen. Abh. Math. Sem. Hansischen Univ. **14**, 285–288 (1941).

F10-8 (3, 271d)

Rademacher, H. A. Correction. Amer. J. Math. **64**, 456 (1942).

Concerning the author's paper "The Fourier series and the functional equation of the absolute modular invariant $J(\tau)$," Amer. J. Math. **61**, 237–248 (1939).

Referred to in F10-30.

F10-9 (6, 208a)

Petersson, Hans. Ein Summationsverfahren für die Poincaréschen Reihen von der Dimension —2 zu den hyperbolischen Fixpunktepaaren. Math. Z. **49**, 441–496 (1944).

Let Γ be a Fuchsian group of the first kind with the matrix elements

$$L=\begin{pmatrix}\alpha & \beta\\ \gamma & \delta\end{pmatrix},$$

where α, β, γ, δ are real numbers and $\alpha\delta-\beta\gamma=1$; let $z=x+iy$, $\zeta=\xi+i\eta$, $y>0$, $\eta<0$; then the Poincaré series

$$f_r=f_r(z, \zeta)=\sum_L \{(\alpha z+\beta)-\zeta(\gamma z+\delta)\}^{-r}$$

is an automorphic form of the variable z with weight r, provided r is an even integer greater than 2. If Γ contains the special parabolic substitution $z\to z+1$, then $f_r(z, \zeta)=f_r(z, \zeta+1)$ and the Fourier expansion

$$f_r=\sum_{k=-\infty}^{\infty} \phi_k e^{2\pi ik\zeta}$$

exists, where the coefficients ϕ_k again are automorphic forms. In former publications the author generalized this expansion in two directions. He considered automorphic forms with arbitrary real weight $r>2$, having an arbitrary multiplier system of absolute value 1, and he replaced the special substitution $z\to z+1$ by an arbitrary parabolic or hyperbolic substitution in Γ; the different expansions of a given Poincaré series implied a number of remarkable relations among automorphic forms. Now he investigates the same problems for the limiting case $r=2$, under the assumption that Γ is a congruence subgroup of the modular group; the proofs become much more delicate, since the series $f_2(z, \zeta)$ is not absolutely convergent. As a possible application of his new results he sketches a method of constructing the period matrix of the Abelian integrals of the first kind for the corresponding algebraic function fields.

C. L. Siegel (Princeton, N. J.).

F10-10 (7, 7e)

Uspensky, J. V. On the arithmetico-geometric means of Gauss. Math. Notae **5**, 1–28 (1945). (Spanish)

If a and b are two positive numbers, their arithmetico-geometric mean is $M(a, b)=\lim_{n\to\infty}a_n=\lim_{n\to\infty}b_n$, where $a_0=a$, $b_0=b$, $a_{n+1}=\frac{1}{2}(a_n+b_n)$, $b_{n+1}=(a_nb_n)^{\frac{1}{2}}$. The paper is the first part of an expository account dealing with Gauss's theory of $M(a, b)$ and its application to the theory of modular functions. In this part, the author derives the differential equation satisfied by $M(a, b)$; he also shows how this function can be used in the calculation of the complete elliptic integral of the second kind.

R. P. Boas, Jr.

Referred to in F10-11.

F10-11 (7, 200c; 7, 200d)

Uspensky, J. V. On the arithmetico-geometric means of Gauss. II. Math. Notae **5**, 57–88 (1945). (Spanish)

Uspensky, J. V. On the arithmetico-geometric means of Gauss. III. Math. Notae **5**, 129–161 (1945). (Spanish)

Continuation of the exposition begun in Math. Notae **5**, 1–28 (1945); these Rev. **7**, 7. These parts consider the arithmetico-geometric mean of two complex numbers and its connections with modular functions.

R. P. Boas, Jr.

Citations: MR 7, 7e = F10-10.

F10-12 (7, 149c)

Wintner, Aurel. A property of the elliptic modular net. Duke Math. J. **12**, 451–454 (1945).

The discriminant of the cubic polynomial

$$(dp/dw)^2=4p^3-g_2p-g_3$$

in $p(w, \omega_1, \omega_2)$ is $\Delta(\omega_1, \omega_2)=g_2^3-27g_3^2=\omega_1^{-12}\Delta(1, \omega)$, where $m_1, m_2=0, \pm1, \pm2, \cdots$, but $(m_1, m_2)\neq(0, 0)$,

$$g_2(\omega_1, \omega_2)=60\sum'(m_1\omega_1+m_2\omega_2)^{-4},$$
$$g_3(\omega_1, \omega_2)=140\sum'(m_1\omega_1+m_2\omega_2)^{-6},$$

and $\omega_2/\omega_1=\omega=x+iy$, $y>0$. The function $\Delta(\omega)=\Delta(1, \omega)$ is regular in the half plane $y>0$ and is relatively invariant under every substitution of the modular group. The x-axis is a natural boundary of $\Delta(\omega)$. The Eisenstein series g_2, g_3 exhibit for $\Delta(\omega)$ a formal pole at every rational x. It turns out that, if a certain x-set Z of measure 0 is discarded, $\Delta(\omega)=\Delta(x+iy)$ tends to a finite nonvanishing limit $\Delta(x)$ as $y\to0$. The exclusion of a zero set Z is essential. The boundary function $\Delta(x)$ proves to exist, for almost all x, not only in the radial sense, but also as a Stolzian limit; that is, if the real number x does not belong to a certain set of measure 0, the function $\Delta(\omega)$ $(y>0)$ tends to a finite limit $\Delta(x)$ as ω tends to x within any fixed wedge $\epsilon<\arg(\omega-x)<\pi-\epsilon$, $\epsilon>0$. The proof is based on an Eulerian factorization

$$\Delta(\omega_1, \omega_2)=(2\pi/\omega_1)^{12}q^2\prod_{n=1}^{\infty}(1-q^{2n})^{24},$$

where $q=e^{i\omega\pi}$, $|q|<1$.

S. C. van Veen (Dordrecht).

F10-13 **(8, 316b)**

Rankin, R. A. A certain class of multiplicative functions. Duke Math. J. **13**, 281–306 (1946).

An elementary method is developed for constructing elliptic modular functions whose coefficients $f(m)$ are multiplicative. The functions $f(m)$ constructed here are of the type $f(m)=\sum P(x_0, \cdots, x_{s-1})$, where $s=2$, 4 or 8 and the rational integers $x_0, \cdots, x_{s-1}$ run through all solutions of $x_0^2+\cdots+x_{s-1}^2=m$; P is a polynomial. These sums can be interpreted in terms of complex numbers, quaternions and the nonassociative Cayley-Dickson algebra. It is shown, if $\zeta=z_0+i_1z_1+\cdots+i_{s-1}z_{s-1}$ and $P(\zeta)$ denotes any polynomial in $z_0, \cdots, z_{s-1}$, that $2s\sum P(\zeta)=\sum\sum P(\xi\eta)$, where ζ, ξ, η run through all numbers of the corresponding number system whose norm is mn, m, n, respectively ($(m, n)=1$). Additional formulas are given for $m=p^l$, $n=p$.

By taking suitable polynomials $P(\zeta)$, multiplicative functions $f(m)$ can be obtained. The corresponding power series $\sum_1^\infty f(m)q^m$ are elliptic modular functions. A number of them are calculated explicitly. Some are known (e.g., Ramanujan's $\frac{1}{256}\theta_2^8\theta_3^8\theta_4^8$), others are new (e.g., $\frac{1}{16}\theta_2^4\theta_3^8\theta_4^4(\theta_4^4-\theta_2^4)$). The proofs are elementary but the formulas for decomposition into 2, 4 and 8 squares are required. *N. G. de Bruijn.*

F10-14 **(8, 316c)**

Kesava Menon, P. Transformation of products of ϑ-functions. J. Indian Math. Soc. (N.S.) **9**, 93–105 (1945).

It is proved that

$$\vartheta_3(x\,|\,\alpha\tau)\vartheta_3(y\,|\,\beta\tau) = \sum_{r=0}^{M-1} q^{r^2(ab^2+\beta d^2)}e^{2r\pi i(bx+dy)}\vartheta_3(ax+cy+rN\tau\,|\,M\tau) \times\vartheta_3(a\alpha y-c\beta x+r\alpha\beta\tau\,|\,\alpha\beta M\tau),$$

where α, β are positive integers, a, b, c, d are integers satisfying the relation $ad-bc=\pm1$ and M and N are equal to $a^2\alpha+c^2\beta$, $ab\alpha+cd\beta$, respectively. A formula of Schröter [Tannery and Molk, Éléments de la Théorie des Functions Elliptiques, v. 2, Paris, 1896, p. 166] follows as a particular case for $a=c=d=1$, $b=0$. By considering other special cases, the author obtains several theorems of which the following is typical. If M is an odd prime greater than α or β and $D(N)$ and $D(N; r, \rho)$ denote, respectively, the number of representations of N in the forms

$$\alpha m^2+\beta n^2,\ M\{(m+\rho/M)^2+\alpha\beta(n+r/M)^2\},$$

where m, n are integers, $\rho^2+\alpha\beta r^2\equiv0 \pmod M$ and $0\leqq\rho\leqq(M-1)/2$, then

$$D(N)=D(N; 0, 0)+2\sum_{r=1}^{(M-1)/2} D(N; r, \rho).$$

The paper concludes with a generalization, too lengthy to reproduce here, for the product $\prod_{j=1}^n\vartheta_3(x_J\,|\,\alpha_J\tau)$.

W. H. Gage (Vancouver, B. C.).

F10-15 **(8, 328g)**

Min, Szu-hoa. A generalized theory of vectorial modular forms of positive dimensions. Acad. Sinica Science Record **1**, 313–318 (1945).

The author refers to an unpublished manuscript of Hua in which the theory of modular forms of positive dimensions, developed by Zuckerman and the reviewer, is extended to vectorial modular forms. By a vectorial modular form of dimension r is meant a vector $V(\tau)=(f_1(\tau), \cdots, f_n(\tau))$ of functions of the complex variable τ regular in the upper τ-half-plane such that $V(\tau)$ satisfies for the modular substitutions a functional equation

$$V\left(\frac{a\tau+b}{c\tau+d}\right)=(-i(c\tau+d))^{-r}V(\tau)\mathfrak{M}(a, b, c, d),$$

where $\mathfrak{M}(a, b, c, d)$ is a matrix of degree n, independent of τ. The author gives a short sketch of a further generalization. He admits finitely many poles in the fundamental region of the modular group. His theory is a generalization of Zuckerman's [Amer. J. Math. **62**, 127–152; these Rev. **1**, 214] and seems to follow Zuckerman's arguments closely. The paper does not contain any detailed proofs.

H. Rademacher (Philadelphia, Pa.).

Citations: MR 1, 214c = F10-1.

F10-16 **(9, 13d)**

Petersson, H. Modulformen und Zahlentheorie. Ber. Math.-Tagung Tübingen 1946, pp. 116–118 (1947).

Brief report of a lecture. *H. S. Zuckerman.*

F10-17 **(9, 273b)**

Chowla, S. Modular equations as solutions of algebraic differential equations of the sixth order. Proc. Nat. Inst. Sci. India **13**, 169–170 (1947).

It is shown that modular equations are solutions of algebraic differential equations. *H. S. Zuckerman.*

F10-18 **(10, 603a)**

Cohn, Harvey. Some Diophantine aspects of modular functions. I. Essential singularities. Amer. J. Math. **71**, 403–416 (1949).

The author considers the behavior of certain modular forms of negative dimension on approach to the boundary of their domain of existence. He defines a "Poincaré theta function" of integral order $m\geqq0$ and degree r to be a single-valued function $f(z)$, regular in the upper half-plane except for a finite number of poles, and satisfying

$$f(z')=(cz+d)^{2m}f(z), \tag{1}$$

where $z'=(az+b)/(cz+d)$ is a modular substitution; the integer r is the order of the pole in the Fourier series $f(z)=(\exp -2\pi irz)(k_0'+k_1'\exp 2\pi iz+\cdots)$, $k_0'\neq0$. In other words, f is a modular form of negative even dimension $-2m$, multiplier $v\equiv1$, and having a pole at infinity of order r. Most of his results concern the Eisenstein series $F_{2m}(z)=\sum(cz+d)^{-2m}$, $m\geqq2$, where (c, d) run over all integer pairs except (0, 0), and the Poincaré series

$$G_{2m}(z)=\sum[cz^2+(a+d)z+b]^{-2m}, \qquad m\geqq2,$$

where the sum is extended over all substitutions $\begin{pmatrix} a & b \\ c & d\end{pmatrix}$ in the full modular group. As noted by Poincaré, $G_{2m}(z)$ vanishes identically unless $m=6$, or $m\geqq8$.

From (1) it is easily seen that $f(z)\asymp(z-p/q)^{-2m}$ as z approaches the rational point p/q in a Stolz neighborhood, i.e., inside the wedge $z=p/q+\rho_1+i\rho_2$, ρ_1, ρ_2 real, $\rho_2>0$, $|\rho_2/\rho_1|\geqq\lambda>0$. ($f\asymp g$ means that $|f/g|$ is bounded away from 0 and ∞.)

Using a generalization of a method of Hardy and Littlewood [Acta Math. **37**, 193–239 (1914)], the author considers approach to an irrational point θ whose continued fraction has bounded partial quotients (this includes the case of real quadratic irrationalities). He proves that if $f(z)$ is a Poincaré theta function of order m without poles, then $f(z)=O[(z-\theta)^{-m}]$ as $z\to\theta$ in a Stolz neighborhood; if $f(z)$ has no zeros as well as no poles, $f(z)\asymp(z-\theta)^{-m}$. As a special case, $G_{2m}(z)=O[(z-\theta)^{-2m}]$, but $G_{12}(z)\asymp(z-\theta)^{-12}$. The last equation is especially interesting because G_{12} is proportional to the square of $\Delta=\eta^{24}(z)$, the Dedekind modular function. Thus $|\eta(z)|$ tends to infinity on approach to irrational θ in the class considered, whereas it is known to tend to zero on approach to all rational real points. The O-estimation can be improved to $\asymp$ only in the case noted above, i.e., in the case G_{12}.

Finally the author states without proof that a Poincaré theta function can satisfy $f(z)\asymp(z-\theta)^s$, s real, only if θ is rational and f is of degree zero, or if θ is irrational and $f(z)=G_{12}(z)^{k/2}\exp g(J(z))$. Here k is an integer, g is an entire function, and $J(z)$ is the absolute modular invariant.

J. Lehner (Philadelphia, Pa.).

F10-19 (11, 15e)

Walton, Jean B. Theta series in the Gaussian field. Duke Math. J. **16**, 479–491 (1949).

Let $\vartheta_r(\tau, \rho, 1)=\sum\mu^r \exp(2\pi i\tau\mu\mu'/4)$, where the sum is taken over all Gaussian integers $\mu\equiv\rho \pmod 4$ and r is a positive integer. Only even values of r are of interest. For $r\equiv 0 \pmod 4$ there are three independent functions given by taking $\rho=0$, $1+i$ and 1. For $r\equiv 2 \pmod 4$ all the functions can be expressed in terms of $\vartheta_r(\tau, 1, 1)$. The behavior of each of these functions under modular transformations on τ is determined. In general the functions are not modular but $\omega_2^{-(r+1)}\vartheta_r(\omega_1/\omega_2, \rho, 1)$ is a modular form of dimension $-(r+1)$ and level 4. Now let $f_r(\tau)=\sum\mu^r \exp(\pi i\tau\mu\mu')$ where μ runs through all Gaussian integers. The only case of interest is $r\equiv 0 \pmod 4$. Then $f_r(\tau)$ can be expressed in terms of the $\vartheta_r(\tau, \rho, 1)$. This makes it possible to obtain transformation formulas for $f_r(\tau)$ and then to express $f_r(\tau)$ in terms of Jacobi's theta functions. This is done and the explicit expressions are given for certain values of r. Finally there is a discussion of the multiplicative properties of the coefficients of $f_r(\tau)$ when it is expanded in powers of $e^{\pi i\tau}$.

H. S. Zuckerman (Seattle, Wash.).

F10-20 (11, 95e)

Petersson, Hans. Über die systematische Bedeutung der Eisensteinschen Reihen. Abh. Math. Sem. Univ. Hamburg **16**, 104–126 (1949).

In previous papers the author has investigated Eisenstein series of dimension $-r$ $(r\geqq 2)$:

$$G_{-r}(\tau, a_1, a_2, N)=\sum{}'(m_1\tau+m_2)^{-r}, \quad (a_1, a_2)=1,$$

where $m_i\equiv a_i(N)$; for $r=2$, convergence fails and the series must be modified by the introduction of a convergence factor due originally to Hecke. Most of the present paper is devoted to the restatement of the author's previous results; toward the end of the paper he extends his theorems to $r=1$, and proves in particular [notation the same as in previous papers; cf., e.g., Math. Nachr. **1**, 218–257 (1948); these Rev. **10**, 525]: the Eisenstein series $G_{-1}(\tau, a_1, a_2, N)$ of level N and dimension -1 constitute a basis for $\mathfrak{N}_1$, the family of modular forms which are orthogonal to every entire cusp-form of the same level and dimension.

J. Lehner (Philadelphia, Pa.).

F10-21 (11, 163b)

Petersson, Hans. Über die lineare Zerlegung der den ganzen Modulformen von höherer Stufe entsprechenden Dirichletreihen in vollständige Eulersche Produkte. Acta Math. **80**, 191–221 (1948).

This paper gives an extension of Hecke's and the author's theory of Dirichlet series with Euler products to the case in which the modular forms involved are not necessarily entire. A typical result is as follows. Let $\mathfrak{S}$ be a linear set of modular forms of dimension $-r$ (r=positive integer), belonging to the divisor t of the "Stufe" N, and having the character (multiplier) ϵ. Let $\mathfrak{S}$ be closed with respect to all operators $\{T_n\}$ with $(n, N)=1$. Define $\mathfrak{S}^+$ as the intersection of $\mathfrak{S}$ with $\mathfrak{C}_r^+$ (the set of entire cusp-forms of dimension $-r$), and $\mathfrak{N}$ as the set of forms in $\mathfrak{S}$ orthogonal to $\mathfrak{S}^+$. Then $\mathfrak{N}$ (as well as $\mathfrak{S}^+$) possesses a finite basis, say $h_j(\tau)$ $(1\leqq j\leqq\kappa)$, which consists entirely of characteristic functions of $\{T_n\}$; let the characteristic values be $\mu_j(n)$. The corresponding Dirichlet series $D(s, h_j)$ have the generalized Euler products:

$$D(s, h_j)=t^{-s}K(s, h_j)\prod_{(p,N)=1}(1-\mu_j(p)p^{-s}+\epsilon(p)p^{r-1}p^{-2s})^{-1},$$

where the "kernel" $K(s, h_j)$ is a Dirichlet series,

$$K(s, h_j)=\sum_{m=1}^{\infty} b_{jm}m^{-s},$$

in which $b_{jm}=0$ whenever m is divisible by other than those primes which divide t but not N/t.

J. Lehner.

F10-22 (11, 343c)

Schoeneberg, Bruno. Multiplikative Gruppen algebraischer Funktionen. Abh. Math. Sem. Univ. Hamburg **16**, nos. 3–4, 136–139 (1949).

Let N be an integer larger than 2. The author exhibits explicit generating elements of the field of algebraic functions which belongs to the principal modular group $\Gamma(N)$ and thus extends an important result of Hecke. His proof is based on Hecke's and Hurwitz's well-known result in which the Nth division values of the Weierstrass $\wp$-function, all of which have dimension -2, are identified as generating elements of the linear space of the Eisenstein series of dimension -2 belonging to the group $\Gamma(N)$. There are $\sigma-1$ independent such forms, where σ denotes the number of rational vertices of the canonical fundamental domain of $\Gamma(N)$. The set of vertices S_i has the following special property: all functions of the form $\sum_{i=1}^{\sigma}\nu_iS_i$, with integers ν_i satisfying $\sum_{i=1}^{\sigma}\nu_i=0$, form a free group with $\sigma-1$ free generators. Thus there are $\sigma-1$ functions $g_i=\mu_iS_i-\mu_iS_\sigma$ whose μ_ith roots are multiplicative radical functions with μ_ith roots of unity for multipliers relative to the surface of $\Gamma(N)$ and a pole and zero of order 1 at S_σ and S_i, respectively. Therefore this special property together with Hecke's theorem on the behaviour of Eisenstein series at the rational vertices of the fundamental domain implies the existence of the field generators. Finally the result is extended to arbitrary congruence groups $\Gamma_1(N)$ modulo N by combining suitable transforms of the fundamental domain of $\Gamma(N)$ and considering appropriate Nth division values of the p-function so as to obtain the right multipliers with respect to $\Gamma_1(N)$.

O. F. G. Schilling (Chicago, Ill.).

F10-23 (12, 12a)

Hasse, Helmut. Osservazioni riguardanti funzioni ellittiche e numeri algebrici. Ann. Mat. Pura Appl. (4) **29**, 225–242 (1949).

Using the congruence groups mod 3 and 4, the author establishes Hurwitz's results on the effect of the modular group $\{S\}$ on the branches of the 12th roots Δ_{12} of the discriminant $g_2^3(W)-27g_3^2(W)$, where

$$W=\begin{pmatrix}W_1\\W_2\end{pmatrix}, \quad \Delta_{12}(SW)=\chi_{12}(S)\Delta_{12}(W).$$

Subsequently, similar results are discussed for quotients of suitably modified elliptic σ-functions. Next, the significance of the nonanalytic function $D(W)=|W|^{\frac{1}{2}}\Delta_{12}(W)^{\frac{1}{2}}\bar{\Delta}_{12}(W)^{\frac{1}{2}}$, and of analogous "normal" elliptic functions, as invariants of ray classes and for the determination of class numbers and units (with generalizations to real quadratic fields) is indicated. In this connection see Dedekind [J. Reine Angew. Math. **121**, 40–123 (1900)].

O. F. G. Schilling.

F10-24 (12, 394a)

Petersson, Hans. Zwei Bemerkungen über die Weierstrasspunkte der Kongruenzgruppen. Arch. Math. **2**, 246–250 (1950).

Let $\Gamma(N)$ be the principal congruence subgroup of Stufe N of the modular group with genus p and with τ_0 a point in a fundamental region $\mathfrak{F}$. Let $M(\tau_0)$ be the set of all automorphic functions belonging to $\Gamma(N)$ which are regular everywhere in $\mathfrak{F}$ except at τ_0. Let $\lambda_i(\tau_0)$ be the ith gap in the sequence of possible pole-orders of the functions in $M(\tau_0)$ and let $\beta(\tau_0)=\beta_N(\tau_0)=\sum_{i=1}^{p}(\lambda_i(\tau_0)-i)$. If $\beta(\tau_0)>0$ the point τ_0 is called a Weierstrass-point of $\Gamma(N)$. By counting in two ways the number of such points in $\mathfrak{F}$ the author gives a rather simple proof that, for $N=1, 2, \cdots$, none of the algebraic forms defined by $\Gamma(N)$ is hyperelliptic. If $A=\beta_N(\infty)$, then by a similar type of argument it is shown that if $N\geqq 7$ we have $6A\equiv 0 \pmod N$ except in the following five cases (q denotes a prime): (a) N not square-free; (b) $N=q\geqq 7$; (c) $N=2q$, $q\geqq 5$, $q\neq 7, 11$; (d) $N=3q$, $q\geqq 5$; (e) $N=6q$, $q\geqq 5$, $q\neq 7$. *T. M. Apostol* (Pasadena, Calif.).

Referred to in F10-27, F10-80, F10-84.

F10-25 (12, 806e)

Petersson, Hans. Konstruktion der Modulformen und der zu gewissen Grenzkreisgruppen gehörigen automorphen Formen von positiver reeller Dimension und die vollständige Bestimmung ihrer Fourierkoeffizienten. S.-B. Heidelberger Akad. Wiss. Math.-Nat. Kl. **1950**, 417–494 (1950).

The construction of the modular and automorphic forms of positive dimension is accomplished by making use of their algebraic properties and relationships, and avoids the extensive use of analytical processes found in the investigations of Hardy and Ramanujan, Rademacher and Zuckerman. The present investigation also differs from the others in that no restrictions are placed on the position or order of the poles.

The modular forms of positive dimension are represented as linear combinations of certain basic functions, analogous to the representation of rational functions by partial fractions. If $F(z)$ is a modular form of positive dimension $r-2$ and has a simple pole at $z=\tau_0$ the corresponding basic function $H(\tau_0, z)$ is obtained by interchanging the roles of variable and parameter in a Poincaré series $H(\tau, z)$. As a function of τ, $H(\tau, z)$ is a modular form of negative dimension $-r<-2$ with a simple pole at $\tau=z$. In case of a pole of higher order, derivatives of $H(\tau, z)$ are also used. Corresponding to a pole at $z=\infty$, certain Fourier series F_{r-2} are used. Not all linear combinations of these basic functions are modular, but necessary and sufficient conditions for modularity are found.

The $H(\tau, z)$ and F_{r-2} are related to other Poincaré series G of dimension $-r$ having poles at ∞. The Fourier coefficients of the G are determined and, from these, the Fourier coefficients of $F(z)$ are found. These coefficients of $F(z)$ finally depend on the coefficients of the principal parts of $F(z)$ at each of its poles, the Fourier coefficients of the G and the values of the G and their derivatives at the poles of $F(z)$.

The results for the automorphic forms, with certain restrictions on their transformation groups, are quite similar. A symmetry property of the modular group is obtained and several isolated topics relating to modular forms are discussed in the light of the above results.

H. S. Zuckerman (Seattle, Wash.).

Referred to in F10-42, F30-26, P72-29.

F10-26 (13, 209c)

Fischer, Wilhelm. On Dedekind's function $\eta(\tau)$. Pacific J. Math. **1**, 83–95 (1951).

The author proves the transformation formula for Dedekind's function $\eta(\tau)=e^{2\pi i\tau}\prod_{n=1}^{\infty}(1-e^{2\pi i m\tau})$, namely

$$\eta\left(\frac{a\tau+b}{c\tau+d}\right)=\epsilon\surd\{-i(c\tau+d)\}\eta(\tau),$$

where a, b, c and d are integers satisfying $ad-bc=1$, $c\geqq 0$. The square root is the principal branch witn positive real part and, since $\eta(\tau)$ is the 24th root of the discriminant, ϵ is a 24th root of unity which depends upon a, b, c and d in a rather complicated manner. Previous determinations of ϵ have used the theory of $\log \eta(\tau)$. The author evaluates ϵ directly from Euler's formula for $\eta(\tau)$ using only Poisson's formula for $\sum_{n=-\infty}^{\infty}\exp\{-\pi(m \mid \alpha)^2 t\}$ ($\Re t>0$), and Gauss sums. *R. A. Rankin* (Birmingham).

Referred to in P72-32.

F10-27 (13, 439c)

Schoeneberg, Bruno. Über die Weierstrass-Punkte in den Körpern der elliptischen Modulfunktionen. Abh. Math. Sem. Univ. Hamburg **17**, 104–111 (1951).

Let $\mathfrak{F}$ be an algebraic function field of one variable of genus $p(\mathfrak{F})\equiv p>0$. Let $\mathfrak{p}$ be a point of the associated Riemann surface. Moreover, let $\mathfrak{G}$ denote the group of automorphisms of $\mathfrak{F}$, and let $\mathfrak{p}$ be a fixed point for the automorphism S of order n. Let $\mathfrak{C}$ be the subfield of $\mathfrak{F}$ which is invariant for the automorphisms S^ν, $\nu=1, 2, \cdots, n$, and let the genus of $\mathfrak{C}$ be $p(\mathfrak{C})$. The author proves that $\mathfrak{p}$ is a Weierstrass point if the condition

$$0\leqq p(\mathfrak{F})-np(\mathfrak{C})<n$$

is not satisfied.

This criterion is used to obtain the following results for $\Gamma(N)$, the principal congruence subgroups of Stufe N of the full modular group $\Gamma(1)$. 1) For $N\geqq 7$ the rational points of the fundamental region of $\Gamma(N)$ are Weierstrass points of the algebraic function field belonging to $\Gamma(N)$ [see also Petersson, Arch. Math. **2**, 246–250 (1950); these Rev. **12**, 394]. 2) The points equivalent to i under $\Gamma(1)$ are Weierstrass points for $N=9$ and $N>10$. For $N\leqq 8$, they are not. 3) The points equivalent to $\rho=e^{(2\pi i)/3}$ under $\Gamma(1)$ are Weierstrass points for $N=10$, 12 and $N>13$. For $N\leqq 8$ they are not. 4) ρ and equivalent points are Weierstrass points for $N=13$. *W. H. Simons* (Vancouver, B. C.).

Citations: MR 12, 394a = F10-24.

Referred to in F10-80, F10-84, F10-92.

F10-28 (14, 250a)

Newman, Morris. Remarks on some modular identities. Trans. Amer. Math. Soc. **73**, 313–320 (1952).

For primes $p>3$ the author considers the functions (r integral)

$$S_r(\tau)=\sum_{n=0}^{p-1}h^r(W^{-pn}\tau),$$

where $h(\tau)=\eta(p^2\tau)/\eta(\tau)$; $\eta(\tau)$ is the Dedekind function $\exp(\pi i\tau/12)\cdot\prod_{n=1}^{\infty}(1-x^n)$ and $x=\exp 2\pi i\tau$; W is the matrix $\binom{1\ 0}{1\ 1}$, so that the matrices W^{-pn} ($n=0, 1, \cdots, p-1$) are a set of right representatives for $\Gamma_0(p^2)$ in $\Gamma_0(p)$ (i.e., the group of all modular matrices $\binom{a\ b}{c\ d}$ for which $c\equiv 0 \pmod p$) and therefore S_r is invariant under the substitutions of $\Gamma_0(p)$. The author studies the behaviour of S_r in the parabolic points $i\infty$, 0 of the fundamental region of $\Gamma_0(p)$. The Ramanujan identities for partitions modulo 5, 7 and Mordell's identity for $\tau(n)$ are obtained as special cases. The author derives also some new identities such as

$$\sum_{n=0}^{\infty}p_r(np+\delta)x^n=p_r(\delta)\prod_{n=1}^{\infty}(1-x^n)^r-p^{\frac{1}{2}r-1}x^\delta\prod_{n=1}^{\infty}(1-x^{np})^r,$$

where $0<r\leqq 24$, $r(p-1)\equiv 0 \pmod{24}$, $\delta=r(p-1)/24$ and $p_r(n)$ is the generalized partition function defined by $\prod_{n=1}^{\infty}(1-x^n)^r=\sum_{n=0}^{\infty}p_r(n)x^n$. *H. D. Kloosterman.*

Referred to in P60-16, P60-17.

F10-29 (15, 105b)

Schoeneberg, Bruno. Über den Zusammenhang der Eisensteinschen Reihen und Thetareihen mit der Diskriminante der elliptischen Funktionen. Math. Ann. **126**, 177–184 (1953).

Making use of the work of Hecke on Eisenstein series

and theta series, the writer shows how to construct the principal function of the congruence group of genus $p=0$, when the number of corners of the fundamental domain $\geqq 3$, by means of Eisenstein series. He also exhibits the functions $\Delta_\lambda(\tau)=(\Delta(\lambda))^{1/\lambda}$, $\lambda|12$, in terms of Eisenstein series. Define the generalized binary theta series

$$\vartheta_k(\tau;\rho,\mathfrak{a},QD^{\frac{1}{2}})=\sum\mu^{k-1}\exp\{2\pi i\tau\mu\mu'/AQ|D|\},$$

the summation extending over all integers of $R(D^{\frac{1}{2}})$ such that $\mu\equiv\rho\pmod{\mathfrak{a}QD^{\frac{1}{2}}}$, where $\rho\in\mathfrak{a}$ and A is the norm of $\mathfrak{a}$. Then $\Delta_\lambda(\tau)$ is represented by means of ϑ_k in such a manner as to obtain the Euler product of the associated Dirichlet series and also to get bounds for the coefficients. Finally the writer indicates a connection between the number of representations of an integer as a sum of $2k$ squares and the Eisenstein series and the functions $\Delta_\lambda(\tau)$. *L. Carlitz.*

F10-30 (15, 290c)

Rosen, S. Modular transformation of certain series. Duke Math. J. **20**, 593–599 (1953).

If $\eta(\tau)=x^{1/24}\prod_{n=1}^{\infty}(1-x^n)$, $x=e^{2\pi i\tau}$, denotes Dedekind's modular function, then $[\eta(2\tau)/\eta(\tau)]^{24}$ is invariant under the sub-group consisting of those transformations $\begin{pmatrix}a & b\\ c & d\end{pmatrix}$ of the modular group in which c is even. This invariance gives rise to a transformation formula for the function $f(x)=\prod_{n=1}^{\infty}(1+x^n)=e^{-\pi i\tau/12}\eta(2\tau)/\eta(\tau)$, this being the generating function for the number Q_n of partitions of n into unequal parts. Hua [Trans. Amer. Math. Soc. **51**, 194–201 (1942); these Rev. **3**, 270] has used this functional equation to obtain a convergent series for Q_n. Hua also showed that if Q_n is defined by its series expansion, then the function $1+\sum Q_nx^n$ is the same as $f(x)$. The author derives the functional equation for $f(x)$ directly from Hua's series for Q_n by extending a method developed by Rademacher [Amer. J. Math. **61**, 237–248 (1939); **64**, 456 (1942); these Rev. **3**, 271] in studying a similar problem concerning $J(\tau)$. The problem is more involved in the case of $f(x)$, partly because of the presence of certain complicated roots of unity in the transformation equation.

T. M. Apostol.

Citations: MR 3, 270c = P72-4; MR 3, 271d = F10-8.

F10-31 (15, 507f)

Koecher, Max. Ein neuer Beweis der Kroneckerschen Grenzformel. Arch. Math. **4**, 316–321 (1953).

Let $\tau=x+iy$ be a complex number, where $y>0$ and let

$$\zeta(\tau;s)=\sum_{m,n}{}'|m\tau+n|^{-2s}\quad(\operatorname{Re}(s)>1),$$

where (m,n) runs through all pairs of integers $\neq(0,0)$. Then if $\eta(\tau;s)=\pi^{-1}y\zeta(\tau;s)-(s-1)^{-1}$, the formula in question is

$$\eta(\tau;1)=-\tfrac{1}{12}\log(\Delta(\tau)\Delta(-\bar\tau))-2\log y+K,$$

where K is a constant ($=2C-2\log 2$, where C is Euler's constant) and $\Delta(\tau)=e^{2\pi i\tau}\prod_{n=1}^{\infty}(1-e^{2\pi in\tau})^{24}$. The author's proof is based on the following well known theorem: If $f(\tau)$ is regular and $\neq0$ for $y>0$, $f(\tau)=f(-\bar\tau)$, $y^{-m}|\log|f(\tau)||$ is bounded for some $m>0$, and if $(c\tau+d)^{-12}f(a\tau+b/c\tau+d)=f(\tau)$ for all modular substitutions $\tau\to a\tau+b/c\tau+d$, then

$$f(\tau)=c\Delta(\tau),$$

where c is a constant. The constant K is determined by taking $\tau=i$ and applying Hurwitz's formula

$$\Delta(i)=(2\pi)^{-24}\Gamma^{24}(\tfrac14).$$

H. D. Kloosterman (Leiden).

Referred to in F10-41.

F10-32 (15, 603d)

Pfetzer, Werner. Die Wirkung der Modulsubstitutionen auf mehrfache Thetareihen zu quadratischen Formen ungerader Variablenzahl. Arch. Math. **4**, 448–454 (1953).

The author applies a method of Hecke [Math. Ann. **97**, 210–242 (1926)] to the problem of determining the level (Stufe) of the modular form given by the theta series based on a positive definite quadratic form (with rational integral coefficients) in n variables, where n is odd, and to a more general series obtained by applying powers of certain linear first-order differential operators in n variables. For an even number of variables, the analogous discussion was given by B. Schoeneberg [ibid. **116**, 511–523 (1939)]. The present paper obtains most of Schoeneberg's results, the principal one being that the class of modular forms has in all cases level $2N$, in some cases level N, where $N=D/K$, D being the determinant of the quadratic form, and K the greatest common divisor of the $(n-1)$-rowed determinants formed from the matrix of the quadratic form. *J. Lehner.*

F10-33 (15, 603f)

Rankin, R. A., and Rushforth, J. M. The coefficients of certain integral modular forms. Proc. Cambridge Philos. Soc. **50**, 305–308 (1954).

If k is even, $k\geqq12$, then the space of cusp-forms of dimension $-k$ belonging to the full modular group has a finite basis $f_k^{(j)}(z)=\sum_{n=1}^{\infty}\lambda_k^{(j)}(n)e^{2\pi inz}$. The real algebraic numbers $\lambda_k^{(j)}(n)$ are shown to be algebraic integers belonging to a field $K_k^{(j)}$. Bounds for the degree of $K_k^{(j)}$ over the field of rational numbers are given. *H. S. Zuckerman.*

F10-34 (15, 941a)

Lekkerkerker, C. G. The elements of the theory of modular forms, derived from properties of theta series. Math. Centrum Amsterdam. Rapport **ZW 1953-006**, 17 pp. (1953).

Expository paper.

F10-35 (16, 16b)

Siegel, Carl Ludwig. A simple proof of

$$\eta(-1/\tau)=\eta(\tau)\sqrt{\tau/i}.$$

Mathematika **1**, 4 (1954).

The author gives a short and extremely elegant proof of the equation in the title, which is a special case of the difficult transformation formula first proved in generality by Dedekind and Hermite. Taking logarithms and expanding in power series, one finds that the formula in question is equivalent to

$$\pi i\frac{\tau+\tau^{-1}}{12}+\frac12\log\frac{\tau}{i}=\sum_{k=1}^{\infty}\frac1k\left(\frac{1}{e^{-2\pi ik\tau}-1}-\frac{1}{e^{2\pi ik/\tau}-1}\right).$$

Let $f(z)=\tau^{-1}\cot z\cot z$, $\nu=(n+\frac12)\pi$, $n=0,1,2,\cdots$, and integrate $z^{-1}f(\nu z)$ over the contour C of the rhombus with vertices at $1,\tau,-1,-\tau$ in the z-plane. Then by the residue theorem

$$\pi i\frac{\tau+\tau^{-1}}{12}+\int_C f(\nu z)\frac{dz}{8z}=\sum_{k=1}^{n}\frac1k\left(\frac{1}{e^{-2\pi ik\tau}-1}-\frac{1}{e^{2\pi ik/\tau}-1}\right).$$

But as $n\to\infty$, $f(\nu z)$ has on the sides of the rhombus the limiting values $1,-1,1,-1$. This gives

$$\lim_{n\to\infty}\int_C f(z)\frac{dz}{z}=4\log\tau/i$$

and completes the proof. *J. Lehner.*

Referred to in F10-40, F10-41, F10-75, F10-119, F65-15, F65-19.

F10-36 **(16, 449c)**

Maass, Hans. Die Differentialgleichungen in der Theorie der elliptischen Modulfunktionen. Math. Ann. **125** (1952), 235–263 (1953).

The differential operator

$$D=-y^2\left(\frac{\partial^2}{\partial x^2}+\frac{\partial^2}{\partial y^2}\right)+(\alpha-\beta)iy\frac{\partial}{\partial x}-(\alpha+\beta)y\frac{\partial}{\partial y}$$

annihilates Eisenstein series of type

$$E(z, w; \alpha, \beta)=\sum_{c,d}\gamma(c, d)(cz+d)^{-\alpha}(cw+d)^{-\beta},$$

where $z=x+iy$, $w=\bar{z}=x-iy$. Let $\{\alpha, \beta\}$ be the linear set of all analytic functions $f(z, w)$, regular in the half-plane $w=\bar{z}$, $\mathfrak{J}(z)>0$, that are annihilated by D. If G is a group of real substitutions $S=\begin{pmatrix} a & b \\ c & d\end{pmatrix}$, $ad-bc=1$. the author considers automorphic forms, belonging to $\{\alpha, \beta\}$, satisfying

$$f(Sz, Sw)(cz+d)^{-\alpha}(cw+d)^{-\beta}=v(S)f(z, w), \quad |v(S)|=1,$$

(where v is a set of multipliers for the group G) and which behave in the usual way in the neighborhood of parabolic fix-points of G. These forms are termed to be of type $\{G; \alpha, \beta; v\}$. If $S_0=\begin{pmatrix} 1 & Q \\ 0 & 1\end{pmatrix}\in G$, $v(S_0)=e^{2\pi i\kappa}$ $(0\leqq\kappa<1)$ the functions of type $\{G; \alpha, \beta; v\}$ have a Fourier development

$$f(z, w)=a_0u(y, \alpha+\beta)+b_0$$

$$+\sum_{n+\kappa\neq 0} a_{n+\kappa}W\left(\frac{2\pi|n+\kappa|}{Q}y; \alpha, \beta, \operatorname{sgn}(n+\kappa)\right)e^{2\pi i(n+\kappa)/Q},$$

where u is an elementary function and W denotes a Whittaker function. If one of the numbers α, β, $\alpha-\beta$ is rational, the Whittaker functions reduce to Bessel functions and exponential functions. The author generalizes the results of Hecke on relations between modular forms and Dirichlet series. If $G=M(Q)$ is the principal congruence subgroup of level Q of the modular group, he also considers the problem of the Euler product development as a generalization of the Hecke-Petersson theory to the theory of the forms $\{M(Q); \alpha, \beta; 1\}$. *H. D. Kloosterman* (Leiden).

Referred to in E12-120, F50-7.

F10-37 **(16, 677d)**

Schoeneberg, Bruno. Über die Quaternionen in der Theorie der elliptischen Modulfunktionen. J. Reine Angew. Math. **193**, 84–93 (1954).

In a previous paper [Math. Ann. **113**, 380–391 (1936)], the author has defined certain theta functions connected with a quaternion algebra, which possess transformation equations of the usual type. In the present work, he considers those theta functions which are modular forms (dimension = 2) of prime level (Stufe). Let

$$(1)\qquad \vartheta(\tau, \rho, \mathfrak{a}, \mathfrak{d})=\sum_{\substack{\mu\equiv\rho\ (\mathfrak{a}\mathfrak{d})\\ \rho\in\mathfrak{a}}}\exp\left(2\pi i\tau\frac{\mu\mu'}{Aq}\right), \quad \operatorname{Im}\tau>0,$$

where q is a rational prime, $\mathfrak{a}$ is an integral right ideal in $\mathfrak{J}$, a maximal order in the definite (generalized) quaternion algebra $\mathfrak{S}$; $\rho\in\mathfrak{a}$, $\mathfrak{d}$ is the different, $\mathfrak{d}^2=(q)$, $(\mathfrak{a}, \mathfrak{d})=1$, $A^2=N(\mathfrak{a})$, and $\mu\mu'$ are not associates. (By a definite quaternion algebra, the author means one in which the product of a number by its conjugate is a definite quadratic form.) The linear family of ϑ obtained by fixing $\mathfrak{a}$ and $\mathfrak{J}$ and varying ρ is partitioned into subsets which are invariant under the substitutions of the irreducible representations of $\mathfrak{M}(q)$, the inhomogeneous modular group mod q. When $\rho=0$, a linear relation is obtained between the ϑ series and the $\wp$ division values of level q. Two numerical examples are given. *J. Lehner* (Los Alamos, N. M.).

F10-38 **(16, 681c)**

van der Blij, F. Even quadratic forms with determinant unity. Quart. J. Math., Oxford Ser. (2) **5**, 297–300 (1954).

Let $q=e^{\pi i\tau}$, $|q|<1$, set $\vartheta_{ij}(0|\tau)=\vartheta_{ij}$ $(i, j=0, 1)$ and define

$$A_k=\tfrac{1}{2}(\vartheta_{00}^{8k}+\vartheta_{01}^{8k}+\vartheta_{10}^{8k}), \quad B_k=\sum_{(m_i)}q^{Q(m_1,\cdots,m_{8k})},$$

where $Q(m_1, \cdots, m_{8k})$ is a quadratic form in $8k$ variables, with even coefficients and determinant unity. The following three theorems are proven: (1) $A_1^2=A_2$. (2) There exist forms Q_k^* such that the corresponding function B_k^* equals A_k. (3) The $[k/3]+1$ functions $A_1^{k-3\alpha}A_3^{\alpha}$ with fixed integer k are linearly independent and A_k can be represented as a sum of these functions, with constant coefficients. (1) follows from the well-known relation $\vartheta_{00}^4=\vartheta_{01}^4+\vartheta_{10}^4$, for which the author gives a simple proof. (2) is proven by actually constructing Q^*, and (3) by induction on k. Some further relations are established between the A_k's, the Eisenstein series of dimension -12 and $\Delta_3=q\prod_{n=1}^{\infty}(1-q^n)^{24}$.

E. Grosswald (Philadelphia, Pa.).

F10-39 **(17, 15e)**

Cohn, Harvey. Modular functions defined by perturbation mappings. Lectures on functions of a complex variable, pp. 341–348. The University of Michigan Press, Ann Arbor, 1955. \$10.00.

Let Π_ε be the region in the upper half z-plane which remains after removing from it all interiors of the circles $C_{p/q}(\varepsilon)$ tangent to the real axis at p/q and of diameter ε/q^2. Here p/q runs through the rational points on the real axis; $0<\varepsilon<1$; $C_{1/0}(\varepsilon)$ is the region $\operatorname{Im} z>1/\varepsilon$. If $\zeta=\zeta_\varepsilon(z)$ is the function which maps Π_ε onto the upper half ζ-plane with point and directions fixed at $z=\zeta=i$ $(d\zeta/dz>0)$, the author proves that the limit

$$\lim_{\varepsilon\to 0}\frac{\zeta_\varepsilon(z)-z}{\varepsilon^2}$$

exists and is equal to $-\pi^2P(z)/12$, where

$$P(z)=z^3-5z/2-\sum_{q=1}^{\infty}\sum_{p}q^{-3}(p+qz)^{-1}$$

(p runs through all integers prime to q). The third derivative of $P(z)$ is an Eisenstein series.

H. D. Kloosterman (Ann Arbor, Mich.).

Referred to in F40-43.

F10-40 **(17, 15f)**

Rademacher, Hans. On the transformation of $\log\eta(\tau)$. J. Indian Math. Soc. (N.S.) **19**, 25–30 (1955).

The author provides an elegant proof of the difficult transformation formula for the Dedekind modular function $\log\eta(\tau)$, where for $\operatorname{Im}\tau>0$,

$$\eta(\tau)=\exp\{\pi i\tau/12\}\prod_{1}^{\infty}(1-\exp\{2\pi im\tau\}).$$

He states that his proof is a generalization of one of Siegel's [Mathematika **1**, 4 (1954); MR **16**, 16] where the special transformation $\tau\to-1/\tau$ was considered, but aside from the fact that contour integration and the calculus of residues are used in both, the two proofs have little in common.

The general transformation formula for

$$\log\eta(\tau)\quad (\tau\to(a\tau+b)/(c\tau+d))$$

can be written as an identity in which the right member

is $-\log z$, while the left member involves Lambert series, an elementary term, and the arithmetic function studied by Dedekind: $s(h,k)=\sum_{\mu=1}^{k-1}(\mu k^{-1}-\frac{1}{2})(\mu hk^{-1}-[\mu hk^{-1}]-\frac{1}{2})$. Here $\tau=(h+iz)/k$, h/k runs over all reduced rational fractions in (0, 1) and Re $z>0$. Rademacher introduces the function (of which the first term is essentially Siegel's)

$$F_n(x)=-\frac{1}{4ix}\coth \pi Nx \cot \frac{\pi Nx}{z}+\sum_{\mu=1}^{k-1}\frac{1}{x}\cdot\frac{e^{2\pi\mu Nx/k}}{1-e^{2\pi Nx}}\cdot\frac{e^{2\pi i\mu^* Nx/kz}}{1-e^{2\pi iNx/z}}$$

with $N=n+\frac{1}{2}$, and the parallelogram C with vertices $z, i, -z, -i$ ($\mu^*\equiv h\mu \pmod k$, $1\leq\mu^*<k$). By direct estimation and with $n\to\infty$, we find $\lim_{n\to\infty}\int_C F_n(x)dx=-\log z$. The remainder of the proof consists in showing that the residues of $F_n(x)$ add up, when $n\to\infty$, to the left member of the above-mentioned identity, which is done by straightforward calculation. The residue at $x=0$ of the general term in the sum of $F_n(x)$ contains the term

$$(\mu k^{-1}-\tfrac{1}{2})(\mu^* k^{-1}-\tfrac{1}{2}).$$

Since from the definition we have $\mu^*k^{-1}=h\mu k^{-1}-[h\mu k^{-1}]$, this is the way the Dedekind sum $s(h,k)$ arises in the final formula.

This proof is shorter and more elementary than the previously known proofs of the Dedekind formula.

J. Lehner (Los Alamos, N.M.).

Citations: MR 16, 16b = F10-35.

Referred to in F10-56, F10-75.

F10-41 (17, 129a)

Meinardus, Günter. Über die Kroneckersche Grenzformel. Math. Z. **62** (1955), 347–351.

Let $\tau=x+iy$ with $y>0$ and for $\text{Re}(s)>1$ set $\zeta(s)\sum_{n=1}^{\infty}n^{-s}$ and

$$Z(\tau,s)=\sum_{\substack{n,m\\ n^2+m^2\neq 0}}|n+m\tau|^{-2s}.$$

Then Kronecker's [S.-B. Preuss. Akad. Wiss. **1885,** 761–784, p. 775; **1889,** 123–135, p. 135] formula

$$(*)\quad \lim_{s\to 1}\{Z(\tau,s)-\pi/y(s-1)\}=-\frac{2\pi}{y}\log\{\eta(\tau)\eta(-\bar\tau)\}-\frac{2\pi}{y}\log y+\frac{2\pi}{y}(\gamma-\log 2)$$

holds; here γ is the Euler constant and $\eta(\tau)$ the Dedekind function. Koecher [Arch. Math. **4** (1953), 316–321; MR **15,** 507] showed that any proof of (**) $(-i\tau)^{\frac{1}{2}}\eta(\tau)=\eta(-1/\tau)$ can be adapted to yield a proof of (*). Siegel [Mathematika **1** (1954), 4; MR **16,** 16] gave a simple new proof of (**) and the present paper gives the corresponding proof of (*). For non-integral w one has

$$(1)\qquad \pi\operatorname{cotg}\pi w=\frac{1}{w}+\sum_{m=1}^{\infty}\left\{\frac{1}{w+m}+\frac{1}{w-m}\right\},$$

and, for $y>0$, $\text{Re}(s)>\frac{1}{2}$,

$$(2)\qquad \int_{-\infty}^{\infty}|w+iy|^{-2s}dw=\frac{\Gamma(\frac{1}{2})\Gamma(s-\frac{1}{2})}{\Gamma(s)}y^{1-2s}$$

holds. If W_N stands for the contour of integration formed by the rectilinear segments between the 4 points $N+\frac{1}{2}\pm i\beta$, $\alpha\pm i\beta$, $0<\alpha<1$, $0<\beta<y/2$, N natural integer, then, by (1) and the theorem on residues,

$$\frac{1}{i}\int_{W_N}\{(w+m\tau)(w+m\bar\tau)\}^{-s}\operatorname{ctg}\pi w\,dw=2\sum_{n=1}^{N}|n+m\tau|^{-2s}.$$

Summing both sides over m, using repeatedly the theorem on residues, the uniformity of convergence of the sum under the integral sign on the left and (2), finally, letting N tend to infinity, one obtains the following: Let

$$K(\tau,s)=Z(\tau,s)-2\pi^{\frac{1}{2}}y^{-2s}\Gamma(s-\tfrac{1}{2})\zeta(2s-1)/\Gamma(s);$$

then $K(\tau,1)=-2\pi y^{-1}\log\{\eta(\tau)\eta(-\bar\tau)\}$. This, however, is equivalent to (*), as $\Gamma'(1)=-\gamma$, $\Gamma'(\frac{1}{2})=-\pi^{\frac{1}{2}}(\gamma+2\log 2)$ and $\lim_{s\to1}(\zeta(s)-1/(s-1))=\gamma$. *E. Grosswald.*

Citations: MR 15, 507f = F10-31; MR 16, 16b = F10-35.

F10-42 (17, 129c)

Petersson, Hans. Über automorphe Formen mit Singularitäten im Diskontinuitätsgebiet. Math. Ann. **129** (1955), 370–390.

Let Γ stand for a Fuchsian group of the first kind, having $\mathfrak{F}$ as one fundamental domain and the real axis as principal circle. Let K be the class of forms $\{\Gamma, -r, v\}$ defined in the upper half-plane of the variable τ, automorphic under Γ, of negative dimension $-r<-2$ and of multipliers v, $|v|=1$; and let $\hat K$ be the complementary class $\{\Gamma, r-2, v^{-1}\}$ of positive dimension $r-2$. As there are no entire automorphic forms of positive dimension (except $F\equiv 0$), the poles and principal parts of a form of $\hat K$ define it uniquely. As a consequence of the theorem on residues and the Riemann-Roch theorem, these poles and principal parts cannot be prescribed arbitrarily, but have to satisfy a "principal-parts condition". If that is satisfied, however, there exists a uniquely determined form F of $\hat K$, satisfying all prescribed conditions. The author indicates an explicit construction of F in the particular case of the modular group, actually valid for any group Γ of the first kind, provided that $\mathfrak{F}$ has a single cusp [S.-B. Heidelberger Akad. Wiss. Math.-Nat. Kl. **1950,** 417–494; MR **12,** 806]. Generalizing these results to the case of arbitrary Fuchsian groups of the first kind, with $\mathfrak{F}$ having any finite number of cusps, the author obtained for F expansions centered at the cusps, involving functions of two complex variables [Math. Ann. **127** (1954), 33–81, cited in what follows as AO; MR **15,** 686]. For each cusp, a different respresentation holds. The analytical apparatus developed in AO did not permit the construction of similar expansions for $F\in\hat K$, around an arbitrary interior point of $\mathfrak{F}$. This the author succeeds in doing in the present paper, using functions of three complex variables. The method follows in the main that of AO. As building blocks are used: (i) functions $P_m(z,s)$, the Fourier coefficients in the expansions of certain generalized Poincaré series $Q(\tau,z,s)$, which will characterize the behaviour of the form at the cusps; and (ii) functions $V_n(z,s,\omega_k)$, characterizing the behaviour at the corners ω_k of F and $V_n(z,s,c_\nu)$, characterizing the behaviour at the poles c_ν. In themselves, these functions are not automorphic forms. But if $\Lambda(z,s)$ is a linear combination of them, $\Lambda(z,s)$ becomes automorphic provided that the coefficients of the linear combination are selected so that the "principal-parts condition" is fulfilled. Accordingly, the main result may be stated as follows: If $\mathfrak{F}$, K, cusps and poles with principal parts are given, such that the "principal-parts condition" holds, then there exists exactly one automorphic form $F(z)$ of class $\hat K$ with the properties: $F(z)$ is regular in $\mathfrak{F}$, except at the cusps, the corners ω_k and the poles c_ν; at the cusps, corners and poles, $F(z)$ has principal parts of a specified form. For every interior point s of $\mathfrak{F}$, $F(z)$ is explicitly represented by $\Lambda(z,s)$. *E. Grosswald.*

Citations: MR 12, 806e = F10-25; MR 15, 686d = R18-19.

F10-43 (17, 968a)

Touchard, J.; et van der Pol, Balth. Equations différentielles linéaires vérifiées par certaines fonctions modulaires elliptiques. Nederl. Akad. Wetensch. Proc. Ser. A. **59**=Indag. Math. **18** (1956), 166–169.

The Fourier expansions for the Eisenstein series can be expressed in the form

$$\sum_{-\infty}^{\infty}{}'\sum_{-\infty}^{\infty}(m+n\tau)^{-2k}=\alpha_{2k-1}(t)\sum_{m=-\infty}^{\infty}{}'m^{-2k},$$

where $t=-2\pi i\tau$ and

$$\alpha_{2k-1}(t)=1+[2/\zeta(1-2k)]\sum_{n=1}^{\infty}e^{-nt}\sigma_{2k-1}(n).$$

The functions α_3 and α_5 are essentially the same as the Weierstrass invariants g_2 and g_3. The authors consider the powers

$$y_k(\tau)=[\alpha_3{}^3(t)-\alpha_5{}^2(t)]^{-k/12}$$

for $k=1, 2, \cdots, 12$. The quotient $y_k{}^{(k+1)}(\tau)/y(\tau)$ is a modular form of dimension $2k+2$ and can be expressed as a polynomial in α_3 and α_5 with rational coefficients. This, of course, results in a linear differential equation satisfied by y_k. The coefficients are determined explicitly for $k=1, 2, \cdots, 12$. In some instances, namely $k=3$, 4, 6 and 12, the differential equation which results is simpler when expressed in terms of the higher α's rather than in terms of α_3 and α_5. *T. M. Apostol* (Pasadena, Calif.).

F10-44 (18, 194h)

Cohn, Harvey. Variational property of cusp forms. Trans. Amer. Math. Soc. **82** (1956), 117–127.

The author proves: A necessary and sufficient condition that a modular form $\varphi(z)$ of dimension -4 belonging to a subgroup G of the modular group be expressible as a linear combination of Eisenstein series with real coefficients is that a function $P(z)$ exists such that $\varphi(z)=P'''(z)$ and for which the function $q_T(z)$ defined by

$$q_T(z)=(cz+d)^2P(Tz)-P(z)$$

(for $T=\begin{pmatrix} a & b \\ c & d \end{pmatrix}\in G$) be a quadratic polynomial with real coefficients. *H. D. Kloosterman* (Leiden).

Referred to in F15-12.

F10-45 (18, 286b)

Bellman, Richard. On a class of functional equations of modular type. Proc. Nat. Acad. Sci. U.S.A. **42** (1956), 626–629.

The Voronoi functions

$$V_a(x, y)=\int_0^\infty \exp(-\pi x^2 s-\pi y^2 s^{-1})s^{-a}ds$$

can be used for building the generalized theta functions

$$f(x, y; u, v; t_1, t_2)=\sum_{m,n=-\infty}^{\infty} V_a((x+m)t_1{}^{1/2}, (y+n)t_2{}^{1/2})e^{2\pi i(mu+nv)}$$

with the functional equation

$$f(x, y; u, v; t_1, t_2)= t_1{}^{-1/2}t_2{}^{-1/2}e^{-2\pi i(xu+yv)}\cdot f(v, u; -y, -x; t_2{}^{-1}, t_1{}^{-1}).$$

As $V_a(x, y)=x^{2a-2}V_a(|xy|)$, the function f can be written in terms of divisor functions. The author indicates several divisor functions. The author indicates several generalizations: (i) to generalized Voronoi functions, (ii) to sums related to totally real algebraic number fields, (iii) to matric fields. He points out that the analogue of $V_a(x, y)$ in finite fields is given by the Kloosterman sums. *N. G. de Bruijn* (Amsterdam).

F10-46 (18, 476d)

Roelcke, Walter. Über die Wellengleichung bei Grenzkreisgruppen erster Art. S.-B. Heidelberger Akad. Wiss. Math.-Nat. Kl. **1953/1955**, 159–267 (1956).

Automorphic wave functions, introduced by H. Maas [Math. Ann. **121** (1949), 141–183; MR **11**, 163] are (non-analytic) eigenfunctions $\phi(x, y)$ belonging to the operator $\Delta=y^2(\partial^2/\partial x^2+\partial^2/\partial y^2)$ and invariant under a Fuchsian group Γ in the upper half plane, which has a fundamental domain with only cusps on the real axis. Thus the Eisenstein-type series $E=\sum y^{\frac{1}{2}s}|m_1\tau+m_2|^{-s}$ $(\tau=x+iy$, summed over an equivalence class of cusps $-m_2/m_1$ under the group $\Gamma)$, satisfies $\Delta E=-[\frac{1}{4}s(2-s)]E$. When Γ is the principal congruence subgroup modulo Q the spectrum is continuous and a complete set of eigenfunctions can be constructed from these E-functions. The multiplicity would equal the number of different equivalent classes of cusps. For Hecke's group, the situation is less conclusive but estimates are given, based on Hilbert-space techniques, (Green's functions, Hellinger's integrals, etc.) The concluding remarks have bearing on the correspondence with Dirichlet series. *H. Cohn.*

Citations: MR 11, 163c = F65-4.

F10-47 (18, 571c)

Rankin, R. A. The construction of automorphic forms from the derivatives of a given form. J. Indian Math. Soc. (N.S.) **20** (1956), 103–116.

Let $f(z)$ be a meromorphic automorphic form of arbitrary dimension k, belonging to the horocyclic group Γ, with the multipliers v. The author determines all polynomials $P(f, f_1, \cdots, f_n)$ in $f(z)$ and its first n derivatives (denoted by subscripts), which are themselves automorphic forms, $P\in\{\Gamma, k', v'\}$. Using relatively simple tools, by skillful but straightforward computations the following results are obtained: A term $Af_0{}^{\alpha_0}f_1{}^{\alpha_1}\cdots f{}^{\alpha_n}$ is said to be of degree r and weight s when $r=\sum_{j=1}^n\alpha_j$, $s=\sum_{j=1}^n j\alpha_j$. If P is automorphic then all its terms are of the same degree and weight. Define $h_r(z)=f_r(z)/\Gamma(k+r)r!$ and, for any integer $m\geq 2$, set $\psi_m(z)=(-1)^{m-1}\|a_{ij}\|$, the terms of the determinant $\|a_{ij}\|$ being $a_{1j}=jh_j$ and, for $i\geq 2$, $a_{ij}=h_{i-j+1}$ if $i-j+1\geq 0$, $a_{ij}=0$ otherwise. In case k is a non-positive integer, set $k=1-N$, $g_r=f_r\Gamma(N-r)/r!$ and let $\phi_m(z)=(-1)^{m-1}\|b_{ij}\|$, the terms b_{ij} being defined as the a_{ij}'s, except that the g_r's now stand for the h_r's. With $\delta_2=g_1h_N+g_0h_{N+1}$ the main result of the paper can be stated as follows: If k is not a non-positive integer, then $f(z)$ and $\psi_m(z)$ $(2\leq m\leq n)$ form a basis for all automorphic forms that are rational functions of f and its first n derivatives. If k is a non-positive integer, then f, $f^{(N)}$ and χ_m (this is ψ_m formed from h_N instead of h_0) are automorphic for $N\geq 1$, $m\geq 2$, while δ_2 is automorphic for $N\geq 2$ and ϕ_m for $N\geq 3$, $2\leq m<N$; these functions are polynomials in f and its first n derivatives and form a basis for all other such polynomials that are automorphic forms. Some examples are considered, where Γ is the full modular group. *E. Grosswald* (Philadelphia, Pa.).

Referred to in F10-88, F10-115, F25-24.

F10-48 (19, 392c)

Fine, N. J. On a system of modular functions connected with the Ramanujan identities. Tôhoku Math. J. (2) **8** (1956), 149–164.

The author discusses modular functions connected with the Dedekind function $\eta(\tau)=x^{1/24}\prod_{m=1}^\infty(1-x^m)$, where $x=\exp 2\pi i\tau$. He starts from the identity

$$\psi(\tau)\equiv(-1)^\lambda\frac{\eta(\tau/q)}{\eta(q\tau)}=1+\sum_{h=1}^{\nu}W_k(\tau),$$

where $q=6\lambda\pm 1$, $\nu=(q-1)/2$ and $W_k(\tau)$ is a power series in x multiplied $x^{6k^2/q-k}$ [cf. Atkin and Swinnerton-Dyer, Proc. London Math. Soc. (3) **4** (1954), 84–106; MR **15**, 685]. He then develops the properties of W_k under transformations of the subgroups $\Gamma_0(q)$ (defined by $q|c$), $\Gamma_0{}^0(q)$ $(q|b, c)$ and $\Gamma(q)$ $(q|b, c, a-1, d-1)$, where $\begin{pmatrix} a & b \\ c & d \end{pmatrix}$ is a modular substitution. This is done by the use of simple operations on infinite products and the transformation formula for one of the theta-functions.

Next, the functions $\psi_r(\tau)=\psi(\tau+r)$, $0\leq r<q$, are studied and it is proved that

$$\psi_r(M\tau)=\psi_{rd^2+bd}(\tau),\quad M=\begin{pmatrix} a & b \\ c & d \end{pmatrix}\in\Gamma_0(q).$$

This formula permits the derivation of the Ramanujan-Watson modular equation for $\eta(\tau/q)/\eta(\tau)$ in a surprisingly simple way. The proof of the modular equation for $q=5, 7$ is very much shorter than Watson's [J. Reine Angew. Math. **179** (1938), 97–128]. The author also works out the modular equation for $q=11$, which may be of some use in investigating Ramanujan's partition congruences to the moduli 11^a. He uses it to develop an identity for the modulus 11, similar to one of the reviewer's.

In the last two sections the author presents, as applications of the preceding theory, proofs of two of Ramanujan's unpublished and unproved identities, of which one is

$$49x \prod_{m=1}^{\infty} (1-x^{7m})^3(1-x^m)^3+8 \prod_{m=1}^{\infty} \frac{(1-x^m)^7}{(1-x^{7m})} = 8-7\sum_{n=1}^{\infty} x^n \sum_{d|n} \left(\frac{d}{7}\right)d^2.$$

He also proves identities of Slater, Newman and Rademacher. *J. Lehner* (E. Lansing, Mich.).

Citations: MR 15, 685d = P76-11.

Referred to in P76-16.

F10-49 (19, 637b)

Petersson, Hans. Über Eisensteinsche Reihen und automorphe Formen von der Dimension −1. Comment. Math. Helv. **31** (1956), 111–144.

It is known that the Eisenstein series span the orthogonal complement $\mathfrak{N}$ of the automorphic cusp forms in the space of all entire automorphic forms. (The forms considered here are automorphic on Γ, a Fuchsian group of the first kind whose elements are real 2×2 matrices, are of dimension -1, and have a given multiplier system v with $|v|=1$.) The author investigates the case $v^2=1$, in which $\mathfrak{N}$ is isomorphic to a certain linear vector space $\mathfrak{R}$, which is characterized uniquely by a real orthogonal skew-symmetric matrix G. He applies knowledge of $\mathfrak{R}$ to investigate $\mathfrak{N}$ and proves, in particular, the following. $\mathfrak{N}$ possesses a system of generators $F_i(\tau)$, associated uniquely with the parabolic vertices P_i of Γ, whose Fourier expansions have the following property: the constant term of F_i in the expansion at P_i has imaginary part 1; at P_j $(j\neq i)$, it has imaginary part 0. For two particular classes of groups the elements of G are determined explicitly: $\Gamma=\Gamma(N)$, the principal congruence subgroup of the modular group of level N; and $\Gamma=\Gamma^0[l, q]=\left\{\begin{pmatrix}\alpha & \beta\\ \gamma & \delta\end{pmatrix}\right\}$, where $\beta\equiv 0 \pmod q$, $\alpha\equiv x^l \pmod q$, $q\equiv 2l+1 \pmod{4l}$.

The remainder of the paper is devoted to the investigation of the dimension of the space $\mathfrak{N}$ for the group $\Gamma=\Gamma^0[l, q]+K_q\Gamma^0[l, q]$, where $K_q=\begin{pmatrix}0 & -q^{\frac12}\\ q^{-\frac12} & 0\end{pmatrix}$. (This group is of particular interest because it possesses the never-vanishing form $\eta(\tau)\eta(\tau/q)$, where η is the classical Dedekind function.) The author specializes to $q=\text{prime}>3$, $q\equiv 3 \pmod 4$, and then proves the following formula: $\mu_1^- - \mu_1^+ = \frac12(h-1)$. Here μ_1^+, μ_1^- are the dimensions of $\mathfrak{N}(\Gamma, -1, v^+)$, $\mathfrak{N}(\Gamma, -1, v^-)$, respectively, where v^+, v^- are certain explicitly given complex-conjugate multipliers; and h is the class number of the field $R(\sqrt{-q})$.
J. Lehner (East Lansing, Mich.).

F10-50 (19, 943a)

Iseki, Shô. The transformation formula for the Dedekind modular function and related functional equations. Duke Math. J. **24** (1957), 653–662.

The author derives the functional equation

$$\sum_{r=0}^{\infty} \{\lambda_p((r+\alpha)z-i\beta)+\lambda_p((r+1-\alpha)z+i\beta)\}$$
$$=(iz)^{p-1}\sum_{r=0}^{\infty} \{\lambda_p((r+\beta)z^{-1}+i\alpha)+\lambda_p((r+1-\beta)z^{-1}-i\alpha)\}$$
$$-\frac{(2\pi z)^p}{(p+1)!}\sum_{\nu=0}^{p+1}\binom{p+1}{\nu}(iz)^{-\nu}B_{p+1-\nu}(\alpha)B_\nu(\beta),$$

where $\lambda_p(x)=\sum_{m=1}^{\infty} m^{-p}e^{-2\pi mx}$, and $B_\nu(t)$ is the Bernoulli polynomial of order ν. The parameter p is required to be a positive odd integer; z is complex, with $\Re(z)>0$; α and β are real, with $0\leqq\alpha\leqq 1$, $0\leqq\beta\leqq 1$ if $p>1$. When $p=1$ at least one of the inequalities $0<\alpha<1$ or $0<\beta<1$ must hold. The functional equation is proved by interchanging the order of summation in the double series $\sum_{m,n}\exp(2\pi i\alpha n+2\pi i\beta m)m^{-p}(zm+in)^{-1}$. When $p=1$, the above formula yields the famous transformation equation for Dedekind's modular function $\eta(\tau)$. In the case of odd $p>1$, it yields a similar transformation formula for the Lambert series $g_p(x)=\sum_{n=1}^{\infty} n^{-p}x^n(1-x^n)^{-1}$. [See Apostol, same J. **17** (1950), 147–157; MR **11**, 641.] *T. M. Apostol.*

Citations: MR 11, 641g = F20-3.

Referred to in F10-63, F10-74, F65-19, P60-28, P68-15.

F10-51 (19, 943b)

Mikolás, Miklós. Über gewisse Lambertsche Reihen. I. Verallgemeinerung der Modulfunktion $\eta(\tau)$ und ihrer Dedekindschen Transformationsformel. Math. Z. **68** (1957), 100–110.

Let $g_p(x)=\sum_{n=1}^{\infty} n^{-p}x^n/(1-x^n)$, $(p=1, 2, \cdots)$; let $Q(x, \omega)=2\sum_{p=0}^{\infty} g_{2p+1}(x)\omega^{2p}$, $(|x|<1, |\omega|<1)$; and let $\tilde{Q}(\tau, \omega)=Q(e^{2\pi i\tau}, \omega)$. Using the residue calculus, the author derives the following elegant functional equation:

$$\tilde{Q}\left(\frac{h+z}{k}, \omega\right)-\tilde{Q}\left(\frac{h'-z^{-1}}{k}, z\omega\right)=\tfrac12[Y(\omega)-Y(z\omega)]+\log z$$
$$+2\pi i\mathfrak{S}_k^{h,1}(\omega, z\omega)+\pi i[(e(\omega)-1)^{-1}+(e(z\omega)-1)^{-1}]$$
$$-\frac{k}{2\pi i}\omega^{-1}(z\omega)^{-1},$$

where

$$Y(\omega)=\frac{\Gamma'(\omega)}{\Gamma(\omega)}-\frac{\Gamma'(-\omega)}{\Gamma(-\omega)}, \quad e(x)=\exp(2\pi ix);$$

$$\mathfrak{S}_k^{h,1}(\omega, z\omega)=$$
$$[e(\omega)-1]^{-1}[e(z\omega)-1]^{-1}\sum_{\lambda=0}^{k-1} e\left(\frac{z\omega\lambda}{k}+\omega\frac{\lambda h}{k}-\omega\left[\frac{\lambda h}{k}\right]\right);$$

h and k are integers, $(h, k)=1$, $hh'\equiv -1 \pmod k$; $\mathfrak{I}(z)>0$; and $\omega\neq n$, $\omega\neq nz^{-1}$ $(n=0, \pm 1, \cdots)$. By equating coefficients of powers of ω, this formula yields the transformation equation for Dedekind's modular function $\eta(\tau)$, as well as the corresponding transformation formula for $g_{2p+1}(x)$. (See the preceding review.)

The author also studies the function

$$xy\mathfrak{S}_c^{a,b}\left(\frac{x}{2\pi i}, \frac{y}{2\pi i}\right)=\sum_{m,n=0}^{\infty}\frac{x^m y^n}{m!n!}\sum_{\lambda=0}^{c-1}\bar{B}_m\left(\frac{\lambda a}{c}\right)\bar{B}_n\left(\frac{\lambda a}{c}\right),$$

where $\bar{B}_n(t)$ is the periodic Bernoulli function of order n, and obtains, as a consequence, the reciprocity laws for Dedekind sums and their various generalizations due to Apostol, Carlitz, and Rademacher. *T. M. Apostol.*

F10-52 (19, 953c)

Newman, Morris. Construction and application of a class of modular functions. Proc. London Math. Soc. (3) **7** (1957), 334–350.

The author considers functions defined for $\Gamma_0(n)$ a

subgroup of the modular group in the τ plane. (Here $c \equiv 0 \bmod n$ in the usual $\begin{pmatrix} a & b \\ c & d \end{pmatrix}$ notation, and $(n, 6)=1$.) In particular, G_n is the (multiplicative) subgroup of the group generated by $\eta(\delta\tau)/\eta(\tau)$ where $\delta | n$; H_n is the subset of G_n with negative valences only at $i\infty$; F_n the entire functions meromorphic at parabolic points; and finally E_n is the totality of F_n with negative valences only at $i\infty$. Let ν be the genus of $\Gamma_0(n)$. Then a polynomial basis of E_n is known to have $\nu+1$ elements by the Riemann-Roch theorem. Since $E_n \supset H_n$ the author would like to choose the polynomial basis of E_n in H_n. This cannot be done generally since when n is a prime the elements of H_n are powers of a single function while the genus is seldom 0; but the conjecture is made that for n composite the basis can be so chosen.

Thus a tremendous advantage accrues from the fact that G_n and hence H_n can be explicitly characterized using the coefficients of the power series expansion in $\exp 2\pi i\tau$. The author considers the case of $n=35$ where $\nu=3$. The basis of E_{35} consists of four functions of valences -4, -5, -6, -7 built with linear combinations of nine functions of G_{35} of which a typical example is $\eta(5\tau)^5\eta(7\tau)/\eta(\tau)\eta(35\tau)^5$. A polynomial basis of F_{35} is also constructed.

The SEAC electronic computer was used to calculate power series coefficients and to reduce the matrices used in determining the aforementioned linear combinations. (The series-length and matrix-size were known in advance.)

Harvey Cohn (Tucson, Ariz.).

Referred to in F10-60.

F10-53 (20# 5765)

Carlitz, L. A note on the irrational modular equation of order seven. Nieuw Arch. Wisk. (3) **5** (1957), 143–145.

The author deduces by elementary means from the irrational modular equation of order 7 that

$$2\frac{\varphi_r(q)}{\psi_r(q)} = -\frac{\psi(q)}{\varphi(q)} \quad (1 \leq r \leq 6),$$

where

$$\varphi(q) = \prod_{m=1}^{\infty} \frac{1+q^{2m}}{1+q^{2m-1}} = \sum_{n=0}^{\infty} a(n)q^n,$$

$$\psi(q) = \prod_{m=1}^{\infty} \frac{1-q^{2m-1}}{1+q^{2m-1}} = \sum_{n=0}^{\infty} b(n)q^n,$$

$$\varphi_r(q) = \sum_{n=0}^{\infty} a(7n+r-1)q^n,$$

$$\psi_r(q) = \sum_{n=0}^{\infty} b(7n+r)q^n.$$

The modular equation of order 23 is also considered and yields a more complicated result.

R. A. Rankin (Glasgow)

F10-54 (21# 1390)

Lehner, Joseph. On modular forms of negative dimension. Michigan Math. J. **6** (1959), 71–88.

Define $e(z)=e^{2\pi iz}$. Let V run through a subset of the matrices $\begin{pmatrix} ab \\ cd \end{pmatrix}$ of the modular group $\Gamma(1)$, such that each second row occurs once and only once (for the purpose on hand the first row is immaterial, as long as $ad-bc=1$). Then, if $s>2$,

$$F_\mu(\tau) = \tfrac{1}{2}\sum_V e(-(\mu-\alpha)V\tau)\varepsilon(V)^{-1}(-i(c\tau+d))^r$$

represents a modular form of real negative dimension $r=-s<-2$. Here μ is a positive integer, $0<\alpha<1$ and $\varepsilon(V)$ is a multiplier system for the dimension r. The series converges absolutely and uniformly in every region $\Im\tau \geq y_0 > 0$, whence the regularity of $F_\mu(\tau)$ in $\Im\tau>0$ and its modular character readily follow. If $s=2$, the series is no longer absolutely convergent. Using an idea of Hecke, Petersson [Math. Ann. **103** (1930), 369–436] introduced a convergence factor $|c\tau+d|^{-\sigma}$ and, letting $\sigma \to 0$, obtained modular forms of dimension -2. In the present paper the author shows that if one sums the series in a certain prescribed order, then it converges to an entire modular form of dimension -2. For that, one defines

$$(*) \qquad F_\mu(\tau) = e(-(\mu-\alpha)\tau)+H(\tau),$$

with

$$H(\tau) = \lim_{K\to\infty} \frac{1}{2}\sum_{k=-K}^{K}\sum_{m=-K}^{K}{}' e(-(\mu-\alpha)V_{k,-m}\tau) \times \varepsilon(V_{k,-m})^{-1}(-i(k\tau-m))^r$$

$$= \lim_{K\to\infty} \sum_{k=1}^{K}\sum_{m=-K}^{K}{}' e(-(\mu-\alpha)V_{k,-m}\tau) \times (V_{k,-m})^{-1}(-i(k\tau-m))^r,$$

with $V_{k,-m}=\begin{pmatrix} m' & k' \\ k & -m \end{pmatrix}$, $mm' \equiv -1 \pmod{k}$, $0<m'<k$ and the inner summation extended only over m prime to k. In the proof of the convergence, use is made of the Assumption A: Define

$$A_{k,\mu}(m) = \sum_{\substack{h=0 \\ (h,k)=1}}^{k-1} \varepsilon^{-1}(V_{k,-h})e[-(\mu-\alpha)h'+(m+\alpha)h/k];$$

then

$$A_{k,\mu}(m) \leq C_\varepsilon(\rho m+\sigma, k)^{1/2}k^{1/2+\varepsilon}$$

for $k \geq 1$ and every $\varepsilon>0$, unless $\alpha=0$, $m=0$, when $A_{k,\mu}(0) \leq C$. For $s>3/2$, and assuming A, the author shows: (i) $F_\mu(\tau)$ is regular in $\Im\tau>0$; (ii) for $W \in \Gamma(1)$, $W=\begin{pmatrix} \cdots \\ \gamma\delta \end{pmatrix}$, $F_\mu(W\tau)=\varepsilon(W)(-i(\gamma\tau+\delta))^s F_\mu(\tau)$; (iii) $F_\mu(\tau)= e(-(\mu-\alpha)\tau)+\sum_0^\infty a_m e((m+\alpha)\tau)$, with

$$(**) \quad a_m = 2\pi\sum_{k=1}^{\infty} k^{-1}A_{k,\mu}(m)\left(\frac{\mu-\alpha}{m+\alpha}\right)^{1/2(r+1)} \times I_{-r-1}(4\pi k^{-1}(\mu-\alpha)^{1/2}(m+\alpha)^{1/2}),$$

where $I_l(z)$ stands for the Bessel function of imaginary argument. Assumption A, however, is proven (by reducing the sums to Kloosterman sums) only for $s=2$. It would be of considerable interest to prove it for $s<2$, as (*) would then represent modular forms of dimension r, $-2<r<-3/2$ and (**) would represent their Fourier coefficients by convergent series (at present no such representations are known). The paper finishes by showing that every modular form $G(\tau)$ of dimension -2 may be written as $\sum_{\nu=1}^{\mu} b_\nu F_\nu(\tau)+K(\tau)$, with constant b_ν's and $K(\tau)$ a cusp form.

E. Grosswald (Princeton, N.J.)

Referred to in F30-50.

F10-55 (21# 2064)

van der Blij, F.; and van Lint, J. H. On some special theta functions. Nederl. Akad. Wetensch. Proc. Ser. A. **61** = Indag. Math. **20** (1958), 508–513.

The authors define a theta function $\vartheta\left(\tau \middle| \begin{matrix} a \\ b \end{matrix}\right)$ in n variables based on a positive definite quadratic form and on two n-dimensional vectors a and b, and discuss its transformation under modular substitutions. By multiplying the theta function by η^{-n}, where $\eta(\tau)$ is the Dedekind modular form, they obtain forms $\varphi\left(\tau \middle| \begin{matrix} a \\ b \end{matrix}\right)$ of dimension 0. In a number of special cases, it is shown how to combine the φ-functions linearly to obtain a modular function.

J. Lehner (East Lansing, Mich.)

F10-56 **(21# 2065)**

van Lint, J. H. On the multiplier system of the Riemann-Dedekind function η. Nederl. Akad. Wetensch. Proc. Ser. A. **61** = Indag. Math. **20** (1958), 522–527.

The Dedekind function

$$\eta(\tau) = e^{\pi i\tau/12}\prod_{n=1}^{\infty}(1-e^{2\pi in\tau})$$

satisfies the transformation formula

$$\eta(L\tau) = \varepsilon(L)(c\tau+d)^{1/2}\eta(\tau)$$

for every modular substitution $L=\begin{pmatrix}a & b\\ c & d\end{pmatrix}$, where v is a complicated 24th root of unity whose explicit dependence on a, b, c, d is a difficult problem first solved by Hermite and Dedekind in somewhat different forms. Their proofs were partly number-theoretic, partly function-theoretic. In recent years several purely function-theoretic proofs have appeared [cf. e.g., Rademacher, J. Indian Math. Soc. (N.S.) **19** (1955), 25–30; MR **17**, 15]. In the present paper, the author proves the Hermite formula—which he apparently attributes to Petersson!—by a combination of group theory and function theory.

The group-theoretic argument proceeds by observing that, since v^2 is a multiplier of dimension -1 on the modular group, it is a character of that group. It is next proved that every one-dimensional character on the modular group is of the form ζ^g, where ζ is a 12th root of unity, $g=f-3c$, c odd; $g=f+3d-3-3cd$, c even; and $f=(a+d)c-bd(c^2-1)$.

We now have $v(L)=\varepsilon(L)\exp\pi ig/12$, where $\varepsilon=\pm 1$. The determination of ε as a quadratic character is accomplished by a theorem of Hecke [Math. Ann. **119** (1944), 266–287; MR **6**, 173], the proof of which makes use of Eisenstein series and of the Gauss lemma in the theory of quadratic characters. *J. Lehner* (East Lansing, Mich.)

Citations: MR 6, 173f = F65-3; MR 17, 15f = F10-40.

F10-57 **(21# 3421)**

Igusa, Jun-ichi. On the transformation theory of elliptic functions. Amer. J. Math. **81** (1959), 436–452.

A complete algebraic account of Kronecker's transformation theory of elliptic functions. Except for the exclusion of characteristic two all things done are compatible with specialization (including reduction mod p). Any elliptic curve is birationally equivalent to a Jacobi quartic $Y^2=1-2\rho X^2+X^4$, where $\rho\neq\pm 1$, ∞, the natural map from these quartics to the space of isomorphism classes of elliptic curves being a galois covering with group S_3. Oversimplifying considerably, consider a rational map $(\rho, x, y)\to(\rho', x', y')$ from one such quartic to another, given by

$$x' = x^mF(x^{-1})F(x)^{-1},\quad y' = G(x)F(x)^{-2}y,$$

where m is an odd integer and $F(X)$, $G(X)$ are polynomials, the former having constant term 1 and the expression for x' being in lowest terms. It is shown that the coefficients of $F(X)$, $G(X)$ are in $Q(\rho, \rho')$, Q being the prime field, and are integral over $Z[8\rho]$ if $\rho'=\rho$. Certain two-variable polynomials over Z that are canonically derived from the division points of given odd order (the quartic being considered an elliptic curve) are shown to be absolutely irreducible. Finally there is Kronecker's congruence relation: If the correspondence $(\rho, x, y)\to(\rho', x', y')$ is of odd prime degree p ($\neq$ characteristic of Q), then

$$F(X) = 1+\sum_{0<2i<p-1}\mu\gamma_iX^{p-2i-1}+\mu X^{p-1},$$

where $\gamma_1, \gamma_2, \cdots$ are integers of $Q(\rho, \mu)$ with reference to $Z[8\rho]$, and $N_{Q(\rho,\mu)/Q(\rho)}(\mu)=(-4/p)p$. *M. Rosenlicht* (Berkeley, Calif.)

Referred to in F10-61.

F10-58 **(21# 3422)**

Igusa, Jun-ichi. Fibre systems of Jacobian varieties. III. Fibre systems of elliptic curves. Amer. J. Math. **81** (1959), 453–476.

[For parts I and II, see same J. **78** (1956), 171–199, 745–760; MR **18**, 935, 936.] This paper gives an algebraic theory of elliptic modular functions and includes generalizations of a number of classical results due, among others, to Klein and Kronecker. First of all, a discussion of canonical forms for elliptic curves shows that it is possible to assign to each such curve A an element $j(A)$ of the universal domain such that $j(A)=j(B)$ if and only if A and B are isomorphic, and such that if an elliptic curve A' is a specialization of A (possibly unequal characteristics) then $j(A)$ has a unique specialization and this is $j(A')$. These properties show that $j(A)$ is contained in any field of definition of A and is uniquely determined up to the transformation $j\to\pm j+$integer; furthermore a model of A exists that is defined over $F(j(A))$, F being the prime field. In general, A has only two automorphisms, $a\to\pm a$, and the identification map, denoted by Ku if A is defined over K, maps A onto a projective line. Letting k be the algebraic closure of F, j a variable over k, A an elliptic curve defined over $k(j)$ and with $j(A)=j$, n an integer prime to the characteristic of k, Ω the n^2 points of A of order n, then the field $k(j, Ku(\Omega))$ is called the field of modular functions of level n. The main results state that $k(j, Ku(\Omega))$ is a galois extension of $k(j)$ with group the unimodular 2×2 integral matrices modulo n modulo its center; give the genus of $k(j, Ku(\Omega))$; and give a complete account of the ramification of this field over $k(j)$. *M. Rosenlicht* (Berkeley, Calif.)

Referred to in F10-81, F10-109, G05-91.

F10-59 **(21# 5728)**

Gel'fer, S. A. The maximum of the conformal radius of the fundamental region of a group of linear fractional transformations. Dokl. Akad. Nauk SSSR **126** (1959), 463–466. (Russian)

Let $\{T\}$ be a discrete group of fractional-linear transformations and $\{D\}$ a family of simply-connected domains D in the w-plane with the following properties: (1) D does not contain points congruent relatively to the group $\{T\}$; (2) D does not contain a system of finite points $a_1, \cdots, a_m$ and ∞, nor points congruent to them by the group $\{T\}$; (3) D contains a given point c_0, different from the fix-points and cyclic points of the transformations in $\{T\}$. The problem is to find the domain $D\in\{D\}$ which has the maximum conformal radius relatively to c_0. The author deals in this paper with groups for which simple automorphic functions exist. He solved in another paper a similar problem for doubly-periodic groups [S. A. Gel'fer, Mat. Sb. (N.S.) **44 (86)** (1958), 213–224; Dokl. Akad. Nauk SSSR **114** (1957), 241–244; MR **20** #1782, #5894].

Denote by $S_a(T)$ the class of functions $w=f(z)=\sum_0^\infty c_nz^n$ regular in $|z|<1$ which provide a univalent mapping of $|z|<1$ on the domains of $\{D\}$. The problem then is to find the max $|f'(0)|$ in the class $S_a(T)$.

The following theorem is proved. If a function $f(z)\in S_a(T)$ gives a maximum value to the functional $|f'(0)|$, then $f(z)$ maps $|z|<1$ on a domain D with the following properties: (1) D, containing the point c_0, is the fundamental region S_0 of the group $\{T\}$ with slits. Its boundary consists of a finite number of analytic arcs pairwise congruent relatively to $\{T\}$ and of piece-wise analytic slits going from the boundary of S_0 to the points $a_1, \cdots, a_m$ or to points congruent to them. (2) To each pair of congruent arcs of the boundary of S_0 and to the simple arcs of the slits correspond on $|z|=1$, through the mapping $w=f(z)$, two arcs of equal length. (3) D is unique for the given group.

In some special cases this theorem helps to find the extremal domain. Thus, for the modular group $\{T\}: w' = (aw+b)/(cw+d)$, $ad-bc=1$, a, b, c, d real integers, and for the subgroup of $\{T\}$ in which b and c are even integers, as well as for groups of which the fundamental regions are images of closed Riemann surfaces of genus $g \geqq 2$, explicit expressions for the upper bound of $|f'(0)|$ are given.

B. A. Amirà (Jerusalem)

F10-60 (21# 6354)

Newman, Morris. Construction and application of a class of modular functions. II. Proc. London Math. Soc. (3) **9** (1959), 373–387.

The author continues the development of his earlier paper [same Proc. **7** (1957), 334–350; MR **19**, 953], concerning functions defined on $\Gamma_0(n)$, where, now, n need not be prime to 6. The author gives integral polynomial bases on F_n (the entire modular functions on $\Gamma_0(n)$) and on E_n (those F_n with negative valence only at $i\infty$) for $n=6$, 10, 14, 15, 21, 22, 26. Typically the bases of E_6 and F_6 are $\{a_1\}$ and $\{a_1, a_3^{-1}\}$, respectively, where

$$a_1 - 5 = \eta(\tau)^5\eta(3\tau)/\eta(2\tau)\eta(6\tau)^5,$$
$$a_3 = \eta(2\tau)^{10}\eta(3\tau)^{14}/\eta(\tau)^2\eta(6\tau)^{22}.$$

These functions are supplied, as before, from the author's theorem I (now extended to include all n regardless of primality to 6): If δ denotes all divisors of n, $\delta\delta'=n$, and if the integers r_δ are so defined that, with $r_1=0$, the two sums $\sum(\delta-1)r_\delta/24$ and $\sum(\delta'-n)r_\delta/24$ are integers and $\prod \delta^{r_\delta}$ is a perfect square, then it follows that $\prod \phi_\delta{}^{r_\delta} = g(\tau)$ is a function on $\Gamma_0(n)$, where $\phi_\delta = \eta(\delta\tau)/\eta(\tau)$. These $g(\tau)$ come in sufficient abundance to provide modular identities for $\eta(\tau)$ on different levels. The study of the expansions at $i\infty$ was aided this time by the IBM 704.

H. Cohn (Tucson, Ariz.)

Citations: MR 19, 953c = F10-52.

F10-61 (21# 7214)

Igusa, Jun-ichi. Kroneckerian model of fields of elliptic modular functions. Amer. J. Math. **81** (1959), 561–577.

A continuation of the author's recent work on elliptic modular functions [Amer. J. Math. **81** (1959), 436–452; MR **21** #3421]. The main result states that there exists a nonsingular projective curve defined over the rationals that is a model for the field of modular functions of level n in characteristic zero whose reduction modulo any prime p not dividing n is a nonsingular model for the modular functions of level n in characteristic p. There follow several highly technical results in which key expressions are modular correspondence and Petersson conjecture on Hecke operators on cusp forms.

M. Rosenlicht (Berkeley, Calif.)

Citations: MR 21# 3421 = F10-57.
Referred to in E28-73.

F10-62 (22# 690)

Carlitz, L. A congruence satisfied by the theta-constant ϑ_3. Proc. Amer. Math. Soc. **10** (1959), 912–916.

Let $\vartheta_3 = \sum_{-\infty}^{\infty} q^{n^2}$ and let p denote an arbitrary odd prime. The following congruence appears incidentally in an earlier paper of the author [Math. Z. **64** (1956), 425–434; MR **17**, 1057]:

$$\text{(i)} \qquad \vartheta_3{}^{2(p-1)} \sum_{r=0}^{m} \binom{m}{r}^2 k^{2r} \equiv 1 \pmod{p},$$

where $p=2m+1$ and k^2 has its usual significance in the theory of elliptic functions. The congruence (i) is to be interpreted in the following way. Using the familiar identity

$$\text{(ii)} \qquad k^2 = 16q \prod_1^\infty \left(\frac{1+q^{2n}}{1+q^{2n-1}}\right)^8,$$

(i) can be written entirely in terms of q or entirely in terms of k^2. It follows from (ii) that

$$\text{(iii)} \qquad k^2 = \sum_{n=1}^\infty a_n q^n \quad (a_1 = 16),$$

where the a_n are rational integers, and that

$$\text{(iv)} \qquad q = \sum_{n=1}^\infty b_n k^{2n} \quad (b_1 = 1/16),$$

where the denominators of the b_n are powers of 2. If we substitute from (iii) into (i) we get a certain set of congruences; if we substitute from (iv) we get another set. By Lemma 1 of the author's earlier paper these congruences are equivalent. The author now shows how the second substitution can be carried out explicitly.

A. L. Whiteman (Princeton, N.J.)

Citations: MR 17, 1057e = B80-14.
Referred to in F10-72.

F10-63 (22# 700)

Iseki, Shô. A generalization of a functional equation related to the theory of partitions. Duke Math. J. **27** (1960), 95–110.

The asympotitic theory of partitions is connected with the transformation formula for the Dedekind modular function $\eta(\tau)$. Special types of partition problems make use of transformation formulas analogous to, or more general than, that of Dedekind. One of these was discovered by E. M. Wright [Acta Math. **63** (1934), 143–191] in his study of partitions into kth powers. Another generalization of the Dedekind functional equation, recently discovered by the author [same J. **24** (1957), 653–662; MR **19**, 943], has the following form:

$$\text{(1)} \quad \sum_{l=0}^\infty \{\lambda((l+\alpha)z - i\beta) + \lambda((l+1-\alpha)z + i\beta)\} + z(\alpha^2 - \alpha + \tfrac16)$$
$$= \sum_{l=0}^\infty \{\lambda((l+\beta)/z + i\alpha) + \lambda((l+1-\beta)/z - i\alpha)\}$$
$$+ (\pi/z)(\beta^2 - \beta + \tfrac16) + 2\pi i(\alpha - \tfrac12)(\beta - \tfrac12),$$

where $\lambda(t) = -\log(1-e^{-2\pi t})$, $\Re(z) > 0$, $0 \leqq \alpha \leqq 1$, $0 < \beta < 1$ (or $0 < \alpha < 1$, $0 \leqq \beta \leqq 1$). In the present paper the author extends this formula in a direction which generalizes Wright's formula. The principal change is that the quantities $(l+\alpha)$ and $(l+1-\alpha)$ which appear on the left of (1) are replaced by their kth powers, where k is a positive integer.

T. M. Apostol (Pasadena, Calif.)

Citations: MR 19, 943a = F10-50.

F10-64 (22# 1553)

van Lint, J. H. Linear relations for certain modular forms. Math. Nachr. **20** (1959), 123–126.

Let f be a modular form of step N, let r be half of an odd integer, and denote by Γ_θ the subgroup of the modular group $\Gamma(1)$ that is generated by $\begin{pmatrix}1 & 2\\ 0 & 1\end{pmatrix}$ and $\begin{pmatrix}0 & -1\\ 1 & 0\end{pmatrix}$. Also, denote by η and θ the Dedekind function and $\sum_n e^{\pi i\tau n^2}$, respectively. In his thesis [Utrecht, 1957; MR **19**, 839] the author proved the following theorem: The only integral modular forms $\in \{\Gamma_0, -r, v\}$ for which linear relations of type $F(p\tau) + \alpha \sum_{l \bmod p} F((\tau+\lambda l)/p) = 0$ exist for all p with $(p, \frac12 N) = 1$ are η, η^3, θ, $(\eta\theta)^{1/2}$, $(\eta^3\theta^{-1})^{1/2}$, $(\eta\theta^5)^{1/2}$, $(\eta\theta)^{3/2}$ and $\eta^4\theta^{-1}$. Continuing the study of the same topic, the author now proves the following. The only modular forms $\in \{\Gamma_\theta, -r, v\}$, where v is not a multiplier system for $\Gamma(1)$, for which singular Hecke operators can be defined for all p with $(p, \frac{1}{2}N)=1$, are those listed above, except η and η^3. For the case of linear relations of order 1, the following is shown: If a linear relation of order 1 exists for a modular form $f\in\{\Gamma_\theta, -r, v\}$, then v is the restriction to Γ_θ of a multiplier system of $\Gamma(1)$ and the relation has the form $f|T[K, \Lambda]=0$, where $\Lambda=\{\Gamma(1), -r, v\}$, unless f is already a modular form of Λ.

E. Grosswald (Princeton, N.J.)

Citations: MR 19, 839f = F25-7.

F10-65 (22# 1554)

Newman, M. Weighted restricted partitions. Acta Arith. **5**, 371–380 (1959).

From the Dedekind eta-function $\eta(\tau)=x^{1/24}\prod(1-x^n)$ $(x=\exp 2\pi i\tau)$, the author defines $B(\tau)=\eta(q\tau)/\eta(\tau)=x^{(q-1)/24}\varphi$, whence $\varphi=\prod(1-x^{nq})/(1-x^n)$. Here $B(\tau)$ is an entire modular function of level q, and we further introduce $g(\tau)=B^r(\tau)B^s(p\tau)$ for p, q different primes, and $p>3$. The author shows that $g(\tau)$ is an entire modular function on $\Gamma_0(pq)$ if $(r+sp)(q-1)/24$ and $(r+s)/2$ are integers. He also shows that $G(\tau)=\sum g(R\tau)$, summed over the coset operations R of $\Gamma_0(q)/\Gamma_0(pq)$, is an entire modular function on $\Gamma_0(q)$.

With $r=-sp$, the main theorem emerges: If $s\geqq 0$, $G(\tau)$ has a pole of order $M=[|s|(p^2-1)(q-1)/24p]$ at $i\infty$ and is pole-free at 0, while if $s<0$, then $G(\tau)$ is pole-free at $i\infty$ and has a pole of order M at 0. If $q=2, 3, 5, 7, 13$, then $\Gamma_0(q)$ has genus 0 and, easily, $G(\tau)$ is a polynomial of degree M in $B(\tau)^{-24/(q-1)}$. This leads to identities among coefficients of $\varphi^s=\sum q_s(n)x^n$ of type

$$pq_1(np+\nu)+(-1)^\nu q_1(n/p) = 2^{(p-1)/2}q_p(n),$$

where $\nu=(p^2-1)/24$, $q=2$ and $5\leqq p\leqq 23$.

Incidentally, the coefficients $q_s(n)$ are weighted restricted partition functions. *H. Cohn* (Tucson, Ariz.)

F10-66 (22# 1670)

Rademacher, Hans. A proof of a theorem on modular functions. Amer. J. Math. **82** (1960), 338–340.

The author gives a new proof of the following theorem. A modular function $\psi(\tau)$ belonging to a modular congruence subgroup modulo N and which is regular and bounded in the half-plane $\Im(\tau)>0$ is a constant.

He avoids the usual contour integration around the fundamental region of $\psi(\tau)$, which necessitates a study of the structure of this region, in particular of its vertices and cusps.

{Correction: For '$\Re(\tau)>0$' read '$\Im(\tau)>0$', both in the theorem and in (1).} *T. Estermann* (London)

F10-67 (22# 12222)

Maak, Wilhelm. Fastautomorphe Funktionen. Bayer. Akad. Wiss. Math.-Nat. Kl. S.-B. **1959**, 289–319 (1960).

In this paper the author discusses almost-periodicity of meromorphic functions on the upper half-plane $H=\{\tau=x+iy|y>0\}$ relative to the modular group G. The space of functions considered, called functions of meromorphic behaviour, is defined to consist of those meromorphic functions $f(\tau)$ in H such that: (1) $f(\tau)$ has only poles in H, in at most finitely many equivalence classes under the action of G; (2) $f(\tau)$ has bounded order of growth upon approaching the poles and the cusps of G (the rational boundary points of H); (3) for any closed subset $D\subset H$ not containing poles of $f(\tau)$, $\|f\|_D=\sup_{T\in G,\,\tau\in D}|f(T\tau)|<\infty$. It then follows that for an open subset $U\subset D$ this space of functions is a Banach space with the norm $\|f\|_U$ as introduced above; and letting G act on this space by putting $Tf(\tau)=f(T\tau)$, $T\in G$, it follows that $\|Tf\|_U=\|f\|_U$. A function $f(\tau)$ as above is called almost-automorphic at a point τ_0 if for some open neighbourhood U of τ_0 the map $T\to Tf$ is an almost-periodic function from G into the function space with norm $\|f\|_U$. The author shows a certain independence from the point τ_0, except of course that the poles of $f(\tau)$ must be omitted. Also the restrictions of $f(\tau)$ to lines $\operatorname{Im}\tau=\eta$, for η suitably large, are almost-periodic on those lines in the customary sense, with customary Fourier expansions. The general results from the Bohr theory apply, so that the sum, convolution, uniform limit, and mean values of almost-periodic functions are again almost-periodic. The concepts are such that almost-periodic functions without poles must be constants; so that the admission of poles is a natural feature. The featured result of the paper is that all finite-dimensional bounded representations of the modular group can be realized by such almost-automorphic functions. *R. C. Gunning* (Princeton, N.J.)

Referred to in F10-68, F10-78.

F10-68 (24# A2027)

Maak, Wilhelm

Elementare fastautomorphe Funktionen.

Bayer. Akad. Wiss. Math.-Nat. Kl. S.-B. **1960**, 95–99.

As a complement to a preceding paper [same S.-B. **1959**, 289–319; MR **22** #12222], the author shows that every irreducible unitary representation $M\to D(M)$ of the inhomogeneous modular group, which has a twelfth root of unity as an eigenvalue for the matrix $D(U)$, $U=\begin{pmatrix}1&1\\0&1\end{pmatrix}\in\Gamma$, can be realized in a space of elementary almost-automorphic functions: these functions are defined in the paper mentioned above.

R. C. Gunning (Princeton, N.J.)

Citations: MR 22# 12222 = F10-67.

F10-69 (23# A325)

Knopp, Marvin Isadore

Construction of a class of modular functions and forms.

Pacific J. Math. **11** (1961), 275–293.

A method due essentially to Rademacher [Amer. J. Math. **61** (1939), 237–248] is used to construct non-constant functions $\mathscr{L}(\tau)=\mathscr{L}(j; b_1, \cdots, b_m; \nu_1, \cdots, \nu_m; \tau)$, invariant under the substitutions $\tau\to T(\tau)=(a\tau+b)/(c\tau+d)$ of $G(j)$, the principal congruence subgroup, of level j, of the modular group. Here $\nu_1, \nu_2, \cdots, \nu_m$ are arbitrary, distinct, positive integers, $m>q(j)$ ($q(j)$ is the number of generators of $G(j)$), while the m constants b_i have to satisfy $q(j)$ linear equations. The method consists in defining functions $\lambda_\nu(j;\tau)=\sum_{n=1}^{\infty}b_n(\nu, j)e^{2\pi in\tau/j}$ (the $b_n(\nu, j)$ are complicated sums involving Kloosterman sums and Bessel functions) and proving that $\lambda_\nu(j;\tau)$ is analytic for $\Im\tau>0$ and satisfies there $\lambda_\nu(j; T(\tau))=\lambda_\nu(j;\tau)+\omega_\nu(j; c, d)$, with ω_ν independent of τ, a and b. If $m>q(j)$, one can select b_i's ($i=1, 2, \cdots, m$) such that $\mathscr{L}(\tau)=\sum_{i=1}^{m}b_i\lambda_{\nu_i}(j;\tau)$ stays invariant when $\tau\to T(\tau)$. A slight generalization of the method permits also the construction of forms (automorphic under $G(j)$) of all positive even dimensions.

E. Grosswald (Philadelphia, Pa.)

Referred to in F10-76.

F10-70 (23# A1036)

Schaeffer, A. C.

Dirichlet series.

Illinois J. Math. **4** (1960), 479–500.

The group H of substitutions $\tau'=(a\tau+b)/(c\tau+d)$ generated by $\tau'=\tau+2$, $\tau'=-1/\tau$ is the appropriate group for studying the behaviour of the theta functions. The author studies the subgroups of H defined by $b\equiv 0 \pmod p$, $b\equiv c\equiv 0 \pmod p$, $b\equiv c\equiv 0 \pmod p$ and $a\equiv d\equiv\pm 1 \pmod p$ which are denoted by $R(p)$, $H(p)$, $\Gamma(p)$, respectively, where p is an odd prime. Much of the paper is devoted to a study of their fundamental regions, and it is proved that the topological genera of $H(p)$ and $\Gamma(p)$ are given by

$$g(H(p)) = \begin{cases} (p^2-3p)/4, & p \equiv 3 \pmod 4, \\ (p^2-3p-2)/4, & p \equiv 1 \pmod 4, \end{cases}$$

$$g(\Gamma(p)) = (p-3)(p^2-p-4)/8.$$

The author does not determine the genus of $R(p)$ but this can be shown to be

$$g(R(p)) = [(p-2)/4].$$

The author develops the (known) transformation formulas for the function $\vartheta(\tau)=\sum_{-\infty}^{\infty} \exp i\pi n^2\tau$ for substitutions of $H(p)$, $\Gamma(p)$ and goes on to construct a set of $(p^3-p)/8$ entire modular functions belonging to $\Gamma(p)$. This is the maximum number of linearly independent functions of this type possible. The important problem of proving that the functions constructed are linearly independent (which would make them a polynomial basis for the functions on $\Gamma(p)$ with suitably restricted behaviour at the parabolic vertices of the fundamental region of $\Gamma(p)$) is left unsettled.

M. Newman (Washington, D.C.)

F10-71 (23# A1037)

Hahn, Hwa S.

Some remarks on A. C. Schaeffer's paper on Dirichlet series.

Illinois J. Math. **4** (1960), 501–506.

It is proved that the $(p^3-p)/8$ functions described in the preceding review are indeed linearly independent for $p=3, 5, 7$. The method is by examining the polar orders of the functions at the parabolic vertices of the fundamental region of $\Gamma(p)$, and apparently cannot be extended to larger p. The computational problems become formidable for large p because of the size of $(p^3-p)/8$.

M. Newman (Washington, D.C.)

F10-72 (23# A2368)

Carlitz, Leonard

On the complete elliptic integral of the third kind.

Boll. Un. Mat. Ital. (3) **15** (1960), 373–378.

Let

$$J(\alpha^2, k^2) = \frac{2}{\pi}\int_0^{\pi/2} \frac{d\phi}{(1-\alpha^2\sin^2\phi)\sqrt{(1-k^2\sin^2\phi)}},$$

let F denote the hypergeometric function, and let

$$T(k^2, \alpha^2) = \sum_{t=0}^{m} (-1)^t \binom{m}{t} \sum_{r=0}^{t-1} (-1)^r \binom{m}{r} \alpha^{2r}k^{2t}.$$

It is shown that

$$F^p(\tfrac12, \tfrac12; 1, \alpha^2k^2) \times \{J(\alpha^2, \alpha^2k^2)-(1-\alpha^2)^m(1-k^2)^m J^p(\alpha^2, \alpha^2k^2)\} \equiv -T(k^2, \alpha^2) \pmod p$$

for any odd prime p. The congruence is to be interpreted in the manner described in the author's earlier paper concerning analogous results for the theta-function ϑ_3 [Proc. Amer. Math. Soc. **10** (1959), 912–916; MR **22** #690].

T. M. Apostol (Pasadena, Calif.)

Citations: MR 22# 690 = F10-62.

F10-73 (23# A2393)

Kolberg, O.

An elementary discussion of certain modular forms.

Univ. Bergen Årbok Naturvit. Rekke **1959**, *no.* 16, 26 *pp.* (1960).

The author applies q-dissection to the functions

$$\varphi(x)^{k_1}\varphi(x^2)^{k_2}\cdots\varphi(x^h)^{k_h}, \quad \varphi(x) = \prod_{n=1}^{\infty}(1-x^n),$$

and obtains many identities and congruences, some well-known. Among the identities obtained, the two that follow are the most striking:

$$\varphi(x^2)^5\varphi(-x)^{-2} = \sum_{n=-\infty}^{\infty}(3n+1)x^{n(3n+2)};$$

$$\varphi(x)^5\varphi(x^2)^{-2} = \sum_{n=-\infty}^{\infty}(6n+1)x^{n(3n+1)/2}.$$

Among the congruences, the following yield interesting number-thoeretic information:

$$p_9(n) \equiv \tfrac14\sigma(8n+3) \pmod 2;$$
$$p_{15}(n) \equiv \tfrac12\sigma(8n+5) \pmod 2;$$
$$p_{21}(n) \equiv \tfrac18\sigma(8n+7) \pmod 2;$$
$$p_8(n) \equiv \sigma(3n+1) \pmod 3;$$
$$p_{16}(n) \equiv \tfrac13\sigma(3n+2) \pmod 3.$$

Here $p_r(n)$ is the coefficient of x^n in $\varphi(x)^r$, and $\sigma(n)$ is the sum of the divisors of n. The author also obtains in an elementary manner such formulas as

$$R(n) = 4\{\sigma(n)-\sigma(\tfrac12 n)+2\sigma(\tfrac14 n)-8\sigma(\tfrac18 n)\}$$

for the number of representations of n by $x^2+y^2+2z^2+2w^2$.

M. Newman (Washington, D.C.)

Referred to in F35-42.

F10-74 (23# A2405)

Iseki, Shô

A proof of a functional equation related to the theory of partitions.

Proc. Amer. Math. Soc. **12** (1961), 502–505.

If $R(s)>0$, $0\leqq\alpha\leqq1$, $0<\beta<1$ (or $0<\alpha<1$, $0\leqq\beta\leqq1$), let

$$\Lambda(z, \alpha, \beta) = \sum_{r=0}^{\infty}\{\lambda((r+\alpha)z-i\beta)+\lambda((r+1-\alpha)z+i\beta)\} + \pi z(\alpha^2-\alpha+1/6)-\pi i(\alpha-1/2)(\beta-1/2),$$

where $\lambda(t)=-\log(1-e^{-2\pi t})$ (the principal value). In an earlier paper [Duke Math. J. **24** (1957), 653–662; MR **19**, 943] the author proved the functional equation $\Lambda(z, \alpha, \beta)=\Lambda(z^{-1}, 1-\beta, \alpha)$, which implies the transformation equation for Dedekind's modular function $\eta(\tau)$. In this paper the author gives a new proof of the functional equation for Λ, using a revision of Rademacher's Mellin-transform approach to $\eta(\tau)$. [J. Reine Angew. Math. **167** (1932), 312–336.] This new proof is much shorter than Rademacher's because the calculation of the residues has been simplified.

T. M. Apostol (Pasadena, Calif.)

Citations: MR 19, 943a = F10-50.

F10-75 (24# A95)

Rieger, G. J.

Ein einfacher Beweis der Funktionalgleichungen der Thetanullwerte.

Arch. Math. **11** (1960), 454–456.

Following in the footsteps of C. L. Siegel [Mathematika **1** (1954), 4; MR **16**, 16] and H. Rademacher [J. Indian Math. Soc. (N.S.) **19** (1955), 25–30; MR **17**, 15], the author gives a simple proof, using Cauchy's theorem, of the transformation formulae for the functions Q, q, G defined for $\operatorname{Im}\tau>0$ by $Q(\tau)=\prod_{k=1}^{\infty}(1+e^{(2k-1)\pi i\tau})$, $q(\tau)=\prod_{k=1}^{\infty}(1-e^{(2k-1)\pi i\tau})$, $G(\tau)=\prod_{k=1}^{\infty}(1+e^{2k\pi i\tau})$.

From these transformation formulae, together with that for the Dedekind η-function, the corresponding formulae for the four theta-functions of Jacobi follow immediately.

A. Sklar (Chicago, Ill.)

Citations: MR 16, 16b = F10-35; MR 17, 15f = F10-40.

F10-76 **(24# A96)**

Knopp, Marvin Isadore

Construction of a class of modular functions and forms. II.

Pacific J. Math. **11** (1961), 661–678.

In Part I [same J. **11** (1961), 275–293; MR **23** #A325] the author defined functions $\lambda_\nu(j;\tau)$ and proved that they satisfy (*) $\lambda_\nu(j;V(\tau))=\lambda_\nu(j;\tau)+\omega_\nu(j;c,d)$ for all $V(\tau)=(a\tau+b)/(c\tau+d)$ that are elements of $G(j)$, the principal congruence subgroup of level j of the modular group $G(1)$. It also was shown how one can form linear combinations of the $\lambda_\nu(j;\tau)$, with constant coefficients, that are invariant under $G(j)$. In the present paper the author generalizes $\lambda_\nu(j;\tau)$ to $\lambda_\nu(\tau)=\lambda_\nu(j,n_1,n_2;\tau)$ by introducing congruence restrictions in the summations defining $\lambda_\nu(j;\tau)$. One observes that this does not affect the validity of (*) (but now $\omega_\nu=\omega_\nu(j,n_1,n_2;c,d)$). The main purpose of the paper is to determine the behaviour of $\lambda_\nu(\tau)$ at the parabolic cusps of a fundamental region of $G(j)$. The method consists (for $j\geqq 3$; the case $j=2$ is treated separately) in studying the behaviour of λ_ν under transformations $V(\tau)\in G^0(j)$ (i.e., $V=\begin{pmatrix}ab\\cd\end{pmatrix}\in G(1)$, $b\equiv 0 \pmod j$)). The result is that $\lambda_\nu(\tau)$ is regular (in the local uniformizing variable) at all but one cusp, where it has a pole of order ν. This, together with (*), shows that $\lambda_\nu(\tau)$ is an abelian integral. It also follows that if V is parabolic, then $\omega_\nu=0$ (although not stated in the paper, the same is true for elliptic V, by the same proof); hence, $\lambda_\nu(\tau)$ are modular functions of $G(j)$, provided that $G(j)$ admits a set of generators consisting only of parabolic [and/or elliptic] transformations, which is the case for groups with fundamental region of genus zero. At higher genus, one can still form linear combinations of the $\lambda_\nu(\tau)$, which are invariant under $G(j)$. These will be investigated in a future paper.

E. Grosswald (Philadelphia, Pa.)

Citations: MR 23# A325 = F10-69.

Referred to in F05-22, F05-27.

F10-77 **(26# 228)**

Smart, John Roderick

On modular forms of levels two and three.

Michigan Math. J. **9** (1962), 233–239.

Let $\Gamma=\Gamma(1)$ denote the (inhomogeneous) modular group, and let $\Gamma(N)$ be the corresponding principal subgroup of level N. Rademacher and Zuckerman [Ann. of Math. (2) **39** (1938), 433–462; Zuckerman, Amer. J. Math. **62** (1940), 127–152; MR **1**, 214] determined the parametrization of $\Gamma(1)$. Maak [Math. Scand. **3** (1955), 44–48; MR **17**, 126] determined all characters on $\Gamma(2)$. Using similar methods, the author determines the characters on $\Gamma(3)$. By methods analogous to those used by Zuckerman, and with the knowledge of the characters of $\Gamma(N)$, one can obtain the parametrization of $\Gamma(N)$, at least if $\Gamma(N)$ is of genus zero (i.e., if there exists a modular invariant which maps the fundamental region one-to-one conformally onto the plane). This is actually carried out by the author for $N=2$ and $N=3$, with the remark that the method should work also for $N=4$ (but not without modification for $N\geqq 5$). *E. Grosswald* (Philadelphia, Pa.)

Citations: MR 1, 214c = F10-1; MR 17, 126d = F70-7.

F10-78 **(26# 2607)**

Dombrowski, Heinz Dieter

Fastautomorphe Funktionen zweiten Grades.

Math. Ann. **149** (1962/63), 71–96.

In 1959 führte Maak [Bayer. Akad. Wiss. Math.-Nat. Kl. S.-B. **1959**, 289–319; MR **22** #12222], in Anlehnung an fastperiodische Funktionen, den Begriff der fastautomorphen (fa) Funktionen ein. Er bewies die Existenz von Darstellungsmoduln (jeder endlichen Dimension n) der Modulgruppe Γ, welche aus fa Funktionen bestehen. Die gegenwärtige Arbeit untersucht ausführlich den Fall $n=2$, sowohl für Γ, als auch für die Hauptkongruenzuntergruppe $\Gamma(2)$. Genauer ausgedrückt befasst sich die Arbeit mit fa Funktionen zweiten Grades, d.h. fa Funktionen die einem 2-dimensionalen irreduziblen Darstellungsmodul von Γ angehören. Die Beweise gründen sich hauptsächlich auf eine Ähnlichkeit genannte Äquivalenzrelation innerhalb der Menge $\mathfrak{D}$ der Matrizendarstellungen n-ten Grades einer Gruppe G: Es sei $\mathfrak{L}$ die lineare Gruppe, $D\in\mathfrak{D}$, $\tilde{D}$ das Tensor-Produkt von D mit einer Darstellung D_1 ersten Grades von G; dann heissen D und D' ähnlich, falls $D'=X\tilde{D}X^{-1}$ für irgend ein $X\in\mathfrak{L}$. Im ersten Teil der Arbeit werden Ähnlichkeitsinvarianten ermittelt (die sich im reellen Falle mit denen von Fricke-Klein decken) und ein kanonisches System von Repräsentanten (Spezialdarstellungen genannt) wird aufgestellt. Es wird, unter anderem, bewiesen: Zwei irreduzible Darstellungen 2. Grades von $\Gamma(2)$ (oder Γ) sind einander genau dann ähnlich, wenn sie in (gewissen) Invarianten übereinstimmen; jede irreduzible Darstellung 2. Grades von $\Gamma(2)$ (oder Γ) ist einer Spezialdarstellung ähnlich. Es gibt (bis auf Ähnlichkeit) genau eine (explizit angegebene) irreduzible Darstellung 2. Grades von Γ, die auf $\Gamma(2)$ reduzibel ist. Der zweite Teil der Arbeit untersucht zweidimensionale Darstellungsmoduln von Γ and $\Gamma(2)$, die aus analytischen Funktionen bestehen. Unter Anlehnung an die klassische Theorie der elliptischen Modulfunktionen wird eine neue (etwas abgeänderte) Definition der Wirtingerintegrale [Wirtinger, S.-B. Kaiserlichen Akad. Wiss. Wien Math.-Nat. Cl. Abt. 2a **111** (1902), 894–900] gegeben. Diese werden nun dazu benützt, um für $\Gamma(2)$ Darstellungsmoduln explizit anzugeben; dasselbe gelingt auch für Γ (für passende Werte der Parameter). Es wird gezeigt, dass die dabei auftretenden Wirtingerintegrale (unter gewissen zusätzlichen Beschränktheitsbedingungen) fa sind. Die hier durch Wirtingerintegrale dargestellten fa Funktionen 2. grades können auch [siehe Maak, Math. Inst. Göttingen Bericht No. 1 (1960)] durch Poincaréreihen dargestellt werden. Diese Tatsache wird nun dahin ausgewertet um die Wirtingerintegrale selber mit Hilfe von Poincaréreihen darzustellen. *E. Grosswald* (Philadelphia, Pa.)

Citations: MR 22# 12222 = F10-67.

F10-79 **(26# 3901)**

Knopp, Marvin Isadore

On abelian integrals of the second kind and modular functions.

Amer. J. Math. **84** (1962), 615–628.

A general problem in the theory of modular functions is to construct modular forms which lie in given form classes. For forms of dimension <-2 the problem is easily solved by the absolutely convergent Poincaré series, but severe difficulties arise for dimension -2. In several previous papers the author has considered forms of positive or zero dimension, for which there is no Poincaré series, and has succeeded in setting up Fourier series which can be shown directly to have the properties of a modular form. In the present paper he extends his methods to the case of abelian integrals.

Let $\Gamma(j)$ be the principal congruence subgroup of level j. Let $w_1,\cdots,w_g$ be the Weierstrass gaps of $\Gamma(j)$ at a fixed parabolic cusp. Then the functions 1, $\hat{\lambda}_{-w_i}$, $1\leqq i\leqq g$, form a basis for the vector space of abelian integrals of the first kind, where $\hat{\lambda}$ is the appropriate "supplementary series" [cf. the author and the reviewer, Illinois J. Math. **6** (1962), 98–106; correction, 713; MR **25** #3168]. A basis for the integrals of the second kind is found by adding the functions λ_ν, $\nu=1,2,\cdots$. Both λ_ν and $\hat{\lambda}_\nu$ are defined by their Fourier series, the coefficients being explicitly given by series of the Petersson-Rademacher-Zuckerman type.

A modular function f on $\Gamma(j)$ is an abelian integral of the second kind with vanishing periods. The author is thus able to determine explicit series expansions for the Fourier coefficients of f in terms of its principal parts.

Results of this general type are accessible from the theory of Poincaré series of dimension -2 by integration. Likewise, the author's results can be interpreted as theorems on abelian differentials (cusp forms of dimension -2). *J. Lehner* (E. Lansing, Mich.)

Citations: MR 25# 3168 = F30-35.

Referred to in F10-83.

F10-80 (26# 6128)

Lewittes, Joseph

Gaps at Weierstrass points for the modular group.

Bull. Amer. Math. Soc. **69** (1963), 578–582.

Let Γ denote the modular group and $\Gamma(N)$ the principal congruence subgroup of level N. Let $S(N)$ be the compactified fundamental region for $\Gamma(N)$. The author gives a new proof that for $N \geqq 7$ the rational cusps of $S(N)$ are Weierstrass points [see also Petersson, Arch. Math. **2** (1950), 246–250; MR **12**, 394; Schoeneberg, Abh. Math. Sem. Univ. Hamburg **17** (1951), 104–111; MR **13**, 439]. Moreover, he gives a method which in some cases is sufficient to determine the gap sequence.

For $P \in S(N)$, $N \geqq 7$, let $1 = \gamma_1(P) < \gamma_2(P) < \cdots < \gamma_g(P) < 2g$ be the gap sequence at P (g is the genus of $S(N)$). If $M(k)$ denotes the number of $\gamma_j(\infty) \equiv k \bmod N$, then the author shows, say, in the case of $N = p$ a prime $\equiv 1 \bmod 4$ (the easiest case to report) that

$$M(0) = (p-5)(p-7)/24,$$

$$M(k) = (p-5)(p-7)/24 + (p-1)/4 - 1,$$

for $k = 1, 2, \cdots, p-1$. Using results of this type, a lower bound for the first non-gap at ∞ and the fact that the non-gaps are closed under addition, he computes the gap sequence at ∞ when $N = 7, 8, 9, 10, 12$. Incomplete results are given for $N = 11$.

Finally it is pointed out that if $G(P) = \sum \gamma_j(P)$ is the sum of the gaps at $P \in S(N)$, then for $N \geqq 7$, $(N, 6) = 1$, $G(\infty) \equiv 0 \bmod N$, $G(i) \equiv 0 \bmod 2$ and $G(\rho) \equiv 0 \bmod 3$, where $i = \sqrt{-1}$ and $\rho = e^{2\pi i/3}$ are elliptic fixed points for Γ. *J. R. Smart* (Madison, Wis.)

Citations: MR 12, 394a = F10-24; MR 13, 439c = F10-27.

Referred to in F10-84, F10-92.

F10-81 (26# 6170)

McQuillan, Donald L.

Ramification in elliptic modular function fields.

Proc. Amer. Math. Soc. **14** (1963), 414–416.

In the classical case, the field of elliptic modular functions of level n is a finite Galois extension K of the field $\mathbf{C}(j)$ generated over $\mathbf{C}$ by the absolute invariant j. The genus is determined by n and the Galois group is LF(2, n). Hecke proved that if n is a prime q, then $K/\mathbf{C}(j)$ is uniquely determined by these two properties. Igusa [Amer. J. Math. **81** (1959), 453–476; MR **21** #3422] has given a geometric theory of elliptic modular functions for any characteristic which does not divide the level and in particular has constructed a Galois covering of a straight line having LF(2, n) as Galois group and a similar formula for the genus. In the present paper the author proves Hecke's theorem for the elliptic modular functions constructed by Igusa. *J. V. Armitage* (Durham City)

Citations: MR 21# 3422 = F10-58.

Referred to in F10-100.

F10-82 (27# 110)

Kloosterman, H. D.

Das Verhalten der Dedekindschen Funktion $\eta(\tau)$ unter Modulsubstitutionen.

Math. Ann. **150** (1963), 130–135.

The Dedekind function $\eta(\tau)$ is defined by the equation

$$\eta(\tau) = \sum_{n=-\infty}^{\infty} (-1)^n \exp 2\pi i\tau(n-\tfrac{1}{6})^2,$$

where τ is a complex variable with positive imaginary part. Let

$$S_B(A) = \sum_{m(\mathrm{mod}\, B)} (-1)^{mA} \exp(\pi i A m^2/B),$$

where A and B are integers, $B \neq 0$, and m ranges over a complete residue system mod B. It is shown that if a, b, c, d are integers such that $ad-bc=1$ and if $c \neq 0$, then

$$\eta\left(\frac{a\tau+b}{c\tau+d}\right) = \varepsilon e^{-(1/4)\pi i \operatorname{sgn} c}(c\tau+d)^{1/2}\frac{S_c(d)}{\sqrt{|c|}}\eta(\tau),$$

where $\varepsilon = \exp\{(1/12)\pi i(c(a+d)+bd(1-c^2))\}$ and the square root is determined from the inequalities $0 < \arg(c\tau+d) < \pi$ if $c > 0$ and $-\pi < \arg(c\tau+d) < 0$ if $c < 0$. The paper also contains some other results involving the η and S functions. *M. V. Subbarao* (Columbia, Mo.)

F10-83 (28# 4110)

Knopp, Marvin Isadore

On generalized abelian integrals of the second kind and modular forms of dimension zero.

Amer. J. Math. **86** (1964), 430–440.

In a previous paper the author treated abelian integrals in the uniformizing plane, i.e., functions $f(\tau)$ satisfying $f(V\tau) = f(\tau) + C(V)$, where $V \in \Gamma(j)$, the principal congruence subgroup of level j, and $C(V)$, independent of τ, is an additive character on $\Gamma(j)$ [same J. **84** (1962), 615–628; MR **26** #3901]. In the present paper he treats generalized abelian integrals, functions satisfying

$$f(V\tau) = v(V)f(\tau) + C(V),$$

where $v(V)$, independent of τ, is a multiplicative character. He makes the restriction that v is a congruence character, i.e., $v \equiv 1$ on some group $\Gamma(nj)$.

The results are similar to those of the previous paper. Since the methods are also similar, the author contents himself with a sketch of the proofs.

The restriction to congruence characters v is made so that the Kloosterman-type sums which occur can be estimated nontrivially by a theorem of Petersson. Also the author uses Petersson's generalization of the Weierstrass gap theorem; in the previous paper the classical theorem was sufficient.

Explicit bases are constructed for the integrals of the first and second kinds and for modular forms. These functions are all exhibited by their Fourier series, the Fourier coefficients being infinite series of the Petersson-Rademacher type. *J. Lehner* (College Park, Md.)

Citations: MR 26# 3901 = F10-79.

F10-84 (28# 5045)

Lehner, J.; Newman, M.

Weierstrass points of $\Gamma_0(n)$.

Ann. of Math. (2) **79** (1964), 360–368.

The authors consider the subgroup of the modular group denoted by $\Gamma_0(n)$ $((a\tau+b)/(c\tau+d)$, where $c \equiv 0 \bmod n)$. The fundamental domain is regarded as a Riemann manifold S with genus $g(n)$; the authors look for Weierstrass points (namely, points P_0 for which a pole structure exists of type P_0^e for $e \leq g(n)$). The property which is used to determine (some) Weierstrass points is a theorem of B. Schoeneberg [Abh. Math. Sem. Univ. Hamburg **17** (1951), 104–111; MR **13**, 439] which is based on $\mathcal{N}$, the normalizer of G (a discrete group (like $\Gamma_0(n)$) in the Lie group of conformal homeomorphisms of the upper half-plane). Then if $M \in \mathcal{N}$ and p is the period of M (least positive p for which $M^p \in G$) the group $G^* = \sum M^k G$ $(1 \leq k \leq p-1)$ is formed and g^* denotes its genus. Finally, if $g^* \neq [g/p]$, then τ, a fixed-point of M, is a Weierstrass point for S. B. Schoeneberg and H. Petersson [H. Petersson, Arch. Math. **2** (1950), 246–250; MR **12**, 394] applied this to the study of $G = \Gamma(n)$, the principal congruence subgroup $((a\tau+b)/(c\tau+d) \equiv \tau \bmod n)$ which is a normal subgroup of the modular group while $\Gamma_0(n)$ is not.

The authors construct the normalizer of $\Gamma_0(n)$ and prove that for n prime $\mathcal{N}/\Gamma_0(n)$ is of order 2. For $\Gamma_0(4n)$ and $\Gamma_0(9n)$ the group G^* is of type $\Gamma_0(2n)$, $\Gamma_0(3n)$; hence a straightforward application of Hecke's formulas yields the theorems that $\tau = 0$ is a Weierstrass point of $\Gamma_0(4n)$ if $g(4n) \geq 2$ except possibly for $4n = 64$, $4p$, $8p$, $16q$, $4pq$ (primes $p \neq q \equiv -1 \bmod 4$). Likewise for $\Gamma_0(9n)$ if $g(9n) \geq 2$; $\tau = 0$ is a Weierstrass point except possibly for $9n = 81$, $9p$, $9pq$ (primes $p \neq q \equiv -1 \bmod 3$).

In particular, using the normalizer $T_n(\tau \to -1/n\tau)$ they find that except for finitely many n, the fixed points of $T_n A$ are Weierstrass points of $\Gamma_0(n)$ $(A \in \Gamma_0(n))$. The proof is based on formulas of Fricke connecting $g(n)$ with class number $h(-4n)$. (It seems necessary to know Siegel's result $h \to \infty$.) Thus the authors justify the Weierstrass points $i/\sqrt{23}$, $\frac{1}{2}(i/\sqrt{23}+1)$, etc., for $\Gamma_0(23)$.

The authors finally consider the problem of when $\Gamma_0(n)$ is hyperelliptic. This is true if and only if a $T \in \mathcal{N}$ has period 2. By identifying images of S under T they obtain a Riemann surface of genus 0 for $\Gamma_0^*(n) = \Gamma_0(n) + T\Gamma_0(n)$. This time, using only less advanced estimates on $h(-4q)$ of P. Bateman [Trans. Amer. Math. Soc. **71** (1951), 70–101; MR **13**, 111], they conclude that for prime $q \equiv -1 \bmod 12$ with $g(q) \geq 2$, $\Gamma_0(q)$ is hyperelliptic exactly when $q = 23, 47, 59, 71$. {In a privately communicated addendum the authors point out that the restriction $q \equiv -1 \bmod 12$ is required so that $\Gamma_0(q)$ is free; otherwise $\mathcal{N}/G$ is isomorphic only to a subgroup of conformal homeomorphisms of S.} Other items in the addenda include the remark that $\Gamma_0(4n)$, $\Gamma_0(9n)$ are free, reference to J. Lewittes [Bull. Amer. Math. Soc. **69** (1963), 578–582; MR **26** #6128], and the remark that $\Gamma_0(37)$ is hyperelliptic but the genus of $\Gamma_0^*(37)$ is 1 since the conformal homeomorphism T need not belong to $\mathcal{N}$. *H. Cohn* (Tucson, Ariz.)

Citations: MR 12, 394a = F10-24; MR 13, 111i = E24-35; MR 13, 439c = F10-27; MR 26# 6128 = F10-80.

Referred to in F10-101.

F10-85 (29# 2391)

Siegel, Carl Ludwig

Bestimmung der elliptischen Modulfunktion durch eine Transformationsgleichung.

Abh. Math. Sem. Univ. Hamburg **27** (1964), 32–38.

If $Tz = (az+b)/(cz+d)$ is a linear fractional transformation, where a, b, c, d are coprime integers and $ad - bc = n > 1$, then the elliptic modular function $j(z)$ and its transform $j(Tz)$ are related by an irreducible algebraic equation over the rationals, $\phi_n(j(Tz), j(z)) = 0$. In the present paper the author shows that, conversely, this transformation equation determines the elliptic modular function in the following sense. If the transformation T as above is a non-periodic elliptic transformation for which the integer n is square-free, and if $f(z)$ is a non-constant analytic function in an open neighborhood of the fixed point ζ of T in the upper half-plane such that

$$\phi_n(f(Tz), f(z)) = 0 \quad \text{and} \quad f(\zeta) = j(\zeta),$$

then $f(z) = j(Mz)$, where M is a linear fractional transformation with the same fixed points as T. In addition, the author investigates the extent to which the Taylor series coefficients of any such function $f(z)$ are determined recursively by the transformation equation ϕ_n itself. *R. C. Gunning* (Princeton, N.J.)

F10-86 (29# 2392)

Iwasaki, Koziro

Note on the modular forms.

Proc. Japan Acad. **39** (1963), 333–337.

If $\sum_{n=1}^{\infty} a_n e^{2\pi i n z}$ is a cusp form of weight k for the modular group, then it is known that the series

$$(*) \qquad \sum_{n=1}^{\infty} a_n (x/n)^{(k+r)/2} J_{k+r}(4\pi\sqrt{(xn)})$$

is Abel summable to $C(k, r) \sum_{0<n<x} a_n (x-n)^r$ for non-integral values $x > 0$, where J_{k+r} is a Bessel function and $C(k, r)$ a suitable constant; general results of this form can be found in Ferrar [Compositio Math. **1** (1934), 344–360; ibid. **4** (1937), 394–405] and in Bochner [Ann. of Math. (2) **53** (1951), 332–363; MR **13**, 920]. In the present paper the author investigates the actual convergence of this series (*) in the cases $r > \frac{1}{2}$ and $r = 0$.

R. C. Gunning (Princeton, N.J.)

Citations: MR 13, 920b = M40-7.

F10-87 (29# 4743)

Wohlfahrt, Klaus

Über die Nullstellen einiger Eisensteinreihen.

Math. Nachr. **26** (1963/64), 381–383.

The author computes the values of the absolute elliptic invariant $J(\tau_0)$ for the zeros of the normalized Eisenstein series (constant term 1) E_k for $k = 12, 16, 18, 20, 22, 26$. These values are rational numbers, but possibly $1728J(\tau_0) \notin Z$. Furthermore, the explicit quadratic equation is given for $J(\tau)$, where τ stands for the two zeros of E_{24} in a fundamental domain.

O. F. G. Schilling (Lafayette, Ind.)

Referred to in F10-118.

F10-88 (30# 4730)

Resnikoff, H. L.

A differential equation for the theta function.

Proc. Nat. Acad. Sci. U.S.A. **53** (1965), 692–693.

For a sufficiently differentiable function f and an integer $n > 1$, define the differential operator D_n by

$$D_n f(z) = (2-2n)^{-1} \{f(z)\}^{3n-2} \frac{d^n}{dz^n} \{f(z)\}^{2-2n},$$

so that $D_n f$ is a polynomial in f and its first n derivatives. The author proves that the theta function θ $(= \theta_\infty = \zeta_3)$ satisfies the differential equation $(D_3\theta)^2 + 32(D_2\theta)^3 + \pi^2\theta^{10}(D_2\theta)^2 = 0$. The methods used are similar to those developed in a paper of the reviewer [J. Indian Math. Soc. (N.S.) **20** (1956), 103–116; MR **18**, 571].

R. A. Rankin (Glasgow)

Citations: MR 18, 571c = F10-47.

F10-89 (30# 4758)

Samuel, Pierre

Travaux d'Igusa sur les formes modulaires de genre 2.

Séminaire Bourbaki, 16e année: 1963/64, Fasc. 2, Exposé 267, 8 pp. Secrétariat mathématique, Paris, 1964.

A report on the results contained in certain papers by

Igusa [Ann. of Math. (2) **72** (1960), 612–649; MR **22** #5637; Amer. J. Math. **84** (1962), 175–200; MR **25** #5040; ibid. **86** (1964), 219–246; MR **29** #2258].

M. Eichler (Basel)

Citations: MR 25# 5040 = F50-22; MR 29# 2258 = F50-27.

F10-90 (32# 5655)

Doi, Koji

On the Jacobian varieties of the fields of elliptic modular functions.

Osaka Math. J. **15** (1963), 249–256.

Let $J_{\Gamma_0(N)}$ be the Jacobian variety of the field of modular functions attached to the group

$$\Gamma_0(N): \begin{pmatrix} a & b \\ c & d \end{pmatrix} \equiv \begin{pmatrix} * & * \\ 0 & * \end{pmatrix} \bmod N.$$

The author considers the cases $N=22, 23, 29, 31$ when the genus is 2. The multiplicator algebras of $J_{\Gamma_0(N)}$ are the matrix algebras of degree 2 over the rational fields $Q, Q(\sqrt{5})$, $Q(\sqrt{2})$, and $Q(\sqrt{5})$, respectively. $J_{\Gamma_0(22)}$ is isogenous to the product of the elliptic curve by itself corresponding to the congruence group $\Gamma_0(11)$; this elliptic curve has no complex multiplications. The proofs follow easily from known facts on abelian varieties. {There is a misprint; the last line must be $A_0(J_{\Gamma_0(N)}) \cong Q(\tau_{p_1,i}) = Q(\tau_{p_2,i})$.}

M. Eichler (Basel)

Referred to in G15-39.

F10-91 (32# 5656)

Matsui, Tokuji

On the endomorphism algebra of Jacobian varieties attached to the fields of elliptic modular functions.

Osaka J. Math. **1** (1964), *no.* 1, 25–31.

The cases $N=41, 47$ are treated similarly. The larger genus (i.e., 3 and 4) requires a refined criterion, coming from the same source as that of Doi [see #5655 above]. Both times $J_{\Gamma_0(N)}$ is simple. The multiplicator algebra is a totally real algebraic number field of degree 4 for $N=41$, and an algebraic number field of degree 8 for $N=47$.

M. Eichler (Basel)

F10-92 (34# 148)

Smart, John Roderick

On Weierstrass points in the theory of elliptic modular forms.

Math. Z. **94** (1966), 207–218.

Let $\{\Gamma, -r, v\}$ denote the class of automorphic forms of dimension $-r$ for the discontinuous group Γ, corresponding to the multiplier system v and having at most a finite number of poles in a fundamental region R; $\nu(\Gamma, -r, v, \mathfrak{d})$ stands for the dimension of the vector space of forms in $\{\Gamma, -r, v\}$, which are multiples of the divisor $\mathfrak{d}$, $\mathscr{H}^+$ stands for the upper half-plane with the rational points adjoined and $\Gamma(n)$ stands for the principal congruence subgroup of the modular group. $z_0 \in \mathscr{H}^+$ is called a gap for the class $\{\Gamma, r-2, v^{-1}\}$ if there exists no form of that class with a pole of order n at z_0 and otherwise regular in R. Let $\mathfrak{a} = \prod \zeta$, the product being taken over the inequivalent parabolic cusps of R with branching value $\lambda=0$, and set $\mu=\nu(\Gamma, -r, v, \mathfrak{a})$; then a theorem of H. Petersson [Math. Ann. **117** (1940), 453–537; MR **2**, 87] states that for every $z_0 \in \mathscr{H}^+$, there exist exactly μ gaps. If these gaps are not (as usually) the integers from 1 to μ, then z_0 is called a Weierstrass point (W.p.). The purpose of the present paper is the investigation of the Weierstrass character of the points $i\infty$, i and $\rho=e^{2\pi i/3}$, for even r, with respect to $\{\Gamma(n), r-2, 1\}$.

Among the results obtained are the following. If $r(\geqq 4)$ is even, then $i\infty$ is a W.p. with respect to $\{\Gamma(n), r-2, 1\}$ for $n\geqq 6$; also, if $\mu=\nu(\Gamma(n), -r, 1, \mathfrak{a})$ and p is the genus of $\Gamma(n)$, then $\mu-p+1$ is a non-gap at $i\infty$ for $n=6$, 7, 8, 9, 10 and 12. For these values of n, the complete gap sequence is actually determined. $z_0=i$ is a W.p. with respect to the class $\{\Gamma(n), r-2, 1\}$ for $n\geqq 6$ and $z_0=\rho$ is a W.p. for $n=6$ and $n\geqq 8$. These, and several other results, generalize and extend theorems due to B. Schoeneberg [Abh. Math. Sem. Univ. Hamburg **17** (1951), 104–111; MR **13**, 439] and J. Lewittes [Bull. Amer. Math. Soc. **69** (1963), 578–582; MR **26** #6128]. The proofs use Lewittes' results, the Riemann-Roch theorem (in Petersson's version) and the above-mentioned theorem of Petersson. An interesting problem left open: are i, ρ and $i\infty$ the only Weierstrass points in R?

E. Grosswald (Philadelphia, Pa.)

Citations: MR 2, 87e = F10-3; MR 13, 439c = F10-27; MR 26# 6128 = F10-80.

F10-93 (34# 4218)

Rademacher, Hans

Über die Transformation der Logarithmen der Thetafunktionen.

Math. Ann. **168** (1967), 142–148.

The author determines the behavior of $\log \vartheta_3(\tau)$ under modular substitutions. His investigations are based on Dedekind's transformation formula for $\log \eta(\tau)$ and on the reciprocity law for Dedekind sums [see the author and A. Whiteman, Amer. J. Math. **63** (1941), 377–407; MR **2**, 249].

O. H. Körner (Marburg)

Citations: MR 2, 249f = F20-1.

F10-94 (34# 7466)

Fomenko, O. M.

Representation of parabolic forms by theta-series. (Russian)

Dokl. Akad. Nauk SSSR **166** (1966), 555–557.

The author sketches a proof of the following theorem. Set $\varphi_i(\tau)=\sum_{n=1}^{\infty} \tau_i(n)e^{2\pi in\tau}$ $(\tau_i(1)=1)$ for $i=1, 2, 3, \cdots, g$ as a basis in the space S of parabolic forms of type $\{\Gamma_0(p), -2\}$ with character $\chi=1$, composed of entire functions of all Hecke operators T_n, $(n,p)=1$ [see H. Petersson, Math. Ann. **117** (1939), 39–64; MR **1**, 294]. Then $\varphi_i(\tau)=\sum_{t=1}^{g^2} \beta_t^{(i)}\vartheta_t'(\tau)$ $(1\leqq i\leqq g)$, where $\vartheta_t'(\tau)$, parabolic form, is the derivative of a quaternary theta-series of degree p (discriminant p^2) and $|\beta_t^{(i)}| < C_\varepsilon p^{5+\varepsilon}$.

References are to the works of Hecke, Eichler, Petersson, Selberg, Shimura and Schoenberg.

{This article has appeared in English translation [Soviet Math. Dokl. **7** (1966), 134–136].}

S. Chowla (University Park, Pa.)

Citations: MR 1, 294c = F65-1.

F10-95 (34# 7469)

Hiramatsu, Toyokazu

Modular forms obtained from L-functions with Grössencharacters of $Q(\sqrt{-3})$.

Comment. Math. Univ. St. Paul. **14** (1966), 65–70.

The Mellin transforms of the L-functions of the title are cusp forms for the commutator subgroup Γ^c of the modular group Γ. The aim of this paper is to express these modular forms explicitly in terms of a standard basis for the space of cusp forms of Γ^c.

R. C. Gunning (Princeton, N.J.)

F10-96 (34# 7511)

Pjateckiĭ-Šapiro, I. I.; Šafarevič, I. R.

Galois theory of transcendental extensions and uniformization. (Russian)

Contemporary Problems in Theory Anal. Functions (Internat. Conf., Erevan, 1965) (*Russian*), *pp.* 262–264. *Izdat. "Nauka", Moscow,* 1966.

In the classical uniformization theory of an algebraic curve X by automorphic functions, one constructs a covering $\tilde{X}$ of X, ramified over only a finite number of points of X, with a transitive group G of automorphisms. Then $X=H\backslash\tilde{X}$, where $H\subset G$ is the group of covering transformations of X. The authors sketch a proposed analogue of this theory for algebraic varieties defined over an arbitrary field K. If X is such a variety, let $\tilde{X}$ be the projective limit of the finite coverings Y of X which are ramified over subvarieties of dimension $<\dim X$. Let G be the group of automorphisms of $\tilde{X}$. In general, G is not transitive, but in many cases $\tilde{X}$ is quasihomogeneous, i.e., one of the orbits of $\tilde{X}$ under G is dense in the topology induced in $\tilde{X}$ by the Zariski topology in the coverings Y. It is this case which the authors promise to investigate more fully. Much of the paper is devoted to the following example. Let Γ be the ordinary modular group operating on the upper half-plane H. For each subgroup $\Delta\subset\Gamma$ of finite index, let X_Δ be a non-singular model of the field of functions automorphic under Δ. Clearly $Y_\Delta=\Delta\backslash H$ can be regarded as a subset of X_Δ with $X_\Delta-Y_\Delta$ finite. Let X, Y be the projective limits of X, Y with respect to the morphisms $X_\Delta\to X_{\Delta'}$, where $\Delta\subseteq\Delta'$. Then $X-Y$ is zero-dimensional, and it is shown that the orbit of any $y\in Y$ is dense in Y. In conclusion it is remarked that if $\tilde{X}$ is quasihomogeneous, then the function field $K(\tilde{X})$ is of finite transcendence degree over K, but not always finitely generated. Of particular interest is the case where there is a finite set $F\subseteq K(\tilde{X})$ such that if $F\subseteq K'\subseteq K(\tilde{X})$, and K' is invariant under the group G of automorphisms of $K(\tilde{X})$, then $K'=K$. In this case the authors suggest the conjecture that G is either a p-adic Lie group or an adelic product of such groups. *B. Gordon* (Los Angeles, Calif.)

F10-97 (35# 1560)

Schoeneberg, B.

Bemerkungen über einige Klassen von Modulformen.

Nederl. Akad. Wetensch. Proc. Ser. A **70** = *Indag. Math.* **29** (1967), 177–182.

Let $K=P(\sqrt{D})$ (P the field of rationals, $0<-D=q\in\mathbf{Z}$), h the number of ideal classes C of K, χ the character of the group of ideal classes; if $\mathfrak{a}\in C$, set $\chi(\mathfrak{a})=\chi(C)$ and let χ_0 and C_1 stand for the principal character and principal ideal class, respectively. For $s=\sigma+it$ ($\sigma>1$), define the coefficients $a(n,C)$ and $a(n,\chi)$ by $\zeta(s,C)=\sum_{\mathfrak{a}\in C}N(\mathfrak{a})^{-s}=\sum_{n>0}a(n,C)n^{-s}$ and

$$\zeta(s,\chi)=\sum_C\chi(C)\zeta(s,C)=\sum_{n>0}a(n,\chi)n^{-s},$$

respectively.

Theorem 1: If $D\equiv 1 \pmod{24}$, then

$$x^{(q+1)/24}\prod_{k>0}(1-x^k)(1-x^{qk})=\sum_{n>0}t_q(n)x^n,$$

where $t_q(n)=a(n,C^{(1)})-a(n,C^{(2)})$ holds for certain ideal classes $C^{(1)}$, $C^{(2)}$ of K. By setting $D=-23$, one obtains a result of F. van der Blij [same Proc. **55** (1952), 498–503; MR **14**, 623]. The method of proof is an extension of that of van der Blij. Some of the steps in the proof of Theorem 1 are used also in the proof of Theorem 2: Let $\eta(\tau)$ stand for Dedekind function, set $\Psi_{q,\varepsilon}{}^r(\tau)=[\eta(q\tau)\eta^{-\varepsilon}(\tau)]^r$, where $\varepsilon=\pm1$, q is an odd, and r is an arbitrary positive integer, satisfying $(q-\varepsilon)r\equiv 0 \pmod{24}$. If Γ_0 is the subgroup of the modular group Γ defined by

$$\left\{\begin{pmatrix}a&b\\c&d\end{pmatrix}\in\Gamma,\ c\equiv 0\ (\mathrm{mod}\ |D|)\right\},$$

then $\psi_{q,\varepsilon}{}^r((a\tau+b)/(c\tau+d))=(d/q)^r(c\tau+d)^{(1-\varepsilon)/2}\psi(\tau)$. This result generalizes one of H. A. Rademacher [Trans. Amer. Math. Soc. **51** (1942), 609–636; MR **3**, 271]. The proof uses the classical transformation formulas of $\eta(\tau)$.

E. Grosswald (Philadelphia, Pa.)

Citations: MR 3, 271c = P60-1; MR 14, 623d = E28-16.

F10-98 (35# 5392)

Meyer, C.

Über die Dedekindsche Transformationsformel für $\log\eta(\tau)$.

Abh. Math. Sem. Univ. Hamburg **30** (1967), 129–164.

Let $q=e^{2\pi i\tau}$, $\eta(\tau)=q^{1/24}\prod_{m=1}^\infty(1-q^m)$. The transformation formula is $\log\eta((a\tau+b)/(c\tau+d))=\log\eta(\tau)+\frac12\log(c\tau+d)+\frac1{12}\pi i((a+d)/c-3\operatorname{sgn}c-12\operatorname{sgn}c\cdot s(a,c))$, where a, b, c, d are integers and $ad-bc=+1$. Further, $s(a,c)=\sum P_1(a\mu/c)P_1(\mu/c)$, $(a,c)=1$, $P_1(x)=x-[x]-\frac12$ and the summation extends over a complete set of residues μ mod c omitting 0. To the four existing proofs of this formula, a new one is added which is related to Iseki's first proof [K. Iseki, J. Math. Soc. Japan **4** (1952), 14–26; MR **14**, 139]. If $\log\eta(\tau)=\pi i\tau/12-\sum(\tau)$, then

$$\sum((a\tau+b)/(c\tau+d))=(2i/(c\tau+d))\sum_{\mu=1}^c\sum_{\nu=1}^c\exp(2\pi ia\mu\nu/c)J_{\mu\nu},$$

$$J_{\mu\nu}=\int_0^\infty\sum_{p=0}^\infty\exp[-\pi(p+\mu/c)^2t^{-2}]\times\sum_{r=0}^\infty\exp[-\pi(r+\nu/c)^2(ict/(c\tau+d))^2]\,dt,$$

and the main problem is the transformation of the asymmetric theta series. For this two methods are used. The first is based on the transformation theory of the Hurwitz zeta function. The representation is

$$\sum_{p=0}^\infty\exp[-\pi(p+\mu/c)^2t^{-2}]=(1/2\pi i)\int_{\sigma-i\infty}^{\sigma+i\infty}\pi^{-s}\Gamma(s)\zeta(2s,\mu/c)t^{2s}\,ds.$$

Here the functional equation is used and gives two distinct types of sums $\sum_{p=0}^\infty\exp[-\pi(p+\lambda/c)^2c^2t^2]$ and

$$\sum_{n=-\infty}^\infty(n+\lambda/c)^{-1}\exp[-\pi(n+\lambda/c)^2c^2t^2]\times{}_1F_1(-\tfrac12;\tfrac12;\pi(n+\lambda/c)^2c^2t^2).$$

The series have elementary multipliers and are summed for λ from 1 to c or 1 to $c-1$. There are also some additional elementary terms. The second method uses Poisson's summation formula. With the aid of these two methods it is shown that $\sum((a\tau+b)/(c\tau+d))-\sum(\tau)$ equals an elementary function plus a complicated remainder. That the latter is actually identically zero involves an elaborate discussion. *E. Hille* (Eugene, Ore.)

Citations: MR 14, 139a = P60-15.

F10-99 (35# 6624)

Schoeneberg, Bruno

Verhalten von speziellen Integralen 3. Gattung bei Modultransformationen und verallgemeinerte Dedekindsche Summen.

Abh. Math. Sem. Univ. Hamburg **30** (1967), 1–10.

Let

$$\eta(\tau;a,b,N)=\exp(\pi i\tau P_2(a/N))\times\prod_{m>0;\,m\equiv a(N)}(1-\zeta^b\exp(2\pi i\tau m/N))\times\prod_{m>0;\,m\equiv -a(N)}(1-\zeta^{-b}\exp(2\pi i\tau m/N)),$$

where for any x, $\exp x=e^x$, $\tau=x+iy$, $y>0$, $\zeta=\exp(2\pi i/N)$, $P_2(x)=(x-[x])^2-(x-[x])+\frac16$, x being real and $[x]$ the largest integer $\leqq x$, and a, b non-negative integers and $N\geqq1$. This function is a generalization of the well-known Dedekind η-function

$$\eta(\tau)=\exp(\pi i\tau/12)\prod_{m>0}(1-\exp 2\pi i\tau m).$$

An important problem, initiated and solved in the case of $\eta(\tau)$ by Riemann and Dedekind, is the study of the behavior of $\log\eta(\tau;a,b,N)=\psi(\tau;a,b,N)$ with regard to the modular substitutions $\tau\to(\alpha\tau+\beta)(\gamma\tau+\delta)^{-1}$, α, β, γ, δ being integers with $\alpha\delta-\beta\gamma=1$. This latter problem was already studied by C. Meyer [*Die Berechnung der Klassenzahl Abelscher Körper über quadratischen Zahlkörpern*, Akademie-Verlag, Berlin, 1957; MR **19**, 531] by using the methods of H. Rademacher [J. Math. **167** (1932), 312–336]. The author solves the problem by using instead E. Hecke's idea [Abh. Math. Sem. Univ. Hamburg **5** (1927), 199–224; reprinted in *Mathematische Werke*, pp. 525–547, Vandenhoeck & Ruprecht, Göttingen, 1959; see MR **21** #3303] that $\psi(\tau; a, b, N)$ is an integral of the third kind and that its derivative is a modular form of dimension -2 and as such is associated with Hecke's generalized Eisenstein series which have simple Fourier expansions.

K. G. Ramanathan (Bombay)

Citations: MR 19, 531f = R02-21; MR 21# 3303 = Z25-14.

F10-100 (35# 6687)

McQuillan, Donald L.

A uniqueness theorem for fields of elliptic modular functions.

Proc. Roy. Irish Acad. Sect. A **65**, 63–68 (1967).

The elliptic modular functions of level n form a normal extension of $\mathbf{C}(j)$ (where j is the absolute invariant) with Galois group $SL(2, Z/2Z)$ and genus $g(1)=g(2)=0$, $g(n)=1+((n-6)n^2/24)\prod_{p|n}(1-p^2)$ $(n>2)$. E. Hecke [*Mathematische Werke*, pp. 568–576, Vandenhoeck and Ruprecht, Göttingen, 1959; MR **21** #3303] showed that there exists but one normal extension of $\mathbf{C}(j)$ with this Galois group and this genus. The author proves a similar uniqueness theorem for function fields over the algebraic closure K_p of the prime field of characteristic p instead of $\mathbf{C}$. There are always three ramification points, their orders are 2, 3 and n, if $p\neq 2, 3$. For $p=2, 3$ the ramifications are slightly more complicated. If the situations of the ramifications are fixed the field is uniquely determined. The proof is a sequel to a previous one by the author [Proc. Amer. Math. Soc. **14** (1963), 414–416; MR **26** #6170], where $n\not\equiv 0 \bmod p$ was assumed.

M. Eichler (Basel)

Citations: MR 21# 3303 = Z25-14; MR 26# 6170 = F10-81.

F10-101 (36# 1646)

Atkin, A. O. L.

Weierstrass points at cusps of $\Gamma_0(n)$.

Ann. of Math. (2) **85** (1967), 42–45.

Let $\Gamma(1)$ be the modular group consisting of all fractional linear transformations $\tau'=(a\tau+b)(c\tau+d)^{-1}$, where $a, b, c, d\in\mathbf{Z}$ and $ad-bc=1$. Let $\Gamma_0(n)$ be the subgroup defined by $c\equiv 0 \pmod n$, and let $g(n)$ be the genus of the Riemann surface $H/\Gamma_0(n)$ (compactified), where H is the upper half τ-plane. If $\tau=i\infty$ is a Weierstrass point of S, one says that $n\in W$.

J. Lehner and M. Newman [same Ann. (2) **79** (1964), 360–368; MR **28** #5045] obtained conditions to ensure that $p^2n\in W$ in the cases $p=2, 3$. The author obtains sufficient conditions for the case where p is any prime $\geqq 5$. He solves, in particular, a problem left open in the cited paper: There are infinitely many values of n such that $(n, 6)=1$ and $n\in W$.

G. G. Weill (Brooklyn, N.Y.)

Citations: MR 28# 5045 = F10-84.

F10-102 (37# 155)

Weil, André

Sur une formule classique.

J. Math. Soc. Japan **20** (1968), 400–402.

The author illustrates a principle—that Dirichlet series can serve the theory of automorphic functions—by the following example. Let $\varphi(s)=\zeta(s)\zeta(s+1)$, $\Phi(s)=(2\pi)^{-2}\Gamma(s)\varphi(s)$; then $\Phi(s)=\Phi(-s)$, by the functional equation for $\zeta(s)$, and one can apply the method of Hecke, although $\Phi(s)$ has poles at $s=0, \pm 1$, while Hecke allowed at most one simple pole. The Mellin transform of Φ is

$$F(\tau) = (1/2\pi i)\int_{\sigma-i\infty}^{\sigma+i\infty}(\tau/i)^{-s}\Phi(s)\,ds = \pi i\tau/12-\log\eta(\tau),$$

where $\sigma>1$, $\operatorname{Im}\tau>0$ and $\eta(\tau)$ is Dedekind's function. Shifting the line of integration to the left, computing the residues at $s=0, \pm 1$, and applying $\Phi(s)=\Phi(-s)$, the classical formula $\log\eta(-1/\tau)=\log\eta(\tau)+\frac{1}{2}\log\tau/i$ is obtained; no proof could be more natural.

A. P. Ogg (Berkeley, Calif.)

Referred to in F65-29.

F10-103 (37# 1365)

Du Val, Patrick

The modular curve for elliptic function transformations of order four.

J. London Math. Soc. **43** (1968), 40–52.

This paper, which is a sequel to one of like character [the author, Ann. Mat. Pura Appl. (4) **70** (1965), 249–270; MR **33** #628], discusses the algebraic relation between the modular invariants of two lattices of complex numbers, each of which is similar to a quarter lattice of the other. The modular invariants used are defined in terms of the modulus k associated with the Jacobian elliptic functions. The author shows the connection between this work and Klein's results concerning the elliptic modular functions.

L. Roth (Pittsburgh, Pa.)

F10-104 (37# 4016)

Eichler, M.

Grenzkreisgruppen und kettenbruchartige Algorithmen.

Acta Arith. **11** (1965), 169–180.

The expansion of a rational number r in a regular continued fraction is connected with the modular group, for it corresponds to an expression $A=S^{m_0}T\cdots S^{m_k}T$, where $A=(ab|cd)$, $A(\infty)=a/c=r$, $S=(11|01)$, $T=(01|-10)$, and the m_i are selected in a certain way. The author generalizes this situation from the modular group to an arbitrary finitely-generated horocyclic group (Fuchsian group of the first kind). Let Γ be such a group; it acts on the upper half-plane and the set of elements $\mathfrak{B}=(B_1, B_2, \cdots, B_h)$ that conjugate pairs of sides of a normal polygon (Dirichlet region) R form a system of generators for Γ. If $A=(ab|cd)\in\Gamma$ and a curve is drawn from some point in R to a point in the fundamental region $A(R)$, the sequence of intervening polygons crossed by the curve can be written as $D_1(R)$, $D_1D_2(R)$, $\cdots$, $D_1D_2\cdots D_m(R)=A(R)$, where each D_i is in $\mathfrak{B}$. Every such curve determines A as a word in the generators $\mathfrak{B}$. The author sets forth the following algorithm: Fix θ, an arbitrary point in R. If $D_1, D_2, \cdots, D_i$ have already been determined, connect ζ_i (the center of the polygon $D_1\cdots D_i(R)$) with $A(\theta)$ by a hyperbolic straight line and write the next polygon crossed by this line as $D_1D_2\cdots D_{i+1}$. Then the word $A=D_1D_2\cdots D_m$, $D_i\in\mathfrak{B}$ is unique.

The author proves that if $A=D_1\cdots D_m$, $D_i\in\mathfrak{B}$, the length l of A is estimated by (1) $l\leqq M_1\log\mu(A)+M_2$, where M_i are constants not depending on A, $\mu(A)=a^2+b^2+c^2+d^2$, and l is defined by counting the factors D_i in a certain way. In Section 5 the author goes back to the modular group and shows how ζ (the center of R) and θ must be chosen to get the regular continued fraction for a rational number by the above algorithm. Then using (1) he obtains (2) $l\leqq M_3\log(3(a^2+c^2)/2)$ for the length (in the ordinary sense) of the regular continued fraction of the rational number a/c. (2) is essentially Lamé's estimate [see J. V. Uspensky and M. A. Heaslet, *Elementary number theory*, pp. 43, 44, McGraw-Hill, New York, 1939; MR **1**, 38].

In Section 4 the author discusses automorphic integrals. Let φ be an automorphic form of degree (or dimension)

$-2n$, n = positive integer, and multiplier system identically 1; then $\Phi(\tau)=\int_{\tau_0}^{\tau} \varphi(\tau')(\tau'-\tau)^{2n-2}\, d\tau'$; $\operatorname{Im} \tau$, $\operatorname{Im} \tau' > 0$, is called an (abelian) automorphic integral of degree (or dimension) $2n-2$. In particular, $n=1$ gives the usual abelian integral. These integrals were mentioned by H. Petersson [Abh. Math. Sem. Univ. Hamburg **12** (1938), 415–472] and investigated by the author [Math. Z. **67** (1957), 267–298; MR **19**, 740]. Writing $\Phi|A=(c\tau+d)^{2n-2}\Phi(A\tau)$, we have $\Phi|A=\Phi+\omega_A$, where $\omega_A(\tau)$ is a polynomial of degree $\leqq 2n-2$; the system of "period polynomials" $\{\omega_A\tau, A\in\Gamma\}$ is used to construct the "Eichler cohomology". The author restricts Φ by the requirement that it be meromorphic (integral of the first or second kind). For Γ a subgroup of finite index in the modular group, he uses (1) and some other results derived by the same methods as (1) to obtain the very interesting estimate (3) $|\omega_A(\tau)|\leqq C(\tau)(\mu(A))^{n-1}\log\mu(A)$, where C depends only on φ, not on A. Then he shows very simply, by the construction of a suitable Poincaré series whose convergence is established by (3), that every system of polynomials $\{\omega_A|A\in\Gamma\}$ of degree $2n-2$ satisfying the consistency ("cocycle") condition $\omega_A|B=\omega_{AB}-\omega_B$, $A, B\in\Gamma$, and the condition (*) $\omega_P\equiv 0$ for certain parabolic P, is the system of period polynomials of an automorphic integral of the second kind. This generalizes the well-known result for ordinary abelian integrals. The condition (*) is stronger than necessary but its use greatly simplifies the proof.

The methods of this paper would seem to be useful in the study of continued fractions based on a finitely-generated horocyclic group Γ, not only for the "rational numbers" $A(\infty)$, $A\in\Gamma$, but for expansions of arbitrary real numbers. Some special cases have already been treated; for the Hecke groups (generated by $\tau'=\tau+\lambda$, $\tau'=-1/\tau$), see D. Rosen [Duke Math. J. **21** (1954), 549–563; MR **16**, 458].

J. Lehner (College Park, Md.)

Citations: MR 1, 38c = Z01-2; MR 16, 458d = A54-20; MR 19, 740a = F15-12.

F10-105 (37# 4021)

Petersson, Hans

Über die logarithmischen Ableitungen der automorphen Formen.

Abh. Math. Sem. Univ. Hamburg **31** (1967), 191–198.

A function $f\in\{\Gamma, -r\}$, i.e., f is an automorphic form of degree (or dimension) $-r$ on the horocyclic group Γ, satisfies $f|_{-r}L=f$ for each $L=(ab|cd)\in\Gamma$, where $f|_{-r}L=(c\tau+d)^{-r}f(L\tau)$. As a consequence $\Lambda(\tau, f)\equiv r^{-1}f'(\tau)/f(\tau)$, with $f\neq 0$, satisfies $\Lambda\|L=\Lambda$, where (1) $f\|L=f|_{-2}L-c/(c\tau+d)$. In this paper the author introduces and investigates the two-stroke operator $\|$. It is assumed that Γ has a fundamental region of finite area.

Let $\mathfrak{L}$ be the set of functions having finitely many poles in a fundamental region F of Γ, meromorphic at the cusps of Γ, and invariant under $\|$. Let $Z(\tau, \tau_0)$ be an "automorphic prime form", i.e., $Z\in\{\Gamma, -r_0\}$ and is regular and zero-free in the upper half-plane H and at the cusps of Γ except for a simple zero at τ_0. (Here r_0 depends on Γ.) Write $\Lambda_0(\tau, \tau_0)=\Lambda(\tau, Z(*, \tau_0))$. Then $\Lambda_0\in\mathfrak{L}$. Let $\mathfrak{L}_1$, $\mathfrak{L}_2$ be the set of linear combinations of $\{\Lambda_0(\tau, \tau_0)|\tau_0\in H$ or $\tau_0=$ cusp$\}$ with real and complex coefficients, respectively, and let $\mathfrak{L}_3$ be the subset of functions of $\mathfrak{L}$ regular at the cusps. The author introduces a $\|$-invariant scalar product $[\varphi, f]$, $\varphi\in\mathfrak{L}$, $f\in\{\Gamma, -2\}$. He sketches the proof of the following theorem. A function $\varphi\in\mathfrak{L}_3$ lies in $\mathfrak{L}_2$ if and only if φ is orthogonal to the space of cusp forms of degree -2.

In the final section (§ 5) the author explains the connection of these ideas with classical concepts. The Poincaré series of degree -2 does not converge absolutely. Hecke introduced a convergence factor $|c\tau+d|^{-s}$ and arrived at functions $E(s, \tau; A, N)$, which are still analytic at $s=0$, and whose "zero-values" $E(0, \tau; A, N)-E(0, \tau; I, N)\in\{\Gamma(N), -2\}$, where $\Gamma(N)$ is the principal congruence subgroup of the modular group of level N. Here A belongs to the full modular group $\Gamma(1)$ and I is the identity matrix. Hecke expanded $E(0, \tau; A, N)$ in a "Fourier series" that contains, besides the usual terms in $\exp 2\pi i\tau/N$, a non-analytic (in τ) term $1/(\tau-\bar{\tau})$; call the analytic part $\Phi(\tau, A, N)$. By using the theorem cited above and the known fact that $E(0, \tau; A, N)$ is orthogonal to the space of cusp forms of degree -2, the author is able to show that $\Phi(\tau, A, N)=\Lambda_0(\tau, A^{-1}\infty)$, where Λ_0 is constructed for the group $\Gamma(N)$. The author states that an analogous construction can be carried out for arbitrary congruence subgroups of $\Gamma(1)$.

J. Lehner (College Park, Md.)

Referred to in F25-26.

F10-106 (38# 125)

Schoeneberg, B.

Über das unendliche Produkt $\prod_{k=1}^{\infty}(i-x^k)$.

Mitt. Math. Gesellsch. Hamburg **9**, *no.* 4, 4–11 (1968).

The author gives a new proof for the transformation formulae for Dedekind's η-function and its logarithm under the substitution $z\to-1/z$. By means of Euler's identity for $\eta(z)$ and a Mellin transformation, a connection between $\eta(z)$ and a Dirichlet L-series is established, which yields the desired transformation formula for $\eta(z)$. As the author points out, this connection is contained as a special case in Hecke's theory on relations between automorphic forms and Dirichlet series. The function $\log\eta(z)$ is similarly treated.

O. H. Körner (Marburg)

F10-107 (38# 4426)

Motohashi, Yoichi

On Hecke's theta-formula.

Math. Japon. **13** (1968), 43–45.

The author gives a direct proof for Hecke's theta-formula which he claims is new. But this is essentially Hecke's proof [see E. Hecke, Nachr. Gesell. Wiss. Göttingen Math. Phys. Kl. **2** (1917), 77–89; ibid. **2** (1917), 299–318].

W. G. H. Schaal (E. Lansing, Mich.)

F10-108 (39# 137)

Petersson, Hans

Über die Eisensteinschen Reihen der Thetagruppe.

Abh. Math. Sem. Univ. Hamburg **31** (1967), 166–178.

The group Γ_ϑ is the subgroup of the modular group consisting of those matrices $(a\ b|c\ d)$ congruent mod 2 to either $(1\ 2|0\ 1)$ or $(0\ -1|1\ 0)$; it is the group of invariance of the theta "zero-values" and so appears in the problem of representing an integer by sums of squares. For the full modular group Γ there is the theorem that every Eisenstein series is a polynomial in the Weierstrass invariants g_2, g_3. In the present paper the author develops the analogue for Γ_ϑ. A special difficulty occurs in the treatment of forms of degree (dimension) -2, for which the usual Eisenstein series fail to converge, and this is handled (as in the case of Γ) by the introduction of the Hecke convergence factor.

The main result is that each everywhere regular modular form of degree $-2m$, $m\geqq 1$ (with multipliers identically 1), is representable as an isobaric polynomial of degree m in E_2 and F_{4i}. Here $i=1$ or ∞, $F_{r1}(\tau)=\sum(m\tau+n)^{-r}$, $m\equiv n\equiv 1 \pmod 2$, $F_{r\infty}(\tau)=\sum(m\tau+n)^{-r}$, $m\not\equiv n \pmod 2$, and E_2 is the form of degree -2 obtained from F_{2i} by means of the Hecke convergence factor.

The remainder of the paper is taken up with application of a certain differential operator discussed in another paper of the author [J. Reine Angew. Math. **231** (1968), 163–191; MR **38** #5718].

J. Lehner (College Park, Md.)

Citations: MR 38# 5718 = F25-24.

F10-109 **(39# 1457)**

Igusa, Jun-ichi

On the algebraic theory of elliptic modular functions.

J. Math. Soc. Japan **20** (1968), 96–106.

The field M_n of elliptic modular functions of level n is an extension of $F(j)$, where j is a transcendental over the prime field F. It is obtained by taking an elliptic curve A in Weierstrass normal form with j as invariant, and adjoining to $F(j)$ the x-coordinates of the points of A of order n. In a previous paper [Amer. J. Math. **81** (1959), 453–476; MR **21** #3422] the author showed the Galois group of $M_n/F(j)$ is $\mathrm{SL}(2, n)/\pm 1$, and he determined the ramification and genus of M_n, all under the assumption that $p\nmid n$ (where $p=\mathrm{char}\ F$). The present paper is devoted to extending these results to the case $n=p^e$, mostly by working directly with the Jacobi normal form for A. The extension $M_n/F(j)$ is inseparable; its Galois group is the subgroup of index 2 in $\mathrm{Gal}(Q(\zeta_n)/Q)$; the ramification is at $j=0$, $j=12^3$, and $j=$the "supersingular invariants", i.e., those j-values corresponding to the elliptic curves with Hasse invariant 0. The genus formula follows from knowing the ramification. As the author remarks, a global treatment over Z would be desirable.

A. Mattuck (Cambridge, Mass.)

Citations: MR 21# 3422 = F10-58.

Referred to in G05-91.

F10-110 **(40# 1339)**

Lehner, Joseph

Automorphic integrals with preassigned periods.

J. Res. Nat. Bur. Standards Sect. B **73B** (1969), 153–161.

The author considers automorphic forms in one variable with respect to an H-group, which means a horocyclic group possessing parabolic elements and a normal fundamental region of finite hyperbolic area. For such forms the reviewer [Math. Z. **67** (1957), 267–298; MR **19**, 740] introduced generalized Abelian integrals. Their periods are polynomials satisfying (1) a global cocycle condition, and (2) local conditions at the cusps. He also gave two proofs for the fact that to given periods there corresponds a generalized Abelian integral also an automorphic form. The first proof uses the Riemann-Roch theorem; the second gives an explicit construction of this Abelian integral as a quotient of certain Poincaré series. But the second proof works only for periods belonging to cusp forms. Now the author constructs more general Poincaré series which solve the problem without restrictions.

M. Eichler (Basel)

Citations: MR 19, 740a = F15-12.

F10-111 **(40# 5563)**

Subrahmanya Sastri, V. V.

A result concerning the Euler's function $f(x)=\prod_1^\infty (1-x^n)$.

Math. Student **35** (1967), 85–87 (1969).

For ω a primitive kth root of unity, the following identity is established: $\prod_{r=0}^{k-1} f(\omega^r x)=\prod_{d|k}\{f(x^{kd})\}^{\sigma(k/d)\mu(d)}$.

D. Rearick (Boulder, Colo.)

F10-112 **(41# 153)**

Ogg, A. P.

Functional equations of modular forms.

Math. Ann. **183** (1969), 337–340.

From the author's introduction: "Let N be a positive integer, and $\mathscr{M}(N,k)$ the space of modular forms of dimension $-k$ for the group $\Gamma_0(N)$, the group of substitutions $\tau\to(a\tau+b)/(c\tau+d)$ of the upper half plane, where $\begin{pmatrix}a b\\ c d\end{pmatrix}\in\mathrm{SL}(2,Z)$, $N|c$. In a previous paper [same Ann. **179** (1969), 101–108]*certain results on the eigenvalues of the Hecke operators $T(p)$ were derived for $p|N$, provided a corresponding eigenfunction satisfies a functional equation. In this paper we show that, conversely, these conditions on the eigenvalues imply the functional equation, in the case where N is square-free. Let k be a fixed positive even integer. If $f(\tau)$ is a function on the upper half plane, and $\begin{pmatrix}a b\\ c d\end{pmatrix}$ is a real matrix with positive determinant, then $f\left|\begin{pmatrix}a b\\ c d\end{pmatrix}\right.(\tau)=(c\tau+d)^{-k}f((a\tau+b)/(c\tau+d))$. Thus, if $f\in\mathscr{M}(N,k)$, then $f|L=f$ for all $L\in\Gamma_0(N)$. For $n\geqq 1$, we let $H_n=\begin{pmatrix}0 & -1\\ n & 0\end{pmatrix}$; we are interested in the question o whether or not $f\in\mathscr{M}(N,k)$ satisfies the functional equation $f|H_n=\pm N^{-k/2}f$." *A. L. Whiteman* (Los Angeles, Calif.)

*MR 42 #4492 = F 25-28.

Citations: MR 42# 4492 = F25-28.

F10-113 **(41# 5297)**

Ogg, A. P.

On product expansions of theta-functions.

Proc. Amer. Math. Soc. **21** (1969), 365–368.

A new proof of the known formula

(*) $\vartheta(\tau,x)=\prod_{n=1}^\infty(1-q^{2n})(1-zq^{2n-1})(1+z^{-1}q^{2n+1})$,

where $\vartheta(\tau,x)=\sum_{n=-\infty}^\infty \exp(2\pi inx+\pi in^2\tau)$ ($\mathrm{Im}\,\tau>0$) and $q=\exp(\pi i\tau)$, $z=\exp(z\pi ix)$. The proof of (*) follows the line of Hecke and Weil; for a more elementary proof see, for instance, G. Pólya and G. Szegő [*Aufgaben und Lehrsätze aus der Analysis. Erster Band: Reihen, Integralrechnung, Funktionentheorie*, p. 8, Problem 53, Springer, Berlin, 1925; second edition, 1954; MR **15**, 512].

P. Szüsz (Stony Brook, N.Y.)

F10-114 **(41# 5298)**

Rankin, F. K. C.; Swinnerton-Dyer, H. P. F.

On the zeros of Eisenstein series.

Bull. London Math. Soc. **2** (1970), 169–170.

Let $E_k(\tau)=\frac{1}{2}\sum_{(c,d)}(c\tau+d)^{-k}$, where (c,d) runs over all pairs of coprime integers c, d, be the Eisenstein series of degree $-k$ on the full modular group. There have been several recent papers devoted to the location of the zeros of $E_k(\tau)$ in the fundamental region R_0: $|\tau|\geqq 1$, $|\mathrm{Re}\,\tau|\leqq\frac{1}{2}$, $|\mathrm{Im}\,\tau|>0$. The authors give an extremely simple proof that all such zeros lie on $|\tau|=1$.

Writing $F_k(\theta)=\exp(ik\theta)\cdot E_k(e^{i\theta})$ we have $F_k(\theta)=2\cos(k\theta/2)+R_1$, where R_1 consists of the terms of the series for which $c^2+d^2>1$. The authors prove $|R_1|<2$ for $\pi/2\leqq\theta\leqq 2\pi/3$, and from this it can be shown that $F_k(\theta)$ oscillates the right number of times to give the known number of zeros of E_k in R_0.

J. Lehner (College Park, Md.)

F10-115 **(41# 6782)**

Bright, George W.

Rational expressions of certain automorphic forms.

Michigan Math. J. **17** (1970), 129–137.

Let Γ be a group of fractional linear transformations of the upper complex half plane and $f(z)$ an automorphic form of weight k with respect to Γ. R. A. Rankin [J. Indian Math. Soc. (N.S.) **20** (1956), 103–116; MR **18**, 571; Michigan Math. J. **4** (1957), 181–186; MR **19**, 1172] and H. L. Resnikoff [Trans. Amer. Math. Soc. **124** (1966), 334–346; MR **34** #4990] considered the differential operator D^m defined by $D^mf=f^{((k+1)m-1)/k}\,d^mf^{(1-m)/k}/dz^m$ $(m=2,3,\cdots)$. D^mf is an automorphic form of weight $(k+2)m$. The D^m are unique in the following sense: If an automorphic form is a polynomial in f, $df/dz, \cdots, d^mf/dz^m$, then it is a quotient of polynomials in f, $D^2f, \cdots, D^mf$. Now the present author proves that such an automorphic form is also a quotient of polynomials in

$$D^{r,s}f = (D^3)^r(D^2)^sf = \underbrace{D^3(\cdots(D^3}_{r\text{-times}}(\underbrace{D^2(\cdots(D^2}_{s\text{-times}}f)\cdots)))\cdots)$$

with $r = \{0, 1\}$, $s = \{0, 1, \cdots, [m/2]\}$, where $3r + 2s = m$.

M. Eichler (Basel)

Citations: MR 18, 571c = F10-47.

F10-116 (42# 197)

Kløve, Torleiv

Recurrence formulae for the coefficients of modular forms.

Math. Scand. **26** (1970), 221–232.

Various authors, e.g., J. H. van Lint [*Hecke operators and Euler products*, Drukkerij "Luctor et Emergo", Leiden, 1957; MR **19**, 839] have noted that for cuspforms of half-integral dimension a restricted theory of Hecke operators $T(p^2)$ can be developed. The author's purpose is to work out the details of this theory for all six multiplier systems on the full modular group $\Gamma(1)$. Let v_0 be the multiplier system of the Dedekind modular form $\eta(\tau)$ of dimension $-\frac{1}{2}$ and let k be an odd positive integer. The six different multiplier systems on $\Gamma(1)$ of dimension $-\frac{1}{2}k$ can be written as v_0^κ when $\kappa \equiv k \pmod{24}$, $0 < \kappa < 24$. Let $C^0 = C^0(\Gamma(1), -\frac{1}{2}k, v_0^\kappa)$ be the corresponding vector space of cuspforms. For p an odd prime and $f \in C^0$, define $f(\tau)|T(p^2) = p^k \sum_i f(PR_i\tau)/(v(R_i)(c_i\tau + d_i)^{k/2})$, where $P = \begin{pmatrix} p^2 & 0 \\ 0 & 1 \end{pmatrix}$ and R_i runs through a certain right-transversal of $\Gamma_0(p^2)$ in $\Gamma(1)$. The author proves the following theorem: There exists a basis f_ν $(1 \leqq \nu \leqq \mu)$ for C^0 such that the f_ν are eigenforms with real eigenvalues for all $T(p^2)$ $(p > 3)$, and for $T(3^2)$ if $k \equiv 0 \pmod 3$ and $\kappa \equiv k \pmod{12}$. That is, there exist real algebraic integers $\rho(\nu, p)$ such that $f_\nu(\tau)|T(p^2) = \rho(\nu, p)f_\nu(\tau)$ $(1 \leqq \nu \leqq \mu)$.

R. A. Rankin (Glasgow)

Citations: MR 19, 839f = F25-7.

F10-117 (42# 275)

Shioda, Tetsuji

Elliptic modular surfaces. I, II.

Proc. Japan Acad. **45** (1969), 786–790; *ibid.* **45** (1969), 833–837.

For each torsion-free subgroup Γ of finite index of the homogeneous modular group SL(2, **Z**), the author shows, in Part I, how to define a compact Riemann surface Δ, a sheaf G over Δ and a meromorphic function J on Δ. By a general construction of K. Kodaira [Ann. of Math. (2) **77** (1963), 563–626; ibid. (2) **78** (1963), 1–40; MR **32** #1730], there exists a (non-singular algebraic) elliptic surface B over Δ with a global holomorphic section having J and G as its functional and homological invariants. The author calls B the elliptic modular surface attached to the Fuchsian group Γ. Let $B^\#$ $[B_0^\#]$ denote the group scheme over Δ associated with B [with the connected component of the identity section in $B^\#$] and let $\Omega(B_0^\#)$ denote the sheaf of germs of holomorphic sections of $B_0^\#$ over Δ. The main results, which are proved in Part II, may be stated as follows. An elliptic modular surface B has only a finite number of global sections over the base curve Δ; the group $H^1(\Delta, \Omega(B_0^\#))$ is isomorphic to the product of a complex torus and a finite group.

Given an elliptic surface B over a non-singular algebraic curve Δ having a global holomorphic section, let $\mathscr{F}(J, G)$ denote the family of elliptic surfaces over Δ with the same functional invariant J and homological invariant G as B. Kodaira has raised the question of whether algebraic surfaces are dense in $\mathscr{F}(J, G)$. The author's results supply an affirmative answer to this question in the case where B is an elliptic modular surface.

C. M. Williams (Manchester)

F10-118 (42# 4493)

Rankin, R. A.

The zeros of Eisenstein series.

Publ. Ramanujan Inst. No. 1 (1968/69), 137–144.

The Eisenstein series considered are the modular forms $E_k(z) = \frac{1}{2}\sum (cz + d)^{-k}$ where the sum is over all coprime pairs of integers c and d, and $\operatorname{Im} z > 0$ and $k \geqq 4$ is an integer. The fundamental region is $F = F_1 \cup F_2$, where $F_1 = \{z: |z| \geqq 1, -\frac{1}{2} \leqq \operatorname{Re} z \leqq 0\}$ and $F_2 = \{z: |z| > 1, 0 < \operatorname{Re} z < \frac{1}{2}\}$. K. Wohlfart [Math. Nachr. **26** (1963/64), 381–383; MR **29** #4743] has established that for $4 \leqq k \leqq 26$, k even, the only zeros of $E_k(z)$ in F lie on $|z| = 1$. The author extends this result to $k = 28$, 30, 32, 34 and 38. Also, for any $k \equiv z \pmod 4$, $k \geqq 4$, it is proved that $E_k(z)$ has no zeros in F with $\operatorname{Re} z > 1$, and for any $k \equiv 0 \pmod 4$, $k \geqq 4$, it is proved that $E_k(z)$ has no zeros in F with $\operatorname{Re} z > 1 + (\log c_k)/2\pi$, where c_k is specified in terms of constants arising in the Fourier expansion of $E_k(z)$, and $c_k = 1 + 4k^{-1} + O(k^{-2})$ is established. The author also studies a class of determinants Δ_n with the property that if $\Delta_n < 0$ for some positive integer n, then E_k for all sufficiently large k would not have all its zeros in F on the boundary of F. However, the author remarks in a postscript that he is able to prove $\Delta_n > 0$ for all $n > 1$ which "adds some weight to the conjecture that all the zeros of E_k in F lie on the unit circle".

I. Niven (Eugene, Ore.)

Citations: MR 29# 4743 = F10-87.

F10-119 (42# 7595)

Schoeneberg, B.

Zur Theorie der verallgemeinerten Dedekindschen Modulfunktionen.

Nachr. Akad. Wiss. Göttingen Math.-Phys. Kl. II **1969**, 119–128.

Es werden verallgemeinerte Dedekindsche Modulfunktionen

$$\eta_{g,h}(\tau; N) = \alpha_{g,h}(N)\exp(\pi i\tau P_2(g/N)) \times \prod_{m>0, m\equiv g(N)} (1 - \exp(2\pi i(m\tau + h)/N)) \times \prod_{m<0, m\equiv -g(N)} (1 - \exp(2\pi i(m\tau - h)/N))$$

untersucht, welche im Fall $g = h = 0$, $N = 1$ mit dem Quadrat der klassischen Dedekind-Funktion übereinstimmen. Zunächst wird der Beweis von C. L. Siegel [Mathematika **1** (1954), 4; MR **16**, 16] über das Verhalten von $\log \eta$ bei der Substitution $\tau \mapsto -1/\tau$ übertragen und das Transformationsgesetz bei beliebigen Modulsubstitutionen hergeleitet. Mittels dieser Gleichung werden Untergruppen der Modulgruppe definiert, unter denen auch Nicht-Kongruenzgruppen vorkommen, und der Modul der durch die Perioden von $\log \eta_{g,h}(\tau; N)$ erzeugten Charaktere wird untersucht.

J. Spilker (Freiburg)

Citations: MR 16, 16b = F10-35.

F10-120 (43# 4764)

Wohlfahrt, Klaus

Eine Anwendung von $\eta(\tau)$. (English summary)

J. Number Theory **2** (1970), 273–278.

Let ${}_1\Gamma = \mathrm{SL}(2, \mathbf{Z})$. Starting from the Dedekind η-function and using the fact that congruence subgroups belong to Riemann surfaces, the author constructs Abelian differentials of four elliptic function fields. The fields belong respectively to the congruence subgroups ${}_m\Gamma_0$, $m = 2$, 3, 5, 11. The absolute invariant j is computed in each of the four cases and is found to be $12^3, 0, -2^4 3^3 109/5^6, -2^{12} 31^3/11^5$, respectively. The argument also yields the fact that the fields corresponding to 2, 3 admit complex multiplication, while the other two do not.

J. V. Armitage (Nottingham)

F10-121 **(44# 3956)**

Kitaoka, Yoshiyuki

On a space of some theta functions.

Nagoya Math. J. **42** (1971), 89–93.

Die Matrizen $\begin{pmatrix} a & b \\ c & d \end{pmatrix}$ aus der Modulgruppe mit $c \equiv 0 \bmod q$ bilden eine Untergruppe $\Gamma_0(q)$. M. M. Eichler [J. Reine Angew. Math. **195** (1956), 156–171; MR **18**, 297] hat bewiesen, daß jede Modulform $(-2m)$-ten Grades $(m = 1, 2, \cdots)$ zu $\Gamma_0(q)$ als Linearkombination von Thetareihen zu den Stufen 1 und q darstellbar ist, sofern q eine hinreichend große Primzahl ist. Der Verfasser beweist denselben Satz für die Fälle $q = 2, 3, 5$ und 11, indem er einen Satz von C. L. Siegel aus der analytischen Theorie der quadratischen Formen anwendet [Ann. of Math. (2) **36** (1935), 527–606].

J. Spilker (Freiburg)

Citations: MR 18, 297d = F15-4.

F10-122 **(44# 6606)**

Lang, Heinrich

Eisensteinsche Reihen höherer Stufe im Falle der komplexen Multiplikation.

Abh. Math. Sem. Univ. Hamburg **35** (1971), 242–250.

The author studies the series

$$C_k(\omega; a_1, a_2, \chi_f) = -\tau(\bar{\chi}_f) f^{k-1} k! (2\pi i)^{-k} \eta^{-2k}(\omega) \times \sum_{h \bmod f} \chi_f(h) \sum_{m_1 \equiv a_1(f), m_2 \equiv a_2(f)} (m_1\omega_1 + m_2)^{-k} \quad (k \geqq 3).$$

He proves that $C_k(\alpha; a_1, a_2, \chi_f)$ is an algebraic integer if α is an integer of an imaginary quadratic field with $\mathrm{Im}(\alpha) > 0$. This is a generalization of a well-known property of the modular function j. Furthermore he gives some congruence relations between the numbers $C_k^*(\alpha; a_1, a_2, \chi_f)$ of the type of Von Staudt congruence for Bernoulli numbers, generalizing some theorems of L. Carlitz [Math. Z. **64** (1956), 425–434; MR **17**, 1057; J. Reine Angew. Math. **202** (1959), 174–182; MR **22** #20].

F. van der Blij (Bilthoven)

Citations: MR 17, 1057e = B80-14; MR 22# 20 = B68-47.

F15 OTHER GROUPS AND THEIR AUTOMORPHIC FORMS (ONE VARIABLE)

See also reviews A54-20, A54-23, A54-24, D48-15, E24-129, E68-38, F10-15, F10-46, F65-27, F99-1, F99-5, G30-31, J28-20, Z05-6.

F15-1 **(15, 785f)**

Lehner, Joseph. Note on the Schwarz triangle functions. Pacific J. Math. 4, 243–249 (1954).

Put $\lambda = 2\cos \pi/q$ $(q = 3, 4, 5, \cdots)$, and define $\phi(z)$ as the function automorphic with respect to the group $\Gamma(\lambda)$ generated by $z \to z + \lambda$ and $z \to -1/z$ and with Fourier expansion

$$\phi(z) = x^{-1} + \sum_0^\infty c_n(\lambda) x^n \quad (x = \exp(2\pi i z/\lambda)).$$

The following results are proved. 1. The coefficients $c_n(\lambda)$ are rational numbers.

2. $c_n(\lambda) \sim (2\lambda)^{-1/2} n^{-3/4} \exp 4\pi n^{1/2}/\lambda \quad (n \to \infty)$.

L. Carlitz (Durham, N. C.).

Referred to in F30-36.

F15-2 **(15, 787a)**

Myrberg, P. J. Über die Picardsche Gruppe. Rend. Circ. Mat. Palermo (2) **2** (1953), 169–176 (1954).

Let G denote the Picard group consisting of the linear fractional transformations $z' = (\alpha z + \beta)/(\gamma z + \delta)$, where $\alpha, \beta, \gamma, \delta$ are Gaussian integers satisfying $\alpha\delta - \beta\gamma = 1$. Let K denote a circle in the z-plane and let $G(K)$ denote the family of limiting sets (Häufungsgebilde) of $\{TK \mid T \in G\}$. The following theorems are established. I. Almost all circles K have the property that $G(K)$ is the set of all circles of the plane. II. There exist K such that $G(K)$ consists of null circles. Every circle of the plane is a cluster circle of the family of these exceptional circles. Several corollaries are given.

M. Heins (Providence, R. I.).

F15-3 **(18, 297c)**

Eichler, Martin. Zur Zahlentheorie der Quaternionen-Algebren. J. Reine Angew. Math. **195** (1955), 127–151 (1956).

This paper contains the arithmetic background for the important results of the author on the representation of modular forms in terms of ϑ-series, which is reviewed below. Suppose that k is a totally real finite algebraic number field in which a finite set of valuations $\{\mathfrak{o}_i\}$, containing the Archimedean valuations of k, is singled out. Let $\mathfrak{i}$ denote the elements of k which are integral for all valuations $\mathfrak{p}$ not in $\{\mathfrak{o}_i\}$; this ring $\mathfrak{i}$ shall be termed the principal order of k. The author considers (unless otherwise mentioned) orders $\mathfrak{J}$ (finite $\mathfrak{i}$-modules with 2, respectively, 4 linearly independent elements) in extensions of k which are either quadratic fields or quaternionic algebras Q in which the valuations $\mathfrak{o}_i$ are ramified (as it is always the case for the Archimedean valuations) or inert. Special emphasis is placed on quaternionic orders. The level $\mathfrak{q}$ of $\mathfrak{J}$ is defined as the inverse $\mathfrak{i}$-ideal of the greatest common divisor of the k-norms of the elements in the complement of $\mathfrak{J}$. It is then shown by local considerations, which incidentally predominate in this paper, that for primes $\mathfrak{p}$ dividing a squarefree $\mathfrak{q}$ the $\mathfrak{p}$-component of $\mathfrak{J}$ is either the unique maximal order of the $\mathfrak{p}$-adic limit $Q_\mathfrak{p}$ (division algebra) or, to within isomorphisms, the ring of all 2×2 matrices from $\mathfrak{i}_\mathfrak{p}$ whose elements in the lower left corner are divisible by the prime $\mathfrak{p}$ of $\mathfrak{i}_\mathfrak{p}$. Next ideals of Q with respect to $\mathfrak{J}$ are defined as intersections of principal ideals relative to the completions $\mathfrak{J}_\mathfrak{p}$ (a fact which is always satisfied for maximal orders); the ambiguous ideals and numbers of integral ideals with the same norm are determined as a preparation for the theory of the ζ-function. Then all ideals with left and right orders of fixed squarefree level $\mathfrak{q}$ form a groupoid. Let H be the number of left ideal classes (equivalence with respect to the non-zero elements of Q), with the representatives $\mathfrak{J} = \mathfrak{M}_1, \cdots, \mathfrak{M}_H$ with respect to a fixed order $\mathfrak{J}$ of level $\mathfrak{q}$. As in the case of maximal orders the right orders $\mathfrak{J}_\nu$ of the $\mathfrak{M}_\nu$ are distributed over T types (sets of non-isomorphic orders) for whose determination the local study of ambiguous ideals is needed. Suppose now that the ideals $\mathfrak{M}_\nu$ are labeled so that $\mathfrak{J}_1, \cdots, \mathfrak{J}_T$ belong to the distinct types and such that $T_{\nu\mu}$ $(\mu = 1, \cdots, H_\nu)$ is a system of representatives of all classes of ambiguous $\mathfrak{J}_\nu$-ideals. Next denote by e_ν the finite (because of the conditions on $\{\mathfrak{o}_i\}$ and k) index of the unit group of $\mathfrak{i}$ in that of $\mathfrak{J}$. Then the measure $M = \sum_{\nu=1}^T H_\nu/e_\nu$ for which an evaluation by means of the ζ-function is given is introduced as a tool for the computation of H and T by means of traces of certain matrices. Now let $\pi_{\mu\nu}(\mathfrak{n})$ be the number of integral $\mathfrak{J}_\mu$-ideals whose norm in k equals $\mathfrak{n}$ and which are left equivalent to $\mathfrak{M}_\mu^{-1}\mathfrak{M}_\nu$. Furthermore denote by $L(\mathfrak{n})$ the matrix with 1 at the position $(\mu, \nu = \lambda(\mu))$ and 0 elsewhere, where $\lambda(\sigma)$ is the permutation of $1, \cdots, H$ so that $\mathfrak{M}_\sigma\mathfrak{n}$ is left equivalent to $\mathfrak{M}_\tau$, $\tau=\lambda(\sigma)$. Then $L(\mathfrak{mn})=L(\mathfrak{m})L(\mathfrak{n})$. Finally let E be the diagonal matrix of the indices e_ν. Then the matrices $P(\mathfrak{n})=(\pi_{\mu\nu}(\mathfrak{n}))$ which were introduced by H. Brandt are shown to satisfy $P(\mathfrak{n})E=P(\mathfrak{n})L(\mathfrak{n})E)'=EL(\mathfrak{n})^{-1}P(\mathfrak{n})'$. Furthermore in analogy to the matrices of E. Hecke the following formulas are proved by ideal-theoretic methods:

$$P(\mathfrak{m})P(\mathfrak{n})=P(\mathfrak{mn}) \text{ if } (\mathfrak{m},\mathfrak{n})=1,$$

$$P(\mathfrak{p}^a)P(\mathfrak{p}^b)=\sum_{\nu=0}^{b} N(\mathfrak{p})P(\mathfrak{p}^{a+b-2\nu})L(\mathfrak{p}^{-1})^\nu \quad (a\geqq b,\ \mathfrak{p}\nmid\mathfrak{q})$$

(a discussion for certain $\mathfrak{p}|\mathfrak{q}$ is also given). As a consequence of these facts the Dirichlet series $\sum_{\mathfrak{n}} P(\mathfrak{n})/N(\mathfrak{n})^s$ has an Euler product for which almost all $\mathfrak{p}$-factors are canonical according to Hecke's definition. After these important preliminary results the author turns to the proof of the important theorem which states that each (commutative) ring which is generated over the field of real numbers by matrices $P(\mathfrak{n})$ and $L(\mathfrak{n})$ must be semi-simple. This result is of special significance for the structure of the multiplication rings of certain fields of modular functions (see the review below). If Sp denotes the trace, the $H=\mathrm{Sp}(P(\mathfrak{i}))$ and $T=2^{-\kappa}\sum_{\mathfrak{t}}\mathrm{Sp}(P(\mathfrak{t}))$, where κ is the number of prime divisors $\mathfrak{t}$ of $\mathfrak{q}$. In turns the traces $\mathrm{Sp}(P(\mathfrak{n}))$ are evaluated in terms of the measure M and a rather complicated correction term whose nature depends on certain quadratic subfields of Q/k (see Theorem 10, p. 143). The author terminates the paper with some special cases which yield among other noteworthy relations between the class numbers of different imaginary quadratic number fields. Furthermore the generalization of the theory to function fields of Kroneckerian dimension 1 is expounded. *O. F. G. Schilling* (Chicago, Ill.).

Referred to in E20-85, F15-7, F15-10, G15-46.

F15-4 (18, 297d)

Eichler, Martin. Über die Darstellbarkeit von Modulformen durch Thetareihen. J. Reine Angew. Math. **195** (1955), 156–171 (1956).

Suppose that K is the field of all modular functions $\varphi(\tau)$ over the field of complex numbers k which are invariant with respect to the congruence group of unimodular transformations $\Gamma_0(q)=\{\tau\to(a\tau+b)/(qc\tau+d);\ a, b, c, d$ being integers, q a squarefree integer$\}$. Denote by g the genus of K. Furthermore let $\{\begin{pmatrix} s & r\\ 0 & t\end{pmatrix}$ with $st=n$, $(n, q)=1$, $s>0$, $(r, s, t)=1$, $1\leqq r\leqq t\}$ denote a complete set of representatives for the left cosets of primitive matrices $\begin{pmatrix} a & b\\ qc & d\end{pmatrix}$, $a, \cdots, d$ again being integers, with determinant n. Next suppose that $\sigma_i(\tau)$, $1\leqq i\leqq g$, is a basis for the vector space of cusp forms of weight -2 which belong to the group $\Gamma_0(q)$. Then each sum

$$\sum_{r,s,t}(s/t)\sigma_i\left(\frac{s\tau+r}{t}\right)d\tau=(\sigma_i(\tau)|\bar\tau_n)d\tau=\sum_{k=1}^{g}\bar t_{ik}(n)\sigma_k(\tau)d\tau$$

is with $\sigma_i(\tau)d\tau$ a differential of the first kind of K, and thus $\tau_n=\sum_{v^2|n}\bar\tau_{nv^{-2}}$ defines the operator of Hecke and a modified operator $\tau_n{}^0=\sum_{v^2|n, v^2\neq n}\bar\tau_{nv^{-2}}$. Using the matrices $\bar T_n=(t_{ik}(n))$ representations T_n and $T_n{}^0$ of τ_n and $\tau_n{}^0$, respectively, are obtained. The author proves in this paper the validity of Hecke's conjecture that the entire modular forms of weight -2 belonging $\Gamma_0(q)$, q a prime, are linear combination of ϑ-series defined by quaternary quadratic forms of level q and discriminant q^2. For the proof the author considers for arbitrary squarefree q the functions

$$\vartheta_{\mu\nu}=\sum_{M\in\mathfrak{M}_\nu^{-1}\mathfrak{M}_\mu}\exp\left(\frac{n(M)\tau}{n(\mathfrak{M}_\nu^{-1}\mathfrak{M}_\mu)}\right)=1+\sum_{n=1}^{\infty}\pi_{\mu\nu}(n)\omega_\nu\exp(n\tau)$$

which are integral modular forms of weight -2 belonging to $\Gamma_0(q)$. The author then forms the matrix

$$\vartheta(\tau)=\sum_{n=0}^{\infty}P(n)\exp(n\tau),$$

where $P(0)$ is the matrix with the rows $(1/w_1, \cdots, 1/w_H)$ with w_ν the number of units in the order $\mathfrak{J}_\nu$ according to the definitions of the preceding review. Application of Hecke's operator τ_p, p a prime not dividing q, yields

$$\vartheta(\tau)|\tau_p=\sum_{n=0}^{\infty}\sum_{r,s,t}P(n)\exp\left(n\left(\frac{s\tau+r}{t}\right)\right)=\sum_{n=0}^{\infty}\left(P(np)+pP\left(\frac{n}{p}\right)\right)\exp(n\tau),$$

where $st=p$, $s>0$, $0\leqq r<p$. Since the matrices $P(n)$ (see the above review) satisfy the same relations as Hecke's τ_n, $(n, q)=1$, one obtains in general $\vartheta(\tau)|\tau_n=P(n)\vartheta(\tau)$. Using the fact that the differences of such quaternary ϑ-series are cusp forms as follows from the proof of their functional equations it is shown that the representation $P(n)$ splits into one belonging to the Eisenstein series

$$c_0+\sum_{n=1}^{\infty}\sum_{t|n,(t,q)=1}t\exp(n\tau)$$

and into another one of dimension $H-1$, $P_{q_1,q_2}(n)$ which is obtained in the subspace of cusp forms generated by ϑ-series. The integers q_1, q_2 are defined by $q=q_1q_2$, where q_2 is the product of the odd number of finite ramifications of a positive definite quaternionic algebra. In the above mentioned paper the author evaluated the trace $\mathrm{Sp}(P_{q_1,q_2}(n))$ in terms of Legendre symbols, class and unit numbers of certain imaginary quadratic orders which depend on n and on the factorization of q. Furthermore the author uses the fact that the matrix $T_n{}^0$ is a representation of $\tau_n{}^0$ considered as a correspondence of K. The latter is defined in the composite of K with an isomorphic field K' relative to a τ'-plane by the ideal $\mathfrak{T}_n{}^0$ which is generated in the subring of all finite sums $\sum\varphi_\nu\varphi_\nu'$, $\varphi_\nu\in K$, $\varphi_\nu'\in K'$, by all products

$$\prod_{r,s,t}\left(\varphi(\tau)-\varphi\left(\frac{s\tau'+r}{t}\right)\right),$$

where φ varies over all functions of K. A result of Hurwitz then states that $\mathrm{Sp}(T_n{}^0)=(d_n{}^0+d_n{}^{0\prime}-c_n{}^0)$, where $d_n{}^0$ and $d_n{}^{0\prime}$ denote the degree of the divisors belonging to $\mathfrak{T}_n{}^0$ in the field composite relative to K' and K, respectively. One finds as a simple consequence of the definition that $d_n{}^0=d_n{}^{0\prime}=\sum_{t|n}t-x=$ the number of prime factors of $\mathfrak{T}_n{}^0$, where $x=1$ if n is a square and $x=0$ otherwise. Finally $c_n{}^0$ is the number of coincidence of $\mathfrak{T}_n{}^0$. This number being the sum of local coincidence numbers $h_\mathfrak{p}$ for all prime divisors $\mathfrak{p}$ of K is then split into a term involving only the rational cusps of a canonical fundamental domain of $\Gamma_0(q)$ which give the total contribution $c_{n,\infty}{}^0$ and a remainder term $c_{n,0}{}^0$. These cusps are represented by the 2^κ points $\tau=\infty, 0, 1/q_1$, where q_1 denotes a typical non-trivial divisor of q. Localization of $\mathfrak{T}_n{}^0$ to the corresponding prime divisor of K then yields by means of a matrix theoretic reduction to the case $\tau=\infty$ that these local multiplicities coincide and equal $2\sum_{t|n,t<\sqrt{n}}t+y$, where $y=\sqrt{n}-1$ if n is a square and $y=0$ otherwise. The evaluation of $c_{n,0}{}^0$ is quite complicated, however not for the contributions at the elliptic boundary points of the fundamental domain where

$$\frac{1}{2}\prod_{p|q}\left(1+\left(\frac{-4}{p}\right)\right)+\frac{2}{3}\prod_{p|q}\left(1+\left(\frac{-3}{p}\right)\right)=\alpha$$

is obtained. The requirement that τ_0 in the upper half plane be an inner point of the fundamental domain of $\Gamma_0(q)$ and have positive coincidence number can be expressed in the form

$$\frac{A\tau_0+B}{qC\tau_0+D}=\tau_0,\ \det\begin{pmatrix}A & B\\ qC & D\end{pmatrix}=n,\ (A, B, C, D)\neq\sqrt{n},$$

$$(*)\qquad N=\begin{pmatrix}A & B\\ C & D\end{pmatrix}=u+vU,\ U\in\Gamma_0(q),$$

u, v rational (the latter inequality expresses that τ_0 is not elliptic.) The author then interprets N as the generator of an imaginary quadratic order $\mathfrak{O}$ with the discriminant Δf^{-2}, where $\Delta=\Delta(N)=\sigma^2-4n$, $A+D=\sigma$. Next let $c(\Delta)$ denote the number of classes (with respect to $\{U\}=\Gamma_0(q)$) of orders $U^{-1}\mathfrak{C}U$ which can be optimally imbedded in $\mathfrak{C}=\left\{\begin{pmatrix}a & b\\ qc & d\end{pmatrix}, a, \cdots, d \text{ integers}\right\}$ (optimal imbedding means that the intersection of $\mathfrak{C}$ with the quotient field of the quadratic order equals the given order). Since the above τ_0 have the coincidence number 1 the desired contribution β equals the number of classes of substitutions $U^{-1}NU$, $U\in\Gamma_0(q)$, which satisfy the condition (*). It follows that $\beta=\sum_{\sigma,f} c(\Delta f^{-2})$ for all σ, f which obey (†) $-2\sqrt{n}<\sigma<2\sqrt{n}$, $0<f$, $\Delta f^{-2}\equiv 0$ or 1 (mod 4), $\Delta f^{-2}<-4$. Finally the arithmetic of the order $\mathfrak{C}$ (for the methods used see also the paper reviewed above) implies that

$$c(\Delta)=\prod_{p|q}\left(1+\left\{\frac{\Delta}{p}\right\}\right)h(\Delta),$$

where $h(\Delta)$ denotes the class number of the order $\mathfrak{O}$ and $\{\cdot\}$ stands for the Legendre symbol $\left(\frac{\Delta}{p}\right)$ if $\Delta p^{-2}\not\equiv 0$ or 1 (mod 4) and for 1 otherwise. Combining the above contributions the author obtains

$$c_{n,0}{}^0=\sum_{\sigma,f}\prod_{p|q}\left(1+\left\{\frac{\Delta f^{-2}}{p}\right\}\right)h(\Delta f^{-2})/w(\Delta f^{-2})-\gamma_{n,0},$$

where (i) the summation is taken over all σ, f obeying (†) except the last inequality, and (ii) $\gamma_{n,0}$ equals 0 if n is not a square and α if n is a square, (iii) $w(\Delta)$ equals half the number of units in the corresponding order $\mathfrak{O}$, this latter correction factor is needed since the condition $\Delta<-4$ is abandoned. Combination of these facts and the results of the author on quaternionic algebras yields ultimately, noting that $\mathfrak{T}_n=\mathfrak{T}_n{}^0$ if n is not a square and $\mathfrak{T}_n=\mathfrak{T}_n{}^0+$the identity if n is a square, that $\mathrm{Sp}(\mathfrak{T}_n)=\mathrm{Sp}(P_{q,1}(n))$ for $(n, q)=1$ if q is a prime, by virtue of a class number relation. This equality of traces implies that the representation of the ring of multiplications on K which is generated by the τ_n with $(n, q)=1$ on the space of cusp forms and the subspace generated by the ϑ-series, respectively, are equivalent. This fact in turn implies that these spaces have the same dimension and that each cusp form equals a linear combination of ϑ-series plus a form whose first $q-1$ Fourier coefficients are 0, and hence by a theorem of Hecke the author's result is reached. Furthermore the author exhibits, using again his method of comparing traces, a whole class of cusp forms which cannot be obtained by means of ϑ-series. Finally it is proved that the entire modular forms of weight $-2k$, $k=1, 2, \cdots$, belonging to $J_0(q)$ are linear combinations of $4k$-fold ϑ-series belonging to the levels 1 and q provided the prime q is sufficiently large. The proof is achieved by observing that the field K is not hyperelliptic for large q and that hence each integral differential $\varphi(\tau)(d\tau)^k$ of degree k is a homogeneous polynomial of degree k of differentials of the first kind. *O. F. G. Schilling.*

Referred to in F10-121, R52-23.

F15-5 (18, 299a)

Eichler, Martin. On the class number of imaginary quadratic fields and the sums of divisors of natural numbers. J. Indian Math. Soc. (N.S.) **19** (1955), 153–180 (1956).

In this paper the author applies the arithmetic results of the two papers reviewed above, in particular those concerning the number of fixed points of Hecke's correspondences T_n (n odd) on the Riemann surface R of genus 0 belonging to the modular group of level 2 (consisting of the matrices $\begin{pmatrix}a & b\\ 2c & d\end{pmatrix}$ of determinant 1, $a, \cdots, d$ being integers) to problems of class number relations for imaginary quadratic orders. For every negative $D\equiv 0$, 1 (mod 4) there exists a quadratic ring $Q(D)$ with D for its discriminant (generated over the integers by $\sqrt{D}$ or $\sqrt{(D/4)}$, respectively). Then denote by $h(n)$ the number of ideal classes in $Q(-n)$ for $n\equiv 0$, 3 (mod 4) (ideal classes defined as in the above papers), $n>4$, and set $h(0)=-1/12$, $(h(3)=1/3$, $h(4)=1/2$, and $h(n)=0$ otherwise. The author shows how the function $H(\tau)=\sum_{n=0}^{\infty} h(n)\exp(n\tau)$ is related to ϑ-functions of one variable, the discriminant function $\Delta(\tau)$ of the theory of modular functions and other "elementary" functions. Thus let $\varphi(\tau)=\sum_{n=1}^{\infty}\lambda(n)\exp(n\tau)$, where $\lambda(n)=\sum_{t|n,t<\sqrt{n}} t+\frac{1}{2}\sqrt{n}$ for n a square, and $=\sum_{t|n,t<\sqrt{n}} t$ for all other n. Let

$$g(\tau)=-\frac{1}{48\pi i}\frac{d\log\Delta(\tau/2)}{d\tau/2}.$$

The first result of the author is the formula

$$H(\tau)\vartheta_{00}(\tau)=2g(4\tau)-2\varphi(4\tau)$$
$$+\tfrac{1}{6}[g(\tau)-g(\tau+1)]-\tfrac{1}{2}[\varphi(\tau)-\varphi(\tau+1)]$$

which implies the known class number relation

$$\sum_{s^2\le 4m} h(4m-s^2)=2\lambda(n)$$

for $n=4m$, and the new result

$$\sum_{s^2\le n} h(n-s^2)=\tfrac{1}{3}\sum_{t|n} t-\sum_{t|n,t\le\sqrt{n}} t$$

for odd n where the sum on the left is further restricted by $s\equiv\frac{1}{2}(n+1)$ (mod 2). These class number formulas are proved directly by interpreting them in terms of fixed point numbers (see the paper reviewed second above), using Lefschetz fixed point formula for R and T_n, and in terms of the number of integral ideals with given norm in a maximal order of the ordinary quaternions. The formula for $H(\tau)$ which is thus obtained by a combination of arithmetic and topological results is then used to establish the new class number relations

$$\sum_{s^2\le 4n}(s^2-n)h(4n-s^2)=-2\sum_{t|n,t\le\sqrt{n}} t^3$$

which are equivalent to the formula

$$\frac{1}{\pi i}\left[H(\tau)\vartheta_{00}'(\tau)-\tfrac{1}{4}(H(\tau)\vartheta_{00}(\tau))'\right]$$
$$+\frac{1}{\pi i}\left[H(\tau+1)\vartheta_{00}'(\tau+1)-\tfrac{1}{4}(H(\tau+1)\vartheta_{00}(\tau+1))'\right]=$$
$$-4\left[\chi(4\tau)-\frac{1}{\pi i}\varphi'(4\tau)\right],$$

where

$$\chi(\tau)=\sum_{n=1}^{\infty}\left(\sum_{t|n,t\le\sqrt{n}}^{*}(t^3+nt)\right)\exp(n\tau),$$

the asterisk indicating that $t=\sqrt{n}$ is counted with the multiplicity 1/2. This formula is proved by lengthy ingenious analytic arguments using contour integrals for suitably defined auxiliary functions and their behavior at $\tau=\infty$, 0. A final inference of the above formula is the interesting functional equation

$$H(\tau)+(-i\tau)^{-3/2}H(-1/\tau)= \frac{-1}{24}\vartheta_{00}(\tau)^3-i^{1/2}\frac{\tau}{4}\int_{-\infty}^{\infty}\frac{1+\exp(\tau\xi)}{1-\exp(\tau\xi)}\exp(-\tau\xi^2)\xi\,d\xi.$$

O. F. G. Schilling (Chicago, Ill.).

F15-6 (18, 299b)

Eichler, Martin. Berichtigung zu der Arbeit "Über die Darstellbarkeit von Modulformen durch Thetareihen". J. Reine Angew. Math. **196** (1956), 155.

The author corrects a detail of the proof for the evaluation the multiplicity number $c_{n,0}{}^0$ (see the second review above; the order which is determined by the substitution N does in turn determine in general a second substitution from which it may arise).

O. F. G. Schilling (Chicago, Ill.).

F15-7 (19, 17e)

Eichler, M. Berichtigung zu der Arbeit "Zur Zahlentheorie der Quaternionen-Algebren". J. Reine Angew. Math. 197 (1957), 220.

A slight reformulation of the proof of Theorem 10 in the article with the given title reviewed in MR 18, 297.

Citations: MR 18, 297c = F15-3.

Referred to in E20-85, R52-23.

F15-8 (18, 565e)

Reiner, Irving; and Swift, J. D. Congruence subgroups of matrix groups. Pacific J. Math. **6** (1956), 529–540.

The author proves the following two theorems.

1. Let G be the group of all 2×2 matrices $\begin{pmatrix} a & b \\ c & d\end{pmatrix}$ with elements a, b, c, d in the ring $\mathscr{D}$ of integers in an algebraic number field. For any ideal $\mathfrak{N}$ in $\mathscr{D}$ let $G(\mathfrak{N})$ denote the subgroup of $\mathscr{D}$ defined by $c\equiv 0 \pmod{\mathfrak{N}}$. Then if H is a subgroup of G satisfying $G(\mathfrak{M}\mathfrak{N})\subset H\supset G(\mathfrak{N})$ and $\mathfrak{M}$ is prime to 6 then $H=G(\mathfrak{D}\mathfrak{N})$ for some $\mathfrak{D}\supset\mathfrak{M}$ [for the special case of the ordinary modular group cf. Newman, Duke Math. J. **22** (1955), 25–32; MR **16**, 801].

2. Let r be a rational integer $\geqq 2$ and let M_r be the group of all $r\times r$ matrices $(a_{i,j})$ $(i, j=1, 2, \cdots, r)$, where the a_{ij} are rational integers. If m and n are positive integers let C_m and R_n be the subgroups of M_r defined by $a_{i1}\equiv 0 \pmod m$ $(i=2, 3, \cdots, r)$ and $a_{rj}\equiv 0 \pmod n$ $(j=1, 2, \cdots, r-1)$ respectively. Then if H is a subgroup of M_r satisfying

$$(C_{am}\cap R_{bn})\subset H\subset (C_m\cap R_n)$$

and a, b, m, n are integers such that $(am, bn)=1$, then $H=C_{\alpha m}\cap R_{\beta n}$ where $\alpha|a$, $\beta|b$. *H. D. Kloosterman.*

Citations: MR 16, 801f = F05-8.

Referred to in F15-9.

F15-9 (19, 17f)

Newman, Morris. An inclusion theorem for modular groups. Proc. Amer. Math. Soc. **8** (1957), 125–127.

From a generalization [I. Reiner and J. D. Swift, Pacific Math. **6** (1956), 529–540; MR **18**, 565] of his earlier theorem [Duke Math. J. **22** (1955), 25–32; MR **16**, 801], the author proceeds to consider G_R, the group of matrices for which the elements $\alpha, \beta, \gamma, \delta$ are members of a ring R in an algebraic number field and $\alpha\delta-\beta\gamma=1$. Then he lets $G_R(\mathfrak{m}, \mathfrak{n})$ be the group of matrices for which $\beta\equiv 0 \bmod \mathfrak{m}$, $\gamma\equiv 0 \bmod \mathfrak{n}$, for ideals satisfying $(\mathfrak{m}, 6)=(\mathfrak{n}, 6)=(\mathfrak{m}, \mathfrak{n})=1$. Then if H is a sub-group of G_R containing $G_R(\mathfrak{m}, \mathfrak{n})$, he shows $H=G_R(\mathfrak{m}_1, \mathfrak{n}_1)$, where $\mathfrak{m}_1$ and $\mathfrak{n}_1$ divide $\mathfrak{m}$ and $\mathfrak{n}$ respectively. The restriction involving "6" can be removed for the rational field, but the author shows that relative primeness can not be removed.

H. Cohn (St. Louis, Mo.).

Citations: MR 16, 801f = F05-8; MR 18, 565e = F15-8.

F15-10 (19, 18a)

Eichler, Martin. Modular correspondences and their representations. J. Indian Math. Soc. (N.S.) **20** (1956), 163-206.

The author observes that modular correspondences [cf. Hecke, Math. Ann. **114** (1937), 1–28] are basically connections between certain subgroups of the modular group. He suggests the possibility of generalization in replacing the modular group by the other appropriate groups, e.g., the groups of units of orders of central simple algebras over algebraic number fields. He here develops this possibility for the groups of units of certain orders of an indefinite quaternion algebra Q over the rational field, using many results of his earlier papers [e.g., J. Math. **195** (1955), 127–151; MR **18**, 297].

Let T be an order of Q of "square-free level," and let ε be a unit of T of norm 1. Then ε can be represented as a 2 by 2 matrix with elements in a real splitting field K of Q. This matrix defines a transformation, $\tau\to\varepsilon\circ\tau$, of the complex upper half plane into itself in the usual way. The transformations belonging to the group U of units of T of norm 1 constitute a faithful representation of $U/\{1, -1\}$. The transformation group is properly discontinuous in the upper half plane and by the identification of equivalent points defines a closed surface S_T with a hyperbolic metric (with appropriate attention to elliptic and parabolic vertices, if any). The author computes the genus of S_T and the number of elliptic vertices (of orders 2 and 3). "Modular correspondences" arise by considering two orders T and T' of rank 4 of Q, and $T^*=T\cap T'$. Let the respective groups of units of norm 1 be U, U' and U^*, transformation groups $\Gamma_T, \Gamma_{T'}, \Gamma_{T^*}$, surfaces $S_T, S_{T'}, S_{T^*}$. Then $[\Gamma_T:\Gamma_{T^*}]$ and $[\Gamma_{T'}:\Gamma_{T^*}]$ are finite, say d' and d, so that $\Gamma_T=\sum_{i=1}^{d'}\Gamma_{T^*}\varepsilon_i'$, $\Gamma_{T'}=\sum_{i=1}^{d}\Gamma_{T^*}\varepsilon_i$. By the definition that the point $\Gamma_{T'}\circ\tau$ of $S_{T'}$ is covered by the points $\Gamma_{T^*}\circ(\varepsilon_i\circ\tau)=\Gamma_{T^*}\circ\tau_i$ $(i=1, \cdots, d)$ of S_{T^*}, the latter appears as a d-sheeted covering surface of $S_{T'}$. Conversely, $\Gamma_{T'}\circ\tau$ is the trace in $S_{T'}$ of the points $\Gamma_{T^*}\circ\tau_i$ in S_{T^*}. Finally, the set-theoretical union of the traces P_i in S_T of all points $P_i{}^*$ of S_{T^*} covering a given point P' in $S_{T'}$, is called the geometrical correspondence of $S_{T'}$ to S_T. Applying this with $T'=\nu T\nu^{-1}$, $\nu\in Q$, ν of positive norm, one has $\Gamma_{T'}=\nu\Gamma_T\nu^{-1}$. The 2 by 2 matrix over K which represents ν maps S_T onto $S_{T'}$ and the geometrical correspondence of $S_{T'}$ to S_T leads to a correspondence of S_T to itself, belonging to the element ν. The set of such correspondences generates, under appropriate combining definition, an associative ring with unit element which the author shows has representations as endomorphisms of Betti groups. In this connection he gives a proof of a fixed-point theorem of Lefschetz [Algebraic topology, Amer. Math. Soc. Colloq. Publ., v. 27, New York, 1942; MR **4**, 84]. *R. Hull* (Los Angeles, Calif.).

Citations: MR 18, 297c = F15-3.

Referred to in E02-7, F02-8, F15-12.

F15-11 (19, 731d)

Hua, Lo-Kèn. Introduction to the theory of vector modular forms. Akad. Nauk Azerbaĭdžan. SSR. Trudy Inst. Fiz. Mat. **3** (1948), 32–43. (Russian. Azerbaijani summary)

F15-12 (19, 740a)

Eichler, M. Eine Verallgemeinerung der Abelschen Integrale. Math. Z. **67** (1957), 267–298.

This is a fundamental, definitive paper to which a review can scarcely do justice; yet it is all based on an explicit manipulation due to G. Bol [Abh. Math. Sem. Univ. Hamburg **16** (1949), nos. 3–4, 1–28; MR **11**, 437, 872]. Let $\varphi(\tau)$ be an automorphic form of degree $-n$ under the linear transformation ε, i.e., $\varphi(\tau)[\varepsilon]^{-n}=\varphi(\tau)$, where $\varepsilon\tau\equiv(a_\varepsilon\tau+b_\varepsilon)/(c_\varepsilon\tau+d_\varepsilon)$ and

$$\varphi(\tau)[\varepsilon]^{-n}\equiv\varphi(\varepsilon\tau)(c_\varepsilon\tau+d_\varepsilon)^{-n}(a_\varepsilon d_\varepsilon-b_\varepsilon c_\varepsilon)^{n/2}.$$

Then if $\Phi(\tau)$ is any $(n-1)$-fold integral of $\varphi(\tau)$,

(1) $$\Phi(\tau)[\varepsilon]^{n-2}-\Phi(\tau)\equiv\Omega_\varepsilon(\tau)$$

is an ordinary polynomial of degree $n-2$ in τ. In analogy to abelian integrals, this polynomial is called a "period". Referring to a fuchsian group $\Gamma=\{1, \varepsilon, \eta, \cdots\}$ in the upper half plane, a Riemann surface is defined as usual by identifying points, etc. The group has consistency relations of the type

(2) $$\Omega_{\varepsilon\eta}-\Omega_\varepsilon[\eta]^{n-2}-\Omega_\eta=0.$$

Here $\varphi(\tau)$ is defined conventionally as being of "first or second type" according to the absence or presence of poles. Furthermore, $n\geqq 2$ and is even. Then every automorphic form of the first or second kind leads to a cohomology class in the mapping of Γ into the polynomial module (via Ω), namely the quotient of the cocycles defined by (2) by the coboundaries trivially defined by taking $\Phi(\tau)$ as a polynomial of degree $n-2$ in (1). The interesting thing is the (converse) correspondence of each such cohomology class to a $\varphi(\tau)$ of first or second kind. The author establishes this by using the defining topology of the Riemann surface for an explicit calculation of the rank of said cohomology group. Integrals of the type

(3) $$I(\varphi, \psi)=\int\Phi(\tau)\psi(\tau)d\tau/(2\pi i),$$

where ψ is an arbitrary automorphic form, are used to build up the desired function coordinatewise from the cohomology class.

The author's ultimate purpose is number-theoretic, and he uses integrals of type (3) to calculate the trace on the space of automorphic forms as produced by certain "modular-group" correspondences of the Riemann surface into itself [cf. Eichler, J. Indian Math. Soc. (N.S.) **20** (1956), 163–206; MR **19**, 18].

The author cites another independent source of the underlying formal manipulations in the work of A. Weil [Abh. Math. Sem. Hamburg. Univ. **11** (1935), 110–115]. {The reviewer can cite two additional independent sources rooted in perturbation-theory (where $n=4$). One is M. Schiffer's and D. C. Spencer's work on the variation kernel or quadratic differential [e.g., Functionals of finite Riemann surfaces, Princeton, 1954, p. 316 ff.; MR **16**, 461]. The other is the reviewer's work involving period polynomials whose coefficients are real [Trans Amer. Math. Soc. **82** (1956), 117–127; MR **18**, 194].} *H. Cohn.*

Citations: MR 18, 194h = F10-44; MR 19, 18a = F15-10.

Referred to in E02-7, F10-104, F10-110, F15-15, F15-16, F15-18, F15-21, F25-12, F25-13, F50-23.

F15-13 (20# 6463)

Dade, Everett C. Abelian groups of unimodular matrices. Illinois J. Math. 3 (1959), 11–27.

An elementary result by the reviewer states that in the modular group (the integral unimodular matrices of order 2 with A and $-A$ identified) the abelian subgroups are cyclic. The author (this paper is his A.B. thesis) proves the following non-elementary generalization. Let G be an abelian subgroup of the group of integral matrices of order n with determinant 1 and elements taken from an algebraic number field of degree d over the rationals. Then the rank of G is at most $d[n^2/4]$, and the minimum number of generators of the periodic subgroup of G is at most $n-1$. These bounds are attained for each field and each n.

The author proves similar results for the abelian subgroups of the group of unrestricted unimodular matrices, and for orders in algebras over algebraic number fields. *K. Goldberg* (Washington, D.C.)

Referred to in F05-16.

F15-14 (22# 5614)

Knopp, Marvin Isadore. Determination of certain roots of unity in the theory of automorphic forms of dimension zero. Duke Math. J. **27** (1960), 497–506.

Let $G(\lambda_q)$ denote the properly discontinuous group generated by the two substitutions $S(\tau)=\tau+q$ and and $T=\tau^{-1}$, where $\lambda_q=2\cos(\pi/q)$. Let Γ denote either $G(\sqrt{2})$ or $G(\sqrt{3})$ ($q=4$ or 6), and suppose that $f(\tau)$ is an automorphic form of dimension 0 belonging to Γ. That is: $f(\tau)$ is regular for $\mathscr{I}(\tau)>0$; and for every $M\in\Gamma$, $f(M\tau)=\varepsilon(M)f(\tau)$, where $\varepsilon(M)$ is a multiplier system and $|\varepsilon(M)|=1$.

The author investigates the multiplier systems $\varepsilon(M)$ for the groups denoted by Γ, and by looking at the structure for the groups Γ, he determines explicitly all multiplier systems $\varepsilon(M)$. *R. Ayoub* (University Park, Pa.)

Referred to in F15-20.

F15-15 (22# 11126)

Shimura, Goro. Sur les intégrales attachées aux formes automorphes. J. Math. Soc. Japan **11** (1959), 291–311.

Eichler developed in his paper in Math. Z. **87** (1957), 267–298 [MR **19**, 740] a theory of the periods of integrals associated to automorphic forms in one complex variable, and showed the usefulness of this theory in obtaining formulas for the traces of modular correspondences. In the present paper the author extends this theory by showing that in certain cases the structure of an Abelian variety can also be given to the periods of such integrals. In more detail, let G be a Fuchsian group of automorphisms of the upper half-plane in one complex variable, and $f(z)$ be a cusp form of weight $n+2$ for G, where n is an even integer. Eichler associated to the function $f(z)$ its $(n+1)$-fold iterated indefinite integral $F(z)$, defined uniquely to within a polynomial of degree n, and then associated to the elements $\sigma\in G$ the periods $x(\sigma)=F(\sigma z)\cdot(d\sigma/dz)^{-n/2}-F(z)$, which are polynomials of degree n defined uniquely to within the obvious equivalence. The equivalence classes of these sets of periods can be interpreted as elements of the first cohomology group of G, with coefficients in the space of polynomials of degree n under the appropriate action of the group G; and the mapping associating to each cusp form its classes of periods is an isomorphism into that cohomology group, the image of the space of cusp forms having half the dimension of the cohomology group [Eichler, loc. cit.]. The present author begins by introducing a convenient paraphrase of the above, essentially considering the coefficients of the polynomials formally as elements of an $(n+1)$-dimensional complex vector space; the periods then appear as elements of the first cohomology group of G with coefficients in an $(n+1)$-dimensional complex vector space, on which the group G acts via a representation corresponding to the above polynomial action. This has the advantage of rewriting the iterated indefinite integrations of Eichler as simple indefinite integrations of vector-valued differential forms, thus exhibiting more explicitly the relations noted by Eichler between this theory and the earlier work of Weil on vector-valued differential forms [J. Math. Pures Appl. (9) **17** (1938), 47–87]. The author then shows that the correspondence associating to the cusp forms the real parts of their periods is actually an isomorphism of the space of cusp forms onto the real cohomology subgroup. If the action of G on the real cohomology group is rational, so that the integral cohomology group is a well-defined lattice, this then induces a lattice into the space of cusp forms, and the quotient space is a compact complex torus. The Petersson inner product is then used to give this torus the structure of an Abelian variety. (Actually the results are more general, since it suffices to have the action of G rational after perhaps an inner automorphism of suitable type.) Some applications to the Hecke correspondences are given in conclusion.

R. C. Gunning (Princeton, N.J.)

Citations: MR 19, 740a = F15-12.

Referred to in F15-16, F15-21, F15-38, F50-23, G10-43.

F15-16 (24# A3311)

Kuga, Michio; Shimura, Goro

On vector differential forms attached to automorphic forms.

J. Math. Soc. Japan **12** (1960), 258–270.

In der Theorie der Modularkorrespondenzen [vgl. Eichler, Math. Z. **67** (1957), 267–298; MR **19**, 740; Shimura, J. Math. Soc. Japan **11** (1959), 291–311; MR **22** #11126] ordnet man den automorphen Formen in bestimmter Weise Vektordifferentialformen zu. Diese in jener Theorie wichtige Zuordnung wird von den Verfassern in der vorliegenden Arbeit unabhängig von diesem Hintergrund untersucht. Es sei G eine Fuchssche Gruppe von linearen Abbildungen $\sigma(z)=(az+b)(cz+d)^{-1}$ der oberen Halbebene H und $M_n(\sigma)$ für natürliches gerades n die folgende Tensordarstellung von G:

$$(cz+d)^n(\sigma(z)^n, \sigma(z)^{n-1}, \cdots, 1) = (z^n, z^{n-1}, \cdots, 1)M_n(\sigma).$$

Gegenstand der Untersuchung sind $(n+1)$-reihige Spalten ω von meromorphen Differentialformen auf H mit dem Transformationsgesetz $\omega \circ \sigma = M_n(\sigma)\omega$, genannt M_n-Differentialformen. Jeder bezüglich G automorphen Form f einer geraden Dimension ν, $2 \leqq \nu \leqq n+2$, wird durch eine explizite Vorschrift eine solche M_n-Differentialform zugeordnet. Dabei entsprechen Spitzenformen f holomorphe M_n-Differentialformen. Die Verfasser zeigen nun umgekehrt, dass sich jede holomorphe M_n-Differentialform als Summe von derartigen aus automorphen Spitzenformen f abgeleiteten M_n-Differentialformen zusammensetzen lässt. Genauer gestattet die volle Schar $F_n(G)$ der holomorphen M_n-Differentialformen eine direkte Zerlegung

$$F_n(G) = S_2{}^{(n)}(G) + \cdots + S_n{}^{(n)}(G) + S_{n+2}^{(n)}(G),$$

wobei $S_\nu{}^{(n)}(G)$ die den Spitzenformen f der Dimension ν zugeordnete Schar der M_n-Differentialformen ist. Es gilt ein analoger Sachverhalt für Funktionen statt Differentialformen. In seiner früheren Arbeit behandelte der zweite Verfasser nur $S_{n+2}^{(n)}(G)$ und zeigte, dass die Periode von $\int^2 \omega$ für $0 \neq \omega \in S_{n+2}^{(n)}(G)$ nicht cohomolog Null ist. Für die übrigen Komponenten obiger Zerlegung von $F_n(G)$ dagegen ist diese Grösse stets cohomolog Null.

H. Klingen (Freiburg)

Citations: MR 19, 740a = F15-12; MR 22# 11126 = F15-15.

Referred to in F65-16.

F15-17 (26# 6127)

Greenberg, Leon

Maximal Fuchsian groups.

Bull. Amer. Math. Soc. **69** (1963), 569–573.

Let D be the unit disk $\{z: |z|<1\}$, $\mathscr{L}$ the group of conformal homeomorphisms of D and $\mathscr{L}'$ the group of angle-preserving homeomorphisms of D. A Fuchsian group is a discrete subgroup of $\mathscr{L}$ and is known to have the presentation: $a_1, b_1, \cdots, a_g, b_g, e_1, \cdots, e_k, h_1, \cdots, h_m, p_1, \cdots, p_r$ with the defining relations $e_1^{\nu_1} = \cdots = e_k^{\nu_k} = 1$ and $(\prod [a_i, b_i])e_1 \cdots e_k h_1 \cdots h_m p_1 \cdots p_r = 1$. This is denoted by $F = F(g; \nu_1, \cdots, \nu_k; m; r)$. The elements h_i are hyperbolic and the p_j are parabolic; D/F is a Riemann surface and the h_i correspond to the boundary curves and the p_j to the punctures.

A geometric isomorphism of a Fuchsian group F is an isomorphism $\gamma: F \to \mathscr{L}$ such that: (1) $\gamma(F)$ is a Fuchsian group; (2) γ maps hyperbolic [parabolic] boundary elements onto hyperbolic [parabolic] boundary elements. Let $\Gamma(F)$ denote the g-isomorphisms of F. $\Gamma(F)$ can be imbedded in $\mathscr{L}^n$, $n=2g+k+m+r$, and then given the relative topology. In $\Gamma(F)$ one says that γ_1 is ρ-equivalent to γ_2 if there exists a $\lambda \in \mathscr{L}'$ such that $\gamma_2(f) = \lambda\gamma_1(f)\lambda^{-1}$ for all $f \in F$. The quotient space $T(F) = \Gamma(F)/\rho$ is the analogue for F of the Teichmüller space of the Riemann surface. Let $A(F)$ denote the group of g-automorphisms of a Fuchsian group F and $I(F)$ the subgroup of inner automorphisms, then $M(F) = A(F)/I(F)$, the modular groups, acts discontinuously on $T(F)$. The author uses results of Fenchel and Nielsen (to appear) to establish the following theorems. Theorem 1: Let F and G be finitely-generated Fuchsian groups with $F \subset G$, $[G: F] < \infty$. Let $i: F \to G$ denote the injection map. The map $\Gamma(G) \to \Gamma(F)$ defined by $\gamma \to \gamma \circ i$ induces a map $m: T(G) \to T(F)$ which has the following properties. (1) m is real-analytic and 1-1. (2) The image $I = m(T(G))$ is a closed subset of $T(F)$. (3) The images of I under the modular group $M(F)$ do not accumulate in $T(F)$.

A finitely-generated Fuchsian group is finitely maximal (f-maximal) if there does not exist a Fuchsian group $G \supset F$ and $[G: F] < \infty$. Let $\mathrm{Max}(F)$ denote the set of points in $T(F)$ which represent f-maximal groups. Theorem 2: Let F be a finitely-generated Fuchsian group. Then one of the following is true. (1) $\mathrm{Max}(F)$ is empty. There is a group G which contains F with finite index such that $m(T(G)) = T(F)$. (2) $\mathrm{Max}(F)$ is an open, everywhere dense subset of $T(F)$ whose complement is an analytic set. The author gives a complete list of the groups for which $\mathrm{Max}(F)$ is empty. This contains some of the triangle groups (a few cases had been found earlier by Petersson and Schulenberg [Petersson, Abh. Math. Semin. Hansische Univ. **12** (1938), 180–199; Schulenberg, ibid. **13** (1939), 144–199]), and some groups of genus 0, 1, and 2. The group G of statement (1) of Theorem 2 is of genus 0 and contains F as a subgroup of index 2. {Reviewer's comment: It would be interesting to know under what conditions a Fuchsian group F which is not f-maximal is contained in a Fuchsian group of genus 0.}

The author notes the connection of these ideas with those of Ahlfors and Bers. *J. R. Smart* (Madison, Wis.)

F15-18 (27# 5747)

Kodama, Tetsuo

On integrals of vector functions attached to automorphic forms.

Mem. Fac. Sci. Kyushu Univ. Ser. A **16** (1962), 9–25.

Diese Arbeit schliesst sich an die fundamentale Arbeit von Eichler über eine Verallgemeinerung der abelschen Integrale an [Math. Z. **67** (1957), 267–298; MR **19**, 740]. Es wird auf das Referat der Eichlerschen Arbeit verwiesen [MR **19**, 740]. Eines der Hauptresultate von Eichler war die Bestimmung der ersten Kohomologiegruppe von Γ, mit Werten im Modul der Polynome $(n-2)$-ten Grades, durch automorphe Formen 1. oder 2. Gattung vom Grade $-n$, modulo den $(n-1)$-fachen Ableitungen. In der vorliegenden Arbeit werden im Anschluss daran die kohomologischen Eigenschaften von vektorwertigen Funktionen untersucht;

die Möglichkeit dazu wurde bereits von Eichler in einer Schlussbemerkung zu der eingangs zitierten Arbeit angedeutet. *P. Roquette* (Tübingen)

Citations: MR 19, 740a = F15-12.

F15-19 **(28# 66)**

Rosen, David

An arithmetic characterization of the parabolic points of $G(2\cos\pi/5)$.

Proc. Glasgow Math. Assoc. **6,** 88–96 (1963).

The problem of characterizing the coefficients of linear fractional transformations $w=(az+b)/(cz+d)$ belonging to the group generated by the transformations $w=-1/z$, $w=z+\lambda$, where $\lambda=2\cos(\pi/q)$, is still unsolved for $q\geqq 5$, and the author derives a certain amount of information for the case $q=5$, basing his work on his theory of λ-fractions [Duke Math. J. **21** (1954), 549–563; MR **16**, 458]. In this case the coefficients a, b, c, d are algebraic integers in the field generated by $\sqrt{5}$, but which algebraic integers can arise in this way is not known; for example, it seems likely that every rational number is a cusp a/c for the group, but this has not yet been proved.

A number of results concerning the approximants P_m/Q_m to the λ-fraction for a cusp a/c are obtained. Here $a=a_1+a_2\lambda$, $c=c_1+c_2\lambda$, where a_1, a_2, c_1, c_2 are rational integers, and the same holds for the approximants. For example, it is shown that c can be expressed in such a way that either $c_2\geqq c_1\geqq 0$ or $c_1=c_2+1$. Also, the 16 possible sets of parities of the four numbers a_1, a_2, c_1, c_2 can be reduced to 5, and the change in parity as one proceeds from one approximant to the next can be specified. In the converse direction, it is shown that each of the units $\{(1+\sqrt{5})/2\}^m$ $(m=0, 1, 2, \cdots)$ is a cusp for the group. *R. A. Rankin* (Bloomington, Ind.)

Citations: MR 16, 458d = A54-20.

Referred to in F15-25.

F15-20 **(29# 2390)**

Smart, John Roderick

Parametrization of automorphic forms for the Hecke groups $G(\sqrt{2})$ and $G(\sqrt{3})$.

Duke Math. J. **31** (1964), 395–403.

In this paper the author considers automorphic forms for the Hecke groups $G(\sqrt{n})$ for $n=2$ and 3. ($G(\sqrt{n})$ is the discontinuous group of linear fractional transformations on the upper half-plane generated by the two transformations $z\to-1/z$ and $z\to z+\sqrt{n}$ [Hecke, Math. Ann. **112** (1936), 664–699].) For $n=2$ and 3 the Riemann surfaces associated to these groups are compact surfaces of genus zero, so the situation is rather similar to that arising in the case of the ordinary modular group $G(1)$. The multiplier systems for these two groups are determined explicitly, using the description of the characters for these two groups given by M. I. Knopp [Duke Math. J. **27** (1960), 497–506; MR **22** #5614], and explicit expansions are derived for all the automorphic forms for these two groups in terms of simple canonical forms. *R. C. Gunning* (Princeton, N.J.)

Citations: MR 22# 5614 = F15-14.

F15-21 **(31# 129)**

Cohn, Harvey; Knopp, M. I.

Note on automorphic forms with real period polynomials.

Duke Math. J. **32** (1965), 115–120.

Let Γ be a discontinuous group of automorphisms of the upper half-plane H, and $g(z)$ be a regular automorphic form of weight $-r-2$ for Γ (for even $r\geqq 2$). Following Eichler [Math. Z. **67** (1957), 267–298; MR **19**, 740] and others, period polynomials $P_T(z)$, $T\in\Gamma$, are associated to $g(z)$ by defining $P_T(z)=(cz+d)^rG(Tz)-G(z)$ for any holomorphic function $G(z)$ in H such that $(d^{r+1}/dz^{r+1})G(z)=g(z)$. The present paper is devoted to a proof of the following theorem (it is, of course, assumed here that H/Γ is compact except for cusps): The period polynomials have real coefficients if and only if $g(z)$ is a real linear combination of Eisenstein series. (In particular, no non-trivial cusp form can have real period polynomials; the latter assertion also follows in Shimura's paper [J. Math. Soc. Japan **11** (1959), 291–311; MR **22** #11126].) *R. C. Gunning* (Princeton, N.J.)

Citations: MR 19, 740a = F15-12; MR 22# 11126 = F15-15.

Referred to in F65-16.

F15-22 **(32# 5633)**

Kubota, Tomio

Ein arithmetischer Satz über eine Matrizengruppe.

J. Reine Angew. Math. **222** (1966), 55–57.

Let F be a totally imaginary algebraic number field of finite degree, which contains the mth $(m\geqq 2)$ roots of unity. Let $G=\left\{\sigma=\begin{pmatrix}\alpha & \beta\\ \gamma & \delta\end{pmatrix},\ \alpha,\ \beta,\ \gamma,\ \delta\in F,\ \alpha\delta-\beta\gamma=1,\ \alpha\equiv\delta\equiv 1 \pmod{m^2},\ \beta\equiv\gamma\equiv 0 \pmod{m^2}\right\}$. If $m^2|M$, let $G_M=\{\sigma\in G|\alpha\equiv\delta\equiv 1,\ \beta\equiv\gamma\equiv 0 \pmod{M}\}$. Let $\left(\frac{\alpha}{\beta}\right)_m$ be the mth power residue symbol. The author proves: If $H=\{\sigma\in G|\gamma=0\}$, put

$$\chi(\sigma)=\begin{cases}\left(\dfrac{\gamma}{\alpha}\right)_m & \text{if } \sigma\in G-H,\\ 1 & \text{if } \sigma\in H;\end{cases}$$

then χ is a character on the group G. Furthermore, χ is nontrivial on every congruence group G_M of G. *D. J. Lewis* (Ann Arbor, Mich.)

Referred to in R40-28.

F15-23 **(33# 5580)**

Yamada, Toshihiko

On the distribution of the norms of the hyperbolic transformations.

Osaka J. Math. **3** (1966), 29–37.

Let Γ be a discrete subgroup of $SL(2, \mathbf{R})$ with compact quotient. Let P denote a hyperbolic element of Γ and $\{P\}$ the conjugate class of P (with respect to Γ). Put $N\{P\}=\alpha^2$ when P is conjugate to $\begin{pmatrix}\alpha & 0\\ 0 & \alpha^{-1}\end{pmatrix}$ $(\alpha>1)$ in G. A hyperbolic class $\{P\}$ is called primitive if it is not a power of exponent >1 of any other classes. The author is concerned with the distribution of $N\{P\}$'s, and proves the following estimate:

$$\sum \log N\{P\}\frac{(\log(x/N\{P\}^n))^2}{1-N\{P\}^{-n}}=x+\textstyle\sum_1^M \chi^{a_\nu}/a_\nu+O(x^{1/2}),$$

where the sum on the left is extended over all primitive $\{P\}$ with $N\{P\}<x$, and $a_1, \cdots, a_M$ are constants which depend on Γ. This is a kind of "Mangold formula" for the Selberg zeta function of Γ [A. Selberg, J. Indian Math. Soc. (N.S.) **20** (1956), 47–87; MR **19**, 531]. *S. Konno* (Osaka)

Citations: MR 19, 531g = F60-2.

Referred to in F15-34.

F15-24 **(36# 2618)**

Doi, Koji; Naganuma, Hidehisa

On the algebraic curves uniformized by arithmetical automorphic functions.

Ann. of Math. (2) **86** (1967), 449–460.

The main result of this paper is a theorem on a canonical model, in the sense of G. Shimura [same Ann. (2) **85** (1967), 58–159; MR **34** #4268], for an algebraic curve uniformized by automorphic functions with respect to a discontinuous group obtained from an indefinite quaternion algebra. The theorem asserts that a canonical model behaves naturally under an automorphism of the basic field. Suggested by their results, including some numerical examples, the authors conjecture that a certain elliptic curve may be isogeneous to a factor of the jacobian variety of a field of elliptic modular functions, or, expressed differently, that there could exist a multiplicative relation, similar to the product decomposition of a Dedekind zeta function into Dirichlet L-series, between Dirichlet series of Hecke type related to quaternion algebras over distinct ground fields. *T. Kubota* (Nagoya)

Citations: MR 34# 4268 = G15-37.

F15-25 (37# 4018)

Leutbecher, Armin

Über die Heckeschen Gruppen $\mathfrak{G}(\lambda)$.

Abh. Math. Sem. Univ. Hamburg **31** (1967), 199–205.

Zwei Untergruppen A, B einer Gruppe G heißen direkt kommensurabel, wenn ihr Durchschnitt endlichen Index in A und in B hat; sie heißen kommensurabel in G, wenn ein $g \in G$ existiert, sodaß A und gBg^{-1} direkt kommensurabel sind. Für die von $z \mapsto z+\lambda_q$ ($\lambda_q = 2\cos\pi/q$, $q=3, 4, \cdots$) und $z \mapsto -1/z$ erzeugte Heckesche Gruppe $\mathfrak{G}(\lambda_q)$ gilt Satz 1: Wenn $q \geqq 5$, $q \neq 6$ ist, dann stimmt die Menge aller lineargebrochenen Abbildungen der Zahlenkugel, für die $\mathfrak{G}(\lambda_q)$ und $g\mathfrak{G}(\lambda_q)g^{-1}$ direkt kommensurabel sind, überein mit $\mathfrak{G}(\lambda_q) \cup J\mathfrak{G}(\lambda_q)$ ($J: z \mapsto -z$). Folgerung: Jede mit $\mathfrak{G}(\lambda_q)$ kommensurable Gruppe holomorpher Automorphismen der oberen Halbebene ist konjugiert zu einer Untergruppe von $\mathfrak{G}(\lambda_q)$, falls $q \geqq 5$, $q \neq 6$ ist, und die Gruppen $\mathfrak{G}(\lambda_q)$, $q \geqq 5$ sind paarweise inkommensurabel. Sodann werden die Spitzen, das sind die Bilder von ∞ unter $\mathfrak{G}(\lambda_q)$, bestimmt. Sie lassen sich durch geeignete Kettenbrüche darstellen. Es folgt Satz 2: Die Spitzen von $\mathfrak{G}(\lambda_q)$ sind ∞ und die Zahlen von $\mathbf{Q}(\sqrt{5})$. Dass die Einheiten von $\mathbf{Q}(\sqrt{5})$ Spitzen sind, wurde schon von D. Rosen [Proc. Glasgow Math. Assoc. **6** (1963), 88–96; MR **28** #66] bewiesen. *J. Spilker* (Freiburg)

Citations: MR 28# 66 = F15-19.

F15-26 (38# 118)

Kubota, Tomio

Über diskontinuierliche Gruppen Picardschen Typus und zugehörige Eisensteinsche Reihen.

Nagoya Math. J. **32** (1968), 259–271.

Let $G = \mathrm{SL}(2, \mathbf{C})$. Every element $\omega \in G$ allows a unique decomposition $\omega = \begin{pmatrix} 1 & z \\ 0 & 1 \end{pmatrix}\begin{pmatrix} v^{1/2} & 0 \\ 0 & v^{-1/2} \end{pmatrix}\omega_0$ with a unitary ω_0, where $z = x+iy \in \mathbf{C}$, $0 < v \in \mathbf{R}$. To ω associate $u(\omega) = \begin{pmatrix} z & -v \\ v & \bar{z} \end{pmatrix}$. Let $\sigma = \begin{pmatrix} \alpha & \beta \\ \gamma & \delta \end{pmatrix}$ be another element of G and put $\tilde{\alpha} = \begin{pmatrix} \alpha & 0 \\ 0 & \bar{\alpha} \end{pmatrix}$, etc. Then $u(\sigma\omega) = (\tilde{\alpha}u(\omega)+\tilde{\beta})(\tilde{\gamma}u(\omega)+\tilde{\delta})^{-1}$. G is thus represented as the group of motions of the 3-dimensional hyperbolic space H^3 with coordinates v, x, y. The Laplace-Beltrami operator is

$$D = v^2(\partial^2/\partial v^2 + \partial^2/\partial x^2 + \partial^2/\partial y^2) - v\partial/\partial v.$$

The author considers subgroups $\Gamma \subset G$ which have fundamental domain of finite volume in H^3. Among these is the Picard modular group $\mathrm{SL}(2, \mathscr{I})$, where $\mathscr{I}$ is the ring of integers of an imaginary quadratic number field. If Γ has a cusp, and if the subgroup which leaves this cusp fixed is denoted by Γ_∞, the author introduces the Eisenstein series $E(u, s, \chi) = \sum_{\sigma \in \Gamma_\infty \backslash \Gamma} \bar{\chi}(\sigma)v(\sigma u)^s$. They converge absolutely for $\mathrm{Re}(s) > 2$ and can be extended analytically to the whole s-plane as meromorphic functions. The Eisenstein series satisfy the following functional and differential equations, respectively: $E(\sigma u, s, \chi) = \chi(\sigma)E(u, s, \chi)$, $DE(u, s, \chi) = s(s-2)E(u, s, \chi)$. In particular, $E(u, s, \chi)$ is periodic in z, having two independent periods. The constant term of the corresponding Fourier series depends trivially on v. As a function of s it is a certain Dirichlet series. Let Γ have exactly h independent cusps, and $E_i(u, s, \chi)$ be the Eisenstein series formed as described above with respect to each of them. Write $\mathscr{E}(u, s, \chi)$ for the column vector formed with the $E_i(u, s, \chi)$. With certain Dirichlet series attached to the constant terms of the Fourier series of the $E_i(u, s, \chi)$, a certain $h \times h$ matrix $\Phi(s, \chi)$ is formed, and the functional equation $\mathscr{E}(u, s, \chi) = \Phi(s, \chi)\mathscr{E}(u, 2-s, \chi)$ holds. The proofs of these facts appear in J. Math. Soc. Japan **20** (1968), 193–207 [MR **37** #4035]. *M. Eichler* (Basel)

Citations: MR 37# 4035 = F65-22.

F15-27 (38# 6064)

Knopp, Marvin I.

Notes on automorphic functions: An entire automorphic form of positive dimension is zero.

J. Res. Nat. Bur. Standards Sect. B **71B** (1967), 167–169.

From the author's summary: "Several new proofs are given of the fact that an entire automorphic form of positive dimension on an H-group is zero. The first proof is modeled on the method used by Hecke to estimate the Fourier coefficients of cusp forms of negative dimension. The other proofs involve well-known theorems of complex function theory. One method applies to a larger class of groups than H-groups and, in particular, applies to compact groups and groups conjugate to H-groups."

R. J. Sibner (New Brunswick, N.J.)

F15-28 (41# 7031a; 41# 7031b)

Mautner, Friedérich Ignaz

[Mautner, Friedrich I.]

Fonctions propres des opérateurs de Hecke.

C. R. Acad. Sci. Paris Sér. A-B **269** (1969), A940–A943.

Mautner, Friederich Ignaz

[Mautner, Friedrich I.]

Fonctions propres des opérateurs de Hecke.

C. R. Acad. Sci. Paris Sér. A-B **270** (1970), A89–A92.

Let $G = \mathrm{PG}(2)$ be the group of all projective transformations

$$g\colon x \to g(x) = \frac{g_{11}x + g_{12}}{g_{21}x + g_{22}}$$

in one variable x, $G_Q = \mathrm{PG}(2, Q)$ the projective group over the rationals, G_Z the modular group $\mathrm{PG}(2, Z)$. The Hecke operators correspond to linear transformations of the space $L(G_Z \backslash G_Q)$ of all complex-valued functions $f(g) = f(\gamma g)$ ($\gamma \in G_Z$, $g \in G_Q$). It turns out that the eigenvalue problem for such operators can be solved explicitly. This is done by reducing the problem to a local one, using $G_Z \backslash G_Q = \prod_{p \neq \infty} G_{Z_p} \backslash G_{Q_p}$, where Q_p is the p-adic field and Z_p is the ring of p-adic integers. Eigenfunctions are then expressed as Fourier polynomials.

Next, looking at the principal series of representations of G_{Q_p}, a complete and explicit description of $L^0(G_Z \backslash G_Q)$ is obtained.

The space $L(G_Z \backslash G_Q / R_Q)$ is also considered, where R_Q is a rotation subgroup of G_Q.

A. Evyatar (Gutwirth) (Haifa)

Referred to in F25-30.

F15-29 **(41# 8426)**

Kuga, Michio

Hecke's polynomial as a generalized congruence Artin L-function.

Algebraic Groups and Discontinuous Subgroups (Proc. Sympos. Pure Math., Boulder, Colo., 1965), *pp.* 333–337. *Amer. Math. Soc., Providence, R.I.,* 1966.

Let L be an indefinite quaternion algebra over $\mathbf{Q}$ (i.e., L is a division algebra such that $L \otimes_{\mathbf{Q}} \mathbf{R} = M_2(\mathbf{R})$) and let $\mathcal{O}$ be a maximal order in L. Set $\Gamma_b = \{\gamma \in \mathcal{O} | \det \gamma = 1, \gamma \equiv 1 \bmod b\mathcal{O}\}$, and let $V = \Gamma_b \backslash X$, where X is the upper half plane. If $\alpha \in \mathcal{O}$ and $\det \alpha = p$, then $\Gamma_b \alpha \Gamma_b$ acts naturally on the holomorphic automorphic forms of weight k, and so gives rise to the endomorphism $(\Gamma_b \alpha \Gamma_b)_k$. When p is prime to the discriminant of L, there is some $\delta \in \Gamma_1$ with $\alpha^2 \equiv p\delta \bmod b\mathcal{O}$; and in this case the Hecke polynomial $H_k(p, u)$ is defined by $H_k(p, u) = \det(I - (\Gamma_b \alpha \Gamma_b)_k u + p(\Gamma_b p\delta \Gamma_b)_k u^2)$. The author studies $H_k(p, u)$ in terms of an algebraic family of two-dimensional abelian varieties $W \to V$ (each fibre having endomorphism ring an order in L) introduced by G. Shimura [*Algebraic groups and discontinuous subgroups* (Proc. Sympos. Pure Math., Vol. IX, Boulder, Colo., 1965), pp. 312–332, Amer. Math. Soc., Providence, R.I., 1966; MR **38** #5789]. He shows that for $k > 2$, $H_k(p, u)$ is a certain formally defined L-function constructed from the field of all l^vth division points of the generic fibre of the family $\overline{W} \to \overline{V}$ obtained by reduction mod $\mathfrak{p}$. Here, $\mathfrak{p}$ is a prime of the number field over which W is defined, $\mathfrak{p}|p$, and l is prime to p. If $k = 2$, $H_2(p, u)$ is the L-function times an elementary factor $(1-u)(1-pu)$.

By using a remark of A. Weil, the author shows that if $p \equiv 1 \bmod bl$, and if K_l is the smallest Galois extension of $\mathbf{Q}$ containing $\mathbf{Q}(\exp(2\pi i/bl))$ and the lth division points of the Jacobian of $\Gamma_{bl} \backslash X$, then when p splits in K_l, we have $H_k(p, u) \equiv (1-u)^{2n(k)} \bmod l$, $k \geqq 2$, where $n(k)$ is a certain well-defined integer depending on k.

S. S. Shatz (Philadelphia, Pa.)

Citations: MR 38# 5789 = G15-47.

F15-30 **(42# 1766)**

Pjateckiĭ-Šapiro, I. I.

Reduction modulo a prime of modular function fields. (Russian)

Izv. Akad. Nauk SSSR Ser. Mat. **32** (1968), 1264–1274.

The results of the present paper generalize the known Shimura relation on the reduction of the Hecke operator and the classical Weber congruence for a modular equation of degree m. Let $j(z)$ be a modular invariant. We denote by $K(p^\infty)$ the field that is obtained by adjoining to the field $\mathbf{Q}$ of rational numbers all functions of the form $j((az+b)/(cz+d))$, where a, b, c, d are integers and $\Delta = ad - bc$ is a divisor of m. The author constructs a homomorphism of the group $\mathrm{PGL}(2, \mathbf{Q}_p)$ into the group $\mathfrak{S}(p^\infty)$ of all automorphisms of the field $K(p^\infty)$ and proves that it is an isomorphism of $\mathrm{PGL}(2, \mathbf{Q}_p)$ onto the subgroup $\mathfrak{S}(p^\infty)$ consisting of the elements that act trivially on the algebraic closure of the field $\mathbf{Q}$ in $K(p^\infty)$. The main result of this article consists of the construction of the reduction of the field $K(p^\infty)$ mod p and of the determination of the quotient ring as a module over the group $\mathrm{PGL}(2, \mathbf{Q}_p)$. To determine the reduction of the field $K(p^\infty)$ it is necessary to construct a subring R invariant with respect to the group $\mathrm{PGL}(2, \mathbf{Q}_p)$ and an invariant ideal $I \subset R$ such that $p \cdot R \in I$. The ring R consists of all elements of the field $K(p^\infty)$ that are representable in the form

$$\varphi(j((p^k z + a)/p^e))/\psi(j(z)),$$

where the numerator is an arbitrary polynomial with integral coefficients in $j((p^k z + a)/p^l)$, $k, l = 0, 1, 2, \cdots$, $a \in \mathbf{Z}$, and the denominator is a polynomial in j with integral coefficients and with the highest coefficient relatively prime to p (the ring R is not integrally closed; its integral closure obviously consists of all elements of the field $K(p^\infty)$ for which the coefficients of the expansion at any parabolic vertex p are integers). The ideal I consists of those $f \in R$ such that all the coefficients of the expansion of f at all parabolic vertices are not relatively prime to p. We will now describe the construction of the quotient ring. We denote by Φ the field of all rational functions of $t, t^{1/p}, \cdots$ with coefficients belonging to the field $\mathbf{Z}_p$ and by X the projective line over the field of p-adic numbers $\mathbf{Q}_p$. The ring $A = R/I$ is isomorphic to the ring of all locally constant functions on X with values in φ. The author shows that the group $\mathrm{PGL}(2, \mathbf{Q}_p)$ acts on A according to the formula $T_g f(x) = f^{k(x,g)}(gx)$, where gx denotes the result of the application of element g to the point $x \in X$ (the group $\mathrm{PGL}(2, \mathbf{Q}_p)$ acts naturally on X), $k(x, g)$ is the dilatation coefficient in the point x, and $f \to f^p$ is the automorphism of the field φ that takes t into t^p. It is very interesting that these formulae are reminiscent of well known formulae from representation theory.

D. Každan (RŽMat **1969** #9 A292)

Referred to in F15-33.

F15-31 **(43# 1924)**

Knopp, Marvin I.; Smart, John Roderick

Hecke basis theorems for groups of genus 0.

J. Res. Nat. Bur. Standards Sect. B **74B** (1970), 131–148.

The groups Γ considered consist of bilinear mappings of the upper complex half plane and they have a canonical system of generators and relations E_μ, P_ν ($\mu = 1, \cdots, e$; $\nu = 1, \cdots, t$): $E_\mu^{l_\mu} = -I$ and $\prod E_\mu P_\nu = (-I)^{e+t}$. The number of parabolic elements P_ν is assumed to be $t > 0$. Examples of such groups are $\Gamma(\lambda_m)$, introduced by Hecke and generated by $E = \begin{pmatrix} 0 & -1 \\ 1 & 0 \end{pmatrix}$ and $P = \begin{pmatrix} 1 & \lambda_m \\ 0 & 1 \end{pmatrix}$, with $\lambda_m = 2\cos(2\pi/m)$. The authors study the space $\mathbf{C}(\Gamma, r, v)$ of holomorphic automorphic forms of weight r (degree $-r$) and of a given multiplier system v. $\mathbf{C}^0(\cdots)$ is the subspace of cusp forms. First they introduce the Eisenstein series $E_r(\Gamma, v: z) = \sum \bar{v}(V)(cz+d)^{-r}$, for $r > 0$, $E_0(\cdots) = 1$, the sum being extended over a system of elements $V = \begin{pmatrix} * & * \\ c & d \end{pmatrix} \in \Gamma$ with given second row. For $r = 2$ convergence difficulties arise; these were solved by H. Petersson [Math. Ann. **115** (1938), 175–204; ibid. **115** (1938), 518–572]; in this case the authors assume that $v = 1$. If $\dim \mathbf{C}^0(\Gamma, r, v) > 0$ then this space contains a form $\Delta(\Gamma, r, v; z)$ without zeros in the finite part of the half plane. In some cases (Theorems 1 and 5), the products $E_k(\Gamma, v; z)\Delta(\Gamma, r, v; z)^l$ for suitable k and l form a basis of $\mathbf{C}^0(\Gamma, r, v)$. These include the above mentioned groups $\Gamma(\lambda_m)$; however, some pairs r, v have to be excluded, when one form is missing. The proof is based on Petersson's generalization of the Riemann-Roch theorem [loc. cit.]. In a few other cases, when Γ is a subgroup of the elliptic modular group, analogous results are derived and listed in a table. Here the application of the Riemann-Roch theorem can be avoided.

M. Eichler (Basel)

F15-32 **(43# 3353)**

Helling, Heinz

On the commensurability class of the rational modular group.

J. London Math. Soc. (2) **2** (1970), 67–72.

In an earlier paper [Math. Z. **92** (1966), 269–280; MR **37** #4017] the author showed that every group commensurable with the modular group is contained in one of a family of groups $\Gamma(f)$, one for each square-free integer f. In this paper the author obtains some further results. In particular, he obtains a formula for the genus of the quotient space of the upper half-plane modulo $\Gamma(f)^+$, where $\Gamma(f)^+$ denotes the subgroup defined by matrices with positive determinant. He gives a table of values for the genus for all f up to 163. {Note a misprint on p. 70, line 9: for $\Gamma(f)^+$ read $\Gamma^0(f)^+$.}

A. M. Macbeath (Birmingham)

Citations: MR 37# 4017 = F40-48.

F15-33 (43# 7669)

Pjateckiĭ-Šapiro, I. I.

Reduction of the fields of modular functions and the rings of functions on p-adic manifolds.

Several Complex Variables, I (Proc. Conf., Univ. of Maryland, College Park, Md., 1970), *pp.* 151–164. *Springer, Berlin,* 1970.

Notations: $\mathbf{Q}_p$ is the field of rational p-adic numbers, $\mathbf{Q}(m)$ is the field of mth roots of unity over $\mathbf{Q}$, $k=\mathbf{Q}(p^\infty)=\bigcup \mathbf{Q}(p^n)$, and K is the field of all elliptic modular functions of levels p^n $(n=0,1,2,\cdots)$ with Fourier expansions whose coefficients lie in k. The group $G_p=\mathrm{PGL}(2,\mathbf{Q}_p)$ can be generated by the matrices $\begin{pmatrix} a & b\\ c & d\end{pmatrix}$, with $a,b,c,d\in\mathbf{Z}$ and $ad-bc=p^n$ $(n=0,1,\cdots)$, and the matrices $\begin{pmatrix}1 & 0\\ 0 & \varepsilon\end{pmatrix}$, with p-adic units ε. By the definitions of the first and second generators of G_p,

$$f(z)\circ\begin{pmatrix} a & b\\ c & d\end{pmatrix} = f((az+b)/(cz+d))(\sum c_n e^{2\pi inp^{-m}z})\circ\begin{pmatrix}1 & 0\\ 0 & \varepsilon\end{pmatrix} = \sum c_n{}^{\varepsilon} e^{2\pi inp^{-m}z},$$

where $c_n\to c_n{}^{\varepsilon}$ means the action of the element of $\mathrm{Gal}(k/Q)$ corresponding to ε, G_p becomes a group of automorphisms of K.

Let $\tilde R$ be the ring of modular functions of K with p-adic integral Fourier coefficients, $\tilde S$ the subring of $\tilde R$ for which some of the Fourier coefficients are p-adic units, and $R=\tilde S^{-1}\tilde R$. Finally, let $\mathfrak{J}$ be the R-ideal, all Fourier coefficients of which are non-units. Now the quotient ring $R/\mathfrak{J}$ has the following properties: Let $\mathbf{F}_p$ be the prime field of characteristic p, t an indeterminate, $\Phi=\mathbf{F}_p(t,\sqrt[p]{t},\cdots)$, X the projective line over $\mathbf{Q}_p$, and $\Phi(X)$ the ring of locally constant functions on X with values in Φ. Then $R/\mathfrak{J}\cong\Phi(X)$. The action of G_p on $\Phi(X)$ can be explained independently, and the above isomorphy is a G_p-operator isomorphy.

The Hecke operator T_p can be studied in this connection. Its well known properties are expressed in the present language.

In the last section similar facts concerning Siegel modular functions are mentioned.

Proofs are only sketched. For details the reader is referred to the following papers: The author and I. R. Šafarevič, Izv. Akad. Nauk SSSR Ser. Mat. **30** (1966), 671–704 [MR **34** #2581]; the author, ibid. **32** (1968), 1264–1274 [MR **42** #1766].

M. Eichler (Basel)

Citations: MR 34# 2581 = F99-4; MR 42# 1766 = F15-30.

F15-34 (44# 1626)

Andrianov, A. N.; Fomenko, O. M.

Distribution of the norms of the hyperbolic elements of the modular group and of the number of classes of indefinite binary quadratic forms. (Russian)

Dokl. Akad. Nauk SSSR **196** (1971), 743–745.

Let $\Gamma'=\Gamma/\{\pm I\}$ be the modular group, where $\Gamma=\mathrm{SL}(2,\mathbf{Z})$. Let P denote a hyperbolic element of Γ' and let $\{P\}$ be the conjugate class of P with respect to Γ'. Put $N\{P\}=\alpha^2$ when P is conjugate to $\begin{pmatrix}\alpha & 0\\ 0 & \alpha^{-1}\end{pmatrix}$ $(\alpha>1)$ in $\mathrm{SL}(2,\mathbf{R})$. The author uses work by A. Selberg [J. Indian Math. Soc. (N.S.) **20** (1956), 47–87; MR **19**, 531] to prove that

$$\tfrac12\sum\log N\{P\}(\log(x/N\{P\}^n))^2/(1-N\{P\}^{-n}) = x+\textstyle\sum_{v=1}^m x^{a_v}/a_v{}^3+O(x^{1/2}).$$

The summation on the left is carried out over all primitive $\{P\}$ with $N\{P\}^n<x$, and $a_1,a_2,\cdots,a_M$ are the real zeros s of $Z(s)$ satisfying the condition $\frac12<s<1$. Here $Z(s)=\prod_{\{P\}}\prod_{n=0}^\infty(1-N\{P\}^{-s-n})$ $(\mathrm{Re}\,s>1)$, where $\{P\}$ runs through all primitive classes. This extends similar results obtained by T. Yamada [Osaka J. Math. **3** (1966), 29–37; MR **33** #5580]. An application is made to the theory of indeterminate binary quadratic forms.

{This article has appeared in English translation [Soviet Math. Dokl. **12** (1971), 217–219].}

R. A. Rankin (Glasgow)

Citations: MR 19, 531g = F60-2; MR 33# 5580 = F15-23.

F15-35 (44# 1628)

Kitaoka, Yoshiyuki

A note on Hecke operators and theta-series.

Nagoya Math. J. **42** (1971), 189–195.

Let $p,p_1,\cdots$ denote primes, let A be an even (i.e., with integral entries that are even on the diagonal) positive $2k\times 2k$ matrix of level N and determinant D. Set $\vartheta(\tau,A)=\sum_{\xi\in\mathbf{Z}^{2k}}e^{\pi iA[\xi]\tau}$, let T_n denote the Hecke operator (of level N) and denote by A_l the representatives of all classes in the genus of A. If $E(A_l)$ denotes the order of the unit group of A_l, set $M(A)=\sum\{E(A_l)\}^{-1}$ and

$$F(\tau,A) = (1/M(A))\textstyle\sum_l\vartheta(\tau,A_l)/E(A_l).$$

For $\tau'=(a\tau+b)(c\tau+d)^{-1}$ with $\begin{pmatrix}ab\\ cd\end{pmatrix}\in\Gamma_0(N)$, one has [see B. Schoeneberg, Math. Ann. **116** (1939), 511–523] $\vartheta(\tau',A_l)=\varepsilon(d)(c\tau+d)^k\vartheta(\tau,A_l)$, with $\varepsilon(d)=((-1)^kD/d)$ (Kronecker symbol), so that $\vartheta(\tau,A_l)$ is a modular form of Hecke type $(-k,N,\varepsilon)$. Finally, let $G(a,b;A)$ denote the Gaussian sums $\sum_{\xi\bmod b}e^{\pi i(a/b)A[\xi]}$, where ξ runs through all vectors in $\mathbf{Z}^{2k}$ (mod $b\mathbf{Z}^{2k}$). Theorem 1: For $(n,N)=1$ the following conditions are equivalent:

(A) $\qquad\vartheta(\tau,A)|T_n-(\sum_{t|n}\varepsilon(t)t^{k-1})\vartheta(\tau,A)$

is a cusp form; (B) either (i) $\sum_{t|n}\varepsilon(t)t^{k-1}=0$, or (ii) $\varepsilon(n)=1$ and, for $p_m|N$, one has $G(1,p^m;A)=G(n,p^m;A)$. (Observe that if $k\geqq 2$ then only (ii) is possible.) Corollary 1: If $N=p$, then (A) and (B) hold if and only if either $\sum_{t|n}\varepsilon(t)t^{k-1}=0$, or $\varepsilon(n)=1$; if N is squarefree and ε is trivial, or if n is a quadratic residue mod N, then (A) and (B) hold. Corollary 2: For $(n,N)=1$, $F(\tau,A)$ is an eigenfunction for T_n if and only if (B) holds; the corresponding eigenvalue is $\sum_{t|n}\varepsilon(t)t^{k-1}$. A consequence of Corollary 2 is that the Dirichlet series associated with $F(\tau,A)^{t|n}$ has an Euler product. Theorem 2: If $N=p$, $k\geqq 2$ and $D\neq p^k$, then the space spanned by $F(\tau,A)$ and $F(\tau,pA^{-1})$ is closed under the operations of all Hecke operators T_n of level p. If $k=2$ and $D=p^2$, or if $k=1$, then $F(\tau,A)$ is an eigenfunction for all T_n of level p. For $k\geqq 3$, C. L. Siegel [Ann. of Math. (2) **36** (1935), 527–606] proved that if A is an even $2k\times 2k$ matrix of level N and determinant D, then $F(\tau,A)$ is an Eisenstein series. The author extends this result to the cases $k=1,2$ and uses it in the proof of one of the nicest results of the present paper, namely Theorem 3: Let k be an imaginary quadratic field with the ring of integers I and, for $\alpha\in I$, let $N(\alpha)$ denote the norm; then there is a single class in each genus of k if and only if $\vartheta(\tau)=\sum_{\alpha\in I}e^{2\pi iN(\alpha)\tau}$ is an Eisenstein series. The proofs rest on the behaviour of modular forms at cusps, the periodicity of Gaussian sums and ideas of H. Maass [Abh. Math. Sem. Univ. Hamburg **12** (1938), 133–162], as well as a lemma of the author (too long to quote here) on the independence of certain ϑ-series. *E. Grosswald* (Philadelphia, Pa.)

F15-36 **(44# 1629)**

Raghavan, S.; Rangachari, S. S.

On ternary quadratic forms and modular forms.

J. Indian Math. Soc. (*N.S.*) **33** (1969), 187–205 (1970).

Nach einem klassischen Verfahren von Jacobi ist jeder m-reihigen positiv-definiten Matrix S mit ganzen rationalen Elementen eine Theta-Reihe $\sum_{n\geq 0}r(S,n)e^{2\pi inz}$ zugeordnet, wobei $r(S,n)$ die Lösungsanzahl der diophantischen Gleichung ${}^t\mathfrak{x}S\mathfrak{x}=n$ in ganzen Vektoren $\mathfrak{x}$ ist und z in der oberen Halbebene variiert. Dieser Ansatz wurde von E. Hecke [Math. Ann. **97** (1926), 210–242] und C. L. Siegel [ibid. **124** (1951), 17–54; MR **16**, 800] auf den indefiniten Fall ausgedehnt. Jeder ganzen Matrix S von der Signatur $(1, m-1)$ läßt sich nach einem ähnlichen Verfahren durch eine Mittelwertbildung eine holomorphe Modulform von der Dimension $m/2-2$ zuordnen. Hecke zeigte, daß diese Thetafunktion in einigen Fällen bei $m=2$ nicht identisch verschwindet; Siegel hat bewiesen, daß sie für den Fall $m\geqq 4$ stets verschwinden. Die Verfasser behandeln den übriggebliebenen Fall $m=3$ und zeigen, daß auch hier in einigen Fällen die zugeordneten Theta-Reihen nicht identisch verschwinden. *J. Spilker* (Freiburg)

Citations: MR 16, 800a = E12-49.

F15-37 **(44# 1741)**

Swan, Richard G.

Generators and relations for certain special linear groups.

Advances in Math. **6**, 1–77 (1971).

Soit $K=\mathbf{Q}(\sqrt{-m})$ un corps quadratique imaginaire, et soit $\mathcal{O}$ l'anneau des entiers de K. L'auteur se propose d'obtenir une présentation du groupe $SL(2,\mathcal{O})$; il part de l'ensemble P des formes hermitiennes positives non dégénérées à 2 variables complexes, et identifie l'ensemble H des classes de formes de P ne différant que par un facteur constant au demi-espace supérieur dans $\mathbf{C}\times\mathbf{R}$. Le groupe $GL(2,\mathbf{C})$ opère dans H comme groupe d'isométries pour la distance non-euclidienne usuelle (demi-espace de Poincaré); on considère l'action sur H du sous-groupe $SL(2,\mathcal{O})$ de $GL(2,\mathbf{C})$; Bianchi et Humbert ont décrit un domaine fondamental B pour l'action de ce sous-groupe, et l'auteur commence par exposer cette théorie en détail, en la complétant sur certains points, et en décrivant une méthode permettant d'obtenir la structure cellulaire de B. Un théorème de A. M. Macbeath sur la présentation d'un groupe d'homéomorphismes d'un espace simplement connexe [Ann. of Math. (2) **79** (1964), 473–488; MR **28** #4058], généralisé par l'auteur, lui permet alors d'obtenir la présentation cherchée. Dans la seconde partie du mémoire, l'auteur applique sa méthode générale à la détermination explicite de la présentation en question pour des valeurs données de m. Il obtient des résultats généraux pour m assez grand, et examine en détail les valeurs 1, 2, 3, 5, 6, 7, 11, 15 et 19 de m. *J. Dieudonné* (Nice)

F15-38 **(44# 2838)**

Rhie, Y. H.; Whaples, G.

Hecke operators in cohomology of groups.

J. Math. Soc. Japan **22** (1970), 431–442.

Let G be a group and Γ be a subgroup. The Hecke ring of the group pair (G,Γ) was defined by G. Shimura [same J. **11** (1959), 291–311; MR **22** #11126].

The authors define a natural action of the Hecke-ring $\mathscr{R}(G,\Gamma)$ on the cohomology group $H^k(\Gamma, A)$ of the group Γ, with a G-module A, and they prove that this action is well defined. They notice that this is a kind of generalization of transfer maps. Also they discuss an example where G is the finite group $SL(2, Z/pZ)$, and

$$\Gamma=\left\{\begin{pmatrix}1, n\\0, 1\end{pmatrix}; n=0,1,\cdots,p-1\right\}$$

and $A=(Z/pZ)^2$. *M. Kuga* (Stony Brook, N.Y.)

Citations: MR 22# 11126 = F15-15.

F15-39 **(44# 3957)**

Orihara, Akio

On the Eisenstein series for the principal congruence subgroups.

Nagoya Math. J. **34** (1969), 129–142.

Let Γ be a Fuchsian group (of finite type) acting on the upper half-plane. To each parabolic cusp κ_i $(i=1,2,\cdots,h)$ there corresponds an Eisenstein series

$$E_i(\tau,s)=\sum_{\Gamma_i\backslash\Gamma}y(\sigma_i^{-1}\sigma\tau)^s,$$

where Γ_i is the stabiliser subgroup of Γ with respect to κ_i and σ_i is an element of $SL(2,R)$, such that $\sigma_i\infty=\kappa_i$; here $y(\tau)$ is the imaginary part of τ. Further, let $E(\tau,s)$ be the $h\times 1$ column matrix with $E_i(\tau,s)$ in the ith row $(i=1,2,\cdots,h)$. It is stated that T. Kubota ["Elementary theory of Eisenstein series" (Japanese), mimeographed seminar notes, Dept. Math., Tokyo Univ., Tokyo, 1968] has proved that $E(\tau,s)$ satisfies the functional equation $E(\tau,s)=\Phi(s)E(\tau,1-s)$.

A direct proof of this is given, using Dirichlet characters and theta-series, for the particular case in which Γ is the principal congruence group of level N. The details are too complicated to be reproduced, but it turns out that $E(\tau,s)$ is meromorphic over the whole s-plane. The meromorphic function $\Phi(s)$ is a sum of matrices each of which can be expressed as a scalar factor (which is a quotient of gamma functions and Dirichlet L-series) times a matrix whose entries are rational functions of d^{-s} where d is a divisor of N. *R. A. Rankin* (Glasgow)

F15-40 **(44# 6605)**

Ihara, Yasutaka

An invariant multiple differential attached to the field of elliptic modular functions of characteristic p.

Amer. J. Math. **93** (1971), 139–147.

Denote by p a fixed prime number. Let F be the prime field of characteristic p, Ω a universal domain of characteristic p and k the algebraic closure of F. Denote by $J\in\Omega$ a transcendental element of Ω. Put $\omega=J^{-1}dJ$, $p=2,3$; $\omega=J^{-a}(J-12^3)^{-b}f(J)(dJ)^r$, $p\neq 2,3$, where $a=\frac{1}{3}(p\mp 1)$ for $p\equiv\pm 1(3)$, and $b=\frac{1}{4}(p\mp 1)$ for $p\equiv\pm 1(4)$. Let S be the set of all $j\in\Omega$ such that the corresponding elliptic curve has vanishing Hasse invariant.

The main result is that ω is invariant (up to sign) under all separable modular transformations.

The main tool in the proof is an infinite extension K_∞^* that is generated by a primitive nth transform of J for all n. *I. I. Pjateckiĭ-Šapiro* (Moscow)

F20 DEDEKIND SUMS AND GENERALIZATIONS

See also reviews B68-61, C20-18, E16-62, F05-17, F10-50, K45-25, P60-15, P72-32, R42-44.

F20-1 **(2, 249f)**

Rademacher, Hans and Whiteman, Albert. Theorems on Dedekind sums. Amer. J. Math. **63**, 377–407 (1941).

Let $((x))=x-[x]-\frac{1}{2}$ for x not an integer and $((x))=0$ for x an integer. Then, in the notation of this paper, the Dedekind sums are defined to be $s(h, k)=\sum_{\mu=1}^{k}((\mu/k))((h\mu/k))$. These sums were used by Dedekind in his "Erläuterungen zu den Riemannschen Fragmenten über die Grenzfälle der elliptischen Modulfunktionen." They are intimately connected with the transformation formula for $\log \eta(\tau)$, where $\eta(\tau)=e^{\pi i\tau/12}\prod_{m=1}^{\infty}(1-e^{2\pi im\tau})$ and where τ is subjected to a modular transformation. The formulas stated by Dedekind were either without proof or were proved by function-theoretic methods. The present paper supplies purely arithmetic proofs for Dedekind's formulas and it includes some new ones. A particularly simple proof of the reciprocity formula $12s(h, k)+12s(k, h)=-3+h/k+k/h+1/hk$, $h>0$, $k>0$, $(h, k)=1$, is given. One section is devoted to verifying that the transformation formulas given by Riemann are actually equivalent to those obtained by Dedekind. The final part of the paper considers congruences involving $s(h, k)$. The principal theorem has to do with three variables. If a, b, c are positive integers, relatively prime in pairs, and if $24|abc$ then

$$\{s(ab, c)-ab/12c\}+\{s(bc, a)-bc/12a\} - \{s(b, ac)-b/12ac\}\equiv 0 \pmod 2.$$

This theorem, together with two less general ones which take up cases where $24\nmid abc$, lead to formulas for the factorization of

$$A_k(n)=\sum_{\substack{h \bmod k\\(h,k)=1}} \exp(\pi is(h, k)-2\pi i(hn/k)),$$

which appear in the formula for the number $p(n)$ of unrestricted partitions of n. These factorization formulas are of the same type as the multiplication theorems of D. H. Lehmer [Trans. Amer. Math. Soc. **43**, 271–295 (1938)].

H. S. Zuckerman (Seattle, Wash.).

Referred to in F10-93, F20-3, F20-35, F20-36, P72-11, P72-32.

F20-2 **(11, 641f)**

Rédei, L. Elementarer Beweis und Verallgemeinerung einer Reziprozitätsformel von Dedekind. Acta Sci. Math. Szeged **12**, Leopoldo Fejér et Frederico Riesz LXX annos natis dedicatus, Pars B, 236–239 (1950).

If $F_m(x)=x^{m-1}+\cdots+x+1$ and if the positive integers m and n are relatively prime, there are uniquely determined polynomials $X_{mn}(x)$ and $X_{nm}(x)$ of degrees $n-1$ and $m-1$ respectively such that: (A) $F_m(x)X_{mn}(x)+F_n(x)X_{nm}(x)=1$. They are given by:

$$X_{mn}=\sum_{k=0}^{n-1}(-\{km'/n\}+\{(k-1)m'/n\} +\{-m'/n\}-\{-2m'/n\})x^k,$$

if the integers m' and n' are chosen such that $mm'+nn'=1$ and where $\{z\}=z-[z]-\frac{1}{2}$ ($[z]$ is the largest integer $\leqq z$). Now, taking $x=1+t$ in (A) and equating the coefficients of t^2, the reciprocity formula

$$S_{mn}+S_{nm}=(12mn)^{-1}(m^2-3mn+n^2+1)$$

can be obtained, where $S_{mn}=\sum_{k=1}^{n-1}\{k/n\}\{mk/n\}$.

H. D. Kloosterman (Leiden).

F20-3 **(11, 641g)**

Apostol, T. M. Generalized Dedekind sums and transformation formulae of certain Lambert series. Duke Math. J. **17**, 147–157 (1950).

In the theory of the transformation of Dedekind's modular function $\log \eta(\tau)$ there appears a certain arithmetic sum,

$$s(h, k)=\sum_{\mu=1}^{k-1}\frac{\mu}{k}\left(\frac{h\mu}{k}-\left[\frac{h\mu}{k}\right]-\frac{1}{2}\right),$$

where h, k with $(h, k)=1$ are coefficients of the modular substitution and $[x]$ is the largest integer not exceeding x. A reciprocity law $12s(h, k)+12s(k, h)=-3+h/k+k/h+1/hk$ was proved by Dedekind using function-theoretic methods. More recently these sums were treated arithmetically in a series of papers by Rademacher [cf. especially Rademacher and Whiteman, Amer. J. Math. **63**, 377–407 (1941); these Rev. **2**, 249]. The author generalizes these sums to $s_p(h, k)=\sum_{\mu=1}^{k-1}\mu k^{-1}\overline{B}_p(h\mu/k)$, $p=$integer $\geqq 1$, where $\overline{B}_p$ is the Bernoulli polynomial $\overline{B}_p(x)=\sum_{s=0}^{p}B_s(p_s)(x-[x])^{p-s}$, B_s being the Bernoulli numbers defined recursively by $B_0=1$, $\sum_{\mu=0}^{s}\binom{s}{\mu}B_\mu=B_s$. (Note that $\overline{B}_1(x)=x-[x]-\frac{1}{2}$.) A generalized reciprocity law is proved:

$$(p+1)\{hk^ps_p(h, k)+kh^ps_p(k, h)\} =pB_{p+1}+\sum_{s=0}^{p+1}\binom{p+1}{s}(-1)^sB_sh^sB_{p+1-s}k^{p+1-s},$$

p odd. Just as $s(h, k)$ appears in the transformation of

$$\log \eta(\tau)=\frac{\pi i\tau}{12}-\sum_{m=1}^{\infty}\sum_{n=1}^{\infty}n^{-1}x^{mn}=\frac{\pi i\tau}{12}-G_1(x),$$

$x=e^{2\pi i\tau}$, so $s_p(h, k)$ is connected with the functions $G_p(x)$ for which the author develops a transformation formula using Rademacher's method [J. Reine Angew. Math. **167**, 312–336 (1932)]. Furthermore, he expresses $s_p(h, k)$ as a sort of Lambert series, generalizing a result of Dedekind for $p=1$, and thus arrives at a closed expression for $s_p(h, k)=\frac{1}{2}(k-k^p)k^{-p}B_p$ when p is an even integer.

J. Lehner (Philadelphia, Pa.).

Citations: MR 2, 249f = F20-1.

Referred to in F10-50, F20-7, F20-8, F20-9, F20-18, F20-26, F20-30, P80-16.

F20-4 **(11, 642a)**

Rademacher, H. Die Reziprozitätsformel für Dedekindsche Summen. Acta Sci. Math. Szeged **12**, Leopoldo Fejér et Frederico Riesz LXX annos natis dedicatus, Pars B, 57–60 (1950).

Calculating the Stieltjes integral $\int_{\epsilon}^{1-\epsilon}((x))d((hx))((kx))$, $\epsilon>0$, in two different ways, the author obtains a simple proof for the reciprocity formula

$$s(h, k)+s(k, h)=(12hk)^{-1}(h^2-3hk+k^2+1)$$

for the Dedekind sums $s(h, k)=\sum_{\mu=1}^{k-1}((\mu/k))((h\mu/k))$, where $((x))=x-[x]-\frac{1}{2}$ or 0 according as x is not or is an integer.

H. D. Kloosterman (Leiden).

F20-5 **(13, 113h)**

Mordell, L. J. The reciprocity formula for Dedekind sums. Amer. J. Math. **73**, 593–598 (1951).

Let p and q be positive integers without a common divisor, and f an arbitrary polynomial. Methods are developed for evaluating $T=\sum f(qx+py)$, where the summation is extended over the lattice points (x, y) lying in the region K defined by $0<x<p$, $0<y<q$, $qx+py<pq$. A detailed discussion is given of the special cases $f(\xi)=\xi$ and $f(\xi)=\xi^2$. This leads to a new proof of Dedekind's result:

$$q\sum_{x=1}^{p-1}x[qx/p]+p\sum_{y=1}^{q-1}y[py/q]=\tfrac{1}{12}(p-1)(q-1)(8pq-p-q-1).$$

W. H. Mills (New Haven, Conn.).

Referred to in F20-6, F20-33.

F20-6 (13, 322b)

Mordell, L. J. Lattice points in a tetrahedron and generalized Dedekind sums. J. Indian Math. Soc. (N.S.) **15**, 41–46 (1951).

Let p, q be two positive integers prime to each other. One form of the reciprocity law for Dedekind sums is given by the formula $s(p, q)+s(q, p)=(pq^{-1}+qp^{-1}+p^{-1}q^{-1}-3)/12$, where $s(p, q)=\sum_{x=1}^{q}x((px/q))/q$ and where $((X))=X-[X]-\frac{1}{2}$ or 0 according as X is not or is an integer. The author's proof of this theorem [Amer. J. Math. **73**, 593–598 (1951); these Rev. **13**, 113] suggests its extension to a set of n positive integers $p, q, r, s, \cdots$ no two of which have common factor. Put $s(p, q, r)=\sum_{x=1}^{r-1}x((pqx/r))/r$ and

$$S_3(p, q, r)=s(p, q, r)+s(q, r, p)+s(r, p, q).$$

Denote by $N_3(p, q, r)$ the number of lattice points in the tetrahedron

$$0\leqq x<p,\ 0\leqq y<q,\ 0\leqq z<r,\ 0<xp^{-1}+yq^{-1}+zr^{-1}<1.$$

Calculating the value of N_3 in two different ways, the author first derives the formula

$$S_3+N_3=\tfrac{1}{6}pqr+\tfrac{1}{4}\sum qr+\tfrac{1}{4}\sum p+\tfrac{1}{12}\sum\frac{qr}{p}+\frac{1}{12pqr}-2,$$

the summations referring to p, q, r. An analogous formula is then obtained for $n=4$. The method of proof shows that for $n>4$, the formula for S_n will depend upon the number of lattice points in sections of an n-dimensional tetrahedron defined by $\lambda<\sum x/p<\lambda+1$ for a number of values of $\lambda\leqq n-1$. *A. L. Whiteman* (Los Angeles, Calif.).

Citations: MR 13, 113h = F20-5.

Referred to in F20-14.

F20-7 (13, 725c)

Apostol, T. M. Theorems on generalized Dedekind sums. Pacific J. Math. **2**, 1–9 (1952).

The author gives a second proof for his reciprocity law for generalized Dedekind sums of the form

$$s_p(h, k)=\sum_{\mu=1}^{k-1}\mu k^{-1}B_p(\{h\mu/k\}),$$

where $(h, k)=1$; B_p denotes the pth Bernoulli polynomial, and $\{x\}=x-[x]$. [See Apostol, Duke Math. J. **17**, 147–157 (1950); these Rev. **11**, 641.] He expresses $s_p(h, k)$ in terms of the Hurwitz zeta function $\zeta(s, a)=\sum_0^\infty(n+a)^{-s}$ by

$$s_p(h, k)=ip!(2\pi ik)^{-p}\sum_{\mu=1}^{k-1}\cot(\pi h\mu/k)\zeta(p, \mu/k)$$

(p odd, $p>1$). Application of the theory of residues to the function $f(z)=\cot(\pi z)\cot(\pi hz/k)\zeta(p, z/k)$ finishes the proof. *N. G. de Bruijn* (Delft).

Citations: MR 11, 641g = F20-3.

F20-8 (14, 847d)

Carlitz, L. Some sums analogous to Dedekind sums. Duke Math. J. **20**, 161–171 (1953).

Working in the field of rational functions $GF(q, x)$, the author constructs analogues of the Dedekind sum $s(h, k)$ suggested by the representation

$$s(h, k)=1/(4k)+(1/k)\sum_{\zeta}(\zeta^{-1}-1)^{-1}(\zeta^h-1)^{-1},$$

where $\zeta\neq 1$ runs through the kth roots of unity. With $\omega_H(u)$ and $\psi(u)$ denoting functions discussed in earlier papers [same J. **1**, 137–168 (1935); **15**, 1001–1012 (1948); Trans. Amer. Math. Soc. **43**, 167–182 (1938); these Rev. **10**, 283], the function $Q_s(v)$ is defined by means of $(\psi(t)-v)^{-1}=\sum_{r=0}^\infty Q_r(v)t^r$, $v\neq 0$, and the sum

$$\sigma_r(H, K)=\sum_{\beta\neq 0}\frac{Q_r(\beta)}{\omega_H(\beta)},$$

where β runs through the roots of $\omega_K(u)=0$, becomes the analogue of the Dedekind sum and of the reviewer's generalization [same J. **17**, 147–157 (1950); these Rev. **11**, 641]. Several properties of the $\sigma_r(H, K)$ are derived, including the following reciprocity law: If $(H, K)=1$ and $q-1\mid r+2$, $r\geqq 0$, then we have

$$H\sigma_r(H, K)+K\sigma_r(K, H)=\sum_{i+j=r+2}b_ib_jH^iK^j-HK\sum_{i+j=r+2}b_ib_j.$$

The b_i are defined by $u/\psi(u)=\sum_{r=0}^\infty b_ru_r$ and can be thought of as analogues of the Bernoulli numbers.

T. M. Apostol (Pasadena, Calif.).

Citations: MR 10, 283h = T55-11; MR 11, 641g = F20-3.

F20-9 (15, 12b)

Carlitz, L. Some theorems on generalized Dedekind sums. Pacific J. Math. **3**, 513–522 (1953).

For a fixed odd integer $p>1$, define

$$G_p(x)=\sum_{m,\,n=1}^{\infty}n^{-p}x^{mn}=\sum_{n=1}^{\infty}n^{-p}\frac{x^n}{1-x^n}\quad(|x|<1),$$

and let $\tau'=(h'\tau+k')/(k\tau-h)$, $hh'+kk'+1=0$, be a unimodular substitution. Then G_p satisfies the transformation formula [see Apostol, Duke Math. J. **17**, 147–157 (1950); these Rev. **11**, 641]

$$G_p(e^{2\pi i\tau})=(k\tau-h)^{p-1}G_p(e^{2\pi i\tau'})+\frac{(2\pi i)^p}{2(p+1)!}f(h, k; \tau).$$

The function $f(h, k; \tau)$ is a polynomial in τ given by

$$f(h, k; \tau)=\sum_{r=0}^{p+1}\binom{p+1}{r}(k\tau-h)^{p-r}c_r(h, k),$$

the coefficients $c_r(h, k)$ being expressible in the form

$$c_r(h, k)=\sum_{\mu=1}^{k}P_{p+1-r}(\mu/k)P_r(h\mu/k),$$

where $P_r(x)=B_r(x-[x])$ is the rth Bernoulli function. Using this transformation formula, the author derives a reciprocity law for the sums $c_r(h, k)$ which can be expressed symbolically as follows:

$$\binom{p+1}{r}k^r(c(h, k)-h)^{p+1-r}$$

$$=\binom{p+1}{r+1}h^{p-r}(c(k, h)-k)^{r+1}+kB_{p+1-r}B_r-hB_{p-r}B_{r+1},$$

where $c^n(h, k)$ must be replaced by $c_n(h, k)$ after expanding, and the B's are Bernoulli numbers. When $r=p$ the sums $c_r(h, k)$ reduce to the generalized Dedekind sums $s_p(h, k)$ considered previously by the reviewer, the case $p=1$ being due to Dedekind.

Further properties of the sums $c_r(h, k)$ are derived, of which we mention the following formula which gives a representation of these sums in terms of the Eulerian numbers:

$$(1)\quad c_r(h, k)=\frac{B_{p+1-r}B_r}{k^p}+\frac{r(p+1-r)}{k^p}\sum_{t=1}^{k-1}\frac{H_{p-r}(\zeta^{ht})H_{r-1}(\zeta^{-t})}{(\zeta^{-ht}-1)(\zeta^t-1)},$$

where $\zeta=e^{2\pi i/k}$ and $H_m(\rho)$ is defined for $\rho^k=1$, $\rho\neq 1$, by $(1-\rho)/(e^t-\rho)=\sum_{m=0}^\infty H_m(\rho)t^m/m!$. *T. M. Apostol.*

Citations: MR 11, 641g = F20-3.

Referred to in F20-11, F20-18.

F20-10 **(15, 12c)**

Carlitz, L. The reciprocity theorem for Dedekind sums. Pacific J. Math. **3**, 523–527 (1953).

Using the Lagrange interpolation formula, the author obtains the identity

$$(1)\quad \frac{1}{k}\sum_{\zeta\neq 1}\frac{\zeta}{x-\zeta}\frac{\zeta-1}{\zeta^h-1}+\frac{1}{h}\sum_{\eta\neq 1}\frac{\eta}{x-\eta}\frac{\eta-1}{\eta^k-1} = \frac{x-1}{(x^k-1)(x^h-1)}-\frac{1}{hk(x-1)},$$

where ζ and η run through the kth roots of unity distinct from 1. This identity is used to obtain a simple proof of the reciprocity law for the Dedekind sums

$$\bar{s}(h,k)=\sum_{r \bmod k}((r/k))((hr/k)),\quad ((x))=x-[x]-\tfrac{1}{2}.$$

By expanding $((hr/k))$ into what amounts to a finite Fourier series the sums $\bar{s}(h,k)$ are expressed as follows:

$$(2)\qquad \bar{s}(h,k)=\frac{1}{4k}+\frac{1}{k}\sum_{\zeta\neq 1}\frac{\zeta}{\zeta-1}\frac{1}{\zeta^h-1}.$$

Putting $x=1+t$ in (1), expanding both members in powers of t and comparing coefficients leads at once to the reciprocity law in question:

$$12hk\{\bar{s}(h,k)+\bar{s}(k,h)\}=h^2+3hk+k^2+1.$$

By a more recondite application of (1), the author also obtains the reciprocity law for the generalized Dedekind sums $s_p(h,k)$ mentioned in the previous review, using formula (1) of that review in place of (2).

T. M. Apostol (Pasadena, Calif.).

F20-11 **(16, 14d)**

Carlitz, L. Dedekind sums and Lambert series. Proc. Amer. Math. Soc. **5**, 580–584 (1954).

In a previous paper [Pacific J. Math. **3**, 513–522 (1953); these Rev. **15**, 12] the author used the transformation formula for the Lambert series $G_p(x)=\sum_{n=1}^{\infty}n^{-p}x^n/(1-x^n)$, $x=e^{2\pi i\tau}$, p odd, to derive the functional equation

$$(1)\quad f(h,k;\tau)=\tau^{p-1}f\left(-k,h;-\frac{1}{\tau}\right)+\frac{1}{\tau}(B+\tau B)^{p+1},$$

where f is a function which appears in the transformation formula for $G_p(x)$. [See these Rev. **15**, 12, for definition of f.] In this paper an elementary proof of (1) is given, based on a representation of f in terms of Eulerian numbers which was obtained in the earlier paper. *T. M. Apostol.*

Citations: MR 15, 12b = F20-9.

Referred to in F20-15.

F20-12 **(16, 14e)**

Rademacher, Hans. Generalization of the reciprocity formula for Dedekind sums. Duke Math. J. **21**, 391–397 (1954).

Let a, b, c be positive integers, pairwise without common divisor and let $aa'\equiv 1 \pmod{bc}$, $bb'\equiv 1 \pmod{ca}$, $cc'\equiv 1 \pmod{ab}$. The author proves that

$$s(bc',a)+s(ca',b)+s(ab',c)=-\frac{1}{4}+\frac{1}{12}\left(\frac{a}{bc}+\frac{b}{ca}+\frac{c}{ab}\right),$$

where $s(a,b)$ is the Dedekind sum

$$\sum_{\mu=1}^{a-1}\left(\frac{\mu}{a}-\left[\frac{\mu}{a}\right]-\frac{1}{2}\right)\left(\frac{b\mu}{a}-\left[\frac{b\mu}{a}\right]-\frac{1}{2}\right).$$

The special case $c=c'=1$ is the reciprocity formula for Dedekind sums. *H. D. Kloosterman* (Leiden).

Referred to in F20-15, F20-17, F20-18, F20-31.

F20-13 **(16, 14f)**

Carlitz, L. A note on generalized Dedekind sums. Duke Math. J. **21**, 399–403 (1954).

The author generalizes a result of Rademacher [see the preceding review]. Writing

$$f\left(\frac{r}{k}\right)=\frac{r}{k}-\left[\frac{r}{k}\right]-\frac{1}{2}+\frac{1}{2k}$$

and

$$s_n(h_1,\cdots,h_n;k) = \sum_{r_r \bmod k} f\left(\frac{r_1}{k}\right)\cdots f\left(\frac{r_n}{k}\right)f\left(\frac{r_1h_1+\cdots+r_nh_n}{k}\right)$$

(the h_i, k and n are integers; $n\geqq 1$), he proves that

$$\sum k_n^{n-2}s_{n-1}(k_1,\cdots,k_{n-1};k_n)=Z_n^{(n)}/n!\quad (n\geqq 2)$$

and

$$\sum k_n^{n-3}s_{n-2}(k_1k'_{n-1},\cdots,k_{n-2}k'_{n-1};k_n) =\sum_{r=1}^{n-1}(-1)^{n-r-1}Z_r^{(n)}/r!+(-1)^{n-1}\left(-1+\frac{1}{k_1\cdots k_n}\right),$$

where $k_1,\cdots,k_n$ are positive integers that are relatively prime in pairs, $k_ik_i'\equiv -1 \pmod{k_1\cdots k_{i-1}k_{i+1}\cdots k_n}$ and the summations on the left hand sides are extended over the cyclic permutations of $k_1,\cdots,k_n$. The $Z_r^{(n)}$ are certain numbers that are related to generalized Bernoulli numbers. The second formula reduces to Rademacher's result if $n=3$.

H. D. Kloosterman (Leiden).

F20-14 **(16, 341b)**

Rademacher, Hans. On Dedekind sums and lattice points in a tetrahedron. Studies in mathematics and mechanics presented to Richard von Mises, pp. 49–53. Academic Press Inc., New York, 1954. \$9.00.

It is proved that if a, b, c are positive integers that are relatively prime in pairs and $s(h,k)$ is the Dedekind sum, then

$$\left(s(bc,a)-\frac{bc}{12a}\right)+\left(s(ca,b)-\frac{ca}{12b}\right)+\left(s(ab,c)-\frac{ab}{12c}\right) \equiv -\frac{1}{4}-\frac{1}{12}abc+\frac{1}{12abc}\pmod 2.$$

By a formula of Mordell [J. Indian Math. Soc. (N.S.) **15**, 41–46 (1951); these Rev. **13**, 322] this is equivalent to

$$N_3(a,b,c)\equiv\tfrac{1}{4}(a+1)(b+1)(c+1)\pmod 2,$$

where $N_3(a,b,c)$ denotes the number of lattice points in the tetrahedron

$$0\leqq x<a,\quad 0\leqq y<b,\quad 0\leqq z<c,\quad 0<\frac{x}{a}+\frac{y}{b}+\frac{z}{c}<1.$$

L. Carlitz (Durham, N. C.).

Citations: MR 13, 322b = F20-6.

Referred to in F20-24.

F20-15 **(17, 946f)**

Carlitz, L. A further note on Dedekind sums. Duke Math. J. **23** (1956), 219–223.

The functional equation

$$f_m(h,k;\tau)=(-1)^m\tau^{m-2}f_m(-k,h;-\tau^{-1})+\tau^{-1}(B+\tau B)^m,$$

derived in an earlier paper [Proc. Amer. Math. Soc. **5** (1954), 580–584; MR **16**, 14] is generalized to the form

$$f_m(h,K;\tau)=(-1)^m(k\tau-h)^{m-2}f_m(h_1,k_1;\tau_1)+f_m(h,k;\tau),$$

where the integers h, k, h_1, k_1, K and the complex numbers τ and τ_1 are related as follows: $(h,k)=1$, $hh'+kk'+1=0$, $\tau_1=(h'\tau+k')/(k\tau-h)$, $(h_1,k_1)=1$, $K=h'k_1-h_1k$. Specialization leads to the three-term relation for Dedekind sums recently discovered by Rademacher [Duke Math. J. **21** (1954), 391–397; MR **16**, 14]. *T. M. Apostol.*

Citations: MR 16, 14d = F20-11; MR 16, 14e = F20-12.

F20-16 **(18, 114d)**

Rademacher, Hans. Zur Theorie der Dedekindschen Summen. Math. Z. **63** (1956), 445–463.

The author proves various results about the values of Dedekind sums

$$s(h,k)=\sum_{\mu \bmod k}\left(\left(\frac{\mu}{k}\right)\right)\left(\left(\frac{h\mu}{k}\right)\right),\quad (h,k)=1,\ k>0,$$

where $((x))=0$ for integers x, $=x-[x]-\frac{1}{2}$ otherwise. The following of his results should be mentioned here: (1) $s(h,k)<s(1,k)$ for $1<h<k$; (2) $s(h,k)>0$ for $0<h<\sqrt{(k-1)}$; (3) let Γ be the group of all modular matrices

$$M=\begin{pmatrix} a & b\\ c & d\end{pmatrix},\quad ad-bc=1.$$

Then the function

$$\Psi(M)=b/d \text{ if } c=0,$$
$$=(a+d)/c-12\operatorname{sgn} c\cdot s(a,|c|)-3\operatorname{sgn}(c(a+d)) \quad \text{if } c\neq 0,$$

depends only on the class of conjugates of M. Further the values of Ψ are integers and

$$\Psi(M)=\Psi(-M),\quad \Psi(M^{-1})=-\Psi(M).$$

Since two modular matrices are conjugate if the corresponding quadratic forms $cx^2+(d-a)xy-by^2$ are equivalent, it is possible to evaluate $s(a,c)$ if the class number h of quadratic forms of discriminant $\Delta=(a+d)^2-4$ is 1. In this way the author proves the interesting result: (4) If $c>0$ and $a(m-a)\equiv 1 \pmod{c}$, then

$$s(a,c)=\frac{(1-c)m}{12c}$$

for $m=0, \pm 1, \pm 3$. He remarks that similar results can be obtained for other small values of h and gives an example for $h=2$. *H. D. Kloosterman* (Leiden).

Referred to in E16-62, F20-17, F20-21.

F20-17 **(19, 395h)**

Dieter, Ulrich. Beziehungen zwischen Dedekindschen Summen. Abh. Math. Sem. Univ. Hamburg **21** (1957), 109–125.

The Dedekind sums $s(d,c)$ investigated in this paper are defined by

$$s(d,c)=\sum_{k \bmod c}\left(\left(\frac{k}{c}\right)\right)\left(\left(\frac{kd}{c}\right)\right),\quad c>0,$$

where $((x))=0$ or $x-[x]-\frac{1}{2}$ according as x is or is not an integer. The major theorem is as follows. Let

$$\tau_1=-\frac{a_3\tau_3+b_3}{c_3\tau_3+d_3},\quad \tau_3=\frac{a_2\tau_2+b_2}{c_2\tau_2+d_2},\quad \tau_2=\frac{a_1\tau_1+b_1}{c_1\tau_1+d_1},$$

be three modular transformations with coefficients c_1, c_2, $c_3>0$ satisfying the relation

$$\varepsilon\begin{pmatrix}1&0\\0&1\end{pmatrix}=\begin{pmatrix}a_3&b_3\\c_3&d_3\end{pmatrix}\begin{pmatrix}a_2&b_2\\c_2&d_2\end{pmatrix}\begin{pmatrix}a_1&b_1\\c_1&d_1\end{pmatrix}\quad (\varepsilon=\pm 1).$$

Then

$$s(d_1,c_1)+s(d_2,c_2)+s(d_3,c_3)=\frac{\varepsilon}{4}-\frac{\varepsilon}{12}\left(\frac{c_1}{c_2c_3}+\frac{c_2}{c_3c_1}+\frac{c_3}{c_1c_2}\right).$$

Two important and interesting consequences may be cited here. The first is Rademacher's extension [Duke Math. J. **21** (1954), 391–397; MR **16**, 14] of the Dedekind reciprocity formula for $s(h,k)$. The second is the following theorem. Let p, d, t be integers such that $(d,t)=1$ if $p\equiv 0 \pmod{t}$ and $d^2\mp pd\equiv 1 \pmod{t}$ if $p\not\equiv 0 \pmod{t}$. Then

$$s(pd\pm 1, pt)=\pm\frac{p^2+2-3pt}{12pt}.$$

The last formula implies a number of similar relations due to Rademacher [Math. Z. **63** (1956), 445–463; MR **18**, 114]. The author's techniques are mostly analytical in character, but in some instances alternative arithmetical proofs are given. *A. L. Whiteman.*

Citations: MR 16, 14e = F20-12; MR 18, 114d = F20-16.

Referred to in F20-21.

F20-18 **(19, 943c)**

Mikolás, M. On certain sums generating the Dedekind sums and their reciprocity laws. Pacific J. Math. **7** (1957), 1167–1178.

Put

$$s_{m,n}\begin{pmatrix}a\ b\\ c\end{pmatrix}=\sum_{\lambda=0}^{c-1}P_m\left(\frac{\lambda a}{c}\right)P_n\left(\frac{\lambda b}{c}\right),$$

where $(a,c)=(b,c)=1$, $c>0$, and $P_m(x)$ is the Bernoulli function (that is, $P_m(x)=B_m(x)$ for $0\leq x<1$, $P_m(x+1)=P_m(x)$). Thus $s_{m,n}$ is essentially the generalized Dedekind sum defined by the reviewer [same J. **3** (1953), 513–522; MR **15**, 12] and in the case $m=1$ by Apostol [Duke Math. J. **17** (1950), 147–157; MR **11**, 641]. Also put

$$\mathfrak{S}_c^{a,b}(x,y)=(e^{2\pi ix}-1)^{-1}(e^{2\pi iy}-1)^{-1}\sum_{\lambda \pmod c} e^{2\pi i\lambda(ax+by)/c},$$

$$\mathfrak{D}_c^{a,b}(w,z)=\sum_{\lambda=1}^{c-1}\zeta(w,\{\lambda a/c\})\zeta(z,\{\lambda b/c\}),$$

where $\{x\}$ denotes the fractional part of x and $\zeta(z,u)=\sum_{n=0}^{\infty}(u+n)^{-z}$.

The principal results of the paper are the following. I. If a, b, c are positive and mutually co-prime, $0\leq R(x)<1$, $-1<R(y)\leq 0$, then

$$\mathfrak{S}_b^{c,a}(ax+by,\ -cx)+\mathfrak{S}_c^{a,b}(cx,\ cy)+\mathfrak{S}_a^{b,c}(-cy,\ ax+by)=(1-e^{2\pi i(ax+by)})^{-1},$$

provided that $ax+by$, cx and cy are not integers. II. If $(a,c)=(b,c)=1$; $c>2$; w, z distinct from 0 and 1; then

$$\mathfrak{D}_c^{a,b}(w,\ z)=(c^{w+z}-1)\zeta(w)\zeta(z)+$$
$$\pi^{-1}(2c\pi)^{w+z-1}\Gamma(1-w)\Gamma(1-z)\{\cos\tfrac{1}{2}\pi(w-z)\mathfrak{D}_c^{b,a}(1-w,1-z)-\cos\tfrac{1}{2}\pi(w+z)\mathfrak{D}_c^{b,-a}(1-w,\ 1-z)\}.$$

Theorem I is proved by contour integration. The result contains, in particular, the three-term relation for Dedekind sum proved by Rademacher [ibid. **21** (1954), 391–397; MR **16**, 14]. *L. Carlitz* (Durham, N.C.).

Citations: MR 11, 641g = F20-3; MR 15, 12b = F20-9; MR 16, 14e = F20-12.

F20-19 **(21# 3396)**

Meyer, C. Über einige Anwendungen Dedekindscher Summen. J. Reine Angew. Math. **198** (1957), 143–203.

The applications of Dedekind sums referred to in the title of this paper concern the problem of the determination of the class number of algebraic number fields K such that the least normal closure of K is an abelian extension of some quadratic field Ω. This problem was completely solved by the author [*Die Berechnung der Klassenzahl Abelscher Körper über quadratischen Zahlkörpern*, Akademie-Verlag, Berlin, 1957; MR **19**, 531; cf. also Hasse, Univ. Roma. Ist. Naz. Alta Mat. Rend. Mat. e Appl. (5) **10** (1951), 84–95; MR **14**, 140]. The solution requires the evaluation of certain L-series $L(s,\mathfrak{k})$ for $s=1$, belonging either to ring classes $\mathfrak{k}$ modulo fp_∞ or ray classes $\mathfrak{k}$ modulo $\mathfrak{f}p_\infty$ in a real quadratic number field Ω with discriminant $d>0$, where f is a rational integer, $\mathfrak{f}$ an integral divisor of

Ω and p_∞ is the infinite rational prime. In the case of ring classes the result is

$$\text{(A)}\quad L(1,\kappa) = \frac{2\pi}{f\sqrt{d}}\,\Im\left(\log\frac{\sqrt[24]{\Delta(a\omega_1+b\omega_2,\ c\omega_1+d\omega_2)}}{\sqrt[24]{\Delta(\omega_1,\omega_2)}}\right),$$

where

$$\sqrt[24]{\Delta(\omega_1,\omega_2)} = \left(\frac{2\pi}{\omega_2}\right)^{1/2}\eta(\tau)$$

is the discriminant in the theory of elliptic functions and

$$\eta(\tau) = q^{1/24}\prod_{m=1}^{\infty}(1-q^m) \quad\text{with}\quad \tau = \frac{\omega_1}{\omega_2},\ \Im(\tau) > 0,$$

is Dedekind's function. The rational integers a, b, c, d with $ad-bc=1$, $c\neq 0$, depend on the choice of a divisor $\mathfrak{c}$ in $\mathfrak{f}$ and on the choice of a basis of the ideal $(\mathfrak{c})_f$ consisting of all multiples of this divisor in the ring of the numbers of Ω whose denominators are prime to f. The value of $L(1,\mathfrak{f})$ must be independent of these choices. The author poses the problem of finding direct elementary proofs for these (and some other) invariance properties [this problem was already mentioned by Hecke in the case of a totally imaginary biquadratic number field in his paper in the Göttinger Nachr. **1921**, 1–23; *Mathematische Werke*, Vandenhoeck and Ruprecht, Göttingen, 1959; MR **21** #3303; pp. 290–312, particularly p. 311]. Since (A) can also be written as

$$L(1,\mathfrak{f}) = -\frac{2\pi^2}{f\sqrt{d}}\operatorname{sgn}\delta(\mathfrak{c})\left(-\frac{a+d}{12c}+\frac{1}{4}\operatorname{sgn}c+\operatorname{sgn}c\cdot s(a,c)\right),$$

where $\delta(\mathfrak{c})$ is the discriminant of a basis for the ideal $(\mathfrak{c})_f$ and $s(a,c)$ is a Dedekind sum, the problem is essentially one about Dedekind sums. In fact its solution follows from the reciprocity formula for these sums. In the first part of his paper the author gives a systematic theory of Dedekind sums. Most of this account is, however, well known from the work of Rademacher and others.—In the case of ray classes considered in the second part of the paper the analogous problem is more complicated. Klein's functions $\sigma_{gh}(\omega_1,\omega_2)$ (essentially "Teilwerte" of Weierstrass's σ-function) must now be considered instead of $\eta(\tau)$. Especially it is necessary to study the behavior of $\log\sigma_{gh}$ under modular substitutions belonging to the principal congruence subgroup $\Gamma(f)$ of the modular group. This led the author already in his book cited above to the introduction of generalized Dedekind sums defined by

$$S_{gh}(a,c) = \sum_{\mu \bmod c} P_1\left(\frac{a\mu}{c}+\frac{ag+ch}{fc}\right)P_1\left(\frac{\mu}{c}+\frac{g}{fc}\right),$$

where μ runs through a complete set of residues modulo c, and $P_1(x)=x-[x]-\frac{1}{2}$. In the second part of the paper the author gives an account of the theory of these sums. They can be reduced to ordinary Dedekind sums and some other sums introduced by Eisenstein and Stern.

H. D. Kloosterman (Leiden)

Citations: MR 14, 140d = R14-18; MR 19, 531f = R02-21; MR 21# 3303 = Z25-14.

F20-20 (21# 3397)

Dieter, Ulrich. Das Verhalten der Kleinschen Funktionen $\log\sigma_{g,h}(\omega_1,\omega_2)$ gegenüber Modultransformationen und verallgemeinerte Dedekindsche Summen. J. Reine Angew. Math. **201** (1959), 37–70.

The behavior of the logarithm of F. Klein's function $\sigma_{gh}(\omega_1,\omega_2)$ (which is essentially $\sigma\left(\frac{g\omega_1+h\omega_2}{f},\ \omega_1,\omega_2\right)$, where $\sigma(u,\omega_1,\omega_2)$ is Weierstrass's σ-function; g, h, f integers) under modular substitutions in ω_1, ω_2, belonging to the principal congruence subgroup $\Gamma(f)$ of level ("Stufe") f has been studied by C. Meyer [see review above]. The author now studies the behavior of the functions σ_{gh} under arbitrary modular substitutions. The method used is that of Rademacher in the case of Dedekind's function $\eta(\tau)$ [same J. **167** (1931), 312–336].

H. D. Kloosterman (Leiden)

Referred to in F20-23.

F20-21 (21# 5601)

Salié, Hans. Zum Wertevorrat der Dedekindschen Summen. Math. Z. **72** (1959/60), 61–75.

For real x let $((x))=0$ if x is an integer and $x-[x]-\frac{1}{2}$ otherwise. Let

$$s(m,n) = \sum_{v \bmod n}\left(\left(\frac{v}{n}\right)\right)\left(\left(\frac{mv}{n}\right)\right),\quad (m,n)=1,\quad n>0,$$

denote the Dedekind sum and put $D(m,n)=12ns(m,n)$. The author introduces the function $T(m,n)$ uniquely defined for all natural integers m, n by means of

$$T(m,n)+T(n,m) = [m/n]+[n/m]-2,\quad m>0,\quad n>0,$$
$$T(m',n) = T(m,n),\quad m'\equiv m \pmod n,$$

and first proves with the aid of the Euclidean algorithm that

$$D(m,n) = m+\bar{m}-n+nT(m,n),\quad m\geqq 1,\quad n>1,$$

where $\bar{m}$ is the smallest positive solution of the congruence $m\bar{m}\equiv 1 \pmod n$, $(m,n)=1$. He then systematically develops a body of arithmetical theorems concerning the values assumed by $T(m,n)$. A typical theorem of this sort states that if $x\geqq 1$, then $T(amx\pm 1,\ m^2x)$ equals $\pm((a,m)^2x-3)$ or $\pm(x-2+[1/x])$ according as $m\geqq 2$ or $m=1$ respectively. Corresponding results for $D(m,n)$ are also derived. Particularly noteworthy is the transformation formula: if $(m,n)=1$, then for every integer $x\geqq 0$

$$D(nx+m,\ ((nx+m)^2-D(m,n)(nx+m)+1)/n) = D(m,n).$$

One application of these results is that the values of $D(m,n)$ are restricted to the five residue classes 0, ± 2, $\pm 6 \pmod{18}$. In each of these classes there are infinitely many values of $D(m,n)$.

The present paper is closely related to two earlier papers by Rademacher [Math. Z. **63** (1956), 445–463; MR **18**, 114] and Dieter [Abh. Math. Sem. Univ. Hamburg **21** (1957), 109–125; MR **19**, 395]. *A. L. Whiteman* (Princeton, N.J.)

Citations: MR 18, 114d = F20-16; MR 19, 395h = F20-17.

F20-22 (22# 10974)

Rieger, G. J. Dedekindsche Summen in algebraischen Zahlkörpern. Math. Ann. **141** (1960), 377–383.

Let $B(x)$ be the Bernoulli function defined as 0 if x is an integer and $x-[x]-\frac{1}{2}$ if x is not an integer. For a rational number $x=u/v$ Eisenstein's well-known formula for $B(x)$ may be written in the form

$$\text{(1)}\qquad B(x) = \frac{i}{2v}\sum_{h=1}^{v-1}e^{2\pi ixh}\cot\frac{\pi h}{v}.$$

Also if $(u,v)=1$ the Dedekind sum $D(x)$ may be expressed in terms of $B(x)$ by means of

$$\text{(2)}\qquad D(x) = \sum_{h=1}^{v}B\left(\frac{h}{v}\right)B(xh).$$

In this paper the author develops direct generalizations of (1) and (2) defined over arbitrary algebraic number fields. Moreover he derives a number of basic properties of the extended functions.

A. L. Whiteman (Los Angeles, Calif.)

Referred to in F65-29.

F20-23 **(23# A1624)**

Meyer, C.

Bemerkungen zu den allgemeinen Dedekindschen Summen.

J. Reine Angew. Math. **205** (1960/61), 186–196.

Let a, c, g, h, f denote integers, and let $(a, c)=1$, $ac\neq 0$, $f\geqq 1$. The generalized Dedekind sums studied in this paper are defined by

$$s_{gh}(a, c) = \sum_{\mu \bmod c} P_1\left(\frac{a\mu}{c}+\frac{ag+ch}{cf}\right)P_1\left(\frac{\mu}{c}+\frac{g}{cf}\right),$$

where $P_1(x)=x-[x]-\frac{1}{2}$, and μ runs over those integers modulo c for which the arguments in both factors are fractional. Dieter [same J. **201** (1959), 37–70; MR **21** #3397] has shown that the sums $s_{gh}(a, c)$ satisfy the following law of reciprocity:

$$\operatorname{sgn} c\cdot s_{gh}(a, c)+\operatorname{sgn} a\cdot s_{gh}(c\ a)$$

$$= \varepsilon\left(\frac{g}{f}\right)\varepsilon\left(\frac{h}{f}\right)P_1\left(\frac{g}{f}\right)P_1\left(\frac{h}{f}\right)$$

$$+\frac{1}{2}\left(\frac{a}{c}P_2\left(\frac{g}{f}\right)+\frac{1}{ac}P_2\left(\frac{ag+ch}{f}\right)+\frac{c}{a}P_2\left(\frac{h}{f}\right)\right)$$

for $g, h\not\equiv 0, 0 \pmod f$, $f>1$. Here $\varepsilon(x)=0$ or 1 according as x is integral or not, and

$$P_2(x) = R^2(x)-R(x)+\tfrac{1}{6}, \quad R(x) = P_1(x)+\tfrac{1}{2}.$$

There is given in this paper a new proof of Dieter's formula. The method involves reducing the generalized Dedekind sums to ordinary Dedekind sums and some other sums named after Eisenstein and Stern.

A. L. Whiteman (Los Angeles, Calif.)

Citations: MR 21# 3397 = F20-20.

F20-24 **(25# 2039)**

Artjuhov, M. M.

On the number of lattice points in certain tetrahedra. (Russian)

Mat. Sb. (*N.S.*) **57** (**99**) (1962), 3–12.

Let p, q, r be positive integers coprime in pairs and let q, r be odd. Let P, Q, R, S, T be the points with respective coordinates $(p, 0, 0)$, $(0, q, 0)$, $(0, 0, r)$, (p, q, r), $(\frac{1}{2}p, \frac{1}{2}q, \frac{1}{2}r)$ in 3-dimensional euclidean space. By an elaborate but elementary argument the author shows that the number of points with integral coordinates (lattice points) strictly within the tetrahedron $SPQR$ is a multiple of 8. He deduces that the number of lattice points strictly within the tetrahedron $TPQR$ is even and that the number strictly within $OPQR$ (where O is the origin) is congruent to $\frac{1}{4}(p-1)(q-1)(r-1)$ modulo 2. These results are related to work on Dedekind sums [cf. H. Rademacher, *Studies in mathematics and mechanics*, pp. 49–53, Academic Press, New York, 1954; MR **16**, 341].

J. W. S. Cassels (Cambridge, England)

Citations: MR 16, 341b = F20-14.

F20-25 **(29# 1172)**

Rademacher, H.

Some remarks on certain generalized Dedekind sums.

Acta Arith. **9** (1964), 97–105.

The author introduces a generalized Dedekind sum

$$(1)\quad s(h, k; x, y) = \sum_{\mu \bmod k}\left(\left(h\left(\frac{\mu+y}{k}+\frac{x}{h}\right)\right)\right)\left(\left(\frac{\mu+y}{k}\right)\right),$$

where h, k are coprime integers, $k>0$, and x, y are real. Special cases of this sum, for rational x, y, have been considered by previous authors. When x and y are both integers, (1) reduces to the classical Dedekind sum.

The main object of the paper is to prove the reciprocity formula:

$$s(h, k; x, y)+s(k, h; y, x) =$$

$$((x))((y))+\frac{1}{2}\left\{\frac{h}{k}\psi_2(y)+\frac{1}{hk}\psi_2(hy+kx)+\frac{k}{h}\psi_2(x)\right\},$$

where $\psi_2(y)=B_2(y-[y])$, $B_2(u)=u^2-u+\frac{1}{6}$. The relation

$$s(h, k; x, y) = s(h-mk, k; x+my, y)$$

is also proved; this permits calculation of s by a euclidean algorithm. *J. Lehner* (College Park, Md.)

Referred to in F20-30.

F20-26 **(29# 3427)**

Carlitz, L.

Generalized Dedekind sums.

Math. Z. **85** (1964), 83–90.

The author derives a reciprocity formula for a generalized Dedekind sum defined by

$$s_p(h, k; x, y) = \sum_{\mu \pmod k} \bar{B}_p\left(h\frac{\mu+y}{k}+x\right)\bar{B}_1\left(\frac{\mu+y}{k}\right),$$

where x, y are real, p, h, k are integers, $p\geqq 0$, $(h, k)=1$, and $\bar{B}_p$, $\bar{B}_1$ are periodic Bernoulli functions. Special cases have been treated by Rademacher [1963 Number Theory Institute in Boulder, Colorado] and by the reviewer [Duke Math. J. **17** (1950), 147–157; MR **11**, 641].

T. M. Apostol (Pasadena, Calif.)

Citations: MR 11, 641g = F20-3.

Referred to in F20-30.

F20-27 **(29# 3446)**

Maak, Wilhelm

Gitterpunktsummen.

Nachr. Akad. Wiss. Göttingen Math.-Phys. Kl. II **1964**, 59–66.

Bekanntlich ist $\Gamma(2)$ (die Gruppe der ganzzahligen Matrizen $\begin{pmatrix}a & b\\ c & d\end{pmatrix}$ mit $a\equiv d\equiv 1$ (4), $b\equiv c\equiv 0$ (2)) eine freie Gruppe von zwei Erzeugenden $A=\begin{pmatrix}1 & 2\\ 0 & 1\end{pmatrix}$ und $B=\begin{pmatrix}1 & 0\\ -2 & 1\end{pmatrix}$. Die Anzahl der Faktoren A bzw. B, aus denen ein Element $L=\begin{pmatrix}a & b\\ c & d\end{pmatrix}\in\Gamma(2)$ aufgebaut ist, ist eine Funktion der ganzrationalen Zahlen a, b, c, d. Es wird eine Methode angegeben, die es gestattet, diese Anzahle durch Abzählen von Gitterpunkten, also ohne eigentliche Rechnung zu bestimmen. Ganz ähnlich Abzählungen können dazu dienen, die Werte der Rademacherschen Φ-Funktion [Rademacher, J. Reine Angew. Math. **167** (1932), 312–336] und damit die der Dedekindsummen zu bestimmen. Es wird die Transformationstheorie der Weierstraßschen σ-Funktion benutzt. Für die angegebenen und weitere Sätze wird demnächst Herr Burde elementare Beweise an anderer Stelle veröffentlichen. Die angegebenen Methoden führen zu einer Fülle weiterer Sätze, die mehr oder weniger interessant erscheinen, je nach der Einstellung, die man gegenüber den Fragestellungen einnimmt, die sie berühren. *J. W. S. Cassels* (Cambridge, England)

Referred to in F20-28.

F20-28 **(31# 114)**

Burde, Klaus-Friedrich

Reziprozitätsgesetze für Gitterpunktsummen.

Dissertation zur Erlangung des Doktorgrades der Mathematisch-Naturwissenschaftlichen Fakultät der Georg-August-Universität zu Göttingen.

Dissertation, Göttingen, 1964. i+37 *pp.*

To any ordered couple (u, v) of coprime rational integers, one makes correspond the point Q of coordinates (v, u), the segment $\sigma = OQ$ and the polygonal line S, formed by the line segment RQ (where R is the point $(2[v/2], 2[u/2])$) together with $\frac{1}{2}(|v|+|u|)$ line segments of length 2, parallel to the axes and uniquely determined by the condition that there are no lattice points enclosed by σ and S. All lattice points of the plane can be subdivided into four equivalence classes, corresponding to the parity of their coordinates. So, e.g., $(3, 4) \equiv (1, 0) \pmod 2$ and the point of coordinates $(3, 4)$ is said to belong to the class P^{10}; the classes P^{00}, P^{01} and P^{11} are similarly defined. For lattice points $P \in S$ one defines

$$\begin{aligned} \operatorname{sig} P &= \;\; 1 \text{ if } P \text{ is above } \sigma \\ &= \;\; 0 \text{ if } P \text{ is on } \sigma \\ &= -1 \text{ if } P \text{ is below } \sigma. \end{aligned}$$

The main object of the paper is the study of the sums $R(u, v) = \sum_{P^{00} \in S} \operatorname{sig} P^{00}$ and $S(u, v) = \sum_{P^{01} \in S} \operatorname{sig} P^{01}, (u,v)=1$, introduced by Maak [Nachr. Akad. Wiss. Göttingen Math.-Phys. Kl. II **1964**, 59–66; MR **29** #3446]. If P_x and P_y stand for the x and y coordinate of P, respectively, then one defines also $\mu(u, v) = \sum_{(v,u) \neq P^{10} \in S} P_y^{10}$, $\nu(u, v) = \sum_{(v,u) \neq P^{01} \in S} P_x^{01}$. One shows that $-R(u, v) = R(v, u) = R(-u, v) = R(u, -v)$; $S(-u, v) = S(u, -v) = -S(u, v)$ and if $g, u > 0$, $(g, u) = 1$, $(g, 2) = 2$, $(u, 2) = 1$, then $\mu(g, u) - \nu(g, u) + \frac{1}{2}g = S(g, u)$. Numerous properties of these sums are established, of which the following may serve as examples: $S(u+v, v) - R(u+v, v) = S(u, v) - R(u, v) + \frac{1}{2}(1+(-1)^v) \operatorname{sig} v(\operatorname{sig}(u+v) - \operatorname{sig} u)$; also, $R(u, v) = (-1)^u S(v, u) - (-1)^v S(u, v)$. If $L = \begin{pmatrix} a & b \\ c & d \end{pmatrix} \in \Gamma(2)$ (i.e., if $L \in \Gamma$, the modular group, and also $\begin{pmatrix} a & b \\ c & d \end{pmatrix} \equiv \begin{pmatrix} 1 & 0 \\ 0 & 1 \end{pmatrix} \pmod 2$), then $S(a, b)$, $R(c, d)$, etc., may be considered as functions on $\Gamma(2)$; $A = \begin{pmatrix} 1 & 2 \\ 0 & 1 \end{pmatrix}$, $B = \begin{pmatrix} 1 & 0 \\ -2 & 1 \end{pmatrix}$ are generators of $\Gamma(2)$. One defines also $\operatorname{sig} L = \frac{1}{2} \operatorname{sig} c(\operatorname{sig} a - \operatorname{sig} d)$. The following results (among others) are proven: $S(b, a) = S(b, d)$; $S(c, a) = S(c, d)$; $R(a, b) + R(c, d) + R(a, c) + R(b, d) = 0$, and even the stronger (double) assertion $R(a, b) = R(d, b) + \operatorname{sig} L$; $R(a, c) = R(d, c) - \operatorname{sig} L$ holds. Next, Rademacher's function $\Phi(L)$ $(L \in \Gamma(2))$ is expressed by the sums R and S as follows:

$$\begin{aligned} \Phi(L) &= 2S(b, a) - 2S(c, d) - 6S(d, c) + 3 \operatorname{sig}(cd) \\ &= 3R(b, a) + 3R(d, c) + S(c, d) - S(b, a) \\ &\qquad + (3/2) \operatorname{sig} c(\operatorname{sig} a + \operatorname{sig} d). \end{aligned}$$

This definition is extended to $L \in \Gamma$, but the corresponding result is complicated. The sums $S(k, h)$ are related to the Dedekind sums $s(h, k)$ [Dedekind, *Gesammelte mathematische Werke*, Band I, pp. 159–172, F. Vieweg, Braunschweig, 1930] by $S(k, h) = 4(s(h, 2k) - s(h+k, 2k))$. Furthermore, it is shown that $(a, 2) = 2$, $(c, 2) = 1$, $(a, c) = 1 \Rightarrow S(a, c) \equiv \frac{1}{2}(c^2 - 3ac + 4a - 1) \pmod 8$ and $S(a, c) \equiv \frac{1}{2}ac \pmod 4$; $(a, c) = (c, 2) = 1, c > 0 \Rightarrow S(c, a) \equiv (-1)^a((a/c) - \frac{1}{2}(c+1)) \pmod 4$ ((a/c) = Jacobi symbol), and similar congruences hold for $R(a, c)$; also, $(a, c) = (a, 2) = (c, 2) = 1$, $a, c > 0 \Rightarrow S(a, c) + S(c, a) \equiv \frac{1}{2}(ac - 1) \pmod 4$. Finally, it is shown that the last congruence is equivalent to the quadratic reciprocity law. All proofs are elementary. They often rely on drawings, whose general validity is not immediately obvious. *E. Grosswald* (Paris)

Citations: MR 29# 3446 = F20-27.
Referred to in F20-29.

F20-29 (35# 111)

Burde, Klaus

Reziprozitätsgesetze für Gitterpunktsummen.

J. Reine Angew. Math. **226** (1967), 159–174.

Essentially a condensed version of the author's dissertation [*Reziprozitätsgesetze für Gitterpunktsummen*, Georg-August-Univ. zu Göttingen, Göttingen, 1964; MR **31** #114]. *A. L. Whiteman* (Princeton, N.J.)

Citations: MR 31# 114 = F20-28.

F20-30 (32# 87)

Carlitz, L.

A theorem on generalized Dedekind sums.

Acta Arith. **11** (1965), 253–260.

Let $B_n(x)$ be the Bernoulli polynomial of degree n and let $\bar{B}_n(x) = B_n(x - [x])$. Then set

$$s_p(h, k; x, y) = \sum_{\mu \pmod k} \bar{B}_p(h(\mu+y)/k + x) \cdot \bar{B}_1((\mu+y)/k).$$

If $(h, k) = 1$ and $0 \leqq x < 1$, $0 \leqq y < 1$, it is proved that for all $p \geqq 0$,

$$(p+1)\{hk^p s_p(h, k; x, y) + kh^p s_p(k, h; y, x)\} = (hB + kB + hy + kx)^{p+1} + p\bar{B}_{p+1}(hy + kx).$$

The power on the right is to be understood symbolically. For the case $p = 1$, this has been obtained by Rademacher [same Acta **9** (1964), 97–105; MR **29** #1172]; in this case, $x = y = 0$ gives the ordinary Dedekind sum. For $p > 1$ and $x = y = 0$, the general result has been proved by Apostol [Duke Math. J. **17** (1950), 147–157; MR **11**, 641]. The present proof is simpler than the earlier proof by the author [Math. Z. **85** (1964), 83–90; MR **29** #3427]. *H. W. Brinkmann* (Swarthmore, Pa.)

Citations: MR 11, 641g = F20-3; MR 29# 1172 = F20-25; MR 29# 3427 = F20-26.

F20-31 (32# 88)

Carlitz, L.

Linear relations among generalized Dedekind sums.

J. Reine Angew. Math. **220** (1965), 154–162.

Rademacher [Duke Math. J. **21** (1954), 391–397; MR **16**, 14] discovered a three-term relation for Dedekind sums $s(h, k) = \sum_{\mu=1}^{k-1} \bar{B}_1(\mu/k)\bar{B}_1(h\mu/k)$. The author discusses linear relations holding among the more general sums $\Phi_{r,s}(h, k) = \sum_{\mu \pmod k} \bar{B}_r(\mu/k)\bar{B}_s(h\mu/k)$, where $\bar{B}_p(x) = B_p(x - [x])$ and $B_p(x)$ is the Bernoulli polynomial of degree p. The results are too lengthy to summarize adequately in a brief review. *T. M. Apostol* (Pasadena, Calif.)

Citations: MR 16, 14e = F20-12.

F20-32 (32# 7515)

Shipp, R. Dale

Table of Dedekind sums.

J. Res. Nat. Bur. Standards Sect. B **69B** (1965), 259–263.

Author's summary: "The Dedekind sums are of importance in the transformation formulae for the Dedekind modular form $\eta(\tau)$, and in discussing the characters of degree 1 of the modular group and its subgroups. These sums are rational numbers and a table of their exact values is given. In addition, a comprehensive bibliography on these sums is included."

F20-33 (35# 5393)

Burde, Klaus

Dedekindsummen als Gitterpunktanzahlen.

J. Reine Angew. Math. **227** (1967), 74–85.

Let a, c denote a pair of relatively prime nonzero integers and let $D(a, c)$ denote the (closed) triangle with coordinates

$(0, 0)$, $(c, 0)$, $(0, a)$. For P a lattice point in $D(a, c)$, put $w(P)=1, \frac{1}{2}, \frac{1}{4}$ or $\frac{1}{8}$ according as P is an inner point, a boundary point but not a vertex, $(c, 0)$ or $(0, a)$. Lattice points are separated into four classes P^{ik} $(i, k=0, 1)$; the class P^{ik} consists of points (x, y) such that $x \equiv i$, $y \equiv k \pmod 2$. Now put $A^{ik}(a, c)=\operatorname{sig}(ac) \sum w(P)$, $K^{ik}(a, c)= \operatorname{sig}(ac) \sum w(P) P_x$, and $H^{ik}(a, c)=\operatorname{sig}(ac) \sum w(P) P_x'$, where each summation is over $P^{ik} \in D(a, c)$, $P=(P_x, P_y)$ and $P_x'=c-P_x-(c/a) P_y$. Also, put $A(a, c)=\sum_{i,k} A^{ik}(a, c)=\frac{1}{2}ac$, and $H(a, c)=\sum_{i,k} H^{ik}(a, c)$, $K(a, c)=\sum_{i,k} K^{ik}(a, c)$. Various relations among these sums are obtained.

The Dedekind sum $s(a, c)=\sum_{\mu \bmod c}((\mu/c))((a\mu/c))$ is expressed in terms of A^{ik} and the reciprocity theorem follows. (Compare L. J. Mordell [Amer. J. Math. **73** (1951), 593–598; MR **13**, 113].) More generally, the author indicates how the more general sum introduced by C. Meyer [*Die Berechnung der Klassenzahl Abelscher Körper über quadratischen Zahlkörpern*, Akademie-Verlag, Berlin, 1957; MR **19**, 531]

$$S_{gh}(a, c) = \sum_{\mu \bmod c} ((a\mu/c+(ga+hc)/fc))((\mu/c+g/fc))$$

can be treated in a similar way.

L. Carlitz (Durham, N.C.)

Citations: MR 13, 113h = F20-5; MR 19, 531f = R02-21.

F20-34 (36# 3708)

Carlitz, L.

A three-term relation for the Dedekind-Rademacher sums.

Publ. Math. Debrecen **14** (1967), 119–124.

The author proves the following theorem which, after suitable specialization of the parameters involved, reduces to many known relations satisfied by Dedekind sums. Theorem: Let $(a, b)=(b, c)=(c, a)=1$; then

$$s(a, b, c; x, y, z)+s(b, c, a; y, z, x)+s(c, a, b; z, x, y) =$$
$$\delta-a\psi(cy-bz)/2bc-b\psi(az-cx)/2ac-c\psi(bx-ay)/2ab,$$

where $\delta=1$ if there exist integers r, s, t such that $(r+x)/a=(s+y)/b=(t+z)/c$, and $\delta=0$ otherwise. The functions ψ and s are defined as follows: $\psi(x)=([x]-x)^2-x+[x]+\frac{1}{6}$, and

$$s(a, b, c; x, y, z) =$$
$$\sum_{t(\bmod c)} \Phi(-x+a(t+z)/c)\Phi(y-b(t+z)/c),$$

where $\Phi(x)=x-[x]-\frac{1}{2}$.

D. A. Klarner (Hamilton, Ont.)

F20-35 (38# 4391)

Burde, Klaus

Verallgemeinerung einer Beziehung zwischen vier Dedekindsummen.

Arch. Math. (*Basel*) **19** (1968), 479–481.

The Dedekind sum $s(a, c)=\sum_{v=1}^{|c|}((v/|c|))((av/|c|))$, where $a, c \in Z$, $c \neq 0$, is usually defined only for $(a, c)=1$. This restriction is easily lifted, however; in fact, in a paper of H. A. Rademacher and A. Whiteman [Amer. J. Math. **63** (1941), 377–407; MR **2**, 249] one finds the (trivial) proof of $s(qa, qc)=s(a, c)$, $q \neq 0$. Dedekind noted the identity: $3s(a, c)=s(2a, c)+s(a, 2c)+s(\frac{1}{2}(a+c), c)$, where a, c are odd, $(a, c)=1$, a proof of which may be found in the paper quoted above. In the present paper the author rewrites this formula by replacing $s(\frac{1}{2}(a+c), c)$ by $s(a+c, 2c)$ and then proves it without restriction on a and c except $c \neq 0$.

J. Lehner (College Park, Md.)

Citations: MR 2, 249f = F20-1.

F20-36 (40# 1325)

Carlitz, L.

The greatest integer function.

Delta (*Waukesha*) **1** (1968/69), 1–12.

The author presents a number of properties of the greatest integer function $[x]$. Some of these are inequalities and simple results of an arithmetic nature by means of which certain quotients of factorials can be proven to be integers. The equation $[x]+[x+1/k]+\cdots+[x+(k-1)/k]=[kx]$ is shown to be a special case of an equation satisfied by the Bernoulli polynomials. Dedekind sums are mentioned and the author sketches the proof of a reciprocity theorem. A full treatment of Dedekind sums can be found in an article by H. Rademacher and A. L. Whiteman [Amer. J. Math. **63** (1941), 377–407; MR **2**, 249].

A. Peluso (New York)

Citations: MR 2, 249f = F20-1.

F20-37 (41# 5299)

Asai, Tetsuya

The reciprocity of Dedekind sums and the factor set for the universal covering group of SL(2, *R*).

Nagoya Math. J. **37** (1970), 67–80.

A new proof of the generalized reciprocity law for Dedekind sums which had first been obtained by H. Rademacher [J. Reine Angew. Math. **167** (1932), 312–336] is given. The method of proof is based on the theorem that the group SL(2, *Z*) is a splitting group for the factor set of the universal covering group of SL(2, *R*). Dedekind sums are exhibited as linear expressions of the function that splits the factor set. The properties of the latter function lead immediately to the desired reciprocity law. This idea was suggested by investigations of T. Kubota [Nagoya Math. J. **37** (1970), 183–189; MR **41** #1647], who derived in a similar way a generalized reciprocity law for the ordinary quadratic residue symbol.

O. H. Körner (Marburg)

Citations: MR 41# 1647 = R40-28.

F20-38 (44# 2691)

Grosswald, Emil

Dedekind-Rademacher sums.

Amer. Math. Monthly **78** (1971), 639–644.

This is a reconstruction of a proof by H. Rademacher from a hint left in one of his manuscripts.

F25 HECKE-PETERSSON OPERATORS, DIFFERENTIAL OPERATORS, TRACE FORMULA (ONE VARIABLE)

See also reviews F10-21, F10-36, F10-46, F10-61, F10-108, F10-112, F10-115, F15-4, F15-28, F30-28, F30-55, F35-29, F65-4, F65-27, F65-29, G30-15, P24-14, R52-23.

F25-1 (2, 39a)

Hecke, E. Die Klassenzahl imaginär-quadratischer Körper in der Theorie der elliptischen Modulfunktionen.

Monatsh. Math. Phys. **48**, 75–83 (1939).

This article begins with a recapitulation of the different known relations between imaginary quadratic fields and modular functions ("complex multiplication," "binary theta-series") and then proceeds to add a new occurrence of the class-number of imaginary quadratic fields in the theory of modular functions. Throughout this paper the author makes use of notations and results of his previous publications on modular forms and Euler products [cf., in particular, Math. Ann. 114, 1–28, 316–351 (1937)].

Let q be an odd prime number not less than 5 and $f^{(\nu)}(\tau)$ ($\nu=1, 2, \cdots, \kappa$) the system of linearly independent cusp-forms (that is, modular forms vanishing in the parabolic points of the fundamental region) of dimension $-k$ belonging to the group $\Gamma_0(q)$ with $c\equiv 0 \pmod q$ in

$$\begin{pmatrix} a & b \\ c & d \end{pmatrix}$$

(on p. 77 this invariance with respect to $\Gamma_0(q)$ is expressed in terms of the quoted papers as follows: the forms $f^{(\nu)}(\tau)$ are of "stufe q" (that is, belong to the principal congruence group $\bar\Gamma(q)$), of "divisor q," "normalized" and of "character $\epsilon(n)=1$"). The linear set generated by the $f^{(\nu)}(\tau)$ goes over into itself under the linear operators T_n and $T_m{}^q$ defined in the second paper quoted above. The automorphisms induced by the $T_m{}^q$ lead to a representation by matrices $\lambda(m)$ of degree κ. The $\lambda(m)$ are connected with the functions $f^{(\nu)}(\tau)$ by the matric equation

$$\sum_{\nu=1}^{\kappa} f^{(\nu)}(\tau)B^{(\nu)} = \sum_{m=1}^{\infty} \lambda(m)e^{2\pi i m\tau}$$

with certain constant matrices $B^{(\nu)}$. The law of composition of the $\lambda(m)$ finds its expression in the formula

$$\sum_{m=1}^{\infty} \lambda(m)m^{-s} = (1-\lambda(q)q^{-s})^{-1} \prod_{p\neq q} (1-\lambda(p)p^{-s}+p^{1-2s})^{-1}.$$

Now the problem of the present paper is the determination of the characteristic roots of $\lambda(q)$ and of its trace $S(\lambda(q))$. For $k=2$ the result is as follows: the characteristic roots are only ± 1, and

$$S(\lambda(q)) = \tfrac{1}{2}\delta_q\cdot h(4q)-1,$$

$h(4q)$ being the class-number of primitive positive binary quadratic forms of determinant $-4q$, and $\delta_q=2$ or $4/3$ for $q\equiv 7$ or $3 \pmod 8$, respectively, and $\delta_q=1$ otherwise.

The method consists in singling out those forms which belong also to the enlarged group $\Gamma^*(q)=\Gamma_0(q)+\Gamma_0(q)H$, where H is the substitution $\tau\to -1/q\tau$. It is shown that the number of linear independent ones of these forms is equal to the number of the negative characteristic roots of $\lambda(q)$, a result which is derived for $k<12$ and $k=14$ since for these dimensions $-k$ there exist no cusp-forms that belong to the full modular group. For $k=2$ the number κ is equal to the genus $p_0(q)$ of $\Gamma_0(q)$, and the number of linear independent forms belonging to $\Gamma^*(q)$ is similarly equal to the genus $p^*(q)$ of $\Gamma^*(q)$. Now Fricke has proved that

$$p^*(q) = \tfrac{1}{2}p_0(q)+\tfrac{1}{2}-\tfrac{1}{4}\delta_q\cdot h(4q),$$

and this yields the above-mentioned result. For $k=4$, 6, 8, 10, 14 the enumerations can be done by means of the Riemann-Roch theorem, and the result is

$$S(\lambda(q)) = (-q)^{k/2-1}\cdot h\cdot \rho_q,$$

with h denoting the class-number of the quadratic field $K(\sqrt{-q})$ and $\rho_q=1$, 2, 1/2 if the quadratic residue symbol $(-q/2)$ is 1, -1, 0, respectively. Analogous results for the other values of the dimension $-k$ are indicated and the connection with a theorem of Petersson concerning the simultaneous transformations of the $\lambda(m)$ into diagonal form is mentioned. *H. Rademacher* (Philadelphia, Pa.).

F25-2 (2, 151a)

Petersson, Hans. Konstruktion der sämtlichen Lösungen einer Riemannschen Funktionalgleichung durch Dirichlet-Reihen mit Eulerscher Produktentwicklung. III. Math. Ann. 117, 277–300 (1940).

In Part I of this series [Math. Ann. 116, 401–412 (1939)] the author has, by means of a metrization in the space of the entire modular forms, proved that the matrices $\lambda(n)$ of Hecke's theory of Euler products [Math. Ann. 114, 1–28, 316–351 (1937)] can, for "Stufe" 1, simultaneously be transformed into diagonal form, which means that Dirichlet series and Euler products with numerical coefficients instead of matrix coefficients can be obtained. The situation for Stufe Q has been studied in Part II [Math. Ann. 117, 39–64 (1939); these Rev. 1, 294]. The simultaneous reduction on diagonal form is also possible for the sets of modular forms belonging to a divisor t of Q which contains only prime factors of $t_1=Q/t$. If, however, t contains primes not dividing t_1, some eigenvalues $\omega(n)$ can be multiple for all operators T_n. In the Euler product of a Dirichlet series which corresponds to such a modular form they give rise to a factor $K(s)$, here called the "kernel." The result of this paper is that the kernel is always a linear combination of a finite number of products of the form

$$q_1^{-(\nu_1-1)s}\left(1-\frac{\alpha_1}{q_1^s}\right)^{-\nu_1}\cdots q_h^{-(\nu_h-1)s}\left(1-\frac{\alpha_h}{q_h^s}\right)^{-\nu_h},$$

where $q_1, \cdots, q_h$ are the primes dividing t but not t_1, $\alpha_1, \cdots, \alpha_h$ characteristic roots of certain linear transformations and $\nu_1, \cdots, \nu_h$ integers which can run up to the multiplicity of the corresponding α at most. For $h=1$ the author proves moreover that each

$$q^{-(\nu-1)s}\left(1-\frac{\alpha}{q^s}\right)^{-\nu}$$

is itself an admissible $K(s)$; this case takes place in particular for $Q=t=q^\alpha$. *H. Rademacher* (Swarthmore, Pa.).

Citations: MR 1, 294c = F65-1.

Referred to in F25-12, F25-27.

F25-3 (2, 251e)

Hecke, E. Über die Darstellung der Determinante einer positiven quadratischen Form durch die Form. Vierteljschr. Naturforsch. Ges. Zürich 85 Beiblatt (Festschrift Rudolf Fueter), 64–70 (1940).

Let $Q(x_1, \cdots, x_{2k})=Ax_1^2+Bx_1x_2+\cdots$ be a positive quadratic form with $2k$ variables and integral coefficients $A, B, \cdots$ and the determinant of the matrix of $2Q$ an odd prime number q. The theta function

$$\vartheta(\tau)=\sum_{(n)} e^{2\pi i\tau Q(n_1,\cdots,n_{2k})}=\sum_{n=0}^{\infty} a(n, Q)e^{2\pi i n\tau}$$

is an entire modular form and $\vartheta(\tau')=\chi(d)(c\tau+d)^k\vartheta(\tau)$ for any modular substitution $\tau'=(a\tau+b)/(c\tau+d)$ with $c\equiv 0 \pmod q$, where $\chi(d)=(d/q)$ is Legendre's symbol. The linear set of all functions $F(\tau)$ with those properties, the type $(-k, q, \chi)$, is transformed into itself by certain operations T_m which have been studied by the author in previous papers [Math. Ann. 114, 1–28 and 316–351 (1937); $T_m=T(m)$ of next review]. A number λ_m is called a characteristic value of T_m if a function F of the given type exists which is transformed by T_m into $\lambda_m F$. These λ_m appear in the multiplicative laws for the representation numbers $a(n, Q)$; in particular, λ_q is connected with the number of representations of q by the quadratic form Q. It is proved that λ_q has the absolute value $q^{(k-1)/2}$. The examples $k=2$, $q=29$ and $k=3$, $q=19$ are investigated. *C. L. Siegel* (Princeton, N. J.).

F25-4 (2, 251f)

Hecke, E. Analytische Arithmetik der positiven quadratischen Formen. Danske Vid. Selsk. Math.-Fys. Medd. 17, no. 12, 134 pp. (1940).

Let $Q=Q(x_1, x_2, \cdots, x_{2k})=Ax_1^2+Bx_1x_2+\cdots$ be a positive quadratic form of $2k$ variables with integral coefficients $A, B, \cdots$. If $n_1, \cdots, n_{2k}$ run over all integers and $a(n, Q)$ denotes the number of representations of n by Q, the function

$$\vartheta(\tau, Q)=\sum_{(n)} e^{2\pi i\tau Q(n_1,\cdots,n_{2k})}=\sum_{n=0}^{\infty} a(n, Q)e^{2\pi i n\tau}$$

is an entire modular form of dimension $-k$ which is invariant under a congruence subgroup of the modular group. There exists for any given Q a certain positive integer N and a character $\epsilon(d)$ modulo N such that (1) $(c\tau+d)^{-k}\vartheta(\tau', Q)=\epsilon(d)\vartheta(\tau, Q)$ for all modular substitutions $\tau'=(a\tau+b)/(c\tau+d)$ with $c\equiv 0 \pmod N$. Consider now all entire modular forms $F=F(\tau)$ of the type $(-k, N, \epsilon)$, that is, modular forms of dimension $-k$ satisfying (1); they are a linear set with a finite basis $F_1, \cdots, F_\kappa$. Let m be an integer relatively prime to N. If α runs over all positive divisors of $m=\alpha\delta$ and β over a complete system of residues modulo α, the linear operation

$$F\to F|T(m)=m^{-1}\sum_{\alpha,\beta}\epsilon(\alpha)\alpha^k F\left(\frac{\alpha\tau+\beta}{\delta}\right)$$

transforms the set $(-k, N, \epsilon)$ into itself and satisfies the law of composition

$$T(m_1)T(m_2)=\sum_{d|(m_1,m_2)} T\left(\frac{m_1m_2}{d^2}\right)\epsilon(d)d^{k-1}.$$

Hence

$$F_\rho|T(m)=\sum_{\sigma=1}^{\kappa}\lambda_{\rho\sigma}(m)F_\sigma,\qquad \rho=1,\cdots,\kappa,$$

and the matrices $\lambda(m)=(\lambda_{\rho\sigma}(m))$ have also the property

$$\lambda(m_1)\lambda(m_2)=\sum_{d|(m_1,m_2)}\lambda\left(\frac{m_1m_2}{d^2}\right)\epsilon(d)d^{k-1}$$

and are therefore commutative. It follows from the results of Petersson [Math. Ann. **116**, 401–412 (1939) and **117**, 39–64 (1939); these Rev. **1**, 294] that the matrices $\lambda(m)$ can be transformed simultaneously into the diagonal form. Consider now the characteristic functions of all the operators $T(m)$, that is, the solutions $F=F(\tau)$ of $F|T(m)=\omega_m F$ $(m=1, 2, \cdots)$ with constant ω_m. If $F(\tau)=\sum_{n=0}^{\infty}a_n e^{2\pi i n\tau}$, then the Dirichlet series $\phi(s)=\sum_{n=1}^{\infty}a_n n^{-s}$ can be written as an infinite product

$$\phi(s)=\prod_p(1-a_p p^{-s}+\epsilon(p)p^{k-1-2s})^{-1}$$

extended over all prime numbers p. There exist κ linearly independent Dirichlet series $\phi_1, \cdots, \phi_\kappa$ corresponding to characteristic functions and the Dirichlet series for any modular form of the type $(-k, N, \epsilon)$ is a linear combination of the κ Euler products $\phi_1, \cdots, \phi_\kappa$. The application of this result to the Dirichlet series

$$\sum_{n=1}^{\infty}a(n, Q)n^{-s}=\sum_{(n)}{}'\,Q(n_1, \cdots, n_{2k})^{-s}$$

gives the generalization of the well-known formula connecting the zeta-functions of the classes of ideals in a quadratic field with the zeta-functions containing the characters of the class-group.

A number of important examples are completely discussed. In these particular cases, the system of all theta-functions $\vartheta(\tau, Q)$ of the same type already gives the basis of an invariant linear set with respect to the operation $T(m)$, and the corresponding representation numbers $a(n, Q)$ are connected by certain multiplicative laws not containing other arithmetical functions than the $a(n, Q)$ alone. It is not known, however, if the $\vartheta(\tau, Q)$ of the same type always are the basis of a closed set for $T(m)$ in the general case. Any further progress seems to depend upon the discovery of new arithmetical notions generalizing the arithmetic of quaternions and adapted to the general quadratic form with an even number of variables. *C. L. Siegel.*

Citations: MR 1, 294c = F65-1.

Referred to in E12-28, E12-143, F30-60, F65-27, R52-3.

F25-5 **(10, 445b)**

Petersson, Hans. Über die Berechnung der Skalarprodukte ganzer Modulformen. Comment. Math. Helv. **22**, 168–199 (1949).

Let Γ be a congruence subgroup of finite index μ in the full modular group. The function $f(\tau)$ is said to belong to $\{\Gamma, -r, v\}$ if and only if (1) f is regular in $\Im(\tau)>0$, (2) $f(L\tau)=v(L)(\gamma\tau+\delta)^r f(\tau)$ for every $L=\binom{\alpha\ \beta}{\gamma\ \delta}\subset\Gamma$, where $|v(L)|=1$ and $r>0$, (3) $f(\tau)$ has at most poles (measured in the local uniformising variable) at the parabolic vertices of Γ. If N is the smallest positive integer such that $\binom{1\ N}{0\ 1}\subset\Gamma$, define κ by $\exp 2\pi i\kappa=v(\binom{1\ N}{0\ 1})$, $0\leqq\kappa<1$. Then f has a Fourier series $f(\tau)=\sum_{n=0}^{\infty}b_n\exp 2\pi i(n+\kappa)\tau/N$.

In previous papers [cf., e.g., Math. Ann. **117**, 453–537 (1940); these Rev. **2**, 87] the author has introduced the scalar product (f, g) of two entire modular forms belonging to $\{\Gamma, -r, v\}$:

$$(f, g; \Gamma)=(f, g)=\iint_{\mathfrak{F}} f(\tau)\overline{g(\tau)}y^{r-2}dxdy,\qquad \tau=x+iy,$$

where $\mathfrak{F}$ is any fundamental region of Γ. In the present paper he establishes a connection between the scalar product of f, g and a certain Dirichlet series built up out of their Fourier coefficients, as follows. Theorem 6: $f(\tau), g(\tau)$ belong to $\{\Gamma, -r, v\}$, $r>0$, and $f(\tau)g(\tau)$ is a cusp-form, i.e., fg vanishes at all parabolic vertices of Γ. Let b_n, c_n $(n\geqq 0)$ be the Fourier coefficients of f, g respectively, and construct the Dirichlet series $D(s; f, g; \Gamma)=\sum_{n+\kappa>0}b_n\overline{c_n}(n+\kappa)^{-s}$. Then the series converges absolutely for $\sigma=\Re(s)>2r$, and $D(s)$ can be continued analytically to the half-plane $\sigma>r-\frac{1}{2}$, and is regular there with the possible exception of the point $s=r$, where it may have a simple pole. Moreover,

$$(1)\qquad \operatorname*{residue}_{s=r} D(s; f, g; \Gamma)=\frac{(4\pi)^{r-1}}{N^r\Gamma(r)}\frac{12}{\mu}(f, g; \Gamma).$$

When $0<r<1$, the above result is essentially true for forms f, g such that fg is not necessarily a cusp-form. With $0<r<1$ and f, g arbitrary entire modular forms belonging to $\{\Gamma, -r, v\}$, the conclusions of theorem 6 hold with the modification that $D(s)$ is analytically continuable to the half-plane $\sigma>\max(r-\frac{1}{2}, 2r-1, 0)$.

The author then calculates, by use of (1), the values of scalar products of various theta functions of dimension $-\frac{1}{2}$ and $-\frac{3}{2}$, e.g.,

$$\vartheta_3(\tau)=\sum_{-\infty}^{\infty}\exp\pi i\tau n^2,\quad \eta(\tau)=\exp\pi i\tau/12\prod_1^{\infty}(1-e^{2\pi i n\tau}),$$

and some of higher level (Stufe),

$$\vartheta_\lambda(\tau, h, N)=\sum_{m\equiv h(N)} m^\lambda\exp\pi i\tau n^2/N,\qquad \lambda=0, 1.$$

A more interesting example is promised in a future work, of which one case is

$$\zeta(3)=\frac{\pi^3}{7}(\vartheta_3{}^8, \vartheta_0{}^4\vartheta_2{}^4);$$

ϑ_3 has been defined above,

$$\vartheta_0(\tau)=\sum_{-\infty}^{\infty}(-1)^n\exp\pi i n^2\tau,\quad \vartheta_2(\tau)=\sum_{-\infty}^{\infty}\exp\pi i(n+\tfrac{1}{2})^2\tau.$$

The scalar product appears in this formula as the analogue of the Bernoulli numbers in the classical expression for $\zeta(2m)$. *J. Lehner* (Philadelphia, Pa.).

Citations: MR 2, 87e = F10-3.

Referred to in M10-7.

F25-6 **(19, 839e)**

Shimura, Goro. La fonction ζ du corps des fonctions modulaires elliptiques. C. R. Acad. Sci. Paris **244** (1957), 2127–2130.

Let M be the field of all elliptic modular functions of level ("Stufe") n. Then M is a field of algebraic functions in one variable over the field C of complex numbers. The author constructs a subfield K of M having the field of rational numbers as its field of constants, which further generates M over C and such that its zeta function can be represented by means of the Riemann ζ-function and an Euler product [as introduced by Hecke, Math. Ann. **114** (1937), 1–28, 316–351]. In addition, the absolute values of the characteristic roots of Hecke's operator T_p for the cusp forms of dimension -2 (differentials of the first kind) do not exceed $2\sqrt{p}$ for almost all prime numbers p.

H. D. Kloosterman (Leiden).

Referred to in F25-11.

F25-7 **(19, 839f)**

van Lint, Jacobus Hendricus. Hecke operators and Euler products. Drukkerij "Luctor et Emergo", Leiden, 1957. 51 pp. (1 insert)

Wohlfart [Dissertation, Münster, 1955] has given a theory of generalized Hecke operators of not necessarily integral dimension. While the original Hecke operators map the set of integral modular forms of dimension $-r$ and step 1 into itself, the generalized operators $T_K{}^\Lambda(Q)$ map the set K of forms $\{\Gamma, -r, v\}$ into the set Λ of forms $\{\theta, -r, v^*\}$, where Γ and θ are subgroups of the modular group $\Gamma(1)$, Q is a matrix with rational elements and positive determinant, and

$$v^*(L)=\frac{\sigma(QLQ^{-1}, Q)}{\sigma(Q, L)}v(QLQ^{-1})$$

for any matrix $L\in\Delta$, where $\Delta=\theta\cap\Gamma(1)\cap Q^{-1}\Gamma Q$ and is of finite index in $\Gamma(1)$ and σ stands for a certain root of unity. In general (with one important exception), all Hecke operators defined on the class $\{\Gamma, -r, v\}$ can be built up from operators $T_K{}^\Lambda(Q)$ defined by $f|T_K{}^\Lambda(Q)=\sum v^*(V)^{-1}f|Q|V$, the summation being extended over a complete system V of representatives of a decomposition of θ into left cosets of Δ. If Γ and θ are arbitrary subgroups of $\Gamma(1)$, in general no non-trivial such operators exist; if they exist, then the determination of Q and, particularly, the proof that v^* has the required value are the main difficulties. Some of the particular cases studied are $\Gamma=\theta=\Gamma(1)$, r integral, $Q=\begin{pmatrix}p&0\\0&1\end{pmatrix}$ (operators denoted $T(p)$) and $Q=\begin{pmatrix}p^2&0\\0&1\end{pmatrix}$ (operators denoted $T(p^2)$); $\Gamma=\theta=\Gamma(1)$, or $\Gamma=\theta=\Gamma_0(2)$, r half odd integer, $Q=\begin{pmatrix}p^2&0\\0&1\end{pmatrix}$; $\Gamma=\Gamma(1)$, $\theta=\Gamma_0(p)$, r half-odd integer, $Q=\begin{pmatrix}1&0\\0&p\end{pmatrix}$, with $p>3$, prime. This theory is used (prove existence of operator, apply it to a function of the first set, compare coefficients of the two members) and permits the derivation in a systematic way of many known results and some new ones.

Applying the operators to even powers $l=2r$ of the (Dedekind) η-function,

$$\eta^l(\tau)=\sum_{0<n\equiv l(\text{mod } 24)}a(n)e^{2\pi i\tau n/24}$$

(observe that $\eta^l\in\{\Gamma(1), -r, v\}$ with integral r; hence, also the classical Hecke operator T_p could be used successfully), the author obtains several theorems due to Newman [Nederl. Akad. Wetensch. Proc. Ser. A. **59** (1956), 204–216; J. London Math. Soc. **30** (1955), 488–493; **31** (1956), 205–208, 350–359; MR **17**, 946, 15; **18**, 194] and some new results. Sample theorems: If $0<l\leqq 24$, l even, then, for $l(p-1)\equiv 0 \pmod{24}$, $\eta^l(\tau)$ is an eigenfunction of $T(p)=(-1)^{r(p-1)/2}pT_p$ for all p; otherwise $\eta^l(\tau)$ is still an eigenfunction of $T(p^2)$ for all $p>3$ and also for $p=3$ if $3|l$. $\eta^{10}(\tau)$ is an eigenfunction for $p\not\equiv 5 \pmod{12}$, while for $p\equiv 5 \pmod{12}$,

$$\eta^{10}(\tau)=p\cdot a(2p)G_4(\tau)\eta^2(\tau)$$
$$=\tfrac{1}{2}\{\eta^{10}(\tau)+G_4(\tau)\eta^2(\tau)/48\}+\tfrac{1}{2}\{\eta^{10}(\tau)-G_4(\tau)\eta^2(\tau)/48\}.$$

The Dirichlet series connected with the two functions in braces have Euler products, too complicated to be quoted. Setting $\prod_{n=1}^\infty(1-x^n)^l=\sum_{n=0}^\infty p_l(n)x^n$ and $\eta^l(\tau)=\sum_{n=0}^\infty a(n)e^{2\pi i\tau n/24}$, one has $p_l(n)=a(24n+l)$. As a corollary of previous results one has, in particular, $p_{10}(n)=0$ if some prime $\equiv 7$ or $\equiv 11 \pmod{12}$ divides $24n+10$ in an odd power, or if all primes $\equiv 5 \pmod{12}$ divide $24n+10$ in even powers. The powers $\eta^l(\tau)$, $l=14$, 16, 18 and 20 are similarly studied. For odd powers, $\eta^l(\tau)\in\{\Gamma(1), -r, v\}$, r is half an odd integer and use of the generalized operators is essential. While, in general, $T(p)$ cannot be defined, $T(p^2)$ exists and its application to $\eta^l(\tau)$ leads to the result: If $0<l<24$ and l is odd, then $\eta^l(\tau)$ is an eigenfunction of $T(p^2)$ for all $p>3$ and also for $p=3$, if $3|l$. Among the consequences for $p_l(n)$, the following may be quoted: $p_{15}(53n^{2k}+15(n^{2k}-1)/24)=0$ (obtained using Newman's result $p_{15}(53)=0$), and $p(5n+4)\equiv 0 \pmod 5$ and $p(7n+5)\equiv 0 \pmod 7$, as was conjectured by Ramanujan and proven by Rademacher [Trans. Amer. Math. Soc. **51** (1942), 609–636; MR **3**, 271]. Application of $T(p^2)$ to $\vartheta^l(\tau)=\sum_{n=0}^\infty r_l(n)e^{\pi i\tau n}$ ($r_l(n)$=number of representations of n as sum of l squares), l odd, $l<8$, leads to proofs of the (known) formulae for $r_l(p^2)$ ($l=3$, 5, 7). Finally, a study is made of modular forms of non-integral dimensions that have an Euler product. Among the results obtained are: $\eta(\tau)$ and $\eta^3(\tau)$ are the only integral modular forms $\in\{\Gamma(1), -r, v\}$, for which linear relations $f(p\tau)+\alpha\sum_{b=0}^{p-1}f((\tau+Nb)/p)=0$ hold for all primes p with $(p, N)=1$. The book ends with a tabulation of the integral modular forms $\{\Gamma_\theta, -r, v\}$, with r a half odd integer and Euler product of the form $\prod_{(p,N)=1}(1+\alpha^{-1}(p)p^{-1-2s})^{-1}$, where Γ_θ is generated by $\begin{pmatrix}1&2\\0&1\end{pmatrix}$ and $\begin{pmatrix}0&-1\\1&0\end{pmatrix}$.

E. Grosswald (Philadelphia, Pa.).

Citations: MR 3, 271e = P60-1; MR 17, 15d = F30-16; MR 18, 194f = F30-21; MR 18, 194g = F30-22.

Referred to in F10-64, F10-116.

F25-8 **(20# 1679)**

Shimura, Gorô. Correspondances modulaires et les fonctions ζ de courbes algébriques. J. Math. Soc. Japan **10** (1958), 1–28.

Let k be a field of characteristic $\neq 2, 3$; let γ_2, γ_3 be elements of k such that $\gamma_2{}^3-27\gamma_3{}^2\neq 0$; and, in the projective plane, let E_1 be the curve (1) $X_0X_2{}^2=4X_1{}^3-\gamma_2X_0{}^2X_1-\gamma_3X_0{}^3$. Taking $(X_0, X_1, X_2)=(0, 0, 1)$ as unit element and setting in (1) $X=X_1/X_0$, $Y=X_2/X_0$ one obtains the elliptic curve (2) $Y^2=4X^3-\gamma_2X-\gamma_3$. For any natural integer N, let $\mathfrak{M}_N$ be the (complete) field of elliptic modular functions of order ("Stufe") N. $\mathfrak{M}_N$ may be represented by the coordinates of points t such that $Nt=0$ on a curve (2), whose invariant is transcendental over the rationals. One defines a homomorphism λ on this elliptic curve, such that $\nu(\lambda)=p$, where p is a prime. This is called a modular correspondence of degree p. The Hecke operator T_p may be interpreted as the differential of the algebraic correspondence defined by λ. Two congruence relations are proven for modular correspondences. These are used to show that the characteristic values corresponding to the Hecke operator T_p, for cusp forms of degree 2 and for almost all primes p, do not exceed $2p^{\frac{1}{2}}$

in absolute value. Some of the present results generalize those of Eichler [Arch. Math. **5** (1954), 355–366; MR **16**, 116], concerning the relation between the Hecke operators and zeta-functions. *E. Grosswald* (Philadelphia, Pa.)

Citations: MR 16, 116c = N40-24.

Referred to in F25-11, F30-41, F50-24, G05-99, R40-20.

F25-9 **(21# 5618)**

Wohlfahrt, Klaus. Über Operatoren Heckescher Art bei Modulformen reeller Dimension. Math. Nachr. **16** (1957), 233–256.

The author generalizes the theory of Hecke operators to automorphic forms of non-integral dimensions. If f is a modular form of class $K=\{\mathrm{K}, -r, \kappa\}$ (i.e., belongs to the group K, has dimension $-r$ and multiplier system κ) he considers linear combinations $g=\sum_Q c_Q\cdot f|Q$, where Q runs through a finite set of matrices $\begin{pmatrix} a & b\\ c & d\end{pmatrix}$ with integral a, b, c, d such that $ad-bc$ is a fixed positive integer n and where $f(\tau)|Q=(c\tau+d)^{-r}f(Q\tau)$. He tries to choose the coefficients c_Q in such a way that $f\to g$ is a linear mapping of K into the class $\Lambda=\{\Lambda, -r, \lambda\}$.

This leads to the consideration of sums

$$g = \sum (\lambda(V))^{-1}f|Q|V,$$

where V runs through a certain finite set of matrices of Λ (in fact a complete set of representatives of the left cosets of $\Delta=\Lambda\cap Q^{-1}\mathrm{K}Q$ in Λ). It must be assumed that Δ has finite index in Λ and that on Δ the multiplier λ is identical with the multiplier (denoted by $\kappa|Q$) which corresponds on $Q^{-1}\mathrm{K}Q$ with the multiplier κ on K. The mapping $f\to g$ is then denoted by $T_K{}^{\Lambda}\langle Q\rangle$. The definition of this operator applies even to certain subgroups of the group of all real unimodular (2×2)-matrices. In the case of the modular group and if r is an even number $\geqq 4$ the relation with Hecke's operators is easily established by means of a normalized representation of $T_K{}^{\Lambda}\langle Q\rangle$ as a linear combination of operators in which the matrices Q are of type $\begin{pmatrix} a & bN\\ 0 & d\end{pmatrix}$, where $ad=n$, $a>0$, $b \bmod d$, $(a, b, d)=1$. This normalized representation applies to the case in which $\mathrm{K}\cap\Lambda$ contains the principal congruence subgroup $\Gamma(N)$ of level N (and some other conditions are satisfied). It leads also to the relation between the Fourier coefficients in the expansion (at ∞) for f and those in the expansion for $f|T_K{}^{\Lambda}\langle Q\rangle$. The author considers an application of the general theory to the theory of quadratic forms in an odd number of variables. The theta-series corresponding to these quadratic forms (which are modular forms of a dimension $\equiv\frac{1}{2}$ (mod 1)) or certain linear combinations of them can be represented as linear combinations of modular forms of the same class, whose Fourier coefficients satisfy relations of type

$$c(m)c(n) = \sum_{t|(m,n)} \gamma(t)c(mn/t^2)$$

if m and n are odd squares and where $\gamma(t)$ is a certain simple arithmetical function involving quadratic residue symbols. The special case $\vartheta^3(\tau)\eta(\tau)$, where $\vartheta(\tau)=\sum_{n=-\infty}^{+\infty}\exp \pi i\tau n^2$ and $\eta(\tau)$ is Dedekind's function, leads to relations between class numbers of imaginary quadratic number fields as a consequence of the fact that these class numbers can be expressed by means of the number of representations of positive numbers as a sum of three squares. *H. D. Kloosterman* (Leiden)

Referred to in F30-28.

F25-10 **(25# 3016)**

Rankin, R. A.

Multiplicative functions and operators of Hecke type. *Acta Math. Acad. Sci. Hungar.* **13** (1962), 81–89.

Let C, I, P denote, respectively, the set of all complex numbers, the set of all positive integers, and the set of all prime numbers. Let V denote a vector space over a non-trivial field F of scalars, where the zero and the identity elements of F are denoted by 0 and 1, respectively.

A mapping ψ of I into F is said to be completely multiplicative if (i) $\psi(1)=1$, (ii) $\psi(mn)=\psi(m)\psi(n)$ for $(m, n)=1$, and (iii) $\psi(p^k)=\{\psi(p)\}^k$ $(p\in P, k\in I)$.

The author then defines $T(n)$, an operator on V. When these operators satisfy the relation $T(m)T(n)=\sum_{d|(m,n)}\psi(d)T(mn/d^2)$ for all m and n in I (ψ is a given mapping of I into F), the operators are ψ-multiplicative. The author shows that if the operators $T(n)$ are ψ-multiplicative, then, with trivial exceptions, the mapping ψ must be completely multiplicative.

Then come ψ-multiplicative functions, i.e., the functions f defined on I which satisfy $f(m)f(n)=\sum_{d|(m,n)}\psi(d)f(mn/d^2)$ for all m and n in I, where ψ is a given completely multiplicative function. It is shown that, under certain conditions, multiplicative functions are linearly independent; this also has applications to the theory of Hecke's T_n operators. (Hecke's T_n operators are examples of ψ-multiplicative operators.)

Finally, when ψ is a given completely multiplicative function, the author shows how various vector spaces of different dimensions can be constructed on which a set of ψ-multiplicative operators is defined. The construction is suggested by the known connection between the Fourier coefficients of a modular form operated on by a Hecke operator T_n and those of the original form.

B. K. Ghosh (Calcutta)

F25-11 **(27# 5735)**

Rangachari, S. S.

Modulare Korrespondenzen und L-Reihen. *J. Reine Angew. Math.* **205** (1960/61), 119–155.

Die Theorie der Heckeschen Operatoren T_n wurde von Hecke entwickelt [Math. Ann. **114** (1937), 1–28; ibid. **114** (1937), 316–351] und zum Studium der Arithmetik von Modulformen und Thetareihen verwendet. Ein neuer Zugang zum Studium dieser Operatoren wurde von Eichler eröffnet [Arch. Math. **5** (1954), 355–366; MR **16**, 116]. Er hat diese Operatoren für Spitzenformen vom Grad -2 zu einer gewissen Untergruppe der Modulgruppe als Differentiale gewisser Korrespondenzen abgeleitet, wobei diese Korrespondenzen einem geeigneten Körper von Modulfunktionen zugehören. Diese Methode von Eichler wurde von Shimura bei seinen Untersuchungen über Modularkorrespondenzen übernommen [C. R. Acad. Sci. Paris **244** (1957), 2127–2130; MR **19**, 839; J. Math. Soc. Japan **10** (1958), 1–28; MR **20** #1679]. Shimura nimmt die Hauptkongruenzuntergruppe $\Gamma_1(N)$ der Modulgruppe $\Gamma(1)$ und ordnet dieser Gruppe einen gewissen Funktionenkörper K über dem rationalen Zahlkörper Q zu. In dieser Arbeit wird der Funktionenkörper $K(\zeta_N)$ über $Q(\zeta_N)$ näher analysiert; dabei bedeutet ζ_N eine primitive N-te Einheitswurzel. Der Verfasser betrachtet $K(\zeta_N)$ als Galoissche Erweiterung des rationalen Funktionenkörpers mit der Galoisschen Gruppe $\Gamma(1)/\Gamma_1(N)$ und verbindet mit jedem Charakter χ dieser Gruppe eine globale Artinsche-Reihe, die analog zur Hasseschen Zetafunktion von $K(\zeta_N)$ definiert ist. Wenn die Stufe N eine ungerade Primzahl $q\geqq 7$ ist, dann sind diese L-Reihen für gewisse Charaktere χ meromorphe Funktionen. Der Beweis gründet sich auf weiteren Korrespondenzrelationen zwischen den Modularkorrespondenzen und den jenigen Korrespondenzen, die den Elementen der endlichen Gruppe $\Gamma(1)/\Gamma_1(q)$ zugeordnet sind. Ausserdem werden einige Resultate von Hecke über irreduzible Darstellungen von $\Gamma(1)/\Gamma_1(q)$ benutzt. Ferner werden einige weitere Nebenresultate über globale

Artinsche L-Reihen im allgemeinen und einige Beispiele für die Stufe q im besonderen diskutiert.

P. Roquette (Tübingen)

Citations: MR 16, 116d = G30-15; MR 19, 839e = F25-6; MR 20# 1679 = F25-8.

F25-12 (28# 3011)

Mori, Mitsuya

Über die rationale Darstellbarkeit der Heckeschen Operatoren.

J. Math. Soc. Japan **15** (1963), 256–267.

Let $\mathbf{Q}$ and $\mathbf{C}$ stand for the fields of rational and complex numbers, respectively; $\mathfrak{H}$ the upper half-plane, Γ a Fuchsian group such that $\mathfrak{H}/\Gamma$ has finite measure, $\mathfrak{K}$ is the field of functions (algebraic, of one variable over $\mathbf{C}$) automorphic under Γ and $\mathfrak{S}_{2\kappa}(\Gamma)$ the vector space of cusp forms of dimension -2κ. ϕ stands for an indefinite algebra of quaternions over $\mathbf{Q}$ of discriminant $d(\phi)$, $\mathfrak{o}$ a maximal order of ϕ, $\mathfrak{a}$ a (two-sided) ideal of $\mathfrak{o}$, Γ_Ξ the group of units of $\mathfrak{o}$ of norm 1; $\Gamma_{\mathfrak{a}}=\{\gamma\in\Gamma_\Xi \mid \gamma\equiv 1 \pmod{\mathfrak{a}}\}$. It may be shown that $\Gamma_{\mathfrak{a}}$ is a Fuchsian group. If $\mathfrak{a}$ and $d(\phi)$ are coprime, then $\mathfrak{a}=N\mathfrak{o}$ (N a positive integer), the group $\Gamma_{\mathfrak{a}}$ is denoted by $\Gamma_N(\mathfrak{o})$ and generalizes the classical principal congruence subgroup $\Gamma(N)$ of level ("Stufe") N. Indeed, if ϕ contains any divisors of zero, then $\phi=M_2(\mathbf{Q})$ (ring of 2×2 matrices over $\mathbf{Q}$) and $\Gamma_N(\mathfrak{o})$ is isomorphic to $\Gamma(N)$. The purpose of the paper is to show that the linear transformations of $\mathfrak{S}_{2\kappa}(\Gamma_N(\mathfrak{o}))$, induced by the (generalized) Hecke operators $T(n; N\mathfrak{o})$, may be rationally represented. In the classical case $\phi=M_2(\mathbf{Q})$; this result can be obtained by combining Eichler's trace formula for the Hecke operators T_n [Eichler, Math. Z. **67** (1957), 267–298; MR **19**, 740] with theorems of Petersson [Math. Ann. **116** (1939), 401–412; ibid. **117** (1939), 39–64; MR **1**, 294; ibid. **117** (1940), 277–300; MR **2**, 151]. Here the result is obtained in the full generality stated above. The proof is rather long and somewhat involved, and will not be described here.

E. Grosswald (Philadelphia, Pa.)

Citations: MR 1, 294c = F65-1; MR 2, 151a = F25-2; MR 19, 740a = F15-12.

F25-13 (34# 7470)

Ihara, Yasutaka

Hecke polynomials as congruence ζ functions in elliptic modular case.

Ann. of Math. (2) **85** (1967), 267–295.

This is a surprisingly beautiful combination of ideas in the theories of elliptic and modular functions, first suggested by M. Kuga and M. Sato, but the difficulties in its completion are equally impressive. The aim is to establish Ramanujan's conjecture on the modular form $\Delta(\tau)$ and its generalization by Petersson in the case of level 1 as special cases of Weil's conjecture on the zeta functions of non singular algebraic varieties.

Let p be a prime; to avoid formal complications, $p>3$ is assumed. F_p means the prime field of p elements and Ω a universal field of characteristic p. For a variable z over Ω, form the elliptic curve E_z with the Weierstrass normal form $y^2=4x^3-tx-t$, with $t=27z(1-z)^{-1}$. The algebraic variety in question is the product $V_r=(z)\times E_z\times\cdots\times E_z$ with r copies of E_z and with (z) meaning the affine straight line. In actual fact, however, this is a simplification, and the E_z have to be replaced by "canonical families" of elliptic curves in which t is multiplied by $cz^m(1-z)^n$ with $c\in F_p$, $m, n\in\mathbf{Z}$. (These families consist of eight inequivalent curves having the same invariant j.) V_r has singularities at $z=0$ and 1 (and at $z=\infty$). The meaning of these canonical families seems to be to secure all elliptic curves with absolute algebraic invariants j, except $j=0$ or 1, to occur as specializations of E_z.

The logarithm of the zeta function $Z_r(u)$ of V_r can be explicitly computed using results of M. Deuring [Abh. Math. Sem. Univ. Hamburg **14** (1941), 197–272; MR **3**, 104]. These tell how many elliptic curves with given invariant exist, whether they are singular or supersingular, and what their zeta function is and especially the number of their points in a given finite field.

On the other hand, let S_k ($k=2, 4, \cdots$) be the space of modular cusp forms of level 1 and weight $-k$, and $T_k(n)$ the matrix representing the Hecke operator $T(n)$ in S_k. With I the unit matrix, call $H_k(u)=\det(I-T_k(p)u+Ip^{k-1}u)$ the Hecke polynomial of weight $-k$ corresponding to the prime p. The generalised Ramanujan conjecture states that its roots have absolute values $p^{-1/2}$. A formula of A. Selberg [J. Indian Math. Soc. (N.S.) **20** (1956), 47–87; MR **19**, 531] and the reviewer [Math. Z. **67** (1957), 267–298; MR **19**, 740] allows one to compute

$$\operatorname{trace}(I-T_k(p)u+Ip^{k-1}u)^{-1} = d\log H_k(u)/du.$$

Comparison of the results of the preceding two paragraphs leads to a formula expressing $H_k(u)$ as a finite product of (positive and negative) powers of some zeta functions $Z_r(p^n u)$ with different r and n and of an elementary factor which is explicitly given. That $\log Z_r(u)$ and $d\log H_k(u)/du$ have something in common is evident at first glance, but the distinguishing of several cases, and extended computational work, is required to establish the final formula.

The author is well aware of the fact that, due to the singular points $z=0, 1, \infty$ of the V_r, Ramanujan's conjecture has not yet fully been reduced to that of Weil. He says that he has vainly sought for a "good" complete and non-singular model of V_r which could resolve the difficulty.

M. Eichler (Basel)

Citations: MR 3, 104g = G20-4; MR 19, 531g = F60-2; MR 19, 740a = F15-12.

Referred to in F25-23.

F25-14 (34# 7471)

Petersson, Hans

Über eine Spurbildung bei automorphen Formen.

Math. Z. **96** (1967), 296–332.

Let Γ be a subgroup of SL$(2, R)$ which, acting as a group of fractional linear transformations of the complex upper half plane, has a finite fundamental domain. Furthermore, let Δ be a subgroup of finite index and $\Gamma=\sum\Delta Q_i$ the division into right cosets. If $f(z)$ is an automorphic function with respect to Δ, $s_{\Gamma/\Delta}(f(z))=\sum_i f(Q_i(z))$ is an automorphic function with respect to Γ. The linear operator $s_{\Gamma/\Delta}$ is independent of the choice of the Q_i; it is the trace with respect to the fields of automorphic functions corresponding to Δ and Γ. This trace operator can be defined in the general situation when $f(z)$ is an automorphic form of complex degree with an arbitrary system of multiplicators (§§ 1, 2). In § 3 the behaviour of fixed points of Γ with respect to Δ is investigated and the Fourier coefficients for a parabolic fixed point of $s_{\Gamma/\Delta}(f)$ are expressed as finite sums over the appropriate Fourier coefficients of f. This can also be done with "Fourier" expansions in a pair of hyperbolic fixed points. The traces of special Poincaré series can explicitly be determined; some of them are, of course, 0 (§ 4). In § 5 Poincaré series are studied which are orthogonal to all cusp forms in the sense of the author's scalar product. § 6 contains some complements of the theory. Particularly interesting is the subgroup Γ_ϑ of the elliptic modular group Γ, generated by the matrices $\begin{pmatrix}1&2\\0&1\end{pmatrix}$ and $\begin{pmatrix}0&1\\-1&0\end{pmatrix}$. All cusp forms of real degree $-s/2$ and multiplicator λ^s, where λ is that of Dedekind's function $\eta(z)$, and all integral modular forms orthogonal to these cusp forms are constructed by means of $\eta(z)$.

M. Eichler (Basel)

Referred to in F25-26.

F25-15 **(34# 7472)**

Rankin, R. A.

Hecke operators on congruence subgroups of the modular group.

Math. Ann. **168** (1967), 40–58.

Let $\Gamma(N)$ be the principal congruence subgroup of the modular group of level N, and let Γ be the subgroup of $\Gamma(1)$ such that $\Gamma(1) \supset \Gamma \supset \Gamma(N)$. Denote by $\{\Gamma, k, v\}$ the space of modular forms belonging to Γ of dimension $-k$ and multiplier system v. It is shown that the Hecke operator T_n of the group $\Gamma(N)$ has a kind of projective representation in $\{\Gamma, k, v\}$, provided $(n, N) = 1$ and k is an integer. The author considers the multiplicative properties of the Fourier coefficients of the modular forms belonging to Γ, where Γ is the commutator subgroup $\Gamma'(1)$ or the group associated to certain theta functions. The method is based on the direct sum decomposition of $\{\Gamma, k, v\}$ by means of the abelian character of $\Gamma(1)/\Gamma$.

S. Konno (Osaka)

F25-16 **(34# 7727)**

Tanaka, Shun'ichi

On some applications of Selberg's trace formula.

Proc. Japan Acad. **42** (1966), 327–329.

The author announces applications of A. Selberg's trace formula [J. Indian Math. Soc. (N.S.) **20** (1956), 47–87; MR **19**, 531] for certain discrete subgroups of $G = \mathrm{SL}(2, \mathbf{R})$. Let H be the upper half plane. Dividing G by its center, we have that the quotient Γ acts effectively on H, with $M = \Gamma/H$ compact. The discussion of the eigenvalue problem $\Delta = -y^2(\partial^2/\partial x^2 + \partial^2/\partial y^2)$ in $L^2(M)$ yields (i) an asymptotic formula for $\alpha(\lambda)/\lambda$, where $\alpha(\lambda)$ is the number of elements in the discrete spectrum Λ of Δ which are smaller than λ, (ii) the unique determination of Γ by Λ, and (iii) the triviality of any deformation of Γ that fixes Λ. In the case of the modular group, M is no longer compact. Λ has a non-vanishing continuous part. For its discrete part, a formula as in (i) is valid.

The results (i) and (iii) are also contained in a paper by I. M. Gel'fand [Proc. Internat. Congr. Mathematicians (Stockholm, 1962), pp. 74–85, Inst. Mittag-Leffler, Djursholm, 1963; MR **31** #273]. *H. Heyer* (Erlangen)

Citations: MR 19, 531g = F60-2.

Referred to in F25-17.

F25-17 **(36# 312)**

Tanaka, Shun'ichi

Selberg's trace formula and spectrum.

Osaka J. Math. **3** (1966), 205–216.

Detailed proofs of results announced previously [Proc. Japan Acad. **42** (1966), 327–329; MR **34** #7727].

H. Heyer (Erlangen)

Citations: MR 34# 7727 = F25-16.

F25-18 **(35# 2830)**

Satake, Ichirô

Spherical functions and Ramanujan conjecture.

Algebraic Groups and Discontinuous Subgroups (Proc. Sympos. Pure Math., Boulder, Colo., 1965), *pp.* 258–264. *Amer. Math. Soc., Providence, R.I.*, 1966.

Let $\mathfrak{S}_\nu$ be the space of all cusp forms of weight $\nu > 0$ (ν even). The Ramanujan-Peterson conjecture states that for all prime p the eigenvalues of the representation on $\mathfrak{S}_\nu$ of the Hecke operator T_p have absolute value $\leqq 2p^{(\nu-1)/2}$. The author translates this conjecture in the language of spherical functions on the p-adic groups (including $p = \infty$) and the adele group attached to the algebraic group $G = \mathrm{PL}(2)$ defined over $\mathbf{Q}$, and alludes to a generalization for the higher-dimensional case. Besides the obvious notations $G_{\mathbf{Z}}$, $G_{\mathbf{Q}}$, $G_p = G_{\mathbf{Q}_p}$, G_A, put $K_p = G_{\mathbf{Z}_p}$ ($p \neq \infty$), $K_\infty = 0(2, \mathbf{R})/\pm 1$, $K = \prod_p K_p$ and $\mathscr{H} = G_\infty/K_\infty$ the upper-half plane. To each $f \in \mathfrak{S}_\nu$ associate a function F on G_∞ given by $F(g) = f(g(i))j(g, i)^{\nu/2}$, where $i = \sqrt{-1}$, $j(g, z) = (\det g)(cz+d)^{-2}$, $z \in \mathscr{H}$, $g = \begin{pmatrix} a & b \\ c & d \end{pmatrix} \in G_\infty$. F has the following properties: (i) $F(\gamma g k) = F(g)\chi_{-\nu}(k)$, $\gamma \in G_{\mathbf{Z}}$, $g \in G_\infty$, $k \in K_\infty$, (ii) $F * \phi = \lambda_\phi F$ for all $\phi \in L_\infty^{(\nu)}$, (iii) $F \in L^2(G_{\mathbf{Z}} \backslash G_\infty)$, where $\chi_\nu(k) = e^{\nu i\theta}$ if k is the rotation of angle θ, and $L_\infty^{(\nu)}$ is the algebra (with convolution product) of all $\mathbf{C}$-valued continuous functions ϕ on G_∞ of compact support such that $\phi(kgk') = \phi(g)\chi_\nu(k)\chi_\nu(k')$, $k, k' \in K_\infty$, $g \in G_\infty$. One knows that there is a unique positive-definite zonal spherical function ω on G_∞ (of type χ_ν) such that $\lambda_\phi = \hat{\omega}(\phi) = \int_{G_\infty} \phi(g)\omega(g^{-1})\,dg$ and that ω belongs to the value $s = s_\infty = \pm(\nu-1)/2$ by the "parametrization" of zonal spherical functions on G_∞: $\omega = \omega_{s_\infty}$. The correspondence $f \leftrightarrow F$ gives the isomorphism $\mathfrak{S}_\nu \approx \mathfrak{M}_{G_{\mathbf{Z}}}(\chi_{-\nu}, \omega_{s_\infty})$, the latter being the space of all $G_{\mathbf{Z}}$-automorphic right spherical functions of type $\chi_{-\nu}$ belonging to ω_{s_∞}. We now pass from $G_{\mathbf{Z}} \backslash G_\infty$ to $G_{\mathbf{Q}} \backslash G_A$. Since G has class number 1, i.e. $G_A = G_{\mathbf{Q}}(K_0 \times G_\infty)$ with $K_0 = \prod_{p \neq \infty} K_p$, the above F gives rise to a function $\tilde{F}$ on G_A by $\tilde{F}(g) = F(G_\infty)$ if $g = \xi(k_0 \times g_\infty)$, $\xi \in G_{\mathbf{Q}}$, $k_0 \in K_0$, $g_\infty \in G_\infty$. By (i), $\tilde{F}$ is well-defined and has properties similar to (i), (ii), (iii), i.e. $\tilde{F}$ is a $G_{\mathbf{Q}}$-automorphic right spherical function on G_A (of type $\chi_{-\nu}$ at infinity). Let $\tilde{\mathfrak{S}}_\nu$ be the space of all $\tilde{F}$ with those properties. Denote by L_p the algebra of all $\mathbf{C}$-valued continuous functions ϕ on G_p of compact support such that $\phi(kgk') = \phi(g)$, $kk' \in K_p$, $g \in G_p$, and put $L^{(\nu)}(G_A, K) = \prod_{p \neq \infty} L_p \times L_\infty^{(\nu)}$. It then turns out that the decomposition of $\tilde{\mathfrak{S}}_\nu \cong \mathfrak{M}_{G_{\mathbf{Z}}}(\chi_{-\nu}, \omega_{s_\infty})$ into eigenspaces under the action of $L^{(\nu)}(G_A, K)$ by convolution from the right:

$$\mathfrak{M}_{G_{\mathbf{Z}}}(\chi_{-\nu}, \omega_{s_\infty}) = \textstyle\sum_j \oplus \mathfrak{M}_{G_{\mathbf{Q}}}(1 \times \chi_{-\nu}, \omega_0^{(j)} \times \omega_{s_\infty}),$$

is analogous to the decomposition of $\mathfrak{S}_\nu$ with respect to the action of the usual Hecke operator. If $\tilde{F} \in \mathfrak{M}_{G_{\mathbf{Q}}}(1 \times \chi_{-\nu}, \omega_0^{(j)} \times \omega_{s_\infty})$ with $\omega_0^{(j)} = (\cdots, \omega_{s_p}, \cdots)$, $s_p \in \mathbf{C}$, $p \neq \infty$, and if the corresponding $f \in \mathfrak{S}_\nu$ belongs to the eigenvalue a_p of T_p for all $p \neq \infty$, the author shows that $a_p = p^{(\nu-1)/2}(p^{s_p} + p^{-s_p})$ and hence the Ramanujan-Peterson conjecture is equivalent to saying that s_p is purely imaginary for all $p \neq \infty$, i.e., $\omega_0^{(j)}$ corresponds to the "principal series" at each p. *T. Ono* (Philadelphia, Pa.)

F25-19 **(35# 2831)**

Tsukamoto, Takashi

On the dimension of the space of automorphic forms. (Japanese)

Sûgaku **13** (1961/62), 154–157.

As an application of the theory of A. Selberg [J. Indian Math. Soc. (N.S.) **20** (1956), 47–87; MR **19**, 531], the author gives an explicit formula for the dimension of the space of cusp forms with respect to ordinary Fuchsian groups. {This result is contained in a paper of H. Shimizu [Ann. of Math. (2) **77** (1963), 33–71; MR **26** #2641], where more general cases are treated.} *T. Kubota* (Nagoya)

Citations: MR 19, 531g = F60-2; MR 26# 2641 = F55-14.

F25-20 **(37# 2691)**

Rademacher, Hans

Eine Bemerkung über die Heckeschen Operatoren $T(n)$.

Abh. Math. Sem. Univ. Hamburg **31** (1967), 149–151.

The author studies Hecke's operator $T(n)$ [E. Hecke, Math. Ann. **114** (1937), 1–28, especially 12–15], and shows that $T(p^r)$ (p a prime) is essentially a Tschebyscheff polynomial of the second kind in $T(p)$.

That $T(p^r)$ is a polynomial in $T(p)$ (of degree r) and that $T(mn)=T(m)T(n)$ for $(m,n)=1$ had previously been proved by Hecke. *S. L. Segal* (Rochester, N.Y.)

F25-21 (38# 3231)

Fomenko, O. M.

A formula for the trace of Hecke's operator in the space of parabolic forms relative to a principal congruence subgroup. (Russian. Uzbek summary)

Izv. Akad. Nauk UzSSR Ser. Fiz.-Mat. Nauk **12** (1968), *no.* 1, 26–28.

The author announces a formula, for the trace of Hecke's operator in the space of parabolic forms relative to a principal congruence subgroup, which is too long to quote here. His formula resembles the well-known Selberg trace formula [J. Indian Math. Soc. (N.S.) **20** (1956), 47–87; MR **19**, 531]. *S. Chowla* (University Park, Pa.)

Citations: MR 19, 531g = F60-2.

F25-22 (38# 4413)

Eichler, M.

Einige Anwendungen der Spurformel im Bereich der Modularkorrespondenzen.

Math. Ann. **168** (1967), 128–137.

Sei $\Gamma=\Gamma(1)=\mathrm{SL}(2,\mathbf{Z})$, $\Gamma(N)$ die Hauptkongruenzgruppe zur Stufe N, d.h. $\Gamma(N)=\left\{M\in\Gamma\,;\,M\equiv\pm\begin{pmatrix}1&0\\0&1\end{pmatrix}\bmod N\right\}$, $\varphi(\tau)$ eine Spitzenform zur Gruppe $\Gamma(N)$ geraden Gewichts $2h\geqq -2$. Übt man auf die Spitzenformen $\varphi(\tau)$ eine Substitution $M\in\Gamma$ aus, so erhält man eine Darstellung $S(\mathfrak{M})$ der Faktorgruppe $\mathfrak{M}=\Gamma|M(N)$. Die Frage nach den Vielfachheiten der irreduziblen Darstellungen von $S(\mathfrak{M})$ ist sehr interessant und ist von E. Hecke, H. Feldmann und anderen in mehreren Arbeiten untersucht worden. Vgl. dazu das Inhaltsverzeichnis der vorliegenden Arbeit. Der Verfasser zeigt, daß diese Vielfachheiten auch mit Hilfe der Spurformel für Modulkorrespondenzen berechnet werden können.

Hinzuweisen ist ferner auf die neuen Modulkorrespondenzen $\hat{T}_n$, welche vom Verfasser mit Hilfe der Heckeschen T_n-Operatoren wie folgt definiert werden:

Sei n eine zu N teilerfremde natürliche Zahl, ferner sei die Kongruenz $n\equiv t^2 \bmod N$ lösbar. t sei eine feste Lösung und $U_t\in M$ mit $U_t\equiv\begin{pmatrix}t&0\\0&t^{-1}\end{pmatrix}\bmod N$. Dann ist $\hat{T}_n=T_nU_t=U_tT_n=\bigcup\Gamma(N)U_tU_a{}^{-1}\begin{pmatrix}a&bN\\0&d\end{pmatrix}$. Es gelingt eine weitgehend explizite (allerdings ziemlich komplizierte) Formel für die Spur $\sigma(\hat{T}_n)$ anzugeben, $\hat{T}_n$ als Operator auf den Spitzenformen $\varphi(\tau)$ aufgefaßt. Diese Formel ist von Interesse, da sie die Klassenzahlen imaginär quadratischer Zahlkörper enthält und damit das Verschwinden von $\sigma(\hat{T}_n)$ Relationen zwischen diesen Klassenzahlen liefert. Am Ende der Arbeit sind zum Teil neue explizite Formeln für die Vielfachheiten der Darstellung $S(\mathfrak{M})$ für eine ungerade Primzahlstufe N angegeben.

H. Popp (Heidelberg)

F25-23 (38# 4481)

Morita, Yasuo

Hecke polynomials $H_k^{(p)}(u)$ ($p=2$ or 3).

J. Fac. Sci. Univ. Tokyo Sect. I **15** (1968), 99–105.

Y. Ihara [Ann. of Math. (2) **85** (1967), 267–295; MR **34** #7470] determined the Euler factors of the Weil zeta function of a certain fibre variety connected with elliptic and elliptic modular functions. He left out the contributions of the exceptional primes $p=2$ and 3. The present author fills this gap. Furthermore, he corrects a minor error in Ihara's formula. *M. Eichler* (Basel)

Citations: MR 34# 7470 = F25-13.

F25-24 (38# 5718)

Petersson, Hans

Über Differentialoperatoren und die Kroneckersche Potenzdarstellung bei automorphen Formen.

J. Reine Angew. Math. **231** (1968), 163–191.

Let Γ be a horocyclic group of the first kind and let $\phi\in\{\Gamma,-r,v\}$, so that ϕ is an automorphic form of dimension $-r$ belonging to Γ, with multiplier system v. It is well known that

$$W(\tau,\phi)=r\phi\phi''-(r+1)(\phi')^2\in\{\Gamma,-2r-4,v^2\},$$

and more general polynomials in ϕ and its derivatives having similar properties are known; see the reviewer [J. Indian Math. Soc. (N.S.) **20** (1956), 103–116; MR **18**, 571], for example. In his first section, the author expresses these results in a vectorial form, which he generalizes in later sections. Thus he writes

$$f(\tau,\phi)=\begin{pmatrix}\tau\phi'(\tau)+r\phi(\tau)\\ \phi'(\tau)\end{pmatrix}=U^\tau\begin{pmatrix}r\phi(\tau)\\ \phi'(\tau)\end{pmatrix},$$

where $U=\begin{pmatrix}1&\tau\\0&1\end{pmatrix}$, so that $W(\tau,\phi)=\det(f(\tau,\phi),f'(\tau,\phi))$. Several applications to particular modular forms are given.

A theory of automorphic vector forms is then set up as follows. Let n be a positive integer and put

$$S=\begin{pmatrix}a&b\\c&d\end{pmatrix},\quad w=\begin{pmatrix}w_1\\w_2\end{pmatrix},$$

where all entries belong to the field C of complex numbers, and let P_n be the module of homogeneous polynomials of dimension $n-1$ in w_1, w_2 over C. Define $h_S\colon P_n\to P_n$ by $h_S(\phi(w))=\phi(Sw)$, for $\phi(w)\in P_n$, and let $q(w)$ be a column vector with elements $\phi_j(w)$ $(1\leqq j\leqq n)$, forming a basis for P_n. Then $h_S(q(w))=q(Sw)=\Lambda(S)q(w)$, where $\Lambda(S)$ is an $n\times n$ matrix over C. It is easily verified that $\Lambda(S_1S_2)=\Lambda(S_1)\Lambda(S_2)$, so that every basis of P_n yields a representation Λ of the group $\mathrm{GL}(2,C)$ of degree n. For the particular choice of basis $\phi_j(w)=w_1{}^{n-j}w_2{}^{j-1}$, put $\Lambda(S)=D(S)=(d_{jk}(S))$; then

$$(aw_1+bw_2)^{n-j}(cw_1+dw_2)^{j-1}=\textstyle\sum_{k=1}^n d_{jk}(S)w_1{}^{n-k}w_2{}^{k-1}$$

and this relation enables the matrices $D(S)$ to be calculated. Note that $D(S)=S$, when $n=2$.

Now let $f(\tau)=(f_j(\tau))$—an $n\times 1$ column vector—and define $f^S(\tau)=D(S^{-1})f(S\tau)(c\tau+d)^{-r-n+1}$ for fixed $r\in C$ and any S. Then f is called an automorphic vector form in $\{\Gamma,-r,v;n\}$ if each component f_j is meromorphic on the upper half-plane, and if $f^L(\tau)=v(L)f(\tau)$ $(L\in\Gamma)$; two further regularity conditions of the usual kind are also imposed. It is shown that, provided that Γ contains parabolic matrices and f does not vanish identically, the components f_j of f are linearly independent. This is deduced from a general theorem that associates with each vector form f another vector function g for which each component $g_j\in\{\Gamma,-(r+2)j,v\}$ $(1\leqq j\leqq n)$. The construction of g is too complicated to be summarised, but depends essentially on the existence of a class of functions $\Lambda(\tau)$, whose most important property is that they satisfy the equation $\Lambda(S\tau)(c\tau+d)^{-2}=\Lambda(\tau)+c/(c\tau+d)$ for all $S\in\Gamma$.

Finally, the differential operators of the first section are generalized by means of the representation D. In place of $f(\tau,\phi)$ $(n=2)$, we have, for arbitrary $n\geqq 2$, the vector form

$$e(\tau, \phi) = D(U^{\tau})\left(\binom{r+n-2}{n-j}(n-j)!\phi^{(j-1)}(\tau)\right),$$

which is shown to belong to $\{\Gamma, -r, v; n\}$, when $\phi \in \{\Gamma, -r, v\}$. The generalization of $W(\tau, \phi)$ is the Wronskian $W(\tau, \phi) = \det(\phi(\tau), \phi'(\tau), \cdots, \phi^{(n-1)}(\tau))$. When $\phi \in \{\Gamma, -r, v; n\}$, it is shown that $W(\tau, \phi) \in \{\Gamma, -n(r+2n-2), v^n\}$. These are only a few of the many different results obtained.

R. A. Rankin (Glasgow)

Citations: MR 18, 571c = F10-47.
Referred to in F10-108.

F25-25 (39# 6825)

Goldstein, L. J.

A necessary and sufficient condition for the Riemann hypothesis for zeta functions attached to eigenfunctions of the Hecke operators.

Acta Arith. **15** (1968/69), 205–215.

Γ denotes the modular group $SL_2(Z)$; σ_k denotes the space of cusp forms of weight k associated to Γ. If $f \in \sigma_k(\Gamma)$, let $f(\tau) = \sum_{n=1}^{\infty} c_n \exp(2\pi i n\tau)$, $\mathrm{Im}(\tau) > 0$ be the Fourier expansion of f about the cusp $i\omega$. The author states the principal facts about the Hecke operators T_n [E. Hecke, Math. Ann. **114** (1937), 1–28; ibid. **114** (1937), 316–351], in particular, that the simultaneous eigenfunctions of the Hecke operators, normalized so that their first coefficient is 1, have associated zeta-functions $\varphi(s) = \sum_{n=1}^{\infty} c_n n^{-s}$, which converge absolutely for $\mathrm{Re}(s) > (k+1)/2$ and converge for $\mathrm{Re}(s) > k/2$, with an Euler product of the form $\varphi(s) = \prod_p (1 - c_p p^{-s} + p^{k-1-2s})^{-1}$ (where the product is extended over all primes p; Hecke [loc. cit., Sätze 40 and 42]). The theory of the function $\varphi(s)$ is completely analogous to the theory of the Riemann zeta-function. The analytic continuation as an entire function satisfies the functional equation

$$(2\pi)^{-s}\Gamma(s)\varphi(s) = (-1)^{k/2}(2\pi)^{s-k}\Gamma(k-s)\varphi(k-s).$$

$1/\varphi(s)$ can be expanded in a Dirichlet series $1/\varphi(s) = \sum_{n=1}^{\infty} \mu(n:\varphi)n^{-s}$, absolutely convergent for $\mathrm{Re}(s) > (k+1)/2$. The function $\mu(n:\varphi)$ can be regarded as a generalization of the Möbius function $\mu(n)$ in the Riemann zeta-function $1/\zeta(s) = \sum_{n=1}^{\infty} \mu(n)n^{-s}$, $\mathrm{Re}(s) > 1$. The function $\mu(n:\varphi)$ is defined as follows: (a) $p =$ prime, $\mu(p:\varphi) = -c_p$, $\mu(p^2:\varphi) = p^{k-1}$, $\mu(p^r, \varphi) = 0$ for other r. (b) m, n positive integers, relatively prime: $\mu(mn:\varphi) = \mu(m:\varphi)\cdot\mu(n:\varphi)$. The main goal of this paper is the proof that the Riemann hypothesis for $\varphi(s)$ (that is, all non trivial zeros of $\varphi(s)$ are on the line $\mathrm{Re}(s) = k/2$) is equivalent to the convergence of the series defined by $\prod_p (1 - c_p p^{-s} + p^{k-1-2s}) = \sum_{n=1}^{\infty} \mu(n:\varphi)n^{-s}$ for $\mathrm{Re}(s) > k/2$. Another result: A necessary and sufficient condition that φ satisfy the Riemann hypothesis is that $\lambda(x) = \sum_{n<x} \mu(n:\varphi) = O(x^{k/2+\varepsilon})$, $x \to \infty$, for all $\varepsilon > 0$, where the constant in the O-term depends on ε. Moreover, $\lambda(x) = \theta(x^{\theta+\varepsilon})$ for all $\varepsilon > 0$ ($\theta =$ sup(abcissae of the zeros of $\varphi(s)$; $\theta \geqq k/2$)).

Based on some empirical evidence, the author ends with the following conjecture, an analogue of Mertens' conjecture: $|\sum_{n<x} \mu(n:\varphi)| < x^{k/2}$. It is clear that this conjecture implies the Riemann hypothesis. *S. C. van Veen* (Delft)

F25-26 (41# 154)

Petersson, Hans

Über Funktionen mit dem Transformationsverhalten der logarithmischen Ableitungen automorpher Formen und die Resultatfunktionen des Heckeschen Summationsverfahrens.

Ann. Acad. Sci. Fenn. Ser. A I No. 445 (1969), 29 *pp.*

In previous papers [Abh. Math. Sem. Univ. Hamburg **31** (1967), 191–198; MR **37** #4021; Math. Z. **96** (1967), 296–332; MR **34** #7471], the author introduced the following concepts: (a) the "double slash" operator $f(\tau)\|S = f(S\tau)(c\tau+d)^{-2} - c/(c\tau+d)$, for $S \in \Gamma$, Γ discrete, $\Gamma \subset SL(2, \mathbf{R})$; (b) spaces of functions $\mathfrak{L}^1 \subset \mathfrak{L}^2 \subset \mathfrak{L}^3 \subset \mathfrak{L}$, all depending on Γ (whenever relevant, this is indicated by a subscript) and defined as follows: $f \in \mathfrak{L}$ if and only if f is meromorphic in the upper half plane $\mathfrak{H}$ and the fundamental domain $\mathfrak{F}_\Gamma$ of Γ contains only a finite number of poles of $f(\tau)$; $f(\tau)\|\mathfrak{L} = f(\tau)$ for $\mathfrak{L} \in \Gamma$; the function $f_A(\tau)$ defined by $f(\tau) = f_A(\tau)\|A$ has only a finite number of negative terms in its Fourier expansion. Let f be automorphic under Γ, of "weight" $-r$ and multiplier system v, i.e., $f \in \{\Gamma, -r, v\}$, and, for $r \neq 0$ set $\Lambda(\tau, f) = r^{-1}(f'/f)(\tau)$. In particular, if the divisor of $f(\tau) = f(\tau, \tau_0)$ reduces to a single place $\tau_0 \in \mathfrak{F}_\Gamma$ (either a cusp, or in $\mathfrak{H}$), one writes simply $\Lambda_0(\tau, \tau_0)$ for $\Lambda(\tau, f(\tau, \tau_0))$ and $\mathfrak{L}^1$ is defined as the set of linear combinations of functions $\Lambda_0(\tau, \tau_0)$ with real coefficients of sum equal to one; $\mathfrak{L}^2$ is similarly defined with complex coefficients, while $\mathfrak{L}^3$ is the set of those functions of $\mathfrak{L}$ that are holomorphic in $\mathfrak{H}$ and at the cusps, except, possibly, for simple poles. (c) A trace operator $\mathrm{Sp}_{\Delta/\Gamma} f(\tau) = \sum_Q v^{-1}(Q)f(\tau)|Q$, where $\Delta \subset \Gamma$ are horocyclic groups of the first kind, $f \in \{\Delta, -r, v\}$, the "slash" is the usual Hecke "slash" and the (necessarily finite) sum is taken over a complete set of representatives Q of (right) cosets of Γ mod Δ. Among the numerous, interesting results of the present paper are the following: The author determines necessary and sufficient conditions for the existence (as finite Cauchy principal values) of the scalar products $[\Phi_1, \Phi_2; \Gamma] = \iint_{\mathfrak{F}_\Gamma} \Phi_1{}^*\overline{\Phi}_2{}^*\, dxdy$ and $[\Phi, f; \Gamma] = \iint_{\mathfrak{F}_\Gamma} \Phi\cdot\bar{f}\, dxdy$ ($\Phi_1, \Phi_2 \in \mathfrak{L}, f \in \{\Gamma, -2, 1\}$, $\Phi^*(\tau) = \Phi(\tau) + (2i\,\mathrm{Im}\,\tau)^{-1}$). If any of the conditions is violated, then the corresponding Cauchy principal value of $\iint_{\mathfrak{B}}$ ($\mathfrak{B} \subset \mathfrak{F}_\Gamma$) approaches ∞ as $\mathfrak{B} \to \mathfrak{F}_\Gamma$. A (fairly complicated) explicit formula is obtained for $[\Phi, f; \Gamma)$ if f has no residues at its poles (i.e., is essentially an abelian differential of the second kind). As easy consequences one obtains now a much simpler formula for $[\Phi_1, f; \Gamma)$ if $\Phi_1 \in \mathfrak{L}^1$, and $[\Phi_1, f; \Gamma) = 0$ if f has no poles (i.e., is of the first kind). One also obtains the characterization of functions of $\mathfrak{L}^2$ (in $\mathfrak{L}^3$), which was the main theorem in the first quoted previous paper: $\Phi_3 \in \mathfrak{L}^3$ belongs to $\mathfrak{L}^2$ if and only if $[\Phi_3, f_1; \Gamma) = 0$ for all $f_1 \in \{\Gamma, -2, 1\}$ of the first kind. Also, a function of $\mathfrak{L}^2$ is uniquely determined by its residues. If $\Delta \subset \Gamma$ are horocyclic of the first kind, with $\mu = [\Gamma:\Delta] < \infty$, then the trace operator maps $\mathfrak{L}_\Delta$ into $\mathfrak{L}_\Gamma$. The trace operator is transitive. If $\varphi \in \mathfrak{L}_\Delta$, $\Phi \in \mathfrak{L}_\Gamma$, $f \in \{\Gamma, -2, 1\}$ and $g \in \{\Delta, -2, 1\}$, then (assuming the existence of the scalar products as Cauchy principal values) $[\varphi, \Phi; \Delta] = \mu[\mathrm{Sp}_{\Delta/\Gamma}\varphi, \Phi; \Gamma]$, $[\varphi, f; \Delta) = \mu[\mathrm{Sp}_{\Delta/\Gamma}\varphi, f; \Gamma)$ and $[\Phi, g; \Delta) = [\Phi, \mathrm{Sp}_{\Delta/\Gamma}\, g; \Gamma)$. In the last part of the paper the author discusses functions of $\{\Gamma, -2, v\}$ (Γ congruence subgroup of the modular group) and the connections of the present results with some of Hecke's work. Sample result: If $G_{-2}(0, \tau; A, N) = \lim_{s\to 0} G_{-2}(s, \tau; A, N)$ is the (generalized, by Hecke summation) Eisenstein series for the natural integer N and the matrix A of the modular group, and if one sets $F(\tau; A, N) = -(2\pi i)^{-1}N^2G_{-2}(0, \tau; A, N) - (2i\,\mathrm{Im}\,\tau)^{-1}$, then $F(\tau; A, N) \in \mathfrak{L}^1_{\Gamma(N)}$. The paper ends with several considerations of which the most intriguing (barely sketched in a note appended in galleys) is the generalization of the last results from congruence subgroups of the modular group to general horocyclic groups of the first kind that contain parabolic elements.

E. Grosswald (Philadelphia, Pa.)

Citations: MR 34# 7471 = F25-14; MR 37# 4021 = F10-105.

F25-27 **(42# 3022)**

Atkin, A. O. L.; Lehner, J.

Hecke operators on $\Gamma_0(m)$.

Math. Ann. **185** (1970), 134–160.

The authors present a complete theory of Hecke operators on $\Gamma_0(m)$, the group of integral unimodular matrices $(a, b; c, d)=\begin{bmatrix} a & b \\ c & d\end{bmatrix}$ with $c\equiv 0 \pmod m$. Here m can be any positive integer; primes that do not divide m are denoted by p and those that do by q. $\langle\Gamma_0(m), k\rangle_0$ denotes the space of cuspforms belonging to $\Gamma_0(m)$ of negative even dimension $-2k$ and constant multiplier system. Every such cuspform f has an expansion $f(\tau)=\sum_{n=1}^{\infty} a(n)x^n$ $(x=e^{2\pi i\tau})$ valid for $\operatorname{Im}\tau>0$. Operators T_p and U_q are defined on $\langle\Gamma_0(m), k\rangle_0$ by $f|T_p=\sum_{n=1}^{\infty}\{a(np)+p^{2k-1}a(n/p)\}x^n$, $f|U_q=\sum_{n=1}^{\infty} a(nq)x^n$. A third operator is defined by $f(\tau)|W_q=q^{k\alpha}(mz\tau+q^{\alpha}w)^{-2k}f(W\tau)$ for any integral matrix W_q of the form $(q^{\alpha}x, y; mz, q^{\alpha}w)$ having determinant q^{α}, where $q^{\alpha}\|m$. The linear fractional transformation associated with the matrix $W_q^{\,2}$ lies in $\Gamma_0(m)$.

The authors show, by methods analogous to those used by Hecke and Petersson [see, for example, H. Petersson, Math. Ann. **116** (1939), 401–412; ibid. **117** (1939), 39–64; MR **1**, 294; ibid. **117** (1940), 277–300; MR **2**, 151], that $\langle\Gamma_0(m), k\rangle_0$ has a basis, each of whose members is an eigenform (i.e., an eigenfunction) of all the operators T_p $(p\nmid m)$ and that the basis forms fall into equivalence classes of eigenforms having the same eigenvalues $\lambda(p)$ $(p\nmid m)$. Moreover, any form in $\langle\Gamma_0(m), k\rangle_0$ which is an eigenform for all T_p $(p\nmid m)$ lies in the vector space spanned by one of the equivalence classes. An eigenform for $\Gamma_0(m)$ may, of course, also be an eigenform for some overgroup $\Gamma_0(m')$, where m' is a proper divisor of m. In fact, if $g(\tau)$ is an eigenform in $\langle\Gamma_0(m'), k\rangle_0$ and d is any divisor of m/m', then $g(d\tau)$ is an eigenform in $\langle\Gamma_0(m), k\rangle_0$ (with the same eigenvalues) and is called an oldform; the set of all such eigenforms for all $d|m/m'$ is called an oldclass. The subspace spanned by the oldforms is denoted by $C^-(m)$ and its orthogonal complement in $\langle\Gamma_0(m), k\rangle_0$ is denoted by $C^+(m)$. Then $C^+(m)$ has a basis consisting of eigenforms, called newforms, and it is the newforms that are of primary interest. The first coefficient of a newform F is necessarily nonzero, so that F can be taken to have the expansion $F(\tau)=\sum_{n=1}^{\infty} a(n)x^n$ $(x=e^{2\pi i\tau})$, where $a(1)=1$. Then not only is it shown that $F|T_p=a(p)F(p\nmid m)$, but also that $F|U_q=a(q)F$, $F|W_q=\lambda(q)F$, where $\lambda(q)=\pm 1$ and where $a(q)=0$ or $-q^{k-1}\lambda(q)$ according as $q^2|m$ or $q\|m$. Further, $\langle\Gamma_0(m), k\rangle_0$ has a basis, which is a direct sum of classes. These classes consist of newclasses and oldclasses. Every form in the same class has the same eigenvalues of T_p for all primes $p\nmid m$. Two forms in different classes have distinct eigenvalues of T_p for an infinity for p. Each newclass consists of a single newform. The vector space spanned by any oldclass can be given an alternative basis consisting of forms which are eigenforms of all the W_q for $q|m$. Finally, any form which is an eigenform of all the T_p, U_q and W_q is a constant multiple of some newform.

These results show that it is possible to obtain a satisfactory theory of Hecke operators on $\Gamma_0(m)$ not only for primes $p\nmid m$, but also for primes that do divide the level m. The paper concludes with a number of more complicated and special results of use in the identification of newforms. {Note: in the enunciation of Theorem 1 it should be mentioned that the primes q_i divide the integer N.}

R. A. Rankin (Glasgow)

Citations: MR 1, 294c = F65-1; MR 2, 151a = F25-2.

Referred to in F02-22.

F25-28 **(42# 4492)**

Ogg, Andrew P.

On the eigenvalues of Hecke operators.

Math. Ann. **179** (1969), 101–108.

Let $\Gamma_0(N)$ be the subgroup of the elliptic modular group whose matrices $\begin{pmatrix} a & b \\ c & d\end{pmatrix}$ have $c\equiv 0 \bmod N$. The spaces of modular forms of weight k, character ε, with respect to $\Gamma_0(N)$ are denoted by $\mathscr{M}(k, N, \varepsilon)$; $\mathscr{T}(k, N, \varepsilon)$ means the cusp forms. The author proves a few facts which were mostly known to Hecke when $N=p$ is a prime [E. Hecke, *Mathematische Werke*, nos. 39, 40, Vandenhoeck & Ruprecht, Göttingen 1959; MR **21** #3303]. Let $N=\prod p^{e_p}$ be the prime decomposition of the level. Theorem 1: Let either $f\in\mathscr{M}(2, N, 1)$ or $f\in\mathscr{T}(k, N, 1)$ with $k<12$ or $k=14$. Then $f|\prod_{p|N}(T(p^{e_p+1})-p^{k-2}T(p^{e_p-1}))=0$. Theorem 2: Let $N=pM$, M prime to p, and ε a character mod M. For $f\in\mathscr{M}(k, N, \varepsilon)$ assume $f|T(p)=c_pf$ and $f|\begin{pmatrix} 0 & 1 \\ -N & 0\end{pmatrix}=\pm i^kN^{-k/2}f$. Then $c_p^{\,2}=\varepsilon(p)p^{k-2}$ or $=p^{k-2}$. Theorem 3: Let $p^2|N$ and $f\in\mathscr{M}(k, N, \varepsilon)$, $f\notin\mathscr{M}(k, N/p, \varepsilon)$, and lastly $f|T(p)=c_pf$. Then $c_p=0$ if and only if ε is a character mod N/p. Theorem 4: Let $N=p^eM$, M prime to p, $e>0$. If ε is not a character mod M and $f\in\mathscr{M}(k, N, \varepsilon)$, we have $f|T(p^e)\begin{pmatrix} 0 & 1 \\ -N & 0\end{pmatrix}T(p^e)=p^{k-1}f|T(p^{e-1})\begin{pmatrix} 0 & 1 \\ -N & 0\end{pmatrix}T(p^{e-1})$.

M. Eichler (Basel)

Citations: MR 21# 3303 = Z25-14.

Referred to in F10-112.

F25-29 **(42# 4494)**

Morita, Yasuo

Hecke polynomials of modular groups and congruence zeta functions of fibre varieties.

J. Math. Soc. Japan **21** (1969), 617–637.

Let p be a prime number and let $Z^{(p)}=\bigcup_{n=0}^{\infty} p^{-n}Z\subset Q$, where Z and Q denote the ring of rational integers and the field of rational numbers, respectively. Let $\Gamma=\mathrm{PSL}(2, Z^{(p)})$ and $\Delta\subset\Gamma$ a subgroup of finite index. Let $\mathfrak{H}$ denote the upper half plane; then Γ operates on $\mathfrak{H}$ as linear fractional transformations. The author defines Hecke operators $T_k(\Delta, m)$ which act on the space of cusp forms of weight k $(k=2, 4, \cdots)$ with respect to the Fuchsian group $\Delta^0=\Delta\cap\mathrm{PSL}(2, Z)$. One defines the Hecke polynomial $H_k(\Delta; u)$ by $H_k(\Delta; u)=\det\{I-(T_k(\Delta, 1)-p^{k-1}I)u+p^{2(k-1)}Iu^2\}$, where u is an indeterminate. One obtains a recursion formula for the $T_k(\Delta, m)$. From this formula and the fact that these operators are self-adjoint, one obtains the formula (1) $\log H_k(\Delta; u)=-\sum_{m=1}^{\infty}\operatorname{tr} U_k(\Delta; m)u^m/m!$ where $U_k(\Delta, m)=T_k(\Delta, m)-p^{k-1}T_k(\Delta, m-1)$.

$\mathscr{P}(\Delta)$ will denote all Δ-equivalence classes of fixed points z in $\mathfrak{H}$ such that Δ_z, the isotropy group of z in Δ, is infinite. Let $\mathscr{P}_\infty(\Delta)$ denote the set of all Δ-equivalence classes of all cuspidal points with respect to Δ^0. Then the author defines a zeta function $Z_k^{\,H}(\Delta; u)$ $(k=2, 4, \cdots)$ by $\log Z_k^{\,H}(\Delta; u)=\sum_{m=1}^{\infty}[\sum_{P\in\mathscr{P}(\Delta)\cup\mathscr{P}_\infty(\Delta)}$ (terms depending on P, k, m)$](p^{k-1}u)^m/m$. For $k=2$, this definition essentially coincides with one given earlier by Ihara. The author then proves what he calls the first equality: (2) $H_k(\Delta; u)\doteqdot Z_k^{\,H}(\Delta; u)$ (equal up to correcting terms). The proof uses (1), and one computes the traces of the $U_k(\Delta, m)$ using the Eichler-Selberg trace formula and theorems which tell "what and how many Δ^0-conjugacy classes are contained in a Δ-conjugacy class $P\in\mathscr{P}(\Delta)\cup\mathscr{P}_\infty(\Delta)$" [Y. Ihara, *On congruence monodromy problems*, Vol. 1, Dept. of Math., Univ. Tokyo, Tokyo, 1968; Vol. 2, 1969; Russian translation of Vol. 1, *Mathematics: Periodical collection of translations of foreign articles, Vol. 14, No. 3*, pp. 40–98, Izdat. "Mir," Moscow, 1970; see MR **41** #3205; *Mathematics: Periodical collection of translations of foreign articles, Vol. 14, No. 4*, pp. 48–77, Izdat. "Mir", Moscow, 1970; *Mathematics: Periodical collection of translations of foreign articles, Vol. 14, No. 5*, pp. 62–101, Izdat. "Mir", Moscow, 1970].

In the last section, the author obtains a relation between the zeta function $Z_k^H(\Delta; u)$ and congruence zeta functions of certain algebraic varieties defined over the finite field F_{p^2}. Thus by (2) one obtains a relation between $H_k(\Delta; u)$ and these congruence zeta functions. The argument of the last section depends on a result of Ihara [op. cit.] which gives the existence of a "separable algebraic extension L over the rational function field $K=F_{p^2}(j)$ such that the decomposition law of the prime divisors of K in L can be written by means of the 'decomposition law' of the Γ-conjugacy classes into Δ-conjugacy classes". *H. Garland* (Ithaca, N.Y.)

F25-30 **(44# 2887)**

Mautner, Friederich I.

Fonctions sphériques et opérateurs de Hecke.

Séminaire Delange-Pisot-Poitou: 1969/70, Théorie des Nombres, Fasc. 1, Exp. 10, 17 pp. Secrétariat mathématique, Paris, 1970.

This is mainly an extended (and very well written) version of two preceding notes by the author [C. R. Acad. Sci. Paris Sér. A-B **269** (1969), A940–A943; MR **41** #7031a; ibid. **270** (1970), A89–A92; MR **41** #7031b]. Some of the eigenvalue calculations are made explicit. Particular attention is given to the case of quadratic extension fields of the rationals. Results of an earlier paper [Amer. J. Math. **80** (1958), 441–457; MR **20** #82] are used. An interesting conjecture is made about some properties of the Riemann zeta function, which would be equivalent to polynomial properties. *A. Evyatar (Gutwirth)* (Haifa)

Citations: MR 20# 82 = E64-2; MR 41# 7031a = F15-28; MR 41# 7031b = F15-28.

F30 FOURIER COEFFICIENTS OF AUTOMORPHIC FORMS (ONE VARIABLE)

Many applications of this theory will be found in **E24, E28.**

See also Section P76.

See also reviews F10-13, F10-19, F10-25, F10-33, F10-42, F10-54, F10-83, F15-1, F25-9, F35-29, F35-35, F40-56, F99-5, P02-22, P72-29, P76-28, P76-31, P76-38, P76-44, R14-34.

F30-1 **(1, 69d)**

Rankin, R. A. Contributions to the theory of Ramanujan's function $\tau(n)$ and similar arithmetical functions. I. The zeros of the function $\sum_{n=1}^{\infty}\tau(n)/n^s$ on the line $\Re s=13/2$. II. The order of the Fourier coefficients of integral modular forms. Proc. Cambridge Philos. Soc. **35**, 351–372 (1939).

Ramanujan's function $\tau(n)$, defined by

$$\sum_{n=1}^{\infty}\tau(n)q^{2n}=q^2\{(1-q^2)(1-q^4)\cdots\}^{24}=\Delta(\tau),\quad q=e^{\pi i\tau},\ \Im\tau>0,$$

possesses multiplicative properties embodied in the formula

$$g(s)=\sum_{n=1}^{\infty}\tau(n)n^{-s}=\prod_p(1-\tau(p)p^{-s}+p^{11-2s}),\ s=\sigma+it,\ \sigma>13/2,$$

and $g(s)$, which can be continued as an entire function satisfying the functional equation

$$(2\pi)^{-s}\Gamma(s)g(s)=(2\pi)^{s-12}\Gamma(12-s)g(12-s),$$

has no zeros in $\sigma>13/2$. It is proved here, in paper I, that $g(s)$ has no zeros on $\sigma=13/2$. The proof is based on the inequality

$$|4\cos A\cos B|\leqq 2+\cos 2A+\cos 2B,\quad \cos A,\cos B \text{ real},$$

(an extension of the classical inequality with $B=0$), and on such properties of the function

$$f(s)=\sum_{n=1}^{\infty}\tau^2(n)n^{-s},\qquad \sigma>12,$$

as can be derived from the multiplicative properties of $\tau(n)$ and from Hardy's inequalities

(1) $A_1n^{12}\leqq\tau^2(1)+\tau^2(2)+\cdots+\tau^2(n)\leqq A_2n^{12},\quad 0<A_1<A_2.$

In paper II the inequalities (1) are replaced by an asymptotic formula. More generally, it is proved that, if

$$H(\tau)=\sum_{n=1}^{\infty}a(n)e^{2\pi in\tau/N},\qquad \tau=x+iy,\ y>0,$$

is an integral modular form of dimensions $-\kappa<0$ and Stufe N, which vanishes at all rational cusps of the fundamental region and is absolutely convergent for $y>0$, then

(2) $$\sum_{n\leqq x}|a(n)|^2=\alpha x^\kappa+O(x^{\kappa-2/5}),\qquad \alpha>0.$$

This implies $a(n)=O(n^{\frac12\kappa-1/5})$, an improvement on the $O(n^{\frac12\kappa-\frac14+\epsilon})$ of Salié and Davenport, and a further step in the direction of Ramanujan's conjecture $|\tau(n)|\leqq n^{13/2}d(n)=O(n^{13/2+\epsilon})$, since $\tau(n)$ is an instance of $a(n)$ with $\kappa=12$, $N=1$. The proof is based on a study of the function

$$f(s)=\sum_{n=1}^{\infty}|a(n)|^2n^{-s},\qquad \sigma>\kappa.$$

When $N=1$ (the simplest case), the author starts from the formula

$$(4\pi)^{-s}\Gamma(s)f(s)=\iint_S y^{s-1}|H(\tau)|^2dxdy,$$

where S is $(|x|\leqq\frac12,\ y\geqq0)$, subdivides S into fundamental regions, and transforms each region into the particular region $D(|x|\leqq\frac12,\ |\tau|\geqq1)$ by a modular substitution. Summation over fundamental regions and multiplication by $2\zeta(2s-2\kappa+2)$ introduce under the integral sign a factor $\xi(s,\tau)=\sum\sum'|m\tau+n|^{-2s+2\kappa-2}$ (summed over all integers m, n, except $m=n=0$), which can be studied by classical methods (as an Epstein zeta-function). The final result is that $f(s)$ can be continued as a meromorphic function satisfying the equation $\varphi(s)=\varphi(2\kappa-1-s)$, where

$$\varphi(s)=(2\pi)^{-2s}\Gamma(s)\Gamma(s-\kappa+1)\zeta(2s-2\kappa+2)f(s),$$

and $\varphi(s)$ is regular at all finite points except for simple poles at $s=\kappa$ and $s=\kappa-1$. An asymptotic formula

$$\sum_{n\leqq x}|a(n)|^2\sim\alpha x^\kappa$$

follows at once from the Wiener-Ikehara theorem, and the more precise relation (2) is obtained by applying a general theorem of Landau to the Dirichlet's series for $\zeta(2s)f(s+\kappa-1)$. The case $N>1$ is similar in principle but more complicated formally. *A. E. Ingham.*

Referred to in F30-2, F30-19, F30-25, F30-46, F30-49, F65-26, G05-98.

F30-2 **(1, 203d)**

Rankin, R. A. Contributions to the theory of Ramanujan's function $\tau(n)$ and similar arithmetical functions. III. A note on the sum function of the Fourier coefficients of integral modular forms. Proc. Cambridge Philos. Soc. **36**, 150–151 (1940).

If $H(\tau)=\sum_1^{\infty}a_ne^{2\pi in\tau/N}$ (absolutely convergent for $\Im\tau>0$)

is an integral modular form of dimensions $-\kappa \leqq -2$ and Stufe N, vanishing at all rational cusps of the fundamental region ("cusp-form"), then

$$\sum_{n\leqq x} a_n = O(x^{\frac{1}{2}\kappa-\frac{1}{10}}).$$

To obtain this improvement of Walfisz's estimate $O(x^{\frac{1}{2}\kappa-1/24+\epsilon})$ [Math. Ann. **108**, 75–90 (1933)] the author follows a similar method, but uses, in place of Kloosterman's theorem $a_n = O(n^{\frac{1}{2}\kappa-\frac{1}{4}+\epsilon})$, his own theorem

$$\sum_{n\leqq x} |a_n|^2 = \alpha x^\kappa + O(x^{\kappa-\frac{2}{5}}),$$

proved in paper II of the series [Proc. Cambridge Philos. Soc. **35**, 357–372 (1939); cf. these Rev. **1**, 69–70 (1940). In this abstract the conjecture of Ramanujan referred to on p. 70, lines 23–24, should read $|\tau(n)| \leqq n^{11/2}d(n) = O(n^{11/2+\epsilon})$].

A. E. Ingham (Berkeley, Calif.).

Citations: MR 1, 69d = F30-1.

Referred to in F35-32.

F30-3 (1, 294d)

Zuckerman, Herbert S. The computation of the smaller coefficients of $J(\tau)$. Bull. Amer. Math. Soc. **45**, 917–919 (1939).

Ramanujan's theorem about the divisibility of $p(25n+24)$ is connected with the multiplicator equation of $J(\tau)$ of the 5th order. The author makes use of this fact and finds $J(\tau)$ expressed by

$$\sum_{n=0}^{\infty} p(25n+24)e^{2\pi i n\tau}$$

and some other modular functions with arithmetically simple coefficients. This enables him to utilize Gupta's table of $p(n)$ for n up to 600 [Proc. London Math. Soc. **39**, 142–149 (1935); **42**, 546–549 (1937)] to compute the first 24 coefficients of $J(\tau)$, the first seven of which agree with values given by Berwick [Quart. J. Math. **47**, 94–103 (1916)].

H. Rademacher (Swarthmore, Pa.).

F30-4 (2, 88a)

Selberg, Atle. Bemerkungen über eine Dirichletsche Reihe, die mit der Theorie der Modulformen nahe verbunden ist. Arch. Math. Naturvid. **43**, 47–50 (1940).

This paper considers two modular forms

$$f(\tau) = \sum_{n=1}^{\infty} \alpha_n e^{2\pi i n\tau}, \quad \phi(\tau) = \sum_{n=1}^{\infty} \beta_n e^{2\pi i n\tau},$$

of positive dimension k, and the Dirichlet series

$$\zeta(2s) \sum_{n=1}^{\infty} \frac{\alpha_n \bar{\beta}_n}{n^{k-1+s}}$$

generated by their coefficients. The Dirichlet series can be expressed in terms of a double integral involving the Epstein zeta-function and it can then be defined over the whole s-plane. Some inequalities concerning the coefficients of the modular forms are given. These include improvements of inequalities of Salié and Walfisz. Only a special case is discussed and the proofs briefly described. The author states that his general results with complete proofs will appear later.

H. S. Zuckerman (Seattle, Wash.).

F30-5 (3, 272c)

Lehmer, D. H. Properties of the coefficients of the modular invariant $J(\tau)$. Amer. J. Math. **64**, 488–502 (1942).

The author considers the coefficients $c(k)$ in the expansion $j(\tau) = 1728J(\tau) = \sum_{k=-1}^{\infty} c(k)x^k$, where $x = e^{2\pi i\tau}$, and finds formulas by means of which $c(k)$ may be found recursively. One of these formulas determines $c(k)$ in terms of earlier c's, $\sigma_{11}(n)$ and $\tau(n)$, where $\sigma_{11}(n)$ is the sum of the eleventh powers of the divisors of n and $\tau(n)$ is Ramanujan's function defined by $\sum_{k=1}^{\infty} \tau(k)x^k = x\{(1-x)(1-x^2)(1-x^3)\cdots\}^{24}$. Multiplication formulas for the $c(k)$ are found, expressing $c(nk)$ in terms of earlier c's, but they are somewhat more complicated than the multiplication property enjoyed by $\tau(k)$. These formulas are useful for the computation of $c(k)$ when k is composite. Some congruence properties of the $c(k)$ are found and the author also discusses the coefficients $c_\nu(k)$ of $\{j(\tau)\}^\nu$. The methods of proof are connected with the transformation equation of the nth order for $j(\tau)$ and certain functional relations involving $j(\tau)$ are also found.

H. S. Zuckerman (Seattle, Wash.).

Referred to in F30-15, F30-23.

F30-6 (5, 36b)

Zuckerman, Herbert S. Certain functions with singularities on the unit circle. Duke Math. J. **10**, 381–395 (1943).

In the method of determining the Fourier coefficients of modular functions of positive dimension [Rademacher and Zuckerman, Ann. of Math. (2) **39**, 433–462 (1938)] the group-theoretical property of the modular functions is used only for obtaining their asymptotic behavior on the Farey arcs. If we prescribe this behavior directly we can still formally carry out the process for obtaining coefficients of an expansion. Whether, however, there exists at all any function of the desired behavior remains uncertain, and thus it is a problem whether the formally obtained expansion shows the required asymptotic properties.

The author shows first through an example that a certain limitation has to be set to the preassignment of properties of $\sum_{n=-\mu}^{\infty} a_n x^n$ on the Farey arcs. Within these limitations, however, he proves four theorems, the type of which may be illustrated by the following specialization of his second theorem. Let r be a nonnegative integer, $\alpha \geqq 0$, $\beta \geqq 2$, $B \geqq 0$, and let $d_{h,k}$ be a set of real or complex numbers defined for $0 \leqq h < k$, $(h, k) = 1$, such that $d_{h,k} = O(k^{r\beta-2-\epsilon})$, $\epsilon > 0$. Put

$$f(x) = \sum_{m=0}^{\infty} a_m x^m$$

with

$$a_m = 2\pi i \sum_{k=1}^{\infty} A_k(m)(B/(k^\beta(\alpha+m)))^{(r+1)/2} I_{r+1}(2(Bk^{-\beta}(\alpha+m))^{\frac{1}{2}}),$$

$$A_k(m) = \sum_{\substack{h \bmod k \\ (h,k)=1}} d_{h,k} e^{-2\pi i m h/k};$$

then we have

$$f(\exp(-2\pi N^{-2} + 2\pi i(\varphi + p/q)) = d_{p,q} i(2\pi)^{r+1}(N^{-2} - i\varphi)^r$$
$$\times \exp(B(2\pi)^{-1}q^{-\beta}(N^{-2} - i\varphi)^{-1} + 2\pi\alpha(N^{-2} - i\varphi)) + O(1),$$

as $N \to \infty$, for $\varphi + p/q$ on the Farey interval of order N about p/q. That in general the term $O(1)$ cannot be replaced by $o(1)$ is shown by the above mentioned example.

H. Rademacher (Swarthmore, Pa.).

F30-7 (8, 198a)

Guinand, A. P. Integral modular forms and summation formulae. Proc. Cambridge Philos. Soc. **43**, 127–129 (1947).

Formulas concerning sums of the coefficients of modular forms are obtained from a more general theorem proved earlier [Quart. J. Math., Oxford Ser. **9**, 53–67 (1938)].

H. S. Zuckerman (Seattle, Wash.).

F30-8 (10, 357a)

Lehner, Joseph. Divisibility properties of the Fourier coefficients of the modular invariant $j(\tau)$. Amer. J. Math. **71**, 136–148 (1949).

If c_ν, $\nu > 1$, are the coefficients of the modular invariant $j(\tau) = x^{-1} + 744 + \sum_{\nu=1}^{\infty} c_\nu x^\nu$, $x = e^{2\pi i\tau}$, then $c_\nu \equiv 0 \pmod{5^{\alpha+1}}$ if $\nu \equiv 0 \pmod{5^\alpha}$, $\alpha = 1, 2, 3, \cdots$; $c_\nu \equiv 0 \pmod{7^\alpha}$ if $\nu \equiv 0 \pmod{7^\alpha}$,

$\alpha=1, 2, 3, \cdots; c_\nu\equiv 0 \pmod{11^\alpha}$ if $\nu\equiv 0 \pmod{11^\alpha}$, $\alpha=1, 2, 3$. The proof depends on subjecting $j(\tau)$ to a certain linear operator and expressing the result in terms of basic modular functions. The identities thus obtained lead directly to the congruence properties. The method is that previously used by Rademacher [Trans. Amer. Math. Soc. **51**, 609–636 (1942); these Rev. **3**, 271] and the author [same J. **65**, 492–520 (1943); these Rev. **5**, 34] to obtain identities involving the partition function. Besides 5, 7, 11 the prime 13 also leads to an identity but not to congruence properties of the c_ν. *H. S. Zuckerman* (Seattle, Wash.).

Citations: MR 3, 271e = P60-1; MR 5, 34d = P76-1.

Referred to in F30-15, F30-23, F30-48, F30-53.

F30-9 (10, 357b)

Lehner, Joseph. Further congruence properties of the Fourier coefficients of the modular invariant $j(\tau)$. Amer. J. Math. **71**, 373–386 (1949).

This is an extension of the paper reviewed above. Using the same notation, it is shown that $c_\nu\equiv 0 \pmod{2^{3\alpha+8}}$ if $\nu\equiv 0 \pmod{2^\alpha}$ and $c_\nu\equiv 0 \pmod{3^{2\alpha+3}}$ if $\nu\equiv 0 \pmod{3^\alpha}$; $\alpha, \nu=1, 2, 3, \cdots$. *H. S. Zuckerman* (Seattle, Wash).

Referred to in F30-23, F30-40, F30-47, F30-53.

F30-10 (11, 421a)

Petersson, Hans. Über den Körper der Fourierkoeffizienten der von Hecke untersuchten Eisensteinreihen. Abh. Math. Sem. Univ. Hamburg **16**, 101–113 (1949).

The series in question are

$$G_r(\tau, a_1, a_2, N)=\sum_{m_i\equiv a_i(N)}{}' (m_1\tau+m_2)^{-r},$$

$$G_r^*(\tau, a_1, a_2, N)=\sum_{m_i\equiv a_i(N)}{}^* (m_1\tau+m_2)^{-r},$$

where $\sum'$ denotes that the term $m_1=m_2=0$ is to be omitted and $\sum^*$ that only the terms with $(m_1, m_2)=1$ are to be taken (N and r are positive integers). If $\tau'=A\tau$ is a modular substitution which transforms a vertex ζ of the fundamental region of $\Gamma(N)$ (the principal congruence group modulo N) to ∞, then the functions G_r and G_r^* can be expanded in Fourier series in the uniformising variable $\exp 2\pi i A\tau/N$ of ζ. The author proves that for the G_r^* all Fourier coefficients lie, for all vertices ζ, in the field of the Nth roots of unity. If N and r are fixed and analytic entire modular forms, not equal to 0, with the given N and r exist, then all coefficients have a common ideal denominator. The same is true for the functions $(-2\pi i)^{-r}N^r(r-1)!G_r(\tau, a_1, a_2, N)$ if $(a_1, a_2, N)=1$. If $F(\tau)$ is a linear combination with constant coefficients of the G_r^* (N and r fixed) then all Fourier coefficients of $F(\tau)$ in all vertices ζ lie in the field obtained by adjunction of $\exp 2\pi i/N$, and of the constant terms in all Fourier expansions of $F(\tau)$, to the field of rational numbers (if $r\geqq 2$; slight modification for $r=1$).

H. D. Kloosterman (Leiden).

Referred to in F40-24.

F30-11 (13, 135a)

van der Pol, Balth. On a non-linear partial differential equation satisfied by the logarithm of the Jacobian theta-functions, with arithmetical applications. I, II. Nederl. Akad. Wetensch. Proc. Ser. A. **54**=Indagationes Math. **13**, 261–271, 272–284 (1951).

The differential equation in question is

$$\partial^2u/\partial s^2=2\partial u/\partial t-(\partial u/\partial s)^2$$

which is satisfied by $u=\log\theta_1(s/2\pi, it/2\pi)$. Expanding the partial derivatives involved, the author is naturally led to consider the functions

$$a_{2k-1}(t)=1+[2/\zeta(1-2k)]\sum_{l=1}^{\infty}e^{-lt}\sigma_{2k-1}(l)$$

which appear in the coefficients. Also considered are the functions $M_k=\theta_0^{4k}+\theta_2^{4k}+(-\theta_3^4)^k$ where $\theta_i=\theta_i(0, it/2\pi)$. Identities are obtained involving the $a_{2k-1}(t)$ and the M_k. These identities lead to numerous formulas, many already known, of various kinds. For example, there are formulas involving the $\sigma_{2k-1}(n)$ alone, formulas expressing $\tau(n)$ in terms of the $\sigma_{2k-1}(n)$, differential equations involving $J(\tau)$, and others. The author rather simply obtains the formula for $r_8(n)$ by first determining M_2 and then finding θ_3^8. Whether this procedure would simplify the computation of $r_{4k}(n)$ for $k>2$ is undecided. *H. S. Zuckerman.*

Referred to in E24-47, F30-15.

F30-12 (14, 139c)

Rankin, R. A. The scalar product of modular forms. Proc. London Math. Soc. (3) **2**, 198–217 (1952).

The author develops methods for effectively calculating the scalar product (f, g) of two modular forms of negative dimension $-k$ belonging to the full group and having unity as multiplier system. His formula when f, g are both cusp forms, for example, is a linear combination of the values of certain Dirichlet series at integral points within their half-plane of absolute convergence. The coefficients in the linear combination are obtained by expressing g, say, in terms of a certain basis of the cusp forms of dimension $-k$. The special case in which the basis consists of one function ($k=12, 16, 18, 20, 22, 26$) is discussed separately and leads to certain identities involving the Fourier coefficients of the modular forms, e.g.,

$$\tau(h)h^{-11}+240\sum_{m=1}^{\infty}\sigma_3(m)\tau(m+h)(m+h)^{-11}=0,\quad h>0.$$

J. Lehner (Los Alamos, N. M.).

F30-13 (14, 248g)

Dragonette, Leila A. Some asymptotic formulae for the mock theta series of Ramanujan. Trans. Amer. Math. Soc. **72**, 474–500 (1952).

The author determines the behaviour of functions of type

$$f(q)=\sum_{n=0}^{\infty}\frac{q^{n^2}}{(1+q)^2(1+q^2)^2\cdots(1+q^n)^2}$$

in the neighbourhood of rational points on the unit circle and obtains a number of results of which the following one is typical: If $(h, k)=1$, h is odd and $hh'\equiv -1 \pmod k$, then for all complex z such that $\Re(z)>0$, $|\Im(z)|\leqq 1/(k+1)$, we have

$$f(e^{\pi i(h+iz)/k})=\epsilon_{h,k}z^{-1/2}e^{-\pi z/24k+\pi z^{-1}/24k}f(-e^{\pi i(h'+iz^{-1})/k})+O(k\log k),$$

where $\epsilon_{h,k}$ is a certain root of unity. These results enable the author to obtain rather precise asymptotic formulae for the coefficients in the power series development

$$f(q)=\sum_{n=0}^{\infty}A(n)q^n.$$

It is proved that

$$A(n)=\sum_{0<k\leqq n^{1/2}}\lambda(k)\exp\{\pi k^{-1}6^{-1/2}(n-1/24)^{1/2}\}+O(n^{1/2}\log n),$$

where $\lambda(n)$ is a certain exponential sum. This formula constitutes a considerable improvement on a hitherto unproved assertion of Ramanujan. Similar results are stated for a number of related functions. *H. D. Kloosterman.*

Referred to in F30-52.

F30-14 **(14, 250b)**

Simons, William H. The Fourier coefficients of the modular function $\lambda(\tau)$. Canadian J. Math. **4**, 67–80 (1952).

The author extends the method of Hardy-Ramanujan-Rademacher to evaluate the Fourier coefficients of a modular function of level (Stufe) 2, namely $\lambda(\tau)$. *L. K. Hua.*

F30-15 **(15, 403a)**

van Wijngaarden, A. On the coefficients of the modular invariant $J(\tau)$. Nederl. Akad. Wetensch. Proc. Ser. A. **56** = Indagationes Math. **15**, 389–400 (1953).

The author presents a table of the coefficients $c(n)$ of Klein's absolute modular invariant $J(\tau)=\sum_{n=-1}^{\infty}c(n)x^n$, where $x=\exp(2\pi i\tau)$, and $\Re\tau>0$ for $n\leqq 100$. Only the values up to $n=25$ were previously available. The $c(n)$, which are positive rational integers, grow very rapidly with n, like $\exp c\sqrt{n}$, where c is a certain positive constant. $c(100)$ is a number of 53 digits.

The calculation was based on the formula

$$J(\tau)=\frac{2}{27}(\theta_2{}^8+\theta_3{}^8+\theta_4{}^8)(\theta_2{}^{-8}+\theta_3{}^{-8}+\theta_4{}^{-8})$$

appearing in van der Pol's paper [same Proc. **54** = Indagationes Math. **13**, 261–271, 272–284 (1951); these Rev. **13**, 135]. Checks on the $c(n)$ were made on the basis of congruences developed by D. H. Lehmer [Amer. J. Math. **64**, 488–502 (1942); these Rev. **3**, 272], the reviewer [ibid. **71**, 136–148, 373–386 (1949); these Rev. **10**, 357], and the author. The author's congruences connect $c(n)$ with certain restricted partition functions tabulated by Watson [Proc. London Math. Soc. (2) **42**, 550–556 (1937)].

Wijngaarden's table verifies a conjecture of the reviewer made in one of the papers cited above for the new values of n, and also for $n=128$; for this purpose the author calculated $c(128)$ modulo 2^{30} from one of Lehmer's formulas.

J. Lehner (Los Alamos, N. Mex.).

Citations: MR 3, 272c = F30-5; MR 10, 357a = F30-8; MR 13, 135a = F30-11.

Referred to in F30-23.

F30-16 **(17, 15d)**

Newman, Morris. An identity for the coefficients of certain modular forms. J. London Math. Soc. **30**, 488–493 (1955).

The author considers the coefficients $p_r(n)$ in the development

$$\prod_{n=1}^{\infty}(1-x^n)^r=\sum_{n=0}^{\infty}p_r(n)x^n.$$

If r is one of the numbers 2, 4, 6, 8, 10, 14, 26 and p is a prime >3 such that $r(p+1)\equiv 0 \pmod{24}$, he proves that $p_r(np+\Delta)=(-p)^{(r/2)-1}p_r(n/p)$, where $\Delta=r(p^2-1)/24$ and $p_r(\alpha)$ is zero if α is not a nonnegative integer. There are no other values of r for which the formula is true.

H. D. Kloosterman (Ann Arbor, Mich.).

Referred to in F25-7, F30-21, F30-43, P76-12.

F30-17 **(17, 240c)**

Look, C. H. On the Fourier coefficients of the function $\mathfrak{T}(\omega_1, \omega_2)$. Acta Math. Sinica **4** (1954), 113–124. (Chinese. English summary)

Under the substitutions of the full modular group the modular function

$$A(\omega_1, \omega_2)=\frac{12\wp(\omega_1/2)}{\wp(\omega_1/4)-\wp(\omega_1/2)}\quad\left(\operatorname{Im}\left(\frac{\omega_2}{\omega_1}\right)>0\right)$$

of the 4th level (Stufe) assumes six values satisfying the equation

$$(A^2-3\times 2^4)^3-j(\omega_1, \omega_2)(A^2-2^6)=0$$

[see R. Fueter, Vorlesungen über die singulären Moduln ⋯, Teubner, Leipzig-Berlin, 1924, p. 104 ff.]. One of these values has the expansion

$$A=\sum_{m=0}^{\infty}a_mq^m,\ \text{where}\ a_0=2^3,\ q=e^{2\pi i\omega_2\omega_1}.$$

The author proves that

$$a_m=\frac{\pi}{\sqrt{m}}\sum_{\substack{0\leq h<k\\(h,k)=1}}^{\infty}\frac{\lambda(h, k)}{k}\cdot e^{-\pi i(h'+4mh)/2k}I_1\left(\frac{2\pi\sqrt{m}}{k}\right).$$

Here $hh'\equiv -1 \pmod{k}$; $\lambda(h, k)$ equals 0, ∓ 1, or $\mp i$ according to the residue classes of h and k (mod 4); and $I_1(z)$ is the Bessel function of order 1 of an imaginary argument. *K. Mahler* (Manchester).

F30-18 **(17, 348g)**

Val′fiš [Walfisz], A. Z. On sums of coefficients of certain modular forms. Soobšč. Akad. Nauk Gruzin. SSR **16** (1955), 417–423. (Russian)

For the entire cusp form $F(\tau)=\sum c_n \exp 2\pi in/N$ of dimension $-k$ and order N the author gives another proof of his result [Math. Ann. **108** (1933), 75–90] $C(x)=\sum_{n\leqq x}c_n=\Omega(x^{\frac{1}{2}k-\frac{1}{4}})$. With $\tau^kF(\tau)=\sum b_n \exp[-2\pi in/(N\tau)]$, by Riemann's transform-method he shows $\Gamma(s)\sum c_nn^{-s}=i^{-k}(N/2\pi)^{k-2s}\Gamma(k-s)\sum b_nn^{s-k}$, making applicable a general theorem of Landau [Nachr. Ges. Wiss. Göttingen. Math.-Phys. Kl. **1924**, 137–150] which yields the main result $\operatorname{Re}\{wC(x_n)\}>a_3x_n{}^{\frac{1}{2}k-\frac{1}{4}}$, $\operatorname{Re}\{wC(y_n)\}<-a_3y_n{}^{\frac{1}{2}k-\frac{1}{4}}$ for a sequence x_n with $x_n<x_{n+1}<x_n+a_nx_n{}^{\frac{1}{2}}$, a like sequence y_n, positive constants a_n, and a complex constant w, depending on $F(\tau)$. [See the paper reviewed below.]

Harvey Cohn (Detroit, Mich.).

F30-19 **(17, 349a)**

Val′fiš [Walfisz], A. Z. On sums of modules of the coefficients of certain modular forms. Soobšč. Akad. Nauk Gruzin. SSR **16** (1955), 497–502. (Russian)

With the notation of the paper reviewed above, the author shows that $D(x)=\sum_{n\leqq x}|c_n|\geqq a_{12}x^{\frac{1}{2}k+\frac{1}{4}}$ directly from the main result quoted in the preceding review. Under the further assumption that $c_n=O(n^{\frac{1}{2}k-\frac{1}{2}+\varepsilon})$, the author shows $D(x)\geqq a_{15}x^{\frac{1}{2}k+\frac{1}{2}-\varepsilon}$ by means of Rankin's result on $\sum|c_n|^2$ [Proc. Cambridge Philos. Soc. **35** (1939), 351–372; MR **1**, 69, 400]. Thus the author notes that the abscissa of absolute convergence of $\sum c_nn^{-s}$ is $\frac{1}{2}k+\frac{1}{2}$. The assumption is applicable to modular functions used by Eichler [Arch. Math. **5** (1954), 355–366; MR **16**, 116]; and Ramanujan's conjecture would imply $\sum_{n\leqq x}|\tau(n)|\geqq ax^{13/2-\varepsilon}$ [see van der Blij, Math. Student **18** (1950), 83–99, p. 90; MR **13**, 328]. *Harvey Cohn* (Detroit, Mich.).

Citations: MR 1, 69d = F30-1; MR 13, 328d = F35-30; MR 16, 116d = G30-15.

Referred to in M40-18.

F30-20 **(17, 946g)**

Newman, Morris. A table of the coefficients of the powers of $\eta(\tau)$. Nederl. Akad. Wetensch. Proc. Ser. A. **59** = Indag. Math. **18** (1956), 204–216.

The numbers $p_r(n)$ defined by the equation

$$\prod_{n=1}^{\infty}(1-x^n)^r=\sum_{n=0}^{\infty}p_r(n)x^n\quad(r=1, 2, \cdots)$$

are tabulated for $1\leqq r\leqq 13$, $1\leqq n\leqq 800$; $r=14$, $1\leqq n\leqq 750$; $r=15$, $1\leqq n\leqq 500$; $r=16$, $1\leqq n\leqq 400$. The computations were performed with the help of the high speed electronic digital computer SEAC of the National Bureau of Standards at Washington, D.C. Two different recursion formulas were used, namely:

$$np_r(n)=\sum_{k=1}^{n}(rk+k-n)\lambda_kp_r(n-k)$$

and

$$np_r(n)=-r\sum_{k=1}^{n}\sigma(k)p_r(n-k),$$

where $\sigma(k)$ is the sum of the divisors of k, and

$$\lambda_k=\begin{cases}(-1)^s \text{ if } k=(3s^2\pm s)/2\\ 0 \text{ otherwise.}\end{cases}$$

T. M. Apostol (Pasadena, Calif.).

F30-21 **(18, 194f)**

Newman, Morris. Generalizations of identities for the coefficients of certain modular forms. J. London Math. Soc. **31** (1956), 205–208.

Denoting the coefficient of x^n in the power series expansion of $\prod_{k=1}^{\infty}(1-x^k)^r$ by $P_r(n)$ (where n is a non-negative integer) and defining $P_r(n)$ to be zero otherwise the author proves for all integral n the identities:

$$(1)\quad P_r(nQ+\delta)=P_r(\delta)P_r(n)-p^{\frac{1}{2}r-1}P_r\Big(\frac{\delta-\Delta}{p}\Big)P_r\Big(\frac{n-\Delta}{p}\Big),$$

where r is even; $0<r\leq 24$; p prime >3; $\Delta=r(p-1)/24$ is an integer; Q is a power of p; $\delta=r(Q-1)/24$.

$$(2)\qquad P_r(nQ+\delta)=(-p)^{\frac{1}{2}r-1}P_r\Big(\frac{\delta-\Delta}{p^2}\Big)P_r\Big(\frac{n}{p}\Big),$$

where $r=2, 4, 6, 8, 10, 14, 26$; p is a prime >3 such that $r(p+1)\equiv 0 \pmod{24}$; $\Delta=r(p^2-1)/24$; Q is an odd power of p; $\delta=r(pQ-1)/24$. — These are generalizations of the case $Q=p$ which the author proved earlier [same J. **30** (1955), 488–493; MR **17**, 15]. *H. D. Kloosterman.*

Citations: MR 17, 15d = F30-16.

Referred to in F25-7.

F30-22 **(18, 194g)**

Newman, Morris. On the existence of identities for the coefficients of certain modular forms. J. London Math. Soc. **31** (1956), 350–359.

Let p be a prime >3; r and K positive integers; $Q_1, Q_2, \cdots, Q_K$ powers of p, either all squares or all non-squares; $\varepsilon=p$ or $=1$ according as the Q_k are squares or non-squares; $\nu_k=(pQ_k-\varepsilon)/24\varepsilon$ $(k=1, 2, \cdots, K)$;

$$\prod_{n=1}^{\infty}(1-x^n)^r=\sum_{n=0}^{\infty}p_r(n)x^n.$$

The author proves the existence of identities

$$\sum_{k=1}^{K}b_kp_r(Q_kn+r\nu_k)=b_0p_r(\varepsilon n/p)$$

for all integers $n\geq 0$ and sufficiently large K and where the b_k are not all zero. *H. D. Kloosterman* (Leiden).

Referred to in F25-7, P76-14.

F30-23 **(20# 5184)**

Newman, Morris. Congruences for the coefficients of modular forms and for the coefficients of $j(\tau)$. Proc. Amer. Math. Soc. **9** (1958), 609–612.

Let $j(\tau)=12^3J(\tau)=x^{-1}+\sum_{n=0}^{\infty}c(n)x^n$ be the absolute modular invariant. The author establishes certain congruences for $c(n)$ to the modulus 13, in particular:

$$c(13n)\equiv-\tau(n),$$
$$c(13np)+c(13n)c(13p)+p^{11}c(13n/p)\equiv 0,$$
$$c(13np^{2a-1})\equiv 0,$$

all modulo 13. In the last congruence, $13|\tau(p)$ and $(n, p)=1$ (for example, $p=7, 11, 157, 179$). Here n and a are positive integers, $\tau(n)$ is Ramanujan's function, and $c(u)=0$ if u is not an integer.

These results extend previously obtained congruences by Lehmer [Amer. J. Math. **64** (1942), 488–502; MR **3**, 272], Lehner, [ibid. **71** (1949), 136–148, 373–386; MR **10**, 357], and van Wijngaarden [Indag. Math. **15** (1953), 389–400; MR **15**, 403].

J. Lehner (East Lansing, Mich.)

Citations: MR 3, 272c = F30-5; MR 10, 357a = F30-8; MR 10, 357b = F30-9; MR 15, 403a = F30-15.

Referred to in F30-37, F30-53.

F30-24 **(20# 7103)**

Raleigh, John. The Fourier coefficients of the invariants $j(2^{\frac{1}{2}};\tau)$ and $j(3^{\frac{1}{2}};\tau)$. Trans. Amer. Math. Soc. **87** (1958), 90–107.

Let $G(\lambda_q)$ denote the properly discontinuous group generated by the two substitutions $S(\tau)=\tau+\lambda_q$ and $T(\tau)=-1/\tau$, where $\lambda_q=2\cos(\pi/q)$ and q is an integer ≥ 3. The class of groups $\{G(\lambda_q)\}$ was initially studied by E. Hecke [Math. Ann. **112** (1936), 664–699]. $G(\lambda_3)$ is the full modular group $G(1)$, the fundamental invariant of which, $j(1;\tau)=12^3J(1;\tau)$, has been widely studied. An invariant for $G(\lambda_4)$, here denoted by $j(2^{\frac{1}{2}};\tau)$, was obtained by J. W. Young [Trans. Amer. Math. Soc. **5** (1904), 81–104] as a quotient of theta-null series, and an invariant $j(3^{\frac{1}{2}};\tau)$ for $G(\lambda_6)$ was obtained by J. I. Hutchinson [Trans. Amer. Math. Soc. **3** (1902), 1–11], also as a quotient of theta-null series. In the present paper the author obtains convergent series for the Fourier coefficients of the invariants $j(2^{\frac{1}{2}};\tau)$ and $j(3^{\frac{1}{2}};\tau)$. The method is an extension of that used by H. Rademacher [Amer. J. Math. **60** (1938), 501–512] for obtaining the Fourier coefficients of the invariant $j(1;\tau)$. *W. H. Simons* (Vancouver, B.C.)

F30-25 **(20# 7104)**

Petersson, Hans. Über Betragmittelwerte und die Fourier-Koeffizienten der ganzen automorphen Formen. Arch. Math. **9** (1958), 176–182.

Let $f(\tau)$, an automorphic form of negative dimension $-r$ on a horocyclic group Γ, have the expansion $f(\tau)=\sum_{n=0}^{\infty}b_{n+\kappa}\exp(2\pi i(n+\kappa)\tau/N)$ at $\tau=i\infty$, where κ, N are constants depending on r, Γ, and the multiplier system v. In a short and simple discussion the author establishes the following estimates for the Fourier coefficients $b_{n+\kappa}$. (1) $b_{n+\kappa}=O(n^{r-1})$, for $r>2$; (2) $b_{n+\kappa}=O(n\log n)$, for $r=2$; $b_{n+\kappa}=O(n^{r/2})$, for $0<r<2$, $r\neq 2^{-h}$ $(h=0, 1, 2, \cdots)$; $b_{n+\kappa}=O(n^{r/2}\log^{r/2}n)$, $r=2^{-h}$ $(h=0, 1, 2, \cdots)$. It can be shown by suitable examples involving Eisenstein series that (1) and (2) cannot be essentially improved.

The principal tool used in the author's elegant proof is the estimation of the partial sums of the Poincaré series in the cases in which the series diverges. The author accomplishes this by applying simple concepts of hyperbolic geometry, just as Poincaré did in proving convergence for $r>2$.

{Reviewer's comment: For automorphic forms which vanish at $\tau=i\infty$, these estimates can be sharpened. The proof, which was given by Hecke in the case of the modular group and its congruence subgroups, is applicable to the general herocyclic group Γ and runs as follows. Let $\tau=x+iy$. Note that $\varphi(\tau)=|y^{r/2}f(\tau)|$ is invariant under Γ. Thus $\varphi(\tau)$ assumes all its values in a fundamental region of Γ and so is bounded in the upper half-plane, since $f(i\infty)=0$ to exponential order (i.e., either $\kappa>0$, or $\kappa=0$ and $b_0=0$). This shows that $f(\tau)=O(y^{-r/2})$ as $y\to 0$, uniformly in x. Now $a_n=(2\pi i)^{-1}\int_L f(\tau)\exp(-2\pi i(n+\kappa)\tau/N)\cdot dx$, where L is the segment $0\leq x<\kappa$, $y=y_0>0$. Hence, $a_n=O(y_0^{-r/2}\exp(2\pi(n+\kappa)y_0/N)$, and for $y_0=n^{-1}$, this becomes (3) $a_n=O(n^{r/2})$, $r>0$. For certain groups, this bound can be further improved. Rankin showed in 1939 [Proc. Cambridge Philos. Soc. **35** (1939), 351–372; MR **1**, 69] that if $f(\tau)$ is a modular form (belonging to the full group or a congruence subgroup) which vanishes at infinity, then $a_n=O(n^{1/2-1/5})$, provided $\kappa=0$. By employing A. Weil's estimates for the Kloosterman sums, this can be reduced to $a_n=O(n^{r/2-\frac{1}{4}+\varepsilon})$. (In the case of the modular group, $\kappa=0$ forces r to be an even integer.)}

J. Lehner (East Lansing, Mich.)

Citations: MR 1, 69d = F30-1.

Referred to in F30-34.

F30-26 (21# 5013)

Lehner, Joseph. The Fourier coefficients of automorphic forms belonging to a class of horocyclic groups. Michigan Math. J. **4** (1957), 265–279.

Let Γ be a discrete subgroup of the group of all linear transformations $z\to Vz=(az+b)/(cz+d)$ with real coefficients a, b, c, d, where z lies in the upper half-plane $\Im(z)>0$. Suppose that Γ is not properly discontinuous at any point (including ∞) of the real axis. The transformations of Γ can be represented by unimodular matrices $\begin{pmatrix} a & b \\ c & d\end{pmatrix}$ with $c>0$, and $a>0$ if $c=0$. The (discrete) set of numbers c occurring in matrices of Γ is denoted by C. For a given $c\in C$ the set of all d such that there exists a matrix $V_{c,d}=\begin{pmatrix} \cdot & \cdot \\ c & d\end{pmatrix}\in\Gamma$ is denoted by D_c. The author makes the assumption that ∞ is a parabolic fixed point of Γ and that all parabolic fixed points of Γ are equivalent under Γ. Entire automorphic forms of real dimension r and multiplier system $\varepsilon(V)$ are analytic functions $F(z)$ regular in the upper half-plane and satisfying the equation $F(Vz)=\varepsilon(V)(-i(cz+d))^{-r}F(z)$ for every $V\in\Gamma$. It is supposed that the $\varepsilon(V)$ have absolute value 1 and are independent of z. If $Sz=z+\lambda$ $(\lambda>0)$ is the generating element of the cyclic subgroup of Γ consisting of all transformations of Γ which preserve ∞, then $t=\exp 2\pi iz/\lambda$ is a uniformizing variable at ∞. If $(-i)^{-r}\varepsilon(S)=\exp 2\pi i\alpha$, $0\leqq\alpha<1$, then $F(z)\cdot\exp(-2\pi i\alpha z/\lambda)$ has a Laurent expansion in t, which is supposed to contain only a finite number of terms with negative powers of t. Thus $F(z)=\sum_{m=-\mu}^{\infty} a_m \exp 2\pi i(m+\alpha)z/\lambda$. The author applies the Hardy-Littlewood circle method for the determination of the a_m with $m\geqq 0$ in terms of the a_m with $m<0$. By means of a suitable dissection (dependent on Γ) of a line segment $0\leqq x\leqq\lambda$, $y=y_0$ $(z=x+iy)$ instead of the usual Farey dissection he obtains the following results. (1) If $F(z)$ is an automorphic form of positive dimension r, then for $m\geqq 0$ we have

$$\lambda a_m = 2\pi\sum_{\nu=1}^{\mu} a_{-\nu}\sum_{c} c^{-1}A_{c,\nu}(m)L_c(m,\nu,r,\alpha),$$

where c runs through those $c\in C$ which are positive and where

$$A_{c,\nu}(m) = \sum_{d\in D_c}\varepsilon^{-1}(V_{c,d})\cdot\exp 2\pi i[(m+\alpha)d-(\nu-\alpha)a]/c\lambda,$$

$$L_c(m,\nu,r,\alpha) = \left(\frac{\nu-\alpha}{m+\alpha}\right)^{(r+1)/2} I_{r+1}(4\pi c^{-1}\lambda^{-1}(\nu-\alpha)^{\frac{1}{2}}(m+\alpha)^{\frac{1}{2}}) \quad (m+\alpha>0,\ r>0),$$

$$L_c(0,\nu,r,0) = \Gamma^{-1}(r+2)(2\pi\nu/c\lambda)^{r+1}$$

and I_r is the Bessel function with purely imaginary argument. This theorem was obtained by Petersson by different methods [S.-B. Heidelberger Akad. Wiss. Math.-Nat. Kl. **1950**, 417–494; MR **12**, 806]. (2) If $F(z)$ is an automorphic form of dimension 0, then

$$\lambda a_m = 2\pi\sum_{\nu=1}^{\mu} a_{-\nu}\sum_{c} c^{-1}A_{c,\nu}(m)L_c(m,\nu,0,\alpha)+O(1) \quad (m\geqq 1),$$

where the summation is over those $c\in C$ for which $0<c<\beta\sqrt{m}$ and β is any positive constant. (3) If $F(z)$ is an automorphic form of dimension -2 and is the derivative of a form of dimension zero, then

$$a_m = (2\pi/\lambda)^2 i(m+\alpha)\sum_{\nu=1}^{\mu} a_{-\nu}\sum_{c} c^{-1}A_{c,\nu}(m)L_c(m,\nu,0,\alpha) \quad (m\geqq 1),$$

where the summation is again over those $c\in C$ for which $0<c<\beta\sqrt{m}$. The author considers also the case $r<-2$ (for negative r the definition of $L_c(m,\nu,r,\alpha)$ must be modified; cf. the correction in the second part of the paper [below].

H. D. Kloosterman (Leiden)

Citations: MR 12, 806e = F10-25.

Referred to in F30-32, F30-35, F30-44.

F30-27 (21# 5014)

Lehner, Joseph. The Fourier coefficients of automorphic forms on horocyclic groups. II. Michigan Math. J. **6** (1959), 173–193.

The author extends the results in the first part of the paper [reviewed above] to the case in which the group Γ has a finite number of inequivalent parabolic fixed points.

H. D. Kloosterman (Leiden)

Referred to in F30-32, F30-34, F30-44.

F30-28 (21# 7192)

Newman, Morris. Modular forms whose coefficients possess multiplicative properties. Ann. of Math. (2) **70** (1959), 478–489.

Let $B(\tau)=\eta^r(\tau)\eta^s(q\tau)$, where $\eta(\tau)$ is Dedekind's modular form, r and s are non-zero integers of the same parity and q is a prime. Put $t=(r+sq)/24$, $t^*=(s+rq)/24$, and let p be a prime greater than 3 such that $t(p-1)$ and $t^*(p-1)$ are integers. Let $g(\tau)=B(p\tau)/B(\tau)$ and

$$G(\tau) = \sum_{k=0}^{p-1} g\{\tau/(1-kq\tau)\}+g\{(\tau-1)/(p_0p-q_0q\tau)\},$$

where $p_0p-q_0q=1$. The functions $g(\tau)$ and $G(\tau)$ are entire modular functions for the groups $\Gamma_0(pq)$ and $\Gamma_0(q)$. The main result proved is that, if $0\leqq\delta=t(p-1)<p$ and $0\leqq t^*(p-1)<p$, then $G(\tau)$ is a constant. This implies that

$$(*)\qquad c(np+\delta) = \beta c(n)-\gamma p^{s-1}c\{(n-\delta)/p\},$$

where β and γ do not depend on n and $c(m)$ is the coefficient of x^m in the product

$$\prod_{n=1}^{\infty}\{(1-x^n)^r(1-x^{nq})^s\}.$$

These inequalities are satisfied by 147 different sets of values q, r, s; for each triple of values the prime q cannot exceed 23 and the prime p must satisfy a congruence $p\equiv 1 \pmod m$, where m is a certain divisor of 24. If $d(n)=c\{t(n-1)\}$, in the case when $\delta>0$, (*) implies that

$$d(np) = d(n)d(p)-\gamma p^{s-1}d(n/p),$$

whenever n is composed only of primes $p\equiv 1 \pmod m$. This gives rise to a 'modified Euler product' for the associated Dirichlet series. There is a slightly simpler result for $\delta=0$.

{These results suggest that there are relationships between the author's work and the general theory of T_n-operators as developed for arbitrary subgroups of the modular group by, for example, K. Wohlfahrt [Math. Nachr. **16** (1957), 233–256; MR **21** #5618] and in the case of the principal congruence group by Petersson [Math. Ann. **117** (1939), 39–64; MR **1**, 294]; these relationships and their generalizations are worth exploration.}

R. A. Rankin (Glasgow)

Citations: MR 1, 294c = F65-1; MR 21# 5618 = F25-9.

Referred to in F30-38.

F30-29 **(23# A137)**

Knopp, Marvin Isadore

Fourier series of automorphic forms of non-negative dimension.

Illinois J. Math. **5** (1961), 18–42.

Let $F(\tau)$ be a modular form of positive dimension r (an even integer) for the full modular group with multiplier 1, so that $F(-1/\tau)=\tau^{-r}F(\tau)$, $F(\tau+1)=F(\tau)$ and the Fourier series of $F(\tau)$ contains only a finite number of negative powers. Rademacher and Zuckerman [Ann. of Math. (2) **39** (1938), 433–462] showed that $F(\tau)$ has the Fourier series expansion

$$F(\tau) = \sum_{m=-\mu}^{\infty} a_m \exp(2\pi i m\tau),$$

where, for $m \geqq 0$,

$$a_m = (-1)^{r/2} \sum_{\nu=1}^{\mu} a_{-\nu} \sum_{k=1}^{\infty} k^{-1}A_{k,\nu}(m)\left(\frac{\nu}{m}\right)^{(r+1)/2} \times I_{r+1}\{4\pi(m\nu)^{1/2}/k\}$$

$$= (-1)^{r/2} \sum_{\nu=1}^{\mu} a_{-\nu}\alpha_m(\nu),$$

with

$$A_{k,\nu}(m) = \sum_{\substack{0\leqq h<k \\ (h,k)=1}} \exp\{-2\pi i(\nu h'+mh)/k\}, \qquad hh' \equiv -1 \pmod k.$$

Here I_{r+1} is the modified Bessel function of the first kind and the formula is a particular case of a more general formula obtained by Rademacher and Zuckerman.

The author considers the converse problem of whether a function $F(\tau)$ possessing such a Fourier series is a modular form. He proves that such a function is holomorphic on the half-plane Im $\tau > 0$ and that

$$F(\tau)-\tau^r F(-1/\tau) = p(\tau),$$

where $p(\tau)$ is a polynomial in τ of degree at most r. This result can be used to construct modular forms $F(\tau)$ in certain cases, for example when $\mu \geqq \frac{1}{2}r+1$.

There results are extended to the zonal horocyclic groups $G(\sqrt{l})$ $(l=2, 3, 4)$ generated by the transformations $\tau'=\tau+\sqrt{l}$, $\tau'=-1/\tau$. The method is based on a paper of Rademacher [Amer. J. Math. **61** (1939), 237–248] and, in particular, upon the rearrangement of certain conditionally convergent double series.

R. A. Rankin (Glasgow)

F30-30 **(23# A138)**

Knopp, Marvin Isadore

Automorphic forms of nonnegative dimension and exponential sums.

Michigan Math. J. **7** (1960), 257–287.

The methods and results of #A137 are extended to automorphic forms of positive integral dimension r with arbitrary multiplier systems of unit modulus for the groups $G(\sqrt{l})$ $(l=1, 2, 3)$. Among the complications necessitated by this generalization is the estimation of certain generalized Kloosterman sums.

R. A. Rankin (Glasgow)

Referred to in F30-33.

F30-31 **(23# A3846)**

Lehner, Joseph

The Fourier coefficients of automorphic forms of horocyclic groups. III.

Michigan Math. J. **7** (1960), 65–74.

The author extends his earlier results on entire automorphic forms [same J. **4** (1957), 265–279; MR **21** #5013; ibid. **6** (1959) 173–193; MR **21** #5014] to automorphic forms that have simple poles. Poles of higher order can be treated in an analogous manner, but the algebraic details become rather complicated.

H. D. Kloosterman (Leiden)

Referred to in F30-44.

F30-32 **(25# 197)**

Knopp, Marvin Isadore

Construction of automorphic forms on H-groups and supplementary Fourier series.

Trans. Amer. Math. Soc. **103** (1962), 168–188.

In the present paper the author extends his previous results concerning automorphic forms from the case of the modular (and similar) groups to general horocyclic groups. Let Γ be horocyclic and denote by $\{\Gamma, r, \varepsilon\}$ the vector space of automorphic forms on Γ of positive, integral dimension r; then (actually, under weaker restrictions) it is known [see J. Lehner, Michigan Math. J. **4** (1957), 265–279; MR **21** #5013; ibid. **6** (1959), 173–193; MR **21** #5014] that $F(\tau)\in\{\Gamma, r, \varepsilon\}$ implies

(1) $$F(\tau) = \sum_{\nu=1}^{\mu} b_\nu e^{2\pi i(-\nu+\kappa)\tau/\lambda} + \sum_{m=0}^{\infty} a_m e^{2\pi i(m+\kappa)\tau/\lambda}$$

($\lambda>0$, $0\leqq\kappa<1$, $S=\begin{pmatrix}1 & \lambda\\ 0 & 1\end{pmatrix}$ generates the translations of Γ and $F(S\tau)=e^{2\pi i\kappa}F(\tau)$), where the b_ν are constants, $a_m=\sum_{\nu=1}^{\mu} b_\nu a_m(\nu, r, \varepsilon)$ and the $a_m(\nu, r, \varepsilon)$ are known functions of their arguments. The main result of the paper is essentially a partial converse of the above statement: If we select arbitrary positive integers r, μ and constants b_ν $(1\leqq\nu\leqq\mu)$ and define $F(\tau)$ by (1), then $F(\tau)$ is regular for $\Im\tau>0$, but in general is not automorphic; instead, it satisfies the equation

(2) $$F(\tau)-\varepsilon^{-1}(V)(-i(\gamma\tau+\delta))^r F(V\tau) = p_V(\tau),$$

for all $V=\begin{pmatrix}\alpha & \beta\\ \gamma & \delta\end{pmatrix}\in\Gamma$, with $p_V(\tau)$ a polynomial of degree at most r. The proof is rather straightforward but lengthy; it consists, essentially, in replacing the $a_m(\nu, r, \varepsilon)$ by their expressions and rearranging the conditionally convergent double series by an appeal to a lemma of Rademacher [Amer. J. Math. **61** (1939), 237–248]. It is now easy to construct automorphic forms for every integral dimension $r>0$. Indeed, Γ is finitely generated by, say, g elements V_j $(j=1, \cdots, g)$, and if $p_{V_j}(\tau)\equiv 0$ for all $j=1, \cdots, g$, then F is automorphic. However, the coefficients of the polynomials $p_V(\tau)$ (of degree $\leqq r$) are linear functions of the b_ν $(1\leqq\nu\leqq\mu)$. Using the fact that the latter vanish, one obtains a system of $(r+1)g$ linear, homogeneous equations in the b_ν's; these have non-trivial solutions at least for $\mu\geqq(r+1)g+1$. In a joint paper of the author and J. Lehner [Illinois J. Math. **6** (1962), 98–106] is introduced the concept of supplementary Fourier series $\hat{F}$. These are essentially the same as (1), after replacement of κ, ν, ε by $\kappa'=1-\kappa$, $\nu'=1-\nu$ $(k>0)$, or $\kappa'=0$, $\nu'=-\nu$ $(\kappa=0)$ and $\varepsilon'(V)=e^{\pi i r}\varepsilon^{-1}(V)$. In terms of the supplementary Fourier series, the conditions on the b_ν's, which ensure that $F(\tau)$ is automorphic, take the simple form: $F(\tau)\in\{\Gamma, r, \varepsilon\}\Leftrightarrow \hat{F}(\tau)\equiv 0$ if $\kappa>0$, $\equiv\sum_{\nu=1}^{\mu}\bar{b}_\nu a_0(\nu', r, \varepsilon')$ if $\kappa=0$. Equivalently, (2) $F(\tau)\in\{\Gamma, r, \varepsilon\}\Leftrightarrow\sum_{\nu=1}^{\mu} b_\nu a_{-m}(\nu, r, \varepsilon)=0$ if $m>\mu$, $=b_m e^{\pi i(r+1)}$ if $1\leqq m\leqq\mu$. Finally, although the real axis is a natural boundary for $F(\tau)$ defined by (1), a certain rearrangement of the defining series (obtained at a stage of the proof of the main result) converges also for $\Im\tau<0$ to a function $F^*(\tau)$ (not the analytic continuation of $F(\tau)$). From (2) follows the corollary: $F(\tau)\in\{\Gamma, r, \varepsilon\}\Leftrightarrow F^*(\tau)\equiv(1-e^{\pi i(r+1)})\sum_{\nu=1}^{\mu} b_\nu e^{2\pi i(-\nu+k)\tau/\lambda}$.

E. Grosswald (Philadelphia, Pa.)

Citations: MR 21# 5013 = F30-26; MR 21# 5014 = F30-27; MR 25# 3168 = F30-35.

Referred to in F30-33.

F30-33 **(25# 5184)**

Knopp, Marvin Isadore

Correction to "Construction of automorphic forms on H-groups and supplementary Fourier series".

Trans. Amer. Math. Soc. **106** (1963), 341–345.

In a recent paper [same Trans. **103** (1962), 168–188; MR **25** #197] the author made use of two lemmas; no proof of these was given, because the statement of each of them closely parallels that of a lemma in a previous paper of the author [Michigan Math. J. **7** (1960), 257–287; MR **23** #A138] quoted in what follows by (A). J. R. Smart pointed out that the proof of the lemmas is still far from trivial. In the present paper the author gives a proof of the second of the lemmas. It contains over three pages of computations, which are not quite the same as in (A) (thus justifying Smart's point of view); at the same time, one may observe that while the proof is rather long and uses ingenious splittings of sums, etc., most (if not all) non-elementary ideas involved can indeed be found in (A). The proof of the first lemma is not given. The author states that it is far more complicated, but does not require any new ideas. At the end of the paper four misprints of (A) are corrected.

E. Grosswald (Philadelphia, Pa.)

Citations: MR 23# A138 = F30-30; MR 25# 197 = F30-32.

F30-34 **(25# 2370)**

Lehner, Joseph

Magnitude of the Fourier coefficients of automorphic forms of negative dimension.

Bull. Amer. Math. Soc. **67** (1961), 603–606.

H. Petersson [Arch. Math. **9** (1958), 176–182; MR **20** #7104] has shown that the Fourier coefficients a_m of certain automorphic forms of small negative dimension r, $0<r<2$, satisfy $a_m=O(m^{r/2})$ if $0<r<2$, $r\neq 2^{-h}$, for $h=0, 1, 2, \cdots$. He also obtained the weaker estimate $a_m=O(m^{r/2}\log^{r/2} m)$ for $r=2^{-h}$. The present author, using a variant of the Hardy-Littlewood circle method discussed in an earlier paper [Michigan Math. J. **6** (1959), 173–193; MR **21** #5014], shows that the stronger estimate $a_m=O(m^{r/2})$ holds for all r in the interval $0<r<2$.

T. M. Apostol (Pasadena, Calif.)

Citations: MR 20# 7104 = F30-25; MR 21# 5014 = F30-27.

Referred to in F30-56.

F30-35 **(25# 3168)**

Knopp, Marvin Isadore; Lehner, Joseph

On complementary automorphic forms and supplementary Fourier series.

Illinois J. Math. **6** (1962), 98–106; *correction*, 713.

For any discontinuous group Γ of linear transformations of the upper half-plane $\mathscr{H}$ onto itself, denote by $\{\Gamma, -r, v\}$ the (complex) vector space of forms automorphic under Γ, of dimension $-r$ and multiplier system v. Two forms $F\in\{\Gamma, -r, v\}$ and $G\in\{\Gamma, -r', v'\}$ are called "complementary" if any one of the following three equivalent conditions is satisfied: (i) FG is a differential; (ii) $FG\in\{\Gamma, -2, 1\}$; (iii) $r+r'=2$ and $vv'=1$. Let $U^\lambda=\begin{pmatrix}1 & \lambda\\ 0 & 1\end{pmatrix}$ $(\lambda>0)$ generate the subgroup of Γ which leaves ∞ invariant and define κ by $v(U^\lambda)=e(\kappa)$ $(0\leqq\kappa<1$, $e(z)=e^{2\pi iz})$. Also, set $t=e(\tau/\lambda)$. Then, if $F_\mu=F_\mu(\tau)\in\{\Gamma, -r, v\}$ is regular in $\mathscr{H}$ and has a pole of order μ at ∞,

$$(*)\qquad e(-\kappa\tau/\lambda)F_\mu(\tau) = t^{-\mu}+\sum_{m=0}^{\infty} a_m t^m$$

and the Fourier coefficients $a_m=a_m(\mu, -r, v)$ can be computed by rather complicated, known formulae [see Lehner, Michigan Math. J. **4** (1957), 265–279; MR **21** #5013]. For given parameters μ, $-r$, v, one may compute coefficients a_m by these formulae and then (*) defines a function F_μ, which, in general, will not be automorphic. Let $\kappa'=1-\kappa$ and $\mu'=1-\mu$ if $\kappa>0$; $\kappa'=0$ and $\mu'=-\mu$ if $\kappa=0$, and set $\hat{a}_m=a_m(\mu', -r, v')$. Then one defines $\hat{F}_{\mu'}$, the series "supplementary" to F_μ, by

$$(**)\qquad e(-\kappa'\tau/\lambda)\hat{F}_{\mu'}(\tau) = t^{-\mu'}+\sum_{m=0}^{\infty}\hat{a}_m t^m.$$

Finally, given $F_\mu\in\{\Gamma, -r, v\}$, one can (following Petersson) formally define a set of Poincaré series $G_\mu=G(\tau, -r', v', \mu)$ which are forms complementary to F (i.e., $G_\mu\in\{\Gamma, -r', v'\}$). The results of the present paper can now be stated as follows: If $F_\mu\in\{\Gamma, -r, v\}$, $r<0$, $\mu\geqq 1$ satisfies (*), then $G(\tau, -r', v', \nu)\equiv 0$, provided that $\nu=\mu-1$ (if $\kappa'>0$) or $\nu=\mu$ (if $\kappa'=0$). If r is an integer, also a converse proposition holds. If v_0 is the multiplier of Dedekind and $-12<r<0$, then $G(\tau, r-2, v_0^{-2r}, \mu)\equiv 0$ if μ is any non-negative integer and $G(\tau, -14, 1, \mu)\equiv 0$ if μ is any positive integer. There are no non-trivial cusp forms in $\{\Gamma(1), r-2, v_0^{-2r}\}$ $(0>r>-12)$, or in $\{\Gamma(1), -14, 1\}$ ($\Gamma(1)=$ the modular group). If F_μ is given by (*) and $\hat{F}_{\mu'}$ by (**), then $F_\mu\in\{\Gamma, -r, v\}$ if and only if $\hat{F}_{\mu'}\equiv 0$ (if $\kappa=0$), or $\hat{F}_{\mu'}\equiv\hat{a}_0$ (if $\kappa>0$). The method used is similar to that of Lehner's quoted paper.

E. Grosswald (Philadelphia, Pa.)

Citations: MR 21# 5013 = F30-26.

Referred to in F10-79, F30-32.

F30-36 **(26# 323)**

Raleigh, J.

On the Fourier coefficients of triangle functions.

Acta Arith. **8** (1962/63), 107–111.

Let G_q be the group of linear-fractional transformations generated by $\tau\to\tau+\lambda_q$, $\tau\to-1/\tau$, where τ is a complex variable restricted to the upper half-plane $\lambda_q=2\cos\pi/q$, $q=3, 4, \cdots, \infty$; $\lambda_\infty=2$. Let $J_q(\tau)$ be the invariant function on G_q normalized so that the vertices of the standard fundamental region are mapped by J_q on 0, 1, ∞. (For $q=3$, J_q coincides with J, Klein's modular invariant.) Writing $J_q(\tau)=\sum_{n=-1}^{\infty}a_n(q)x_q^n$, $x_q=\exp(2\pi i\tau/\lambda_q)$, the author finds closed expressions for $a_n(q)$, $n=-1, 0, 1, 2, 3$. For $0\leqq n\leqq 3$ the quantity $A_n=a_nq^{2n+2}a_{-1}{}^n$ has the form $A_n=P_{n+1}(q^2)/R_{n+1}$, where P_{n+1} is a polynomial of degree $n+1$ and R_{n+1} is a rational integer. The result suggests the change of variable $x_q=a_{-1}q^2Z_q$, $J_q(\tau)=J_q{}^*(Z_q)$; then $q^2J_q{}^*(Z_q)=Z_q^{-1}+\sum_{n=0}^{\infty}A_n(q)Z_q{}^n$, which accords with the reviewer's result [Pacific J. Math. **4** (1954), 243–249; MR **15**, 785] that $A_n(q)$ is a rational number for $n\geqq 0$ and $q\geqq 3$.

The calculation makes use of the well-known differential equation for the function inverse to J_q. The paper closes with some remarks and conjectures.

J. Lehner (E. Lansing, Mich.)

Citations: MR 15, 785f = F15-1.

F30-37 **(26# 1287)**

Kolberg, O.

Congruences for the coefficients of the modular invariant $j(\tau)$.

Math. Scand. **10** (1962), 173-181.

This paper provides new congruences for $\{c(n)\}$, the Fourier coefficients of the modular invariant $j(\tau)$. For example,

$$c(3n+1)\equiv 54\sigma_1(3n+1) \pmod{3^4},$$

$$c(n)\equiv 2n\sigma_3(n) \pmod 7 \text{ if } \left(\frac{n}{7}\right)=1,$$

and similar congruences for the moduli 5^2, 11, and 13. Here $\sigma_k(n)$ is the sum of the kth powers of the divisors of n. From these congruences and one of M. Newman [Proc. Amer. Math. Soc. **9** (1958), 609–612; MR **20** #5184], $c(13n) \equiv -\tau(n) \pmod{13}$, exact divisibility properties of $c(n)$ to the above moduli may be deduced. The author also develops congruences to the moduli 17, 19, and 23 in terms of a function $\tau_k(n)$ generalizing the τ-function of Ramanujan.

The method used is elementary, essentially manipulation of power series and utilization of identities of Euler, Jacobi, and Ramanujan. No use is made of the transformation theory of modular functions.

J. Lehner (E. Lansing, Mich.)

Citations: MR 20# 5184 = F30-23.
Referred to in F30-47, F30-48.

F30-38 (26# 3676)

Newman, Morris

Modular forms whose coefficients possess multiplicative properties. II.

Ann. of Math. (2) **75** (1962), 242–250.

Part I appeared in same Ann. (2) **70** (1959), 478–489 [MR **21** #7192]. Let

$$\varphi(\tau) = \prod_{n=1}^{\infty} (1-x^n)^r(1-x^{nq})^s = \sum_{n=0}^{\infty} c(n)x^n,$$

where $x = \exp 2\pi i\tau$, and let

$$\Delta = (r+sq)(p^2-1)/24,\ \Delta^* = (s+rq)(p^2-1)/24.$$

From φ a certain function $G(\tau)$, of a rather complicated form, is constructed and is shown to be an entire modular function for the group $\Gamma_0(q)$. Its valence is determined in certain cases, and it is shown that $G(\tau)$ is a constant when $0 \leqq \Delta < p^2$ and $0 \leqq \Delta^* < p^2$.

A table of values of r and s such that $rs \neq 0$, $r \not\equiv s \pmod 2$ and $G(\tau) = c$ (a constant) is given. For these the coefficients $c(n)$ of $\varphi(\tau)$ satisfy

$$c(np^2+\Delta) - \gamma_n c(n) + p^{2\varepsilon-2}c\{(n-\Delta)/p^2\} = 0,$$

where $\varepsilon = \frac{1}{2}(r+s)$,

$$\gamma_n = p^{2\varepsilon-2}c - \left(\frac{\theta}{p}\right)p^{\varepsilon-3/2}\left(\frac{n-\Delta}{p}\right),$$

and $\theta = (-1)^{1/2-\varepsilon}2q^s$. Several special cases are given.

R. A. Rankin (Glasgow)

Citations: MR 21# 7192 = F30-28.

F30-39 (27# 2466)

Maier, W.

Teilerpotenzsummen und ihre Erzeugenden.

Arch. Math. **14** (1963), 238–242.

The sums in question are $\sigma_a(n)$, the sum of the ath powers of the divisors of n. The author discusses a number of known identities involving these sums and derives some new ones. For example, if $0 < \operatorname{Im}(\beta) < \operatorname{Im}(\tau)$ we have

$$\int_{\beta}^{\beta+1} \Theta(w)H\binom{a+1}{\tau-w}\,dw = \frac{2(-2\pi i)^{a+1}}{\Gamma(a+1)}\sum_{n=1}^{\infty} e^{2\pi i\tau n^2}\sigma_a(n^2),$$

where $\Theta(w) = \sum_{g=-\infty}^{\infty} e^{2\pi i w g^2}$ and

$$H\binom{s}{w} = \frac{(-2\pi i)^s}{\Gamma(s)}\sum_{n=1}^{\infty} e^{2\pi i w n}\sigma_{s-1}(n).$$

T. M. Apostol (Pasadena, Calif.)

F30-40 (28# 1288)

Kolberg, O.

The coefficients of $j(\tau)$ modulo powers of 3.

Årbok Univ. Bergen Mat.-Natur. Ser. **1962**, *no.* 16, 7 *pp.*

Let $j(\tau) = x^{-1} + c_0 + c_1x + \cdots$ be Klein's modular invariant, where $\operatorname{Im}\tau > 0$ and $x = \exp 2\pi i\tau$. The reviewer gave a congruence

$$c(3^a n) \equiv 0 \pmod{3^{2a+3}}, \qquad a > 0,$$

for the coefficients $c_n = c(n)$ [Amer. J. Math. **71** (1949), 373–386; MR **10**, 357] and observed that this congruence states the exact power of 3 dividing $c(3^a)$ for $3^a \leqq 24$, these values being known numerically. The author proves that this observation is true for all n by showing that

$$c(3^a n) \equiv \mp 3^{2a+3}10^{a-1}\sigma(n)/n \pmod{3^{2a+6}}$$

if $n \equiv \pm 1 \pmod 3$; thus in particular $c(3^a) \not\equiv 0 \pmod{3^{2a+4}}$. The method of proof is by induction on a, and important use is made of the relation

$$j = f^{-1} + 28\cdot 3^3 + 10\cdot 3^9 f + 4\cdot 3^{14}f^2 + 3^{18}f^3,$$

with $f = x\varphi(x)^{-12}\varphi(x^3)^{12}$, φ being the Euler product $\prod_1^{\infty}(1-x^m)$.

J. Lehner (College Park, Md.)

Citations: MR 10, 357b = F30-9.
Referred to in F30-47.

F30-41 (28# 2096)

Fomenko, O. M.

Estimates of Petersson's inner product with an application to the theory of quaternary quadratic forms. (Russian)

Dokl. Akad. Nauk SSSR **152** (1963), 559–562.

Let $E(x_1, \cdots, x_4)$ be a positive definite quadratic form with rational integral coefficients of g.c.d. 1, let F be the matrix of the form. D the discriminant, q the "Stufe", $\tau = x+iy$ $(y>0)$, L, X integral 4-vectors, $t = $ g.c.d. $(q, \bar{L}FL/2q)$. Construct $\vartheta_F(\tau/L) = \sum \alpha_F(n, L)\exp(2\pi i t\tau n/q)$, where $\alpha_F(n, L)$ is the number of vector solutions X to $2qtn = (q\bar{X}+\bar{L})F(qX+L)$. Then decompose $\vartheta = E+S$ into an Eisenstein series E and a cusp series (parabolic form) S with coefficients $\varepsilon_F(n, L)$ and $\omega_F(n, L)$ (for the term $\exp 2\pi i t\tau n/q$). The author considers estimates on ω.

Previously, Eichler [Arch. Math. **5** (1954), 355–366; MR **16**, 116] showed $|\omega_F(n, 0)| < c_{F,\varepsilon}n^{1/2+\varepsilon}$, where $(n, Q) = 1$ for a certain integer Q. The result was improved by Shimura [J. Math. Soc. Japan **10** (1958), 1–28; MR **20** #1679] and Andrianov [Dokl. Akad. Nauk SSSR **141** (1961), 9–12; MR **24** #A2560] to the new result $|\omega_F(n, L)| < c_{F,L}\tau(n)n^{1/2}$, $(n, Q) = 1$, for $\tau(n)$ the divisor function.

The author extends these results to $|\omega_F(n, 0)| < Cq^4 \ln\ln qn^{1/2}\tau(n)$. He uses Petersson's inner product formula for the system of forms belonging to $\{\Gamma(q), -2\}$ [see Gunning, *Lectures on modular forms*, Princeton Univ. Press, Princeton, N.J., 1962; MR **24** #A2664]. Some of the author's methods are used again in the following paper [#2097].

H. Cohn (Tucson, Ariz.)

Citations: MR 16, 116d = G30-15; MR 20# 1679 = F25-8; MR 24# A2560 = E20-65; MR 24# A2664 = F02-7.

F30-42 (28# 2097)

Fomenko, O. M.

Fourier coefficients of Poincaré series of dimension −2. (Russian)

Dokl. Akad. Nauk SSSR **153** (1963), 1273–1275.

The author considers Fourier coefficients of Poincaré series of dimension -2 for certain congruence subgroups $\Gamma(N)$ of the modular group (mod N). Then summing for (matrix) M in coset $A\Gamma(N)$ $(A \in \Gamma(1))$, we have

$$G_{-2}(\tau, A, N, \nu) = \sum \exp(2\pi i M\tau\nu/N)/(\text{den } M)^2 = \sum_{l=1}^{\infty} a_l(\exp 2\pi i\tau l/N),$$

and $a_l = \delta_l^{\nu} - 2\pi l^{1/2} S(A, N, l, \nu)/N\nu^{1/2}$. The author shows that if $(l/(l, N), N) = 1$, then

$$S(A, N, l, \nu) = O(\tau(l)\nu^{5/6}N^{7/4});$$

and if in addition $(\nu/(\nu, N), N) = 1$, then

$$S(I, N, l, \nu) = O(\tau(l)\tau(\nu)N^6).$$

The proof uses lemmas on Petersson's inner product as developed in the previous article [see #2096] and again applies relatively elementary methods to deep results, such as Salié's estimates on Kloosterman sums [Salié, Math. Z. **36** (1932), 263–278]. *H. Cohn* (Tucson, Ariz.)

F30-43 **(29# 1188)**

Gupta, H.

On the coefficients of the powers of Dedekind's modular form.

J. London Math. Soc. **39** (1964), 433–440.

Let $\varphi(x)$ denote the Euler product, $\varphi(x) = \prod_{n=1}^{\infty}(1-x^n)$, and for arbitrary r define $p_r(n)$ as the coefficient of x^n in $\varphi(x)^r$, i.e., $\varphi(x)^r = \sum_{n=0}^{\infty} p_r(n)x^n$. Then $\varphi(x)$ is a polynomial in r of degree n which was studied by the reviewer [J. London Math. Soc. **30** (1955), 488–493; MR **17**, 15], who gave the polynomials explicitly for $n \leqq 10$. The coefficients of $p_r(n)$ tend to become large, and the author observes that if $p_r(n)$ be expressed in terms of the binomial coefficients $\binom{r}{k}$, $0 \leqq k \leqq n$, the coefficients involved are much smaller. Thus, setting

$$(-1)^n p_r(n) = \sum_{k=0}^{n} C_k(n)\binom{r}{k},$$

the author gives recurrence formulas for the integers $C_k(n)$ and gives their actual values for $0 < k \leqq n \leqq 50$. The tables were checked against tables of the partition function by choosing $r = -1$. It would be of fundamental interest to compute the zeros of these polynomials.

Morris Newman (Washington, D.C.)

Citations: MR 17, 15d = F30-16.

F30-44 **(29# 2230)**

Lehner, Joseph

On automorphic forms of negative dimension.

Illinois J. Math. **8** (1964), 395–407.

Let Γ be a horocyclic group and assume that the function $F(\tau)$ is regular in the upper half-plane and is an automorphic form (with respect to Γ) of dimension $-r$ and multiplier system v. At the finite parabolic cusps p_k, $F(\tau)$ admits a (generalized) Fourier expansion of the form

$$(\tau - p_k)^r e(-\kappa_k A_k \tau/\lambda_k) F(\tau) = \sum_{m=-\mu_k}^{\infty} a_m^{(k)} e(mA_k\tau/\lambda_k) \quad (\mu_k \geqq 0)$$

(the exact definitions of the constants κ_k, A_k, λ_k are lengthy and may be found in the author's book [*Discontinuous groups and automorphic functions*, Amer. Math. Soc., Providence, R.I., 1964; MR **29** #1332]). Generalizing the classical circle method, the author [see Michigan Math. J. **4** (1957), 265–279; MR **21** #5013; ibid. **6** (1959), 173–193; MR **21** #5014; ibid. **7** (1960), 65–74; MR **23** #A3846] has obtained explicit expressions for the Fourier coefficients $a_m^{(k)}$ as functions of the principal parts of $F(\tau)$ at the parabolic cusps, provided that the dimension is positive or zero, in the latter case with a bounded error term, this is still, in a sense, a "best possible" result, the forms of dimension zero being determined by their principal parts only up to an additive constant. No such results could be expected in the case of forms of negative dimensions, because these are not completely determined by their principal parts at the cusps; indeed, there exist non-constant automorphic forms of negative dimension that are regular everywhere. In the present paper the author shows that the circle method can still be used to determine the Fourier coefficients of forms of negative dimension, with an error term of the order of magnitude of the Fourier coefficients of an everywhere regular form. The Cauchy integral representation of the $a_m^{(k)}$ is obtained easily, and the major part of the paper is devoted to the way in which the path of integration has to be partitioned and to the estimation of the corresponding integrals.

E. Grosswald (Paris)

Citations: MR 21# 5013 = F30-26; MR 21# 5014 = F30-27; MR 23# A3846 = F30-31; MR 29# 1332 = F02-12.

F30-45 **(29# 2231)**

Knopp, Marvin Isadore; Smart, John Roderick

On Kloosterman sums connected with modular forms of half-integral dimension.

Illinois J. Math. **8** (1964), 480–487.

Es sei Γ die elliptische Modulgruppe, r eine reelle Zahl und v ein Multiplikatorsystem für Γ und die Dimension r. Insbesondere ist dann $v(M)$ für jedes $M \in \Gamma$ eine komplexe Zahl mit $|v(M)| = 1$. Speziell für $U = \begin{pmatrix} 1 & 1 \\ 0 & 1 \end{pmatrix}$ sei $v(U) = e^{2\pi i\kappa}$, $0 \leqq \kappa < 1$. Mit vorgegebenen ganzen Zahlen c, n, μ, $c > 0$ wird die Exponentialsumme

$$W(c, n, \mu, v) = \sum_{\substack{0 < d \leqq c \\ (c,d)=1}} \bar{v}(M_d) \exp\left[\frac{2\pi i}{c}\{(n+\kappa)a + (\mu+\kappa)d\}\right]$$

gebildet. Dabei ist M_d für jedes d mit $0 < d \leqq c$, $(c, d) = 1$, irgendeine Matrix $M_d = \begin{pmatrix} a & b \\ c & d \end{pmatrix} \in \Gamma$ mit $(c \quad d)$ als zweiter Zeile. Die Summe $W(c, n, \mu, v)$ ist unabhängig davon, in welcher Weise $M_d \in \Gamma$ so gewählt wird. Die Verfasser beweisen für halbganze Dimensionen r und für $c \to +\infty$ die asymptotische Abschätzung

$$(*) \qquad W(c, n, \mu, v) = O(c^{1/2+\varepsilon}), \quad \varepsilon > 0.$$

Die dabei eingehende Konstante hängt von μ und v, aber nicht von n ab. Der Beweis kombiniert eine Methode von H. Petersson [Abh. Deutsch. Akad. Wiss. Berlin Kl. Math. Allg. Natur. **1954**, no. 2; MR **17**, 129] mit einem Resultat von A. V. Malyšev [Vestnik Leningrad. Univ. **15** (1960), no. 13, 59–75; MR **23** #A2391]. Die Verfasser formulieren ferner die folgende Vermutung: Zu jeder reellen nicht halbganzen Dimension r gibt es ganze Zahlen n, μ und ein Multiplikatorsystem v derart, daß (*) nicht gilt. Schließlich wird noch eine Anwendung von (*) auf die Abschätzung der Fourierkoeffizienten von Spitzenformen erwähnt. *E. Gottschling* (Berlin)

Citations: MR 17, 129b = P72-25; MR 23# A2391 = L05-20.

F30-46 **(31# 2216)**

Andrianov, A. N.; Fomenko, O. M.

Fourier coefficients of parabolic forms. (Russian)

Dokl. Akad. Nauk SSSR **158** (1964), 255–257.

The parabolic forms referred to in the title are cuspforms (Spitzenformen) of dimension $-k$ belonging to the principal congruence group $\Gamma(N)$. Let $\lambda(n)$ be the nth Fourier coefficient of such a cuspform f. Let p be a prime and let l take one of the values $1, 2, \cdots, p-1$. The authors state the following two theorems: (i) If $M \gg p^2$, then

$$\sum_{m \leqq M} |\lambda(mp+l)|^2 = \beta M^k + (M^{k-0.332}p^{k+3.672});$$

(ii) if $p \ll M^{0.07}$, then $\sum_{m \le M} |\lambda(mp+l)|^2 \ll M^k p^{k-1}$ (misprint corrected). The positive number β depends on p and is $O(p^{k-1})$. These results are improvements of similar results obtained by J. V. Linnik [Proc. Internat. Congr. Math. (Stockholm, 1962), pp. 270–284, Inst. Mittag-Leffler, Djursholm, 1963; MR **31** #4775] by a different method. A very brief sketch of the proofs is given. They appear to be based essentially on the reviewer's work [Proc. Cambridge Philos. Soc. **35** (1939), 351–372; MR **1**, 69; errata, MR **1**, p. 400] on $\sum_{n \le M} |\lambda(n)|^2$, supplemented by estimates, due to N. G. Čudakov [*Introduction to the theory of Dirichlet's L-functions* (Russian), OGIZ, Moscow, 1947; MR **11**, 234] and the authors, of the magnitude of certain Dirichlet series.

{This article has appeared in English translation [Soviet Math. Dokl. **5** (1964), 1203–1205].}

R. A. Rankin (Glasgow)

Citations: MR 1, 69d = F30-1; MR 11, 234b = M02-1; MR 31# 4775 = P02-22.

F30-47 (31# 3388)

Aas, Hans-Fredrik

Congruences for the coefficients of the modular invariant $j(\tau)$.

Math. Scand. **14** (1964), 185–192.

Let $j(\tau) = x^{-1} + c_0 + \sum_1^\infty c(n)x^n$, $x = \exp 2\pi i\tau$, be the modular invariant. Continuing work of Kolberg [Årbok Univ. Bergen Mat.-Natur. Ser. **1962**, no. 16; MR **28** #1288], the author proves that $c(5^a n) \equiv -3^{a-1}5^{a+1} n\sigma(n) \pmod{5^{a+2}}$ for $a > 0$ and $n > 0$, where $\sigma(n)$ is the sum of the divisors of n. In particular, $c(5^a) \not\equiv 0 \pmod{5^{a+2}}$, a conjecture of the reviewer [Amer. J. Math. **71** (1949), 373–386; MR **10**, 357]. The paper also contains a new proof of Kolberg's congruence [Math. Scand. **10** (1962), 173–181; MR **26** #1287] $c(n) \equiv 10n\sigma(n) \pmod{5^2}$, $n \equiv 2, 3 \pmod 5$.

J. Lehner (College Park, Md.)

Citations: MR 10, 357b = F30-9; MR 26# 1287 = F30-37; MR 28# 1288 = F30-40.

F30-48 (31# 3389)

Aas, Hans-Fredrik

Congruences for the coefficients of the modular invariant $j(\tau)$.

Math. Scand. **15** (1964), 64–68.

Let $c(n)$ be the coefficient of $\exp 2\pi i n\tau$ in the modular invariant $j(\tau)$, where $n \geqq -1$ and $c(-1) = 1$. J. Lehner [Amer. J. Math. **71** (1949), 136–148; MR **10**, 357] showed that $c(7^a n) \equiv 0 \pmod{7^a}$, and the author sharpens this result by showing that $c(7^a n) \equiv -7^a 5^{a-1} n\sigma_3(n) \pmod{7^{a+1}}$. It follows that $c(7^a n) \equiv 0 \pmod{7^{a+1}}$ when n is not a quadratic residue modulo 7. The proof, which is elementary but complicated, uses methods similar to those employed by Lehner [loc. cit.], O. Kolberg [e.g., Math. Scand. **10** (1962), 173–181; MR **26** #1287] and the author [#3388 above] to deduce similar congruences to other moduli.

R. A. Rankin (Glasgow)

Citations: MR 10, 357a = F30-8; MR 26# 1287 = F30-37.

F30-49 (32# 93)

Selberg, Atle

On the estimation of Fourier coefficients of modular forms.

Proc. Sympos. Pure Math., Vol. VIII, pp. 1–15. *Amer. Math. Soc., Providence, R.I.*, 1965.

This is a survey paper describing two of the methods which have been used to obtain estimates of the Fourier coefficients of modular forms. The paper also contains a number of new results by the author although they date back ten years.

Let Γ denote the modular group of linear fractional transformations, Γ' a subgroup of Γ, k a positive real number and χ a multiplier system for k and Γ'. Let $f(z)$ be a modular form of dimension $-k$ for Γ' with the multiplier system χ; then f has the Fourier expansion $f(z) = \sum_1^\infty C_n \exp((n-\alpha)z/q)$, where α is a real number, $0 \leqq \alpha < 1$, depending on χ, and q is an integer depending on Γ'. Rankin [Proc. Cambridge Philos. Soc. **35** (1939), 357–372; MR **1**, 69] showed that $\sum_{n \le x} |C_n|^2/n^{k-1} = Ax + O(x^{3/5})$ and consequently $C_n = O(n^{k/2-1/5})$, this result being valid for Γ' a congruence group in Γ and χ arbitrary. Kloostermann [Abh. Math. Sem. Univ. Hamburg **5** (1927), 337–352] introduced a second method for estimating these coefficients which later led to the result $C_n = O(n^{k/2-1/4+\varepsilon})$ following Weil's result $S(m, n; c, \chi, \Gamma') = O(|c|^{1/2+\varepsilon})$ on Kloostermann sums. This is now known to be valid for k half integral and χ a multiplier system which is identically 1 on a congruence subgroup.

Some of the new results of this paper: (1) If Γ' is a subgroup of finite index in Γ and χ is a multiplier system for Γ' and k, then $C_n = O(n^{k/2-1/5})$; (2) The result $\sum_{n \le x} |C_n|^2/(n-\alpha)^{k-1} = Ax + O(x^{1-\delta})$ is false for fixed $\delta > 0$ even on subgroups of finite index in Γ; (3) If G is a discontinuous group acting on the upper half-plane and f is an automorphic cusp form of dimension $-k$ for G, then $\sum_{n \le x} |C_n|^2/n^{k-1} = Ax + o(x)$; (4) The Kloostermann sums $S(m, n, c; \chi, \Gamma')$ are not $O(c|^{1-\delta})$, $\delta > 0$, even for even integral k on all subgroups of finite index in Γ. There are other results of a similar nature, and the author closes the paper with comments concerning the relative merits of the two approaches.

J. R. Smart (Madison, Wis.)

Citations: MR 1, 69d = F30-1.

Referred to in F30-54.

F30-50 (32# 7516)

Smart, John Roderick

On modular forms of dimension -2.

Trans. Amer. Math. Soc. **116** (1965), 86–107.

The author extends a method going back in its essentials to papers by Rademacher [Amer. J. Math. **61** (1939), 237–248] and the reviewer [Michigan Math. J. **6** (1959), 71–88; MR **21** #1390]. This method works as follows. Let Γ be a subgroup of finite index in the modular group M, and let v be a multiplier system of integral dimension on Γ. The Poincaré series of dimension -2 on Γ with multiplier v does not converge absolutely and so cannot be used directly to represent modular forms of that dimension. One shows, however, that the Poincaré series does converge conditionally and uniformly when summed in a certain order; its sum is an analytic function, and is, in fact, a modular form, whose Fourier coefficients can be calculated from the Poincaré series.

The method involves proving a "Rademacher lemma" for the group Γ, whose purpose is to permit rearrangement of the conditionally convergent series. Crucial in the proof is the nontrivial estimation of the Kloosterman sums, which arise from the multiplier system v.

The author carries out all this for Γ a subgroup of finite index in M and v a multiplier system for which the Kloosterman estimates are valid. At the end of the paper he gives a number of cases in which v satisfies the required condition. Thus if Γ is a congruence subgroup of M and v is a character on Γ, the estimates hold, as he deduces from a result of Petersson [Abh. Deutsch. Akad. Wiss. Berlin. Kl. Math. Allg. Natur. **1954**, no. 2; MR **17**, 129]. Several other examples are given. In the last section he introduces a scalar product in the space of modular forms of dimension -2 and proves the Petersson scalar product formula.

This leads to a proof of the completeness theorem for the Poincaré series in question.

J. Lehner (College Park, Md.)

Citations: MR 17, 129b = P72-25; MR 21# 1390 = F10-54.

F30-51 **(33# 2603)**

Andrianov, A. N.; Fomenko, O. M.

On square means of progressions of Fourier coefficients of parabolic forms. (Russian)

Trudy Mat. Inst. Steklov. **80** (1965), 5–15.

Let $\Gamma(1)$, $\Gamma(N)$ be the well-known groups of integral unimodular matrices [see R. C. Gunning, *Lectures on modular forms*, Princeton Univ. Press, Princeton, N.J., 1962; MR **24** #A2664]; $\tau = x + iy$;

$$f(\tau) = \sum_{n=1}^{\infty} \lambda(n) \exp\left(\frac{2\pi i \tau n}{N}\right)$$

is a parabolic form of type $\{\Gamma(N), -k\}$; p, typical prime, $(p, 2N) = 1$; $l = 1, 2, 3, \cdots, p-1$. Also, write

$$f_{l,p}(\tau) = \sum_{n \equiv l(p)} \lambda(n) \exp\left(\frac{2\pi i \tau n}{Np}\right),$$

which is a parabolic form of type $\{\Gamma(Np), -k\}$. Let f, g be parabolic forms of type $\{G, -k\}$, where G is the genus-group of the group $\Gamma(1)$. Next, write

$$(f, g)_G = \iint_{D(G)} f(\tau)\overline{g(\tau)} y^{k-2}\, dx dy,$$

where $D(G)$ is the fundamental domain of G in the τ-half-plane; $[\Gamma(1) : \Gamma(N)]$ is the index of $\Gamma(N)$ in $\Gamma(1)$;

$$\alpha = \frac{12(4\pi)^{k-1}(f(\tau), f(\tau))_{\Gamma(N)}}{[\Gamma(1) : \Gamma(N)]N^k k!},$$

$$\beta = \frac{12(4\pi)^{k-1}(f_{l,p}(\tau), f_{l,p}(\tau))_{\Gamma(Np)}}{[\Gamma(1) : \Gamma(Np)]N^k k!}.$$

Using the notation $T \ll S$ made familiar by I. M. Vinogradov, the authors prove the following theorems.

Theorem 1: For $M \gg p^2$,

$$\sum_{m \leq M} |\lambda(mp+l)|^2 = \beta M^k + O(M^{k-.332} p^{k+3.672}).$$

Theorem 2: For $p \ll M^{.07}$,

$$\sum_{m \leq M} |\lambda(mp+l)|^2 \ll M^k p^{k-1}.$$

These theorems could throw light on a well-known unsolved hypothesis of H. Petersson [Math. Ann. **117** (1939), 39–64; MR **1**, 294]. *S. Chowla* (University Park, Pa.)

Citations: MR 1, 294c = F65-1; MR 24# A2664 = F02-7.

F30-52 **(34# 157)**

Andrews, George E.

On the theorems of Watson and Dragonette for Ramanujan's mock theta functions.

Amer. J. Math. **88** (1966), 454–490.

This paper continues the work by L. A. Dragonette [Trans. Amer. Math. Soc. **72** (1952), 474–500; MR **14**, 248] on the coefficients of Ramanujan's mock theta functions. Five third-order functions are treated, the first of which, $f(q) = \sum_{n=0}^{\infty} q^{n^2} \prod_{j=1}^{n} (1+q^j)^{-2} = \sum A(n) q^n$, is discussed fully. The coefficients $A(n)$ were given by Dragonette in the form of an exponential sum of $\sqrt{n}$ terms with an error term $O(n^{1/2} \log n)$. The coefficients $\lambda_n(k)$ in this sum were given in terms of some unspecified roots of unity. In the present paper, the author proves that $\lambda_n(k)$ is essentially the same as the well-known $A_{2k}(n)$ that occur in the Hardy-Ramanujan series for the partition function. This more explicit result is used to obtain $O(n^{\varepsilon})$ for the error term. The methods used are the traditional ones but their execution is very elaborate.

D. H. Lehmer (Berkeley, Calif.)

Citations: MR 14, 248g = F30-13.

F30-53 **(35# 5390)**

Atkin, A. O. L.; O'Brien, J. N.

Some properties of $p(n)$ and $c(n)$ modulo powers of 13.

Trans. Amer. Math. Soc. **126** (1967), 442–459.

Let $j(\tau) = x^{-1} + \sum_{n=1}^{\infty} c(n) x^n$, $x = \exp(2\pi i \tau)$, $\operatorname{Im} \tau > 0$, be Klein's modular invariant. The $c(n)$ are rational integers, and in 1949 the reviewer [Amer. J. Math. **71** (1949), 136–148; MR **10**, 357; ibid. **71** (1949), 373–386; MR **10**, 357] proved in particular the following congruences for them: if $n \equiv 0 \pmod{2^a 3^b 5^c 7^d}$, then (1) $c(n) \equiv 0 \pmod{2^{3a+8} 3^{2b+3} 5^{c+1} 7^d}$. The moduli occurring in (1) are exactly those primes p for which $\Gamma_0(p)$—the subgroup of the modular group with $c \equiv 0 \pmod p$ in $\begin{pmatrix} a & b \\ c & d \end{pmatrix}$—is of genus zero, with one exception: $\Gamma_0(13)$ is of genus zero, but there is no congruence like (1) for 13. In 1958, however, M. Newman [Proc. Amer. Math. Soc. **9** (1958), 609–612; MR **20** #5184] proved that (2) $c(13^2 n) \equiv 8c(13n) \pmod{13}$, and setting $t(n) = -c(13n) \equiv c(13n/c(13) \pmod{13}$, he showed that (3) $t(np) - t(n)t(p) + p^{-1}t(n/p) \equiv 0 \pmod{13}$, where $p \neq 13$ is a prime. Equation (3) reminds one of the identical formulae characteristic of the Fourier coefficients of the Hecke modular forms. Since the present $c(n)$ are exponentially large, trivial order of magnitude considerations show that an identical formula of the Hecke type is impossible here; instead, however, one has the congruence (3). Equation (2) may be regraded as a ramified case of (3) with $p = 13$.

Continuing, Newman observed that $c(91) \equiv 0 \pmod{13}$, and it follows from (3) that (4) $c(91n) \equiv 0 \pmod{13}$ if $(n, 7) = 1$. Thus the density of those $c(n)$ that are divisible by 13 is positive.

The paper under review makes a noteworthy contribution to the literature in this field. The authors generalize (2) as follows. Theorem 1: For each $\alpha \geq 1$ there exists a constant k_α not divisible by 13 such that for all n, $c(13^{\alpha+1} n) \equiv k_\alpha c(13^\alpha n) \pmod{13^\alpha}$. They also offer the following conjecture: Let $\alpha \geq 1$ and write $t(n) \equiv c(13^\alpha n)/c(13^\alpha) \pmod{13}$; then $t(np) - t(n)t(p) + p^{-1}t(n/p) \equiv 0 \pmod{13^\alpha}$. {The first author has informed the reviewer that Conjecture 1 has since been proved by the authors. It represents the congruential analogue of the Hecke identical formulae. Thus Hecke's theory, valid originally only for modular forms of negative dimension, has been extended to modular functions (which are of zero dimension).}

In addition the authors demonstrate that $c(n)$ is divisible by 13^3 for infinitely many n, and that $c(n)$ fills all residue classes (prime to 13) modulo 13^α ($\alpha \geq 1$) infinitely often.

The basic tool used in the above developments is the modular equation, the algebraic equation connecting the modular functions $\eta(169\tau)/\eta(\tau)$ and $\eta^2(169\tau)/\eta^2(13\tau)$, where $\eta(\tau) = x^{1/24} \prod (1 - x^m)$ is the Dedekind function. The modular equation was developed by the second author.

The second part of the paper is concerned with $p(n)$, the partition function, which can be defined by $x^{1/24} \eta^{-1}(\tau) = \sum_0^{\infty} p(n) x^n$. The famous Ramanujan congruences for $p(n)$ are of type (1) and were, of course, the inspiration for the discovery of (1). Of the moduli mentioned in (1) only 5 and 7 appear here, and the corresponding Ramanujan conjectures (modified slightly in one case) were proved by G. N. Watson [J. Reine Angew. Math. **179** (1938), 97–128]. H. S. Zuckerman [Duke Math. J. **5** (1939), 88–110] and M. Newman [Canad. J. Math. **9** (1957), 549–552; MR **19**,

1160; ibid. **10** (1958), 577–586; MR **20** #4543] found congruences involving $p(n)$ modulo 13.

Let $P(N)=p(24n-1)$ if and only if $N=24n-1>0$, otherwise $P(N)=0$. The authors prove an analogue of Theorem 1. Theorem 2: For all $\alpha \geqq 1$ there is an integer K_α not divisible by 13 such that for all N, $P(13^{\alpha+2}N) \equiv K_\alpha P(13^\alpha N) \pmod{13^\alpha}$. Besides this they conjecture (Conjecture 2) the existence of a three-term relation involving $P(N)$ somewhat similar to (3); this conjecture is proved in the paper for $\alpha=1$ and 2, and has since been proved for all α by Atkin (private communication to the reviewer). Finally, it is proved that $P(59^3 \cdot 13N)$ is divisible by 13 for $(N, 59)=1$, that $p(n)$ is divisible by 13^4 infinitely often, that $p(n)$ fills all residue classes (prime to 13) modulo 13^α infinitely often, and some congruences modulo 13^2.

Theorem 2 is again proved by the modular equation, but Conjecture 2 requires in addition certain recurrence formulae established by M. Newman in the second Canad. Math. J. paper mentioned above.

Unlike the Hecke theory, these results depend on extensive numerical calculation. Basically this is because the present theory is a congruential one: certain constants left unevaluated in the Hecke formulae must be determined to certain moduli in the present case in order to obtain congruences. *J. Lehner* (College Park, Md.)

Citations: MR 10, 357a = F30-8; MR 10, 357b = F30-9; MR 19, 1160b = P76-13; MR 20# 4543 = P76-14; MR 20# 5184 = F30-23.

F30-54 (37# 159)

Malyšev, A. V.

The Fourier coefficients of modular forms. (Remarks on the article "A generalization of Kloosterman sums and their estimates"). (Russian)

Zap. Naučn. Sem. Leningrad. Otdel. Mat. Inst. Steklov. (LOMI) **1** (1966), 140–163.

Let $K_r(u, v; l, L; q) = \sum_{x \equiv l \,(\mathrm{mod}\, L)} (x/r) e^{2\pi i(ux+vx')/q}$, where q is a positive integer, r is an odd positive integer all prime divisors of which divide q, u and v are integers, L is a positive integer dividing q, and l is an integer. The summation is extended over a reduced set of residues x modulo q which satisfy $x \equiv l \pmod L$, and $xx' \equiv 1 \pmod q$. By using his earlier estimate of a simpler Kloosterman sum [Vestnik Leningrad. Univ. **15** (1960), no. 13, 59–75; MR **23** #A2391], the author proves that

$$|K_r(u, v; l, L; q)| \leqq q^{1/2} \min\{\tau(u^*)(u, q)^{1/2}, \tau(v^*)(v, q^{1/2})\},$$

where $u^* = q/(u, q)$, $v^* = q(v, q)$ and $\tau(u^*)$ is the number of divisors of u^*. This estimate is used to prove that $c_n = O(n^{s/2-1/4}(\log n)^{3/2}\sigma_{-1/2}(n))$, where $\sigma_{-1/2}(n) = \sum_{d|n} d^{-1/2}$ and c_n is the nth Fourier coefficient of an entire modular cusp form $F(z) = \sum_{n=1}^\infty c_n e^{2\pi i n z/N}$ of integral dimension $-s$ and level N (with constant multiplier system). The previous best estimate, using A. Weil's estimates of Kloosterman sums, was $c_n = O(n^{s/2-1/4+\varepsilon})$ (for arbitrary $\varepsilon > 0$); see, for example, A. Selberg [Proc. Sympos. Pure Math. (California Institute of Technology, Pasadena, Calif., 1963), Vol. VIII: *Theory of Numbers*, pp. 1–15, Amer. Math. Soc., Providence, R.I., 1965; MR **32** #93]. The author's analysis could presumably be simplified by use of the known explicit formulae for Fourier coefficients of Poincaré series which span the finite vector space of cusp forms. *R. A. Rankin* (Glasgow)

Citations: MR 23# A2391 = L05-20; MR 32# 93 = F30-49.

Referred to in Z10-48.

F30-55 (37# 2690)

Atkin, A. O. L.

Multiplicative congruence properties and density problems for $p(n)$.

Proc. London Math. Soc. (3) **18** (1968), 563–576.

The leading idea of this paper is the conjecture that the theory of Hecke operators for cusp forms of negative dimensions has an analogon for modular forms of non-negative dimensions that vanish at the cusp $\tau = i\infty$. To the multiplicative equalities of Fourier coefficients of the Hecke theory correspond here multiplicative congruences. This conjecture is verified in at least one important instance and, as applications, a large number of linear congruences of a new type are obtained for the partition function $p(n)$. Also, results concerning the density of those n for which $p(n) \equiv 0 \pmod m$ (m a given integer) are obtained. As usually, the primes $q = 5, 7, 13$ (for which $\Gamma_0(q)$ is of genus zero) play a special role. For $|x| < 1$, set $x = \exp(2\pi i\tau)$ $(\mathrm{Im}\, \tau > 0)$ and $f(x) = \prod_{r=1}^\infty (1-x^r) = \exp(-\pi i\tau/12)\eta(\tau) = \{\sum_{n=0}^\infty p(n)x^n\}^{-1}$. Also, let $N = 24n-1$ and set $P(N) = p(n)$ if $N \geqq -1$, $N \equiv -1 \pmod{24}$; otherwise (also, in particular, for non-integral N), $P(N) = 0$. Finally, for primes $p \geqq 5$, set

$$t(N) = t_p(N) = p^3 P(Np^2) + p(-3N/p)P(N) + P(Np^{-2}),$$

where (a/b) stands for the Legendre symbol. With these notations the Ramanujan congruences (in the definitive form proven by Watson and by the author) take the neat form $P(q^\alpha N) \equiv 0 \pmod{q^\beta}$, where $\beta = \beta(q, \alpha) = \alpha$ for $q = 5$ and 13, $\beta = [(\alpha+2)/2]$ for $q = 7$. The main results of the paper are the following: For $p \geqq 5$, $q = 5$, 7, or 13, $\alpha = |q-11|$ and $(-N/q) = -1$, $t_p(N) \equiv \gamma_p P(N) \pmod{q^\alpha}$, with γ_p an integer independent of N satisfying $\gamma_p \equiv p(p+1)(3/p) \pmod q$. If p_i ($i = 1$ to 6) are distinct primes $\geqq 11$, with $p_i \equiv -2 \pmod{5 \cdot 7 \cdot 13}$, $p_7 = 5$, $p_8 = 7$, $p_9 = 13$ and all N with $(-N/p_i) = -1$ $(1 \leqq i \leqq 9)$, one has $P(r^2 N) \equiv 0 \pmod{5^6 7^4 13^2}$, where $r = \prod_{i=1}^6 p_i$. Using Dirichlet's theorem on primes in arithmetic progressions, the last result leads to an infinite set of independent linear congruences of the form $p(r^3 \cdot 5 \cdot 7 \cdot 13\, n + c) \equiv 0 \pmod{5^6 7^4 13^2}$. Let $d(m) = \liminf x^{-1} \sum_n 1$, the sum being taken over all integers $n \leqq x$, for which $p(n) \equiv 0 \pmod m$; explicit positive lower bounds are obtained for $d(q)$ and for some $d(q^\alpha)$ (q prime, $5 \leqq q \leqq 31$). The proof uses functions invariant under $\Gamma_0(p)$ or $\Gamma_0(p^2)$, and congruence properties of the modular invariant $j(\tau) \pmod{q^\alpha}$. Various generalizations are indicated. *E. Grosswald* (Philadelphia, Pa.)

Referred to in P76-45.

F30-56 (38# 3232)

Ogg, A. P.

On modular forms with associated Dirichlet series.

Ann. of Math. (2) **89** (1969), 184–186.

Let f be an entire automorphic form of degree (= dimension) $-k$, $k > 0$, on the Hecke group $G(\lambda)$ generated by $\tau \to \tau + \lambda$, $\tau \to -1/\tau$, where $\lambda = 2\cos \pi/q$, $q = 3, 4, 5, \cdots$. Let $f(\tau) = \sum_{n=0}^\infty a_n e^{2\pi i n\tau/\lambda}$ be its Fourier series. The author proves that a_n grows no faster than a power of n; specifically, he shows that (1) $a_n = O(n^k)$.

This is an old result. A sharper form of it, valid for arbitrary H-groups and arbitrary multiplier systems is known, namely, (2) $a_n = O(n^{k/2})$ if $0 < k < 2$, $a_n = O(n \log n)$ if $k = 2$ and $a_n = O(n^{k-1})$ if $k > 2$. See, for example, the reviewer's paper in Bull. Amer. Math. Soc. **67** (1961), 603–606 [MR **25** #2370].

The author's proof is simple, utilizing Petersson's scalar product and Parseval's formula.

J. Lehner (College Park, Md.)

Citations: MR 25# 2370 = F30-34.

F30-57 **(39# 1407)**

Atkin, A. O. L.

Congruences for modular forms.

Computers in Mathematical Research, pp. 8–19. North-Holland, Amsterdam, 1968.

The author describes his attempts to extend and generalize certain congruence properties of the Fourier coefficients of modular forms with the aid of the Atlas computer. The discussion is confined mainly to the coefficients $c(n)$ of Klein's Hauptmodul $j(\exp 2\pi i x)$. For example, a theorem tested extensively by the computer and later proved, is as follows. Let $q=13$ and write $t(n)=c(13^a n)/c(13^a)$; then $t(13n)\equiv t(13)t(n) \pmod{13^a}$ and $t(np)-t(n)t(p)+t(n/p)/p\equiv 0 \pmod{13^a}$ holds for every prime p different from 13. The discussion extends to primes $q\leqq 37$. For primes $q\geqq 29$ the theory is analogous to the Hecke theory of modular forms in that integers are now replaced by elements in $\mathrm{GF}(q^2)$.

D. H. Lehmer (Berkeley, Calif.)

F30-58 **(40# 1337)**

Atkin, A. O. L.

Note on a paper of Rankin.

Bull. London Math. Soc. **1** (1969), 191–192.

The Eisenstein series $E_k(\tau)=\frac{1}{2}\sum\sum(c\tau+d)^{-k}$, where the double sum is over all coprime pairs of integers c and d, and $\operatorname{Im}\tau>0$, has zeros at points congruent to $\rho=e^{2\pi i/3}$ when $k\not\equiv 0 \pmod 3$ ($k\geqq 4$, k even). For $4\leqq k\leqq 14$ the zero is simple when $k\equiv 1 \pmod 3$ and double when $k\equiv 2 \pmod 3$, and the reviewer conjectured (Publ. Ramanujan Inst. **1** (1969), 137–144, to appear) that this is true in general. By showing that $E_k(\tau)\equiv E_l(\tau) \pmod{13}$ when $k\equiv l \pmod{12}$—the first congruence means that the corresponding Fourier coefficients are congruent—the author proves that, for $n\geqq 0$, $E_{12n+k}(\tau)\equiv E_k(\tau)\Delta^n(\tau)\{j(\tau)-5\}^n \pmod{13}$, from which the result follows since $j(\rho)=0$ and $\Delta(\rho)\neq 0$.

R. A. Rankin (Glasgow)

F30-59 **(40# 2608)**

Lahiri, D. B.

Congruences for the Fourier coefficients of the modular invariant $j(\tau)$.

Proc. Nat. Inst. Sci. India Part A **32** (1966), 95–103.

The author derives some new arithmetical properties of the Fourier coefficients $c(n)$ of the modular invariant $j(\tau)$. In particular, it is shown that if $n\equiv 0 \bmod(2^a3^b5^c7^d)$, then $c(n)\equiv 0 \bmod(2^{3a+12}3^{2b+5}5^{c+2}7^{d+1})$ for almost all such values of n. The proof uses identities from J. Lehner's *Discontinuous groups and automorphic functions* [Amer. Math. Soc., Providence, R.I., 1964; MR **29** #1332]. Also included are some more general results and explicit expressions for the least residues of $c(p^\lambda)$ to moduli which are suitable powers of p.

M. S. Cheema (Tucson, Ariz.)

Citations: MR 29# 1332 = F02-12.

F30-60 **(40# 5544)**

Kolberg, O.

Note on the Eisenstein series of $\Gamma_0(p)$.

Årbok Univ. Bergen Mat.-Natur. Ser. **1968**, *no.* 6, 20 *pp.* (1969).

Let $\Gamma=\left\{\begin{pmatrix}ab\\cd\end{pmatrix}\middle| a,b,c,d\in\mathbf{Z},\ ad-bc=1\right\}$, considered as a group of transformations on the upper half-plane $\operatorname{Im}\tau>0$; let $\Gamma_0(q)=\left\{\begin{pmatrix}ab\\cd\end{pmatrix}\in\Gamma \middle| c\equiv O \pmod q\right\}$ and, for $x=e^{2\pi i\tau}$ ($\operatorname{Im}\tau>0$), define $U_{r,p}(\tau)=\sum_{m=1}^\infty\sum_{n=1}^\infty(m/p)n^{r-1}x^{mn}$ ($r\geqq 2$) $V_{r,p}(\tau)=A_{r,p}+\sum_{m=1}^\infty\sum_{n=1}^\infty(n/p)n^{r-1}x^{mn}$ ($r\geqq 1$), with p an odd prime, r a positive integer, $r\equiv\frac{1}{2}(p-1) \pmod 2$ and $2rA_{r,p}=-\sum_{v=0}^{r-1}(r/v)B_vp^{v-1}\sum_{n=1}^{p-1}(n/p)n^{r-v}$ ($B_v=$ Bernoulli numbers). For $S\in\Gamma_0(p)$, both $U_{r,p}$ and $V_{r,p}$ satisfy [see E. Hecke, Danske Vid. Selsk. Math.-Fys. Medd. **17** (1940), no. 12; MR **2**, 251] $X_{r,p}(S\tau)=(d/p)(c\tau+d)^rX_{r,p}(\tau)$. Using this, some similar formulae valid only for $S\tau=-1/\tau$ and some lemmas concerning the behaviour of Dedekind's η-function under transformations $\tau\to S\tau$ with $S\in\Gamma$ or $S\in\Gamma_0(q)$ ($q\in\mathbf{Z}$), the author proves Theorem 1: Let p be an odd prime and let r and s be integers, s odd, satisfying $(p+1)r\equiv 0 \pmod{12}$ and $(p-1)s\equiv 2r \pmod{24}$; then $\eta(\tau)^{-2r-s}\eta(p\tau)^sU_{r,p}(\tau)$ (for $r\geqq 2$) and $\eta(\tau)^{-2r-s}\eta(p\tau)^sV_{r,p}(\tau)$ (for $r\geqq 1$) are functions on $\Gamma_0(p)$. Theorem 2 states the analogous result for $q=9$ and Theorems 3, 4 and 5 give the results for the case of the principal character and $q=p$, $q=9$ and $q=4$, respectively. If one writes out explicitly the identities that express the invariance of the functions under the respective groups of transformations, one obtains formulae that contain as particular cases many of the Ramanujan (and Ramanujan type) formulae, such as $\sum_{n=1}^\infty(n/7)x^n(1+x^n)(1-x^n)^{-3}=x\prod_{n=1}^\infty(1-x^n)^3\times(1-x^{7n})^3+8x^2\prod_{n=1}^\infty(1-x^{7n})^7(1-x^n)^{-1}$, as well as a large number of new ones, of which the following may serve as an example: $\sum_{m=1}^\infty\sum_{n=1}^\infty(n/5)(n^5-m^5)x^{mn}\equiv 5\eta(\tau)^3\eta(5\tau)^9 \pmod{67}$ (congruences taken for coefficients of power series in x). Most of these identities are obtained by setting $p=3$, 5, 7 or 13 in Theorem 1; the author expresses his doubts that similar results could be expected for other primes.

E. Grosswald (Philadelphia, Pa.)

Citations: MR 2, 251f = F25-4.

F30-61 **(41# 6780)**

Lang, Heinrich

Kummersche Kongruenzen für die normierten Entwicklungskoeffizienten der Weierstrassschen $\wp$-Funktion.

Abh. Math. Sem. Univ. Hamburg **33** (1969), 183–196.

For $\omega=\omega_2/\omega_1$ ($\operatorname{Im}\omega>0$), let $g_2=60G_2$, $g_3=140G_3$, Δ, j, γ_2, γ_3 have their usual meaning [see, e.g., H. Weber, *Lehrbuch der Algebra*, Vol. 3, Vieweg, Braunschweig, 1891; second edition, 1908; reprint, Chelsea, New York, 1961] and set $C_n=(2n)!\Delta^{-n/6}G_n$. All these quantities (and also A_p and $E_n(j)$ to be introduced later) depend, of course, on ω, but, in order to simplify the notations, this dependence will usually not be indicated. It is known [see A. Hurwitz, Math. Ann. **51** (1898/99), 196–226; G. Herglotz, Ber. Verh. Sächs. Akad. Wiss. Leipzig Math.-Phys. Kl. **73** (1921), 303–310; ibid. **74** (1922), 269–289; also H. Niemeyer, "Bernoullische Zahlen in imaginär-quadratischen Zahlkörpern", Staatsexamenarbeit, Univ. Hamburg, Hamburg, 1966] that

$$(*)\quad C_n=(-1)^{n+1}\gamma_2{}^u\gamma_3{}^vj^t/6+\sum_{(p-1)|2n}p^{-1}A_p{}^{2n/(p-1)}+\gamma_2{}^u\gamma_3{}^vE_n(j),$$

where $E_n(j)\in\mathbf{Z}[j]$, $n=6t+2u+3v$ and A_p is the coefficient of x in the equation satisfied by

$$x=(\Delta(\omega_1/p,\omega_2)/\Delta(\omega_1,\omega_2))^{1/12}.$$

If ω ($\operatorname{Im}\omega>0$) belongs to an imaginary quadratic field Ω, then j, γ_2, γ_3, A_p and $E_n(j)$ are algebraic integers, C_n are algebraic numbers and (*) is the analog of the von Staudt-Clausen formula for Bernoulli numbers. The purpose of the present paper is to prove for the C_n the analog of Kummer's congruences. The method is essentially that of Herglotz and uses the classical result of Kummer for Bernoulli numbers in conjunction with $\eta^{4n}C_n=B_n+$

$(-1)^n 4n \sum_{\nu=1} \nu^{2n-1}q^\nu(1-q^\nu)^{-1}$ ($\eta=\eta(\omega)$ is Dedekind's η-function). One has to use also the above mentioned equation for x and the fact that an entire modular function $f(\omega)=\sum_{r=0}^N a_r j(\omega)$ has coefficients a_r in a given ring R if and only if the Fourier expansion $f(\omega)=\sum_{v=-N}^\infty b_v e^{2\pi iv\omega}$ has its coefficients b_v in R. The main result is the congruence $\sum_{s=0}^m (-1)^s \binom{m}{s} C_{k+s(p-1)/2} A_p^{m-s}/(k+\frac{1}{2}s(p-1))\equiv 0$ (mod p^m) for $k\geqq\max(2, \frac{1}{2}(m+1))$, $(p-1)\nmid 2k$. If ω_1, ω_2 are the basis of an ideal in Ω and p does not split in Ω, then, under the same conditions as above,

$$C_{k+m(p-1)/2}/(k+\tfrac{1}{2}m(p-1)) \equiv 0 \pmod{p^m}.$$

The case when p does split in Ω is considered only in the nine cases when the class number of Ω is one and the results are similar. *E. Grosswald* (Philadelphia, Pa.)

F30-62 **(42# 3023)**

Gandhi, J. M.

Three theorems for the co-efficients of the powers of the Dedekind's modular form.

Math. Student **36** (1968), 218–221 (1969).

The author considers the integers $C_k(n)$ defined by $(\prod_{j=1}^\infty (1-x^j)-1)^k=\sum_{n=k}^\infty (-1)^n C_k(n)x^n$. These quantities are easily related to the generalized partition functions and to the Fourier coefficients of Dedekind's η-function. It is shown that for any prime p, $C_{kp}(np)\equiv C_k(n)$ mod p, $C_{p+1}(np+t)\equiv 0$ mod p for $t\not\equiv j(3j\pm 1)/2$ mod p. These results depend on identities for formal power series and the Eulerian pentagonal number theorem. {The third statement of the paper and its proof are not quite clear to the reviewer.} *H. Klingen* (Freiburg)

F30-63 **(44# 1627)**

Erevik, Olaf Reidar

Congruences for the coefficients of $\sqrt[3]{j(\tau)}$ and $\sqrt{(j(\tau)-1728)}$ where $j(\tau)$ is the modular invariant.

Årbok Univ. Bergen Mat.-Natur. Ser. **1966**, *no.* 9, 28 *pp.* (1967).

Let $j(\tau)=x^{-1}+744+c_1x+c_2x^2+\cdots$, $x=\exp(2\pi i\tau)$, Im $\tau>0$, be Klein's modular invariant. Many arithmetic properties of the Fourier coefficients c_n, which are rational integers, have been discovered in the last 25 years. Now j has a zero of order 3 at $\tau=\rho=\exp(2\pi i/3)$ and $j-12^3$ has a zero of order 2 at $\tau=i$, so that $j^{1/3}(\tau)=\sum_{-1}^\infty a(n)x^{n/3}$, $(j(\tau)-12^3)^{1/2}=\sum_{-1}^\infty b(n)x^{n/2}$ are still holomorphic; moreover $a(n)$ and $b(n)$ are integers. The author establishes a number of congruences satisfied by the $a(n)$ and $b(n)$, for example: $a(2^{2m}n)\equiv -2^{3m+7}\beta((n-5)/6)$ (mod 2^{3m+12}) for $m, n>0$, where $\prod_1^\infty (1+x^n)^{20}=\sum_0^\infty \beta(n)x^n$, $b(5^m n)\equiv 0$ (mod 5^{m+1}), and others to the moduli 3^k and 7^l. *J. Lehner* (College Park, Md.)

F35 THE RAMANUJAN τ-FUNCTION

See also Section F30.

See also reviews A22-3, A30-30, A30-31, B80-26, E24-19, E28-16, F10-28, F30-1, F30-11, F30-12, F30-16, F30-19, F30-23, F60-2, F65-1, F65-8, M40-35, N28-13, N36-25, P28-75, P56-4, P76-36.

F35-1 **(4, 265g)**

Banerji, D. P. Congruence properties of Ramanujan's function $\tau(n)$. J. London Math. Soc. **17**, 144–145 (1942).

Ramanujan's function $\tau(n)$ is defined by

$$x[(1-x)(1-x^2)(1-x^3)\cdots]^{24}=\sum_1^\infty \tau(n)x^n.$$

The author proves two congruences which do not seem to have been noticed before, namely,

$$\tau(3m-r)\equiv 0 \pmod 3, \qquad r=0, 1,$$
$$\tau(4m-r)\equiv 0 \pmod 4, \qquad r=0, 1, 2.$$

If $r=0$, stronger results hold: $\tau(3m)\equiv 0$ (mod 9) and $\tau(4m)\equiv 0$ (mod 64). *E. Hille* (New Haven, Conn.).

F35-2 **(5, 35b)**

Lehmer, D. H. Ramanujan's function $\tau(n)$. Duke Math. J. **10**, 483–492 (1943).

In trying to disprove Ramanujan's hypothesis that $|\tau(p)|<2p^{11/2}$, p a prime, the author computed the values of $\tau(p)$ for $p<300$ and $p=571$ without finding a case in which the hypothesis is false. The reason for testing $p=571$ is not explained. The values of $\tau(n)$ for all $n\leqq 300$ are tabulated and they are discussed in relation to questions arising from the problem of the order of $\tau(n)$. In this connection the numerical value of Rankin's formula for $\lim_{n\to\infty}\sum_{\nu\leqq n}\tau(\nu)^2$ is determined. *H. S. Zuckerman.*

Referred to in F35-4, F35-26.

F35-3 **(6, 37b; 6, 37c)**

Ramanathan, K. G. Congruence properties of Ramanujan's function $\tau(n)$. Proc. Indian Acad. Sci., Sect. A. **19**, 146–148 (1944).

Ramanathan, K. G. Congruence properties of $\sigma(n)$, the sum of the divisors of n. Math. Student **11**, 33–35 (1943).

These papers contain simple proofs of the congruences

$$\sigma(kn-1)\equiv\tau(kn-1)\equiv 0 \pmod k,$$

where k is any divisor of 24 greater than 2. These are based on the congruence theory of power series and on well-known identities of the generating functions of σ and τ. *D. H. Lehmer* (Berkeley, Calif.).

Referred to in A30-2, A30-6, A30-8, A30-30, F35-4, F35-5, F35-7.

F35-4 **(7, 50a)**

Gupta, Hansraj. Congruence properties of $\tau(n)$. Proc. Benares Math. Soc. **5**, 17–22 (1943).

Ramanujan's function $\tau(n)$ is generated by

$$\sum_{n=1}^\infty \tau(n)x^n=x\prod_{m=1}^\infty (1-x^m)^{24}.$$

A proof is given that, for odd n, $\tau(n)$ is congruent modulo 8 to the number of solutions of the equation $4n=a^2+b^2+c^2+d^2$, where a, b, c, d are odd and positive. Separate proofs are given for the special cases $\tau(p)\equiv 2$(mod 4) if $p\equiv 1$(mod 4) is a prime; $\tau(p)\equiv 4$(mod 8) if $p\equiv 3$(mod 8) is a prime; $\tau(8k+7)\equiv 0$(mod 8). The theorem, in view of a result of Legendre, could have been stated as follows:

$$\tau(2m+1)\equiv\sigma(2m+1) \pmod 8,$$

where $\sigma(k)$ is the sum of the divisors of k, from which the special cases follow at once [cf. Ramanathan, Proc. Indian Acad. Sci., Sect. A. **19**, 146–148 (1944); Math. Student **11**, 33–35 (1943); these Rev. **6**, 37]. The author proves that $\tau(n)$ is odd if and only if n is an odd square. On page 22 there is a table of $\tau(n)$ for $n\leqq 130$. A comparison of this table with an earlier more extensive table [Lehmer, Duke Math. J. **10**, 483–492 (1943); these Rev. **5**, 35] reveals no discrepancies. *D. H. Lehmer.*

Citations: MR 5, 35b = F35-2; MR 6, 37b = F35-3.

Referred to in F35-7, F35-26.

F35-5 **(8, 10a)**

Ramanathan, K. G. Congruence properties of Ramanujan's function $\tau(n)$. II. J. Indian Math. Soc. (N.S.) **9**, 55–59 (1945).

[For part I see Proc. Indian Acad. Sci., Sect. A. **19**, 146–148 (1944); these Rev. **6**, 37.] Congruences are given for Ramanujan's function $\tau(n)$ taken with respect to the moduli 3, 4 and 7. All three theorems of the paper may be combined as follows. Let k be 3, 4 or 7 and let n be any positive integer. If k is not prime to n then $\tau(n)$ is divisible by k. If k is prime to n we may write $n=PQ$, where Q is divisible only by primes which are quadratic residues of k. Then if P is not a square, $\tau(n)$ is divisible by k; if P is a square, $\tau(n)$ is congruent modulo k to the number of divisors of Q. For $k=7$ this result is due to J. R. Wilton [Proc. London Math. Soc. (2) **31**, 1–10 (1930)]. The paper uses elementary methods based on identities between familiar elliptic modular functions. *D. H. Lehmer* (Berkeley, Calif.).

Citations: MR 6, 37b = F35-3.

Referred to in F35-9.

F35-6 (8, 10b)

Lahiri, Debabrata. Congruence properties of Ramanujan's function $\tau(n)$. Science and Culture **12**, 52 (1946).

The author gives all solutions x of the congruence $\tau(x)\equiv a \pmod{k}$, $k=3, 4$. These results can be obtained at once from a paper of K. G. Ramanathan [cf. the preceding review]. Corresponding results for the modulus 8 are said to be too lengthy for inclusion in the present note.

D. H. Lehmer (Berkeley, Calif.).

F35-7 (8, 10c)

Gupta, Hansraj. A congruence relation between $\tau(n)$ and $\sigma(n)$. J. Indian Math. Soc. (N.S.) **9**, 59–60 (1945).

The author proves that if $\tau(n)$ is Ramanujan's function defined by

$$x\{(1-x)(1-x^2)(1-x^3)\cdots\}^{24}=\sum_{n=1}^{\infty}\tau(n)x^n,$$

if $\sigma(n)$ is the sum of the divisors of n and if r is any divisor of 24 prime to n then $\tau(n)$ and $\sigma(n)$ are congruent modulo r. [Cf. H. Gupta, Proc. Benares Math. Soc. **5**, 17–22 (1943); K. G. Ramanathan, Proc. Indian Acad. Sci., Sect. A. **19**, 146–148 (1944); Math. Student **11**, 33–55 (1943); these Rev. **7**, 50; **6**, 37.] *D. H. Lehmer* (Berkeley, Calif.).

Citations: MR 6, 37b = F35-3; MR 7, 50a = F35-4.

Referred to in F35-16, F35-19.

F35-8 (8, 10d)

Banerjee, D. P. On the new congruence properties of the arithmetic function $T(n)$. Proc. Nat. Acad. Sci. India. Sect. A. **12**, 149–150 (1942).

For Ramanujan's function [cf. the preceding review] the author notes the congruence properties

$$\tau(2^n m)\equiv 0 \pmod{8^n},\quad \tau(7^n m)\equiv 0 \pmod{7^n},$$
$$\tau(10m)\equiv 0 \pmod{40}.$$

D. H. Lehmer (Berkeley, Calif.).

F35-9 (8, 315h)

Gupta, Hansraj. A congruence property of $\tau(n)$. Proc. Indian Acad. Sci., Sect. A. **24**, 441–442 (1946).

Let $\tau(n)$ be the coefficient of x^{n-1} in the expansion of the 24th power of the product (1) $(1-x)(1-x^2)(1-x^3)\cdots$. The author gives a simple proof without the use of elliptic function identities of the fact that $\tau(n)\equiv n\sigma_3(n) \pmod{7}$, where $\sigma_3(n)$ is the sum of the cubes of the divisors of n. The method uses Jacobi's triangular number theorem about the cube of (1) and the fact that a prime is uniquely representable by the form x^2+7y^2 whenever it is a quadratic residue of 7. [See J. Indian Math. Soc. (N.S.) **9**, 55–59 (1945); these Rev. **8**, 10 for another proof by Ramanathan.]

D. H. Lehmer (Berkeley, Calif.).

Citations: MR 8, 10a = F35-5.

F35-10 (8, 445e)

Bambah, R. P. Two congruence properties of Ramanujan's function $\tau(n)$. J. London Math. Soc. **21**, 91–93 (1946).

Proofs are given of the congruences $\tau(2k+1)\equiv\sigma_3(2k+1) \pmod{32}$, $\tau(n)\equiv n\sigma_9(n) \pmod{25}$, where $\sigma_k(m)$ denotes the sum of the kth powers of the divisors of m and $\tau(n)$ is the coefficient of x^{n-1} in the expansion of the 24th power of the infinite product $(1-x)(1-x^2)(1-x^3)\cdots$. It follows that $\tau(n)$ is divisible by 32 and 25 for almost all n. The method is based on certain identities of Ramanujan.

D. H. Lehmer (Berkeley, Calif.).

F35-11 (9, 12b)

Lehmer, D. H. The vanishing of Ramanujan's function $\tau(n)$. Duke Math. J. **14**, 429–433 (1947).

The author shows that $\tau(n)\neq 0$ for all n less than the prime 3316799. It is first shown, by an argument which makes use of some of the elementary properties of algebraic integers, that n_0, the least value of n for which $\tau(n)=0$, must be prime. By means of known congruences connecting $\tau(n)$ with the function $\sigma_k(n)$ (the sum of the kth powers of the divisors of n) for various values of k and for the moduli 32, 3, 25, 7 and 691, it is deduced that if $\tau(p)=0$, where p is a prime, then p must be congruent to one of three residue classes modulo $2^5\cdot 3\cdot 5^2\cdot 7\cdot 691=11608800$. By applying a rather complicated theorem due to Wilton [Proc. London Math. Soc. (2) **31**, 1–10 (1930)] on the residue of $\tau(n)$ modulo 23, the number of possible values of p less than $2\cdot 10^7$ is reduced to one, namely the prime 3316799. Whether $\tau(3316799)$ is zero or not is unknown. A sketch of an elementary proof of Wilton's theorem is included.

R. A. Rankin (Cambridge, England).

Referred to in F35-31, F35-35.

F35-12 (9, 12c)

Bambah, R. P., and Chowla, S. A note on Ramanujan's function $\tau(n)$. Quart. J. Math., Oxford Ser. **18**, 122–123 (1947).

It is shown that $\tau(n)$ is divisible by $801007200=2^5\cdot 3^2\cdot 5^2\cdot 7\cdot 23\cdot 691$ for almost all n. An extension of this result to 3460351104000 would appear to be possible.

D. H. Lehmer (Berkeley, Calif.).

F35-13 (9, 78g)

Bambah, R. P. Ramanujan's function $\tau(n)$—a congruence property. Bull. Amer. Math. Soc. **53**, 764–765 (1947).

A short proof of the congruence $\tau(n)\equiv n\sigma_3(n) \pmod{7}$.

D. H. Lehmer (Berkeley, Calif.).

F35-14 (9, 78h)

Bambah, R. P., Chowla, S., and Gupta, H. A congruence property of Ramanujan's function $\tau(n)$. Bull. Amer. Math. Soc. **53**, 766–767 (1947).

A short proof of the congruence $\tau(n)\equiv\sigma(n)$ or $0 \pmod{8}$ according as n is odd or even. *D. H. Lehmer.*

Referred to in F35-16.

F35-15 (9, 79a)

Bambah, R. P., and Chowla, S. A new congruence property of Ramanujan's function $\tau(n)$. Bull. Amer. Math. Soc. **53**, 768–769 (1947).

A short proof of the congruence $\tau(n)\equiv n^2\sigma(n) \pmod{9}$.

D. H. Lehmer (Berkeley, Calif.).

Referred to in F35-16.

F35-16 (9, 135a)

Bambah, R. P., Chowla, S., Gupta, H., and Lahiri, D. B. Congruence properties of Ramanujan's function $\tau(n)$. Quart. J. Math., Oxford Ser. **18**, 143–146 (1947).

Another proof is given of the fact that, if d is any divisor of 24 which is prime to n, then $\tau(n)\equiv\sigma(n)$ (mod d). [Cf. Gupta, J. Indian Math. Soc. (N.S.) **9**, 59–60 (1945); Bambah, Chowla and Gupta, Bull. Amer. Math. Soc. **53**, 766–767 (1947); Bambah and Chowla, ibid., 768–769 (1947); these Rev. **8**, 10; **9**, 78, 79.] *D. H. Lehmer.*

Citations: MR 8, 10c = F35-7; MR 9, 78h = F35-14; MR 9, 79a = F35-15.

Referred to in A30-30.

F35-17 (9, 225f)

Lahiri, D. B. On Ramanujan's function $\tau(n)$ and the divisor function $\sigma_k(n)$. II. Bull. Calcutta Math. Soc. **39**, 33–52 (1947).

Ramanujan's function $\tau(n)$ is defined by

$$\Delta(x)=\sum_{n=1}^{\infty}\tau(n)x^n=x[(1-x)(1-x^2)(1-x^3)\cdots]^{24}.$$

No less than 171 congruences of the form

$$(1)\qquad A\tau(n)\equiv\sum_{k=0}^{6}P_k(n)\sigma_{2k+1}(n)\pmod{M}$$

are tabulated. Here A is a constant and P is a polynomial, both depending on n, while $\sigma_r(n)$ denotes the sum of the rth powers of the divisors of n. The moduli M are among the divisors of $2^{13}\cdot3^6\cdot5^3\cdot7\cdot11\cdot13\cdot691$. Not all these 171 congruences are independent since there are numerous congruences between the σ's. These were developed by the author in his previous paper I [same Bull. **38**, 193–206 (1946); these Rev. **8**, 567]. Also in many cases the constant A is not prime to the modulus M so that a congruence for $\tau(n)$ itself is not obtained modulo M. This occurs whenever M is divisible by 2^{11}, 3^6, 11 or 13. If one regards the functions $\sigma_r(n)$ as known and wishes only to express $\tau(n)$ in terms of them and various moduli the following five independent congruences give the necessary information:

$$\begin{aligned}\tau(n)\equiv{}&(175n^2+499n)\sigma_7(n)\\&+(473n^3+235n^2-157n)\sigma_5(n)\\&+(224n^4-390n^3+155n^2+473n)\sigma_3(n)\\&+(48n^5+76n^4+396n^3-53n^2-105n)\sigma(n)\pmod{2^{10}},\end{aligned}$$
$$\tau(n)\equiv n^2\sigma_7(n)-18n^2\sigma_5(n)+9n^2(2n+5)\sigma_3(n)-45n^3\sigma(n)\pmod{3^5},$$
$$\tau(n)\equiv 36n\sigma_9(n)-30n\sigma_5(n)-40n^2\sigma_3(n)+35n\sigma(n)\pmod{5^3},$$
$$\tau(n)\equiv n\sigma_3(n)\pmod{7},$$
$$\tau(n)\equiv\sigma_{11}(n)\pmod{691}.$$

The author considers with Ramanujan the functions

$$\Phi_{r,s}(x)=\sum_{n=1}^{\infty}\sum_{m=1}^{\infty}n^rm^sx^{mn}=\sum_{n=1}^{\infty}n^r\sigma_{s-r}(n)x^n$$

and finds all 41 products $P(x)$ of Φ's which can be expressed linearly in terms of other Φ's and the function $\Delta(x)$ in the form $MP(x)=A\Delta(x)+\sum A_{ks}\Phi_{k,s}(x)$, where M is an integer. Identifying coefficients of x^n on both sides and taking this identity modulo M one obtains a congruence relation of type (1). Further ones follow from this by using congruence relations between the σ_r's. *D. H. Lehmer.*

Citations: MR 8, 567b = A30-4.

Referred to in F35-25, F35-34, F35-35.

F35-18 (9, 226a)

Bambah, R. P., and Chowla, S. Congruence properties of Ramanujan's function $\tau(n)$. Bull. Amer. Math. Soc. **53**, 950–955 (1947).

The authors prove two congruence properties of Ramanujan's function for the moduli 81 and 125 in the cases where n is prime to the modulus. Their results are

$$\tau(n)\equiv 5n^2\sigma_7(n)-4n\sigma_9(n)\pmod{125},$$
$$\tau(n)\equiv(n^2+k)\sigma_7(n)\pmod{81},$$

where $k=0$ or 9 according as $n\equiv1$ or 2 (mod 3). Here $\sigma_k(n)$ denotes as usual the sum of the kth powers of all the divisors of n. The usual method of proof involving Ramanujan's functions P, Q and R is employed. *D. H. Lehmer.*

Referred to in F35-31.

F35-19 (9, 272e)

Bambah, R. P., and Chowla, S. A congruence property of Ramanujan's function $\tau(n)$. Proc. Nat. Inst. Sci. India **12**, 431–432 (1946).

Another proof is given of the fact that $\tau(n)\equiv\sigma(n)$ (mod 3) when n is not divisible by 3 [for other proofs cf. Gupta, J. Indian Math. Soc. (N.S.) **9**, 59–60 (1945); these Rev. **8**, 10]. This proof is based on the fact that the number of representations of an odd integer n as the sum of 24 squares is a linear combination of $\tau(n)$ and $\sigma_{11}(n)$. *D. H. Lehmer* (Berkeley, Calif.).

Citations: MR 8, 10c = F35-7.

F35-20 (9, 272f)

Bambah, R. P., and Chowla, S. On a function of Ramanujan. Proc. Nat. Inst. Sci. India **12**, no. 8, 1 p. (1946).

The authors announce the following congruences for Ramanujan's function $\tau(n)$:

$$\tau(n)\equiv\sigma_{11}(n)\pmod{256}\qquad(n\text{ odd}),$$
$$\tau(p)\equiv-4p\sigma_9(p)+5p^2\sigma_7(p)\pmod{125},$$

where p is a prime not equal to 5. *D. H. Lehmer.*

F35-21 (9, 331i)

Bambah, R. P., and Chowla, S. On a function of Ramanujan. Proc. Nat. Inst. Sci. India **12**, 433 (1946).

The authors announce the congruences $\tau(n)\equiv\sigma_{11}(n)$ (mod 256) (n odd), $\tau(n)\equiv5n^2\sigma_7(n)-4n\sigma_9(n)$ (mod 125) $(n,5)=1$; these are proved in the two papers reviewed below. *D. H. Lehmer* (Berkeley, Calif.).

Referred to in F35-31.

F35-22 (9, 331j)

Bambah, R. P., and Chowla, S. The residue of Ramanujan's function $\tau(n)$ to the modulus 2^8. J. London Math. Soc. **22**, 140–147 (1947).

The authors prove that if $n=2^mk$, k odd, $m\leqq0$, then Ramanujan's $\tau(n)$ enjoys the congruence property

$$\tau(n)\equiv(-2)^{3m}(2m+1)\sigma_{11}(k)\pmod{2^8}.$$

Here $\sigma_{11}(k)$ denotes the sum of the eleventh powers of the divisors of k. *D. H. Lehmer* (Berkeley, Calif.).

F35-23 (9, 332a)

Chowla, S. A note on multiplicative functions. Proc. Nat. Inst. Sci. India **12**, 429–430 (1946).

A function f is said to be multiplicative if $f(mn)=f(m)f(n)$ whenever m and n are coprime integers. The author defines a function f to be multiplicative mod k if $f(mn)\equiv f(m)f(n)$ (mod k) whenever m, n and k are prime to each other in pairs. This idea is used to prove that

$$\tau(n)\equiv5n^2\sigma_7(n)-4n\sigma_9(n)\pmod{5^3},$$

where $\tau(n)$ is Ramanujan's function, a multiplicative function. The right side of the above congruence is shown to be multiplicative mod 125. *D. H. Lehmer* (Berkeley, Calif.).

F35-24 (9, 332c)

Chowla, S. On a theorem of Walfisz. J. London Math. Soc. **22**, 136–140 (1947).

Let m be any number of the form $m=2^a3^b5^c7^d23^e691^f$, where the exponents are arbitrary nonnegative integers. This note contains the proof of the fact that Ramanujan's function $\tau(n)$ is divisible by m for almost all n. This is made to follow from the lemma: let r and k be arbitrary positive integers; then almost all positive integers contain at least r different primes of the form $kn-1$ each raised to an odd power. The theorem then follows from known congruence properties of $\tau(n)$ with respect to the moduli 2, 3, 5, 7, 23, and 691. *D. H. Lehmer* (Berkeley, Calif.).

F35-25 (9, 411c)

Bambah, R. P., and Chowla, S. **Some new congruence properties of Ramanujan's function $\tau(n)$.** Math. Student **14**, 24–26 (1946).

Congruence properties of the usual type, connecting Ramanujan's $\tau(n)$ with the sum $\sigma_k(n)$ of the kth powers of the divisors of n, are given with respect to the moduli 2^5, 3^4, 5^3 and 7^2. All these results except the last follow from the tables of D. B. Lahiri [Bull. Calcutta Math. Soc. **39**, 33–52 (1947); these Rev. **9**, 225]. This is true even of the conjecture $\tau(n)\equiv\sigma_{11}(n)$ (mod 2^8) (n odd) made by the authors. For the modulus 49 they give

$$\tau(n)\equiv 8n^4\sigma_3(n)-14\{2(1-n-n^3)\sigma_3(n)+(2n^2-3)\sigma(n)+\Sigma\} \pmod{49},$$

where n is not divisible by 7 and $\Sigma=\sum_{u+7v=n}\sigma(u)\sigma_3(7v)$. No proofs are given. *D. H. Lehmer* (Berkeley, Calif.).

Citations: MR 9, 225f = F35-17.

Referred to in F35-36.

F35-26 (10, 104c)

Gupta, Hansraj. A table of values of $\tau(n)$. Proc. Nat. Inst. Sci. India **13**, 201–206 (1947).

A table of the first 400 coefficients $\tau(n)$ in the power series $\{(1-x)(1-x^2)\cdots\}^{24}=\sum_{n=1}^{\infty}\tau(n)x^{n-1}$ is given. [For earlier tables of this function see Lehmer, Duke Math. J. **10**, 483–492 (1943); Gupta, Proc. Benares Math. Soc. **5**, 17–22 (1943); these Rev. **5**, 35; **7**, 50.] Six congruence properties due to various authors are quoted. *D. H. Lehmer.*

Citations: MR 5, 35b = F35-2; MR 7, 50a = F35-4.

Referred to in F35-28.

F35-27 (10, 354e)

Sengupta, H. M. On Ramanujan function $\tau(n)$. Math. Student **15** (1947), 9–10 (1948).

If p is a prime, the formula $\tau(p^n)=\tau(p)\tau(p^{n-1})-p^{11}\tau(p^{n-2})$ is a well-known result conjectured by Ramanujan and proved by Mordell. This implies that $\tau(p^n)$ is a polynomial in $\tau(p)$ and p^{11}. The author finds this polynomial. It is the same as the polynomial which expresses csc x sin nx in powers of 2 cos x. *D. H. Lehmer* (Berkeley, Calif.).

F35-28 (10, 514c)

Watson, G. N. A table of Ramanujan's function $\tau(n)$. Proc. London Math. Soc. (2) **51**, 1–13 (1949).

This table gives the coefficient $\tau(n)$ of x^{n-1} in the 24th power of Euler's product $(1-x)(1-x^2)(1-x^3)\cdots$ for all integers $n\leqq 1000$. The most extensive previous table is that of Gupta for $n\leqq 400$ [Proc. Nat. Inst. Sci. India **13**, 201–206 (1947); these Rev. **10**, 104]. Besides $\tau(n)$, the function $\tau^*(n)=n^{-11/2}\tau(n)$ is given to 5 decimals. This function, according to the as yet unproved "Ramanujan hypothesis," should be less than 2 in absolute value for all prime values of n. The table shows that $\tau^*(p)$, for p a prime, lies between $\tau^*(103)=-1.91881$ and $\tau^*(479)=1.90410$, at least when $p<1000$. Let $\tau^*(p)=2\cos\pi r_p$; then, for $p<1000$, not only is r_p real, but also $\frac{1}{6}<r_p<\frac{5}{6}$ except for the 6 primes $p=103$, 313, 479, 619, 719, and 877. This table will be of much use in the further investigation of this interesting numerical function. *D. H. Lehmer* (Berkeley, Calif.).

Citations: MR 10, 104c = F35-26.

F35-29 (10, 514d)

v. d. Blij, F. S. Ramanujan's function $\tau(n)$. Math. Centrum Amsterdam. Rapport **ZW 1948-010**, 18 pp. (1948). (Dutch)

This report is a topical history of the function $\tau(n)$ of Ramanujan defined as the coefficient of x^{n-1} in the power series development of the 24th power of the product $(1-x)(1-x^2)(1-x^3)\cdots$. The report is in 7 sections whose titles might have been (1) introduction, congruence properties of $\tau(n)$; (2) properties of modular functions, especially Δ and η; (3) the Fourier coefficients of modular forms; (4) the associated Dirichlet series and their Euler products; (5) quadratic forms and their associated theta functions; (6) miscellaneous results on quadratic forms and their numbers of representations; (7) bibliography. The last section extends through 1947 and contains 73 titles by 33 authors. There are references to other problems related to those concerning $\tau(n)$. This section is an especially valuable feature of the report since no proofs (or even indications of proofs) are given in the text. The author presents the subject matter in clear and concise manner. The reviewer has noticed only one mistake. The erroneous identity

$$\sum_{n=1}^{\infty}\tau(n)e^{-sn^{\frac{1}{2}}}=(2\pi)^{23/2}\Gamma(25/2)\sum_{n=1}^{\infty}\tau(n)(s^2+4n\pi^2)^{-25/2}$$

is incorrectly quoted from Hardy ["Ramanujan," Cambridge University Press, 1940, p. 124; these Rev. **3**, 71] who, in turn, has made an error. In fact the left member should read $2^{-\frac{1}{2}}s^{-1}\sum_{n=1}^{\infty}\tau(n)e^{-2sn^{\frac{1}{2}}}$. *D. H. Lehmer.*

Citations: MR 3, 71d = Z20-4.

Referred to in F35-30.

F35-30 (13, 328d)

van der Blij, F. The function $\tau(n)$ of S. Ramanujan (an expository lecture). Math. Student **18**, 83–99 (1950).

"Somewhat enriched translation" of Math. Centrum Amsterdam. Rapport **ZW1948-010** (1948); these Rev. **10**, 514.

Citations: MR 10, 514d = F35-29.

Referred to in F30-19.

F35-31 (10, 514e)

Gupta, Hansraj. The vanishing of Ramanujan's function $\tau(n)$. Current Sci. **17**, 180 (1948).

By using certain congruence properties of Ramanujan's function $\tau(n)$ the reviewer has shown that, for $n<3316799$, $\tau(n)\neq 0$ [Duke Math. J. **14**, 429–433 (1947); these Rev. **9**, 12]. By using recent results of Bambah and Chowla [Bull. Amer. Math. Soc. **53**, 950–955 (1947); Proc. Nat. Inst. Sci. India **12**, 433 (1946); J. London Math. Soc. **22**, 140–147 (1947); these Rev. **9**, 226, 331], the author asserts that $\tau(n)$ fails to vanish for $n<1791071999$. [An unpublished result of the reviewer is that this number may be replaced by the prime 214928639999.] *D. H. Lehmer* (Berkeley, Calif.).

Citations: MR 9, 12b = F35-11; MR 9, 226a = F35-18; MR 9, 331i = F35-21.

F35-32 (13, 209d)

Pennington, W. B. On the order of magnitude of Ramanujan's arithmetical function $\tau(n)$. Proc. Cambridge Philos. Soc. **47**, 668–678 (1951).

The best-known estimate for the order of magnitude of the "sum-function" $T(x)=\sum_{n\leq x}\tau(n)$ of Ramanujan's $\tau(n)$ is $T(x)=O(x^{6-1/10})$, obtained by Rankin [Proc. Cambridge Philos. Soc. **36**, 150–151 (1940); these Rev. **1**, 203]. If, for prime p, the conjecture $|\tau(p)|\leqq 2p^{11/2}$ of Ramanujan were true, it would follow that $T(x)=O(x^{6-1/6+\epsilon})$. The author obtains results in the opposite direction, namely,

$$\liminf_{x\to\infty} \frac{T(x)}{x^{6-\frac{1}{4}}} = -\infty, \quad \limsup_{x\to\infty} \frac{T(x)}{x^{6-\frac{1}{4}}} = +\infty,$$

by a method similar to that developed by Ingham [ibid. **36**, 131–138 (1940); these Rev. **2**, 149] in treating classical lattice-point problems. Equation (12) should contain $\underline{\lim}$ instead of $\overline{\lim}$. *T. M. Apostol* (Pasadena, Calif.).

Citations: MR 1, 203d = F30-2; MR 2, 149f = N40-3.

Referred to in N36-25.

F35-33 (13, 209e)

Lehmer, D. H. Ramanujan's function with respect to the modulus 49. Proc. Nat. Inst. Sci. India **17**, 67–70 (1951).

Let $\tau(n)$ be Ramanujan's function. If p is a prime which is a quadratic non-residue of 7 so that p is congruent to 3, 5 or 6 (mod 7), then $\tau(p)\equiv 3p(p^3+1)$ (mod 49). This is proved by suitable manipulations of the Ramanujan identities connecting the power series with coefficient $1728\tau(n)$ and the power series whose coefficients are of the form $n^r\sigma_{s-r}(n)$. One consequence of this result is that if p and q are primes which are quadratic non-residues of 7 and if 49 divides $p-q$, then 49 divides $\tau(p)-\tau(q)$. Another result is that if p is a prime, then 49 divides $\tau(p)$ if and only if p is congruent to 19, 31 or 48 (mod 49). *L. Schoenfeld* (Urbana, Ill.).

F35-34 (14, 249f)

Rushforth, J. M. Congruence properties of the partition function and associated functions. Proc. Cambridge Philos. Soc. **48**, 402–413 (1952).

The author has made a thorough study of a manuscript left by Ramanujan entitled, "Properties of $p(n)$ and $\tau(n)$ defined by the relations

$$\sum p(n)x^n = \prod_{\nu=1}^{\infty}(1-x^\nu)^{-1}, \quad \sum \tau(n)x^n = x\prod_{\nu=1}^{\infty}(1-x^\nu)^{24}, \text{"}$$

excerpts of which have been published by Hardy and Watson. The more fragmentary parts of the work have been filled in by the author who has supplied proofs for a number of new congruence properties of $p(n)$ and $\tau(n)$. Among these are cited

$$\tau(n) \equiv n^3\sigma_5(n) \quad (\text{mod } 32).$$

(This is equivalent to a result given by Lahiri [Bull. Calcutta Math. Soc. **39**, 33–52 (1947); these Rev. **9**, 225]) and

$$p(49n+k)\equiv 0 \quad (\text{mod } 49), \quad k=19, 33, 40, 47,$$
$$p(121n-s)\equiv 0 \quad (\text{mod } 121).$$

Results are given for the moduli 13, 17, 19, and 23. These involve the functions $\tau_k(n)$ introduced by Ramanujan and defined by

$$\sum_{n=1}^{\infty}\tau_k(n) = xQ^rR^s\prod_{\nu=1}^{\infty}(1-x^\nu)^{24}, \quad 2r+3s=k=2, 3, 4, 5, 7.$$

Here Q and R are essentially the Weierstrass invariants,

$$Q=1+240\sum_{n=1}^{\infty}\sigma_3(n)x^n, \quad R=1-504\sum_{n=1}^{\infty}\sigma_5(n)x^n.$$

An example of the more complicated results obtained for these larger moduli is the identity

$$\prod_{\nu=1}^{\infty}(1-x^\nu)\sum_{n=1}^{\infty}p(529n-22)x^n = 5\sum_{n=1}^{\infty}\tau_6(n)x^n+23J,$$

where J denotes a power series with integral coefficients. These results are obtained by expanding appropriate powers of the discriminant $Q^3-R^2=12^3\sum\tau(n)x^n$ as polynomials in Q, R, and $P=1-24\sum_{n=1}^{\infty}\sigma(n)x^n$ and reducing the coefficients with respect to the modulus concerned. *D. H. Lehmer.*

Citations: MR 9, 225f = F35-17.

F35-35 (17, 1186b)

Schoeneberg, Bruno. Über die Diskriminante der elliptischen Funktionen und ihre Quadratwurzel. Math. Z. **65** (1956), 16–24.

Put

$$e^{2\pi i\tau}\prod_1^{\infty}(1-e^{2\pi i\tau n})^{24} = \sum_1^{\infty}\tau(n)e^{2\pi i\tau n},$$

$$e^{\pi i\tau}\prod_1^{\infty}(1-e^{2\pi i\tau n})^{12} = \sum_{n\equiv 1(2)}\tau_2(n)e^{\pi i\tau n}.$$

D. H. Lehmer [Duke Math. J. **14** (1947), 429–433; MR **9**, 12] showed that if $\tau(n)$ ever vanishes the smallest value of n is a prime; he also showed that $\tau(n)\neq 0$ for $n<3316799$. In the present paper explicit expressions for $\tau(n)$ and $\tau_2(n)$ are obtained in terms of certain positive definite quadratic forms in 8 and 4 variables and certain associated harmonic functions [cf. Schoeneberg, Math. Ann. **116** (1939), 511–523]. It is proved that

$$64\tau(n) = \sum_{Q_{16}(\Pi)=n} n_1^4 - 80n^2\sigma_7(n),$$

$$\sum_{Q_{16}(\Pi)=n} n_1^4 = 144n^2\sigma_3(n)+144\cdot 240\sum_1^{n-1}(n-i)^2\sigma_3(n-i)\sigma_3(i),$$

whence

$$(*) \quad \tau(n) = \frac{n^2}{4}\{9\sigma_3(n)-5\sigma_7(n)\} + 9\cdot 240\sum_1^{n-1}(n-1)^2\sigma_3(n-i)\sigma_3(i).$$

This implies

$$(**) \quad \tau(n) \equiv \frac{n^2}{4}\{9\sigma_3(n)-5\sigma_7(n)\} \ (\text{mod } 9.240);$$

hence if $\tau(p)=0$, $p\neq 2, 3, 5$, it is necessary that $5p^7-9p^3-4\equiv 0$ (mod $2^6\cdot 3^3\cdot 5$), which implies $p\equiv -1$ (mod $2^2\cdot 3^3\cdot 5$). (The formula (*) as it stands seems to be incorrect; the coefficient $9\cdot 240$ in the right member should apparently read $9\cdot 60$. This change implies a corresponding change in (**) and the result obtained from it. Incidentally the correct form of (*) had been proved in a different way by Lahiri [Bull. Calcutta Math. Soc. **39** (1947), 33–52, in particular p. 35, formula (7.2); MR **9**, 225].

As for the function $\tau_2(n)$, it is proved that

$$(***) \quad \tau_2(n) = n\{2\sigma_1(n)-\sigma_3(n)+48\sum_{2i<n}(n-2i)\sigma_1(n-2i)\sigma_1'(i),$$

where $\sigma_1'(n)$ denotes the sum of the odd divisors of n. It follows from (***) that

$$\tau_2(n)\equiv n\{2\sigma_1(n)-\sigma^3(n)\} \quad (\text{mod } 48).$$

Thus if $\tau_2(p)=0$, $p\neq 2$ or 3, then

$$p^3-2p^2-1\equiv 0 \quad (\text{mod } 48).$$

It is also proved that $\tau_2(n)\equiv\sigma_5(n)$ (mod 2^8); hence $\tau_2(p)=0$ implies $p\equiv -1$ (mod 8). *L. Carlitz.*

Citations: MR 9, 12b = F35-11; MR 9, 225f = F35-17.

F35-36 (20# 5755)

McCarthy, P. J. A congruence property of Ramanujan's function. Quart. J. Math. Oxford Ser. (2) **8** (1957), 141–142.

Ramanujan's function $\tau(n)$ is defined by

$$\sum_1^{\infty}\tau(n)x^n = x\prod_1^{\infty}(1-x^n)^{24} \quad (|x|<1).$$

Using results of Ramanujan [Collected Papers, University Press, Cambridge, 1927] the author proves

$$\tau(n)\equiv 26\sigma_3(n)+3\sigma_7(n)+21\sigma_{11}(n)+34U_{3,7}(n) \ (\text{mod } 49),$$

where $U_{r,s}(n)=\sum_1^{n-1}\sigma_r(k)\sigma_s(n-k)$ $(n>1)$, $U_{r,s}(1)=0$, and $\sigma_a(n)=\sum_{d|n}d^a$. This is simpler than a result of Bambah and Chowla [Math. Student **14** (1946), 24–26;

MR 9, 411]. When $n \equiv 3, 5, 6 \pmod 7$, the residue of $\tau(n)$ (mod 49) is very simply expressed by $\sigma_a(n)$, a result of D. H. Lehmer. *S. Chowla* (Boulder, Colo.)

Citations: MR 9, 411c = F35-25.

F35-37 (23# A132)

McCarthy, P. J.

Some congruences involving Ramanujan's function $\tau(n)$.

Math. Student **27** (1959), 13–15.

Ramanujan's function $\tau(n)$ is defined by $\sum_1^\infty \tau(n)x^n = x\prod_1^\infty (1-x^n)^{24}$ ($|x|<1$). The author tries to obtain certain congruences involving $\tau(n)$ for the moduli 11 and 13, and in addition he obtains a congruence for $\tau(n)$ for the modulus 17. He makes use of the expressions introduced by Ramanujan,

$$P = 1-24\sum_{n=1}^{\infty}\frac{nx^n}{1-x^n} = 1-24\sum_1^\infty \sigma_1(n)x^n,$$

$$Q = 1+240\sum_{n=1}^{\infty}\frac{n^3x^n}{1-x^n} = 1+240\sum_1^\infty \sigma_3(n)x^n,$$

$$R = 1-504\sum_{n=1}^{\infty}\frac{n^5x^n}{1-x^n} = 1-504\sum_1^\infty \sigma_5(n)x^n,$$

where $\sigma_k(n)$ is the sum of the kth powers of all the positive divisors of n. Ramanujan proved the identity (A) $Q^3-R^2 = 1728\sum_1^\infty \tau(n)x^n$, from which the author obtains $\tau(n) \equiv n\sigma_5(n)+9S_{5,3}(n) \pmod{11}$, where $S_{r,s}(n)=\sum_1^{n-1} k\sigma_r(k)\times\sigma_s(n-k)$, $(n>1)$, $S_{r,s}(1)=0$ (the author writes abusively $\sum_1^{n-1} k\sigma_r(n)\sigma_s(n-k)$). To obtain a congruence for the modulus 13, the author uses the following relation of W. H. Simons [Bull. Amer. Math. Soc. **50** (1944), 883–892; MR **6**, 118]: $6(R^2-I) = -3\sum_1^\infty \tau(n)x^n+13I$, where I is a power series in x with integral coefficients. He obtains: $\tau(n) \equiv \sigma_5(n)+8T_5(n) \pmod{13}$, where $T_r(n)=\sum_1^{n-1}\sigma_r(k)\times\sigma_r(n-k)$, $(n>1)$, $T_r(1)=0$ (the author writes abusively $\sum_1^{n-1}\sigma_r(n)\sigma_r(n-k)$). Simons [loc. cit., p. 888] gives still another relation: $8(Q^3-R^2)+14R^2+3 \equiv \sum_1^n \sigma_{11}(n)x^n \pmod{17}$, from which the author obtains: $\tau(n) \equiv 13\sigma_5(n)+15\sigma_{11}(n)+5T_5(n) \pmod{17}$. As an example of another congruence the author obtains from (A):

$$24\tau(n) \equiv 35n\sigma_5(n)-11n\sigma_9(n) \ (\mathrm{mod}\ 2^4\cdot 3\cdot 5^2\cdot 7 = 8400).$$

S. C. van Veen (Delft)

Citations: MR 6, 118a = P76-2.

F35-38 (24# A710)

Gandhi, J. M.

The nonvanishing of Ramanujan's τ-function.

Amer. Math. Monthly **68** (1961), 757–760.

The non-vanishing of $\tau(n)$ defined by

$$x\prod_1^\infty (1-x^n)^{24} = \sum_1^\infty \tau(n)x^n \quad (|x|<1)$$

was conjectured by D. H. Lehmer. The author proves for $1 \leq \theta \leq 9$:

$$\text{(A)} \qquad 2^\theta \| \tau(p) \quad \text{if} \quad 2^\theta \| (p+1)$$

($2^\theta \| m$ means that 2^θ is the highest power of 2 contained in m), where p is an odd prime. He conjectures (as D. H. Lehmer also did) that (A) is true for all positive integers θ. It is easy to see that the truth of (A) for all positive integers θ would imply the non-vanishing of $\tau(n)$ ($n=1, 2, 3, \cdots$). *S. Chowla* (Boulder, Colo.)

F35-39 (24# A1263)

Lehmer, D. H.

Some functions of Ramanujan.

Math. Student **27** (1959), 105–116 (1961).

This is a very interesting expository account of Ramanujan's τ-function, and related functions.

S. Chowla (Boulder, Colo.)

F35-40 (27# 1431)

Gandhi, J. M.

Congruences for $p_r(n)$ and Ramanujan's τ function.

Amer. Math. Monthly **70** (1963), 265–274.

Die verallgemeinerten Partitionenfunktionen $p_r(n)$ sind die Koeffizienten der Potenzreihenentwicklung von $\phi(x)^r$, wobei $\phi(x)=\prod_{v=1}^\infty (1-x^v)$ ist. Insbesondere ist $p_{-1}(n)$ die Anzahl der uneingeschränkten Partitionen der natürlichen Zahl n und $p_{24}(n-1)=\tau(n)$ die von Ramanujan eingeführte τ-Funktion. Der Verfasser zeigt vermöge einfacher Beziehungen zwischen den erzeugenden Funktionen eine Reihe von Kongruenzen für $p_r(n)$, welche insbesondere bekannte Resultate enthalten wie z.B. $p_{-2}(5n+2)$, $p_{-2}(5n+3)$, $p_{-2}(5n+4) \equiv 0$ mod 5 (Ramanathan), $\tau(3n+2) \equiv 0$ mod 3 (Lahiri), $p_{-1}(n) \equiv \sum p_{-1}(t)$ mod 2, wobei t über alle ganzen Zahlen der Form $(2n-j(j+1))/8$ mit ganzem nichtnegativen j läuft (MacMahon). Die Resultate des Verfassers sind in der Einleitung in den Aussagen (I)–(V) übersichtlich zusammengestellt. *H. Klingen* (Freiburg)

F35-41 (28# 1155)

Kolberg, O.

Note on Ramanujan's function $\tau(n)$.

Math. Scand. **10** (1962), 171–172.

Writing $\tau(n)$ for Ramanujan's function and $\sigma_k(n)$ for the sum of the kth powers of the divisors of n, the author proves the congruence $\tau(n) \equiv n\sigma_9(n) \pmod{7^2}$, provided the Legendre symbol $(n/7)=-1$. There is a number of well-known congruences of similar type.

A. C. Woods (Columbus, Ohio)

F35-42 (28# 2095)

Kolberg, O.

Congruences for Ramanujan's function $\tau(n)$.

Årbok Univ. Bergen Mat.-Natur. Ser. **1962**, *no.* 11, 8 *pp.*

The author derives some new, very simple congruences for Ramanujan's function $\tau(n)$, defined by $x\prod_{m=1}^\infty (1-x^m)^{24} = \sum_{n=1}^\infty \tau(n)x^n$. He proves, namely,

$$\tau(8n+l) \equiv a_l\sigma_{11}(8n+l) \ (\mathrm{mod}\ 2^{b_l}),$$

where $(l, 8)=1$, $a_1=1$, $a_3=1217$, $a_5=1537$, $a_7=705$, $b_1=11$, $b_3=13$, $b_5=12$, $b_7=14$;

$$\tau(3n+1) \equiv \sigma_{11}(3n+1) \ (\mathrm{mod}\ 3^5),$$

$$\tau(3n+2) \equiv 53\sigma_{11}(3n+2) \ (\mathrm{mod}\ 3^6).$$

The proof uses some standard devices from the theory of modular functions combined with identities involving $\varphi(x)=\prod_1(1-x^m)$ which appear in an earlier paper [Univ. Bergen Årbok Naturvit. Rekke **1959**, no. 16; MR **23** #A2393]. *J. Lehner* (College Park, Md.)

Citations: MR 23# A2393 = F10-73.

F35-43 (29# 80)

Kesava Menon, P.

Series associated with Ramanujan's function $\tau(n)$.

J. Indian Math. Soc. (N.S.) **27** (1963), 57–65.

The series

$$F(s) = \sum_1^\infty \frac{\tau(n)}{n^s}, \qquad f(s) = \sum_1^\infty \frac{\tau^2(n)}{n^s}$$

satisfy known functional equations. The former has an Euler product conjectured by Ramanujan and proved by

Mordell. The author introduces a few other functions involving $\tau(n)$ and establishes identities between them.
S. Chowla (University Park, Pa.)

F35-44 **(30# 3072)**

Lehmer, D. H.

The primality of Ramanujan's tau-function.

Amer. Math. Monthly **72** (1965), *no. 2, part II*, 15–18.

The tables of $\tau(n)$ end at $n=10{,}000$ (unpublished), but despite this fact the author shows that $\tau(n)$ is prime for the first time when $n=251^2=63{,}001$. Here τ is a 26 digit number which is tested by a Fibonacci-type criterion: If $F_0=0$, $F_1=1$, $F_{n+1}=F_n+F_{n-2}$, then N is prime if, for all primes $p|(N+1)$, $N|F_n$ for $n=N+1$ but not for $n=(N-1)/p$. The test is so good that it takes only 20 seconds of computer time, and the author saves the proof for a later paper. By the multiplicative properties of $\tau(n)$ (once he excludes $\tau(n)=0$) it is clear he need test only $n=p^t$. If $|\tau(n)|=2$, then $p\equiv 1 \pmod{691\times 32}$, using $\tau(n)\equiv\sigma_{11}(n) \pmod{691}$ and $\tau(n)\equiv\sigma_3(n) \pmod{32}$. If $|\tau(n)|>2$, the oddness of $\tau(n)$ leads to $n=p^{2t}$, and if $t\geqq 2$, 63,001 is not so hard to reach. If we come finally to $n=p^2$ ($p\leqq 251$), the case $p\equiv 1 \pmod 6$ determines a few cases of $p \pmod{691}$, where $\tau(p^2)=\pm 3$ (since $\tau(p^2)\equiv\sigma_3(p^2)\equiv 0 \bmod 3$). The case $p\equiv -1 \pmod 6$ is left. The special cases $3p=u^2+23v^2$ are excluded by $p^{11}\equiv(p/23)=1 \pmod{23}$ and $\tau(p)\equiv -1$, hence $\tau(p^2)=|\tau(p)|^2-p^{11}\equiv 1$ or $\tau(p^2)=\pm 23$. This is again excluded by congruences on $\sigma_{11}(n) \pmod{691}$. The remaining cases of $p\equiv -1 \pmod 6$ were tested by computer (by John Brillhart on the Stanford IBM 7090).
H. Cohn (Tucson, Ariz.)

F35-45 **(35# 4152)**

Gandhi, J. M.

A congruence for $\tau(p^{4m})$.

Amer. Math. Monthly **74** (1967), 413–414.

Let $\tau(n)$ be Ramanujan's function and let p be an odd prime. Let 2^θ be the highest power of 2 dividing $\tau(p)$. Let $\alpha=2^K R$, where $K\geqq 2$ and R is odd. The author proves that the highest power of 2 dividing $\tau(p^\alpha)-1$ is $2^{K+2\theta-2}$.
D. H. Lehmer (Berkeley, Calif.)

F35-46 **(39# 5464)**

Serre, Jean-Pierre

Une interprétation des congruences relatives à la fonction τ de Ramanujan.

Séminaire Delange-Pisot-Poitou: 1967/68, *Théorie des Nombres, Fasc.* 1, *Exp.* 14, 17 *pp. Secrétariat mathématique, Paris,* 1969.

The author makes a survey of results on Ramanujan's τ-function.
B. Stolt (Stockholm)

F35-47 **(41# 3372)**

Lahiri, D. B.

Identities connecting the partition, divisor and Ramanujan's functions.

Proc. Nat. Inst. Sci. India Part A **34** (1968), *suppl.* 1, 96–103.

The sum $\sigma_k(n)$ of the kth powers of the divisors of n is expressed in terms of the partition function $p(n)$ for $k=1$, 3, 5, 7 and 9. The case $k=1$ is a classical pentagonal number formula of Euler. These identities are used to show that $5474304\tau(n)=2275\sigma_{11}(n)-691\sum_v \pm P(v,n)vp(n-v)$, where the sum is over pentagonal numbers and $P(v,n)$ is an explicit fifth degree polynomial in n with integer coefficients. {Reviewer's remark: Since $5474304=2275+(691)(7919)$, the last formula implies Ramanujan's congruence $\tau(n)\equiv\sigma_{11}(n) \pmod{691}$.}
T. M. Apostol (Pasadena, Calif.)

F35-48 **(41# 3400)**

Rankin, Robert A.

Ramanujan's function $\tau(n)$.

Symposia on Theoretical Physics and Mathematics, Vol. 10 (*Inst. Math. Sci., Madras,* 1969), *pp.* 37–45. *Plenum, New York,* 1970.

As the author states, the object of the paper is to give a survey of problems concerning the Ramanujan function $\tau(n)$ defined by

$$\Delta(z) = e^{2\pi iz}\prod_{n=1}^\infty (1-e^{2\pi inz})^{24} = \sum_{n=1}^\infty \tau(n)e^{2\pi inz},$$

where $\operatorname{Im} z>0$ and $\Delta(z)$ is the so-called discriminant function from the theory of elliptic modular functions. Recalling first the multiplicative properties $\tau(mn)=\tau(m)\tau(n)$ $((m,n)=1)$, $\tau(p^{k+1})=\tau(p^k)\tau(p)-p''\tau(p^{k-1})$, the author discusses the Ramanujan conjecture $|\tau(p)|<2p^{u/2}$. It is known that $\tau(n)=O(n^{6-1/4+\varepsilon})$. Also, $T(x)=\sum_{n\leqq x}\tau(n)=O(x^{6-1/10})$, $T^*(x)=\sum_{n\leqq x}\tau(n)=O(x^{13/2})$.

Let $\sigma(g)$ denote the abscissa of convergence of $g(s)=\sum_{n=1}^\infty \tau(n)/n^s$ and define $\sigma(f)$ and $\sigma(g^*)$ similarly for $f(s)=\sum_{n=1}^\infty \tau^2(n)/n^s$, $g^*(s)=\sum_{n=1}^\infty |\tau(n)|/n^s$. Then $\sigma(f)=12$ and $6-\frac14\leqq\sigma(g)\leqq 6-1/10$, $6+\frac14\leqq\sigma(g^*)\leqq 6+\frac12$. Both $f(s)$ and $g(s)$ satisfy simple functional equations; $g(s)$ is an entire function while $f(s)$ has a simple pole at $s=1$.

Finally, the question of the possible vanishing of $\tau(n)$ is discussed. Let

$$G_k(z,m) = \tfrac12 \sum_{(c,d)=1} (cz+d)^{-k}\exp\{2\pi im(az+b)/(cz+d)\},$$

where k is an even integer greater than 2, m is a positive integer and the summation is over all coprime c, d and for each pair two integers a, b are chosen such that $ad-bc+1$. Then (*) $G_{12}(z,m)=\tau(m)/11\alpha m''\,\Delta(z)$, where α is a certain positive constant. It is known that $G_k(z,m)$ vanishes identically for $k=4$, 6, 8, 10, 14. Hence, as the author remarks, it is not likely to be easy to show that $G_{12}(z,m)$ takes nonzero values.
L. Carlitz (Durham, N.C.)

F35-49 **(43# 166)**

Lehmer, D. H.

Note on the distribution of Ramanujan's tau function.

Math. Comp. **24** (1970), 741–743.

Let $\tau(n)$ denote the Ramanujan tau function. When p is a prime, write $\tau(p)=2p^{11/2}\cos\theta_p$. Then, according to a conjecture of Ramanujan, θ_p should be real. Assuming the truth of this conjecture, Sato and Tate conjectured that θ_p is distributed over $[0,\pi]$ according to the following law:

The density of those primes p for which $a<\theta_p<b$ is $2\pi^{-1}\int_a^b \sin^2/\theta\, d\theta$. This paper reports on a test of this conjecture for the primes $<10^4$.
K. Thanigasalam (Bronx, N.Y.)

F35-50 **(43# 169)**

Joris, Henri

Un Ω-théorème pour la fonction arithmétique de Ramanujan.

C. R. Acad. Sci. Paris Sér. A-B **272** (1971), A295.

The author announces the following result concerning the sum-function of Ramanujan's arithmetic function $\tau(n)$: $\sum_{n\leqq x}\tau(n)=\Omega_\pm(x^{23/4}\log\log\log x)$.
T. Metsänkylä (Turku)

F35-51 **(43# 4781)**

de Branges, Louis

A proof of the Ramanujan hypothesis.

J. Math. Anal. Appl. **30** (1970), 335–352.

Ramanujan's τ-function is defined by $\sum_1^\infty \tau(n)x^n = x\prod_1^\infty (1-x^n)^{24}$, valid for $|x|<1$. The "hypothesis" referred to in the title is the conjectured inequality $|\tau(n)| \leq n^{11/2} d(n)$, where $d(n)$ is the number of divisors of n. The conjecture has attracted considerable attention (e.g., D. H. Lehmer and E. Lehmer, R. A. Rankin, G. H. Hardy, A. Weil, G. Shimura and M. Kuga, P. Deligne). The reviewer has not understood the author's claimed proof. In view of the great interest evoked by the author's claim, it seems very desirable that a clarification of the proof be published.

{In the later article [same J. **35** (1971), 285–311] the author points out that there is a gap in the above proof.}
S. Chowla (Princeton, N.J.)

Referred to in F35-52.

F35-52 **(44# 154)**

de Branges, Louis

The Riemann hypothesis for modular forms.

J. Math. Anal. Appl. **35** (1971), 285–311.

Unfortunately a gap occurs in the author's proof of the Ramanujan hypothesis for the τ-function [same J. **30** (1970), 335–352; MR **43** #4781]. He acknowledges this at the end of the present paper, which depends essentially on the earlier one. *S. Chowla* (Princeton, N.J.)

Citations: MR 43# 4781 = F35-51.

F40 HILBERT AND HILBERT-SIEGEL MODULAR GROUPS AND THEIR AUTOMORPHIC FORMS

See also reviews F50-10, F55-15, F55-16, F55-31, F65-22.

F40-1 **(2, 213d)**

Maass, Hans. Über Gruppen von hyperabelschen Transformationen. S.-B. Heidelberger Akad. Wiss. **1940**, no. 2, 26 pp. (1940).

Let T be the space of n complex variables $\tau_k = x_k + iy_k$ with $y_k > 0$ $(k=1, \cdots, n)$ and Γ a discontinuous group of simultaneous linear fractional transformations

$$\tau_k \to \frac{\alpha_k \tau_k + \beta_k}{\gamma_k \tau_k + \delta_k}$$

of T into itself. Since the differential form

$$ds^2 = \sum_{k=1}^{n} y_k^{-2}(dx_k^2 + dy_k^2)$$

is invariant under Γ, it defines a distance $\overline{PP^*}$ for any two points P and P^* of T. Let P_0 be any given point of T and $P_0, P_1, P_2, \cdots$ the system of images of P_0 under Γ. A fundamental domain F with respect to Γ is formed by the set of all points P of T satisfying the inequalities $\overline{PP_0} \leqq \overline{PP_k}$ $(k=1, 2, \cdots)$. It is important for the theory of the corresponding automorphic functions to determine the shape of F in the neighborhood of the boundary of T. This is performed in the special case of Hilbert's modular group; then $\alpha_k, \beta_k, \gamma_k, \delta_k$ $(k=1, \cdots, n)$ run over the conjugates of all integers $\alpha, \beta, \gamma, \delta$ with $\alpha\delta - \beta\gamma = 1$ in a totally real algebraic number field Z of degree n. In this case another construction of a fundamental domain F^* is given, using the properties of the ideals of Z. The domain F^* is bounded by a finite number of analytic manifolds, and there are exactly h inequivalent boundary points of F^* on the boundary of T, where h denotes the class number of Z. The latter result corrects an erroneous statement of Blumenthal, to whom the definition of F^* is due [Math. Ann. **56**, 509–548 (1903)].
C. L. Siegel (Princeton, N. J.).

Referred to in F40-5, F40-7, F40-32.

F40-2 **(3, 272b)**

Maass, Hans. Modulformen und quadratische Formen über dem quadratischen Zahlkörper $R(\sqrt{5})$. Math. Ann. **118**, 65–84 (1941).

Notation: M a modular group in $R(\sqrt{5})$, that is, the system of matrices

$$S = \begin{pmatrix} \alpha & \beta \\ \gamma & \delta \end{pmatrix}$$

with integral $\alpha, \beta, \gamma, \delta$ in $R(\sqrt{5})$ and $\alpha\delta - \beta\gamma = 1$; U a subgroup of M, in particular T the subgroup defined by the condition $\beta \equiv \gamma \equiv 0 \pmod 2$ or $\alpha \equiv \delta \equiv 0 \pmod 2$; a function $\phi(\tau, \tau')$ of two independent complex variables τ, τ', not identically vanishing, is called a modular form with the group U, the dimension $-r$ and the multiplier system $v(S)$ if it is regular in a fundamental domain of U and satisfies for all S in U the equation

$$\phi\left(\frac{\alpha\tau+\beta}{\gamma\tau+\delta}, \frac{\alpha'\tau'+\beta'}{\gamma'\tau'+\delta'}\right) = v(S)(\gamma\tau+\delta)^r(\gamma'\tau'+\delta')^r\phi(\tau, \tau'),$$

where $\alpha', \beta', \gamma', \delta'$ are the conjugates of $\alpha, \beta, \gamma, \delta$; let $a(r)$ be the number of linearly independent modular forms with the group M and the dimension $-r$.

The first result is concerned with the possible values of r and $v(S)$. In the case $U = M$, the dimension is necessarily a rational integer and $v(S) = 1$; in the case $U = T$, the number $2r$ is a rational integer and there are exactly 4 possible systems of multipliers $v(S)$. In a former publication [Math. Ann. **117**, 538–578 (1940); cf. these Rev. **2**, 87] the author had proved the inequality $a(r) < cr^2$, with constant c. Now he uses results of F. Götzky [Math. Ann. **100**, 411–437 (1928)] and demonstrates that $a(1) = 0$, $a(2) = 1$, $a(3) \leqq 2$, $a(4) \leqq 3$. This leads to the three identities: $G_2^2 = G_4$, $G_2 = \theta_4$, $G_4 = \theta_8$, where G_r $(r = 2, 4)$ denotes the Eisenstein series of M with the dimension $-r$ whose Fourier expansion at the point ∞ has the constant term 1; moreover,

$$\theta_{2r} = \sum \exp(\pi i \operatorname{tr} Q(x_1, \cdots, x_{2r})\tau/\sqrt{5}),$$

where $Q(x_1, \cdots, x_{2r}) = Q_{2r}$ is a certain positive even quadratic form in $R(\sqrt{5})$ with determinant 1 and $2r$ variables, with integral rational coefficients in the case $r = 4$, and the summation is carried over all systems of integers $x_1, \cdots, x_{2r}$ in $R(\sqrt{5})$. It follows that for every integer in $R(\sqrt{5})$ the number of representations by Q_8 is the same as the number of representations by $Q_4(x_1, \cdots, x_4) + Q_4(x_5, \cdots, x_8)$, whereas those two quadratic forms are not equivalent in $R(\sqrt{5})$. There exist in $R(\sqrt{5})$ exactly two classes of positive even quadratic forms with determinant 1 and 8 variables, and one such class with 4 variables. *C. L. Siegel.*

Referred to in E12-31.

F40-3 **(5, 261a)**

Maass, Hans. Theorie der Poincaréschen Reihen zu den hyperbolischen Fixpunktsystemem der Hilbertschen Modulgruppe. Math. Ann. **118**, 518–543 (1942).

Recently the theory of automorphic functions of a single variable has been greatly simplified by the application of an integral covariant, due to H. Petersson; in particular, Petersson has proved that the set of automorphic forms of given real dimension (< -2), with a multiplier system of absolute value 1 for a group of first kind, possesses a finite basis consisting of Poincaré series of special simple types [Abh. Math. Sem. Hansischen Univ. **14**, 22–60 (1941); these Rev. **3**, 204]. In a former publication the author generalized Petersson's investigation by considering certain classes of automorphic functions of several variables, in particular for the case of Hilbert's modular group [Math. Ann. **117**, 538–578 (1940); these Rev. **2**, 87]; however, he introduced only the Poincaré series corresponding to the first of Petersson's three types (parabolic fixed points). In the present paper his results are extended to the two other types of Poincaré series. The proof used Dirichlet's theorem concerning algebraic units. *C. L. Siegel.*

F40-4 **(8, 8d)**

de Bruijn, Nicolaas Govert. Over Modulaire Vormen van Meer Veranderlijken. [On Modular Forms in Several Variables]. Thesis, Free University of Amsterdam, 1943. xvi+63 pp. (Dutch)

Modular functions of several variables were first associated with algebraic fields by Hilbert and by Blumenthal [Math. Ann. **56**, 509–548 (1903); **58**, 497–527 (1904)]. The purpose of the present paper is to extend Blumenthal's results in the direction which Hecke and his associates have followed in the theory of modular functions of one variable.

Let K be a totally real algebraic field of degree n. The matrix $\binom{\alpha\ \beta}{\gamma\ \delta}$ with $\alpha, \beta, \gamma, \delta\varepsilon K$ and $\alpha\delta-\beta\gamma=\sigma\neq 0$ gives rise to a set of substitutions

$$(1) \qquad \tau_1^{(i)}=\frac{\alpha^{(i)}\tau^{(i)}+\beta^{(i)}}{\gamma^{(i)}\tau^{(i)}+\delta^{(i)}}, \qquad i=1, \cdots, n,$$

where $\alpha^{(i)}, \beta^{(i)}, \gamma^{(i)}, \delta^{(i)}$ are the conjugates of $\alpha, \beta, \gamma, \delta$ and $\tau^{(i)}$ are complex variables. Blumenthal studied the group H of substitutions with $\alpha, \beta, \gamma, \delta$ algebraic integers and σ a totally positive unit.

A modular form of dimension $-k$ is defined as a function of n variables $\tau^{(1)}, \cdots, \tau^{(n)}$, subject to certain regularity conditions and with the property that

$$(2) \qquad F\left(\frac{\alpha^{(1)}\tau^{(1)}+\beta^{(1)}}{\gamma^{(1)}\tau^{(1)}+\delta^{(1)}}, \cdots, \frac{\alpha^{(n)}\tau^{(n)}+\beta^{(n)}}{\gamma^{(n)}\tau^{(n)}+\delta^{(n)}}\right) =\prod_{i=1}^{n}(\gamma^{(i)}\tau^{(i)}+\delta^{(i)})^kF(\tau^{(1)}, \cdots, \tau^{(n)})$$

in the region $\mathfrak{J}(\tau^{(i)})>0$. Instead of the Hilbert group H a wider group Γ_0 (already mentioned by Hurwitz) is studied which is defined as follows. Let $\mathfrak{e}$ be such an ideal of K (not necessarily entire) that $\mathfrak{e}^2$ is a principal ideal; then the substitution with the matrix $\binom{\alpha\ \beta}{\gamma\ \delta}$ belongs to Γ_0 if $\alpha, \beta, \gamma, \delta$ lie in $\mathfrak{e}$ and $\sigma=\alpha\delta-\beta\gamma$ fulfills $(\sigma)=\mathfrak{e}^2$. Hilbert's group H is a subgroup of Γ_0, and so is the group Γ_1, with $\alpha, \beta, \gamma, \delta$ entire and $\sigma=1$.

For Γ_0 the determinant σ does not need to be positive. The region $\mathfrak{J}(\tau^{(i)})>0$ is then transformed through (1) into $\sigma^{(i)}\mathfrak{J}(\tau^{(i)})>0$. Therefore regions T_w are introduced, where $w=(w^{(1)}, \cdots, w^{(n)})$ is a signature, $w^{(i)}$ being ± 1, and T_w is determined by $w^{(i)}\mathfrak{J}(\tau^{(i)})>0$, $i=1, \cdots, n$. If $M=\binom{\alpha\ \beta}{\gamma\ \delta}$, the author defines (following Kloosterman)

$$F(\tau)\,|\,M=N(\gamma\tau+\delta)^{-k}F\left(\frac{(\alpha\tau+\beta)}{(\gamma\tau+\delta)}\right),$$

where $F(\tau)$ is an abbreviation for $F(\tau^{(1)}, \cdots, \tau^{(n)})$. A modular form of type $(\Gamma_1, -k)$ is now defined as a function $F(\tau)$ which satisfies the conditions (1) $F(\tau)\,|\,L=F(\tau)$ for all $L\varepsilon\Gamma_1$, (2) $F(\tau)$ is regular in all T_w, (3) for every matrix $M=\binom{\alpha\ \beta}{\gamma\ \delta}$ with determinant $\sigma\neq 0$ there exists an ideal $\mathfrak{m}$ such that for any signature w and $\tau\varepsilon T_w$ there exists an absolutely convergent expansion

$$(3) \qquad F(\tau)\,|\,M=c(0)+\sum_{w\nu>0,\ \nu\equiv 0(\mathfrak{m})} c(\nu)\exp 2\pi i S(\nu\tau).$$

Condition (3) refers to the "cusps" of the fundamental region in which regularity is demanded.

A still finer classification of modular forms is obtained by the use of the wider group Γ_0 instead of Γ_1 in the following way. The subgroup $\Gamma_{(k)}$ of those substitutions L of Γ_0 for which the ideal $\mathfrak{e}$ is a principal ideal (μ) with $N(\mu)^k>0$ is normal and of finite index in Γ_0. Let χ be a character of the factor group $\Gamma_0/\Gamma_{(k)}$. Then the form F is said to be of type $(\Gamma_0, -k, \chi)$ if conditions (1), (2), (3) are fulfilled and if also, for any substitution $M=\binom{\alpha\ \beta}{\gamma\ \delta}$ of Γ_0, $\alpha\equiv\beta\equiv\gamma\equiv\delta\equiv 0 \pmod{\mathfrak{e}}$, $(\sigma)=\mathfrak{e}^2$, the equation $N(\mathfrak{e})^kF\,|\,M=\chi(M)F$ is satisfied. Any function of type $(\Gamma_1, -k)$ can then be written as a sum of functions of type $(\Gamma_0, -k, \chi)$, the sum extended over all χ.

After this preparation, the analogues of Hecke's operators $T(n)$ can be introduced. First it can be seen that χ can be defined for all "singular numbers" σ, that is, those whose principal ideal is a square, by just putting $\chi(\sigma)=\chi(M)$, where σ is the determinant of M; second, χ can then be extended to all numbers, not equal to 0, of K. Let now $\mathfrak{n}$ be an entire ideal which is equivalent to the square of an ideal. The operator $T(\mathfrak{n}, \chi)$ is then defined by

$$(4) \qquad F\,|\,T(\mathfrak{n}, \chi)=N(\mathfrak{n})^{k-1}N(\mathfrak{b})^k\bar{\chi}(\sigma)\sum_{i=1}^{s}F\,|\,M_i.$$

Here $M_1, \cdots, M_s$ is a complex system of left classes modulo Γ_1 of matrices "of order $\mathfrak{n}$ with determinant σ," that is, with $\alpha\delta-\beta\gamma=\sigma$, $(\sigma)=\mathfrak{n}\mathfrak{b}^2$, $\alpha\equiv\beta\equiv\gamma\equiv\delta\equiv 0 \pmod{\mathfrak{b}}$. The definition (4) does not depend on the choice of σ.

These operators are commutative as in Hecke's case and the author obtains, for two entire ideals $\mathfrak{N}$ and $\mathfrak{n}$ which are equivalent with ideal squares, for each form F of type $(\Gamma_0, -k, \chi)$, the formula

$$F\,|\,T(\mathfrak{N}, \chi)T(\mathfrak{n}, \chi)=\sum_{\mathfrak{c}\,|\,(\mathfrak{N}, \mathfrak{n})} N(\mathfrak{c})^{k-1}F\,|\,T(\mathfrak{N}\mathfrak{n}/\mathfrak{c}^2, \chi),$$

in full analogy to Hecke's formula. Parallel with this goes, as in Hecke's theory, a relation between the coefficients of expansions in cusp points:

$$c(\mathfrak{n}, F\,|\,T(\mathfrak{N}, \chi))=\sum_{\mathfrak{c}\,|\,(\mathfrak{N}, \mathfrak{n})} N(\mathfrak{c})^{k-1}c(\mathfrak{N}\mathfrak{n}/\mathfrak{c}^2, F),$$

where the $c(\mathfrak{n}, F)$ are defined on the basis of the expansion (3).

An analogue for Hecke's representation of the operators $T(n)$ by matrices $\lambda(n)$ is still missing since the finiteness of a basis of the linear family of forms of given dimension is a function-theoretical problem which the author leaves untouched. However, for eigenfunctions F of the operators $T(\mathfrak{n}, \chi)$, that is, for functions which fulfill $F\,|\,T(\mathfrak{n}, \chi)=\lambda(\mathfrak{n})F$ with complex numbers $\lambda(\mathfrak{n})$, these form a representation of the ring of the $T(\mathfrak{n}, \chi)$. Eigenfunctions can indeed be constructed by means of Eisenstein's series [Kloosterman, Abh. Math. Sem. Hamburgischen Univ. **6**, 163–188 (1928)].

The second part of the paper applies some of the methods to "special" ϑ-series in n variables. Let N be an even number and let $\xi=(\xi_1, \cdots, \xi_N)$ be a vector whose components are numbers of K. The quadratic form $Q(\xi, \xi)=\sum_{i,j=1}^{N}\alpha_{ij}\xi_i\xi_j$ is called totally definite if there exists a signature w such that $w^{(i)}Q(\xi^{(i)}, \xi^{(i)})>0$ for all ξ; w is then called the signature of Q. If $\mathfrak{b}$ is an ideal and $\rho=(\rho_1, \cdots, \rho_N)$ a vector, $\rho_i\varepsilon K$, and Q such a form that $\alpha_{ij}\varepsilon\mathfrak{b}^{-2}\mathfrak{d}^{-1}$, $\alpha_{ii}\varepsilon 2\mathfrak{b}^{-2}\mathfrak{d}^{-1}$,

$$Q(\rho)=\sum_{j=1}^{N}\alpha_{ij}\rho_j\,\varepsilon\,\mathfrak{b}^{-1}\mathfrak{d}^{-1},$$

with $\mathfrak{d}$ the "differente" of K, then

$$\theta(\tau, Q, \rho, \mathfrak{b})=\sum_{\xi\equiv\rho \pmod{\mathfrak{b}}}\exp \pi i S(\tau Q(\xi, \xi))$$

is introduced as a "special ϑ-series." For the sake of convergence, $\tau\varepsilon T_{\mathrm{sgn}\ Q}$. The series θ is of a certain level (Stufe) $\mathfrak{M}$, depending on the quadratic form Q, that is, for the group $\Gamma_1(\mathfrak{M})$ of all those matrices L for which

$$L\equiv\binom{1\ 0}{0\ 1} \bmod \mathfrak{M},$$

we have $\theta\,|\,L=\theta$. The author finally constructs special ϑ-series of level 1 by means of a known definite quadratic form in the rational field of 8 variables and determinant 1, which goes back to Korkine and Zolotareff and which has recently been studied again by Mordell [J. Math. Pures Appl. (9) **17**, 47–87 (1938)]. *H. Rademacher.*

Referred to in F40-6.

F40-5 (10, 434e)

Maass, H. Über die Erweiterungsfähigkeit der Hilbertschen Modulgruppe. Math. Z. **51**, 255–261 (1948).

Let $\tau_1, \cdots, \tau_n$ be n complex variables, and let T be the domain $\Im(\tau_k)>0$, $k=1, \cdots, n$. If Z is a totally real algebraic number field of degree n, and $\alpha_1, \cdots, \delta_1$ are integers of Z such that $\alpha_1\delta_1-\beta_1\gamma_1=1$, Hilbert's modular group M consists of the hyperabelian transformations $\tau_k\rightarrow(\alpha_k\tau_k+\beta_k)/(\gamma_k\tau_k+\delta_k)$, where $\alpha_k, \cdots, \delta_k$ are the conjugates of $\alpha_1, \cdots, \delta_1$. It is discontinuous in T [cf. Maass, S.-B. Heidelberger Akad. Wiss. **1940**, no. 2; these Rev. **2**, 213]. The author proves that the maximal extension of M which is discontinuous in T is Hurwitz's group H, which consists of the hyperabelian transformations

$$\tau_k\rightarrow S_k(\tau_k),\quad S_k=\begin{pmatrix}\alpha_k/\sqrt{\omega_k}, & \beta_k/\sqrt{\omega_k}\\ \gamma_k/\sqrt{\omega_k}, & \delta_k/\sqrt{\omega_k}\end{pmatrix},$$

where now $\alpha_1, \cdots, \delta_1, \omega$ are integers of Z such that ω is totally positive, $\alpha_k\delta_k-\beta_k\gamma_k=\omega_k$, and the coefficients of S are algebraic integers. *R. Hull* (Lafayette, Ind.).

Citations: MR 2, 213d = F40-1.

Referred to in F55-18.

F40-6 (15, 940d)

Herrmann, Oskar. Über Hilbertsche Modulfunktionen und die Dirichletschen Reihen mit Eulerscher Produktentwicklung. Math. Ann. **127**, 357–400 (1954).

In his thesis [Free Univ. of Amsterdam, 1943; these Rev. **8**, 8] the reviewer gave a first approach to a theory of Hecke's T-operators for Hilbert's modular functions. The present author goes much further and obtains the generalization of the entire Hecke-Petersson theory. The main features are: (1) The author constructs a fundamental domain for the Hilbert group of modular substitutions in a totally real field K, and more generally for the groups $\Gamma_1(K_a)$ (see below). These domains have cusp points (h is the number of ideal classes of K). He shows that the linear family of modular forms of a given dimension has a finite basis. Further, applying Petersson's metrization method [Math. Ann. **116**, 401–412 (1939)] he shows that the linear family of cusp forms is spanned by forms which are eigenfunctions of all T-operators. Finally, he constructs, by Mellin's transformation, the corresponding Dirichlet series. The eigenfunctions of the T-operators correspond to Dirichlet series with an Euler product expansion. (2) The reviewer was able to define suitable operators $T(\mathfrak{n})$ only if $\mathfrak{n}$ is equivalent to an ideal square, so that a closed theory was to be expected only in the case where h is odd. The present author solves this difficulty by replacing modular forms by vectors of h different forms, belonging to h different transformation groups $\Gamma_1(K_a)$ $(a=1, \cdots, h)$, which do not seem to have been studied before. These groups are described in terms of ideal numbers: The set of numbers $\neq 0$ of K is extended to a multiplicative system Z^+ of ideal numbers, corresponding to ideals of K, in such a way that no new units are involved [see Hecke, Math. Z. **6**, 11–51 (1920)]. K_a is the subset corresponding to the ideals of class C_a ($C_1, \cdots, C_h$ are the ideal classes of K; C_1 is the unit ideal class, and $K_1=K$). Now $\Gamma_1(K_a)$ is defined as the set of all matrices $\begin{pmatrix}\alpha & \beta\\ \gamma & \delta\end{pmatrix}$ where $\alpha\delta-\beta\gamma=1$, α, β, γ, δ integers, $\alpha\in K$, $\delta\in K$, $\gamma\in K_a$, $\beta\in(K_a)^{-1}$. The fact that $K_1, \cdots, K_h$ need not be totally real is irrelevant. $\Gamma_1(K_1)$ is the Hilbert group.

The use of ideal numbers has the advantage that no nonintegral ideals or auxiliary ideals are needed. On the other hand it has the disadvantage that the ranges of the complex variables τ can be entirely different, and that the relations between the several groups are not easily noticed. Some of these, not mentioned by the author, are (i) $\Gamma_1(K_a)$ is isomorphic (similarity) with a group $\Gamma(\mathfrak{a})$ whose intersection with the Hilbert group Γ_1 has the same finite index both in $\Gamma(\mathfrak{a})$ and in Γ_1. Here $\mathfrak{a}$ is an integral ideal of class C_a, and $\Gamma(\mathfrak{a})$ consists of all matrices $\begin{pmatrix}\lambda & \mu\\ \nu & \rho\end{pmatrix}$ with $\lambda,\mu,\nu,\rho\in K$, $\lambda\rho-\mu\nu=1$, $\lambda\in(1)$, $\rho\in(1)$, $\mu\in\mathfrak{a}$, $\nu\in\mathfrak{a}^{-1}$. Therefore, $\Gamma(\mathfrak{a})$ contains the Hilbert group of level ("Stufe") $\mathfrak{a}$, and so the author's modular forms are trivially related to special modular forms of level $\mathfrak{a}$ in the sense of Kloosterman [Abh. Math. Sem. Univ. Hamburg. **6**, 163–188 (1928)]. (ii) There is also an isomorphism $\Gamma(\mathfrak{a})\simeq\Gamma(\mathfrak{b})$, if $\mathfrak{a}\mathfrak{b}^{-1}$ is equivalent to the square of an ideal. This fact furnishes the connection between the author's results and those of the reviewer, whose T-operators were defined in a different way.

Misprints: In the definition of the T-operator on page 379 $R(\eta, \kappa, \sigma, K)$ should be $R(\eta, \kappa, \sigma, K_a)$. In the formula for $D(s, \lambda)$ on page 397 the factor $N(\sigma)^{-s}$ should be added on the right. *N. G. de Bruijn* (Amsterdam).

Citations: MR 8, 8d = F40-4.

Referred to in F40-11.

F40-7 (16, 16a)

Herrmann, Oskar. Eine metrische Charakterisierung eines Fundamentalbereichs der Hilbertschen Modulgruppen. Math. Z. **60**, 148–155 (1954).

Let K be a totally real field of degree n, and let $\mathfrak{G}$ be a group of totally positive units. Then the Hilbert group Γ is defined as the group of all transformations

$$\tau_k'=(\alpha^{(k)}\tau_k+\beta^{(k)})/(\gamma^{(k)}\tau_k+\delta^{(k)})$$

in the domain $\operatorname{Im}\tau_1>0, \cdots, \operatorname{Im}\tau_n>0$. Here α, β, γ, δ are integers of K, $\alpha\delta-\beta\gamma\in\mathfrak{G}$, and (k) denotes kth conjugate. The author determines a fundamental domain for Γ which is essentially simpler than the one of Maass [S.-B. Heidelberger Akad. Wiss. **1940**, no. 2; these Rev. **2**, 213]. It is determined by the set of inequalities:

(i) $\mathbf{N}|\gamma\tau+\delta|^2\geqq 1$ for all pairs $\gamma\in K$, $\delta\in K$, $(\gamma, \delta)=1$;
(ii) $\mathbf{S}\log\epsilon(\log\epsilon+2\log\operatorname{Im}\tau)\geqq 0$ for all $\epsilon\in\mathfrak{G}$;
(iii) $\mathbf{S}\mu(\mu+2\operatorname{Re}\tau)\geqq 0$ for all integers $\mu\in K$.

($\mathbf{N}$ and $\mathbf{S}$ denote norm and trace, and in these formulas $\tau_1, \cdots, \tau_n$ are formally interpreted as the conjugates of τ.) It is also shown that the domain can already be described by a finite number of these inequalities.

N. G. de Bruijn (Amsterdam).

Citations: MR 2, 213d = F40-1.

Referred to in F40-16.

F40-8 (16, 1000a)

Gundlach, Karl-Bernhard. Über die Darstellung der ganzen Spitzenformen zu den Idealstufen der Hilbertschen Modulgruppe und die Abschätzung ihrer Fourierkoeffizienten. Acta Math. **92**, 309–345 (1954).

This paper carries over to the Hilbert modular group the methods and results of the Hecke-Petersson theory for functions of one variable.

The Hilbert modular group Γ is defined as follows: Let K be a totally real algebraic number field of finite degree n over the rational field. $\tau^{(1)}, \cdots, \tau^{(n)}$ are n complex variables lying in the half-space $\operatorname{Im}\tau^{(k)}>0$. By a substitution $L\tau$ belonging to Γ we mean a set of n simultaneous linear fractional transformations

$$L\tau:\quad \tau^{(k)}\rightarrow\frac{a^{(k)}\tau^{(k)}+b^{(k)}}{c^{(k)}\tau^{(k)}+d^{(k)}}\quad (k=1, 2, \cdots, n),$$

where a, b, c, d are integers in K, and $\{a^k\}$ are the conjugates of a. L_T is associated with the matrix $\begin{pmatrix} a & b \\ c & d \end{pmatrix}$, Γ is the group of all unimodular matrices, and $\Gamma(\mathfrak{c})$, the principal congruence subgroup of level $\mathfrak{c}$, is the subgroup of all unimodular matrices congruent elementwise to the identity matrix. Here $\mathfrak{c}$ is an integral ideal in K. Both Γ and $\Gamma(\mathfrak{c})$ are properly discontinuous and have fundamental regions with cusps lying on the boundary of the half-space $\operatorname{Im} \tau^{(k)} > 0$.

The Hecke-Petersson method offers a recipe for the determination of the Fourier coefficients of an entire modular form of rational integral dimension $-r$ ($r \geqq 2$). One subtracts from the given modular form a suitable linear combination of Eisenstein series (whose Fourier coefficients are known) so that the difference is an entire cusp form, i.e., a form vanishing at all the vertices of the fundamental region. By means of a completeness theorem, the discussion of the cusp forms is reduced to that of the Poincaré series. The latter are expanded in Fourier series, whose coefficients can be estimated non-trivially by using recent estimates of the Kloosterman sums developed by A. Weil [Proc. Nat. Acad. Sci. U. S. A. **34**, 204–207 (1948); MR **10**, 234]. The case $r=2$ is particularly difficult because the Poincaré series do not converge, and it is necessary to use a convergence factor method introduced by Hecke.

All these steps must now be carried out for the Hilbert modular group. The author first treats the case $r>2$. The required Eisenstein series have been discussed by Kloosterman [Abh. Math. Sem. Hamburg. Univ. **6**, 163–188 (1928); Math. Ann. **103**, 279–299 (1930)]. The completeness theorem for the Poincaré series was proved by Maass [Math. Ann. **117**, 538–578 (1940); MR **2**, 87]. The difficult reduction of the occurring Kloosterman sums to the usual sums is accomplished by the author (§4). The analytical details are very complicated.

The final result is: If $a^*(\nu)$ are the Fourier coefficients of an entire cusp form of rational integral dimension $-r(r>2)$ belonging to the group $\Gamma(\mathfrak{c})$, then

$$|a^*(\nu)| = O(N(\nu)^{\frac{1}{2}r-\frac{1}{4}+\epsilon}),$$

where $N(\nu)$ is the norm of ν. In §3 the author demonstrates that this estimate is correct also for $r=2$. *J. Lehner.*

Citations: MR 10, 234e = T25-5.

Referred to in F40-10, F40-11, F40-24.

F40-9 (16, 1000b)

Gundlach, Karl-Bernhard. Über die Darstellung der ganzen Spitzenformen zu den Idealstufen der Hilbertschen Modulgruppe und die Abschätzung ihrer Fourierkoeffizienten. Dissertationen der Mathematisch-Naturwissenschaftlichen Fakultät der Westfälischen Wilhelms-Universität zu Münster in Referaten, Heft 5, pp. 5–6. Aschendorffsche Verlagsbuchhandlung, Münster, 1954. DM 3.50.

Summary of the paper reviewed above.

F40-10 (17, 1059a)

Herrmann, Oskar. Über den Rang der Schar der Spitzenformen zu Hilbertschen Modulgruppen. Math. Z. **64** (1956), 457–466.

The author considers the non-identical vanishing of the Poincaré series in complex variables τ_1, τ_2 for the Hilbert modular group for a real quadratic field of discriminant d. The transformation matrices are conjugates of a unimodular integral matrix M in $R(d^{\frac{1}{2}})$ with denominator $\gamma\tau+\delta$. With k a rational integer $\geqq 3$ and μ an integer of $R(d^{\frac{1}{2}})$, the series

$$G = \sum_{(\gamma,\delta)} \sum_{\lambda} N(\gamma\tau+\delta)^{-k} \exp 2\pi i S(\mu\lambda^2 M\tau d^{-\frac{1}{2}})$$

is defined in the usual manner (to avoid repetitions in summation), with N and S as norm and trace respectively. In the Fourier expansion of G, the coefficients of $\exp 2\pi i S(\nu\tau d^{-\frac{1}{2}})$ for ν in $R(d^{\frac{1}{2}})$ break up into the combination of Kloosterman sums and Bessel functions. Estimates verify the non-identical vanishing of G when the principal term $(\gamma, \delta)=(0, 1)$ predominates as it does except for a finite set of k ($\leqq 9$) and d ($\leqq 109$). Similar results are shown to hold for ideal class generalizations of the group [see Gundlach, Acta. Math. **92** (1954), 309–345; MR **16,** 1000], and lower estimates can be made on the dimensionality of the cusp forms. *Harvey Cohn.*

Citations: MR 16, 1000a = F40-8.

Referred to in F40-14.

F40-11 (18, 195d)

Gundlach, Karl-Bernhard. Poincáresche und Eisensteinsche Reihen zur Hilbertschen Modulgruppe. Math. Z. **64** (1956), 339–352.

In a previous paper, the author constructed a Hecke-Petersson theory for the Hilbert modular group [Acta Math. **92** (1954), 309–345; MR **16**, 1000]. This is a hyperabelian substitution group based on a totally real algebraic field K of degree n in which the complex variable vector $(\tau^{(1)}, \cdots, \tau^{(n)})$ is restricted to lie in the region $\operatorname{Im} \tau^{(j)}>0$, $j=1, \cdots, n$. In the present paper, the author points out that one may just as well consider the 2^n groups obtained by allowing the $\tau^{(j)}$ to have an arbitrary combination of signs, since in each case, the domain of the vector is mapped into itself by all the transformations of the group.

Moreover, O. Herrmann [Math. Ann. **127** (1954), 357–400; MR **15**, 940] has discussed besides the Hilbert group, a whole series of related groups corresponding to the ideal classes of K. In the present paper, the author treats the Poincaré and Eisenstein series in the related groups $\Gamma_1(K_{\mathfrak{c}})$ ($\mathfrak{c}$ an ideal in K) in all of the 2^n regions. He obtains results similar to those in his first paper: the Poincaré series form a basis for the entire cusp forms; the Fourier coefficients of the entire cusp-forms have the estimate of the previous paper; and the Eisenstein series span the orthogonal complement (in the space of entire forms) of the cusp forms. These results hold for $r\geqq 2$ ($-r$ is the dimension of the modular form). The last section treats the linear independence of the Eisenstein series for $r=1$. *J. Lehner* (Los Alamos, N.M.).

Citations: MR 15, 940d = F40-6; MR 16, 1000a = F40-8.

Referred to in F40-13, F40-15.

F40-12 (19, 260e)

Gundlach, Karl-Bernhard. Modulfunktionen zur Hilbertschen Modulgruppe und ihre Darstellung als Quotienten ganzer Modulformen. Arch. Math. **7** (1956), 333–338.

By using a recent result of Siegel [Nachr. Akad. Wiss. Göttingen. Math.-Phys. Kl. IIa. **1955**, 71–77; MR **17**, 530], the author gives a short proof of the following theorem: Every set of $n+1$ modular functions belonging to the Hilbert modular group on n variables is algebraically dependent. Every modular function is the quotient of two entire modular forms. *J. Lehner.*

F40-13 (19, 396c)

Gundlach, Karl-Bernhard. Ganze Nichtspitzenformen der Dimension -1 zu den Hilbertschen Modulgruppen reellquadratischer Zahlkörper. Arch. Math. **7** (1957), 453–456.

In a previous paper [Math. Z. **64** (1956), 339–352; MR **18**, 195] the author has treated Poincaré and Eisenstein series defined on a series of groups related to the Hilbert modular group. In the present paper the author proves the following theorem: Every entire modular form of dimension -1 on $\Gamma(1, \mathfrak{c})$ is the sum of a linear combination of Eisenstein series of dimension -1 and a cusp form. Here $\Gamma(1, \mathfrak{c})$ is the group of unimodular matrices $\begin{pmatrix} a & b \\ c & d \end{pmatrix}$ with a, d integers in K, $b \equiv 0 \pmod{\mathfrak{c}}$, $c \equiv 0 \bmod \mathfrak{c}^{-1}$; K is a totally real algebraic field and $\mathfrak{c}$ is an ideal in K.

J. Lehner (E. Lansing, Mich.).

Citations: MR 18, 195d = F40-11.

F40-14 (19, 953d)

Herrmann, Oskar. Über den Rang der Schar der Spitzenformen zu Hilbertschen Modulgruppen beliebiger totalreeller Körper. Arch. Math. 8 (1957), 322–326.

The author extends his work on the existence of nonvanishing cusp forms [Math. Z. **64** (1956), 457–466; MR **17**, 1059] to an arbitrary totally real field of degree n. He shows in fact that the rank r of the cusp forms of dimension $-k$ of the Hilbert modular group of a fixed field satisfies:

$$\liminf_{k\to\infty} \frac{r}{k^n} \geq \frac{R|d|^{\frac{1}{2}}}{2(\pi e)^n},$$

where R is the regulator, d is the discriminant and only those k are considered for which nk is even, the other ranks being trivially zero.

The special device is the Poincaré series in τ

$$G_\mu = \sum_{(\gamma,\delta)} \sum_{\lambda} \mathrm{N}(\gamma\tau+\delta)^{-k} \exp 2\pi i \mathrm{S}\Big(\frac{\mu\lambda^2}{\partial}\Gamma\tau\Big),$$

where μ is totally positive, and $\Gamma\tau$ runs over the group matrices with $(\gamma\tau+\delta)$ as denominator while λ runs over the units mod ± 1. The different, ∂, is assumed to be principal, for convenience. Then in the Fourier series,

$$G_\mu = \sum_{\nu} a_{\mu\nu} \exp 2\pi i\, \mathrm{S}\Big(\frac{\nu\tau}{\partial}\Big),$$

$a_{\mu\nu}$ can be expanded into a sum of the type: $\delta_{\mu\nu}+$"small terms" (i.e., combinations of Kloosterman sums and Bessel functions), while from now on μ and ν are specialized to a sequence of inequivalent totally positive integers ordered by norm: $\mu_1, \mu_2, \cdots, \mu_r$. The main theorem is based on an estimate of how big r can be made without disturbing the dominance of the main diagonal of determinant $|a_{\mu\nu}|$, thus ensuring linear independence of these r series G_μ.

Harvey Cohn (Tucson, Ariz.).

Citations: MR 17, 1059a = F40-10.

F40-15 (21# 3395)

Gundlach, Karl-Bernhard. Dirichletsche Reihen zur Hilbertschen Modulgruppe. Math. Ann. **135** (1958), 294–314.

The author continues his earlier development [Math. Z. **64** (1956), 339–352; MR **18**, 195] and establishes a functional equation for his Hecke-Eisenstein series in a totally real field of degree n:

$$G_{-r}^*(\tau, s, \mathfrak{a}, \Gamma(1, \mathfrak{c})) = \sum N(m_1^*\tau+m_2^*)^{-r}|N(m_1^*\tau+m_2^*)|^{-s}$$

for m_1^*, m_2^* determined by the ideals $\mathfrak{a}$ and $\mathfrak{c}$ in a complicated manner described in the earlier paper. By a direct transformation of Fourier series, he relates the series to

$$G_{-r}^*(\tau, 2(1-r)-s, \mathfrak{q}, \Gamma(1, \mathfrak{c}))$$

for $\mathfrak{q} \sim \mathfrak{c}\mathfrak{a}^{-1}\mathfrak{d}^{-1}$ ($\mathfrak{d}$ = different). The natural restriction is Re $s+r>2$ but the author finds the residue (for $r=0$) at $s=2$, and effects analytic continuation. The main significance of the result seems to be a proof that for the Fourier coefficients $a(\mu+\kappa) = ON(\mu+\kappa)^{r/2-1/(4n+1)}$. Here μ belongs to an appropriate module (and κ is taken from a finite set of residues as required to cancel out the multipliers introduced by the translations of the modular group). The determination of κ is described in the author's work [Math. Ann. **117** (1940), 538–540]. The asymptotic result is not as strong as the author's result in the work last cited: $a(\mu) = ON(\mu)^{r/2-1/4+\varepsilon}$.

H. Cohn (Tucson, Ariz.)

Citations: MR 18, 195d = F40-11.

F40-16 (22# 12095)

Tamagawa, Tsuneo. On Hilbert's modular group. J. Math. Soc. Japan **11** (1959), 241–246.

The author determines a fundamental domain for Hilbert's modular group. The methods are quite arithmetical, and seem to be simpler than those of O. Hermann [Math. Z. **60** (1954), 148–155; MR **16**, 16].

Let $\mathfrak{k}$ be a totally real field of degree d, and $\alpha \to \alpha^{(1)}, \cdots, \alpha \to \alpha^{(d)}$ distinct isomorphisms of $\mathfrak{k}$ into the complex field. $\mathfrak{k}$ is then identified with a subset of the d-dimensional complex space C^d. Let P be the set of points $(\tau^{(1)}, \cdots, \tau^{(d)})$ in C^d such that $\mathrm{Im}(\tau^{(i)})>0$. Denote by $\mathfrak{o}$ the ring of integers of $\mathfrak{k}$. The Hilbert modular group Γ is the group of transformations

$$\tau \to \frac{\alpha\tau+\beta}{\gamma\tau+\delta} = \Big(\frac{\alpha^{(1)}\tau^{(1)}+\beta^{(1)}}{\gamma^{(1)}\tau^{(1)}+\delta^{(1)}}, \cdots, \frac{\alpha^{(d)}\tau^{(d)}+\beta^{(d)}}{\gamma^{(d)}\tau^{(d)}+\delta^{(d)}}\Big),$$

where $\tau \in P$, α, β, γ, $\delta \in \mathfrak{o}$, and $\alpha\delta-\beta\gamma=1$.

If $x \in C^d$, define $|x| = (|x^{(1)}|, \cdots, |x^{(d)}|)$; if the components are real, let $\|x\|$ be the Euclidean norm; if the components are real and positive, define $\log x = (\log x^{(1)}, \cdots, \log x^{(d)})$. Let E be the group of units and $\mathfrak{a}$ an ideal of $\mathfrak{k}$. A point $\tau=\xi+i\eta \in P$ is called $\mathfrak{a}$-reduced if: (a) $\|\xi+\alpha\| \geqq \|\xi\|$, for all $\alpha \in \mathfrak{a}$; (b) $\|\log \eta + 2 \log |\varepsilon|\| \geqq \|\log \eta\|$, for all $\varepsilon \in E$.

Let $\mathfrak{a}_1, \cdots, \mathfrak{a}_h$ be a set of representatives of the ideal classes of $\mathfrak{k}$ such that (i) each $\mathfrak{a}_i$ is integral, and (ii) $\mathfrak{a}_i$ has minimum norm among the integral ideals in its class. $\mathfrak{a}_1$ is assumed to represent the principal class.

Define F_i to be the set of all $\tau \in P$ such that (1) τ is $\mathfrak{a}_i^{-2}$-reduced, and (2) $\prod_{n=1}^{d} |\gamma^{(n)}\tau^{(n)}+\delta^{(n)}| \geqq 1$ for all pairs $(\gamma, \delta) \neq (0, 0)$ with $\gamma \in \mathfrak{a}_i$, $\delta \in \mathfrak{a}_i^{-1}$. It is shown that the infinitely many inequalities which define F_i may be replaced by a finite number among them.

Let γ_i, δ_i be integers generating $\mathfrak{a}_i$. Then there exist α_i, $\beta_i \in \mathfrak{a}_i^{-1}$ such that $\alpha_i\delta_i-\beta_i\gamma_i=1$. Let A_i denote the transformation $\tau \to (\alpha_i\tau+\beta_i)/(\gamma_i\tau+\delta_i)$. Theorem: The set $F=F_1 \cup A_2^{-1}F_2 \cup \cdots \cup A_h^{-1}F_h$ is a fundamental domain for the group Γ.

L. Greenberg (Copenhagen)

Citations: MR 16, 16a = F40-7.

F40-17 (22# 12244)

Baily, Walter L., Jr. On the Hilbert-Siegel modular space. Amer. J. Math. **81** (1959), 846–874.

The symplectic modular group $\Gamma = \mathrm{Sp}(n, Z)$ acts in a well-known manner as a properly discontinuous group of complex-analytic automorphisms on the space S_n of complex symmetric $n \times n$ matrices $Z=X+iY$ with Y positive definite [C. L. Siegel, Math. Ann. **116** (1939), 617–657; MR **1**, 203]; the proof of the theorem that the quotient space S_n/Γ can be "compactified" in such a manner that the result is (complex-analytically isomorphic to) a normal complex projective variety was given in detail by H. Cartan and I. Satake [*Séminaire H. Cartan, 1957/58*, Paris, 1958; MR **21** #2750; especially Lectures 11–17]. More generally, for a totally real algebraic number field K, with $\sigma_1, \cdots, \sigma_p$ being the distinct isomorphisms of K into the real numbers, the group $\mathrm{Sp}(n, K)$ can be imbedded in $(\mathrm{Sp}(n, R))^p$ by the isomorphism i: $M \to (M^{\sigma_1}, \cdots, M^{\sigma_p})$; the imbedded group $\Gamma^* = i(\mathrm{Sp}(n, K))$, called the Hilbert-Siegel modular group, acts as a properly discontinuous group of complex analytic automorphisms on the space $S_n{}^p = S_n \times \cdots \times S_n$ [I. I. Pyateckiĭ-Šapiro, Amer. Math. Soc. Transl. (2) **10** (1958), 13–58; MR **20**, 991b]. In this paper the author proves that the quotient space $S_n{}^p/\Gamma^*$ can also be compactified to yield a normal complex projective variety. The proof closely parallels that of Cartan and Satake [loc. cit.], but the generalization is by no means trivial.

R. C. Gunning (Princeton, N.J.)

Citations: MR 1, 203f = F50-1; MR 20# 991b = F50-17; MR 21# 2750 = F02-5.

Referred to in F40-25, F40-28, F50-30.

F40-18 (23# A356)

Klingen, Helmut

Eisensteinreihen zur Hilbertschen Modulgruppe n-ten Grades.

Nachr. Akad. Wiss. Göttingen Math.-Phys. Kl. II **1960**, 87–104.

The group considered by the author is the analogue of Siegel's modular group of order n over a totally real algebraic number-field K; the author indicates two ways of defining, for this group, the Eisenstein series of degree g (which coincide only if K has the ideal-class number 1), and proves that they both converge for $g > n+1$ and fail to do so for $g = n+1$; the difficulties which would arise (because of the so-called "failure of the method of elementary divisors" over algebraic number-fields) in trying to follow Siegel's methods are circumvented by a series of lemmas, in a manner somewhat similar to that of H. Braun in discussing the Hermitian modular group over an imaginary-quadratic field [H. Braun, Ann. of Math. (2) **50** (1949), 827–855; MR **11**, 333]. The second part of the paper generalizes to the Hilbert modular group, and to the two types of Eisenstein series introduced here, the classical formula for the Fourier coefficients of the Eisenstein series for the modular group and deduces from this the order of magnitude of these coefficients.

A. Weil (Princeton, N.J.)

Citations: MR 11, 333a = F55-1.

F40-19 (23# A3120)

Klingen, Helmut

Volumbestimmung des Fundamentalbereichs der Hilbertschen Modulgruppe n-ten Grades.

J. Reine Angew. Math. **206** (1961), 9–19.

Let K be a totally real algebraic number field of degree r over the rational field P, and let $V_n(K)$ be the volume (in the symplectic metric) of a fundamental region of the associated Hilbert modular group $\Gamma_n(K)$ of degree $n \geqq 1$. The author proves that

$$V_n(K) = 2\pi^{-rn(n+1)/2} d^{n^2+n/2} \prod_{k=1}^{n} [\{(k-1)!\}^r \zeta_K(2k)],$$

where k is the discriminant of K and $\xi_K(s)$ is the Dedekind zeta-function. Previously, formulae for $V_1(K)$ and $V_n(P)$ only have been known [C. L. Siegel, Trans. Amer. Math. Soc. **39** (1936), 209–218; Amer. J. Math. **65** (1943), 1–86; MR **4**, 242]. The author's proof is by induction on n using the result for $V_1(K)$, but considerable difficulties have to be overcome, mainly because of the fact that the fundamental region may have cusps, and this necessitates greater care in the inversion of limit processes. The volume $V_n(K)$ is a rational multiple of π.

R. A. Rankin (Glasgow)

Citations: MR 4, 242b = F50-2.

F40-20 (23# A3283)

Gundlach, Karl-Bernhard

Some new results in the theory of Hilbert's modular group.

Contributions to function theory (Internat. Colloq. Function Theory, Bombay, 1960), *pp.* 165–180. *Tata Institute of Fundamental Research, Bombay,* 1960.

Let P be the rational number field, K a totally real algebraic extension of degree n over P, I its ring of integers; then

$$\Gamma = \{A \mid A = \begin{pmatrix} a & b \\ c & d \end{pmatrix}, a, b, c, d \in I, |A| = 1\}$$

defines the Hilbert modular group. Denote conjugates by superscripts, let $\mathfrak{H}^{(j)} = \{\tau^{(j)} = x^{(j)} + iy^{(j)} \mid y^{(j)} > 0\}$. One observes that Γ acts on $\mathfrak{H} = \mathfrak{H}^{(1)} \times \mathfrak{H}^{(2)} \times \cdots \times \mathfrak{H}^{(n)}$ as a properly discontinuous group of analytic automorphisms. One may compactify $\mathfrak{H}$ by adjoining the set of parabolic cusps, obtaining a space $\overline{\mathfrak{H}}$; one then proves that $\overline{\mathfrak{H}}/\Gamma$ is a compact Hausdorff space. For some applications (e.g., a generalization of the Riemann-Roch theorem) one would need to know that $\overline{\mathfrak{H}}/\Gamma$ is a complex manifold. This, however, is actually not the case. Indeed, the author shows that (for $n > 1$) the elliptic fixed points and (at least for $n = 2$) the parabolic cusps are non-uniformizable points of $\overline{\mathfrak{H}}/\Gamma$. Furthermore, Γ always has fixed points of order 2 and 3 (fixed points of order $t > 3$ may (but need not) occur only if $\phi(2t) \mid 2n$). Some (non-hyperabelian) extension $\hat{\Gamma}$ of Γ, may, however, lead to quotient spaces $\overline{\mathfrak{H}}/\hat{\Gamma}$ that are manifolds. In the case $n = 2$ a necessary and sufficient condition is given for the existence of uniformizing parameters for the cusp ∞. This is used to construct groups $\hat{\Gamma}$ such that $\overline{\mathfrak{H}}/\hat{\Gamma}$ is a complex manifold. Example: Let K have class number one, $[K:P] = 2$, $\Gamma^* = \{A \mid A = \begin{pmatrix} a & b \\ c & d \end{pmatrix}, a, b, c, d \in I, |A| = \text{positive unit in } K\}$, $\varepsilon_0 =$ fundamental unit in K, discriminant of $K = 4p$, $p > 3$, prime, $p + 2 = m^2$ $(m \in P)$, $\varepsilon_0 \equiv +1 \pmod{p^{1/2}}$,

$$\Gamma^*(p^{1/2}) = \{A \mid A \in \Gamma^*, A \equiv \begin{pmatrix} 1 & 0 \\ 0 & 1 \end{pmatrix} \bmod p^{1/2}\};$$

$\hat{\Gamma}^*(p^{1/2}) =$ symmetric extension of $\Gamma^*(p^{1/2})$ (by $\tau' + i\tau'' \leftrightarrow \tau'' + i\tau'$). Then $\overline{\mathfrak{H}}/\hat{\Gamma}^*(p^{1/2})$ is a complex manifold. The proofs are sketchy, but their basic idea is clear enough: assuming the existence of uniformizing parameters at elliptic fixed points, or at parabolic cusps, one would obtain power series expansions, which can be shown (by elementary methods) not to exist.

E. Grosswald (Philadelphia, Pa.)

Referred to in F40-29.

F40-21 (24# A2055)

Gundlach, Karl-Bernhard

Quotientenraum und meromorphe Funktionen zur Hilbertschen Modulgruppe.

Nachr. Akad. Wiss. Göttingen Math.-Phys. Kl. II **1960**, 77–85.

Théorème: Soit Γ un groupe de transformations hyperabélien du type du groupe modulaire de Hilbert. Soit $\mathfrak{H}$ le "demi-plan généralisé", $\overline{\mathfrak{H}}$ sa complétion. Alors $\overline{\mathfrak{H}}/\Gamma$ est un espace analytique normal, analytiquement isomorphe à une variété algébrique projective.

La démonstration résulte facilement d'un théorème du référent sur le prolongement des espaces analytiques normaux [Math. Ann. **136** (1958), 97–110; MR **20** #5891], et en appliquant la méthode utilisée par W. L. Baily [Amer. J. Math. **80** (1958), 348–364; MR **20** #5890] pour traiter le cas des fonctions modulaires de Siegel. La situation est d'autant plus facile à traiter, que $\bar{\mathfrak{H}}/\Gamma$ ne diffère de $\mathfrak{H}/\Gamma$ que par un nombre fini de points (isolés).

Le théorème précédent entraîne, lorsque la dimension n est $\geqq 2$, que toute fonction méromorphe dans $\mathfrak{H}$ et invariante par Γ est égale au quotient de deux formes modulaires. L'auteur donne de ce résultat une démonstration directe (indépendante du théorème précédent et du théorème de Levi sur le prolongement des fonctions méromorphes), qui utilise le lemme suivant: soit $\mathfrak{N} \subset \mathfrak{H}$ un sous-ensemble analytique de codimension 1, invariant par Γ; soit $\delta(r)$ la dimension de l'espace vectoriel formé des traces, sur $\mathfrak{N}$, des "Spitzenformen" de poids $-r$; alors $\delta(r) = 0(r^{n-1})$. *H. Cartan* (Paris)

Citations: MR 20# 5890 = F45-5; MR 20# 5891 = F45-6.

F40-22 (24# A2056)

Siegel, Carl Ludwig

Über die algebraische Abhängigkeit von Modulfunktionen n-ten Grades.

Nachr. Akad. Wiss. Göttingen Math.-Phys. Kl. II **1960**, 257–272.

Encouragé par l'exemple donné par Gundlach pour les fonctions modulaires de Hilbert [cf. #A2055], l'auteur donne, pour $n \geqq 2$, une "démonstration directe" (c'est-à-dire indépendante de la compactification de Satake) du théorème suivant: Toute fonction modulaire (de Siegel) est le quotient de deux formes modulaires.

La démonstration a l' "avantage" de n'utiliser, de la théorie générale des fonctions analytiques de plusieurs variables, que les idées connues depuis longtemps dans la théorie classique, au sens de Weierstrass; autrement dit, elle est indépendante de toute théorie des espaces analytiques complexes. En revanche, elle nécessite quinze pages de préliminaires, au moyen de 10 lemmes où interviennent des majorations qui introduisent successivement 11 constantes absolues (c'est-à-dire ne dépendant que de n). *H. Cartan* (Paris)

F40-23 (24# A2057)

Andreotti, Aldo; Grauert, Hans

Algebraische Körper von automorphen Funktionen.

Nachr. Akad. Wiss. Göttingen Math.-Phys. Kl. II **1961**, 39–48.

Les auteurs donnent une nouvelle démonstration, indépendante de la compactification de Satake, du fait que, pour $n \geqq 2$, toute fonction modulaire de Siegel est quotient de deux formes modulaires (pour une autre démonstration récente, cf. C. L. Siegel [#A2056 ci-dessus]. Cette démonstration met en œuvre une notion nouvelle, intéressante en elle-même et susceptible d'autres applications.

Un ouvert $G \subset \mathbf{C}^m$ est "pseudo-concave" en un point $z_0 \in \partial G$ si z_0 possède un système fondamental de voisinages ouverts U tels que l'enveloppe convexe de $U \cap G$ vis-à-vis des fonctions holomorphes dans U contienne z_0 à son intérieur. On donne une condition suffisante de pseudo-concavité au moyen des fonctions plurisousharmoniques. Soit maintenant Γ un groupe d'automorphismes (holomorphes) de G; on dit que Γ opère d'une manière pseudo-concave (ou simplement que Γ est pseudo-concave) s'il existe un ouvert relativement compact G' de G tel que tout point de $\partial G'$ soit Γ-équivalent soit à un point intérieur à G' soit à un point frontière pseudo-concave de G'. Il est immédiat que tout groupe commensurable à Γ est alors aussi pseudo-concave. On a le théorème (Satz 3): si le corps $K(\Gamma)$ des fonctions méromorphes dans G et Γ-invariantes contient m éléments algébriquement indépendants $f_1, \cdots, f_m$, et si Γ est pseudo-concave, $K(\Gamma)$ est une extension algébrique finie du sous-corps engendré par $f_1, \cdots, f_m$.

Prenant alors pour G le demi-plan généralisé de Siegel, de dimension $n(n+1)/2$, et pour Γ le groupe modulaire de Siegel, les auteurs montrent facilement que, pour $n \geqq 2$, Γ opère dans G d'une manière pseudo-concave. Le corps des fonctions modulaires de Siegel a donc un degré de transcendance égal à $n(n+1)/2$; un théorème de pure algèbre permet alors de conclure qu'il est identique au sous-corps formé des quotients de formes modulaires. *H. Cartan* (Paris)

Referred to in E60-44, F55-15.

F40-24 (25# 2041)

Klingen, Helmut

Über den arithmetischen Charakter der Fourierkoeffizienten von Modulformen.

Math. Ann. **147** (1962), 176–188.

The author generalizes theorems of H. Petersson [Abh. Math. Sem. Univ. Hamburg **16** (1949), 101–113; MR **11**, 421; erratum, MR **11**, 872] on the arithmetic nature of the coefficients of an entire modular form on the principal congruence subgroups of the modular group to the principal congruence subgroups of the Hilbert modular group. Five theorems are proved. The first lays the foundation for the discussion and the last provides a far-reaching generalization of the theorems of Petersson referred to above. These are as follows. (1) Let f be an entire modular form (in the sense of K. Gundlach [Acta Math. **92** (1954), 309–345; MR **16**, 1000]) of dimension $-k$, $k \geqq 2$ on the principal congruence subgroup $\Gamma(n)$ of the Hilbert modular group Γ over a totally real field K, where n is an ideal in K. Then if all but a finite number of coefficients of f lie in a number field Σ, then so does its constant term. (2) Let f be an entire modular form orthogonal to the space of entire cusp forms on $\Gamma(n)$ of dimension $-k$, $k \geqq 2$, and let $\alpha_1, \cdots, \alpha_q$ be the values of f at a complete set of inequivalent cusps of $\Gamma(n)$. Then the Fourier coefficients of f at an arbitrary cusp of $\Gamma(n)$ all lie in the number field obtained by adjoining $\alpha_1, \cdots, \alpha_q$ to the field of the $N(n)$th roots of unity, where $N(n)$ is the norm of the ideal n. *M. Newman* (Washington, D.C.)

Citations: MR 11, 421a = F30-10; MR 16, 1000a = F40-8.

Referred to in F40-58.

F40-25 (25# 5194)

Christian, Ulrich

Über die Multiplikatorensysteme gewisser Kongruenzgruppen ganzer Hilbert-Siegelscher Modulsubstitutionen.

Math. Ann. **144** (1961), 422–459.

In two preceding papers [same Ann. **138** (1959), 363–397; MR **22** #5732; Ann. of Math. (2) **73** (1961), 134–153; MR **23** #A3284] the author derived a classification of the factors of automorphy (Multiplikatorensysteme) for the integral symplectic modular group, the subgroup of the symplectic modular group consisting of the transformations of the form $Z \to U'ZU+S$, where U is an $n \times n$ unimodular integral matrix and S is an $n \times n$ symmetric integral matrix [Siegel, Math. Ann. **116** (1939), 617–657; MR **1**, 203]. In the present paper the author extends his classification to the corresponding subgroup of some Hilbert-Siegel modular groups [Baily, Amer. J. Math. **81** (1959), 846–874; MR **22** #12244]. The techniques are similar to those used in the author's preceding papers, with some additional technical complications. *R. C. Gunning* (Princeton, N.J.)

Citations: MR 1, 203f = F50-1; MR 22# 5732 = F45-10; MR 22# 12244 = F40-17; MR 23# A3284 = F45-15.

F40-26 **(26# 2425)**

Cohn, Harvey

Cusp forms arising from Hilbert's modular functions for the field of $3^{1/2}$.

Amer. J. Math. **84** (1962), 283–305.

This is a continuation of two previous papers [same J. **82** (1960), 301–322; MR **22** #4686; ibid. **83** (1961), 33–56; MR **24** #A110] on the number of representations of an integer μ as a sum of squares in the field of $\sqrt{D}$ for $D=2, 3, 5$. In this paper an investigation is made of the "error function", here denoted by $4L(\mu)$, namely, the amount by which the number of representations of μ as a sum of 4 squares in the field of $\sqrt{3}$ differs from the appropriate divisor function. $L(\mu)$ turns out to be like Ramanujan's tau function. L is a multiplicative function whose values for powers of a fixed prime form a second-order recurring series. As might be expected, no good formula is available for $L(\mu)$ when μ is a prime. $L(\mu)=0$ if μ is a prime whose norm is $\equiv 11 \pmod{12}$. $L(\mu)$ is tabulated for primes $\mu \equiv +5 \pmod{12}$, $\mu<89$, and also for primes whose norms are less than 1000 and are $\equiv 1 \pmod{12}$. These results come out of a study of three modular forms of dimension -2 in two independent complex variables using Hecke operator methods.

D. H. Lehmer (Berkeley, Calif.)

Citations: MR 22# 4686 = E24-78; MR 24# A110 = E24-79.

F40-27 **(26# 2640)**

Christian, Ulrich

Über Hilbert-Siegelsche Modulformen und Poincarésche Reihen.

Math. Ann. **148** (1962), 257–307.

Für einen total-reellen Zahlkörper K vom Grade m und natürliches n besteht die Hilbert-Siegelsche Modulgruppe $\Gamma(n, K)$ aus allen $2n$-reihigen in K ganzen Lösungen M der Matrizengleichung

$$M^tJM = J, \qquad J = \begin{pmatrix} O & E \\ -E & O \end{pmatrix}.$$

Dabei ist E die n-reihige Einheitsmatrix. $\Gamma(n, K)$ gestattet die bekannte birationale Darstellung

$$Z \to M\langle Z\rangle = (AZ+B)(CZ+D)^{-1}, \quad M = \begin{pmatrix} A & B \\ C & D \end{pmatrix}$$

in dem kartesischen Produkt von m Siegelschen Halbräumen, wobei in den einzelnen Komponenten jeweils die Konjugierten von M zu verwenden sind. Der Verfasser legt beliebige Kongruenzgruppen Ψ der Idealstufe $\mathfrak{q}$ zugrunde; dies sind Untergruppen der symplektischen Gruppe, welche die Hauptkongruenzgruppe ($M \equiv E \bmod \mathfrak{q}$) von endlichem Index enthalten. Es werden nützliche Fundamentalmengen konstruiert, welche Vereinigung von endlich vielen Bereichen sind, denen analoge Eigenschaften zukommen wie dem Siegelschen Fundamentalbereich. Das Auftreten von Spitzen im Endlichen bedingt technische Komplikationen. Für $mn>1$ werden Multiplikatorsysteme vom Typ

$$I(M, Z) = d(M) \det{}^s (CZ+D)$$

zugelassen und s als notwendig rational erkannt. Das Hauptresultat der Arbeit (Satz 5) ist ein Darstellungssatz für die Schar $\mathfrak{m}(\Psi, I)$ der Modulformen zur Gruppe Ψ und Multiplikatorsystem I mittels Poincaréscher Reihen. Im Gegensatz zum Siegelschen Fall treten dabei Poincarésche Reihen zu Kongruenzgruppen auf, auch wenn man sich auf $\Gamma(n, K)$ beschränken würde. Hieraus erhellt die prinzipielle Rechtfertigung für den allgemeinen Ansatz des Autors. Die Methoden von Petersson, Maass, Braun in früher behandelten Fällen werden voll benutzt. Entscheidende Hilfsmittel sind die Peterssonsche Metrisierung, der von Siegel eingeführte ϕ-Operator sowie die Charakterisierung von Spitzenformen durch $\phi \det^{-s}(CZ+D)f(M\langle Z\rangle)=0$ für alle symplektischen M aus K. Abschliessende Bemerkungen beziehen sich auf die Fourierentwicklung der Poincaréschen Reihen und den Siegelschen Fall ($m=1$). *H. Klingen* (Freiburg)

Referred to in F40-29, F40-42.

F40-28 **(26# 6158)**

Katayama, Koji

On the Hilbert-Siegel modular group and abelian varieties.

J. Fac. Sci. Univ. Tokyo Sect. I **9**, 261–291 (1962).

Let $\mathfrak{o}$ be the ring of integers in a totally real algebraic number field. Isomorphism classes of polarized abelian varieties of type $\mathfrak{o}$ (injection maps of $\mathfrak{o}$ into endomorphism rings of abelian varieties are specified) belonging to certain systems are represented by points of quotient spaces of the generalized Hilbert-Siegel upper half-plane by discrete groups commensurable with the Hilbert-Siegel modular group; the fields of modular functions belonging to such groups are known to be fields of algebraic functions over **C** [Pjateckiĭ-Šapiro, Izv. Akad. Nauk SSSR Ser. Mat. **20** (1956), 53–98; MR **20** #991a; Amer. Math. Soc. Transl. (2) **10** (1958), 13–58; MR **20** #991b]. For a given ring $\mathfrak{r}$ with finite basis over **Z**, Shimura algebraico-geometrically constructed the fields of modular functions for systems of polarized abelian varieties of type $\mathfrak{r}$, and gave a general criterion for the determination of the fields of definition for such fields of modular functions; further, he treated the case in which $\mathfrak{r}$ is an order of an indefinite quaternion algebra [Shimura, Ann. of Math. (2) **70** (1959), 101–144; MR **21** #6370]. The author applies Shimura's theory to the case in which $\mathfrak{r}$ is the ring of integers in a given totally real algebraic number field, and by using one of Baily's results [Amer. J. Math. **81** (1959), 846–874; MR **22** #12244] obtains results similar to those of Shimura, that is to say, the fields of modular functions belonging to the Hilbert-Siegel (para-) modular groups are defined over **Q**.

T. Hayashida (Yokohama)

Citations: MR 20# 991b = F50-17; MR 21# 6370 = F55-11; MR 22# 12244 = F40-17.

Referred to in F40-31.

F40-29 **(28# 2256)**

Christian, Ulrich

Zur Theorie der Hilbert-Siegelschen Modulfunktionen.

Math. Ann. **152** (1963), 275–341.

Die vorliegende Arbeit setzt die früheren Untersuchungen [dieselben Ann. **148** (1962), 257–307; MR **26** #2640] des Verfassers über die Hilbert-Siegelschen Modulfunktionen fort. Damals wurden Fundamentalbereiche, Multiplikatorsysteme, Peterssonsche Metrisierung und Darstellungssatz für beliebige Kongruenzgruppen behandelt. In dem jetzigen zweiten Teil wird — grob gesprochen — die Theorie vervollständigt zu dem Umfang, der bei den Siegelschen Modulfunktionen bislang erreicht war. Es werden dabei bekannte Methoden für die Siegelschen, Hilbertschen und Hermiteschen (insbesondere bei der Behandlung der Spitzenformen) Modulfunktionen verwendet, wobei zahlreiche technische Schwierigkeiten zu überwinden sind.

Daneben bringt die Arbeit zwei interessante neuartige Resultate: (1) Die Kompaktifizierung des Quotientenraums der oberen Halbebene nach einer Kongruenzgruppe wird bezüglich lokaler Uniformisierbarkeit untersucht. Ist n der Grad der Modulfunktionen und m der Grad des zugrunde liegenden total-reellen algebraischen Zahlkörpers, so existieren für $nm>1$ stets nicht-uniformisierbare Punkte; dabei beschränkt sich der Verfasser im rationalen Fall auf die Hauptkongruenzgruppen und schliesst die volle Modulgruppe zweiten Grades aus. Bislang war dies nur bekannt für die parabolischen Spitzen der vollen Hilbertschen Modulgruppe in quadratischen Zahlkörpern [Gundlach, *Contributions to function theory* (Internat. Colloq. Function Theory, Bombay, 1960), pp. 165–180, Tata Inst. Fundamental Res., Bombay, 1960; MR **23** #A3283]. Zum Beweise werden Hilfsmittel der Humbertschen Reduktionstheorie und Thetareihen herangezogen. (2) Für die Siegelschen Modulfunktionen n-ten Grades zur Hauptkongruenzgruppe q-ter Stufe wird eine notwendige und hinreichende Bedingung dafür angegeben, dass sich jede Modulfunktion rational durch Eisensteinreihen ausdrücken lässt, nämlich: n ungerade oder n gerade und $q=1, 2, 4, p^\nu, 2p^\nu$ ($\nu=1, 2, 3, \cdots$) mit einer ungeraden Primzahl p. Dieses Ergebnis beruht auf Trennungseigenschaften der Eisensteinreihen im Endlichen. *H. Klingen* (Freiburg)

Citations: MR 23# A3283 = F40-20; MR 26# 2640 = F40-27.

Referred to in F40-42, F45-23, F50-34, F50-35.

F40-30 (29# 1186)

Gundlach, Karl-Bernhard

Die Bestimmung der Funktionen zur Hilbertschen Modulgruppe des Zahlkörpers $Q(\sqrt{5})$.

Math. Ann. **152** (1963), 226–256.

La determinazione delle funzioni invarianti per il gruppo modulare hilbertiano Γ del campo $K=Q(\sqrt{5})$—ove Q è il campo razionale—si vale in modo essenziale dello studio di una particolare funzione Θ (prodotto di 10 funzioni thêta speciali) della quale interessano, tra l'altro, gli zeri appartenenti al campo fondamentale del gruppo Γ. La conoscenza della funzione Θ consente di determinare le forme modulari relative al gruppo Γ ed in conseguenza le funzioni invarianti. Nella dimostrazione vengono usate proprietà speciali del campo fondamentale del gruppo Γ; non sembra quindi che i risultati ottenuti possano estendersi direttamente a tipi di campi diversi da K. *M. Rosati* (Rome)

Referred to in F40-36, F40-51, F50-41, F55-27.

F40-31 (29# 5824)

Katayama, Koji

On the Hilbert-Siegel modular group and abelian varieties. II.

J. Fac. Sci. Univ. Tokyo Sect. I **9**, 433–467 (1963).

Es sei F ein total reeller algebraischer Zahlkörper vom Grade r über dem Körper der rationalen Zahlen. Es sei $\mathfrak{g}$ der Ring der ganzen Zahlen von F. Für eine natürliche Zahl n sei 1_n die n-reihige Einheitsmatrix und $I=\begin{pmatrix} 0 & 1_n \\ -1_n & 0 \end{pmatrix}$. Für jede Primstelle $\mathfrak{p}$ von F sei $F_\mathfrak{p}$ die $\mathfrak{p}$-Vervollständigung von F. Für die endlichen Primstellen $\mathfrak{p}$ sei $\mathfrak{g}_\mathfrak{p}$ der Ring der ganzen Zahlen von $F_\mathfrak{p}$ und $\mathfrak{u}_\mathfrak{p}$ die Gruppe der Einheiten von $F_\mathfrak{p}$. Der Verfasser betrachtet dann die Gruppen

$$G = \{\sigma \in \mathrm{GL}(2n, F) \mid \sigma I^t\sigma = m(\sigma)I,\ m(\sigma) \in F\},$$

$$G_\mathfrak{p} = \{\sigma \in \mathrm{GL}(2n, F_\mathfrak{p}) \mid \sigma I^t\sigma = m(\sigma)I,\ m(\sigma) \in F_\mathfrak{p}\},$$

$$\mathfrak{U}_\mathfrak{p} = \{\sigma \in \mathrm{GL}(2n, \mathfrak{g}_\mathfrak{p}) \mid \sigma I^t\sigma = m(\sigma)I,\ m(\sigma) \in \mathfrak{u}_\mathfrak{p}\}.$$

Zwei $\mathfrak{g}$-Gitter $\mathfrak{M}$, $\mathfrak{N}$ im $2n$-dimensionalen Zeilenvektorraum $\mathfrak{V}=\mathfrak{V}(2n, F)$ über F heißen G-äquivalent, wenn es ein $\sigma \in G$ mit $\mathfrak{M}\sigma=\mathfrak{N}$ gibt. Analog wird für endliches $\mathfrak{p}$ die $\mathfrak{G}_\mathfrak{p}$-Äquivalenz zweier $\mathfrak{g}_\mathfrak{p}$-Gitter $\mathfrak{M}_\mathfrak{p}$, $\mathfrak{N}_\mathfrak{p}$ von $\mathfrak{V}_\mathfrak{p}=\mathfrak{V}(2n, F_\mathfrak{p})$ definiert. Die beiden $\mathfrak{g}$-Gitter $\mathfrak{M}$, $\mathfrak{N}$ heißen zu demselben Geschlecht gehörig, wenn für jedes endliche $\mathfrak{p}$ die $\mathfrak{p}$-Vervollständigungen $\mathfrak{M}_\mathfrak{p}$, $\mathfrak{N}_\mathfrak{p}$ von $\mathfrak{M}$, $\mathfrak{N}$ $G_\mathfrak{p}$-äquivalent sind. Das erste Resultat der vorliegenden Arbeit ist dann: Jedes Geschlecht von $\mathfrak{g}$-Gittern besteht aus genau h G-Äquivalenzklassen, wobei h die Klassenzahl von F ist (Theorem 1). Es seien $\mathfrak{p}_1, \cdots, \mathfrak{p}_r$ die unendlichen Primstellen von F. Es werden dann die direkten Produkte $J_{G,\infty}=G_{\mathfrak{p}_1}\times\cdots\times G_{\mathfrak{p}_r}$ und

$$J_{G,0} = \{s \in \prod_{\mathfrak{p}<\infty} G_\mathfrak{p} \mid s_\mathfrak{p} \in \mathfrak{U}_\mathfrak{p} \text{ für fast alle } \mathfrak{p} < \infty\}$$

betrachtet, wobei $s_\mathfrak{p}$ jeweils die $\mathfrak{p}$-Koordinate von s ist. Das direkte Produkt $J_G=J_{G,\infty}\times J_{G,0}$ heißt die Idelgruppe von G. Unter Benutzung früherer Ergebnisse des Verfassers [dasselbe J. **9** (1962), 261–291; MR **26** #6158] konstruiert der Verfasser zu jedem Element von J_G eine polarisierte Abelsche Mannigfaltigkeit vom Typ $\mathfrak{g}$ und zeigt, daß auf diese Weise auch alle polarisierten Abelschen Mannigfaltigkeiten vom Typ $\mathfrak{g}$ erhalten werden (Theorem 5). Die Elemente $D_\infty \in J_{G,\infty}$ können in der Form

$$D_\infty = \left(\begin{pmatrix} A^{(1)} & B^{(1)} \\ C^{(1)} & D^{(1)} \end{pmatrix}, \cdots, \begin{pmatrix} A^{(r)} & B^{(r)} \\ C^{(r)} & D^{(r)} \end{pmatrix}\right)$$

geschrieben werden, wobei $A^{(i)}$, $B^{(i)}$, $C^{(i)}$, $D^{(i)}$ n-reihige quadratische Matrizen mit reellen Elementen sind. Es sei $\mathfrak{K}_\infty=\{D_\infty \in J_{G,\infty} \mid A^{(i)}=D^{(i)}, C^{(i)}=-B^{(i)} \text{ für } i=1, \cdots, r\}$ und $\mathfrak{K}=\mathfrak{K}_\infty\times\mathfrak{U}_0$ mit $\mathfrak{U}_0=\prod_{\mathfrak{p}<\infty}\mathfrak{U}_\mathfrak{p}$. Zu zwei Elementen $D, D' \in J_G$ seien gemäß Theorem 5 polarisierte Abelsche Mannigfaltigkeiten $\wp$, $\wp'$ vom Typ $\mathfrak{g}$ konstruiert. Der Verfasser zeigt, daß $\wp$ und $\wp'$ genau dann isomorph sind, wenn $GD\mathfrak{K}=GD'\mathfrak{K}$ gilt. Der zu G gehörige Heckesche Ring $\mathfrak{R}$ wird mit Hilfe von $J_{G,0}$ und $\mathfrak{U}_0$ in Anlehnung an Shimura [Ann. of Math. (2) **76** (1962), 237–294] definiert. Der Verfasser zeigt, daß $\mathfrak{R}$ kommutativ ist. Aufgrund von Theorem 1 gilt eine Zerlegung $J_{G,0}=\bigcup_{\lambda=1}^h Gs_\lambda\mathfrak{U}_0$ mit gewissen $s_\lambda \in J_{G,0}$. Mit einem geeigneten $D_\infty \in J_{G,\infty}$ wird $D_\lambda=D_\infty\times s_\lambda \in J_G$ gesetzt und gemäß Theorem 5 eine zu D_λ gehörige polarisierte Abelsche Mannigfaltigkeit A_λ vom Typ $\mathfrak{g}$ konstruiert. Man setze $A=A_1\times\cdots\times A_h$. Der Verfasser zeigt dann, daß jedes Element von $\mathfrak{R}$ eine Isogenie von A definiert. *E. Gottschling* (Berlin)

Citations: MR 26# 6158 = F40-28.

F40-32 (30# 4729)

Cohn, Harvey

On the shape of the fundamental domain of the Hilbert modular group.

Proc. Sympos. Pure Math., Vol. VIII, pp. 190–202. *Amer. Math. Soc., Providence, R.I.*, 1965.

As several authors (e.g., H. Maass [S.-B. Heidelberger Akad. Wiss. **1940**, no. 2 (1940); MR **2**, 213]) have previously shown, there always exists a fundamental domain of the Hilbert modular group of a totally real algebraic number field K with $|\gamma z+\delta|^2|\gamma' z'+\delta'|^2\cdots \geqq 1$, where γ, δ are integers in K and the accent denotes the conjugates with respect to the rational field Q. Actually, a part of the boundary consists of varieties defined thus with the equality sign. The author calls this part of the boundary the "floor". He restricts himself to quadratic fields $K=Q(\sqrt{m})$ with class number 1, and improves earlier estimates of the floor. He shows that the floor consists, in general, of more than one such surface, except perhaps for $m=2, 3, 13, 21$, or $m\equiv 5 \bmod 24$. Eventually he determines all elliptic vertices. The fact that these lie on the floor allow an estimate (which he does not give explicitly) of the class number of quadratic extensions of K generated by roots of unity (whose orders must be 3, 4, or 5) in terms of data of the fundamental domain. *M. Eichler* (Basel)

Citations: MR 2, 213d = F40-1.

Referred to in R26-31.

F40-33 **(31# 387)**

Lal, Sunder

On the Fourier coefficients of Hilbert-Siegel modular forms.

Math. Z. **88** (1965), 207–243.

Für Hauptkongruenzuntergruppen einer Hilbert-Siegelschen Modulgruppe werden Modulformen mit geeigneten Multiplikatorsystemen untersucht. Jeder solchen Modulform f wird nach dem Heckeschen Verfahren eine Linearkombination φ Eisensteinscher Reihen zugeordnet, deren Fourierentwicklung sich explizit angeben läßt. Das Integral, das einen Fourierkoeffizienten von $f-\varphi$ darstellt, wird mittels einer Farey-Zerlegung abgeschätzt. Bei dieser Methode von Siegel ergeben sich hier zusätzliche Komplikationen, da jeder Fundamentalbereich den endlichen Rand des Darstellungsraumes berührt und $f-\varphi$ im allgemeinen keine Spitzenform ist. Falls man an die Stufe der zugrundeliegenden Kongruenzgruppe eine geeignete Bedingung stellt, erhält man eine Abschätzung der Fourierkoeffizienten von f, die zahlentheoretische Konsequenzen hat: Verfasser verallgemeinert eine asymptotische Formel von Siegel für die Anzahl ganzer Darstellungen einer Matrix durch eine ganze, total positive quadratische Form über einem total reellen, algebraischen Zahlkörper.

J. Spilker (Freiburg)

F40-34 **(31# 4769)**

Cohn, Harvey

Some elementary aspects of modular functions in several variables.

Bull. Amer. Math. Soc. **71** (1965), 681–704.

This is an expository lecture delivered at a meeting of the American Mathematical Society. The author chiefly treats Hilbert modular functions for quadratic number fields, fundamental domains of the underlying groups, and representation of integers as sums of squares. The procedures followed are generalisations of those known for elliptic modular functions; they are explained here as such. The paper concludes with some remarks on compactification and the behaviour of finite fixed points of the group.

M. Eichler (Basel)

F40-35 **(32# 2382)**

Gundlach, Karl-Bernhard

Zusammenhänge zwischen Modulformen in einer und in zwei Variablen.

Nachr. Akad. Wiss. Göttingen Math.-Phys. Kl. II **1965**, 47–88.

Verfasser entwickelt eine neue Methode zur Behandlung von Modulformen zu Hilbertschen Modulgruppen in einem reell-quadratischen Zahlkörper: Durch Restriktion der Modulformen auf eindimensionale analytische Untermengen wird die Theorie der automorphen Formen einer Variablen für die Hilbertschen Modulformen nutzbar gemacht.

Betrachtet wird eine beliebige Gruppe G, die zur engeren Hilbertschen Modulgruppe eines reell-quadratischen Zahlkörpers kommensurabel ist und wie üblich als Gruppe linear gebrochener Abbildungen auf dem Produkt zweier Halbebenen H operiert. Neben G wird stets die zugehörige symmetrische Gruppe betrachtet, was im Hinblick auf Strukturuntersuchungen des Körpers der automorphen Funktionen wichtig ist. Diese ist eine Erweiterung von G vom Index zwei, welche aus G durch Hinzufügen der Variablenvertauschung entsteht. Ihre Existenz stellt eine Bedingung für G dar, welche etwa bei der engeren Hilbertschen Modulgruppe erfüllt ist. Es sei $\{G, -r, v\}$ die Schar der Modulformen bezüglich G der Dimension $-r$ zum Multiplikatorsystem v und A eine eindimensionale irreduzible analytische Menge in H. Die Restriktion der Funktionen aus $\{G, -r, v\}$ auf A liefert eine Abbildung $\sigma_r: \{G, -r, v\} \to \{{}_1G, -r, v\}$, wobei ${}_1G$ die Fixuntergruppe von A in G ist und die letztgenannte Schar aus den automorphen Formen auf der Normalisierung von A bezüglich ${}_1G$ besteht. Hieraus resultiert die Zerlegung $\{G, -r, v\} = B_r \oplus \text{Kern}\,\sigma_r$ mit $B_r \simeq \text{Bild}\,\sigma_r$. Mit Hilfe der früheren Ergebnisse des Verfassers [dieselben Nachr. IIa **1958**, 59–66; MR **20** #1793] und Shimizu [Ann. of Math. (2) **77** (1963), 33–71; MR **26** #2641] wird eine Rangformel für $\{G, -r, v\}$ aufgestellt. Die Dimension dieser Schar ist ein quadratischer Ausdruck in r, in dem der Koeffizient des linearen Gliedes und das konstante Glied noch von r modulo q abhängen. Der Modul q ist durch die Fixpunktordnungen von G allein bestimmt. Ausserdem bekommt man vermöge des Riemann-Rochschen Satzes eine Rangformel für $\{{}_1G, -r, v\}$. Ist nun σ_r für alle hinreichend grossen r surjektiv, so wird aus obiger Zerlegung auf Grund der beiden Rangformeln geschlossen, dass $\text{Kern}\,\sigma_r = 0$ für kleine r ist. Hierdurch gelingt ein neuer Zugang zu den Modulformen kleinen Gewichtes r.

Die Brauchbarkeit der Methode, die ja von der geeigneten Wahl von A abhängt, demonstriert der Verfasser an mehreren Beispielen. Unter anderem werden sämtliche symmetrischen Modulformen zur engeren Hilbertschen Modulgruppe des Körpers $Q(\sqrt{3})$ für kleine r explizit bestimmt und Aussagen über Darstellungsanzahlen gewisser quadratischer Formen gemacht. In einer inzwischen erschienenen Arbeit [J. Reine Angew. Math. **220** (1965), 109–153] benutzt der Verfasser seine Methode zum Nachweis der Rationalität des Körpers der symmetrischen Hilbertschen Modulfunktionen zu $Q(\sqrt{2})$ und $Q(\sqrt{3})$.

H. Klingen (Freiburg)

Citations: MR 20# 1793 = F50-18; MR 26# 2641 = F55-14.

Referred to in F40-36.

F40-36 **(33# 1290)**

Gundlach, Karl-Bernhard

Die Bestimmung der Funktionen zu einigen Hilbertschen Modulgruppen.

J. Reine Angew. Math. **220** (1965), 109–153.

In den letzten Jahren konnte das schwierige Problem der Strukturuntersuchung des graduierten Ringes der Modulformen in mehreren Veränderlichen in einigen Spezialfällen gelöst werden. J.-I. Igusa [Amer. J. Math. **84** (1962), 175–200; MR **25** #5040] und E. Freitag [Nachr. Akad. Wiss. Göttingen Math.-Phys. Kl. II **1965**, 151–157] behandelten die Siegelsche Modulgruppe zweiten Grades, Verfasser [Math. Ann. **152** (1963), 226–256; MR **29** #1186] die symmetrische Hilbertsche Modulgruppe zu $Q(\sqrt{5})$, W. F. Hammond (gleichzeitig und unabhängig zur vorliegenden Arbeit) die symmetrische Hilbertsche Modulgruppe zu $Q(\sqrt{2})$ und $Q(\sqrt{5})$, E. Freitag (erscheint demnächst) die erweiterte Hermitesche Modulgruppe zweiten Grades zu $Q(\sqrt{-1})$ und eine spezielle Siegelsche Stufengruppe zweiten Grades. In allen diesen Fällen erwies sich der Körper der Modulfunktionen als rational.

Verfasser untersucht in der vorliegenden Arbeit die Hilbertschen Modulgruppen $\Gamma_{Q(\sqrt{2})}$ und $\Gamma_{Q(\sqrt{3})}$ der Zahlkörper $Q(\sqrt{2})$, $Q(\sqrt{3})$, wobei die im zweiten Fall mögliche Erweiterung vom Index 2 und in beiden Fällen die durch Hinzunahme der Variablenvertauschung entstehende Symmetrisierung bereits vollzogen seien. Ferner muss bei $Q(\sqrt{3})$ zwischen den Operationsgebieten H (Produkt zweier oberer Halbebenen) und H^* (Produkt der oberen und der unteren Halbebene) unterschieden werden. Die entsprechenden linearen Scharen von Modulformen der Dimension $-r$ zum Multiplikatorsystem 1 seien $\{\Gamma_{Q(\sqrt{2})}, -r\}$, $\{\Gamma_{Q(\sqrt{3})}, -r\}$ und $\{\Gamma^*_{Q(\sqrt{3})}, -r\}$. Die Dimension

$-r$ stellt sich notwendig als ganzzahlig heraus. Die Struktursätze lauten: (1) Jede Funktion aus $\{\Gamma_{Q(\sqrt{2})}, -r\}$ ist für gerades r isobares Polynom in den Eisensteinreihen der Dimension -2, -4, -6. Der Fall eines ungeraden r wird durch die Formel $\{\Gamma_{Q(\sqrt{2})}, -r\} = \{\Gamma_{Q(\sqrt{2})}, -(r-9)\}GH$ auf den vorigen Fall zurückgeführt, wobei G, H aus Eisensteinreihen der Dimension -1 zu Kongruenzgruppen explizit konstruiert werden. (2) Jede Funktion aus $\{\Gamma_{Q(\sqrt{3})}, -r\}$ ist isobares Polynom in den drei Eisensteinreihen der Dimension -2, -3, -4. Jede Funktion aus $\{\Gamma^*_{Q(\sqrt{3})}, -r\}$ ist isobares Polynom in den drei Eisensteinreihen der Dimension -1, -4, -6. Die zugehörigen Körper von Modulfunktionen sind also in allen drei Fällen rational und können von den entsprechenden Eisensteinreihenquotienten erzeugt werden.

Die Methode des Verfassers besteht darin, dass durch Projektion der Hilbertschen Modulformen auf geeignete eindimensionale analytische Untermengen die Theorie der automorphen Funktionen einer Variablen nutzbar gemacht wird. Verfasser hatte dieses Vorgehen, in welchem die Rangformel von H. Shimizu [Ann. of Math. (2) **77** (1963), 33–71; MR **26** #2641] eine wesentliche Rolle spielt in Nachr. Akad. Wiss. Göttingen Math.-Phys. Kl. II **1965**, 47–88 [MR **32** #2382] entwickelt und dokumentiert nun die Tragweite seiner Betrachtungen. Bei den vorliegenden Fällen ist die Wahl der analytischen Untermengen von recht einfacher Natur; z.B. wird man in den beiden ersten Fällen bei der Projektion auf die rationale Modulgruppe geführt. Im Verlaufe des Beweises müssen gemäss [Verfasser, loc. cit.] spezielle Modulformen konstruiert werden. Alle diese Funktionen sind von bekannter Bauart, nämlich Eisensteinreihen zu Kongruenzgruppen oder Thetareihen. *H. Klingen* (Freiburg)

Citations: MR 25# 5040 = F50-22; MR 26# 2641 = F55-14; MR 29# 1186 = F40-30; MR 32# 2382 = F40-35.

Referred to in F40-57.

F40-37 (33# 4015)

Christian, Ulrich

Über die Uniformisierbarkeit elliptischer Fixpunkte Hilbert-Siegelscher Modulgruppen.

J. Reine Angew. Math. **223** (1966), 113–130.

Ψ sei eine Kongruenzuntergruppe einer Hilbert-Siegelschen Modulgruppe. Z sei ein elliptischer Fixpunkt von Ψ in der verallgemeinerten oberen Halbebene $\mathfrak{Z}$, k die komplexe Dimension von $\mathfrak{Z}$ und $\Psi(Z)$ die Untergruppe von Ψ, die Z fest läßt. Eine geeignete biholomorphe Abbildung bildet $\mathfrak{Z}$ so auf ein beschränktes Gebiet ab, daß Z in den Nullpunkt und $\Psi(Z)$ in eine Gruppe $\Phi(Z)$ linearer Transformationen mit Fixpunkt O übergeht. Uniformisierbarkeit von Z im Quotientenraum $\Psi\backslash\mathfrak{Z}$ ist gleichbedeutend mit der Existenz von k konvergenten Potenzreihen der Form $P_t(W) = \sum_{j=1}^{\infty} H_j^t(W)$, $H_j^t(W)$ homogenes Polynom vom Grad j, $1 \leq t \leq k$, die gegen $\Phi(Z)$ invariant sind, und die Eigenschaft haben, daß jede in einer Umgebung von O konvergente und gegen $\Phi(Z)$ invariante Potenzreihe sich als Potenzreihe in den $P_t(W)$ schreiben läßt. Verfasser beweist den folgenden Sachverhalt. Bezeichnet $\mathfrak{H}(Z)$ die Algebra, welche durch die gegen $\Phi(Z)$ invarianten homogenen Polynome über **C** erzeugt wird und $d(Z)$ die Elementezahl eines minimalen Erzeugendensystems von $\mathfrak{H}(Z)$ über **C**, so ist Z genau dann uniformisierbar, wenn $d(Z) = k$ ist. Ist $d(Z) = k$, so ist jedes minimale Erzeugendensystem von $\mathfrak{H}(Z)$ in $\mathfrak{H}_h(Z)$ enthalten ($h = \text{ord}\,\Phi(Z)$, $\mathfrak{H}_h(Z)$ = Teilmenge der Polynome der Ordnung $\leq h$ in $\mathfrak{H}(Z)$). Ist $A \subset \mathfrak{H}_h(Z)$ so beschaffen, daß jedes Polynom aus $\mathfrak{H}_h(Z)$ sich als Polynom in Elementen aus A schreiben läßt, so ist $d(Z) = k$, also Z uniformisierbar, dann und nur dann, wenn es in A eine Teilmenge M aus k Elementen gibt, die die Variablen trennen. Ob die Elemente von M die Variablen trennen, hängt von der Lösungsanzahl eines gewissen mit Elementen von M gebildeten Gleichungssystems ab. *K.-B. Gundlach* (Münster)

F40-38 (33# 4016)

Cohn, Harvey

A numerical survey of the floors of various Hilbert fundamental domains.

Math. Comp. **19** (1965), 594–605.

The groups considered in this paper are groups of linear fractional transformations of the space of two complex variables $Z = X + iY$, $Z' = X' + iY'$, with Y and Y' positive, onto itself via $Z \to (\alpha Z + \beta)/(\gamma Z + \delta)$, $Z' \to (\alpha' Z' + \beta')/(\gamma' Z' + \delta')$, where the Greek letters are integers in the quadratic field generated by the square root of k, with $k = 2, 3, 5, 6, 7, 11, 13, 14, 17, 21, 29, 33$, and satisfy $\alpha\delta - \beta\gamma = \varepsilon$, $\alpha'\delta' - \beta'\gamma' = \varepsilon'$ with ε and ε' positive units in the field.

The object of the paper is to explore the lower parts, called the floor, of the three-dimensional boundary of the fundamental region of each group. Only the case $k = 5$ gives a simple floor consisting of a single analytic piece. The reader should consult the paper for the many details, especially of the case $k = 6$. *D. H. Lehmer* (Berkeley, Calif.)

Referred to in F40-45, F40-53, F40-54.

F40-39 (33# 5573)

Cohn, Harvey

Note on how Hilbert modular domains become increasingly complicated.

J. Math. Anal. Appl. **15** (1966), 55–59.

K sei ein total-reeller Zahlkörper vom Grad $n > 1$, die Klassenzahl von K sei 1, und Γ sei die erweiterte Hilbertsche Modulgruppe zu K. Es ist bekannt, daß dann der Fundamentalbereich von Γ "nach unten" durch endlich viele Hyperflächen der Form $|N(c\tau + d)| = 1$ mit teilerfremden ganzen Zahlen c, d aus K berandet wird. Verfasser zeigt durch einige einfache zahlentheoretische Betrachtungen: Ist n eine Primzahl, k eine natürliche Zahl, und ist die Diskriminante von K größer als eine von n und k abhängige Schranke, so treten mindestens k Hyperflächen der Form $|N(c\tau + d)| = 1$ mit verschiedenen Werten von $|N(c)|$, also etwa $|N(c_j\tau + d_j)| = 1$, $1 \leq j \leq k$, mit $|N(c_1)| < |N(c_2)| < \cdots < |N(c_k)|$ als Randflächen des Fundamentalbereichs von Γ auf. *K.-B. Gundlach* (Münster)

F40-40 (34# 1281)

Hammond, William F.

The modular groups of Hilbert and Siegel.

Amer. J. Math. **88** (1966), 497–516.

$\mathfrak{S}_n$ bezeichne die Siegelsche obere Halbebene n-ten Grades, also die Menge der n-reihigen quadratischen Matrizen $Z = X + iY$ mit $Z = {}^tZ$ und $Y > 0$. $\text{Sp}(n, \mathbf{R})$ bezeichne die symplektische Gruppe n-ten Grades, die Gruppe der analytischen Automorphismen von $\mathfrak{S}_n$. Durch

$$\varphi_0((z_1, \cdots, z_n)) = \text{diag}(z_1, \cdots, z_n)$$

erhält man eine holomorphe Einbettung von $\mathfrak{S}_1{}^n = \mathfrak{S}_1 \times \cdots \times \mathfrak{S}_1$ in $\mathfrak{S}_n$ und gleichzeitig für die Gruppe $\text{Sp}(1, \mathbf{R})^n = \text{Sp}(1, \mathbf{R}) \times \cdots \times \text{Sp}(1, \mathbf{R})$ von analytischen Automorphismen von $S_1{}^n$ einen natürlichen Monomorphismus $\Phi_0 : \text{Sp}(1, \mathbf{R})^n \to \text{Sp}(n, \mathbf{R})$ mit $\Phi_0(S)(\varphi_0(z)) = \varphi_0(S(z))$ für $S \in \text{Sp}(1, \mathbf{R})^n$ und $z \in S_1{}^n$. Ist $N \in \text{Sp}(n, \mathbf{R})$, so ist $\varphi = N\varphi_0$ eine weitere holomorphe Einbettung von $\mathfrak{S}_1{}^n$ in $\mathfrak{S}_n$ mit einem zugehörigen Monomorphismus $\Phi(S) = N\Phi_0(S)N^{-1}$. Die Hilbertsche Modulgruppe $\text{Sp}(1, K)$ eines totalreellen Zahlkörpers K vom Grad n läßt sich bekanntlich in natürlicher Weise als Untergruppe von $\mathrm{Sp}(1, \mathbf{R})^n$ auffassen. Verfasser bezeichnet eine Einbettung $\varphi = N\varphi_0$ als modular, wenn sie die beiden folgenden Eigenschaften hat: (1) $\Phi(\mathrm{Sp}(1, K))$ liegt in der Siegelschen Modulgruppe n-ten Grades $\mathrm{Sp}(n, \mathbf{Z})$, und (2) ist f eine ganze Siegelsche Modulform vom Gewicht w, so ist $f\varphi$ eine ganze Hilbertsche Modulform vom Gewicht w. Verfasser beweist: Eine modulare Einbettung existiert dann und nur dann, wenn die engere Idealklasse der Differente von K in der engeren Idealklassengruppe von K ein Quadrat ist. Im quadratischen Falle ($n = 2$) ist das gleichbedeutend damit, daß die Diskriminante von K die Summe zweier Quadrate ist. Die Einbettung hat dann die Form $\varphi(z) = L(A\varphi_0(z)^t A)$, worin A eine nicht-singuläre quadratische Matrix und $L \in \mathrm{Sp}(n, \mathbf{Z})$ ist. Ist $n \leqq 7$, so kann man erreichen, daß A orthogonal ist.

K sei jetzt reell-quadratisch, die Diskriminante von K sei die Summe zweier Quadrate und φ sei eine feste modulare Einbettung, o.B.d.A. mit $L = E$ und orthogonalem A. Ist f eine ganze Siegelsche Modulform, so stellt sich heraus, daß $f\varphi(z_1, z_2)$ eine ganze Hilbertsche Modulform, $f\varphi_0(z_1, z_2)$ in jeder Variablen eine ganze Modulform zur rationalen Modulgruppe und $f\varphi(z, z) = f\varphi_0(z, z)$ ist. Hieraus zeigt Verfasser, daß für die beiden Eisensteinreihen G_4 und G_6 zur Siegelschen Modulgruppe $G_4\varphi(z, z)$ und $G_6\varphi(z, z)$ algebraisch unabhängig sind, während für das Produkt Θ der 10 Thetareihen vom Geschlecht 2 sich $\Theta\varphi(z, z) = 0$ ergibt, woraus der bemerkenswerte Satz folgt, daß $G_4\varphi$, $G_6\varphi$ und $(\Theta\varphi)^2$ algebraisch unabhängige ganze symmetrische Modulformen zur Hilbertschen Modulgruppe sind. Eine genauere Untersuchung der Nullstellen der Thetafunktionen ergibt noch, daß im Falle, daß K der quadratische Zahlkörper der Diskriminanten 8 ist, sich jede ganze symmetrische Modulform zur Hilbertschen Modulgruppe als Polynom in h_2, $G_6\varphi$, $(\Theta_2\varphi)^2$ schreiben läßt, worin h_2 die Eisensteinreihe der Dimension -2 zur Hilbertschen Modulgruppe und Θ_2 ein gewisses Teilprodukt von Θ ist. *K.-B.* Gundlach (Münster)

Referred to in F40-41, F40-44, F40-51.

F40-41 (34# 7468)

Hammond, William F.

The modular groups of Hilbert and Siegel.

Algebraic Groups and Discontinuous Subgroups (Proc. Sympos. Pure Math., Boulder, Colo., 1965), *pp.* 358–360. *Amer. Math. Soc., Providence, R.I.,* 1966.

Brief outline of another paper by the author [Amer. J. Math. **87** (1966), 497–516; MR **34** #1281].

M. Eichler (Basel)

Citations: MR 34# 1281 = F40-40.

F40-42 (36# 431)

Christian, Ulrich

Some remarks on symplectic groups, modular groups and Poincaré's series.

Amer. J. Math. **89** (1967), 319–362.

Die vorliegende Arbeit setzt die Untersuchungen des Verfassers [Math. Ann. **148** (1962), 257–307; MR **26** #2640; ibid. **152** (1963), 275–341; MR **28** #2256] über Hilbert-Siegelsche Modulformen fort. Die ergänzenden Ergebnisse betreffen zunächst ein Kriterium für die Uniformisierbarkeit elliptischer Fixpunkte und das Verschwinden der ersten Homologiegruppe des Quotientenraumes, der aus dem Siegelschen Halbraum durch Identifizieren von bezüglich der Siegelschen Modulgruppe äquivalenten Punkten entsteht. Der Beweis für die letzte Behauptung wird durch die Angabe von Erzeugenden der Modulgruppe erbracht, die sämtlich Fixpunkte besitzen.

Der größere Teil der Arbeit betrifft Poincarésche Reihen zu Hilbert-Siegelschen Modulgruppen. Es werden zwei Typen eingeführt. Der erste entsteht durch Quersummation aus den Fourierentwicklungen von Modulformen, der zweite wird gebildet durch Summation von festen Potenzen der Funktionaldeterminanten, wobei man die Gruppe auf dem Einheitskreis operieren läßt. Um auch Nichtspitzenformen zu erfassen, werden Poincarésche Reihen angesetzt, welche den niederdimensionalen Randkomponenten der oberen Halbebene in bestimmter Weise entsprechen. Der vom Referenten [ibid. **168** (1967), 157–170; MR **34** #7828] im Siegelschen Fall gemachte Ansatz kann übertragen werden. Verfasser läßt Kongruenzgruppen, nicht-ganzzahlige Gewichte und Multiplikatorsysteme zu. Es werden detaillierte Aussagen über die gleichmäßige Konvergenz gemacht und frühere Beweise vereinfacht. Die Resultate gehen auch im Siegelschen Fall über die Ergebnisse des Referenten hinaus bezüglich ihrer Unabhängigkeit von weiteren Parametern, welche in die Reihen eingehen. Anwendungen beziehen sich auf die Separation von Punkten der oberen Halbebene durch Modulfunktionen. Man vergleiche in diesem Zusammenhang auch W. L. Baily, Jr. and A. Borel [Ann. of Math. (2) **84** (1966), 442–528; MR **35** #6870].

H. Klingen (Freiburg)

Citations: MR 26# 2640 = F40-27; MR 28# 2256 = F40-29; MR 34# 7828 = F50-49; MR 35# 6870 = F50-31.

F40-43 (36# 2835)

Cohn, Harvey

How perturbations satisfying Hilbert's modular group affect the invariant metric.

J. Analyse Math. **18** (1967), 53–59.

In an earlier paper [*Lectures on functions of a complex variable*, pp. 341–348, Univ. Michigan Press, Ann Arbor, 1955; MR **17**, 15] the author showed that a series expansion $P(z)$ arising in the study of automorphic forms for the classical modular group (a triple indefinite integral of the Eisenstein series $E_4(z)$) could be derived as a perturbation of the modular configuration, as follows: letting D_h be the complement in the upper half-plane of the union of all translates by the modular group of the set $\{z : \mathrm{Im}(z) > 1/h\}$ and f_h be an analytic homeomorphism from D_h to the upper half-plane, $P(z) = -(12/\pi^2) \lim_{h\to 0}[(f_h(z) - z)/h^2]$. In the present paper the author examines heuristically a similar construction for the Hilbert mod'lar group, considering the Bergman kernel function rather than the Riemann mapping function. *R. C. Gunning* (Princeton, N.J.)

Citations: MR 17, 15e = F10-39.

F40-44 (36# 3727)

Freitag, Eberhard; Schneider, Volker

Bemerkung zu einem Satz von J. Igusa und W. Hammond.

Math. Z. **102** (1967), 9–16.

Es sei Γ_K die Hilbertsche Modulgruppe zu einem totalreellen Zahlkörper K vom Grade n und $\Gamma(T)$ die Siegelsche paramodulare Gruppe zur n-reihigen Elementarteilermatrix T. Verfasser studiert die Menge aller Einbettungen A von Γ_K in $\Gamma(T)$ von folgendem Typ:

$$M \in \Gamma_K \Rightarrow \begin{pmatrix} A & O \\ O & A'^{-1} \end{pmatrix} M^* \begin{pmatrix} A & O \\ O & A'^{-1} \end{pmatrix}^{-1} \in \Gamma(T).$$

Hierbei ist A eine n-reihige reelle invertierbare Matrix, und M^* bedeutet das direkte Produkt der Konjugierten von M. Jede solche Einbettung impliziert, dass die in naheliegender Weise gebildeten Restriktionen von Modulformen zu $\Gamma(T)$ stets Hilbertsche Modulformen zu K ergeben. Die Bedeutung einer solchen Einbettung besteht darin, dass Strukturaussagen über den graduierten Ring der Hilbertschen Modulformen aus entsprechenden Aussagen für $\Gamma(T)$ gewonnen werden können (vgl. W. F.

Hammond [Amer. J. Math. **88** (1966), 497–516; MR **34** #1281]).

Das Hauptresultat des Verfassers besagt, dass die Einbettungen von Γ_K in $\Gamma(T)$ umkehrbar eindeutig gewissen Zerlegungen der reziproken Differente von K entsprechen. Insbesondere existiert zu jedem K ein T, so dass Γ_K in $\Gamma(T)$ eingebettet werden kann.

H. Klingen (Freiburg)

Citations: MR 34# 1281 = F40-40.

F40-45 (36# 5081)

Cohn, Harvey

A numerical study of topological features of certain Hilbert fundamental domains.

Math. Comp. **21** (1967), 76–86.

The author continues his study [Math. Comp. **19** (1965), 594–605; MR **33** #4016] of the three-dimensional floors of the four-dimensional fundamental domains of Hilbert's modular group H_k over the field $\sqrt{k}$. This time he restricts k to 2, 3, 6, and he is concerned with the way the various analytic pieces of the floor are paired off under H_k. This is explored and portrayed by printing crude norms of each point on the floor, giving weird propeller-shaped regions in cross-sections.

D. H. Lehmer (Berkeley, Calif.)

Citations: MR 33# 4016 = F40-38.

Referred to in F40-53, F40-54.

F40-46 (37# 156)

Claus, G.

Die Randmannigfaltigkeiten und die "tiefsten" Punkte des Fundamentalbereichs für drei Hilbertsche Modulgruppen.

Math. Ann. **176** (1968), 225–256.

Let K be a totally real algebraic number field with ideal class number 1. It is known that the Hilbert modular group of K has a fundamental domain with only one cusp which is defined by a finite number of equations of the following kind: $\prod_\nu |\gamma_\nu z_\nu + \delta_\nu| \geqq 1$, where the γ_ν, δ_ν are the conjugates to two integers γ, $\delta \in K$ and z_ν the variables. The author determines these γ, δ in the cases $K = Q(\sqrt{m})$, $m = 2, 3, 5$. Furthermore, he determines the "lowest points" of these fundamental domains, more specifically the minimum of $\prod_\nu y_\nu$, $y_\nu = \operatorname{Im}(z_\nu)$. The first task is solved by elementary though not short discussions; the second involved some numerical computation for which an electronic computer was employed. *M. Eichler* (Basel)

F40-47 (37# 4015)

Cohn, Harvey

Sphere fibration induced by uniformization of modular group.

J. London Math. Soc. **43** (1968), 10–20.

K sei ein reell-quadratischer Zahlkörper, das Bild eines Elementes $a' \in K$ unter dem nicht-trivialen Automorphismus von K sei a''. Γ sei eine Untergruppe von endlichem Index in der Hilbertschen Modulgruppe von K, die auf die übliche Weise als Transformationsgruppe auf $\{(z', z'') | \operatorname{Im} z' > 0, \operatorname{Im} z'' < 0\}$ operiere. Die Untergruppe Γ_∞ von Γ, die den Randpunkt (∞, ∞) festläßt, besteht aus Abbildungen $(z', z'') \to (\varepsilon' z' + b', \varepsilon'' z'' + b'')$, $\varepsilon' \in E$, $b' \in M$, wobei E eine Untergruppe der Gruppe der total-positiven Einheiten von K, M ein Untermodul des Moduls der ganzen Zahlen in K, jeweils mit endlichem Index, ist, und $\varepsilon' M \subset M$ für jedes $\varepsilon' \in E$ gilt. M sei symmetrisch, d.h. zu $b' \in M$ sei auch $b'' \in M$. $\hat{\Gamma}$ bzw. $\hat{\Gamma}_\infty$ entstehe durch Hinzunahme der Abbildung $(z', z'') \to (-z'', -z')$. Setzt man $z' = x' + iy'$, $z'' = x'' - iy''$, $y'y'' = t$, $c[(y'/y'') - 1] \cdot [(y'/y'') + 1]^{-1} = s$, c passend reell, und ist P ein Fundamentalparallelogramm für die Translationen $(x', x'') \to (x' + b', x'' + b'')$, $b' \in M$, so ist $P \times \{s | 0 \leqq s \leqq 1\} \times \{t | t > 0\}$ Fundamentalbereich für $\hat{\Gamma}_\infty$. In der reellen x', x''-Ebene sei Σ die Gruppe der Translationen $(x', x'') \to (x' + u, x'' + v)$, u, v ganz rational. T_0, T_1 seien unimodulare Transformationen der Ordnung 2, Σ_0 die Erweiterung von Σ durch T_0, Σ_1 die Erweiterung von Σ durch T_1. Verfasser geht aus von dem Würfel $0 \leqq x', x'', s \leqq 1$ und identifiziert zwei Randpunkte (x_1', x_1'', s) und (x_2', x_2'', s), wenn (x_1', x_1'') und (x_2', x_2'') bei Σ äquivalent sind, auf der Grundfläche des Würfels $(s = 0)$ auch bei Äquivalenz bei Σ_0, und auf der Deckfläche $(s = 1)$ bei Äquivalenz bei Σ_1. Erfüllen T_0, T_1 eine gewisse Verträglichkeitsbedingung, so ergibt sich ein kompakter topologischer Raum H mit trivialer Fundamentalgruppe. Nach einem Satz von Seifert ist H eine 3-Sphäre, wenn man H als Faserraum mit einer 1-Sphäre als Faser und einer 2-Sphäre als Basis erhalten kann. Verfasser konstruiert nun K, E, M so, daß der Ausgangswürfel durch eine passende Transformation in $P \times \{s | 0 \leqq s \leqq 1\}$ übergeht und sich gerade die durch $\hat{\Gamma}_\infty$ induzierten Identifizierungen der Randpunkte ergeben. Da außerdem die Uniformisierbarkeitsbedingungen für die Spitze ∞ von $\hat{\Gamma}$ erfüllt sind, lassen sich Ortsuniformisierende zu dieser Spitze verwenden, um die gewünschte Faserung von H zu gewinnen.

K.-B. Gundlach (Münster)

F40-48 (37# 4017)

Helling, Heinz

Bestimmung der Kommensurabilitätsklasse der Hilbertschen Modulgruppe.

Math. Z. **92** (1966), 269–280.

Let $\Gamma(\mathbf{C})$ be the group of two-rowed complex matrices. Two subgroups Γ and Γ' of $\Gamma(\mathbf{C})$ are said to be "direct commensurable" if $\Gamma \cap \Gamma'$ is of finite index in both Γ and Γ'. They are said to be "commensurable" if either Γ or Γ', say Γ, can be transformed, by means of a matrix in $\Gamma(\mathbf{C})$, into a group Γ^* such that Γ^* and Γ' are direct commensurable. All groups commensurable to a given group constitute a commensurability class. The author determines explicitly the commensurability class of the Hilbert modular group of an algebraic number field K.

Let K be of finite degree over $\mathbf{Q}$ the field of rational numbers and $\mathfrak{o}$ the maximal order in K. Let $\mathfrak{a}$ be an arbitrary ideal and f an integral square free ideal of K. Then $A[\mathfrak{a}:f] = \left\{ \begin{pmatrix} \alpha & \beta \\ \gamma & \delta \end{pmatrix} \middle| \alpha, \delta \in \mathfrak{o}, \gamma \in \mathfrak{a}, \beta \in \mathfrak{a}^{-1} f \right\}$ is an order in the two-rowed matrix algebra $\mathfrak{M}_2(K)$ over K. The elements $\begin{pmatrix} \alpha & \beta \\ \gamma & \delta \end{pmatrix}$ in $A[\mathfrak{o}:\mathfrak{o}]$ with $\alpha\delta - \beta\gamma$ equal to a unit in $\mathfrak{o}$ form the homogeneous Hilbert modular group of K. The "corresponding substitutions" $z \mapsto (\alpha z + \beta)(\gamma z + \delta)^{-1}$ form the inhomogeneous Hilbert modular group $\Gamma^0(\mathfrak{o}, \mathfrak{o})$. For every divisor t of f, let an integral ideal $\mathfrak{c}$ be chosen in each (absolute) ideal class of K whose square is the class of the ideal t^{-1}. Denote by $R(t)$ the system of such ideals. The principal class will always be represented by $\mathfrak{o}$. Further, $R(t)$ is empty if t does not belong to the principal genus of K. Define now $G(\mathfrak{a}:f) =$

$$\bigcup_{t|f} \bigcup_{\mathfrak{c} \in R(t)} \left\{ S = \begin{pmatrix} a & b \\ c & d \end{pmatrix} \in \mathfrak{c} A[\mathfrak{a}:f] \,\middle|\, \det S = \mathfrak{c}^2 t,\ a, d \in \mathfrak{c} t \right\}.$$

Let $\Gamma(\mathfrak{a}:f)$ be the group of substitutions corresponding to $G(\mathfrak{a}:f)$. The main result proved by the author is that any subgroup of $\Gamma(\mathbf{C})$ which is commensurable with the inhomogeneous Hilbert modular group $\Gamma^0[\mathfrak{o}:\mathfrak{o}]$ can be transformed into a subgroup of $G(\mathfrak{a}:f)$ for suitably chosen $\mathfrak{a}$ and f. The proofs are elementary.

K. G. Ramanathan (Bombay)

Referred to in F15-32.

F40-49 **(37# 4019)**

Prestel, Alexander

Die elliptischen Fixpunkte der Hilbertschen Modulgruppen.

Math. Ann. **177** (1968), 181–209.

H. Shimizu [Ann. of Math. (2) **77** (1963), 33–71; MR **26** #2641] determined the dimension of the space of cusp forms corresponding to discontinuous groups operating on H^m (product of m upper half planes). In the case of the Hilbert modular group Γ_K, corresponding to a totally real number field K of degree m over the rationals, this dimension turns out to be the sum of terms, depending on the volume of the fundamental region, on the cusps, and on (a system of representatives of) the elliptic fixed points, respectively. The first two can be computed when K is given. The contribution of the elliptic points has been determined by K.-B. Gundlach [Math. Ann. **157** (1965), 369–390; MR **37** #5153] for real quadratic fields K of discriminants 5, 8 and 12, by actually exhibiting a complete set of representatives of the elliptic points. The purpose of the present paper is to determine for arbitrary totally real K the contribution of the elliptic points to the dimension of the space of cusp forms. This requires the determination of the number of elliptic points incongruent mod Γ_K and of the corresponding rotation factors. The method is an extension of the algebraic approach of Shimizu. A correspondence is established between the subgroups of Γ_K that leave a given elliptic point invariant and orders in certain quadratic extensions of K. In the last two paragraphs effective computations are made for the particular situation when K is real quadratic over the rationals, and in an appendix the results are tabulated for all such fields with (squarefree) discriminants up to 100.

E. Grosswald (Philadelphia, Pa.)

Citations: MR 26# 2641 = F55-14; MR 37# 5153 = F40-50.

F40-50 **(37# 5153)**

Gundlach, Karl-Bernhard

Die Fixpunkte einiger Hilbertscher Modulgruppen.

Math. Ann. **157** (1965), 369–390.

Let Γ denote the Hilbert modular group of the real-quadratic algebraic number field k with discriminant d_K. Let $\mathfrak{H}=\mathfrak{H}^+\times\mathfrak{H}^+$ and $\mathfrak{H}_0=\mathfrak{H}^+\times\mathfrak{H}^-$, where $\mathfrak{H}^+$ denotes the upper and $\mathfrak{H}^-$ the lower half-plane of the complex plane. It is well known that the knowledge of the maximal finite subgroups of Γ is essential for the study of the quotient space $\mathfrak{H}/\Gamma$ or $\mathfrak{H}_0/\Gamma$ and for the study of the space of entire cusp forms belonging to Γ. In this paper the author completes this study for the small discriminants $d_K=5$, 8, 12. Consequently, with the help of the formula of H. Shimizu [Ann. of Math. (2) **77** (1963), 33–71; MR **26** #2641] he obtains in the above cases the exact value of the rank of the space of entire cusp forms belonging to Γ. He also discusses (Satz 5) the uniformisability of the points of $\mathfrak{H}$ and $\mathfrak{H}_0$. By extending the group Γ, he gives examples of groups for which the compactified quotient space is a compact complex analytic manifold. *Sunder Lal* (Zbl **134**, 301)

Citations: MR 26# 2641 = F55-14.

Referred to in F40-49.

F40-51 **(38# 4412)**

Fomenko, O. M.

Hilbert's modular forms and functions for the field $\mathbf{Q}(\sqrt{2})$. (Russian)

Mat. Zametki **4** (1968), 129–136.

Es sei Γ die Hilbertsche Modulgruppe des Körpers $(\mathbf{Q}\sqrt{2})$, $\mathfrak{R}$ der graduierte Ring der symmetrischen Modulformen geraden Gewichtes zu Γ und $\mathfrak{N}$ der Körper aller Modulformen zu Γ. Die Struktursätze über $\mathfrak{R}$ und $\mathfrak{N}$ sind von K.-B. Gundlach [Math. Ann. **152** (1963), 226–256; MR **29** #1186] für den Körper $\mathbf{Q}(\sqrt{5})$ und von W. Hammond [Amer. J. Math. **88** (1966), 497–516; MR **34** #1281] für $\mathbf{Q}(\sqrt{2})$ und $\mathbf{Q}(\sqrt{5})$ bewiesen worden. Hammond benutzte Moduleinbettungen und wandte J. Igusas entsprechende Resultate [ibid. **86** (1964), 392–412; MR **29** #6061] über Siegelsche Modulformen zweiten Grades an. Die Methode von Gundlach ist eine Verallgemeinerung des klassischen Verfahrens der elliptischen Diskriminanten. Verfasser benutzt dasselbe Verfahren im Fall $\mathbf{Q}(\sqrt{2})$. Es kommt darauf an, durch ein Produkt von Thetareihen eine Modulform θ^2 zu konstruieren, deren Nullstellenmenge im Fundamentalbereich aus einem einzigen irreduziblen Zweig besteht. Struktursatz 1: $\mathfrak{R}$ ist ein Polynomring in drei Unbestimmten, nämlich zwei Modulformen G_{-2} und G_{-4} vom Gewicht -2 und -6 und der Spitzenform θ^2 vom Gewicht -4. Struktursatz 2: Der Körper der symmetrischen Modulfunktionen zu $\mathbf{Q}(\sqrt{2})$ ist rational; $\mathfrak{N}$ ist quadratische Erweiterung dieses Körpers (ein primitives Element der Erweiterung, also eine schiefsymmetrische Modulfunktion, wird explizit bestimmt).

J. Spilker (Freiburg)

Citations: MR 29# 1186 = F40-30; MR 29# 6061 = F50-33; MR 34# 1281 = F40-40.

F40-52 **(39# 1684)**

Christian, Ulrich

Hilbert-Siegelsche Modulformen und Integralgleichungen.

Monatsh. Math. **72** (1968), 412–418.

Let Γ denote a congruence subgroup of Hilbert-Siegel modular group. It is shown that every cusp form with respect to Γ satisfies an integral equation whose kernel is the Poincaré series. *S. Konno* (Osaka)

F40-53 **(40# 89)**

Cohn, Harvey

Some computer-assisted topological models of Hilbert fundamental domains.

Math. Comp. **23** (1969), 475–487.

Author's summary: "The Hilbert modular group **H** for the integral domain $\mathbf{O}(k^{1/2})$ has a four-dimensional fundamental domain **R** which should be represented geometrically (like the classic modular group). Computer assistance (by the Argonne CDC 3600) was used for outlining cross sections of the three-dimensional 'floor' of **R**, which is a mosaic of an intractably large number of boundary pieces identified under **H**. The cross sections shown here might well contain enough information when $k=2$, 3, 5, 6 to form some 'incidence matrices' and see **R** (at least) combinatorially. For special symmetrized subgroups of **H**, it is plausible to see homologously independent 2-spheres in (the corresponding) **R**. The program is a continuation of one outlined in two earlier issues of this journal [the author, Math. Comp. **19** (1965), 594–605; MR **33** #4016; ibid. **21** (1967), 76–86; MR **36** #5081]. (Errata for these articles are appended to this paper.)"

Citations: MR 33# 4016 = F40-38; MR 36# 5081 = F40-45.

F40-54 **(41# 3399)**

Cohn, Harvey

Application of computer to algebraic topology on some bicomplex manifolds.

Computational Problems in Abstract Algebra (*Proc. Conf., Oxford*, 1967), *pp.* 371–381. *Pergamon, Oxford*, 1970.

The author describes part of a series of numerical investigations of the nature of the fundamental domain of certain of the simpler Hilbert modular functions of two independent complex variables.

The associated quadratic field is chosen as $Q(2^{1/2})$, and three groups are dealt with. To appreciate the complexity of the problem the reader is referred to previous papers [Math. Comp. **19** (1965), 594–605; MR **33** #4016; ibid. **21** (1967), 76–86; MR **36** #5081].

D. H. Lehmer (Berkeley, Calif.)

Citations: MR 33# 4016 = F40-38; MR 36# 5081 = F40-45.

F40-55 (41# 8595)

Selberg, Atle

Recent developments in the theory of discontinuous groups of motions of symmetric spaces.

Proceedings of the Fifteenth Scandinavian Congress (Oslo, 1968), Lecture Notes in Mathematics, Vol. 118, *pp.* 99–120. *Springer, Berlin,* 1970.

Let G be a noncompact semisimple Lie group and Γ a lattice in G, i.e., Γ is discrete and volume $(\Gamma\backslash G)<\infty$. Questions of the following kind are discussed: (1) Under what conditions is Γ rigid? (2) When is Γ commensurable to an arithmetic group? Work done on these questions in the last decade is briefly reviewed. As far as the second question is concerned, the author discusses extensively the situation in $\mathrm{SL}(2, R)\times\cdots\times\mathrm{SL}(2, R)$ and the relationship of such a Γ to the Hilbert modular groups. In particular, the author gives a sketch of his ideas on how to accomplish a proof of the statement that an irreducible lattice in $\mathrm{SL}(2, R)^n$ is commensurable with a Hilbert modular group. Question (2) is also discussed for the rank 1 case, and reference is made to the work of H. Garland and Raganuthan (see the report of Raganuthan in Proc. Internat. Congr. Mathematicians (Nice, September, 1970), to appear). Conjectures and hints to possible ways of attack for the rank >1 case are put forward.

W. T. van Est (Leiden)

F40-56 (43# 155)

Hiramatsu, Toyokazu

Eichler maps and hyperbolic Fourier expansion.

Nagoya Math. J. **40** (1970), 173–192.

Let $F(z_1, z_2)=\sum C_\mu e^{2\pi i(\mu_1 z_1+\mu_2 z_2)}$ be the Fourier expansion of a Hilbert modular form of weight k attached to the real quadratic field $\Omega=\mathbf{Q}(\sqrt{p})$, p a prime. Here μ runs over the totally positive numbers in some ideal of Ω, and μ_1, μ_2 are the images of μ in $\mathbf{R}$. By the specialization $z_1 z_2=-q$, q another prime with $(-q/p)=-1$, we obtain an automorphic form $f(z)=F(z, -q/z)z^{-k}$ of weight $2k$ with respect to a group $\Gamma(p, q)$ which represents the group of units of an order in a certain quaternion division algebra. In particular, the map $z\to\varepsilon^2 z$ with a unit ε of Ω belongs to $\Gamma(p, q)$, and so there is an expansion $f(z)=\sum c_n e^{\pi i n(\log z)/\log\varepsilon}$. The author determines the coefficients c_n, using a method of H. Petersson [Abh. Math. Sem. Univ. Hamburg **14** (1941), 22–60; MR **3**, 204]. The final formula extends over 3 lines. It is an infinite series extending over the μ and containing the C_μ. Its coefficients are again infinite series which seem not to have occurred in the previous literature.

M. Eichler (Basel)

F40-57 (43# 7404)

Freitag, Eberhard

Über die Struktur der Funktionenkörper zu hyperabelschen Gruppen. I.

J. Reine Angew. Math. **247** (1971), 97–117.

In some cases it is known that the fields of Hilbert modular functions are rational function fields; the latest reference is to the paper by K.-B. Gundlach [same J. **220** (1965), 109–153; MR **33** #1290]. The ultimate goal of this paper is to provide examples of these function fields that are not rational. Theorem 4: Let $L=\mathbf{Q}(\sqrt{d})$ with $d\equiv 3 \bmod 4$ be a real quadratic number field with class number 1, let the Hilbert modular group Γ of L operate on z_1, z_2 with $\mathrm{Im}\, z_1>0$, $\mathrm{Im}\, z_2<0$, and adjoin the substitution $z_1\to -z_2$, $z_2\to -z_1$ to Γ; in the enlarged group $\hat\Gamma$ there exists a subgroup $\hat\Gamma_0$ of index 2 such that the field of automorphic functions with respect to $\hat\Gamma_0$ is not rational.

At least as important as this result are the single steps of the proof. It rests firstly on the theorem of H. Hironaka [Ann. Math. (2) **79** (1964), 109–203; ibid. (2) **79** (1964), 205–326; MR **33** #7333] that there exists a non-singular model of a field of algebraic functions. Secondly, it uses Castelnuovo's criterion of rationality [see O. Zariski, Illinois J. Math. **2** (1958), 303–315; MR **20** #6426]. Thirdly, it applies and generalizes an idea of S. Matsushima and G. Shimura [Ann. Math. (2) **78** (1963), 417–449; MR **27** #5274] by which all holomorphic differential forms of degree 4 dimension can be shown to vanish.

The author makes 3 important observations. A point on an algebraic variety is said to be quasiregular if it has a neighbourhood that in turn has a regular covering. If all points of a variety are quasiregular it is called a quasiregular variety. Theorem 1: Let X be a quasiregular variety and $\tilde X$ a desingularization; a differential form that is holomorphic at all regular points of X has a regular extension on $\tilde X$. Now a group $\hat\Gamma$ is studied, operating on the product of n upper half planes, and it is assumed that the automorphic functions with respect to $\hat\Gamma$ form a finite algebraic function field of transcendence degree n. Finite fixed points are always quasiregular; furthermore (Theorem 2) a cusp of $\hat\Gamma$ constitutes a regular point at most if it is contained in a subvariety of fixed points of codimension 1. This is only possible if $n\leqq 2$. Conversely (Theorem 3) for $n=2$, a symmetric cusp (i.e., one which is equivalent with $(z_1, z_2)\to(\infty, \infty)$ and invariant under $z_1\leftrightarrow z_2$) is quasiregular. With all these tools the proof of Theorem 4 is easy, all that is needed is to show that the arithmetic genus is >0, and this consists of the explicit construction of a theta series which is a holomorphic differential of degree 2.

M. Eichler (Basel)

Citations: MR 33# 1290 = F40-36.

F40-58 (44# 2706)

Siegel, Carl Ludwig

Über die Fourierschen Koeffizienten von Modulformen.

Nachr. Akad. Wiss. Göttingen Math.-Phys. Kl. II **1970**, 15–56.

Diese Arbeit verallgemeinert weitreichend eine frühere Untersuchung des Verfasser über den arithmetischen Charakter der Fourierkoeffizienten von Modulformen und der Rationalität von Zetawerten [dieselben Nachr. **1969**, 87–102; MR **40** #5570]. Sei $\mathfrak{K}$ ein totalreeller algebraischer Zahlkörper vom Grade n, d seine Diskriminante; $\mathfrak{c}$ und $\mathfrak{f}$ seien ganze Ideale aus $\mathfrak{K}$ und $\mathfrak{E}_\mathfrak{f}$ sei die Gruppe der total-positiven Einheiten $\equiv 1 \pmod{\mathfrak{f}}$. Für jede natürliche Zahl $k>1$ liegt der folgende Ausdruck im Körper der f-ten Einheitswurzeln ($f=N(\mathfrak{f})$): $R_k=(\pi i)^{-kn}d^{1/2}N(\mathfrak{c}^{-k})\sum_\mu N(\mu^{-k})$, wobei μ ein vollständiges System bezüglich $\mathfrak{E}_\mathfrak{f}$ nicht-assoziierter Zahlen aus $\mathfrak{K}$, $\mu\neq 0$, $\mu\equiv 1 \pmod{\mathfrak{f}\mathfrak{c}^{-1}}$ durchläuft. Dieses Resultat wurde von H. Klingen bewiesen [Math. Ann. **147** (1962), 176–188; MR **25** #2041]. Die Idee ist, R_k als 0-ten Fourierkoeffizienten einer Eisensteinreihe (zur Hauptkongruenzuntergruppe der Stufe $\mathfrak{f}$ in der Hilbertschen Modulgruppe für den Körper $\mathfrak{K}$) zu deuten, deren höhere Fourierkoeffizienten alle im Körper der f-ten Einheitswurzeln liegen, und zu zeigen, daß der 0-te Fourierkoeffizient einer solchen Modulform in einem algebraischen Zahlkörper liegt, wenn alle höheren darin liegen. Für diesen Beweis wurden die algebraischen Relationen zwischen Eisensteinreihen sowie der Hilbertsche Basissatz benutzt. In der vorliegenden Arbeit werden diese beiden Schritte durch ein umfangreiches konstruktives Verfahren ersetzt. Das gelingt so: Der Verfasser geht von den R_k zu ähnlich gebildeten Ausdrücken Q_k über, deren Rationalität er zeigen muß. Die Q_k treten jetzt auf als konstante Glieder der Fourierreihe einer elliptischen Modulform höherer Stufe, deren weitere Fourierkoeffizienten $u_1, u_2, \cdots$ ganze rationale Zahlen sind. Der Hauptteil der Untersuchung besteht aus einem effektiven Rechenverfahren, um aus den Fourierkoeffizienten $u_1, u_2, \cdots, u_{T-1}$ der Modulform das absolute Glied u_0 zu berechnen; dabei ergibt sich $T < \frac{1}{3}f^{20}k^3n^3$, und für den gekürzten Nenner von Q_k gilt $(f^2kn)^{f^6k^2n^2}$. Auch der Fall $k=1$ wird in die Untersuchung einbezogen, jedoch hängen im speziellen Fall $\mathfrak{f}=\mathfrak{o}$ dann die beiden oberen Schränken noch von der Diskriminanten d ab. Die Rationalität Q_k impliziert leicht, daß die Zetafunktion jeder Strahlklasse zu einem algebraischen Zahlkörper an allen Stellen $0, -1, -2, \cdots$ rational ist. *J. Spilker* (Freiburg)

Citations: MR 25# 2041 = F40-24; MR 40# 5570 = R42-50.

F40-59 **(44# 3958)**

Busam, Rolf

Eine Verallgemeinerung gewisser Dimensionsformeln von Shimizu.

Invent. Math. **11** (1970), 110–149.

Für Transformationsgruppen Γ vom Typ der Hilbertschen Modulgruppen auf einem Produkt H^n von n oberen Halbebenen hat H. Shimizu [Ann. of Math. (2) **77** (1963), 33–71; MR **26** #2641] aus der Selbergschen Spurformel eine explizite Formel für $\dim_{\mathbf{C}} S_\Gamma(r)$ hergeleitet. Dabei ist $S_\Gamma(r)$ der endlich-dimensionale Vektorraum der ganzen Spitzenformen vom Gewicht r (der Dimension $2r$ in anderer Terminologie) zu Γ, $r \in \mathbf{N}$, $r \geqq 2$. Die Gruppen Γ sind Untergruppen der Zusammenhangskomponente der Eins der Automorphismengruppe von H^n. Die entsprechenden Untergruppen $\hat{\Gamma}$ der vollen Automorphismengruppe von H^n unterscheiden sich von den Gruppen Γ dadurch, daß in den Transformationen von $\hat{\Gamma}$ noch Variablenvertauschungen auftreten können. Der Verfasser zeigt, daß man auf dem von Shimizu angegebenen Weg auch $\dim_{\mathbf{C}} S_{\hat{\Gamma}}(r)$ bestimmen kann. Gegenüber der Dimensionsformel von Shimizu treten hier zusätzliche Glieder auf, die von den Klassen konjugierter Elemente in $\hat{\Gamma}$ herrühren, die Fixpunktmengen höherer Dimension als 0 besitzen. Da über diese Fixpunktmengen für $n>2$ wenig bekannt ist, wird die Endformel für $\dim_{\mathbf{C}} S_{\hat{\Gamma}}(r)$ nur für den Fall $n=2$ hergeleitet. *K.-B. Gundlach* (Münster)

Citations: MR 26# 2641 = F55-14.

F45 SIEGEL (SYMPLECTIC MODULAR) GROUPS AND GENERALIZATIONS: ACTION ON A SPACE

For the algebraic structure of these groups, see **E56**.

See also reviews E12-81, E12-102, E12-115, E12-120, E56-16, E60-44, F50-30, F70-18, F99-3, F99-4, G10-45, R32-72.

F45-1 **(14, 623b)**

Siegel, Carl Ludwig. Die Modulgruppe in einer einfachen involutorischen Algebra. Festschrift zur Feier des zweihundertjährigen Bestehens der Akademie der Wissenschaften in Göttingen. I. Math.-Phys. Kl., pp. 157–167. Springer-Verlag, Berlin-Göttingen-Heidelberg, 1951.

In the present paper the author considers previously elaborated concepts of the theory of discontinuous groups in a general algebraic setting.

Let A be a simple algebra of finite degree over the field of rational numbers which possesses an involution $X \to X^*$, and $A^{(2)}$ the algebra of 2-rowed matrices with elements in A. By extension from the rational to the reals, let $A \to \bar{A}$ and $A^{(2)} \to \overline{A^{(2)}}$, the involution also being extended to $\bar{A}$, $\overline{A^{(2)}}$. The author defines the symplectic group Σ in $\bar{A}$ as the set of all $\mathfrak{M} = \begin{pmatrix} \mathfrak{A} & \mathfrak{B} \\ \mathfrak{C} & \mathfrak{D} \end{pmatrix}$ in $\overline{A^{(2)}}$ which satisfy $\mathfrak{M}^* \mathfrak{J} \mathfrak{M} = \mathfrak{J}$, where $\mathfrak{J} = \begin{pmatrix} 0 & \mathfrak{E} \\ -\mathfrak{E} & 0 \end{pmatrix}$, $\mathfrak{E}$ being the unit matrix, and discusses its representation by linear fractional transformations $\mathfrak{Z} \to (\mathfrak{A}\mathfrak{Z} + \mathfrak{B})(\mathfrak{C}\mathfrak{Z} + \mathfrak{D})^{-1}$.

The modular group M in O, an order in A, is then defined as the set of all elements in Σ which are units in $O^{(2)}$, the corresponding order in $A^{(2)}$. M is shown to be a properly discontinuous subgroup of Σ of the first kind: it possesses a fundamental region F with the following properties: (1) every compact portion of Σ is covered by a finite number of copies of F; (2) only a finite number of copies of F intersect F; (3) F has a finite volume, measured in the invariant metric. It follows that M is generated by a finite number of elements. The proof is made by utilizing the regular representation of A and $\bar{A}$ and the reduction theory of quadratic forms. *J. Lehner* (Los Alamos, N. M.).

Referred to in G10-45.

F45-2 **(17, 602d)**

Siegel, Carl Ludwig. Zur Theorie der Modulfunktionen n-ten Grades. Comm. Pure Appl. Math. **8** (1955), 677–681.

In the theory of automorphic functions of one variable, the fundamental region F of a Fuchsian group of the first kind (limit-circle group) can be compactified by adjoining the parabolic boundary points (if any). In the case of the modular group one adds the infinite point $(i\infty)$ of F, or equivalently the point $q=0$ of the corresponding local variable $q=e^{2\pi iz}$.

In this paper Siegel accomplishes the compactification of the fundamental region of the matrix modular group of degree n. Let $Z=X+iY$, $Y>0$, where X, Y are real symmetric matrices of order n. Siegel proves the existence of ν $(\nu=\frac{1}{2}n(n+1))$ variables $q_1, \cdots, q_\nu$ such that when $Z \to \infty$ $(y_{nn} \to \infty)$ there is a subsequence on which one of the q's$\to 0$ while the others tend to limits lying in $|q_k|<1$. The q's and z's are related by a reversible analytic transformation. F is then made compact by adding the finite number of surfaces $q_k=0$ $(k=1, 2, \cdots, \nu)$. In the proof decisive use is made of the arithmetic properties of the modular group via Minkowski's reduction theory of positive quadratic forms.

The case $n=2$ is worked out explicitly. Set $z_{11}=z_1$, $z_{12}=z_2$, $z_{22}=z_3$, and $q_k=\exp 2\pi i w_k$ $(k=1, 2, 3)$, with $w_1=z_1-2z_2$, $w_2=z_2$, $w_3=z_3-z_1$. By the reduction theory we have $0 \leqq 2y_2 \leqq y_1 \leqq y_2$. When $y_3 \to \infty$, it is immediately verified that there is a subsequence on which the above requirements on the q's are satisfied. The local variable is shown to be $q_1 q_2^2 q_3$. *J. Lehner* (Los Alamos, N.M.).

Referred to in F50-19.

F45-3 **(18, 299c)**

Klingen, Helmut. Diskontinuierliche Gruppen in symmetrischen Räumen. I, II. Math. Ann. **129** (1955), 345–369; **130** (1955), 137–146.

Continuing the work of Siegel [Amer. J. Math. **65** (1943), 1–86; MR **4**, 242] and Braun [Ann. of Math. (2) **53** (1951), 143–160; MR **12**, 482], the author studies in I the first three types of irreducible bounded symmetric domains:

$H_1: \frac{1}{2i}(Z-\tilde{Z})>0$; $H_2: \frac{1}{2i}(Z-\tilde{Z})>0$, $Z'Z=-E$;

$$H_3 \frac{1}{2i}(Z-\tilde{Z})>0, \ Z'=Z;$$

where Z is an $n\times n$ matrix and $\tilde{Z}$ is the conjugate complex transposed matrix. He characterizes the group of one-to-one analytic mappings of H_ν on itself ($\nu=1, 2, 3$), studies their geometric properties under a Riemannian metric, and treats discontinuous groups of mappings. He shows that the mappings of $H_2(H_3)$ on itself can always be extended to H_1 with one exception ($n=4$, H_2). Every discontinuous group of mappings of H_ν on itself possesses a fundamental region with the usual properties.

II is devoted to examples of discontinuous groups and their fundamental regions. The groups, which are of the first kind, are developed by number-theoretic means, involving the group of units of certain Hermitian forms. The fundamental regions are then constructed with the help of the Humbert reduction theory of positive definite forms in an algebraic number field. Among the groups treated is the modular group. *J. Lehner.*

Citations: MR 4, 242b = F50-2; MR 12, 482c = F55-3.

Referred to in F50-28.

F45-4 **(18, 934c)**

Satake, Ichiro. On the compactification of the Siegel space. J. Indian Math. Soc. (N.S.) **20** (1956), 259–281.

Soit $\mathscr{H}_n$ le demi-plan généralisé de Siegel. formé des matrices symétriques Z à n lignes et n colonnes, à termes complexes, telles que $\operatorname{Im} Z$ soit définie positive. Le groupe modulaire M_n opère dans $\mathscr{H}_n$; l'espace-quotient $\mathscr{V}_n=M_n\backslash\mathscr{H}_n$ est un espace analytique, et même une V-variété au sens de Satake. Comme bien connu, $\mathscr{V}_n$ n'est pas compact; il est classique que $\mathscr{V}_1$ se compactifie par adjonction d'un point à l'infini $\mathscr{V}_0$; récemment, Satake [Proc. Internat. Symposium Algebraic Number Theory, Tokyo and Nikko, 1955, Science Council of Japan, Tokyo, 1956, pp. 107–129; MR **18**, 731] a défini une compactification $\bar{\mathscr{V}}_2$ de $\mathscr{V}_2$ en utilisant la théorie de Minkowski pour la réduction des formes quadratiques; $\bar{\mathscr{V}}_2$ est une V-variété réalisable comme sous-variété algébrique dans un espace projectif (Baily). Dans le présent travail, Satake définit une compactification $\mathscr{V}_n{}^*$ de $\mathscr{V}_n$ pour tout n; pour $n=2$, $\mathscr{V}_2{}^*$ est un quotient de $\bar{\mathscr{V}}_2$; dans le cas général, $\mathscr{V}_{n-1}{}^*$ s'identifie à un sous-espace fermé de $\mathscr{V}_n{}^*$, dont le complémentaire est $\mathscr{V}_n$, et on a donc $\mathscr{V}_n{}^*=\mathscr{V}_n\cup\mathscr{V}_{n-1}\cup\cdots\cup\mathscr{V}_0$. Pour définir la topologie de $\mathscr{V}_n{}^*$, l'auteur utilise le domaine fondamental de M_n et la théorie de Siegel.

Pour tout entier pair $m\geqq 0$, on a la notion de forme modulaire de poids m; d'une façon précise, pour tout ouvert U de $\mathscr{V}_n$, on a un espace $\mathscr{A}_m{}^{(n)}(U)$ de formes modulaires sur l'ouvert de $\mathscr{H}_n$, image réciproque de U; les $\mathscr{A}_m{}^{(n)}(U)$ définissent un faisceau $\mathscr{A}_m{}^{(n)}$ sur $\mathscr{V}_n$. Tout $f\in\mathscr{A}_m{}^{(n)}(U^*\cap\mathscr{V}_n)$, U^* un ouvert de $\mathscr{V}_n{}^*$, définit, pour chaque entier $r<n$, un élément $\Phi_r{}^n(f)\in\mathscr{A}_m{}^{(r)}(U^*\cap\mathscr{V}_r)$. En fait, l'auteur considère (cf. coroll. 2 du th. 3) une topologie sur $\mathscr{H}_n{}^*=\mathscr{H}_n\cup\mathscr{H}_{n-1}\cup\cdots\cup\mathscr{H}_0$ (cette topologie est définie par la donnée de „filtres convergents"; il semble au rapporteur que la topologie de $\mathscr{V}_n{}^*$ n'est autre que la topologie-quotient de celle de $\mathscr{H}_n{}^*$). Si on note $\Phi_n{}^*$ l'application naturelle: $\mathscr{H}_n{}^*\to\mathscr{V}_n{}^*$, et si f est une forme modulaire holomorphe dans $\mathscr{H}_n\cap\Phi_n{}^{*-1}(U^*)$, f se prolonge par continuité à $\Phi_n{}^{*-1}(U^*)$; alors la restriction de ce prolongement à $\mathscr{H}_r\cap\Phi_n{}^{*-1}(U^*)$ n'est autre que $\Phi_r{}^n(f)$. L'auteur définit ainsi, sur l'espace $\mathscr{V}_n{}^*$, le faisceau $\mathscr{A}_m{}^{(n)*}$ des formes modulaires de poids m: pour chaque ouvert $U^*\subset\mathscr{V}_n{}^*$, on a un espace $\mathscr{A}_m{}^{(n)*}(U^*)$ formé de fonctions sur $\Phi_n{}^{*-1}(U^*)$. En particulier, le faisceau $\mathscr{A}_0{}^{(n)*}$ définit la structure d'espace analytique de $\mathscr{V}_n{}^*$. L'auteur affirme (sans démonstration) que $\mathscr{V}_n{}^*$ est bien un espace analytique, mais n'est pas une V-variété pour $n\geqq 2$; il ignore si $\mathscr{V}_n{}^*$ est réalisable comme sous-variété algébrique d'un espace projectif. *H. Cartan.*

Citations: MR 18, 731a = F50-12.

Referred to in F02-8, F02-10, F45-5, F50-19.

F45-5 **(20# 5890)**

Baily, Walter L., Jr. Satake's compactification of V_n. Amer. J. Math. **80** (1958), 348–364.

Soit H_n le demi-plan généralisé de Siegel (espace des matrices complexes symétriques à n lignes et n colonnes, dont la partie imaginaire est définie positive); soit M_n le groupe modulaire $\operatorname{Sp}(n, Z)$ qui opère dans H_n. L'espace $V_n=H_n/M_n$ est un espace analytique normal; il a été compactifié par I. Satake [J. Indian Math. Soc. (N.S.) **20** (1956), 259–281; MR **18**, 934]. Le compactifié

$$V_n{}^*=V_n\cup V_{n-1}\cup\cdots\cup V_1\cup V_0$$

est muni par Satake d'une structure d'espace annelé, dont il faut démontrer que c'est bien une structure d'espace analytique normal. L'auteur le prouve en établissant d'abord un théorème général de prolongement des espaces analytiques normaux (th. 1); ce théorème de prolongement a été ultérieurement amélioré par le rapporteur [voir l'analyse ci-dessous]. Il s'applique ici grâce aux propriétés des formes automorphes d'un poids donné assez grand.

L'auteur démontre ensuite que $V_n{}^*$ est isomorphe (comme espace analytique compact) à une variété algébrique projective, projectivement normale; il en résulte que, pour $n\geqq 2$, toute fonction méromorphe invariante par M_n est le quotient de deux formes automorphes de même poids. L'auteur annonce des résultats analogues dans le cas où le groupe M_n est remplacé par un sous-groupe d'indice fini de M_n. Signalons que, pour tout groupe M' commensurable à M_n, des résultats plus précis relatifs au plongement projectif du compactifié de H_n/M' ont été obtenus postérieurement par I. Satake et le rapporteur* [Séminaire H. Cartan; 10e année: 1957/58, Secrétariat Math., Paris, 1958; cf. notamment exposé 17]. *H. Cartan* (Paris)

*See MR **21** #2750 = F02-5

Citations: MR 18, 934c = F45-4; MR 21# 2750 = F02-5.

Referred to in F02-8, F40-21, F50-22, F55-13.

F45-6 **(20# 5891)**

Cartan, Henri. Prolongement des espaces analytiques normaux. Math. Ann. **136** (1958), 97–110.

Let X be a locally compact space; let V be an open subset which is everywhere dense, and let $W=X-V$. Suppose V is a normal complex analytic space of dimension m. The problem of analytic prolongation is to define on X a structure of normal analytic space in such a way that: (α) The structure of V is that induced from X; (β) W is an analytic subspace of dimension $<m$.

It is easily seen that there cannot be more than one structure of analytic space on X which satisfies (α) and (β), namely, for each $x\in X$ we define the stalk A_x of germs of holomorphic functions at x as the stalk of germs of continuous functions which belong to B_y for $y\in V$ sufficiently close to x. (Here B is the sheaf defining the analytic structure on V.)

The main result of the paper is Theorem 2: Suppose (i) Each $x_0\in W$ has (in X) a fundamental system of open neighborhoods U such that $V\cap U$ is connected; (ii) every $x_0\in W$ has a neighborhood U such that the functions on U which are continuous and holomorphic on $V\cap U$ separate the points of $V\cap U$; (iii) A defines on W the structure of analytic space of dimension $<m$: then A

defines the structure of analytic normal space on X.

The origin of this problem stems from the Satake compactification of the fundamental domain for the symplectic modular group in Siegel's upper half plane. Baily [see the preceding review] has proved that this compactification is a normal analytic space; Baily's theorem is an easy consequence of the results of this paper.

L. Ehrenpreis (Waltham, Mass.)

Referred to in F40-21.

F45-7 **(21# 5617)**

Siegel, Carl Ludwig. Zur Bestimmung des Volumens des Fundamentalbereichs der unimodularen Gruppe. Math. Ann. **137** (1959), 427–432.

In an earlier work [Trans. Amer. Math. Soc. **39** (1936), 209–218] the author verified Minkowski's formula for the volume of the fundamental region of the unimodular group of the nth order, by analytical methods involving the zeta-function for the ring of $n\times n$ matrices over the rational field. This was generalized to the case of an arbitrary algebraic number field. The present note draws attention to a gap in his proof (p. 211, where two divergent integrals are introduced) and remedies it.

J. H. H. Chalk (Hamilton, Ont.)

F45-8 **(21# 5683)**

Newman, M.; and Reiner, I. Inclusion theorems for congruence subgroups. Trans. Amer. Math. Soc. **91** (1959), 369–379.

Let $G_t=\mathrm{GL}_t^+[J]=\mathrm{SL}_t[J]$ be the group of $t\times t$ matrices with rational integral elements and determinant 1. The set of matrices $\begin{pmatrix}A & B\\ C & D\end{pmatrix}$ with $\dim A=r$, $0<r<t$, $C\equiv 0 \bmod n$, $n>1$, forms a proper subgroup $G_r(n)$. Moreover, if $n|m$, then $G_r(n)\supset G_r(m)$. Theorem 1: If $G_r(n)\supset H\supset G_r(m)$, then $H=G_r(q)$ for some q, $n|q$, $q|m$. The set of matrices above with $\dim A=r$, $C\equiv 0 \bmod n$, $B\equiv 0 \bmod m$, forms a subgroup $G_r(m,n)$. Theorem 2: Suppose $t=2r$, $(m,n)=1$, $G_r(m,n)\subset H\subset G_{2r}$. Then $H=G_r(m_1,n_1)$ with $m_1|m$, $n_1|n$. Both theorems 1 and 2 are generalized in various directions, and extended to the symplectic group.

J. L. Brenner (Palo Alto, Calif.)

Referred to in F45-18, F45-22.

F45-9 **(21# 5748)**

Gottschling, Erhard. Explizite Bestimmung der Randflächen des Fundamentalbereiches der Modulgruppe zweiten Grades. Math. Ann. **138** (1959), 103–124.

Denote by $\mathfrak{H}$ the set of complex, symmetric matrices $Z=X+iY$, of order n, with Y positively definite, and let Γ be the (inhomogeneous) modular group of order n on $\mathfrak{H}$. For every (possibly complex) matrix $W=(w_{kl})$, $k, l=1, 2, \cdots, n$, denote the absolute value of the determinant of W by abs W. It is known [Siegel, Math. Ann. **116** (1939), 617–657; Amer. J. Math. **65** (1943), 1–86; MR **4**, 242] that one may define a fundamental domain of Γ in $\mathfrak{H}$ by the conditions (i) $|x_{kl}|\leqq \frac{1}{2}$; (ii) Y reduced (in the sense of Minkowski); (iii) abs $(CZ+D)\geqq 1$. Here (iii) has to be satisfied for all pairs of coprime, symmetric matrices C, D. Siegel has shown [loc. cit.] that the infinite set of inequalities (iii) follows from a finite subset of them, but the exact number of independent inequalities in (iii) was not known for any $n>1$. For $n=1$, Γ becomes the ordinary modular group and it is a classical result that a fundamental domain in the plane of the complex variable $z=x+iy$ is defined (essentially) by (i) $|x|\leqq\frac{1}{2}$; (ii) $y\geqq 0$; (iii) $|z|\geqq 1$. In the case $n=2$,

$$Z=\begin{pmatrix} z_1 & z_3\\ z_3 & z_2\end{pmatrix}=\begin{pmatrix} x_1 & x_3\\ x_3 & x_2\end{pmatrix}+i\begin{pmatrix} y_1 & y_3\\ y_3 & y_2\end{pmatrix},$$

(i) and (ii) become $|x_i|\leqq\frac{1}{2}$ and $y_2\geqq y_1\geqq 2y_3\geqq 0$, respectively. In the present paper the author shows that (iii) contains exactly 19 inequalities, namely $|z_1|\geqq 1$, $|z_2|\geqq 1$, $|z_1+z_2-2z_3\pm 1|\geqq 1$, and 15 others of the form abs $|Z+S|\geqq 1$, where S runs through a set of 15 (explicitly indicated) matrices, whose elements are $+1$, -1, or 0.

E. Grosswald (Princeton, N.J.)

Citations: MR 4, 242b = F50-2.

Referred to in E56-23.

F45-10 **(22# 5732)**

Christian, Ulrich. Über die Multiplikatorensysteme zur Gruppe der ganzen Modulsubstitutionen n-ten Grades. Math. Ann. **138** (1959), 363–397.

Consider the group of analytic automorphisms of the generalized upper half-plane of degree n [Siegel, Math. Ann. **116** (1939), 617–657] of the form $T: Z\to U'ZU+S$, where S is a symmetric integral matrix, U is a unimodular integral matrix, and U' is the transpose of U. A factor of automorphy (Multiplikatorensysteme) for this group is a set of holomorphic, nowhere-vanishing functions $I(T,Z)$ associated to the transformations T of the group such that $I(T_1T_2,Z)=I(T_1,T_2Z)I(T_2,Z)$ for each pair of transformations T_1, T_2. The author gives a complete classification of these factors of automorphy for $n\geqq 3$; modulo the usual notion of equivalence [Gunning, Amer. J. Math. **78** (1956), 357–382; MR **18**, 933] the only factors of automorphy are the trivial factor $I(T,Z)=1$ and, for even n, the factor $I(T,Z)=\det U$ when the transformation T is written as above. This classification involves, in addition to the more or less standard analytical techniques, a careful study of the algebraic properties of the group of unimodular matrices.

R. C. Gunning (Princeton, N.J.)

Referred to in F40-25, F45-15.

F45-11 **(23# A357)**

Gottschling, Erhard

Über die Fixpunkte der Siegelschen Modulgruppe.

Math. Ann. **143** (1961), 111–149.

Let A, B, C, D be $n\times n$ matrices with integral elements, set $M=\begin{pmatrix}A & B\\ C & D\end{pmatrix}$ and denote the transpose of M by M'; set $J=\begin{pmatrix}O & E\\ -E & O\end{pmatrix}$, where E is the unit matrix of order n. The set of matrices M satisfying $MJM'=J$ forms (under matrix multiplication) the (homogeneous) modular group of degree n. Identification of M with $-M$ leads to the inhomogeneous modular group Δ. The set of $n\times n$ symmetric matrices $Z+iY$, such that Y is positively definite, is the generalized upper half-plane and is denoted by $\mathfrak{H}$. If $Z\in\mathfrak{H}$ and $M\in\Delta$, then $M(Z)=(AZ+B)(CZ+D)^{-1}$ defines a one-to-one mapping of $\mathfrak{H}$ onto itself. The purpose of the present paper is to study the set of fixed points of the transformation $Z\to M(Z)$, i.e., the set of solutions Z of the equation $AZ+B=Z(CZ+D)$, $M\in\Delta$ being kept fixed. The results are too complicated to be quoted in full; one of the simplest is the following: Theorem 5: Let $\rho=e^{2\pi i/3}$, $\omega=e^{2\pi i/5}$, $\eta=\frac{1}{3}(1+2\cdot 2^{1/2}i)$. Then the set of all isolated fixed points is given (modulo Δ) by the formulae:

$$\text{(a)}\quad Z=\begin{pmatrix}\omega & \omega+\omega^{-2}\\ \omega+\omega^{-2} & -\omega^{-1}\end{pmatrix},\ \begin{pmatrix}\omega & -(\omega^2+\omega^{-1})\\ -(\omega^2+\omega^{-1}) & -\omega^{-1}\end{pmatrix},$$

$$\begin{pmatrix}-\omega^{-1} & \omega+\omega^{-2}\\ \omega+\omega^{-2} & \omega\end{pmatrix},\ \begin{pmatrix}-\omega^{-1} & -(\omega^2+\omega^{-1})\\ -(\omega^2+\omega^{-1}) & \omega\end{pmatrix};$$

$$\text{(b)}\quad Z=\begin{pmatrix}\eta & \frac{1}{2}(\eta-1)\\ \frac{1}{2}(\eta-1) & \eta\end{pmatrix},\ \begin{pmatrix}-\eta^{-1} & \frac{1}{2}(-\eta^{-1}+1)\\ \frac{1}{2}(-\eta^{-1}+1) & -\eta^{-1}\end{pmatrix};$$

$$\text{(c)}\quad Z=\begin{pmatrix}i & 0\\ 0 & i\end{pmatrix};$$

(d) $Z = \begin{pmatrix} \rho & 0 \\ 0 & \rho \end{pmatrix}, \begin{pmatrix} \rho & 0 \\ 0 & -\rho^{-1} \end{pmatrix}, \begin{pmatrix} -\rho^{-1} & 0 \\ 0 & \rho \end{pmatrix}, \begin{pmatrix} -\rho^{-1} & 0 \\ 0 & -\rho^{-1} \end{pmatrix}$;

(e) $Z = 3^{-1/2} i \begin{pmatrix} 2 & 1 \\ 1 & 2 \end{pmatrix}$;

(f) $Z = \begin{pmatrix} \rho & 0 \\ 0 & i \end{pmatrix}, \begin{pmatrix} -\rho^{-1} & 0 \\ 0 & i \end{pmatrix}$.

E. Grosswald (Philadelphia, Pa.)

Referred to in E56-23, F45-12, F45-21.

F45-12 (23# A1719)

Gottschling, Erhard

Über die Fixpunktuntergruppen der Siegelschen Modulgruppe.

Math. Ann. **143** (1961), 399–430.

Let Δ be the (inhomogeneous) modular group of degree n and $\mathfrak{H}$ the set of all symmetric matrices $Z = X + iY$, with complex coefficients, and with positive-definite imaginary part Y. If $M = \begin{pmatrix} A & B \\ C & D \end{pmatrix} \in \Delta$, then the set of entire matrices (i.e., of matrices M with $C = 0$) forms a subgroup Γ of Δ. The mapping $M(Z) = (AZ + B)(CZ + D)^{-1}$ of $\mathfrak{H}$ onto itself is one-to-one and analytic (in each of the $\frac{1}{2}n(n+1)$ elements of Z) and Siegel has shown [Amer. J. Math. **65** (1943), 1–86; MR **4**, 242] that $M_1(Z) = M_2(Z)$ for all $Z \in \mathfrak{H}$ implies $M_1 = M_2$. If for some $M \in \Delta$ and some $Z \in \mathfrak{H}$ one has (*) $M(Z) = Z$, i.e., (*) $AZ + B = Z(CZ + D)$, then Z is called a fixed point of M. Keeping M fixed, one may ask for the set $\mathfrak{H}(M)$ of all matrices $Z \in \mathfrak{H}$, for which (*) holds. This problem was treated by the author in a previous paper, quoted in what follows by (I) [Math. Ann. **143** (1961), 111–149; MR **23** #A357] and solved completely in the case $n = 2$. The present paper discusses the dual problem: To determine the set $\Delta(Z)$ of all matrices $M \in \Delta$, such that (*) holds for some fixed $Z \in \mathfrak{H}$. One observes that the set $\Delta(Z)$ is actually a (finite) group under matrix multiplication. Let also $\Gamma(Z)$ be defined for Γ the way $\Delta(Z)$ is defined for Δ, and, for an arbitrary point-set $\mathfrak{M}$, let $\bigcap_{Z \in \mathfrak{M}} \Delta(Z) = \Delta(\mathfrak{M})$ and $\bigcap_{Z \in \mathfrak{M}} \Gamma(Z) = \Gamma(\mathfrak{M})$. A first general theorem permits one to obtain $\Delta(\mathfrak{M})$, if one knows $\Gamma(\mathfrak{M})$, for any point-set $\mathfrak{M}$. A second general theorem deals with properties of regions $\mathfrak{B}$, defined for fixed $M = \begin{pmatrix} * & * \\ C & D \end{pmatrix}$ by absolute value of determinant of $CZ + D \geqq 1$. The other results are valid only for $n = 2$; they are obtained by using the first general theorem in conjunction with the results of (I). Clearly, $\Delta(Z)$ reduces to the identity, unless Z is a fixed point, as determined in (I). In these cases, $\Delta(Z)$ contains a normal subgroup $\Delta_0(Z)$, such that the factor group $\Delta(Z)/\Delta_0(Z)$ is either cyclic, or is the group of a regular polyhedron. In general $\Delta_0(Z)$ is the identity. The exceptions occur if Z is one of the fixed points defined by Theorem 5 of (I) under either (c) or (d) [see (I), or MR **23** #A357], when $\Delta_0(Z)$ is the dihedral group of order 8 or of order 12, respectively. For $n = 2$, the complete structure of $\Delta(Z)$ is obtained in all cases.

E. Grosswald (Philadelphia, Pa.)

Citations: MR 4, 242b = F50-2; MR 23# A357 = F45-11.

Referred to in F45-21.

F45-13 (23# A1839)

Koecher, Max

Beiträge zu einer Reduktionstheorie in Positivitätsbereichen. I.

Math. Ann. **141** (1960), 384–432.

The author introduced positivity regions first in Amer. J. Math. **79** (1957), 575–596 [MR **19**, 867] to deal simultaneously with the different kinds of modular functions in several complex variables. This paper presents the construction of fundamental domains. Voronoï [J. Reine Angew. Math. **133** (1908), 97–178; **134** (1908), 198–287; **136** (1909), 67–181] considered the representation $\mathfrak{H} \to \mathfrak{A}^t\mathfrak{H}\mathfrak{A}$ ($\mathfrak{A}$ unimodular) of the unimodular group Ω in the space Y of all positive definite real symmetric matrices $\mathfrak{H}$. The author extends these ideas to arbitrary positivity regions. Let X be an n-dimensional vector space over the real field R and $\sigma(a, b)$ a positive definite symmetric bilinear form over X. A topology on X is introduced by the norm $|a| = \sqrt{\sigma(a, a)}$. Then a subset $Y \subset X$ is called a positivity region if: (1) Y is open and not empty; (2) $\sigma(a, b) > 0$ for all $a, b \in Y$; (3) for x not in Y, there is an $a \neq 0$ in the topological closure $\bar{Y}$ of Y with $\sigma(a, x) \leqq 0$. In Voronoï's case X is the space of real symmetric m-rowed matrices, $n = \frac{1}{2}m(m+1)$, $\sigma(\mathfrak{A}, \mathfrak{B}) = \operatorname{trace}(\mathfrak{A}\mathfrak{B})$, Y the region of positive definite matrices. Let D be a discrete subset of $\bar{Y} - \{0\}$ and $\mu(y)$ the minimum of the linear form $\sigma(d, y)$ over D for fixed $y \in Y$. The points, where this minimum is attained, span a convex pyramid $P(y)$. Under certain conditions on D (D zulässig) there exist n-dimensional $P(y)$, and they cover Y without gaps and overlappings. Using these facts an useful fundamental domain F is constructed explicitly for a wide class of discontinuous groups Ω of automorphisms of Y, which map D onto itself. F is contained in the union of a finite number of n-dimensional pyramids $P(y)$ and has only a finite number of neighbors. Hence, by a well-known argument, Ω can be finitely generated. In Voronoï's example one may take for D the set of all $\mathfrak{g}\mathfrak{g}^t$, where $\mathfrak{g}$ runs over all columns $\neq 0$ of m rational integers. Then $\mu(\mathfrak{H})$ has the usual meaning $\mu(\mathfrak{H}) = \min_{\mathfrak{g} \neq 0} \mathfrak{g}^t\mathfrak{H}\mathfrak{g}$.

The author shows further that definite quadratic forms over arbitrary algebraic number fields (Minkowski, Siegel, Humbert) and quadratic forms over the quaternions (Weyl) are contained in his general investigations. One gets further results, for instance, the finiteness of the class number, if one assumes D to be contained in a lattice of X. Finally the main results of Minkowski's reduction theory, such as the Minkowski-Siegel inequalities or the finiteness theorem for the volume of the fundamental domain, are proved in a new way simultaneously for all the examples mentioned above. Generalizations to indefinite quadratic forms and to modular groups seem to be possible following the ideas of C. L. Siegel.

H. Klingen (Heidelberg)

Referred to in F45-17.

F45-14 (23# A3262)

Christian, Ulrich

On certain factors of automorphy for the modular group of degree n.

Monatsh. Math. **65** (1961), 82–87.

Let Γ be the modular group of degree n consisting of all symplectic matrices

$$M = \begin{pmatrix} A & B \\ C & D \end{pmatrix}$$

with integral $n \times n$ matrices A, B, C, D. Let $\mathfrak{Z}$ be the generalized upper half-plane consisting of all complex symmetric $n \times n$ matrices $Z = X + iY$, where Y is positive definite. Then the image of $\mathfrak{Z}$ by M is $M(Z) = (AZ + B) \times (CZ + D)^{-1}$ and Det $(CZ + D) \neq 0$ for $Z \in \mathfrak{Z}$. It is shown that, if $n \geqq 2$, the functions $I_t(M; Z) = \{\operatorname{Det}(CZ + D)\}^t$, for complex t, form a system of factors of automorphy for holomorphic forms $F(Z)$ if and only if t is a rational integer. The sufficiency part is obvious. To prove necessity the author sets up an elaborate relation involving products of powers of five special matrices in Γ, which he optimistically states to be obvious. Even if the definition of the matrix M_5 were made clear, the verification of this relation would be onerous. It is also shown that, when n is even and positive and t is odd, there exist modular forms of all sufficiently large weights t.

R. A. Rankin (Glasgow)

F45-15 **(23# A3284)**

Christian, Ulrich

On the factors of automorphy for the group of integral modular substitutions of second degree

Ann. of Math. (2) **73** (1961), 134–153.

In an earlier paper [Math. Ann. **138** (1959), 363–397; MR **22** #5732] the author obtained a classification of the factors of automorphy for the subgroup of the symplectic modular group of degree $n \geqq 3$ consisting of the transformations of the form: $Z \to U'ZU+S$, where U is an $n \times n$ unimodular integral matrix, S is an $n \times n$ symmetric integral matrix, and Z is a point in the Siegel generalized upper half-plane of rank n. The present paper presents a corresponding classification for the case $n=2$; the classification is more complicated, and, unlike the case $n \geqq 3$, there are infinitely many classes of such factors of automorphy.

R. C. Gunning (Princeton, N.J.)

Citations: MR 22# 5732 = F45-10.
Referred to in F40-25.

F45-16 **(24# A188)**

Selberg, Atle

On discontinuous groups in higher-dimensional symmetric spaces.

Contributions to function theory (Internat. Colloq. Function Theory, Bombay, 1960), pp. 147–164. *Tata Institute of Fundamental Research, Bombay,* 1960.

Let G be the group of all $n \times n$ real matrices of determinant one. A matrix will be called algebraic if all its entries are algebraic numbers. The main result proven in this paper is the following. Theorem: If $n \geqq 3$ and Γ is a discrete subgroup of G with compact quotient $\Gamma \backslash G$, then we can, by an inner automorphism of G, bring Γ to such a form $T\Gamma T^{-1}$, that all the elements of $T\Gamma T^{-1}$ are algebraic matrices. This result stands in sharp contrast to the case $n=2$, where there are families of discontinuous groups of 2×2 matrices of determinant one with compact fundamental domain (in the hyperbolic plane) and depending non-trivially on continuous parameters. In general, if Γ is a discrete subgroup of G with $\Gamma \backslash G$ of finite measure, Γ is said to be deformable, provided that it can be imbedded in a family of groups $\Gamma^{(t)}$ (continuous dependence on the continuous parameter t, $0 \leqq t \leqq \vartheta$) such that $\Gamma^{(t)}$ is discrete, $\Gamma^{(t)} \backslash G$ is of finite measure and $\Gamma^{(0)} = \Gamma$. If $\Gamma^{(t)} = T\Gamma T^{-1}$ ($T \in G$), the deformation is called trivial; groups with no non-trivial deformations are called rigid. The proof of the theorem depends on several lemmas that fall naturally into two categories. In the first (Lemmas 1 to 7), criteria are obtained permitting one to assert that a given deformation is trivial. Lemma **5**, for instance, states that a deformation which preserves the traces of those elements of Γ which have real eigenvalues with distinct absolute values is a trivial deformation. Some of these lemmas are valid under more general assumptions (G a locally compact group, Γ discrete), but the compactness of $\Gamma \backslash G$ is required. The last two lemmas (8 and 9) show that if Γ is discrete and $\Gamma \backslash G$ compact (here this requirement may be relaxed to that of finite measure), then Γ can be deformed into a group of algebraic matrices. The proof of the theorem is completed by showing that Lemma 5 is applicable and the deformation is actually a trivial one. More general situations can be handled by this method in an attempt to prove the theorem for all symmetric spaces of dimension $n \geqq 3$ (except certain product spaces) and discontinuous groups whose fundamental domains have finite volume. Similar results (including the case of isotropic spaces of negative curvature, not covered by the present theorem) were obtained by Calabi and Vesentini [Ann. of Math. (2) **71** (1960), 472–507; MR **22** #1922b], and a note added in proof mentions that A. Weil has proven the rigidity of groups with compact fundamental domain for all remaining symmetric spaces.

E. Grosswald (Philadelphia, Pa.)

F45-17 **(25# 232)**

Koecher, Max

Beiträge zu einer Reduktionstheorie in Positivitätsbereichen. II.

Math. Ann. **144** (1961), 175–182.

B. A. Venkov [Izv. Akad. Nauk SSSR Ser. Mat. **4** (1940), 37–52; MR **2**, 147] gave a general method of determining fundamental domains of the unimodular group U of degree n. He considered the usual representation $\mathfrak{Y} \to \mathfrak{U}^t\mathfrak{Y}\mathfrak{U}$ ($\mathfrak{U} \in U$) of U in the space $Y = \{\mathfrak{Y}\}$ of n-rowed positive symmetric matrices. Let $\mathfrak{F} \in Y$ be any non-fixed point of U; then $F(\mathfrak{F}) = \{\mathfrak{Y} \in Y \mid \operatorname{tr}(\mathfrak{F}\mathfrak{Y}) \leqq \operatorname{tr}(\mathfrak{F}\mathfrak{U}^t\mathfrak{Y}\mathfrak{U})$ for all $\mathfrak{U} \in U\}$ represents such a fundamental domain in Y. Because of the fact that the set of non-fixed points is everywhere dense in Y, there is enough arbitrariness in the choice of $F(\mathfrak{F})$ to be useful for applications. Furthermore, he proved that the number of $\mathfrak{U} \in U$ for which the equality $\operatorname{tr}(\mathfrak{F}\mathfrak{Y}) = \operatorname{tr}(\mathfrak{F}\mathfrak{U}^t\mathfrak{Y}\mathfrak{U})$ holds is uniformly bounded in $F(\mathfrak{F})$.

Continuing his earlier work [Math. Ann. **141** (1960), 384–432; MR **23** #A1839], the present author carries these theorems over to discontinuous groups U operating on general positivity domains Y. The only restriction on U is the same finiteness condition already used in part I. Now the concept and theorems are so wide that all the situations are covered which appear in the theory of modular functions in several complex variables. The concept of a complete form due to Voronoï is again important.

H. Klingen (Heidelberg)

Citations: MR 2, 147c = E12-2; MR 23# A1839 = F45-13.

F45-18 **(26# 6265)**

Newman, M.; Smart, J. R.

Modulary groups of $t \times t$ matrices.

Duke Math. J. **30** (1963), 253–257.

Let I be the $t \times t$ identity matrix, Γ the group of rational, integral $t \times t$ matrices of determinant 1, $\Gamma(n)$ the principal congruence subgroup of Γ of level n, i.e., $\Gamma(n) = \{A \in \Gamma \mid A \equiv I \pmod{n}\}$. Then, if $a \mid b$, $\Gamma(b)$ is a normal subgroup of $\Gamma(a)$. Hence, one may form the quotient group $\Gamma(a)/\Gamma(b)$, which is called the modulary group $\mathfrak{M}(a, b)$. The authors study the structure of $\mathfrak{M}(a, b)$; among their results are the following. For $(m, nr) = 1$ and arbitrary d, $\mathfrak{M}(dn, dmn) \cong \mathfrak{M}(dr, dmr)$. For $(m, n) = 1$ and arbitrary d, $\mathfrak{M}(d, dmn) \cong \mathfrak{M}(d, dm) \times \mathfrak{M}(d, dn)$ and $\mathfrak{M}(dmn, dm^2n^2) \cong \mathfrak{M}(dm, dm^2) \times \mathfrak{M}(dn, dn^2)$. Let d and $n = \prod_{p \mid n} p^{\beta_p}$ be arbitrary and denote by α_p the highest power to which the prime factor p of n divides d. Then $\mathfrak{M}(d, dn) = \prod_{p \mid n} \mathfrak{M}(p^{\alpha_p}, p^{\alpha_p + \beta_p})$ ($\prod$ stands here for the direct product). The order of $\mathfrak{M}(1, p^m)$ is $p^{m(t^2-1)} \prod_{j=2}^{t} (1-p^{-j})$; more generally, the order of $\mathfrak{M}(1, n) = n^{t^2-1} \prod_{p \mid n} \prod_{j=2}^{t} (1-p^{-j})$. If $s \mid m$, then $\mathfrak{M}(m, ms)$ is abelian. If $1 \leqq u \leqq v$, then $\mathfrak{M}(p^v, p^{u+v})$ is abelian of order $p^{u(t^2-1)}$, type $(p^u, \cdots, p^u)$, and a set of generators of simple form is indicated. More generally, if $s \mid m$, then $\mathfrak{M}(m, sm)$ is the direct product of factors of the form $\mathfrak{M}(p^v, p^{u+v})$, of known structure. The question is raised under what conditions $\mathfrak{M}(p^\alpha, p^\beta) \cong \mathfrak{M}(p^\gamma, p^\delta)$; the necessary condition $\beta - \alpha = \delta - \gamma$ is not sufficient. The method uses one of the isomorphism theorems (if G and

H are normal subgroups of Γ, then $GH/G \cong H/G \cap H)$ and previous results by Newman and Reiner [Trans. Amer. Math. Soc. **91** (1959), 369–379; MR **21** #5683] and Fine and Niven [Bull. Amer. Math. Soc. **50** (1944), 89–93; MR **5**, 169] follow. *E. Grosswald* (Philadelphia, Pa.)

Citations: MR 5, 169f = C20-5; MR 21# 5683 = F45-8.

Referred to in F45-22, F45-26.

F45-19 (29# 166)

Newman, M.; Smart, J. R.

Symplectic modulary groups.

Acta Arith. **9** (1964), 83–89.

Let I_t denote the $t \times t$ unit matrix, M' the transpose of a matrix M, and set

$$J = \begin{pmatrix} 0 & I_t \\ -I_t & 0 \end{pmatrix}.$$

Consider matrices whose entries are rational integers, and write $M \equiv N \pmod n$ to indicate elementwise congruence.

The symplectic modular group Γ consists of all $2t \times 2t$ matrices M (with rational integral entries) such that $MJM' = J$. Its principal congruence subgroup $\Gamma(n)$ consists of all $M \in \Gamma$ such that $M \equiv I_{2t} \pmod n$. If a divides b, define the symplectic modulary group $\mathfrak{M}(a, b) = \Gamma(a)/\Gamma(b)$.

The authors prove various results about the structure of $\mathfrak{M}(a, b)$. A typical theorem is as follows: Let p^u divide m, where p is prime. Then $\mathfrak{M}(m, mp^u)$ is an abelian group of type $(p^u, \cdots, p^u)$, the number of factors being $2t^2 + t$.

Of independent interest is the preliminary theorem which the authors establish: If $NJN' \equiv J \pmod n$, then there exists an $M \in \Gamma$ such that $M \equiv N \pmod n$.

I. Reiner (Urbana, Ill.)

Referred to in F45-20, F45-26.

F45-20 (30# 3100)

Newman, Morris

A theorem on the automorphs of a skew-symmetric matrix.

Michigan Math. J. **12** (1965), 61–63.

Consider matrices with rational integral entries. Let K be a nonsingular skew-symmetric matrix. Call N K-symplectic if $NKN' = K$. The author gives a simple proof of the following result: If M is an integral matrix satisfying $MKM' \equiv K \pmod n$, there exists a K-symplectic matrix N such that $N \equiv M \pmod n$. The proof depends upon reducing this problem to the special case in which

$$K = \begin{pmatrix} 0 & I \\ -I & 0 \end{pmatrix},$$

where I is the identity matrix. The result for the special case was established earlier [the author and J. R. Smart, Acta Arith. **9** (1964), 83–89; MR **29** #166].

I. Reiner (Urbana, Ill.)

Citations: MR 29# 166 = F45-19.

F45-21 (30# 3239)

Christian, Ulrich

Über die Uniformisierbarkeit der Fixpunkte der Modulgruppe zweiten Grades.

Nachr. Akad. Wiss. Göttingen Math.-Phys. Kl. II **1964**, 211–231.

Es sei $Z(n)$ die verallgemeinerte obere Halbebene und $\Gamma(n)$ die Siegelsche Modulgruppe n-ten Grades. Der Quotientenraum $Q(n) = Z(n)/\Gamma(n)$ werde nach Satake in der Form $\bar{Q}(n) = Q(n) \cup Q(n-1) \cup \cdots \cup Q(0)$ kompaktifiziert. Der Verfasser hatte früher [Math. Z. **85** (1964), 1–28; ibid. **85** (1964), 29–39; MR **29** #6063] die Uniformisierbarkeit der Punkte von $Q(1) \cup Q(0)$ in $\bar{Q}(2)$ behandelt. In der vorliegenden Arbeit werden seine Betrachtungen für $n = 2$ zum Abschluss gebracht durch die Untersuchung der Punkte aus $Q(2)$. Wegen der vorliegenden Resultate von Igusa [Amer. J. Math. **84** (1962), 175–200; MR **25** #5040] in dieser Richtung legt der Verfasser Wert auf elementare Beweise. Es ist klar, dass Nichtfixpunkte von $\Gamma(2)$ in $Z(2)$ beim Übergang zum Quotientenraum zu uniformisierbaren Punkten führen. Für die Untersuchung der Fixpunkte benutzt der Verfasser wesentlich die von Gottschling [Math. Ann. **143** (1961), 399–430; MR **23** #A1719; ibid. **143** (1961), 111–149; MR **23** #A357] gegebene explizite Bestimmung aller Fixpunkte und die strukturellen Aussagen über die Fixpunktgruppen (zyklische Gruppen oder Drehungsgruppen der regulären Körper). Es stellt sich heraus, dass ein Teil der Fixpunkte uniformisierbar ist, insbesondere diejenigen, welche von den komplex zweidimensionalen Fixpunktmannigfaltigkeiten herrühren; es gibt aber auch nichtuniformisierbare Fixpunkte in $Q(2)$, die alle explizit bestimmt werden. Zum Schluss wird der Zusammenhang mit Igusas Resultaten hergestellt. *H. Klingen* (Freiburg)

Citations: MR 23# A357 = F45-11; MR 23# A1719 = F45-12; MR 25# 5040 = F50-22; MR 29# 6063 = F50-35.

F45-22 (31# 4840)

Houghton, C. H.

A question of M. Newman and J. R. Smart.

Duke Math. J. **32** (1965), 541–543.

For $a|b$, let $M(a, b)$ be a modulary group of $t \times t$ matrices. Then Newman and Smart [same J. **30** (1963), 253–257; MR **26** #6265] reduced the study of the structure of $M(a, b)$ to that of $M(p^\alpha, p^\beta)$ (p a prime). In particular, they proved that $M(p^\alpha, p^\beta) \cong M(p^\delta, p^\varepsilon)$ provided that $1 \leqq \alpha \leqq \beta \leqq 2\alpha$, $1 \leqq \delta \leqq \varepsilon \leqq 2\delta$, and $\beta - \alpha = \varepsilon - \delta$. The problem of determining necessary conditions for such an isomorphism was left open, but they showed by the counterexample $M(p, p^3) \not\cong M(p^2, p^4)$ that $\beta - \alpha = \varepsilon - \delta$ alone is not sufficient. The present author solves the problem by proving that the full set of sufficient conditions of Newman and Smart are also necessary. The proof is based on (i) the fact (proven in the present paper) that if $0 \leqq \alpha \leqq \gamma \leqq \beta$, then $M(p^\gamma, p^\beta)$ is a normal subgroup of $M(p^\alpha, p^\beta)$ and $M(p^\alpha, p^\beta)$ is an extension of $M(p^\gamma, p^\beta)$ by $M(p^\alpha, p^\gamma)$, and on (ii) the known [see Newman and Reiner, Trans. Amer. Math. Soc. **91** (1959), 369–379; MR **21** #5683] lemma: If S is an integral $t \times t$ matrix, $\det S \equiv 1 \pmod m$, then there exists an integral matrix A, with $\det A = 1$, such that $A \equiv S \pmod m$. Furthermore, from the fact that $M(p^{\beta-\alpha}, p^\beta)$ is central in $M(p^\alpha, p^\beta)$, it follows that if r is the greatest integer satisfying $r\alpha < \beta$, then the nilpotency class of $M(p^\alpha, p^\beta)$ is $\leqq r$, with equality at least for $t > 2$.

E. Grosswald (Philadelphia, Pa.)

Citations: MR 21# 5683 = F45-8; MR 26# 6265 = F45-18.

F45-23 (31# 5844)

Christian, Ulrich

Über die Uniformisierbarkeit nicht-elliptischer Fixpunkte Siegelscher Modulgruppen.

J. Reine Angew. Math. **219** (1965), 97–112.

Der Verfasser [z.B. Math. Ann. **152** (1963), 275–341; MR **28** #2256] und Igusa [Amer. J. Math. **84** (1962), 175–200; MR **25** #5040] haben in mehreren früheren Arbeiten die lokale Uniformisierbarkeit der nach Satake und Christian kompaktifizierten Quotientenräume zu Modulgruppen und verwandten Gruppen untersucht. Jetzt behandelt der Verfasser einen Fall, der mit seinen früheren Methoden nicht erfasst werden konnte. Es sei ψ eine beliebige Kongruenzgruppe n-ten Grades über dem rationalen Zahlkörper, welche auf dem Siegelschen Halbraum $H(n)$

in der üblichen Weise operiert und

$$R(n)/\psi = H(n)/\psi \cup R_1(n)/\psi \cup \cdots \cup R_n(n)/\psi$$

der kompaktifizierte Quotientenraum. Die Punkte aus $R_1 \cup \cdots \cup R_n$ heissen nicht-elliptische Fixpunkte von ψ. Das Hauptergebnis besagt, dass für $n \geq 3$ kein nicht-elliptischer Fixpunkt uniformisierbar ist. Für $n=2$ wird ein Kriterium für Uniformisierbarkeit angegeben, welches allerdings nicht unmittelbar auf ψ anwendbar ist. Zum Beweise genügt es, die sogenannten einfachen Fixpunkte aus R_1 zu betrachten, weil diese in der Menge aller nicht-elliptischen Fixpunkte dicht liegen. Die einfachen Fixpunkte aus R_1 zerfallen in zwei Arten, von denen die erste wie früher vom Verfasser [loc. cit.] behandelt wird. Neue Überlegungen sind notwendig für die sogenannten einfachen Fixpunkte zweiter Art. *H. Klingen* (Freiburg)

Citations: MR 25# 5040 = F50-22; MR 28# 2256 = F40-29.

Referred to in F50-51.

F45-24 (32# 7790)

Pjateckiĭ-Šapiro, I. I.

Arithmetic groups in complex domains. (Russian)

Uspehi Mat. Nauk **19** (1964), *no.* 6 (120), 93–121.

Let $\mathscr{D}$ be a homogeneous bounded domain and Γ a discrete group of analytic automorphisms of $\mathscr{D}$. The main object of the paper is to construct a suitable extension $\mathscr{M}$ of the quotient space $\mathscr{D}/\Gamma$, which is a normal analytic space containing $\mathscr{D}/\Gamma$ as an everywhere dense open subspace. The method depends essentially on a recent result of the author, stated without proof, that any homogeneous analytic fibration of $\mathscr{D}$ coincides with the natural fibration in some realization of $\mathscr{D}$ in the form of a Siegel domain of the third kind [cf. Uspehi Mat. Nauk **20** (1965), no. 2 (122), 3–51]; no mention is made of the uniqueness of this realization, though it is implicit and used frequently in the paper. The author defines a Γ-rational boundary component of $\mathscr{D}$ as a base space $\mathscr{D}'$ of such a fibration of $\mathscr{D}$ satisfying a certain rationality condition; in case $\mathscr{D}$ is a homogeneous space of an algebraic group G defined over $\mathbf{Q}$ and Γ is an "arithmetic" subgroup (i.e., commensurable with $G_{\mathbf{Z}}$), this condition is shown to be equivalent to the condition that the group of "parallel translations" (defined in connection with the realization of $\mathscr{D}$ as a Siegel domain of the third kind corresponding to $\mathscr{D}'$) is an algebraic subgroup of G defined over $\mathbf{Q}$. Then $\mathscr{M}$ is defined as the quotient space $\mathfrak{M}/\Gamma$, where $\mathfrak{M}$ is the set-theoretical union of $\mathscr{D}$ and all Γ-rational boundary components endowed with a topology depending again on the realizations of $\mathscr{D}$ as a Siegel domain of the third kind. In case $\mathscr{D}$ is a symmetric domain and Γ is an arithmetic subgroup of the group of all analytic automorphisms of $\mathscr{D}$, the extension $\mathscr{M}$ thus obtained is proved to be a compact Hausdorff space by virtue of a reduction theory of Borel [Colloq. Théorie des Groupes Algébriques (Bruxelles, 1962), pp. 23–40, Librairie Universitaire, Louvain, 1962; MR **26** #6173]; more specifically, this connection is established by using the notion of "bounded holomorphic envelopes", introduced in the first section of the paper, and a detailed consideration of j-algebras developed previously by the author (with Vinberg and Gindikin) [Trudy Moskov. Mat. Obšč. **12** (1963), 359–388; MR **28** #1638]. (Note that the topology on $\mathfrak{M}$ in this paper is weaker than the one introduced on the same space in a recent paper of Baily and Borel treating a similar subject [Bull. Amer. Math. Soc. **70** (1964), 588–593; MR **29** #6058]. Finally, $\mathscr{M}$ becomes a normal analytic space embeddable in a projective space, whence one obtains the theorem of algebraic dependence of automorphic functions. (As for the proofs of these assertions, the author only indicates that the proofs are analogous to those given previously for the case of classical domains. Cf. his *Geometry of classical domains and the theory of automorphic functions* (Russian), Fizmatgiz, Moscow, 1961 [MR **25** #231].) As another approach to the same theorem, it is also shown that the criterion of Andreotti-Grauert ("pseudo-concavity") is applicable to all arithmetic groups. The paper contains also interesting remarks on the desingularization-problem of $\mathscr{M}$ and some (mostly known) results on Hecke rings. As a whole, the paper is written in a very suggestive way, but the proofs are often too sketchy to convince the reader. Some of the results of this paper are obtained independently (with a more complete proof) by Borel and Baily [loc. cit.].

{This article has appeared in English translation [Russian Math. Surveys **19** (1964), no. 6, 83–109].}

I. Satake (Chicago, Ill.)

Citations: MR 25# 231 = F02-10; MR 26# 6173 = E60-6; MR 29# 6058 = F50-30.

Referred to in F99-4.

F45-25 (33# 5630)

Baily, Walter L., Jr.

On the orbit spaces of arithmetic groups.

Arithmetical Algebraic Geometry (Proc. Conf. Purdue Univ., 1963), *pp.* 4–10. *Harper & Row, New York,* 1965.

This is an expository note on the recent development of the theory of compactification [cf., especially, the author and Borel, Ann. of Math. (2) **84** (1966), 442–528]. In the last part of the paper, the author considers a quotient space of the form $\mathscr{S}/\Gamma$, where $\mathscr{S}$ is a hermitian symmetric space with compact factors and Γ is an arithmetic subgroup of the group of all isometries of $\mathscr{S}$, and shows how the generalization of Kodaira's criterion can be used to find a projective imbedding of $\mathscr{S}/\Gamma$. *I. Satake* (Chicago, Ill.)

Citations: MR 35# 6870 = F50-31.

F45-26 (34# 1401)

Kolmer, S. K.

Generalization of the symplectic modular group.

Acta Arith. **11** (1965/66), 281–291.

Let K be a rational integral skew-symmetric $2t \times 2t$ matrix in standard form; i.e., $K = \begin{pmatrix} 0 & H \\ -H & 0 \end{pmatrix}$, $H = \operatorname{diag}(h_1, \cdots, h_t)$, where, for all i, $h_i > 0$ and h_{i-1} divides h_i. A rational integral matrix $M = \begin{pmatrix} A & B \\ C & D \end{pmatrix}$ is called K-symplectic if $MKM' = K$. For $(\det K, n) = 1$, M is called K symplectic modulo n if $MKM' \equiv K \pmod{n}$. The author generalizes some of the results of M. Newman and J. R. Smart [Duke Math. J. **30** (1963), 253–257; MR **26** #6265; Acta Arith. **9** (1964), 83–89; MR **29** #166] to K-symplectic groups. The main theorem asserts that if M is K-symplectic modulo n, then there is a K-symplectic N with $N \equiv M \pmod{n}$. *B. Maskit* (Cambridge, Mass.)

Citations: MR 26# 6265 = F45-18; MR 29# 166 = F45-19.

F45-27 (34# 4215)

Christian, Ulrich

Einführung in die Theorie der paramodularen Gruppen.

Math. Ann. **168** (1967), 59–104.

Es sei F eine n-reihige Diagonalmatrix, deren Diagonalelemente $f_1, \cdots, f_n$ ganze rationale Zahlen sind und $f_1 | f_2 | \cdots | f_n$ erfüllen. Unter der parasymplektischen Gruppe $\Sigma(n, F)$ versteht man die Gruppe aller reellen $2n$-reihigen Lösungen M der Matrixgleichung ${}^tMJM = J$, $J = \begin{pmatrix} 0 & F \\ -F & 0 \end{pmatrix}$. Sie ist in $\mathrm{GL}(2n, \mathbf{R})$ konjugiert zur symplektischen Gruppe und lässt sich daher in naheliegender

Weise als Gruppe aller biholomorphen Abbildungen des Siegelschen Halbraumes darstellen. Die paramodulare Gruppe $\Pi(n, F)$ besteht aus allen ganzen $M \in \Sigma(n, F)$. Diese Gruppe wurde in Verallgemeinerung der Siegelschen Modulgruppe, Spezialfall $F = E$ (Einheitsmatrix), von Pjateckiĭ-Šapiro und Siegel eingeführt. Verfasser gibt detaillierte Untersuchungen dieser Gruppe und gewisser Kongruenzuntergruppen in Verallgemeinerung von bekannten Resultaten im Spezialfall $F = E$. Sie betreffen Erzeugende, Gruppenindizes, Uniformisierbarkeit von elliptischen Fixpunkten und Gewichte von Multiplikatorensystemen. Diese Resultate sind wichtig für die Theorie der zugehörigen automorphen Funktionen.

H. Klingen (Freiburg)

F45-28 (36# 3756)

Christian, Ulrich

Über teilerfremde symmetrische Matrizenpaare.

J. Reine Angew. Math. **229** (1968), 43–49.

Let C be a nonsingular $n \times n$ matrix. A residue class $A \bmod C$ is called symmetric if it contains a matrix D such that C, D form a symmetric pair in the sense of Siegel (i.e., $CD^t = DC^t$). Let $\varphi(n, C)$ denote the number of symmetric residue classes prime to C. The author gives a procedure for determining $\varphi(n, C)$ which depends finally on a recurrence formula for $\varphi(n, pE)$, E being the $n \times n$ identity matrix and p being a prime dividing the entries of the diagonal matrix in Smith normal form equivalent to C.

J. Lehner (College Park, Md.)

F45-29 (36# 4020)

Satake, Ichirô

A note on holomorphic imbeddings and compactification of symmetric domains.

Amer. J. Math. **90** (1968), 231–247.

Let $D = G/K$, $D' = G'/K'$ be symmetric domains. A holomorphic imbedding $\rho: D \to D'$ is a (not necessarily injective) holomorphic map induced by a homomorphism $\tilde{\rho}: G \to G'$ such that $\tilde{\rho}(K) \subset K'$. From earlier work of the author [Ann. of Math. (2) **71** (1960), 77–110; MR **22** #9546] and of S. Ihara [Proc. Japan Acad. **42** (1966), 193–197; MR **34** #370; J. Math. Soc. Japan **19** (1967), 261–302; MR **35** #5656], one has a complete classification of all such imbeddings. The subject of the present paper is the study of the correspondence under ρ of the boundary components of D and D' in the canonical Harish-Chandra realization. It is almost immediate that ρ is a linear map induced by the differential $d\tilde{\rho}$, and that the image of any boundary component is contained in a unique boundary component of D'. Using some earlier work of the reviewer and J. A. Wolf [Ann. of Math. (2) **81** (1965), 265–288; MR **30** #4980; Amer. J. Math. **87** (1965), 899–939; MR **33** #229], the author proceeds to a much more detailed explicit description of this correspondence. The discussion here is made fairly transparent by a systematic use of "Hermann maps", i.e., certain universal imbeddings of polydiscs into symmetric domains. Next, it is assumed that Γ, Γ' are arithmetically defined subgroups of G, G' such that $\rho(\Gamma) \subset \Gamma'$. (This amounts to assuming that G_C, G_C' are algebraic linear groups over Q and $\tilde{\rho}$ is rational, defined over Q.) It is well known from the work of the author, W. L. Baily and A. Borel [see Ann. of Math. (2) **84** (1966), 442–528; MR **35** #6870] that the quotient spaces $V = \Gamma \backslash D$ and $V' = \Gamma' \backslash D'$ have compactifications V^*, V'^* which are normal analytic spaces in a natural way. The main result of the present paper is that the map of V into V' induced by ρ extends to a holomorphic map of V^* into V^*. The proof consists of showing that rational boundary components of D are mapped by ρ into rational boundary components of D', and then showing that ρ regarded as a map of the union of D and its rational boundary components is continuous with respect to the topology used in the construction of the compactifications.

A. Korányi (New York)

Citations: MR 35# 6870 = F50-31.

Referred to in F45-34.

F45-30 (37# 6245)

Christian, Ulrich

Über die Anzahl der Spitzen Siegelscher Modulgruppen.

Abh. Math. Sem. Univ. Hamburg **32** (1968), 55–60.

${}_n\Gamma$ sei die Siegelsche Modulgruppe n-ten Grades, Ψ eine Untergruppe von endlichem Index. Sind im Falle $n = 1$ ${}_1\Gamma_1$, Ψ_1 die Untergruppen von ${}_1\Gamma$, Ψ, die ∞ festlassen, so ist (falls die negative Einheitsmatrix in Ψ liegt) $[{}_1\Gamma_1 : \Psi_1]$ die Spitzenbreite von Ψ in ∞. Ist Ψ Normalteiler in ${}_1\Gamma$, so haben alle Spitzen von Ψ die gleiche Breite und ihre Anzahl ist $A(\Psi) = [{}_1\Gamma : \Psi]/[{}_1\Gamma_1 : \Psi_1]$. Für $n > 1$ zerfällt die Spitze ∞ von ${}_n\Gamma$, wie man etwa bei der Kompaktifizierung des Quotientenraumes sieht, in n verschiedene Teile, der Teil der Nummer j wird durch die Untergruppe ${}_n\Gamma_j$ derjenigen Modulmatrizen charakterisiert, deren zweite Zeilen (C, D) die Gestalt $C = \begin{pmatrix} * & 0 \\ 0 & 0 \end{pmatrix}$, $D = \begin{pmatrix} * & * \\ 0 & * \end{pmatrix}$ haben, wenn man C, D in Kästchen einteilt mit einer j-reihigen quadratischen Untermatrix in der rechten unteren Ecke. Ψ_j sei die entsprechende Untergruppe von Ψ. Verfasser definiert in naheliegender Weise eine Spitzenanzahl $A(\Psi, j)$ für den Teil der Nummer j und zeigt, daß für Normalteiler Ψ auch hier $A(\Psi, j) = [{}_n\Gamma : \Psi]/[{}_n\Gamma_1 : \Psi]$ gilt. Für Hauptkongruenzuntergruppen ${}_n\Gamma(q)$ der Stufe q werden die $A({}_n\Gamma(q), j)$ explizit bestimmt. Da Verfasser für $n = 1$ und $2 \leq q \leq 13$ die Werte numerisch ausrechnet und für $q = 2$ auf die Übereinstimmung mit Klein-Fricke verweist, erscheint es nützlich, anzumerken, daß diese Endformel für $n = 1$ seit Jahrzehnten wohlbekannt ist. Ist Ψ kein Normalteiler, so braucht die Formel nicht mehr zu stimmen, was an dem altbekannten Beispiel der Gruppe ${}_1\Gamma_0(2)$ mit einer Spitze der Breite 1, einer Spitze der Breite 2 und dem Index 3 erläutert wird.

K.-B. Gundlach (Münster)

F45-31 (37# 6264)

Christian, Ulrich

Über die erste Zeile paramodularer Matrizen.

Nachr. Akad. Wiss. Göttingen Math.-Phys. Kl. II **1967**, 239–245.

Let $f_1, \cdots, f_n$ be rational integers with f_i/f_{i+1} ("divides"). $F = \operatorname{diag}(f_1, \cdots)$, $J_F = \begin{pmatrix} 0 & F \\ -F & 0 \end{pmatrix}$. The paramodular group with respect to F is the group of $2n \times 2n$ matrices $M = \begin{pmatrix} A & B \\ C & D \end{pmatrix}$ with rational integral coefficients satisfying $M^t J_F M = J_F$. One can also consider congruence subgroups $M \equiv 1$ (unit matrix) mod q. The author proves the following theorem: A pair A, B of $n \times n$ matrices is the first line of a paramodular matrix in the congruence subgroup if and only if the following conditions are satisfied: $AF^{-1}B^t = BF^{-1}A^t$; $A \equiv F^{-1}A^tF \equiv 1$, $B \equiv F^{-1}B^tF \equiv 0 \bmod q$; the coefficients of A and B (together) have g.c.d. 1.

M. Eichler (Basel)

F45-32 (39# 2768)

Kodama, Tetsuo

On $t_n(p)$ and $T_{p^2}(m)$ in the Hecke ring.

Math. Rep. General Ed. Department Kyushu Univ. **3** (1965), 1–17.

From the author's paper: "Let Z be the ring of integers, and let Z_l be the set of all square matrices of size l with entries in Z. We denote the unit matrix of size n by $E^{(n)}$, and $\begin{pmatrix} 0 & E^{(n)} \\ -E^{(n)} & 0 \end{pmatrix}$ by $J^{(n)}$. Let $G_n^{(m)} = \{M \mid {}^tMJ_nM = mJ_n, M \in Z_{2n}\}$, where ${}^tM$ denotes the transposed matrix of M. Then $G_n^{(1)}$ is identical with the symplectic modular group, and we denote it by G_n. Let $G_n \backslash G_n^{(m)}$ be the set of all left cosets of $G_n^{(m)}$ by G_n, and $G_n \backslash G_n^{(m)}/G_n$ be the set of all double cosets of $G_n^{(m)}$ by G_n. Let R be the free Z-module generated by all double cosets for all m. We call the ring R the Hecke ring and state the law of multiplication in R following G. Shimura [Proc. Nat. Acad. Sci. U.S.A. **49** (1963), 824–828; MR **28** #250]. Let G_nKG_n, G_nLG_n and G_nMG_n be three cosets in R, and let $G_nKG_n = \bigcup_i G_nK_i$, $G_nLG_n = \bigcup_j G_nL_j$ be their disjoint expressions. By $\mu(G_nKG_n \cdot G_nLG_n, G_nMG_n)$ we denote the number of (i, j) which satisfy $G_nK_iL_j = G_nM$, and we define the product

$$G_nKG_n \cdot G_nLG_n = \sum_{G_nMG_n \subset G_nKG_nLG_n} \mu(G_nKG_n \cdot G_nLG_n, G_nMG_n)G_nMG_n.$$

With this law of multiplication R becomes a commutative ring. Since the diagonal matrices $[e_1, \cdots, e_n, f_1, \cdots, f_n]$ such that $e_if_i = m$, e_{i+1} are divisible by e_i for $1 \leq i \leq n-1$, are the complete system of representatives of $G_n \backslash G_n^{(m)}/G_n$, we denote the corresponding cosets by $T(e_1, \cdots, e_n; f_n, \cdots, f_1)$ and denote the element $\sum T(e_1, \cdots, e_n; f_n, \cdots, f_1)$ in R by $t_n(m)$, where the summation ranges over the above e_i and f_j for an integer m. We denote

$$T(\overbrace{1, \cdots, 1}^{r}, \overbrace{p, \cdots, p}^{n-r}; p, \cdots, p, p^2, \cdots, p^2)$$

by $T_{p^2}(r)$. Primarily $t_n(p)$ and $T_{p^2}(m)$ are considered, because $t_n(p)$ and $T_{p^2}(m)$ are generators of R over the ring of rational integers." *N. Kuhlmann* (Bochum)

Citations: MR 28# 250 = F50-24.

F45-33 **(39# 4449)**

Evgrafov, M. A.; Postnikov, M. M.

A certain property of Siegel's modular group. (Russian)

Mat. Sb. (*N.S.*) **78** (**120**) (1969), 485–500.

Sei $\mathfrak{Z}_n$ die Siegelsche obere Halbebene aller symmetrischen komplexen n-reihigen Matrizen $Z = X + iY$ mit positiv definitem Y. Für $Z_0, Z_1 \in \mathfrak{Z}_n$ sei

$$R(Z_0, Z_1) = (Z_1 - Z_0)(Z_1 - \bar{Z}_0)^{-1}(\bar{Z}_1 - \bar{Z}_0)(\bar{Z}_1 - Z_0)^{-1}.$$

Seien $r_1, \cdots, r_n$ die der Größe nach geordneten Eigenwerte von $R(Z_0, Z_1)$ (es gilt stets $0 \leq r_k < 1$),

$$t_k = (1 + \sqrt{r_k})(1 - \sqrt{r_k})^{-1}$$

und $T = T(Z_0, Z_1)$ die Diagonalmatrix mit den Diagonalelementen $t_1, \cdots, t_n$. Bekanntlich läßt sich jedes Paar $Z_0, Z_1 \in \mathfrak{Z}_n$ durch einen holomorphen Automorphismus von $\mathfrak{Z}_n$ in das Paar iE, iT transformieren; dabei bedeutet E die n-reihige Einheitsmatrix [C. L. Siegel, Amer. J. Math. **65** (1943), 1–86; MR **4**, 242]. Verfasser behandeln nun die Frage der Transformierbarkeit für modulare Automorphismen von $\mathfrak{Z}_n$, d.h. Automorphismen, in deren Darstellung $Z \to (AZ+B)(CZ+D)^{-1}$ die Matrizen A, B, C, D ganzzahlig sind. Es wird folgender Satz bewiesen: Zu jedem $\varepsilon > 0$ existiert ein modularer Automorphismus von $\mathfrak{Z}_n$, der das Punktepaar Z_0, Z_1 in das Paar $(X_\varepsilon + iE + U_\varepsilon)\mu_\varepsilon$, $(X_\varepsilon + iT + V_\varepsilon)\mu_\varepsilon$ überführt. Dabei ist ε eine positive Zahl, X_ε eine reelle Matrix und U_ε und V_ε sind komplexe Matrizen, deren Koeffizienten einen Betrag $\leq \varepsilon$ haben. *O. Forster* (Regensburg)

Citations: MR 4, 242b = F50-2.

F45-34 **(40# 7483)**

Satake, Ichirô

On modular imbeddings of a symmetric domain of type (IV).

Global Analysis (*Papers in Honor of K. Kodaira*), *pp.* 341–354. *Univ. Tokyo Press, Tokyo*, 1969.

This paper is a supplement to an earlier one by the author [Nagoya Math. J. **27** (1966), 435–446; MR **35** #1602; correction, ibid. **31** (1968), 295–296; MR **36** #2624]. The author considers a suitable arithmetic group Γ_0 acting on a bounded symmetric domain $\mathscr{D}$ of type IV and constructs holomorphic embeddings into a Siegel upper half-plane $\mathscr{D}'$ compatible with homomorphisms of Γ_0 into the Siegel modular group Γ'. As shown earlier by the author [Amer. J. Math. **90** (1968), 231–247; MR **36** #4020], such an embedding yields a morphism $\rho: \mathscr{V}^* \to \mathscr{V}'^*$ of the natural compactifications of $\Gamma_0 \backslash \mathscr{D}$ and $\Gamma' \backslash \mathscr{D}'$. It is shown that $\rho(\mathscr{V}^*)$ is birationally equivalent to the quotient of $\mathscr{V}^*$ by a finite group of automorphisms, whose structure is studied. This also gives some information on the quotient $\mathbf{C}(\mathscr{V}^*)/\mathbf{C}(\rho(\mathscr{V}^*))$ of the fields of meromorphic functions on $\mathscr{V}^*$ and $\rho(\mathscr{V}^*)$. *A. Borel* (Princeton, N.J.)

Citations: MR 35# 1602 = F55-21; MR 36# 2624 = F55-23; MR 36# 4020 = F45-29.

F50 SIEGEL (SYMPLECTIC MODULAR) GROUPS AND GENERALIZATIONS: AUTOMORPHIC FORMS

See also reviews E12-10, F40-21, F40-22, F40-40, F40-42, F55-10, F55-12, F55-18, F55-24, F55-27, F55-30, F60-10, F70-22, G10-46, G15-37, G15-40, G15-51, G15-52, G25-49.

F50-1 **(1, 203f)**

Siegel, Carl Ludwig. Einführung in die Theorie der Modulfunktionen n-ten Grades. Math. Ann. **116**, 617–657 (1939).

In this paper the author continues the paper: "Über die analytische Theorie der quadratischen Formen" [Ann. of Math. **36**, 527–606 (1935)]. Let x_i and y_i $(i = 1, 2, \cdots, 2n)$ be two systems of $2n$ cogredient variables; he studies the transformations T

$$(1) \qquad x_i' = \sum_k a_{ik}x_k, \quad y_i' = \sum_k a_{ik}y_k, \quad i, k = 1, 2, \cdots, 2n,$$

with integer coefficients, which leave invariant the bilinear form

$$(2) \qquad \sum_1^n (x_iy_{n+i} - y_ix_{n+i}).$$

The group Γ of these transformations is the modular group of genus (or degree) n. This group is arrived at by a generalization of the well-known modular group for the elliptic curves to the curves of genus n. Using the calculus of matrices, Siegel finds, with great simplicity, the algebraic properties of the transformations (1). The matrix corresponding to a transformation (1) is denoted by

$$\begin{pmatrix} A & B \\ C & D \end{pmatrix},$$

where A, B, C, D are square matrices of n rows and columns.

If V, W are two other matrices of order n, the author writes

$$V_1 = AV + BW,\quad W_1 = CV + DW \quad \text{or} \quad \begin{pmatrix} V_1 \\ W_1 \end{pmatrix} = \begin{pmatrix} A & B \\ C & D \end{pmatrix} \begin{pmatrix} V \\ W \end{pmatrix},$$
$$Z = VW^{-1}, \qquad Z_1 = V_1 W_1^{-1},$$

or, with a symbolic notation,

$$(3) \qquad Z_1 = (AZ+B)(CZ+D)^{-1}.$$

He also puts $Z = X + iY$, $Z_1 = X_1 + iY_1$, where X, Y, X_1, Y_1 are real matrices, and proves that, if Z is symmetric and the imaginary part Y is the matrix of a positive quadratic form, Z_1 also possesses the analogous properties. The coefficients of X, Y are considered as Cartesian coordinates of a point in an Euclidean hyperspace S. If Z satisfies the preceding hypothesis, the corresponding point belongs to an open convex region P, the boundary of which consists of a finite number of algebraic surfaces. The transformations (3) transform this region P into itself. The author succeeds in finding inside P a fundamental region F for the group of the transformations (3); he proves that this fundamental region F is connected and that its boundary also consists of a finite number of algebraic surfaces. Siegel calls the functions $\varphi(Z)$ of the coefficients of the matrices Z (which satisfy the preceding conditions) modular forms if they are regular inside P, bounded inside F, and satisfy, for every transformation (3), the functional equation

$$\varphi(Z_1) = |CZ+D|^{g}\varphi(Z), \qquad g = \text{const.}$$

He studies not only these forms by means of their Fourier development, but also the algebraic equations, which can connect many modular forms; he makes use also of series which can be considered as a generalization of Eisenstein's series (the difference being that in Siegel's problems coefficients and variables are no longer numbers, but matrices). The ratio of two modular forms, corresponding to the same value of g, is called a modular function. Siegel proves that these functions are the functions of an algebraic field, which contains precisely $n(n+1)/2$ independent functions, and that they can all be obtained by using Eisenstein's series; he studies their development into Fourier series, thus obtaining theorems which are important for arithmetical applications.

It goes without saying that the paper is also important for the analytical theory of the algebraic moduli of an algebraic curve. *G. Fubini* (Princeton, N. J.).

Referred to in E60-35, F40-17, F40-25, F50-2, F50-5, F50-6, F50-10, F50-13, F50-16, F50-25, F50-28, F50-29, F50-52, F50-60, F50-62, F55-1, F55-8, F60-1, F70-3.

F50-2 (4, 242b)

Siegel, Carl Ludwig. Symplectic geometry. Amer. J. Math. **65**, 1–86 (1943).

Siegel has introduced modular functions of degree n, that is, of $m = \frac{1}{2}n(n+1)$ complex variables [Math. Ann. **116**, 617–657 (1939); these Rev. **1**, 203]. Similarly generalized automorphic functions can be defined [Sugawara, Ann. of Math. (2) **41**, 488–494 (1940); these Rev. **2**, 37]. Such a theory is based on (1) a suitable definition of the domain H of the m complex variables, which for $m=1$ has to go over into the upper half-plane, (2) the theory of the group Ω of analytic transformations which leave H invariant, (3) the theory of discontinuous subgroups Δ of Ω, culminating in the discussion of a fundamental region for Δ. This geometric and group-theoretical basis of the theory of automorphic functions of m variables is given in the present paper.

The $m = \frac{1}{2}n(n+1)$ complex variables are the elements $z_{kl} = z_{lk}$ $(1 \leqq k \leqq l \leqq n)$ of a symmetric matrix $\mathfrak{Z} = \mathfrak{X} + i\mathfrak{Y}$, where $\mathfrak{X} = \frac{1}{2}(\mathfrak{Z} + \bar{\mathfrak{Z}})$ and $\mathfrak{Y} = (1/2i)(\mathfrak{Z} - \bar{\mathfrak{Z}})$ are the real and imaginary parts of $\mathfrak{Z}$. Inequalities, needed to define certain areas, are introduced by the definition: $\mathfrak{H} > 0$ means that $\mathfrak{H} = \bar{\mathfrak{H}}$ is the matrix of a positive definite Hermitian form. If $\mathfrak{E}$ is the unit matrix of n rows and columns, then the domain E with $\mathfrak{E} - \mathfrak{Z}\bar{\mathfrak{Z}} > 0$ for symmetric $\mathfrak{Z}$ corresponds to the unit circle, and the domain H with $\mathfrak{Y} = (1/2i)(\mathfrak{Z} - \bar{\mathfrak{Z}}) > 0$ to the upper half-plane in the case $m = n = 1$. The domain H is mapped onto itself by all substitutions

$$\mathfrak{W} = (\mathfrak{A}\mathfrak{Z} + \mathfrak{B})(\mathfrak{C}\mathfrak{Z} + \mathfrak{D})^{-1}$$

of the (nonhomogeneous) symplectic group Ω [cf. H. Weyl, The Classical Groups, Princeton University Press, Princeton, N. J., 1939; these Rev. **1**, 42], where $\mathfrak{A}$, $\mathfrak{B}$, $\mathfrak{C}$, $\mathfrak{D}$ are real matrices of n rows and columns satisfying

$$\begin{pmatrix} \mathfrak{A}' & \mathfrak{C}' \\ \mathfrak{B}' & \mathfrak{D}' \end{pmatrix} \begin{pmatrix} 0 & \mathfrak{E} \\ -\mathfrak{E} & 0 \end{pmatrix} \begin{pmatrix} \mathfrak{A} & \mathfrak{B} \\ \mathfrak{C} & \mathfrak{D} \end{pmatrix} = \begin{pmatrix} 0 & \mathfrak{E} \\ -\mathfrak{E} & 0 \end{pmatrix}.$$

The matrix

$$\mathfrak{M} = \begin{pmatrix} \mathfrak{A} & \mathfrak{B} \\ \mathfrak{C} & \mathfrak{D} \end{pmatrix}$$

of $2n$ rows and columns is called a symplectic matrix. Theorem 1 states that every analytic mapping of H onto itself is symplectic. Since the transformation

$$\mathfrak{Z}_0 = (\mathfrak{Z} - i\mathfrak{E})(\mathfrak{Z} + i\mathfrak{E})^{-1}$$

established a one-to-one correspondence between the points $\mathfrak{Z}$ of H and $\mathfrak{Z}_0$ of E, it suffices to prove that an analytic mapping $\mathfrak{Z}_0 \to \mathfrak{W}_0$ of E into itself with the fixed point 0 is always represented by

$$\mathfrak{W}_0 = \mathfrak{U}'\mathfrak{Z}_0\mathfrak{U}$$

with constant unitary $\mathfrak{U}$. This is established by the introduction of an auxiliary complex variable t in the unit circle $|t| \leqq 1$.

The further discussion is based on a generalization of Poincaré space. For two points $\mathfrak{Z}$, $\mathfrak{Z}_1$ of H the matrix

$$\mathfrak{R}(\mathfrak{Z}, \mathfrak{Z}_1) = (\mathfrak{Z} - \mathfrak{Z}_1)(\mathfrak{Z} - \bar{\mathfrak{Z}}_1)^{-1}(\bar{\mathfrak{Z}} - \bar{\mathfrak{Z}}_1)(\bar{\mathfrak{Z}} - \mathfrak{Z}_1)^{-1}$$

generalizes a cross ratio. The characteristic roots of $\mathfrak{R}$ are real numbers of the interval $0 \leqq r < 1$. Two pairs of points $\mathfrak{Z}$, $\mathfrak{Z}_1$ and $\mathfrak{W}$, $\mathfrak{W}_1$ of H can be mapped on each other if and only if $\mathfrak{R}(\mathfrak{Z}, \mathfrak{Z}_1)$ and $\mathfrak{R}(\mathfrak{W}, \mathfrak{W}_1)$ have the same characteristic roots. Any pair $\mathfrak{Z}$, $\mathfrak{Z}_1$ can be transformed into $i\mathfrak{E}$, $i\mathfrak{T}$, $\mathfrak{T}$ being a diagonal matrix with real diagonal elements $t_1, \cdots, t_n$, $1 \leqq t_1 \leqq \cdots \leqq t_n$. The Hermitian differential form

$$ds^2 = \text{trace}\,(\mathfrak{Y}^{-1}d\mathfrak{Z}\mathfrak{Y}^{-1}d\bar{\mathfrak{Z}})$$

is invariant under Ω and defines a Riemann metric in H. Any two points of H can be connected by one and only one geodesic in this metric. The distance $\rho(\mathfrak{Z}, \mathfrak{Z}_1)$ of $\mathfrak{Z}$ and $\mathfrak{Z}_1$ is given by

$$\rho^2 = \text{trace}\left(\log \frac{1 + \mathfrak{R}^{\frac{1}{2}}}{1 - \mathfrak{R}^{\frac{1}{2}}}\right)^2, \qquad \mathfrak{R} = \mathfrak{R}(\mathfrak{Z}, \mathfrak{Z}_1).$$

A generalization of the Gauss-Bonnet formula by Allendoerfer and Fenchel yields the Euler characteristic χ of a closed manifold F in the above Riemann metric:

$$\chi = c_n(-\pi)^{-\frac{1}{2}n(n+1)} \int_F dv,$$

where dv is the Euclidean volume element in the space of $\mathfrak{X}, \mathfrak{Y}^{-1}$ and c_n a certain rational number depending only on n. Let Δ be a discontinuous subgroup of Ω and let D_1, D_2, $\cdots$ be its elements, D_1 being the identity. Let $\mathfrak{Z}_k$ be the image $D_k(\mathfrak{Z}_1)$ of $\mathfrak{Z}_1$, $\mathfrak{Z}_1$ being taken as a point of H which is not a fixed point under any transformation D_k $(k = 2, 3, \cdots)$. A fundamental region F for Δ can then be defined as consisting of all those points $\mathfrak{Z}$ of H for which

$$\rho(\mathfrak{Z}, \mathfrak{Z}_1) \leqq \rho(\mathfrak{Z}, \mathfrak{Z}_k)$$

for all $k=2, 3, \cdots$. This F is a "star" with respect to $\mathfrak{Z}_1$, that is, if $\mathfrak{Z}$ belongs to F then the whole geodesic arc $\mathfrak{Z}\mathfrak{Z}_1$ also belongs to F.

In analogy to Fuchsian groups a discontinuous symplectic group Δ is said to be of the first kind if there exists a fundamental domain F such that (1) every compact domain in H is covered by a finite number of images of F, (2) only a finite number of images of F are neighbors of F, (3) the integral $V(\Delta)=\int_F dv$ converges. The group Δ is certainly of the first kind if H is compact relative to Δ, that is, if there exists for every infinite sequence of points $\mathfrak{Z}^{(k)}$ $(k=1, 2, \cdots)$ in H at least one compact sequence of images $\mathfrak{Z}_{ik}{}^{(k)}$ under Δ.

The second and longer part of the paper is devoted to the discussion of special discontinuous symplectic groups defined by arithmetical properties. Let K be a totally real algebraic field of finite degree h, let r be a totally positive number of K; then the field $K_0=K(\sqrt{-r})$ is totally imaginary and of degree $2h$. Let $\mathfrak{H}$ be a Hermitian and $\mathfrak{G}$ be a nonsingular symmetric matrix, both of order $2n$, and with elements of K_0 and let all conjugates of $\mathfrak{H}$, except $\mathfrak{H}$ and $\bar{\mathfrak{H}}$, be positive. Let us further assume the relationship

$$\mathfrak{H}\mathfrak{G}^{-1}\bar{\mathfrak{H}}=s\mathfrak{G}$$

with a positive s of K. The numbers r and s can be taken as integers. Then the matrices $\mathfrak{U}$ with integral elements of K_0 satisfying the conditions

$$\mathfrak{U}'\mathfrak{G}\mathfrak{U}=\mathfrak{G}, \quad \mathfrak{U}'\mathfrak{H}\bar{\mathfrak{U}}=\mathfrak{H}$$

form a multiplicative group $\Lambda=\Lambda(\mathfrak{G}, \mathfrak{H})$ which is discontinuous and discrete. There exists a constant matrix $\mathfrak{C}$ (not unique) such that the matrices $\mathfrak{M}=\mathfrak{C}^{-1}\mathfrak{U}\mathfrak{C}$ are symplectic. Identifying $\mathfrak{M}$ and $-\mathfrak{M}$, we have a discontinuous subgroup $\Delta(\mathfrak{G}, \mathfrak{H})$ of Ω. The most important case is the modular group Γ obtained by

$$\mathfrak{G}=\begin{pmatrix} 0 & \mathfrak{E} \\ -\mathfrak{E} & 0 \end{pmatrix}, \quad \mathfrak{H}=i\mathfrak{G}, \qquad h=1; r=1.$$

The group $\Delta(\mathfrak{G}, \mathfrak{H})$ is of the first kind. Instead of using the above defined fundamental region, which may have a very complicated shape, the author introduces fundamental regions based on special arithmetic properties of $\Delta(\mathfrak{G}, \mathfrak{H})$, using for the modular group Minkowski's theory of reduction of quadratic forms and for general $\Delta(\mathfrak{G}, \mathfrak{H})$ P. Humbert's extension of Minkowski's theory to an arbitrary field K_0. For this purpose the space H is first mapped on the space S of all symplectic positive symmetric matrices $\mathfrak{S}$.

The volume of the fundamental region of the modular group is

$$(*) \qquad V_n=2\prod_{k=1}^{n}\{(k-1)!\pi^{-k}\zeta(2k)\}.$$

The proof is obtained by recursion from n to $n-1$; Riemann's ζ-function comes into play by a summation over lattice points. The formula (*) admits of an interesting interpretation in terms of densities of real and of p-adic matrix solutions of certain conditions. For the commensurability of two groups $\Delta(\mathfrak{G}, \mathfrak{H})$ and $\Delta(\mathfrak{G}_1, \mathfrak{H}_1)$, that is, for the existence of subgroups of finite indices which are conjugate in Ω, a necessary and sufficient condition is given in theorem 13. For $n=2$ another example of a discontinuous symplectic group $\Delta(\mathfrak{T})$ of the first kind is furnished by the theory of units of quinary quadratic forms of signature 2, 3.

Even a lengthy review can indicate only a few outstanding marks among the abundant results and methods of this important paper. *H. Rademacher* (Swarthmore, Pa.).

Citations: MR 1, 203f = F50-1.

Referred to in E60-8, F02-3, F40-19, F45-3, F45-9, F45-12, F45-33, F50-3, F50-7.

F50-3 (29# 1362)

Siegel, Carl Ludwig

Symplectic geometry.

Academic Press, New York-London, 1964. viii+86 *pp.* \$4.00.

A reprinting, together with a page of errata, of the author's classical paper [Amer. J. Math. **65** (1943), 1–86; MR **4**, 242].

Citations: MR 4, 242b = F50-2.

F50-4 (13, 210a)

Maass, Hans. Über die Darstellung der Modulformen n-ten Grades durch Poincarésche Reihen. Math. Ann. **123**, 125–151 (1951).

This is an extension, to the Siegel matrix modular forms of degree n, of Petersson's theory of Poincaré series. A modular form of degree n and dimension $-k$ is an analytic function of the complex variables in the symmetric matrix (of degree n) $Z=(z_{\mu\nu})=X+iY$, regular in the half-space $Y>0$, and satisfying there the transformation equation (1) $g_{-k}(\sigma(Z))=|CZ+D|^k g_{-k}(Z)$ for every modular substitution $\sigma=\begin{pmatrix} A & B \\ C & D\end{pmatrix}$ of degree n. Siegel has shown that $g_{-k}(Z)$ possesses a Fourier expansion

$$(2) \qquad g_{-k}(Z)=\sum_{T\geqq 0} a(T) \exp 2\pi i \operatorname{Sp}(TZ),$$

extended over all non-negative symmetric matrices T with semi-integer elements; Sp=trace. Following Petersson ($n=1$), the author obtains from (2) by a process of summation a Poincaré series

$$(3) \qquad g_{-k}(Z, T)=\sum_{\sigma} \exp 2\pi i \operatorname{Sp}(T\sigma(Z))\times|CZ+D|^{-k}$$

with $T\geqq 0$, σ runs over a complete set of non-associated modular substitutions of degree n. (For the modular concepts, cf. Siegel, Math. Ann. **116**, 617–657 (1939); these Rev. **1**, 203.) The case $T=0$ yields the Eisenstein series.

The author's first goal is the proof of the following Theorem I. For $k>\min(2n, n+1+\operatorname{rank} T)$, the Poincaré series (3) converges absolutely and uniformly in every closed bounded subdomain of $Y>0$ and defines there a modular form of dimension $-k$. The modular behavior of the Poincaré series would follow at once from its boundedness in $\mathfrak{F}_n$, the Siegel fundamental region of the modular group in the space $Y>0$. However, for $T\neq 0$, no majorant independent of Z is available. The author therefore expands the Poincaré series in a Fourier series

$$(4) \qquad g_{-k}(Z, T)=\sum_{T_0} a(T, T_0) \exp 2\pi i \operatorname{Sp}(T_0 Z),$$

T_0=symmetric semi-integral matrix, and shows that $a(T, T_0)=0$ whenever $T<0$, a condition equivalent to the boundedness of g_{-k}. This he does by introducing the scalar product (first defined by Petersson for $n=1$) of two modular forms

$$(5) \qquad (h(Z), g(Z))=\int\cdots\int_{\mathfrak{F}_n} h(Z)\overline{g(Z)}\,|Y|^{n-k-1}d(X)d(Y),$$

where $d(X)=\prod_{\mu\leqq\nu}dx_{\mu\nu}$, $dY=\prod_{\mu\leqq\nu}dy_{\mu\nu}$, $z_{\mu\nu}=x_{\mu\nu}+iy_{\mu\nu}$. He shows that the scalar product exists for $h=g_{-k}(Z)$, $g=g_{-k}(Z, T)$, provided that in the Fourier expansion (2) of $g_{-k}(Z)$ we have $a(T)=0$ whenever $|T|=0$—these are the so-called cusp-forms—and gives explicit formulas for the value of the scalar product; in particular, the scalar product is proportional to the Fourier coefficient $a(T)$.

The second object of the paper is the Representation Theorem II. Let $k\geqq 2n+2$ and even. Every modular form of degree n and dimension $-k$ can be written uniquely in the form $g_{-k}(Z)+h_{-k}(Z)$, $g_{-k}(Z)\varepsilon\mathfrak{N}_k{}^{(n)}$, $h_{-k}(Z)\varepsilon\mathfrak{S}_k{}^{(n)}$, where $\mathfrak{S}_k{}^{(n)}$ is the (linear) family of all cusp-forms of degree n and dimension $-k$, and $\mathfrak{N}_k{}^{(n)}$ is the family of all forms

h_{-k} which are orthogonal to every cusp-form under the scalar-product (5). In the proof of this theorem important use is made of the following observation of Siegel. Write $Z=\binom{Z^*\ n}{n'\ \lambda}$, where $Z^*=Z^{*(n-1)}$, n=column of zeros, $\lambda>0$. Then $g_{-k}(Z^*)=\lim_{\lambda\to\infty} g_{-k}(Z)$ is a modular form of degree $n-1$. Since the representation theorem for $n=1$ was proved by Petersson [Jber. Deutsch. Math. Verein. **49**, 49–75 (1939)], the author can proceed by induction.

The position of the Poincaré series in the family of modular forms is shown by Theorem III. Let $k\geqq 2n+2$ and even. The Poincaré series $g_{-k}(Z, T)$, where T has rank n, is orthogonal to every cusp-form whose Fourier coefficient $a(T)=0$. This property characterizes $g_{-k}(Z, T)$ uniquely apart from a constant factor. *J. Lehner.*

Citations: MR 1, 203e = R54-1.

Referred to in F50-49, F50-53, F50-56, F55-9, F60-1.

F50-5 (15, 603e)

Koecher, Max. Zur Theorie der Modulformen n-ten Grades. I. Math. Z. **59**, 399–416 (1954).

Siegel's definition [Math. Ann. **116**, 617–657 (1939); these Rev. **1**, 203] of modular forms of degree n includes restrictions on the behavior of the forms at infinity. The principal purpose of the present paper is to show that these restrictions can be dropped for $n>1$. Regularity and the existence of suitable transformation formulas are enough to insure proper behavior at infinity. This is proved for certain subgroups of the symplectic group as well as for the modular group of degree n. The corresponding field of modular functions is also considered. *H. S. Zuckerman.*

Citations: MR 1, 203f = F50-1.

Referred to in E56-18, F50-8, F50-25, F55-6, F55-9.

F50-6 (16, 338a)

Pyateckiĭ-Šapiro, I. I. Abelian modular functions. Doklady Akad. Nauk SSSR (N.S.) **95**, 221–224 (1954). (Russian)

A discussion of the author's extension of Siegel's definitions of modular group and modular functions of degree (genus) n [Math. Ann. **116**, 617–657 (1939); these Rev. **1**, 203] to the following. Let Ω be the set of matrices ω with p rows and $2p$ columns $\omega_1, \cdots, \omega_{2p}$ for which there exists a non-degenerate Abelian function with periods $\omega_1, \cdots, \omega_{2p}$. Let $\mathfrak{A}$ be the multiplication algebra of some irreducible matrix ω. Denote by R_0 a rational skew-symmetric matrix of order $2p$, and let $\Omega_{\mathfrak{A}}$ be the set of all ω in Ω with multiplication algebra $\mathfrak{A}$ and such that $\omega R_0\omega'=0$ and $\overline{i\omega}R_0\omega'>0$. Then the modular group $\Gamma_{\mathfrak{A}}$ on $\Omega_{\mathfrak{A}}$ is the set of all unimodular matrices U of order $2p$ such that if $\omega \in \Omega_{\mathfrak{A}}$, then also $\omega U' \in \Omega_{\mathfrak{A}}$. *W. H. Simons* (Vancouver, B. C.).

Citations: MR 1, 203f = F50-1.

Referred to in F02-8.

F50-7 (16, 449d)

Maass, Hans. Die Differentialgleichungen in der Theorie der Siegelschen Modulfunktionen. Math. Ann. **126**, 44–68 (1953).

Let $X=(x_{\mu\nu})$ and $Y=(y_{\mu\nu})$ $(\mu, \nu=1, 2, \cdots, n)$ be $n\times n$ symmetric matrices and let $Z=X+iY=(z_{\mu\nu})$, $W=X-iY=(w_{\mu\nu})$ where the $z_{\mu\nu}$ and $w_{\mu\nu}$ are independent complex variables. The author considers the differential operators defined by

$$D_z=(e_{\mu\nu}\partial/\partial z_{\mu\nu}),\qquad D_w=(e_{\mu\nu}\partial/\partial w_{\mu\nu}),$$
$$K_\alpha=\alpha E+(Z-W)D_z,\quad \Lambda_\beta=-\beta E+(Z-W)D_w$$

and

$$\Omega_{\alpha\beta}=\Lambda_{\beta-\frac{1}{2}(n+1)}K_\alpha+\alpha(\beta-\tfrac{1}{2}n-\tfrac{1}{2})E,$$

where $e_{\mu\nu}=\frac{1}{2}(1+\delta_{\mu\nu})$, $\delta_{\mu\nu}$ is the Kronecker symbol and $E=(\delta_{\mu\nu})$ is the unit matrix. He proves that the Eisenstein series

$$G(Z, W; \alpha, \beta)=\sum_{C, D}\gamma(C, D)\,|CZ+D|^{-\alpha}|CW+D|^{-\beta}$$

in Siegel's theory of modular forms of order n (C, D run through a complete set of nonassociated coprime pairs of symmetric matrices) satisfy the n^2 differential equations $\Omega_{\alpha\beta}G(Z, W; \alpha, \beta)=0$. The author determines the behavior of the differential operators under symplectic substitutions

$$Z\to(AZ+B)(CZ+D)^{-1},\quad W\to(AW+B)(CW+D)^{-1}.$$

The operator $\Delta=-\text{Trace}\,(Z-W)((Z-W)D_w)'D_z$ (A' is the transposed matrix of A) is shown to be invariant under symplectic substitutions. This operator is the Laplace-Beltrami operator for the symplectic metric [C. L. Siegel, Amer. J. Math. **65**, 1–86 (1943); MR **4**, 242]. Let $\{\alpha, \beta\}$ be the set of all analytic functions $f(Z, W)$ which are regular in the domain $W=\bar{Z}$ (=complex conjugate of Z), $Y>0$ and which satisfy the differential equations $\Omega_{\alpha\beta}f=0$. If for any symplectic substitution σ the symbol $f(Z, W)|\sigma$ is defined by

$$f(Z, W)|\sigma=|CZ+D|^{-\alpha}|CW+D|^{-\beta}f(\sigma Z, \sigma W),$$

the set $\{\alpha, \beta\}$ is shown to be invariant under symplectic substitutions: $\{\alpha, \beta\}|\sigma=\{\alpha, \beta\}$. The author further constructs certain differential operators M_α and N_β which transform the Eisenstein series $G(Z, W; \alpha, \beta)$ into $\epsilon_n(\alpha)G(Z, W; \alpha+1, \beta-1)$ and $\epsilon_n(\beta)G(Z, W; \alpha-1, \beta+1)$, respectively (the ϵ_n are certain constants). The author surmises that not only the Eisenstein series but even all modular forms f for any group $\mathcal{G}$ of symplectic substitutions (for which $f(Z, W)\in\{\alpha, \beta\}$ and $f(Z, W)|\sigma=v(\sigma)f(Z, W)$, where $v(\sigma)$ is a certain set of multipliers for $\mathcal{G}$) show the same behavior under the operators M_α and N_β but he has not been able to prove this conjecture except for $n=1$ and $n=2$ [for $n=1$ cf. the paper reviewed above].

The author finally considers the problem of the Fourier expansion of periodic modular forms of order n. The solution of this problem requires the determination of those functions in $\{\alpha, \beta\}$ which have the form

$$a(Y, T)\exp[i\,\text{Trace}\,(TX)],$$

where T is an arbitrary $n\times n$ symmetric real matrix. The linear set $\{\alpha, \beta, T\}$ of functions $a(Y, T)$ is determined by a system of differential equations. This system is completely solved for $n=2$. The maximal number of linearly independent functions in $\{\alpha, \beta, T\}$ is finite. *H. D. Kloosterman* (Leiden).

Citations: MR 4, 242b = F50-2; MR 16, 449c = F10-36.

F50-8 (16, 801c)

Koecher, Max. Zur Theorie der Modulformen n-ten Grades. II. Math. Z. **61**, 455–466 (1955).

The definitions of part I [Math. Z. **59**, 399–416 (1954); MR **15**, 603] are used. The definition of a cusp-form is altered. A scalar product is obtained, thereby furnishing the set of cusp-forms with a metric. This is done for a class, congruence subgroups, of subgroups of the symplectic group, and is a generalization of results of Petersson and Maass. *H. S. Zuckerman* (Seattle, Wash.).

Citations: MR 15, 603e = F50-5.

Referred to in F55-9.

F50-9 (17, 1058a)

Koecher, Max. Zur Operatorentheorie der Modulformen n-ten Grades. Math. Ann. **130** (1956), 351–385.

Let Γ denote the modular group and let $\{\Gamma, k\}$ stand for the set of integral modular forms of negative dimension k. For every integer g, Hecke defined the operator $T(g)$ of $\{\Gamma, k\}$ into itself, as follows: If $f \in \{\Gamma, k\}$, then

$$f|T(g)=g^{-k-1}\sum_{\mathfrak{A}} (c\tau+d)^k f\left(\frac{a\tau+b}{c\tau+d}\right),$$

the sum being extended over all non-equivalent (under Γ) matrices $\mathfrak{A}=\begin{pmatrix} a & b \\ c & d\end{pmatrix}$ with integral elements and $ad-bc=g$. The set of the $T(g)$ forms a commutative ring, whose structure is defined by

$$(1) \qquad T(g)T(h)=\sum_{d|(g,h)} d^{-k-1}T(gh/d^2).$$

As the Fourier coefficients of many modular forms are important number-theoretical functions, the Hecke operator is a very valuable tool in number theory. Also the Fourier coefficients of some modular forms in several variables have number-theoretical significance; therefore, the generalization of the Hecke operator to the case of modular of degree n is an important problem. Maass [Math. Ann. **124** (1951), 87–122; MR **13**, 823] defined the most general operator of this kind, in which the domain and the range of the operators are still the same. Formally, several further generalizations seem possible. The author is guided by heuristic considerations of the complex multiplication of abelian functions of n variables, as natural generalization of the complex multiplication of elliptic functions. Thus he is led to a set of rather general operators, forming again a ring. However, the generality achieved is paid for by a certain loss of simplicity. In the first place, the domain and range of the operators are distinct sets of functions; hence, the "inverse operator" is actually an operator of a different kind. Finally, two further operators are needed, that reduce to the identity operator, if $n=1$. Hence, four distinct operators are defined. The precise definition of these operators requires rather lengthy explanations and cannot be given in a few words. The operators $T(\mathfrak{H}, \mathfrak{H}\mathfrak{R})$ and $T^*(\mathfrak{H}\mathfrak{R}, \mathfrak{H})$ (the first argument stands for the domain of definition, the second for the range of the operator) however, satisfy relations generalizing (1) for the particular case $(g, h)=1$; the generalization of (1) for the general case $(g, h)>1$ is not obtained. The operators $V(\mathfrak{H}, \mathfrak{H}\mathfrak{G}^2)$ and $V^*(\mathfrak{H}\mathfrak{G}^2, \mathfrak{H})$ (same meaning of the arguments as for the T-operators) satisfy $V\cdot V^*=1$, while $V^*\cdot V\neq 1$ in general; but the operator $W(\mathfrak{H}; \mathfrak{G})=\delta(H\cdot G^{-2})V^*(\mathfrak{H}, \mathfrak{H}\mathfrak{G}^{-2})V(\mathfrak{H}\mathfrak{G}^{-2}, \mathfrak{H})$ (here $\delta(\mathfrak{A})=1$ if $\mathfrak{A}$ is in canonical form, with integral, positive elementary divisors on the main diagonal; $\delta(\mathfrak{A})=0$ otherwise) acts upon the functions f_j of certain orthogonal bases of cusp forms like $f_j|W(\mathfrak{H}; \mathfrak{G})=\chi_j(\mathfrak{H}; \mathfrak{G})f_j$ with $\chi_j=0$ or 1. Finally, the "Euler product" decomposition of the Hecke operator,

$$T_s=\prod_p(1-p^{-s}T(p)+p^{-k-1-2s})^{-1}, \quad T_s=\sum_{g=1}^{\infty} g^{-s}T(g)$$

can be generalized and an analogous relation holds for certain operators $T(\mathfrak{G})$, derived from the $T(\mathfrak{H}\mathfrak{G}^{-1}, \mathfrak{H})$.

E. Grosswald (Philadelpia, Pa.).

Citations: MR 13, 823g = F60-1.

F50-10 (18, 19c)

Pyateckiĭ-Šapiro, I. I. On the theory of abelian modular functions. Dokl. Akad. Nauk SSSR (N.S.) **106** (1956), 973–976. (Russian)

The author gives a unified approach to the modular functions of Hilbert, Siegel [Math. Ann. **116** (1939), 617–657; MR **1**, 203] and Braun [Ann. of Math. (2) **50** (1949), 827–855; MR **11**, 333]. The approach is based on a connection between E. Cartan's first three bounded symmetric domains [see Siegel, Analytic functions of several complex variables, Inst. Advanced Study, Princeton, N.J., 1950; MR **11**, 651] and the irreducible components of the multiplier algebra $\mathfrak{A}$ [see Albert, Ann. of Math. **35** (1934), 500–515]. These algebras are rational square matrices of order $2p$ for which every element A determines a complex square matrix α of order p such that $\omega A=\alpha\omega$. Here ω is a complex matrix of order $p\times 2p$ for which $\omega R_0\omega'=0$, $i\bar{\omega}R_0\omega'>0$, where, finally, R_0 is a rational skew-symmetric matrix of order $2p$ for which the transformation $R_0A'R_0^{-1}$ maps $\mathfrak{A}$ onto itself. The modular group consists of (say) integral square matrices U of order $2p$ for which $U'R_0U=R_0$, $U'A=AU'$ for all A in $\mathfrak{A}$. Modular forms of weight m on ω are defined by the properties $f(\alpha\omega)=|\alpha|^{-m}f(\omega)$, $f(\omega U)=f(\omega)$, (with suitable boundedness) and the set of equivalence classes $\omega\sim\alpha\omega$ determines the domain with irreducible components identified as Cartan's third, first, or second domain according as the irreducible components of the real envelope of $\mathfrak{A}$ are reals, complex numbers, or quaternions respectively. General proofs on the existence of modular functions are also outlined.

Harvey Cohn (St. Louis, Mo.).

Citations: MR 1, 203f = F50-1; MR 11, 333a = F55-1; MR 11, 651c = F02-3.

Referred to in F02-8.

F50-11 (18, 389g)

Lapin, A. I. On modular functions of degree two. Izv. Akad. Nauk SSSR. Ser. Mat. **20** (1956), 325–336. (Russian)

Extending Siegel's work [Math. Ann. **116** (1939), 617–657] the author shows that the field of modular functions of degree two is isomorphic to the field of rational functions of three independent variables.

A. J. Lohwater (Ann Arbor, Mich.).

Referred to in F50-25, F50-40.

F50-12 (18, 731a)

Satake, Ichiro. On Siegel's modular functions. Proceedings of the international symposium on algebraic number theory, Tokyo & Nikko, 1955, pp. 107–129. Science Council of Japan, Tokyo, 1956.

Let $\mathfrak{H}_n$ be the space of all complex symmetric matrices $Z=X+iY$ of order n, with $Y>0$ and let M_n be Siegel's modular group of degree n; then Siegel's modular functions $F(Z)$ are defined as quotients of two modular forms on $\mathfrak{V}_n=M_n\backslash\mathfrak{H}_n$, regular at the points at infinity. If one wants to define them directly as meromorphic functions on $\mathfrak{V}_n$, difficulties arise because the quotient space $M_n\backslash\mathfrak{H}_n$ is not compact. The author tries to obviate these difficulties by a compactification procedure. In order to do that, he introduces complex analytic manifolds with ramifications, called V-manifolds. Their precise definition is rather complicated and cannot be recorded here, but it is possible to define meromorphic functions on a V-manifold and the $\mathfrak{V}_n$, in particular, are V-manifolds. Denote by $\mathfrak{W}_{n-1}$ the V-manifold consisting of the equivalence classes under M_n of the limit points of the sequences $Z^{(k)}=(z_{ij}^{(k)})$, such that $\lim_{k\to\infty} y_{nn}^{(k)}\to\infty$, while all other elements stay bounded. Next, a "junction" of V-manifolds $\mathfrak{V}_n$ and $\mathfrak{W}_m$ $(m<n$, $\mathfrak{V}_n\cap\mathfrak{W}_m=\emptyset)$ is defined as the V-manifold sturcture on $\mathfrak{V}_n\cup\mathfrak{W}_m$, such that $\mathfrak{V}_n$ becomes an open V-submanifold and $\mathfrak{W}_m$ a regularly imbedded V-submanifold of $\mathfrak{V}_n\cup\mathfrak{W}_m$, in case such a V-structure can be defined. In general, taking as $\mathfrak{W}_m$ the previously defined $\mathfrak{W}_{n-1}$, the new V-manifold $\mathfrak{V}_n\cup\mathfrak{W}_{n-1}$ is still not compact. However, if $\mathfrak{W}_{n-1}$ itself is first completed to a compact V-manifold $\overline{\mathfrak{W}}_{n-1}$, and then joined to $\mathfrak{V}_n$, the resulting V-manifold

$$\overline{\mathfrak{V}}_n=\mathfrak{V}_n\cup\overline{\mathfrak{W}}_{n-1}$$

is compact. The author conjectures that this should be

possible for every n, as would follow from a proof that $\bar{\mathfrak{V}}_n$ is a projective variety. In the particular case $n=2$, the V-structure of $\mathfrak{W}_1$ is trivial ($\mathfrak{W}_1 \approx C\times C$, whence $\bar{\mathfrak{W}}_1 \not\approx \bar{C}\times\bar{C}$, C being the complex plane and $\bar{C}=C\cup\{\infty\}$ the complex sphere) and the author shows that

$$\bar{\mathfrak{V}}_2=\mathfrak{V}_2\cup\bar{\mathfrak{W}}_1$$

is compact. This proof, however, is far from trivial and succeeds mainly because in this case $n-1=1$ and one has at his disposal the well developed theories of theta-functions and of elliptic functions. *E. Grosswald.*

Referred to in F45-4, F50-19.

F50-13 (19, 173g)

Rosati, Mario. Qualche aspetto della teoria delle funzioni ellittiche modulari ed abeliane modulari. Archimede **8** (1956), 145–153.

Klassifizierung der algebraischen Kurven mittels birationellen Invarianten. Für Kurven vom Geschlechte $p=1$ (elliptische Kurven) die birationell äquivalent mit einer ebenen Kurve dritter Ordnung ohne Doppelpunkt sind, kann man dazu erstens den algebraischen Modul $\mathfrak{J}$ benutzen, d.h. eine geeignete symmetrische Funktion der sechs verschiedenen Doppelverhältnisse von vier Tangenten aus einem Punkte der kubischen Kurve an diese Kurve. An zweiter Stelle ergibt sich eine tranzendente Invariante als der Quotient $z=\omega_1/\omega_2$ der primitiven Perioden des der ebenen Kurven zugehörigen elliptischen Integrals. Zwei elliptische Kurven sind birationell äquivalent wenn die zugehörigen Werte z und z' äquivalent in Bezug auf die modulare Substitution $z'=(\alpha z+\beta)/(\gamma z+\delta)$ (α, β, γ, δ ganz; $\alpha\delta-\beta\gamma=1$) sind, und umgekehrt. Aus diesen Betrachtungen ergibt sich, dass der algebraische Modul $\mathfrak{J}$ der Beziehung $\mathfrak{J}(z)=\mathfrak{J}((\alpha z+\beta)/(\gamma z+\delta))$ genügt. Beim Übergang zu dem Falle $p>1$ wird die Variable z ersetzt durch eine komplexe Matrix

$$Z=X+iY=\|z_{hk}\|=\|x_{hk}+iy_{hk}\|$$

($z_{hk}=z_{kh}$; $h, k=1, 2, \cdots, p$) mit definit positiven Y. Die (geeignet definierten) analytischen Funktionen der Elemente z_{hk} der Matrix Z, die bei Substitutionen der beschränkten modularen Gruppe invariant bleiben, sind Abelsche Modular-Funktionen mehrer Variablen [Siegel, Math. Ann. **116** (1939), 617–657; MR **1**, 203]. *S. C. van Veen* (Delft).

Citations: MR 1, 203f = F50-1.

F50-14 (19, 740b; 19, 740c)

Myrberg, P. J. Über eine Klasse von automorphen Funktionen mehrerer Variablen, die vermittels periodischer Funktionen darstellbar sind. I. Kommutative Gruppen. Ann. Acad. Sci. Fenn. Ser. A. I. no. **235** (1957), 10 pp.

Myrberg, P. J. Über eine Klasse von automorphen Funktionen mehrerer Variablen, die vermittels periodischer Funktionen darstellbar sind. II. Die nichtkommutativen Gruppen. Ann. Acad. Sci. Fenn. Ser. A. I. no. **238** (1957), 16 pp.

The functions under discussion are the automorphic functions of a group Γ of transformations S_ν: $x'=x+\omega_\nu$, $y'=y+\tau_\nu(x)$, ω_ν constants, $\tau_\nu(x)$ entire functions. Introducing a new variable $z=y-\varphi(x)$, where $\varphi(x+\omega_1)-\varphi(x)=\tau_1(x)$, puts Γ into a simpler form. Apart from special cases, if Γ is commutative it can be reduced to a group of transformations $x'=x+\omega_\nu$, $z'=z+\eta_\nu$, η_ν constants, with $\omega_1=2\pi i$, $\omega_2=0$, $\eta_1=0$, $\eta_2=2\pi i$. Then if Γ is generated by N transformations its automorphic functions are determined by $f(x+2\pi i, z)=f(x, z)$ if $N=1$ and by $f(x+2\pi i, z)=f(x, z+2\pi i)=f(x, z)$ if $N=2$. For $N=3$ there are meromorphic, but not entire, automorphic functions. For $N=4$ automorphic functions exist only under certain conditions. When Γ is not commutative the situation is much more complicated and the groups having automorphic functions are fairly restricted. *H. S. Zuckerman* (Seattle, Wash.).

F50-15 (19, 740d)

Christian, Ulrich. Zur Theorie der Modulfunktionen n-ten Grades. Math. Ann. **133** (1957), 281–297.

A function is here defined to be a modular function if it is invariant and properly behaved (meromorphic) when the fundamental region has been compactified. It is proved that every $n(n+1)/2+1$ modular functions are algebraically dependent over the complex numbers. Every modular function is the quotient of two modular forms and can be expressed rationally in terms of generalized Eisenstein series. *H. S. Zuckerman.*

Referred to in F50-19.

F50-16 (20# 991a)

Pyateckiĭ-Šapiro, I. I. Singular modular functions. Izv. Akad. Nauk SSSR. Ser. Mat. **20** (1956), 53–98. (Russian)

In this paper is given a generalization of the abelian modular functions introduced by Siegel.

The Riemann-Frobenius condition on the periods of abelian functions of p variables is, if by ω we denote the ($p\times 2p$) matrix of $2p$ strongly independent vector-periods, that there exist a rational skew-symmetric matrix R of order $2p$ for which $\omega R\omega'=0$, $i\bar{\omega}R\omega'>0$. The set $N\omega$ of such R satisfies $R_1, R_2\in N\omega \Rightarrow r_1R_2+r_2R_2\in N\omega$ for any rational $r_i>0$. Any set N of rational skew-symmetric matrices of order $2p$ satisfying such a condition is called a cone. If it is of the form $N\omega$ for some ω it is called admissible; the set of admissible cones was enumerated by A. A. Albert [Ann. of Math. (2) **35** (1934), 500–515]. For admissible N, let $\Omega_N=\{\omega|N\subseteq N\omega\}$, and let H_N be Ω_N reduced modulo equivalence $\sim$, where $\omega_1\sim\omega$ if $\omega_1=\alpha\omega$, α a non-degenerate square complex matrix. Let L_N be the group of integer-valued unimodular matrices U of order $2p$ such that $\omega\in\Omega_N\Rightarrow\omega U'\in\Omega_N$. Since the mapping $\omega\to\omega U'$ preserves equivalence, L_N may be regarded as operating on H_N. The quotient group of L_N by the normal subgroup of matrices inducing the identity map is called the modular group Γ_N, and the functions on H_N automorphic with respect to Γ_N are called modular functions.

The modular functions considered in this paper correspond to cones of the following description. Let k be a totally real algebraic number field of degree n, R_0 a rational skew-symmetric matrix of order $2p$, $p=np_0$, and $\alpha\to A(\alpha)$ a representation of k by rational matrices of order $2p$, where $AR_0=R_0A'$ for any matrix A of the representation. Then the set $N(k)$ of skew-symmetric matrices $R=AR_0$, where A runs over all matrices of the representation with positive eigenvalues, is an admissible cone, and $H_{N(k)}$ is the product $H_{p_0}{}^n$ of n generalized upper half planes of degree p_0. The modular group $\Gamma_{N(k)}$ is commensurable with the following special case of the above construction (two groups are commensurable if their intersection has a finite index in each). Consider the group of matrices U of order $2p_0$, with elements which are algebraic integers in k, satisfying

$$U'IU=I,\ U=\begin{pmatrix}A & B\\ C & D\end{pmatrix},\ I=\begin{pmatrix}0 & E\\ -E & 0\end{pmatrix}.$$

To every such U associate the transformation $(Z_1, \cdots, Z_n)\to(\tilde{Z}_1, \cdots, \tilde{Z}_n)$ of $H_{p_0}{}^n$ given by $\tilde{Z}_s=(A^{(s)}Z_s+B^{(s)})\times(C^{(s)}Z_s+D^{(s)})^{-1}$, where $V^{(s)}$ is the matrix whose elements are the sth conjugates of those of V. The group $\Gamma_{p_0}(k)$ of these transformations is here called a Hilbert-Siegel group, being due to Hilbert for $p_0=1$ and any k, to Siegel for any p_0 and $n=1$.

The main results, for any group Γ commensurable with $\Gamma_{p_0}(k)$, are: (1) For every $z_0 \in H_{p_0}{}^n$ which is not a fixed point for any group transformation except the identity, there exist $m=np_0(p_0+1)/2$ functions regular at z_0, automorphic with respect to Γ, and with Jacobian $\neq 0$ at z_0. (2) If $z_1, z_2 \in H_{p_0}{}^n$ are not equivalent under Γ, there exists an automorphic function h regular at z_1 and z_2 with $h(z_1)\neq h(z_2)$. (3) The field of functions automorphic with respect to Γ is isomorphic to a field of algebraic functions in m variables.

(3) was proved for $n=1$ by Siegel [Math. Ann. **116** (1939), 617–657; MR **1**, 203] and for $p_0=1$ by Maass [ibid. **117** (1940), 538–578; MR **2**, 87]; (1) and (2) were proved in a less precise form for $n=1$ by Siegel [op. cit.] and for $p_0=1$ by Steinitz [ibid. **71** (1912), 328–354]. The methods used in the present paper are developments of those of Siegel. To prove existence of modular functions, the author makes use of ordinary Poincaré series in a bounded domain, rather than (as did Siegel and Maass) of generalized Poincaré series in the upper half plane. Other simplifications are also achieved, in part by systematic use of majorant functions.

Adapted from the introduction

Citations: MR 1, 203f = F50-1.
Referred to in F02-8, F50-17.

F50-17 (20# 991b)

Pyateckiĭ-Šapiro, I. I. Singular modular functions. American Mathematical Society Translations, Ser. 2, Vol. 10, pp. 13–58. American Mathematical Society, Providence, R. I., 1958. iv+409 pp. $6.60.

Translation of #991 a.

Citations: MR 20# 991a = F50-16.
Referred to in F40-17, F40-28.

F50-18 (20# 1793)

Gundlach, Karl-Bernhard. Über den Rang der Schar der ganzen automorphen Formen zu hyperabelschen Transformationsgruppen in zwei Variablen. Nachr. Akad. Wiss. Göttingen. Math.-Phys. Kl. IIa. **1958**, 59–66.

The following theorem was proved by Hervé [Ann. Sci. Ecole Norm. Sup. (3) **69** (1952), 277–302; MR **14**, 633]: Let Γ be a discontinuous group of transformations on a bounded region of the space of two complex variables, and let Γ have a compact fundamental region. Then the dimension of the vector space of automorphic forms of dimension $-r$ ($r>0$) is a quadratic polynomial in r, provided r is sufficiently large. In the present paper the author extends this result to a class of hyperabelian transformation groups in two complex variables whose fundamental regions are not compact.

J. Lehner (East Lansing, Mich.)

Referred to in F40-35.

F50-19 (21# 4255)

Christian, Ulrich. Zur Theorie der Modulfunktionen n-ten Grades. II. Math. Ann. **134** (1958), 298–307.

[For part I, see same Ann. **133** (1957), 281–297; MR **19**, 740.] Let $\mathfrak{Z}_n$ be the space (with complex dimension $k=\frac{1}{2}n(n+1)$) of all complex symmetric $(n\times n)$ matrices Z such that $\mathfrak{I}(Z)$ is positive definite and let Γ_n be Siegel's modular group of degree n. The problem of the compactification of the fundamental domain $\mathfrak{G}_n$ of Γ_n in $\mathfrak{Z}_n$ by adding a suitable complex manifold at infinity was solved by Siegel himself [Comm. Pure Appl. Math. **8** (1955), 677–681; MR **17**, 602] and also by Satake [Proc. Internat. Symposium Algebraic Number Theory, Tokyo and Nikko, 1955, pp. 107–129, Science Council of Japan, Tokyo, 1956; J. Indian Math. Soc. **20** (1956), 259–281; MR **18**, 731, 934]. The latter introduced a topological space $\mathfrak{H}_n=\bigcup_{0\leq\nu\leq n}\mathfrak{F}_\nu$, where $\mathfrak{F}_\nu$ is the quotient space $\mathfrak{Z}_\nu/\Gamma_\nu$ and $\mathfrak{F}_\nu \cap \mathfrak{F}_\mu$ is empty if $\nu\neq\mu$. The present author introduces local coördinates in $\mathfrak{H}_n$ (which was not done yet by Satake) which makes it possible to apply Siegel's method [Nachr. Akad. Wiss. Göttingen. Math.-Phys. Kl. IIa **1955**, 71–77; MR **17**, 530] for proving that $k+1$ meromorphic functions on $\mathfrak{H}_n$ are algebraically dependent.

H. D. Kloosterman (Leiden)

Citations: MR 17, 602d = F45-2; MR 18, 731a = F50-12; MR 18, 934c = F45-4; MR 19, 740d = F50-15.

F50-20 (23# A135)

Klingen, Helmut

Zur Transformationstheorie von Thetareihen indefiniter quadratischer Formen.

Math. Ann. **140** (1960), 76–86.

Siegel's theory of indefinite quadratic forms rests in part on the study of the theta-series connected with such forms; these are non-analytic functions of a complex variable in the Poincaré half-plane (this corresponds to the problem of the representation of a number by a form) or more generally of a matrix variable in the Siegel space (corresponding to the problem of the representation of a form by a form). In both cases, it is essential to investigate the behavior of the theta-series under the modular group; the most general case, which had not been discussed by Siegel, is treated here; it leads to a unitary representation of the Siegel modular group which is described explicitly and involves generalized Gaussian sums.

A. Weil (Princeton, N.J.)

F50-21 (25# 233)

Satake, Ichirô

On modular functions of several variables (the compactification and its application). (Japanese)

Sûgaku **11** (1959/60), 170–175.

The classical theory of modular functions can be extended to the case of several variables by various methods. Though some results have been proved by using certain special properties of modular groups of higher dimensions, the essential point of the proof is that the quotient space by modular group is embedded into its compactification. This is similar to the case of one variable. However, strong contrast appears from the fact that in the definition of modular forms, no additional conditions on the behavior at the points at infinity is necessary for several variables.

In the present paper, the author gives an actual construction of the compactification, the so-called Satake compactification, for Siegel's modular group, and discusses the Siegel modular functions in detail. Further theory is published in Séminaire H. Cartan, 10e année: 1957/58 [Sécretariat Mathématique, Paris, 1958; MR **21** #2750] and this paper serves as an introduction to it.

S. Hitotumatu (Tokyo)

Citations: MR 21# 2750 = F02-5.

F50-22 (25# 5040)

Igusa, Jun-ichi

On Siegel modular forms of genus two.

Amer. J. Math. **84** (1962), 175–200.

Let $\mathfrak{S}_n$ be the variety of complex, symmetric matrices of degree n with positive-definite imaginary parts, Γ_n the homogeneous modular group of degree n operating on $\mathfrak{S}_n$ and $F_n=\Gamma_n\backslash\mathfrak{S}_n$, the Siegel fundamental domain of degree n. A modular form of degree n and (even) weight w is a function $\psi(\tau)$ ($\tau\in\mathfrak{S}_n$) holomorphic in $\mathfrak{S}_n$ (if $n=1$, exceptionally, also at $\tau=i\infty$) and satisfying $\psi(M\tau)=\det(c\tau+d)^w\psi(\tau)$ for every $M\in\Gamma_n$. If, in particular, $w=0$, we speak of invariants, or modular functions. The special functions $\psi_w(\tau)=\sum_{\{c,d\}}\det(c\tau+d)^{-w}$ ($\tau\in\mathfrak{S}_n$, $\{c,d\}$, inequivalent second rows of $M\in\Gamma_n$) are called Eisenstein series (of degree n, weight w). The set of finite sums of modular forms is a graded ring. The elliptic case ($n=1$) is classical, but already for $n=2$ very little was known. The present paper clarifies the structure of this subring (corresponding to $n=2$) by proving a number of theorems, some of which are of an unexpected beauty and whose importance (in this reviewer's opinion) can hardly be overestimated. It seems, unfortunately, that the methods used do not generalize in any obvious way to $n\geqq 3$. In fact, the present work relies heavily on some previous results obtained by the author [Ann. of Math. (2) **72** (1960), 612–649; MR **22** #5637] to the effect that the projective variety associated with the graded ring of even projective invariants of binary sextics is a compactification of the variety of moduli of curves of genus two. In addition, besides some standard theorems of algebraic geometry, a considerable amount of classical material is used (theta functions, elliptic modular forms), due to Jacobi, Rosenhain and Hurwitz. The principal results are the following (all for $n=2$): The field of meromorphic functions on F_2 can be identified with the field of absolute invariants such that holomorphic functions correspond to constants (this already follows from Baily, Amer. J. Math. **80** (1958), 348–364 [MR **20** #5890]). The structure of the ring of "algebraic" (i.e., with $w\equiv 0 \pmod 6$) modular forms is determined (6 generators, 3 relations), as well as the dimension N_w of the complex vector space of such forms of given weight $w(\equiv 0 \pmod 6)$. Adjoining the Eisenstein series ψ_4 to the ring of algebraic modular forms, one obtains (after normalization) the graded ring of all modular forms, which therefore turns out to be generated (over the field of complex numbers) by four algebraically independent modular forms of respective weights 4, 6, 10, 12 (for the first one may take ψ_4). Hence the dimension of the complex vector space of modular forms of weight w is equal to the number of non-negative integral solutions of the Diophantine equation $4p+6q+10r+12s=w$. Next, it is shown that the form of weight six is essentially ψ_6, while the other two are cusp forms (denoted, except for numerical factors, by χ_{10} and χ_{12}, respectively), expressible as simple polynomials in ψ_4, ψ_6, ψ_{10} and ψ_{12}. Consequently, we obtain the extremely interesting result that every modular form (with $n=2$, of course) is a polynomial of Eisenstein series of weight 4, 6, 10 and 12. Using the relation between algebraic modular forms and differentials, the three absolute invariants are found to be $\psi_4\chi_{10}^2/\chi_{12}^2$, $\psi_6\chi_{10}^3/\chi_{12}^3$, χ_{10}^6/χ_{12}^5; this solves a problem raised by Siegel [Ann. of Math. (2) **36** (1935), 527–606, p. 604]. In the last section, the structure of the Satake compactification Y of F_2 is discussed. It is shown that Y has the same Betti numbers as the three-dimensional complex projective space. Finally, in an appendix, the author discusses the connection of his results with A. Selberg's "trace formula", which also leads to a formula for N_w.

E. Grosswald (Philadelphia, Pa.)

Citations: MR 20# 5890 = F45-5.

Referred to in F10-89, F40-36, F45-21, F45-23, F50-27, F50-29, F50-33, F50-35, F50-39, F50-40, F50-41, F50-51, F50-69, F55-27.

F50-23 (27# 152)

Rangachari, S. S.

Abelian varieties attached to automorphic forms.

J. Math. Soc. Japan **14** (1962), 300–311.

Let G be a discontinuous group of analytic automorphisms on the upper half-plane H such that the quotient space H/G can be compactified by finitely many points (cusps). The space of cusp forms of degree $n+2$ for G is canonically isomorphic to a cohomology group $H^1(G, M_n)$ introduced by Eichler, where M_n is a linear representation of the group G in the space of polynomials of degree n and the cohomology is in the sense of the cohomology theory of abstract groups [Eichler, Math. Z. **67** (1957), 267–298; MR **19**, 740]; and Shimura [J. Math. Soc. Japan **11** (1959), 291–311; MR **22** #11126] has shown that for certain classes of groups G, there is a lattice in $H^1(G, M_n)$ whose associated torus is an abelian variety. In the present paper, the author extends these results to cusp forms with multipliers, with a corresponding modification of the Eichler cohomology groups, provided that the multiplier has a kernel of finite index in G. By using this generalization, the author is also able to introduce an interesting decomposition of the abelian varieties associated to a subgroup $H\subset G$ of finite index, in terms of the abelian varieties associated to various multipliers for G.

R. C. Gunning (Princeton, N.J.)

Citations: MR 19, 740a = F15-12; MR 22# 11126 = F15-15.

F50-24 (28# 250)

Shimura, Goro

On modular correspondences for $Sp(n, Z)$ and their congruence relations.

Proc. Nat. Acad. Sci. U.S.A. **49** (1963), 824–828.

This paper is a brief survey of some very interesting recent work of the author on modular correspondences for the Siegel modular function fields. Let G be the integer symplectic group, $G=Sp(n, Z)$; let S be the set of all $2n\times 2n$ integer matrices B such that ${}^tBJB=r(B)J$ for some rational integer $r(B)>0$; and let L be the free Z-module generated by the double cosets GBG for $B\in S$. The module L is given the structure of a commutative integral domain. The author introduces and investigates the formal Dirichlet series with coefficients in the ring L, defined by $D(s)=\sum (GBG)r(B)^{-s}$, where the summation is extended over the double cosets GBG with $B\in S$. It is shown that this series has an Euler product $D(s)=\prod_p D_p(s)$, where $D_p(s)$ is the corresponding sum extended over those double cosets for which $r(B)$ is a power of the prime p. It is conjectured that $D_p(s)=E(p^{-s})/F(p^{-s})$, where E and F are polynomials of degrees 2^n-2 and 2^n with integer coefficients; for $n=1$ this is a result due to Hecke [Math. Ann. **114** (1937), 1–28; ibid. **114** (1937), 316–351], while for $n=2$ the author determines the polynomials E and F explicitly. The ring L is then realized as a ring of algebraic correspondences of an algebraic variety V defined over the rationals, where the function field of V is the field of Siegel's modular functions of degree n; this construction rests upon some results from the author's earlier study of these function fields [Ann. of Math. (2) **78** (1963), 149–192; MR **27** #5934; ibid. (2) **70** (1959), 101–144; MR **21** #6370]. By studying the reduction modulo a prime p of these correspondences, the author derives congruence relations for the correspondences which generalize the congruences derived earlier by Eichler [Arch. Math. **5** (1954), 355–366; MR **16**, 116] and the author [J. Math. Soc. Japan **10** (1958), 1–28; MR **20** #1679; ibid. **13** (1961), 275–331; MR **26** #84] for the modular correspondences of the fields of elliptic modular functions and of some other automorphic functions of one variable. For $n=2$ the congruence relations lead to a factorization of the denominator of the formal Dirichlet series $D_p(s)$.

R. C. Gunning (Princeton, N.J.)

Citations: MR 16, 116d = G30-15; MR 20# 1679 = F25-8; MR 21# 6370 = F55-11; MR 26# 84 = G30-31; MR 27# 5934 = F55-16.

Referred to in F45-32, F50-65, F50-72, F60-8.

F50-25 **(28# 251)**

Fritzsche, Reiner

Beitrag zur Theorie der Modulfunktionen 2. Grades. *Inauguraldissertation zur Erlangung der Doktorwürde der Mathematisch-Naturwissenschaftlichen Fakultät der Martin-Luther-Universität Halle-Wittenberg, Halle,* 1962. iii + 42 *pp.*

Let E and 0 stand for the $n\times n$ unit and zero matrices, respectively, set $I=\begin{pmatrix}0 & E\\ -E & 0\end{pmatrix}$ and let Γ_n stand for the multiplicative group of $2n\times 2n$ matrices M with rational, integral entries and such that $M^TIM=I$. Define also H_n as the set of square, symmetric matrices T with complex entries, $T=U+iV$ (V positive definite); then, if $M=\begin{pmatrix}A & B\\ C & D\end{pmatrix}\in\Gamma_n$, $T^*=M\langle T\rangle=(AT+B)(CT+D)^{-1}=U^*+iV^*$, with V^* positive definite and, furthermore, $M\langle T\rangle=(-M)\langle T\rangle\neq N\langle T\rangle$ for $N\in\Gamma_n$, $N\neq\pm M$. Identifying M and $-M$, one obtains the group $\mathfrak{M}_n$. Following Siegel [Math. Ann. **116** (1939), 617–657; MR **1**, 203] and Koecher [Math. Z. **59** (1954), 399–416; MR **15**, 603], a modular form of degree $n>1$ is a function $\varphi(T)$ of the $\frac{1}{2}n(n+1)$ independent complex variables of T, analytic and regular for $T\in H_n$ and satisfying $M\varphi(T)$ $(=_{\rm def}\varphi(M\langle T\rangle),\ M\in\mathfrak{M}_n)=|M(T)|^g\varphi(T)$ (the "weight" g is an even rational integer). This generalizes the classical situation $n=1$ of the elliptic modular forms (where one requires, however, in addition, that $\varphi(z)$ be bounded in a fundamental region). The ratio of two modular forms of degree n and equal weight g is called a (Siegel) modular function. The set of these functions is a field of transcendence degree $\frac{1}{2}n(n+1)$ over the complex numbers and is denoted by $C\{\mathfrak{M}_n\}$; the relation of the modular functions of degree n to Abelian functions of n independent variables is similar to the relation between elliptic modular functions and elliptic functions. Also, just as in the classical case, one may define congruence subgroups of rank (Stufe) q, etc. It is still partly an open problem to investigate which properties of the elliptic modular functions remain valid for $n>1$, or how the corresponding statements have to be modified. The present booklet investigates a specific problem of this kind for $n=2$. In this particular case, the equation $f(x,y)=0$, which defines the field of (hyperelliptic) functions, may be reduced (by a birational transformation) to $y^2=\prod_{i=1}^6(x-a_i)$ ($a_i\neq a_j$ for $i\neq j$). Set $\lambda_j=(a_j-a_5)/(a_j-a_6)\cdot(a_4-a_6)/(a_4-a_5)$ ($j=1, 2, 3$) and $\vartheta_{jk}=\vartheta_{jk}(0;\ T)$; then the λ_j's are rational in the $\vartheta_{jk}{}^2$ [Weierstrass; see also Lapin, Izv. Akad. Nauk SSSR Ser. Mat. **20** (1956), 325–336; MR **18**, 389], so that $\lambda_j=\lambda_j(T)$. Denoting also the principal congruence subgroup of rank q of $\mathfrak{M}_2$ by $\mathfrak{M}_2(q)$, the principal results may be formulated as follows. Theorem 1: Let $\mathfrak{S}_6$ be the symmetric group of degree 6; then $\mathfrak{S}_6\cong\mathfrak{M}_2/\mathfrak{M}_2(2)$ (in a certain canonical way). Theorem 2: Let $\mathfrak{H}_2{}^{(j)}=\{M|M\in\mathfrak{M}_2,\ \lambda_j(M\langle T\rangle)=\lambda_j(T)\}$; then $C\{\mathfrak{H}_2{}^{(j)}\}$ (i.e., the field of functions automorphic under $\mathfrak{H}_2{}^{(j)}$) is a simple algebraic extension of $C\{\mathfrak{M}_2\}$ of degree $m=90$ and λ_j ($j=1, 2, 3$) is a primitive element. Theorem 3: $C\{\mathfrak{M}_2(2)\}$ is a simple algebraic extension of $C\{\mathfrak{H}_2{}^{(j)}\}$ of degree 8 and λ_k is a primitive element ($j, k=1, 2, 3;\ j\neq k$). Theorem 4: $C\{\mathfrak{M}_2(2)\}$ is a simple algebraic extension of $C\{\mathfrak{M}_2\}$, of degree 720. Theorem 5 [Lapin, loc. cit.]: $C\{\mathfrak{M}_2(2)\}$ is isomorphic to the field of rational functions in three indeterminates. A less precise version of Theorem 2 (but in a much more general setting) is due to Koecher [loc. cit.]. Theorem 4 follows readily from Theorems 2 and 3; Theorem 5 is an easy consequence of Theorems 2, 3, 4, a lemma of the author and a result of Koecher. The method for the proof of Theorems 1, 2 and 3 is essentially that of Lapin and cannot be generalized in any obvious way to $n\geqq 3$, because it makes essential use of the fact that for $n=2$ the inversion of the abelian integral of first kind leads to the most general abelian function of n ($=2$) variables. This, however, is true only for $n=2$; for $n\geqq 3$ the number $\frac{1}{2}n(n+1)$ of parameters on which an abelian function of n variables depends exceeds the number of parameters (namely, $3n-3$) of an algebraic curve of genus n. *E. Grosswald* (Philadelphia, Pa.)

Citations: MR 1, 203f = F50-1; MR 15, 603e = F50-5; MR 18, 389g = F50-11.

Referred to in F50-26.

F50-26 **(28# 3156)**

Fritzsche, Reiner

Beitrag zur Theorie der Modulfunktionen 2. Grades. *Math. Ann.* **154** (1964), 135–146.

This is an abridged version of the author's 1962 dissertation (Martin-Luther-Univ. Halle-Wittenberg, Halle), which was reviewed earlier [MR **28** #251].

Citations: MR 28# 251 = F50-25.

Referred to in F50-43.

F50-27 **(29# 2258)**

Igusa, Jun-ichi

On the graded ring of theta-constants. *Amer. J. Math.* **86** (1964), 219–246.

Es sei g eine natürliche Zahl. Die Menge $\mathfrak{S}_g$ der komplexen Matrizen g-ten Grades mit positiv-definitem Imaginärteil bildet eine konvexe offene Teilmenge des $\frac{1}{2}g(g+1)$-dimensionalen komplexen Vektorraumes. $\mathfrak{S}_g$ heisst die "Siegelsche obere Halbebene vom Grade g". Die reelle symplektische Gruppe $\mathrm{Sp}(g, \mathbf{R})$ operiert folgendermassen auf $\mathfrak{S}_g$: Man schreibe $M\in\mathrm{Sp}(g, R)$ in der Form $M=\begin{pmatrix}a & b\\ c & d\end{pmatrix}$, wobei a, b, c, d Matrizen g-ten Grades sind; dann ist $M\cdot\tau=(a\tau+b)(c\tau+d)^{-1}$ für $\tau\in\mathfrak{S}_g$. Der Verfasser betrachtet diskrete Untergruppen Γ von $\mathrm{Sp}(g, \mathbf{R})$, die mit der "Siegelschen Modulgruppe" $\mathrm{Sp}(g, \mathbf{Z})$ kommensurabel sind in dem Sinne, dass $\Gamma\cap\mathrm{Sp}(g, \mathbf{Z})$ endliche Indizes in Γ und in $\mathrm{Sp}(g, \mathbf{Z})$ besitzt. Eine analytische Funktion ψ auf $\mathfrak{S}_g$ heisst "Modulform vom Gewicht k bezüglich Γ", wenn $\psi(M\cdot\tau)=\det(c\tau+d)^k\psi(\tau)$ für $M\in\Gamma$, $\tau\in\mathfrak{S}_g$; im Falle $g=1$ kommt hierzu noch in geläufiger Weise eine Analytizitätsbedingung im Unendlichen. Es bedeute $A(\Gamma)_k$ den komplexen Vektorraum der Modulformen vom Gewicht k. Durchläuft k die positiven ganzrationalen Zahlen, so ist die direkte Summe $A(\Gamma)=\sum_k A(\Gamma)_k$ ein graduierter ganzabgeschlossener Integritätsbereich. Er ist endlich erzeugt über dem Körper $\mathbf{C}=A(\Gamma)_0$ der komplexen Zahlen und bestimmt daher eine projektive Mannigfaltigkeit $\mathrm{proj}\,A(\Gamma)$ über $\mathbf{C}$. Man nennt $\mathrm{proj}\,A(\Gamma)$ die "Modulmannigfaltigkeit" bezüglich Γ; sie enthält die Quotientenmannigfaltigkeit $\Gamma\backslash\mathfrak{S}_g$ als offene Teilmenge im Sinne der Zariskischen Topologie. Der Verfasser stellt sich die Aufgabe, die Struktur der Modulmannigfaltigkeit $\mathrm{proj}\,A(\Gamma)$ zu untersuchen.

Das Hauptergebnis der vorliegenden Arbeit bezieht sich auf die Kongruenzuntergruppe $\Gamma_g(4, 8)$ von $\mathrm{Sp}(g, \mathbf{Z})$; sie besteht aus denjenigen Matrizen $M=\begin{pmatrix}a & b\\ c & d\end{pmatrix}\in\mathrm{Sp}(g, \mathbf{Z})$, für welche $M\equiv 1 \bmod 4$, $(a^tb)_0\equiv(c^td)_0\equiv 0 \bmod 8$ (hier bedeutet s_0 den Vektor der Diagonalkoeffizienten der quadratischen Matrix s). Der Verfasser zeigt: Der graduierte Ring $A(\Gamma_g(4, 8))$ ist die ganzabgeschlossene Hülle des graduierten Ringes $\mathbf{C}[\theta_m\theta_n]$, der über $\mathbf{C}$ durch die Produkte von "Thetakonstanten" θ_m erzeugt wird. Letztere werden wie folgt erklärt: m sei ein Vektor in $\mathbf{Z}^{2g}$; $m', m''\in\mathbf{Z}^g$ sind die

Vektoren der ersten bzw. letzten g Komponenten von $\mathfrak{m}$. Durch

$$\theta_{\mathfrak{m}}(\tau, z) = \sum_{p\in \mathbf{Z}^g} \exp 2\pi i[\tfrac{1}{2}\cdot{}^t(p+\tfrac{1}{2}\mathfrak{m}')\tau(p+\tfrac{1}{2}\mathfrak{m}') + {}^t(p+\tfrac{1}{2}\mathfrak{m}')(z+\tfrac{1}{2}\mathfrak{m}'')]$$

wird eine analytische Funktion der beiden Variablen $\tau \in \mathfrak{S}_g$, $z \in \mathbf{C}^g$ definiert: die Thetafunktion der Charakteristik $\mathfrak{m}$. Durch $\theta_{\mathfrak{m}}(\tau) = \theta_{\mathfrak{m}}(\tau, 0)$ wird eine analytische Funktion $\theta_{\mathfrak{m}}$ der Variablen $\tau \in \mathfrak{S}_g$ definiert; man nennt $\theta_{\mathfrak{m}}$ die Funktion der Thetakonstanten der Charakteristik $\mathfrak{m}$. Zum Beweis des Hauptergebnisses wird erstens gezeigt, dass $A(\Gamma_g(4, 8))$ ganzalgebraisch ist über $\mathbf{C}[\theta_{\mathfrak{m}}\theta_{\mathfrak{n}}]$; hierzu wird das folgende Lemma verwendet: Seien $\psi_1, \cdots, \psi_n$ Modulformen bezüglich Γ ohne gemeinsame Nullstelle in der Quotientenmannigfaltigkeit $\Gamma\backslash\mathfrak{S}_g$ und ihrem Rande. Dann ist $A(\Gamma)$ ganzalgebraisch über $\mathbf{C}[\psi_1, \cdots, \psi_n]$. Zweitens wird gezeigt, dass der (homogene) Quotientenkörper $F(\Gamma_g(4, 8))$ übereinstimmt mit dem durch die Thetaquotienten erzeugten Körper $\mathbf{C}(\theta_{\mathfrak{m}}/\theta_{\mathfrak{n}})$. Vermöge der Galoisschen Theorie von $F(\Gamma_g(4, 8))$ über $F(\mathrm{Sp}(g, \mathbf{Z}))$ wird diese Behauptung zurückgeführt auf den Satz, dass $F(\mathrm{Sp}(g, \mathbf{Z}))$ in $\mathbf{C}(\theta_{\mathfrak{m}}/\theta_{\mathfrak{n}})$ enthalten ist. Der Beweis dieses Satzes bildet den Hauptteil dieser Arbeit; die Beweisschritte beruhen auf Ideen von Wirtinger [*Untersuchungen über Thetafunctionen*, Teubner, Leipzig, 1895]. Für vorgegebenes g kann die ganzabgeschlossene Hülle von $\mathbf{C}[\theta_{\mathfrak{m}}\theta_{\mathfrak{n}}]$ und damit auch $A(\Gamma_g(4, 8))$ explizit bestimmt werden. Hieraus kann dann auch $A(\mathrm{Sp}(g, \mathbf{Z}))$ als Teilring davon bestimmt werden. In den Fällen $g = 1, 2$ ist $\mathbf{C}[\theta_{\mathfrak{m}}\theta_{\mathfrak{n}}]$ selbst ganzabgeschlossen; die hieraus folgenden Konsequenzen sollen für $g = 2$ in einer weiteren Arbeit des Verfassers diskutiert werden. Die Fälle $g = 1, 2, 3$ wurden mit einer anderen Methode vom Verfasser bereits früher behandelt [der Verfasser, Amer. J. Math. **84** (1962), 175–200; MR **25** #5040; Proc. Internat. Congr. Mathematicians (Stockholm), 1962, pp. 522–525, Inst. Mittag-Leffler, Djursholm, 1963]. *P. Roquette* (Tübingen)

Citations: MR 25# 5040 = F50-22.

Referred to in F10-89, F50-33, F50-44, F50-69.

F50-28 (29# 2434)

Klingen, Helmut

Über einen Zusammenhang zwischen Siegelschen und Hermiteschen Modulfunktionen.

Abh. Math. Sem. Univ. Hamburg **27** (1964), 1–12.

The Siegel upper half-plane $\mathfrak{S}_n$ is the space of symmetric $n \times n$ complex matrices Z such that $\operatorname{Im} Z = (2i)^{-1}(Z - \bar{Z})$ is positive definite, and the Siegel modular functions are those meromorphic functions on $\mathfrak{S}_n$ which are invariant under the action of the symplectic modular group Γ_n [Siegel, Math. Ann. **116** (1939), 617–657; MR **1**, 203]. The Hermitian upper half-plane $\mathfrak{H}_n$ is the space of $n \times n$ complex matrices Z such that $(2i)^{-1}(Z - \bar{Z}')$ is positive definite Hermitian, and correspondingly, Hermitian modular functions are meromorphic functions on $\mathfrak{H}_n$ which are invariant under the action of Hermitian modular groups Φ_n [Braun, Ann. of Math. (2) **50** (1949), 827–855; MR **11**, 333]. The space $\mathfrak{S}_n$ is embedded in $\mathfrak{H}_n$ as an analytic submanifold in a natural manner, namely,

$$\mathfrak{S}_n = \{Z \in \mathfrak{H}_n | Z = Z'\};$$

and Γ_n is then the subgroup of Φ_n consisting of those transformations which preserve the submanifold $\mathfrak{S}_n$ [Klingen, Math. Ann. **129** (1955), 345–369; MR **18**, 299]. The purpose of the present paper is to show that the Siegel modular functions consist precisely of the restrictions to $\mathfrak{S}_n$ of those Hermitian modular functions which are not everywhere singular on $\mathfrak{S}_n \subset \mathfrak{H}_n$. *R. C. Gunning* (Princeton, N.J.)

Citations: MR 1, 203f = F50-1; MR 11, 333a = F55-1; MR 18, 299c = F45-3.

Referred to in F50-58.

F50-29 (29# 3473)

Siegel, Carl Ludwig

Moduln Abelscher Funktionen.

Nachr. Akad. Wiss. Göttingen Math.-Phys. Kl. II **1963**, 365–427.

Let $\Omega = (Z, T)$ be a $2n \times n$ period matrix, where $T = \operatorname{diag}(t_1, \cdots, t_n)$ with natural integers t_i and $Z = X + iY$ symmetric, $Y > 0$. If $t_1 \geqq 3$, the Jacobian theta functions yield a singularity-free model of the corresponding Abelian manifold in the projective space of dimension $t = |T|$. Let $\vartheta_i(w) = \vartheta_i(w_1, \cdots, w_n)$ be these theta functions and consider as many indeterminates $\xi_1, \cdots, \xi_t$. With $(n+1)t$ further indeterminates λ_{ik} form $\eta_i = \sum \lambda_{ik}\xi_k$ and $j_i(w) = \sum \lambda_{ik}\vartheta_k(w)$. Now let $\Phi(\lambda, \eta)$ be a homogeneous polynomial in the λ and η of minimal degree in the latter which vanishes for $\eta_i = j_i(w)$. It has the following properties. (1) The degree is $m = n!t$. (2) If $\Phi(\lambda, \eta) = \sum \lambda_{ik}\Phi_{ik}(\xi)$, all algebraic equations between the $\vartheta_i(w)$ are consequences of $\Phi_{ik}(\vartheta(w)) = 0$. (3) The coefficients of Φ depend naturally on the period matrix. (4) Φ can explicitly be described as follows: let $\varphi_l(\xi)$, $l = 1, \cdots, h$, all be power products of the ξ_i in some order and $\alpha_l = \alpha_l(\lambda)$ the $(h-1)$-rowed subdeterminants of the matrix $(\varphi_l(\vartheta_k(w)))$, then

$$\Phi = \sum_{l=1}^{h} \alpha_l\varphi_l(\xi). \tag{1}$$

The chief object of the paper is the study of the behavior of the coefficients of Φ under modular transformation of the period matrix Z (T being left fixed throughout). A tool for this is the following Hermitian scalar product of theta functions. Put $w = Zu + Tv$ with real vectors u and w and for two Jacobian functions $f(w)$, $g(w)$

$$(f, g) = \int_W f(w)\overline{g(w)}e^{(\pi/2)Y[w-\bar{w}]}\,du_1\cdots dv_1\cdots,$$

where W is the period torus. It is easily shown that the integrand is a function defined on W_1 and that two different theta functions are orthogonal while $(\vartheta_i, \vartheta_i) = 2|Y|^{-1/2}$.

Now Jacobian functions of characteristic xy are considered which are linear combinations of these theta series

$$\vartheta(x, y; Z, w) = \sum_m \exp \pi i(Z[m + T^{-1}x] + 2(m + T^{-1}x)^t(w + y)). \tag{2}$$

To these functions the transformations

$$Z_1 = (TAT^{-1}Z + TB)(CT^{-1}Z + D)^{-1},$$
$$w_1 = ((CT^{-1}Z + D)^t)^{-1}w$$

are applied, where A, B, C, D are rational integral matrices with

$$\begin{pmatrix} A & B \\ C & D \end{pmatrix}^t \begin{pmatrix} 0 & T \\ -T & 0 \end{pmatrix} \begin{pmatrix} A & B \\ C & D \end{pmatrix} = s\begin{pmatrix} 0 & T \\ -T & 0 \end{pmatrix}$$

with a further rational integer s. If $s = 1$, these matrices form the modular group $\Gamma(T)$; subsequently the following normal subgroup $\Delta(T)$ will be used:

$$(A-E)T^{-1},\ BT^{-1},\ CT^{-1},\ (D-E)T^{-1} \text{ integral.}$$

With a substitution described above and a Jacobian function $f(w_1)$ of characteristic xy and period matrix (Z_1T)

$$f_1(w) = \exp(-\pi i(s^{-1}w^tT^{-1}C^tw_1))f(w_1)$$

is a Jacobian function of characteristic

$$x_1 = A^tx+C^ty+\tfrac{1}{2}\{A^tTC\}, \qquad y_1 = B^tx+D^ty+\tfrac{1}{2}\{B^tTD\}$$

and period matrix $s(ZT)$, where $\{\cdots\}$ denotes the vector whose components are the diagonal elements of the matrix in parentheses. Furthermore, the scalar product remains invariant: $(f,g)=(f_1,g_1)$.

This transformation is specially applied to theta functions of the more general type (2) and under the restriction to $w=0$. It yields a unitary representation of the group $\Gamma(T)$ whose coefficients can of course be written in terms of Gaussian sums. The kernel of this representation turns out to be the subgroup $\Theta(T)\subset\Delta(T)$ defined by the conditions that $AT^{-1}B^t$, $CT^{-1}D$ have even coefficients in the diagonal. A similar result which is less easy to formulate concerns the transformation of the functions (2) with $w\neq 0$; it is a decisive tool in the following problem.

Under the transformations Z, $w\to Z_1$, w_1 belonging to the modular group $\Gamma(T)$, the coefficients $\alpha_l=\alpha_l(\lambda)$ undergo corresponding transformations. The ratios $\alpha_{l_1}:\alpha_{l_2}$, however, remain invariant if and only if the transformation belongs to the congruence subgroup $\Delta(T)$. It is now very easy to form invariants for the whole modular group $\Gamma(T)$ by symmetrization. Now the α_l are polynomials in the indeterminates λ_{ik} the coefficients of which are functions of Z and the w_i. Let $q_0, q_1, \cdots, q_g$ be all these coefficients, then the quotients $f_i=q_i/q_0$ are functions of Z only. The author even proves that to every $Z=Z_0$ there is such an ordering of the q_i that the f_i are regular in the neighborhood of this point. (The statement has been somewhat simplified; in fact, this is only true if the $\alpha_l(\lambda)$ are relatively prime polynomials in the λ, the formulation of the theorem in the general case being more complicated.)

The last fact is necessary to prove the following deep theorem: All modular functions of $\Delta(T)$ are rational functions of the f_i. The proof is of course rather involved. Among other things it uses the fact that all modular functions can be represented as quotients of Eisenstein series [the author, Math. Ann. **116** (1939), 617–657; MR **1**, 203]. In the case $T=tE$ it is eventually shown that all modular functions can be represented as quotients of Fourier series with integral rational coefficients.

Taking into account the contents of the author's paper quoted before [loc. cit.] (which has to be generalised, however, since it assumes $T=E$) and furthermore the result of Igusa [Amer. J. Math. **84** (1962), 175–200; MR **25** #5040], we may expect the story to end here. But the author continues, attempting to determine all algebraic equations between the functions f_i or, what is the same, all homogeneous algebraic equations between the q_i. The latter do not only depend on Z but also on the w_i. The principle of determining these equations consists of two theorems. (1) Let $Q(Z,w)$ be a homogeneous polynomial in the q_i. If sufficiently many of the initial coefficients of the development of Q in a power series in the w_i vanish, then Q vanishes identically. (2) If sufficiently many of the initial coefficients in the Fourier expansion of Q with respect to Z vanish, then Q vanishes identically. The latter theorem has been proved and used by the author on previous occasions. From these theorems we can easily derive a "constructive procedure" to obtain all algebraic relations between the f_i since we know them to be generated by those of a bounded degree. However, the conditions seem rather involved, and it may be premature to expect explicit information. *M. Eichler* (Basel)

Citations: MR 1, 203f = F50-1; MR 25# 5040 = F50-22.

Referred to in G15-34.

F50-30 (29# 6058)

Baily, W. L., Jr.; Borel, A.

On the compactification of arithmetically defined quotients of bounded symmetric domains.

Bull. Amer. Math. Soc. **70** (1964), 588–593.

This is a brief announcement of the results extending earlier results [*Séminaire H. Cartan*, 1957/58, Secrétariat mathématique, Paris, 1958; MR **21** #2750; W. L. Baily, Jr., Amer. J. Math. **81** (1959), 846–874; MR **22** #12244; I. I. Pjateckiĭ-Šapiro, *Geometry of classical domains and theory of automorphic functions*, Fizmatgiz, Moscow, 1961; MR **25** #231] to the most general case, of which a full account is supposed to be published elsewhere. Let X be a hermitian symmetric space of non-compact type. One considers a (connected) semi-simple linear algebraic group G ($\subset GL(m,\mathbf{C})$) defined over $\mathbf{Q}$ such that the symmetric space associated with $G_{\mathbf{R}}$ is equal to X, i.e., $X=K\diagdown G_{\mathbf{R}}$, where K is a maximal compact subgroup of $G_{\mathbf{R}}$. (As usual, for every subring B of $\mathbf{C}$, one puts $G_B=G\cap GL(m,B)$.) Let Γ be an "arithmetic subgroup" of G, i.e., a subgroup of $G_{\mathbf{Q}}$ commensurable with the group $G_{\mathbf{Z}}$ of units of G; then Γ acts on X (from the right) in a properly discontinuous manner, and the quotient space X/Γ carries a natural ringed structure with which it becomes an irreducible normal analytic space. Since the main purpose of the paper is to construct a suitable compactification of X/Γ, one may assume that X/Γ is not compact, which implies, in particular, that $G_{\mathbf{R}}$ has no compact simple factor $\neq(e)$; for simplicity, one further assumes that G is strictly simple over $\mathbf{Q}$ (i.e., that it has no proper invariant subgroup $\neq(e)$ over $\mathbf{Q}$). Now the first step is to define the notion of "rational boundary component" for the natural compactification $\bar{X}$ of X (i.e., the closure of X in the Harish-Chandra realization as a bounded symmetric domain). This being done in a very ingenious way, it turns out that, for a rational boundary component F of X (with respect to Γ), the complexification $\mathfrak{N}(F)_{\mathbf{C}}$ of the normalizer $\mathfrak{N}(F)=\{g\in G_{\mathbf{R}}|\ Fg=F\}$ is a proper maximal parabolic subgroup defined over $\mathbf{Q}$ of G, and actually the map $F\to\mathfrak{N}(F)_{\mathbf{C}}$ gives a one-to-one correspondence between the rational boundary components of X (with respect to Γ) and the proper maximal parabolic subgroups over $\mathbf{Q}$ of G (Theorem 1). Then, denoting by X^* the union of X and all rational boundary components, one introduces a topology on X^* in a natural way (but still making use of a fundamental set for Γ) so that $V^*=X^*/\Gamma$ becomes a compact Hausdorff space. From the construction, one has $V^*=V\cup V_1\cup\cdots\cup V_t$ with $V_i=F_i/\Gamma(F_i)$, where $V=X/\Gamma$ is open, everywhere dense, the F_i's are such that the corresponding groups $\mathfrak{N}(F_i)_{\mathbf{C}}$ form a system of representatives for the equivalence-classes, modulo inner automorphisms by elements of Γ, of proper maximal parabolic subgroups over $\mathbf{Q}$ of G, and $\Gamma(F_i)$ is an arithmetic group acting on F_i, obtained as a homomorphic image of $\mathfrak{N}(F_i)\cap\Gamma$. Next, to define an analytic structure on V^*, one calls a complex-valued function f defined on an open subset U of V^* an $\mathscr{H}$-function on U if it is continuous and if its restriction to $V\cap U$ and to $V_i\cap U$ is analytic in the given analytic structure $(1\leq i\leq t)$. Then, by arguments similar to those used in the previous papers [loc. cit.] and by considerations of Poincaré-

Eisenstein series, the constructions of which depend essentially on the realization of X as a Siegel domain of the third kind for a given boundary component [cf. Pjateckiĭ-Šapiro, loc. cit.; and A. Korányi and J. Wolf, "Generalized Cayley transforms of bounded symmetric domains", Ann. of Math. (2) (to appear)], the authors show finally that V^*, provided with the ringed structure defined by the sheaf of $\mathscr{H}$-functions, becomes a normal analytic space projectively embeddable as a projectively normal algebraic variety by means of a set of automorphic forms for Γ of some suitably high weight (Theorem 3). As a corollary, a generalization of Köcher's theorem and the finiteness of the dimension of the space of automorphic forms (for G with dim $G > 3$) are mentioned, together with some comments on the other approaches to the same results. *I. Satake* (Chicago, Ill.)

Citations: MR 21# 2750 = F02-5; MR 22# 12244 = F40-17; MR 25# 231 = F02-10.

Referred to in F45-24, F50-40.

F50-31 (35# 6870)

Baily, W. L., Jr.; Borel, A.

Compactification of arithmetic quotients of bounded symmetric domains.

Ann. of Math. (2) **84** (1966), 442–528.

The subject of this paper is the extension of the theory of the Siegel modular group (as presented in the Cartan seminar of 1957/58 [Séminaire Henri Cartan, 1957/58, *Fonctions automorphes*, 2 Vols., Sécretariat mathématique, Paris, 1958; MR **21** #2750]) to what seems to be its proper range of generality. The authors start with an arbitrary bounded symmetric domain X and an arithmetically defined discontinuous group Γ of automorphisms of X. (The group $H(X)$ of holomorphic automorphisms of X is always a subgroup of finite index in the group G_R of real points of a linear algebraic R-group G, namely the automorphism group of the complexification h_c of the Lie algebra h of $H(X)$. G can be given, generally in many ways, a rational structure by fixing a rational subalgebra h_Q such that $h = h_Q \otimes_Q R$. $\Gamma \subset G$ is called arithmetic if for some, and hence all, rational matrix representations ρ of G, $\rho(\Gamma)$ is commensurable with the group of integral matrices in $\rho(G)$.)

The paper consists of three parts. The subject of the first is to construct (as a topological space) a compactification V^* of $V = X/\Gamma$, generalizing Satake's construction for the Siegel case. In order to do this the authors first summarize, adapt, and at points extend results obtained in recent years by several authors (mainly Pjateckiĭ-Šapiro, J. A. Wolf and the reviewer) about the geometric structure of the canonical Harish-Chandra realization of X as a bounded domain D in $\mathbf{C}^n$. The main facts are the following. (i) $\bar{D} - D$ is a union of locally closed analytic subsets of $\mathbf{C}^n$, called boundary components, which are themselves bounded symmetric domains imbedded in certain affine subspaces of $\mathbf{C}^n$. (ii) The subgroups $N(F)$ which keep a boundary component fixed as a set are exactly the maximal parabolic subgroups of $G_R{}^0$ (topological identity component of G_R). (iii) If $Z(F)$ is the subgroup fixing each point of F, the group $G(F) = N(F)/Z(F)$ is exactly the connected automorphism group of F. (iv) To each F there is associated an unbounded realization S_F of X ("Siegel domain of type III") obtainable as a generalized Cayley transform of D, and a kind of fibering of X over F whose fibers are affine subspaces of $\mathbf{C}^n$ and orbits of $Z(F)^0$. Next, it is pointed out that if X/Γ is not compact (which is the only non-trivial case in the present context), then G has a non-trivial maximal Q-split torus and a non-trivial system of Q-roots. The restriction map from R-roots to Q-roots is considered in detail; it turns out, for example, that there are only two systems of simple roots that can occur. Here and also in the following section a number of important references are made to a paper of the second author and J. Tits [Inst. Hautes Études Sci. Publ. Math. **27** (1965), 55–150; MR **34** #7527]. The fundamental notion of a rational boundary component is introduced next: F is rational if $N(F)_c$ is defined over Q. This is equivalent to saying that $U(F)/(U(F) \cap \Gamma)$ is compact for some, and hence for all, arithmetic groups Γ ($U(F)$ denotes the unipotent radical of $N(F)$). The authors prove that if F is rational then $\Gamma(F)$, the image of $\Gamma \cap N(F)$ under the natural map $N(F) \to N(F)/Z(F)$, is discrete and is an arithmetic subgroup of $G(F)$. The construction of V^* is performed now along the lines of Satake. An important role is played in the construction by certain fundamental open sets for Γ (called "Siegel domains" and studied earlier by Borel and Harish-Chandra). V^* is the quotient by Γ of the union of D and its rational boundary components with an appropriately defined topology; it can be regarded as the union of V and finitely many $V_i = G(F_i)/\Gamma(F_i)$. This finishes Part I, which takes up more than half of the paper.

Part II deals with automorphic forms constructed as Poincaré-Eisenstein series. There are such series associated to every type of boundary component (or every unbounded realization of X); they are simultaneous generalizations of the classical Poincaré and Eisenstein series. After quoting some general results of Harish-Chandra and Godement, the authors proceed to the construction of convergent majorants and to the study of the series in the neighborhood of rational boundary components. This is rather complicated, involving the Bruhat decomposition, representation theory and some fairly explicit information about Siegel domains and Jacobian determinants. It turns out that every Poincaré-Eisenstein series adapted to the rational boundary component F has a limit on F, which is a Poincaré series for F; one has therefore a generalization of the Φ-operator of Maass. Important information about the range of Φ is also obtained (showing that the range is large).

Part III is concerned with the extension of the first author's work on the Satake compactification. A sheaf of germs of functions is constructed on V^* and it is shown that this makes V^* into an irreducible normal analytic space in a natural way. For the proof a new version of the analyticity criterion of Baily and Cartan is needed; this is stated and proved in a separate section. It now follows easily that V^* has an imbedding as a projectively normal subvariety in some $P(N, C)$, that the field of Γ-automorphic functions is isomorphic with the field of rational functions on V^* and that every automorphic function is the quotient of two automorphic forms. With the aid of an extension theorem of Serre, a generalization of Koecher's principle is also proved. There is an appendix in which the question of the number of connected components of $H(X)$ and G_R is clarified. *A. Korányi* (New York)

Citations: MR 21# 2750 = F02-5.

Referred to in E60-44, F40-42, F45-25, F45-29, F50-53, F50-71.

F50-32 (29# 6060)

Maass, Hans

Über die gleichmässige Konvergenz der Poincaréschen Reihen n-ten Grades.

Nachr. Akad. Wiss. Göttingen Math.-Phys. Kl. II **1964**, 137–144.

Let $S(Z) = (AZ+B)(CZ+D)^{-1}$ be a transformation of the Siegel modular group of degree n. The Poincaré series of dimension $-k$ is defined as

$$g_{-k}(Z, T) = e^{2\pi i\sigma(TS(Z))}|CZ+D|^{-k},$$

where k is an even positive integer, $Z=X+iY$, $Y>0$, $T\geqq 0$ is a semi-integral symmetric matrix of rank r, S runs over a certain reduced set of modular matrices, and σ is the trace. The object of this paper is to prove the Theorem: The series $g_{-k}(Z,T)$ for $k>n+1+r$ converges absolutely and uniformly in each region $Y\geqq(1/m)E$, $\sigma(X^2)\leqq m$. Here $m>0$ and E is the identity matrix.

Up to now only the absolute convergence of the Eisenstein series ($T=0$) had been known. Both the plan of the proof and Lemma 1 are attributed to C. L. Siegel.

The author proceeds by introducing a majorant for g_{-k}, which is essentially

$$\sum_{\{C,D\}}\varphi(Z;C,D)\|CZ+D\|^{-k},$$

with

$$\varphi(Z;C,D)=\sum_P e^{-2\pi\delta\sigma(Y_S(P))},$$

where δ, $0<\delta<1$, depends on T, Y_S is the imaginary part of $S(Z)$, and C, D, P are matrices with certain ranges. Lemma 1: $|Y|\Delta_h(Z)\geqq c\Delta_h(iE)$, where Δ_h is a principal subdeterminant of the matrix $\begin{pmatrix}Y&0\\0&Y^{-1}\end{pmatrix}\begin{pmatrix}C'\\XC'+D'\end{pmatrix}$; C and D form the lower row of a transformation $S(Z)$, and c depends only on m and n. Lemma 2: For $k>n+1$ the Eisenstein series $g_{-k}(Z,0)$ converges uniformly in each domain of the type stated in the Theorem.

The proof of Lemma 2 is made from the estimate

$$\varphi_p(Z;C,D)\|CZ+D\|^{-k}\leqq c_1p^{-2(k-r)},$$

where φ_p is φ restricted to $\sigma(P'P)\geqq p^2$ and c_1 depends on m,n,r,δ,C,D.

The Theorem follows from the above three results.

J. Lehner (College Park, Md.)

Referred to in F50-53.

F50-33 (29# 6061)

Igusa, Jun-ichi

On Siegel modular forms of genus two. II.

Amer. J. Math. **86** (1964), 392–412.

The author continues his intrepid investigation [Part I appeared in same J. **84** (1962), 175–200; MR **25** #5040] of the modular varieties in genus 2, using in an essential way the ideas and results of his work on theta constants [ibid. **86** (1964), 219–246; MR **29** #2258].

Let $\Gamma(n)$ be the modular group of level n acting on the Siegel upper half-plane $\mathfrak{S}_2$ of genus 2. Thus $\Gamma(1)=\mathrm{Sp}(2,\mathbf{Z})$ and there is a chain of natural subgroups $\Gamma(1)\supset\Gamma(2)\supset\Gamma(2,4)\supset\Gamma(4,8)$. Let $A(\Gamma)$ be the graded ring of modular forms with respect to Γ of different weights, and let $V(\Gamma)=\operatorname{proj}A(\Gamma)$ denote the corresponding projective variety. The main geometric results then are that $V(\Gamma(2,4))$ is nonsingular; thus $V(\Gamma(1))$ and $V(\Gamma(2))$ have a nonsingular covering. On the other hand, it is proved that there is a singular point on $V(\Gamma(4))$ which has no local nonsingular covering, and this result easily extends to all $V(\Gamma(n))$, $n\geqq 3$.

The general line of argument uses the ten theta constants θ_m for genus 2. He proves $\mathbf{C}(\theta_m\theta_n)$ is integrally closed, which shows by the second paper cited above that it coincides with $A(\Gamma(4,8))$; this gives a hold on the structure of the latter. One then obtains the other $A(\Gamma)$ as the subrings of $A(\Gamma(4,8))$ invariant under the corresponding finite groups; the passage from $A(\Gamma(2))$ to $A(\Gamma(1))$ requires an analysis of the representation of $\Gamma(2)/\Gamma(1)$ on the former ring. The result about $V(\Gamma(4))$ is obtained by studying it locally as a covering of the nonsingular $V(\Gamma(2,4))$.

Along the way, a new proof is given for the structure of $A(\Gamma(1))$, and explicit formulas for the basic Eisenstein series of level one in terms of the θ_m are given. The paper is almost entirely algebraic.

A. Mattuck (Cambridge, Mass.)

Citations: MR 25# 5040 = F50-22; MR 29# 2258 = F50-27.

Referred to in F40-51, F50-47, F50-51, F50-69.

F50-34 (29# 6062)

Christian, Ulrich

Bestimmung des Körpergrades der Siegelschen Modulfunktionen über den Eisensteinreihen.

Abh. Math. Sem. Univ. Hamburg **27** (1964), 171–172.

Es sei $\Gamma(q)$ die Hauptkongruenzuntergruppe q-ter Stufe der Siegelschen Modulgruppe n-ten Grades Γ. Früher [Math. Ann. **152** (1963), 275–341; MR **28** #2256] hatte der Autor bemerkt, dass der Körper $m(q)$ der zugehörigen Modulfunktionen nur in den Fällen $n\equiv 1$ (2) und $n\equiv 0$ (2), $q=1,2,4,p^\nu,2p^\nu$ (p ungerade Primzahl, $\nu=1,2,\cdots$) durch die Eisensteinreihen erzeugt wird. In der vorliegenden Note wird der Körpergrad von $m(q)$ über dem Körper $e(q)$ derjenigen Modulfunktionen, welche durch die Eisensteinreihen rational dargestellt werden können, ergänzend angegeben. Es sei $n\equiv 0$ (2), $q\geqq 3$. Die zu $\Gamma(q)$ gebildeten Eisensteinreihen sind nämlich in Wahrheit sogar Modulformen bezüglich der Kongruenzgruppe $\Gamma^*(q)=\{M\in\Gamma\mid M\equiv uE\ (q),\ u^2\equiv 1\ (q)\}$, und nach früheren Resultaten ist einerseits der zugehörige Funktionenkörper $m^*(q)=e(q)$ und andererseits $[m(q):m^*(q)]=\frac{1}{2}[\Gamma^*(q):\Gamma(q)]$. Es ergibt sich also durch elementare Bestimmung des Gruppenindex $[\Gamma^*(q):\Gamma(q)]$ das Resultat $[m(q):e(q)]=2^{r+s-1}$, wobei r die Anzahl der ungeraden Primteiler von q und $s=0,1,2$ je nachdem $4\nmid q$, $4\mid q$ und $8\nmid q$, $8\mid q$ ist.

H. Klingen (Freiburg)

Citations: MR 28# 2256 = F40-29.

F50-35 (29# 6063)

Christian, Ulrich

Über die Modulgruppe zweiten Grades. I, II.

Math. Z. **85** (1964), 1–28; *ibid.* **85** (1964), 29–39.

Seien $Z(n)$ der Siegelsche Halbraum und $\Gamma(n)$ die Siegelsche Modulgruppe n-ten Grades. Der Quotientenraum $Q(n)=Z(n)/\Gamma(n)$ lässt sich nach Satake, Siegel, und Verfasser in der Gestalt

$$\bar{Q}(n)=Q(n)\cup Q(n-1)\cup\cdots\cup Q(0)$$

kompaktifizieren. Die Frage nach der Uniformisierbarkeit der Punkte von $\bar{Q}(n)$ wurde früher für $n\geqq 3$ vom Verfasser [Math. Ann. **152** (1963), 275–341; MR **28** #2256] und für $n=2$ von Igusa [Amer. J. Math. **84** (1962), 175–200; MR **25** #5040] mit recht tiefliegenden Hilfsmitteln behandelt. Die vorliegende Arbeit betrifft den Fall $n=2$ und gibt einfache neue Beweise für die Ergebnisse von Igusa in expliziter Darstellung. Das Hauptresultat von Teil I ist der Nachweis der Uniformisierbarkeit des Punktes $Q(0)$ in $\bar{Q}(2)$. Verfasser benutzt seine verwendete Beschreibung [loc. cit.] der Umgebungen von $Q(0)$. In die Rechnungen geht wesentlich ein die einfache Gestalt der Minkowskischen Reduktionsbedingungen im binären Fall. Als Ortsuniformisierende von $Q(0)$ werden Funktionen folgender Art verwendet:

$$F(Z)=\sum e^{2\pi i\,\mathrm{Sp}(SZ)},$$

wobei über alle symmetrischen S summiert wird, die zu einer festen Kantenmatrix der Minkowskischen Pyramide unimodular äquivalent sind. Anschliessend werden einige Folgerungen aus diesem Uniformisierungssatz gezogen. Im zweiten Teil werden Thetafunktionen benutzt, um die Uniformisierbarkeit der Punkte von $Q(1)$ in $\bar{Q}(2)$ zu untersuchen. Sämtliche Punkte von $Q(1)$ sind uniformisierbar mit der genauen Ausnahme von denjenigen, die i und $1/2+i\sqrt{3}/2 \in Z(1)$ entsprechen. Dort liegen Singularitäten vor. *H. Klingen* (Freiburg)

Citations: MR 25# 5040 = F50-22; MR 28# 2256 = F40-29.

Referred to in F45-21, F50-40.

F50-36 **(30# 1984)**

Siegel, Carl Ludwig

Über die Fourierschen Koeffizienten der Eisensteinschen Reihen.

Mat.-Fys. Medd. Danske Vid. Selsk. **34**, *no.* 6, 20 *pp.* (1964).

Let Z be the variable matrix in the symplectic upper half plane of degree n, $g>n+1$, and let $s_g(Z)=\sum_{C,D}|CZ+D|^{-g}$ be the Eisenstein series of weight g. The author considers the coefficients $a_g(T)$ of the Fourier expansion $s_g(Z)=\sum_{T\geqq 0} a_g(T)e^{\pi i\,\mathrm{tr}(TZ)}$. He proves the following theorem. Let d_g be the product of the numerators of $2B_g/g$ and B_{2k}/k for $k=1,\cdots,g-1$, where B_k is the kth Bernoulli number. Furthermore, let $2z_g$ be the largest power of 2 which is less than g. If $g\equiv 0 \bmod 4$, the common denominator of all $a_g(T)$ divides d_g, and otherwise it divides $d_g z_g$.

The proof is based on the following fact. If T has rank r, there exists a primitive representation $T=T_1[N]$ by an integral r-rowed definite matrix T_1 with even elements in the diagonal. Put

$$S=S^{2g}=\begin{pmatrix}0 & E^g\\ E^g & 0\end{pmatrix},$$

with E^g the g-rowed unit matrix, and let $A_q(S_1T_1)$ be the number of solutions of $S[M]\equiv T_1 \bmod q$. Then

$$(1)\quad a_g(T)= (-1)^{gr/2}\frac{\rho_{sg}}{\rho_{2g-r}}|T_1|^{(2g-1)/2}\lim_{q\to\infty} q^{r(r+1)/2-2gr}A_q(S_1T_1).$$

The right-hand side is evaluated by the author's analytic theory of quadratic forms [Ann. of Math. (2) **36** (1935), 527–606; ibid. (2) **37** (1936), 230–263].

This is easy in the case $g\equiv 0 \bmod 4$, for then there exists an integral definite quadratic form S_0 in $2g$ variables with even terms on the diagonal and of determinant 1. Using S_0 instead of S in (1) gives the same value. If S_k runs over a system of class representatives in the genus of S_0, the right-hand side in (1) is, up to sign,

$$(2)\qquad \sum_k \frac{A(S_k,T_1)}{E(S_k)}\Big/\sum_k\frac{1}{E(S_k)},$$

where $A(S_k,T_1)$ is the number of representations of T_1 by S_k and $E(S_k)$ the number of units of S_k. The denominator of this fraction is, therefore, the measure of the genus of the S_k and this, in its turn, has been known explicitly since the time of Minkowski. Its value, involving the Bernoulli numbers, gives the announced theorem.

If g is but once divisible by 2 there does not exist such a definite form S_0. Now S is replaced by a suitable indefinite quadratic form S_0, with determinant 1, which again does not affect the right-hand side of (1), and this is in principle the quotient (2), but $A(S_k,T_1)$ and $E(S_k)$ have to be replaced by certain measures which are the inverses of the volumes of certain unit groups of indefinite quadratic forms operating in certain metric spaces.

The metric of these spaces has a constant scalar curvature because of the transitivity of the group of real automorphisms of the quadratic forms which leave the metric invariant. The computation of the scalar curvature can be simplified by showing that it is (up to a sign) equal to that of the corresponding space attached to the real orthogonal group. Thus, knowing the curvature, the author applies the generalized Gauss-Bonnet formula, which links the volume with the Euler characteristic. The latter is computed by a theorem of Hopf and Samelson [Comment. Math. Helv. **13** (1941), 240–251; MR **4**, 3]. The application of the Gauss-Bonnet formula raises two difficulties. (1) Elements of finite order of the respective unit groups cause metric singularities. These can be avoided, however, by considering the subgroups of units whose matrices are congruent to the unit matrix modulo a suitable q. The volume is thus multiplied by the group index. (2) The fundamental domains of the unit groups are not compact. Therefore the cusps are first cut off. Now the Gauss-Bonnet formula contains some surface integrals over those cuts. In showing that these surface integrals tend to 0 as the cuts tend to infinity, the computation of the volumes is complete.

After assembling the results, the verification of the theorem follows the procedure in the first case (where a definite S_0 existed). *M. Eichler* (Basel)

F50-37 **(30# 1985)**

Maass, Hans

Die Fourierkoeffizienten der Eisensteinreihen zweiten Grades.

Mat.-Fys. Medd. Danske Vid. Selsk. **34**, *no.* 7, 25 *pp.* (1964).

Using formula (1) in the preceding review [#1984], the author explicitly calculates the coefficients $a_g(T)$ for primitive matrices T, under the assumption $n=2$. The limit on the right of (1) can be written as an Euler product whose factors are of an elementary nature, save for a finite number of exceptions. The formula is, of course, complicated; it shows some similarity with the class number formula for imaginary quadratic fields, as was to be expected. For imprimitive T a recurrence formula is proved linking $a_g(T)$ with the values for primitive T. The result allows one to infer that the $a_g(T)$ are divisible by $4g(g-1)/(B_gB_{2k-2})$, with the exception of those T whose determinants are either 1 or a quarter of a prime dividing the denominator of B_{2g-2}. In the exceptional cases a modified common divisor is given. *M. Eichler* (Basel)

F50-38 **(30# 2010)**

Shimura, Goro

On the field of definition for a field of automorphic functions. II.

Ann. of Math. (2) **81** (1965), 124–165.

The results of two previous papers [same Ann. (2) **80** (1964), 160–189; MR **29** #4739; ibid. (2) **80** (1964), 444–463; MR **30** #65] are extended to the case of congruence subgroups of the arithmetic groups studied in the earlier papers (this corresponds to the "marking" of finitely many points of finite order on the abelian varieties under study). The results are of the same general type as those previously obtained. As an application, the author determines the fields of definition for certain varieties, fibered by abelian varieties over varieties of moduli, which will play the main part in some forthcoming joint work with M. Kuga. *A. Weil* (Princeton, N.J.)

Citations: MR 29# 4739 = G15-27; MR 30# 65 = G15-29.

Referred to in F50-42, G15-32, G15-34, G15-47.

F50-39 **(31# 178)**

Igusa, Jun-ichi

Structure theorems of modular varieties.

Proc. Internat. Congr. Mathematicians (*Stockholm*, 1962), *pp.* 522–525. *Inst. Mittag-Leffler, Djursholm*, 1963.

A discussion of several of the author's contributions to the theory of modular varieties [Ann. of Math. (2) **72** (1960), 612–649; MR **22** #5637; Amer. J. Math. **84** (1962), 175–200; MR **25** #5040].

Citations: MR 25# 5040 = F50-22.

F50-40 **(31# 2218)**

Gindikin, S. G.; Pjateckiĭ-Šapiro, I. I.

On the algebraic structure of the field of Siegel modular functions. (Russian)

Dokl. Akad. Nauk SSSR **162** (1965), 1226–1229.

Let $\mathscr{X}_p$ be the Siegel half-plane of degree p. Denote by Γ_p the Siegel modular group, and by $\Gamma_p(q)$ the congruence subgroup of Γ_p for the modulus q:

$$\Gamma_p = Sp(p, Z), \qquad \Gamma_p(q) = \{\gamma \in \Gamma_p : \gamma \equiv E_{2p} \pmod{q}\}$$

(E_{2p} is the unit matrix of order p). A. I. Lapin [Izv. Akad. Nauk SSSR Ser. Mat. **20** (1956), 325–336; MR **18**, 389] and J. Igusa [Amer. J. Math. **84** (1962), 175–200; MR **25** #5040; ibid. **86** (1964), 392–412; MR **29** #6061; also cf. Ulrich Christian, Math. Z. **85** (1964), 1–28; ibid. **85** (1964), 29–39; MR **29** #6063] have shown that, in the cases of $\Gamma_2(1)$ and $\Gamma_2(2)$, the field of automorphic functions on $\mathscr{X}_p$ are rational function fields. The authors of the present paper sketch a proof of the following theorem: The field of $\Gamma_p(q)$-automorphic functions on $\mathscr{X}_p$ is not a rational function field for $q \geqq 6$; $q \geqq 4$, $p \geqq 3$; $q \geqq 3$, $p \geqq 5$; $q \geqq 2$, $p \geqq 6$. For $p \geqq 13$ the field of automorphic functions has this property for every subgroup of finite index in Γ_p which does not contain any elements of finite order.

The proof involves the following steps. (1) Construction of a compactification Ω^n of the fundamental domain Ω of the group Γ (Ω^n is an analytic normal space [W. L. Baily and A. Borel, Bull. Amer. Math. Soc. **70** (1964), 588–593; MR **29** #6058; the second author, Uspehi Mat. Nauk **19** (1964), no. 6 (120), 93–121]). (2) Construction of another compactification Ω^r; for all arithmetical groups Ω^r is again an analytic normal space, but in some cases, e.g., for the groups $\Gamma_p(q)$, $q \geqq 3$, Ω^r is a nonsingular complex manifold; Ω^r is a covering of Ω^n. (3) Finding the conditions in order that an automorphic form $\varphi(Z)$ may yield a holomorphic differential; these are obtained as the vanishing of certain coefficients in the Fourier-Jacobi expansion of $\varphi(Z)$ around the "cusps". (4) Proving the following asymptotic formula for the dimension of spaces of automorphic forms: Lemma: Let $\chi(\gamma)$ be a unitary representation of Γ_p of dimension m; denote by $N(p, k; \chi)$ the dimension of Γ_p-automorphic vector forms of type χ and order k; then for $k \to \infty$,

$$N(p, k; \chi) \sim \operatorname{Vol}(\Gamma_p) \cdot m \cdot \left(\frac{(p+1)k}{4\pi}\right)^{p(p+1)/2}.$$

This yields for the plurigenera p_k of the algebraic variety corresponding to the field of automorphic functions an assessment of the form $p_k \sim \alpha \cdot k^n$. The lemma, which is of independent interest, is proved by the method of A. Selberg. The note poses the problem: Describe all arithmetical groups for which the field of automorphic functions is rational.

{This article has appeared in English translation [Soviet Math. Dokl. **6** (1965), 831–835].}

T. S. Bhanu Murthy (Princeton, N.J.)

Citations: MR 18, 389g = F50-11; MR 25# 5040 = F50-22; MR 29# 6058 = F50-30; MR 29# 6063 = F50-35.

F50-41 **(31# 5845)**

Hammond, William F.

On the graded ring of Siegel modular forms of genus two.

Amer. J. Math. **87** (1965), 502–506.

Der Verfasser überträgt eine Methode des Referenten [Math. Ann. **152** (1963), 226–256; MR **29** #1186] auf die Modulgruppe 2. Grades und erhält einen einfacheren Beweis für den Satz von Igusa [Amer. J. Math. **84** (1962), 175–200; MR **25** #5040], dass jede ganze Modulform geraden Gewichts zur Modulgruppe 2. Grades als isobares Polynom in den (algebraisch unabhängigen) Eisensteinreihen G_4, G_6, G_{10}, G_{12} darstellbar ist. Die Modulgruppe 2. Grades ist eine diskrete Transformationsgruppe Γ im Raum der symmetrischen Matrizen $W = \begin{pmatrix} w_1 & w_2 \\ w_2 & w_3 \end{pmatrix}$ mit positiv definitem Imaginärteil. Die Einschränkung einer ganzen Modulform f vom Gewicht m auf die Teilmenge der W mit $w_2 = 0$ ist in w_1 und w_3 symmetrisch und in jeder der Variablen eine ganze Modulform gleichen Gewichts zur rationalen Modulgruppe. Alle Funktionen dieser Art auf $w_2 = 0$ sind isobare Polynome in den Einschränkungen von G_4, G_6, G_{12} (die auf $w_2 = 0$ algebraisch unabhängig sind) auf $w_2 = 0$, wie eine einfache Abzählung zeigt. Subtrahiert man also ein passendes Polynom in den Eisensteinreihen von f, so erhält man eine ganze Modulform f_0, die auf $w_2 = 0$ verschwindet. Es wird nun eine Thetafunktion $\theta(W)$ angegeben, die die Bilder von $w_2 = 0$ unter Γ als genaue Nullstellenmenge hat. Ausserdem gilt: Ist f_0 eine ganze Modulform vom Gewicht m, die auf $w_2 = 0$ verschwindet, so ist f_0/θ^2 eine ganze Modulform vom Gewicht $m - 10$. Da nur für positives Gewicht nicht-konstante ganze Modulformen existieren, erhält man f als Polynom in den Eisensteinreihen und θ^2. θ^2 wird schliesslich noch selbst durch die Eisensteinreihen ausgedrückt.

K.-B. Gundlach (Münster)

Citations: MR 25# 5040 = F50-22; MR 29# 1186 = F40-30.

F50-42 **(32# 7514)**

Shimura, Goro

On the field of definition for a field of automorphic functions. III.

Ann. of Math. (2) **83** (1966), 377–385.

Some complements to Parts I [same Ann. (2) **80** (1964), 160–189; MR **29** #4739] and II [ibid. (2) **81** (1965), 124–165; MR **30** #2010] of this series of papers. They concern the explicit description of a certain class field and simplify proofs.

M. Eichler (Basel)

Citations: MR 29# 4739 = G15-27; MR 30# 2010 = F50-38.

Referred to in G15-47.

F50-43 **(33# 1372)**

Fritzsche, Reiner

Beitrag zur Theorie der Modulfunktionen 2. Grades. II.

Math. Ann. **164** (1966), 54–57.

Let $\mathfrak{M}_n$ be the modular group of degree n; $\mathfrak{G}_n$ a subgroup of $\mathfrak{M}_n$; K the field of complex numbers; $K\{\mathfrak{G}_n\}$ the field of meromorphic functions of $\frac{1}{2}n(n+1)$ complex variables, invariant under $\mathfrak{G}_n$ and which are quotients of modular forms of degree n belonging to $\mathfrak{G}_n$; H the Galois group of $K\{\mathfrak{M}_2(2)\}$ over $K\{\mathfrak{M}_2\}$, where $\mathfrak{M}_n(2)$ stands for the principal congruence subgroup of level 2. For $G \subseteq H$, let G_b be the fixed field (intermediate between $K\{\mathfrak{M}_2\}$ and $K\{\mathfrak{M}_2(2)\}$, left elementwise invariant by all automorphisms) of G, and, for $K\{\mathfrak{M}_2\} \subseteq \Lambda \subseteq K\{\mathfrak{M}_2(2)\}$, let $\Lambda_\#$ denote the group of automorphisms of $K\{\mathfrak{M}_2(2)\}$ that leave Λ (elementwise) invariant. If $\mathfrak{G}$ is a group, $\mathfrak{M}_2(2) \subseteq \mathfrak{G} \subseteq \mathfrak{M}_2$, then $\mathfrak{G}^b$ stands for the (field of) modular functions belonging to $\mathfrak{G}$; if Λ is a field, $K\{\mathfrak{M}_2\} \subseteq \Lambda \subseteq K\{\mathfrak{M}_2(2)\}$, then $\Lambda^\#$ stands for that subset of $\mathfrak{M}_2$ under which the elements of Λ are modular functions. Continuing his previous work [same Ann. **154** (1964), 135–146; MR **28** #3156], the author shows that for every field Λ with $K\{\mathfrak{M}_2\} \subseteq \Lambda \subseteq K\{\mathfrak{M}_2(2)\}$, there exists a group $\mathfrak{G}$ such that $\Lambda = K\{\mathfrak{G}\}$ and if $\mathfrak{G} \subseteq \mathfrak{G}'$, then

$(K\{\mathfrak{G}\}: K\{\mathfrak{G}'\}) = [\mathfrak{G}': \mathfrak{G}]$. Also, $\mathfrak{G} \subseteq \mathfrak{G}'$ implies $\mathfrak{G}^b \supseteq \mathfrak{G}'^b$, $\Lambda \subseteq \Lambda'$ implies $\Lambda^\# \supseteq \Lambda'^\#$, $\mathfrak{G} \subseteq \mathfrak{G}^{b\#}$, $\Lambda \subseteq \Lambda^{\#b}$. The main result is the theorem: If $\mathfrak{M}_2(2) \subseteq \mathfrak{G} \subseteq \mathfrak{G}' \subseteq \mathfrak{M}_2$ and $K\{\mathfrak{M}_2\} \subseteq \Lambda \subseteq K\{\mathfrak{M}_2(2)\}$, then $\mathfrak{G}^{b\#} = \mathfrak{G}$, $\Lambda^{\#b} = \Lambda$ and $\mathfrak{G}^b = K\{\mathfrak{G}\}$ is a simple algebraic extension of $\mathfrak{G}'^b = K\{\mathfrak{G}'\}$, with $(\mathfrak{G}^b : \mathfrak{G}'^b) = [\mathfrak{G}' : \mathfrak{G}]$. *E. Grosswald* (Philadelphia, Pa.)

Citations: MR 28# 3156 = F50-26.

F50-44 (34# 375)

Igusa, Jun-ichi

On the graded ring of theta-constants. II.

Amer. J. Math. **88** (1966), 221–236.

The paper is concerned with the general theta function $\theta_m(\tau, z) = \sum_{p \in \mathbf{Z}^g} \exp \pi i[{}^t(p+m')\tau(p+m') + 2{}^t(p+m')(z+m'')]$ and the theta constants $\theta_m(\tau) = \theta_m(\tau, 0)$. Here τ denotes a matrix in the Siegel upper half-plane of degree g, z a variable vector in C^g, and m a vector in $\mathbf{Q}^{2g}$ with parts m', m''. First, the author proves the following remarkable necessary and sufficient condition for the vanishing of $\theta_m(\tau)$: $2m \in \mathbf{Z}^{2g}$ and $\exp 4\pi i {}^t m' m'' = -1$. Second, he determines the eighth root of unity occurring in the functional equation of $\theta_m(\tau, z)$, up to sign, provided the transformation matrix lies in the principal congruence subgroup mod 2. Third, he proves the following theorem. For a rational integer r, form all theta constants $\theta_m(\tau)$ with $rm \in \mathbf{Z}^{2g}$ and, furthermore, the (graded) ring generated by all products of any two such theta constants. The integral closure of this ring in its field of fractions coincides with the ring of holomorphic Siegel modular forms with respect to the following subgroup of $\mathrm{Sp}(g, \mathbf{Z})$: $M \equiv 1_{2g} \bmod r$ and $M = \begin{pmatrix} a & b \\ c & d \end{pmatrix}$ with $a^t b$ and $c^t d$ having diagonal elements divisible by $2r$. The paper contains simplifications of an earlier one [same J. **86** (1964), 219–246; MR **29** #2258] and can be read independently of it. *M. Eichler* (Basel)

Citations: MR 29# 2258 = F50-27.
Referred to in F50-61, F50-69.

F50-45 (34# 2943)

Spilker, Jürgen

Werte von Modulformen.

Nachr. Akad. Wiss. Göttingen Math.-Phys. Kl. II **1965**, 125–132.

In analogy to a result by N. Kuhlmann [Proc. Conf. Complex Analysis (Minneapolis, Minn., 1964), pp. 155–172, Springer, Berlin, 1965; MR **30** #4977], the author constructs a compact set K in the Siegel half-plane such that every Siegel modular form of degree $n > 1$ and even weight assumes each value on K that is approximated on the fundamental domain. As a consequence he obtains the known estimates of the dimension of the space of all modular forms of given weight. *H. Röhrl* (La Jolla, Calif.)

F50-46 (34# 6157)

Gottschling, Erhard

Die Uniformisierbarkeit der Fixpunkte eigentlich diskontinuierlicher Gruppen von biholomorphen Abbildungen.

Math. Ann. **169** (1967), 26–54.

Ist X ein n-dimensionaler komplexer Raum und Γ eine eigentlich diskontinuierliche Gruppe biholomorpher Abbildungen von X auf sich, so ist der Quotientenraum X/Γ wieder ein komplexer Raum. In der klassischen Theorie der automorphen Funktionen ist X immer eine Mannigfaltigkeit (ein Gebiet im $\mathbf{C}^n$), X/Γ kann jedoch auch in diesem Fall nicht-uniformisierbare Punkte enthalten, braucht also keine Mannigfaltigkeit zu sein. X/Γ läßt sich dann aber lokal in der Umgebung jedes Punktes x/Γ, $x \in X$, in der Form U/Γ_x, $\Gamma_x = \{\gamma : \gamma \in \Gamma, \gamma(x) = x\}$, mit $\gamma(U) = U$ für $\gamma \in \Gamma_x$ darstellen, wobei U eine offene Umgebung von x in X ist, die zu einer offenen Punktmenge des $\mathbf{C}^n$ biholomorph äquivalent ist. Γ_x ist endlich. Die Eigenwerte der Funktionalmatrix einer Abbildung $\gamma \in \Gamma_x$ im Punkte x sind offenbar unabhängig von der Wahl der lokalen Koordinaten in der Umgebung von x. γ heißt Spiegelung, wenn höchstens einer dieser Eigenwerte von 1 verschieden ist. Verfasser beweist den folgenden Satz: x/Γ ist dann und nur dann ein uniformisierbarer Punkt von X/Γ, wenn Γ_x von den in Γ_x enthaltenen Spiegelungen erzeugt wird. Zum Beweis zeigt Verfasser, daß es bei passender Wahl der lokalen Koordinaten in der Umgebung von x im Falle der Uniformisierbarkeit von x/Γ ein System von Ortsuniformisierenden zu x/Γ gibt, die sich als Polynome in den lokalen Koordinaten bei x schreiben lassen. Die Existenz eines derartigen Systems von Polynomen ist aber nach einem Satz von G. C. Shephard und J. A. Todd gleichbedeutend damit, daß Γ_x durch die in Γ_x enthaltenen Spiegelungen erzeugt wird [Canad. J. Math. **6** (1954), 274–304; MR **15**, 600]. Als Anwendung wird gezeigt, daß elliptische Fixpunkte zur Siegelschen Modulgruppe n-ten Grades für $n > 2$ stets nicht-uniformisierbar sind. Für $n = 2$ wird festgestellt, welche elliptischen Fixpunkte uniformisierbar und welche nicht-uniformisierbar sind. *K.-B. Gundlach* (Münster)

F50-47 (34# 7467)

Freitag, Eberhard

Zur theorie der Modulformen zweiten Grades.

Nachr. Akad. Wiss. Göttingen Math.-Phys. Kl. II **1965**, 151–157.

J. Igusa gave two proofs that the ring of modular forms of degree (genus) 2 is generated by the four Eisenstein series G_4, G_6, G_{10}, G_{12} [Amer. J. Math. **86** (1964), 392–412; MR **29** #6061]. The author gives another proof, very short and elementary. The forms are defined on H_2, the Siegel upper half-plane of degree 2. The author restricts them to the subspace $H_1 \times H_1$ of diagonal matrices; generators for the resulting ring of restricted forms are known from the theory of the elliptic modular functions, and the kernel of the restriction map is determined by showing that the product of a certain ten even and odd theta-functions of genus 2 has a simple zero on $H_1 \times H_1$ and vanishes nowhere else in the fundamental domain. *A. Mattuck* (Cambridge, Mass.)

Citations: MR 29# 6061 = F50-33.
Referred to in F55-27.

F50-48 (34# 7827)

Baily, Walter L., Jr.

Classical theory of θ-functions.

Algebraic Groups and Discontinuous Subgroups (Proc. Sympos. Pure Math., Boulder, Colo., 1965), pp. 306–311. *Amer. Math. Soc., Providence, R.I.*, 1966.

This paper is a survey of some results on theta functions, as background for other seminars of this symposium. In addition to classical results (from A. Krazer [*Lehrbuch der Thetafunktionen*, Teubner, Leipzig, 1903]), some more recent results of the author are also described. *R. C. Gunning* (Princeton, N.J.)

F50-49 (34# 7828)

Klingen, Helmut

Über Poincarésche Reihen zur Siegelschen Modulgruppe.

Math. Ann. **168** (1967), 157–170.

Es seien Z und W quadratische n-reihige komplexe Matrizen, ferner $\mathfrak{H}_n = \{Z = X + iY : Z' = Z,\ Y > 0\}$ die verallgemeinerte obere Halbebene und $\mathfrak{E}_n = \{W : W' = W,\ E - \overline{W}W > 0\}$ der verallgemeinerte Einheitskreis (E = n-reihige Einheitsmatrix). Für vorgegebenes $Z^* = X^* +$

$iY^* \in \mathfrak{H}_n$ sei die reelle Matrix F durch $E = FY^*F'$ bestimmt. Dann ist durch

$$Z \to W = L_{Z^*}\langle Z\rangle = F(Z - Z^*)(Z - \overline{Z^*})^{-1}F^{-1}$$

eine biholomorphe Abbildung von $\mathfrak{H}_n$ auf $\mathfrak{E}_n$ gegeben, welche Z^* in den Nullpunkt überführt. Es sei ferner Γ_n die Siegelsche Modulgruppe n-ten Grades, welche aus allen $2n$-reihigen ganz-rationalen symplektischen Matrizen besteht. Bei Aufspaltung von M in n-reihige Untermatrizen erhält man durch

$$Z \to M\langle Z\rangle = (AZ+B)(CZ+D)^{-1}, \qquad M = \begin{pmatrix} A & B \\ C & D \end{pmatrix},$$

eine Gruppe von biholomorphen Automorphismen von $\mathfrak{H}_n$. Für eine Spitzenform $f(Z)$ zu Γ_n vom Gewichte k (kn gerade) sei $\hat{f}$ durch $\hat{f}(W) = |Z - \overline{Z^*}|^k f(Z)$ definiert.

Im ersten Paragraphen der vorliegenden Arbeit wird die Peterssonsche Metrisierungstheorie [H. Petersson, Abh. Math. Sem. Hansischen Univ. **14** (1941), 22–60; MR **3**, 204] für die Siegelsche Modulgruppe bezüglich eines beliebigen Entwicklungspunktes $Z^* \in \mathfrak{H}_n$ dargestellt. Die dabei verwendeten Poincaréschen Reihen sind von der Form

$$P_{k,n}(Z; Z^*, \varphi) = \sum_{M \in \Gamma_n} \frac{\varphi(L_{Z^*}M\langle Z\rangle)}{|M\langle Z\rangle - \overline{Z^*}|^k |CZ+D|^k},$$

wobei φ ein beliebiges Polynom in $\frac{1}{2}n(n+1)$ Variablen mit komplexen Koeffizienten ist. Es sei m_ν die Dimension des komplexen Vektorraumes aller homogenen Polynome ν-ten Grades in $\frac{1}{2}n(n+1)$ Variablen mit komplexen Koeffizienten. Durch eine Orthogonalitätsforderung bestimmt der Verfasser für jedes $\nu = 0, 1 \cdots$ eine Basis $\varphi_{\nu_1}, \cdots, \varphi_{m_\nu}$ dieses Vektorraums und schreibt die Potenzreihenentwicklung von $\hat{f}(W)$ im Nullpunkt in der Form $\hat{f}(W) = \sum_{\nu=0}^{\infty} (\sum_{\mu=1}^{m_\nu} a_{\nu\mu}\varphi_{\nu\mu}(W))$. Das Hauptergebnis des ersten Paragraphen der vorliegenden Arbeit sind dann die Grundformeln der Metrisierungstheorie

$$\{f(Z), P_{k,n}(Z; Z^*, \varphi_{\nu\mu})\} = 2^{n(n-2k+1)+1}|Y^*|^{-k}a_{\nu\mu}(f, Z^*),$$

wobei für zwei Spitzenformen f, g vom Gewichte k das Skalarprodukt $\{f, g\} = \int_{\mathfrak{F}_n} f(Z)\overline{g(Z)}|Y|^{k-n-1}\,dX\,dY$ benutzt wird ($\mathfrak{F}_n$ ein Fundamentalbereich von Γ_n in $\mathfrak{H}_n$). Aus diesen Grundformeln werden analog zu den oben zitierten Peterssonschen Betrachtungen die Hauptergebnisse der Metrisierungstheorie gefolgert, z.B. die metrische Charakterisierung der Poincaréschen Reihen $P_{k,n}(Z; Z^*, \varphi_{\nu\mu})$ und die Darstellungssätze für Spitzenformen. Die Darstellungssätze wurden zum Teil schon von R. Godement [*Séminaire Henri Cartan, 1957/58, Fonctions automorphes*, Vol. 1, Exposé 10, Secrétariat mathématique, Paris, 1958; cf. MR **21** #2750] behandelt, allerdings mit komplizierteren Hilfsmitteln.

Im zweiten Paragraphen betrachtet der Verfasser drei Typen von Poincaréschen Reihen, nämlich Typus 1: $\{P_{k,n}(Z; Z^*, 1)$: Parameter $Z^* \in \mathfrak{H}_n\}$, Typus 2: $\{P_{k,n}(Z; Z^*, \varphi)$: $Z^* \in \mathfrak{H}_n$ fest, Parameter φ ein beliebiges Polynom$\}$. Der Typus 3 wurde von H. Maass [Math. Ann. **123** (1951), 125–151; MR **13**, 210] durch Quersummation aus der Fourierentwicklung von Spitzenformen gewonnen. Um auch die Nichtspitzenformen in die Betrachtungen mit einbeziehen zu können, wird für jedes ganze r mit $0 \leq r \leq n$ eine Untergruppe $\mathfrak{A}_r$ von Γ_n betrachtet. Zu jedem $\mathfrak{A}_r$ werden gewisse modifizierte Poincarésche Reihen der obigen drei Typen eingeführt. Der Zusammenhang zwischen den drei Typen von modifizierten Reihen wird aufgedeckt und es wird gezeigt, daß die Reihen eines jeden Typus jeweils die volle Schar aller Modulformen vom Gewicht k erzeugen (k gerade, $k > \mathrm{Min}(2n, n+r+1)$ vorausgesetzt).

Im dritten Paragraphen untersucht schließlich der Verfasser die Konvergenz aller betrachteten Poincaréschen Reihen. Seine Ergebnisse sind auch für den Fall $n = 1$ schärfer als die bisher bekannten Resultate über die Konvergenz Poincaréscher Reihen.

E. Gottschling (Berlin)

Citations: MR 13, 210a = F50-4; MR 21# 2750 = F02-5.

Referred to in F40-42, F50-53.

F50-50 (36# 432)

Spilker, Jürgen

Darstellung automorpher Formen durch Poincaré-Reihen.

Math. Z. **99** (1967), 216–234.

Zu festem natürlichen n sei $\mathfrak{D}$ die Menge aller n-reihigen symmetrischen Matrizen Z, für welche die Hermitesche Matrix $E - \bar{Z}Z$ positiv definit ist. Die Gruppe der holomorphen Automorphismen von $\mathfrak{D}$ besteht genau aus den Abbildungen $\gamma_M: Z \to M\langle Z\rangle = (AZ+B)(\bar{B}Z+\bar{A})^{-1}$, wobei die Beziehungen (*) $M = \begin{pmatrix} A & B \\ \bar{B} & \bar{A} \end{pmatrix}$, ${}^tA\bar{B} = {}^t\bar{B}A$, ${}^tA\bar{A} - {}^t\bar{B}B = E$ gelten. Die Matrizen (*) bilden eine Gruppe, welche durch die Zuordnung $M \to \gamma_M$ homomorph auf die Gruppe der holomorphen Automorphismen von $\mathfrak{D}$ mit dem Kern $\{\pm E\}$ abgebildet wird. Eine Untergruppe dieser Matrizengruppe ist genau dann diskret, wenn ihr Bild bei $M \to \gamma_M$ diskontinuierlich auf $\mathfrak{D}$ operiert. Es sei Γ eine diskrete Gruppe von Matrizen der Form (*). Jede meßbare Lösung f der Funktionalgleichungen $f(M\langle Z\rangle)j_M{}^m(Z) = f(Z)$, $M \in \Gamma$, $Z \in \mathfrak{D}$ heißt Γ-automorphe Form vom ganzzahligen Gewicht m. Dabei ist $j_M(Z) = \det^{-1}(\bar{B}Z + \bar{A})$ gesetzt. Es sei $\mathfrak{A}(m, \Gamma)$ der komplexe Vektorraum aller dieser Formen. Für reelles $p \geq 1$ bilden die $f \in \mathfrak{A}(m, \Gamma)$ mit $\|f\|_p = (\int_{\mathfrak{F}} |f(Z) \det^{m/2}(E - \bar{Z}Z)|^p\, dv)^{1/p} < \infty$ einen Unterraum $\mathfrak{A}_p(m, \Gamma)$. Dabei ist $\mathfrak{F}$ ein Fundamentalbereich von Γ in $\mathfrak{D}$ und $dv = \det^{-n-1}(E - \bar{Z}Z)\, dw$ mit dem euklidischen Volumenelement dw in $\mathfrak{D}$. Ferner sei $\mathfrak{A}_\infty(m, \Gamma)$ der durch $\|f\|_\infty = \text{wes sup}_{Z \in \mathfrak{D}} |f(Z) \det^{m/2}(E - \bar{Z}Z)| < \infty$ definierte Unterraum von $\mathfrak{A}(m, \Gamma)$. Ist schließlich $\mathfrak{H}$ der Vektorraum aller in $\mathfrak{D}$ holomorphen Funktionen, so wird gesetzt $\mathfrak{H}(m, \Gamma) = \mathfrak{A}(m, \Gamma) \cap \mathfrak{H}$, $\mathfrak{H}_p(m, \Gamma) = \mathfrak{A}_p(m, \Gamma) \cap \mathfrak{H}$, $1 \leq p \leq \infty$. Wenn Γ nur aus der Identität besteht, so seien die betrachteten Vektorräume einfach durch $\mathfrak{A}(m)$, $\mathfrak{H}(m)$, $\mathfrak{A}_p(m)$, $\mathfrak{H}_p(m)$ bezeichnet. In der vorliegenden Arbeit untersucht der Verfasser die Räume $\mathfrak{A}_p(m, \Gamma)$ und $\mathfrak{H}_p(m, \Gamma)$ insbesondere hinsichtlich ihrer Erzeugbarkeit durch Poincarésche Thetareihen. Von der Vielzahl der Resultate seien nur die beiden wichtigsten Ergebnisse genannt. Wenn f eine in $\mathfrak{D}$ meßbare Funktion ist, so heißt $\theta f(Z) = e^{-1}\sum_{M \in \Gamma} f(M\langle Z\rangle)j_M{}^m(Z)$ die zugeordnete Poincarésche Thetareihe. Dabei ist $e = 1$ oder $e = 2$ je nachdem, ob $-E \notin \Gamma$ oder $-E \in \Gamma$ gilt. Es ist dann $\theta\mathfrak{H}_1(m) \to \mathfrak{H}_1(m, \Gamma)$ ein stetiger Homomorphismus, der für $m > n(n+1)$ surjektiv ist. Wenn $m > 2n$ ist, existiert zu jedem $g \in \mathfrak{H}_\infty(m, \Gamma)$ ein $f \in \mathfrak{H}_\infty(m)$ mit $\theta f = g$. Es wird ferner z.B. eine Isomorphie von $\mathfrak{H}_\infty(m, \Gamma)$ und dem Dualraum $\mathfrak{H}_1{}^*(m, \Gamma)$ bewiesen. Besondere Sorgfalt verwendet der Verfasser darauf, auf ähnliche Sätze in der Literatur hinzuweisen. In diesem Zusammenhang sind besonders die Autoren L. V. Ahlfors, L. Bers und R. Godement zu nennen.

E. Gottschling (Berlin)

F50-51 (36# 1439)

Igusa, Jun-ichi

A desingularization problem in the theory of Siegel modular functions.

Math. Ann. **168** (1967), 228–260.

Let g be an integer ≥ 2. Let $\mathfrak{S}_g$ be the Siegel upper-half space of degree g and $\Gamma_g(\lambda)$ the principal congruence group of degree g and of level λ; let $\mathscr{S}(\Gamma_g(\lambda))$ denote the usual compactification of the quotient space $\Gamma_g(\lambda)\backslash\mathfrak{S}_g$, which is a normal projective variety associated with the graded ring of Siegel modular forms belonging to $\Gamma_g(\lambda)$. It had been observed [U. Christian, J. Reine Angew. Math. **219** (1965), 97–112; MR **31** #5844] that all "boundary points" of $\mathscr{S}(\Gamma_g(\lambda))$ (i.e., the points in $\mathscr{S}(\Gamma_g(\lambda))-\Gamma_g(\lambda)\backslash\mathfrak{S}_g$) are singular except for the case $(g,\lambda)=(2,1)$. (More precisely, $\mathscr{S}(\Gamma_g(\lambda))$ does not even admit a non-singular covering locally at any boundary point except for the cases $(g,\lambda)=(2,1),(2,2)$, in which case it is a V-manifold.) In this paper, in an attempt to find a natural desingularization of $\mathscr{S}(\Gamma_g(\lambda))$, the author considers the monoidal transform $\mathscr{M}(\Gamma_g(\lambda))$ of $\mathscr{S}(\Gamma_g(\lambda))$ along its "boundary". The main result is that, for $\lambda\geqq 3$, the points of $\mathscr{M}(\Gamma_g(\lambda))$ lying over a g_1th boundary component of $\mathscr{S}(\Gamma_g(\lambda))$ (i.e., a conjugate of $\Gamma_{g_0}(\lambda)\backslash\mathfrak{S}_{g_0}$ under the action of $\mathrm{Sp}(g,\mathbf{Z}/\lambda\mathbf{Z})$, where $g_0=g-g_1$) are actually non-singular for $g_1\leqq 3$, but not for $g_1=4$. The structure of the fibers of the monoidal transformation $\mathscr{M}\to\mathscr{S}$ is also given explicitly for small g_1; for $g_1=1$, the fiber over the point conjugate to (the equivalence class of) $t_0\in\mathfrak{S}_{g_0}$ is an abelian variety $T(t_0)$ with the period matrix (t_0,l_{g_0}), and, for $g_1=2$, it is an extension of a two-fold product of $T(t_0)$ by a reducible rational variety composed of a certain number of projective lines $P_1(\mathbf{C})$, of which the combinatorial schema is explicitly given. These results are derived from a detailed analysis of the analytic local rings in terms of the Fourier-Jacobi series of I. I. Pjateckiĭ-Šapiro [*Geometry of classical domains and theory of automorphic functions* (Russian), Fizmatgiz, Moscow, 1961; MR **25** #231; French translation, Dunod, Paris, 1966; MR **33** #5949], which depends essentially on some results in reduction theory of quadratic forms which in part dates back to the 19th century. Furthermore, for the case $g=2$, the definition of $\mathscr{M}(\Gamma)$ is extended to an arbitrary discrete subgroup Γ of $\mathrm{Sp}(2,\mathbf{R})$ commensurable with $\Gamma_2(1)$ by a functorial requirement, and it is shown that the following statements are not true in general: (i) $\mathscr{M}(\Gamma)\to\mathscr{S}(\Gamma)$ is a monoidal transformation along the boundary of $\mathscr{S}(\Gamma)$; (ii) $\mathscr{M}(\Gamma)$ is non-singular. With the help of the author's previous results on modular forms of degree 2 [Amer. J. Math. **84** (1962), 175–200; MR **25** #5040; ibid. **86** (1964), 392–412; MR **29** #6061], it is also shown that for $\Gamma=\Gamma_2(2)$ both (i), (ii) are true, and for $\Gamma=\Gamma_2(1)$ they are true except for the points over the two singular points in the first boundary component of $\mathscr{S}(\Gamma_2(1))$; in this latter case, the sheaf of ideals defining the blowing up $\mathscr{M}(\Gamma_2(1))\to\mathscr{S}(\Gamma_2(1))$ is explicitly determined.

The result in reduction theory mentioned above is the following. Let σ_0 be a $g\times g$ matrix whose (i,j)-entry is $=1$ for $i=j$ and $=\frac{1}{2}$ for $i\neq j$, and define the corresponding "fundamental cone" $F=F_{\sigma_0}$ ["central cone" $C=C_{\sigma_0}$] as the set of all real positive symmetric matrices y of degree g satisfying the condition $\mathrm{tr}(\sigma_0 uy^tu)\geqq\mathrm{tr}(\sigma_0 y)$ for all $u\in GL(g,\mathbf{Z})$ [$\mathrm{tr}(\sigma y)\geqq\mathrm{tr}(\sigma_0 y)$ for all half-integral positive-definite symmetric matrices σ of degree g]. To a symmetric matrix $y=(y_{ij})$ of degree g one associates a symmetric matrix $Y=(y_{ij})$ of degree $g+1$ by the condition $\sum_{j=1}^{g+1}y_{ij}=0$ $(1\leqq i\leqq g+1)$, and calls y_{ij} $(1\leqq i<j\leqq g+1)$ the "normal coordinates" of y. Then, C consists of all y such that all the normal coordinates are non-positive, and one has $F=C$ for $g\leqq 3$, but not for $g\geqq 4$. *I. Satake* (Chicago, Ill.)

Citations: MR 25# 231 = F02-10; MR 25# 5040 = F50-22; MR 29# 6061 = F50-33; MR 31# 5844 = F45-23; MR 33# 5949 = F02-11.

F50-52 (36# 1707)

Klingen, Helmut

Bemerkungen zur Konvergenz von Poincaréschen Reihen.

Nachr. Akad. Wiss. Göttingen Math.-Phys. Kl. II **1966**, 1–9.

Let $T=\begin{pmatrix}T_1&0\\0&0\end{pmatrix}$, T_1 be a symmetric $r\times r$ matrix with rational integral coefficients and $T_1\gg 0$. Let U run over all unimodular $n\times n$ matrices of the form $U=\begin{pmatrix}E&0\\ *&*\end{pmatrix}$, E the unit matrix of r rows, and S over all integral symmetric $n\times n$ matrices. Then the $2n\times 2n$ matrices $M_r=\begin{pmatrix}U&SU^{-t}\\0&U^{-t}\end{pmatrix}$ (where $U^{-t}=(U^t)^{-1}$) form a subgroup Γ_r of the Siegel modular group Γ^n. The author first studies the Poincaré series $g_k(Z,T)=\sum e^{2\pi is(TM\langle Z\rangle)}|CZ+D|^{-k}$, summed over a set $M=\begin{pmatrix}A&B\\C&D\end{pmatrix}$ of left cosets of Γ_r in Γ^n. He shows that it converges absolutely and uniformly in a vertical "strip" $Z=X+iY$, $Y-mE\gg 0$ with $m>0$, if $k>\min(2n,n+r+1)$. The proof reduces the convergence of the series to that of an integral of the type of Euler's beta function. If $k>2n$ the proof of convergence can be simplified even further by transforming the (Siegel) generalized upper half-plane into the correspondingly generalized unit circle, and by an idea which was first used by Poincaré in the case $n=1$.

Second, the author studies another Poincaré series. Let M_r be the matrices as above but with S that have 0 in the upper left $r\times r$ corner. They form a subgroup $\Gamma_r'\subset\Gamma_r$. Let Z_r^* be a matrix in the $r\times r$ Siegel upper half plane and $M\langle Z\rangle_r$ the upper left $r\times r$ part of $M\langle Z\rangle$. Put $P_k(Z,Z_r^*)=\sum|CZ+D|^{-k}|M\langle Z\rangle_r+Z_r^*|^{-k}$, summed over a set $M=\begin{pmatrix}A&B\\C&D\end{pmatrix}$ of left cosets of Γ_r' in Γ^n. Now the author proves the interesting formula

$$P_k(Z,Z_r^*)=\tau(r,k)^{-1}\textstyle\sum_{T_1\gg 0}|T_1|^{k-(r+1)/2}g_k(Z,T)e^{2\pi is(T_1Z_r^*)}$$

with

$$\tau(r,k)=(4\pi)^{r(r-1)/4}(2\pi i)^{-rk}\Gamma(k)\Gamma(k-\tfrac{1}{2})\cdots\Gamma(k-\tfrac{1}{2}(r-1)).$$

The proof uses the Poisson summation formula and a result of C. L. Siegel [Math. Ann. **116** (1939), 617–657; MR **1**, 203]. *M. Eichler* (Basel)

Citations: MR 1, 203f = F50-1.

Referred to in F50-63.

F50-53 (36# 2555)

Klingen, Helmut

Zum Darstellungssatz für Siegelsche Modulformen.

Math. Z. **102** (1967), 30–43.

This paper gives essential simplifications of former work on the representation of Siegel modular forms by series of Poincaré type, namely, that of H. Maass [Math. Ann. **123** (1951), 125–151; MR **13**, 210; Nachr. Akad. Wiss. Göttingen Math.-Phys. Kl. II **1964**, 137–144; MR **29** #6060] and of R. Godement [Séminaire Henri Cartan: 1957/58. *Fonctions automorphes*, 2 vols., Secrétariat mathématique, Paris, 1958; see MR **21** #2750]. See also the author's paper [Math. Ann. **168** (1967), 157–170; MR **34** #7828]. Some of the methods can be extended to more general groups and are related to those used by W. L. Baily, Jr. and A. Borel [Ann. of Math. (2) **84** (1966), 442–528; MR **35** #6870].

Let Γ^n be the Siegel modular group of $2n$ rows and $0\leqq r\leqq n$. The matrices of Γ^n whose elements are 0 in the left lower corner of $n-r$ rows and $n+r$ columns form a subgroup $\Gamma_r^n\subseteq\Gamma^n$. The left upper $r\times r$ part of an n-rowed matrix Z will be written Z_r. Now let f be a modular form of degree r and weight $-k$. The author introduces the following important generalisation of the Eisenstein series $E_r^k(Z,f)=\sum f(M\langle Z\rangle_r)|CZ+D|^{-k}$, to be summed over a set $M=\begin{pmatrix}A&B\\C&D\end{pmatrix}$ of representatives of the left cosets of

Γ_r^n in Γ^n. They converge absolutely and uniformly for $k>n+r+1$ and $Z=X+iY$, $Y-mE\gg 0$ $(m>0)$. They are modular forms in Z of degree n and weight $-k$. If $r=0$, they are the conventional Eisenstein series. The essential feature of the $E_r^k(Z,f)$ is their behaviour under the Φ-operator: $\Phi^{n-r}E_r^k(Z,f)=f(Z_r)$. Application of this fact allows one to construct inductively all modular forms as such Eisenstein series. The space $\mathfrak{M}^k$ of all modular forms of even weight k is the direct sum of the subspaces $\mathfrak{M}_r^k$ defined as follows: $\mathfrak{M}_n^k$ is the space of cusp forms, $\mathfrak{M}_{n-1}^k$ is perpendicular to the cusp forms with respect to the Petersson metric and $\Phi\mathfrak{M}_{n-1}^k$ consists of cusp forms only, and so forth. $\mathfrak{M}_r^k$ is generated by the $E_r^k(Z,f)$ for all cusp forms f of degree r.

It is clear from the preceding that all types of Poincaré series occurring in earlier literature can be generated by the author's generalized Eisenstein series. The actual formulas are given explicitly. *M. Eichler* (Basel)

Citations: MR 13, 210a = F50-4; MR 21# 2750 = F02-5; MR 29# 6060 = F50-32; MR 34# 7828 = F50-49; MR 35# 6870 = F50-31.

Referred to in F50-54.

F50-54 **(37# 4020)**

Klingen, Helmut

Berichtigung zu: "Zum Darstellungssatz für Siegelsche Modulformen".

Math. Z. **105** (1968), 399–400.

A small gap in the proof in the original paper [same Z. **102** (1967), 30–43; MR **36** #2555] is removed. The results remain unchanged. *M. Eichler* (Basel)

Citations: MR 36# 2555 = F50-53.

F50-55 **(36# 3726)**

Allan, Nelo D.

On the commensurability class of the Siegel modular group.

Bull. Amer. Math. Soc. **74** (1968), 115–118.

Let O be the ring of integers of a number field k of finite degree. Let G be either the symplectic group $\mathrm{Sp}(n)$ or the special linear group $\mathrm{SL}(n)$. The author determines the commensurability class of G_O, and proves that there exists a countable family of arithmetic groups in G such that every maximal arithmetic group is conjugate to one group of the family. The proof uses the strong approximation theorem of M. Kneser [Proc. Internat. Congr. Math. (Stockholm, 1962), pp. 260–263, Inst. Mittag-Leffler, Djursholm, 1963; MR **31** #172]. *S. Konno* (Osaka)

Citations: MR 31# 172 = E68-10.

F50-56 **(36# 4028)**

Christian, Ulrich

Siegelsche Modulformen und Integralgleichungen.

Math. Z. **101** (1967), 299–305.

Verfasser behandelt die bekannte Integralgleichung für Spitzenformen. Er leitet sie her unter Verwendung der von H. Maass [Math. Ann. **123** (1951), 125–151; MR **13**, 210] eingeführten Poincaréschen Reihen und der diesbezüglichen Metrisierungsformeln. Dies ist möglich, weil der Kern der Integralgleichung bezüglich seiner Fourierentwicklung erzeugende Funktion der oben genannten Poincaréschen Reihen ist. *H. Klingen* (Freiburg)

Citations: MR 13, 210a = F50-4.

F50-57 **(37# 157)**

Takeuchi, Kisao

A remark on the Riemann-Roch-Weil theorem.

J. Fac. Sci. Univ. Tokyo Sect. I **12**, 235–245 (1966).

Γ sei eine Grenzkreisgruppe 1. Art. Nimmt man zur oberen Halbebene H die Menge P der parabolischen Fixpunkte hinzu, so entsteht ein Raum $H^*=H\cup P$, dessen Quotientenraum $R=\Gamma\backslash H^*$ eine kompakte Riemannsche Fläche ist. t sei Ortsuniformisierende zu einem Punkt $\Gamma\backslash\tau$ aus R. Ist τ kein Fixpunkt von Γ, so läßt sich ein lokaler Divisor durch eine meromorphe Funktion $f(t)$ repräsentieren mit $f\not\equiv 0$ (was man auch so ausdrücken kann: f ist im Ring der bei $t=0$ meromorphen Funktionen invertierbar). Ist τ Fixpunkt, so muß man ein Produkt $t^\alpha f(t)$ nehmen; hier wird nur der Fall betrachtet, daß α rational ist und daß, falls τ elliptischer Fixpunkt der Ordnung n ist, $n\alpha$ ganz ist. Nach dem Vorbild von A. Weil [J. Math. Pures Appl. **17** (1938), 47–87] wird die Definition des lokalen Divisors auf r-reihige quadratische Matrizen ausgedehnt, was darauf hinausläuft, daß an Stelle von $f(t)$ eine r-reihige quadratische Matrix mit meromorphen Elementen tritt, die meromorph invertierbar ist, und an Stelle von t^α eine Diagonalmatrix mit Diagonalelementen $t^{\alpha_1},\cdots,t^{\alpha_r}$ steht. Ein Divisor θ auf R wird wie üblich durch lokale Divisoren definiert, die mit Ausnahme höchstens endlich vieler Punkte durch die Einheitsmatrix repräsentiert sein müssen. Wegen der Nichtkommutativität der Matrizenmultiplikation gibt man jetzt einen Divisor θ für r-reihige Matrizen und einen Divisor θ' für r'-reihige Matrizen vor. Verfasser untersucht die Dimension des Vektorraumes derjenigen r-reihigen, r'-spaltigen Matrizen M, für die die Elemente von $\theta M\theta'^{-1}$ in allen Punkten nichtnegative Ordnung haben, wobei als Elemente von M wahlweise meromorphe Funktionen auf R bzw. meromorphe Differentiale auf R genommen werden. Verfasser leitet in der üblichen Weise einen Riemann-Rochschen Satz her und benutzt ihn, um die Dimension des Vektorraumes der ganzen automorphen Formenvektoren vom Gewicht m zu Γ zu bestimmen, die sich bei den Transformationen von Γ nach einer endlichen Darstellung von Γ durch r-reihige Matrizen umsetzen. In der zitierten Arbeit von Weil waren nur Gruppen ohne parabolische Fixpunkte behandelt worden. *K.-B. Gundlach* (Münster)

F50-58 **(37# 1652)**

Freitag, Eberhard

Fortsetzung von automorphen Funktionen.

Math. Ann. **177** (1968), 95–100.

Wenn man den Siegelschen Halbraum n-ten Grades in natürlicher Weise in den Hermiteschen Halbraum einbettet, dann läßt sich jede Siegelsche Modulfunktion zu einer Hermiteschen Modulfunktion (eines beliebigen imaginärquadratischen Zahlkörpers) fortsetzen. Dieser Satz von H. Klingen [Abh. Math. Sem. Univ. Hamburg **27** (1964), 1–12; MR **29** #2434] und sein Beweis werden vom Verfasser verallgemeinert. Sodann wird ein Fortsetzungssatz für folgende Situation hergeleitet. Sei $\iota: Y\to X$ eine abgeschlossene Einbettung irreduzibler komplexer Räume und X abzählbar im Unendlichen; $\iota(Y)$ werde mit Y identifiziert. Γ sei eine eigentlich diskontinuierliche Gruppe analytischer Automorphismen von X und Γ_0 die Gruppe aller analytischer Automorphismen von Y, welche zu Elementen von Γ fortsetzbar sind. Ferner seien die komplexen Räume Y/Γ_0 und X/Γ isomorph zu quasiprojektiven algebraischen Mannigfaltigkeiten Y^* und X^*. Eine automorphe Funktion bez. Γ ist eine auf X meromorphe, Γ-invariante Funktion, welche auf X^* eine rationale Funktion induziert. Satz: Wenn für jede automorphe Funktion bez. Γ, welche irgendwo auf Y holomorph ist, die Restriktion auf Y automorphe Funktion bez. Γ_0 ist, dann läßt sich jede automorphe Funktion bez. Γ_0 zu einer solchen von Γ fortsetzen. Die Voraussetzungen sind bei den

Modulfunktionen der verschiedenen Typen stets erfüllt. Abschließend wird der Satz auf Diagonaleinbettungen Siegelscher Halbräume angewendet.

J. Spilker (Freiburg)

Citations: MR 29# 2434 = F50-28.

F50-59 **(37# 2692)**

Spilker, Jürgen

Eine Anzahlfunktion bei diskontinuierlichen Gruppen.

Arch. Math. (*Basel*) **18** (1967), 597–602.

Let D be the domain consisting of those complex symmetric matrices Z such that $E-\bar{Z}Z>0$, let $k(Z)=\det^{-1}(E-\bar{Z}Z)$, let Γ_0 be the (transitive) group of all holomorphic automorphisms of E and let Γ be a discrete subgroup of Γ_0. The first part of the paper obtains upper estimates of the form c_1r^n and, in case D/Γ has finite volume, lower estimates of the form c_2r^n ($c_2>0$), for the number of elements Z in a Γ-orbit satisfying the inequality $k(z)<r$. These results are applied to prove convergence theorems for Poincaré series, and integral theorems for Γ-automorphic forms. *A. M. Macbeath* (Birmingham)

F50-60 **(37# 4022)**

Siegel, Carl Ludwig

Über die Fourierschen Koeffizienten von Eisensteinschen Reihen der Stufe T.

Math. Z. **105** (1968), 257–266.

Es sei $T=[t_1,\cdots,t_n]$ eine Diagonalmatrix, deren Elemente $1|t_1|t_2|\cdots|t_n$ erfüllen, und

$$\varphi(Z)=\sum_{C,D}|CT^{-1}Z+D|^{-g},$$

g gerade, $>n+1$, eine Eisenstein-Reihe zur Paramodulgruppe $\Gamma(T)$ der Stufe T, d.h. das Paar C, D durchlaufe die zweiten Matrizenzeilen eines Vertretersystems der rechtsseitigen Nebenklassen von $\Gamma(T)$ nach der Untergruppe der Matrizen mit $C=0$. Hauptresultat ist die Rationalität der Fourier-Koeffizienten von φ. In dem Spezialfall $T=$ Einheitsmatrix wurde das Resultat vom Verfasser schon früher bewiesen [Math. Ann. **116** (1939), 617–657; MR **1**, 203], und der vorliegende allgemeine Fall ist eine Ausdehnung jener Beweismethode: Alle Reihenglieder, für welche die Matrix C einen festen Rang hat, werden zusammengefaßt, und die Fourier-Koeffizienten werden mit Lösungsanzahlen von Matrix-Kongruenzen in Verbindung gebracht. *J. Spilker* (Freiburg)

Lines 5–8: "d.h. das Paar C, D... mit $C=0$." should be changed to read "d.h. C, D laufen über ein volles system von linksseitig nicht-assoziierten teilerfremden Paaren n-reihiger Matrizen, welche noch die Gleichung $(CT^{-1}D')'=CT^{-1}D'$ erfüllen."

Citations: MR 1, 203f = F50-1.

F50-61 **(37# 5217)**

Igusa, Jun-ichi

Modular forms and projective invariants.

Amer. J. Math. **89** (1967), 817–855.

Let S_g denote the Siegel upper half plane of degree $g\geqq 1$ consisting of complex g-rowed symmetric matrices whose imaginary parts are positive definite. Let $\Gamma_g(l)$ be the principal congruence subgroup of level l of the Siegel modular group $\Gamma_g(1)$. Let $A(\Gamma_g(l))$ be the graded ring of modular forms on S_g belonging to $\Gamma_g(l)$. A consequence of compactification theory is that $A(\Gamma_g(l))$ is a ring of finite type. Further, there exists a suitably chosen ring of theta constants such that $A(\Gamma_g(l))$ is the integral closure of this ring in its quotient field [the author, same J. **88** (1966), 221–236; MR **34** #375]. Using this the author now studies a certain subring R of $A(\Gamma_g(1))$ which contains all elements of even weights and also polynomials, with complex coefficients, in the theta constants, and shows that there exists a ring homomorphism ρ of R into the graded ring S of projective invariants of a binary form of degree $2g+2$. The subring R is shown to coincide with $A(\Gamma_g(1))$ if g is odd or $g=2$ or 4. Further, if $A(\Gamma_g(1))$ contains an element of odd weight and there exists at least one monomial ψ in the theta constants defining an element of $A(\Gamma_g(2))$ of odd weight such that $\psi(\tau)\neq 0$ at some point τ of S_g associated with a hyperelliptic curve, then ρ can be extended to $A(\Gamma_g(1))$. The author obtains some interesting consequences of these results. He shows that for $g=1$, ρ is a one-to-one mapping onto S. If $g=2$ the mapping ρ is one-to-one. If $g=3$, the kernel of ρ is a principal ideal (in $A(\Gamma_g(1))$ which equals R since g is odd) generated by a cusp form χ_{18} of weight 18. From these the author deduces a new proof of the structure theorem of $A(\Gamma_1(1))$. In the case of $g=3$ again, the author shows that there exist no cusp forms of weight less than 12. This leads to an answer, in the affirmative, to a question of E. Witt [Abh. Math. Sem. Univ. Hamburg **14** (1941), 323–337; MR **3**, 163]. According to Witt the genus of even positive quadratic forms of determinant unity in 16 variables consists of 2 classes represented by T_1 and T_2. Let $Z=Z_g$ be any element of S_g and let for $k=1,2$, $f_k(Z_g)=\sum_X e^{2\pi i\sigma(X'T_kXZ)}$, where X runs through all integral matrices of 16 rows and g columns. Witt showed that $f_1(Z_g)=f_2(Z_g)$ if $g=1$ or 2. The author's result shows that this is true also for $g=3$. In case $g=4$, however, the author shows that $f_1(Z_4)-f_2(Z_4)$ is a cusp form of weight 8. Finally, by using χ_{18}, the author is able to characterise completely the points on S_3 which correspond to a hyperelliptic jacobian variety.

K. G. Ramanathan (Bombay)

Citations: MR 3, 163d = E12-10; MR 34# 375 = F50-44.

F50-62 **(38# 119)**

Köhler, Günter

Ein Trennungssatz für Eisensteinsche Reihen zweiten und dritten Grades der Stufe T.

J. Reine Angew. Math. **231** (1968), 47–74.

Let $T=\mathrm{diag}(t_1,\cdots,t_n)$ with rational integers, where t_i divides t_{i+1}. With $J_T=\begin{pmatrix}0 & T\\ -T & 0\end{pmatrix}$, let $\Gamma(T)$ be the group of integral $2n\times 2n$ matrices M satisfying $M^tJ_TM=J_T$. $\Gamma(T)$ is the natural generalisation of the Siegel modular group $\Gamma^n=\Gamma(E)$, where E is the unit matrix. The author considers the Eisenstein series $\psi_{g,T}(Z)=\sum|CT^{-1}Z+D|^{-g}$, the sum being extended over a system of matrices $M=\begin{pmatrix}A & B\\ C & D\end{pmatrix}$ representing the right cosets of $\Gamma(T)$ mod the subgroup defined by $C=0$. These series converge absolutely and uniformly for all $Z=X+iY$ with $Y\geqq E/m$, $\mathrm{trace}(X^2)\leqq m$ for any $m>0$, if $g>n+1$. The $\psi_{g,T}(Z)$ are modular forms with respect to a certain group $\Lambda(T)$ which contains $\Gamma(T)$ with index 2^l, where l is the number of primes which divide the quotients t_{i+1}/t_i in equal powers. The quotients $f_{g,k,T}(Z)=\psi_{gk,T}(Z)\psi_{g,T}(Z)^{-k}$ are modular functions. Now let $f_{g,k,T}(Z_1)=f_{g,k,T}(Z_2)$, and assume that Z_1 does not lie on a certain finite number of surfaces. Then $Z_2=M(Z_1)$, where $M=M_1M_2$ with $M_1\in\Lambda(T)$ and M_2 belongs to a finite set of rational matrices. If $n=2$ or 3, the author even proves $M\in\Lambda(T)$. This fact entails that the field of all quotients of integral modular forms of equal weights with respect to $\Lambda(T)$ is generated by the quotients $f_{g,k,T}(Z)$. For $T=E$ and any n, C. L. Siegel has shown the same [Math. Ann. **116** (1939), 617–657; MR **1**, 203] and the author applies his method.

M. Eichler (Basel)

Citations: MR 1, 203f = F50-1.

Referred to in F55-29.

F50-63 **(39# 127)**

Christian, Ulrich

Untersuchung einer Poincaréschen Reihe. I.

J. Reine Angew. Math. **233** (1968), 37–88.

Let Z, W be symmetric complex matrices of n rows in the Siegel upper half space and $M=\begin{pmatrix} A & B \\ C & D \end{pmatrix}$ run over the Siegel modular group. The author considers the Poincaré series

$$G_g(W, Z) = \sum_M \|W(AZ+B)+CZ+D\|^{-g},$$

where $\|\cdots\|$ denotes the absolute value of the determinant. It is known [cf., e.g., H. Klingen, Nachr. Akad. Wiss. Göttingen Math.-Phys. Kl. II **1966**, 1–9; MR **36** #1707] that G_g converges for $g>2n$. The present author shows that it diverges for $g<2n$. The proof is a comparatively easy consequence of an estimation whose proof is extremely long and complicated. Let $G_{g,r}(W, Z)$ be the partial sum of $G_g(W, Z)$ summed over those M for which C has rank r. Put $Z=X+iY$ and form the integral $\Theta_{g,r}(Y)=\int G_{n,r}(-\bar{Z}, Z)|y|^g\,dx_{11}\cdots dx_{nn}$ over the cube $-\frac{1}{2}\leq x_{ij}\leq\frac{1}{2}$. Assume Y to be reduced in the sense of Minkowski, and denote the coefficients of Y by $y_1, \cdots, y_n$. Then, for every $\varepsilon>0$, there exist constants c_1, c_2 such that

$$c_1(y_1\cdots y_r)^{n+r-g-\varepsilon}y_{r+1}^{r+1}\cdots y_n{}^n \leq \Theta_{n,r}(Y) \leq c_2(y_1\cdots y_r)^{n+r-g}y_{r+1}^{r+1}\cdots y_n{}^n.$$

M. Eichler (Basel)

Citations: MR 36# 1707 = F50-52.

Referred to in F50-64.

F50-64 **(40# 1338)**

Christian, Ulrich

Untersuchung einer Poincaréschen Reihe. II.

J. Reine Angew. Math. **237** (1969), 12–25.

This is the continuation of a former paper of the author [same J. **233** (1968), 37–88; MR **39** #127]. Here the estimation of the integral, which was needed there for the proof of convergence of a certain Poincaré series, is improved. The reader is not informed whether these—again—highly technical considerations are useful for some applications in the theory of modular forms.

M. Eichler (Basel)

Citations: MR 39# 127 = F50-63.

F50-65 **(39# 2705)**

Andrianov, A. N.

Rationality of multiple Hecke series of the full linear group and Shimura's hypothesis on Hecke series of the symplectic group. **(Russian)**

Dokl. Akad. Nauk SSSR **183** (1968), 9–11.

Verfasser gibt in diesem Ergebnisbericht ohne Beweis einige Resultate über Heckesche Dirichletreihen zu gewissen Hecke-Ringen an. Der erste Fall betrifft die Hecke-Ringe der vollen linearen Gruppen, gebildet über einer zentralen Divisionsalgebra endlichen Ranges über einem p-adischen Zahlkörper. Diese Ringe sind von I. Satake [Inst. Hautes Études Sci. Publ. Math. No. 18 (1963), 5–69; MR **33** #4059] näher untersucht worden. Die zugehörigen Hecke-Reihen stellen sich jetzt als rationale Funktionen heraus. Der zweite Fall betrifft die lokalen Heckeschen Dirichletreihen zu den Siegelschen Modulgruppen, von denen G. Shimura [Proc. Nat. Acad. Sci. U.S.A. **49** (1963), 824–828; MR **28** #250] vermutet hatte, daß sie rationale Funktionen sind. Diese Vermutung wird bestätigt. Zusätzlich werden in beiden Fällen Angaben über die analytische Fortsetzung der Zetafunktionen zu den betreffenden Gruppen gemacht.

{This article has appeared in English translation [Soviet Math. Dokl. **9** (1968), 1295–1297].}

K.-B. Gundlach (Münster)

Citations: MR 28# 250 = F50-24; MR 33# 4059 = E64-10.

Referred to in F50-66.

F50-66 **(41# 6778)**

Andrianov, A. N.

Rationality theorems for Hecke series and Zeta functions of the groups GL_n and Sp_n over local fields. **(Russian)**

Izv. Akad. Nauk SSSR Ser. Mat. **33** (1969), 466–505.

Es handelt sich um die ausführliche Darstellung der Beweise der vom Verfasser in einem Ergebnisbericht [Dokl. Akad. Nauk SSSR **183** (1968), 9–11; MR **39** #2705] bereits angekündigten Resultate.

K.-B. Gundlach (Münster)

Citations: MR 39# 2705 = F50-65.

Referred to in F50-72.

F50-67 **(40# 1340)**

Resnikoff, H. L.

Non trivial cusp forms in several complex variables.

Complex Analysis (Proc. Conf., Rice Univ., Houston, Tex., 1967).

Rice Univ. Studies **54** (1968), *no.* 4, 55–61.

Verfasser hat in einer früheren Arbeit [Trans. Amer. Math. Soc. **124** (1966), 334–346; MR **34** #4490] Differentialoperatoren untersucht, die automorphe Formen (in einer Variablen) wieder in automorphe Formen überführen. In einer Arbeit ("On singular automorphic forms in several complex variables", zu erscheinen), hat er in analoger Weise Differentialoperatoren konstruiert, die automorphe Formen in mehreren Variablen zu gewissen Gruppen in einem der klassischen Gebiete wieder in automorphe Formen überführen. Er zeigt, daß die Anwendung eines solchen Differentialoperators auf eine nicht identisch verschwindende automorphe Form im allgemeinen, d.h. bis auf den Fall gewisser kritischer Gewichte, eine nichttriviale Spitzenform liefert. Er benutzt dieses Ergebnis, um zur Siegelschen und zur Hermiteschen Modulgruppe Spitzenformen kleinen Gewichts zu konstruieren.

K.-B. Gundlach (Münster)

F50-68 **(41# 3401)**

Resnikoff, H. L.

A differential equation for an Eisenstein series of genus two.

Proc. Nat. Acad. Sci. U.S.A. **65** (1970), 495–496.

Verfasser gibt eine nichtlineare Differentialgleichung der Ordnung 8 für die Eisensteinreihe vom Gewicht 4 zur Siegelschen Modulgruppe 2. Grades an. Sie spielt hier eine ähnliche Rolle wie die Differentialgleichung der Weierstraßschen $\wp$-Funktion in der Theorie der elliptischen Funktionen. Man erhält Rekursionsformeln für die Fourierkoeffizienten und kann von hier aus die Rationalität der Fourierkoeffizienten aller Eisensteinreihen zur Modulgruppe 2. Grades zeigen.

K.-B. Gundlach (Münster)

F50-69 **(42# 6000)**

Igusa, Jun-ichi

Geometric and analytic methods in the theory of theta-functions.

Algebraic Geometry (Internat. Colloq., Tata Inst. Fund. Res., Bombay, 1968), pp. 241–253. Oxford Univ. Press, London, 1969.

This paper gives an informative, condensed survey of recent and new results in the theory of theta-functions, including the important contributions of A. Weil [Acta Math. **111** (1964), 143–211; MR **36** #6421; ibid. **113** (1965), 1–87; MR **29** #2324] and of the author [Amer. J. Math. **84** (1962), 175–200; MR **25** #5040; ibid. **86** (1964), 392–412; MR **29** #6061; ibid. **86** (1964), 219–246; MR **29** #2258; ibid. **88** (1966), 221–236; MR **34** #375].

H. H. Martens (Trondheim)

Citations: MR 25# 5040 = F50-22; MR 29# 2258 = F50-27; MR 29# 2324 = E12-104; MR 29# 6061 = F50-33; MR 34# 375 = F50-44; MR 36# 6421 = E12-105.

F50-70 **(42# 7596)**

Baily, Walter L., Jr.

Automorphic forms with integral Fourier coefficients.
Several Complex Variables, I (Proc. Conf., Univ. of Maryland, College Park, Md., 1970), *pp.* 1–8. *Springer, Berlin,* 1970.

Von M. Eichler [Aequationes Math. **3** (1969), 93–111; MR **41** #2056] stammt folgendes Resultat: Der graduierte Ring der Siegelschen Modulformen besitzt ein endliches Erzeugendensystem von Formen, welche ganze rationale Fourier-Koeffizienten besitzen. Der Verfasser verallgemeinert das Problem auf Kegel-Gebiete und arithmetisch definierte diskrete Holomorphismengruppen. Er beweist, daß unter 3 Voraussetzungen, welche im Siegelschen Fall erfüllt sind, die Behauptung des Eichlerschen Satzes erhalten bleibtnämlich: Es existiert eine endliche Menge Θ von automorphen Formen $\neq 0$ mit ganzrationalen Fourier-Koeffizienten und folgenden Eigenschaften: (1) Jede automorphe Form ist Quotient zweier isobarer Polynome in Elementen aus Θ; (2) Der größte gemeinsame Teiler der Gewichte aller Formen aus Θ ist 1; (3) Sei E der von Θ erzeugte Unterring im Ring R aller automorphen Formen. Dann ist R ganz über $E \otimes_{\mathbf{Z}} \mathbf{C}$.

J. Spilker (Freiburg)

Citations: MR 41# 2056 = F55-30.

F50-71 **(42# 7597)**

Eichler, M.

Algebraic methods in the theory of modular forms.
Several Complex Variables, I (Proc. Conf., Univ. of Maryland, College Park, Md., 1970), *pp.* 88–96. *Springer, Berlin,* 1970.

Es wird ein kurzer Abriß von neuen Resultaten über Modulformen gegeben, welche sich mit Methoden aus der algebraischen Geometrie gewinnen lassen. Ausgehend von dem Resultat von W. L. Baily, Jr. und A. Borel [Ann. of Math. (2) **84** (1966), 442–528; MR **35** #6870], daß der graduierte Ring J der Modulformen unter weiten Voraussetzungen endlich erzeugt ist, untersucht der Verfasser ein projektives Modell H dieses Ringes, benutzt eine verallgemeinerte Riemann–Roch-Formel und zeigt, daß unter geeigneten Voraussetzungen darin die Moduln $\mathrm{Ext}^i(J, H)$ verschwinden. Dies Resultat hat zahlentheoretische Konsequenzen: Die Gruppe von genügend regulären Divisorklassen in J ist trivial.

J. Spilker (Freiburg)

Citations: MR 35# 6870 = F50-31.

F50-72 **(44# 216)**

Andrianov, A. N.

Spherical functions for GL_n over local fields, and the summation of Hecke series. (Russian)
Mat. Sb. (N.S.) **83 (125)** (1970), 429–451.

Der Verfasser untersucht Heckesche Dirichletreihen und Zetafunktionen zu den Gruppen $\mathrm{GL}_n(D)$ für eine Divisionsalgebra D endlichen Ranges über einem diskret bewerteten Körper k mit endlichem Restklassenkörper sowie die entsprechenden Funktionen zu den Siegelschen Modulgruppen über k. Er hatte bereits früher [Izv. Akad. Nauk SSSR Ser. Mat. **33** (1969), 466–505; MR **41** #6778] gezeigt, daß es sich um rationale Funktionen handelt. Es gelingt ihm jetzt, die Summation der Reihen im einzelnen auszuführen und damit unter anderem die Vermutung von Satake über die genaue Form des Nenners [I. Satake, Inst. Hautes Études Sci. Publ. Math. No. 18 (1963), 5–69; MR **33** #4059] und die Vermutung von G. Shimura über die Grade von Zähler und Nenner [Proc. Nat. Acad. Sci. U.S.A. **49** (1963), 824–828; MR **28** #250] zu beweisen. Wesentlichstes Hilfsmittel ist die explizite Bestimmung der zonalen Kugelfunktionen. Der Verfasser erhält hier ähnliche Formeln, wie sie I. G. Macdonald [Bull. Amer. Math. Soc. **74** (1968), 520–525; MR **36** #5141] auf anderem Wege für die zonalen Kugelfunktionen einer p-adischen Chevalley-Gruppe hergeleitet hat.

{This article has appeared in English translation [Math. USSR-Sb. **12** (1970), 429–452].}

K.-B. Gundlach (Münster)

Citations: MR 28# 250 = F50-24; MR 33# 4059 = E64-10; MR 36# 5141 = E64-17; MR 41# 6778 = F50-66.

F55 OTHER GROUPS AND THEIR AUTOMORPHIC FORMS (SEVERAL VARIABLES)

See also reviews E12-49, E12-81, E20-8, E20-21, E20-22, E56-56, E60-20, E60-24, E60-35, F15-8, F15-33, F40-21, F45-3, F50-10, F50-28, F50-58, F50-67, G10-43, G15-24, G15-45, R40-26.

F55-1 **(11, 333a)**

Braun, Hel. Hermitian modular functions. Ann. of Math. (2) **50**, 827–855 (1949).

The Hermitian modular group of degree n is defined as the group of all matrices

$$M=\begin{pmatrix} A & B \\ C & D \end{pmatrix}$$

(where A, B, C, D are matrices with n rows and columns whose elements are integral numbers of a given imaginary quadratic field $\mathfrak{K}$ of discriminant d) satisfying $\tilde{M}JM=J$, where

$$J=\begin{pmatrix} 0 & E \\ -E & 0 \end{pmatrix},$$

E is the n-rowed unit matrix and $\tilde{M}$ is the transpose conjugate complex to M. The Poincaré-Eisenstein series belonging to this group are defined as follows. A pair of n-rowed square matrices A and B with elements in $\mathfrak{K}$ is termed a Hermitian pair if the matrix (AB) has rank n and if $A\tilde{B}=B\tilde{A}$. It is called integral if the elements of A and B are integral. It is called coprime if it is integral and if for any row vector x the assumption that xA and xB are integral implies that x is integral. Two coprime Hermitian pairs of A, B and A_1, B_1 of $\mathfrak{K}$ are termed associate (or are said to belong to the same class) if $A_1=UA$, $B_1=UB$, where U is unimodular (a matrix U of $\mathfrak{K}$ is called unimodular if it is integral and has an integral inverse U^{-1}). Now if Z is an n-rowed square matrix whose elements are complex variables and such that $i^{-1}(Z-\tilde{Z})$ is a matrix of a positive Hermitian form define $\varphi_g(Z)=\sum_{A,B}|AZ+B|^{-g}$, where A, B run over a complete system of class representatives of coprime n-rowed Hermitian pairs of $\mathfrak{K}$ ($|AZ+B|$ is the determinant of the matrix $AZ+B$). It is supposed that g is an even positive integer and that $4|g$ if $d=-4$, $6|g$ if $d=-3$. Each class of Hermitian pairs of $\mathfrak{K}$ is proved to contain coprime pairs. The author proves that the series of the absolute values of the terms of the series $\varphi_g(Z)$ converges for all real values of $g>2n$, but diverges for $g=2n$. Writing $Z=\dot{Z}+\omega\ddot{Z}$, $Z'=\dot{Z}+\bar{\omega}\ddot{Z}$, where $\omega=\frac{1}{2}(d+\sqrt{d})$, $\bar{\omega}=\frac{1}{2}(d-\sqrt{d})$ and where Z' is the transposed matrix of Z, the matrices $\dot{Z}=(\dot{Z}_{kl})$ and $\ddot{Z}=(\ddot{Z}_{kl})$ have the properties $\ddot{Z}'=-\ddot{Z}$ and $\dot{Z}'=\dot{Z}+d\ddot{Z}$. Considering $\varphi_g(Z)$ as a function of the variables $\ddot{Z}_{kl}$ $(k<l)$ and $\dot{Z}_{kl}$ $(k\leqq l)$ it has the period 1 in each of these variables. It therefore has a Fourier expansion which is of the form $\sum_F a(F)\exp[2\pi i\sigma(FZ)]$, where σ is the trace of the matrix FZ and where $F=(f_{kj})$ runs through all Hermitian matrices of $\mathfrak{K}$ for which f_{kk} and $d^{\frac{1}{2}}f_{kj}$ $(j\neq k)$ are integral. The coefficients $a(F)$ are evaluated and the author proves that they are rational numbers. The proofs are modeled on those of the analogous theorems for modular forms of degree n by C. L. Siegel [Math. Ann. **116**, 617–657 (1939); these Rev. **1**, 203]. *H. D. Kloosterman* (Leiden).

Citations: MR 1, 203f = F50-1.

Referred to in F40-18, F50-10, F50-28, F55-6, F55-8, F55-9, F55-13.

F55-2 **(11, 333c)**

Braun, Hel. Hermitian modular functions. II. Genus invariants of Hermitian forms. Ann. of Math. (2) **51**, 92–104 (1950).

[See the preceding review.] This second part contains the proof of an identity which gives a partial fraction series for the analytic genus invariant of a nonnegative integral Hermitian matrix H of $\mathfrak{K}$. It is an analytic equivalent of the author's main theorem on Hermitian forms [Abh. Math. Sem. Hansischen Univ. **14**, 61–150 (1941); these Rev. **3**, 70]. The identity has the form

$$(1)\quad \sum_K \frac{1}{\mathfrak{M}(H)}\sum_{j=1}^{\lambda}\frac{\mathfrak{A}(H_j,K)}{\mathfrak{A}(H_j)}\exp[2\pi i\sigma(KZ)] = \sum_{A,B}\nu(H,A,B)|AZ+B|^{-r}.$$

On the left K runs through all nonnegative integral n-rowed Hermitian matrices K of $\mathfrak{K}$; the H_j are a complete set of representatives of the classes in the genus of H; $\mathfrak{A}(H,K)$ denotes for given nonnegative matrices H and K the number of representations of K by H, i.e., the number of integral matrices C of $\mathfrak{K}$ such that $\bar{C}HC=K$ and $OC=C$. Here O is a so-called right-idem of H, that is to say an integral matrix of $\mathfrak{K}$ with the same rank r as H and such that $HO=H$ ($\mathfrak{A}(H,K)$ does not depend on the choice of O). Moreover, $\mathfrak{A}(H)$ is the number of representations of H by itself and the measure $\mathfrak{M}(H)$ of the genus of H is defined by

$$\mathfrak{M}(H)=\sum_{j=1}^{\lambda}1/\mathfrak{A}(H_j).$$

On the right-hand side of (1), A, B run through a complete set of n-rowed non-associate, coprime, positive Hermitian pairs of $\mathfrak{K}$. The coefficients $\nu(H,A,B)$ are of absolute value not exceeding 1 and are (except for numerical factors) generalized Gaussian sums. The identity (1) is the analogue for Hermitian forms of the identity given by Siegel for quadratic forms [same Ann. (2) **38**, 212–291 (1937)]. *H. D. Kloosterman* (Leiden).

Citations: MR 3, 70i = E12-7.

Referred to in F55-3, F55-9.

F55-3 **(12, 482c)**

Braun, Hel. Hermitian modular functions. III. Ann. of Math. (2) **53**, 143–160 (1951).

[For part II see the same Ann. (2) **51**, 92–104 (1950); these Rev. **11**, 333.] The author studies the (homogeneous Hermitian modular) group $\mathfrak{H}$ consisting of all $2n\times 2n$ matrices M whose elements are integral numbers in an imaginary quadratic number field $\mathfrak{K}$ and such that $\bar{M}JM=J$. Here $\bar{M}$ is the conjugate complex of the transposed matrix of A and $J=\left(\begin{smallmatrix}0&E\\-E&0\end{smallmatrix}\right)$, where E is the $n\times n$ unit matrix. The group $\mathfrak{H}$ is therefore the group of all linear transformations with integral coefficients in $\mathfrak{K}$ which transform the bilinear Hermitian form $\sum_{k=1}^{n}(\bar{y}_kx_{k+n}-\bar{y}_{k+n}x_k)$ into itself. The author proves that the determinant of each M of $\mathfrak{H}$ is the square of a unit of $\mathfrak{K}$. Let $\mathfrak{Z}$ be the space consisting of all complex $n\times n$ matrices Z, such that the Hermitian matrix $Y=\frac{1}{2}i(\bar{Z}-Z)$ is positive definite. To the matrices $M=\left(\begin{smallmatrix}C&D\\F&G\end{smallmatrix}\right)$ (where C, D, F, G are $n\times n$ matrices) of $\mathfrak{H}$ correspond mappings $Z\to Z_1=(CZ+D)(FZ+G)^{-1}$ of $\mathfrak{Z}$ onto itself. The group $\mathfrak{H}_0$ of all these mappings (inhomogeneous Hermitian modular group) is isomorphic to the quotient group $\mathfrak{H}/\mathfrak{E}$, where $\mathfrak{E}$ is the subgroup of $\mathfrak{H}$ consisting of all matrices $\epsilon E^{(2n)}$, where ϵ is a unit of $\mathfrak{K}$ and $E^{(2n)}$ is the $2n\times 2n$ unit matrix. The author constructs a special fundamental domain **F** for $\mathfrak{H}_0$ in $\mathfrak{Z}$ by means of the reduction theory of Humbert for Hermitian forms over $\mathfrak{K}$. It is bounded by a finite number of algebraic surfaces. The domain **F** is not compact (indeed no fundamental domain for $\mathfrak{H}_0$ in $\mathfrak{Z}$ is compact). There exists however a positive number c such that the determinant $|Y|$ of Y is $\geqq c$ for all Z in **F**. If dZ is the matrix whose elements are the differentials of the elements of Z the differential form $ds^2=$ trace of $Y^{-1}dZY^{-1}d\bar{Z}$ defines a line element in $\mathfrak{Z}$ which is invariant under all transformations $Z_1=(CZ+D)(FZ+G)^{-1}$, where $\left(\begin{smallmatrix}C&D\\F&G\end{smallmatrix}\right)=M$ is an arbitrary complex matrix such that $\bar{M}JM=J$. Measured in this metric the volume of **F** is finite. Only a finite number of images of **F** under transformations of $\mathfrak{H}_0$ are neighbors of **F**. Every compact set in $\mathfrak{Z}$ can be covered by a finite number of images of **F**. *H. D. Kloosterman* (Leiden).

Citations: MR 11, 333c = F55-2.

Referred to in F45-3, F55-6, F55-7, F55-8, F55-9.

F55-4 **(11, 421c)**

Maass, Hans. Automorphe Funktionen von mehreren Veränderlichen und Dirichletsche Reihen. Abh. Math. Sem. Univ. Hamburg **16**, 72–100 (1949).

The automorphic functions which the author considers are solutions of the differential equation

$$(1)\quad \left[x_k^{k+1}\sum_{j=0}^{k}\frac{\partial}{\partial x_j}\left(x_k^{1-k}\frac{\partial}{\partial x_j}\right)+r^2+\tfrac{1}{4}k^2\right]f=0.$$

This equation is a $(k+1)$-dimensional analogue of the two-dimensional equation

$$\left[y^2\left(\frac{\partial^2}{\partial x^2}+\frac{\partial^2}{\partial y^2}\right)+\lambda^2\right]f(\tau)=0\qquad(\tau=x+iy).$$

The latter is invariant under the hyperbolic group $\tau\to(\alpha\tau+\beta)(\gamma\tau+\delta)^{-1}$ ($\alpha,\beta,\gamma,\delta$ real; $\alpha\delta-\beta\gamma=1$). According to Vahlen [Math. Ann. **55**, 585–593 (1902)] the $(k+1)$-dimensional hyperbolic group can be represented as

$$x\to(\alpha x+\beta)(\gamma x+\delta)^{-1},$$

where x is a vector $x_0+x_1i_1+x_2i_2+\cdots+x_ki_k$ in the Clifford algebra C_k of rank 2^k which is generated by units $i_1, i_2, \cdots, i_k$ satisfying $i_p^2+1=0$, $i_pi_q+i_qi_p=0$ ($p,q=1,2,\cdots,k$; $p\neq q$) and where $\alpha,\beta,\gamma,\delta$ are suitably chosen Clifford numbers from C_{k-1}. Every function $f(x)$ which is a solution of (1), which satisfies certain regularity conditions and is invariant under the translations of a k-dimensional lattice in the space V_{k-1}: $(x_0, x_1, \cdots, x_{k-1})$ has a Fourier expansion

$$f(x)=u(x_k)+\sum a(\beta)x_k^{\frac{1}{2}k}K_{ir}(2\pi|\beta|x_k)\exp 2\pi i\Re(\beta x),$$

where the summation is extended over all vectors

$\beta=(\beta_0, \beta_1, \cdots, \beta_{k-1})\neq 0$ of a k-dimensional lattice in V_{k-1}; K_{ir} is a Bessel function; $|\beta|$ is the norm of the vector β; $\Re(\beta x)$ denotes the real part of the element βx of C_k and $u(x)=a_1x^{\frac{1}{2}k+ir}+a_2x^{\frac{1}{2}k-ir}$ if $r\neq 0$, $u(x)=x^{\frac{1}{2}k}(a_1+a_2\log x)$ if $r=0$. The author now proves that (if $k>1$) necessary and sufficient conditions for the validity of $f(x)=f(-x^{-1})$ are that the functions

$$F_n(y, P_n)=u_n(y)+\sum a(\beta)P_n(\beta)y^{\frac{1}{2}k+n}K_{ir}(2\pi|\beta|y)$$

$(n=0, 1, 2, \cdots; y>0)$ satisfy $F_n(y^{-1}, P_n)=(-1)^nF(y, P_n')$. Here $P_n(\beta)=P_n(\beta_0, \beta_1, \cdots, \beta_{k-1})$ is a spherical harmonic of degree n, P_n' is the conjugate spherical harmonic of P_n and $u_n(y)=u(y)$ or $=0$ according as $n=0$ or $n>0$. By means of the Mellin transformation

$$4\int_0^\infty (F_n(y, P_n)-u_n(y))y^{2s-\frac{1}{2}k-n-1}dy = \pi^{-2s}\Gamma(s+\tfrac{1}{2}ir)\Gamma(s-\tfrac{1}{2}ir)\varphi(s, P_n)=\xi(s, P_n)$$

the linear set of the functions $f(x)$ mentioned above is proved to be in one-to-one correspondence with the linear set of Dirichlet series $\varphi(s, P_n)=\sum a(\beta)P_n(\beta)|\beta|^{-2s}$ satisfying the functional equation $\xi(\frac{1}{2}k+n-s, P_n)=(-1)^n\xi(s, P_n')$ and in addition certain regularity conditions. A special case is considered in more detail. It deals with zeta-functions of those biquadratic number fields which contain an imaginary quadratic field $R(\sqrt{d})$. The corresponding functions $f(x)$ are proved to be invariant under the principal congruence group of the field $R(\sqrt{d})$, the level (Stufe) of which is a certain ideal of this field.

H. D. Kloosterman (Leiden).

F55-5 (16, 801b)

Koecher, Max. Über Thetareihen indefiniter quadratischer Formen. Math. Nachr. **9**, 51–85 (1953).

Let $\mathfrak{S}=(s_{kl})$ be a real symmetric matrix with m rows and columns and let the s_{kk}, $2s_{kl}$ be integers. The corresponding quadratic form is supposed to be indefinite and of signature $(\mu, m-\mu)$, so that $\mu(m-\mu)>0$. Let $\mathfrak{P}$ be a "majorant" of $\mathfrak{S}$, satisfying $\mathfrak{P}\mathfrak{S}^{-1}\mathfrak{P}=\mathfrak{S}$, $\mathfrak{P}'=\mathfrak{P}>0$. If further $\mathfrak{A}$ is a rational matrix with m rows and n columns $(n\leqq m)$ and such that $2\mathfrak{S}\mathfrak{A}$ is an integral matrix, and if $\mathfrak{Z}_1$ and $\mathfrak{Z}_2$ are variable complex symmetric matrices with n rows and columns, the author considers theta series of the following type:

$$f_{\mathfrak{A}}(\mathfrak{Z}_1, \mathfrak{Z}_2, \mathfrak{P}) = \sum_{\mathfrak{B}\equiv\mathfrak{A}(1)} \exp \pi i\sigma\{\mathfrak{S}[\mathfrak{B}](\mathfrak{Z}_1+\mathfrak{Z}_2)+\mathfrak{P}[\mathfrak{B}](\mathfrak{Z}_1-\mathfrak{Z}_2)\},$$

where the summation is extended over all rational matrices $\mathfrak{B}$ which are congruent mod 1 with the given matrix $\mathfrak{A}$, and where $\sigma\{\mathfrak{U}\}$ denotes the trace of the matrix $\mathfrak{U}$. The series is convergent for $\mathfrak{J}(\mathfrak{Z}_1)>0$, $\mathfrak{J}(-\mathfrak{Z}_2)>0$. The author studies the behaviour of the function if $\mathfrak{Z}_\nu$ $(\nu=1, 2)$ are replaced by $(\mathfrak{F}\mathfrak{Z}_\nu+\mathfrak{G})(\mathfrak{C}\mathfrak{Z}_\nu+\mathfrak{D})^{-1}$, where $\mathfrak{M}=\begin{pmatrix}\mathfrak{F} & \mathfrak{G}\\ \mathfrak{C} & \mathfrak{D}\end{pmatrix}$ is an element of Siegel's modular group M_n of degree n.

In order to eliminate the special choice of the fixed majorant $\mathfrak{P}$ the functions f are integrated over the fundamental domain on the space P of the majorants $\mathfrak{P}$ of a certain subgroup of the group of automorphs of $\mathfrak{S}$ (the group of all integral matrices which transform $\mathfrak{S}$ into itself). The resulting functions $g(\mathfrak{Z}_1, \mathfrak{Z}_2, \mathfrak{S})=\int f(\mathfrak{Z}_1, \mathfrak{Z}_2, \mathfrak{P})dv$ show the same behaviour under M_n as the functions f. They are solutions of certain partial differential equations of order $2n$ which in the case $n=1$ reduce to the confluent hypergeometric differential equation. *H. D. Kloosterman.*

F55-6 (16, 801d)

Braun, Hel. Der Basissatz für hermitische Modulformen. Abh. Math. Sem. Univ. Hamburg **19**, 134–148 (1955).

In some earlier papers [Ann. of Math. (2) **50**, 827–855 (1949); **51**, 92–104 (1950); **53**, 143–160 (1951); MR **11**, 333; **12**, 482] the author developed a theory of hermitian modular forms. She did not succeed at that time in proving the basis theorem stating that the rank of the linear set of hermitian modular forms of a given dimension is finite. Now using some idea of Koecher [Math. Z. **59**, 399–416 (1954); MR **15**, 603] she gives a proof of the basis theorem.

H. D. Kloosterman (Leiden).

Citations: MR 11, 333a = F55-1; MR 12, 482c = F55-3; MR 15, 603e = F50-5.

Referred to in F55-8, F55-9.

F55-7 (17, 603a)

Becker, Hugo. Poincarésche Reihen zur hermitischen Modulgruppe. Math. Ann. **129** (1955), 187–208.

The author studies Poincaré series associated with certain discontinuous subgroups $G^{(n)}$ of the hermitian modular group $H^{(n)}$ of degree n [for definitions and notation see Braun, Ann. of Math. (2) **53** (1951), 143–160; MR **12**, 482]. Let $G^{(n)}$ be a congruence subgroup modulo q over an imaginary quadratic field K. The Poincaré series

$$g_{-k}(Z, F)=\sum_{\sigma\in V(f)} e^{2\pi i \mathrm{Sp}(\sigma F(Z))}v(\sigma)^{-1}|C_\sigma Z+D_\sigma|^{-k}$$

is shown to converge absolutely in Z when $k>\min(4n-2, 2(n+s))$, $k\equiv O(w)$, and to represent a modular form of dimension $-k$ belonging to $G^{(n)}$ and having multipliers $v(\sigma)$ $(|v(\sigma)|=1)$. Here F is an "exponent matrix" of rank s, $V(F)$ runs over a set of inequivalent substitutions of $G^{(n)}$, and w is the number of roots of unity in K. For the modular groups $H^{(n)}$ the author establishes a lower bound for the number of linearly independent modular forms of dimension $-k$ (provided $k>4n-2$, $k\equiv O(w)$).

J. Lehner (Los Alamos, N.M.).

Citations: MR 12, 482c = F55-3.

Referred to in F55-9.

F55-8 (20# 31)

Klingen, Helmut. Zur Theorie der hermitischen Modulfunktionen. Math. Ann. **134** (1958), 355–384.

Let Σ be an imaginary quadratic number field of discriminant $\delta\neq-4, -3$. Generalizing Siegel's modular functions of degree n [Math. Annalen **116** (1939), 617–657; MR **1**, 203], one makes the following definitions: Let E be the unit matrix of order n, set $I=\begin{pmatrix}0 & E\\ -E & 0\end{pmatrix}$ and, for every matrix Z, with elements in Σ, denote by $\tilde{Z}$ the transposed complex conjugate $\bar{Z}'$; define $\mathfrak{H}_n$, the "generalized upper half-plane" (of n^2 complex dimensions) as the set of matrices Z, such that the hermitian matrix $(Z-\tilde{Z})/2i$ is positively definite. The set $\mathfrak{M}_n$ of square matrices M of order $2n$, with elements in Σ and satisfying $\tilde{M}IM=I$ constitutes the hermitian modular group. If $Z\in\mathfrak{H}_n$ and $M=\begin{pmatrix}A & B\\ C & D\end{pmatrix}\in\mathfrak{M}_n$, then also $M\langle Z\rangle=(AZ+B)(CZ+D)^{-1}\in\mathfrak{H}_n$. Meromorphic functions of n^2 complex variables, defined on $\mathfrak{H}_n$ and invariant under the transformations $Z\to M\langle Z\rangle$, $M\in\mathfrak{M}_n$, are called hermitian modular functions. For $n=1$, one obtains the classical modular functions. One knows [H. Braun, Ann. of Math. (2) **50** (1949), 827–855; **53** (1951), 143–160; MR **11**, 333; **12**, 482] how to determine a fundamental domain of $\mathfrak{M}_n$ in $\mathfrak{H}_n$, and that the generalized Eisenstein series $\varphi_g(Z)=$

$\Sigma_{\{C,D\}}|CZ+D|^g$ (summation extended over the coprime matrices C, D of Σ) converge for $g<-2n$. The author proves that $\varphi_g(Z)$ are holomorphic modular forms of dimension g in $\mathfrak{H}_n$. Hermitian modular functions are now defined as quotients of modular forms of equal dimensions. They form a field of degree of transcendency at least n^2 over the complex numbers. The most striking difference between the present theory and that of Siegel's modular functions of degree n is that in the hermitian case one has to take into account the congruence subgroups already for the proof of the fundamental (basis) theorem on functions modular under the full hermitian group $\mathfrak{M}_n$ [see also H. Braun, Abh. Math. Sem. Univ. Hamburg **19** (1955), 134–148; MR **16**, 801]. The author studies the fields of functions modular under subgroups of $\mathfrak{M}_n$. Restricting $\mathfrak{H}_n$ by the condition $Z=Z'$, one obtains modular functions, forming a subfield of degree $\frac{1}{2}n(n+1)$ of the field Λ of (Siegel) modular functions of degree n. Finally, the author discusses the characterization of hermitian modular forms by differential equations. The Eisenstein series corresponding to certain subgroups of $\mathfrak{M}_n$ satisfy a set of $2n^2$ differential equations, which characterize pencils of automorphic forms. The paper concludes with the establishment of functional relations between different pencils of hermitian modular forms.

E. Grosswald (Philadelphia, Pa.)

Citations: MR 1, 203f = F50-1; MR 11, 333a = F55-1; MR 12, 482c = F55-3; MR 16, 801d = F55-6.

F55-9 (20# 1794)

Braun, Hel. Darstellung hermitischer Modulformen durch Poincarésche Reihen. Abh. Math. Sem. Univ. Hamburg 22 (1958), 9–37.

In the theory of automorphic forms in several complex variables, the so-called representation theorems have been achieved only for the Siegel modular group [Maass, Math. Ann. **123** (1951), 125–151; MR **13**, 210]. In previous papers the author has discussed the Hermitian modular group of degree n and its automorphic forms [Ann. of Math. (2) **50** (1949), 827–855; **51** (1950), 92–104; **53** (1951), 143–160; Abh. Math. Sem. Univ. Hamburg **19** (1955), 134–148; MR **11**, 333; **12**, 482; **16**, 801], and Becker has introduced Poincaré series on this group and its congruence subgroups [Math. Ann. **129** (1955), 187–208; MR **17**, 603]. In the present paper, she establishes a representation theorem for the congruence subgroups of the Hermitian modular group of degree n, and so, in particular, for the full group. She proves, in fact, that every automorphic form of sufficiently high negative dimension k ($-k\geqq 4n$, k=even integer) is a finite linear combination of Poincaré series.

The principal tool used in the proof is the scalar product of two automorphic forms as developed by Maass [cf. above] and Koecher [Math. Z. **59** (1954), 399–416; **61** (1955), 455–466; MR **15**, 603; **16**, 801]. The representation theorem is first proved for cusp forms. The extension to the general case is then made by an inductive argument using the Siegel operator Φ, which maps forms of degree n into those of degree $n-1$.

J. Lehner (East Lansing, Mich.)

Citations: MR 11, 333a = F55-1; MR 11, 333c = F55-2; MR 12, 482c = F55-3; MR 13, 210a = F50-4; MR 15, 603e = F50-5; MR 16, 801c = F50-8; MR 16, 801d = F55-6; MR 17, 603a = F55-7.

F55-10 (21# 4202)

Harish-Chandra. Automorphic forms on a semisimple Lie group. Proc. Nat. Acad. Sci. U.S.A. **45** (1959), 570–573.

Let G be a connected semisimple Lie group with finite center and K a maximal compact subgroup of G. Let Γ be a discrete subgroup of G and σ and μ unitary representations of K and Γ respectively on a finite-dimensional Hilbert space U. $\sigma(K)$ acts on U on the left and $\mu(\Gamma)$ acts on U on the right. Let $\mathfrak{Z}$ be the (commutative) algebra of differential operators on G which are invariant under all left and right translations of G. Fix a homomorphism χ of $\mathfrak{Z}$ into the field of complex numbers. A C^∞ function f from G to U is called an automorphic form of type (σ, μ, χ) if (1) $f(kx\gamma)=\sigma(k)f(x)\mu(\gamma)$ $(k\in K,\ x\in G, \gamma\in\Gamma)$ and (2) $zf=\chi(z)f$ $(z\in\mathfrak{Z})$. Such a function is always analytic. The author studies the space $\mathfrak{F}_0(\sigma, \mu, \chi)$ of automorphic forms on G which satisfy a certain growth condition at infinity. The main result is that $\dim \mathfrak{F}_0(\sigma, \mu, \chi)<\infty$ under a suitable condition on Γ (too complicated to describe here). This condition is stronger than finiteness of the volume of G/Γ. However it is fulfilled, for example, when $\Gamma=\mathrm{Sp}(n, Z)$ (Siegel's modular group) and $G=\mathrm{Sp}(n, R)$. The result is applied to the decomposition of the representation λ of G on $L^2(G/\Gamma)$ induced by the action of G on G/Γ. It is shown that each discrete irreducible component of λ occurs only a finite number of times in λ.

S. Helgason (New York, N.Y.)

Referred to in F55-20.

F55-11 (21# 6370)

Shimura, Goro. On the theory of automorphic functions. Ann. of Math. (2) **70** (1959), 101–144.

For a given Z-algebra $\mathfrak{r}$ with finite basis, define a polarized abelian variety of type $\mathfrak{r}$ to be an abelian variety A with a given polarization (meaning, roughly, a class of projective embeddings) and a given isomorphism from $\mathfrak{r}$ into the endomorphism ring of A. For such data a field of moduli is defined; this is, roughly, the least field over which an isomorphic polarized variety of type $\mathfrak{r}$ can be defined. If now we are given an analytic family of polarized abelian varieties of type $\mathfrak{r}$, parametrized by a connected open subset $\mathfrak{Z}$ of C^m (that is, for each $z\in\mathfrak{Z}$ we are given a Riemann matrix of specified type, etc.), then there exist meromorphic functions $f_1(z), \cdots, f_\alpha(z)$ on $\mathfrak{Z}$ and an analytic subset $\mathfrak{S}$ of $\mathfrak{Z}$, of codimension one and containing the polar locus of each f_i, such that $Q(f_1(z), \cdots, f_\alpha(z))$ is the field of moduli of the polarized abelian variety of type $\mathfrak{r}$ corresponding to any point $z\in\mathfrak{Z}-\mathfrak{S}$; in addition, k being a countable subfield of C, a condition is given for $k(f_1, \cdots, f_\alpha)$ to be a regular extension of k, linearly disjoint from C over k. The last part of the paper considers polarized abelian varieties of dimension 2 with endomorphism rings isomorphic to an order of an indefinite quaternion algebra, i.e., a central simple Q-algebra of degree 2 possessing a faithful representation by real 2×2 matrices; analytic families of such polarized abelian varieties are constructed, parametrized by the upper half plane of C, for which the moduli are precisely the automorphic functions on the upper half plane corresponding to a certain transformation group, and the field of moduli is shown to be defined over Q.

M. Rosenlicht (Berkeley, Calif.)

Referred to in F40-28, F50-24, F55-16, G15-22, G15-34, G30-31.

F55-12 (21# 6371)

Shimura, Goro. Fonctions automorphes et variétés abéliennes. Séminaire Bourbaki; 10e année: 1957/1958. Textes des conférences; Exposés 152 à 168; 2e éd. corrigée, Exposé 167, 9 pp. Secrétariat mathématique, Paris, 1958. 189 pp. (mimeographed)

This can be considered as an exposé of the special case of the paper reviewed above, in which one considers the family of polarized abelian varieties given by the Siegel variety; the field of moduli here is precisely the field of modular functions of Siegel. There is also a brief discussion of the modular functions obtained from the division points of a certain order on a variable abelian variety.

M. Rosenlicht (Berkeley, Calif.)

F55-13 (23# A3285)

Klingen, Helmut

Quotientendarstellung Hermitescher Modulfunktionen durch Modulformen.

Math. Ann. **143** (1961), 1–18.

The fact that every modular function (every group-invariant meromorphic function) can be represented as the quotient of two holomorphic modular forms was first proved by W. L. Baily, using the technique of compactification of the quotient space [Amer. J. Math. **80** (1958), 348–364; MR **20** #5890]; another proof, using more classical means, was given by C. L. Siegel [Nachr. Akad. Wiss. Göttingen Math. Phys. Kl. II **1960**, 257–272]. The present paper carries Siegel's proof of the theorem over to the case of the Hermitian modular functions of H. Braun [Ann. of Math. (2) **50** (1949), 827–855; MR **11**, 333]; the transition is not trivial, since the structures of the standard fundamental domains in the two cases are quite dissimilar.

R. C. Gunning (Princeton, N.J.)

Citations: MR 11, 333a = F55-1; MR 20# 5890 = F45-5.

F55-14 (26# 2641)

Shimizu, Hideo

On discontinuous groups operating on the product of the upper half planes.

Ann. of Math. (2) **77** (1963), 33–71.

In this paper, H^n is the direct product of n copies of the upper half-plane, Γ a discrete subgroup of the identity component G of the group of conformal transformations of H^n with a fundamental domain F of finite invariant volume $v(F)$. Mainly for convenience, it is also assumed that Γ is "irreducible", that is, not commensurable with the product of two discrete subgroups belonging to two proper invariant complementary subgroups of G. The first part of the paper gives two conditions equivalent to irreducibility and proves some results on parabolic points, announced, with some ideas of proof, by I. I. Pjateckiĭ-Šapiro [Dokl. Akad. Nauk SSSR **124** (1959), 760–763; MR **21** #3581]; the second and main part of the paper is concerned with the dimension of the space of cusp forms for Γ. A point $x \in \bar{H}^n$, where $\bar{H}^n$ is the usual compactification of H^n, is parabolic for Γ if it is fixed under a unipotent element $\gamma \neq e$ of Γ. Among other things, the following is proved: there are finitely many equivalence classes of parabolic points, the quotient of the greatest unimodular subgroup of G leaving a parabolic point x fixed by its intersection $\Gamma_x^{(1)}$ with Γ is compact; if $x=(\infty, \cdots, \infty)$, $\Gamma_x^{(1)}$ leaves $U_\mu=\{z=(z_1, \cdots, z_n) | \prod \operatorname{Im} z_i > \mu\}$ invariant for μ large enough and admits there a fundamental set V_μ of the type known for the Hilbert-Blumenthal group. In the sequel, Γ is assumed moreover to have a fundamental domain F which is the union of a relatively compact set F_0 and of finitely many "cusps", equivalent to the above V_μ, one for each class of parabolic points. It is not known whether this is not a consequence of the previous assumptions on Γ. It follows then from results of A. Selberg [Seminars on Analytic Functions (Institute for Advanced Study, Princeton, N.J., 1957), Vol. 2, pp. 152–161, U.S. Air Force, Washington, D.C.], also proved in Cartan's Seminar on automorphic functions [Séminaire Henri Cartan, 10e année: 1957/1958, Exp. 8, Exp. 10. Secrétariat mathématique, Paris, 1958; MR **21** #2750], that the dimension of the space $\mathfrak{S}_r$ of cusp forms of weight $r=(r_1, \cdots, r_n)$ $(r_i>1, 1 \leq i \leq n)$ is finite and equal to the trace of a certain integral operator. The kernel of the latter is an infinite sum over Γ; if H^n/Γ is compact, then the integral over F and the sum over Γ can be permuted, and Selberg's trace formula can be used. Otherwise, a modified procedure has to be used. After a rather long analysis, it is shown that dim $\mathfrak{S}_r$ is the sum of $v(F)(4\pi)^{-n} \prod (2r_i-1)$ and of finitely many terms, explicitly described, corresponding to the classes of elliptic and of parabolic points. A less precise formula of this type, for r large, had already been mentioned by Selberg [loc. cit.]. This formula is further transformed in the cases where Γ is the Hilbert-Blumenthal group or the group of elements of reduced norm 1 in a maximal order of an indefinite quaternion algebra A over a totally real number field of degree $m>n$ which has exactly n completions at infinity over which A splits.

A. Borel (Princeton, N.J.)

Citations: MR 21# 2750 = F02-5.

Referred to in F25-19, F40-35, F40-36, F40-49, F40-50, F40-59, F60-6.

F55-15 (26# 5188)

Spilker, Jürgen

Algebraische Körper von automorphen Funktionen.

Math. Ann. **149** (1962/63), 341–360.

Andreotti and Grauert [Nachr. Akad. Wiss. Göttingen Math.-Phys. Kl. II **1961**, 39–48; MR **24** #A2057] have introduced the notion of pseudo-concavity for a properly discontinuous group Γ operating on a domain $H \subset C^m$ and have shown that Siegel's modular group is pseudo-concave if $m>1$. In the present paper, pseudo-concavity is established when Γ is either the Hilbert-Siegel modular group or the hermitian modular group and H the corresponding symmetric domain (and $m>1$). The proof makes use of various properties of fundamental sets for Γ in H, due notably to P. Humbert, H. Klingen, H. Braun and the author, and is technically more involved than in the case of the Siegel modular group, but it is essentially analogous to that of Andreotti and Grauert [loc. cit.]. As shown there, the result is then valid for any properly discontinuous group of automorphisms of H which is commensurable with Γ, and implies that the automorphic functions for Γ are quotients of automorphic forms and form an algebraic function field of transcendence degree $m=\dim H$.

A. Borel (Princeton, N.J.)

Citations: MR 24# A2057 = F40-23.

F55-16 (27# 5934)

Shimura, Goro

On analytic families of polarized abelian varieties and automorphic functions.

Ann. of Math. (2) **78** (1963), 149–192.

This is a sequel to a previous paper by the author [same Ann. (2) **70** (1959), 101–144; MR **21** #6370]. Let L be a division algebra over $\mathbf{Q}$, endowed with a positive involution ρ. Let A be an abelian variety, $\mathscr{A}(A)$ its endomorphism ring, $\mathscr{C}$ a polarization of A, and θ a monomorphism of L into $\mathscr{A}_0(A)=\mathscr{A}(A) \otimes \mathbf{Q}$ which carries ρ into the involution associated to $\mathscr{C}$. After having recalled Albert's classification of the algebras (L, ρ), the author gives necessary conditions for the representation Φ of L, of degree $n=\dim A$, obtained via θ and the identification of A with a quotient of $\mathbf{C}^n$. He then constructs analytic families of polarized abelian varieties of type $(A, \mathscr{C}, \theta)$, in which $\mathscr{A}(A) \cap \theta(L)$ contains a given order $\mathfrak{M}$ of L. They are parametrized by certain bounded symmetric domains $\mathscr{H}$, and the isomorphism classes of elements in a family correspond to the orbits of a suitable discontinuous group of automorphisms Γ of $\mathscr{H}$. The possible $\mathscr{H}$ and Γ are described. Using the results of the paper quoted above, the author then shows the existence of finitely many automorphic functions f_i ($1 \leq i \leq k$) for Γ and of an analytic subset $\mathscr{W}$ of $\mathscr{H}$, of codimension one, with the following properties: the f_i's are holomorphic on $\mathscr{H}-\mathscr{W}$, their values at $z \in \mathscr{H}-\mathscr{W}$ generate over $\mathbf{Q}$ the field of moduli of the triplet $(A, \mathscr{C}, \theta)$ represented by z, they separate the orbits of Γ in a suitable open invariant subset containing $\mathscr{H}-\mathscr{W}$, and the field $\mathbf{C}(f_1, \cdots, f_k)$ is defined over a number field of finite degree. If $\mathscr{H}/\Gamma$ is compact or has a "good" compactification, then $\mathbf{C}(f_1, \cdots, f_k)$ is the field of all automorphic functions. This happens, for instance, when Γ is the Hilbert-Siegel group (and also, according to Baily [see #5935 below], in the other cases considered here). The author also determines all cases in which $\theta(\mathfrak{L}) \neq \mathscr{A}_0(A)$, when A is a generic member of the above analytic family. Finally, he extends some of his results to analytic families of abelian varieties $(A, \mathscr{E}, \theta)$, where $\mathscr{E}$ is a "weak" polarization, i.e., a family of polarizations of the form $\mathscr{C} \cdot \theta(b)$, where b runs through the totally positive units of the maximal central totally real subfield of L.

A. Borel (Princeton, N.J.)

Citations: MR 21# 6370 = F55-11.

Referred to in F50-24, G10-45, G15-22, G15-32, G15-34.

F55-17 (27# 5935)

Baily, Walter L., Jr.

On the theory of automorphic functions and the problem of moduli.

Bull. Amer. Math. Soc. **69** (1963), 727–732.

This report discusses analytic families of polarized abelian varieties whose endomorphism ring contains a given order in a division algebra with positive involution over Q, their relations with bounded symmetric domains H and certain discontinuous groups of automorphisms Γ of H, following in part Shimura [see #5934 above]. The author also recalls his results on the compactification of H/Γ when Γ is the Hilbert-Siegel group, and states that some of them can be extended to more general cases containing those considered by Shimura.

A. Borel (Princeton, N.J.)

F55-18 (30# 2008)

Ramanathan, K. G.

Discontinuous groups. II.

Nachr. Akad. Wiss. Göttingen Math.-Phys. Kl. II **1964**, 145–164.

Nach Hecke ist die elliptische Modulgruppe maximale diskrete Untergruppe der symplektischen Gruppe 1. Grades über dem reellen Zahlkörper R. Dagegen ist dies nach Maass [Math. Z. **51** (1948), 255–261; MR **10**, 434] für die Hilbertschen Modulgruppen nicht immer richtig. Der Verfasser beantwortet die zugrundeliegende Frage in sehr weitreichender Weise.

Es sei zunächst K ein algebraischer Zahlkörper mit r_1 reellen und r_2 Paaren konjugierter Körper und Ω das Produkt von r_1 symplektischen Gruppen n-ten Grades über R und r_2 solchen Gruppen über dem Körper der komplexen Zahlen C. Die Modulgruppe Γ von K besteht aus allen Elementen von Ω mit ganzen Matrixelementen aus K. Unter einer Erweiterung von Γ versteht man eine diskrete Untergruppe H von Ω, die Γ enthält. Über diese Erweiterungen zeigt der Verfasser die folgenden drei Sätze: (1) Die Elemente von H sind von der Gestalt $h=\omega V$ mit einer quadratischen ganzen algebraischen Zahl ω über K und einer Matrix V mit Elementen aus K; die Matrixelemente von h sind ganze algebraische Zahlen; H/Γ ist endlich und von 2-Potenzordnung. (2) Es existieren maximale Erweiterungen von Γ. (3) Bei Klassenzahl 1 sind die Elemente von H von der Form $h=\sqrt{\varepsilon}\, V$, wobei V ganze Matrixelemente in K hat und ε ein Repräsentantensystem der totalpositiven Einheiten modulo den Einheitenquadraten von K durchläuft. Aus (3) wird sofort ersichtlich, dass z.B. die Siegelsche Modulgruppe n-ten Grades für beliebiges n nicht erweiterungsfähig ist.

Der vorstehende Sachverhalt mit dem schönen neuen Resultat über die Siegelsche Modulgruppe ist nur ein Spezialfall der vom Verfasser untersuchten Situation. Es gelingt ihm, Analoga der oben beschriebenen Sätze zu beweisen für beliebige diskrete Untergruppen der klassischen Gruppen, welche arithmetisch definierte Untergruppen enthalten. Wesentliches Hilfsmittel beim Beweis ist die Verwendung der sogenannten Gruppenalgebra einer diskontinuierlichen Gruppe, die bereits im ersten Teil [Nachr. Akad. Wiss. Göttingen Math.-Phys. Kl. II **1963**, 293–323; MR **28** #2112] eine wesentliche Rolle spielte.

H. Klingen (Freiburg)

Citations: MR 10, 434e = F40-5; MR 28# 2112 = E60-8.

Referred to in E60-22.

F55-19 (31# 385)

Jacquet, Hervé

Mémoire de Langlands sur la dimension des espaces de formes automorphes.

Séminaire Bourbaki, 16e année: 1963/64, Fasc. 1, Exposé 261, 15 pp. Secrétariat mathématique, Paris, 1964.

A clear though condensed report on Langlands' paper [Amer. J. Math. **85** (1963), 99–125; MR **27** #6286], in which he computes the dimension of the space of automorphic forms with the help of Selberg's trace formula.

W. Klingenberg (Mainz)

F55-20 (34# 7465)

Borel, Armand

Introduction to automorphic forms.

Algebraic Groups and Discontinuous Subgroups (Proc. Sympos. Pure Math., Boulder, Colo., 1965), *pp.* 199–210. *Amer. Math. Soc., Providence, R.I.,* 1966.

This paper surveys some of the basic results of the modern theory of automorphic forms on semisimple algebraic groups. The starting point is Harish-Chandra's definition of an automorphic form on a semisimple Lie group G with respect to a discrete subgroup Γ [Harish-Chandra, Proc. Nat. Acad. Sci. U.S.A. **45** (1959), 570–573; MR **21** #4202], which encompasses the classical notions of holomorphic as well as non-holomorphic automorphic forms in one or more complex variables. The author then points out how one of the conditions in this definition can be interpreted geometrically via factors of automorphy on Γ, and how another condition in the definition is related to holomorphy. He then shows how automorphic forms can be constructed under suitable hypotheses. In particular, there is given a result of R. Godement [Séminaire H. Cartan, 1957/58, Exposé 10, Secrétariat mathématique, Paris, 1958; see MR **21** #2750] which enables one to construct analogues on G of the classical Poincaré series. Also given is the proof of a lemma of Godement which makes it possible to construct analogues on G of the classical Eisenstein series. (See R. Langlands, *Algebraic groups and discontinuous subgroups* (Proc. Sympos. Pure Math., Boulder, Colo., 1965), pp. 235–252, Amer. Math. Soc., Providence, R.I., 1966.)

The author has included several standard and illuminating examples of these notions which further enhance the value of this survey.

R. A. Gangolli (Princeton, N.J.)

Citations: MR 21# 2750 = F02-5; MR 21# 4202 = F55-10; MR 40# 2784 = F60-10.

F55-21 **(35# 1602)**

Satake, I.

Clifford algebras and families of abelian varieties.

Nagoya Math. J. **27** (1966), 435–446.

Let $\mathscr{D}=G/K$ be a bounded symmetric domain. In the theory of automorphic functions on $\mathscr{D}$, as developed by M. Kuga and G. Shimura [Ann. of Math. (2) **82** (1965), 478–539; MR **32** #2413], an important role is played by families of polarized abelian varieties parametrized by $\mathscr{D}$. In this paper the author shows how to construct such families in the case when G is the spin group of an indefinite quadratic form. The construction is given quite explicitly in terms of the Clifford algebra of the quadratic form.

If V is the vector space with quadratic form S, then the points of $\mathscr{D}$ correspond to decompositions $V=V^+\oplus V^-$ in which S is positive [negative] definite on V^+ [V^-]. Given such a decomposition (and assuming say that S is defined over **Q**), the author shows how to construct an abelian variety whose universal covering is the even Clifford algebra $C^+(V,S)$. He also investigates the endomorphism ring of this abelian variety.

The case when $\dim V^+=2$ is particularly interesting because in this case $\mathscr{D}$ has a complex structure and the family of abelian varieties is complex analytic [see the following review #1603]. *M. F. Atiyah* (Oxford)

Citations: MR 32# 2413 = G15-32.
Referred to in F45-34, F55-23.

F55-22 **(35# 1603)**

Kuga, Michio; Satake, Ichirô

Abelian varieties attached to polarized K_3-surfaces.

Math. Ann. **169** (1967), 239–242.

Quartic surfaces in projective 3-space belong to the family of compact complex surfaces known as K_3-surfaces. These can be characterized by the vanishing of the first Betti number and the first Chern class, and the study of the moduli (or parameter space) of K_3-surfaces presents a fascinating problem. More precisely, one considers polarized algebraic K_3-surfaces (i.e., surfaces S with a preferred one-dimensional subspace X of $H^2(S,\mathbf{Q})$ containing the class of a hyperplane section in some projective embedding). The orthogonal complement of X (with respect to the cup-product in H^2) gives a space V of dimension 21, and the cup-product on V gives a quadratic form of type (2, 19). Moreover, the Hodge structure of V, i.e., the decomposition of $V\otimes_{\mathbf{Q}}\mathbf{C}$ given by forms of type (2, 0), (1, 1) and (0, 2), defines in a natural way a point of the symmetric space D of the orthogonal group of V. It is a conjecture of Weil that in this way one obtains a bijective correspondence between polarized K_3-surfaces and points of a quotient Γ/D for a suitable discrete group Γ.

In this paper the authors show (along the lines of the paper reviewed above [#1602]) how to construct an analytic family of polarized abelian varieties parametrized by D—or, equivalently, a holomorphic map of D into the Siegel space D'. In particular, this construction therefore attaches a polarized abelian variety A to each polarized K_3-surface S. The authors examine in particular the following two cases: (i) S is a generic K_3-surface; (ii) S is a "singular" K_3-surface, i.e., possesses 20 linearly independent polarizations. In the first case they show that A is isogenous to a product of 2^{10} copies of a simple abelian variety of dimension 2^9 without complex multiplication. In the second case A is isogenous to a product of 2^{19} copies of an elliptic curve whose endomorphism algebra is $Q\sqrt{-1}$. *M. F. Atiyah* (Oxford)

Referred to in F55-24.

F55-23 **(36# 2624)**

Satake, I.

Corrections to: "Clifford algebras and families of abelian varieties".

Nagoya Math. J. **31** (1968), 295–296.

The original article appeared in same J. **27** (1966), 435–446 [MR **35** #1602].

Citations: MR 35# 1602 = F55-21.
Referred to in F45-34.

F55-24 **(35# 6697)**

Satake, I.

Corrections to: "Abelian varieties attached to polarized K_3-surfaces".

Math. Ann. **173** (1967), 322.

The original article appeared in same Ann. **169** (1967), 239–242 [MR **35** #1603].

Citations: MR 35# 1603 = F55-22.

F55-25 **(35# 1713)**

Godement, R.

The spectral decomposition of cusp-forms.

Algebraic Groups and Discontinuous Subgroups (Proc. Sympos. Pure Math., Boulder, Colo., 1965), *pp.* 225–234. *Amer. Math. Soc., Providence, R.I.*, 1966.

Let G be a connected reductive algebraic linear group defined over **Q**, $G_{\mathbf{R}}$ the set of real points of G and Γ an arithmetic subgroup of G. Let P be a parabolic subgroup of G, U its unipotent radical, and put $U_\Gamma=U_{\mathbf{R}}\cap\Gamma$. A function Φ on $G_{\mathbf{R}}/\Gamma$ is called a cusp-form if $\Phi\in L^2(G_{\mathbf{R}}/\Gamma)$ and if for every unipotent subgroup U which is the unipotent radical of some parabolic subgroup P, one has $\int_{U_{\mathbf{R}}/U_\Gamma}\Phi(gu)\,du=0$ for almost all $g\in G$. The space of cusp-forms is denoted by $L_0{}^2(G_{\mathbf{R}}/\Gamma)$. It is stable under the action induced on it by the left regular action of $G_{\mathbf{R}}$ on $G_{\mathbf{R}}/\Gamma$.

The various group algebras of $G_{\mathbf{R}}$ also act on this space. In this paper, the author studies the action of the group algebra $\mathscr{D}(G_{\mathbf{R}})$ of compactly supported C^∞ functions on $G_{\mathbf{R}}$, on the space $L_0{}^2(G_{\mathbf{R}}/\Gamma)$. The following result is proved. Let $F\in\mathscr{D}(G_{\mathbf{R}})$ and let T_F denote the operator induced on $L_0{}^2(G_{\mathbf{R}}/\Gamma)$ by left convolution by F. Thus, if $\Phi\in L_0{}^2(G_{\mathbf{R}}/\Gamma)$, then $(T_F\Phi)(x)=\int_{G_{\mathbf{R}}}F(xy^{-1})\Phi(y)\,dy$. Then the operator T_F is compact.

This result has the immediate consequence that the representation of $G_{\mathbf{R}}$ on $L_0{}^2(G_{\mathbf{R}}/\Gamma)$ decomposes into a discrete direct sum of irreducible subrepresentations each occurring with finite multiplicity. Once this result is proved for $G_{\mathbf{R}}/\Gamma$, it is relatively easy to deduce a similar result for the space $G_{\mathbf{A}}/G_{\mathbf{Q}}$, where $G_{\mathbf{A}}$ is the adelized group of $G_{\mathbf{Q}}$, and $G_{\mathbf{Q}}$ is regarded as a discrete subgroup of $G_{\mathbf{A}}$ via the diagonal map.

The method of proof is quite direct, and proceeds by first obtaining a majorant for the kernel of the convolution operator T_F when it is regarded as an operator on functions on $G_{\mathbf{R}}/U_\Gamma'$, where U_Γ' is a suitable subgroup of finite index in U_Γ. This estimate is then used to get information on the size of $(T_F\Phi)(x)$. There results an estimate of the form $|(T_F\Phi)(x)|\leqq C_{F,x}\|\Phi\|_{G_{\mathbf{R}}/\Gamma}$ for $\Phi\in L_0{}^2(G_{\mathbf{R}}/\Gamma)$, where $C_{F,x}$ is a constant depending only on F and (continuously) on x. This estimate together with some structure theory leads quickly to the fact that the set

$$\mathscr{E}=\{T_F\Phi\colon\Phi\in L_0{}^2(G_{\mathbf{R}}/\Gamma),\ \|\Phi\|\leqq 1\}$$

is precompact, proving that T_F is a compact operator.

{See also #1712 above.}

R. A. Gangolli (Princeton, N.J.)

Citations: MR 35# 1712 = F70-16.
Referred to in F70-16.

F55-26 **(35# 3010)**

Langlands, R. P.

Dimension of spaces of automorphic forms.

Algebraic Groups and Discontinuous Subgroups (*Proc. Sympos. Pure Math., Boulder, Colo.*, 1965), *pp.* 253–257. *Amer. Math. Soc., Providence, R.I.*, 1966.

This article sketches a method for computing the dimension of certain spaces of automorphic forms, associated with discrete subgroups Γ of semi-simple Lie groups G such that G/Γ is compact. The method is essentially the same as that described (in more detail) in a previous paper by the author [Amer. J. Math. **85** (1963), 99–125; MR **27** #6286]. The article concludes with some interesting conjectures, which generalize a known relationship between representation theory and automorphic forms on the one hand, and the Borel-Weil theorem on the other.

H. Garland (New Haven, Conn.)

F55-27 **(35# 5391)**

Freitag, Eberhard

Modulformen zweiten Grades zum rationalen und Gaußschen Zahlkörper.

S.-B. Heidelberger Akad. Wiss. Math.-Natur. Kl. **1967**, 3–49.

Die in der Literatur behandelten Körper von automorphen Funktionen zu arithmetisch definierten diskontinuierlichen Gruppen sind algebraische Funktionenkörper. Weitergehende Resultate sind bei mehreren Variablen nur in Einzelfällen bekannt. K.-B. Gundlach [Math. Ann. **152** (1963), 226–256; MR **29** #1186] zeigte für verschiedene Hilbertsche Modulgruppen, J.-I. Igusa [Amer. J. Math. **84** (1962), 175–200; MR **25** #5040] und der Verfasser [Nachr. Akad. Wiss. Göttingen Math. Phys. Kl. II **1965**, 151–157; MR **34** #7467] zeigten für die Siegelsche Modulgruppe zweiten Grades die Rationalität des Funktionenkörpers. Verfasser beweist in der vorliegenden Arbeit die Rationalität für die um $Z \to {}^tZ$ erweiterte Hermitesche Modulgruppe zweiten Grades zum Gaußschen Zahlkörper und—in engem Zusammenhang damit—für eine spezielle Siegelsche Paramodulgruppe zweiten Grades. Das entscheidende Hilfsmittel ist eine Hermitesche Modulform vom Gewicht 10, welche als Produkt von Thetareihen konstruiert wird. Ihre Nullstellenmenge N ist vom Typ des Siegelschen Halbraumes zweiten Grades; sämtliche Nullstellen haben die Ordnung 1. Der Zusammenhang mit der erwähnten Paramodulgruppe zweiten Grades ergibt sich aus der Tatsache, daß durch Restriktion von Hermiteschen Modulformen auf N Modulformen zu dieser Paramodulgruppe induziert werden. Hierdurch gelingt die Rückführung der Fragestellung für die Hermitesche Modulgruppe auf eine Gruppe, welche mit der Siegelschen Modulgruppe zweiten Grades kommensurabel ist. Die Untersuchung der Funktionen zu der zuletzt genannten Gruppe kann ähnlich wie bei dem Verfasser [loc. cit.] auf die elliptische Modulgruppe reduziert werden. Die Erzeugenden ergeben sich sämtlich explizit durch Thetareihen.

Bei der Hermiteschen Modulgruppe handelt es sich um Funktionen in vier komplexen Variablen, woraus der prinzipielle Fortschritt und die Erschwernis gegenüber dem früher behandelten Fall (Dimension 3) ersichtlich wird. Darüber hinaus waren bei der Durchführung neue Schwierigkeiten zu überwinden. Zum Beispiel kann das Verschwinden der Thetareihen nicht mehr allein auf Grund ihres Bildungsgesetzes diskutiert werden. Es sind tiefliegende allgemeine Sätze über die Nullstellen von Modulformen heranzuziehen.

H. Klingen (Freiburg)

Citations: MR 25# 5040 = F50-22; MR 29# 1186 = F40-30; MR 34# 7467 = F50-47.

F55-28 **(36# 2834)**

Baily, Walter L., Jr.

Fourier-Jacobi series.

Algebraic Groups and Discontinuous Subgroups (*Proc. Sympos. Pure Math., Boulder, Colo.*, 1965), *pp.* 296–300. *Amer. Math. Soc., Providence, R.I.*, 1966.

Fourier-Jacobi series were introduced by I. I. Pjateckiĭ-Šapiro in § 15 of his book *The geometry of classical domains and the theory of automorphic functions* (Russian) [Fizmatgiz, Moscow, 1961; MR **25** #231; French translation, Dunod, Paris, 1966; MR **33** #5949]. They can be used for the representation of holomorphic automorphic forms on symmetric domains. Here the author discusses them in the context of the more recent work of himself and A. Borel about arithmetic discontinuous groups. He sketches a proof, based largely on ideas of Pjateckiĭ-Šapiro, of the fact that (the case of the unit disc in one variable being excluded) every holomorphic automorphic form of even weight has a limit on every proper rational boundary component, and this limit is again an automorphic form with respect to an arithmetic discontinuous group.

A. Korányi (New York)

Citations: MR 25# 231 = F02-10; MR 33# 5949 = F02-11.

F55-29 **(41# 1649)**

Köhler, Günter

Erweiterungsfähigkeit paramodularer Gruppen.

Nachr. Akad. Wiss. Göttingen Math.-Phys. Kl. II **1967**, 229–238.

Let $T = \mathrm{diag}(t_1, \cdots, t_n)$ with natural numbers t_v dividing t_{v+1} and $t_1 = 1$. The generalized Siegel modular group $\Gamma(T)$ is the group of all $2n$ rowed matrices M satisfying $M^t\begin{pmatrix} 0 & T \\ -T & 0 \end{pmatrix}M = \begin{pmatrix} 0 & T \\ -T & 0 \end{pmatrix}$. If t_n is square-free, all discrete extensions of $\Gamma(T)$ consisting of rational matrices satisfying the same equation have been determined by L. A. Gutnik [Vestnik Leningrad. Univ. Ser. Math. Meh. Astronom. **12** (1957), no. 19, 47–78; MR **20** #6464]. The present author determines such extensions in which $\Gamma(T)$ is a normal subgroup if t_n contains a square factor. They are all contained in one such extension the index of which is a power of 2. He remarks that the determination of non-normal extensions seems difficult.

Furthermore, he simplifies and extends his earlier proof on the separation of points by Eisenstein series [the author, J. Reine Angew. Math. **231** (1968), 47–74; MR **38** #119].

M. Eichler (Basel)

Citations: MR 20# 6464 = E56-16; MR 38# 119 = F50-62.

F55-30 **(41# 2056)**

Eichler, M.

Zur Begründung der Theorie der automorphen Funktionen in mehreren Variablen.

Aequationes Math. **3** (1969), 93–111.

Unter geeigneten Voraussetzungen über den Fundamentalbereich der Gruppe und die Entwickelbarkeit in Fourierreihen (welche für die klassischen Gruppen erfüllt sind), beweist Verfasser zentrale Sätze aus der Theorie automorpher Formen mit teilweise einfacheren Methoden. (A) Es gibt $n+1$ algebraisch unabhängige automorphe Formen (in einem Gebiet des $\mathbf{C}^n$). (B1) Die Dimension des Vektorraumes der automorphen Formen vom Grad h ist $\leq ch^n$. (B2) Die Quotienten automorpher Formen gleichen Grades bilden einen algebraischen Funktionenkörper in n Variablen. (C1) Je $n+1$ algebraisch unabhängige automorphe Formen bilden den Quotientenraum auf einen offenen und dichten Teil einer endlich-blättrigen Überlagerung des n-dimensionalen projektiven Raumes ab.

(C2) Der graduierte Ring der automorphen Formen besitzt ein endliches Erzeugendensystem. (D) Die Siegelschen Modulformen können durch Formen erzeugt werden, deren Fourier-Koeffizienten ganze rationale Zahlen sind. *J. Spilker* (Freiburg)

Referred to in F50-70.

F55-31 (42# 5912)

Hall, Michael H.

On the topological classification of the floors of certain Hilbert fundamental domains.

Proc. Amer. Math. Soc. **28** (1971), 67–70.

Author's summary: "Associated to the field $Q(k^{1/2})$ (k a positive square free integer greater than one), there is a group of transformations of the product of two upper half planes which is analogous to the Hilbert modular group. This group has been shown to have a fundamental domain bounded by a finite number of hypersurfaces. Of particular interest is a subspace of the domain known as the 'floor'. This floor is a quotient space of a fiber bundle over the circle which is determined by the field $Q(k^{1/2})$. The principal result of this paper is that, conversely, the topological type (indeed the homotopy type) of this fiber bundle determines the field $Q(k^{1/2})$ which gives rise to it. This is accomplished by computing the homology groups of the fiber space and showing that the integer k can be determined from these groups." *J. Spilker* (Freiburg)

F55-32 (43# 4762)

Katayama, Koji

On certain zeta-functions attached to the tensor representations of $SL(2, R)$.

Amer. J. Math. **92** (1970), 869–893.

Let M be the symmetric tensor representation of odd degree $\nu > 1$ of $G = SL(2, R)$. Namely M is the matrix representation of G, defined by ${}^t(u_1{}^\nu, u_1{}^{\nu-1}v_1, \cdots, v_1{}^\nu) = M(g){}^t(u^\nu, u^{\nu-1}v, \cdots, v^\nu)$, for $g = \begin{pmatrix} a & b \\ c & d \end{pmatrix}$, where u, v and u_1, v_1 are variables related by the equation

$$\begin{pmatrix} u_1 \\ v_1 \end{pmatrix} = \begin{pmatrix} a & b \\ c & d \end{pmatrix}\begin{pmatrix} u \\ v \end{pmatrix}.$$

Since the representation M leaves an alternating matrix A invariant, M is an isomorphism of G to $G_0 = Sp(A, R)$, the symplectic group of the alternating form A. We take an isomorphism φ defined over Q of $Sp(A, R)$ to the standard symplectic group $Sp((\nu+1)/2, R)$, and we put $\varphi \circ M = N_\varphi$. Take a maximal compact subgroup K_0 of G_0 such that $M(K) \subset K_0$, where $K = SO(2, R)$. Then, M induces an immersion of the upper half plane $H = G/K$ into the homogeneous space G_0/K_0, which is isomorphic with the Siegel half space $\tilde{H}$. The isomorphism is determined by the isomorphism $\varphi: G_0 \cong Sp((\nu+1)/2, R)$. The induced map of H into $\tilde{H}$ is denoted by Φ_φ. The map Φ_φ is equivariant with N_φ: $\Phi_\varphi(gx) = N_\varphi(g)(\Phi_\varphi(x))$. However Φ_φ is not holomorphic. Take arithmetic discontinuous groups Γ of G and Γ_0 in G_0 such that $M(\Gamma) \subset \Gamma_0$. Γ_0 operates on $\tilde{H}$ via φ. If the choice of φ is appropriate, we can choose Γ and Γ_0 in such a way that Γ_0 is a finite index subgroup of Siegel's paramodular group, Γ with finite index in $SL(2, Z)$. By the pull-back process $\Phi_\varphi{}^*: f \to f \circ \Phi_\varphi$, a Γ_0-automorphic form f on $\tilde{H}$ with an automorphic factor $J(\gamma, z)$ goes to a (real analytic) Γ-automorphic form $f_\varphi = f \circ \Phi_\varphi$ on H with the automorphic factor $J_\varphi(\sigma, \tau) = J(M(\sigma), \Phi_\varphi(\tau))$.

The purpose of this paper is to investigate various properties of such automorphic forms f_φ, especially those f_φ for which f is a theta function.

The author first conjectures that if φ is appropriate and $J(\gamma, Z) = \det(CZ + D)$, then J_φ is a product of a certain power of $cz+d$ and a power of $\overline{cz+d}$: and he proves this conjecture for $\nu = 3$ and for $\nu = 5$. Therefore, if this conjecture is true and $\begin{pmatrix} 0 & 1 \\ -1 & 0 \end{pmatrix} \in \Gamma$, then $f_\varphi(-1/iy) = \pm (iy)^k f_\varphi(iy)$. So, by following the same argument as in Hecke's famous works, the author shows that the Mellin transform $\zeta(s, \varphi) = \int_0^\infty f_\varphi(iy) y^{k-1}\, dy$ of f_φ satisfies a functional equation. And even in the case $\begin{pmatrix} 0 & 1 \\ -1 & 0 \end{pmatrix} \notin \Gamma$, the author proves similar formulas by taking a certain vector of theta functions in place of a single theta function.

Moreover he conjectures a formula that expresses $\zeta(s, \varphi)$ as an infinite sum of terms involving Appell-Pochhammer's generalized hypergeometric series in several variables. And he proves the formula, which he calls the "Dirichlet series formula", in the case $\nu = 3$.

Finally he also conjectures a certain formula called the "partial Euler product formula", and proves the formula for $\nu = 3$.

He makes a vague suggestion about the possibility of defining a new kind of "zeta-functions" which are perhaps not Dirichlet series, but series of sums of values at lattice points of fundamental solutions of differential equations whose coefficients involve the parameter s.

M. Kuga (Stony Brook, N.Y.)

F60 HECKE-PETERSSON OPERATORS, DIFFERENTIAL OPERATORS, TRACE FORMULA (SEVERAL VARIABLES)

See also reviews E56-56, E68-27, F40-6, F40-8, F40-27, F40-59, F50-7, F50-9, F55-4, F55-14, F65-16, R54-33.

F60-1 (13, 823g)

Maass, Hans. Die Primzahlen in der Theorie der Siegelschen Modulfunktionen. Math. Ann. **124**, 87–122 (1951).

In the Hecke-Petersson theory of modular forms, a set of operators $\{T(m)\}$ is introduced each of which maps the family $\mathfrak{M}_k{}^{(1)}$ of modular forms of dimension $-k$ ($k \geqq 4$ and even) into itself. An end result is the theorem that it is possible to select a finite set of modular forms which constitutes a basis for $\mathfrak{M}_k{}^{(1)}$ and at the same time are eigenfunctions of $\{T_m\}$. Furthermore, the eigenvalues are Fourier coefficients of the basis functions and possess a multiplicative arithmetic property.

In the present paper the author makes an attempt to construct a similar theory for the Siegel modular forms of degree n. (For concepts and definitions, see Siegel, Math. Ann. **116**, 617–657 (1939); these Rev. **1**, 203; and Maass, ibid. **123**, 125–151 (1951); these Rev. **13**, 210.) First he defines a generalized operator $\tau(m)$:

$$f(Z) \mid \tau(m) = c_{nk}(m) \sum f(Z) \mid \sigma,$$

where f is a modular form of dimension $-k$ and degree n, m is a positive integer, the $C_{nk}(m)$ are certain constants chosen so that in particular $\tau(m)$ reduces to $T(m)$ when $n = 1$, σ runs over a set of representatives of the cosets of the modular group of degree n in the set of substitutions of order m, and

$$f(Z) \Big| \sigma = f(Z) \Big| \begin{pmatrix} A & B \\ C & D \end{pmatrix} = f(\sigma(Z)) \mid CZ + D \mid^{-k}.$$

(σ is of order m if $\sigma' i \sigma = mi$, where

$$i=\begin{pmatrix} 0 & E \\ -E & 0 \end{pmatrix},$$

and the entries in A, B, C, D are integers.) The author restricts himself to the case $m=p$, prime, and must assume $k\geqq 2n+2$ in order to insure the convergence of the Poincaré series used in the proof.

The set $\mathfrak{M}_k^{(n)}$ of modular forms of dimension $-k$ and degree n is made into a metric space by means of the Petersson scalar product which Maass has generalized in the paper quoted above. Let $\mathfrak{S}_k^{(n)}$ denote the family of cusp forms in $\mathfrak{M}_k^{(n)}$; $\mathfrak{N}_k^{(n)}$, the orthogonal complement of $\mathfrak{S}_k^{(n)}$. The Siegel operator Φ:

$$f(Z)\,|\,\Phi=\lim_{\lambda\to\infty} f\begin{pmatrix} Z^* & \mathfrak{n} \\ \mathfrak{n}' & i\lambda \end{pmatrix},$$

maps $\mathfrak{M}_k^{(n)}$ onto $\mathfrak{M}_k^{(n-1)}$. Maass proves the existence of a unique decomposition $\mathfrak{M}_k^{(n)}=\mathfrak{S}_{k,0}^{(n)}+\cdots+\mathfrak{S}_{k,n-1}^{(n)}+\mathfrak{S}_k^{(n)}$, such that $\mathfrak{S}_{k,0}^{(n)}+\cdots+\mathfrak{S}_{k,j}^{(n)}$ is mapped one-to-one onto $\mathfrak{M}_k^{(j)}$ by Φ^{n-j}, $0\leqq j\leqq n-1$. Interest centers on $\mathfrak{S}_{k,0}^{(n)}+\mathfrak{S}_{k,1}^{(n)}$, the set mapped by Φ^{n-1} on $\mathfrak{M}_k^{(1)}$, the space of the usual modular forms. The author next establishes the commutativity $\Phi\tau(p)=\tau(p)\Phi$. This step requires a long, complicated proof.

According to the Petersson theory mentioned earlier [cf. Math. Ann. **116**, 401–412 (1939)] there exist eigenfunctions $f_\nu\,|\,\tau(p)=a_\nu(p)f_\nu$, $\nu=1,2,\cdots,\rho_1$. Define the forms g_ν by $g_\nu\,|\,\Phi^{n-1}=f_\nu$, $\nu=1,2,\cdots,\rho_1$; these functions lie in $\mathfrak{S}_{k,0}^{(n)}+\mathfrak{S}_{k,1}^{(n)}$ and constitute a basis thereof. We have then

$$g_\nu\,|\,\tau(p)\Phi^{n-1}=[g_\nu\,|\,\Phi^{n-1}]\,|\,\tau(p)=f_\nu\,|\,\tau(p)$$
$$=a_\nu(p)f_\nu=a_\nu(p)g_\nu\,|\,\Phi^{n-1},$$

from which it follows that (*) $g_\nu\,|\,\tau(p)=a_\nu(p)g_\nu$, $1\leqq\nu\leqq\rho_1$, i.e., the g_ν are eigenfunctions of the set $\{\tau(p)\}$. The $\{a_\nu(p)\}$ are Fourier coefficients of f_ν; therefore, of g_ν. These three properties characterize the g_ν to within a multiplicative factor. By expanding both sides of (*) into Fourier series the author obtains a complicated equation $a_\nu(p)a_\nu(T)=\cdots$, which is intended to generalize the multiplication law $a_\nu(r)a_\nu(s)=\sum_{d\,|\,(r,s)}a_\nu(rs/d^2)\cdot d^{k-1}$ of the Hecke theory. For the case $n=2$, which is treated in detail in the last section of the paper and without the restriction $m=p$, the multiplication law is obtained in a simple form. *J. Lehner.*

Citations: MR 1, 203f = F50-1; MR 13, 210a = F50-4.

Referred to in F50-9.

F60-2 (19, 531g)

Selberg, A. Harmonic analysis and discontinuous groups in weakly symmetric Riemannian spaces with applications to Dirichlet series. J. Indian Math. Soc. (N.S.) **20** (1956), 47–87.

This article outlines an extensive theory concerning certain eigenvalue problems and Dirichlet series associated with a group G of isometries of a Riemannian space S. The metric $ds^2=\sum g_{ij}dx^idx^j$ of S is to be positive definite, the g_{ij} being analytic in the $x^1,\cdots,x^n$. G is to be locally compact and must act transitively on S, but need not be the full group of isometries. The eigenvalue problems relate to linear operators L on functions $f(x)$ defined for $x\in S$. Such an L is termed invariant if it commutes with the operation $f(x)\to f(mx)$ for all $m\in G$. An integral L of the form $Lf(x)=\int_S k(x,y)f(y)dy$, where dy is the invariant volume element derived from the metric, is invariant if k is a "point-pair invariant", i.e., if $k(mx,my)=k(x,y)$ for all $x,y\in S$, $m\in G$. Invariant differential operators are constructed first at some $x_0\in S$, at which point they are equivalent to a ring of polynomials in $\partial/\partial x^1,\cdots,\partial/\partial x^n$ with constant coefficients, subject to invariance under a certain group of orthogonal transformations; they can then be extended to the whole of S by the rule $[Lf(x)]_{x=mx_0}=[Lf(mx)]_{x=x_0}$. For this ring there exists at least one minimal basis $D_1,\cdots,D_l$. Since further developments depend on the commutativity of the invariant operators, a sufficient condition to ensure this is postulated, namely that S is "weakly symmetric". There is to be a fixed isometry μ of S, such that $\mu G\mu^{-1}=G$, $\mu^2\in G$, with the property that for any $x,y\in S$ there is an $m\in G$ such that $mx=\mu y$ and $my=\mu x$. This requirement is in fact weaker than that of symmetry in the sense of E. Cartan.

An eigenfunction $f(x)$ is to be a simultaneous solution of $D_if(x)=\lambda_if(x)$ $(i=1,\cdots,l)$ for some set of constants λ_i; when suitably normed and symmetrised it is uniquely fixed by the λ_i. It is necessarily also an eigenfunction of any other invariant L, so that $Lf(x)=\Lambda(\lambda_1,\cdots,\lambda_l)f(x)$. Eigenfunctions can be given explicitly if one assumes there to exist a subgroup T of G which is simply transitive on S, and also functions $\phi(t)$ on T such that $\phi(t_1t_2)=\phi(t_1)\phi(t_2)$.

The first section of the article concludes by illustrating the concepts so far introduced by the case in which S is the space of positive definite symmetric n by n matrices $Y=(y_{ij})$ with the metric $ds^2=\sigma(Y^{-1}dY\,Y^{-1}dY)$, $\sigma=$trace, and the isometries G are $Y\to AYA'$, where A is any real non-singular n by n matrix, A' being its transpose; μ is taken as $Y\to Y^{-1}$. For this case the author sketches the mode of calculation of the eigenvalues of integral operators, making contact with an investigation of H. Maass [same J. **19** (1955), 1–23; MR **17**, 588].

The next stage is to consider a discrete subgroup Γ of G, whose action on S is properly discrete; let $\mathscr{D}$ be a fundamental domain of Γ in S. Let $\chi(M)$, $M\in\Gamma$, be a representation of Γ by ν by ν matrices, and consider ν-vectors or column matrices $F(x)$, $x\in S$, such that $F(Mx)=\chi(M)f(x)$. The formula

$$\int_S k(x,y)F(y)dy=\int_{\mathscr{D}}K(x,y;\chi)F(y)dy$$

where $K(x,y;\chi)=\sum_{M\in\Gamma}\chi(M)k(x,My)$ leads to a study of the latter integral operator in the Hilbert space of $F(x)$ with inner product $(F_1,F_2)=\int_{\mathscr{D}}\bar{F}_1'(x)F_2(x)dx$, where $\bar{F}_1'$ is the conjugate transpose of F_1.

Under certain conditions, including the compactness of $\mathscr{D}$, one has an eigenfunction expansion of $K(x,y;\chi)$ of the form $\sum_{M\in\Gamma}\chi(M)k(x,My)=\sum_i h(\lambda^i)F_i(x)\bar{F}_i'(y)$, where $\lambda^i=\lambda_1^i,\cdots,\lambda_l^i$, and the F_i are eigenfunctions of the $D_1,\cdots,D_l$. Taking the trace of this identity, and transforming the right-hand side into a sum over conjugacy classes in Γ, the author obtains the "trace-formula" ((2.12), p. 67), constituting the centre of his investigation; it may be used to investigate the distribution of either the λ^i or the conjugacy classes in Γ, and may also be viewed as a generalisation of the Poisson summation formula. The section concludes with a brief account of generalisations, one in connection with the Hecke operator for the modular group, and the other concerning the case in which $\mathscr{D}$ has finite volume but is not compact, when the spectrum may cease to be discrete.

The remainder of the paper deals with special cases. There is first the case when S is the hyperbolic plane $z=x+iy$, $y>0$, with the metric $ds^2=y^{-2}(dx^2+dy^2)$, and the isometries of G are $z\to(az+b)/(cz+d)$, $ad-bc=1$, a, b, c and d real. The eigenfunctions have the form y^s, the point-pair invariants the form $k(z,z')=k(|z-z'|^2/(yy'))$; formulae concerning the eigenvalues are also given.

The trace-formula is given in full for the case in which Γ has a compact $\mathscr{D}$, and leads to the consideration of the zeta-function

$$Z_\Gamma(s;\chi)=\prod_{\{P\}_\Gamma}\prod_{k=0}^{\infty}|E_\nu-\chi(P)(N\{P\})^{-s-k}|,$$

for $\Re\{s\}>1$, where E_ν is the ν by ν identity matrix, $|\cdot|$ indicates the determinant, the first product is taken over a set of representatives, one from each primitive hyperbolic conjugacy class $\{P\}_\Gamma$ of Γ, and the norm $N\{P\}$ is derived from that element of the conjugacy class which is a pure magnification. $Z_\Gamma(s;\chi)$ and $Z_\Gamma(1-s;\chi)$ are connected by a functional equation. The complex zeros have real part $\frac{1}{2}$. After discussing modifications required when $\mathscr{D}$ is not compact, the author discusses other special spaces S. Some details are given for the case in which S is the space of 3 by 3 symmetric matrices with determinant unity, Γ is the group of 3 by 3 matrices with determinant unity and integral rational elements; there arises the Dirichlet series in two variables

$$\sum (X'YX)^{-s}(Z'Y^{-1}Z)^{-s'}=\zeta_Y(s,s'),$$

where the summation is over pairs of column vectors X, Z with integral rational components subject to $X'X>0$, $Z'Z>0$, $X'Z=0$. This series satisfies four functional equations. Generalisations are indicated.

The final section of the paper deals with the space (z,ϕ), $z=x+iy$, $y>0$, ϕ being identified with $\phi+2\pi$. The group G has elements m_α, where

$$m_\alpha(z,\phi)=((az+b)/(cz+d),\ \phi+\arg(cz+d)+\alpha),$$

where a, b, c and d are as before; a suitable metric is $ds^2=y^{-2}(dx^2+dy^2)+(d\phi-\frac{1}{2}y^{-1}dx)^2$. The author outlines the argument leading to formulae for the number of analytic automorphic forms of various classes. The special case of one-dimensional $\chi(M)$, together with the generalisation leading to Hecke operators, yields a formula for the trace of this operator acting on the space of cusp-forms of dimension $-k$, a special case being an explicit formula for Ramanujan's function $\tau(n)$. Extensions are indicated to spaces of higher dimensionality.

F. V. Atkinson (Canberra).

Citations: MR 17, 588e = F65-11.

Referred to in E68-27, F02-10, F02-13, F15-23, F15-34, F25-13, F25-16, F25-19, F25-21, F60-3, F60-5.

F60-3 (21# 1954)

Kuga, Michio. Topological analysis and its applications in weakly symmetric Riemannian spaces. (Introduction to the work of A. Selberg.) Sûgaku **9** (1957/58), 166–185. (Japanese)

This is the reproduction in Japanese, with several remarks, of a work of A. Selberg [J. Indian Math. Soc. (N.S.) **20** (1956), 47–87; MR **19**, 531]. *K. Yano* (Tokyo)

Citations: MR 19, 531g = F60-2.

F60-4 (23# A958)

Tamagawa, Tsuneo

On Selberg's trace formula.

J. Fac. Sci. Univ. Tokyo Sect. I **8** (1960), 363–386.

This article presents a self-contained exposition and a broad generalization of Selberg's trace formula (for the case of discrete subgroups with compact quotient) within the framework of the theory of locally compact groups. By aiming straight at that formula, and by-passing all considerations on differential operators, unitary representations, etc., while making use of some ideas originated by Gelfand and by Godement, the author succeeds in giving a concise and beautifully direct proof of his main result, which will now be described. Let G be a unimodular locally compact group, and U a compact subgroup of G; call $C(G,U)$ the set of continuous functions on G satisfying $f(x)=f(uxu')$ for all $x\in G$, $u\in U$, $u'\in U$, and $L(G,U)$ the set of functions $f\in C(G,U)$ with compact support; assume that convolution is commutative in $L(G,U)$; then the closure $L_1(G,U)$ of $L(G,U)$ in $L_1(G)$ (the algebra of integrable functions on G) is a commutative normed algebra; this has a unit (the characteristic function of U) if U is compact; in that case, put $A(G,U)=L_1(G,U)$; otherwise, call $A(G,U)$ the commutative normed algebra obtained by adding a unit element to $L_1(G,U)$. As in I. Gelfand, Dokl. Akad. Nauk SSSR **70** (1950), 5–8 [MR **11**, 498], say that a function $\omega\in C(G,U)$ is zonal spherical if the mapping $f\to\hat\omega(f)=\int f(x^{-1})\omega(x)dx$ is a homomorphism of the algebra $L(G,U)$ into the complex number-field; such functions are characterized by the functional equation $\int_U \omega(xuy)du=\omega(x)\omega(y)$, where du is normalized by $\int_U du=1$. Call $\mathfrak{S}$ the set of all zonal spherical functions (other than 0), $\mathfrak{S}_1$ the set of those which are bounded, $\mathfrak{P}$ the set of those which are positive-definite; there is a one-to-one correspondence between $\mathfrak{S}_1$ and the set of all maximal ideals other than $L_1(G,U)$ in $A(G,U)$; by Gelfand's theory of normed algebras, there is, to every $f\neq 0$ in $L(G,U)$, an $\omega\in\mathfrak{S}_1$ such that $\hat\omega(f)\neq 0$. For the usual "weak" topology (the weakest one making every function $\omega\to\hat\omega(f)$ continuous), $\mathfrak{S}_1$ is closed in $\mathfrak{S}$ and locally compact (compact if U is open in G), and $\mathfrak{P}$ is closed in $\mathfrak{S}_1$. Say that a continuous function φ on G is right-spherical if $\varphi(ux)=\varphi(x)$ for all $u\in U$, $x\in G$, and if it is an eigenfunction of the operator $T_f\colon \varphi\to f*\varphi$ for every $f\in L(G,U)$; then there is a zonal spherical function ω such that $\int_U \varphi(xuy)du=\varphi(x)\omega(y)$; φ is said to belong to ω. Now let Γ be a discrete subgroup of G, such that G/Γ is compact; the author calls a function φ on G automorphic if it is right-spherical (for U) and satisfies $\varphi(x\gamma)=\varphi(x)$ for all $x\in G$, $\gamma\in\Gamma$; it is shown that, when φ is such, the zonal spherical function to which φ belongs is positive-definite. Let H be the Hilbert space $L_2(G/\Gamma)$; this consists of the functions on G which are locally square integrable and satisfy $f(x\gamma)=f(x)$ for $x\in G$, $\gamma\in\Gamma$, with the norm $(\int_{G/\Gamma}|f(x)|^2dx)^{1/2}$; the functions $f\in H$ invariant under U operating on G/Γ, i.e., satisfying $f(ux)=f(x)$ for $u\in U$, $x\in G$, make up a closed subspace H_0 of H. For every $f\in L(G,U)$, the operator $K_f\colon g\to f*g$ on H is normal and completely continuous; it is given by

$$(K_fg)(x)=\int_{G/\Gamma}k_f(x,y)g(y)\,dy,$$

with the continuous kernel $k_f(x,y)=\sum_{\gamma\in\Gamma}f(x\gamma y^{-1})$; it maps H into H_0. In particular, the operators K_f induce on H_0 a commutative algebra of completely continuous normal operators. Call $\Lambda(G)$ the set of all zonal spherical functions ω on G such that the space $M(\omega)$ of automorphic functions belonging to ω has a dimension $m(\omega)>0$. Then each $M(\omega)$ has a finite dimension; the $M(\omega)$ are mutually orthogonal and span H_0; they provide a complete decomposition of H_0 for the operators K_f; moreover, if ω_0 is the constant 1, $M(\omega_0)$ consists of the constant functions on G. The trace-formula is now:

$$\sum_\omega m(\omega)\cdot\hat\omega(f)=\sum_\alpha \mu(G_\alpha/\Gamma_\alpha)\cdot\int_{G/G_\alpha}f(x\alpha x^{-1})\,d_\alpha\bar x;$$

here the summation in the left-hand side is over all $\omega\in\Lambda(G)$; the summation in the right-hand side is over a complete set of representatives α for the classes of conjugate elements in Γ; for each α, G_α is the group of the elements of G which commute with α; $\Gamma_\alpha=\Gamma\cap G_\alpha$; in the integral, $f(x\alpha x^{-1})$ is considered as a function of $\bar x=xG_\alpha\in G/G_\alpha$; $d_\alpha\bar x$ is an invariant measure in G/G_α (for G operating on G/G_α); $\mu(G_\alpha/\Gamma_\alpha)=\int_{G_\alpha/\Gamma_\alpha}d_\alpha'y$, where $d_\alpha'y$ is the invariant measure on G_α satisfying (in an obvious sense) the symbolic equation $dx=d_\alpha\bar x\cdot d_\alpha'y$; $\mu(G_\alpha/\Gamma_\alpha)$ is finite (and consequently G_α is unimodular, and $d_\alpha\bar x$ exists) because G_α/Γ_α is compact. The trace-formula is valid under the following conditions: (i) the left-hand side is absolutely convergent; (ii) $f\in C(G,U)\cap L_1(G,U)$; (iii) the series $k_f(x,y)=\sum_\gamma f(x\gamma y^{-1})$ is absolutely convergent, uniformly on every compact subset of $G\times G$. Poisson's formula is the special case when G is commutative and $U=\{e\}$. The paper also contains a number of useful auxiliary results, and a discussion of zonal spherical functions on products and on restricted infinite products of the type occurring in the theory of adele groups, thus paving the ground for applications to such groups which are to be developed later. The article is marred by a number of misprints (none of which should give serious trouble to an attentive reader).

A. Weil (Princeton, N.J.)

Referred to in R54-33.

F60-5 **(23# A3790)**

Kuga, Michio

On a uniformity of distribution of 0-cycles and the eigenvalues of Hecke's operators. I, II.

Sci. Papers Coll. Gen. Ed. Univ. Tokyo **10** (1960), 1–16, 171–186.

By a positive 0-cycle Z of degree $d=\deg(Z)$ in a space X, understand a formal sum of d points of X, or in other words, any formal sum $Z=\sum n_ix_i$ of points $x_i\in X$ with integral coefficients $n_i\geqq 0$ such that $\sum n_i=d$; write $f(Z)=\sum n_if(x_i)$ if f is any function on X. If (Z_λ) is any sequence (or direct family) of such cycles, and if $\lim \deg(Z_\lambda)^{-1}f(Z_\lambda)=\int f\cdot d\mu$ (where μ is a measure on X) for every continuous function f with compact support on X, one says that (Z_λ) is uniformly distributed with respect to μ. Now let Γ be a discrete subgroup of the group G operating on a weakly symmetric Riemannian space in the sense of Selberg's theory [J. Indian Math. Soc. (N.S.) **20** (1956), 47–87; MR **19**, 531]; assume that G/Γ is compact. Take for X the compact quotient-space $\Gamma\backslash S$ of S by the equivalence relation determined by Γ; it will be understood that μ is always the measure determined on X by the invariant measure in S. By a "positive M-correspondence", the author understands any formal finite sum $\Omega=\sum m_i\cdot(\Gamma\alpha_i\Gamma)$, with integral coefficients $m_i\geqq 0$, of double cosets $\Gamma\alpha_i\Gamma$, each of which is a finite union of right cosets and also a finite union of left cosets of Γ in G; because of this, one can also write $\Omega=\sum n_j\cdot(\Gamma\beta_j)$; put $\#(\Omega)=\sum n_j$. Then, for every $x\in X$, one can define in an obvious manner the positive 0-cycle Ωx, of degree $\#(\Omega)$, on X. If H is the Hilbert space $L^2(X)$, Ω determines the bounded operator $F(x)\to F(\Omega x)$ on H; this is a generalization of the Hecke operators. The author now considers a sequence (or a directed family) (Ω_λ) of correspondences, such that the operators $T_\lambda: F(x)\to F(\Omega_\lambda x)$ on H are normal and commute with each other. Then one can find for H an orthonormal basis (F_ν), where each F_ν is an eigenfunction of all the T_λ and also of all the invariant differential operators on S, and where $F_0=1$. It is shown that the following two assertions are equivalent: (a) for every $x\in X$, the cycles $\Omega_\lambda x$ are uniformly distributed; (b) for every $\nu\neq 0$, $\lim d_\lambda^{-1}\cdot(T_\lambda F_\nu)/F_\nu=0$, where $d_\lambda=\#(\Omega_\lambda)$; $(T_\lambda/F_\nu)/F_\nu$ is, of course, the eigenvalue of T_λ for the eigenfunction F_ν. This is then applied to the following two examples. Let A be an indefinite quaternion algebra over the rational number-field Q; let $\mathfrak{o}$ be a maximal order of A, and call E the group of the units of $\mathfrak{o}$ with norm $+1$. By identifying A_R (the extension of A by the real number-field) with $M_2(R)$ (the algebra of real 2×2 matrices), one identifies the group A_+ of elements with positive norm in A with a subgroup of $GL^+(2, R)$, the group of real 2×2 matrices M with $\det M>0$; putting $\psi(M)=(\det M)^{-1/2}\cdot M$, we get a homomorphism ψ of A_+ into $G_0=SL(2, R)$; this induces on E an isomorphism of E onto a discrete subgroup $\Gamma_0=\psi(E)$ of G_0, such that G_0/Γ_0 is compact. Now consider the two cases: (A) Take $G=G_0$, $\Gamma=\Gamma_0$, and let G (the hyperbolic group) operate on the upper half-plane S in the usual manner; (B) Take $G=G_0\times K_0$, where K_0 is the subgroup $SO(2, R)$ of G_0; take $\Gamma=\Gamma_0\times\{1\}$; take $S=G_0$, and let G operate on S by $(\sigma, k)u=\sigma uk^{-1}$ [cf. Selberg, loc. cit., p. 81]. For every integer $m>0$, call $\Omega(m)$ the set of the elements $\psi(\alpha)$ in case (A), respectively $(\psi(\alpha), 1)$ in case (B), when one takes for α all the elements of $\mathfrak{o}$ with the norm m. The main result of the author is that, for every prime p not dividing the discriminant D of A, the correspondences $\Omega(p^\lambda)$, for $\lambda=1, 2, \cdots$, satisfy the condition (b) above, hence also (a), so that they determine uniformly distributed sequences of 0-cycles, both in case (A) and in case (B). Some of the lemmas involved in this are of independent interest; in particular, the author determines the eigenfunctions of the ring of the invariant differential operators in the space H for the case (B) in terms of the solution of the corresponding problem in case (A) and of the automorphic forms for the group Γ in the usual sense. He also observes that (with a suitable adjustment of the concept of "uniform distribution" to the case of 0-cycles of infinite degree) the final result for case (B) can be described by saying that the $\Omega(p^\lambda)$ themselves, considered as subsets of G_0, are uniformly distributed with respect to the Haar measure. As a consequence, let $F(x)=x_0^2+dx_1^2+qx_2^2+dqx_3^2$ be the norm-form of A (d, q are negative integers, and d is not the norm of a number in $Q(q^{1/2})$); the hypersurface $F=1$ is nothing else than the multiplicative group of elements of norm 1 in A_R, which is isomorphic to G_0; for any integer $m>0$, call $S(m)$ the set of all rational solutions of $F(x)=1$ such that the mx_i are integers; then, for every prime p not dividing $2dq$, the sets $S(p^\lambda)$, for $\lambda=1, 2, \cdots$, are (in the modified sense mentioned above) uniformly distributed with respect to the Haar measure on $F=1$. *A. Weil* (Princeton, N.J.)

Citations: MR 19, 531g = F60-2.

F60-6 **(28# 5197)**

Shimizu, Hideo

On traces of Hecke operators.

J. Fac. Sci. Univ. Tokyo Sect. I **10**, 1–19 (1963).

Let $\mathfrak{F}_n$ be the product of n copies of the complex plane minus the real axis, on which the product G of n copies of the group $\mathbf{GL}(2, \mathbf{R})$ of 2×2 invertible real matrices acts in the obvious way. Let Γ be a subgroup of G which is properly discontinuous on F_n, χ a finite-dimensional unitary representation of Γ with kernel of finite index and α an element of G such that $\alpha\Gamma\alpha^{-1}\cap\Gamma$ has finite intersection in Γ and $\alpha\Gamma\alpha^{-1}$. It is assumed that the intersection of Γ with the identity component of G has, on the product of the n upper half-planes, a fundamental domain satisfying condition (F) of a previous paper [Ann. of Math. (2) **77** (1963), 33–71; MR **26** #2641]. One main purpose of the paper is to compute the trace of the Hecke operator $\mathfrak{T}(\Gamma\alpha\Gamma)$ on the space of cusp forms with values in the representation space of χ for an automorphy factor which is a product of n factors of the form $(\dot{c}z+d)^{-k}|\det\gamma|^{-k/2}$. For this, the author uses the known projector from square integrable automorphic forms to cusp forms [cf. Godement, Séminaire H. Cartan, 1957/1958, Exp. 8, Secrétariat mathématique, Paris, 1958; MR **21** #2750], the trace formula, and evaluates the integrals occurring in the latter. He then considers the case where Γ is the group of units of a maximal order in an indefinite quaternion algebra over a totally real number field and computes the trace of the operator $\mathfrak{T}(\mathfrak{q})$ introduced by Shimura [Ann. of Math. (2) **76** (1962), 237–294].

A. Borel (Princeton, N.J.)

Citations: MR 21# 2750 = F02-5; MR 26# 2641 = F55-14.

Referred to in R52-23.

F60-7 **(31# 372)**

Selberg, Atle

Discontinuous groups and harmonic analysis.

Proc. Internat. Congr. Mathematicians (*Stockholm*, 1962), *pp.* 177–189. *Inst. Mittag-Leffler, Djursholm*, 1963.

A survey of some results and problems related to certain rings of integral operators that arise naturally when a discontinuous group is allowed to operate on a symmetric Riemannian space.

Referred to in F60-9, F65-31.

F60-8 **(37# 158)**

Andrianov, A. N.

Shimura's hypothesis for Siegel's modular group of genus 3. (Russian)

Dokl. Akad. Nauk SSSR **177** (1967), 755–758.

Ausgehend vom ursprünglichen Ansatz der Theorie der Hecke-Operatoren zur rationalen Modulgruppe hat G. Shimura [Proc. Nat. Acad. Sci. U.S.A. **49** (1963), 824–828; MR **28** #250] für die Siegelsche Modulgruppe n-ten Grades Γ folgendes bewiesen. S sei die Menge der $2n$-reihigen quadratischen Matrizen B, für die ${}^TBJB=r(B)J$ mit einer von der betreffenden Matrix B abhängigen ganzen rationalen Zahl $r(B)$ ist. Führt man in dem freien **Z**-Modul, der von den Doppelnebenklassen $\Gamma B\Gamma$ mit $B\in S$ erzeugt wird, in geeigneter Weise eine Multiplikation ein, so erhält man einen Integritätsbereich, und die formale Dirichletreihe $D(s)=\sum(\Gamma B\Gamma)r(B)^{-s}$ besitzt ein Eulerprodukt (die Summation ist über die Doppelnebenklassen zu erstrecken). Im Eulerprodukt treten die lokalen Dirichletreihen $D_p(s)$ auf, die man erhält, indem man nur über die $\Gamma B\Gamma$ summiert, für die $r(B)$ eine Potenz der Primzahl p ist. Shimura vermutete, daß $D_p(s)=E(p^{-s})F(p^{-s})^{-1}$ ist mit Polynomen E und F vom Grade 2^n-2 und 2^n und bewies diese Vermutung für $n=2$, indem er E und F explizit bestimmte (für $n=1$ stammt das entsprechende Ergebnis schon von Hecke). Verfasser beweist die Vermutung von Shimura für $n=3$, indem er auch hier E und F explizit ausrechnet.

{This article has appeared in English translation [Soviet Math. Dokl. **8** (1967), 1474–1478].}

K.-B. Gundlach (Münster)

Citations: MR 28# 250 = F50-24.

F60-9 **(38# 1216)**

Harish-Chandra

Automorphic forms on semisimple Lie groups.

Notes by J. G. M. Mars. Lecture Notes in Mathematics, No. 62.

Springer-Verlag, Berlin-New York, 1968. x+138 *pp.* *DM* 14.00; $3.50.

From Harish-Chandra's preface: "These lectures are largely based on an important but, unfortunately, as yet unpublished, manuscript of R. P. Langlands, with the title 'On the functional equations satisfied by Eisenstein series'. However, they do not cover the last and the most difficult part (Chapter VII) of this manuscript. Langlands himself has given a brief account of his work in a short paper [*Algebraic groups and discontinuous subgroups*, (Proc. Sympos. Pure Math., Boulder, Colo., 1965), pp. 235–252, Amer. Math. Soc., Providence, R.I., 1966].

"In the last ten years, the analytic theory of automorphic forms has been pushed forward mainly through the contributions of Atle Selberg, I. M. Gel'fand and I. I. Pjateckiĭ-Šapiro, and Langlands. In my opinion, here Selberg's ideas were decisive. But since only a very sketchy account of Selberg's work is available [Proc. Internat. Congr. Mathematicians (Stockholm, 1962), 177–189, Inst. Mittag-Leffler, Djursholm, 1963; MR **31** #372], they have not attracted the notice which they undoubtedly deserve. After some of the arithmetic aspects of the theory of discontinuous groups began to be understood, it became clear that one needed analytical tools, in order to apply this newly acquired knowledge to the theory of automorphic forms. It is here that Langlands succeeded in adapting and extending Selberg's methods so as to fit them to the more general situation.

"Let me now give an outline of the main steps which lead to the analytic continuation and the functional equations of the Eisenstein series. (1) Definition of the space of cusp forms and proof of the theorem of Gel'fand and Pjateckiĭ-Šapiro which says that for any $\alpha\in C_c^\infty(G)$, the operator ${}^0\lambda(\alpha)$ is compact (Theorem 2, § 2, Chapter I). We also verify that $\dim\mathscr{A}(G/\Gamma,\alpha,\chi)<\infty$ (Theorem 1, § 2, Chapter I) and prove a simple but important result of Langlands (Theorem 4, § 5, Chapter I). (2) Definition and elementary properties of Eisenstein series corresponding to a cuspidal subgroup P of rank q. In particular we show that this series lies in $\mathscr{A}_q(G/\Gamma,\sigma)$ (see §§ 4, 8, Chapter II). Also we derive a certain scalar product formula (Lemma 40). (3) Given $f\in\mathscr{A}_q(G/\Gamma,\sigma)$, we obtain an estimate for $|f|$ in terms of its constant terms f_P corresponding to the cuspidal subgroups P of rank q (Theorems 6 and 6′ of Chapter III). (4) The Maass-Selberg relations for forms of type 1. Previously Selberg has considered these relations only in the case $l=1$ ($l=\operatorname{rank}_Q G$). But Langlands found, for arbitrary l, a dissection of G/Γ into disjoint sets, which imitates Selberg's method of cutting off the cusps. By using this dissection, it becomes possible to extend Selberg's ideas to the case $l>1$ (§§1, 2, Chapter IV). (5) Proof of the analytic continuation and the functional equation of the Eisenstein series of type 1. Here we follow the method of Selberg (§§ 5–8, Chapter IV). (6) An induction on $q=\operatorname{rank} P$, which enables us to obtain similar results for Eisenstein series of type q (Theorems 8 and 9, § 2, Chapter V). This is entirely due to Langlands."

J. G. M. Mars' introduction: "Let G be a connected semisimple Lie group with finite center, and let Γ be a closed subgroup of G, which we assume to be unimodular. Let μ denote the invariant measure on G/Γ. We have the obvious representation λ of G on $L_2(G/\Gamma)=L_2(G/\Gamma,\mu)$. The main problem here is to carry out, as explicitly as possible, the reduction of λ. Let K be a maximal compact subgroup of G. In case $\Gamma=K$, this problem has been solved. Similarly if $\Gamma=\{1\}$, it has been more or less solved. (It is then essentially the same problem as the explicit determination of the Plancherel formula.)

"Let $\mathscr{E}$ be the set of all equivalence classes of irreducible unitary representations of G. Fix $\omega\in\mathscr{E}$. We say that an element $f\in L_2(G/\Gamma)$ is of type ω if the smallest closed invariant subspace V_f of $L_2(G/\Gamma)$ containing f is irreducible under λ and the corresponding representation λ_f lies in ω. Let $\mathscr{H}_\omega$ be the smallest closed subspace of $L_2(G/\Gamma)$ containing all elements of type ω. Then $\mathscr{H}_\omega$ can be written as an orthogonal sum of irreducible subspaces. Let $m(\omega)$ denote the number of irreducible subspaces in this sum. Then $m(\omega)$ is called the multiplicity of ω in λ. It is an important problem to compute $m(\omega)$.

"ω is said to occur discretely in λ if $m(\omega)>0$. For example, if G is not compact and $\Gamma=K$, $m(\omega)=0$ for all ω and therefore λ has no discrete components. If $\Gamma=\{1\}$, the discrete components occur if and only if G has a compact Cartan subgroup. Moreover, one then knows which discrete components occur. Finally, $m(\omega)=\infty$ for every discrete component ω, provided G is not compact.

"A class $\omega\in\mathscr{E}$ is said to be L_p ($p=1,2$) if some matrix coefficient of ω lies in $L_p(G)$. If Γ is a discrete subgroup of G such that G/Γ is compact, then $m(\omega)<\infty$ for every ω and $L_2(G/\Gamma)=\mathrm{Cl}(\sum_\omega\mathscr{H}_\omega)$. Moreover, if ω is an L_1-class, there exists an explicit formula for $m(\omega)$. It is important to generalize this formula in two directions. Firstly we should drop the assumption that ω is L_1 and, secondly, we should relax the condition that G/Γ be compact. However, no general results in this direction have been obtained so far.

"From now on we assume that Γ is a discrete subgroup of G such that G/Γ has finite invariant measure. For $G=\mathrm{SL}(2, \mathbf{R})$ and $\Gamma=\mathrm{SL}(2, \mathbf{Z})$ (and perhaps also for some other Γ), the problem of the reduction of λ was solved by Selberg. The case $G=\mathrm{SL}(n, \mathbf{R})$, $\Gamma=\mathrm{SL}(n, \mathbf{Z})$ has been considered by Gel'fand and Pjateckiĭ-Šapiro. Finally, the case when G is any real algebraic semisimple group defined over $\mathbf{Q}$, and Γ any arithmetic subgroup of G, has been studied by Langlands and he has obtained the deepest and the most general results so far. In this case it is possible to show that $m(\omega)<\infty$. However, the problem of computing $m(\omega)$ remains largely untouched.

"There is another way of approaching the problem of the reduction of $L_2(G/\Gamma)$. Let $\mathfrak{Z}$ be the algebra of all differential operators on G which commute with both left and right translations. Let $\mathfrak{G}$ be the Lie algebra of G and $\mathfrak{U}$ the universal enveloping algebra of $\mathfrak{G}_c$. Then $\mathfrak{U}$ may be identified with the algebra of all left-invariant differential operators on G and $\mathfrak{Z}$ is the center of $\mathfrak{U}$. Put $\mathscr{H}=L_2(G/\Gamma)$ and let $\mathscr{H}_\infty$ denote the subspace of all $f\in\mathscr{H}$ such that the mapping $x\to\lambda(x)f$ of G into H is of class C^∞. Then one gets in a natural way a representation of $\mathfrak{U}$ on $\mathscr{H}_\infty$, which we denote by λ_∞. For any differential operator D on G, let D^* denote its adjoint, so that $\int Df\cdot g\,dx=\int f\cdot D^*g\,dx$ ($f, g\in C_c^\infty(G)$). (dx is the Haar measure on G.) Then $\mathfrak{U}^*=\mathfrak{U}$ and $\mathfrak{Z}^*=\mathfrak{Z}$. Let η denote the conjugation of $\mathfrak{G}_c$ with respect to $\mathfrak{G}$. We say that an element $z\in\mathfrak{Z}$ is hermitian if $\eta(z^*)=z$. Lemma: If $z\in\mathfrak{Z}$ is hermitian, then $\lambda_\infty(z)$ is an essentially self-adjoint operator in the sense of Hilbert-space theory.

"Now $\mathscr{H}_\infty$ is stable under $\lambda(x)$ ($x\in G$) and $\lambda_\infty(z)$ ($z\in\mathfrak{Z}$) commutes with $\lambda(x)$. Hence we may regard our reduction problem, at least as a first approximation, as that of obtaining a simultaneous spectral decomposition for all the operators $\lambda_\infty(z)$ ($z\in\mathfrak{Z}$). So, roughly speaking, it becomes an eigenfunction expansion problem. Given $f\in L_2(G/\Gamma)$, we have to express it as a linear combination of eigenfunctions of $\mathfrak{Z}$ on G/Γ. Fix a maximal compact subgroup K of G. There is no essential loss of generality in assuming that f is K-finite on the left. Then the eigenfunctions that we are looking for, may also be assumed to be left K-finite. It is not difficult to show that such eigenfunctions are in fact analytic.

"Thus it is natural to introduce the following definition. Let σ be a unitary representation of K on a finite-dimensional complex Hilbert space V and χ a character of $\mathfrak{Z}$, i.e., a homomorphism of $\mathfrak{Z}$ into $\mathbf{C}$ such that $\chi(1)=1$. By an automorphic form of type (σ,χ) we mean a C^∞ function $f\colon G/\Gamma\to V$ such that $f(kx)=\sigma(k)f(x)$ ($k\in K$, $x\in G$) and $zf=\chi(z)f$ ($z\in\mathfrak{Z}$). However, one finds that some of these eigenfunctions have nothing to do with harmonic analysis on G/Γ, since they grow much too fast at infinity. Therefore we impose, in addition, a mild growth condition on f, so as to exclude these extraneous functions.

"Let $\mathscr{A}(G/\Gamma,\sigma,\chi)$ denote the space of all automorphic forms of type (σ,χ). Then the first result is that $\dim\mathscr{A}(G/\Gamma,\sigma,\chi)<\infty$ (provided Γ satisfies certain reasonable conditions). For example, this is true if $G=\mathrm{SL}(n, \mathbf{R})$, $\Gamma=\mathrm{SL}(n, \mathbf{Z})$. In the case of $G=\mathrm{Sp}(n, \mathbf{R})$, $\Gamma=\mathrm{Sp}(n, \mathbf{Z})$ and holomorphic forms, this result was first proved by Siegel.

"Now a few words about how to construct such eigenfunctions. When G/Γ is compact, no general method of constructing them explicitly is known (except when G has a discrete series). However, their existence is assured from the fact that $L_2(G/\Gamma)$ reduces, in this case, to a discrete orthogonal sum of irreducible subspaces. Every such subspace then consists of eigenfunctions.

"So let us now consider the case when G/Γ is not compact, e.g., $G=\mathrm{SL}(n, \mathbf{R})$, $\Gamma=\mathrm{SL}(n, \mathbf{Z})$. Then we have the Iwasawa decomposition $G=KAN$, where $K=\mathrm{SO}(n)$, $A=$ the group of diagonal matrices in G with all diagonal elements >0, and $N=\left\{\begin{pmatrix}1 & * \\ 0 & 1\end{pmatrix}\right\}$. Let $x=kan$ ($k\in K$, $a\in A$, $n\in N$). We write $k(x)=k$ and $H(x)=\log a\in\mathfrak{A}=$ Lie algebra of A. Then $dx=e^{2\rho(\log a)}\,dk\,da\,dn$, where ρ is a certain linear function on $\mathfrak{A}$. Let σ be a unitary representation of K on a finite-dimensional space V as above. Then for any linear function λ on $\mathfrak{A}_c$, the function $x\to\sigma(k(x))e^{(\lambda-\rho)(H(x))}$ ($x\in G$) from G to the space $\mathscr{E}(V)$ of endomorphisms of V, is an eigenfunction of $\mathfrak{Z}$. Let χ_λ denote the corresponding character of $\mathfrak{Z}$. Then $\chi_{s\lambda}=\chi_\lambda$ for $s\in W$ ($=$Weyl group of $(\mathfrak{G},\mathfrak{A})$). This function may be considered as a function on G/N. Therefore if the series

$$E_\lambda(x) = \sum_{\gamma\in\Gamma/\Gamma\cap N}\sigma(k(x\gamma))e^{(\lambda-\rho)(H(x\gamma))}$$

converges, then it gives an eigenfunction of $\mathfrak{Z}$ on G/Γ. Now the series does converge for suitable λ. But the corresponding χ_λ is such that it is clearly not the infinitesimal character of an irreducible unitary representation of G. Therefore we are forced to study $E_\lambda(x)$ as a function of λ and show that, by analytic continuation, it can be extended to a meromorphic function of λ on $\mathfrak{A}_c{}^*$ ($=$dual of $\mathfrak{A}_c$).

"For simplicity, let us consider the case when $\sigma=1$ and $V=\mathbf{C}$. Normalize the Haar measure dn on N in such a way that $N/N\cap\Gamma$ has measure 1. Then

$$e^{\rho(\log a)}\int_{N/N\cap\Gamma}E_\lambda(an)\,dn = \sum_{s\in W}c(s:\lambda)e^{s\lambda(\log a)}\ (a\in A),$$

where the $c(s:\lambda)$ are meromorphic functions on $\mathfrak{A}_c{}^*$ and $c(1:\lambda)=1$. Moreover, we have the functional equations $c(st:\lambda)=c(s:t\lambda)c(t:\lambda)$ and $E_\lambda=c(s:\lambda)E_{s\lambda}$ ($s, t\in W$). Since E_λ is actually defined by means of a Dirichlet series, there is a certain obvious analogy with the ζ-functions and L-series of number theory. In particular, the functions $c(s:\lambda)$ seem to have a product formula. On the other hand there is also a strong analogy with the theory of elementary spherical functions. If we put

$$\phi_\lambda(x) = \int_K e^{(\lambda-\rho)(H(xk))}\,dk\ (x\in G),$$

then it is known that $\phi_{s\lambda}=\phi_\lambda$ ($s\in W$).

"For $G=\mathrm{SL}(n, \mathbf{R})$ and $\Gamma=\mathrm{SL}(n, \mathbf{Z})$ Selberg had obtained the analytic continuation of all the Eisenstein series (and not just those mentioned above). Langlands has now done this in the general case. Actually he does not confine himself to the arithmetic case but makes a certain set of assumptions on (G,Γ). In view of the recent work of two Russians, Vinberg and Makarov, where they construct non-arithmetic discrete groups Γ such that G/Γ has finite measure, it seems conceivable that the assumptions of Langlands are more general. However, they are rather unwieldy and so we shall confine ourselves to the arithmetic case." *J. A. Wolf* (Berkeley, Calif.)

Citations: MR 31# 372 = F60-7; MR 40# 2784 = F60-10.

Referred to in F60-10.

F60-10 **(40# 2784)**

Langlands, R. P.

Eisenstein series.

Algebraic Groups and Discontinuous Subgroups (*Proc. Sympos. Pure Math., Boulder, Colo.*, 1965), *pp.* 235–252. *Amer. Math. Soc., Providence, R.I.*, 1966.

This is a very short account of the author's unpublished

work "On the functional equations satisfied by Eisenstein series". An idea is given of the method which leads to the analytic continuation of Eisenstein series on semisimple Lie groups.

In the meantime, Harish-Chandra has given a simpler (and for the reviewer incomprehensible) proof for the Eisenstein series attached to a cuspidal (=parabolic) subgroup of rank 1 [see Harish-Chandra, *Automorphic forms on semisimple Lie groups*, Springer, Berlin, 1968; MR **38** #1216]. The author's complete proof for cuspidal subgroups of higher rank can be found in Harish-Chandra's lecture notes [op. cit.]. *J. G. M. Mars* (Utrecht)

Citations: MR 38# 1216 = F60-9.

Referred to in E56-56, E60-24, F55-20, F60-9.

F65 DIRICHLET SERIES AND FUNCTIONAL EQUATIONS ASSOCIATED WITH MODULAR FORMS

See also reviews E44-38, E44-42, F10-95, F10-102, F15-3, F15-24, F15-35, F15-39, F25-1, F25-8, F25-11, F25-13, F25-25, F30-1, F30-4, F35-43, F40-6, F40-15, F50-24, F50-65, F55-4, F60-8, M05-6, M40-7, M40-10, M40-16, M40-35, N36-13, N36-25, R42-14, R52-23, R52-24, R54-33, R54-38, R54-47, R54-53, Z10-59, Z10-66.

F65-1 (1, 294c)

Petersson, Hans. Konstruktion der sämtlichen Lösungen einer Riemannschen Funktionalgleichung durch Dirichlet-Reihen mit Eulerscher Produktentwicklung. II. Math. Ann. **117**, 39–64 (1939).

This paper and the previous Part I [Math. Ann. **116**, 401–412 (1939)] extend the work of Hecke [Math. Ann. **114**, 1–28, 316–351 (1937)] on Dirichlet series $D(s)=\sum_1^\infty a(n)n^{-s}$ associated with integral modular forms $f(\tau)=\sum_0^\infty a(n)e^{2\pi in\tau/Q}$ of "type $(-k, Q)$" (that is, dimension $-k$ and Stufe Q; k and Q positive integers). The significance of the title is that the transformation formulae for the $f(\tau)$ correspond to functional equations, or systems of functional equations, for the analytic functions defined by the $D(s)$, and that attention is focused on those $D(s)$ which have Euler products. In Part I it was proved that, when $Q=1$, the linear set of all $D(s)$ has a (linearly independent) basis $D_1(s), \cdots, D_\kappa(s)$, and only one (except for order), in which each $D_i(s)$ has an Euler product; or, what is the same thing after Hecke, that the linear set of all $f(\tau)$ has a basis $f_1(\tau), \cdots, f_\kappa(\tau)$, and only one (apart from order and constant factors), made up of eigenfunctions of a certain commutative ring of linear operators introduced by Hecke. Here, in Part II, the more complicated case $Q>1$ is discussed. The author considers the linear set $S(t, \epsilon, Q)$ of cusp-forms $f(\tau)$ associated in the manner defined by Hecke with a given divisor t of Q and a given character $\epsilon(n)$ mod Q (the "complementary" set $E(t, \epsilon, Q)$ of Eisenstein series having already been analyzed by Hecke), and shows that results analogous to the above hold in $S(t, \epsilon, Q)$ and in the associated set of $D(s)$ if $t=1$ or if every prime factor of t divides Q/t. The proof consists in finding a normal orthogonal basis of $S(t, \epsilon, Q)$ in the metric introduced by the author in Part I. If t contains a prime factor which does not divide Q/t, a complete reduction in the sense of the above theorems is not always possible, and the failure is analyzed in detail in the case $Q=q$, an odd prime. On the basis of this discussion a generalization of Ramanujan's conjecture $|\tau(n)|\leqq n^{11/2}d(n)$ for the coefficients in $x\{(1-x)(1-x^2)\cdots\}^{24}=\sum_1^\infty \tau(n)x^n$ is proposed, and an analogy with the Riemann hypothesis for congruence zeta-functions is indicated. *A. E. Ingham.*

Referred to in F10-94, F25-2, F25-4, F25-12, F25-27, F30-28, F30-51.

F65-2 (5, 263b)

Guinand, A. P. Functional equations and self-reciprocal functions connected with Lambert series. Quart. J. Math., Oxford Ser. **15**, 11–23 (1944).

The Lambert series considered is

$$\varphi(z)=\sum_{n=1}^{\infty}\frac{1}{e^{2\pi nz}-1}=\sum_{n=1}^{\infty}d(n)e^{-2\pi nz}.$$

Writing $F(z)=\varphi(z)-(2\pi z)^{-1}(\gamma-\log 2\pi z)$, $\Re(z)>0$, the author shows that $F(z)$ is self-reciprocal with respect to the Fourier kernel $2x\pi^{-1}(x^2-1)^{-1}$ and that $F(z)+(i/z)F(1/z)$ can be continued analytically over the z-plane cut from 0 to $+i\infty$, while $F(z)-(i/z)F(1/z)$ can be continued over the z-plane cut from 0 to $-i\infty$. If square brackets denote the analytic continuation of the whole expression inside them, then $F(z)$ satisfies the functional equation

$$[F(z)-(i/z)F(1/z)]+[F(-z)-(i/z)F(-1/z)]=0$$

except for z on a cut from 0 to $-i\infty$; $\varphi(iy)$, for y not on the negative real axis, satisfies

$$\left[\varphi(iy)-\frac{1}{y}\varphi\left(-\frac{i}{y}\right)\right]+\left[\varphi(-iy)-\frac{1}{y}\varphi\left(\frac{i}{y}\right)\right]=\frac{1}{2}-\frac{1}{2y};$$

and, for real positive y,

$$\lim_{\alpha\to+0}\left\{\sum_{n=1}^{\infty}d(n)e^{-2\pi ny\sin\alpha}\cos(2\pi ny\cos\alpha)\right.$$
$$\left.-(1/y)\sum_{n=1}^{\infty}d(n)e^{-2\pi n(\sin\alpha)/y}\cos(2\pi n(\cos\alpha)/y+\alpha)\right\}$$
$$=\tfrac14-1/4y.$$

The last relation gives a meaning to the formal result, obtainable from Voronoï's summation formula,

$$-\tfrac14+\sum_{n=1}^{\infty}d(n)\cos 2\pi ny$$
$$=-(1/4y)+(1/y)\sum_{n=1}^{\infty}d(n)\cos(2\pi n/y),$$

in which the series neither converge nor are summable by any ordinary method. Similar results are given for series involving $\sigma_k(n)$, the sum of the kth powers of the divisors of n. *R. P. Boas, Jr.* (Cambridge, Mass.).

Referred to in M05-20.

F65-3 (6, 173f)

Hecke, E. Herleitung des Euler-Produktes der Zetafunktion und einiger L-Reihen aus ihrer Funktionalgleichung. Math. Ann. **119**, 266–287 (1944).

The main purpose of this paper is to obtain the expansions of $\eta(\tau)$, $\vartheta(\tau)$, $\eta^3(\tau)$ and $\eta^4(\tau)/\vartheta(\tau)$ from their functional properties alone. These functions are modular forms of dimension half an odd integer. The expansions are of the form $\sum_{n=0}^\infty a(n)z^n$, with $z=e^{2\pi i\tau/\lambda}$, λ a suitable divisor of 24. Corresponding to this expansion, the Euler product expansion of the function $\varphi(s)=\sum_{n=1}^\infty a(n)n^{-s}$ is also determined. The author has previously shown [Math. Ann. **112**, 664–699 (1936)] that if $\varphi(s)$ has the functional properties of $\zeta(2s)$ then the corresponding modular form has the functional properties of $\vartheta(\tau)$. Therefore the Euler expansion of $\zeta(s)$ is obtained from the functional properties of $\zeta(s)$. The functions $\varphi(s)$ corresponding to the remaining modular forms considered are various L-series.

H. S. Zuckerman (Seattle, Wash.).

Referred to in F10-56.

F65-4 **(11, 163c)**

Maass, Hans. Über eine neue Art von nichtanalytischen automorphen Funktionen und die Bestimmung Dirichletscher Reihen durch Funktionalgleichungen. Math. Ann. **121**, 141–183 (1949).

In Hecke's theory of Dirichlet series with Euler products we associate, roughly speaking, a Dirichlet series with an automorphic function; the invariance of the latter under linear substitutions is used, together with the Mellin transform, to derive a functional equation for the Dirichlet series. This suffices for the discussion of the ζ-function of an imaginary quadratic field, for example, but not of a real quadratic field. In order to handle the latter case, the author defines a class of functions ("automorphic wave functions") to take the place of the analytic automorphic functions of Hecke's theory. Such a function, $g(x+iy)$, is a solution of

(1) $$\partial^2 g/\partial x^2+\partial^2 g/\partial y^2+(r^2+\tfrac{1}{4})y^{-2}g=0, \qquad r\geqq 0.$$

We consider a system of such functions $g_k(\tau)$, $k=1, 2, \cdots, N$, satisfying (1), regular in the half-plane $y>0$, having a prescribed (uniform) growth as $y\to\infty$ or $y\to 0$, and enjoying a certain transformation property with respect to the group $G(\lambda/q)$ generated by $\tau\to\tau+\lambda/q$, $\tau\to -1/\tau$ (q a fixed integer); each $g_k(\tau)$ has an expansion in certain Bessel functions with coefficients $a_n^{(k)}$. This system is made to correspond, again by the Mellin transform, with a system of Dirichlet series; each g_k is associated with two series, $\varphi_k(s)$, $\psi_k(s)$, corresponding essentially to g_k, $\partial g_k/\partial x$, and employing the coefficients $a_n^{(k)}$. The functions $(s-1-ir)(s-1+ir)\varphi_k(s)$ and $\psi_k(s)$ are entire functions of finite genus. Certain linear combinations of φ_k (and also of ψ_k) weighted by "Γ-factors" satisfy a functional equation involving the transition $s\to 1-s$. In case $\lambda/q=1$ or 2 so that $G(\lambda/q)$ is the modular group or a particular one of its subgroups, and if a certain additional restriction is satisfied, it is shown that the number of linearly independent systems of functions φ_k, ψ_k ($k=1, \cdots, N$) is finite. The author illustrates his theory with a discussion of the Hecke $\zeta(s, \lambda)$ functions of a real quadratic field and of an analogue of the Eisenstein-Hecke series of higher Stufe. Finally, the author carries over the Hecke-Petersson theory of the T_n-operators, which leads to the expression of the Dirichlet series as linear combinations of Euler products, to the automorphic wave functions and obtains quite analogous results. *J. Lehner* (Philadelphia, Pa.).

Referred to in F10-46, F65-6, F99-1.

F65-5 **(11, 230h)**

Maass, Hans. Automorphe Funktionen und indefinite quadratische Formen. S.-B. Heidelberger Akad. Wiss. Math.-Nat. Kl. **1949**, no. 1, 42 pp. (1949).

Set $\Delta=y^2(\partial^2/\partial x^2+\partial^2/\partial y^2)$, let k be a nonnegative integral rational number and r a real parameter. If, in the half plane $y>0$, the $(2k+2)$-fold differentiable function $g(\tau)$ satisfies the system of differential equations:

$$\prod_{\nu=0}^{k}(\Delta-(r+\nu)(r+\nu-1))\tau^{\mu}g(\tau)=0, \qquad \mu=0, 1, \cdots, k,$$

as well as the relationship $g(S\tau)=v(S)(c\tau+d)^k g(\tau)$ for S an element of the group G of real 2 by 2 unimodular substitutions, $v(s)$ having the properties: $v(S_1)v(S_2)=v(S_1S_2)$ and $v(-E)=(-1)^k$, where E is the identity matrix, then $g(\tau)$ is called a "wave form" [Wellenform] of dimension $-k$ and parameter r. The principal theorem consists of a relationship between automorphic wave forms of dimension -1 and Dirichlet series in the form of a general theorem on the solutions of functional equations of the following type:

$$\xi(s)=\left\{\frac{\lambda}{\pi}\right\}^s\Gamma\left\{\frac{s+r+\frac{1}{2}}{2}\right\}\Gamma\left\{\frac{s-r-\frac{1}{2}}{2}\right\}\varphi(s), \qquad \varphi(s)=\sum_{n\neq 0}a_n/|n|^s,$$

$\eta(s)$ obtained from the above by replacing $r+\frac{1}{2}$ by $r-\frac{1}{2}$ and a_n by $a_n \operatorname{sgn} n$, $\xi(s)=\pm\eta(2-s)$. An application of this result is made to Siegel's

$$\zeta(S, s)=\sum_{t=1}^{\infty}M(S, t)t^{-s},$$

where M is the mass of the indefinite quadratic form S. *B. W. Jones* (Boulder, Colo.).

Referred to in F65-30, P28-29.

F65-6 **(12, 319e)**

Maass, Hans. Modulformen zweiten Grades und Dirichletreihen. Math. Ann. **122**, 90–108 (1950).

The author develops a Hecke theory of Dirichlet series satisfying functional equations for a particular case ($n=2$) of Siegel's matrix modular forms. The method is analogous to that by which Hecke treated modular forms on the Hilbert modular group (double ϑ-series) and extracted from them his $\zeta(s, \lambda)$ functions for a real quadratic field. Siegel's modular forms are functions $g(Z)$ of three complex variables

$$z_0, z_1, z_2; \quad Z=\begin{pmatrix} z_0 & z_1\\ z_1 & z_2\end{pmatrix}=\begin{pmatrix} x_0 & x_1\\ x_1 & x_2\end{pmatrix}+i\begin{pmatrix} y_0 & y_1\\ y_1 & y_2\end{pmatrix}=X+iY,$$

analytic in the space $Y>0$ and having the automorphic property $g(Z')=|CZ+D|g(Z)$ for every modular substitution of degree 2, i.e., $Z'=(AZ+B)(CZ+D)^{-1}$, where $AB'=BA'$, $CD'=DC'$, $AD'-BC'=E$ (unit matrix), A, B, C, D are quadratic matrices with integer elements; $-k$ is the "dimension" of g. The function $g(Z)$ is expanded in a Fourier series (1) $\sum a(Z)\exp\{2\pi i\cdot\operatorname{trace}(TZ)\}$, summed over all nonnegative symmetric

$$T=\begin{pmatrix} t_0 & t_1\\ t_1 & t_2\end{pmatrix}.$$

To this we associate through the Mellin transform the Dirichlet series $\xi_1+\xi_2$, where

$$\xi_\nu(s, \tau; g)=(2\pi)^{-2s}\Gamma(2s)\sum a(T)(\operatorname{trace}(TY_1))^{-2s}$$

over T of rank ν, where we have set $X=0$, parameterized

$$Y=uY_1, \quad Y_1=y^{-1}\begin{pmatrix} x^2+y^2 & x\\ x & 1\end{pmatrix}, \quad u>0, y>0,$$

and put $\tau=x+iy$.

In Hecke's theory, we subtract off the constant term of the Fourier series (1); the remainder, when subjected to the Mellin transform, yields a series whose Fourier coefficients are the associated Dirichlet series; under certain conditions, the process is reversible: the modular form and the Dirichlet series determine each other uniquely. In the present paper the author by analogy subtracts off from (1) not only the constant term but all terms in which T is of rank 1; i.e., he considers $\xi_2(s, \tau; g)$ and subjects it to a Fourier analysis, obtaining in this way the desired Dirichlet series. Calling $R(s; e, g)$ the Fourier coefficient of ξ_2, he obtains R as a Dirichlet series multiplied by Γ-factors, as in Hecke's theory; by means of another representation of R he shows that R is a meromorphic function of s in the whole plane having a finite number of simple poles. Furthermore, R satisfies the functional equation $R(k-s; e, g)=(-1)^k R(s; e, g)$.

The Fourier analysis of ξ_2 is not made with respect to the exponential function, as in Hecke's case, but in terms of certain "automorphic wave-functions" which the author introduced in an earlier paper [same Ann. **121**, 141–183 (1949); these Rev. **11**, 163]. These are the functions $e(\tau)$ in

$R(s; e, g)$. They are the analogues of the Hecke "Grössencharakter" λ^n in Hecke's Dirichlet series $\sum_{(\mu)} \lambda^n(\mu)/|N(\mu)|^s$ extended over certain principal ideals in the real quadratic field. Whether conversely, the Dirichlet series for R determines the modular form g is not settled in this paper.
J. Lehner (Philadelphia, Pa.).

Citations: MR 11, 163c = F65-4.

Referred to in F65-7, F65-9, F65-11.

F65-7 (13, 15b)

Bellman, Richard. On the functional equations of the Dirichlet series derived from Siegel modular forms. Proc. Nat. Acad. Sci. U. S. A. **37**, 84–87 (1951).

H. Maass has developed a Hecke theory of Dirichlet series satisfying functional equations for the particular case $n=2$ of Siegel's matrix modular forms [Math. Ann. **122**, 90–108 (1950); these Rev. **12**, 319]. The author sketches a new proof of the functional equation, which he states is applicable to the general case of $n\times n$ matrices. His proof follows the general lines of Riemann's second proof (involving theta-functions) of the functional equation of $\zeta(s)$. Details are promised in a future paper. *J. Lehner.*

Citations: MR 12, 319e = F65-6.

F65-8 (14, 21h)

Shapiro, George. On the Dirichlet series associated with Ramanujan's τ-function. Amer. J. Math. **74**, 401–409 (1952).

Let p_k denote the kth prime. The author proves that, for every fixed $\sigma=\Re s>13/20$, the sequences $\{Z_n(s)\}$ and $\{\operatorname{Log} Z_n(s)\}$ tend in relative measure to $Z(s)$ and $\operatorname{Log} Z(s)$. Here

$$Z_n(s)=\prod_{k=1}^{n}\{1-\tau(p_k)p_k^{-11/2-s}+p_k^{-2s}\}^{-1},$$

$$Z(s)=\prod_{k=1}^{\infty}\{1-\tau(p_k)p_k^{-11/2-s}+p_k^{-2s}\}^{-1}=\sum_{n=1}^{\infty}\tau(n)n^{-11/2-s},$$

$\tau(n)$ is Ramanujan's function, and $\operatorname{Log} Z$ denotes a particular branch of the logarithm. The infinite products and series converge absolutely if $\sigma>1$. A method similar to that used by H. Bohr [Acta Math. **40**, 67–100 (1915)] is used. The asymptotic distribution functions of $Z(s)$ and $\operatorname{Log} Z(s)$ are also investigated by methods similar to those used by Jessen and Wintner [Trans. Amer. Math. Soc. **38**, 48–88 (1935)]. It is shown that both asymptotic distribution functions are absolutely continuous; their densities $D_\sigma(x)$, $\bar{D}_\sigma(x)$ possess continuous partial derivatives of all orders. Also, for any fixed $\lambda>0$, $D_\sigma(x)=O(e^{-\lambda|x|^2})$, $\bar{D}_\sigma(x)=O(e^{-\lambda\log^2|x|})$ as $|x|\to\infty$. Further, if $13/20<\sigma<1$, $D_\sigma(x)>0$ for all x and $\bar{D}_\sigma(x)=0$ if and only if $x=0$. Other properties are also proved. The lower bound of the abscissa 13/20 depends upon the reviewer's estimate, $\tau(n)=O(n^{29/5})$; presumably it can be replaced by 5/8 by using the estimate $\tau(n)=O(n^{23/4+\epsilon})$ which may be obtained by using A. Weil's results on Kloosterman sums [Proc. Nat. Acad. Sci. U. S. A. **34**, 204–207 (1948); these Rev. **10**, 234]. *R. A. Rankin* (Birmingham).

Citations: MR 10, 234e = T25-5.

F65-9 (15, 290a)

Koecher, Max. Über Dirichlet-Reihen mit Funktionalgleichung. J. Reine Angew. Math. **192**, 1–23 (1953).

The Dirichlet series under consideration are generalizations of Epstein's zeta function suggested by C. L. Siegel's work on the analytic theory of quadratic forms. If $\mathfrak{S}$ is a positive symmetric $m\times n$ matrix, define

$$(1)\qquad \zeta_n(\mathfrak{S}^{(m)}, s)=\sum_{\mathfrak{A}}|\mathfrak{A}'\mathfrak{S}\mathfrak{A}|^{-s},\quad m\geqq n,$$

where the summation extends over a complete system of non-right-associate integral $m\times n$ matrices $\mathfrak{A}$ of rank n. As usual, $\mathfrak{A}'$ denotes the transpose of $\mathfrak{A}$ and $|\mathfrak{A}|$ the determinant. The author establishes the absolute convergence of (1) for $\operatorname{Re}(s)>m/2$, uses Siegel's generalization of the integral representation for the gamma function to obtain the analytic continuation of (1) in the whole s-plane and then derives the functional equation

$$R_n(\mathfrak{S}, s)=|\mathfrak{S}|^{-n/2}R_n(\mathfrak{S}^{-1}, \tfrac{1}{2}m-s),$$

where

$$(2)\qquad R_n(\mathfrak{S}, s)=\pi^{n(n-1-4s)/4}\Gamma(s)\Gamma(s-\tfrac{1}{2})\cdots\times\Gamma(s-\tfrac{1}{2}(n-1))\zeta_n(\mathfrak{S}, s).$$

The difficulties which distinguish the previously known case $n=1$ are side-stepped here by using induction on n. When $m=n$, the series in (1) reduces to a product of Riemann zeta functions:

$$\zeta_m(\mathfrak{S}^{(m)}, s)=|\mathfrak{S}|^{-s}\zeta(2s)\zeta(2s-1)\cdots\zeta(2s-m+1).$$

Taking $\mathfrak{S}$ to be the unit matrix in this case leads to a particularly simple derivation of Minkowski's formula for the volume of the domain of reduced positive quadratic forms with determinant $\leqq 1$.

The methods used here also suffice to extend Hecke's theory (on the connection between modular forms and Dirichlet series with certain types of functional equations) to the modular forms of nth degree considered by Siegel [Math. Z. **43**, 682–708; **44**, 398–426 (1938)]. The Fourier development of a modular form f of degree n and weight k is obtained from a series of the form $\sum A(\mathfrak{T})\exp(2\pi i\operatorname{trace}\mathfrak{T}\mathfrak{Z})$, $\mathfrak{Z}=\mathfrak{Z}'=\mathfrak{X}+i\mathfrak{Y}$, $\mathfrak{Y}>0$, by putting $\mathfrak{Z}=i\mathfrak{Y}$. The summation extends over all half-integral non-negative symmetric $n\times n$ matrices. The associated Dirichlet series is

$$D_n(f; s)=2^{-ns}\sum a(\mathfrak{T})|\mathfrak{T}|^{-s},\quad a(\mathfrak{T})=A(\mathfrak{T})/E(\mathfrak{T}),$$

where $E(\mathfrak{T})$ denotes the number of units of $\mathfrak{T}$ and the summation now extends over a complete system of non-equivalent positive matrices. If one now forms $R_n(f; s)$ according to (2) with $\zeta_n(\mathfrak{S}, s)$ replaced by $D_n(f; s)$, the functional equation $R_n(f; s)=(-1)^{nk/2}R_n(f; k-s)$ holds. Using different methods, Maass [Math. Ann. **122**, 90–108 (1950); these Rev. **12**, 319] has recently considered the special case $n=2$. The converse problem of characterizing a modular form of degree n by the associated Dirichlet series is also treated. In contrast to Hecke's theory, there is no unique correspondence in the general case. *T. M. Apostol.*

Citations: MR 12, 319e = F65-6.

Referred to in E44-42.

F65-10 (16, 222f)

Košlyakov, N. S. Investigation of some questions of the analytic theory of the rational and quadratic field. III. Izvestiya Akad. Nauk SSSR. Ser. Mat. **18**, 307–326 (1954). (Russian)

The author continues his detailed investigation of various analytic identities that exist for the functions which correspond in quadratic fields to the zeta-function and theta functions of the rational field. In particular, in this paper, among other things, he generalizes a formula of Ramanujan for the sums $\sum_{n=1}^{\infty} n^{4m+1}/(e^{2\pi n}-1)$ to obtain results for the sums $\sum_{n=1}^{\infty} F(n)n^{4m+1}\sigma(n)$ in terms of the values of the zeta-function of the field. *R. Bellman.*

F65-11 (17, 588e)

Maass, Hans. Die Bestimmung der Dirichletreihen mit Grössencharakteren zu den Modulformen n-ten Grades. J. Indian Math. Soc. (N.S.) **19** (1955), 1–23.

Generalizing a previous paper [Math. Ann. **122** (1950), 90–108; MR **12**, 319], the author sets up, by the same method, a one-one correspondence between a matrix modular form of degree n and even integral dimension $-k$ and a Dirichlet series. The paper is essentially devoted to establishing the explicit formula

$$\int_{Y>0} e^{-2\pi \operatorname{tr}(TY)} u(Y)|Y|^{s-\frac{1}{2}(n+1)}[dY] = (2\pi)^{-ns}\Gamma(s-\alpha_1)\cdots\Gamma(s-\alpha_n)\pi^{\frac{1}{4}n(n-1)}u_1(E).$$

Here $Y=(y_{\mu\nu})$ is a positive real matrix of order n, $u(Y)$ is a bounded eigensolution of Selberg's differential system

$$\{\operatorname{tr}(Y\partial/\partial Y)^k+\lambda_k\}u(Y)=0\ (k=1, \cdots, n),$$

where $\partial/\partial Y=\{e_{\mu\nu}\partial/\partial y_{\mu\nu}\}$, $e_{\mu\nu}=1$ $(\mu=\nu)$, $\frac{1}{2}$ $(\mu\neq\nu)$, E is the unit matrix, $u_1(y)=u(Y)[S^{-1}]$, $T=SS'>0$, and the α's are determined uniquely by the λ's. *J. Lehner.*

Citations: MR 12, 319e = F65-6.

Referred to in F60-2.

F65-12 (17, 602c)

Siegel, Carl Ludwig. Die Funktionalgleichungen einiger Dirichletscher Reihen. Math. Z. 63 (1956), 363–373.

Hecke has introduced into the theory of Eisenstein series a convergence factor $|c\tau-a|^{-z}$, as in

$$\Phi_m(\tau, z)=1+\sum \gamma^m\left(\frac{a}{c}\right)(c\tau-a)^{-m/2}|c\tau-a|^{-z},$$

which by analytic continuation reduces to the theta-functions $\Phi_m(\tau, 0)=\vartheta_m(\tau, 0)$ when $z=0$ $(m=1, 3, 4)$. Considered as a function of z, $\Phi_m(z)$ is meromorphic and satisfies a simple functional equation.

Generalizing this situation the author defines

$$\varphi(\tau, z)=\eta^{z/2}\sum Q(M_\tau, \tau)\vartheta(\infty)|c\tau-a|^{-z}\quad (\tau=\xi+i\eta),$$

where Q is the multiplier in the transformation law of $\vartheta(\tau)$ and M_τ runs over a set of inequivalent modular substitutions. Siegel proves that $\varphi(\tau, 0)=\vartheta(\tau)$, that φ satisfies the same transformation equation (in τ) as $\vartheta(\tau)$ does, and satisfies also the functional equation

$$\psi(\tau, z)=\psi(\tau, 1-z),$$

where $\psi=\varphi(\tau, z)\cdot(2^{z/2}+2^{-z/2})\pi^{-z}\Gamma(z)\zeta(2z)$, ζ being the Riemann zeta-function.

At the end of the paper Siegel generalizes Riemann's second proof of the functional equation for $\zeta(z)$ (the one which uses ϑ-functions) by setting up an analogous integral $\varrho(s, z)$. We have $\varrho(s, 0)=\zeta(s)$, and $\varrho(s, z)$ is developed as an Eisenstein series. The author proposes the problem of discussing the zeros of $\varrho(s, z)$ on the line $\Re s=\frac{1}{2}$. *J. Lehner* (Los Alamos, N.M.).

F65-13 (19, 838g)

Maass, Hans. Zetafunktionen mit Grössencharakteren und Kugelfunktionen. Math. Ann. 134 (1957), 1–32.

In a previous paper [J. Indian Math. Soc. (N.S.) 20 (1956), 117–162; MR 19, 252] the author discussed the problem whether the series

$$\phi_0(s, S; u, v)=\sum_G u(QG)\ v\ (S[G])|S[G]|^{-s-k}$$

define zeta-functions, i.e., meromorphic functions which satisfy a functional equation of Riemann's type. Here $u(X)$ denotes a spherical function of type (m, n) and degree $2nk$, $v(Y)$ an angular character of quadratic forms, S a positive matrix of type $S^{(m)}$ and Q the positive matrix defined by $S=Q'Q$. G runs through a complete system of integral right non-associated matrices of type $G^{(m,n)}$ and rank n. The answer is affirmative if $u(X)$ is harmonic. The problem for an arbitrary spherical function $u(X)$ is related to that involving polynomials $u(X)$ with the invariance property $u(XV)=u(X)$ for orthogonal matrices V. In this case generalized theta-functions related to the problem can be defined. In general however the application of Mellin's transformation to these functions leads not to ϕ_0 but to a different function ϕ. If $u(X)$ satisfies the condition $u(XV)=|V|^{2k}u(X)$ for $|V|\neq 0$, ϕ and ϕ_0 coincide apart from an elementary factor, and a result of the required type is obtained. *E. C. Titchmarsh.*

Citations: MR 19, 252a = E12-60.

Referred to in E12-68.

F65-14 (22# 12223)

Kaufhold, Günter. Dirichletsche Reihe mit Funktionalgleichung in der Theorie der Modulfunktion 2. Grades. Math. Ann. **137** (1959), 454–476.

Let $Z=X+iY$ be an $n\times n$ complex symmetric matrix with $Y>0$. Let A, B, C, D be $n\times n$ matrices with rational integral entries, satisfying certain conditions, and let $\{A, B\}$ be the set of pairs UA, UB with U unimodular. It is known that the Dirichlet series

$$\varphi(s) = |Y|^{s/2}\sum_{\{A,B\}}\operatorname{abs}(AZ+B)^{-s},$$

$$\psi(s) = |Y|^{s/2}\sum_{\{C,D\}}\operatorname{abs}(CZ+D)^{-s}$$

have $n+1$ as the exact abscissa of absolute convergence [H. Braun, Math. Z. **44** (1939), 387–397]. (Here $|A|$ is the determinant and abs A is the absolute value of the determinant of the matrix A.) The author inquires as to the analytic continuation of $\varphi(s)$, $\psi(s)$ and the existence of functional equations which they satisfy.

He confines himself to the case $n=2$ and proves: $\varphi(s)$ is meromorphic in the whole s-plane and has a pole of first order at $s=3$ with residue $90/\pi^2$. It satisfies the functional equation $\omega(s)=\omega(3-s)$, where $\omega(s)=\rho(s)\rho(2s-2)\varphi(s)$ and $\rho(s)=\pi^{-s/2}\Gamma(s/2)\zeta(s)$. Similar results hold for $\psi(s)$. Some of the intermediate calculations are carried out for $n>2$. *J. Lehner* (E. Lansing, Mich.)

F65-15 (26# 3678)

Glaeske, Hans-Jürgen

Zur Herleitung einer asymptotischen Funktionalgleichung gewisser Lambertscher Reihen.

Wiss. Z. Friedrich-Schiller-Univ. Jena **11** (1962/63), 111–113.

Define

$$L_{-s}(\tau) = \sum_{n=1}^{\infty} n^{-s}(e^{-2\pi i\tau n}-1)^{-1}\quad (\operatorname{Im}\tau > 0).$$

The author derives an asymptotic functional equation, which expresses $L_{-s}(\tau)-(-\tau)^{s-1}L_{-s}(\tau^{-1})$ as

$$-\tfrac{1}{2}\zeta(s)+(-2\pi i\tau)^{s-1}\Gamma(1-s)\zeta(1-s)-(2\pi i\tau)^{-1}\zeta(s+1) + (\pi i)^{-1}\sum_{n=1}^{\infty}\zeta(2n)\zeta(s+1-2n)\tau^{2n-1};$$

the latter series is an asymptotic series for $\tau\to 0$. The case $s=0$ is due to S. Wigert [Acta Math. **41** (1918), 197–218]. The author's method imitates a proof of Siegel [Mathematika **1** (1954), 4; MR **16**, 16] for the functional equation of the elliptic modular function η, which can be interpreted as the case $s=1$. The case of general s is more difficult since the integrand can be multi-valued. The method consists of integrating z^{-s} ctg z ctg τz along a path starting at infinity, encircling the origin and leading back to infinity. On the one hand it can be evaluated by the residue calculus, which produces the series $L_{-s}(\tau)$, $L_{-s}(\tau^{-1})$; on the other hand it can be expanded asymptotically for $\tau\to 0$.

The author excludes the case that s is an even integer. {The reviewer remarks that in this case the series arising from the author's series by a formal limit process is still valid as an asymptotic series; it may involve a term $\tau^{s-1}\log\tau$.} *N. G. de Bruijn* (Eindhoven)

Citations: MR 16, 16b = F10-35.

Referred to in F65-18, F65-19.

F65-16 (33# 1292)

Shimura, Goro

On Dirichlet series and abelian varieties attached to automorphic forms.

Ann. of Math. (2) **76** (1962), 237–294.

Let Ω be a totally real finite algebraic number field, and D a quaternion algebra over Ω which is not ramified at the infinite prime spots $\mathfrak{p}_{\infty,\rho}$, $\rho=1,\cdots,r$. Let $\Omega_{\mathfrak{p}_{\infty,\rho}}$, $D_{\mathfrak{p}_{\infty,\rho}}$ be the corresponding $\mathfrak{p}_{\infty,\rho}$-adic completions which are isomorphic to the real field $\mathbf{R}$ and the matrix algebra $M_2(\mathbf{R})$. Take r independent complex variables z_ρ and associate to every $v\in D$ the mapping

$$(z_1,\cdots,z_r)\to\left(\frac{a_1z_1+b_1}{c_1z_1+d_1},\cdots,\frac{a_rz_r+b_r}{c_rz_r+d_r}\right),$$

$$v_\rho=\begin{pmatrix}a_\rho & b_\rho\\ c_\rho & d_\rho\end{pmatrix}\in D_{\mathfrak{p}_{\infty,\rho}},$$

of the space $\mathfrak{F}^r$ consisting of all vectors with nonreal components z_ρ. The group $\Gamma(\mathfrak{o})$ of units of a maximal order $\mathfrak{o}$ of D is discontinuous on $\mathfrak{F}^r$, and a fundamental domain has a finite invariant measure. There exist automorphic functions in these r variables with respect to $\Gamma(\mathfrak{o})$.

The author considers corresponding automorphic forms in the following general sense: Let $\Phi_n(v)$ be the representation of $M_2(\mathbf{R})$ which is the nth "symmetric power" of the natural representation (its degree is $n+1$) and a representation $\varphi(v)$ of the group of residues of $\Gamma(\mathfrak{o})$ modulo an integral two-sided ideal $\mathfrak{a}$ of $\mathfrak{o}$. The automorphic forms considered are vectors of functions satisfying

$$f(v(z))\prod_{\rho=1}^{r}(c_\rho z_\rho+d_\rho)^{-n_\rho}=\varphi(v)\otimes\Phi_{n_1}(v_1)\otimes\cdots\otimes\Phi_{n_r}(v_r)f(z).$$

In the case $\Omega=\mathbf{Q}$, $D=M_2(\mathbf{Q})$, only cusp forms are allowed. Now the Hecke operators are introduced and investigated, which can be done in but one obvious way, and which requires that several maximal orders $\mathfrak{o}$, representing all isomorphy classes, and all 2^r nonconnected parts $\operatorname{Im}(z_\rho)\gtrless 0$ of $\mathfrak{F}^r$ be considered. The elementary properties of the Hecke operators are all contained in the following Euler product:

$$Z(s,\xi)=\sum_{\mathfrak{n}}\xi_0(\mathfrak{n})T(\mathfrak{n})N(\mathfrak{n})^{-s}=\prod_{\mathfrak{p}}(E-\xi_0(\mathfrak{p})T(\mathfrak{p})N(\mathfrak{p})^{-s}+U_{\mathfrak{p}}\xi_0(\mathfrak{p}^2)N(\mathfrak{p})^{1-2s})^{-1},$$

where ξ denotes an arbitrary Grössencharakter in the idèle group of D and ξ_0 the corresponding Grössencharakter of the ideal group of Ω. $T(\mathfrak{n})$ is the matrix representing the Hecke operator in the space of such automorphic forms. $U_{\mathfrak{p}}$ is some unitary matrix depending on (the class of) $\mathfrak{p}$. Finally, $\mathfrak{n}$, $\mathfrak{p}$ run over all integral ideals and all prime ideals of Ω.

This zeta function satisfies a functional equation of the type

$$F(s,\xi)=W_\xi D(s,\xi)F'(2-s,\xi'),$$

$$F(s,\xi)=Z(s,\xi)\prod_{\rho=1}^{r}\Gamma(s+\alpha_\rho),$$

common to all known Dirichlet series with Grössencharakter. The accents on F and ξ on the right mean an involutorial change of the underlying representations $\Phi_{n_\rho}(v)$ and of the Grössencharakter. W_ξ is a constant of the type of a Gaussian sum, and $D(s,\xi)$ is a finite product depending on the arithmetical data, e.g., the discriminant of D/Ω and the ideal $\mathfrak{a}$ mentioned above. The proof of this functional equation uses the method of Iwasawa-Tate which expresses $F(s,\xi)$ as a Haar integral over the idèle group of D and which has previously been employed in similar but simpler cases by Fujisaki [J. Fac. Sci. Univ. Tokyo Sect. I **7** (1958), 567–604; MR **20** #2367] and Tamagawa [Ann. of Math. (2) **77** (1963), 387–405; MR **26** #2468]. As far as the reviewer knows this is the first example where this method yields a functional equation which was not known from other, more conventional considerations. It would be interesting to find out whether such methods could also lead as far.

In a second part of the paper the author restricts himself to the case $r=1$, thus treating automorphic functions and forms which were discovered by Fricke [see R. Fricke and F. Klein, *Vorlesungen über die Theorie der automorphen Funktionen*, Bd. I, Teubner, Leipzig, 1897]. He extends results obtained previously by M. Kuga and himself [J. Math. Soc. Japan **12** (1960), 258–270; MR **24** #A3311] in the case $\Omega=\mathbf{Q}$. The most important of these concerns the holomorphic forms $f(z)$ mentioned above with $n_1=2$, their integrals $\int f(z)\,dz$, and the periods of the latter. These are elements of the first cohomology group $H^1(\Gamma(\mathfrak{o}),\Phi(v),\mathbf{C})$. If the representation $\Phi(v)$ of $\Gamma(\mathfrak{o})$ entering in the definition of $f(z)$ has rational integral coefficients and satisfies $\Phi(v)^tY\Phi(v)=Y$ with a real symmetric matrix Y of a certain kind, the quotient space $H^1(\Gamma(\mathfrak{o}),\Phi(v),\mathbf{R})/H^1(\Gamma(\mathfrak{o}),\Phi(v),\mathbf{Z})=A_{\mathfrak{o}}$ is an Abelian variety. Such representations $\Phi(v)$ always exist. The Hecke operators $T(\mathfrak{n})$ can be applied in $H^1(\Gamma(\mathfrak{o}),\Phi(v),\mathbf{R})$ and $H^1(\Gamma(\mathfrak{o}),\Phi(v),\mathbf{Z})$ in an obvious way, and they constitute algebraic mappings of the Abelian variety $A_{\mathfrak{o}}$ into $A_{\mathfrak{o}'}$, where $\mathfrak{o}'$ is the maximal order of D connected with $\mathfrak{o}$ by an ideal of norm $\mathfrak{n}$.

The paper closes with a surprisingly easy geometric explanation of the Abelian varieties $A_{\mathfrak{o}}$ which does not mention automorphic functions at all. The reviewer wonders whether there is a connection between this fact and a recent discovery by H. Cohn and M. Knopp [Duke Math. J. **32** (1965), 115–120; MR **31** #129] that the periods of the integrals of certain automorphic forms attached to the classical Eisenstein series in the case $D=M_2(Q)$ are real. *M. Eichler* (Basel)

Citations: MR 20# 2367 = R54-27; MR 24# A3311 = F15-16; MR 26# 2468 = R54-33; MR 31# 129 = F15-21.

Referred to in G15-37.

F65-17 (34# 154)

Glaeske, Hans-Jürgen

Funktionalgleichungen von Gitterfunktionen.

Math. Nachr. **32** (1966), 95–105.

The author considers first the function $H(\omega;s;\alpha,\beta)=\sum_{g=-\infty}^{\infty}\sum_{h=0}^{\infty}[g+\beta+\omega(h+\alpha)]^{-s}$, where $\operatorname{Im}\omega>0$, $\sigma>2$, $0<\alpha\leqq1$, $0\leqq\beta\leqq1$. The special case $H(\omega;s)=H(\omega;s;1,0)$ has been discussed by W. Maier [Math. Ann. **113** (1936), 363–379; Arch. Math. **9** (1958), 186–190; MR **20** #5758]. The author shows first that $H(\omega;s;\alpha,\beta)$ is an entire function of s. Moreover, he shows that for $\omega\to0$ and $k=0,1,2,\cdots$,

$$H(\omega;s;\alpha,\beta)=\delta_\beta\zeta(s,\alpha)\omega^{-s}+\frac{(-2\pi i)^{s-1}l_{2-s}(e^{2\pi i\beta})}{\Gamma(s)\omega}+\frac{1}{\Gamma(s)}\sum_{r=0}^{k}\frac{(-1)^{r+1}B_{r+1}(\alpha)l_{1-r-s}(e^{2\pi i\beta})}{(r+1)!}+O(\omega^{k+\eta}),$$

where $0<\eta<1$, $s\not\equiv0(1)$ when $\beta=0$ or 1, $\delta_\beta=0$ $(0<\beta<1)$, $\delta_\beta=1$ $(\beta=0$ or $1)$, $\zeta(s,\alpha)$ is the Hurwitz zeta-function,

$l_s(e^{2\pi ix}) = \sum_{n=1}^{\infty} n^{-s}e^{2\pi inx}$ and $B_n(\alpha)$ is the Bernoulli polynomial of degree n.

Next, the author introduces the function $V(a,b;s;\alpha,\beta) = \sum_{g,h=0}^{\infty} [a(g+\alpha)+b(h+\beta)]^{-s}$ for $\sigma > 2$, $|\arg b/a| < \pi$, $0 < \alpha \leqq 1$, $0 \leqq \beta \leqq 1$. The special case $V(a,b;s) = V(a,b;s;1,1)$ was introduced by Maier in the first paper cited above. The author shows that $V(a,b;s;\alpha,\beta)$ is a meromorphic function of s with simple poles at $s=1$ and $s=2$; the residues at these poles are $(\frac{1}{2}-\alpha)/a + (\frac{1}{2}-\beta)/b$ and $1/ab$, respectively. He also obtains a functional equation relating $V(\omega,1;s;\alpha,\beta)$ to $H(\omega;s;\alpha,\beta)$, and an asymptotic development for $V(\omega,1;s;\alpha,\beta)$ both for $\omega \to 0$ and $\omega \to \infty$. These results imply an asymptotic functional equation for $H(\omega;s;\alpha,\beta)$ that the author has proved elsewhere [J. Math. Soc. Japan **18** (1966), 253–266; MR **34** #1280].

L. Carlitz (Durham, N.C.)

Citations: MR 20# 5758 = M40-20; MR 34# 1280 = F65-19.

F65-18 (34# 1279)

Glaeske, Hans-Jürgen

Über die Modultransformation einer Halbgitterfunktion.

Arch. Math. (Basel) **17** (1966), 438–442.

If $\mathrm{Im}(\omega) > 0$ and $\mathrm{Re}(s) > 2$, the Lambert series $L_{-s}(\omega) = \sum_{n=1}^{\infty} n^{-s}e^{2\pi in\omega}(1-e^{2\pi in\omega})^{-1}$ is related to the semilattice function $H(\omega;s) = \sum_{g=-\infty}^{\infty}\sum_{h=1}^{\infty}(g+\omega h)^{-s}$ by the equation $L_{-s}(\omega) = (-2\pi i)^{s-1}\Gamma(1-s)H(\omega;1-s)$, a connection noted by W. Maier [Math. Ann. **113** (1936), 363–379]. In an earlier paper [Wiss. Z. Friedrich-Schiller-Univ. Jena **11** (1962/63), 111–113; MR **26** #3678] the author obtained an asymptotic functional equation relating $L_{-s}(\omega)$ to $L_{-s}(-\omega^{-1})$. More recently [#1280 below] he extended this result to the generalized Lambert series $L_{-s}(\omega;\alpha,\beta) = \sum_{n=1}^{\infty} n^{-s}e^{2\pi in(\alpha\omega+\beta)}(1-e^{2\pi in\omega})^{-1}$. In this paper he uses the extended formula and a technique of Shô Iseki to determine the behavior of $L_{-s}(\omega)$ under a general modular transformation. Limiting cases of this far-reaching generalization include the transformation formula for the Dedekind modular function $\eta(\tau)$ as well as many other known formulas.

T. M. Apostol (Pasadena, Calif.)

Citations: MR 26# 3678 = F65-15.

F65-19 (34# 1280)

Glaeske, Hans-Jürgen

Eine asymptotische Funktionalgleichung für eine Funktion eines ebenen Halbgitters.

J. Math. Soc. Japan **18** (1966), 253–266.

For $\mathrm{Im}\ \omega > 0$ the author considers the function

$$H = H(\omega, s; \alpha, \beta) = \sum_{-\infty<g<\infty}\ \sum_{0\leqq h<\infty} \{g+\beta+\omega(h+\alpha)\}^{-s}$$

($\sigma > 2$; $0 \leqq \alpha, \beta \leqq 1$; $\alpha+\beta(1-\beta) \neq 0$). The analytic continuation of H leads to an entire function of s and is (with $e(\rho) = \exp(2\pi i\rho)$) given by the generalized Lambert series $H = (-2\pi i)^s\Gamma^{-1}(s)\sum_{1\leqq n<\infty} n^{s-1}e(n(\alpha\omega+\beta))(1-e(n\omega))^{-1}$ ($\mathrm{Im}\ \omega > 0$). Using a method of Siegel [Mathematika **1** (1954), 4; MR **16**, 16] the author derives (for any $k > 0$) the following asymptotic functional equation for $L_{-s}(\omega;\alpha,\beta) = (-2\pi i)^{s-1}\Gamma(1-s)H(\omega,1-s;\alpha,\beta)$:

$$L_{-s}(\omega;\alpha,\beta) - e(s/2)L_{-s}(\omega;1-\alpha,1-\beta) -$$

$$\omega^{s-1}\{L_{-s}(-\omega^{-1};1-\beta,\alpha) - e(\pm s/2)L_{-s}(-\omega^{-1};\beta,1-\alpha)\} =$$

$$-(2\pi i)^s \sum_{0\leqq n\leqq k} B_n(\alpha)\zeta(n-s,\beta)$$

$$\times\{n!\Gamma(1+s-n)\}^{-1}\omega^{n-1} + R_k(\omega),$$

where $R_k(\omega) = O(\omega^k)$ for $\omega \to 0$; $\pm$ means $+$ for $0 < \arg\omega < \pi/2$ and $-$ for $\pi/2 < \arg\omega < \pi$; the B_n are the Bernoulli polynomials. This functional equation generalizes a former result of the author [Wiss. Z. Friedrich-Schiller-Univ. Jena/Thüringen **11** (1962/63), 111–113; MR **26** #3678]. Special cases give results of S. Wigert [Acta Math. **41** (1917), 197–218] and S. Iseki [Duke Math. J. **24** (1957), 653–662; MR **19**, 943], and the transformation formula for Dedekind's

$$\eta(\omega) = \exp(\pi i\omega/12)\prod_{1\leqq n<\infty}(1-e(n\omega)).$$

{See also #1279 above.}

W. Schwarz (Freiburg)

Citations: MR 16, 16b = F10-35; MR 19, 943a = F10-50; MR 26# 3678 = F65-15.

Referred to in F65-17, F65-20.

F65-20 (34# 4216)

Glaeske, Hans-Jürgen

Eine asymptotische Funktionalgleichung für eine verallgemeinerte Halbgitter-funktion.

Duke Math. J. **34** (1967), 23–32.

For real a, α, β and complex s, ω with $R(s) > 1$, $\mathrm{Im}(\omega) > 0$, let $\zeta_s(a) = \sum_{n=1}^{\infty} n^{-s}e^{2\pi ina}$, and define $L_{-s}^{(\lambda)}(\omega;\alpha,\beta) = \sum_{m=0}^{\infty}\zeta_s[(m+\alpha)^\lambda\omega+\beta]$, where λ is a positive integer. The function $L_{-s}^{(\lambda)}$ is related to the semilattice function $H^{(\lambda)}(\omega;s;\alpha,\beta) = \sum_{g=-\infty}^{\infty}\sum_{h=0}^{\infty}[g+\beta+\omega(h+\alpha)^\lambda]^{-s}$ by the equation

$$L_{-s}^{(\lambda)}(\omega;\alpha,\beta) = (-2\pi i)^{s-1}\Gamma(1-s)H^{(\lambda)}(\omega;1-s;\alpha,\beta).$$

In a recent paper [J. Math. Soc. Japan **18** (1966), 253–266; MR **34** #1280] the author obtained an asymptotic functional equation describing the behavior of the function $L_{-s}^{(1)}(\omega;\alpha,\beta)$ under the modular transformation $\omega' = -\omega^{-1}$. In this paper he extends the result to all positive integers λ.

T. M. Apostol (Pasadena, Calif.)

Citations: MR 34# 1280 = F65-19.

F65-21 (34# 7473)

Weil, André

Über die Bestimmung Dirichletscher Reihen durch Funktionalgleichungen.

Math. Ann. **168** (1967), 149–156.

E. Hecke [same Ann. **112** (1936), 664–699] set up a one-to-one correspondence between Dirichlet series with a certain functional equation and modular forms for a certain group (on two generators) of substitutions of the upper half plane. The author shows by Hecke's methods that modular forms for the congruence subgroup $\Gamma_0(A)$ of the modular group are characterized by functional equations for many associated Dirichlet series.

The result is the following. Given a sequence $a_1, a_2, \cdots$ of complex numbers, $a_n = O(n^{\mathrm{const}})$, define $F(\tau) = \sum_{n=1}^{\infty} a_n e^{2\pi in\tau}$ ($\mathrm{Im}\ \tau > 0$), $L(s) = \sum_{n=1}^{\infty} a_n n^{-s}$, $\Lambda(s) = (2\pi)^{-s}\Gamma(s)L(s)$. Given also $C = \pm 1$, and positive integers k, A, define $L_\chi(s) = \sum_{n=1}^{\infty} a_n\chi(n)n^{-s}$, $\Lambda_\chi(s) = (m/2\pi)^s\Gamma(s)L_\chi(s)$ for every character χ of the integers whose conductor m is relatively prime to A, and let $g(\chi)$ be the Gauss sum $g(\chi) = \sum_{x \bmod m}\chi(x)e^{2\pi ix/m}$. Finally, let ε be a real character of the integers modulo A. Then $F(\tau)$ is a modular form of dimension $-k$ and character ε for the group $\Gamma_0(A)$ of modular substitutions $\begin{pmatrix} a & b \\ c & d \end{pmatrix}$ with $A|c$, and satisfies $F(\tau) = CA^{k/2}(A\tau/i)^{-k}F(-1/A\tau)$, if and only if $\Lambda(s)$ and $\Lambda_\chi(s)$ are entire, bounded in every vertical strip, and satisfy the functional equations $\Lambda(s) = CA^{k/2-s}\Lambda(k-s)$, $\Lambda_\chi(s) = C_\chi A^{k/2-s}\Lambda_{\bar{\chi}}(k-s)$, for every χ of conductor m relatively prime to A, where $C_\chi = C\varepsilon(m)\chi(-A)g(\chi)(g(\bar{\chi}))^{-1}$. Furthermore, $F(\tau)$ is a cusp form if $L(s)$ converges absolutely for some $s = k-\delta$, $\delta > 0$.

The theorem leads to the following (rather startling) conjecture on the zeta-function of an elliptic curve C defined over the rational numbers. Let $L(s) = \prod_p L_p(s)$ be the numerator of this zeta-function; thus $L_p(s) = (1-C_p p^{-s}+p^{1-2s})^{-1}$ at good primes p, where C has non-degenerate reduction and $1+p-C_p$ is the number of points on the reduced curve rational over the field of p elements. At bad primes p, one knows how to define $L_p(s)$; one also knows how to define an integer A, called the conductor of C, whose prime factors are the bad primes. The Hasse-Weil conjecture states that $L(s)$ has an analytic continuation to the whole s-plane and a functional equation. The author now makes the more precise conjecture, "on certain theoretical grounds", that $L(s)$ and the modified $L_\chi(s)$ satisfy precisely the above functional equations, with $k=2$ and $\varepsilon=1$. It would then follow, by the theorem, that $L(s)$ corresponds to a cusp form of dimension -2 for $\Gamma_0(A)$. *A. P. Ogg* (Berkeley, Calif.)

Referred to in E44-41, E68-38, F65-27, F65-28, G05-111, Z10-69.

F65-22 (37# 4035)

Kubota, Tomio

On a special kind of Dirichlet series.

J. Math. Soc. Japan **20** (1968), 193–207.

The author sketches a method for obtaining new zeta-functions satisfying functional equations of the usual kind. These zeta-functions arise from the Fourier coefficients of Eisenstein series containing characters of certain discontinuous groups, e.g., discontinuous groups of Hilbert type. As a simple example of his method, the author treats the case of subgroups of $SL(2, J)$, where J is the ring of Gaussian integers. He mentions several possible applications of his method, e.g., to Kummer's conjecture on cubic characters. *O. H. Körner* (Marburg)

Referred to in F15-26.

F65-23 (37# 5165)

Glaeske, Hans-Jürgen

Über eine Integralgleichung n-dimensionaler Gitterfunktionen.

Wiss. Z. Friedrich-Schiller-Univ. Jena/Thüringen **14** (1965), 351–357.

The first part of this paper deals with the n-dimensional grid function

$$V_n(a_1, a_2, \cdots, a_n; s) \equiv V_n(a_\nu; s) = \sum_{\nu_i=1; (i=1,\cdots,n)}^{\infty} (a_1\nu_1 + a_2\nu_2 + \cdots + a_n\nu_n)^{-s},$$

where $\mathrm{Re}(a_\nu)>0$ and $\mathrm{Re}(s)>\eta$. For $n=1$ and 2, V_n reduces, respectively, to the Riemann zeta function and Maier's grid function. For convenience, all the equations are given in terms of the function $Q_n(a_\nu; s)=\Gamma(s)V_n(a_\nu; s)$. It is shown that Q_n is a meromorphic function of s with poles at the points $(n-\nu)$, is invariant under permutations of the symmetric group σ_n, and is the unique solution of a certain integro-functional equation. In the second part of the paper the function $q(a_\nu; s)$, the inverse Mellin transform of $Q(a_\nu; s)$, is studied. This is shown to satisfy a certain functional equation. The cases $n=1, 2, 3$ are studied in some detail. *H. E. Fettis* (Dayton, Ohio)

F65-24 (37# 6251)

Glaeske, Hans-Jürgen

Über eine Charakterisierung einer Gitterfunktion.

Wiss. Z. Friedrich-Schiller-Univ. Jena/Thüringen **14** (1965), 359–362.

Let $Q_n(a_1, a_2, \cdots, a_n; s)=\Gamma(s)\sum_{\nu_i=1}^{\infty}(a_1\nu_1+\cdots+a_n\nu_n)^{-s}$, $\sigma=R(s)>n$, $\mathrm{Re}\, a_\nu>0$. It is shown that Q_2 satisfies the functional-cum-integral equation

$$\begin{aligned}(1/2\pi i)\int \{&Q(a_1, a_2; u)Q(a_3, a_4; s-u)-Q(\alpha, a_1; u)\\ &\times[Q(a_2, a_3; s-u)+Q(a_2, a_4; s-u)+Q(a_3, a_4; s-u)]\\ &-Q(\alpha, a_2; u)Q(a_3, a_4; s-u)-Q_1(\alpha, u)\\ &\times[Q(a_1, a_2; s-u)+Q(a_1, a_3; s-u)+Q(a_1, a_4; s-u)\\ &+Q(a_2,a_3;s-u)+Q(a_2,a_4;s-u)+Q(a_3,a_4;s-u)]\}\, du =\\ &Q(\alpha,a_1;s)+Q(\alpha,a_2;s)+Q(\alpha,a_3;s)+Q(\alpha,a_4;s)+Q_1(\alpha;s),\end{aligned}$$

for $\sigma>4$, $\mathrm{Re}\, a_\nu>0$. This equation characterizes $Q(a, b; s)$ in the sense that these are the only solutions which possess the symmetry property $Q(a, b; s)=Q(b, a; s)$, which are homogeneous so that $Q(za, zb; s)=z^{-s}Q(a, b; s)$ and which are Mellin transforms of some function of the form $q(a, b; x)$ which is meromorphic in a and b and singular for $(0, 0)$. *R. P. Srivastav* (Stony Brook, N.Y.)

F65-25 (39# 712)

Maak, Wilhelm

Dirichletreihen mit Funktionalgleichung.

Nachr. Akad. Wiss. Göttingen Math.-Phys. Kl. II **1968**, 199–223.

Verfasser zeigt, daß die Fourier-Reihen $\sum_{\lambda>0} a(\lambda)e^{i\lambda\tau}$ analytisch fastperiodischer Funktionen $\Phi(\tau)$, welche gewisse Wachstumsbedingungen erfüllen, und die Dirichlet-Reihen $\sum a(\lambda)/\lambda^s$ (mit Wachstumsbedingung) bijektiv vermöge einer Integraltransformation vom Typ der Mellin-Transformierten aufeinander abgebildet werden können. Dabei genügt die Dirichlet-Reihe genau dann einer Funktionalgleichung nach Art der Riemannschen ζ-Funktion, wenn Φ eine Funktionalgleichung erfüllt. Beispiele für fastperiodische Funktionen mit Funktionalgleichung sind ganze fastautomorphe Formen. Solche Formen werden mittels verallgemeinerter Poincaré-Reihen konstruiert und die zugehörigen Funktionalgleichungen mit den Darstellungen der Modulgruppe in Verbindung gebracht. Einige dieser Resultate wurden für den speziellen Fall von Modulformen schon von E. Hecke gefunden [Math. Ann. **114** (1937), 1–28; ibid. **114** (1937), 316–351]. *J. Spilker* (Freiburg)

F65-26 (40# 7203)

Doi, Koji; Naganuma, Hidehisa

On the functional equation of certain Dirichlet series.

Invent. Math. **9** (1969/70), 1–14.

Let $f(\tau)=\sum_{n=1}^{\infty} a_n e^{2\pi i n\tau}$ be a cusp form on the upper half complex plane with respect to $SL_2(\mathbf{Z})$ of weight k, and let $\varphi(s)=\sum_{n=1}^{\infty} a_n n^{-s}$ be the corresponding Dirichlet series. Assume that $\varphi(s)$ has an Euler product and satisfies a functional equation of the usual type. Form the Dirichlet series $\varphi(s, \chi)=\sum_{n=1}^{\infty}\chi(n)a_n n^{-s}$ for a class character χ with respect to a real quadratic number field F of class number one. The representation $\varphi(s)\varphi(s,\chi)=\sum_A C(A)N(A)^{-s}$ with suitable constants $C(A)$ gives rise to the Dirichlet series $D(s)=D(s, \varphi, \chi, \xi)=\sum_A \xi(A)C(A)N(A)^{-s}$ for any Grössencharacter ξ of F. Here A ranges over all integral ideals of F. The authors prove that, if the conductor of ξ is one, the function $D(s)$ can be continued holomorphically to the whole s-plane, that it can be expressed as an Euler product, and that it satisfies a functional equation similar to those of zeta-functions of quaternion algebras. This is done by expressing $D(s)$ as a convolution of $\varphi(s)$ and an L-function of F and making use of a method of R. A. Rankin [Proc. Cambridge Philos. Soc. **35** (1939), 351–372; MR **1**, 69; errata, MR **1**, p. 400]. *O. H. Körner* (Marburg)

Citations: MR 1, 69d = F30-1.

F65-27 **(41# 1648)**

Ogg, Andrew

Modular forms and Dirichlet series.

W. A. Benjamin, Inc., New York-Amsterdam, 1969. xvi+173 *pp.* (*not consecutively paged*) \$8.50; \$3.95 *paperbound.*

Diese Berkeley-Noten sind eine schöne Einführung in die Ideen von E. Hecke über den Zusammenhang von Modulformen und Dirichlet-Reihen.

Kapitel 1: Von E. Hecke [Math. Ann. **112** (1936), 664–699] stammt die Entdeckung, daß sich die Funktionalgleichung der Riemannschen ζ-Funktion aus der Transformationsgleichung der Theta-Funktion für $\tau \mapsto -1/\tau$ herleiten läßt. Genauer gilt unter gewissen Konvergenzvoraussetzungen: Die Fourier-Reihe $f(\tau)=\sum_{n\geqq 0} a_n e^{2\pi i n\tau/\lambda}$ erfüllt in der oberen Halbebene $f(\tau)=C(\tau/i)^{-k}f(-1/\tau)$ genau dann, wenn für die zugeordnete Dirichlet-Reihe $\varphi(s)=\sum_{n\geqq 1} a_n n^{-s}$, $\Phi(s)=(2\pi/\lambda)^{-s}\Gamma(s)\varphi(s)$ gesetzt, gilt: $\Phi(s)+a_0/s+Ca_0/(k-s)$ ist eine ganze Funktion, ist in jedem Vertikalstreifen beschränkt und erfüllt $\Phi(s)=C\Phi(k-s)$. Damit ist die Suche nach den Dirichlet-Reihen mit gegebener Funktionalgleichung zurückgeführt auf das Auffinden aller Modulformen zur Hecke-Gruppe $G(\lambda)$ vom Gewicht k und mit Multiplikator C. Im Rest des Kapitels wird mit den bekannten Methoden die Dimension der Vektorraüme dieser Modulformen für alle $\lambda>0$ bestimmt.

Der andere Teil dieses Buches behandelt die Euler-Produktentwicklung von Dirichlet-Reihen. In Kapitel 2 werden Hecke-Operatoren zur vollen Modulgruppe eingeführt und der auf Hecke zurückgehende Satz bewiesen [ibid. **114** (1937), 1–28]: Die Dirichlet-Reihe $\sum_{n\geqq 1} a_n n^{-s}$ besitzt genau dann ein Euler-Produkt, wenn $\sum_{n\geqq 0} a_n e^{2\pi i n\tau}$ Eigenfunktion aller Hecke-Operatoren $T(p)$ ist und diese hat die Form $\sum_{n\geqq 1} a_n n^{-s}=\prod_p (1-a_p p^{-s}+p^{k-1-2s})^{-1}$. Da die Eisenstein-Reihen Eigenfunktionen sind, ist die Aufgabe, eine Basis von Eigenfunktionen zu finden, auf Spitzenformen reduziert. Kapitel 3 behandelt das Skalarprodukt von Modulformen, bezüglich dessen die $T(n)$ Hermitesche Operatoren sind, und daraus resultiert die Peterssonsche Lösung dieser Aufgabe.

In Kapitel 4 wird die Theorie der Hecke-Operatoren nach Heckes Vorbild [ibid. **114** (1937), 316–351] auf Hauptkongruenzuntergruppen zur Modulgruppe ausgedehnt.

Kapitel 5 behandelt eine neuere Untersuchung von A. Weil [ibid. **168** (1967), 149–156; MR **34** #7473] zum ersten Fragenkreis. Die Eigenschaft einer holomorphen Funktion, Modulform zu einer Hauptkongruenzuntergruppe zu sein, drücken Funktionalgleichungen zu jeder der endlich vielen Erzeugenden aus. Jede dieser Funktionalgleichungen läßt sich übersetzen in eine Funktionalgleichung einer zugeordneten Dirichlet-Reihe. Auf diese Weise erhält man als Ausdehnung des Heckeschen Satzes eine Charakterisierung von Modulformen zu gewissen Hauptkongruenzuntergruppen durch Funktionalgleichungen vieler Dirichlet-Reihen.

In Kapitel 6 schließlich wird die ebenfalls auf Hecke [Danske Vid. Selsk. Math.-Fys. Medd. **17** (1940), no. 12; MR **2**, 251] zurückgehende Konstruktion von Modulformen zu Hauptkongruenzuntergruppen durch Theta-Reihen positiv-definiter ganzer quadratischer Formen behandelt.

Das Buch ist sehr klar geschrieben und kann empfohlen werden, zumal es eine Vielzahl schöner mathematischer Ideen, welche meist auf Hecke zurückgehen, beschreibt. {Druckfehler: Auf S. I-16 in Pro. 3 lies $f(L\tau)$ statt $f(-1/\tau)$.}

J. Spilker (Freiburg)

Citations: MR 2, 251f = F25-4; MR 34# 7473 = F65-21.

F65-28 **(41# 6857)**

Weil, André

Zeta-functions and Mellin transforms.

Algebraic Geometry (Internat. Colloq., Tata Inst. Fund. Res., Bombay, 1968), *pp.* 409–426. *Oxford Univ. Press, London*, 1969.

In an earlier paper [Math. Ann. **168** (1967), 149–156; MR **34** #7473] which has justly aroused considerable interest, the author, by an extension of the work of Hecke which relates Dirichlet series and automorphic forms, showed the plausibility of a rather striking suggestion relating the zeta-function of an elliptic curve over the rationals to certain modular forms. In the present paper the extensions of Hecke's work necessary to justify the suggestion over an arbitrary global field are treated. It should be remarked that a report of further progress is to be found in notes of the author's lectures at the Institute for Advanced Study.

R. P. Langlands (Princeton, N.J.)

Citations: MR 34# 7473 = F65-21.

Referred to in E68-38.

F65-29 **(42# 5921)**

Asai, Tetsuya

On a certain function analogous to $\log|\eta(z)|$.

Nagoya Math. J. **40** (1970), 193–211.

A. Weil [J. Math. Soc. Japan **20** (1968), 400–402; MR **37** #155] obtained the functional equation relating $\log\eta(z)$ to $\log\eta(-1/z)$ by using the functional equation of $\zeta(s)\zeta(s+1)$ ($\zeta(s)=$ Riemann's zeta function). In the present paper the author generalizes this method and obtains, among his results, a function analogous to $\log|\eta(z)|$ for algebraic number fields (for a different kind of generalization of $\eta(z)$ to algebraic number fields see G. J. Rieger [Math. Ann. **141** (1960), 377–383; MR **22** #10974]) and some Kronecker limit formula type results. The first generalization is to the Gaussian field $F=\mathbf{Q}(i)$; in a second step, F is any algebraic field of class number one (this restriction may be motivated mainly by technical simplicity). In case $F=\mathbf{Q}(i)$, denote the Dedekind zeta function $\zeta_F(s)$ by $Z(s)$ and set $\varphi(s)=Z(s)Z(s+1)$ and $\Phi(s)=\pi^{-(2s+1)}\Gamma(s)\Gamma(s+1)\varphi(s)$. Let $H_{\mathbf{q}}$ be the quaternion upper half-space, the three-dimensional space of elements $z=\begin{pmatrix} x & -y\\ y & \bar{x}\end{pmatrix}$ with complex x and $y>0$. The group $\mathrm{SL}(2,\mathbf{C})$ operates on $H_{\mathbf{q}}$ by $z\to\sigma\langle z\rangle=(\alpha z+\beta)(\gamma z+\delta)^{-1}$ for $\sigma\in\mathrm{SL}(2,\mathbf{C})$, the complex numbers, say α, being identified with the quaternions $\begin{pmatrix}\alpha & 0\\ 0 & \bar{\alpha}\end{pmatrix}$. The subgroup $\mathrm{SL}(2,Z[i])$ operates discontinuously on $H_{\mathbf{q}}$ and the Laplace-Beltrami operator

$$D_{\mathbf{q}} = y^2(4\,\partial^2/\partial x\partial\bar{x}+\partial^2/\partial y^2)-y\,\partial/\partial y$$

is a differential operator on $H_{\mathbf{q}}$, invariant under $\mathrm{SL}(2,\mathbf{C})$. Also, let $K_s(u)$ be the (modified) Bessel function. With this terminology the following are proved. Theorem 1: The function $h(z)$, defined for $z=\begin{pmatrix} x & -y\\ y & \bar{x}\end{pmatrix}\in H_{\mathbf{q}}$ by $8\pi^{-2}y^2Z(2)+4\sum_{\mu,\nu\in\mathbf{Z}[i],\mu\nu\neq 0}\left|\frac{\nu}{\mu}\right|K_1(2\pi|\mu\nu|y)ye^{2\pi i\,\mathrm{Re}(\mu\nu x)}$, has the following properties: (I) $h(z)$ is real valued, real analytic on $H_{\mathbf{q}}$ (of variables $x,\bar{x},y$) and $D_{\mathbf{q}}h=0$; (II) for $\sigma\in\mathrm{SL}(2,\mathbf{Z}[i])$, $h(z)=2\log(|\gamma x+\delta|^2+|\gamma|^2y^2)+h(\sigma\langle z\rangle)$. (On account of (II), $h(z)$ is said to be the harmonic modular form on $H_{\mathbf{q}}$.) Theorem 2: $h(z)$ is associated with the Dirichlet series $Z(s)Z(s+1)$ (essentially under Mellin transform). The proofs follow those in the quoted paper of Weil and use also the following lemma: The function $e_s(z,\alpha)=K_{2s-1}(|\alpha|y)ye^{i\,\mathrm{Re}(\alpha x)}$ ($s\in\mathbf{C}$, $\alpha\in\mathbf{C}$, $z\in H_{\mathbf{q}}$) satisfies $D_{\mathbf{q}}e_s(z,\alpha)=4s(s-1)e_s(z,\alpha)$, so that it is an eigenfunction of $D_{\mathbf{q}}$. For the generalization to fields of degree $n=r_1+2r_2$, set

$\mathscr{H}=\prod_{j=1}^{r_1+r_2} H_j$ ($H_j=H_c$, complex upper half plane, or $H_j=H_q$ as previously defined, accordingly as $j\leqq r_1$ or $j\geqq r_1+1$); $\mathbf{z}=(z_j)\in\mathscr{H}$ is a vector with $z_j=x_j+iy_j$, or $z_j=\begin{pmatrix} x_j & -y_j \\ y_j & \bar{x}_j\end{pmatrix}$, respectively, accordingly as $j\leqq r_1$ or $j\geqq r_1+1$, respectively, $N\mathbf{y}=\prod_{j=1}^{r_1+r_2} y_j^{e_j}$ ($e_j=1$ if $j\leqq r_1$, $=2$ otherwise). Then $E(\mathbf{z},s)=\sum_{(\mu,\nu)\neq(0,0)} N\mathbf{y}(\mu,\nu;\mathbf{z})^s$ ($y(\mu,\nu;\mathbf{z})=y(\mu^{(j)},\nu^{(j)};z_j)$ and

$$y(\mu^{(j)},\nu^{(j)};z_j) = y_j/\{|\mu^{(j)}x_j+\nu^{(j)}|^2+|\mu^{(j)}|^2y_j^2\},$$

$\mu,\nu\in\mathfrak{o}$, the ring of integers of F) is essentially a non-holomorphic Eisenstein series (also a kind of Epstein zeta function). Theorem 3: $\lim_{s\to1}\{E(\mathbf{z},s)-t/(s-1)\}=t(\alpha_0-2r_1\log 2-2r_2-\log N\mathbf{y}(\mathbf{z})+h(\mathbf{z}))$, where

$$\alpha_0 = 2\lim_{s\to1}\{2^{r_2+1}\pi^{r_1+r_2}t^{-1}\Delta^{-1/2}\zeta_F(s)-(s-1)^{-1}\},$$

$h(\mathbf{z})$(defined on $\mathscr{H}$) $=$

$$t^{-1}\zeta_F(s)N\mathbf{y}(\mathbf{z})+(2^{r_2+1}\omega/R)\sum_{(\mu,\nu)',\mu\nu\neq0}|N\nu/N\mu|^{1/2} \times e^{2\pi i S(\mu\nu\omega x)}\prod_{j=1}^{r_1+r_2}K_{e_j/2}(2e_j\pi|(\mu\nu\omega)^j|y_j)y_j^{e_j/2}$$

($t=2^{n-1}\pi^nR/w\Delta$, $S(\cdots)$ stands for the trace, ω^{-1} is the different, the other notations being standard). Theorem 4: (I) $h(\mathbf{z})$ is real valued on $\mathscr{H}$, depending on $2r_1+3r_2$ variables. If D is a polynomial without constant term in the Laplace-Beltrami operators on the component spaces of $\mathscr{H}$, then $Dh(\mathbf{z})=0$. (II) $h(\mathbf{z})$ is a modular form with (explicitly given) automorphic factor, with respect to $\mathrm{SL}(2,\mathfrak{o})$. Theorem 5: $h(\mathbf{z})$ is associated with the family of Dirichlet series $\zeta_F(s,\lambda)\zeta_F(s+1,\lambda)$, where the λ's are certain Grössen-character). *E. Grosswald* (Philadelphia, Pa.)

Citations: MR 22# 10974 = F20-22; MR 37# 155 = F10-102.

F65-30 (43# 4763)

Schwandt, Ernst A.

Non-degenerate modular wave forms with wave parameter $\rho=1$.

J. London Math. Soc. (2) **3** (1971), 183–186.

A modular wave form (introduced by H. Maass [S.-B. Heidelberger Akad. Wiss. Math.-Natur. Kl. **1949**, no. 1; MR **11**, 230]) is a function $\phi(x,y)=\phi(z)$ with $z=x+iy$, $y>0$ satisfying the following conditions: (1) $\phi(z)$ is C^{2r+2} for some natural r, (2) $\prod_{\nu=0}^{r}(\Delta-(\rho+\nu)(\rho+\nu-1))z^{\mu}\phi(z)$ for $\mu=0,1,\cdots,r$, (3) $\phi((az+b)/(cz+d))(cz+d)^{-r}=\phi(z)$ for $\begin{pmatrix} a & b\\ c & d\end{pmatrix}\in\mathrm{SL}(2,\mathbf{Z})$. r is called the dimension of $\phi(z)$ and ρ the parameter. $\Delta=y^2(\partial^2/\partial x^2+\partial^2/\partial y^2)$ is the Laplace-Beltrami operator. The author shows that if $\rho=1$ then the operator $\bar{B}^r$ with $\bar{B}=y^2(\partial/\partial x+i\,\partial/\partial y)$ maps the $\mathbf{C}$-module of such wave forms bijectively on the module of regular analytic modular forms of the same dimension.

M. Eichler (Basel)

Citations: MR 11, 230h = F65-5.

F65-31 (44# 3969)

Maass, H.

Some remarks on Selberg's zeta functions.

Several Complex Variables, I (Proc. Conf., Univ. of Maryland, College Park, Md., 1970), *pp.* 122–131. *Springer, Berlin,* 1970.

Für die analytische Fortsetzung und die Bestimmung der Funktionalgleichung von ζ-Funktionen verfügt man seit langem über die Methode, mit Hilfe gewisser Thetafunktionen eine Integraldarstellung für die ζ-Funktion herzuleiten, aus der sich auf Grund der bekannten Eigenschaften der Thetafunktionen analytische Fortsetzung und Funktionalgleichung der ζ-Funktion ergeben. Dieses Verfahren stieß bei den von A. Selberg als Eisensteinreihen zur unimodularen Gruppe eingeführten Zetafunktionen [Selberg, Inst. Theory of Numbers (Univ. Colorado, Boulder, Colo., 1959), pp. 207–210, Amer. Math. Soc., Providence, R.I., 1959] auf erhebliche Schwierigkeiten, da bei den Thetafunktionen in diesem Fall störende Glieder auftreten. Selberg gelangte zunächst mit anderen Methoden ans Ziel (skizzenhafte Angaben findet man bei Selberg, Proc. Internat. Congr. Mathematicians (Stockholm, 1962), pp. 177–189, Inst. Mittag-Leffler, Djursholm, 1963 [MR **31** #372]). Der Verfasser skizziert nun in diesem Ergebnisbericht, wie man durch die Verwendung passender Differentialoperatoren die störenden Glieder entfernen und sich gleichzeitig auch die sonst nötige Berechnung von Residuen ersparen kann. Eine ausführliche Darstellung ist inzwischen erschienen [der Verfasser, *Siegel's modular forms and Dirichlet series*, Springer, Berlin, 1971]. *K.-B. Gundlach* (Münster)

Citations: MR 31# 372 = F60-7.

F70 REPRESENTATION THEORY OF THE ABOVE GROUPS

See also reviews E12-49, E12-104, E56-56, E60-50, E64-17, E64-22, E68-9, E68-30, F15-10, F25-22, F50-20, F55-10, F55-25, F55-26.

F70-1 (9, 12g)

Kloosterman, H. D. The behaviour of general theta functions under the modular group and the characters of binary modular congruence groups. I. Ann. of Math. (2) **47**, 317–375 (1946).

The object of this paper is to use the transformation theory of general ϑ-functions for the study of the matric representations and the characters of the binary modulary congruence group modulo p^λ. [I suggest and shall use in the sequel the phrase "modulary group" for the German "Modulargruppe" in contradistinction to "modular group" for the German "Modulgruppe."]

For the definition of the ϑ-functions in question we need first an integral square matrix Q of degree n; the quadratic form $x'Qx$ is assumed as definite positive, x being a vector of n components. Let $\Delta>0$ be the determinant of Q. A vector a of n components is called "special" if Qa is divisible by Δ. Let N be a positive integer, τ a complex variable of positive imaginary part and z a complex vector with n components. If g, h, a are special vectors then the following definition is given:

$$\vartheta_{gh}(z|\tau;a,N)=\sum_{m\equiv a(N\Delta)}(-1)^{h'Q(m-a)/N\Delta^2} \times\exp\left\{\frac{\pi i\tau}{N\Delta^2}(m+\tfrac{1}{2}g)'Q(m+\tfrac{1}{2}g)+\frac{2\pi i}{\Delta}(m+\tfrac{1}{2}g)'Qz\right\}.$$

For fixed Q, N, g, h this furnishes for different vectors a exactly $N^n\Delta$ functions which are shown to be linearly independent.

The transformation of the function under $\tau\to\tau+\beta$ with β a rational integer is obvious; for $\tau\to-1/\tau$ the Poisson sum formula is used. Hecke's variant of Hermite's method gives the transformation formula for a general modular substitution through the investigation of certain Gaussian sums; N and Δ are now taken as odd. It turns out that any of the ϑ-functions goes over into a linear aggregate of them, however in general with different g, h. Through a particular choice of g modulo 2 it can be achieved that ϑ_{00} goes over into an aggregate of ϑ_{00}'s. In order to get a linear relation with constant coefficients the following quotients are introduced:

$$x_a(z|\tau)=\vartheta_{00}(z|\tau;a,N)/\vartheta_{00}^N(z|\tau;0,1).$$

These functions are subjected to substitutions of the principal congruence modular group $G(\epsilon_n)$:

$$U=\begin{pmatrix}\alpha & \beta\\ \gamma & \delta\end{pmatrix}\equiv\begin{pmatrix}1 & 0\\ 0 & 1\end{pmatrix} \pmod{\epsilon_n},$$

where ϵ_n is the greatest elementary divisor of the matrix Q. Here U operates on a function $x_a(z|\tau)$ as follows:

$$x_a(z|\tau)U=(\gamma\tau+\delta)^{\frac{1}{2}n(N-1)}x_a\left(\frac{z}{\gamma\tau+\delta}\middle|\frac{\alpha\tau+\beta}{\gamma\tau+\delta}\right).$$

The results about the ϑ_{gg} are used now to show that

$$x_aU=\sum_{b \bmod N\Delta}^{*} A(a,b)x_b,$$

where the asterisk denotes that the summation is to be taken only over "special" vectors. Finally, for a simplification of the transformation matrix, instead of the $x_a(z|\tau)$ the functions

$$u_a(z|\tau)=(-1)^{v'Q(a+c)}x_{a+c}(z|\tau)$$

are introduced, where v and c are certain special vectors defined in terms of Q, N, Δ, g. Then

$$(*)\qquad u_aU=\sum_{b \bmod N\Delta}^{*} C_0(a,b)u_b,$$

where the $C_0(a,b)$ are explicitly determined. It follows that the correspondence (*) $U\rightarrow(C_0(a,b))$ is a matrix representation of the group $G(\epsilon_n)$; this representation, denoted by R_0, is $N^n\Delta$-rowed. Since it turns out that $(C_0(a,b))$ is the identity matrix for all substitutions

$$U\equiv\begin{pmatrix}1 & 0\\ 0 & 1\end{pmatrix} \pmod{N\epsilon_n}$$

of the principal congruence subgroup $G(N\epsilon_n)$ of $G(\epsilon_n)$, (*) actually gives a representation of the quotient group $G(\epsilon_n)/G(N\epsilon_n)$, which is simply isomorphic with the binary modulary group modulo N.

This representation is now studied, especially for $N=p^\lambda$, p odd. This requires first an examination of the sets of conjugate elements in the modulary group modulo p^λ, which are enumerated in a table. The number of complete sets of conjugates is $p^\lambda+4\sum_{\nu=0}^{\lambda-1}p^\nu$. The representation R_0 is found to be the direct sum of Δ identical representations formed by all those u_a for which $a\equiv 0 \pmod\Delta$. This reduced representation of N^n rows, called R, is further studied.

Some invariant subspaces of R are found, first by the use of ϑ-relations for N, N_1, N_2, when $N=N_1^2N_2$, and second by considering automorphs modulo N of the quadratic form $x'Qx$. In this way a complete decomposition of R into its irreducible components can be achieved for $n=1$, $N=p^\lambda$. A table shows the 2λ different irreducible characters thus obtained, which are only a part of the total number of all characters. *H. Rademacher* (Philadelphia, Pa.).

Referred to in F70-3, F70-6, F70-19.

F70-2 (9, 13b)

Kloosterman, H. D. The behaviour of general theta functions under the modular group and the characters of binary modular congruence groups. II. Ann. of Math. (2) **47**, 376–447 (1946).

In part I [see the preceding review] a matrix representation R of the group G, the modulary congruence group modulo N, was obtained by means of theta functions of n variables belonging to the quadratic positive definite form $x'Qx$. This representation is studied here for $n=2$, $N=p^\lambda$, p an odd prime. A complete decomposition into irreducible representations is achieved. A number of irreducible characters of G are obtained, which form the complete set for $\lambda=1$ (for this case already found by Frobenius). Tables of the characters are included. The complicated details of the investigation cannot be indicated briefly. The terminology of quadratic fields instead of quadratic forms is used. Of interest is the appearance of certain sums of roots of unity which are generalizations of the "Kloosterman sums"; for these generalizations the author proves here estimates similar to those of Davenport and Salié. *H. Rademacher.*

Referred to in F70-3, F70-6.

F70-3 (9, 228d)

van der Blij, Frederik. Theta functions of degree *m*. Thesis, University of Leiden, 1947. 47 pp.

The theta functions considered are of the form

$$\theta_{GH}(Z|T;P,\nu)=\sum_{M\equiv P(\bmod\ \Delta\nu)} e\left\{\frac{(M-P)H'}{\Delta\nu}\right\}$$
$$\times e\left\{\frac{(M+\frac{1}{2}G)T(M+\frac{1}{2}G)'}{\Delta\nu}\right\}e\{2Z(M+\tfrac{1}{2}G)'\},$$

where $e\{X\}=e^{(\pi i/\Delta)\sigma(QX)}$; G, H, P, Q are integral matrices satisfying certain conditions; Z and T are certain matrices with complex elements; ν is a positive integer; $\Delta=|Q|$; $\sigma(X)$ is the trace of X. These functions are formally similar to the theta functions considered by H. D. Kloosterman [Ann. of Math. (2) **47**, 317–375, 376–447 (1946); these Rev. **9**, 12, 13] but vectors have here been replaced by matrices and it has become necessary to introduce the trace into the exponentials; cf. C. L. Siegel [Ann. of Math. (2) **36**, 527–606 (1935)]. The results closely parallel some of those of Kloosterman. The dependence of the theta functions on the parameters is determined. Also studied is the behavior of the functions under generalized modular transformations. Here Z is replaced by $Z(CT+D)^{-1}$ and T by $(AT+B)(CT+D)^{-1}$ with A, B, C, D matrices such that $U=\binom{A\ B}{C\ D}$ is modular; i.e., $U'IU=I$ with $I=\binom{N\ \ E}{-E\ N}$, N the zero matrix, E the unit matrix; cf. Siegel [Math. Ann. **116**, 617–657 (1939); these Rev. **1**, 203]. Similarly, generalized Gaussian sums are defined and analogous transformation formulas for them are determined.

H. S. Zuckerman (Seattle, Wash.).

Citations: MR 1, 203f = F50-1; MR 9, 12g = F70-1; MR 9, 13b = F70-2.

F70-4 (9, 228e)

van der Blij, F. A matric representation of binary modular congruence groups of degree *m*. Nederl. Akad. Wetensch., Proc. **50**, 942–951 = Indagationes Math. **9**, 453–462 (1947).

This first communication announces results whose proofs will apparently be completed in further publications. Continuing the work reviewed above the author states that he will obtain generalizations of more of Kloosterman's results and will finally obtain matrix representations of certain modular congruence groups. Some preliminary results are obtained in this communication. *H. S. Zuckerman.*

F70-5 (9, 228f)

van der Blij, F. A matric representation of binary modular congruence groups of degree *m*. II. Nederl. Akad. Wetensch., Proc. **50**, 1084–1091 = Indagationes Math. **9**, 498–505 (1947).

Continuing the work reviewed above the author obtains generalizations of more of Kloosterman's results. The final results are matrix representations of certain modular congruence groups. *H. S. Zuckerman* (Seattle, Wash.)

F70-6 **(13, 628c)**

Kloosterman, H. D. The characters of binary modulary congruence groups. Proceedings of the International Congress of Mathematicians, Cambridge, Mass., 1950, vol. 1, pp. 275–280. Amer. Math. Soc., Providence, R. I., 1952.

In two earlier papers [Ann. of Math. (2) **47**, 317–375, 376–447 (1946); these Rev. **9**, 12, 13] the author has considered the problem of determining the characters and representations of the binary modulary congruence groups modulo N by deriving the transformation formulae under modular substitutions of certain multiple theta series. By using binary theta series only he succeeded in determining explicitly the greater part of the characters and irreducible representations and conjectured that the remaining irreducible representations might be determined by considering ternary or higher theta series. By well-known methods the problem can be reduced to the case $N=p^\lambda$ where p is a prime number. In the second paper referred to above the binary theta series were defined in terms of a positive definite quadratic form of determinant Δ, where $\Delta\not\equiv 0 \pmod p$. In this case $\Gamma(\Delta)/\Gamma(N\Delta)\cong\Gamma(1)/\Gamma(N)=G(N)$, and the representation of the quotient group $\Gamma(\Delta)/\Gamma(N\Delta)$ obtained by means of the theta series is also a representation of $G(p^\lambda)$. In this way the greater part of the irreducible representations of $G(p^\lambda)$ were found. The author has now discovered that the remaining irreducible representations can be found by considering binary quadratic forms of discriminant Δ where $\Delta\equiv 0 \pmod p$. If $\Delta\not\equiv 0 \pmod{p^2}$ we now have the isomorphism $\Gamma(\Delta)/\Gamma(N\Delta)\cong\Gamma(p)/\Gamma(p^{\lambda+1})$. This does not give immediately a representation of the group $G(p^\lambda)$, but only a representation of a subgroup of $G(p^{\lambda+1})$. However, this representation induces one of the whole group $G(p^{\lambda+1})$ and this induced representation can be split up into its irreducible constituents by means of the same devices as used in the case $\Delta\not\equiv 0 \pmod p$. Detailed proofs are to appear elsewhere.

R. A. Rankin (Birmingham).

Citations: MR 9, 12g = F70-1; MR 9, 13b = F70-2.

F70-7 **(17, 126d)**

Maak, Wilhelm. Fastperiodische Funktionen auf der Modulgruppe. Math. Scand. 3 (1955), 44–48.

In order to be able to characterize all almost periodic functions over a finite group it is sufficient to obtain a complete system of non-equivalent, irreducible, unitary representations of the group [see Maak, Fastperiodische Funktionen, Springer, Berlin, 1950; MR **13**, 29]. This characterization alone is however insufficient for the actual construction of the almost periodic functions. The problem of their construction is solved here for the particular case of the principal congruence subgroup $\Gamma(2)$ of the full modular group, and for the case of unitary representations of first degree. The free group $\Gamma(2)$ is generated by $S(\tau)=\tau+2$ and $T(\tau)=\tau/(-2\tau+1)$; if $X\in\Gamma(2)$, then $X=S^{n_1}T^{m_1}\cdots S^{n_r}T^{m_r}$. If the unitary representations of S and T are $D(S)=A$, $D(T)=B$, respectively, with $|A|=|B|=1$, then $D(X)=A^sB^t$ with $s=n_1+\cdots+n_r$, $t=m_1+\cdots+m_r$. Using results of Rademacher [J. Reine Angew. Math. **167** (1932), 312–336] on the transformation of Dedekind's η-function and on the reciprocity formula for the Dedekind sums $s(h,k)$, the author shows that $\exp\left(\frac{1}{12}\pi i\Psi_{\alpha\beta}\begin{pmatrix}a & b\\ c & d\end{pmatrix}\right)$ is a representation of first degree of $\Gamma(2)$. Here

$$\Psi_{\alpha\beta}\begin{pmatrix}a & b\\ c & d\end{pmatrix}=\alpha\phi(M_1)+\beta\phi(M_2)-(\alpha+\beta)\phi(M_3),$$

M_1, M_2, M_3 belong to the modular group, but not, in general, to $\Gamma(2)$, and are simply related to $\begin{pmatrix}a & b\\ c & d\end{pmatrix}\in\Gamma(2)$; finally,

$$\phi(M)=\phi\begin{pmatrix}a & b\\ c & d\end{pmatrix}=\begin{cases}b/d \text{ if } c=0\\ (a+d)/c-12\operatorname{sgn} cs(a,|c|) \text{ otherwise.}\end{cases}$$

From the reality of $\Psi_{\alpha\beta}$ follows that the representation is unitary and the parameters α, β can always be determined so that $\Psi_{\alpha\beta}(S)=A$, $\Psi_{\alpha\beta}(T)=B$, provided that $|A|=|B|=1$, thus proving the completeness of the system of representations. *E. Grosswald* (Philadelphia, Pa.).

Referred to in F10-77, F70-8.

F70-8 **(20# 3220)**

Maak, W. Zur Theorie der Modulgruppe. Abh. Math. Sem. Univ. Hamburg **22** (1958), 267–275.

The paper deals with unitary representations of degree s for the principal congruence subgroup $\Gamma(2)$ of the modular group. For $s=1$ this problem of representation has been solved [see Maak, Math. Scand. 3 (1955), 44–48; MR **17**, 126]. For $s>1$, let $L\in\Gamma(2)$, let $D_{\rho\sigma}(L)$ ($\rho,\sigma=1,2,\cdots,s$) be a unitary representation of degree s for $\Gamma(2)$, and let $\{f_\rho(\tau)\}$ be a set of linearly independent functions such that $f_\rho(L\tau)=\sum_{\sigma=1}^{s}D_{\rho\sigma}(L)f_\sigma(\tau)$. The s-dimensional space $\mathfrak{M}$ spanned by the functions $\{f_\rho\}$ is a representation module for the $D_{\rho\sigma}(L)$. The main purpose of the paper is the characterization of functions belonging to such modules. The set of functions $f(\tau)$, defined, bounded and analytic in $\mathfrak{J}\tau>0$ form a Banach space under the norm $\|f\|=\sup_\tau|f(\tau)|$. For $L\in\Gamma(2)$, let $Lf=f(L\tau)$. If f, as element of the Banach space, is almost periodic, then $f(\tau)$ is called an entire almost automorphic function; all such functions reduce, however, to constants. One may relax the restrictions on f in two ways: (a) by admitting (polar) singularities, the functions then being called almost automorphic functions; and (b) by retaining the regularity condition, but admitting not only zero, but any non-negative integer k in $Lf=Lf(\tau)=(c\tau+d)^{-k}f(L\tau)$; $L\in\Gamma(2)$. In the latter case f is called an entire almost automorphic form of dimension $-k$. The author proves, among others: Thm. 4: To every unitary representation of $\Gamma(2)$, there exists a module $\mathfrak{M}$ containing only almost automorphic functions. Thm. 6: to every unitary representation of $\Gamma(2)$, there exists a module $\mathfrak{M}$, containing only entire automorphic forms of even dimension $-k$, with $k\geqq 4$. The proofs use Poincaré series and results of Bohr on almost periodic functions.

E. Grosswald (Philadelphia, Pa.)

Citations: MR 17, 126d = F70-7.

F70-10 **(31# 130)**

Lehner, J.

Representations of discrete groups.

Proc. Sympos. Pure Math., Vol. VIII, pp. 203–208. *Amer. Math. Soc., Providence, R.I.*, 1965.

The modular group can be presented abstractly as $\{x,y;x^2=y^3=1\}=M$ or as a real matrix group $\bar{M}=$ {rational integral unimodular matrices}, the latter providing a concrete representation. This process is generalized for groups G (euclidean motions excluded) which are defined abstractly by generators or as real matrix groups $\bar{G}$. Call $\bar{G}$ compact if its fundamental polygon lies above the real axis. One could call G compact if the relationship were independent of representation. This is so [see A. M. Macbeath, *Discontinuous groups and birational transformations*, Proc. Summer School in Math., Geometry and Topology, July 1961, Univ. St. Andrew's, Queen's College, Dundee, 1962]. The author considers invariant properties of a noncompact group G which can be either a free group or the free product of cyclic groups of which at least one is of finite order. *H. Cohn* (Tucson, Ariz.)

F70-11 **(32# 1174)**

Schoeneberg, Bruno

Über die Eisensteinschen Reihen von Primzahlstufe.

Abh. Math. Sem. Univ. Hamburg **26** (1963/64), 145–154.

Let q be an odd prime. The Eisenstein series $G_k(\tau;a_1,a_2,q)$ of degree $-k\leqq -1$ and level q yield a representation of the homogeneous modular congruence group $\Gamma/\Gamma(q)$. By simple group-theoretical considerations, the author determines the multiplicities of the irreducible representations of $\Gamma/\Gamma(q)$, listed by I. Schur, which are contained in this given representation. They are all 0 or 1. Particularly interesting is the result for $k=-1$, where there are fewer linearly independent Eisenstein series than formally might exist. *M. Eichler* (Basel)

F70-12 **(32# 5737)**

Lehner, J.; Newman, M. [Newman, Morris]

Real two-dimensional representations of the modular group and related groups.

Amer. J. Math. **87** (1965), 945–954.

Let Δ be the abstract modular group (the free product of a cyclic group of order 2 and a cyclic group of order 3). Let Λ be the group of real non-singular 2×2 matrices, and Ω the group of real 2×2 matrices of determinant 1 modulo its centre. The authors consider the problem of determining all faithful representations of Δ by a discrete subgroup of Ω. Let

$$T=\begin{pmatrix}0 & 1\\ -1 & 0\end{pmatrix},\qquad R_\rho=\begin{pmatrix}0 & -\rho\\ 1/\rho & 1\end{pmatrix},$$

and G_ρ the group generated by T and R_ρ. The authors prove that (1) for $\rho\geqq 1$, G_ρ is the free product of a cyclic group of order 2 and a cyclic group of order 3; (2) every discrete faithful representation of Δ by a subgroup of Ω is conjugate over Λ to a G_ρ for some $\rho\geqq 1$; (3) a representation of Δ of the type under consideration is horocyclic if and only if it belongs to the conjugacy class determined by $\rho=1$. The paper also contains generalizations to the Hecke groups. *J. R. Smart* (Madison, Wis.)

F70-13 **(32# 7513)**

Andrianov, A. N.

On the representations of the modular group on spaces of parabolic forms. (Russian)

Dokl. Akad. Nauk SSSR **165** (1965), 735–737.

Es sei Γ die inhomogene Modulgruppe, G ein Normalteiler von Γ mit endlichem Index in Γ und $\mathfrak{N}_{2k}(G)$ der Vektorraum der ganzen Spitzenformen der Dimension $-2k$ zu G (k ganz, $\geqq 1$). Ist $\sigma\in\Gamma$, $\sigma(z)=(\alpha z+\beta)(\gamma z+\delta)^{-1}$, so ist mit $F\in\mathfrak{N}_{2k}(G)$ auch $F(z)\circ\sigma=(\gamma z+\delta)^{2k}F(z)$ in $\mathfrak{N}_{2k}(G)$. Man erhält auf diese Weise eine Darstellung $\Omega_{2k}(\Gamma/G)$ von Γ/G auf $\mathfrak{N}_{2k}(G)$. Der Verfasser stellt den folgenden Satz auf: Ist $r_{2k}(\chi)$ die Vielfachheit, mit der die irreduzible Darstellung von Γ/G zu dem Nicht-Hauptcharakter χ in $\Omega_{2k}(\Gamma/G)$ auftritt, so ist

$$r_{2k}(\chi)+r_{2k}(\bar\chi)=\tfrac{1}{6}\chi(1)(2k-1)-\frac{1}{N}\sum_{n \bmod N}\chi(\tau_0{}^n)$$
$$+\tfrac{1}{2}(-1)^k\chi(\sigma_0)+\frac{1}{3}\left(\frac{k+1}{3}\right)(\chi(\sigma_0\tau_0)+\chi((\sigma_0\tau_0)^2)),$$

worin $\bar\chi$ der konjugiert-komplexe Charakter zu χ ist, $\sigma_0,\tau_0\in\Gamma$ durch $\tau_0(z)=z+1$, $\sigma_0(z)=-1/z$ gegeben sind, N die kleinste natürliche Zahl mit $\tau_0{}^N\in G$ ist, und $((k+1)/3)$ das Legendre-Symbol ist.

Es handelt sich um die Verallgemeinerung eines Satzes von Hecke [Math. Ann. **116** (1939), 469–510] über die Darstellung von Γ/G im Raum $\mathfrak{N}_2(G)$ der Differentiale 1. Gattung der zu G gehörenden Riemannschen Fläche. (Die ganzen Spitzenformen der Dimension -2 sind gerade die Differentiale 1. Gattung.) Der Beweis ist skizziert.

{This article has appeared in English translation [Soviet Math. Dokl. **6** (1965), 1482–1485].}

K.-B. Gundlach (Münster)

F70-14 **(33# 1291)**

Menalda, A.

Representations of modulary congruence groups.

Nederl. Akad. Wetensch. Proc. Ser. A **68** = *Indag. Math.* **27** (1965), 760–767.

The author defines a "$\mathfrak{p}$-adic analogue" of theta-functions, and proceeding as in the classical case, obtains a representation of the congruence group $M(\mathfrak{p}^m)=\Gamma(1)/\Gamma(p^m)$, where $\Gamma(\mathfrak{m})$ denotes the group of all 2×2 matrices X whose entries are integers in an algebraic number field, and which satisfy $X\equiv I \pmod{\mathfrak{m}}$.

The author's theta-functions $\theta_\rho(\tau,z)$ are no longer functions of a complex variable; in fact, the variable z ranges over a certain finite set of residue classes in a p-adic number field, and their transformation formulas yield a representation of $M(\mathfrak{p}^m)$.

The author also indicates some submodules of the representation module. *Rimhak Ree* (Vancouver, B.C.)

F70-15 **(33# 7422)**

Fluch, W.

Maximal-Fastperiodizität von Gruppen. I, II.

Math. Scand. **16** (1965), 148–158; 159–163.

An abstract group is called maximally [minimally] almost periodic, abbreviated max.a.p. [min.a.p.], if the intersection of the kernels of all its finite-dimensional unitary representations is the identity [the whole group]. Clearly every subgroup [quotient group] of a max.a.p. [min.a.p.] group is max.a.p. [min.a.p.]. In the spirit of a paper of von Neumann and Wigner [Ann. of Math. (2) **41** (1940), 746–750; MR **2**, 127], this pair of papers obtains these properties for several types of groups, including the following. These groups are max.a.p.: SL(k,R) for $k=1,2,3,\cdots$, where R is the polynomial ring in m ($\geqq 0$) transcendentals over the ring of all integers of an algebraic number field K, or over the ring of all elements of K with denominators relatively prime to a fixed prime ideal; the Hilbert and Siegel modular groups; free groups on sets of cardinality $\leqq 2^{\aleph_0}$; all finitely generated function groups in the sense of L. R. Ford [*Automorphic functions*, second corrected edition, p. 64, Chelsea, New York, 1951]; all finitely generated matrix groups; and the fundamental groups of all closed surfaces. However SL$(2,K)$, K as above, and SL$(2,\mathbf{Q}[x])$ are min.a.p. The author states that some of these results are of interest for the theory of almost automorphic functions. *W. F. Reynolds* (Medford, Mass.)

F70-16 **(35# 1712)**

Godement, R.

The decomposition of $L^2(G/\Gamma)$ for $\Gamma=\mathrm{SL}(2,Z)$.

Algebraic Groups and Discontinuous Subgroups (*Proc. Sympos. Pure Math., Boulder, Colo.*, 1965), *pp.* 211–224. *Amer. Math. Soc., Providence, R.I.*, 1966.

The author considers the problem of decomposing the left-regular representation of $G=\mathrm{SL}(2,R)$ on $L^2(G/\Gamma)$, where $\Gamma=\mathrm{SL}(2,Z)$. Let U be the subgroup of G consisting of unipotent upper triangular matrices, u denoting a typical element $\begin{pmatrix}1 & u\\ 0 & 1\end{pmatrix}$; H the diagonal subgroup with elements $h=\begin{pmatrix}t & 0\\ 0 & t^{-1}\end{pmatrix}$, $t\neq 0$; M the subgroup of orthogonal matrices $m=\begin{pmatrix}\cos\theta & \sin\theta\\ -\sin\theta & \cos\theta\end{pmatrix}$. Let $\beta: H\to R$ be the character of H defined by $\beta(h)=t^2$, where $h=\begin{pmatrix}t & 0\\ 0 & t^{-1}\end{pmatrix}$. Then one has, as usual, $G=MHU$ and $dg=\beta(h)\,dm\,dh\,du$. For a complex number s, $\mathscr{H}(s)$ is the Hilbert space of functions φ on

G which satisfy $\varphi(ghu) = \varphi(g)\beta(h)^{s-1}$, the inner product being $\langle\varphi, \psi\rangle_s = \int_M \varphi(m)\overline{\psi(m)}\, dm$. The action of G by left translation gives a representation of G on $\mathscr{H}(s)$ which is unitary when $\operatorname{Re} s = \frac{1}{2}$. These representations constitute the so-called principal series of representations of G.

Let Φ be a modular function on G, that is, a function satisfying $\Phi(g\gamma) = \Phi(g)$ for $g \in G$, $\gamma \in \Gamma$. For fixed $g \in G$, the function $\Phi(gu)$ on U is right-invariant under $\Gamma_\infty = \Gamma \cap U$, and can therefore be regarded as a function on U/Γ_∞, which is isomorphic to a circle. It can therefore be developed into a Fourier series $\Phi(gu) \sim \sum_n \Phi^n(g)e^{2\pi inu}$. Φ is said to be a cusp-form if $\Phi^0(g) = 0$ a.e. and if $\Phi \in L^2(G/\Gamma)$. The space of cusp forms is denoted by $L_0{}^2(G/\Gamma)$. It is stable under the left action of G.

The author uses the method of his paper reviewed below [#1713] to show that the representation of G on $L_0{}^2(G/\Gamma)$ decomposes into a discrete direct sum of irreducible subrepresentations each occurring with finite multiplicity. This is done in § 9 and § 10.

The remainder of the paper is devoted to studying the representation of G on the orthocomplement of $L_0{}^2(G/\Gamma)$ in $L^2(G/\Gamma)$. To this end, the author defines: (a) for $\Phi \in L^2(G/\Gamma)$, a formal Laplace transform $\hat{\Phi}(g, s)$ by $\hat{\Phi}(g, s) = \int_H \Phi^0(gh)\beta(h)^{s-1}\, dh$, whenever this makes sense; (b) for each $\varphi \in \mathscr{D}(G/U)$ = the space of compactly supported C^∞ functions on G/U, a theta-series θ_φ by $\theta_\varphi(g) = \sum_{\gamma\in\Gamma/\Gamma_\infty} \varphi(g\gamma)$; (c) for $\varphi \in \mathscr{D}(G/U)$, an L-function $L_\varphi(g, 2s) = \int_H \varphi(gh)\beta(h)^{2s}\, dh$; and (d) the Eisenstein series $E_\varphi(g, 2s) = \sum_{\gamma\in\Gamma/\Gamma_\infty} L_\varphi(g\gamma, 2s)$, $\varphi \in \mathscr{D}(G/U)$.

For $\varphi \in \mathscr{D}(G/U)$, one has $\theta_\varphi(\cdot, s) \in \mathscr{H}(s)$, and $L_\varphi(\cdot, 2s) \in \mathscr{H}(1-s)$. It can be shown that θ_φ is orthogonal to $L_0{}^2(G/\Gamma)$. Thus, a first step in the study of the action of G on the orthocomplement of $L_0{}^2(G/\Gamma)$ would be to study the action of G on the span of θ_φ, with $\varphi \in \mathscr{D}(G/U)$.

Under the hypothesis that $\varphi \in \mathscr{D}(G/U)$ and that θ_φ is orthogonal to 1 in $L^2(G/\Gamma)$, the author shows the following: (i) $\zeta(2s)E_\varphi(g, s)$ is, for fixed $g \in G$, an entire function of s, and is invariant under the substitution $(s, \varphi) \to (1-s, \hat{\varphi})$. Here $\hat{\varphi}$ is the Euclidean Fourier transform of φ when the latter is regarded as a function on R^2. This can be done by noting that $G/U \cong R^2 - \{0\}$. Of course ζ is the Riemann zeta function. (ii) $\hat{\theta}_\varphi(g, s)$ is holomorphic for $\operatorname{Re} s \geq \frac{1}{2}$ and is meromorphic in the complex plane. (iii) $\|\theta_\varphi\|_{G/\Gamma}{}^2 = c\int \|\hat{\theta}_\varphi(\cdot, s)\|_s{}^2\, ds$, where c is a constant and the integral is over $\operatorname{Re} s = \frac{1}{2}$, $\operatorname{Im} s > 0$.

(iv) $$\theta_\varphi(g) = (1/4\pi)\int_{\operatorname{Re} s=1/2} E_{\theta_\varphi}(g, s)\, ds.$$

The relation (iii) is nothing but the decomposition of the left-regular representation of G on the subspace of $L^2(G/\Gamma)$ spanned by those θ_φ, $\varphi \in \mathscr{D}(G/U)$, that are orthogonal to 1 in $L^2(G/\Gamma)$. It shows that this representation decomposes into a direct integral of the representations of the principal series. $E_{\theta_\varphi}(\cdot, s)$ is the "component" of θ_φ in $\mathscr{H}(s)$, and (iv) is analogous to the Fourier inversion formula.

Since the representation of G on the constant functions in $L^2(G/\Gamma)$ is trivial, it follows that modulo getting sufficiently many theta-series to span the orthocomplement of $L_0{}^2(G/\Gamma)$ in $L^2(G/\Gamma)$, the above results are a qualitatively complete description of the spectral composition of $L^2(G/\Gamma)$. {As evidenced by a recent lecture of the author delivered in Princeton, he has been able to settle this point also.} The proofs in the present paper are complete, a welcome departure (noted as such by the author also) from the practice of putting forth theorems without proof, a practice that has been common in this subject and has been threatening to become sanctified by usage. The author also notes that the work of Langlands is an exception to this practice, and that the author's method is different from Langlands' method in his more general work.

R. A. Gangolli (Princeton, N.J.)

Citations: MR 35# 1713 = F55-25.
Referred to in F55-25.

F70-17 (35# 5519)

Wohlfahrt, Klaus
Über Kleinsche Darstellungen der Modulgruppe.
Math. Ann. **171** (1967), 110–130.

Let $\Gamma(1)$ be the group of modular matrices $M = \begin{pmatrix} a & b \\ c & d \end{pmatrix}$ with a, b, c, d integers satisfying $ad - bc = 1$. For any integer $n \geq 1$, let $\Gamma(n)$ be the subgroup of $\Gamma(1)$ consisting of all M in $\Gamma(1)$ satisfying $M \equiv E = \begin{pmatrix} 1 & 0 \\ 0 & 1 \end{pmatrix} \pmod n$. $\Gamma(n)$ is a normal subgroup of $\Gamma(1)$ of finite index and is called the Principal congruence subgroup of level n. Any subgroup of $\Gamma(1)$ which contains $\Gamma(n)$ for some n is called a congruence subgroup of $\Gamma(1)$. An important, but as yet not completely solved, problem is to construct all subgroups of $\Gamma(1)$ of finite index which are not congruence groups. Examples of such subgroups occur in the classical work of Klein, Fricke and Pick.

For a prime $q \equiv 3 \pmod 4$, Klein obtained an $r = \frac{1}{2}(q-1)$ rowed matrix representation of the finite group $\Gamma(1)/\Gamma(q)$ by means of matrices whose elements are in the cyclotomic field generated by $\rho = e^{2\pi i}/q$. E. Hecke in his very important work [same Ann. **116** (1939), 469–510] has shown, among others, that this representation of Klein's is irreducible and is equivalent to a representation with elements in the quadratic field $Q(\sqrt{-q})$, Q being the field of rationals. Denote by Ω the ring generated by these r-rowed matrices. In view of certain applications, to be given in a future paper, to the problem about subgroups mentioned above, the author says that it is important to investigate the nature of the ring Ω. The main theorem of the author states that there exists a matrix B such that $B^{-1}\Omega B$ consists precisely of the maximal order of r-rowed integral matrices—integral in $Q(\sqrt{-q})$—in the algebra $\mathfrak{M}_r(Q(\sqrt{-q}))$ of all r-rowed square matrices over $Q(\sqrt{-q})$. The author's main theorem in particular implies that Klein's representation is equivalent to a representation by matrices with elements which are integers of $Q(\sqrt{-q})$. In the case $q = 7$ the author explicitly writes down these matrices. The proofs use only elementary ideas about the calculus of matrices but are somewhat involved.

K. G. Ramanathan (Bombay)

F70-18 (35# 6694)

Satake, Ichirô
Symplectic representations of algebraic groups satisfying a certain analyticity condition.
Acta Math. **117** (1967), 215–279.

The most interesting fact in this paper is that among algebraic groups it is only "classical groups" that can produce the analytic families of polarized abelian varieties induced from the Siegel family. In a previous paper [Amer. J. Math. **87** (1965), 425–461; MR **33** #4326] the author solved the problem of Kuga on holomorphic imbedding of symmetric domains into a Siegel space "over **R**". However, the problem came primarily from that of construction of families of abelian varieties, and one finds it necessary to reconsider the problem "over **Q**". For this purpose, since no systematic Galois theory of representations of algebraic groups existed previously, the author develops (in the first two parts of this three-part paper) such a theory from the beginning over any field of characteristic zero; this lays the foundations not only for the problem of Kuga but for many other problems on algebraic groups.

The contents of Parts I and II are as follows. Let G be an algebraic group defined over a field k_0 of characteristic zero. The study of a completely reducible representation of G defined over k_0 is reduced to that of the k_0-primary representation, i.e., a representation ρ which is a direct sum of a certain number of mutually k_0-equivalent k_0-irreducible representations. Then, by the Galois theory, such a ρ can be described by any one of the absolutely irreducible constituents, say ρ_1, defined over $\bar{k}_0$, the algebraic closure of k_0; conversely, for a given absolutely irreducible representation ρ_1 defined over $\bar{k}_0$, there always exists a k_0-primary representation ρ containing ρ_1. Let K_{ρ_1} be the finite extension of k_0 corresponding to the subgroup $\mathscr{G}_{\rho_1}=\{\sigma\in\mathscr{G}(k_0),\ \rho_1{}^\sigma\sim\rho_1\}$, where $\mathscr{G}(k_0)$ denotes the Galois group of $\bar{k}_0/k_0$. Hence, for each $\sigma\in\mathscr{G}_{\rho_1}$, there is a $\bar{k}_0$-isomorphism φ_σ of representation spaces of ρ_1 and $\rho_1{}^\sigma$ such that $\rho_1{}^\sigma(g)=\varphi_\sigma\rho_1(g)\varphi_\sigma{}^{-1}$ for all $g\in G$. By Schur's lemma, such a φ_σ is uniquely determined up to a scalar multiple and so one has $\varphi_\sigma{}^\tau\varphi_\tau=\lambda_{\sigma,\tau}\varphi_{\sigma\tau}$ with a 2-cocycle $\{\lambda_{\sigma,\tau}\}$ of $\mathscr{G}_{\rho_1}$ in $(\bar{k}_0)^*$, the multiplicative group of nonzero elements in $\bar{k}_0$, whose cohomology class in $H^2(K_{\rho_1},(\bar{k}_0)^*)=H^2(K_{\rho_1},E)$ is well-defined, where E denotes the multiplicative group of all roots of unity. Let $\mathfrak{K}_{\rho_1}$ be the division algebra (variety) defined over K_{ρ_1} representing the algebra class corresponding to the inverse of that cohomology class, i.e. the class containing $\{\lambda_{\sigma,\tau}^{-1}\}$; we also denote by $c(\mathfrak{K}_{\rho_1})$ this inverse class. Then, there is a unique right $\mathfrak{K}_{\rho_1}$-space V_1 defined over K_{ρ_1} and a K_{ρ_1}-homomorphism P_1 of G into $\mathrm{GL}(V_1/\mathfrak{K}_{\rho_1})$ (=the group of all non-singular $\mathfrak{K}_{\rho_1}$-linear automorphisms of V_1) such that $\rho_1(g)=\theta_1(\mathrm{P}_1(g))$, $g\in G$, where θ_1 is a unique absolutely irreducible representation defined over $\bar{k}_0$ of the algebra of all $\mathfrak{K}_{\rho_1}$-linear endomorphisms of V_1 (Proposition 1), and any k_0-primary representation (V,ρ) containing ρ_1 can be obtained as $(V,\rho)=R_{K_{\rho_1}/k_0}(\hat{V}_1,\hat{\rho}_1)$, where $\hat{V}_1=V_1\otimes_{\mathfrak{K}_{\rho_1}}V_2$, V_2 being a suitable left $\mathfrak{K}_{\rho_1}$-space defined over K_{ρ_1} with trivial action of G, and R is the Weil functor for the restriction of the field of definition (Proposition 2). If, in particular, G is connected and semi-simple, then $\mathfrak{K}_{\rho_1}$ is determined in terms of a certain invariant $\gamma(G)\in H^2(k_0,Z)$, Z being the center of G, which generalizes the Hasse-Minkowski invariant, in such a way that $\gamma(G)$ is mapped on $c(\mathfrak{K}_{\rho_1})$ under the natural homomorphism $H^2(K_{\rho_1},Z)\to H^2(K_{\rho_1},E)$ obtained by the restriction of ρ_1 on Z (Theorem 2). The determination of $\gamma(G)$, which is the theme of Part II, is complete for classical groups; for exceptional groups, the author restricts himself to the case of local and number fields, since he needs the results of M. Kneser [Math. Z. **89** (1965), 250–272; MR **32** #5658] and the reviewer [Ann. of Math. (2) **82** (1965), 88–111, especially p. 107; MR **31** #2249].

Let V be a vector space defined over k_0, A a non-degenerate alternating form defined over k_0 on $V\times V$, and $\mathrm{Sp}(V,A)$ the symplectic group viewed as an algebraic group defined over k_0. Let G be arbitrary. A completely reducible k_0-primary representation $\rho\colon G\to\mathrm{GL}(V)$ is said to be symplectic if $\rho(G)\subset\mathrm{Sp}(V,A)$. Denoting by ρ_1 an absolutely irreducible constituent of ρ as before, one has to distinguish the following two cases: (a) ${}^t\rho_1{}^{-1}\sim\rho_1$; (b) ${}^t\rho_1{}^{-1}\nsim\rho_1$ but $\sim\rho_1{}^{\sigma_0}$ for some $\sigma_0\in\mathscr{G}(k_0)$. In case (a), $\mathfrak{K}_{\rho_1}$ has an involution ι_0 of the first kind defined over K_{ρ_1}. In case (b), letting K_0 be the fixed subfield of $\sigma_0|K_{\rho_1}$ in K_{ρ_1}, $\mathfrak{K}_{\rho_1}$ has an involution ι_0 of the second kind inducing σ_0 on the center K_{ρ_1} which is quadratic over K_0. The main result (Theorem 1) of Part I is then the modification of Propositions 1 and 2 mentioned above, in view of the presence of the alternating form A. More precisely, in case (a), there exist on V_1 a non-degenerate ε-hermitian form F_1 with respect to $(\mathfrak{K}_{\rho_1},\iota_0)$, on V_2 a non-degenerate $(-\varepsilon)$-hermitian form F_2 with respect to $(\mathfrak{K}_{\rho_1},\iota_0)$, both defined over K_{ρ_1}, and a K_{ρ_1}-homomorphism P_1 of G into the unitary group $\mathrm{U}(V_1/\mathfrak{K}_{\rho_1},F_1)$, which is absolutely irreducible as a representation of G in $\mathfrak{K}_{\rho_1}$, such that ρ is factorized in the following manner:

$$\left.\begin{array}{c} G\xrightarrow{\mathrm{P}_1}\mathrm{U}(V_1/\mathfrak{K}_{\rho_1},F_1)\\ \times\\ \mathrm{U}(\mathfrak{K}_{\rho_1}\backslash V_2,F_2)\end{array}\right\}\xrightarrow{\otimes}\mathrm{Sp}(\hat{V}_1,\hat{A}_1)\xrightarrow{R_{K_{\rho_1}/k_0}}\mathrm{Sp}(V,A),$$

where $\hat{A}_1$ is a suitable alternating form on $\hat{V}_1=V_1\otimes_{\mathfrak{K}_{\rho_1}}V_2$. A similar statement holds for case (b). In either case $\mathfrak{K}_{\rho_1}$, V_1, V_2, P_1 and the multiplicative equivalence classes of F_1, F_2 are invariants of ρ, and, conversely, any symplectic representation so constructed is k_0-primary and of type (a), (b), respectively.

In Part III the solution of the Kuga problem over $\mathbf{Q}$ is given by combining the above general results and the solution over $\mathbf{R}$ [the author, loc. cit.]. Let G be connected semi-simple defined over $\mathbf{Q}$, $G_{\mathbf{R}}{}^0$ the topological component of the identity of the Lie group $G_{\mathbf{R}}$. Assume that G is of hermitian type, i.e., that the associated symmetric space $D=G_{\mathbf{R}}/K$ admits a $G_{\mathbf{R}}{}^0$-invariant complex structure, K being a maximal compact subgroup of $G_{\mathbf{R}}$. Let V be a vector space defined over $\mathbf{Q}$ and A a non-degenerate alternating form defined over $\mathbf{Q}$ on V. Kuga's problem is then, for a given K, to determine all symplectic representations $\rho\colon G\to G'=\mathrm{Sp}(V,A)$ defined over $\mathbf{Q}$ together with a maximal compact subgroup K' of $G_{\mathbf{R}}{}'$ such that the induced map $D\to D'=G_{\mathbf{R}}{}'/K'$ is (non-constant) holomorphic with respect to the given complex structures on D and D', this being the analyticity condition called (H_1). By the general theory, the problem can first be reduced to the case where ρ is $\mathbf{Q}$-primary. The author makes the further assumption that ρ comes essentially from an absolutely irreducible representation of just one absolutely simple factor of G, this being the case if the group $G_{\mathbf{R}}$ has no compact factor. Then one can assume that G is $\mathbf{Q}$-simple. Under these assumptions, the author gives, in § 8, all possible solutions: namely, besides the standard solution (coming from the identical representation) for the groups of type (I), (II), (III 1), (III 2), there are also non-standard solutions for the groups of type (I′), (IV 1), (IV 2) and for the groups of the mixed type (II–IV 2) if the number of the quaternion variables is four. Thus, exceptional groups (including the trialitarian form of type (D_4)) are (un)fortunately shut out of the Siegel family.

T. Ono (Philadelphia, Pa.)

Citations: MR 31# 2249 = E68-12; MR 32# 5658 = E72-7.

F70-19 **(36# 6541)**

Tanaka, Shun'ichi

On irreducible unitary representations of some special linear groups of the second order. I, II.

Osaka J. Math. **3** (1966), 217–227; 229–242.

Let $\mathbf{K}$ be a non-discrete totally disconnected locally compact field with a residue class field of odd characteristic. Let $\mathbf{L}=\mathbf{K}(\sqrt{\tau})$ be a quadratic extension of $\mathbf{K}$. There is a natural embedding of $\mathrm{SL}(2,\mathbf{K})$ into the symplectic group $\mathrm{Sp}(\mathbf{L})$ defined by A. Weil [Acta Math. **111** (1964), 143–211;

MR **29** #2324]. The restriction to SL(2, **K**) of a representation of Sp(**L**) constructed by Weil [loc. cit.] is shown to constitute a unitary representation T of SL(2, **K**) on $L^2(\mathbf{L})$. Let C be the compact group of elements of norm 1 in **L**. For each $t \in C$ the map $f(x) \to f(tx)$ of $L^2(\mathbf{L})$ is unitary and commutes with T. Thus the decomposition of the corresponding representation of C yields at the same time a decomposition of T. The author shows that the sub-representations of T which arise comprise the discrete series of I. M. Gel'fand, M. I. Graev and I. I. Pjateckiĭ-Šapiro [*Theory of representations and automorphic functions* (Russian), Izdat. "Nauka", Moscow (1966); MR **36** #3725; Uspehi Mat. Nauk **18** (1963), no. 4 (112), 29–99; MR **27** #5864]. In Part II the author applies similar techniques to construct representations of the binary congruence group. Let p be an odd prime, λ a natural number, $\Gamma(p^\lambda)$ the principal congruence subgroup mod p^λ of SL(2, **Z**) and $G(p^\lambda) = \mathrm{SL}(2, \mathbf{Z})/\Gamma(p^\lambda)$. There is a natural homomorphism of $G(p^\lambda)$ into Sp(G), where $G = \mathbf{Z}/(p^\lambda) \times \mathbf{Z}/(p^\lambda)$. Thus the representation of Sp(G) defined by Weil gives rise to a unitary representation of $G(p^\lambda)$, which is a representation constructed by H. Kloosterman [Ann. of Math. (2) **47** (1946), 317–375; MR **9**, 12]. By taking $G = \mathbf{Z}/(p^\lambda) \times \mathbf{Z}/(p^{\lambda-1})$, $\lambda \geqq 2$, the author constructs a new representation of $G(p^\lambda)$. For $\lambda = 2$ this representation is decomposed into irreducible ones and a comparison of the traces of these representations with the traces calculated by H. Rohrbach [Schr. Math. Sem. Inst. Angew. Math. Univ. Berlin **1** (1932), 33–94] shows that these representations constitute all the irreducible representations absent from Kloosterman's work. *A. Kleppner* (College Park, Md.)

Citations: MR 9, 12g = F70-1; MR 29# 2324 = E12-104; MR 36# 3725 = F02-18.

F70-20 (37# 6380)

Takahashi, Reiji

Über p-adische Kugelfunktionen und unitäre Darstellungen der Modulargruppen.

J. Math. Soc. Japan **20** (1968), 350–364.

Sei p eine Primzahl $\neq 2$ und K die Gruppe aller Matrizen $\begin{pmatrix} a & b \\ c & d \end{pmatrix}$ mit ganzen p-adischen Zahlen und $ad - bc = 1$ und K^m die Untergruppe derjenigen Matrizen, welche kongruent zur Einheitsmatrix modulo p^m sind. Die Faktorgruppe K/K^m ist die (homogene) Modulargruppe zur Stufe p^m. Sie ist kompakt in der p-adischen Topologie. Die irreduziblen Darstellungen dieser Modulargruppen wurden von J. A. Shalika, T. Shintani und S. Tanaka [siehe Tanaka, Osaka J. Math. **4** (1967), 65–84; MR **36** #2714] bestimmt. In dieser Arbeit wird die Godementsche Theorie der Kugelfunktionen der Klasse χ benutzt, um eine Reihe irreduzibler Darstellungen dieser Gruppe herzuleiten, welche bei klassischen Gruppen der Hauptserie entspricht. *J. Spilker* (Freiburg)

F70-21 (38# 5787)

Iyanaga, Kenichi

Arithmetic of special unitary groups and their symplectic representations.

J. Fac. Sci. Univ. Tokyo Sect. I **15** (1968), 35–69.

Let K be a quadratic extension of a finite algebraic number field k and $R_{K/k}$ the Weil functor of lowering the field of definition, from K to k, of an algebraic variety defined over K. To a non-degenerate hermitian space (V, H) over K/k, an alternating space (V', A') over k is naturally assigned with $V' = R_{K/k}V$. For a lattice L in V_K, L' denotes a lattice in V_k' determined by L canonically. In Chapter II of the paper, the author describes the elementary divisors of L' in terms of the invariants of L when L is "modular". Chapter I contains definitions and elementary properties of modular lattices and their invariants. Chapter III starts with the following setting: Let (V, H) be as above, let $\Lambda^r H$, $1 \leq r \leq n$, $n = \dim V$, be the hermitian form on $\Lambda^r V$ given by

$$\Lambda^r H(v_1 \wedge \cdots \wedge v_r, u_1 \wedge \cdots \wedge u_r) = \det(H(v_i, u_j)),$$

$v_i, u_j \in V$. Put, anew, $(V', A') = R_{K/k} \circ \Lambda^r(V, H)$ and put $G = \mathrm{SU}(V, H)$, the special unitary group, $G' = S_p(V', A')$, the symplectic group. The functor $R_{K/k} \circ \Lambda^r$ induces a k-homomorphism $\rho: G \to G'$, a symplectic representation. Denoting by L' the lattice in V_k' naturally obtained by an L in V_K, one has $\rho(G_L) \subset G_{L'}'$, where $G_L = \{g \in G_K, gL = L\}$, $G_{L'}' = \{g' \in G_k', g'L' = L'\}$. Assume now that k is totally real and K totally imaginary. Under a mild condition on Witt indices of H with respect to infinite places of k, the groups G, G' determine symmetric bounded domains D, D' on which G_L, $G_{L'}'$ act discontinuously, respectively. The representation ρ induces a "holomorphic imbedding" $D \subset D'$ in the sense of Satake. Let F be the field of automorphic functions on D with respect to G_L and F' be the subfield of F consisting of those functions which can be extended to automorphic functions on D' with respect to $G_{L'}'$. Then, what is the structure of the field extension F/F'? The author's partial answer to this interesting question is substantially as follows: assuming $k = \mathbf{Q}$, for simplicity, under some conditions (too complicated to reproduce here), the extension F/F' is abelian with the Galois group isomorphic to a subgroup of the first cohomology group $H^1(g, (\zeta_n))$, where $\zeta_n = \exp(2\pi i n^{-1})$ and g is the Galois group of a certain extension K'/K, where K' is a Kummer extension of $K(\zeta_n)$. In an appendix some conditions for the vanishing of that cohomology group are studied, which imply, in turn, the stronger result $F' = F$. The paper also contains some results concerning the rational boundary components of the symmetric bounded domain of type (I). *T. Ono* (Philadelphia, Pa.)

F70-22 (43# 2111)

Lenglends, R. P. [Langlands, R. P.]

Euler products. (Russian)

Mathematics: Periodical Collection of Translations of Foreign Articles, Vol. 15, No. 1 (Russian), pp. 14–43. Izdat. "Mir", Moscow, 1971.

The author gives some applications of group representation theory to the theory of automorphic forms.

For any commutative ring R, denote by G_R the group of all simplectic $2n \times 2n$ matrices over R. Let A be the ring of elements $(a_p) \in \prod_p \mathbf{Q}_p$, where almost all the a_p are integers of $\mathbf{Q}_p$; the group G_A has a locally compact topology and $G_\mathbf{Q}$ is a discrete subgroup of it. Let $C = G_\mathbf{Q} \backslash G_A$, the group of ideals, whose characters are to be considered as basic automorphic forms. Any character χ of C defines a character χ_p of the group $\mathbf{Q}_p$. Consider the L-series $L(s, \chi) = \prod_p 1/(1 - \chi_p{}^{(p)}/p^s)$ (over those p that divide the conductor f_χ). $L^2(G_\mathbf{Q} \backslash G_A)$ is expressed as a direct integral of certain Hilbert spaces and with any such space one can associate an Eulerian product, with analytic properties similar to those of $L(s, \chi)$.

In § 2 the author defines the Euler product $L(s, \pi, \varphi) = \prod_p 1/\det(1 - \pi(g_p)/p^s)$, starting with a semisimple Lie algebra over **Q**. He proves that for almost all simple groups there is a nontrivial representation for which the function $L(s, \pi, \varphi)$ is meromorphic in **C**. In §§ 3 and 4 the above product converges absolutely for Re(s) sufficiently large and the author uses some results of Harish-Chandra, Gindikin and Karpelevič to establish a formula similar to the Weyl formula for characters. In the last two paragraphs he defines the Eisenstein series and determines the Dynkin diagrams for some Lie algebras. *O. Stănăşilă* (Bucharest)

F99 NONE OF THE ABOVE, BUT IN THIS CHAPTER

See also reviews E44-5, Z10-1.

F99-1 **(12, 319d)**

Bellman, Richard. Generalized Eisenstein series and nonanalytic automorphic functions. Proc. Nat. Acad. Sci. U. S. A. **36**, 356–359 (1950).

The author introduces a new class of "nonanalytic automorphic functions" [cf. Maass, Math. Ann. **121**, 141–183 (1949); these Rev. **11**, 163]. These new functions are obtained from the classical theta-functions, and the author uses the theta transformation formula to expand the new functions into generalized Eisenstein series. The associated Dirichlet series are the Epstein ζ-functions. The author indicates two generalizations of his result: one, to the Siegel modular functions; the other, to the function $f_k(x)=\sum_{n=1}^{\infty} d_k(n) V_k(n^2x^2)$, where V_k is the Voronoi function defined by $\int_0^\infty V_k(x)x^{s-1}dx=\{\Gamma(s)\}^k$. Proofs and details are promised in a subsequent paper. *J. Lehner.*

Citations: MR 11, 163c = F65-4.

F99-2 **(20# 2323)**

Häuslein, Günter. Über die Modulfunktionen arithmetischer Körper höheren Grades. Math. Nachr. **16** (1957), 73–78.

Suppose that $K=k(x, y)$ is a field of algebraic functions of one variable with the defining (absolutely irreducible) equation $f(x, y)=0$ over the algebraic number field k of absolute degree g. Using the isomorphisms $k\to k^{(i)}$ into the field of all complex numbers C the author associates to K the function fields $CK^{(i)}/C$ by replacing the coefficients of $f(x, y)$ by their ith conjugates. The fields $K^{(i)}$ have the same genus p as K. Furthermore, denote by $\sigma_j^{(i)}$, $1\leqq j\leqq p$, half systems of retrosections on the Riemann surfaces of the $CK^{(i)}$, which can be augmented to canonical systems of retrosections. Now observe that the differentials of the first kind in each field $K^{(i)}$ form modules $M^{(i)}$ of rank pg over the ring of integers. Systems of generators $w^{(i)}$ for these modules are picked as follows: Let ϕ_j, $1\leqq j\leqq p$, be a k-basis of the module of differentials of the first kind in K/k. Denoting by $\Gamma=C_1Z+\cdots+C_gZ$, Z the ring of integers, the maximal order of K, Steinitz' theorem implies $M=\Gamma\phi_1+\cdots+\Gamma\phi_{p-1}+\mathfrak{b}\phi_p$, with an ideal $\mathfrak{b}=b_1Z+\cdots+b_gZ$ of Γ. Then the elements $W_1=C_1\phi_1, \cdots, W_{p-1}=C_1\phi_{p-1}, W_p=b_1\phi_p, \cdots, W_{p(g-1)+1}=C_g\phi_1, \cdots, W_{pg-1}=C_g\phi_{p-1}, W_{pg}=b_g\phi_p$ form a basis of M over Z. Passage to the fields $K^{(i)}$, replacing the coefficients of these expressions with respect to x, y and their multipliers by their conjugates, determines similar bases $w_\nu^{(i)}$ for the modules $M^{(i)}$. Finally set $A_j^{(i)}=((\sigma_\alpha^{(i)}, w_\beta^{(i)}))$ and $Z(w, \sigma)=(A_j^{(i)})$ with $1\leqq j\leqq g$, $1\leqq\alpha\leqq p$, $(j-1)p+1\leqq\beta\leqq jp$, where $(\sigma, w)=\int_\sigma w$. With this notation the author shows, taking advantage of results of C. L. Siegel and Hel Braun on modular forms, that $\sum|\det Z(w, \sigma)|^{-s}$, summation being taken over $\{\sigma^{(1)}, \cdots, \sigma^{(g)}\}$, complete sets of non-associated half-systems of retrosections, is formally a modular function which is analytic for $R(s)>p+1$. *O. F. G. Schilling* (Chicago, Ill.)

F99-3 **(33# 7309)**

Skubenko, B. F.

The distribution of integer matrices and calculation of the volume of the fundamental domain of a unimodular group of matrices. (Russian)

Trudy Mat. Inst. Steklov. **80** (1965), 129–144.

Let Ω be a Jordan-measurable set on the hypersurface $\det(x_{ij})=1$, where the x_{ij} are n^2 variables. Then the number of integral points on the surface $\det(x_{ij})=N$ which lie in $N^{1/n}\Omega$ is asymptotically

$$\frac{\operatorname{mes}\Omega}{\zeta(2)\cdots\zeta(n)}\prod_i\frac{(p_i^{k_i+1}-1)\cdots(p_i^{k_i+n-1}-1)}{(p_i-1)(p_i^2-1)\cdots(p_i^{n-1}-1)},$$

where $N=\prod_i p_i^{k_i}\to\infty$, and the number of such integral points where the greatest common divisor of the $(n-1)$ by $(n-1)$ minors is unity is given asymptotically by

$$\frac{\operatorname{mes}\Omega}{\zeta(2)\cdots\zeta(n)}N^{n-1}\prod_i\frac{p_i^n-1}{p_i^{n-1}(p_i-1)}.$$

Here mes Ω is the measure of Ω with respect to an appropriate measure. It follows that the measure of the quotient space of the group of real unimodular matrices by integral ones is $\vartheta_n=\zeta(2)\cdots\zeta(n)$.

{This result is said to have been first obtained by Weil using the theory of adeles (but see C. L. Siegel [Ann. of Math. (2) **46** (1945), 340–347; MR **6**, 257]).} The present proof is by induction on n and makes use of trigonometric sums to estimate the numbers of solutions of inequalities. *J. W. S. Cassels* (Cambridge, England)

Citations: MR 6, 257b = H25-2.

F99-4 **(34# 2581)**

Pjateckiĭ-Šapiro, I. I.; Šafarevič, I. R.

Galois theory of transcendental extensions and uniformization. (Russian)

Izv. Akad. Nauk SSSR Ser. Mat. **30** (1966), 671–704.

Let D be a bounded symmetric domain, G its group of automorphisms and Γ a discrete group of automorphisms of D. The following (not mutually exclusive) cases are considered: (1) D/Γ is compact; (2) D is the unit disc and D/Γ has finite invariant area; (3) Γ is arithmetic. A main object of study in the paper is the inductive limit $K(\Gamma)$ of the fields K_Δ of automorphic functions of the subgroups Δ of finite index of Γ. Let $\mathfrak{G}$ be its Galois group over $\mathbf{C}$, topologized using the finitely generated subfields of $K(\Gamma)$. Let Γ' be the group of $g\in G$ such that $g\cdot\Gamma\cdot g^{-1}$ is commensurable with Γ, and $\mathfrak{G}'$ its completion with respect to the groups Δ. There is a natural monomorphism of $\mathfrak{G}'$ into $\mathfrak{G}$, which is shown to be an isomorphism in cases (1), (2), and in case (3) if moreover Γ is associated to a $\mathbf{Q}$-structure on G whose $\mathbf{Q}$-rank is equal to the rank of D, as a symmetric space. (This last restriction is dictated by the proof, but is not shown to be necessary.) In case (1) this follows from the fact that D/Γ is a minimal model for K_Δ, and in the other ones, the proof is based on Proposition 4 mentioned below. In case (3), there is a natural homomorphism of $\mathfrak{G}'$ into the finite part of the adele group of G, whose image is described, using Galois cohomology. The authors consider next the projective limit $X(\Gamma)$ [$Y(\Gamma)$] of the quotients D/Δ [of the normal compactifications $\tilde{D}/\Delta$ of the quotients D/Δ in the non-compact cases]. It is a finite-dimensional proalgebraic projective variety, on which $\mathfrak{G}'$ operates, and which is quasi-homogeneous (i.e., there are regular points whose orbits under the automorphism group of the variety are dense), which is a model for $K(\Gamma)$. Proposition 4 states that in cases (1), (2), and in case (3) with the above conditions on ranks, the inductive limit $A(\Gamma)$ of the graded rings A_Δ of square-integrable automorphic forms for Δ is isomorphic to the inductive limit $D(\Gamma)$ of the rings of regular differentials of the fields K_Δ, and the projective spectrum of $A(\Gamma)$ is $X(\Gamma)$ in case (1), the projective limit $W(\Gamma)$ of suitable desingularisations W_Δ of $\tilde{D}/\Delta$ in the non-compact case. The proof depends on delicate properties of the W_Δ, which so far have been only partially stated by the first author [Uspehi Mat. Nauk **19** (1964), no. 6 (120),

93–121; MR **32** #7790] and J. Igusa [Proc. Sympos. Pure Math. Vol. 9, pp. 301–305, Amer. Math. Soc., Providence, R.I., 1966] (whose statements do not seem, in fact, to the reviewer to fully agree on all points). The paper ends with an application to the modular group: Let S be a set of primes, and $P(S)$ the inductive limit of the fields of automorphic functions for the principal congruence subgroups $\Gamma(m)$ of the modular group, where m runs through the power products of elements in S; then the only subfields of $P(S)$ invariant under its Galois group over $\mathbf{C}$ are $\mathbf{C}$ and $P(S)$. Throughout the paper, the case where Δ runs through suitable families of subgroups of Γ of finite index is also considered. The paper also contains a discussion of proalgebraic varieties.

{Reviewer's remarks: On p. 678 D is not necessarily connected, and $K(\Gamma)$ therefore not necessarily a field; the statement about Γ' presupposes that G has no $\mathbf{Q}$-factor whose group of real points is compact. On p. 679 the compactness of ker $\bar{\varphi}$ does not imply that $\bar{\varphi}$ is proper. One has to know that Im $\bar{\varphi}$ is closed, but this is easily proved directly.} *A. Borel* (Princeton, N.J.)

Citations: MR 32# 7790 = F45-24.

Referred to in E60-36, F02-20, F15-33, F99-6.

F99-5 (42# 201)

Venugopal Rao, V.

Averages involving Fourier coefficients of non-analytic automorphic forms.

Canad. Math. Bull. **13** (1970), 187–198.

If f is a (holomorphic) automorphic form belonging to the group generated by the transformations $\tau \to \tau+\lambda$, $\tau \to -1/\tau$, then f has a Fourier expansion $f(\tau)=a_0+\sum a_n \exp(2i\pi n\tau/\lambda)$ and the quantity $\sum a_n(x-n)^\delta$ $(0<n\leqq x$, $\delta>0)$ is evaluated in classical works. When f is non-analytical there is still a Fourier expansion (with Whittaker functions replacing exp). The aim of the author is to represent the same quantity as a convergent series of analytic functions. *H. Jacquet* (New York)

F99-6 (43# 1955)

Robert, Alain

Automorphism groups of transcendental field extensions.

J. Algebra **16** (1970), 252–270.

This paper contains a few theorems and several examples about transcendental Galois theory. This subject has been started by I. I. Pjateckiĭ-Šapiro and I. R. Šafarevič [Izv. Akad. Nauk SSSR Ser. Mat. **30** (1966), 671–704; MR **34** #2581] in order to get an algebraic analogue to the theory of uniformization of algebraic varieties by automorphic functions. These ideas were further developed by Y. Ihara [*On congruence monodromy problems*, Vol. 1, Math. Dept., Univ. of Tokyo, Tokyo, 1968; Vol. 2, 1969] including number theoretical aspects.

The theorems of the paper under review are influenced by the papers mentioned above, the examples are good illustrations showing the transcendental traps. Different examples can be found in a paper of R. Baer [Math. Z. **114** (1970), 217–240; MR **41** #3452].

W.-D. Geyer (Heidelberg)

Citations: MR 34# 2581 = F99-4.

G. DIOPHANTINE GEOMETRY

G02 BOOKS AND SURVEYS

See also reviews D02-13, D02-18, D02-23, D02-24, D72-53, D72-55, E02-17, F02-4, G05-11, G05-29, G05-100, G10-9, G10-12, G10-16, G10-21, G15-19, G15-20, G15-28, G15-47, G15-48, G20-7, G20-8, G20-10, G20-36, G25-12, G25-44, G30-46, G30-50, G35-25, G35-54, R02-35, R02-47, R02-53, R58-10, R58-12, R58-39, S35-8, T50-8, Z02-42, Z02-44, Z02-67, Z02-75, Z10-23, Z10-26, Z15-89.

G02-1 **(4, 239c)**

Hasse, Helmut. Zur arithmetischen Theorie der algebraischen Funktionenkörper. Jber. Deutsch. Math. Verein. **52**, 1–48 (1942).

This, the author states, is the introductory section of a report, the writing of which was interrupted. The report was to cover the following topics, which the author lists as the most important results hitherto achieved in the study of algebraic curves over arithmetically significant fields of constants: (I) Weil's theorem of the finite basis [A. Weil, Acta Math. **52**, 281–315 (1928)]; (II) Siegel's theorem on the finite number of integral solutions [C. L. Siegel, Abh. Preuss. Akad. Wiss. Phys.-Math. Kl. **1929**, part 2]; (III) Lutz's theorem on elliptic curves over p-adic fields [E. Lutz, J. Reine Angew. Math. **177**, 238–247 (1937)]; (IV) Hasse's proof of the Riemann hypothesis for elliptic curves over Galois-fields [H. Hasse, J. Reine Angew. Math. **175**, 55–62, 69–88, 193–208 (1936)] [this has now been superseded by the proof obtained for arbitrary genus by A. Weil, Proc. Nat. Acad. Sci. U. S. A. **27**, 345–347 (1941); these Rev. **2**, 345]; (V) Deuring's algebraic construction of the Abelian extensions of the function-field of an algebraic curve [M. Deuring, Math. Ann. **106**, 77–102 (1932)]. These topics were to be treated from a "unified point of view," which, needless to say, is supplied by the consideration of the Jacobian variety (or, in the language of the author, the Abelian function-field) belonging to the curve. The greater part of the present paper is devoted to an exposition of some of the more elementary properties of the Jacobian variety, in purely algebraic terms and without the use of the convenient tools supplied in the case of characteristic 0 by classical function-theory. These properties are of course couched in the arithmetico-algebraic language of the author and his school, which will be familiar to readers of his papers on elliptic function-fields, but may act as a deterrent on other classes of readers, and does not seem to the reviewer to be as well adapted to those questions as the language of algebraic geometry. Some new lemmas, mainly of technical interest, are stated and proved; some of the basic results of the classical theory are stated as unproved assertions in the abstract case. A final section is devoted to an exposition, restricted to algebraic curves, of Weil's so-called distribution-theory [loc. cit. chap. I], with the quantitative complements due to Siegel [loc. cit.]. One may express the hope that circumstances will soon restore the author to his mathematical studies and enable him to complete his report. *A. Weil* (Bethlehem, Pa.).

Citations: MR 2, 345b = G20-3.
Referred to in R58-17.

G02-2 **(9, 303c)**

Weil, André. Foundations of Algebraic Geometry. American Mathematical Society Colloquium Publications, vol. 29. American Mathematical Society, New York, 1946. xix+289 pp. $5.50.

Advances in the more arithmetic branches of modern algebra and their application to number theory naturally lead, as we may venture to say today, to problems which to the well-informed mathematician either appeared familiar as part of the heritage of classical algebraic geometry or seemed to be intrinsically adapted to a solution by more conceptual geometric methods. Furthermore, since major parts of the theory of algebraic functions of one variable had been fitted into the system of algebra it was sensible that similar interpretations and attempts at solutions were (and had to be) tried for higher dimensional problems. In order to understand and appreciate the ultimate significance of this book the reader may well keep in mind the preceding twofold motivation for the interest in algebraic geometry. Classical algebraic geometry made free use of a type and mode of reasoning with which the modern mathematician often feels uncomfortable, though the experience based on a rich and intricate source of examples made the founders of this discipline avoid serious mistakes in final results which lesser men might have been prone to make. The main purpose of this treatise is to formulate the broad principles of the intersection theory for algebraic varieties. We find those fundamental facts without which, for example, a good treatment of the theory of linear series would be difficult. The doctrine of this book is that an unassailable foundation (and thereby justification) of the basic concepts and results of algebraic geometry can be furnished by certain elementary methods of algebra. Thus, the reader will agree after some time that he is finding a delicate tool which can serve him to remove the traces of insecurity which occasionally accompany geometric reasoning. Incidentally, the term "elementary" used here and by the author is to be understood in a restricted technical sense, in the sense that general ideal theory and the theory of power series rings are not brought into play too often. The proofs require the general plan of using the "principles of specialization," as formulated algebraically by van der Waerden; and they are by no means elementary in the customary connotation. To some readers the adherence to a definite type of approach, where another author may have deemed it more instructive or appropriate to use slightly different methods, may tend to cloud occasionally immediate understanding by the less adept. However, once the reader has grasped the real geometric meaning of a definition or theorem (he then has to forget occasionally the fine points resulting from the facts that the author imposes no restriction on the characteristic of the underlying field of quantities) he will recognize how skilfully the language and methods of algebra are used to overcome certain limitations of spatial intuition.

The author begins his work with judiciously selected results from the theory of algebraic and transcendental extensions of fields [chapter I, Algebraic preliminaries]. Special emphasis has to be placed on inseparable extensions, which incidentally means a more complete account than is found in books on algebra. The further plan of the book is perhaps best appreciated if one starts to ponder over a more or less heuristic definition of "algebraic variety," and then asks one's self informally how one should define "intersections with multiplicities" of "subvarieties." Then, in view of the principle of local linearization in classical analysis, the author's arrangements of topics is more or less dictated by the ultimate subject under discussion, provided one does not place the interpretation of geometrical concepts by ideal theory at the head of the discussion. Therefore the technical definitions of point, variety, generic point and point set attached to a variety [chapter IV, The geometric language] must be preceded by suitable algebraic preparations [essentially in chapter II, Algebraic theory of specializations] and more arithmetic studies [chapter III, Analytic theory of specializations]. Crucial results in this connection, based on arithmetical considerations, are found in proposition 7 on page 60 and theorem 4 on page 62, where the existence of a well-defined multiplicity is proved for specializations. For further work, the author next introduces the concept of simple point of a variety in affine space by means of the linear variety attached to the point. [See the significant propositions 19 to 21 on pages 97–99.] Next, the intersection theory of varieties in affine space is presented through the following stages of increasing complexity: (i) intersection with a linear subspace of complementary dimension, the 0-dimensional case, with the important criterion for multiplicity 1 in proposition 7 on page 122, and ultimately the criterion for simple points in theorem 6 on page 136; (ii) intersection with a linear subspace of arbitrary dimension, with theorem 4 on page 129 which justifies the invariant meaning of the term "intersection multiplicity of a variety with a linear variety along a variety" [chapter V, Intersection multiplicities, special case]. In chapter VI, entitled General intersection theory, the results for the linear case are extended so as to culminate in the important theorem 2 on page 146 concerning the proper components of the intersection of two subvarieties in a given variety. Furthermore, all important properties of intersection multiplicities are established. Later, in appendix III, it is shown that the properties established for a certain symbol are characteristic for intersection multiplicities and uniquely define that concept. It may be mentioned that the topological definition of the chain intersections on manifolds coincides with the algebraically defined concept of this book. Of course, the underlying coefficient field has to be the field of all complex numbers and further simplifying assumptions on the variety have to be made. However, this comparison cannot be made at the level of chapters V and VI, since there one deals with affine varieties to which the ordinary topological considerations are not directly applicable.

The subsequent chapter VII, Abstract varieties, provides the necessary background for the aforementioned connections and also contains complete proofs of those results which one might have formulated first had one deliberately adopted ideal-theoretic intentions at an early stage. The abstract varieties of this chapter are obtained by piecing together varieties in affine spaces by means of suitably restricted birational transformations. This definition of the author has turned out to be very fruitful for the work on the Riemann hypothesis for function fields and the study of Abelian varieties in general. In the course of the work, the results of the preceding chapters are extended so as to lead up to the important theorem 8 on page 193 related to Hopf's "inverse homomorphism." The chapter ends with a theory of cycles of dimension s, that is, formal integral combinations of simple abstract subvarieties of dimension s. The notion of the intersection product of cycles is also introduced here [page 202], by means of which the investigation of equivalence theories can be initiated. This is done more explicitly in chapter IX, Comments and discussion; apparently the Riemann-Roch theorem for surfaces should now be accessible to a careful re-examination. As a further result, the theory of quasi-divisibility of Artin and van der Waerden is developed in theorems 3 and 4 on pages 224–225 and theorem 6 on page 230. These theorems exhibit the relations between the theory of cycles of highest dimension and the theory of quasi-divisibility, where naturally some of the results in appendix II, Normalization of varieties, are to be added for the necessary integral closure of the required rings of functions. In this appendix the author relates his results on the normalization of algebraic varieties to those of Zariski. At this point the individual reader may well compare the elementary and the ideal-theoretic approach to a group of theorems. In appendix I, Projective spaces, often used properties and facts concerning projective spaces are quickly developed on the basis of the preceding work. This brief discussion not only deals with results which are generally useful in algebraic geometry, but also contains one of the theorems on linear series of divisors which was frequently used in the classical work [see page 266]. Because of the wealth of material and the excellent "advice to the reader" prefacing this rich and important book the reviewer feels that he should mention some of the highlights and not delve into a discussion of technical details. In short, the only way to appreciate this treatise is actually to read it.

O. F. G. Schilling (Chicago, Ill.).

Referred to in G10-1, G10-9, G10-25, G20-8, G20-9, G20-15.

G02-3 (12, 852e)

Segre, Beniamino. Questions arithmétiques sur les variétés algébriques. Algèbre et Théorie des Nombres. Colloques Internationaux du Centre National de la Recherche Scientifique, no. 24, pp. 83–91. Centre National de la Recherche Scientifique, Paris, 1950.

A compact survey of, and an excellent guide to the arithmetical questions which arise when algebraic varieties are considered over any commutative field, not necessarily the field of complex numbers. In this branch of mathematics, which the author has considerably enriched by his own results, the tendency is to produce arithmetical results out of geometrical results. A comprehensive bibliography is appended.

D. Pedoe (London).

G02-4 (13, 273c)

Segre, Beniamino. Arithmetical Questions on Algebraic Varieties. University of London, The Athlone Press, London, 1951. v+55 pp. 10/6d.

This booklet is based upon three lectures which the author gave at the University of London in 1950. It gives an account of problems and results in which algebraic geometry and number theory are interrelated. The topics treated represent chiefly the author's own contributions. For details of proofs the reader is referred to the original research papers, but the proofs are usually sketched and most of the necessary concepts and definitions are introduced in the text. The exposition is divided into three chapters. Chapter I deals with the theory of quadratic forms over an arbitrary commutative field. The topics include Dieudonné's results on the automorphisms of a quadratic form, representations between quadrics, and the determination of the linear spaces belonging to a quadric. In chapter II certain special types of Diophantine equations are studied by algebro-geometric methods (cubic and quartic surfaces, Severi-Brauer varieties, etc.). In chapter III the author studies some problems concerning rational varieties; gives applications to the Hilbert problem in the theory of resolvents; gives a partial solution of a problem (proposed orally by the reviewer) concerning the birational equivalence of hypercones; and discusses the arithmetical questions which come up when Severi's theory of the base is applied toward the determination of the birational transformation of an algebraic variety into itself. *O. Zariski.*

Referred to in G02-5.

G02-5 **(13, 578d)**

Segre, Beniamino. Arithmetical properties of algebraic varieties. Proceedings of the International Congress of Mathematicians, Cambridge, Mass., 1950, vol. 1, pp. 490–493. Amer. Math. Soc., Providence, R. I., 1952.

Expository lecture. See the author's recent book "Arithmetical questions on algebraic varieties" [Athlone Press, London, 1951; these Rev. **13**, 273]. *D. Pedoe* (London).

Citations: MR 13, 273c = G02-4.

G02-6 **(13, 579d)**

Weil, André. Number-theory and algebraic geometry. Proceedings of the International Congress of Mathematicians, Cambridge, Mass., 1950, vol. 2, pp. 90–100. Amer. Math. Soc., Providence, R. I., 1952.

Ici nous trouvons à la fois un manifeste et un programme. Comme dans plusieurs de ses écrits récents, introductions ou analyses, l'auteur s'insurge contre l'emprise absolue de l'algèbre "pure" sur ses applications; et, s'opposant à la nombreuse lignée de Dedekind et d'Emmy Noether, il met l'accent sur les idées, un peu oubliées, de Kronecker. Ainsi sont passés en revue les quelques résultats modernes qui font partie du programme Kronéckérien, et les nombreux problèmes que pose la réalisation de celui ci.

Est d'abord examinée la notion de dimension, définie comme longueur d'une suite de spécialisations succéssives. On voit que, dans toute question de géométrie algébrique, on peut, par passage à une variété de dimension supérieure, opérer sur une extension algébrique du corps premier. D'autre part les spécialisations d'inégales caractéristiques accroissent d'une unité la dimension des corps de caractéristique nulle; par exemple les corps de dimension 1 sont les corps de nombres algébriques et les corps de fonctions algébriques d'une variable sur un corps fini, cas bien étudiés, dont l'analogie est féconde, mais qui présentent de nombreux problèmes non résolus, comme ceux relatifs à la fonction zèta. Plus difficile encore semble la généralisation de la fonction zèta aux cas de dimension supérieure; une définition naturelle en est donnée, et plusieurs conjectures faites à son sujet.

Mais les questions locales introduisent d'autres corps et anneaux de base que les corps absolument algébriques; ce sont les anneaux locaux complets en général, les p-adiques en particulier, et pour étudier les places à l'infini, les corps réel et complexe (qu'un arithméticien aurait ainsi été amené à étudier, si l'histoire n'avait suivi la marche inverse). Divers résultats appartenant à la géométrie sur les anneaux et corps locaux sont passés en revue, ceux de Skolem, Chabauty et Lutz dans le cas p-adique, ceux de Zariski et Chow dans le cas général. On est ici un peu surpris de l'hommage rendu à ceux des fidèles de Dedekind et E. Noether qui ont développé la théorie des anneaux locaux dans le cadre de l'algèbre pure.

Le programme Kronéckérien vise, entre autres choses, à la création d'une géométrie algébrique sur les entiers. Un exemple typique est l'étude, par Kronecker lui même, d'une correspondance sur une surface dont on déduit de nombreux résultats sur les transformations des fonctions elliptiques, la multiplication complexe par exemple.

L'auteur montre enfin comment la définition Kronéckérienne des idéaux par adjonction d'indéterminées est réliée aux "formes associées" de Chow, à la théorie des séries linéaires, et à la notion de degré d'une variété. L'analogue arithmétique de cette notion de degré est celle de "hauteur" d'un point algébrique [Ann. of Math. (2) **53**, 412–444 (1951); ces Rev. **13**, 66] essentielle dans les travaux de l'auteur, de Siegel, de Northcott et d'autres. Il est rappelé comment la théorie des "distributions" (ibid.) permet d'étudier cette notion, et d'établir une inégalité fondamentale entre les hauteurs de deux points algébriques se correspondant par transformation birationnelle.

P. Samuel (Clermont-Ferrand).

Citations: MR 13, 66d = G35-25.

G02-7 **(18, 719f)**

Deuring, M. The zeta-functions of algebraic curves and varieties. J. Indian Math. Soc. (N.S.) **20** (1956), 89–101.

This paper is expository in character. The author reviews in some detail the conjectures (and proofs for some special cases beyond the definite conclusions of Hasse and Weil for function fields of one variable over a finite field) on the zeta functions of algebraic varieties of finite Kroneckerian dimension. The bibliography of the paper includes the important work of Shimura, Taniyama and Weil on complex multiplications; Lang's recent results on the class field theory of algebraic varieties are not included. *O. F. G. Schilling* (Chicago, Ill.).

G02-8 **(19, 1078a)**

Weil, André. Abstract versus classical algebraic geometry. Proceedings of the International Congress of Mathematicians, 1954, Amsterdam, vol. III, pp. 550–558. Erven P. Noordhoff N.V., Groningen; North-Holland Publishing Co., Amsterdam, 1956. $7.00.

Die "klassischen" und die "abstrakten" Methoden in der algebraischen Geometrie werden ihrem Wesen und ihrer Reichweite nach miteinander verglichen. Zur Erläuterung dienen mehrere Beispiele: Castelnuovos Satz über den Äquivalenzdefekt einer Korrespondenz zweier Kurven (für den ein einfacher Beweis im klassischen Fall gegeben wird); der Zusammenhang dieses Satzes mit der Riemannschen Vermutung in Funktionenkörpern; Verallgemeinerung der Riemannschen Vermutung für höhere Dimension; Lefschetzs Fixpunktformel und der Zusammenhang mit den "arithmetischen" Zetafunktionen.

P. Roquette (Hamburg).

Referred to in G25-23, G25-40.

G02-9 **(26# 119)**

Lang, Serge

Diophantine geometry.

Interscience Tracts in Pure and Applied Mathematics, No. 11.

Interscience Publishers (a division of John Wiley & Sons), New York-London, 1962. x+170 *pp.* $7.45.

This book is concerned with the interactions of diophantine analysis and algebraic geometry. It is up to the author's usual high standard, and should do much to renew profitable interest in the subject it treats. The first two chapters are concerned with absolute values and the arithmetic of the classical fields, ideal theory, divisors, units and ideal classes. The account given of these matters is one of the cleanest in the current literature, and is beautifully done. Chapters III and IV are concerned with heights. Suppose K is a field with a family of absolute values v_α satisfying the product formula. If $p=(x_0, \cdots, x_n)$ is a point in projective n-space over K, its height is defined to be the product over all α of $\sup_i v_\alpha(x_i)$. By virtue of the product formula, this is well-defined; the height depends only on p and not on the choice of its homogeneous coordinates. With this notion it is possible to achieve a twentieth-century version of the method of infinite descent. One wonders what comments there might be from the shade of Fermat, provided he has kept in touch with our earthly endeavours. Chapter V is devoted to the Mordell-Weil Theorem: If K is a finitely generated field over the prime field and A is an abelian variety over K, then the group of rational points of A is finitely generated. A relative version is also given for abelian varieties over function fields and this is applied to give a proof of the theorem of the base. In Chapter VI the Thue-Siegel-Roth Theorem is proved under very general circumstances (which obtain for number and function fields). It is then reformulated in geometric terms which in turn lead to some interesting comments on the direction of future progress on these questions. Chapter VI is concerned with Siegel's Theorem: If C is an affine curve of genus $\geqq 1$ over a ring R, finitely generated over Z, then it has only a finite number of points in R. The content of this theorem can be appreciated by anyone who has used rational parametrizations for solving diophantine equations corresponding to rational curves. The proof, however, is not easy; it uses Roth's improvement of the Thue-Siegel Theorem, a result that was not available to Siegel at the time he gave his original proof. The question of when a rational curve has infinitely many integral points is settled. The Hilbert irreducibility theorem is treated in Chapter VIII. Suppose $f(t_1, \cdots, t_r, X_1, \cdots, X_s)$ is an irreducible polynomial in $r+s$ variables over a field k. The main question is the existence of specializations $(t)\to(t')$ with $t'\in k$ such that the resulting polynomial in (X) is still irreducible over k. It is shown that for an abelian variety or curve or genus $\geqq 1$ over a field of finite type over Q, there are an infinity of non-degenerate specializations of it into a number field, each inducing an injection on the sets of rational points. Some applications of the irreducibility theorem to Galois theory are also given. The historical notes throughout the book are of very high order. These include conjectures as to the future history as well, which possibly constitute one of the more valuable features of the book. {There is the usual canonical remark about Jacobian varieties replacing theta functions, of course for perfectly good reasons. However, is not the time perhaps due for this situation to be turned? It is not impossible that geometry may now have something new to say about the analytic problems of abelian and theta functions.} *W. E. Jenner* (Chapel Hill, N.C.)

Referred to in G05-71, G10-29, G30-35, J68-58, R32-53.

G02-10 (26# 3705)

Kähler, Erich

Infinitesimal-Arithmetik.

Univ. e Politec. Torino Rend. Sem. Mat. **21** (1961/62), 5–29.

This paper is an account of the lecture given by the author during the conference on algebraic geometry in Turin (Italy), May 24–27, 1961. It contains (without proofs) statements of the author's ideas of what a birationally invariant theory of arithmetic varieties (arithmetic of the coefficient field being incorporated for the definition of homomorphisms of a finitely generated field) should be. Topics covered range from the indication of elementary definitions to statements about deep-lying properties of modular forms and zeta functions. See also an earlier paper of the author [Ann. Mat. Pura Appl. (4) **45** (1958); MR **21** #4155]. *O. F. G. Schilling* (Lafayette, Ind.)

G02-11 (30# 2004)

Manin, Ju. I.

Rational points on algebraic curves. (Russian)

Uspehi Mat. Nauk **19** (1964), *no.* 6 (120), 83–87.

A short, extremely general, survey article.

J. W. S. Cassels (Cambridge, England)

G02-12 (31# 167)

Cassels, J. W. S.

Arithmetic on an elliptic curve.

Proc. Internat. Congr. Mathematicians (*Stockholm*, 1962), *pp.* 234–246. *Inst. Mittag-Leffler, Djursholm*, 1963.

An expository paper describing the current status of arithmetic on curves of genus 1.

G02-13 (31# 168)

Tate, John

Duality theorems in Galois cohomology over number fields.

Proc. Internat. Congr. Mathematicians (*Stockholm*, 1962), *pp.* 288–295. *Inst. Mittag-Leffler, Djursholm*, 1963.

A primarily expository paper having close connections with that by Cassels reviewed above (#167), but in a more abstract setting.

Referred to in G05-105, R32-56, R34-31, R34-32, R34-33, S25-20.

G02-14 (32# 7520)

Serr, Ž. P. [Serre, J. P.]

Zeta-functions and L-functions. (Russian)

Uspehi Mat. Nauk **20** (1965), *no.* 6 (126), 19–26.

Translation of the elegantly formulated expository lecture which was delivered at the A.M.S. Summer School of Algebraic Geometry in Woods Hole, Mass., U.S.A., in July 1964. {The lecture has also been published in *Arithmetical algebraic geometry* (Proc. Conf. Purdue Univ., 1963), pp. 82–92 [Harper & Row, New York, 1965].}

J. W. S. Cassels (Cambridge, England)

Referred to in G02-15.

G02-15 (33# 2606)

Serre, Jean-Pierre

Zeta and L functions.

Arithmetical Algebraic Geometry (*Proc. Conf. Purdue Univ.*, 1963), *pp.* 82–92. *Harper & Row, New York*, 1965.

An elegant exposition of the general properties of zeta functions and Artin L-functions in the setting of schemes and dealing mainly with the formal side of the theory. A Russian translation is already available [Uspehi Mat. Nauk **20** (1965), no. 6 (126), 19–26; MR **32** #7520].

J. W. S. Cassels (Cambridge, England)

Citations: MR 32# 7520 = G02-14.

G02-16 (33# 7299)

Cassels, J. W. S.

Diophantine equations with special reference to elliptic curves.

J. London Math. Soc. **41** (1966), 193–291.

The author has written a very lively and interesting survey on diophantine equations with particular attention to rational points on elliptic curves. The article emphasizes the geometric aspect of diophantine equations and accordingly geometric language is used throughout. The author begins with some very general comments on diophantine equations and quickly moves on to survey the geometric theory of elliptic curves. He then proceeds to discuss the arithmetic properties (both local and global) of these curves, culminating with a discussion of various unsolved problems and conjectures. While many proofs are omitted or only sketched, footnotes and asides abound, as do references to a very ample bibliography (about 150 titles). This article should serve as a satisfactory introduction and guide to this very active field of research.

D. J. Lewis (Ann Arbor, Mich.)

Referred to in G02-17, G05-87, G05-91, G05-116, G05-122.

G02-17 **(34# 2523)**

Cassels, J. W. S.

Corrigenda: "Survey article—Diophantine equations with special reference to elliptic curves".

J. London Math. Soc. **42** (1967), 183.

The original article appeared in same J. **41** (1966), 193–291 [MR **33** #7299].

Citations: MR 33# 7299 = G02-16.

Referred to in G05-87, G05-91, G05-122.

G02-18 **(34# 1329)**

Tèĭt, Dž. [Tate, J.]

Algebraic classes of cohomologies. (Russian)

Uspehi Mat. Nauk **20** (1965), *no.* 6 (126), 27–40.

This is a translation of an article read at the Summer Institute in Algebraic Geometry at Woods Hole, Mass., 1964. The object of the article is to discuss various hypotheses rather than to prove theorems. If V is an irreducible scheme, projective and smooth over k, and $\bar{V}$ is obtained by extending k to its algebraic closure, then the main subject of discussion is the cohomology group $H_l^i(\bar{V}) = Q_l \otimes_{Z_l} (\varprojlim_n H^i(\bar{V}_{\text{étale}}, Z/l^n Z))$, where $\bar{V}_{\text{étale}}$ denotes the étale topology of $\bar{V}$. An important feature of this étale cohomology with l-adic coefficients is that it admits operations by the Galois group of $\bar{k}$ over k. A variation of the above definition yields $H_l^i(\bar{V})(m)$, the m-fold twisting of $H_l^i(\bar{V})$.

Then, for example, mapping the group $\mathfrak{Z}^i(\bar{V})$ of cycles (in the algebraic-geometric sense) of codimension i into $H_l^{2i}(\bar{V})(i)$, one gets a homomorphism whose kernel consists of cycles $\mathfrak{Z}_h^i(\bar{V})$ which are l-adic cohomologous to 0. It is suggested that $\mathfrak{Z}_h^i(\bar{V})$ may be independent of l, in fact may consist of cycles numerically equivalent to 0, assertions both true in the case of characteristic 0. A further conjecture is that the image of $\mathfrak{A}^i(\bar{V}) = \mathscr{Z}^i(\bar{V})/\mathscr{Z}_h^i(\bar{V})$ in $H_l^{2i}(\bar{V})(i)$ consists of those elements whose stationary subgroups are open in the Galois group of $\bar{k}$ over k.

The relation of this cohomology to the zeta-function is studied. For example, a conjecture is that the rank of $\mathfrak{A}^i(\bar{V})$ coincides with the order of a certain pole of $\zeta(X, s)$, where $f: X \to Y$ is a morphism with Y regular, X irreducible, and general fiber coinciding with the given morphism $V \to \operatorname{spec} k$. It is noted that this conjecture is related to a conjecture of B. J. Birch and H. P. F. Swinnerton-Dyer [J. Reine Angew. Math. **218** (1965), 79–108; MR **31** #3419] that the rank of the group of k-rational points on the Picard variety of V is the order of a certain pole of the appropriate zeta-function.

A. H. Wallace (Philadelphia, Pa.)

Citations: MR 31# 3419 = G05-75.

Referred to in G15-42, G35-45.

G02-19 **(36# 6418)**

Manin, Ju. I.

Diophantine equations and algebraic geometry. (Russian)

Proc. Fourth All-Union Math. Congr. (Leningrad, 1961) (Russian), Vol. II, pp. 15–21. *Izdat. "Nauka", Leningrad,* 1964.

Expository paper. *J. W. Cassels* (Cambridge, England)

G02-20 **(37# 6287)**

Swinnerton-Dyer, P.

The conjectures of Birch and Swinnerton-Dyer, and of Tate.

Proc. Conf. Local Fields (Driebergen, 1966), *pp.* 132–157. *Springer, Berlin,* 1967.

In the last few years, it has become evident that the study of the zeta-function of an algebraic variety can yield valuable information about that variety. These facts grew out of the attempt to apply Siegel's works on quadratic forms to elliptic curves. Many extensive computations concerning rational points on elliptic curves were done by Birch and the author and through these works they published many important conjectures. Then J. Tate has put forward and produced evidence for these conjectures. The present article is an exposition of those conjectures on zeta-functions and L-series of (1) elliptic curves over Q, (2) elliptic curves with complex multiplication, (3) elliptic curves parametrized by modular functions, (4) abelian varieties over algebraic number fields, (5) varieties over finite fields, and (6) varieties over algebraic number fields. *Y. Nakai* (Hiroshima)

Referred to in G05-104.

G05 ELLIPTIC CURVES OVER GLOBAL FIELDS

See **G20** for other ground fields.

See also Sections G15, R58.

See also reviews D02-23, D24-90, D28-9, D28-14, D48-62, D99-5, E64-13, F10-57, F10-81, F10-100, F10-109, F15-24, F15-40, F25-13, F65-21, F65-28, G02-12, G02-13, G02-16, G02-20, G10-20, G10-24, G10-44, G15-3, G15-5, G15-7, G15-8, G15-21, G15-53, G20-22, G20-39, G20-43, G25-56, G30-7, G30-9, G30-21, R40-20, R58-50, Z02-48, Z10-8, Z10-67, Z15-84.

G05-1 **(1, 166e)**

Châtelet, François. Groupe exceptionnel d'une classe de cubiques. C. R. Acad. Sci. Paris **210**, 200–202 (1940).

Using definitions, methods and results of earlier papers [C. R. Acad. Sci. Paris **206**, 1532–1533 (1938); **209**, 90–92 (1940)], the author constructs sets of groups of exceptional points of classes of cubic curves in an algebraic field k', when a curve in a field k is given. Several illustrations of the process are given. *V. Snyder* (Ithaca, N. Y.).

G05-2 **(1, 266a)**

Billing, G. and Mahler, K. On exceptional points on cubic curves. J. London Math. Soc. **15**, 32–43 (1940).

Sur une cubique de genre un, on appelle exceptionnels les

points qui donnent lieu à une succession finie de tangentiels. Les auteurs donnent une construction linéaire par laquelle, à partir de cinq points arbitrairement choisis dans le plan, on détermine une succession de points appartenants à une cubique. Si celle-ci est de genre un, les valeurs du paramètre elliptique qui les caractérisent sont les multiples positifs et négatifs d'une valeur fixe. Pour certaines configurations du groupe de cinq points initials, on voit géométriquement que la succession se réduit à un groupe de 5, 6, 7, 8 ou 9 points exceptionnels. La construction linéaire indiquée permet de calculer les coordonnées homogènes des points successifs et d'écrire enfin la condition pour que la succession vienne se fermer à un certain moment. Pour le cas d'un cycle de onze points les auteurs rencontrent l'équation $x_1^2x_2-x_1x_2^2-x_1x_3^2+x_2^2x_3=0$ que, dans le cas qu'une telle configuration de points exceptionnels, avec coordonnées rationnelles, existe sur une cubique à coefficients rationnels, devrait admettre une solution rationnelle différente de (100), (010), (001), (110), (111) (équation que pour le même objet avait été determinée précédemment par B. Levi [Atti Accad. Sci. Torino **43** (1908)]). Par un procédé donné par Billing [Nova Acta Soc. Sci. Upsaliensis (4) **11**, 1–165 (1937)] ils réussissent à démontrer la non-existence d'une telle solution.

B. Levi (Rosario).

G05-3 (3, 14c)

Châtelet, François. Courbes réduites dans les classes de courbes de genre 1. C. R. Acad. Sci. Paris **212**, 320–322 (1941).

In earlier papers [C. R. Acad. Sci. Paris **206**, 1532–1533 (1938); **208**, 487–489 (1939)] the author discusses, by group theory considerations, the question of transforming an algebraic curve, with coefficients in the rational field R, into a cubic in R by means of a birational transformation in R. In the present paper a similar question is considered for any algebraic field k. A series of curves W_n are constructed through definite points c_i such that the Galois group of this extension is multiply isomorphic to the direct product of two cyclic groups. *V. Snyder* (Ithaca, N. Y.).

G05-4 (4, 239b)

Hasse, Helmut. Der n-Teilungskörper eines abstrakten elliptischen Funktionenkörpers als Klassenkörper, nebst Anwendung auf den Mordell-Weilschen Endlichkeitssatz. Math. Z. **48**, 48–66 (1942).

The author has distilled an abstract essence from Mordell's proof of his well-known theorem [L. J. Mordell, Proc. Cambridge Philos. Soc. **21**, 179–192 (1922)], according to which the rational points on a curve of genus 1 form an Abelian group with a finite basis. His work is based on the version given by Weil of that proof [A. Weil, Bull. Sci. Math. (2) **54**, 182–191 (1930)]. Mordell's proof consisted of two parts, the first one of which studies the arithmetical properties of the bisection of elliptic functions, while the other applies these to an "infinite descent." The main part of the present paper deals with the first step; the purely algebraic results, which are implicit in Mordell and were in part made explicit by Weil [loc. cit., and Acta Math. **52**, 281–315 (1928)], are here developed, in the language peculiar to the author and his school, for an elliptic function-field over an arbitrary (perfect) field of constants, and the division by n. The main result is stated as a theorem on the decomposition of a prime divisor of degree 1, belonging to the given function-field, in the Abelian extension of degree n^2 determined by the division by n (the divisors of order n being assumed to be in the field of constants). As pointed out by the author, there is an interesting analogy between this and the law of reciprocity in ordinary classfield theory. The author states that this has its source in the classical theorem of the "exchange of parameter and argument" for an Abelian integral of the third kind; it seems to the reviewer that this is not quite correct; the source of the result in question is rather to be looked for in Cauchy's theorem applied to the integral $\int \log \varphi \cdot d(\log \psi)$, where φ and ψ are in the function-field; all the available evidence points to that integral as being the correct analogue of the law of reciprocity. The final section of the paper deals with the "infinite descent" in the case of an algebraic number-field; this is here carried out on the basis of the so-called distribution-theory, and essentially in the same way as had been done by Mordell and Weil, except that a different birational model is used for the curve. *A. Weil.*

G05-5 (7, 70g)

Wiman, A. Über den Rang von Kurven $y^2=x(x+a)(x+b)$. Acta Math. **76**, 225–251 (1945).

Poincaré's conjecture [J. Math. Pures Appl. (5) **7**, 161–233 (1901)] that, on any given rational plane cubic C of genus 1, the totality of the rational points can be deduced from a finite number by repeated application of the tangent and chord process was proved by L. J. Mordell [Proc. Cambridge Philos. Soc. **21**, 179–192 (1922)]. The minimum number r of rational points of C, from which all the others can thus be deduced, is called the rank of C. It is not known whether r is bounded or not, and all the concrete examples where r has been determined have $r\leqq 4$. Here a number of cubics of the form (I) $y^2=x(x+a)(x+b)$, where a and b are rational, are obtained, of ranks not less than 4, 5 or 6.

The cubic (I) always contains 4 trivial rational points (the point at infinity of the y-axis and the three intersections with the x-axis), but at most two of these points are independent on (I). The author shows how a and b can be chosen so that (I) contains $\rho=2, 3, 4$ additional unrelated rational points; then he proves in several numerical cases that these points and the former two are independent on (I), and so $r\geqq 2+\rho$ (the exact determination of r is an intricate problem, whose solution is not attempted for any of the examples). The proof of the independence of the $2+\rho$ rational points is based on the distribution of the rational points (x, y) of (I) in classes depending on the common factors of the numbers x, $x+a$, $x+b$ taken in pairs, and the consideration of these classes as elements of a convenient Abelian group.

The author investigates first the curves (I) having $a+b=0$. By direct verification he obtains $\rho=2$ nontrivial rational points when

$$a=-b=2\cdot3\cdot5\cdot7,\quad 2\cdot3\cdot5\cdot11,\quad 2\cdot3\cdot5\cdot7\cdot13,\quad 2\cdot3\cdot5\cdot7\cdot17,\quad 3\cdot5\cdot7\cdot11,\quad 5\cdot11\cdot13\cdot17,$$

and $\rho=3$ with

$$a=-b=2\cdot3\cdot5\cdot7\cdot11\cdot13\cdot17.$$

Then he proves that these curves have $r\geqq 4$ and $r\geqq 5$, respectively, and conjectures that there exist curves $y^2=x(x^2-a^2)$ having $r\geqq 6$ and an infinity of them having $r\geqq 5$. By considering a more general class of curves, he obtains the curves (I) with

$$(a, b)=(10, 22),\ (16, 34),\ (32, 66),\ (14, 36),\ (22, -20),\ (-12, 30),\ (-2, 100);$$
$$(a, b)=(-26, 76),\ (22, 556);$$
$$(a, b)=(46, 292);$$

and proves that they have $r\geqq 4$, $r\geqq 5$, $r\geqq 6$, respectively. He also gives a method for deducing other curves of the last type, probably an infinity of them, each of which is presumably of rank not less than 6; for these, however, a and b are very large. *B. Segre* (Manchester).

Referred to in G05-20.

G05-6 (7, 323b)

Wiman, A. Über rationale Punkte auf Kurven $y^2=x(x^2-c^2)$. Acta Math. **77**, 281–320 (1945).

In a previous paper the author has studied the rank of the cubics $y^2=x(x+a)(x+b)$ [Acta Math. **76**, 225–251 (1945); these Rev. **7**, 70]. Here similar methods are applied to the curve $y^2=x(x^2-c^2)$, where c is a positive integer free from square factors. It is proved that the rank r of this curve is not greater than $2n+2$, where n denotes the number of odd prime factors of c. A lower upper bound of r can sometimes be found, and the exact value of r may be obtained in certain cases by using the Abelian group associated with the rational points of the curve; thus it is shown, for example, that $r=4, 5$ if $c=2\cdot3\cdot5\cdot11$, $2\cdot3\cdot11\cdot19$, respectively.

The case $n=1$ is studied in detail. If c is a prime number of the form $8k+3$, then $r=2$; if $c=8k+5$ or $8k+7$, then $2\leqq r\leqq3$; if $c=8k+1$, then $2\leqq r\leqq4$. For example, $r=3$ for $c=5, 13, 29, 37, 61$ and $r=4$ for $c=41, 137, 761$. If $c=2p$ is the double of a prime number of the form $p=8k+5$ or $16k+9$, then $r=2$; if $p=8k+3$ or $8k+7$, then $2\leqq r\leqq3$; if $p=16k+1$, then $2\leqq r\leqq4$. For example, $r=3$ for $c=2\cdot31$, $2\cdot47$, $2\cdot79$, and $r=4$ for $c=2\cdot17$, $2\cdot97$, $2\cdot113$. In order that $r>4$ it is necessary that $n\geqq2$, but this condition is, of course, far from being sufficient. It is shown that $r\geqq5$ if $c=2\cdot3\cdot5\cdot7\cdot17\cdot43$, $2\cdot3\cdot7\cdot11\cdot19\cdot67$, $2\cdot3\cdot11\cdot19$; $r=5$ if $c=2\cdot3\cdot7\cdot17\cdot31$, $2\cdot3\cdot73\cdot97$, $2\cdot3\cdot97\cdot193$, and a method is given for deriving other curves (probably infinite in number) having $r\geqq5$. Finally, it is proved that $r\geqq6$ if $c=2\cdot3\cdot7\cdot17\cdot41$. *B. Segre* (Manchester).

Referred to in G05-20.

G05-7 (7, 477f)

Châtelet, François. Les correspondances birationnelles à coefficients rationnels sur une courbe. C. R. Acad. Sci. Paris **222**, 351–353 (1946).

If γ is an algebraic curve of genus p belonging to the rational field R, that is, represented by one or more equations with rational coefficients, the birational group of γ in R consists of all the birational transformations of γ in itself which are representable by equations with rational coefficients. This group is finite if $p>1$, and then its transformations can be obtained by means of algebraic operations. The author has already studied the case $p=0$ [Ann. Sci. École Norm. Sup. (3) **61**, 249–300 (1944); these Rev. **7**, 323]. Now he investigates how the group above can be determined for $p=1$ by transforming γ in a plane cubic $C: y^2=x^3-ax-b$ (a, b rational, $4a^3-27b^2\neq0$) by means of a suitable birational transformation with algebraic coefficients. If γ is neither harmonic nor equianharmonic, and so $ab\neq0$, the birational group of γ in R is isomorphic either with the group of the rational points of C or with the birational group of C in R. The second alternative occurs if C and γ are of the same class, but the converse is not true. *B. Segre* (Manchester).

Citations: MR 7, 323a = G35-11.

G05-8 (8, 88c)

Sansone, G. Su un problema di analisi indeterminata e sui punti razionali di una famiglia di curve ellittiche dipendenti da un parametro. Ann. Mat. Pura Appl. (4) **20**, 105–135 (1941).

The following is an extract from the author's summary. The author proves that the family of elliptic cubics $C^3(v)$:

$$Y^2=4\left(X-\frac{v^4+1}{6}\right)\left(X+\frac{v^4-6v^2+1}{12}\right)\left(X+\frac{v^4+6v^2+1}{12}\right)$$

possesses, for every rational value of v, a configuration of eight rational points and shows that the existence of a ninth rational point on $C^3(v)$ implies the existence on that $C^3(v)$ of infinitely many rational points. He also shows that there exist rational values of v for which $C^3(v)$ possesses only eight rational points, and values of v, for example

$$v=(\xi-1)(\xi^2+3\xi+1)/(\xi+1)(\xi^2-3\xi+1)$$

with ξ rational, for which all $C^3(v)$ have infinitely many rational points. *D. B. Scott* (London).

G05-9 (8, 220g)

Sansone, Giovanni. La formula di bisezione della $\wp u$ di Weierstrass, e un teorema sui punti razionali delle cubiche ellittiche a coefficienti razionali. Atti Accad. Italia. Rend. Cl. Sci. Fis. Mat. Nat. (7) **2**, 124–128 (1941).

The author gives a demonstration of the bisection formula for the function $\wp(u)$ of Weierstrass, namely

$$\wp(\tfrac{1}{2}u)=\wp(u)+\sqrt{\wp(u)-e_1}\sqrt{\wp(u)-e_2}+\sqrt{\wp(u)-e_2}\sqrt{\wp(u)-e_3}+\sqrt{\wp(u)-e_3}\sqrt{\wp(u)-e_1}.$$

He states that this formula has not been explicitly mentioned in any of the handbooks of the theory of elliptic functions. [See, however, among others, Whittaker and Watson, A Course of Modern Analysis, 4th ed., Cambridge University Press, 1927, § 20.33, ex. 5; Tannery and Molk, Éléments de la Théorie des Fonctions Elliptiques, v. 1, Paris, 1893, p. 197 (XVI_1).] By means of this formula the following theorem on the cubic C^3: $y^2=4x^3-g_2x-g_3=4(x-e_1)(x-e_2)(x-e_3)$ with rational e_1, e_2, e_3, $e_1>e_2>e_3$, $e_1+e_2+e_3=0$, is obtained. A necessary and sufficient condition that a point (x, y) of C^3, with rational coordinates, and $x>e_1$, is a tangential point of another point (X, Y) of C^3, with rational coordinates, is that $x-e_1$, $x-e_2$, $x-e_3$ are the squares of rational numbers. *S. C. van Veen* (Delft).

Referred to in G05-17.

G05-10 (8, 315d)

Nagell, Trygve. Sur la résolubilité des équations diophantiennes cubiques à deux inconnues dans un domaine relativement algébrique. Nova Acta Soc. Sci. Upsaliensis (4) **13**, no. 3, 34 pp. (1942).

Let $f(x, y, z)$ be a homogeneous cubic polynomial with coefficients from a field Ω. The purpose of the author is to develop the basis of a theory of the solvability of $f=0$ in an extension field over Ω. Since Hilbert and Hurwitz [Acta Math. **14**, 217–224 (1891)] have treated the case where $f=0$ is a unicursal curve, the discussion is limited to curves of genus one. It is first shown that, if $f=0$ is solvable only by $x=y=z=0$ in Ω, it cannot be solved in a field obtained by adjoining to Ω an algebraic number whose degree, relative to Ω, is prime to 3. In case $f=0$ has a solution other than 0, 0, 0 in Ω, corresponding to the point P say, the author has previously shown [Acta Math. **52**, 93–126 (1928)] that there exists a birational transformation with coefficients in Ω which reduces $f=0$ to (1) $Y^2=X^3-AX-B$, A and B in Ω. If X^3-AX-B is irreducible in Ω, (1) is solvable in a quadratic field generated by a number of the form $\sqrt{\Delta}$, $\Delta=a^3-Aa-B$, a in Ω. Calling $\Omega(\sqrt{\Delta})$ a quadratic resolvent field (root field) of f, the author proves the existence of infinitely many such fields when Ω is algebraic; also the existence of infinitely many cubic resolvent fields, defined analogously.

Next, (1) can be represented parametrically by the Weierstrassian elliptic functions $X=\wp(u)$, $2Y=\wp'(u)$. The field $\Omega(\sqrt{\Delta})$ having been obtained from a point P on the cubic, say that this is an ordinary resolvent field in case P is the point with argument $u=0$, otherwise a singular resolvent field. Then a point P can generate at most two singular resolvent fields when $z^3-Az-B=0$ has a single root in Ω, and at most three when this equation has all roots in Ω. Resolvent quadratic fields are discussed in detail in several special cases: $Y^2=X^3-B$ with $B=-1$, 3^3 and $2^4 3^3 c^2$, where $4c$ is not a cube in the rational field; $Y^2=X^3-bX$ with $b=1$ and 2.

Following Weierstrass, the writer shows that for a quartic $R(x)$ without double roots, $\Delta y^2=R(x)$ can be reduced by a birational transformation to a cubic, and thus certain corollaries are obtained concerning such a quartic equation. There is an extensive bibliography and a commentary on some of the works cited. *I. Niven* (West Lafayette, Ind.).

Referred to in D44-79, G30-11.

G05-11 (8, 502d)

Mordell, L. J. A Chapter in the Theory of Numbers. Cambridge, at the University Press; New York, The Macmillan Company, 1947. 31 pp. $.40.

This inaugural lecture is an interesting historical account of the Diophantine equation $y^2=x^3+k$.
H. W. Brinkmann (Swarthmore, Pa.).

G05-12 (8, 565a)

Châtelet, F. Sur l'arithmétique des courbes de genre un. Ann. Univ. Grenoble. Sect. Sci. Math. Phys. (N.S.) **22**, 153–165 (1946).

A curve C of genus one with rational coefficients is transformable by a birational transformation $\mathfrak{R}$ into a Weierstrass cubic W of the form $y^2=x^3+Ax+B$. It is shown that W may be chosen to have rational coefficients, the coefficients of $\mathfrak{R}$ being in a normal algebraic extension k of the rational ground-field. The existence of a rational point on C is equivalent to the existence on W of a rational point satisfying certain conditions depending on the Galois group of k.

Mordell [Proc. Cambridge Philos. Soc. **21**, 179–192 (1922)] and Weil [Bull. Sci. Math. (2) **54**, 182–191 (1930)] have demonstrated the existence of a "base" for rational points on W, but it is not known how to determine such a base. If a base for W is given then a finite number of operations will determine whether or not C contains a rational point. *D. B. Scott* (Aberdeen).

G05-13 (8, 565b)

Châtelet, François. Méthode galoisienne et courbes de genre un. Ann. Univ. Lyon. Sect. A. (3) **9**, 40–49 (1946).

Generalisation of the results of the paper reviewed above to ground fields other than the field of rational numbers.
D. B. Scott (Aberdeen).

Referred to in G20-5.

G05-14 (9, 100b; 9, 100c)

Nagell, Trygve. Les points exceptionnels sur les cubiques planes du premier genre. Nova Acta Soc. Sci. Upsaliensis (4) **14**, no. 1, 34 pp. (1946).

Nagell, Trygve. Les points exceptionnels sur les cubiques planes du premier genre. II. Nova Acta Soc. Sci. Upsaliensis (4) **14**, no. 3, 40 pp. (1947).

Let C be a plane cubic of genus one. Let P_0 be a point of C. The tangent to C at P_0 cuts C again at a point P_1, the tangential of P_0. Let P_2 be the tangential of $P_1, \cdots, P_{r+1}$ the tangential of P_r. The point P_0 is said to be exceptional if the sequence $(P_0, \cdots, P_r, \cdots)$ has only a finite number of distinct terms. The object of these papers is to study the exceptional points of C with coordinates in some given field Ω of characteristic zero which contains the coefficients of some equation of C. The points of C whose coordinates are in Ω will be called rational. If C has at least one rational point, it is birationally equivalent over Ω to a Weierstrass cubic W of equation $y^2=4x^3-g_2x-g_3$ and we can parametrize C by means of the elliptic argument on W. Let $\{\omega, \omega'\}$ be a basic system of periods for the elliptic functions belonging to W. The condition for three points of elliptic arguments u_1, u_2, u_3 on C to be collinear is $u_1+u_2+u_3\equiv 3\theta$ (mod ω, ω'), where θ is a constant. The exceptional points of C are then the points $u+\theta$, where u is the argument of an exceptional point of W, and the arguments u of the exceptional points of W are the numbers such that $nu\equiv 0$ (mod ω, ω') for some integral $n\neq 0$. This shows that, if C has at least one rational point, it has exactly as many rational exceptional points as W, and that the rational exceptional points of W form a group. In case Ω is a field of finite degree over the rational numbers, the group of rational exceptional points of W is finite. The author indicates a method of determining this group completely when an upper bound for its order is known.

When Ω is the field Q of rational numbers, it is known that the group of rational exceptional points is either cyclic or product of two cyclic groups. If $\Omega=Q(\sqrt{\Delta})$, Δ an integer, then the author determines entirely the group of rational exceptional points for a cubic W which is of one of the forms $y^2=x^3-Ax$ or $y^2=x^3-B$; the result is too complicated to be stated here.

Let C_1 be the cubic $y^2=x^3-Ax-B$, where A and B are in Ω, and let C_2 be the cubic $y^2=x^3-A\Delta^2x-B\Delta^3$, where $\Delta\varepsilon\Omega$, $\sqrt{\Delta}\bar{\varepsilon}\Omega$. Assume that the groups G_1, G_2 of exceptional points in Ω of C_1, C_2 are of finite orders n_1, n_2; then the group of exceptional points of C_1 (or C_2) in $\Omega(\sqrt{\Delta})$ has for order one of the numbers n_1n_2, $\frac{1}{2}n_1n_2$ or $\frac{1}{4}n_1n_2$. The orders $\frac{1}{2}n_1n_2$, $\frac{1}{4}n_1n_2$ can occur only if n_1 is even; $\frac{1}{4}n_1n_2$ can occur only if all half periods belong to G_1. If C is a cubic which has no rational exceptional point in Ω, and if α is algebraic of degree not congruent to 0 (mod 3) over Ω, then C has no rational exceptional point over $\Omega(\alpha)$.

The author also gives the form which the invariants of a cubic must have if it is known that its exceptional group over a field Ω is of order divisible by one of the integers 3, 4, 5, 6 or 7. *C. Chevalley* (Princeton, N. J.).

Referred to in G05-38, G05-39, G05-45.

G05-15 (9, 156e)

Nagell, Trygve. Sur la classification des cubiques planes du premier genre par des transformations birationnelles dans un domaine de rationalité quelconque. Nova Acta Soc. Sci. Upsaliensis (4) **12**, no. 8, 34 pp. (1941).

The author considers plane cubic curves of genus one over an arbitrary coefficient field Ω. Two such cubics C and C_1 (in homogeneous coordinates) are called "collinearly equivalent" in Ω if one may be transformed into the other by a linear transformation with coefficients in Ω. Similarly, if there exists a birational transformation with coefficients in Ω which carries C into C_1, then C and C_1 are called "equivalent" in Ω. It is proved that, if C and C_1, with coefficients in Ω, are equivalent in Ω, then they are collinearly equivalent in the field $\Omega(\chi, \chi_1)$, where χ and χ_1 are the coordinates of any point of inflection of C and C_1, respectively. The reduction of these cubics to a Weierstrass normal form is studied; the form and the requisite birational transformation are determined. Given two cubics C and C_1 over Ω, the problem is considered to determine whether or not they are equivalent in Ω. This problem is solved in the case where the two given cubics both have the Weierstrass normal form. *H. N. Shapiro* (Princeton, N. J.).

Referred to in G05-39.

G05-16 (9, 225b)

Lind, Carl-Erik. Untersuchungen über die rationalen Punkte der ebenen kubischen Kurven vom Geschlecht Eins. Thesis, University of Uppsala, 1940. 97 pp.

Working on a special type of rational plane cubic, the author rediscovers the transformation of order 2 of elliptic functions, and derives from it a criterion [substantially a special case of that given by A. Weil, Bull. Sci. Math. (2)

54, 182–191 (1930)] for a rational point to arise from duplication in the group of rational points on the cubic. As usual [cf. loc. cit.], this leads to associated equations of the type $z^2=P(x, y)$, with P a biquadratic form. From this, using congruence properties and some special results of Euler, the author derives results about points of finite order and about the nonexistence of points of infinite order in certain cases, and solves completely a number of such cases.

A. Weil (Chicago, Ill.).

Referred to in D32-83, G05-43.

G05-17 (10, 14c)

Huff, Gerald B. Diophantine problems in geometry and elliptic ternary forms. Duke Math. J. **15**, 443–453 (1948).

The author proves first the following extension of a result by G. Sansone [Atti Accad. Italia. Rend. Cl. Sci. Fis. Mat. Nat. (7) 2, 124–128 (1941); these Rev. **8**, 220]: if e_1, e_2, e_3 are distinct numbers in some field k of algebraic numbers, then a point (x, y) in k on the curve $y^2=(x+e_1)(x+e_2)(x+e_3)$ is the tangential of a point in k on the same curve if, and only if, $x+e_1$, $x+e_2$, $x+e_3$ are all squares of numbers in k. This enables him to go deeply into a procedure of finding new rational points on an elliptic cubic, as tangent points of given rational points, leading to a geometric characterization of the plane cubic C: $az_1(z_2^2-z_3^2)=bz_2(z_1^2-z_3^2)$, which is then investigated for different fields. Thus, as a consequence of more general results, it is shown that (when k is the field of rational numbers) the curve C contains either eight rational points or an infinite number of rational points if $a=l^2+m^2$, $b=lm$, where l and m are relatively prime rational integers; moreover, C contains a set of sixteen rational points (never extendible either by the tangents and chords process or by the procedure above) if a, b and $a+b$ are all squares of rational integers which are relatively prime each to each. Applications are made to three geometric problems, one of them giving a new infinite planar rational distance set, i.e., a set of rational points lying on a plane and having rational distances two by two.

B. Segre (Bologna).

Citations: MR 8, 220g = G05-9.

G05-18 (10, 60f)

Néron, André. Une propriété arithmétique des faisceaux linéaires de courbes de genre 1. C. R. Acad. Sci. Paris **226**, 1781–1783 (1948).

Let us consider a finite algebraic field k, and choose arbitrarily on a plane (x, y) 8 points over k such that no 3 of them are on a line and no 6 of them are on a conic. If $\varphi(\lambda)$ denotes any rational function over k and $f(x, y)$, $g(x, y)$ are two independent cubic polynomials over k vanishing at the 8 points, then there is an infinity of values of λ in k such that the plane cubic $f(x, y)+\varphi(\lambda)g(x, y)=0$ has rank $r\geqq 8$ over k. The proof of this theorem is only sketched, and consists of two parts, one geometric and the other arithmetic in character. The first part deals with some covariant curves of a pencil of plane cubics and leads also to other geometric results. The second part is based on the following theorem, which is only stated. Let E be a finite set of plane algebraic curves over k irreducible and of genus greater than or equal to 1, and let $\Phi(x, y, \lambda)$ be a polynomial in x, y whose coefficients are rational functions of λ over k; then there is an infinity of values of λ in k for each of which no point over k lies simultaneously on E and on the curve $\Phi(x, y, \lambda)=0$. [Reviewer's remark. One has obviously to disregard the points over k, if any, lying on E and on the curve $\Phi(x, y, \lambda)=0$ for all λ of k.] *B. Segre.*

Referred to in G30-7, G30-9.

G05-19 (10, 434b)

Cassels, J. W. S. A note on the division values of $\wp(u)$. Proc. Cambridge Philos. Soc. **45**, 167–172 (1949).

Let $x=\wp(u)$, $y=\frac{1}{2}\wp'(u)$, where the Weierstrass elliptic $\wp$-function has the invariants $g_2=4A$, $g_3=4B$; then (1) $y^2=x^3-Ax-B$. [Note: the definitions of x and y are printed incorrectly in the paper and should be as above.] A classical result is that $\wp(nu)=x-\psi_{n-1}\psi_{n+1}/\psi_n{}^2$, where $\psi_n=\psi_n(u)=\sigma(nu)/\sigma(u)^{n^2}$, with the Weierstrass σ-function, from which it follows that $\wp(nu)$ is a rational function of $\wp(u)$. The author introduces the notation ψ_n to mean $(-1)^{n+1}$ times the classical ψ_n function. He also defines two new functions ϕ_m and ω_m by the relations: $\phi_m=x\psi_m^2-\psi_{n-1}\psi_{m+1}$, $4y\omega_m=\psi_{m+2}\psi_{m-1}^2-\psi_{m-2}\psi_{m+1}^2$. The functions ϕ_m, ψ_m^2 are polynomials in x, A, B with rational integral coefficients. The author defines congruence, $\phi_m\equiv 0 \pmod m$, to signify that all the coefficients of the polynomial ϕ_m are divisible by m. The author proves [theorem I]: $\phi_m'\equiv(\psi_m^2)'\equiv 0 \pmod m$, where $\phi_m'=(\partial/\partial x)\phi_m$, etc. If m is even, the stronger theorem II holds: let $2^k|m$ $(k>0)$, then $\phi_m\equiv(x^2+A)^{m^2/2} \pmod{2^{2k+1}}$, and $2^k|\psi_m$. Theorem III is a more complicated result of the same kind for m divisible by 3.

Theorems IV and V concern the zeros of $\psi_m^2(x)$, i.e., the "division values" $x_{\lambda\mu}=\wp((\lambda\Omega_1+\mu\Omega_2)/m)$, where Ω_1, Ω_2 are a pair of basic periods and $0\leqq\lambda, \mu<m$. Let A, B take integral values in an algebraic number field F. A solution (x_1, y_1) of (1) $(x_1, y_1\varepsilon F)$ is of finite order m if and only if m is the smallest integer for which mu_1 is a period of $\wp(u)$, where u_1 is the argument corresponding to (x_1, y_1). Hence a solution of order m satisfies $\psi_l{}^2(x)=0$ if and only if $m|l$. Theorem IV states: if (x_1, y_1) has order p^k $(p\neq 2)$, there is an integral ideal $\mathfrak{t}$ in F such that $x_1\mathfrak{t}^2$ and $y_1\mathfrak{t}^2$ are integral and $\mathfrak{t}^r|p$ $(p\neq 3)$, $\mathfrak{t}^s|3$ $(p=3)$, where $r=p^k-p^{k-1}$, $s=3^{2k}-3^{2k-2}$; all other solutions of finite order are integers in F. Theorem V discusses the divisibility of the discriminant $4A^3-27B^2$ with respect to y_1 and $\mathfrak{t}$. It is stated that theorems IV and V generalize results of Mahler, Lutz, Billing, Weil, and Châtelet. *J. Lehner* (Philadelphia, Pa.).

Referred to in G05-87.

G05-20 (10, 472c)

Wiman, A. Über rationale Punkte auf Kurven dritter Ordnung vom Geschlechte Eins. Acta Math. **80**, 223–257 (1948).

In a previous paper the author has studied the rank r of the elliptic cubics (I) $y^2=x(x+a)(x+b)$, where a and b are rational [Acta Math. 76, 225–251 (1945); these Rev. **7**, 70]; then, in another paper, he has applied his methods to the harmonic cubics (II) $y^2=x(x^2-c^2)$ [Acta Math. **77**, 281–320 (1945); these Rev. **7**, 323]. He now obtains several further cubics, of the form (I) and (II), having the rank not less than 6 or 5 respectively. For this purpose he uses again the methods explained in the former work; but the difficulty of the discussion necessary for finding the new examples is much increased, and shows the extreme intricacy of the still unsolved problem of determining whether r is bounded or not and of finding, in the affirmative case, an upper bound for it.

The paper is divided into three parts. Part I deals with the rank of the families of curves obtained by the author's methods, and also considers the different ways of writing the equation of a given cubic in form (I); to the former end certain assumptions are made which, though probable, seem rather difficult to prove. Part II is concerned with the equations (II). The author, in the second paper quoted above, has shown that $r\geqq 6$ if $c=2\cdot 3\cdot 7\cdot 17\cdot 41$; he is now doubtful whether there are other curves (II) having $r\geqq 6$, but obtains several cases in which $r \geqq 5$, i.e.,

$$c = 2\cdot3\cdot5\cdot7\cdot13\cdot17\cdot19,\quad 2\cdot5\cdot7\cdot11\cdot13\cdot17\cdot19,\quad 2\cdot3\cdot5\cdot7\cdot11\cdot19\cdot23,\quad 2\cdot3\cdot5\cdot7\cdot11\cdot13\cdot19\cdot23,\quad 2\cdot3\cdot5\cdot7\cdot19\cdot41.$$

In the first paper quoted the author obtained the curve (I) with $a=46$, $b=292$ and proved that it has $r \geqq 6$. In part III he adds many more curves having $r \geqq 6$, namely the curves (I) with

$$(a,b) = (9\cdot61,\ 12\cdot283),\quad (18\cdot53,\ 12\cdot419),\quad (-2^6\cdot185\cdot17\cdot23,\ 2\cdot185\cdot5\cdot641),\quad (77\cdot17\cdot64,\ 77\cdot11\cdot547),\quad (-14\cdot13\cdot25\cdot157,\ 14\cdot13\cdot31\cdot112),\quad (7\cdot29\cdot512,\ -49\cdot167).$$

He also shows that the rank of the general curve of one of his families may be lower than one would expect.

B. Segre (Bologna).

Citations: MR 7, 70g = G05-5; MR 7, 323b = G05-6.

Referred to in D02-23.

G05-21 (11, 81i)

Podsypanin, V. D. On the indeterminate equation $x^3 = y^2 + Az^6$. Mat. Sbornik N.S. **24**(66), 391–403 (1949). (Russian)

Points (x, y) on $C(A): x^3 - A = y^2$ can be written as $x = \wp(t)$, $y = \frac{1}{2}\wp'(t)$, where $\wp$ is the Weierstrass elliptic function of invariants $g_2 = 0$, $g_3 = 4A$. Let $A = f^2 g \neq 0$ be an integer, f^2 its greatest square factor, hence g squarefree. By Mordell's theorem [Proc. Cambridge Philos. Soc. **21**, 179–192 (1922)], the arguments t of the points $T(x, y)$ on $C(A)$ with rational x, y form an Abelian group G of finite basis; denote by $a_1T_1 + a_2T_2$ the point of argument $a_1t_1 + a_2t_2$ if T_1 and T_2 belong to t_1 and t_2, respectively, and a_1, a_2 are integers. By a theorem of Fueter, there corresponds to every rational point $T(x, y)$ on $C(A)$ a rational point (x', y') on $C(-27A)$ defined by

$$(1)\qquad x' = \frac{x^3 - 4A}{x_2},\quad y' = \frac{y(x^3 + 8A)}{x^3},$$

while, conversely, there corresponds to this point (x', y') a new rational point $T^*(x^*, y^*)$ on $C(A)$ given by

$$(2)\qquad x^* = \frac{x'^3 + 108A}{x'^2},\quad y^* = \frac{y'(x'^3 - 216A)}{x'^3}.$$

On eliminating x', y' from (1) and (2), it is seen that $T^* = 3T$. Denote by H the set of all rational points T^* on $C(A)$ derivable from a rational point (x', y') on $C(-27A)$, but not necessarily of the form $3T$ where $T \varepsilon G$; $T^*(x^*, y^*)$ belongs to H if and only if $y^* + \sqrt{(-A)}$ is the cube of an element of the quadratic field $R(\sqrt{(-A)}) = R(\sqrt{(-g)})$. One shows that H is a subgroup of G; evidently $G \supset H \supset 3G$, where $3G$ consists of all points $3T$ with $T \varepsilon G$ and is a subgroup of H. Both quotient groups G/H and $H/3G$ are direct products of cyclical groups of order 3, say of k and l such groups, respectively. Since on changing over from $C(A)$ to $C(-27A)$ these two numbers k and l are interchanged, it suffices to investigate k. The author gives for this number the upper bound $k \leqq n_1 + n_2 + n_3 + n_4$, where n_1 is the number of prime factors of f which split in $R(\sqrt{(-g)})$ into prime ideals of the first order prime to the discriminant of this field; 3^{n_2} is the number of ideal classes of $R(\sqrt{(-g)})$ the cube of which is the principal class; n_3 is 1 when $g \equiv 7 \pmod 8$ and 0 otherwise; and n_4 is 0 when $g > 0$ and $g \neq 3$, and 1 otherwise. The paper concludes with a table of the bases of G for $1 \leqq |A| \leqq 89$ and the values of k and l in these cases.

K. Mahler (Manchester).

Referred to in G05-54.

G05-22 (12, 11a)

Cassels, J. W. S. The rational solutions of the diophantine equation $Y^2 = X^3 - D$. Acta Math. **82**, 243–273 (1950).

The equation of the title is a special case of

$$Y^2 = X^3 - CX - D,$$

where C and D are integers. The values of the parameter u corresponding to rational solutions form an additive group, $\mathfrak{U}$, when the usual parametrization $Y = \frac{1}{2}\wp'(u)$, $X = \wp(u)$ is employed. Weil [Acta Math. **52**, 281–315 (1929)] has given a far-reaching generalization of the theorem which states that this group has a finite basis. Using an algorithm which underlies Weil's theorem, the author gives a complete solution of $Y^2 = X^3 - D$ for all $|D| \leqq 50$ in the sense that he gives a complete basis for $\mathfrak{U}$. With one exception $(D = -15)$ his results confirm those of Billing's thesis [Nova Acta Soc. Sci. Upsaliensis (4) **11**, 1–165 (1938)] in the range $|D| \leqq 25$. The proofs involve detailed developments of the arithmetical properties of the relevant cubic number fields. A table of class-numbers and units for all cubic fields $R(D^{\frac{1}{3}})$ with $|D| \leqq 50$ is included. Among the numerous applications the following may be cited. The equation $y^2 = x^3 - Dt^6$, where $t \neq 0$, $(x, t) = (y, t) = 1$, $27 \nmid D$ and D is sixth-power-free, has no integral solutions for $D = -11, -39, +43, -46, -47$ though rational solutions exist. Mordell [Proc. London Math. Soc. (2) **13**, 60–80 (1914)] has shown in the remaining cases $D = +21, +22, +29, +30, +38, +50$ (where the author obtains rational but no integral solutions) that no integral solutions exist. In general, however, the author's method appears unsuitable for discussing integral as opposed to rational solutions.

A. L. Whiteman (Los Angeles, Calif.).

Referred to in D24-24, D28-10, G05-23, G05-31, G05-54, R16-17.

G05-23 (12, 481f)

Cassels, J. W. S. The rational solution of the diophantine equation $Y^2 = X^3 - D$. Acta Math. **84**, 299 (1951).

Addenda and corrigenda to a paper of the same title in the same Acta **82**, 243–273 ((1950); these Rev. **12**, 11.

Citations: MR 12, 11a = G05-22.

G05-24 (12, 50a)

Segre, Beniamino. Alcune questioni diofantee. Boll. Un. Mat. Ital. (3) **5**, 33–43 (1950).

A geometrical proof is given of the theorem of Hurwitz [Mathematische Werke, vol. 2, pp. 446–468, in particular, § 8 = Vierteljschr. Naturforsch. Ges. Zürich **62**, 207–229 (1917)] that if a plane binary cubic curve of genus 1, with rational coefficients, has only four rational points then those points together with their tangents form one of two configurations. In one of these cases the cubic can be transformed to (1) $x(x+z)(y+z) + ay^2z = 0$ in homogeneous coordinates x, y, z where a is rational [Hurwitz, loc. cit.]. The author uses a method of descent to prove that for $a = -1/12$ there are indeed only four rational points [similar results hold for $a = -1/4$ [Hurwitz, loc. cit.] and for $a = -1/8$ [B. Levi, Atti Accad. Sci. Torino **43**, 99–120 (1908)]]. This result is used to show that there are no nontrivial rational solutions of

$$(2)\qquad x_1^2 + y_1^2 = x_2^2 + y_2^2 = x_3^2 + y_3^2;\quad x_1^3 + y_1^3 = x_2^3 + y_2^3 = x_3^3 + y_3^3.$$

The curve (2) (in homogeneous coordinates) decomposes into a curve of degree 8 with no real points, six quartics, and four lines. The quartics are equivalent to (1) with $a = -1/12$ and so all their rational solutions are known (and trivial); the lines give trivial solutions. This solves a prob-

lem of Moessner [same Boll. (3) 4, 146 (1949)].
J. W. S. Cassels (Cambridge, England).

Referred to in G05-25, G05-26.

G05-25 (12, 200e)

Segre, Beniamino. Problèmes arithmétiques en géométrie algébrique. Colloque de géométrie algébrique, Liège, 1949, pp. 123–142. Georges Thone, Liège; Masson et Cie., Paris, 1950. 200 Belgian francs; 1400 French francs.

The first part of this paper is an incomplete discussion of a problem completely solved by the author [Boll. Un. Mat. Ital. (3) 5, 33–43 (1950); these Rev. 12, 50]. The second part discusses quadratic forms in a field γ of arbitrary characteristic. Many of the results were already obtained by Witt [J. Reine Angew. Math. **176**, 31–44 (1936)] but with the restriction that the characteristic of γ is not 2. If f', f'' are forms, write $f' \xrightarrow{\gamma} f''$, $f' \overset{\gamma}{\leftrightarrow} f''$ for "f' represents f'' in γ" and "f' is equivalent to f'' in γ," respectively. If $f(x_1, \cdots, x_n) \overset{\gamma}{\leftrightarrow} f'(y_1, \cdots, y_n)$, where for some $r>0$ the coefficients of all terms involving $y_1, \cdots, y_r$ are zero, then f is called singular, otherwise nonsingular. Let $f_1' = f' + \bar{f}'$; $f_1'' = f'' + \bar{f}''$, where f', $\bar{f}'$, f'', $\bar{f}''$ are nonsingular forms in different variables and f_1', f_1'' are also nonsingular. Then

(a) $f_1' \xrightarrow{\gamma} f_1''$ and $f' \overset{\gamma}{\leftrightarrow} f''$ imply $\bar{f}' \xrightarrow{\gamma} \bar{f}''$

(b) $f_1' \overset{\gamma}{\leftrightarrow} f_1''$ and $f' \xrightarrow{\gamma} f''$ imply $\bar{f}'' \xrightarrow{\gamma} \bar{f}'$

(c) $f_1' \overset{\gamma}{\leftrightarrow} f_1''$ and $f' \overset{\gamma}{\leftrightarrow} f''$ imply $\bar{f}' \overset{\gamma}{\leftrightarrow} \bar{f}''$.

Further, every $f(x_1, \cdots, x_n)$ is equivalent in γ to a form $y_1 y_1' + \cdots + y_n y_n' + \phi(z_1, \cdots, z_k)$ where ϕ does not represent 0 and $2h + k \leqq n$, with equality if and only if f is nonsingular. Here h, k are invariants of f, and ϕ is unique up to equivalence. Further, if $f \xrightarrow{\gamma} f'$ then $h \geqq h'$, $h+k \geqq h'+k'$ (h, k correspond to Sylvester's index of inertia). Proofs depend on the invariant characterisation of h, k in terms of the geometry of the "quadric surface" $f(x_1, \cdots, x_n) = 0$ ($x_1, \cdots, x_n$ in γ). Further results are indicated, some without proof.

The third part of the paper considers two varieties U, V defined in γ and birationally equivalent in some field over γ and asks: (1) Is U birationally equivalent to V in γ? (2) If not, in what fields over γ is U equivalent to V? (3) Can we construct in γ a variety W, connected with U in some simple way and birationally equivalent to V in γ? It is shown that problem (3) can be solved subject to certain conditions if U is a hypersurface (so that V is a "generalised Severi-Brauer variety") and that this gives an approach to (1) and (2). *J. W. S. Cassels* (Cambridge, England).

Citations: MR 12, 50a = G05-24.
Referred to in D28-26.

G05-26 (12, 200f; 12, 200g)

Errera, A. Un problème diophantien de M. Segre. Bull. Soc. Roy. Sci. Liège **19**, 177–186 (1950).
Errera, A. Un problème diophantien de M. Segre: Addenda. Bull. Soc. Roy. Sci. Liège **19**, 213–214 (1950).

It is shown that the only rational solutions x, y of $y^2 = 3x(x^2+x+1)$ are the trivial ones $x=y=0$, $x=1$, $y=\pm 3$. This solves a problem of Segre [see the preceding review; for another solution see Segre, Boll. Un. Mat. Ital. (3) 5, 33–43 (1950); these Rev. 12, 50]. It is also shown that there are no integer solutions x, y of $y^2 = p^u x(x^2+x+1)$, $u \geqq 0$, p prime, except $x=y=0$ and $p=3$, $u \equiv 1$ (2), $x=1$.
J. W. S. Cassels (Cambridge, England).

Citations: MR 12, 50a = G05-24.
Referred to in D40-17, G05-27.

G05-27 (12, 853a)

Errera, A. Un problème diophantien de M. Segre. Extrait d'une lettre de M. Siegel. Bull. Soc. Roy. Sci. Liège **19**, 404–405 (1950).

Repairs an omission and simplifies a step in an earlier paper [same Bull. **19**, 177–186, 213–214 (1950); these Rev. **12**, 200]. *J. W. S. Cassels* (Cambridge England).

Citations: MR 12, 200f = G05-26; MR 12, 200g = G05-26.
Referred to in D40-17.

G05-28 (12, 590c)

Buquet, A. L'équation diophantienne

$$f(t) \equiv At^4 + Bt^3 + Ct^2 + Dt + E = s^2$$

en nombres rationnels et les polygones de Poncelet. Mathesis **59**, 233–236 (1950).

From one rational solution of the given equation, Euler obtained an infinite sequence of rational solutions, in general all different. Euler's method employs a parameter, say m, and the sequence of solutions corresponds to a sequence of points (t, m) which form the (Poncelet) polygon mentioned in the title. Certain geometric properties of this polygon are studied, the details of which are omitted here. Reference should also be made to work of Mordell [Quart. J. Pure Appl. Math. **45**, 170–186 (1914)]. *I. Niven.*

Referred to in G05-33, G05-47.

G05-29 (12, 852a)

Nagell, Trygve. Sur quelques questions dans la théorie arithmétique des cubiques planes du premier genre. Algèbre et Théorie des Nombres. Colloques Internationaux du Centre National de la Recherche Scientifique, no. 24, pp. 59–64. Centre National de la Recherche Scientifique, Paris, 1950.

The present paper summarizes some of the results obtained by Poincaré, Mordell, Weil, Nagell, Billing, Mahler, Wiman and Néron in the arithmetical theory of the plane cubics of genus 1. After having recalled the reduction of the equation of such a cubic to Weierstrass form and the Mordell-Weil theorem on the finite basis, many other results are given concerning the rank, the resolvent fields (especially the quadratic ones) the study of birational and linear equivalence by means of Aronhold invariants, and the exceptional points. It is shown that the Mordell-Weil theorem cannot be extended to arbitrary fields, and that the number of exceptional points is not a birational invariant.
B. Segre (Rome).

Referred to in G05-39.

G05-30 (12, 852b)

Châtelet, François. Points exceptionnels des cubiques. Algèbre et Théorie des Nombres. Colloques Internationaux du Centre National de la Recherche Scientifique, no. 24, pp. 71–72. Centre National de la Recherche Scientifique, Paris, 1950.

By using the methods of E. Lutz [J. Reine Angew. Math. **177**, 238–247 (1937)] the author shows how the problem of rational exceptional points upon an elliptic cubic of genus 1 can be solved in any algebraic field k, by determining the order of these points, i.e. their order in the Abelian group of points of the cubic belonging to k. Also some extensions of the problem above are considered. *B. Segre* (Rome).

G05-31 **(13, 13i)**

Selmer, Ernst S. The Diophantine equation

$$ax^3+by^3+cz^3=0.$$

Acta Math. **85**, 203–362 (1 plate) (1951).

The principal equations discussed are

$$(1) \qquad f(x, y, z)=ax^3+by^3+cz^3=0$$

where a, b, c are cube-free rational integers, relatively prime in pairs, (2) $x^3+y^3=Az^3$ with $A=abc$, and (3) $x^3-my^3=nz^3$ which is obtained from (1) by multiplying by a^2 and replacing ax by $-x$. Various known results are reviewed at the start, such as the connection between (1) and (2). It is indicated that recent work of Cassels [Acta Math. **82**, 243–273 (1950); these Rev. **12**, 11] can be used to demonstrate the impossibility (apart from $x=y=z=0$) of (1) in certain cases. Further cases in which (1) is not solvable can be decided by simple congruence conditions, although Skolem [Avh. Norske Vid. Akad. Oslo. I. **1942**, no. 4; these Rev. **8**, 7] has proved that $f(x, y, z)\equiv 0 \pmod p$ is solvable for any prime $p>7$ for which $(p, abc)=1$.

The author gets at equation (1) largely through (3), which, factored in $R(\sqrt[3]{m})$, leads to equations of the form (4) $[x-y\sqrt[3]{m}]=\mathfrak{r}\mathfrak{a}^3$ where $\mathfrak{r}$ is an ideal from a finite set. The impossibility of (4) is established in various cases by class number considerations. If such an exclusion fails, then an auxiliary cubic, arising from comparison of coefficients of $m^{\frac{1}{3}}$ in (4), is studied. To facilitate discussion of this auxiliary cubic, an extensive examination is made of cubic residues in the field $R(\sqrt[3]{m})$, yielding further necessary conditions for the solvability of (1). These conditions enable the author to handle nearly all equations (3) with $2\leqq m<n\leqq 50$, m and n cube-free. A table lists the cases proved impossible, others which are solvable (with a solution given, and the methods used for finding the solution), and four undecided cases. Another table lists equations of type (1) with $a<b<c$, $abc<500$, again there being four undecided cases in addition to the solvable and nonsolvable ones. Cases are exhibited where $f\equiv 0 \pmod p$ is solvable for every prime p and yet (1) is not solvable, Skolem [ibid.] having established such a result for certain nonhomogeneous cubics. The methods are also applied to the equation $x^3-3x^2y+y^3=3^\lambda pz^3$, and a table contains all cases with $\lambda=0$ or 1, $9^{1-\lambda}p\leqq 500$. On the basis of the table for (1) the author makes certain conjectures, such as: if A is an integer such that among all factorizations $A=abc$ with $a<b<c$ there is exactly one cubic f with $f\equiv 0 \pmod p$ solvable for every modulus, then the corresponding equation (1) is solvable.

The known impossible cases of (2) are extended as follows. Let r and q be primes with $r\equiv -q\equiv 1 \pmod 3$, q being a cubic nonresidue of r. Then (2) has only the trivial solution with $z=0$ in case $A\not\equiv\pm 1 \pmod 9$ has any of the forms qr, q^2r, qr^2, q^2r^2. Again, let A be the product of three different primes, exactly one of which, say p, has the form $1+3k$. Then (2) has only the trivial solution if the four possible equations (1) with $abc=A$, $1\leqq a<b<c$ can all be excluded by elementary congruence considerations mod 9 and mod p. Numerical cases are again given.

The paper is very well annotated, with clear references to other work on these equations. *I. Niven* (Eugene, Ore.).

Citations: MR 8, 7d = D24-9; MR 12, 11a = G05-22.
Referred to in D24-59, D28-10, D28-12, D28-39, G05-32, G05-44, G05-59, G05-88.

G05-32 **(14, 621c)**

Selmer, Ernst S. Homogeneous Diophantine equations. Den 11te Skandinaviske Matematikerkongress, Trondheim, 1949, pp. 296–300. Johan Grundt Tanums Forlag, Oslo, 1952. 27.50 kr.

The full details of this paper were published in Acta Math. **85**, 203–362 (1951); these Rev. **13**, 13.

Citations: MR 13, 13i = G05-31.

G05-33 **(13, 535d)**

Buquet, A. Structure en réseau des solutions en nombres rationnels de l'équation diophantienne

$$f(t)\equiv At^4+Bt^3+Ct^2+Dt+E=s^2.$$

Mathesis **60**, 239–243 (1951).

Associated with the given equation are certain quadratic equations with discriminant $f(t)$, and the author extends his previous study [Mathesis **59**, 233–236 (1950); these Rev. **12**, 590] by determining certain algebraic relations between two such auxiliary quadratics. *I. Niven* (Eugene, Ore.).

Citations: MR 12, 590c = G05-28.
Referred to in G05-47.

G05-34 **(14, 140c)**

Hasse, Helmut. Rein-arithmetischer Beweis des Siegelschen Endlichkeitssatzes für binäre diophantische Gleichungen im Spezialfall des Geschlechts 1. Abh. Deutsch. Akad. Wiss. Berlin. Kl. Math. Nat. **1951**, no. 2, 19 pp. (1952).

Suppose that $f(x, y)=0$ is an irreducible equation with coefficients in an algebraic number field Ω, which defines an elliptic field K. The author proves, using his arithmetic theory of elliptic function fields, the elliptic case of Siegel's theorem that there exists only finitely many pairs of integers $a, b \in \Omega$ for which $f(a, b)=0$. It is the aim of this paper to reformulate clearly the essential component steps of the proof for the elliptic case so as to obtain hints for further algebraization of Siegel's original proof which referred strongly to the analytically founded theory of abelian functions. Thus the author first works out by means of Weil's theory of distributions a birationally invariant formulation of an intermediate problem as Hypothesis (A_n): There exists an integral square-free divisor $\mathfrak{z}_n$ of K/Ω of degree n^2 such that $\mathfrak{z}_n(\mathfrak{p})\doteq 1$ (equivalence meant in the sense of Weil) for infinitely many prime divisors $\mathfrak{p}$ of K. It is shown that Weil's finiteness theorem in a weakened form (if D is the divisor class group of degree 0, then D/D^n is finite) implies the validity of (A_n) as a consequence of (A_1), where (A_1) is a birationally invariant form of the hypothesis which is customarily shown to lead to a contradiction. Thus a recasting of Siegel's method from the theory of diophantine approximations is employed to set (A_n), for sufficiently large n, into contradiction to the theorem of Thue-Siegel. As to the generalization for arbitrary genus it will be useful to add to the author's bibliography the following papers which deal precisely with the necessary extensions of the elliptic case so that a complete algebraization of some essential steps in Weil's thesis [Acta Math. **52**, 281–315 (1929)] become evident: A. Weil, Variétés abéliennes et courbes algébriques, Hermann, Paris, 1948; Ann. of Math. **53**, 412–444 (1951); these Rev. **10**, 621; **13**, 66; W.-L. Chow, Amer. J. Math. **72**, 247–283 (1950); these Rev. **11**, 615.

O. F. G. Schilling (Chicago, Ill.).

Citations: MR 10, 621d = G10-1; MR 13, 66d = G35-25.

G05-35 **(14, 450e)**

Buquet, A. Sur un critère d'indépendance de deux solutions données de l'équation diophantienne en nombres rationnels $x^3+dx+e=z^2$. Mathesis **61**, 183–193 (1952).

It was established by Mordell [Proc. Cambridge Philos. Soc. **21**, 179–192 (1922)] that the rational solutions of the equation of the title can be obtained rationally from a finite number of basic solutions. The writer calls two solutions independent if they cannot be obtained rationally from the same basic solution. If M_1 and M_2 are two rational points on the cubic, and if M_3 with coordinates (x_3, z_3) is the point on the cubic such that $M_1M_2M_3$ form a straight line, then it is well-known that M_3 is rational and the point $(x_3, -z_3)$ is called the resultant of M_1 and M_2. The tangential T of any rational point M on the curve is the rational point where the tangent at M cuts the curve. It is proved that if no point P exists on the curve having M_1, M_2, or their resultant as tangential, then M_1 and M_2 are independent. Various other geometric properties are obtained, and examples are given. *I. Niven* (Eugene, Ore.).

Referred to in G05-40, G05-47.

G05-36 (14, 451f)

Bergman, Gösta. A generalization of a theorem of Nagell. Ark. Mat. **2**, 299–305 (1952).

If A, B belong to a field Ω and satisfy the condition $4A^3-27B^2\neq 0$, then the equation $y^2=x^3-Ax-B$ defines a plane elliptic curve Γ, belonging to Ω, representable parametrically with Weierstrass equations:

$$x=\wp(u; 4A, 4B), \quad y=\tfrac{1}{2}\wp'(u; 4A, 4B).$$

The point (x, y) of Γ belongs to Ω if both x and y are in Ω; moreover, (x, y) is called an exceptional point of Γ, of order n (where n is a natural number) if nu is a period, while $n'u$ is not a period if $0<n'<n$.

In the present paper it is proved that, if Ω is an algebraic number field, of which A and B are integers, and if (x, y) belongs to Ω and is an exceptional point of Γ of order $n>1$, then x and y are integers in Ω in the following cases: i) if n is not a power of an odd prime; ii) if n is a power of 3 and 3 is not divisible by the 8th power of any prime ideal in Ω; iii) if n is a power of a prime $p>3$ and p is not divisible by the $(p-1)$th power of any prime ideal in Ω (the pth power does not suffice).

These results are obtained through the study of the algebraic equation in $x=\wp(u)$ given by $\sigma(nu)=0$. The case when $\Omega=k(1)$ had been considered first by T. Nagell [Skr. Norske Vid.-Akad. Oslo I. **1935**, no. 1], who proved that x and y are then always ordinary integers. An incomplete extension of this result to quadratic and cubic fields had been obtained by G. Billing [Nova Acta Soc. Sci. Upsaliensis (4) **11**, no. 1 (1938)]. *B. Segre* (Rome).

G05-37 (14, 539f)

Selmer, Ernst S. On the Dixon elliptic functions in the equianharmonic case. Norsk Mat. Tidsskr. **34**, 105–116 (1952).

The elliptic functions $x=\mathrm{sm}\,u$, $y=\mathrm{cm}\,u$, which satisfy the equation $x^3+y^3-3\alpha xy=1$, were investigated by A. C. Dixon [Quart. J. Pure Appl. Math. **24**, 167–233 (1890)]. In the present paper the writer is concerned with the special case $\alpha=0$; he writes $\mathrm{sip}\,u$, $\mathrm{cop}\,u$ in place of $\mathrm{sm}\,u$, $\mathrm{cm}\,u$. These functions have been employed by Koschmieder [Math. Ann. **83**, 280–285 (1921)] to obtain a simple proof of the cubic reciprocity theorem. The author has shown that the functions possess simple trisection formulas. He now discusses in detail the behavior of the functions inside the period parallelogram and derives formulas suitable for numerical computation. *L. Carlitz* (Durham, N. C.).

G05-38 (14, 789f)

Nagell, Trygve. Problems in the theory of exceptional points on plane cubics of genus one. Den 11te Skandinaviske Matematikerkongress, Trondheim, 1949, pp. 71–76. Johan Grundt Tanums Forlag, Oslo, 1952. 27.50 kr.

Let $Y^2=X^3-AX-B$ be the equation of an elliptic cubic C, where A and B are in a given field Ω. Then it is well known that the elliptic arguments of the points of C having coordinates in Ω constitute an Abelian group G, and that the points of C corresponding to the elements of a finite subgroup $\bar{G}$ of G are exceptional points of C over Ω. In a previous paper [Nova Acta Soc. Sci. Upsaliensis (4) **14**, no. 1 (1946); no. 3 (1947); these Rev. **9**, 100], the author has given necessary and sufficient conditions on A, B in order that C admit a group $\bar{G}$ of order $n=3, 4, 5, 6, 7$; now he studies the case $n=9$. Then, if G is non-cyclic, all the nine points of inflection of C have coordinates in Ω, the number $\sqrt{-3}$ must belong to Ω, and A, B can be expressed in the form

$$A=\sqrt{-3}cd(c^2-d^2-\sqrt{-3}cd),$$
$$4B=(c^2+d^2)(c^4+d^4-6c^2d^2-2\sqrt{-3}c^3d+2\sqrt{-3}cd^3),$$

where c, d are elements of Ω such that C has a non-zero discriminant; and vice versa. A similar result is reached, for an arbitrary Ω, in the case when C admits a cyclic group $\bar{G}$ of order 9, and gives A and B as forms in two indeterminates, with integer coefficients, of degrees 12 and 18 respectively. *B. Segre* (Rome).

Citations: MR 9, 100b = G05-14; MR 9, 100c = G05-14.

G05-39 (14, 1010c)

Nagell, Trygve. Recherches sur l'arithmétique des cubiques planes du premier genre dans un domaine de rationalité quelconque. Nova Acta Soc. Sci. Upsaliensis (4) **15**, no. 6, 66 pp. (1952).

The present paper deals chiefly with elliptic plane cubics over an arbitrary commutative field, Ω. In the first of the two parts into which it is divided, a Weierstrass cubic $y^2=x^3-Ax-B$ is considered (A, B in Ω), together with the Abelian group G formed by its exceptional points, and any finite subgroup G_1 of G. Then the general expressions for A and B are obtained, when each of the exceptional points of G_1 is supposed to be rational (i.e., to have coordinates x, y in Ω) and G_1 has the order $n=3, 4, 5, 6, 7, 9, 15$; for $n=4, 9$, the two possibilities for G_1 to be cyclic or non-cyclic are investigated. The cases $n=3, 4, 5, 6, 7$ have already been studied by the author [Acta Math. **52**, 93–126 (1928); Nova Acta Soc. Sci. Upsaliensis (4) **14**, no. 1 (1946); Colloq. Internat. Centre Nat. Recherche Sci., no. **24**, 59–64 (1950); these Rev. **9**, 100; **12**, 852], and the proofs are here completed. The new case $n=15$ is particularly laborious and leads to a number of interesting incidental results, such as the following one: the plane quartic

$$u^3(v-2w)+u^2(-2v^2+4vw-w^2)$$
$$+u(v^3-3v^2w+4vw^2-2w^3)+vw(v-w)^2=0$$

has in $K(1)$ only six rational points, i.e., (1, 1, 0), (0, 1, 1), (1, 1, 1), (1, 0, 0), (0, 1, 0), (0, 0, 1).

In part II there are some properties of resolvent fields of a conic or cubic, and of rational triplets on a Weierstrass cubic. Then the equianharmonic cubics (1) $ax^3+by^3+cz^3=0$ and the cubics represented by the Hesse normal form (2) $x^3+y^3+z^3-3\alpha xyz=0$ are considered, and criteria for the linear and birational equivalence in Ω of two cubics of the same type (1) or (2) are given. For instance, in $K(1)$ there is an infinity of cubics $x^3+py^3+p^2z^3=0$, two-by-two non-equivalent; and, over a field not containing $\sqrt{-3}$, two cubics (2) are equivalent only if they have the same coefficient α. At the end, some calculations leading to a result stated in a previous paper [T. Nagell, Nova Acta Soc. Sci. Upsaliensis (4) **12**, no. 8 (1941); these Rev. **9**, 156] are sketched. *B. Segre* (Rome).

Citations: MR 9, 100b = G05-14; MR 9, 156e = G05-15; MR 12, 852a = G05-29.

Referred to in G05-45.

G05-40 **(15, 400c)**

Buquet, A. Sur un critère d'indépendance de plusieurs solutions données de l'équation diophantienne en nombres rationnels $x^3+dx+e=z^2$. Mathesis **62**, 281–289 (1953).

The writer continues his investigations [Mathesis **61**, 181–193 (1952); these Rev. **14**, 450] of geometric properties of the rational solutions of $x^3+dx+e=z^2$. Two rational points A_1 and A_2 on the curve determine a third such point called the resultant [cf. the earlier paper or the review thereof] designated by A_1A_2. This operation is commutative and associative, and so a set of points $A_1, A_2, \cdots, A_r$ determine a system $\sum n_iA_i$, the n_i being any integers. Systems of points are classified in various ways, the details being too numerous to permit delineation here. The classification enables the writer to formulate an elaborate algorithm which is employed to test the independence of solutions. *I. Niven* (Eugene, Ore.).

Citations: MR 14, 450e = G05-35.

Referred to in G05-47, G05-58.

G05-41 **(15, 645f)**

Peeples, W. D., Jr. Elliptic curves and rational distance sets. Proc. Amer. Math. Soc. **5**, 29–33 (1954).

By using the method of tangentials and some simple arguments of valuation theory, conditions are obtained sufficient to ensure that a rational cubic curve

$$ax(y^2-1)-by(x^2-1)=0$$

will contain an infinite number of rational points. This occurs if, for example, $x=m/n$, $y=p/q$ is a point of the curve, where m, n, p, q are non-zero integers, of which m, p are even and n, q are odd. Correspondingly, there is an infinite number of points $(u, 0)$, where $u=2by/(y^2-1)$ and (x, y) is a rational point of the cubic curve, which together with $(0, \pm a)$ and $(0, \pm b)$ form a set in which all distances are rational. *B. Segre* (Rome).

G05-42 **(15, 779d)**

Deuring, Max. Die Zetafunktion einer algebraischen Kurve vom Geschlechte Eins. Nachr. Akad. Wiss. Göttingen. Math.-Phys. Kl. Math.-Phys.-Chem. Abt. **1953**, 85–94 (1953).

Let k be an algebraic number field and let C be a plane algebraic curve over k defined by the (absolutely irreducible) equation $f(x, y)=0$ with coefficients in k; let C be of genus g. Let p denote a prime divisor of k. Then $f(x, y)$ is absolutely irreducible and defines an algebraic curve C/p of genus g for almost all p. Define the zeta-function

$$\zeta(s, C, k, p)=\sum_a \frac{1}{(Na)^s} \quad (\Re s>1),$$

where a runs through the integral divisors of $(k/p)(x, y)$. Then it is known that

$$\zeta(s, C, k, p)=\frac{L(s, C, k, p)}{(1-Np^{-s})(1-Np^{1-s})},$$

where $L(s, C, k, p)$ is a polynomial in Np^{-s} of degree $2g$; moreover,

$$L(s, C, k, p)=\prod_{r=1}^{2g}(1-\pi_r Np^{-s}) \quad (|\pi_r|=Np^{1/2}).$$

Now define

$$\zeta(s, C, k)=\zeta(s, k)\zeta(s-1, k)\prod_p L(s, C, k, p),$$

where $\zeta(s, k)$ is the Dedekind zeta-function. Then $\zeta(s, C, k)$ is regular for $\Re s>3/2$ except for a pole at $s=2$. For $g=0$ it is easy to extend the function to the entire s-plane and to show that it satisfies a functional equation of the usual kind. It is therefore natural to ask whether the same is true for $g\geqq 1$. A. Weil [Trans. Amer. Math. Soc. **73**, 487–495 (1952); these Rev. **14**, 452] showed that for the equation $ax^n+by^m+c=0$, the product $\prod L(s, C, k, p)^{-1}$ is the product of $2g$ Hecke L-series of argument $s-\frac{1}{2}$. He conjectured that this result holds when $g=1$ in the case of complex multiplication. The truth of this conjecture is proved in the present paper. *L. Carlitz* (Durham, N. C.).

Citations: MR 14, 452d = G30-10.

Referred to in G05-50, G05-52, G05-55, G30-15, G30-18.

G05-43 **(15, 894a)**

Bergman, Gösta. On the exceptional points of cubic curves. Ark. Mat. **2**, 489–535 (1954).

According to T. Nagell [Skr. Norske Vid. Akad. Oslo. I. **1935**, no. 1 (1936)] a point (x, y) of the elliptic cubic curve

$$(1) \qquad y^2=x^3-Ax-B \quad (4A^3-27B^2\neq 0)$$

is called an exceptional point of order n, if—in connection with the classical parametric representation of the curve (1) by means of elliptic functions $x=\wp(u)$, $y=\frac{1}{2}\wp'(u)$, with invariants $4A$, $4B$ and a pair of primitive periods ω, ω'—the value of the parameter u which corresponds to (x, y) (defined by this point mod ω, ω') is commensurable with a period, n being the smallest natural number that makes nu a period. If A and B belong to a field Ω, the values of u belonging to those exceptional points which have their coordinates in Ω constitute an Abelian group, called the exceptional group in Ω on the curve (1) [F. Châtelet, C. R. Acad. Sci. Paris **210**, 90–92 (1940); these Rev. **1**, 166]. On account of a result of A. Weil [Acta Math. **52**, 281–315 (1929)], this group is finite if Ω is an algebraic field; then the group contains at most two independent elements having as order any assigned prime [G. Billing, Nova Acta Soc. Sci. Upsaliensis (4) **11**, no. 1 (1938)], and so there is only a finite number of a priori possible structures, indicated here by a simple notation, for an exceptional group of a given order.

In the present paper, parametric expressions for A and B are obtained in correspondence with groups of several types, and precisely of the types (4, 2), (8), (2, 5), (2, 2, 3), (4, 3), (4, 4), (8, 2), (2, 3, 3). Further, the exceptional group is determined when the curve (1) is harmonic ($B=0$) or equianharmonic ($A=0$) and Ω is an algebraic field of degree n, where $n=2$, 4 or an odd number in the harmonic case, and $n=2$, 3 or a number not divisible by 2, 3 in the equianharmonic case. The many results obtained cannot all be described, and we shall give details only on a few of them.

While C. E. Lind [Thesis, Uppsala, 1940; these Rev. **9**, 225] has shown that the groups (4, 2, 3) and (2, 2, 5) are impossible in $k(1)$, here it is proved that each of these groups is possible in an infinity of quadratic fields, even on supposing A and B to be rational. If Ω is an algebraic field of odd degree, A is an arbitrarily given number of Ω and C denotes any number of Ω, then the harmonic curve $y^2=x^3-Ax$ has the following exceptional group in Ω:

$$(2), \text{ if } A\neq C^2, A\neq -4C^4; \qquad (2, 2), \text{ if } A=C^2; \qquad (4), \text{ if } A=-4C^4.$$

If Ω is an algebraic field of degree not divisible by 2, 3, B is an arbitrarily given number of Ω and C denotes any number of Ω, then the equianharmonic curve $y^2=x^3-B$ has the following exceptional group in Ω:

(1), if $B\neq C^3$, $B\neq -C^2$, $B\neq 432C^6$;
(2), if $B=C^3$, $B\neq -C^6$;
(3), if $B=-C^2$ or $B=432C^6$, but $B\neq -C^6$;
(2, 3), if $B=-C^6$.

B. Segre (Rome).

Citations: MR 1, 166f = G20-1; MR 9, 225b = G05-16.

G05-44 **(16, 14g)**

Selmer, Ernst S. A conjecture concerning rational points on cubic curves. Math. Scand. **2**, 49–54 (1954).

The author reports that using an electronic computor he has found solutions for all the equations for which he could give no decision in an earlier memoir [Acta Math. **85**, 203–362 (1951); these Rev. **13**, 13] except in two cases where he can prove insolubility by different criteria. This and other numerical evidence to be presented elsewhere later leads to interesting conjectures. If the L.H.S. of the Diophantine equation $x^3+y^3=az^3$ is factorised in the Eisenstein field of cube roots of 1 and coefficients are equated, there result a finite number of equations of the type $w^3=f(u,v)$ where $f(u,v)$ is a ternary cubic with rational integer coefficients. The number of these which are soluble is closely related to the number of generators of the group of rational solutions in the usual sense. By congruence considerations equations $w^3=f(u,v)$ may often be shown to be insoluble. One can now factorise $f(u,v)$ in the relevant cubic fields and so obtain new equations of the type $\phi(u',v',w')=0$, where ϕ is a ternary cubic with integer coefficients. These can be again sometimes eliminated by congruence considerations ("second descent"). The author remarks that in a large number of cases an even number of generators is eliminated by the second descent and conjectures that this always happens. Indeed he conjectures that when a second descent exists the difference between the number of generators allowed by the first descent and that actually existing is even. He also shows that a second descent can be made with $Y^2=X^3-AX-B$ and makes similar conjectures.

J. W. S. Cassels (Cambridge, England).

Citations: MR 13, 13i = G05-31.

Referred to in G05-51, G05-59.

G05-45 **(16, 15a)**

Nagell, Trygve. Sur la division des périodes de la fonction $\wp(u)$ et les points exceptionnels des cubiques. Nova Acta Soc. Sci. Upsaliensis (4) **15**, no. 8, 28 pp. (1953).

In previous papers the author has discussed the group Γ of exceptional points on a plane cubic curve $y^2=x^3-Ax-B$ of genus one over a field Ω by means of the well-known parametrization of the cubic in Weierstrassian elliptic functions [cf., e.g., same Acta (4) **14**, no. 1 (1946), no. 3 (1947); these Rev. **9**, 100]. He has considered subgroups G_n of Γ of various finite orders n; the difficult case of a G_{15} was examined earlier [ibid. **15**, no. 6 (1952); these Rev. **14**, 1010]. In the present paper he continues this investigation and obtains among other results: (1) Necessary and sufficient that a cubic over Ω should admit a G_{15} is that the cubic $y^2=4x^3-7x^2+4x$ should have on it a rational point (in Ω) distinct from 20 specified points; (2) when $\Omega=K(1)$, $K(i)$, a cubic of genus one cannot have a G_{15}; (3) there are infinitely many quadratic fields Ω (characterized by a necessary and sufficient condition) in which there exist cubics of genus one with a G_{15}. *J. Lehner* (Los Alamos, N. M.).

Citations: MR 9, 100b = G05-14; MR 14, 1010c = G05-39.

G05-46 **(16, 15b)**

Bergman, Gösta. On the exceptional group of a Weierstrass curve in an algebraic field. Acta Math. **91**, 113–142 (1954).

Let Ω be an algebraic field, and let A, B be two of its numbers satisfying $4A^3-27B^2\neq 0$. The plane elliptic curve (1) $y^2=x^3-Ax-B$ can then be represented parametrically by

$$x=\wp(u;4A,4B),\quad y=\tfrac{1}{2}\wp'(u;4A,4B);$$

we denote by ω, ω' a primitive pair of periods of the $\wp$-function. A point u of the curve (1) is said to be a point in Ω if its coordinates (x,y) belong to Ω; it is called an exceptional point of order q if u is commensurable with a period and if q is the smallest natural number such that $qu\equiv 0 \pmod{\omega,\omega'}$. It is well known that the u-values of the exceptional points in Ω form an abelian group, called the exceptional group in Ω of the curve (1).

This paper, by a deep arithmetical analysis of the elliptic functions which express the coordinates x, y or an exceptional point, and of the relations among the points νu ($\nu=0,\pm1,\pm2,\cdots$), proves that the order q of an exceptional point in Ω of a given plane elliptic curve is bounded, and actually determines an upper bound for q.

For this purpose, it is first of all remarked that, if α and $\mathfrak{p}$ denote a number $\neq 0$ and a prime ideal in Ω, the curve (1) and $y^2=x^2-A\alpha^4x-B\alpha^6$ are equivalent, so that A and B can be supposed to be integers mod $\mathfrak{p}$. Hence it is shown that, if $\mathfrak{p}$ is a divisor of 2, then the (x,y)-coordinates of any exceptional point in Ω, not at infinity, are integers mod $\mathfrak{p}$. Denote by N the norm of $\mathfrak{p}$, by $q=2^\lambda t$ the order of an exceptional point in Ω (where $\lambda\geqq 0$, and t is an odd number $\geqq 1$), and suppose $\mathfrak{p}^m\|2$; if $\mathfrak{p}^4|A$, then $\mathfrak{p}^6\nmid B$; if $\mathfrak{p}^m\|B$, then $\mathfrak{p}|A$ (here $\mathfrak{p}^n\|\alpha$ expresses that n is the integer such that $\alpha=\mathfrak{p}^n\mathfrak{a}/\mathfrak{b}$, where $\mathfrak{a}$ and $\mathfrak{b}$ are convenient integral ideals in Ω and $\mathfrak{p}\nmid\mathfrak{a}\mathfrak{b}$). A limit for q which depends only on Ω is then given by proving the following inequalities:

$$t\leqq 2N+1;\quad 2^\lambda\leqq\max[2N,4(3(m+1))^{1/2}];$$
$$q\leqq\max[2N+1,3(6(m+1))^{1/2}],\quad\text{if}\quad t=3;$$
$$q\leqq(2N+1)(2(m+1))^{1/2},\quad\text{if}\quad t\geqq 5.$$

Similar inequalities are obtained in the remaining case, i.e. when $\mathfrak{p}\nmid A$; $\mathfrak{p}^m\|B$.

These results imply a new proof of a theorem by A. Weil [Acta Math. **52**, 281–315 (1929)], according to which the exceptional group in an algebraic field is always finite, and also make it possible to find the points of this group by a regular process. *B. Segre* (Rome).

G05-47 **(16, 335m)**

Buquet, A. Etude des solutions rationnelles de l'équation diophantienne $G(x)\equiv ax^4+bx^3+cx^2+dx+e=z^2$. Mathesis **63**, 240–250 (1954).

It has been known since Euler and Fermat that a series of rational solutions of the equation of the title can be obtained from one such solution. The present paper continues the detailed study of various geometric properties of such chains of solutions, earlier papers having treated also the problem of a cubic polynomial equal to a square [Mathesis **59**, 233–236 (1950); **60**, 239–243 (1951); **61**, 183–193 (1952); **62**, 281–289 (1953); these Rev. **12**, 590; **13**, 535; **14**, 450; **15**, 400]. *I. Niven* (Eugene, Ore.).

Citations: MR 12, 590c = G05-28; MR 13, 535d = G05-33; MR 14, 450e = G05-35; MR 15, 400c = G05-40.

G05-48 **(17, 347j)**

Buquet, A. Sur un critère d'indépendance de plusieurs solutions données de l'équation diophantienne en nombres rationnels $G(x)=ax^4+bx^3+cx^2+dx+e=z^2$. Mathesis **64** (1955), 231–241.

G05-49 **(16, 740d)**

Selmer, Ernst S. The exceptional points of a cubic curve which is symmetric in the homogeneous variables. Math. Scand. **2**, 227–236 (1954).

The present paper deals with symmetric cubic elliptic curves

(1) $a(x+y+z)^3+b(xy+xz+yz)(x+y+z)+cxyz=0,$

where a, b, c are rational integers satisfying the inequality

$$c(27a+9b+c)(b^3+b^2c-ac^2)\neq 0;$$

these are precisely the cubic elliptic curves which possess three rational inflections: $(0, 1, -1)$, $(-1, 0, 1)$, $(1, -1, 0)$. In the general case when $c\neq -3b$, i.e. if the tangents at these three points are non-concurrent and the cubic is not equianharmonic, by a convenient choice of coordinates the equation of the cubic can be written in the reduced form, (2) say, deducible from (1) by assuming $b=0$.

Using a method due to A. Hurwitz [Vierteljschr. Naturforsch. Ges. Zürich **62**, 207–229 (1917)], for any rational point (x, y, z) of the curve (2)—where x, y, z are integers with no common factor—the weight $|xyz|$ is considered, and this number is then compared to the weight of the tangential point of (x, y, z). Hence it is proved that, if the tangential point is not an inflection, its weight is never smaller than the weight of the original point; moreover, the cases when the two weights can be equal are investigated. This leads to the possibility of studying the exceptional points of the curves (1) or (2), and to the determination of those among these curves which have an exceptional subgroup of order nine (cyclic in a real field), six or twelve. Among other related results it is also shown that, when a is squarefree, the number of exceptional points of the curve (2) can only be three (the inflections) or six.

B. Segre (Rome).

Referred to in G05-61.

G05-50 (17, 17c)

Deuring, Max. Die Zetafunktion einer algebraischen Kurve vom Geschlechte Eins. II. Nachr. Akad. Wiss. Göttingen. Math.-Phys. Kl. IIa. **1955,** 13–42 (1955).

In part I [same Nachr. **1953**, 85–94; MR **15**, 779] the author defined the zeta-function of a curve C over the number field k by means of

$$(*)\qquad \zeta(s, C, k)=\prod_{\mathbf{p}}{}' \zeta(s, C, k, \mathbf{p}).$$

Let C be defined by $f(x, y)=0$. The prime in the right member of (*) indicates that the product is restricted to prime divisors $\mathbf{p}$ such that the curve $C/\mathbf{p}$ defined by $f(x, y)\equiv 0 \pmod{\mathbf{p}}$ is absolutely irreducible and has the same genus as C; moreover, for such $\mathbf{p}$, $\zeta(s, C, k, \mathbf{p})$ denotes the zeta-function of the field of algebraic functions on $C/\mathbf{p}$. The principal result of I states that if C is of genus 1, admits of complex multiplication and contains at least one rational point relative to k, then

$$(**)\quad \zeta(s, C, k)= =\zeta(s, k)\zeta(s-1, k)L_0(s-\tfrac{1}{2}, k, \chi)^{-1}L_0(s-\tfrac{1}{2}, k, \bar{\chi})^{-1},$$

where $\zeta(s, k)$ is the zeta-function of k, x is a primitive „Grössencharakter" of k and $L_0(s, k, \chi)$ is "essentially" the L-series $L(s, k, \chi)=\prod \{1-\chi(\mathbf{p})N\mathbf{p}^{-s}\}^{-1}$.

The writer now raises the question whether the definition of $\zeta(s, C, k)$ can be altered in such a manner that that in (**) the L_0's will be replaced by L's. Let $K=k(x, y)$, the field of algebraic functions on C, K of genus 1. Assume that the extension $\mathbf{p}^*$ of $\mathbf{p}$ is such that if u is a non-constant function of K then $u/\mathbf{p}^*$ is not constant, secondly the field of constants of $K/\mathbf{p}^*$ is identical with $k/\mathbf{p}$, and finally the genus of $K/\mathbf{p}^*$ is 1. Then the extension is called regular and u is $\mathbf{p}$-regular. It is proved that a given $\mathbf{p}$ has either a uniquely determined extension (which is independent of u) or it has none; the proof is simple for $\mathbf{p}\nmid 2$, less simple for $\mathbf{p}|2$. Now define

$$\zeta(s, K)=\prod_{\mathbf{p}} \zeta(s, K, \mathbf{p}),$$

where the product is over all prime divisors of k and $\zeta(s, K, \mathbf{p})$ is the zeta-function of $K/\mathbf{p}$ for regular $\mathbf{p}$ while for irregular $\mathbf{p}$ it is the zeta-function of $k/\mathbf{p}$ of genus 0. Then we have the following main result:

$$(***)\ \zeta(s, K)=\zeta(s, k)\zeta(s-1, k)L(s-\tfrac{1}{2}, k, \chi)^{-1}L(s-\tfrac{1}{2}, k, \bar{\chi})^{-1},$$

where L denotes a Hecke L-series and moreover the conductor of χ contains just the irregular $\mathbf{p}$. The proof will be completed in a later paper. *L. Carlitz.*

Citations: MR 15, 779d = G05-42.

Referred to in G05-52, G05-55, G30-20.

G05-51 (17, 711f)

Selmer, Ernst S. The Diophantine equation $\eta^2=\xi^3-D$. A note on Cassels' method. Math. Scand. 3 (1955), 68–74.

The author has recently set up a "second descent" for the diophantine equation $\eta^2=\xi^3-C\xi-D$ the "first descent" being related to halving the elliptic argument ("On Cassels' conditions for the solubility of the diophantine equation $\eta^2=\xi^3-D$", to appear in Archiv for Math. og Naturv.). Here he gives strong numerical evidence that the number of generators "lost" in the second descent is even, at least when $C=0$ and $-D$ is a perfect square. He uses the known relation between (*) $x^3+y^3+Az^3=0$ and $\eta^2=\xi^3+2^4A^2$ together with his extensive numerical information about (*). [For a somewhat analogous "second descent" for (*) (the first descent being related to division of the argument by $\sqrt{(-3)}$) and for a similar conjecture, see Selmer, Math. Scand. **2** (1954), 49–54; MR **16**, 14.] *J. W. S. Cassels* (Cambridge, England).

Citations: MR 16, 14g = G05-44.

G05-52 (18, 113e)

Deuring, Max. Die Zetafunktion einer algebraischen Kurve vom Geschlechte Eins. III. Nachr. Akad. Wiss. Göttingen. Math.-Phys. Kl. IIa. 1956, 37–76.

[For parts I, II of this paper see same Nachr. **1953**, 85–94; **1955**, 13–42; MR **15**, 779; **17**, 17.] Let K be a singular elliptic function-field over the algebraic field k of constants. It is assumed that K has at least one prime divisor $\mathfrak{o}$ of degree 1. The multiplier ring R of K is an order in an imaginary quadratic field Σ, the elements of R may be identified with those of k. The ring classfield Ω_R of Σ is contained in k. The zeta function $\zeta(s, K)$ of K is defined by means of

$$\zeta(s, K)=\prod_{p} \zeta(s, K, p),$$

where the product is over all the prime divisors of k and $\zeta(s, K, p)$ is the zeta function of K/p. Then

$$\zeta(s, K, p)=\frac{(1-\chi(p)Np^{\frac{1}{2}-s})(1-\bar{\chi}(p)Np^{\frac{1}{2}-s})}{(1-Np^{-s})(1-Np^{1-s})},$$

where $|\chi(p)|=1$ for regular p, $\chi(p)=0$ for irregular p (for definitions see review of II).

The principal result of the present paper is contained in the following theorem.

χ is a proper "Grössencharakter" of k; its conductor F_χ contains all the irregular places of K and no other prime divisors of k.

$$\zeta(s, K)=\zeta(s, k)\zeta(s-1, k)L(s-\tfrac{1}{2}, k, \chi)^{-1}L(s-\tfrac{1}{2}, k, \bar{\chi})^{-1},$$

where $\zeta(s, k)$ is the Dedekind zeta function of k and $L(s, k, \chi)$ is the Hecke L-function of k for the Grössencharakter χ. $\zeta(s, K)$ is a meromorphic function of s that satisfies the functional equation

$$(NF_\chi)^{-s}\zeta(s, K)=(NF_\chi)^{-(2s)}\zeta(2-s, K).$$

L. Carlitz (Durham, N.C.).

Citations: MR 15, 779d = G05-42; MR 17, 17c = G05-50.

Referred to in G05-55.

G05-53 **(18, 718b)**

Buquet, A. Démonstration élémentaire du théorème de Mordell-Weil pour l'équation diophantienne en nombres rationnels $X(X^2+CX+D)=Z^2$. Mathesis **65** (1956), 379–390.

It was established by L. J. Mordell [Proc. Cambridge Philos. Soc. **21** (1922), 179–192] that all the rational points on the cubic curve $4x^3-g_2x-g_3=y^2$ could be found by the chord and tangent process starting from a finite number of them. In this paper the author gives an elementary proof of this theorem for the title equation. It is shown that the basic solutions can be selected among four types of points, the classification of which is too complicated to be given here. Use is made of some results due to Rignaux concerning the diophantine equation $x^4+Cx^2y^2+Dy^4=z^2$. At last examples are given.

W. Ljunggren (Blindern).

G05-54 **(19, 120b)**

Selmer, Ernst S. The rational solutions of the Diophantine equation $\eta^2=\xi^3-D$ **for** $|D|\leqq 100$. Math. Scand. **4** (1956), 281–286.

The author lists the number of generators (in the sense of Poincaré-Mordell-Weil) of infinite order for the rational solutions of the title equation for integers D in $|D|\leqq 100$. He gives the appropriate number of linearly independent solutions. He states that he has not verified that they are in fact a system of generators for the rational solutions but that he has verified that no solution listed, or the sum or difference of solutions listed, is either 2 or 3 times a rational solution in the sense of addition on the curve. It is further stated whether the solutions given are $\sqrt{(-3)}$ times a solution of $\eta^2=\xi^3+27D$ in the sense of complex multiplication. Earlier tables covering a more restricted range of D have been given by the reviewer [Acta Math. **82** (1950), 243–273; MR **12**, 11] and by Podsypanin [Mat. Sb. N.S. **24** (66) (1949), 391–403; MR **11**, 81]. A list of errata to Podsypanin's table is given.

The author also lists for $50\leqq D\leqq 100$ elements of the purely cubic fields which are ideal squares but not the product of a unit by a square of a number of the field. This extends the table of the reviewer (loc. cit.) for $0<D\leqq 50$ and supplements the author's table which gives other information about these fields [Avh. Norske Vid. Akad. Oslo. I. **1955**, no. 5; MR **18**, 286].

J. W. S. Cassels (Cambridge, England).

Citations: MR 11, 81i = G05-21; MR 12, 11a = G05-22; MR 18, 286e = R16-17.

G05-55 **(19, 637a)**

Deuring, Max. Die Zetafunktion einer algebraischen Kurve vom Geschlechte Eins. IV. Nachr. Akad. Wiss. Göttingen. Math.-Phys. Kl. IIa. **1957**, 55–80.

Let k be an algebraic number field, K an elliptic function field with the field of constants k. Let K be singular; that is, let the multiplier ring **R** of K be complex, so that **R** is an order of an imaginary quadratic field. Also assume that K contains at least one prime divisor of the first degree. Then the main result of parts I–III [same Nachr. **1953**, 85–94; **1955**, 13–42; **1956**, 37–76; MR **15**, 779; **17**, 17; **18**, 113] can be summed up in the following statement. The zeta-function $\zeta(s, K)$ of K has the representation

(*) $\zeta(s,K)=\zeta(s,k)\zeta(s-1,k)\{L(s-\frac{1}{2},\chi,k)L(s-\frac{1}{2},\bar{\chi},k)\}^{-1}$,

where $L(s,\chi,k)$ is the L-function corresponding to a certain Hecke "grössen" character of k.

The field K is regular for the prime divisor $\mathbf{p}$ of k provided $\mathbf{p}$ possesses a continuation such that $K\ (\mathrm{mod}\ \mathbf{p})$ is an elliptic function-field $\bar{K}$ over the field of constants $\bar{k}(=k(\mathrm{mod}\ \mathbf{p}))$. Let $\zeta(s,K,\mathbf{p})$ denote the zeta-function of $\bar{K}/\mathbf{p}$ or the zeta-function of genus 0 over $k/\mathbf{p}$, according as K is regular or irregular for $\mathbf{p}$; then we define

(**) $$\zeta(s,K)=\prod_{\mathbf{p}}\zeta(s,K,\mathbf{p}).$$

It is remarked that this definition is immediately applicable to the case that K is an elliptic function-field with at least one prime divisor of the first degree.

The object of the present paper is a proof of the following result corresponding to (*).

Let K be an elliptic function-field with at least one prime divisor of the first degree over the number field k. As above, let the multiplier ring **R** of K be complex, so that **R** is an order of an imaginary quadratic field Σ. It is assumed that Σ is not contained in k, so that K has no complex multipliers. Then we have

(***) $\zeta(s,K)=\zeta(s,k)\zeta(s-1,k)\{L(s-\frac{1}{2},\chi,k\Sigma)\}^{-1}$.

The Hecke L-function $L(s,\chi,k\Sigma)$ satisfies (compare (*))

$$\zeta(s,K\Sigma)=\zeta(s,k\Sigma)\zeta(s-1,k\Sigma)\{L(s-\tfrac{1}{2},\chi,k\Sigma)L(s-\tfrac{1}{2},\bar{\chi},k\Sigma)\}^{-1},$$

where $K\Sigma$ denotes the composition of K with Σ and is an elliptic function-field with field of constants $k\Sigma$. Note that in the present case the functions $L(s,\chi,k\Sigma)$ and $L(s,\bar{\chi},k\Sigma)$ are the same.

L. Carlitz (Durham, N.C.).

Citations: MR 15, 779d = G05-42; MR 17, 17c = G05-50; MR 18, 113e = G05-52.

G05-56 **(20# 867)**

Shafarevich, I. R. Birational equivalence of elliptical curves. Dokl. Akad. Nauk SSSR (N.S.) **114** (1957), 267–270. (Russian)

Elliptische Kurven über einem nicht algebraisch abgeschlossenen Körper k können möglicherweise erst in einer endlichen Erweiterung K von k auf die Weierstraßsche Normalgestalt $y^2=x^3+ax+b$ gebracht werden. 2 Kurven sind dann bei Gleichheit der absoluten Invariante $j=4a^3/(4a^3+27b^2)$ zueinander birational äquivalent. In der vorliegenden Note wird weiterhin gezeigt: Jede über k definierte elliptische Kurve, die zu einer über K erklärten Kurve in Weierstraßscher Normalgestalt äquivalent ist, definiert ein System von Automorfismen des algebraischen Funktionenkörpers $K(x,y)$ über K. Bei algebraischem k wird ferner bewiesen: Es gibt nur eine endliche Zahl nicht birational äquivalenter Kurven über k mit gleicher Invariante j und einem Primdivisor ersten Grades in einer gegebenen endlichen Erweiterung K/k. Ist k ein $\mathfrak{p}$-adischer Zahlkörper, der ja nur endlich viele Erweiterungen endlichen Grades besitzt, so läßt sich der letztgenannte Satz noch in folgender Weise verschärfen: Es gibt nur endlich viele birational verschiedene Kurven gegebenen Grades und gegebener Invariante j über dem $\mathfrak{p}$-adischen Körper k.

W. Burau (Hamburg)

Referred to in G10-31, G20-24.

G05-57 **(20# 881)**

Shafarevich, I. R. Exponents of elliptic curves. Dokl. Akad. Nauk SSSR (N.S.) **114** (1957), 714–716. (Russian)

Unter dem Exponenten f einer algebraischen Kurve γ vom Geschlecht g über dem Körper k versteht der Verf. den kleinsten positiven Grad eines Divisors auf γ. Es gilt $f|2g-2$, sodaß nur bei elliptischen Kurven ($g=1$) mehr als endlich viele Werte für f in Frage kommen. Verf. zeigt nun in der vorliegenden Note, daß es im Falle des rationalen Zahlkörpers R elliptische Kurven über R mit beliebig großem f gibt. Es wird hierzu vor allem die von A. Weil [Amer. J. Math. **77** (1955), 493–512; MR **17**, 533] eingeführte Gruppe $H(\omega)$ aller birational äquivalenten elliptischen Kurven mit gegebener Jacobischen Kurve ω herangezogen und gezeigt daß $H(\omega)$ über dem rationalen Zahlkörper R Elemente beliebig hoher Ordnung besitzt.

W. Burau (Hamburg)

G05-58 (21# 3411)

Buquet, A. Sur la recherche directe de l'indépendance de plusieurs points rationnels donnés d'une cubique. Mathesis **68** (1959), 24–37.

A set of p rational points $A_1, A_2, \cdots, A_p$ on a plane cubic curve are "independent" if it is not possible to find q $(<p)$ rational points $B_1, B_2, \cdots, B_q$ on the curve from which one can find the A_j by repeated operation of alignment. In a previous paper [Mathesis **62** (1953), 281–289; MR **15**, 400] the author has considered the special case of cubics of the form $x^3+dx+e=z^2$; this investigation is now extended to arbitrary cubics. The problem is reduced to that of determining whether certain equations of the fourth degree (in a single unknown) have rational solutions.

L. Carlitz (Durham, N.C.)

Citations: MR 15, 400c = G05-40.

G05-59 (22# 24)

Cassels, J. W. S. Arithmetic on curves of genus 1. I. On a conjecture of Selmer. J. Reine Angew. Math. **202** (1959), 52–99.

The subject of this paper is not quite so wide as the title would indicate. For all but one brief section the discussion is restricted to points (x, y, z) on $x^3+y^3+dz^3=0$ where the ground-field K is not of characteristic 3 and contains a non-trivial cube root of unity. In section 2 a discussion is given of the algebraic background of the subject and of the link with Weil's proof of the Mordell-Weiss finite basis theorem, but the rest of the paper is independent of this section. The author believes that the methods used for the special cubic are capable of generalization along the line he indicates.

The paper investigates the circumstances which will permit the conclusion that the curve has a point over K from the fact that the curve has a point over every p-adic completion of K. The basic method is the consideration of homomorphisms of a group structure defined on points of the curve by the choice of $(1, -1, 0)$ as neutral point together with the principle of linear equivalence to various subgroups of $K^*/(K^*)^3$ defined by the curve. In developing this theory and the reciprocity theorems which follow from it the author is able to generalize the methods of descent used by E. S. Selmer in a number of papers in Acta Math. and Math. Scand. beginning with his memoir "The Diophantine equation $ax^3+by^3+cz^3=0$" [Acta Math. **85** (1951), 203–362; MR **13**, 13]. In an appendix the author takes as an example $d=5610$; he is able to show the absence of non-trivial points by discussing only the field $R(\rho, 5610^{1/3})$ where R is the rational field and $\rho^2+\rho+1=0$, while Selmer had to consider 40 fields in this case. A conjecture of Selmer regarding the number of generators of the groups involved is also shown to be true [Math. Scand. **2** (1954), 49–54; MR **16**, 14].

The following theorem (VII) is chosen as reasonably typical while not requiring extended definitions. Let m_1, m_2 be in K^* but not in $(K^*)^3$. Suppose that there are points (X_1, Y_1, Z_1), (X_2, Y_2, Z_2) defined over K on $m_j^{-1}X_j^3+m_jY_j^3+dZ_j^3=0$ $(j=1, 2)$. Then m_2 is the norm of an element of $K(m_1^{1/3})$.

J. D. Swift (Los Angeles, Calif.)

Citations: MR 13, 13i = G05-31; MR 16, 14g = G05-44.
Referred to in G05-67, G10-13.

G05-60 (22# 1542)

Nagell, T. Les points exceptionnels rationnels sur certaines cubiques du premier genre. Acta Arith. **5**, 333–357 (1959).

The principal result is theorem II: Let Ω be an algebraic number field with class-number 1 and suppose either that there are no units E, E_1 of Ω such that $1+E+E_1=0$ or that the only such units are cube roots of 1. Let a, b, c, be cube-free integers of Ω. Then there are no exceptional points defined over Ω on

(1) $$ax^3+by^3+cz^3=0$$

except when the equation (1) can be reduced to the shape

(2) $$x'^3+y'^3+c'z'^3=0$$

by writing $x=\varepsilon_1x'$, $y=\varepsilon_2y'$, $z=\varepsilon_3z'$ with unit factors $\varepsilon_1, \varepsilon_2, \varepsilon_3$. If Ω is as above, all the exceptional points defined over Ω on the curve (2) can be specified completely. (An exceptional point is one which gives rise to only finitely many distinct points under the "chord and tangent process".) It is shown, further, that if Ω is either a quadratic field or a cubic field with negative discriminant and has class-number 1, then it satisfies the criterion of theorem II except in a finite number of cases which can be dealt with separately.

J. W. S. Cassels (Cambridge, England)

Referred to in G05-62, R04-27, R04-39.

G05-61 (22# 4714)

Gutwirth, A.; Jabotinsky, E. An alignment matrix and its applications to plane cubic curves and their rational points. Bull. Res. Council Israel. Sect. A **6** (1956), 11–41.

An alignment matrix is defined to be a matrix of three rows (x_i, y_i, z_i) $(i=1, 2, 3)$ such that the sum $(=\mu)$ and the product $(=\lambda)$ of the elements in each row is the same, the coordinates being taken from an arbitrary field K. The authors enunciate a large number of identities which hold amongst the elements of an alignment matrix, perhaps the most striking being that

$$(x_1x_2x_3)^{1/3}+(y_1y_2y_3)^{1/3}+(z_1z_2z_3)^{1/3} = 0,$$

for an appropriate choice of the cube roots, provided only that two of the cube roots are in K. These identities are proved on the assumption that the alignment matrix is non-degenerate, in a sense which is defined; but the authors also investigate how far they continue to be valid for degenerate alignment matrices. As they point out, the three rows of a non-degenerate alignment matrix are the homogeneous coordinates of the intersection of a line with the cubic $\mu^3xyz=\lambda(x+y+z)^3$ of genus 1, and this places their results in a wider setting. The authors give a geometric interpretation of degenerate alignment matrices. Finally, they discuss when a general curve of genus 1 can be brought into their canonical form, and the condition under which the group of the rational points (over K) on the curve contains elements of order 3 and 9 [cf., e.g., Selmer, Math. Scand. **2** (1954), 227–236; MR **16**, 740].

J. W. S. Cassels (Cambridge, England)

Citations: MR 16, 740d = G05-49.

G05-62 (23# A3709)

Nagell, T.

Les points exceptionnels sur les cubiques $ax^3+by^3+cz^3=0$.

Acta Sci. Math. Szeged **21** (1960), 173–180.

Theorem: Let Ω be an algebraic number field which does not contain $\sqrt{(-3)}$ and such that there are no units E, E_1 for which $1+E+E_1=0$. Let a, b, c be integers of Ω coprime in pairs, no one of them being divisible by the cube of a prime ideal. Then the number of exceptional points defined over Ω on the title curve is 0, 1, 2 or 3. The exceptional points are just the inflexions which happen to be defined over Ω. The cases when the number is not 0 are characterized in terms of a, b, c. For a similar theorem in which, however, Ω is required to have class number 1, see the author's recent paper, Acta Arith. **5** (1959), 333–357 [MR **22** #1542].

The author also discusses when a totally complex

quartic field Ω satisfies the condition of this or his earlier theorem. *J. W. S. Cassels* (Cambridge, England)

Citations: MR 22# 1542 = G05-60.

Referred to in R04-27.

G05-63 (26# 3669)

Birch, B. J.; Swinnerton-Dyer, H. P. F.

Notes on elliptic curves. I.

J. Reine Angew. Math. **212** (1963), 7–25.

This note is the first of a series of papers in which the authors give numerical evidence in support of several fascinating conjectures concerning rational points on algebraic varieties. Let Γ be an elliptic curve of genus 1 with a rational point. Then Γ has an equation of the form $y^2z=x^3-Axz^2-Bz^3$, where $4A^3-27B^2\neq 0$. Mordell showed that the set A of rational points on Γ is a finitely generated group, and Miss Lutz completely determined the torsion subgroup of A. This paper is primarily concerned with the practical computation of the number g of independent generators of A of infinite order.

In the first part of the paper the authors develop a theory that enables them to compute $g+t$, where 2^t is the number of elements of order 2 in the Tate-Šafarevič group of Γ. In addition they can sometimes compute g. Briefly, this theory goes as follows. The set of 2-coverings of Γ forms an abelian group whose elements have order at most 2. Let G be those 2-coverings of Γ which have points in all local fields and let G' be those 2-coverings of Γ which have a rational point. G' is a subgroup of G of order 2^{g+g_2}, where g_2 is the number of elements of A of finite, even order ($g_2=0$, 1 or 2 as $f(x)=x^3-Ax-B$ has 0, 1 or 3 real roots). The order of G is 2^k, where $k=g+g_2+t$. The authors prove that each 2-covering of Γ is given by a curve of the form $y^2=g(x)$, where $g(x)$ is a quartic form with rational coefficients and with invariants related to the invariants of $f(x)$. Two curves $y^2=g(x)$ and $y^2=g^*(x)$ give the same 2-covering if and only if there are rational numbers α, β, γ, δ, μ such that

$$g(x) = \mu^2(\gamma x+\delta)^4g^*((\alpha x+\beta)/(\gamma x+\delta)).$$

By developing a theory of reduced quartic forms (essentially a finite-descent process), the authors are able to determine representations $y^2=g(x)$ of each of the various 2-coverings of Γ. A Hensel-type lemma is given to determine which of these lie in G, and the elements of G' are determined from these by inspection for rational points.

The second part of the paper consists of a discussion of the programming of a method to determine k (and sometimes g) based on this theory. The paper concludes with four tables. The first gives $g+t$ for all curves of the form $y^2=x^3-Ax-B$ with $0<|A|\leqq 20$, $0\leqq |B|\leqq 30$. The others give $g+t$, and lower bounds for g, for all curves of the form $y^2=x^3-D$ with $|D|\leqq 400$ and $y^2=x^3-Dx$ with $|D|\leqq 200$. The authors point out that their computations have not been completely double-checked, but they agree with previously published results.

D. J. Lewis (Ann Arbor, Mich.)

Referred to in D02-23, G05-74, G05-75, G05-87.

G05-64 (26# 6171)

Cassels, J. W. S.

Arithmetic on curves of genus 1. V. Two counter-examples.

J. London Math. Soc. **38** (1963), 244–248.

Part IV appeared in J. Reine Angew. Math. **211** (1962), 95–112. The author considers the abelian variety $\mathscr{C}$ consisting of the elliptic curve defined by $x^2=y^2-t^2$, $z^2=y^2+t^2$ and the group law $x_1+x_2=x_3$, given by: $x_3=x_2t_2y_1z_1-x_1t_1y_2z_2$, $y_3=y_2t_2z_1x_1-y_1t_1z_2x_2$, $z_3=z_2t_2x_1y_1-z_1t_1x_2y_2$, $t_3={t_2}^2{x_1}^2-{t_1}^2{x_2}^2$, whose zero element is the point $\mathfrak{o}=(1, 1, 1, 0)$. Let l, m, n be any non-zero rational numbers and let $\mathfrak{X}=(X, Y, Z, T)$ be the generic point of the curve $\mathscr{D}$: $mnX^2=nlY^2-T^2$, $lmZ^2=nlY^2+T^2$. Let λ be the birational correspondence between $\mathscr{D}$ and $\mathscr{C}$, and let $\lambda\mathfrak{X}=((lm)^{1/2}X, (mn)^{1/2}Y, (nl)^{1/2}Z, T)$. The author defines in $\mathscr{D}$ a structure of homogeneous space over $\mathscr{C}$, relative to the field Q, by

$$\mathfrak{X}+\mathfrak{n} = \lambda^{-1}(\lambda\mathfrak{X}+\mathfrak{n}),$$

where $\mathfrak{X}$, $\mathfrak{n}$ are generic points of $\mathscr{D}$, $\mathscr{C}$, respectively. One can determine l, m, n in such a fashion that the homogeneous space has order 2 and index 4, and that the canonical map of the rational divisors of degree 0 on $\mathscr{D}$ into the rational points of its Jacobian $\mathscr{C}$ is not surjective. The author found, in proofs, a generalization of the foregoing counter-examples for any curve $\mathscr{B}$ defined over a perfect field k, based on the exactness of the following sequence

$$0\to C/\pi D\to \operatorname{Ker}[H^2(\Gamma, \bar{k}^*)\to H^2(\Gamma, \bar{k}(\mathfrak{X})^*)],$$

where D is the group of divisors, C the divisor class group, π the canonical homomorphism $D\to C$, $\bar{k}$ the algebraic closure of k and Γ the Galois group of $\bar{k}/k$.

P. Abellanas (Madrid)

Citations: MR 29# 1214 = G05-70.

Referred to in G05-66, G05-70.

G05-65 (28# 2103)

Gerl, Peter

Punktfolgen auf Kurven und Flächen.

Monatsh. Math. **67** (1963), 401–432.

The larger part of this paper deals with curves of degree 3 and genus 1, parametrized by $x=p(u)$, $y=p'(u)$, where p is the Weierstrass elliptic function. According to a theorem of Mordell, the set of those u's that produce rational points of the curve form a module with a finite set of generators $u_1, \cdots, u_n$. These points $m_1u_1+\cdots+m_nu_n$ (with integral m_i) can be arranged such that $|m_1|+\cdots+|m_n|$ is non-decreasing. This sequence is shown to be uniformly distributed mod ω, where ω is a period. The sequence of u's corresponds to a sequence of points on the curve, and the detailed study of its density on the curve is, of course, nothing but a study of ds/du, where ds is the line element.

There are also some definitions concerning density of a sequence on a surface. The author studies curves of constant density, but fails to remark that his definition depends on the special Gaussian parameters, and that these curves are not invariant with respect to bending of the surface.

{The reviewer remarks that the lemma proved on pp. 406–407 is a well-known theorem, of which better and shorter proofs are available in standard texts, e.g., N. Jacobson [*Lectures in abstract algebra*, Vol. II, Chapter II, Section 9, Theorem 7, Van Nostrand, Toronto, 1953; MR **14**, 837].} *N. G. de Bruijn* (Eindhoven)

G05-66 (29# 104)

Cassels, J. W. S.

Arithmetic on curves of genus 1. VI. The Tate-Šafarevič group can be arbitrarily large.

J. Reine Angew. Math. **214/215** (1964), 65–70.

Part V appeared in J. London Math. Soc. **38** (1963), 244–248 [MR **26** #6171]. Let **C** be the 1-dimensional abelian variety consisting of the curve

(1) $$x^3+y^3+dz^3 = 0$$

with an addition in which (1, −1, 0) is the zero point. Let us consider the set of homogeneous spaces over **C** defined by the curves

(2) $$mx^3+m^{-1}y^3+dz^3 = 0,$$

where m is an element of the multiplicative group Q^* of rationals. Equation (2) defines a map $\omega: Q^* \to WC$, where WC is the group of classes of homogeneous spaces over **C**. The Tate-Šafarevič group Ш consists of those elements of WC which have points in every p-adic field and in the reals, but no rational points. The author proves that if $m|P^2$, $m>1$, where $P=\prod_{1\leq j\leq T} p_j$ and the p_j are distinct positive rational primes of the form $9n+8$, then $\omega(m)\in$ Ш. Hence, the order of Ш is at least 3^T.

P. Abellanas (Madrid)

Citations: MR 26# 6171 = G05-64.
Referred to in G05-73.

G05-67 (29# 1211)

Cassels, J. W. S.
Arithmetic on curves of genus 1. II. A general result.
J. Reine Angew. Math. **203** (1960), 174–208.

On généralise ici les résultats d'un article antérieur [même J. **202** (1959), 52–99; MR **22** #24; errata, MR **22**, p. 2545] dont on reprend les notations. On désigne par C une courbe algébrique de genre un sur un corps de nombres algébriques R, par P un point de C défini sur R et par $X \to \nu X$ une application φ de C en C qui est définie sur R et laisse le point P invariant. On précise au préalable certaines propriétés des recouvrements et des conséquences du théorème de finitude de Mordell-Weil. En particulier, les théorèmes de descente permettent de définir un groupe $M^{(1)}$ de ν-recouvrements particulier. On obtient alors le résultat suivant (théorème I): si ν^2 est un entier rationnel et si chaque point du noyau de φ est défini sur R, il existe une application bilinéaire symétrique gauche des paires d'éléments de $M^{(1)}$ dans les entiers rationnels modulo un.

J. Guérindon (Zbl **94**, 26)

Citations: MR 22# 24 = G05-59.

G05-68 (29# 1212)

Cassels, J. W. S.
Arithmetic on curves of genus 1. III. The Tate-Šafarevič and Selmer groups.
Proc. London Math. Soc. (3) **12** (1962), 259–296.

L'auteur continue l'étude du groupe G des points d'une courbe C de genre 1, définie sur un corps de nombres k, algébrique et de degré fini [voir #1211 ci-dessus]. Il passe aux complétions P-adiques de k et donne un algorithme permettant de déterminer effectivement le groupe de Tate-Šafarevič, pris modulo les éléments qui sont divisibles par une puissance élevée d'un nombre premier fixé q. Enfin on étudie le problème de savoir si deux espaces homogènes principaux sur C sont dans la même classe, élément du groupe de Weil-Chatelet. *J. Guérindon* (Zbl **106**, 37)

Referred to in G05-75.

G05-69 (29# 1213)

Cassels, J. W. S.
Corrigendum: "Arithmetic on curves of genus 1. III. The Tate-Šafarevič and Selmer groups".
Proc. London Math. Soc. (3) **13** (1963), 768.

The author points out an imprecision in the reasoning of § 5 of the paper mentioned in the title [#1212] and shows how to rectify it.

G05-70 (29# 1214)

Cassels, J. W. S.
Arithmetic on curves of genus 1. IV. Proof of the Hauptvermutung.
J. Reine Angew. Math. **211** (1962), 95–112.

Let k be an algebraic number field, $\mathscr{C}$ an abelian variety of dimension 1 and Ш the corresponding Tate-Šafarevič group of classes of principal homogeneous spaces for $\mathscr{C}$ defined over k which are everywhere locally trivial. The author constructs a pairing $l(\xi, \eta)$ over Ш with values in the group Q/Z of the rationals modulo 1 and he shows that $l(\xi, \eta)$ is linear in η and that $l(\xi, \eta)$ is skew-symmetric. Tate's lemma is then given: If A is a Γ-module which, when considered only as a Z-module, is isomorphic to $Z/qZ \oplus Z/qZ$, where q is a rational prime and Γ is the Galois group of the algebraic closure $\bar{k}$ of the algebraic number field k over k; then an element of $H^2(\Gamma, A)$ is trivial if it is everywhere locally trivial. By means of Tate's lemma, it is proved that if q is a prime, a necessary and sufficient condition for $\xi\in$ Ш to be divisible by q in Ш is that $l(\xi,\eta)=0$ for all $\eta\in$ Ш with $q\eta=0$. From this lemma follows the theorem: Let m be a natural number and suppose that $l(\xi,\eta)=0$ for all $\xi\in$ Ш such that $m\xi=0$; then $\eta=mH$ for some $H\in$ Ш. One proves also the following theorems: (i) Let $(\mathscr{D}, \mu)$ be a homogeneous space over an abelian variety $\mathscr{C}$ of dimension 1 defined over an algebraic number field. Suppose that $(\mathscr{D}, \mu)$ corresponds to an element of Ш. Then the map induced by μ of the divisors on $\mathscr{D}$ defined over k of degree 0 into the points of $\mathscr{C}$ defined over k is surjective. (ii) In the language of Lang and Tate [Amer. J. Math. **80** (1958), 659–684; MR **21** #4960] the index of an element of Ш is always equal to its order in the group Ш.

{Part V has already appeared [J. London Math. Soc. **38** (1963), 244–248; MR **26** #6171].} *P. Abellanas* (Madrid)

Citations: MR 21# 4960 = G10-10; MR 26# 6171 = G05-64.
Referred to in G05-64, G05-76, G10-31.

G05-71 (29# 2220)

Lang, Serge
Diophantine approximations on toruses.
Amer. J. Math. **86** (1964), 521–533.

Author's introduction: "The main purpose of this paper is to make precise certain analogies between diophantine approximations on the multiplicative group and elliptic curves and to show how these are related to approximations on the additive group by means of the exponential mapping. We shall state two conjectures."

The first conjecture is as follows. Let Γ be a finitely-generated subgroup of the group G_K of points defined over the number field K on the multiplicative group G and let ϕ be a nonconstant function on G defined over K. Then the logarithmic heights $h(P)$ of points P in Γ which are bounded away from 0 and ∞ and satisfy the inequality $|\phi(P)| < |h(P)|^{-rm-\varepsilon}$ are bounded, where m is the rank of Γ and r is the maximum multiplicity of a zero of ϕ. (The logarithmic height is the logarithm of the more usual height.) On taking logarithms, this conjecture is seen to be substantially equivalent to the conjecture that a set of logarithms of m elements of K behaves for linear diophantine approximation like "almost any" set of m real numbers provided that they are linearly independent over the rationals. The second conjecture relates to functions on an elliptic curve defined over an algebraic number field and is similarly motivated.

Of interest are (1) a new type of "Lipschitz principle" [cf. Davenport, J. London Math. Soc. **26** (1951), 179–183;

MR **13**, 323], which is said to be more useful in applications and which is used to obtain an asymptotic estimate of the number of units of K with height less than a given number; and (2) a proof, due to Tate, that the (logarithmic) height of a rational point on an abelian variety is essentially given by a quadratic form (conjecture of Néron [cf. Lang, *Diophantine geometry*, Interscience, New York, 1962; MR **26** #119]).

J. W. S. Cassels (Cambridge, England)

Citations: MR 13, 323d = P28-14; MR 26# 119 = G02-9.
Referred to in G10-27.

G05-72 (29# 2699)

Baur, Arnold

Rationale Punkte auf Kurven dritter Ordnung vom Geschlecht Eins.

Math.-Phys. Semesterber. **10** (1963/64), 241–251.

K sei eine ebene Kubik vom Geschlecht 1 über dem rationalen Zahlkörper mit dem rationalen Punkt R. Dann ist bekanntlich auch der Tangentialpunkt T von R, rational, und man erhält so eine Kette von rationalen Punkten, die endlich oder unendlich sein kann und nur bei einem Wendepunkt aufhört. Der Verfasser nennt K Zwillingskurve, wenn es auf ihr einen rationalen Punkt T gibt, der Tangentialpunkt von 2 rationalen Punkten ist; gibt es sogar 4 rationale Tangenten von T aus, so heißt die Zwillingskurve Quadrupelkurve. Ebene Kubiken, die keine Zwillingskurven sind, nennt er Einfachkurven. Als Grenzfall gehören auch die Kubiken mit einem rationalen Wendepunkt zu den Zwillingskurven. Diese lassen sich auf die Normalgestalt

$$ax^2y+by^2+2cxy+dx+ey = 0$$

mit rationalen Koeffizienten transformieren. Der Verfasser beweist, daß auf ihnen alle rationalen Punkte paarweise auftreten. Im allgemeinen besitzt die Zwillingskurve bei $ae-bd\neq 0$ 6 rationale Punkte. Der Verfasser gibt Beispiele für Zwillingskurven mit 1, 3, 4, 8, 9 und unendlich vielen rationalen Punkten. Es folgen dann Beispiele von Quadrupelkurven, die geschlossene Ketten von je 12, 16 und 26 rationalen Punkten besitzen. Bei Einfachkurven ist die Frage offen, ob es solche mit einer geschlossenen Kette von endlich vielen rationalen Punkten gibt. Doch gibt es Einfachkurven mit unendlich vielen rationalen Punkten. Hinreichend ist dafür die Existenz eines rationalen Anfangspunktes R_0 auf K mit 4 irrationalen Tangenten durch R_0 an K.

W. Burau (Hamburg)

G05-73 (30# 92)

Cassels, J. W. S.

Arithmetic on curves of genus 1. VII. The dual exact sequence.

J. Reine Angew. Math. **216** (1964), 150–158.

Part VI appeared in same J. **214/215** (1964), 65–70 [MR **29** #104]. Let k be an algebraic number field, and let C be an abelian variety of dimension 1 defined over k. Denoting by p any place (non-archimedean or archimedean) of k, there is a natural map $\varphi\colon H^1(k,C)\to\sum_p H^1(k_p,C)$, and hence an exact sequence

$$(*)\quad 0\to \operatorname{Ker}\varphi\to H^1(k,C)\to \sum_p H^1(k_p,C)\to \operatorname{Cok}\varphi\to 0.$$

Here Ker φ is known as the Tate-Šafarevič group, and it is widely believed that Ker φ is finite. Taking all groups to be discrete, we get the dual exact sequence of compact groups

$$(*)^*\quad 0\to(\operatorname{Cok}\varphi)^*\to\Big(\sum_p H^1(k_p,C)\Big)^* \to (H^1(k,C))^*\to(\operatorname{Ker}\varphi)^*\to 0.$$

Now, $(\sum_p H^1(k_p,C))^*=\prod_p (H^1(k_p,C))^*$ and, according to Tate,

$$H^1(k_p,C)^* = G_p' = \varprojlim_n C_{k_p}/nC_{k_p},$$

where $G_p'=C_{k_p}$ if p is non-archimedean, and $G_p'=C_{k_p}$ modulo its identity component if p is archimedean. Then the group C_k is mapped in an obvious way into the product $\prod_p G_p'$. The author proves that the closure of the image of C_k is precisely equal to (Cok φ)*, provided 0 is the only divisible element (by any natural number) of Ker φ (Theorem 1.1). In § 3, assuming the finiteness of Ker φ, an explicit description of $H^1(k,C)^*$ and the duality between (*) and (*)* is given. The author remarks that Tate has generalized the results of this paper to abelian varieties of arbitrary dimension [cf. Tate, Proc. Internat. Congr. Mathematicians (Stockholm, 1962), pp. 288–295, Inst. Mittag-Leffler, Djursholm, 1963].

T. Ono (Philadelphia, Pa.)

Citations: MR 29# 104 = G05-66.
Referred to in G05-76, G05-123.

G05-74 (30# 4759)

Birch, B. J.

Conjectures concerning elliptic curves.

Proc. Sympos. Pure Math., Vol. VIII, pp. 106–112. *Amer. Math. Soc., Providence, R.I.*, 1965.

A racy and readable account of the present state of ignorance about elliptic curves defined over the rational field, with particular reference to the experimental work of Swinnerton-Dyer and the author [J. Reine Angew. Math. **212** (1963), 7–25; MR **26** #3669, and forthcoming papers], which have revealed what a rich structure of theory there must be, waiting to be discovered.

J. W. S. Cassels (Cambridge, England)

Citations: MR 26# 3669 = G05-63.
Referred to in G05-75.

G05-75 (31# 3419)

Birch, B. J.; Swinnerton-Dyer, H. P. F.

Notes on elliptic curves. II.

J. Reine Angew. Math. **218** (1965), 79–108.

In recent years the authors have made extensive computations concerning rational points on elliptic curves. An account of their methods of computation was given in Part I [same J. **212** (1963), 7–25; MR **26** #3669]. These computations have led them to a number of important and deep conjectures. A few of these conjectures have now been proved [see Cassels, #3420 below], and others have been reformulated in response to recent developments in the theory of algebraic groups. In the present paper the authors describe their computations and conjectures as of April, 1964. For a somewhat earlier report on the subject, see Birch [Proc. Sympos. Pure Math., Vol. VIII, pp. 106–112, Amer. Math. Soc., Providence, R.I., 1965; MR **30** #4759]. Some of the conjectures have since given rise to other more general conjectures by Tate and by the authors. All these conjectures (if true) represent profound discoveries on the arithmetical structure of algebraic groups.

Let Γ be an elliptic curve, with equation $y^2z=x^3-Axz^2-Bz^3$. Γ is an abelian group (points being added by the chord construction), and the rational points $\mathscr{A}$ on Γ constitute a subgroup. Mordell proved in 1922 that

$\mathscr{A}$ is finitely generated. Methods for determining the torsion part of $\mathscr{A}$, which is finite, have been given by Nagell [Skr. Norske Vid.-Akad. Oslo I (1935), No. 1, 1–25]. One of the most significant unsolved problems in number theory is that of determining the number g of independent generators of the torsion free part of $\mathscr{A}$. The general aim of the authors is to relate g to the densities of the p-adic points on Γ, for the totality of all primes p. It is plausible that greater densities of p-adic points will correspond to larger values of g.

A measure of the density of p-adic points is $\lim_{n\to\infty} N_{p^n}/p^n$, where N_{p^n} denotes the number of solutions of the congruence $y^2z\equiv x^3-Axz^2-Bz^3 \pmod{p^n}$. By Hensel's lemma, this limit is N_p/p, except for finitely many p. Thus the authors were led to examine the function $f(P)=\prod_{p\leq P}(N_p/p)$ for large P, and for a number of curves Γ. Their calculations suggested that (1) $f(P)\sim C(\log P)^g$ as $P\to\infty$, where $C=C(\Gamma)$. Since $f(P)$ oscillates wildly, it was impossible to identify C.

The ζ-function associated with Γ (defined by Deuring) is expressible as $\zeta_\Gamma(s)=\zeta(s)\zeta(s-1)/L_\Gamma(s)$, where (except for finitely many p)

$$L_\Gamma(s) = \prod_p (1+(N_p-p-1)p^{-s}+p^{1-2s})^{-1}.$$

Thus formally, $L_\Gamma(1)=\prod (N_p/p)^{-1}$, but for general Γ it is not known whether this product converges. (Hasse has conjectured that it does, and that $L_\Gamma(s)$ can be continued to the left of $s=1$.) The authors conjecture, as a parallel to (1), that (2) $\zeta_\Gamma(s)\sim C'(s-1)^{g-1}$ as $s\to 1$.

In the special cases when Γ admits complex multiplication, $L_\Gamma(s)$ is expressible as a Hecke L-series with a Grössencharakter and (as Deuring proved) can be continued over the whole plane. In particular, for the curve Γ_D given by $y^2z=x^3-Dxz^2$, the authors obtain an expression for $L_{\Gamma_D}(1)=L_D(1)$ as a finite sum containing quartic residue symbols and division values of the Weierstrass $\wp$-function with periods ω, $i\omega$ (ω being a certain computable absolute constant). By an ingenious proof (which uses among other things classical class-field theory, specifically, Kronecker's Jugendtraum), the authors prove: Let D be a fourth-power free integer, not divisible by 4; then

$$L_D(1) = \begin{cases} D^{1/4}\omega\sigma(D), & \text{for } D>0,\\ (-4D)^{1/4}\omega\sigma(D), & \text{for } D<0,\end{cases}$$

where $\sigma(D)$ is a rational integer. This enables $L_D(1)$ to be determined exactly from a computation of only moderate accuracy. The value found for $\sigma(D)$ for some 1,300 values of D support the conjecture (implicit in (2)) that (3) $\sigma(D)=0$ if and only if $g=0$. All the values found for $\sigma(D)$ are of the form 2^ab^2, which suggests that $\sigma(D)\geqq 0$; however, this has not been proved.

The authors next turn to giving an interpretation of $\sigma(D)$ when it does not vanish. If $\mathscr{A}$ is finite, the Tamagawa number of the curve Γ_D is given by $\int_{\mathfrak{A}/\mathscr{A}}\omega$, where $\mathfrak{A}$ is the adèle curve for Γ_D and ω is the canonical measure on the adèle group. This suggested investigating the related number $\tau(D)=\prod_p\int_{\Gamma_{D,p}}\omega_p$, where $\Gamma_{D,p}$ is the p-adic curve for Γ_D and ω_p is the canonical measure on the p-adic field. The authors prove that $\sigma(D)\tau(D)=4\prod_{p|2D}\int_{\Gamma_{D,p}}\omega_p$, and the right-hand side is easily evaluated. The authors go on to conjecture: (4) If $g=0$, then the order of the Tate-Šafarevič group of Γ_D is $\eta^2(D)/\tau(D)$, where $\eta(D)$ is the number of rational points on Γ_D.

The tangible evidence for this conjecture is not as great as for the others. Indeed, at present there is no example of a curve known with certainty to have a finite Tate-Šafarevič group. However, in all the authors' examples where $g=0$, it is seen that (a) $\tau(D)$ is a square, which is consistent with the fact that if the Tate-Šafarevič group is finite, its order is a square [Cassels, Proc. London Math. Soc. (3) **12** (1962), 259–296; MR **29** #1212]; (b) when the order of the 2-Sylow subgroup of the Tate-Šafarevič group is known, it agrees with the power of 2 in $\eta^2(D)/\tau(D)$; (c) in instances where the second descent fails to determine g, there is reason to believe that the 2-component of the Tate-Šafarevič group is large, and in these instances $\eta^2(D)/\tau(D)$ is divisible by an appropriate large power of 2. Whenever g is known to be positive, $\tau(D)=0$.

Many of the values of g needed for the verifications mentioned above were determined in Part I. There the authors developed a theory of first descent for an elliptic curve, which enabled them to compute $g+t$, where 2^t is the order of the 2-Sylow subgroup of the Tate-Šafarevič group of the curve. The method was based on 2-coverings of the curve. With this information they were able to determine g and t for most curves with A and B of reasonable size. In the present paper a somewhat different method of descent is given for the curves Γ_D, based on 2-isogenous coverings. With this approach they give a second descent and announce that their method gives a third descent. With their second descent they have eliminated many of the gaps in their earlier tables for g; however, to eliminate more of the gaps the third descent will be necessary. *D. J. Lewis* (Ann Arbor, Mich.)

Citations: MR 26# 3669 = G05-63; MR 29# 1212 = G05-68; MR 30# 4759 = G05-74.

Referred to in D02-23, G02-18, G05-79, G05-87, G05-88, G05-93, G05-96, G05-122.

G05-76 (31# 3420)

Cassels, J. W. S.

Arithmetic on curves of genus 1. VIII. On conjectures of Birch and Swinnerton-Dyer.

J. Reine Angew. Math. **217** (1965), 180–199.

The author defines a kind of "relative Tamagawa number" for isogenous elliptic curves and obtains various expressions for it in terms of Galois cohomology. Let k be a number field and A an abelian variety of dimension 1 defined over k. For a valuation v of k, let k_v be the completion at v, dx_v the normalized Haar measure of the additive group k_v, and let $\omega=f(\xi)dx(\xi)$ be a differential of the first kind on A defined over k, where $x(\xi)$ is one of the coordinates of the generic point ξ of A. The differential ω induces a Haar measure on the compact abelian group A_{k_v} (the group of points in A which are rational over k_v); namely,

$$\mu_v(\omega, E) = \int_{\xi\in E} |f(\xi)|_v\, dx_v(\xi)$$

for any Borel set $E\subset A_{k_v}$. This measure is independent of the particular expression $f\,dx$ chosen for the differential ω. Now, let $\lambda: A\to B$ be an isogeny of abelian varieties of dimension 1 defined over k. Denoting by ω, ω' differentials of the first kind on A, B, respectively, the author defines the number $T(A/B)$, which depends only on A, B and k, not on the choice of ω, ω', by

$$T(A/B) = \prod_v \frac{\mu_v(\omega', B_{kv})}{\mu_v(\omega, A_{k_v})}.$$

To get cohomological expressions for $T(A/B)$, the basic exact sequences are the following:

$$\begin{array}{ccccccc} 0\to \operatorname{Cok}\lambda_k & \to & H^1(k, A_\lambda) & \to & H^1(k,A)_\lambda & \to & 0\\ \downarrow & & \downarrow j_v & & \downarrow & & \\ 0\to \operatorname{Cok}\lambda_{k_v} & \to & H^1(k_v, A_\lambda) & \to & H^1(k_v,A)_\lambda & \to & 0,\end{array}$$

$$0\to \operatorname{Cok}\lambda_k \to S(A)\to (\check{S}(A))_\lambda\to 0,$$

where λ_k [respectively, λ_{k_v}] is the restriction of λ on A_k

$[A_{k_v}]$, $S(A)=\{\xi \in H^1(k, A_\lambda);\ j_v\xi \in \operatorname{Cok} \lambda_{k_v}$ for all $v\}$ (the Selmer group), $\check{S}(A)=\operatorname{Ker}(H^1(k, A)\to\prod_v H^1(k_v, A))$ (the Tate-Šafarevič group), and one uses the convention of putting $G_\lambda=\operatorname{Ker}\lambda$ for the homomorphism λ and the homomorphisms derived naturally from λ. The principal theorem is Theorem 1.1. Let $\lambda: A\to B$, $\mu: B\to A$ be conjugate isogenies defined over k. Then $T(A/B)=[S(A)][(B_k)_\mu]/[S(B)][(A_k)_\lambda]$, where [*] denotes the number of elements in a set *.

Combining this theorem and his earlier results (Part IV of the series [same J. **211** (1962), 95–112; MR **29** #1214]), the author proves that (*) $T(A/B)=[B_k]^2[\check{S}(A)]/[A_k]^2[\check{S}(B)]$, provided that all groups on the right-hand side are finite. The author says that (*) is in agreement with the Birch–Swinnerton-Dyer heuristic definition of the "Tamagawa number $t(A)$ for abelian varieties" and its conjectural value (which is analogous to the reviewer's formula for the Tamagawa number of algebraic tori).

Part VII appeared in same J. **216** (1964), 150–158 [MR **30** #92]. *T. Ono* (Philadelphia, Pa.)

Citations: MR 29# 1214 = G05-70; MR 30# 92 = G05-73.

G05-77 (33# 4008)

Ogaĭ, S. V.

On rational points on the curve $y^2=x(x^2+ax+b)$. (Russian)

Trudy Mat. Inst. Steklov. **80** (1965), 110–116.

For each prime p, the author gives rather elaborate tables giving the possible p-adic solutions of the equation in the title. These are used to discuss the "first descents" in the investigation of the rational points on the curve by means of the isogeny of order 2.

J. W. S. Cassels (Cambridge, England)

G05-78 (34# 664)

Lapin, A. I.

On the rational points of an elliptic curve. (Russian)

Izv. Akad. Nauk SSSR Ser. Mat. **29** (1965), 701–716.

Let $k=C(x)$ be the field of rational functions in one variable x over the field C of complex numbers. Let p be a positive integer. The author considers elliptic curves Γ, defined over k by an equation of the form $Y^2=\prod_{1\leq i\leq 3}(X-e_i(x))$, where the $e_i(x)$ are polynomials of degree $2p+2$. He proves the existence of such curves Γ with the property that Γ has at least p independent rational points in k whose coordinates are integral, i.e., are polynomials in x (see also the author, same Izv. **28** (1964), 953–988 [MR **33** #7337]). *P. Roquette* (Tübingen)

Referred to in G30-55, Z10-43.

G05-79 (34# 1263)

Birch, B. J.; Stephens, N. M.

The parity of the rank of the Mordell-Weil group.

Topology **5** (1966), 295–299.

It has been conjectured by the first author and Swinnerton-Dyer [J. Reine Angew. Math. **218** (1965), 79–108; MR **31** #3419] that the rank g of the group of rational points on a curve Γ of genus one is equal to the order γ of the zero of $L_\Gamma(s)$, at $s=1$, where the zeta-function $\zeta_\Gamma(s)$ of the curve is given by $\zeta_\Gamma(s)=\zeta(s)\zeta(s-1)/L_\Gamma(s)$. In many cases $L_\Gamma(s)$ is a Hecke L-function "mit Grössencharakteren" and then, as Shimura pointed out to the authors, at least the parity of γ can be decided from the function equation. The authors use this approach to give explicit formulae for the parity of γ in the two cases $y^2=x^3-Dx$ and $y^3=x^3+A$, where D and A are given integers. They then show that $\gamma\equiv g \pmod 2$ provided that the 2-component of the Tate-Šafarevič group is finite. In particular, there should be infinitely many rational points if the parity of γ, as given by their formula, is odd. They note that this statement implies conjectures of Sylvester and others.

J. W. S. Cassels (Cambridge, England)

Citations: MR 31# 3419 = G05-75.

G05-80 (34# 1320)

Ogg, A. P.

Abelian curves of 2-power conductor.

Proc. Cambridge Philos. Soc. **62** (1966), 143–148.

Let A be an Abelian variety of dimension 1 defined over the field of rational numbers Q. Let Δ be the discriminant of A, p a prime number and n_p the number of distinct components of the reduction of A modulo p in the sense of A. Néron [Inst. Hautes Études Sci. Publ. Math. No. 21 (1964); MR **31** #3423]. Then $N=\Pi_p p(\operatorname{ord}_p(\Delta)+1-n_p)$ is called the conductor of A. The zeta-function of A over Q may be written as $\zeta(s)\zeta(s-1)/L(s)$, where $\zeta(s)$ is the Riemann zeta-function. There is a conjecture of Weil that $L(s)$ is the Dirichlet series corresponding to a cusp form of weight 2 for the subgroup $\Gamma_0(N)$ of the modular group $z\to az+b/cz+d$ defined by N/c. This conjecture suggests that the genus $p(N)$ of the upper-half plane modulo $\Gamma_0(N)$ is positive. On the other hand, it is known that $p(N)=0$ for $N=1, 10, 12, 13, 16, 18, 25$. Therefore, the conjecture suggests that there is no Abelian variety of dimension 1 with such conductors. In this paper, it is shown that there is no Abelian variety of dimension 1, defined over Q, with the conductors $N=2^i$, $0\leq i\leq 4$, by finding all such Abelian varieties with 2 power conductors.

T. Matsusaka (Waltham, Mass.)

Citations: MR 31# 3423 = G10-25.

G05-81 (34# 7510)

Stephens, N. M.

Conjectures concerning elliptic curves.

Bull. Amer. Math. Soc. **73** (1967), 160–163.

Let E_D be the elliptic curve $X^3+Y^3=DZ^3$, where D is a cube-free positive integer. The zeta-function of E_D is given by $\zeta(s)\zeta(s-1)/L_D(s)$, where $L_D(s)$ is a Hecke L-function. The author reports his numerical experiments about the behavior of $L_D(s)$ for $s=1$ and he conjectures, among others, the following: $L_D(s)\sim(f\gamma\kappa/\eta^2)(s-1)^g$, where g is the rank of E_D, f is a product of factors due to "bad" primes, γ is the order of the Tate-Šafarevič group, κ is the inverse of the "measure" for the density of rational points on E_D and η is the number of rational points of finite order. *T. Ono* (Philadelphia, Pa.)

G05-82 (35# 1592)

Ogg, A. P.

Abelian curves of small conductor.

J. Reine Angew. Math. **226** (1967), 204–215.

The author sets up a complete list of the abelian varieties of dimension one defined over the rationals whose conductor is of the shape $3\cdot2^n$ or $3^2\cdot2^n$, where n is a non-negative integer. He also shows that there are no such varieties of conductor 10 or 22. An essential first step is to show that there is always a rational point of order two: for if not, its coordinates would generate an unramified extension of degree three of the rationals or of a quadratic extension of the rationals whose class number is prime to 3. The results then follow on regarding the expression for the discriminant of a minimal model as a diophantine equation for the coefficients of the latter.

J. W. S. Cassels (Cambridge, England)

Referred to in G05-124.

G05-83 (36# 1440)

Dem'janenko, V. A.

Points of finite order of elliptic curves. (Russian)

Izv. Akad. Nauk SSSR Ser. Mat. **31** (1967), 1327–1340.

Let K be an algebraic number field of degree n, let Γ, with equation $y^2 = x^3 + rx + s$, be an elliptic curve defined over K, let D be its discriminant and let O_m be a point of order m on Γ. The following results are proved. Theorem 1: If $m > 12n + 4$ the coordinates x, y of O_m are integral over K and $D \equiv O(y^2)$. Theorem 2: Divide the set of all elliptic curves into classes with respect to birational equivalence over extensions of K. Then in any one of these classes there is only a finite number of curves with points of order $m > 2$. Theorem 3: Let $\nu_\mathfrak{p}(\mathbf{m})$ be the $\mathfrak{p}$-exponent of the divisor $\mathbf{m}$ [Z. I. Borevič and I. R. Šafarevič, *Theory of numbers* (Russian), Izdat. "Nauka", Moscow, 1964; MR **30** #1080; German translation, Birkhäuser, Basel, 1966; MR **33** #4000; English translation, Academic Press, New York, 1966; MR **33** #4001; French translation, Gauthier-Villars, Paris, 1967; MR **34** #5734]. Let p be a prime $\neq 2$ and $\mathfrak{p}$ be an odd divisor of y not dividing r and $3s$. Then $\nu_\mathfrak{p}(D) \equiv O(p)$.

A number of computations are carried out to illustrate these theorems in special cases.

A. H. Wallace (Philadelphia, Pa.)

Citations: MR 30# 1080 = Z02-44; MR 33# 4001 = Z02-46; MR 34# 5734 = Z02-47.

G05-84 (36# 1453)

Serre, Jean-Pierre

Groupes de Lie l-adiques attachés aux courbes elliptiques.

Les Tendances Géom. en Algèbre et Théorie des Nombres, pp. 239–256. *Éditions du Centre National de la Recherche Scientifique, Paris,* 1966.

k sei ein Zahlkörper, $\bar{k}$ sei eine algebraisch abgeschlossene Hülle von k. $G(\bar{k}/k)$ sei die Galoisgruppe von $\bar{k}$ über k. Es sei E eine elliptische Kurve, welche über k definiert ist und welche einen k-rationalen Punkt O besitzt. E kann dann als algebraische Gruppe (abelsche Mannigfaltigkeit) aufgefasst werden, so dass der Punkt O das neutrale Element der Gruppenoperation ist. Das soll im folgenden geschehen. Es sei l eine Primzahl und $n \geqq 0$ eine ganze Zahl. Mit E_{l^n} sei die Untergruppe von E bezeichnet, welche aus allen Punkten x von E besteht mit Koordinaten in $\bar{k}$, sodass $l^n \cdot x = 0$ ist. (E_{l^n} ist die Gruppe der l^n-Teilungspunkte von E mit Koordinaten in $\bar{k}$.) Man weiss, dass E_{l^n} ein freier $Z/l^n\mathbf{Z}$-Modul vom Rang 2 ist. Es sei $T_l = \varprojlim_n E_{l^n}$ der l-adische Tate-Modul von E. T_l ist ein freier Modul vom Rang 2 über den ganzen l-adischen Zahlen Z_l. Es sei $V_l = T_l \otimes Q_l$ der zugehörige Vektorraum über den l-adischen Zahlen Q_l.

Die Galoisgruppe $G(\bar{k}/k)$ operiert auf jedem der Moduln E_{l^n} als lineare Gruppe und deshalb auch auf T_l und V_l. Man erhält einen Homomorphismus $\pi_l: G(\bar{k}/k) \to \mathrm{Gl}(T_l)$. Es sei G_l das Bild von $G(\bar{k}/k)$ bei $\pi_l \cdot G_l$ ist eine abgeschlossene Untergruppe der l-adischen Lie-Gruppe $\mathrm{Gl}(T_l)$ und als solche selbst eine Lie-Gruppe. $\mathfrak{g}_l$ sei die zu G gehörige Lie-Algebra, welche Teilalgebra der Lie-Algebra $\mathfrak{g}_l(V_l)$ ist. Die Lie-Algebren $\mathfrak{g}_l$ werden in der vorliegenden Arbeit studiert. (Diese Algebren $\mathfrak{g}_l$ haben ihre Bedeutung beim Studium derjenigen algebraischen Erweiterungen von k, welche von den Koordinaten der Punkte aus T_l erzeugt werden [vgl. Verfasser, Izv. Akad. Nauk SSSR Ser. Mat. **28** (1964), 3–20; MR **28** #3994].

Es folgen einige Ergebnisse der vorliegenden Arbeit: (1) Ist die absolute Invariante j der elliptischen Kurve E nicht ganz (j ist eine Zahl aus k), so ist $\mathfrak{g}_l = \mathfrak{gl}(V_l)$. (2) Hat die Kurve E komplexe Multiplikation, und ist K der zugehörige imaginär-quadratische Zahlkörper, so gilt: (a) die Lie-Algebra $\mathfrak{g}_l$ ist die durch $K_l = K \otimes Q_l$ definierte Cartan-Teilalgebra von $\mathfrak{gl}(V_l)$. Weiter gilt, genau dann, wenn die Primzahl l in K zerfällt, kann die Algebra $\mathfrak{g}_l$ auf Diagonalgestalt gebracht werden. (b) Unter den obigen Voraussetzungen gilt, G_l ist genau dann kommutativ, wenn k in K enthalten ist. (c) Ist Σ die Menge der nicht archimedischen Stellen v von k welche die Eigenschaft haben, dass die Reduktion Ev von E modulo v (Ev ist wieder eine elliptische Kurve) die Hasse-Invariante null hat (Ev hat dann keine nichttrivialen p_v-Teilungspunkte, p_v = Charakteristik des Restklassenkörpers von v). Dann gilt, eine Stelle v aus k ist genau dann in Σ, wenn p_v nicht in K zerfällt. (d) Man kann die Dichte der Menge Σ innerhalb der Menge aller nicht archimedischen Primstellen von k angeben. Die Dichte ist 0, wenn k Teilkörper von K ist und $\frac{1}{2}$ sonst. (3) Es sei die Invariante j von E ganz in k aber E habe keine komplexe Multiplikation. Dann ergeben sich aus der Arbeit für die Algebra $\mathfrak{g}_l$ die folgenden Möglichkeiten: (a) $\mathfrak{g}_l = \mathfrak{gl}(V_l)$, (b) $\mathfrak{g}_l$ ist eine Cartan-Teilalgebra von $\mathfrak{gl}(V_l)$, G_l ist kommutativ und die Dichte von Σ ist Null. Das in (3) angegebene Ergebnis wird nun erst recht interessant durch das folgende in der Arbeit bewiesene Resultat 4. (4) Der in (3b) zitierte Fall tritt für eine elliptische Kurve E, welche über k definiert ist nicht ein, wenn der Körper k in den reellen Zahlkörper eingebettet werden kann. Der Verfasser vermutet, dass der Fall (3b) gar nicht vorkommt.

Noch zwei Bemerkungen: (I) Wir haben nur einige der "globalen Ergebnisse" dieser Arbeit angeführt. Die entsprechenden Sätze für elliptische Kurven über lokalen Körpern sind in dieser Arbeit ebenfalls bewiesen und werden beim Beweis der "globalen Ergebnisse" laufend benutzt. (II) Der Verfasser diskutiert am Ende der Arbeit mehrere Probleme, welche mit den angeführten in Zusammenhang stehen. Auf diese sei besonders hingewiesen.

H. Popp (Lafayette, Ind.)

Citations: MR 28# 3994 = G10-22.

G05-85 (36# 2595)

Swinnerton-Dyer, H. P. F.

An application of computing to class field theory.

Algebraic Number Theory (*Proc. Instructional Conf., Brighton,* 1965), *pp.* 280–291. *Thompson, Washington, D.C.*, 1967.

The author explains some conjectures concerning congruence zeta-functions that are supported by numerical calculations. In the introduction he says, "For Abelian varieties, very few number-theoretical theorems have yet been proved. The most interesting results are conjectures, based on numerical computation of special cases, and the fact that one has no idea how to attack these conjectures suggests that there must be important theorems which have not yet even been stated." *K. Masuda* (Nagoya)

Referred to in Z10-29.

G05-86 (37# 2751)

Dem'janenko, V. A.

An estimate of the remainder term in Tate's formula. (Russian)

Mat. Zametki **3** (1968), 271–278.

Soient K un corps de nombres algébriques de degré n sur le corps des rationnels, Γ une courbe elliptique non dégénérée, définie sur K, $P_1, \cdots, P_m$ des points de Γ, $t_1, \cdots, t_m$ des entiers; d'après Ju. Ī. Manin [Izv. Akad. Nauk SSSR Ser. Mat. **28** (1964), 1363–1390; MR **30** #3886], la formule de Tate s'écrit: $c_1 \leqq h(\sum_{i=1}^m t_i P_i) - \sum_{i,j=1}^m a_{ij} t_i t_j \leqq c_2$, où $a_{ij} = a_{ji}$, et où c_1 et c_2 sont des constantes indépendantes des t_i. L'auteur donne de ces constantes une évaluation dépendant de n et en déduit que, dans un

ensemble M de courbes elliptiques birationnellement équivalentes sur une extension de K, il n'y en a qu'un nombre fini qui possèdent au moins un point d'ordre $g > 2$.
J.-E. Bertin (Paris)

Citations: MR 30# 3886 = G10-24.
Referred to in G05-115.

G05-87 (37# 4079)

Rajwade, A. R.
Arithmetic on curves with complex multiplication by $\sqrt{-2}$.
Proc. Cambridge Philos. Soc. **64** (1968), 659–672.

In this paper the author verifies certain conjectures of B. J. Birch and H. P. F. Swinnerton-Dyer [J. Reine Angew. Math. **212** (1963), 7–25; MR **26** #3669; ibid. **218** (1965), 79–108; MR **31** #3419] on the zeta function and the Tamagawa number of elliptic curves over $\mathbf{Q}$ admitting complex multiplication by $\sigma=\sqrt{-2}$. Such curves Γ are given by $y^2=x(x^2-4Dx+2D^2)$, $D\in\mathbf{Z}$. For this purpose he first develops an explicit table of the σ^nth division points of Γ for $1\leqq n\leqq 5$ and examines the effect of multiplication by σ on these sets. Next he determines the number of $\mathbf{Z}_p$-rational points on the reduced curves Γ_p for "good" primes p ($p\nmid 2D$) by showing how the complex primes $\pi, \bar\pi$ dividing p must be normalized for the Frobenius mapping: π and $\bar\pi$ must be congruent to some of the residue classes mod 4σ in the set

$$\Lambda = \{1, 3, 1+\sigma, 1+3\sigma, 3+3\sigma, 5+2\sigma, 7+2\sigma\}.$$

Then $N_p=p+1$ for $p\equiv-1, -3 \pmod 8$, and $N_p=p+1-(D/\pi)_2\bar\pi-(D/\pi)\pi$, for $p\equiv 1, 3 \pmod 8$; here $(\alpha/\beta)_2$ denotes the quadratic residue symbol for $\mathbf{Q}(\sigma)$, i.e., that unit ± 1 which is $\equiv\alpha^{(N(p)-1)/2} \pmod\beta$ for relatively prime integers α, β of $\mathbf{Q}(\sigma)$, β a prime distinct from σ. Using these facts it is found that $\zeta_\Gamma(s)=\prod_{p\,\text{good}}\zeta_{\Gamma_p}(s)=\zeta(s)\zeta(s-1)\times L_D(s)^{-1}$ with

$$L_D(s) = \prod_{\pi\equiv l\in\Lambda}\{1-(D/\pi)_2\bar\pi/N(\pi)^s\}^{-1} = \sum_{\lambda\in\Lambda}(D/\lambda)_2(\bar\lambda/N(\lambda)^s),$$

where the product is taken over all the relevant primes, real or complex, of $\mathbf{Q}(\sigma)$. (Note in this connection that D may be taken in $\mathbf{Z}[\sigma]$.) Now write $D=\Delta F$, where $\Delta\in\Lambda$ and F is the product of powers of σ and the units ± 1. Next the sum $L_D(s)$ is rewritten by fixing a set $\{\beta\}$ of representatives for the residue classes mod Δ, and $\{\gamma\}$ a set of representatives for those residue classes mod K lying in Λ, here K is taken to be 4σ if $D\in\mathbf{Z}[\sigma]$. Expansion of the terms in $L_D(s)$ yields summands of the form $1+(1-s)\bar\alpha/\bar\mu-s\alpha/\mu$, μ from $\lambda=K\Delta\mu+(K\beta+\Delta\lambda)=K\Delta\mu+\rho$ whose presence implies divergence for $s\to 1$, and which lead to the introduction of the Weierstrass function with the periods 1, σ. A suitable manipulation of the terms yields

$$L_D(1) = \frac{\Theta}{K\Delta}\sum_{\beta,\gamma}\left(\frac{D}{\rho}\right)_2\left[\frac{\wp'(\Theta\beta/\Delta)-\wp'(\Theta\gamma/K)}{\wp(\Theta\beta/\Delta)-\wp(\Theta\gamma/K)}\right]$$

if $\Delta\neq 1$, and somewhat more complicated expressions for $\Delta=1$. Here $\wp(u)$ is the Weierstrass function with the periods Θ and $\sigma\Theta$ which uniformizes Γ. Furthermore, the author proves that for square free $D>1$ and real period Θ of the $\wp$-function for $y^2=x^3-4x^2+2$, the quotients $8(\sqrt{D})L_D(1)/\Theta$ and $8(\sqrt{2D})L_{-D}(1)/\Theta$ are rational integers. His proof of rationality depends, among other results, on the determination of the galois group, over $\mathbf{Q}(\sigma)$, of the field of 8Δ-division points as a subgroup of the multiplicative group of prime residues mod 8Δ in $\mathbf{Q}(\sigma)$, and J. W. S. Cassel's pairing operation for 8Δ-division points [J. London Math. Soc. **41** (1966), 193–291; MR **33** #7299; correction, ibid. **42** (1967), 183; MR **34** #2523]. In order to establish the integral character, Cassel's estimates on the ideal denominator of the division points of $\{\Gamma, \infty\}$ relative to the ideal denominator of x are used [Proc. Cambridge Philos. Soc. **45** (1949), 167–172; MR **10**, 434]. Finally it is proved that $(\sqrt{D})/\Theta$ and $(\sqrt{2D})/\Theta$ are the contributions of $p=\infty$ to the Tamagawa number.
O. F. G. Schilling (Lafayette, Ind.)

Citations: MR 10, 434b = G05-19; MR 26# 3669 = G05-63; MR 31# 3419 = G05-75; MR 33# 7299 = G02-16; MR 34# 2523 = G02-17.
Referred to in G05-92.

G05-88 (37# 5225)

Stephens, N. M.
The diophantine equation $X^3+Y^3=DZ^3$ and the conjectures of Birch and Swinnerton-Dyer.
J. Reine Angew. Math. **231** (1968), 121–162.

The zeta-function of an abelian variety Γ of dimension 1 which is defined over the rationals and has complex multiplication can be expressed in terms of the Riemann zeta-function and a Hecke L-function $L_\Gamma(s)$. B. J. Birch and H. P. F. Swinnerton-Dyer [same J. **218** (1965), 79–108; MR **31** #3419] made the following two conjectures, largely on the basis of numerical evidence for complex multiplication by the Gaussian integers. Conjecture 1: The order of the zero of $L_\Gamma(s)$ at $s=1$ is the rank g of the Mordell-Weil group of rational points on Γ. Conjecture 2: If $g=0$ and η is the number of rational points of finite order, then (*) $L_\Gamma(1)/f=|Ш|/\eta^2$, where $|Ш|$ is the order of the Tate-Šafarevič group (conjectured finite) and f is a well-defined correcting factor for the "bad" primes.

The author presents considerable numerical evidence for these conjectures in the case of the curve of the title and also for the following conjecture which he attributes to J. Tate [Séminaire Bourbaki: Vol. 1965/66, Exposé 306; W. A. Benjamin, New York, 1966; see MR **34** #5605]. Conjecture 3: The gth derivative of $L_\Gamma(s)$ satisfies $L_\Gamma^{(g)}(1)/f=g!\mathfrak{X}|Ш|/\eta^2$, where $\mathfrak{X}$ is the following measure of the "density" of the rational points on Γ. Let $P_1, \cdots, P_g$ be generators of the Mordell-Weil group modulo torsion. Then the Tate-Néron canonical height $\hat h$ gives a quadratic form $\hat h(\sum_{j=1}^g a_jP_j)=\sum_{i,j=1}^g h_{ij}a_ia_j$ ($a_i\in\mathbf{Z}$). We have $\mathfrak{X}=\det(h_{ij})$. The evidence is copious for $g=1$, there are four cases with $g=2$ and one with $g=3$.

The evidence is presented in extensive tables. They use the tables of E. S. Selmer [Acta Math. **85** (1951), 203–362; MR **13**, 13; ibid. **92** (1954), 191–197; MR **16**, 674] of rational points on curves related to the curves of the title and the author also gives tables considerably extending Selmer's.

There is a useful and fairly full discussion of the theoretical basis of the work which shows that the considerations of Birch and Swinnerton-Dyer for their case have analogues here. In particular, it is shown that the left hand side of (*) for the equation of the title is an integer with bounded denominator.
J. W. S. Cassels (Cambridge, England)

Citations: MR 13, 13i = G05-31; MR 16, 674e = D28-10; MR 31# 3419 = G05-75.

G05-89 (37# 6242)

Birch, B. J.
How the number of points of an elliptic curve over a fixed prime field varies.
J. London Math. Soc. **43** (1968), 57–60.

Let $1+p-E_p$ be the number of points on the reduction modulo p of an elliptic curve Γ defined over the rationals; write $E_p=2p\cos\theta_p$, where $0<\theta_p<\pi$. If Γ has no complex

multiplications, then Sato found experimentally a $\sin^2$ distribution for θ_p as a function of p; later J. T. Tate [*Arithmetical algebraic geometry* (Proc. Conf. Purdue Univ., 1963), pp. 93–110, Harper and Row, New York, 1965; MR **37** #1371] gave a conjectural theoretical explanation. (The author reverses the order.) The author considers the analogous problem of the distribution of the E_p for all (finitely many) Γ over the field of p elements, i.e., he fixes the prime and lets the curve vary, and shows that $\mathrm{mean}[E_p(\Gamma)^{2R}] \sim 2R!p^R/(R!(R+1)!)$ as $p\to\infty$ (for $R=1, 2, \cdots$). The proof depends on the Selberg trace formula.
A. P. Ogg (Berkeley, Calif.)

Citations: MR 37# 1371 = G35-45.
Referred to in G05-90.

G05-90 (38# 5720)

Atkin, A. O. L.
Note on a paper of Birch.
J. London Math. Soc. **44** (1969), 282.

B. J. Birch [same J. **43** (1968), 57–60; MR **37** #6242] considered a number $\gamma(p)=\gamma_R(p)$, essentially a certain exponential sum, for $R=1, 2, \cdots$, and showed that $|\gamma(p)|<2p^{3/2}$ for $R=5$. The author conjectures that $\gamma(p)=\lambda(p)/p$, where $\lambda(p)$ is the eigenvalue of the Hecke operator $T(p^2)$ on $F(\tau)=\eta^4(\tau)\eta(5\tau)$, where $\eta(\tau)=e^{\pi i\tau/12}\times\prod_{n=1}^{\infty}(1-e^{2\pi i n\tau})$, and states there is agreement for $p\leq 311$.
A. P. Ogg (Berkeley, Calif.)

Citations: MR 37# 6242 = G05-89.

G05-91 (37# 6283)

Levin, Martin
On the group of rational points on elliptic curves over function fields.
Amer. J. Math. **90** (1968), 456–462.

Let K denote an algebraic function field in one variable with constant field k and with genus $g(K)$, and let A be an elliptic curve defined over K such that its absolute invariant j is transcendental over k. Denote by A_K the group of K-rational points on A, and by $T(A_K)$ the torsion subgroup of A_K. The author proves that the order of $T(A_K)$ has a computable upper bound depending only on $g(K)$. (This result is a particular case of the conjecture that for a given field K the order of the torsion part of the group of k-rational points of an elliptic curve defined over K is bounded in terms of K; see J. W. S. Cassels [J. London Math. Soc. **41** (1966), 193–291, especially p. 264; MR **33** #7299; corrigenda, ibid. **42** (1967), 183; MR **34** #2523].)

The idea of the proof is as follows: Let a be a point of $T(A_K)$ of order n. If A' is any elliptic curve defined over $k(j)$ with the same absolute invariant j as A and if w is the image of a under any isomorphism of A with A', then $K=K(\mathrm{Ku}(a))=K(\mathrm{Ku}(w))$, where Ku is the Kummer morphism. Therefore $k(j, \mathrm{Ku}(w))$ is a subfield of K, and hence its genus g_n is at most equal to $g(K)$. Now g_n can easily be computed as a function of n by methods given by J. Igusa in Amer. J. Math. **81** (1959), 453–476 [MR **21** #3422] for the case $p=\mathrm{char}(k)\nmid n$, and for the case $n=p^e$, by Igusa in J. Math. Soc. Japan **20** (1968), 96–106. Putting $n=q^e$ with q prime and $e\geq 1$, we then get an upper bound on q and e.

Let C be a subgroup of $A_{\bar{K}_s}$, where $\bar{K}_s$ is the separable algebraic closure of K. We say that C is defined over K if C is stable under any automorphism of K_s over K. The author proves that if C is finite, cyclic, defined over K, and of order n not divisible by the characteristic, then n has an upper bound which depends only on the genus $g(K)$ of K. This result was conjectured by Tate (in a letter to Igusa). Its proof proceeds as above, employing a formula by Igusa [Amer. J. Math. reference cited above] for the genus g_c of $k(j, j_c)$, where j_c is the invariant of the quotient elliptic curve A/C.
D. Laksov (New York)

Citations: MR 21# 3422 = F10-58; MR 33# 7299 = G02-16; MR 34# 2523 = G02-17; MR 39# 1457 = F10-109.

G05-92 (38# 2142)

Rajwade, A. R.
Arithmetic on curves with complex multiplication by the Eisenstein integers.
Proc. Cambridge Philos. Soc. **65** (1969), 59–73.

In this paper the author presents another verification of the conjecture of Birch and Swinnerton-Dyer on Tamagawa numbers for the zeta function of elliptic curves [see the author, same Proc. **64** (1968), 659–672; MR **37** #4079]. If $L_B(s)=\prod_{p\,\mathrm{good}}[1+(N_p-p-1)p^{-s}+p^{1-2s}]^{-1}$ for the curve $y^2=x^3-B$, then the following theorem holds: If $D=-4B$ is a positive integer, free of sixth powers, and Θ is the real period of the Weierstrass function satisfying $\wp'^2=\wp^3+1$, then $72\cdot\sqrt[6]{D}\cdot L_B(1)\Theta^{-1}$ and $72\cdot\sqrt[6]{(27D)}\cdot L_{-B}(1)\Theta^{-1}$ are rational integers. The method of proof is mutatis mutandis the same as in the cited paper.
O. F. G. Schilling (Lafayette, Ind.)

Citations: MR 37# 4079 = G05-87.

G05-93 (38# 4389)

Swinnerton-Dyer, P.
The use of computers in the theory of numbers.
Proc. Sympos. Appl. Math., Vol. XIX, pp. 111–116. *Amer. Math. Soc., Providence, R.I.*, 1967.

A popularization for the general mathematical reader of some of the results of the author and B. J. Birch [J. Reine Angew. Math. **218** (1965), 79–108; MR **31** #3419]. Particular attention is paid to the reduction of the calculations involved in verifying a conjecture about the number of independent generators of the group of rational points on a cubic $y^2=x^3-ax$ to a point where the result could be tested directly by a computer.
J. D. Swift (Los Angeles, Calif.)

Citations: MR 31# 3419 = G05-75.

G05-94 (38# 5788)

Lichtenbaum, Stephen
The period-index problem for elliptic curves.
Amer. J. Math. **90** (1968), 1209–1223.

Let A be an abelian variety over a field k, and let V be a principal homogeneous space for A over k, i.e., a variety on which A acts simply and transitively. Such a V is trivial if and only if it has a point rational over k. In any case there exist finite separable extensions K of k which split V (i.e., over which V has a rational point); the index [separable index] of V is the g.c.d. of the degrees of finite extensions [finite separable extensions] of k splitting V. On the other hand, one can regard the isomorphism class of V as an element of the first cohomology group $H^1(k, A)$, and its period is defined to be its order as an element of that group. S. Lang and J. Tate [same J. **80** (1958), 659–684; MR **21** #4960] showed that the period divides the index, which divides the separable index, and all three numbers have the same prime factors. In general, one asks whether the period is equal to the index, say for fields of arithmetic interest k and under various conditions on A.

In the present paper, the author gives a rather definitive treatment of the case $\dim A=1$, showing in that case that (a) for any field k, the index is equal to the separable index, (b) the period is equal to the index if k is p-adic, and (c) the period is equal to the index if k has trivial Brauer group. The result (c) contains results of I. R. Šafarevič [Trudy Mat. Inst. Steklov. **64** (1961), 316–346; MR **29**

#110; translated in Amer. Math. Soc. Transl. (2) **37** (1964), 85–114; see MR **28** #3907] and the reviewer [Ann. of Math. (2) **76** (1962), 185–212; MR **27** #5758], without assuming, as they did, that the period is prime to the characteristic. The author also gives an example of an A of dimension 2 over a p-adic field k, with a V of period l and index l^2, for a prime $l \neq p$.

A. P. Ogg (Berkeley, Calif.)

Citations: MR 21# 4960 = G10-10; MR 27# 5758 = G10-19; MR 29# 110 = G10-23.

Referred to in G05-107, G20-50, G25-56.

G05-95 (38# 5790)

Tèĭt, D. T. [Tate, J. T.]; Šafarevič, I. R.

The rank of elliptic curves. (Russian)

Dokl. Akad. Nauk SSSR **175** (1967), 770–773.

Authors' introduction: "Let k be a finite field, $K = k(t)$, and A an elliptic curve defined over K. The object of this note is to prove that the rank of the group A_k of rational points may assume arbitrarily large values under suitable choice of the curve A, the field K being fixed. Analogous examples have been constructed over the field $k(t)$, when k is an algebraically closed field of characteristic zero, by A. I. Lapin [Izv. Akad. Nauk SSSR Ser. Mat. **28** (1964), 953–988; MR **33** #7337]."

G05-96 (39# 4097)

Stephens, N. M.

A corollary to a conjecture of Birch and Swinnerton-Dyer.

J. London Math. Soc. **43** (1968), 146–148.

Consider the elliptic curve $\Gamma_D: X^3 + Y^3 = DZ^3$. It has a global zeta-function $\zeta_D = \zeta(s)\zeta(s-1)/L_D(s)$, where $\zeta(s)$ is the Riemann zeta and $L_D(s)$ is a Hecke L-function with Grossencharactere. If the free part of the rational group of Γ_D has g generators (the group is finitely generated by Mordell-Weil) and $L_D(S)$ has a zero order γ at $s = 1$, then a conjecture of B. J. Birch and H. P. F. Swinnerton-Dyer [J. Reine Angew. Math. **28** (1965), 79–108; MR **31** #3419] implies that $g = \gamma$.

The author's intention is to prove that the density of integers which are sums of rational cubes is positive ($> 1/8$) (it is known that the density of integers which are sums of integral cubes is zero), provided that $g = \gamma$ for all D, which would hold if the Birch and Swinnerton-Dyer conjecture were true.

In the proof, the author counts with a slightly different function than one would think to use, and here employs an expression for $(-1)^\gamma$. But on the Birch and Swinnerton-Dyer conjecture, this expression is also one for $(-1)^g$.

The counting method itself is fairly elementary, but interesting.

B. Berlowitz (Berkeley, Calif.)

Citations: MR 31# 3419 = G05-75.

G05-97 (39# 6856)

Yamamoto, Yoshihiko; Naganuma, Hidehisa; Doi, Koji.

Experimental integer theory. (Japanese)

Sûgaku **18** (1966), 95–103.

This is an experimental report containing two numerical tables which are concerned with characteristic roots of Hecke operators and Sato's conjecture on elliptic curves over the rational number field without complex multiplication.

One of the tables gives the value of a_n ($n \leqq 740$) of $q^2 \prod_{n=1}^\infty (1-q^n)^2(1-q^{23n})^2 = \sum_{n=1}^\infty a_n q_n$.

Let E_1 and E_2 be the elliptic curves defined by $y^2 = x^3 + x - 1$ and $y^2 = x^3 - x + 1$. For prime p, let θ_p denote the same absolute value of the amplitude of the two characteristic roots π_1, π_2 of the pth power endomorphism of the elliptic curve E_p over the finite field, obtained by taking E ($= E_1$ or E_2) mod p. The other table gives the distribution of θ_p for 2000 number of prime numbers p (for each of E_1, E_2), and it is compared with Sato's conjecture that the distribution of θ_p for the elliptic curve E over the rational number field without complex multiplication is the $\sin^2\theta$ distribution. (The present result seems rather affirmative data.)

K. Masuda (Nagoya)

G05-98 (40# 88)

Ogg, A. P.

On a convolution of L-series.

Invent. Math. **7** (1969), 297–312.

Let f be a cusp form of dimension $-k$ for the group $\Gamma_0(N)$ of matrices $(ab|cd)$ with $c \equiv 0 \pmod N$, and let $\phi(s) = \sum_{n=1}^\infty a_n n^{-s}$ be the associated Dirichlet series. Then f is said to be normalized of level N when $\phi(s)$ has the Euler product

$$\phi(s) = \prod_{p|N} (1-a_p p^{-s})^{-1} \prod_{p\nmid N} (1-a_p p^{-s}+p^{k-1-2s}),$$

and $\Phi(s) = \pm(-1)^{k/2}\Phi(k-s)$, where

$$\Phi(s) = (2\pi/\sqrt{N})^{-s}\Gamma(s)\phi(s).$$

Write $L_{f,g}(s) = \zeta_N(2s)\sum_{n=1}^\infty a_n\bar{b}_n n^{-(s+k-1)}$, where the b_n are the Dirichlet series coefficients of a series associated with the cusp form g of the same dimension and $\zeta_N(s) = \sum_{(n,N)=1} n^{-s}$. By methods similar to those used by the reviewer [Proc. Cambridge Philos. Soc. **35** (1939), 351–372; MR **1**, 69], the author shows that $L_{f,g}(s)$ is entire if f and g are orthogonal to each other, but otherwise has a simple pole at $s = 1$. This is used to prove that, if f and g are normalized and satisfy the "Petersson conjecture" that $|a_p| \leqq 2p^{(k-1)/2}$, $|b_p| \leqq 2p^{(k-1)/2}$, then $\mathrm{ord}_{s=1} L_{f,g}(s) = -1$ or 0 according as $f = g$ or $f \neq g$.

Now suppose that A and B are two abelian curves over the rationals and that $\phi(s)$ and $\psi(s)$ are the one-dimensional parts of their zeta-functions, corresponding to cusp forms f and g, with $k = 2$. A conjecture of J. Tate asserts that $\sum_{n=1}^\infty a_n b_n n^{-s}$ has a pole at $s = 1$ of order δ, where $\delta = 1$ or 0 according as A and B are isogenous over the rationals, or not. The truth of the conjecture in this case follows from the author's results.

R. A. Rankin (Glasgow)

Citations: MR 1, 69d = F30-1.

G05-99 (40# 2683)

Honda, Taira

Formal groups and zeta-functions.

Osaka J. Math. **5** (1968), 199–213.

$C/\mathbf{Q}$ sei eine elliptische Kurve über dem rationalen Zahlkörper. $C^*/\mathbf{Z}$ sei das Néron'sche minimale Modell von $C/\mathbf{Q}$ über den ganzen Zahlen $\mathbf{Z}$. Nach Néron kann $C^*/\mathbf{Z}$ affin durch eine Gleichung der Gestalt $Y^2 + \lambda XY + \mu Y = X^3 + \alpha X^2 + \beta X + \gamma$ beschrieben werden, wobei $\lambda, \mu, \alpha, \beta, \gamma$ ganze Zahlen sind und die Diskriminante der Gleichung minimal ist. Ist p eine Primzahl in $\mathbf{Z}$, so ist die Reduktion C_p^* von $C^*/\mathbf{Z}$ modulo p eine irreduzibel Kurve, welche einen Knoten oder eine Spitze als Singularitäten haben kann. Man definiert die lokalen L-Reihen $L_p(s)$ von C wie folgt: (1) Ist C_p^* elliptisch, so sei $L_p(s) = (1 - a_p p^{-s} + p^{1-2s})^{-1}$, wobei $1 - a_p U + pU^2$ der Zähler der Zeta-Funktion von C_p^* ist. (2) Hat C_p^* einen Knoten als Singularität, so setzt man $\varepsilon_p = +1$ oder -1, falls der Knoten über dem Primkörper F_p rationale Tangenten hat oder nicht und setzt weiter $L_p(s) = (1 - \varepsilon_p \cdot p^{-s})^{-1}$. (3) Hat C_p^* eine Spitze als Singularität, so wird $L_p(s) = 1$ gesetzt. $L(s, C) = \prod_p L_p(s) = \sum_{n=1}^\infty a_n n^{-s}$ ist die Zeta-Funktion von C. $t = X/Y$ ist ein lokaler Parameter im Nullpunkt von C^*. Dann ist $4t$ ein lokaler Parameter im Nullpunkt von C_p^* für alle p. Schreibt man die Gruppenoperation von C als Potenzreihe in t, so erhält man eine formale Gruppe $F(x, y)$ über $\mathbf{Z}$.

Jede formale Gruppe über $\mathbf{Z}$, welche zu $F(x, y)$ im strengen Sinne isomorph ist, heißt ein formales minimales Modell von $C/\mathbf{Q}$ über $\mathbf{Z}$.

Der Autor zeigt, daß ein sehr enger Zusammenhang zwischen der Zeta-Funktion der elliptischen Kurve $C/\mathbf{Q}$ und der formalen minimalen Modelle von C besteht. Es gilt folgendes: (1) Es gibt ein formales minimales Modell $G(x, y)$ von C über $\mathbf{Z}$, so daß das zugehörige invariante Differential dieselben Koeffizienten hat wie die Zeta-Funktion von C. (2) Ist C_p^* eine elliptische Kurve, so ist $\bar{a}_p = a_p$ modulo p die Hasse Invariante von C_p ($\bar{a}_p$ verschwindet genau dann, wenn C_p^* keine p-Teilungspunkte hat). (3) Ist $a_p = 0$, so hat die Kurve $C/\mathbf{Q}$ formale komplexe Multiplikation über der quadratischen, unverzweigten Erweiterung von $\mathbf{Q}_p$. ($\mathbf{Q}_p$ = Komplettierung von $\mathbf{Q}$ nach p.)

Einige dieser Ergebnisse finden sich schon bei M. Eichler [Arch. Math. **5** (1954), 355–366; MR **16**, 116; G. Shimura, J. Math. Soc. Japan **10** (1958), 1–28; MR **20** #1679] allerdings dort nur für elliptische Kurven $C/\mathbf{Q}$, welche zu Kongruenzuntergruppen gehören.

Der Beweis der angegebenen Ergebnisse folgt aus allgemeinen Sätzen, welche es gestatten, gewisse formale Gruppen über endlichen Körpern, über den ganzen p-adischen Zahlen und über den rationalen Zahlen zu konstruieren und zu klassifizieren. Wir führen das hier nicht weiter aus, obwohl diese Sätze interessant sind. Wir machen jedoch noch auf folgendes aufmerksam: Ist K ein quadratischer Zahlkörper, O der Ring der ganzen Zahlen in K und D die Diskriminante von K, so gilt: Die Dirichletsche L-Reihe $\sum_{n=1}^{\infty} (D/n)n^{-s}$ kann aus einer formalen Gruppe $G(x, y)$ über $\mathbf{Z}$ erhalten werden, d.h. $\sum_{n=1}^{\infty} (D/n)n^{-s}$ hat dieselben Koeffizienten wie das kanonische, invariante Differential von $G(x, y)$. Setzt man weiter $F(x, y) = x + y + (\sqrt{D})\cdot xy$, so ist F ein formales Gruppengesetz, welches über O streng isomorph zu G ist. Dies kann nun, wie die Ausführungen der Arbeit zeigen, wie folgt interpretiert werden: Die Zeta-Funktion eines kommutativen Gruppenschemas ist diejenige L-Reihe, deren Koeffizienten eine Normalform für das Gruppengesetz ergeben.

H. Popp (Lafayette, Ind.)

Citations: MR 16, 116d = G30-15; MR 20# 1679 = F25-8.

G05-100 (40# 7265)

van der Blij, F.

The plane cubic curve. (Dutch)

Math. Centrum Amsterdam Afd. Zuivere Wisk. **1969**, ZW-002, 9 *pp.*

Expository paper on an elementary level. Topics discussed: group of an elliptic cubic curve; cubic curves over special fields; endomorphism ring; zeta functions.

C. G. Lekkerkerker (Amsterdam)

G05-101 (41# 1638)

Baker, A.; Coates, J.

Integer points on curves of genus 1.

Proc. Cambridge Philos. Soc. **67** (1970), 595–602.

A well known theorem of C. L. Siegel [Abh. Deutsch. Akad. Wiss. Berlin Kl. Phys.-Mat. **1929**, no. 1] states that there are only finitely many integer points on a curve of genus $\geqq 1$. Siegel's proof makes use of his work on diophantine approximations (Thue-Siegel-Roth theorem) and the Mordell-Weil theorem, both of which are of a non-effective character. As such Siegel's arguments cannot lead to an algorithm determining the integer points on such curves. The authors prove: If $F(x, y)$ is an absolutely irreducible polynomial of degree n and integer coefficients of height H such that the curve $F(x, y) = 0$ has genus 1, then the integer points on $F(x, y) = 0$ satisfy

$$\max(|x|, |y|) < \exp\exp\exp\{(2H)^{10^{n^{10}}}\}.$$

Thus one can effectively determine the integer points on curves of genus 1. Their method of proof is necessarily different from Siegel's and actually gives a simpler proof for the case of genus 1. Their methods do not extend in any obvious way to curves of higher genus. Their bound is too large to be of practical use, but for any specific curve their methods will usually give a much smaller bound which when combined with the method of the first author and H. Davenport [Quart. J. Math. Oxford Ser. (2) **20** (1969), 129–137; MR **40** #1333] will usually enable one to get all integral points on the specific curve.

Their proof makes use of the second author's [Proc. Cambridge Philos. Soc. **68** (1970), 105–123; MR **41** #3477] explicit construction of rational functions on curves with prescribed poles and the Riemann-Roch theorem to show that the integer points on the curve $F(x, y) = 0$ are birationally related to the integer points in a fixed algebraic field K of a curve $Y^2 = f(X)$, where f is cubic and has coefficients in K. They then modify the arguments given by the first author [ibid. **65** (1969), 439–444; MR **38** #3226] for such curves when the coefficients are rational to get bounds for X, Y and their conjugates and so get bounds for x, y.

D. J. Lewis (Ann Arbor, Mich.)

Citations: MR 38# 3226 = D40-51; MR 40# 1333 = D20-25; MR 41# 3477 = G30-53.

G05-102 (41# 3397)

Dem'janenko, V. A.

The representation of numbers by a binary cubic irreducible form. (Russian)

Mat. Zametki **7** (1970), 87–96.

Let $f(x, y) = ax^3 + bx^2y + cxy^2 + dy^3$ be a cubic form with rational integer coefficients and discriminant $D \neq 0$. Let k be a cube-free integer and suppose that the Mordell-Weil group of rational points on $f(x, y) = k$ has rank one. Then if $|D|k^2 > 6^{144}$, there are at most 3 integral points on $f(x, y) = k$ except possibly when D is a perfect square, and then there are at most 9.

J. W. S. Cassels (Cambridge, England)

Referred to in G05-103.

G05-103 (44# 6603)

Dem'janenko, V. A.

The representation of numbers by a binary cubic irreducible form. (Russian)

Mat. Zametki **10** (1971), 69–71.

The author improves his previous result [see same Zametki **7** (1970), 87–96; MR **41** #3397].

{This article has appeared in English translation [Math. Notes **10** (1971), 466–467].}

B. Novák (Prague)

Citations: MR 41# 3397 = G05-102.

G05-104 (41# 3478)

Birch, B. J.

Diophantine analysis and modular functions.

Algebraic Geometry (Internat. Colloq., Tata Inst. Fund. Res., Bombay, 1968), *pp.* 35–42. *Oxford Univ. Press, London,* 1969.

Heegner studied the curves parametrised by modular functions from the viewpoint of the theory of complex multiplication and proved that there exist exactly nine imaginary quadratic fields with class number one [K. Heegner, Math. Z. **56** (1952), 227–253; MR **14**, 725]. His original proof which had not been accepted because of a gap was later reconstructed by M. Deuring [Invent. Math. **5** (1968), 169–179; MR **37** #4044]. The author shows that Heegner's method is effective not only for the class number problem but also for the study of conjectures on rational points of elliptic curves [H. P. F. Swinnerton-Dyer, Proc. Conf. Local Fields (Driebergen, 1966), pp. 132–157, Springer, Berlin, 1967; MR **37** #6287]. For example, if p is a prime number with $p \equiv 3 \pmod 8$, then the curve $y^2 = x(x^2+p^2)$ has infinitely many rational points over Q. Further, if p is a prime number with $p \equiv 3 \pmod 4$ and $(p/17)=1$, then there exists a family of elliptic curves defined over Q such that each of these curves has infinitely many points rational over $Q(\sqrt{(-p)})$. *E. Inaba* (Tokyo)

Citations: MR 14, 725j = R14-23; MR 37# 4044 = R14-71; MR 37# 6287 = G02-20.

G05-105 (41# 6853)

Bašmakov, M. I.

The Šafarevič-Tate group of an elliptic curve. (Russian)

Mat. Zametki **7** (1970), 79–86.

The author establishes three theorems about a commutative diagram naturally arising from the definition of the group of the title and which are too technical to describe here. Two of them were enunciated by J. Tate without proof [Proc. Internat. Congr. Mathematicians (Stockholm, 1962), pp. 288–295, Inst. Mittag-Leffler, Djursholm, 1963; MR **31** #168].

{This article has appeared in English translation [Math. Notes **7** (1970), 48–52].}

J. W. S. Cassels (Cambridge, England)

Citations: MR 31# 168 = G02-13.

G05-106 (41# 8420)

Novodvorskiĭ, M. E.; Pjateckiĭ-Šapiro, I. I.

Some remarks on the torsion of elliptic curves. (Russian)

Mat. Sb. (*N.S.*) **82** (**124**) (1970), 309–316.

Let k be an algebraic extension of finite degree of the rational field Q and let N be a natural number. The authors find conditions which ensure that the set of elliptic curves which possess a point of order N, both curve and point being defined over k, fall into a finite number of isogeny classes. The condition generalizes one of Ju. I. Manin for the case when N is the power of a fixed prime p [Izv. Akad. Nauk SSSR Ser. Mat. **33** (1969), 459–466]*.

To explain the conditions we must introduce more notation. For a natural number a denote by $Y(a)$ the curve parametrizing the set of elliptic curves with a distinguished cycle of order a (the Transformationsgleichung) and let $J(a)$ be its Jacobian. Let A be an abelian subvariety of $J(a)$ defined and irreducible over k and denote by rk A_k and rk $\mathrm{End}_k^{(A)}$ the rank of the group of its k-rational points and k-rational complex multiplications, respectively. Then the condition is (*) $\tau(n)\,\mathrm{rk}\,\mathrm{End}_k(A) > \mathrm{rk}\,A_k$, where $\tau(u)$ is the number of divisors of n. More generally, the condition (*) implies that there are only finitely many k-rational points on $Y(N)$.

The proof uses the classical action of the modular group on the upper half-plane and the theory of infinite unitary representations to show that $J(N)$ contains $\tau(n)$ independent copies of A (up to isogeny). The authors can then invoke Manin's generalization [loc. cit.] of V. A. Dem'janenko's criterion [ibid. **30** (1966), 1373–1396; MR **34** #5816] for the finiteness of the number of points on a curve.

In the final section there is a generalization to other arithmetic groups acting on the upper half-plane.

J. W. S. Cassels (Cambridge, England)

*MR 42 #7667 = G05-115.

Citations: MR 34# 5816 = G30-40; MR 42# 7667 = G05-115.

G05-107 (41# 8421)

Olson, Loren D.

Galois cohomology of cycles and applications to elliptic curves.

Amer. J. Math. **92** (1970), 75–85.

The techniques of Galois cohomology and some theorems from algebraic number theory are applied to the study of algebraic cycles on a smooth projective variety X over an arbitrary ground field k. The first results concern the group of divisor classes invariant under the absolute Galois group of k modulo the subgroup generated by the divisors rational over k. This quotient group is proved a subgroup of the Brauer group of k and its order r is shown to divide the index I of X (I is the greatest common divisor of the degrees of the points of X). Now, applied to an elliptic curve E over an algebraic number field k, the next theorems assert notably that an element X of the (Weil-Chatelet) group WC of equivalence classes of principal homogeneous spaces has index I which divides the square of its period P (viz., its order in WC); this result removes some previous restrictions on its validity. Some of the results in the second part of the article were obtained independently by S. Lichtenbaum [same J. **90** (1968), 1209–1223; MR **38** #5788]; moreover, some of Lichtenbaum's techniques and other results have been incorporated into the proofs.

S. L. Kleiman (Cambridge, Mass.)

Citations: MR 38# 5788 = G05-94.

G05-108 (42# 274)

Ginatempo, Nicola

Alcune questioni diofantee sulle curve di genere uno. (English summary)

Atti Soc. Peloritana Sci. Fis. Mat. Natur. **14** (1968), 565–575.

It has been shown that if a cubic curve of genus one which is represented by an algebraic equation of the third degree with rational coefficients has four rational points one of which is a point of inflection and the other three are noncollinear, then its equation in homogeneous projective coordinates can be written as $ax_1x_2^2 + x_3(x_2+x_1)(x_3+x_1) = 0$, where a is rational and can take on three particular values. In this paper the author shows that in such a case the values that a can take on are exactly three. Equation $y^2 + k = x^3$ is also discussed. There are a few printing mistakes. *J. Verdina* (Long Beach, Calif.)

G05-109 (42# 1827)

Ogaĭ, S. V.

Curves that admit a second degree rational transformation. (Russian)

Proc. Eleventh Sci. Conf. of the Professorial Teaching Staff Fac. Phys. Math. (*Math. Section*) (*Russian*), *pp.* 58–60. *Kirgiz. Gos. Univ., Frunze*, 1963.

The elliptic curve $y^2 = x(x^2+av+b)$ admits a canonical isogeny of degree 2 defined over the field of constants. Studying this isogeny, the author estimates by a well-known method the rank of the curve in question.

Ju. Manin (RŽMat **1963** #11 A208)

G05-110 **(42# 4548)**

Bachmakov, Marc

Un théorème de finitude sur la cohomologie des courbes elliptiques.

C. R. Acad. Sci. Paris Sér. A-B **270** (1970), A999–A1001.

Let E be an elliptic curve over a number field k, and A a subgroup of $E(k)$, stable under $R = \mathrm{End}_k(E)$; for a prime number p we denote by A_p the group of elements $y \in E(\bar{k})$ such that for some $n \geqq 0$, $p^n y \in A$; denote by L_p the smallest field containing k over which all elements of A_p are rational, and let $\Gamma_p = \mathrm{Gal}(L_p/k)$. Theorem: Suppose A is torsion free; then for almost all p, $H^1(\Gamma_p, A_p) = 0$. We are looking forward to detailed proofs, which will appear soon.

Corrections to the paper, communicated by the author: On page 1000, first line, read: "Let L be the smallest field containing k over which all elements of $\bar{A}$ are rational" (and the analogous correction on page 999 in the definition of K). Theorem 2: Let r be the rank of A as an R-module, etc. Theorem 4: Suppose A is torsion free, etc.

F. Oort (Amsterdam)

G05-111 **(42# 4549)**

Birch, B. J.

Elliptic curves and modular functions.

Symposia Mathematica, Vol. IV (INDAM, Rome, 1968/69), pp. 27–32. *Academic Press, London,* 1970.

Let E: $y^2 = x^3 + Ax + B$ with A, B rational integers, be an elliptic curve. The Mordell-Weil theorem tells us that the group $E_{\mathbf{Q}}$ of rational points on E (as a projective curve) is finitely generated. Associated with E is the family of curves $E^{(D)}$: $Dy^2 = x^3 + Ax + B$ which are equivalent to E over $\mathbf{Q}(\sqrt{D})$, but not usually over $\mathbf{Q}$. It has been conjectured by A. Weil [Math. Ann. **168** (1967), 149–156; MR **34** #7473] that for square-free D, the parity of the rank of the group $E_{\mathbf{Q}}^{(D)}$ of rational points on $E^{(D)}$ is determined by the sign of D and the congruence class of D modulo a power of $6N$, where N is the conductor of E. The author examines a number of cases and for these shows that $E_{\mathbf{Q}}^{(D)}$ is infinite when the conjectures predict odd rank. The curves considered are each parametrized by $j(z)$, $j(Nz)$, where j is the modular invariant, and N is some integer; and the proofs make use of the theory of modular forms.

D. J. Lewis (Ann Arbor, Mich.)

Citations: MR 34# 7473 = F65-21.

G05-112 **(42# 4550)**

Dem'janenko, V. A.

The points of finite order of elliptic curves. **(Russian)**

Mat. Zametki **7** (1970), 563–567.

The author gives a complete description of all the elliptic curves which possess a point of order ten over any algebraic number field. The author also corrects an error in the proof of Y. Hellegouarch [C. R. Acad. Sci. Paris **260** (1965), 6256–6258; MR **31** #5862b] of the classical result that there are no points of fourteenth order on elliptic curves over the rational numbers.

{This article has appeared in English translation [Math. Notes **7** (1970), 340–342].}

D. Lieberman (Waltham, Mass.)

Citations: MR 31# 5862b = G20-22.

G05-113 **(42# 5995)**

Neumann, O.

Über die rationalen Punkte auf elliptischen Kurven.

Number Theory (Colloq., János Bolyai Math. Soc., Debrecen, 1968), *pp.* 161–164. *North-Holland, Amsterdam,* 1970.

Estimates (without proof) of the number of generators of the Mordell-Weil group in certain special cases. In one family of cases (indexed by the primes of the form $a^2 + 64$) the existence of points of infinite order is asserted.

J. W. S. Cassels (Cambridge, England)

G05-114 **(42# 7644)**

Washio, Tadashi

A remark on the trace formula for an inseparable correspondence in an algebraic function field.

Mem. Fac. Sci. Kyushu Univ. Ser. A **24** (1970), 231–237.

Let N_1 be the number of prime divisors of degree one of an elliptic function field k having $GF(p^h)$ as its field of constants. The author proves that the trace of the Hasse invariant A of k is given by $A^{1+p+\cdots+p^{h-1}} = \overline{1-N_1}$, where $\overline{1-N_1}$ denotes the residue class of $1-N_1$ mod p.

M. L. Madan (Columbus, Ohio)

G05-115 **(42# 7667)**

Manin, Ju. I.

The p-torsion of elliptic curves is uniformly bounded. (Russian)

Izv. Akad. Nauk SSSR Ser. Mat. **33** (1969), 459–465.

This paper is a very important contribution to the arithmetic on elliptic curves. Let X be an elliptic curve defined over the field of complex numbers C. Let D be a cyclic subgroup of X of order p^m. The absolute invariants $j(X)$ and $j(X/D)$ are connected by the modular equation of level p^m: $F_m[j(X), j(X/D)] = 0$. Let K be a number field. The above correspondence commutes with the action of $\mathrm{Gal}(\bar{K}/K)$.

The author shows that for large values of m the curve $F_m(X, Y) = 0$ contains a finite number of K-rational points.

This plus the fact that the torsion of curves with fixed invariant $j \in K$ is bounded [V. A. Dem'janenko, Mat. Zametki **3** (1968), 271–278; MR **37** #2751] gives the main result of the paper: If K is a number field, then there exists a constant c such that the order of the p-torsion group of the K-rational points of an elliptic curve defined over K does not exceed c.

The proof of the finiteness of the number of K-rational points on $F_m(X, Y) = 0$ is based on the following result: Let X ($X(K)$, $A(K)$ denote sets of K-rational points on X and A, respectively) be a curve and A a K-simple abelian variety contained in the jacobian of X with multiplicity $m(X, A)$ (to within isogeny). If $m(X, A) >$ rk $A(k)$/rk $\mathrm{End}_k A$, then the set $X(K)$ is finite.

The above is obtained as a corollary to the following important theorem proved in this paper: Let $A(X)$ be the group of K-homomorphisms of a normal projective variety X into an abelian variety A taking a fixed point $x \in X(K)$ into zero. Assume that the rank of the Néron-Severi group of X is 1. If rk $A(X) >$ rk $A(K)$, then the set $X(K)$ is finite.

The author also proves the following: Let X be an elliptic curve over k that has no complex multiplication. Then on the set of its K-forms the order of a maximal cyclic p-subgroup rational over K is bounded.

J. Blass (Ann Arbor, Mich.)

Citations: MR 37# 2751 = G05-86.

Referred to in G05-106, G05-116, G05-117, G05-118.

G05-116 **(43# 216)**

Hellegouarch, Y.

Étude des points d'ordre fini des variétés abéliennes de dimension un définies sur un anneau principal.

J. Reine Angew. Math. **244** (1970), 20–36.

In what follows A is an elliptic curve defined over the field of fractions K of a Dedekind ring R, and all the points of order 2 on A are defined over K. A rational prime p is said to be "idoine" if $(-2)^m \equiv -1 \pmod{p}$ for some integer m. When $R = \mathbf{Z}$, the rational integers, it is shown that there is no point of order p^2 defined over K, where p is an idoine prime, provided that Fermat's equation $x^p + y^p = z^p$ is insoluble. When $R = k[t]$ is a simple transcendental extension of a field k (not necessarily algebraically closed) and the invariant j of A (in the classical notation) is transcendental over k, then no point of A defined over K has odd order $\geqq 5$.

The proofs depend on writing the equation of A in the shape $Y^2 = X(X-A)(X-B)$ (sic!), where A and B are in R. The author then investigates the factorization of x, $x-A$ and $x-B$ at a point (x, y) defined over K and of finite order by using Tate's unpublished θ-function parametrization [see, e.g., the reviewer, J. London Math. Soc. **41** (1966), 193–291; MR **33** #7299].

From now on we confine attention to the case $R = \mathbf{Z}$. Let (x, y) be of odd prime order n and write $\nu(x, y) = (x_\nu, y_\nu)$ for $n \nmid \nu$ (group addition on A). Then there are u_ν, u_ν', u_ν'', w_ν, w_ν', $w_\nu'' \in \mathbf{Z}$ such that $x_\nu = u_\nu^2 w_\nu^2 w_\nu'^2$, $x_\nu - A = u_\nu'^2 w_\nu^2 w_\nu''^2$, $x_\nu - B = u_\nu''^2 w_\nu'^2 w_\nu''^2$. Further, on putting $n = 2r+1$ we have $w_\nu = \varepsilon_\nu a_1^{(\nu)_n} \cdots a_r^{(r\nu)_n}$ $(1 \leqq \nu \leqq n-1)$ for certain $a_1, \cdots, a_r \in \mathbf{Z}$, where $\varepsilon_\nu = \pm 1$ or ± 2 and where $(\alpha)_n$ denotes the least non-negative integer congruent to $\pm\alpha \pmod{n}$: and similarly for w_ν' and w_ν''. There are similar but more complicated formulae for $n = p^2$, where p is prime. The identities connecting the (x_ν, y_ν) which are given by the formulae for addition on A now lead to diophantine equations relating the a_j. If p is idoine these imply the existence of a solution of Fermat's equation.

The ideas underlying the proof seem to have considerable affinity with those of V. A. Dem'janenko [see #217 below]. For other recent work on the torsion group of elliptic curves, see Ju. I. Manin [Izv. Akad. Nauk SSSR Ser. Mat. **33** (1969), 459–465; MR **42** #7667] and A. N. Paršin [#218 below].
J. W. S. Cassels (Cambridge, England)

Citations: MR 33# 7299 = G02-16; MR 42# 7667 = G05-115.
Referred to in G05-121, G05-125.

G05-117 (43# 217)

Dem'janenko, V. A.
The torsion points of elliptic curves. (Russian)
Izv. Akad. Nauk SSSR Ser. Mat. **34** (1970), 757–774.

Let $\mathscr{K}$ be an algebraic number field and let $p > 3$ be a rational prime. The author in effect establishes the existence of an integer C depending only on $\mathscr{K}$ and p and enjoying the following property: Let $\mathscr{I}$ be an elliptic curve defined over $\mathscr{K}$ which has a point of order $2p^2$ defined over $\mathscr{K}$. Then the order of any point of finite order defined over $\mathscr{K}$ is at most C.

The proof depends on writing the equation of the curve in the shape $y^2 = x^4 + ax^2 + b$ and then investigating the factorization of x and y at points of finite order. Identities between the co-ordinates of multiples of a given point then lead to equations of the type $r^p + \varepsilon_0 s^p = \sigma_0''$, for given ε_0 and σ_0'', to be solved for r, s in a given extension of $\mathscr{K}$.

The ideas underlying the proof seem to have considerable affinity with those of Y. Hellegouarch [#216 above]. For other recent work on the torsion group of elliptic curves, see the papers by Ju. I. Manin [Izv. Akad. Nauk SSSR Ser. Mat. **33** (1969), 459–465; MR **42** #7667] and A. N. Paršin [#218 below].
J. W. S. Cassels (Cambridge, England)

Citations: MR 42# 7667 = G05-115.
Referred to in G05-121.

G05-118 (43# 218)

Paršin, A. N.
Isogenies and torsion of elliptic curves. (Russian)
Izv. Akad. Nauk SSSR Ser. Mat. **34** (1970), 409–424.

Let K be a finite extension of Q, let C be an elliptic curve defined over K, and let $C(K)$ be the group of K-rational points on C. By Mordell-Weil the torsion subgroup of $C(K)$ is finite and it has long been conjectured that its order is bounded when K is fixed and C varies. Let $\#C(K)^{\text{tors}} = \prod l^{n_C(l)}$ be its prime factorization. It was shown by Ju. I. Manin [same Izv. **33** (1969), 459–465; MR **42** #7667] that $\sup_C n_C(l) < \infty$. The author obtains the stronger result $\sup_C \sum_l n_C(l) < \infty$ in the case when C is without complex multiplication and C has a rational subgroup of prime order p, $p \geqq 19$.

The paper has two sections, the first geometric, the second arithmetic. In § 1 a subgroup Γ of finite index in $SL(2, Z)$ acts on the upper half plane H, and a family B of elliptic curves is defined over the quotient $Y = H/\Gamma$. $X = \bar{Y}$ is the compactification of Y obtained by adding parabolic points, and $A \to X$ is the Neron minimal model of $B \to Y$. A canonical section imbeds X in A, and the invertible sheaf L on X is taken as the conormal bundle of this imbedding. The rest of § 1 establishes various functorial properties of L and checks that $\deg L > 0$.

In § 2 it is first shown, using a moduli scheme of Mumford, that if $\Gamma = \Gamma(l)$ is a congruence subgroup, then $Y(K)$ classifies pairs (C, β), where C is an elliptic curve defined over K with $C^{(l)} \subset C(K)$ ($C^{(l)}$ is the subgroup of C of points of order l) and β is a basis for $C^{(l)}$. The Tate height h_L is defined on X using the invertible sheaf L of § 1, and it is shown that if B_x and B_y are isogenous, then $h_L(x) = h_L(y)$. A result of Mumford is used to show that if the genus of X is greater than 1, then there is an N such that the number of points in $X(K)$ of any given height is less than N. These considerations, and several technical lemmas, lead to the following result: If $C(K)$ contains a subgroup of prime order l, $l \geqq 19$, then there is an N such that the number of curves defined over K and K-isogenous to C is less than N (N depends only on K and l). The bound on $\sum_l n(l)$ now follows easily. *N. Greenleaf* (Austin, Tex.)

Citations: MR 42# 7667 = G05-115.

G05-119 (43# 3240)

Milne, J. S.
Elements of order p in the Tate-Šafarevič group.
Bull. London Math. Soc. **2** (1970), 293–296.

Let K be a global field (a number field, or a function field in one variable over a finite field), A an abelian variety over K and $Ш = Ш(A/K)$ its Tate-Šafarevič group, i.e., the group of principal homogeneous spaces over A that are trivial for every valuation of K. It is known that for any integer m prime to char(K) the group Ш has only finitely many elements of order dividing m [cf., S. Lang and J. Tate, Amer. J. Math. **80** (1958), 659–684; MR **21** #4960]; in this paper the author proves that the result holds for all m. In the proof, he considers a factorization of the isogeny $[p]: A \to A$, multiplication by $p = \text{char}(K)$, into isogenies having a kernel of prime order. After a finite separable extension of the ground field such a kernel is $\mathbf{Z}/p$, $\boldsymbol{\alpha}_p$ or $\boldsymbol{\mu}_p$. In each of these cases the kernel of the natural map $H^1(K, N) \to \Pi' H^1(K_v, N)$ from the cohomology of the kernel N into the restricted topological product of the local cohomology groups can be expressed in terms of the additive [multiplicative] group K [K^*], and the result follows. *F. Oort* (Amsterdam)

Citations: MR 21# 4960 = G10-10.

G05-120 **(43# 6215)**

Neumann, Olaf

Zur Reduktion der elliptischen Kurven.

Math. Nachr. **46** (1970), 285–310.

The author uses very classical methods to investigate the places of good reduction of elliptic curves. In particular, he characterizes the j invariants of elliptic curves E over a field k equipped with a discrete valuation w such that E has good reduction modulo w. The author has also given alternative proofs of many well-known theorems. Although the proofs do not differ drastically from those that the reviewer has already seen, this paper forms a fine compendium of the basic results due to M. Deuring and A. P. Ogg [see J.-P. Serre and J. Tate, Ann. of Math. (2) **88** (1968), 492–517; MR **38** #4488 for references] on the places of bad reduction of an elliptic curve defined over a number field. There is a certain cleverness in the author's manipulation via classical methods that may encourage a reader who has initial difficulty with the more sophisticated work in this area. *M. Fried* (Stony Brook, N.Y.)

In lines 9 and 10 "results due to M. Deuring and A. P. Ogg" should read "results due to M. Deuring, I. R. Šafarevič and A. P. Ogg".

Citations: MR 38# 4488 = G10-36.

G05-121 **(44# 2755)**

Dem'janenko, V. A.

The torsion of elliptic curves. (Russian)

Izv. Akad. Nauk SSSR Ser. Mat. **35** (1971), 280–307.

The author purports to prove the long-standing conjecture that the Mordell-Weil rank of an elliptic curve (= abelian variety of dimension one) over an algebraic number field is bounded by a constant depending only on the field. Unfortunately, the exposition is so obscure that the reviewer has yet to meet someone who would vouch for the validity of the proof; on the other hand he has yet to be shown a mistake that unambiguously and irretrievably vitiates the argument. Ideas appearing in the proof were previously exploited by the author [same Izv. **34** (1970), 757–774; MR **43** #217] and independently by Y. Hellegouarch [J. Reine Angew. Math. **244** (1970), 20–36; MR **43** #216].

J. W. S. Cassels (Cambridge, England)

Citations: MR 43# 216 = G05-116; MR 43# 217 = G05-117.

G05-122 **(44# 2758)**

Damerell, R. M.

L-functions of elliptic curves with complex multiplication. I.

Acta Arith. **17** (1970), 287–301.

Let $\mathscr{C}$ be an elliptic curve $y^2 = 4x^3 - ax - b$, $a, b \in \mathbf{Q}$, with complex multiplication, so the ring $\mathbf{S} = \mathrm{End}_{\mathrm{C}}\,\mathscr{C}$ is an order in some complex quadratic field $k = \mathbf{Q}(\sqrt{-d})$. Let $L_{\mathscr{C}}(s)$ denote the associated L-function (J. W. S. Cassels [J. London Math. Soc. **41** (1966), 193–291; MR **33** #7299; correction, ibid. **42** (1967), 183; MR **34** #2523] and note that the author follows Cassels in replacing the s of the Birch and Swinnerton-Dyer conjectures by $s - \frac{1}{2}$). In the case $\mathbf{S} = \mathbf{Z}[\sqrt{-1}]$, B. J. Birch and H. P. F. Swinnerton-Dyer [J. Reine Angew. Math. **218** (1965), 79–108; MR **31** #3419] showed how to construct a number α such that $L_{\mathscr{C}}(\frac{1}{2}) \cdot \alpha = \tau(\mathscr{C}) \in \mathbf{Z}$ (the notation suggests Tamagawa numbers).

The function $L_{\mathscr{C}}(s)$ has a product $\prod_{\mathfrak{p}} (1 - \lambda(\mathfrak{p})/N(\mathfrak{p})^s)^{-1}$, where $\mathfrak{p}$ runs through the "good" primes of S (good reduction mod $\mathfrak{p}$) and λ is a Hecke Grössencharakter on the ideals of S. More generally one considers $L_{\mathscr{C}}^{[n]}(s) = \prod_{\mathfrak{p}} (1 - \lambda^n(\mathfrak{p})/(N\mathfrak{p})^s)^{-1}$ and it is natural to ask whether or not there exists $\alpha = \alpha(\mathscr{C}, n)$ such that $L_{\mathscr{C}}^{[n]}(\frac{1}{2}) \cdot \alpha \in \mathbf{Z}$. (The generalized $L_{\mathscr{C}}^{[n]}(s)$ are suspected of having applications to the study of the rational points of $\mathscr{C}$, but as far as the reviewer knows it is no more than a suspicion.)

This paper is the first of a series in which it is promised that the existence of an α with the foregoing properties will be proved for all the 13 complex quadratic rings with class number 1. The author considers the Hecke zeta function $\zeta(s, \lambda) = \sum_{\mathfrak{a}} \lambda(\mathfrak{a})/(N\mathfrak{a})^s$ formed with a Grössencharakter λ defined on the ideals $\mathfrak{a}$ of S prime to some $\mathfrak{m}$. Let s_0 be such that $\frac{1}{2}n - s_0 \in \mathbf{Z}$ and $0 < s_0 \leqq \frac{1}{2}n$. Let x be so chosen as to ensure that $g_2(\mathbf{S}x)$, $g_3(\mathbf{S}x)$ (in the usual notation) are algebraic numbers (that this is possible is a consequence of a theorem of H. Hasse [ibid. **157** (1937), 115–139]). Then $\zeta(s, \lambda)$ is regular at $s = s_0$ and the number $\zeta(s_0, \lambda)\pi^{n(2-s_0)}/x^n$ is algebraic. This establishes the first step in the proof of the desired result. In subsequent papers [see, e.g., Acta Arith. **19** (1971), 311–317] questions of rationality and integrality will be taken up.

J. V. Armitage (Nottingham)

Citations: MR 31# 3419 = G05-75; MR 33# 7299 = G02-16; MR 34# 2523 = G02-17.

G05-123 **(44# 5319)**

Bachmakov, Marc [Bašmakov, M. I.]

Cohomologie des courbes elliptiques.

Séminaire Delange-Pisot-Poitou: 1969/70, *Théorie des Nombres, Fasc.* 1, *Exp.* 12, 4 *pp. Secrétariat mathématique, Paris*, 1970.

In this paper, the author generalizes a duality theorem of J. W. S. Cassels [J. Reine Angew. Math. **216** (1964), 150–158; MR **30** #92] for the Galois cohomology of elliptic curves defined over algebraic number fields. Let E be an elliptic curve over a number field k, v a place of k, k_v the v-completion of k, and G $[G_v]$ the Galois group of the algebraic closure of k $[k_v]$. Let B be the cokernel of the well-known homomorphism $i: H^1(G, E) \to \bigoplus_v H^1(G_v, E)$. The kernel of i is by definition the Tate-Šafarevič group Ш of E. Under the assumption that Ш [the p-component of Ш] is finite, Cassels has computed the dual (in the sense of locally compact abelian groups) to B, $\mathrm{Char}(B)$ [Char (the p-component of B)]. The author generalizes this result to the situation in which no assumption is made on the finiteness of Ш. More specifically: Let p be a prime number, and let S' be the set of places of k dividing p, the places where E has bad reduction, and the archimedean places. For any set S of places containing S', consider the homomorphism $i_S: H_p^1(G_S, E) \to \sum_{v \in S} H^1(G_v, E)$ where the subscript p denotes the p-component, and G_S is the Galois group of the maximal extension of k unramified outside of S, and let B_S denote the cokernel. The author computes $\mathrm{Char}(B_S)$ with no assumptions on Ш. *L. D. Olson* (Oslo)

Citations: MR 30# 92 = G05-73.

G05-124 **(44# 5320)**

Neumann, Olaf

Die elliptischen Kurven mit den Führern 3.2^m und 9.2^m.

Math. Nachr. **48** (1971), 387–389.

A simplified proof of results of A. P. Ogg [J. Reine Angew. Math. **226** (1967), 204–215; MR **35** #1592].

J. W. S. Cassels (Cambridge, England)

Citations: MR 35# 1592 = G05-82.

G05-125 **(44# 6703)**

Hellegouarch, Yves

Points d'ordre fini sur les courbes elliptiques.

C. R. Acad. Sci. Paris Sér. A-B **273** (1971), A540–A543.

In order to review this paper, the reviewer found it necessary to read an earlier paper by the author [J. Reine

Angew. Math. **244** (1970), 20–36; MR **43** #216]. Recently V. A. Dem'janenko [Mat. Zametki **7** (1970), 563–567; MR **42** #4450] has shown there exists a constant $C>0$ such that (*) an elliptic curve $A/\mathbf{Q}$ has no rational point of order $n>C$. This delicate Diophantine problem amounts to showing that most of the modular equations have no $\mathbf{Q}$-rational points. The author's work improves on the constant C in (*) (determining it effectively) when n is assumed special.

For example, if A has a rational point of order p^h (p a prime $\geqq 17$, and $h>1$), then (1) $\sum_{n=0}^{m} x_i^{p^{h-1}}=0$ has at least $(p-1)/2$ distinct (non-trivial) solutions in $\mathbf{Z}^{m+1}$, with m (effectively calculable) independent of p and h.

If A admits a point of order $2\cdot p^h$, even more implausibly (2) $x_1^{p^{h-1}}+x_2^{p^{h-1}}=x_3^{p^{h-1}}$, $y_1^{p^{h-1}}+y_2^{p^{h-1}}=2y_3^{p^{h-1}}$ have $(p-1)/2$(non-trivial) solutions in $\mathbf{Z}^6$ (if the reviewer understands the author).

In general the author relates the existence of special rational points to solutions of Fermat-type equations, where for special primes he can refer to classical diophantine results.

The idea of the proofs divides into two cases. Let A be defined over a number field K with nonarchimedian valuation v and j-invariant $j(A)$. If $v(j(A))\geqq 0$, then E. Lutz's theory [J. Reine Angew. Math. **177** (1937), 238–247] gives a bound to the order of the torsion group of A/K (dependent on K and v). If $v(j(A))<0$ (so that, in particular, A has bad reduction at v) the Jacobi-Tate model of A (as a torus formed from $K_v{}^*$) provides a classical description of the coordinates of division points in terms of θ-functions. The author exploits this in his earlier paper [op. cit.] to associate with a division point its v-adic characteristic.

In each of the author's papers, the reader is reminded that details are to appear in a forthcoming thesis.

M. Fried (Ann Arbor, Mich.)

Citations: MR 43# 216 = G05-116.

G10 ABELIAN VARIETIES OF HIGHER DIMENSION OVER ARBITRARY GROUND FIELDS

See also Section G15.

See also reviews F02-5, F02-16, F10-90, F15-15, F15-29, F40-28, F40-31, F50-23, F50-29, F55-11, F55-16, F55-21, F65-16, F70-18, G02-1, G02-13, G02-20, G05-119, G20-34, G20-35, G20-37, J76-45, J76-51, J76-58, M02-5, R58-17, R58-19, Z10-59.

G10-1 (10, 621d)

Weil, André. Variétés abéliennes et courbes algébriques. Actualités Sci. Ind., no. 1064 = Publ. Inst. Math. Univ. Strasbourg 8 (1946). Hermann & Cie., Paris, 1948. 165 pp.

This book is a continuation of the author's test of the comprehensive methods developed in his "Foundations of Algebraic Geometry" [Amer. Math. Soc. Colloquium Publ., v. 29, New York, 1946; these Rev. **9**, 303], which was begun in his "Sur les courbes algébriques et les variétés qui s'en déduisent" [Actualités Sci. Ind., no. 1041 = Publ. Inst. Math. Univ. Strasbourg **7** (1945); these Rev. **10**, 262] with the proof of the Riemann hypothesis for function fields of one variable. Now the theory of Abelian functions and of the Jacobian variety attached to a curve is developed over arbitrary coefficient fields. All the classical results (i.e., one works over the field of all complex numbers) are generalized and new theorems enriching the classical theory are added. An essential tool, though this at first glance may appear to be trivial, is the concept of function defined on a variety U [abstract in the sense of "Foundations . . ." pp. 167 ff.] with values in another variety V. This is naturally done by means of special [regularity in the sense of "Foundations . . ." p. 107] subvarieties of the Cartesian product $U\times V$; it is significant that heretofore a systematic exploitation of this particular concept was not used appreciably in modern algebra. Thus the type of reasoning of analysis and combinatorial topology can now find fuller application in arithmetic and algebraic geometry.

Already, for the proof of the Riemann hypothesis, it was necessary to consider Cartesian products of a curve involving more than two factors [theorem 10 of "Sur les courbes . . ."]; only in this fashion, it appears, the full force of algebraic geometry can be brought to bear upon certain delicate parts of the class field theory of function fields; this involves a detailed study of the ring of correspondences [e.g., the positiveness of certain traces, and L-series in § 5 of "Sur les courbes . . ."]. The full details of the pertinent facts are given in this book by means of a systematic theory of Abelian varieties, i.e., complete ["Foundations . . ." p. 168] algebraic varieties which are group spaces in §§ II, III and IV (see the beginning of this review for the possibility of this definition). A basic result for the theory of Abelian varieties is embodied in theorem 9 on page 34 which states that a function on an Abelian variety B into an Abelian variety A is (essentially) a homomorphism in the sense of the given group operations on the varieties. (This result is a "dual" of the known direct imbedding of differentials.) In § V the existence of Abelian varieties is established by means of the Jacobian varieties of curves. It is noteworthy that, as in the classical theory, the theory of curves and their attached Jacobian varieties is material in order to enrich the theory of general Abelian varieties [see the useful theorem 10 on p. 39, and later results starting with theorem 22 on p. 79 to theorem 24 on p. 87 leading up to important facts concerning the anti-isomorphism of the ring of endomorphisms].

To a homomorphism λ of an Abelian variety A into an Abelian variety B the norm $\nu(\lambda)$ is associated by means of the theory of cycles and projections, and this norm is investigated in relation to the group of points $x\varepsilon A$ which are mapped upon $0\varepsilon B$ by means of λ [in theorem 12 with corollary and proposition 9, pp. 42, 43]. In particular, it is shown that $\nu(\lambda)=0$ implies the existence of an Abelian subvariety of A which does not reduce to a point. Results of this kind are continued subsequently in the generalization of Poincaré's famous result on the reducibility of integrals of the first kind in theorem 26 on page 94 (exploitation of $\nu(a)>0$, a an integer, in § VII, also important later for the proof of semi-simplicity of the algebra of homomorphisms of an Abelian variety), with the subsequent work on categories of Abelian varieties (defined by means of isogeny, i.e., equality of dimension and existence of homomorphisms upon each other). Thus the algebraic structure of the algebra of homomorphisms (ring of homomorphisms of an Abelian variety into itself extended by the field of rational numbers) is related to the decomposition of categories [theorem 29 on p. 101 in § VII]. These results comprehend incidentally a first step in the direction of an algebraic structure theory of certain function fields as subfields of direct products of function fields with special properties such as that of having multiplication algebras which are division algebras, in other words, here are the roots of an algebraic theory of "fibered" fields. The preparations for results of this kind are not easy, and intermediate statements using the theorem of Riemann-Roch have to be established. We mention theorem 19 on page 70 which concerns itself with the canonical mapping of the classes of divisors of degree 0 on a curve onto the group of points on the attached Jacobian variety, and theorem 21 on page 77 where connections between homomorphisms of Jacobian varieties and algebraic correspondences of the related curves are made precise. As a consequence an important part of an algebraic analogue of Hurwitz' transcendental description of algebraic correspondences is obtained.

Already the qualitative study of the homomorphisms λ of Abelian varieties leads in theorem 14 on page 49 to a representation $M_l(\lambda)$ of λ by matrices with elements in the additive l-adic group modulo l, where l is relatively prime to the characteristic of the underlying coefficient field as is shown subsequently (the representation for the characteristic is of no special interest in the present work). In order to determine the precise degree of the matrices, as is done in theorem 23 and its corollaries 1 and 2 on pages 126–127, one has to pass through the delicate § VIII where the difficult work of theorem 23 in § VII is resumed. The degree in question is uniformly $2n$ if n is the dimension of the variety; in other words de Jonquières' formula is obtained. Thus the author succeeds in finding $2n$-dimensional representations $M_l(\lambda)$ of the ring of homomorphisms of an Abelian variety whose traces and norms coincide [theorem 36 on p. 136, passing through the theorem on Jacobian varieties in theorem 34 on p. 131] with the trace and norm which were previously defined without recourse to matrix representations [e.g., section 27 on p. 43 for the norm]. With this result the climax of the investigation is reached. Now a rather complete analogue has been found for Hurwitz's transcendental description of correspondences, and the proof of Artin's conjecture on the L-series of nonprincipal characters is completed [p. 137 and § V, pp. 72–85 in "Sur les courbes . . ."].

Finally in § X the famous result on the "finiteness of the base" of the ring of homomorphisms over the ring of integers is proved in theorem 37 on page 138. The proof is first given for simple Abelian varieties (no proper Abelian subvarieties are present, or equivalently the ring of homomorphisms lies in a division algebra); the theorem 31 on page 117 on the positiveness of certain traces is essential in order to set up a useful symmetric bilinear form on homomorphisms [p. 139]. The proof is then completed by a straightforward application of the theory of categories [theorem 29 on p. 101], and results of the theory of Riemann matrices become applicable [theorem 32 on p. 144], where naturally the originally important matrices of periods do not occur.

In the terminating § XI it is explained how one can map divisors of an n-dimensional Abelian variety upon $2n$-dimensional l-adic matrices where the mapping is a homomorphism acting upon classes in the sense of linear equivalence ["Foundations . . . ," chapter VIII]. These results offer extensions of facts, up to now restricted to the application of combinatorial topology to algebraic geometry, dealing with the arithmetic theory of homomorphisms [proposition 33 on p. 160, a kind of decomposition theory of ideals], and necessary and sufficient conditions (involving factor sets) for a divisor to be linearly equivalent to a multiple of another divisor [proposition 33 on p. 163].

O. F. G. Schilling (Chicago, Ill.).

Citations: MR 9, 303c = G02-2; MR 10, 262c = G20-8.

Referred to in G05-34, G10-2, G10-9.

G10-2 (15, 464g)

Morikawa, Hisasi. On abelian varieties. Nagoya Math. J. 6, 151–170 (1953).

En utilisant l'existence de variétés abéliennes quotients [Chow, Proc. Nat. Acad. Sci. U. S. A. **38**, 1039–1044 (1952); ces Rev. **14**, 580] et le plongement des jacobiennes dans l'espace projectif, l'auteur démontre d'abord que toute variété abélienne abstraite est isomorphe (sur la clôture algébrique de son corps de définition) à une variété abélienne projective; le traitement des phénomènes d'inséparabilité parait insuffisant au rapporteur, mais il pense qu'il est facile de combler cette lacune. Soit alors A une variété abélienne; notons $\sim$ l'équivalence linéaire des diviseurs sur A, X_t le translaté du diviseur X par $t \in A$, et $X \equiv Y$ la relation $X_t - X \sim Y_t - Y$ pour tout $t \in A$ [cf. Weil, Variétés abéliennes et courbes algébriques, Hermann, Paris, 1948, no. 57; ces Rev. **10**, 621]; l'auteur appelle cette dernière l'équivalence algébrique, mais ne démontre pas qu'elle coïncide avec l'équivalence algébrique au sens classique. En notant $G_l(A)$ (resp. $G_a(A)$) le groupe des diviseurs X sur A tels que $X \sim 0$ (resp. $X \equiv 0$), on démontre l'existence d'une variété abélienne A^0 isogène à A [Weil, loc. cit., no. 53] et isomorphe (en tant que groupe additif) à $G_a(A)/G_l(A)$; cette "variété de Picard" de A est déterminée à un isomorphisme purement inséparable près. La méthode des matrices q-adiques de Weil [loc. cit. no. 77] permet de montrer que l'on a $A = A^{00}$ sous certaines conditions peu restrictives.

L'auteur passe alors à une étude arithmétique des anneaux d'endomorphismes de variétés abéliennes. Un lemme montre que, si un corps K de nombres algébriques admet une involution s telle que $\mathrm{Tr}_{K/Q}(x \cdot s(x)) > 0$ pour tout $x \neq 0$ dans K, alors K est totalement réel ou totalement imaginaire. Il en est donc ainsi du centre de l'anneau des endomorphismes d'une variété abélienne simple.

Le reste du mémoire est consacré à la démonstration purement algébrique du théorème suivant, dû à Frobenius: si A est une variété abélienne sur un corps de caractéristique 0, et si X est un diviseur positif sur A tel que l'on ait $X_t \sim X$ pour seulement un nombre fini de points t de A, alors la dimension $l(X)$ de l'espace vectoriel des fonctions f sur A telles que $(f) \geqq -X$ est égale à la racine carrée de l'entier $\prod_q q^{e(q)}$, où $e(q)$ est l'exposant du nombre premier q dans le déterminant de la matrice q-adique $E_q(X)$ attachée à X [cf. Weil, loc. cit., no. 76]. La démonstration de ce résultat est délicate. Elle fait intervenir tous les résultats précédemment démontrés, une classe de variétés abéliennes (dites "spéciales") qui jouissent de mainte propriété des jacobiennes, et un résultat de Siegel sur la représentation sous forme de sommes de quatre carrés des entiers totalement positifs d'un corps de nombres totalement réel.

P. Samuel (Clermont-Ferrand).

Citations: MR 10, 621d = G10-1.

G10-3 (17, 87e)

Lang, Serge. Abelian varieties over finite fields. Proc. Nat. Acad. Sci. U.S.A. **41**, 174–176 (1955).

Soient K_1/k_1 un corps de fonctions algébriques, et k un sous corps de k_1. L'auteur donne une condition suffisante pour que K_1 provienne, par extension du corps de base, d'un corps de fonctions algébriques K/k. Si K/k est un corps de fonctions algébriques, et si k_1 est une extension de k telle que Kk_1/k_1 soit un corps de fonctions abéliennes, il existe un modèle V de K/k qui est birégulièrement équivalent à une variété abélienne sur k_1. De plus, si k_1 est séparable sur k, V est une variété abélienne sur k si et seulement si elle admet un point rationnel sur k. Supposons maintenant que k soit un corp fini à q éléments, et que V soit une variété définie sur k et admette une structure de variété abélienne sur la clôture algébrique de k; l'étude de l'application $x \rightarrow x^q$ de V sur V montre que V admet un point rationnel sur k, et est donc une variété abélienne sur k. *P. Samuel* (Clermont-Ferrand).

Referred to in G25-6.

G10-4 (17, 87f)

Mattuck, Arthur. Abelian varieties over p-adic ground fields. Ann. of Math. (2) **62,** 92–119 (1955).

Let k be an ultrametric field (i.e. a field with a real-valued non-archimedian valuation) which is complete and of characteristic 0, and let A be a d-dimensional Abelian variety over k. The author proves that the group of points of A rational over k contains a subgroup isomorphic to the direct sum of d times the additive group of integers of k; moreover, if k is locally compact, then this subgroup is of finite index (which implies that A has only a finite number of points of finite orders rational over k). The theorem is first proved in the case where A is the Jacobian variety of a curve C rational over k and having a rational point over k. In this case, the method is an adaptation of the proof that J is a torus group in the case where the basic field is that of complex numbers. Denoting by $\mathfrak{m}_1+\cdots+\mathfrak{m}_g=\mathfrak{M}$ (g=genus of C) a suitable non-special divisor of degree g of C, the points of a neighbourhood of 0 in J are represented by the divisors $\mathfrak{P}-\mathfrak{M}$, where $\mathfrak{P}=\mathfrak{p}_1+\cdots+\mathfrak{p}_g$, each $\mathfrak{p}_i$ being a point near $\mathfrak{m}_i$ on C. Any differential du of the first kind on C defines by integration a function u_i on a neighbourhood of $\mathfrak{m}_i$, and $\sum_{i=1}^{g} u_i(\mathfrak{p}_i)=v(\mathfrak{P}-\mathfrak{M})$ defines a holomorphic function v on on a neighbourhood of 0 in J. If $du_1, \cdots, du_g$ form a base of the space of differentials of the first kind, the corresponding functions v yield a uniformization of a neighbourhood of 0 in J, and this uniformization transforms the addition in J into the addition in a g-dimensional vector space over k; the theorem now follows easily. To go over to the general case, the author imbeds the Abelian variety A into the Jacobian variety of a curve with a rational point over k; this is possible because A, having a rational point over k (the zero element), has, in the neighbourhood of this point, points which are rational over k but generic over a suitable field of definition of A, from which it follows that A contains sufficently general curves having rational points over k. One then uniformizes locally the ambient Jacobian variety J in the manner indicated above; since A is a subgroup of J, it will be represented locally by a linear variety in the parameter space, from which the theorem follows. *C. Chevalley* (Paris).

G10-5 (19, 981c)

Roquette, Peter. Über das Hassesche Klassenkörper-Zerlegungsgesetz und seine Verallgemeinerung für beliebige abelsche Funktionenkörper. J. Reine Angew. Math. **197** (1957), 49–67.

Let A be an abelian variety defined over a field k, let G be a finite subgroup of the group $A(k)$ of points on A rational over k, and let $B=A/G$ be the quotient variety. Then G is a group of translation automorphisms of the function field $K=k(A)$ and the fixed field of G is $L=k(B)$. Let $D_a(A, k)$, resp. $D_l(A, k)$, be the group of divisors on A rational over k which are algebraically, resp. linearly, equivalent to zero, and let $\hat{A}(k)$ be the group of points rational over k on the Picard variety $\hat{A}$ of A. Since G consists of translations of A, it operates trivially on $\hat{A}$ and the exact sequence $\hat{A}(k)\approx D_a(A, k)/D_l(A, k)$ yields a coboundary homomorphism δ_0: $\hat{A}(k)=H^0(G, \hat{A}(k))\to H^1(G, D_l(A, k))$. Since K/L is unramified, the kernel of δ_0 is $\varepsilon\hat{B}(k)$, where $\varepsilon:\hat{B}\to\hat{A}$ is the dual isogeny to the canonical map $A\to B=A/G$. The exact sequence $D_l(A, k)\approx K^*/k^*$ yields $\delta_1:H^1(G, D_l(A, k))\to H^2(G, k^*)$, and the kernel of δ_1 is zero by Hilbert's Theorem 90. Thus, the composed map $h=\delta_1\delta_0$ is a homomorphism of $\hat{A}(k)$ into $H^2(G, k^*)$ with kernel $\varepsilon\hat{B}(k)$. Let $C\in\hat{A}(k)$ and let $c_{\sigma,\tau}$ be a 2-cocycle representing $h(C)$. Given a constant field extension $k'\supset k$, it is clear from the naturality of h that the equation $\varepsilon D=C$ has a solution $D\in\hat{B}(k')$ if and only if the equations $c_{\sigma,\tau}=d_\sigma d_\tau/d_{\sigma\tau}$ have a solution $\{d_\sigma\}$ in k'^*. Since $\varepsilon:\hat{B}\to\hat{A}$ is surjective, such fields k' do exist, and it follows that $c_{\sigma,\tau}=c_{\tau,\sigma}$. Moreover, if we build the abelian k-algebra Γ having as k-basis a set of elements $\{u_\sigma\}$, $\sigma\in G$, with $u_\sigma u_\tau=u_{\sigma\tau}c_{\sigma,\tau}$, then the above condition on k' is equivalent with the existence of a k-homomorphism $\Gamma\to k'$. Assume now that k contains a primitive n_0th root of unity, where n_0 is the exponent of G, and let X be the kernel of ε. Then $X\subset\hat{B}(k)$ and the function field $\bar{L}=k(\hat{B})$ is abelian over $\bar{K}=k(\hat{A})$ with Galois group X, and by Kummer theory, $X\approx\text{Hom}(G, k)$. From the theory of algebras of type Γ one can see directly that for each $C\in A(k)$ there is a smallest field of type k', namely the "kernel field" of Γ, and this smallest k' is abelian over k with Galois group isomorphic to a subgroup of X. Thus, the way in which a point $C\in\hat{A}(k)$ decomposes in the extension $\bar{L}/\bar{K}$ is described by the cohomology class $h(C)$. This is the author's generalization of Hasse's reciprocity law. If instead of treating a rational point C of $\hat{A}$ over k we treat a generic point x of $\hat{A}$ over k, we find that the algebra Γ constructed with a representative cocycle of $h(x)$ is a field, and the extension $\Gamma/k(x)$ is isomorphic to $k(\hat{B})/k(\hat{A})$, i.e. to $\bar{L}/\bar{K}$.

When G is taken to be the group of division points of period n_0 on A, then B can be identified with A, and ε becomes simply multiplication by n_0. Thus h induces an isomorphism of the factor group $\hat{A}(k)/n_0\hat{A}(k)$ (divisor classes of K algebraically equivalent to zero modulo their n_0th powers) onto a subgroup $h(\hat{A}(k))$ of $H^2(G, k^*)$. In case k is a number field the author gives a simple proof of Weil's weak finiteness theorem by showing that there exists a finite set S of primes of k such that every element of $h(\hat{A}(k))$ can be represented by a cocycle whose elements are S-units, and consequently that $h(\hat{A}(k))$ is finite. *J. Tate* (Cambridge, Mass.).

Referred to in G10-12.

G10-6 (21# 1311)

Lang, S.; and Néron, A. Rational points of abelian varieties over function fields. Amer. J. Math. **81** (1959), 95–118.

A simplified proof of the theorem of the base for divisors is given in this article. The base theorem asserts, as is well known, that the group of rational divisors over a ground field modulo algebraic equivalence is finitely generated, and this was proved by A. Néron [Bull. Sci. Math. France **80** (1952), 101–166; MR **15**, 151].

The authors reduce the assertion first to the following.

Let K be a finitely generated regular extension of a field k. Let A be an abelian variety defined over K, and let (B, τ) be its K/k-trace, namely, B is an abelian variety, τ is a homomorphism $B\to A$ defined over K, and for any abelian variety C defined over an extension E of k which is free from K over k and homomorphism $\alpha: C\to A$ defined over KE, there exists a homomorphism $\alpha': C\to B$ defined over E such that the diagram

$$C \xrightarrow{\ \alpha\ } A, \qquad C \xrightarrow{\ \alpha'\ } B \xrightarrow{\ \tau\ } A$$

is commutative. Then A_K/B_k is finitely generated. [The notion of K/k-traces was studied by W. L. Chow, Trans. Amer. Math. Soc. **78** (1955), 582–586; MR **17**, 193.]

Then the authors prove the assertion reducing to the case where k is algebraically closed and K is of transcendence degree 1 over k.

Finite generation of the group of rational points of an

abelian variety over an algebraic number field is also proved. *M. Nagata* (Kyoto)

Citations: MR 15, 151a = G30-13.
Referred to in G10-23, G30-35.

G10-7 **(21# 3425)**

Lang, Serge. Reciprocity and correspondences. Amer. J. Math. **80** (1958), 431–440.

Let V, W be two complete varieties, non-singular in co-dimension 1. Let D be a divisor on the product $V \times W$ and $\mathfrak{a}$ and $\mathfrak{b}$ be respectively 0-cycles on V and W. If $D(\mathfrak{a})$ is defined and is the divisor of a function f on V, and if no component of $\mathfrak{b}$ is contained in a component of $D(\mathfrak{a}) = (f)$, $f(\mathfrak{b}) = \prod f(b_i)^{n_i}$ ($\mathfrak{b} = \sum n_i b_i$) is defined. If $\mathfrak{b}$ is of degree 0, $f(\mathfrak{b})$ is independent of the choice of f. Assume that $\mathfrak{a}$ and $\mathfrak{b}$ are both of degree 0 and that they are in the kernels of the canonical mappings of the groups of 0-cycles of degree 0 on V and W into the corresponding Albanese varieties. The main theorem of this paper asserts that if no component of $\mathfrak{a} \times \mathfrak{b}$ lies in the support of D, $D(\mathfrak{a}, \mathfrak{b})$ and ${}^tD(\mathfrak{b}, \mathfrak{a})$ are defined and equal. This is first proved on Abelian varieties and the general case is deduced from there. This is a generalization of Weil's reciprocity theorem $f((g)) = g((f))$, where f and g are functions on a complete non-singular curve C, which can be obtained from this theorem by putting $V = W = C$, D = diagonal. Two applications of the main theorem are mentioned. (i) Let K be a finite Galois extension of a field k with the Galois group G, and A, B be Abelian varieties defined over k. Then a well-defined bilinear mapping of $H^1(G, A_K)$ and B_k into $H^2(G, K^*)$ is defined in terms of the operation $D(\ ,\ )$ (A_K [resp. B_k] is the group of rational points of A [resp. B] over K [resp. k], and K^* is the multiplicative group of K), generalizing the pairing of Tate on Jacobian varieties. (ii) Let A, B be Abelian varieties, D a divisor on the product $A \times B$, and $\mathfrak{a}$, $\mathfrak{b}$ two 0-cycles on A and B respectively, of degree 0, such that $nS(\mathfrak{a}) = 0$, $nS(\mathfrak{b}) = 0$. If no component of $\mathfrak{a} \times \mathfrak{b}$ lies in the support of D, ${}^tD(n\mathfrak{b}, \mathfrak{a})/D(n\mathfrak{a}, \mathfrak{b}) = \varepsilon_{n,D}(a, b)$ is an nth root of unity, where $a = S(\mathfrak{a})$, $b = S(\mathfrak{b})$. $\varepsilon_{n,D}(a, b)$ depends only on the correspondence class of D and of a, b. On the other hand, $(n\delta)^{-1}\ ({}^tD(\mathfrak{b}))$ is the divisor of a function f. When u is a generic point of A, $f(u+a)/f(u) = e_{n,D}(a, b)$ is also an nth root of unity. It is proved that $\varepsilon_{n,D}(a, b) = e_{n,D}(a, b)$, giving a complement to Kummer theory arising from the theory of divisorial correspondences. *T. Matsusaka* (Evanston, Ill.)

G10-8 **(21# 4162)**

Tate, J. *WC*-groups over $\mathfrak{p}$-adic fields. Séminaire Bourbaki; 10e année: 1957/1958. Textes des conférences; Exposés 152 à 168; 2e éd. corrigée, Exposé 156, 13 pp. Secrétariat mathématique, Paris, 1958. 189 pp. (mimeographed)

Let k be a $\mathfrak{p}$-adic number field, K the algebraic closure of k, and G the Galois group of K/k. Let A be an abelian variety defined over k, and A_K the group of points of A rational over K. Let $WC(A/k)$ denote the one-dimensional cohomology group $H^1(G, A_K)$ constructed with cochains coming from finite extensions of k in K. The main result of the paper then says that the discrete abelian group $WC(A/k)$ is canonically dual to the compact abelian group B_k of the points rational over k on the Picard variety B of A. For the proof, a canonical pairing of $WC(A/k)$ and B_k into the Brauer group Br(k) is defined by geometric method, and then a pairing of the same groups into the reals mod. 1 by using local class field theory; the latter is then proved to be a dual pairing of discrete $WC(A/k)$ and compact B_k.

As an application, the following result is also stated: If Γ is an algebraic curve defined over, and with rational point in, k, and if L/k is a finite Galois extension with group S, then $H^1(S, C_L) = 0$, where C_L is the group of idèle classes of the field of rational functions on Γ defined over L. *K. Iwasawa* (Cambridge, Mass.)

Referred to in G10-13, G20-38, G25-56, R34-18, R34-26.

G10-9 **(21# 4959)**

Lang, Serge. Abelian varieties. Interscience Tracts in Pure and Applied Mathematics. No. 7. Interscience Publishers, Inc., New York; Interscience Publishers Ltd., London; 1959. xii + 256 pp. $7.25.

This book deals with the theory of general Abelian varieties and also that of Albanese and Picard varieties of given varieties. It is chiefly based on the lectures given by A. Weil during 1954–1955 (together with the author's own contribution). Also Chow's work on the trace and image is treated in the last chapter.

Generally speaking, this book is very well written and would give investigators an excellent account of what has been done, without going through many papers. Also it is convenient that this book contains all results in Weil's book on Abelian varieties [*Variétés abéliennes et courbes algébriques*, Actualités Sci. Ind. no. 1064, Hermann, Paris, 1948; MR **10**, 621] (except possibly a construction of a group variety from a variety having a normal law of composition); some proofs are simplified and are made lucid. However, it is regrettable that some of the basic and useful theorems on Abelian varieties (such as duality, absence of torsion, Riemann-Roch theorem, theorem of Frobenius, etc.) had to be omitted (partly because these were not available at the time when the book was being prepared). The following list of chapter headings and comments will make the scope of this book clear.

In the following, we assume that all ambient varieties are non-singular in co-dimension 1. Chapter I contains preparatory remarks about group varieties, and some of them have no proofs (references are given). It might have been a good idea, in order to make this book self-contained, to include at least a construction of a group variety from a variety with a normal law of composition. Contents of Chapter II are: properties of rational mappings of varieties into Abelian varieties (which include the Poincaré complete reducibility theorem); construction of Jacobian varieties of curves; construction of Albanese varieties of given varieties. Chapter III starts with the definition of algebraic equivalence of cycles and gives a proof of Weil's theorem of the square: $X(a, b) - X(a, b') - X(a', b) + X(a', b') \sim 0$ on a product $U \times V \times W$. From this, it follows that if X is a divisor on $G \times W$, where G is a group variety, $X(a_1) - X(a_2) - X(a_3) + X(a_4) \sim 0$ if $a_1 a_3^{-1} = a_2 a_4^{-1}$, which is a fundamental theorem in the theory of Picard varieties as treated here. After this, the symbol φ_X is defined for a divisor X on a commutative group variety G, as a homomorphism $a \to \mathrm{Cl}(X_a - X)$ of G into the group of divisor classes Pic (G) of G with respect to linear equivalence. Then the theorem of the square shows that the kernel of φ_X is the algebraic subgroup of G. Chapter IV begins by proving an existence of a positive non-degenerate divisor X on an Abelian variety A^r (X is such that the kernel of φ_X is finite). From this, the Picard variety of A is constructed. This chapter contains a proof of the theorem that $\nu(\sum m_i \alpha_i)$ is homogeneous of degree $2r$ in the m_i with rational coefficients (in particular $\nu(n\delta) = n^{2r}$), together with related topics, which is simpler than the one given by Weil originally and is based on the author's own contribution. In Chapter V, first the transpose ${}^t\alpha$ of a homomorphism α of an Abelian variety A into another Abelian variety B is defined, then some related formulas are proved. Next, assuming $A = B$, an involution $\alpha \to$

$\varphi_X^{-1}\,{}^t\alpha\,\varphi_X=\alpha'$ is given and the Castelnuovo inequality $\mathrm{tr}(\alpha\alpha')>0$ (if $\alpha\neq 0$) is proved. From this, it is proved that if A is defined over a finite field k with q elements, absolute values of characteristic roots of the Frobenius endomorphism relative to k are all equal to $\sqrt{q}$. The chapter ends with a few remarks about positive endomorphisms. Chapter VI begins with the existence theorem of the Picard variety of a given variety. Then the theorem of divisorial correspondences is given. Using this and results of Chapter V, a proof of the Riemann hypothesis for curves over finite fields is given. Finally, the reciprocity theorem $f((g))=g((f))$ on curves is generalized to Abelian varieties. In Chapter VII, l-adic representations of homomorphisms are discussed, more neatly than in Weil's book. As a consequence, the structure of the module of homomorphisms is given, among other things. The chapter ends with a remark about a polarized Abelian variety. In Chapter VIII, Chow's theory of K/k-image and K/k-trace of an Abelian variety defined over K is given. It also contains results about exact sequences, which are sometimes useful. Finally, an Appendix is added to include some auxiliary results about correspondences used in this book. Readers will find an "Historical Note" at the end of each chapter, about works of algebraic geometers, mainly those which were done after Weil's *Foundations of algebraic geometry* [Amer. Math. Soc., New York, 1946; MR **9**, 303] had appeared. This might be helpful sometimes. Also some problems are mentioned. {Remarks: In the Note to Chapter VI, the theory of correspondences, as formulated here, is attributed to Severi, but at least Hurwitz's name should have been mentioned also, since the theory of correspondences itself is essentially due to him (expressed in terms of Abelian integrals). Also, elsewhere, a remark is made that the seesaw principle is implicit in Severi's work, but as far as the reviewer knows, it was rather explicit.}
T. Matsusaka (Evanston, Ill.)

Citations: MR 9, 303c = G02-2; MR 10, 621d = G10-1.
Referred to in G10-23, G25-18.

G10-10 **(21# 4960)**

Lang, Serge; and Tate, John. Principal homogeneous spaces over abelian varieties. Amer. J. Math. **80** (1958), 659–684.

Let K/k be a Galois extension with the Galois group $G(K/k)$ (possibly infinite), A be an algebraic group defined over k, $A(K)$ be the group of points of A which are rational over K. A cochain $a(\alpha_1, \cdots, \alpha_r)$ of $G(K/k)$ with values in $A(K)$ is of finite type if there is a finite subextension F such that it depends only on the effects of the automorphisms α_i on F. Denoting by $C(K/k, A)$ the complex formed by these finite cochains, let $H^r(K/k, A)$ be its cohomology groups (sets, if A is not commutative). First, most results in Galois cohomology theory are extended to this case (for more general functor $A(K)$). Then using Weil's result on the field of definition of an algebraic variety, it is shown that there is a canonical bijection of $H^1(K/k, A)$ to the set of classes of k-isomorphic principal homogeneous spaces for A which have rational points over K. This generalizes Chatelet's result.

Further study of $H^1(K/k, A)$ is made, assuming that A is an Abelian variety defined over k. First, assuming that k is a local field, $H^1(K/k, A)$ is studied in relation with the reduction mod p. Passing to m-global fields (number fields, function fields over algebraically closed ground fields, fields of finite type, etc.; a characterization of m-global fields is given) ($m\not\equiv 0 \bmod p$, p being the characteristic of k), and showing that $A(k)/mA(k)$ is finite, the finiteness of the m-primary part of $H^r(K/k, A)$ is proved when r is positive and K/k is finite. This is used to show that the group of elements of $H^1(K/k, A)$ which split at all primes has the property that its subgroup of elements of order m ($m\not\equiv 0 \bmod p$) is finite. Finally, a theorem is given which shows that when k is a global field $H^1(K/k, A)$ is a large group. *T. Matsusaka* (Evanston, Ill.)

Referred to in G05-70, G05-94, G05-119, G10-13, G10-20, G10-23, G10-31, G20-24.

G10-11 **(21# 4961)**

Šafarevič, I. R. The group of principal homogeneous algebraic manifolds. Dokl. Akad. Nauk SSSR **124** (1959), 42–43. (Russian)

The author puts together without proofs some theorems about the group $H(\alpha, k)$ of the principal homogeneous algebraic manifolds, connected with an abelian manifold α, introduced by A. Weil [Amer. J. Math. **77** (1955), 355–391, 493–512; MR **17**, 533]. *W. Burau* (Hamburg)

G10-12 **(22# 9492)**

Roquette, Peter. Some fundamental theorems on abelian function fields. Proc. Internat. Congress Math. 1958, pp. 322–329. Cambridge Univ. Press, New York, 1960.

Topics are picked up from the author's papers in Jber. Deutsch. Math. Verein. **60** (1957) Abt 1, 1–21 [MR **21** #3405], and J. Reine Angew. Math. **197** (1957), 49–67 [MR **19**, 981]. These topics are related with the celebrated finiteness theorem of Severi-Néron. *M. Nagata* (Kyoto)

Citations: MR 19, 981c = G10-5; MR 21# 3405 = G35-37.

G10-13 **(23# A110a; 23# a110b)**

Poitou, Georges

Remarques sur la division des fonctions abéliennes.
C. R. Acad. Sci. Paris **252** (1961), 648–650.

Poitou, Georges

À propos d'une conjecture de Cassels.
C. R. Acad. Sci. Paris **252** (1961), 968–970.

The author discusses the reviewer's work on rational points on curves of genus 1 [J. Reine Angew. Math. **202** (1959), 52–99; **203** (1960) 174–208; MR **22** #24] in the light of work on abelian varieties [Lang and Tate, Amer. J. Math. **80** (1958), 659–684; MR **21** #4960; Tate, Séminaire Bourbaki 1957/58, Exp. 156, Secrétariat mathématique, Paris, 1958; MR **21** #4162]. He indicates how some of the reviewer's results extend to abelian varieties.
J. W. S. Cassels (Cambridge, England)

Citations: MR 21# 4162 = G10-8; MR 21# 4960 = G10-10; MR 22# 24 = G05-59.

G10-14 **(24# A2581)**

Blanchard, André; Poitou, Georges

Sur les composantes primaires du groupe des espaces homogènes principaux localement triviaux relatifs à une même variété abélienne.
C. R. Acad. Sci. Paris **253** (1961), 2309–2310.

The authors sketch a proof of the existence of a skew-symmetric form on the Tate-Šafarevič group of an abelian variety defined over an algebraic number field (i.e., the group of classes of principal homogeneous spaces defined over the field which are everywhere locally trivial) whose kernel is precisely the infinitely divisible elements of the group. Unfortunately, the proof depends on the false result enunciated by Poitou in same C. R. **253** (1961), 1745–1746. A correction has since appeared [ibid. **254** (1962), 206]. Some of the ideas introduced may nevertheless be useful in the study of the Tate-Šafarevič group.
J. W. S. Cassels (Cambridge, England)

Referred to in G10-15.

G10-15 **(26# 3639)**

Poitou, Georges

Rectification de deux notes précédentes.

C. R. Acad. Sci. Paris **254** (1962), 206.

The proofs of the results announced in two previous notes [the author, same C. R. **253** (1961), 1745–1746; MR **25** #63; Blanchard and the author, ibid. **253** (1961), 2309–2310; MR **24** #A2581] are unfortunately invalid. The author states that, however, something can be saved.

J. W. S. Cassels (Cambridge, England)

Citations: MR 24# A2581 = G10-14; MR 25# 63 = R34-4.

G10-16 **(25# 2068)**

Tate, John

Principal homogeneous spaces for Abelian varieties.

J. Reine Angew. Math. **209** (1962), 98–99.

A laconic but useful review of the existing state of knowledge for different types of groundfield.

J. W. S. Cassels (Cambridge, England)

G10-17 **(25# 5066)**

Morikawa, Hisasi

Theta functions and abelian varieties over valuation fields of rank one. I.

Nagoya Math. J. **20** (1962), 1–27.

The classical theory of theta functions, which concerns the complex number field, is extended to the case of an arbitrary algebraically closed base field that is complete with respect to a given rank one valuation. In analogy with the classical theory, after a choice of basic matrices and an exponential change of variable, theta functions are defined as formal power series of certain types in variables $u_1, \cdots, u_r, u_1^{-1}, \cdots, u_r^{-1}$ with coefficients in the base field. A number of results are purely formal, for example, the computation of the dimension of the vector space of theta functions of a certain type, but most results depend on convergence, which in fact holds for all $u_1, \cdots, u_r$ in the base field and distinct from zero. Defining abelian functions as quotients of theta functions of the same type, all abelian functions with given periods are shown to form the function field of an abelian variety of dimension r defined over the base field. Furthermore, again classically, the theta functions can be used to get a specific projective embedding of the abelian variety, and the usual relations are shown between the endomorphism ring of the abelian variety and the matrices used at the beginning.

M. Rosenlicht (Paris)

Referred to in G10-18.

G10-18 **(26# 2443)**

Morikawa, Hisasi

On theta functions and abelian varieties over valuation fields of rank one. II. Theta functions and abelian functions of characteristic $p(>0)$.

Nagoya Math. J. **21** (1962), 231–250.

In the author's previous paper [same J. **20** (1962), 1–27; MR **25** #5066], analogously to the classical theory, theta functions were defined by explicit power series and abelian functions as quotients of certain theta functions, and the usual connections with abelian varieties were shown. Here explicit addition formulas are given for certain abelian functions for characteristic $p \geqq 3$, and explicit expressions are given for the invariant differentials and derivations on the related abelian varieties. Finally, certain "$\wp$-functions" are defined explicitly and a number of their properties given.

M. Rosenlicht (Paris)

Citations: MR 25# 5066 = G10-17.

G10-19 **(27# 5758)**

Ogg, A. P.

Cohomology of abelian varieties over function fields.

Ann. of Math. (2) **76** (1962), 185–212.

Es sei A eine d-dimensionale abelsche Mannigfaltigkeit, definiert über einem algebraischen Funktionenkörper k in einer Variablen mit algebraisch abgeschlossenem Konstantenkörper k_0. g sei das Geschlecht von k. Für jeden Primdivisor $\mathfrak{p}$ von k sei $k_\mathfrak{p}$ die zugehörige Komplettierung von k. Es wird die erste Kohomologiegruppe $H^1(k, A)$ und die kanonische Abbildung $H^1(k, A) \to \oplus \sum_\mathfrak{p} H^1(k_\mathfrak{p}, A)$ untersucht. Für eine von der Charakteristik von k verschiedene Primzahl q bedeute $H^1(k, A, q)$ den q-primären Bestandteil von $H^1(k, A)$. Es werde vorausgesetzt: (1) Die k/k_0-Spur von A im Sinne von Chow verschwindet, sodass nach dem Mordell-Weilschen Satze die Gruppe der rationalen Punkte von A über k endlich erzeugt ist; sei r ihr Rang. (2) Der Körper $k(A_q)$ der Koordinaten der q-Teilungspunkte von A ist über k regulär verzweigt. Unter diesen Voraussetzungen beweist der Verfasser den Satz: Die kanonische Abbildung $H^1(k, A, q) \to \oplus \sum_\mathfrak{p} H^1(k_\mathfrak{p}, A, q)$ ist surjektiv, und ihre Kern $X(q)$ besitzt eine Untergruppe von endlichem Index, die isomorph ist zu der direkten Summe von r_0 Exemplaren von Q_q/Z_q (die q-adischen rationalen Zahlen modulo den q-adischen ganzen Zahlen), wobei $r + r_0 = 4d(g-1) + \sum_\mathfrak{p} \varepsilon_\mathfrak{p}$, wobei $\varepsilon_\mathfrak{p}$ eine gewisse ganze Zahl zwischen 0 und $2d$ ist. Und zwar ist $\varepsilon_\mathfrak{p}$ dadurch definiert, dass $H^1(k_\mathfrak{p}, A, q)$ isomorph zur direkten Summe von $2d - \varepsilon_\mathfrak{p}$ Exemplaren von Q_q/Z_q ist. Es ist $\varepsilon_\mathfrak{p} = 0$, wenn $\mathfrak{p}$ regulär für A ist, d.h. wenn A eine nichtausgeartete Reduktion $\mathfrak{p}$ besitzt; insbesondere ergibt sich, dass $\varepsilon_\mathfrak{p} = 0$ für fast alle $\mathfrak{p}$. Bei dem Beweis des genannten Satzes (der noch in allgemeinerer Form formuliert wird), wird wesentlich Gebrauch gemacht von dem Grothendieckschen Resultat über die Galoissche Gruppe der maximalen Erweiterung T_S von k, die höchstens über einer vorgegebenen endlichen Menge S von Primdivisoren p verzweigt, dort aber regulär verzweigt ist: diese Gruppe kann durch Erzeugende und definierte Relationen genau wie im klassischen Falle beschrieben werden [Grothendieck, Séminaire Bourbaki, 1958/59, Exp. 182, Secrétariat mathématiques, Paris, 1959; MR **28** #1091]. Die Resultate des Verfassers wurden, teilweise in verschärfter Form, inzwischen auch von Šafarevič veröffentlicht [Trudy Mat. Inst. Steklov. **64** (1961), 316–346].

P. Roquette (Tübingen)

Citations: MR 28# 1091 = Z10-14.

Referred to in G05-94, G10-23, G20-20, G20-28.

G10-20 **(27# 5762)**

Honda, Taira

Isogenies, rational points and section points of group varieties.

Japan. J. Math. **30** (1960), 84–101.

Es seien G, H zusammenhängende algebraische Gruppen und $\lambda: G \to H$ eine separable Isogenie, definiert über einem Körper k. Zunächst gibt der Verfasser eine verallgemeinerte "Kummersche exakte Sequenz" an, die im Spezialfall kommutativer Gruppen in die von Lang-Tate angegebene Sequenz übergeht [Lang und Tate, Amer. J. Math. **80** (1958), 659–684; MR **21** #4960]. Dabei handelt es sich um eine Abschätzung für die Gruppe $H_k/\lambda(G_k)$, wobei G_k, H_k die Gruppen der in k rationalen Punkte von G bezw. H bedeuten. $\lambda(G_k)$ ist Normalteiler von H_k, und die Faktorgruppe $H_k/\lambda(G_k)$ ist abelsch von einem Exponenten, der Teiler des Grades $\nu(\lambda)$ ist. Ist k ein p-adischer Zahlkörper, so ergibt sich die Endlichkeit von $H_k/\lambda(G_k)$. Aber auch im Falle eines algebraischen Zahlkörpers ergibt sich eine gewisse Endlichkeitsaussage, welche als die Verallgemeinerung des sogenannten "schwachen

Mordell-Weilschen Endlichkeitssatzes" angesehen werden kann, und zwar folgendermassen: Ein Primdivisor $\mathfrak{p}$ heisst "regulär" (oder "ohne Defekt") für die Isogenie $\lambda: G \to H$, wenn G und H $\mathfrak{p}$-einfach im Sinne der Reduktionstheorie von Shimura [ibid. **77** (1955), 134–176; MR **16**, 616] sind, wenn ferner das Kompositionsgesetz für G und H sich auf die reduzierten Mannigfaltigkeiten $G\mathfrak{p}$, $H\mathfrak{p}$ derart überträgt, dass diese algebraische Gruppen werden, und wenn schliesslich sich auch die Isogenie λ zu einer separablen Isogenie $\lambda\mathfrak{p}: G\mathfrak{p} \to H\mathfrak{p}$ vom selben Grade wie λ überträgt. Fast alle $\mathfrak{p}$ sind regulär für λ. Ein Punkt aus G_k [bezw. H_k] wird $\mathfrak{p}$-endlich genannt, wenn seine Reduktion modulo $\mathfrak{p}$ ein Punkt aus $G\mathfrak{p}$ [$H\mathfrak{p}$] ist. Ein für λ regulärer Primdivisor $\mathfrak{p}$ ist unverzweigt in dem Koordinatenkörper $k(\lambda^{-1}(b))$ für jeden $\mathfrak{p}$-endlichen Punkt b von H; diese Tatsache ist eine Verallgemeinerung des Zerlegungsgesetzes von Primdivisoren in Einheitswurzelkörpern und in Kummerschen Erweiterungskörpern. Nun sei S eine endliche Menge von Primdivisoren von k, welche alle irregulären $\mathfrak{p}$ enthält. Die Gruppe derjenigen Punkte aus G_k, welche $\mathfrak{p}$-endliche sind für alle $\mathfrak{p} \notin S$, heisst die "S-Einheitengruppe" von G_k und wird mit $G_k(S)$ bezeichnet; entsprechend $H_k(S)$. Dann lässt sich die in Rede stehende Endlichkeitsaussage wie folgt formulieren: $G_k(S)$ besitzt endlichen Index in $H_k(S)$. Wenn G und H abelsche Mannigfaltigkeiten sind, so ist $G_k(S) = G_k$ und daher erhalten wir den schwachen Mordell-Weilschen Endlichkeitssatz. (Bemerkung: Der "starke" Mordell-Weilsche Endlichkeitssatz lässt sich nicht auf beliebige algebraische Gruppen übertragen.) Nun sei $G = A$ eine abelsche Mannigfaltigkeit und λ die Multiplikation von A mit einer Primzahl l; es werde vorausgesetzt, dass $A_1 \subset A_k$. Für den (nach Mordell-Weil endlichen) rationalen Rang $\rho_k(A)$ von A_k gibt der Verfasser die Abschätzung $\rho_k(A) \leqq 2r(s + eu + 2[k:Q] + h_k(l) - 1)$ wobei bedeutet: s die Anzahl derjenigen für A irregulären Primdivisoren von k, für welche $N(p) \equiv 1 \bmod l$; u die Anzahl der reellen unendlichen Primstellen von k; $h_k(l)$ der l-Rang der absoluten Divisorklassengruppe von k; $e = 0$ oder 1 je nachdem ob $l > 2$ oder $l = 2$. Der Verfasser behandelt noch die folgende Frage: Sei $K \supset k$ eine endliche Erweiterung; wie verhalten sich $\rho_K(A)$ und $\rho_k(A)$ zueinander? Der Verfasser zeigt für gewisse abelsche Mannigfaltigkeiten A, die in der Theorie der komplexen Multiplikation von Shimura und Taniyama [*Complex multiplication of abelian varieties and its applications to number theory*, Math. Soc. Japan, Tokyo, 1961; MR **23** #A2419] auftreten, dass $\rho_K(A) = [K:k]\rho_k(A)$. Die Arbeit enthält noch eine Kummersche Theorie der Teilungskörper von abelschen Mannigfaltigkeiten (im Zusammenhang mit dem sogenannten "Hasseschen Klassenkörperzerlegungsgesetz"), sowie eine Untersuchung spezieller Isogenien von gewissen elliptischen Kurven im Zusammenhang mit den Zerfällungskörpern kubischer Gleichungen. *P. Roquette* (Tübingen)

Citations: MR 21# 4960 = G10-10; MR 23# A2419 = G15-19.

G10-21 (28# 1200)

Manin, Ju. I.

Theory of commutative formal groups over fields of finite characteristic. (Russian)

Uspehi Mat. Nauk **18** (1963), *no.* 6 (114), 3–90.

About half of this long paper is a survey of the basic facts about commutative formal groups over a field k of characteristic $p > 0$. The other and more interesting half consists of detailed proofs of the author's announced results on (1) the "varieties of moduli" of certain classes of such formal groups and (2) the formal groups obtained by localizing algebraic groups.

Chapter I gives the basic properties of commutative formal groups, starting with a definition in abstract categories and leading to their classification by means of Dieudonné modules over a certain ring E_k. In Chapter II, they are classified to within isogeny over algebraically closed k. These results were originally due to Dieudonné [Amer. J. Math. **77** (1955), 429–452; MR **17**, 174; Math. Ann. **134** (1957), 114–133; MR **20** #4608], with improvements by Barsotti and Gabriel.

Chapter III contains the author's theorem on varieties of moduli of certain Dieudonné modules over algebraically closed k. The theorem applies to those modules whose classification under isogeny gives no unipotent components. In each such module M, he constructs a unique maximal special submodule M_0 such that M/M_0 has finite length (as an E_k-module). There are two finiteness theorems: (1) In each isogeny class there are only a finite number of non-isomorphic special modules; (2) Given a special module M_0, there is an upper bound on the possible length of M/M_0, where M runs over all supermodules for which M_0 is the maximal special submodule. Finally, he shows that the space of isomorphy classes of the supermodules M of M_0 considered in (2) has the natural structure of a reducible k-variety. Hence the space of isomorphy classes of Dieudonné modules lying in a fixed isogeny class has a natural k-variety structure. The author shows by examples that his finiteness theorems break down if unipotent components are allowed. The varieties of moduli obtained here are constructible. The construction is actually carried through in some special cases.

In Chapter IV the author considers formal groups obtained by localizing algebraic groups. The main results are: (1) The classification of the localizations of abelian varieties X over finite fields k (to within isogeny over the algebraic closure of k) depends only on the characteristic polynomial of the Frobenius endomorphism of X. (2) Every commutative formal group over an algebraically closed k is isogenous to a subgroup of the localization of some algebraic group. The latter result only requires the classification of the localizations of the Jacobians of the Davenport-Hasse curves using (1). A by-product of (1) is a certain symmetry property for the localizations of abelian varieties. The author conjectures that every commutative formal group satisfying this property is such a localization.

The author seems to have the mistaken impression that one of Dieudonné's rings, called E_F here, is an extension of another, called E. This makes some of his proofs false, but they can be fixed easily. *E. C. Dade* (Pasadena, Calif.)

Referred to in G10-32, G15-42.

G10-22 (28# 3994)

Serre, Jean-Pierre

Sur les groupes de congruence des variétés abéliennes. (Russian summary)

Izv. Akad. Nauk SSSR Ser. Mat. **28** (1964), 3–20.

From the author's Russian summary: "Let A be an abelian variety defined over a field k of finite degree over the rationals and let $A(k)$ be the group of points on A defined over k. A subgroup Γ of $A(k)$ is called a congruence subgroup if there exists a finite set I of valuations $\mathfrak{p}$ of k and open subgroups $U_\mathfrak{p}$ of $A(k_\mathfrak{p})$ for $\mathfrak{p} \in I$ such that $\Gamma = \bigcap_{\mathfrak{p} \in I} U_\mathfrak{p}$. (Open means here open in the $\mathfrak{p}$-adic topology.)

"In this paper the author investigates the nature of the closure $\widetilde{A(k)}$ of $A(k)$ in the injection $A(k) \to \prod_\mathfrak{p} A(k_\mathfrak{p})$ (cf. the addresses of the reviewer and Tate to the Stockholm Congress [Cassels, Proc. Internat. Congr. Mathematicians

(Stockholm, 1962), pp. 234–246, Inst. Mittag-Leffler, Djursholm, 1963; Tate, ibid., pp. 288–295]). In particular, is it true that $\widetilde{A(k)} = \text{proj lim}_n\, A(k)/nA(k)$ (with the limit topology)? This is equivalent to the statement that every subgroup of $A(k)$ of finite index contains a congruence subgroup. The author considers the following more general property C_S: For every finite subset S of prime divisors on k and for every subgroup Γ of finite index, Γ contains a congruence subgroup defined by a set I of divisors which is disjoint from S.

"The principal result of the paper (Theorems 4 and 5) is that C_S is true if A is either (a) of dimension 1 or (b) an abelian variety with a sufficient number of complex multiplications.

"The proof depends on some other results of independent interest. Clearly it is enough to prove C_S for subgroups of index p^n, where p is any prime: we call the corresponding assertion $C_S(p)$. By considering the exact cohomology sequence associated with multiplication by p^n on A the author shows that $C_S(p)$ is true if

$$(*)\qquad \text{proj lim}_n\, H_S{}^1(k, A_{p^n}) = 0,$$

where $H_S{}^1(k, A_{p^n})$ is the subgroup of elements of $H^1(G(\bar{k}/k), A_{p^n})$ which vanish when restricted to the splitting groups of the prime divisors outside S. Here $G(\bar{k}/k)$ is the Galois group of $\bar{k}/k$, where $\bar{k}$ is the algebraic closure of k and A_{p^n} is the group of points on A of order dividing p^n.

"Let G be a profinite group (projective limit of finite groups) and M any topological G-module. Following Tate, the author denotes by $H_*{}^1(G, M)$ the subgroup of $H^1(G, M)$ consisting of all the elements which vanish when restricted to any one-parameter subgroup of G (i.e., the closed subgroups with one topological generator). Let $T_p(A) = \text{proj lim}_n\, A_{p^n}$ be the Tate module of the abelian variety A and let $V_p(A)$ be the extension of this module to a module over the p-adic numbers. Then it is shown that (*) is true if

$$(**)\qquad H^1(G(\bar{k}/k), T_p(A)) = 0.$$

"It is well known that $T_p(A)$ is a free module over the ring $\mathbf{Z}_p$ of p-adic integers of dimension $2d$, where d is the dimension of A. Its group of automorphisms is just the linear group $GL(2d, \mathbf{Z}_p)$. Consequently, the action of $G(\bar{k}/k)$ on $T_p(A)$ gives a group homomorphism $\pi: G(\bar{k}/k) \to GL(2d, \mathbf{Z}_p)$. The group $GL(2d, \mathbf{Z}_p)$ is a p-adic Lie group in an appropriate sense and $\pi G(\bar{k}/k)$ is a closed subgroup. Hence it can be given the structure of a p-adic Lie group with a Lie algebra $\mathfrak{g}_p$. The representation π gives naturally a representation of $\mathfrak{g}_p$ in $V_p(A)$. The algebra $\mathfrak{g}_p$ and this representation are unchanged if k is replaced by any finite algebraic extension. The author shows that (**) is true if

$$(***)\qquad H_*{}^1(\mathfrak{g}_p, V_p(A)) = 0,$$

where $H_*{}^1$ is defined for Lie algebras as for groups. Finally he verifies that (***) is true in the two cases (a) and (b), and indeed shows that $H^1(\mathfrak{g}_p, V_p(A)) = 0$.

"Amongst others the author mentions the following unsolved problems: (1) Is there a relation between the $\mathfrak{g}_p$ for different p (e.g., do they have the same dimension)? (2) In the numerical examples of elliptic curves considered by the author $\mathfrak{g}_p$ is either abelian of dimension 2 (if A has complex multiplication) or the full matrix group (if not). Is this always true? (3) Is the main result of the paper true for all abelian varieties? (4) To what extent is the main result true for other algebraic groups? Examples are known of other groups for which it is true [Chevalley, J. Math. Soc. Japan **3** (1951), 36–44; MR **13**, 440], but Klein showed that it is false for the special linear group of dimension 2." *J. W. S. Cassels* (Cambridge, England)

Citations: MR 13, 440a = R38-4.
Referred to in G05-84, G10-49.

G10-23 (29# 110)

Šafarevič, I. R.

Principal homogeneous spaces defined over a function field. (Russian)

Trudy Mat. Inst. Steklov. **64** (1961), 316–346.

Es sei A eine über dem Körper k definierte abelsche Mannigfaltigkeit der Dimension d. Gegenstand der Untersuchung ist die erste Kohomologiegruppe $H^1(G, A_K)$, wobei K die maximale separabel-algebraische Erweiterung von k bezeichnet, A_K die Gruppe der in K rationalen Punkte von A, und G die Galois-Gruppe von K/k. Zur Abkürzung werde $H^1(G, A_K) = H^1(k, A)$ gesetzt. Die Elemente dieser Gruppe sind die prinzipalen homogenen Räume über A; sie entsprechen grob gesprochen denjenigen über k definierten Mannigfaltigkeiten, die über K zu A biregulär äquivalent werden. Jedes Element von $H^1(k, A)$ besitzt endliche Ordnung. Es wird vornehmlich der Fall untersucht, in dem k ein algebraischer Funktionenkörper in einer Variablen über einem algebraisch abgeschlossenen Konstantenkörper k_0 ist. Die angewendete Betrachtungsweise ist die in der Zahlentheorie übliche Methode des Übergangs vom Lokalen zum Globalen. Zuerst wird die lokale Seite des Problems untersucht, d.h. als Grundkörper wird die komplette Hülle $k_{\mathfrak{p}}$ des Körpers k nach einem seiner Primdivisoren $\mathfrak{p}$ genommen. Es bedeute $\hat{A}$ die zu A duale Mannigfaltigkeit (Picardsche Mannigfaltigkeit), und $\hat{A}_{k_{\mathfrak{p}}}{}^0$ die Gruppe derjenigen in $k_{\mathfrak{p}}$ rationalen Punkte von $\hat{A}$, die durch sämtliche zur Charakteristik p von k_0 primen Zahlen teilbar sind. Ferner bedeute B_n die Gruppe der Elemente der Periode n der abelschen Gruppe B. Das Hauptresultat im lokalen Falle ist der Dualitätssatz: Ist n prim zu p, so sind die Gruppen $H^1(k_{\mathfrak{p}}, A)_n$ und $(\hat{A}_{k_{\mathfrak{p}}}{}^0)_n$ dual zueinander, d.h. jede ist isomorph zur Charaktergruppe der anderen. Diese Dualität wird vermittelt durch die von A. Weil für abelsche Mannigfaltigkeiten über beliebigen Körpern angegebene Paarung $e_n(x, \xi)$, $x \in A_n$, $\xi \in \hat{A}_n$ [vgl. S. Lang, *Abelian varieties*, insbesondere S.189, Interscience, New York, 1959; MR **21** #4959]. Wenn A eine reguläre Reduktion modulo $\mathfrak{p}$ besitzt, so ergibt sich aus allgemeinen Sätzen über abelsche Mannigfaltigkeiten, dass $(\hat{A}_{k_{\mathfrak{p}}}{}^0)_n$ direktes Produkt von $2d$ zyklischen Gruppen der Ordnung n ist; dasselbe gilt daher nach dem Dualitätssatz auch für $H^1(k_{\mathfrak{p}}, A)_n$. Im allgemeinen Falle ist $H^1(k_{\mathfrak{p}}, A)_n$ direktes Produkt von $d' + 2d''$ zyklischen Gruppen der Ordnung n, wobei sich die Invarianten d' und d'' aus dem Verhalten von A bei Reduktion modulo $\mathfrak{p}$ bestimmen; es ist $d' + d'' \leqq d$.

Bei der Behandlung des globalen Problems wird die folgende Zusatzvoraussetzung gemacht: Alle Punkte von zu p primer Ordnung von A sind rational über der maximalen Erweiterung K' von k, die keine höhere Verzweigung über k besitzt. (Für $p = 0$ bedeutet dies keine Einschränkung.) Diese Zusatzvoraussetzung ist anscheinend oft erfüllt. Sie ist notwendig, weil die Galois-Gruppe G' von K'/k nach Grothendieck [Séminaire Bourbaki, 1958/59, Exp. 182, Secrétariat mathématique, Paris, 1959; MR **28** #1091] wohl bekannt ist: sie besitzt nämlich dieselbe Struktur wie im klassischen Falle, wo k_0 der Körper der komplexen Zahlen ist. Es sei $\varphi_{\mathfrak{p}}$ der durch die Einbettung $k \subset k_{\mathfrak{p}}$ definierte Homomorphismus $\varphi_{\mathfrak{p}}: H^1(k, A) \to H^1(k_{\mathfrak{p}}, A)$. Bei gegebenem $a \in H^1(k, A)$ ist $\varphi_{\mathfrak{p}}(a) = 0$ für alle Primdivisoren $\mathfrak{p}$ von k bis auf endlich viele. Also definieren die $\varphi_{\mathfrak{p}}$ durch Zusammensetzung einen verschwinden? Zu (1): Es sei n prim zur Charakteristik p. Nach Satz 1 haben wir einen Homomorphismus

$$\varphi_n: H^1(k, A)_n \to \sum_{\mathfrak{p}} H^1(k_{\mathfrak{p}}, A)_n = \sum_{\mathfrak{p}} \operatorname{Char}(\hat{A}_{k_{\mathfrak{p}}}{}^0)_n = \operatorname{Char} \prod_{\mathfrak{p}} (\hat{A}_{k_{\mathfrak{p}}}{}^0)_n,$$

wobei die Charaktergruppe und das Produkt $\prod$ im topologischen Sinne zu verstehen sind. Es sei $\mathfrak{t}$ die Gruppe derjenigen Elemente aus $\hat{A}_k$, die endliche, zu p prime Ordnung besitzen und die für jedes $\mathfrak{p}$ vermöge $\varphi_{\mathfrak{p}}$ in $\hat{A}_{k_{\mathfrak{p}}}{}^0$ abgebildet werden. Durch die Einbettungen $k \subset k_{\mathfrak{p}}$ wird ein Homomorphismus $\psi_n: \mathfrak{t}_n \to \prod_{\mathfrak{p}} (\hat{A}_{k_{\mathfrak{p}}}{}^0)_n$ definiert, aus dem durch Dualisierung ein Homomorphismus $\psi_n{}^*$ der entsprechenden Charaktergruppen in umgekehrter Richtung entsteht. Satz 2: Die Sequenz

$$H^1(k, A)_n \xrightarrow[\varphi_n]{} \sum_{\mathfrak{p}} H^1(k_{\mathfrak{p}}, A)_n \xrightarrow[\psi_n^*]{} \operatorname{Char}(\mathfrak{t}) \to 0$$

ist exakt.

Zu (2): Es sei $\mathfrak{h}$ der Kern von φ. Satz 3: Wenn $\mathfrak{t}=0$, so ist $\mathfrak{h}$ unbeschränkt teilbar; und zwar ist $\mathfrak{h}$ dann isomorph zum e-fachen Produkt der Gruppe der Einheitswurzeln von zu p primer Ordnung mit sich selbst, wobei $e = 2d(m+2g-2) - \sum_{\mathfrak{p}} e_{\mathfrak{p}} - r$. Hierbei bedeuten: g das Geschlecht von k; r den Rang von A über k, wobei $(A_k : nA_k) = n^r \cdot ((A_k)_n : 1)$ [Lang und Néron, Amer. J. Math. **81** (1959), 95–118; MR **21** #1311]; m die Anzahl derjenigen $\mathfrak{p}$, für die A keine reguläre Reduktion modulo $\mathfrak{p}$ besitzt; für ein solches $\mathfrak{p}$ bedeutet $e_{\mathfrak{p}}$ eine gewisse Invariante, die von dem Verhalten von A bei Reduktion modulo $\mathfrak{p}$ abhängt, und zwar ist $e_{\mathfrak{p}}$ der Rang der ersten Homotopiegruppe $\pi_1(A_{k_{\mathfrak{p}}})$ im Sinne von Serre [Inst. Hautes Études Sci. Publ. Math. No. 7 (1960); MR **22** #9493], wobei $A_{k_{\mathfrak{p}}}$ als proalgebraische Gruppe über k_0 aufzufassen ist ($e_{\mathfrak{p}}=0$, wenn A eine reguläre Reduktion modulo $\mathfrak{p}$ besitzt).

Es wird noch die Gruppe $\mathfrak{t}$ eingehender untersucht und insbesondere ein Kriterium dafür angegeben, dass $\mathfrak{t}=0$. Eine abelsche Mannigfaltigkeit A/k heisst unverzweigt, wenn sie eine reguläre Reduktion nach jedem Primdivisor $\mathfrak{p}$ von k besitzt. Die maximale unverzweigte Teilmannigfaltigkeit A_0 von A heisst die unverzweigte Spur von A. Die Existenz der unverzweigten Spur wird durch die gleichen Überlegungen bewiesen, mit denen die Existenz der Chowschen k/k_0-Spur A^* von A bewiesen wird [vgl. Lang, loc. cit.]; es gilt $A^* \subset A_0$. Satz 4: $\mathfrak{t}$ ist isomorph zur Gruppe der Punkte mit endlicher, nicht durch p teilbarer Ordnung von $(A_0)_k$. Satz 5: Wenn $k = k_0(t)$ der rationale Funktionenkörper ist, so ist $A_0 = A^*$, d.h. A_0 ist schon über k definiert. Insbesondere ist dann $\mathfrak{t}$ und also auch $\mathfrak{h}$ unbeschränkt teilbar. Wenn k/k_0 nicht rational ist, so ist die Situation verwickelter; Verfasser zeigt, dass A_0 im Falle der Dimension 1 in gewissem Sinne den Typus eines Faserraumes besitzt, während das im höherdimensionalen Falle nicht notwendig richtig ist.
Homomorphismus φ: $H^1(k, A) \to \sum_{\mathfrak{p}} H^1(k_{\mathfrak{p}}, A)$, wobei $\sum$ die Bildung der direkten Summe andeutet. Gegenstand der Untersuchung ist Bild und Kern dieses Homomorphismus, d.h. die Beantwortung der folgenden Fragen: (1) Welche Systeme lokaler Invarianten können über k realisiert werden? (2) Wie sind diejenigen Elemente aus $H^1(k, A)$ beschaffen, für welche alle lokalen Invarianten

Der Verfasser betrachtet noch genauer den Fall, in dem $A = A^*$ über k_0 definiert ist; in diesem Falle vereinfachen sich die obigen Ergebnisse sehr. Auch kann dann die Theorie unter der allgemeineren Annahme entwickelt werden, dass k der Funktionenkörper einer singularitätenfreien Mannigfaltigkeit X beliebiger Dimension über k_0 ist. In dem ersten, der lokalen Theorie gewidmeten Teil der Arbeit findet sich ein Beispiel dafür, dass Index und Exponent eines Elements $a \in H^1(k_{\mathfrak{p}}, A)$ nicht notwendig zusammenfallen, wenn $d > 1$, und zwar kann der Exponent $n \not\equiv 0 \bmod p$ beliebig vorgegeben werden. Dagegen ist für $d=1$ und $k_{\mathfrak{p}}$ als Grundkörper stets Index = Exponent. (Vgl. hierzu auch: Lang und Tate [Amer. J. Math. **80** (1958), 659–684; MR **21** #4960].) Die Hauptresultate dieser Arbeit wurden unabhängig davon auch von Ogg veröffentlicht [Ann. of Math. (2) **76** (1962), 185–212; MR **27** #5758].

P. Roquette (Tübingen)

Citations: MR 21# 1311 = G10-6; MR 21# 4959 = G10-9; MR 21# 4960 = G10-10; MR 27# 5758 = G10-19; MR 28# 1091 = Z10-14.

Referred to in G05-94, G20-20, G20-51.

G10-24 (30# 3886)

Manin, Ju. I.

The Tate height of points on an Abelian variety, its variants and applications. (Russian)

Izv. Akad. Nauk SSSR Ser. Mat. **28** (1964), 1363–1390.

The author, in the first section of this paper, reproduces an unpublished proof by Tate of the conjecture of Néron that the (logarithmic) height $h(P)$ of points P on an abelian variety is approximately given by a quadratic form; more precisely, there is a quadratic form $\hat{h}(P)$ such that $h(P) = \hat{h}(P) + O(1)$ for all points P. In the second section, the author shows that the construction also gives a pairing between the points, A_k, of the abelian variety A and those of its Picard variety $P(A)$, the kernel on A consisting of the subgroup $A_k{}^0$ generated by the points of finite order (together with the points of the k/k_0-trace in the function-field case, where k_0 is the constant field), the kernel on $P(A)$ being similar.

In the third section, the author considers the case in which the ground-field K is the function-field of an algebraic curve defined over an algebraically closed field k. Subject to certain conditions about the existence of a suitable minimal model (which he says have been shown by Šafarevič to be satisfied for abelian varieties of dimension 1), he shows that there is a subgroup of finite index of the group A_k of points on an abelian variety A defined over K, on which the Tate height (i.e., the height whose existence is proved in the first section) is the sum of local components, one for each place of K. The local components are just combinations of certain intersection-multiplicities.

In the fourth section, the author considers a pencil of cubics through nine base-points, defined over k as a single abelian variety over the function-field K, given by the parameter, and determines the group of rational points over K. If one of the nine base-points is taken as zero, it turns out that the group of points generated by the other eight fixed points (which, of course, give points defined over K) is of index 3 in the full group. This problem is shown to be the same as that of determining all the exceptional curves of the first kind on the cubic surface obtained by taking k as the base-field; and so this result answers questions of Coble [Bull. Amer. Math. Soc. **28** (1922), 329–364] and M. Nagata [Mem. College Sci. Univ. Kyoto Ser. A Math. **33** (1960/61), 271–293; MR **23** #A3740].

In the fifth section, the author shows that also when the ground-field is the field of rationals and the abelian variety is a curve $y^2 = x^3 - ax$ (a rational), the Tate height is a sum of local components. Finally, in the sixth section, the author shows that there are only finitely many rational points on certain curves of higher genus, related to curves of genus 1 on which the group of rational points has rank 1.

In a footnote added in proof, the author notes that more general results about the expression of the Tate height as a sum of local components have been obtained by Néron and announced by Lang [S. Lang, Séminaire Bourbaki, 16ième année, 1963/64, Fasc. 3, Exposé 274, Secrétariat mathématique, Paris, 1964].

J. W. S. Cassels (Cambridge, England)

Referred to in D02-23, G05-86, G35-42.

G10-25 (31# 3423)

Néron, André

Modèles minimaux des variétés abéliennes sur les corps locaux et globaux.

Inst. Hautes Études Sci. Publ. Math. No. 21 (1964), 128 *pp.*

This paper contains two theorems of fundamental importance for the theory of abelian varieties over local or global fields, as well as a large number of interesting facts of a general nature concerning reductions of varieties "mod p". The terminology used follows closely that of Weil [*Foundations of algebraic geometry*, Amer. Math. Soc., New York, 1946; MR **9**, 303] and Shimura [Amer. J. Math. **77** (1955), 134–176; MR **16**, 616], and the author has given resumés of some of his results in that language [Séminaire Bourbaki, 1961/62, Fasc. 1, Exposé 227, deuxième édition, corrigée, Secrétariat mathématique, Paris, 1962; MR **26** #3561]. It would be very useful to have a clear exposition of his theory in the language of schemes.

Chapter I serves as an introduction to the study of varieties over local fields and is full of new results, of which only a few can be mentioned here: Let R be a complete discrete valuation ring with field of fractions k and perfect residue field k_0. Let t be a generator of the maximal ideal p of R and let f be a rational function on affine n-space Spec $R[x_1, \cdots, x_n]$ over Spec R, which is regular at a rational point $(x^0) \in$ Spec $k_0[x_1, \cdots, x_n]$. The author introduces formally the "value of the derivative" $(\partial f/\partial t)^0(x^0)$ of f at (x^0), also in the unequal characteristic case. This allows him to derive a number of results analogous to classical ones, such as a Jacobian criterion for regularity of a closed subscheme of Spec $R[x]$ at (x^0).

Suppose now that V is a projective variety over Spec k, and consider projective schemes $\bar{V}$ over Spec R, reduced and irreducible, whose general fibre is V. The closed fibre V_0 of $\bar{V}$ is a reduction of V modulo p. Let $V_n=$ Spec$(O_{\bar{V}} \otimes_R R/p^{n+1})$, and let F_n be the Greenberg functor [Ann. of Math. (2) **73** (1961), 624–648; MR **23** #A3745] for the ring R/p^{n+1}, so that $F_n(V_n)$ is the scheme over Spec k_0 whose points parametrize sections of V_n over Spec R/p^{n+1}. Proposition 21 asserts if V is a smooth variety over Spec k, then $F_{n+1}(V_{n+1})$ is a vector bundle over $F_n(V_n)$ for sufficiently large n.

Put $F(\bar{V})=\varprojlim F_n(V_n)$ (this projective limit is actually representable as a scheme). In Section 24 the structure of $F(\bar{V})$ is studied. The main result (Theorem 2 and Corollary) is the interesting fact that the set of constructible sets of $F(\bar{V})$ depends only on the variety V over Spec k, and not on the choice of the reduction (V is assumed smooth). Section 27 contains a local uniformization theorem for certain valuations of $\bar{V}$ lying over R.

In Chapter II the following fundamental theorem is proved. Suppose R is a discrete valuation ring (not necessarily complete) and let A be an abelian variety defined over k. There exists a group scheme $\bar{A}$ smooth over Spec R (the "Néron model") having the following universal property: Every rational map $X \to \bar{A}$ over Spec R, with X/Spec R smooth, is induced by a morphism $X \to \bar{A}$. In particular, every rational point of A over Spec k extends to a section of $\bar{A}$ over Spec R.

The result extends immediately to give a "global model" if k is a global field, and the theorem is stated also for abelian homogeneous spaces, which are defined independently of an a priori structure group. The elegant proof gives an "explicit" projective embedding using the theorem of the square. A key step is the following assertion (Chapter I, Section 29 and Chapter II, Sections 3,4): There exists a finite set of "provarieties" which is invariant under rational translation. These provarieties correspond to simple components of a suitable reduction of A (mod p), and it follows easily that the group law in A induces a birational law of composition on this set of components.

Chapter III contains a detailed study of elliptic curves V/k and their reductions. The main theorem is that there exists a regular model $\bar{V}$ proper over Spec R which is minimal among regular models. The possible configurations of curves making up the reductions are listed explicitly, together with an analysis of the group structure on the closed fibre of the Néron model in each case. The results are similar to ones obtained previously and independently by Kodaira [*Analytic functions*, pp. 121–135, Princeton Univ. Press, Princeton, N.J., 1960; MR **25** #3939] in the complex-analytic case.

M. Artin (Bures-sur-Yvette)

Citations: MR 9, 303c = G02-2.

Referred to in G05-80, G10-36, G20-28, G35-54, Z10-36.

G10-26 (31# 3424)

Néron, A.

Quasi-fonctions et hauteurs sur les variétés abéliennes.

Ann. of Math. (2) **82** (1965), 249–331.

Let K be a field. When V is an algebraic variety defined over K, V_K denotes the set of K-rational points of V; $K(V)$ and $K(V)^*$ denote the function field of V over K and its multiplicative group. Start with a set M of valuations of K such that two different members of M are not equivalent to each other; here a valuation is understood to be either an archimedian or non-archimedian valuation, additively expressed (using $-\log$). When L is an algebraic extension field of K, M_L denotes the set of prolongations of members of M to L. $\bar{K}$ denotes the algebraic closure of K. Let $\Lambda(V)$ be the set of mappings $V_{\bar{K}} \times M_{\bar{K}} \to \mathbf{R}$ (=real number field); multiplication in $\Lambda(V)$ is defined by the sum of images. Let $H(V)$ be the subgroup of $\bar{K}(V)^* \times \Lambda(V)$ consisting of all (f, λ) such that $v(f(x))=\lambda(x, v)$ for any $x \in V_{\bar{K}}$ and $v \in M_{\bar{K}}$. Then elements of $(K(V)^* \times \Lambda(V))/H(V)$ are defined to be elementary quasi-functions on V. A quasi-function on V is defined by certain patching of elementary quasi-functions on open subsets of V. This theory of quasi-functions (Chapter I) is said by the author to be an adaption of the theory of distributions of A. Weil. In Chapter II, for each pair $(X, \mathfrak{a})$ of a divisor X and a cycle $\mathfrak{a}$ of degree zero and of dimension zero, a real-valued function $(X, \mathfrak{a})$ on M_K is defined, and the value $(X, \mathfrak{a})_v$ at v is called the v-degree of intersection of X and $\mathfrak{a}$. Many of the properties of this function are proved in Chapter III. This function depends bilinearly on X and $\mathfrak{a}$ and has the property that if $X \sim 0$, then for a rational function f such that $X=(f)$, $(X, \mathfrak{a})_v=v(f(\mathfrak{a}))$. In order to define this function, the author makes use of quasi-functions and also defines a canonical quasi-function on an abelian variety. These and some other notions and results are applied in proving a conjecture made by the author at the Edinburgh Congress, 1958, which asserts that there is a unique quadratic map $q: A_K \to \mathbf{R}$ (A being an abelian variety over K and M being assumed to satisfy the product formula) such that $q(\mathfrak{a})-h(\mathfrak{a})$ is bounded; here h stands for height. The conjecture was solved by Tate and the proof was published by S. Lang [Séminaire Bourbaki, 1963/64, Fasc. 3, Exposé 274, Secrétariat mathématique, Paris, 1964; MR **31** #1252]. The author says that the approach of Tate is used here, but in the attempt to see more, the method of this paper becomes more complicated than that of Tate.

M. Nagata (Cambridge, Mass.)

Citations: MR 31# 1252 = G35-42.

Referred to in G10-27, G10-28, G30-54, G35-54.

G10-27 **(35# 2901)**

Néron, A.

Hauteurs des points rationnels d'une variété abélienne définie sur un corps global.

Proc. Internat. Colloq. Algebraic Geometry (Madrid, 1965) (Spanish), pp. 49–56. *Inst. Jorge Juan del C.S.I.C.-Internat. Math. Union, Madrid,* 1966.

This note sketches a proof of the quadratic nature of the height function on an abelian variety over a number field K. It differs from the proof of Tate [see S. Lang, Amer. J. Math. **86** (1964), 521–533; MR **29** #2220] in that it is primarily local, and realizes the quadratic function as an infinite sum, indexed by the primes of K. A detailed exposition has appeared [the author, Ann. of Math. (2) **82** (1965), 249–331; MR **31** #3424].

N. Greenleaf (Rochester, N.Y.)

Citations: MR 29# 2220 = G05-71; MR 31# 3424 = G10-26.

G10-28 **(39# 1451)**

Néron, A.

Degré d'intersection en géométrie diophantienne.

Proc. Internat. Congr. Math. (Moscow, 1966), pp. 485–495. *Izdat. "Mir", Moscow,* 1968.

This is a brief and readable account of the author's theory of the normalized height function, interpreted as an intersection number (in the generalized sense of Diophantine geometry). The full account is given in Ann. of Math. (2) **82** (1965), 249–331 [MR **31** #3424].

A. Mattuck (Cambridge, Mass.)

Citations: MR 31# 3424 = G10-26.

G10-29 **(32# 7560)**

Lang, Serge

Division points on curves.

Ann. Mat. Pura Appl. (4) **70** (1965), 229–234.

The author formulates the following conjecture. Let A be either an abelian variety or a product of multiplicative groups defined over the complex field. Let V be an absolutely irreducible curve in A passing through the neutral point of A; moreover, denote by Γ_0 a finitely generated subgroup of A and by Γ the division group of Γ_0, i.e., the group of points P on A such that, for some $n \geqq 1$ (depending on P), nP lies in Γ_0. Then, whenever $V \cap \Gamma$ is an infinite set, V is a group subvariety of A.

When A is an abelian variety, on substituting the hypothesis on $V \cap \Gamma$ with the stronger assumption that $V \cap \Gamma_0$ is infinite, the above conjecture is equivalent with the Mordell conjecture [the author, *Diophantine geometry*, Interscience, New York, 1962; MR **26** #119; Inst. Hautes Études Sci. Publ. Math. No. 6 (1960), 27–43; MR **24** #A86].

A special case in which the conjecture can be proved occurs when A is a product of multiplicative groups and Γ_0 coincides with the neutral point of A, so that Γ consists of roots of unity. The proof is given here on taking A as the multiplicative plane of two variables x, y, and assuming the curve V in the form $y = g(x)$ or, more generally, $f(x, y) = 0$, where g, f denote a rational function and a polynomial, respectively (in the two cases, respectively, Ihara and Tate have indicated the procedure to the author and a similar proof was shown to him by Serre).

A geometric interpretation for the proof is then given and a connection with recent work by Serre on Galois groups of division points of elliptic curves is established by showing that, when A is an abelian variety and Γ_0 is its neutral point (so that Γ is the group of torsion points of A), the previous conjecture can be reduced to establishing the following criterion. Let k be a field of definition for A finitely generated over the rationals. There exists then an integer $c \geqq 1$ such that, for any point x of period n on A, the inequality $(G_n : G) \leqq c$ holds, where G_n denotes the multiplicative group of integers (mod n) prime to n and G is the subgroup of G_n consisting of the integers d for which dx is conjugate to x over k.

B. Segre (Rome)

Citations: MR 24# A86 = G30-26; MR 26# 119 = G02-9.

G10-30 **(33# 2632)**

Vvedenskiĭ, O. N.

Duality in abelian manifolds over a local field. **(Russian)**

First Republ. Math. Conf. of Young Researchers, Part II (Russian), pp. 112–117. *Akad. Nauk Ukrain. SSR Inst. Mat., Kiev,* 1965.

Let k be the residue field of a local field K, G the Galois group of a finite normal extension L of K, and F the Galois group of the separable closure of K. If the reduction A' of A is not degenerated and contains p^r points of order p ($p = \text{char } k$, $r = \dim A$), then $H^1(F, A)$ is dual to $\pi_1(A_K)$, $\hat{H}^n(G, A_L)$ is dual to $\hat{H}^{-n}(G, A_L)$, and this last is naturally isomorphic to $\hat{H}^{1-n}(G, \pi(A_L))$ (A_K = group of rational points of A over K).

E. Lluis (Mexico City)

G10-31 **(34# 2574)**

Bašmakov, M. I.

On the divisibility of principal homogeneous spaces over Abelian varieties. **(Russian)**

Izv. Akad. Nauk SSSR Ser. Mat. **28** (1964), 661–664.

Let l be a prime number and k a finite algebraic number field satisfying the following conditions: (i) l is a power of a prime divisor in k; (ii) k contains the primitive lth roots of unity; (iii) the class number of k is prime to l. The author considers abelian varieties, defined over k, which admit a regular reduction modulo every prime divisor in k not dividing l. Let A be such an abelian variety and ν an isogeny of A onto itself, defined over k, whose norm is a power of l. Let $\bar{A}$ denote the group of points of A which are rational over the algebraic closure $\bar{k}$ of k, and let $\bar{A}_\nu$ denote the kernel of ν; this is a finite group of l-power order in $\bar{A}$. The author considers the map $i: H^1(G, \bar{A}_\nu) \to H^1(G, \bar{A})$ defined by the inclusion $\bar{A}_\nu \subset \bar{A}$; here G denotes the Galois group of $\bar{k}$ over k, and $H^1(G, \bar{A})$ can be interpreted as the group of principal homogeneous spaces of A over k. Theorem: Let $f \in H^1(G, \bar{A}_\nu)$. A necessary and sufficient condition for the principal homogeneous space $i(f)$ to have a rational point in every completion $k_\mathfrak{p}$ with $\mathfrak{p} \nmid l$ is that $i(f)$ have a rational point in some finite extension K of k in which all prime divisors $\mathfrak{p} \nmid l$ of k are unramified. (Only the necessity is proved; the author states that the sufficiency follows from the work of M. J. Greenberg ["Pro-algebraic structure on the rational subgroup of a p-adic abelian variety", Ph.D. thesis, Princeton Univ., Princeton, N.J., 1959].) Now let k_l denote the maximal l-extension of k in which all $\mathfrak{p} \nmid l$ are unramified. From the above theorem it follows that k_l is a splitting field for every $i(f)$ which is locally trivial everywhere. On the other hand, the Galois group of k_l over k is a free pro-l-group [I. R. Šafarevič, Inst. Hautes Études Sci. Publ. Math. No. 18 (1963), 71–95; MR **31** #1247]. From this the author deduces the fact that every such $i(f)$ is divisible by an arbitrary power of ν, in the group of all principal homogeneous spaces. This answers a question raised by J. W. S. Cassels [J. Reine Angew. Math. **211** (1962), 95–112; MR **29** #1214], for the special cases considered in this paper. The author mentions the following examples: (1) $k=Q(\varepsilon)$, the field of lth roots of unity over the rational numbers Q, where l is a regular prime number, and A the Jacobian variety of the curve $x^l+y^l=1$, and $\nu=\sigma-\sigma^{-1}$, where σ is the automorphism of A defined by the automorphism $y\to y\varepsilon$ of the function field of the curve; (2) $k=Q(\varepsilon)$ as in (1), and A the Jacobian variety of the curve $y^l=x^r(1-x)$, with $1\leqq r\leqq l-2$, and $\nu=\sigma-\sigma^{-1}$, where again σ is defined by $y\to y\varepsilon$. The Jacobian variety of the Fermat curve in example (1) is isogeneous to the direct product of the varieties in example (2).

Further references: S. Lang and J. Tate [Amer. J. Math. **80** (1958), 659–684; MR **21** #4960], I. R. Šafarevič [Dokl. Akad. Nauk SSSR **114** (1957), 267–270; MR **20** #867].

P. Roquette (Tübingen)

Citations: MR 20# 867 = G05-56; MR 21# 4960 = G10-10; MR 29# 1214 = G05-70; MR 31# 1247 = R38-34.

Referred to in G10-35.

G10-32 (34# 5829)

Tate, John

Endomorphisms of abelian varieties over finite fields.
Invent. Math. **2** (1966), 134–144.

Suppose that A/k is an abelian variety of dimension g which is defined over the field k with algebraic closure $\bar{k}$. Let $A(\bar{k})$ be the abelian variety obtained from A by extending k to $\bar{k}$. Furthermore, let l be a prime distinct from the characteristic of k. Then the groups A_{l^n} of points $a_n\in A_{l^n}$ satisfying $l^na_n=0$ determine, by the homomorphisms $a_{n+1}\to la_{n+1}\in A_{l^n}$, a projective limit which is a free **Z**-module of rank $2g$, $T_l(A)$, on which the Galois group G of $\bar{k}|k$ operates in the obvious manner. The author proves, as a first most noteworthy result, that the canonical (injective) map (*) $\mathbf{Z}_l\otimes H_k(A',A'')\to\mathrm{Hom}_G(T_l(A'),T_l(A''))$ is bijective for abelian varieties A'/k and A''/k if k is a finite field. He first reduces this statement (no restriction on k being needed) to the equivalent proposition that the map (**) $\mathbf{Q}_l\otimes\mathrm{End}_k(A)\to\mathrm{End}_G(\mathbf{Q}_l\otimes_{\mathbf{Z}_l}T_l(A))$ be bijective for every abelian variety A/k (Lemma 3). Next, implications of a hypothesis $\mathrm{Hyp}(k,A,d,l)$ which was suggested by Lichtenbaum are discussed. This hypothesis is as follows: there exist (up to k-isomorphism) only a finite number of abelian varieties B defined over k such that (a) there is a polarization ψ of B of degree d^2 defined over k, (b) there is a k-isogeny $B\to A$ of l-power degree. Using a polarization of A to its dual (see, in this connection, D. Mumford [*Geometric invariant theory*, Ergeb. Math. Grenzgeb. (N.F.), Band 34, Academic Press, New York, 1965]) and the associated bilinear form on $\mathbf{Q}_l\otimes_{\mathbf{Z}_l}T_l(A)$ (special care must be taken so that the various polarizations match, pp. 136–137, proof of Proposition 1), it is shown that $\mathrm{Hyp}(k,A,d,l)$, together with the assumption that the algebra which is generated in $\mathrm{End}(\mathbf{Q}_l\otimes_{\mathbf{Z}_l}T_l(A))$ by the elements of G is isomorphic to a product of copies of $\mathbf{Q}_l$, implies that the map (**) is bijective (this subalgebra then turns out to be the commutator algebra of the image of $\mathbf{Q}_l\otimes\mathrm{End}_k(A)$ by (**); see Lemma 4 and Proposition 2, its semi-simplicity being equivalent to the bijectivity of (**)). Hence the map (*) is also bijective. Finally, results of Mumford [Invent. Math. **1** (1966), 287–354; MR **34** #4269] imply that $\mathrm{Hyp}(k,A,d,l)$ holds for finite fields. To this end, the author shows that the dimension of $\mathrm{End}_G(\mathbf{Q}_l\otimes_{\mathbf{Z}_l}T_l(A))$ does not depend on l. For the proof, an integer $r(f_A,f_B)$ is associated with a pair of abelian varieties A, B whose Frobenius automorphisms have the characteristic polynomials f_A,f_B; if $f_A=\prod P^{a(P)}$, $f_B=\prod P^{b(P)}$ with irreducible factors in a field $K/\mathbf{Q}$, then $r(f_A,f_B)=\sum_P a(P)b(P)\deg P$. This positive integer is independent of K and is equal to the dimension of $\mathrm{Hom}_G(\mathbf{Q}_l\otimes_{\mathbf{Z}_l}T_l(A),\mathbf{Q}_l\otimes_{\mathbf{Z}_l}T_l(B))$, and the rank of $\mathrm{Hom}_k(A,B)$ equals $r(f_A,f_B)$.

The author's main result has decisive consequences for problems concerning the ζ-functions of abelian varieties and Hasse's sum formula for the invariants of $\mathbf{Q}\otimes\mathrm{End}_k(A)$ [see the author, *Arithmetical algebraic geometry* (Proc. Conf. Purdue Univ., 1963), pp. 93–110, Harper & Row, New York, 1965]. To mention a few: $f_B|f_A$ if and only if B is k-isogeneous to an abelian subvariety of A defined over k; $\mathbf{Q}[\pi]$, π the Frobenius endomorphism of A/k, is the center of $\mathbf{Q}\otimes\mathrm{End}_k(A)$;

$$2g\leqq\dim_{\mathbf{Q}}(\mathbf{Q}\otimes\mathrm{End}_k(A))=r(f_A,f_A)\leqq(2g)^2$$

(compare with the classical case $k=\mathbf{C}$); $r(f_A,f_A)=2g$ if and only if $\mathbf{Q}\otimes\mathrm{End}_k(A)=\mathbf{Q}[\pi]$; on the other hand $r(f_A,f_A)=(2g)^2$ if and only if $\mathbf{Q}\otimes\mathrm{End}_k(A)$ is isomorphic to the algebra of all g by g matrices with coefficients in the division algebra which is ramified at p and ∞ (for $g=1$ compare with the results of Hasse and Deuring on the supersingular invariants). Finally, the author indicates that (i) appealing to results of Ju. I. Manin [Uspehi Mat. Nauk **18** (1963), no. 6 (114), 3–90; MR **28** #1200; translated as Russian Math. Surveys **18** (1963), no. 6, 1–83], the Hasse invariant $\mathrm{inv}_v(\mathbf{Q}\otimes\mathrm{End}_k(A))$ is $\equiv i_v\pmod{\mathbf{Z}}$ for all valuations v of $\mathbf{Q}(\pi)$, where $\|\pi\|_v=q^{-i_v}$, and the Artin-Whaples product formula $\prod_v\|\pi\|_v=1$ then implies Hasse's sum formula $\sum_v\mathrm{inv}_v(\mathbf{Q}\otimes\mathrm{End}_k(A))\equiv 0\ (\mathbf{Z})$, and that (ii) for schemes X which are products of curves and abelian varieties with the Néron-Severi group $\mathrm{NS}_k(X)$, the rank of $\mathrm{NS}_k(X)$ equals the order of the pole of the zeta function of X at $s=1$ [see the author, loc. cit., pp. 108–109].

O. F. G. Schilling (Lafayette, Ind.)

Citations: MR 28# 1200 = G10-21; MR 37# 1371 = G35-45.

Referred to in G10-33, G10-37, G20-35, G35-45.

G10-33 (37# 5216)

Honda, Taira

Isogeny classes of abelian varieties over finite fields.
J. Math. Soc. Japan **20** (1968), 83–95.

This important paper gives a complete classification of Abelian varieties up to isogeny over a finite field k_a with p^a elements, as follows: An algebraic number π is said to be of type (A_0) with order a if for any conjugate π^0 of π we have $\pi^\sigma\pi^{\sigma\rho}=p^a$, where ρ is the ordinary complex conjugation. There is a mapping Φ_a from $\{k_a$-isogeny classes of k_a-simple Abelian varieties $A\}$ to $\{$conjugacy classes of numbers π of type (A_0) with order $a\}$ defined by assigning to A its Frobenius endomorphism π.

Classification theorem: Φ_a is bijective.

Half of this theorem, namely the injectivity of Φ_a, had already been proved by J. Tate [Invent. Math. **2** (1966), 134–144; MR **34** #5829]. The author proves the surjectivity by applying a basic theorem of Shimura-Taniyama on reducing an Abelian variety of CM-type and the criterion of Néron-Ogg-Šafarevič, which guarantees a good reduction by a finite extension of the field of definition.

Some applications: (1) By a fundamental theorem of Manin-Tate, the prime ideal decomposition of the Frobenius endomorphism of an Abelian variety A over a finite field k determines the formal group structure of A over the algebraic closure Ω of k, up to isogeny. This theorem reduces existence problems of commutative algebroid formal groups over Ω to problems of finding ideals of type (A_0) with certain properties. The author is thus able to give a short proof of Manin's conjecture that the formal group $G_{m,n} \times G_{n,m}$ is algebroid. (2) The author announces conditions (analogous to those for Riemann matrices of complex tori) for an ℓ-adic matrix to be the representation matrix of the Frobenius endomorphism of some Abelian variety. Here $\ell \neq p$, but the author also obtains conditions for the p-adic representation. No details are given. *M. J. Greenberg* (Santa Cruz, Calif.)

Citations: MR 34# 5829 = G10-32.

G10-34 (37# 5226)

Milne, J. S.

Extensions of abelian varieties defined over a finite field.

Invent. Math. **5** (1968), 63–84.

The author has given in a later paper [Invent. Math. **6** (1968), 91–105] a formula for the order of the Tate-Šafarevič group of certain constant abelian schemes in the function field case (thus confirming in that case the conjecture of Birch and Swinnerton-Dyer). In this paper the way is prepared by deriving results about Ext-groups of abelian varieties over finite fields. It is shown that $\mathrm{Ext}_k{}^1(A, B)$ and $\mathrm{Ext}_k{}^1(B, A)$ are dual (finite) groups, and that the compact group $\mathbf{Z} \otimes \mathrm{Hom}_k(A, B)$ is dual to the discrete group $\mathrm{Ext}_k{}^2(A, B)$ (Theorem 2). In Theorem 3 an elegant formula is given which expresses the cardinality of $\mathrm{Ext}_k{}^1(A, B)$ in terms of the determinant of the bilinear form $\mathrm{Hom}_k(A, B) \times \mathrm{Hom}_k(B, A) \to \mathbf{Z}$ (which takes two homomorphisms to the trace of their composite), and in terms of the roots of the characteristic polynomials of the Frobenius endomorphisms of A and B relative to the finite field. The proofs use the results (as derived by Tate) on p-divisible groups, and the interpretation of these characteristic polynomials via p-adic representations on the Dieudonné-modules of the p-divisible groups associated with the abelian varieties. *F. Oort* (Amsterdam)

Referred to in G10-37.

G10-35 (38# 1090)

Bašmakov, M. I.

The rank of abelian varieties. (**Russian**)

Dokl. Akad. Nauk SSSR **181** (1968), 1031–1033.

Let Γ be an abelian variety defined over an algebraic number-field k and let p be a rational prime. The author considers the homology of various groups of points on Γ both globally and locally at the primes of a finite set S which includes all the prime divisors of p and all the primes at which the reduction is bad. He produces a commutative diagram and deduces relations between the p-ranks of various occurring groups. The results are too technical to reproduce. In particular, he gets more information in the case he considered earlier [Izv. Akad. Nauk SSSR Ser. Mat. **28** (1964), 661–664; MR **34** #2574] when S consists of a single first-degree prime.

{This article has appeared in English translation [Soviet Math. Dokl. **9** (1968), 954–956].}

J. W. S. Cassels (Cambridge, England)

Citations: MR 34# 2574 = G10-31.

G10-36 (38# 4488)

Serre, Jean-Pierre; Tate, John

Good reduction of abelian varieties.

Ann. of Math. (2) **88** (1968), 492–517.

Let K be a field, v a discrete valuation of K, O_v the valuation ring of v, k its perfect residue field of characteristic p, K_s a separable closure of K, $\bar{v}$ an extension of v to K_s, and $I(\bar{v})$ the inertia group of $\bar{v}$. A set on which the Galois group $\mathrm{Gal}(K_s/K)$ operates is said to be unramified at v if $I(\bar{v})$ acts trivially on it. Let A be an abelian variety over K; A is said to have good reduction at v if A comes from an abelian scheme over $\mathrm{Spec}(O_v)$, and is said to have potential good reduction at v if A has good reduction at a prolongation of v to some finite extension of K.

The first fundamental theorem is the criterion of Néron-Ogg-Šafarevič for good reduction: Let A_m be the group of points of order dividing m in the group of K_s-points of A, and for a prime $l \neq p$, let $T_l(A)$ be the inverse limit of the groups A_{l^n} as $n \to \infty$. Then the following are equivalent: (a) A has good reduction at v. (b) A_m is unramified at v for all m prime to p. (c) $T_l(A)$ is unramified at v for some prime $l \neq p$. Some immediate corollaries of this criterion are: (1) Having good reduction is a property of the isogeny class of A. (2) Given an exact sequence $0 \to A' \to A \to A'' \to 0$ of abelian varieties over K, then A has good reduction if and only if both A' and A'' have. (3) If K' is a finite unramified extension of K, and A has good reduction over K', then A already has good reduction over K (same statement if K' is the completion of K at v).

The proof of this criterion is a beautiful application of Néron's theory of minimum models [A. Néron, Inst. Hautes Études Sci. Publ. Math. No. 21 (1964); MR **31** #3423].

Another immediate consequence of the criterion is that if ρ_l is the l-adic representation of $\mathrm{Gal}(K_s/K)$ on $T_l(A)$, then A has potential good reduction at v if and only if the image of $I(\bar{v})$ under ρ_l is finite. If this is the case, then ρ_l has the same kernel in $I(\bar{v})$ for all $l \neq p$ and its character on $I(\bar{v})$ has integer values independent of l; if moreover k is finite with q elements, and σ is a lift to the decomposition group $D(\bar{v})$ of the Frobenius automorphism over k, then the characteristic polynomial of $\rho_l(\sigma)$ has integral coefficients independent of l, and the absolute values of its roots are equal to $q^{1/2}$.

Suppose O_v is Henselian with algebraically closed residue field. Then Ogg has defined a measure δ_l of wild ramification of A_l; in the case of elliptic curves, he has proved that δ_l is independent of l [A. P. Ogg, Amer. J. Math. **89** (1967), 1–21; MR **34** #7509]. The authors generalize this result to higher dimensional abelian varieties under the assumption of potential good reduction (an assumption which Grothendieck has announced to be unnecessary).

In the rest of the paper, the authors give applications to abelian varieties with complex multiplication, defined over a global field. They first show that such a variety has potential good reduction everywhere (generalizing the fact that the j-invariant of an elliptic curve with complex multiplication is integral). They then show that for any finite set S of places which is "ordinary" in a technical sense, the variety can be twisted so as to have good reduction at S (a result due to Deuring in dimension one, except that he did not point out the necessity of excluding the special case). Finally, they show that over a number field, such a variety has good reduction outside the support of a corresponding Grössencharakter (a result also due to Deuring in the case of elliptic curves).

M. J. Greenberg (Santa Cruz, Calif.)

Citations: MR 31# 3423 = G10-25; MR 34# 7509 = G20-28.

Referred to in G05-120.

G10-37 (39# 5581)

Milne, J. S.

The Tate-Šafarevič group of a constant abelian variety.

Invent. Math. **6** (1968), 91–105.

Let B be an abelian variety over a global field K. The Tate-Šafarevič group Ш(B/K) is defined as the group of equivalence classes of principal homogeneous spaces for B over K which become isomorphic over all completions of K. It is conjectured that this group is finite, and there even should be a nice formula for its order (the conjecture of Birch and Swinnerton-Dyer, cf. J. Tate, Séminaire Bourbaki: Vol.

1965/1966, Exposé 306, Benjamin, New York, 1966 [see MR **34** #5605]). It seems that this conjecture is not yet proved for a single abelian variety over a number field. In this paper the author proves the conjecture in case of a constant abelian variety over a function field in one variable over a finite field. First it is shown that the extension groups with base X over $A = \mathrm{Alb}(X)$ with finite kernel can be described via flat cohomology in case X is, e.g., an algebraic curve (Theorem 1). Together with an elegant formula proved by the author in an earlier paper [Invent. Math. **5** (1968), 63–84; MR **37** #5226], an explicit formula for $H^1(X, B)$ follows, where X is an algebraic curve over a finite field k, and B an abelian variety over k. As the Tate-Šafarevič group can be defined in terms of flat cohomology (Lemma 1), the formula for $Ш(B/K)$ follows (Theorem 3). The author shows that his result confirms the Birch, Swinnerton-Dyer conjecture in this special case: combination with a result of Tate [cf. J. Tate, ibid. **2** (1966), 134–144; MR **34** #5829] proves that the number of generators of the Mordell-Weil group is the order of the zero of $L(s)$ at $s = 1$, and the main theorem of the paper yields the conjectured value for $\lim_{s\to 1} L(s)/(s-1)^r$. Various interesting remarks conclude the paper. *F. Oort* (Amsterdam)

Citations: MR 34# 5829 = G10-32; MR 37# 5226 = G10-34.

G10-38 (40# 2685)

Neumann, Olaf

Zur Galois-Kohomologie Abelscher Mannigfaltigkeiten.

Math. Nachr. **40** (1969), 367–378.

Let (A, k) be the group of points rational over k on an abelian variety A defined over a number field k. For a positive integer m, one has the exact sequence $0 \to (A, k)/m(A, k) \to RS^{(m)} \to ST_m \to 0$, where $RS^{(m)}$ is the Reichardt-Selmer group of A, ST_m is the m-torsion part of the Šafarevič-Tate group of A (i.e., the group of locally trivial principal homogeneous spaces of period dividing m for A over k). Determining the first and third groups in the above sequence is a fundamental arithmetic problem; the present paper contributes to this question by giving an upper bound for the number of elements of $RS^{(p^n)}$ in terms of various numerical invariants attached to A, k, and p (where p is a prime). *A. P. Ogg* (Berkeley, Calif.)

G10-39 (40# 7270)

Deligne, Pierre

Variétés abéliennes ordinaires sur un corps fini.

Invent. Math. **8** (1969), 238–243.

This paper gives an explicit description of the isomorphism classes of ordinary abelian varieties over a finite field, and thus partially refines the results of T. Honda and J. Tate [see J. Tate, Séminaire Bourbaki, *Vol. 1968/1969: Textes des conférences*, Exposé 352, Secrétariat mathématique, Paris, 1969; fascimile reprint, Hermann, Paris, 1969] which describe only the isogeny classes. (An abelian variety of dimension d over a field of characteristic p is said to be ordinary if it has the maximum number p^d of points of order p in some algebraically closed field.)

J.-P. Serre and J. Tate have shown [unpublished] that an ordinary abelian variety A over a finite field k has a canonical lifting to an abelian scheme $\tilde{A}$ over the Witt vectors of the algebraic closure of k. The author defines $T(A)$ to be the first integral homology group of the complex abelian variety deduced from $\tilde{A}$ by an extension of scalars, and F to be the endomorphism of $T(A)$ induced by the Frobenius endomorphism of A. Then the map $A \mapsto (T(A), F)$ extends to give an equivalence between the category of ordinary abelian varieties over k and a category of pairs, Z-module with endomorphism, satisfying certain natural conditions. *J. S. Milne* (Ann Arbor, Mich.)

G10-40 (41# 213)

Murasaki, Takeaki

On rational cohomology classes of type (p, p) on an abelian variety.

Sci. Rep. Tokyo Kyoiku Daigaku Sect. A **10**, 66–74 (1969).

Question: If A is an abelian variety of dimension n over the complex number-field, then is it true that $H_Q{}^{p,p}(A)$, $1 \leqq p \leqq n$, is generated by $H_Q{}^{1,1}(A)$ over the rational number-field Q? (Here, $H_Q{}^{p,q}(A)$ for $1 \leqq p \leqq n$, $1 \leqq q \leqq n$ stands for the rational de Rham cohomology classes of type (p, q).) An affirmative answer obtains in case A is generic [A. Mattuck, Proc. Amer. Math. Soc. **9** (1958), 88–98; MR **20** #5207], whereas for A's of CM-type, the answer is in general negative as shown by an example due to Mumford [H. Pohlmann, Ann. of Math. (2) **88** (1968), 161–180; MR **37** #4080]. The present author shows that if A is an n-fold product E^n of an elliptic curve E, with or without complex multiplication, the answer to the above question is yes. The proof is based on explicit calculations of de Rham differential forms. In an appendix, the dimension of the Q-module $H_Q{}^{p,p}(E^n)$ is computed: It is $\binom{n}{p}^2$ when E is with complex multiplication, and is $\binom{n}{p}^2 - \binom{n}{p-1}\binom{n}{p+1}$ otherwise.

T. Kambayashi (De Kalb, Ill.)

Citations: MR 37# 4080 = G15-44.

G10-41 (41# 3480)

Miller, Leonhard

Über die Punkte der Ordnung p auf einer Jacobischen k-Varietät, char $k = p > 0$.

Nachr. Akad. Wiss. Göttingen Math.-Phys. Kl. II **1969**, 9–23.

The author proves the following theorem: Let k be a field of characteristic $p > 0$. For a geometrically regular curve X over k let $J_p(X)$ be the group of $\bar{k}$-rational points of order p on the Jacobian variety of X ($\bar{k}$ the algebraic closure of k). Let M_g be the moduli scheme of curves of genus g ($g \geqq 2$). Then for each σ, $1 \leqq \sigma \leqq g$, there is a subscheme $M_{g,\sigma}$ of M_g, whose k-rational points correspond to the curves X, such that $J_p(X)$ has order less than p^σ and such that X satisfies a certain (technical) condition E.

The proof uses an explicit description of the Cartier operator of a curve X. The author conjectures that each geometrically regular curve is birationally equivalent to one satisfying E, which would allow the removal of condition E in the above theorem.

Ernst Kunz (Regensburg)

G10-42 (41# 6861)

Voskresenskiĭ, V. E.

Birational properties of linear algebraic groups. (Russian)

Izv. Akad. Nauk SSSR Ser. Mat. **34** (1970), 3–19.

The main idea of the paper seems to be based on the fact that (in characteristic 0) the similarity class of the Picard module (over a Galois group) of any projective nonsingular variety (and hence also the first Galois cohomology group of the module) is a birational invariant (Theorem 1). This result was proved (over any perfect field) by Ju. I. Manin [Inst. Hautes Études Sci. Publ.

Math. No. 30 (1966), 55–113; MR **37** #1373] and I. R. Šafarevič [*Lectures on minimal models and birational transformations of two dimensional schemes*, Tata Inst. Fund. Res., Bombay, 1966; MR **36** #163] in the case of surfaces. Having this connection of birational properties of varieties and cohomology, the author is able to use cohomology technique in order to obtain interesting theorems on birational properties of algebraic groups. Here are the main results of the paper. Let k be a fixed field of characteristic 0 and let G be the Galois group of an algebraic closure $\bar{k}$ over k. Let X be an algebraic variety defined over k. Then the group $\mathrm{Pic}(\bar{X})$ (for any algebraic variety Z defined over k, $\bar{Z}$ denotes $Z\times_k \mathrm{Spec}(\bar{k})$) has a natural structure of a G-module. The first theorem of the paper says that if X, Y are non-singular and birationally equivalent (over k) projective varieties, then the G-modules $\mathrm{Pic}(\bar{X})$, $\mathrm{Pic}(\bar{Y})$ are similar, i.e., there exist trivial G-modules M_1, M_2 such that $\mathrm{Pic}(\bar{X})+M_1=\mathrm{Pic}(\bar{Y})+M_2$ (a G-module is called trivial if it is a finite direct sum of G-modules of the form $Z[G]\otimes_{Z[U]} Z$, where U is a subgroup of G of finite index). As a corollary one obtains that if X is rational over k, then $H^1(K, \mathrm{Pic}(\bar{X}))=0$ for any finite extension K of k. Next the author considers an affine and connected algebraic group G defined over k. Since k is of characteristic 0, there exists a non-singular projective variety (called in the sequel a projective model of G) containing G as an open subvariety. Then the author proves the existence of an exact sequence of G-modules: $0\to\hat{G}\to M\to\mathrm{Pic}(\bar{V})\to\mathrm{Pic}(\bar{G})\to 0$, where M is trivial. Applying the above results to the case where the algebraic group considered is a torus T, the author proves that for any rational (over k) torus T there exists an exact sequence $0\to\hat{T}\to\hat{M}\to\hat{N}\to 0$, where $\hat{M}$, $\hat{N}$ are trivial G-modules (the problem whether the converse holds remains open). As an application one constructs a torus T which is not rational but has a cyclic split extension $K\supset k$. On the other hand the next theorem shows that if T is a torus (over k) with a cyclic split extension K of k and V is a projective model of T, then $H^1(k, \mathrm{Pic}(\bar{V}))=0$. In the case where k is an algebraic number field the author gives an interesting interpretation of the group $H^1(k, \mathrm{Pic}(\bar{V}))$ (where V as above is a projective model of T). Namely, he shows that there exists an exact sequence: $0\to A(T)\to H^1(k, \mathrm{Pic}(\bar{V}))\to Ш(T)\to 0$, where $A(T)=\prod_\nu T(k_\nu)/\overline{T(k)}$ (ν runs over the set of all non-equivalent norms of k, k_ν is the ν-adic completion of k, $\overline{T(k)}$ is the closure of $T(k)$ diagonally imbedded in $\prod_\nu T(k_\nu)$ considered with the product topology). Hence if T is rational (over k), then $A(T)=Ш(T)=0$. The next results of the paper concern toruses of the form $R_{L/K}^{(1)}(G_m)$, where L is a finite extension of k. For instance, one of the results says that the torus $R_{L/K}^{(1)}(G_m)$ is not rational if the Galois group of L over K contains a subgroup of the form $Z_p\oplus Z_p$, where p is a prime. *Andrzej Białynicki-Birula* (Warsaw)

Citations: MR 37# 1373 = G35-46.

G10-43 (41# 8431)

Kuga, Michio; Leahy, J. V.

Shimura's abelian varieties as Weil's higher Jacobian varieties.

J. Fac. Sci. Univ. Tokyo Sect. I **16** (1969), 229–253.

From the authors' text: "G. Shimura [J. Math. Soc. Japan **11** (1959), 291–311; MR **22** #11126] has constructed an abelian variety attached to the space of Γ-automorphic forms of even dimension, where Γ is an arithmetically defined Fuchsian group operating on the upper half plane X. M. Kuga [*Fibre varieties over a symmetric space whose fibres are abelian varieties*, Math. lecture notes, Univ. Chicago, Chicago, Ill., 1964] has considered a projective algebraic variety V which is a fibred variety over the compact Riemann surface $\Gamma\backslash X$ and in which the fibres are abelian varieties. A. Weil [Amer. J. Math. **74** (1952), 865–894; MR **14**, 314] has constructed abelian varieties called higher Jacobian varieties attached to odd-dimensional cohomology groups of a Hodge manifold.

"In this paper, we shall show that the higher Jacobian variety of the fibred algebraic variety V is isogenous to the direct sum of several of Shimura's abelian varieties and several complex conjugates of Shimura's abelian varieties." *M. J. Greenberg* (Santa Cruz, Calif.)

Citations: MR 22# 11126 = F15-15.

G10-44 (42# 196)

Hellegouarch, Yves

Application de la théorie des fonctions thêta à un problème de théorie des nombres.

C. R. Acad. Sci. Paris Sér. A-B **269** (1969), A883–A884.

Author's summary: "On sait trouver les points d'ordre fini rationnels d'une variété abélienne définie sur un corps de nombres lorsque l'on connaît une borne supérieure de leur hauteur. C'est à la détermination d'une telle borne que l'on va s'intéresser."

G10-45 (42# 1861)

Siegel, C. L.

Lectures on Riemann matrices.

Notes by S. Raghavan and S. S. Rangachari. Tata Institute of Fundamental Research Lectures on Mathematics, No. 28.

Tata Institute of Fundamental Research, Bombay, 1963. iii + 127 + ii *pp.* $2.00.

This is a self-contained exposition of the classical theory of the multiplicator algebras of Abelian varieties, ending up with the explicit construction of the 4 types of existing simple multiplicator algebras and with a study of the corresponding modular groups as defined previously by the author [*Festschrift zur Feier des zweihundertjährigen Bestehens der Akad. der Wissensch. in Göttingen, I, Math.-Phys. Kl.*, pp. 157–167, Springer, Berlin, 1951; MR **14**, 623]. Table of contents: (1) Introduction, Abelian functions. (2) The commutator algebra. (3) Division algebras over **R** with a positive involution. (4) Cyclic algebras. (5) Division algebras over **Q** with involutions of the second kind. (6) Positive involutions of the second kind in division algebras. (7) Existence of matrices with given commutator algebra. (8) Modular groups associated with Riemann matrices.

The function theoretic and algebraic geometric aspects of the theory are but very briefly touched. A reader interested in these may find them in a paper by G. Shimura [Ann. of Math. (2) **78** (1963), 149–192; MR **27** #5934]. *M. Eichler* (Basel)

Citations: MR 14, 623b = F45-1; MR 27# 5934 = F55-16.

G10-46 (43# 7405)

Pjateckiĭ-Šapiro, I. I.

Induced rings and reduction of fields of automorphic functions. (Russian)

Funkcional. Anal. i Priložen. **4** (1970), *no.* 1, 94.

The author formulates some results on the structure of a ring arising by reduction modulo p of the abelian modular functions. The main result is that this ring may be represented as a ring of k-valued functions on the p-adic symplectic group, where k is some perfect field of characteristic p, that is induced by some homomorphism of the parabolic subgroup in Aut k.

{This article has appeared in English translation [Functional Anal. Appl. **4** (1970), 86–87].}

A. N. Andrianov (Leningrad)

Referred to in G10-47.

G10-47 **(44# 155)**

Pjateckiĭ-Šapiro, I. I.

Induced rings and the reduction of fields of Abelian modular functions. (Russian)

Izv. Akad. Nauk SSSR Ser. Mat. **34** (1970), 532–546.

The author proves the results formulated in an earlier paper [Funkcional. Anal. i Proložen. **4** (1970), no. 1, 94; MR **43** #7405]. *A. N. Andrianov* (Leningrad)

Citations: MR 43# 7405 = G10-46.

G10-48 **(44# 5287)**

Shimura, Gorô

On the zeta-function of an abelian variety with complex multiplication.

Ann. of Math. (2) **94** (1971), 504–533.

Let A be an abelian variety of dimension n over an algebraic number field k of finite degree whose endomorphism algebra End(A) contains an isomorphic image $\Theta(K)$ of an algebraic number field K of degree $2n$. The author considers the following two problems: (I) Determination of the zeta-function of A over k in the case when the elements of $\Theta(K) \cap \mathrm{End}(A)$ are not necessarily defined over k. (II) Construction of an abelian variety A with a given Grössen-character, and study of the relation between the isomorphism-class or the isogeny-class of A and the character.

As to the first problem, let F be the maximal real subfield of K and let k_1 be an algebraic number field of finite degree, over which A and the elements of $\Theta(F) \cap \mathrm{End}(A)$ are rational. The author defines the zeta-function of A over k_1 relative to F, denoted by $\zeta(s, A/k_1, F)$, by means of the l-adic representations on A for the prime ideals l in F. He proves that there is an algebraic number field K', determined by (A, Θ), with the property that the elements of $\Theta(K) \cap \mathrm{End}(A)$ are rational over the composite k_1K'. Then the main result is that if $K' \not\supset k_1$, then $\zeta(s, A/k_1, F)$ is exactly the L-function $L(s, \psi)$ with a Grössen-character ψ of k_1K' (Theorem 7).

As to the second problem, let ψ be a Grössen-character of k or $K'k$, according as $K' \supset k$ or $K' \not\supset k$. The author gives a necessary and sufficient condition on ψ that there exists an abelian variety A over k whose zeta-function is given by ψ (Theorem 6, 10). If $K' \not\supset k$, an assumption is made that k has at least one real archimedean prime, without which the theorem is shown by an example to be false.

In the final section the author generalizes these results by taking a more general type of subfield of K instead of F. *A. N. Andrianov* (Leningrad)

G10-49 **(44# 6702)**

Serre, Jean-Pierre

Sur les groupes de congruence des variétés abéliennes. II. (Russian summary)

Izv. Akad. Nauk SSSR Ser. Mat. **35** (1971), 731–737.

Let k be an algebraic number field, A an algebraic variety defined over k and $A(k)$ the group of points of A defined over k. The author deduces from his earlier work [same Izv. **28** (1964), 3–20; MR **28** #3994] and a general criterion for the vanishing of the cohomology of a Lie algebra that any subgroup of finite index of $A(k)$ is a congruence subgroup. In the earlier paper he proved this in some special cases.

The Lie algebra theorem is as follows. Let V be a finite-dimensional vector space over a field K and let $\mathfrak{g}$ be a subalgebra of the Lie algebra $\mathfrak{gl}(V)$ of K-endomorphisms of V; let N be a nonnegative integer and suppose that there is an $x \in \mathfrak{g}$ such that $\lambda_1 + \cdots + \lambda_{N+1} \neq \mu_1 + \cdots + \mu_N$ for any eigenvalues $\lambda_1, \cdots, \mu_N$ of x (in the algebraic closure of K); then $H^n(\mathfrak{g}, V) = 0$ for all $n \leqq N$.

In the abelian variety context the author deduces that $H^n(\mathfrak{g}_p, V_p) = 0$ for all primes p and all n. Here $V_p = \mathbf{Q}_p \otimes T_p$, where T_p is the Tate module and $\mathfrak{g}_p$ is the Lie algebra of the closed subgroup G_p of GL(V_p) given by the action of Galois. The author had already shown [op. cit.] that the congruence subgroup theorem follows from the case $n = 1$. It also follows, by the use of results of M. Lazard [Inst. Hautes Études Sci. Publ. Math. No. 26 (1965), 1–219; MR **35** #188], that $H^n(G_p, V_p) = 0$ and that $H^n(G_p, T_p)$ is a finite p-group.

J. W. S. Cassels (Cambridge, England)

Citations: MR 28# 3994 = G10-22.

G15 COMPLEX MULTIPLICATION AND MODULI OF ABELIAN VARIETIES; CONNECTIONS WITH CLASS FIELD THEORY OF NUMBER FIELDS

See also reviews B44-9, B80-7, D80-71, F02-8, F02-16, F10-120, F10-122, F15-29, G02-20, G05-42, G05-50, G05-87, G05-88, G05-92, G05-104, G05-122, G20-4, Q05-83, R14-23, R14-94, R20-46, R36-42, R38-3, R40-14, R42-33, R56-6, S35-3, Z15-20.

G15-1 **(6, 144c)**

Schilling, O. F. G. On a special class of Abelian functions. Bull. Amer. Math. Soc. **51**, 133–136 (1945).

Let k be a totally real field of algebraic numbers of finite degree n and let $\mathfrak{o}$ be an order of maximal rank in k. Let μ be a totally negative number in k, and let $\mathfrak{O}$ be an order of maximal rank in $k(\mu^{\frac{1}{2}})$. It is shown how one can construct fields of Abelian functions of genus n admitting either $\mathfrak{o}$ or $\mathfrak{O}$ as their rings of complex multiplications. The construction depends on the use of certain Riemann matrices which were defined by Blumenthal. The proofs given are rather sketchy; thus, it is not immediately clear why (in the notation of the author) $\mathfrak{A}(\Omega_2)$ could not be the direct sum of two fields isomorphic with k, or why the condition that the τ_{ji}'s be transcendental implies that $\mathfrak{A}(\Omega_2) = k$.

C. Chevalley (Princeton, N. J.).

G15-2 **(7, 380g)**

Fueter, Rud. Über die Quaternionenmultiplikation regulärer vierfachperiodischer Funktionen. Experientia **1**, 57 (1945).

In dieser vorläufigen Mitteilung gibt der Verfasser bekannt, dass die "Theorie der komplexen Multiplikation der elliptischen Funktionen weitgehend auf den Bereich der vierfachperiodischen Funktionen übertragen" werden kann. Er geht dabei von Ergebnissen einer früheren Arbeit aus [Monatsh. Math. Phys. **48**, 161–169 (1939); diese Rev. **1**, 115], worin er die Darstellung jeder beliebigen vierfachperiodischen rechtsregulären Funktion angibt, zunächst unter einer gewissen Voraussetzung, die dann später von W. Nef bewiesen wurde [Comment. Math. Helv. **16**, 215–241 (1944); diese Rev. **5**, 241]. *P. Thullen* (Quito).

G15-3 **(8, 318d)**

Deuring, Max. Teilbarkeitseigenschaften der singulären Moduln der elliptischen Funktionen und die Diskriminante der Klassengleichung. Comment. Math. Helv. **19**, 74–82 (1946).

Suppose that Σ is an imaginary quadratic field with the maximal order $\mathfrak{O}$ and the ideal classes $k_1, \cdots, k_h$. Set $j(k)=j(\alpha_1/\alpha_2)$ with $(\alpha_1, \alpha_2)=\mathfrak{a}\varepsilon k$, where $j(\tau)$ is the classical modular invariant of elliptic fields. The author uses the results of his paper [Abh. Math. Sem. Hansischen Univ. **14**, 197–272 (1941); these Rev. **3**, 104] to determine the rational primes p which divide the discriminant D_Σ of the equation $\prod_{\nu=1}^{h}(t-j(k_\nu))=0$. The technique consists in reducing a suitable elliptic field K over the coefficient field $C \supseteq \Sigma(j(k_1), j(k_2))$ with respect to a prime ideal divisor $\mathfrak{p}_1$ of p in C. If K has the ring of multiplicators $\mathfrak{o} \subset \Sigma$ then the invariant $j(k_0)$ of K is associated with a fixed ideal class k_0 of $\mathfrak{o}$ and $j(k)$ is the invariant of the subfield $\cup_\lambda K^\lambda = K_\mathfrak{a} \subseteq K$, where $\mathfrak{a}=\{\lambda\}$ is an integral ideal in k_1 with $k=k_0k_1^{-1}$ and where the fields K^λ are isomorphic subfields of K. This definition of $j(k)$ differs from the classical determination by an automorphism of the class field $\Sigma(j(k))/\Sigma$. Then, for given k_1 and k_2, the field K/C contains the elliptic fields K_1 and K_2 which belong to $j(k_1)$ and $j(k_2)$, respectively. Reduction of K/C modulo $\mathfrak{p}_1$ leads to the elliptic fields $\bar{K}_1$, $\bar{K}_2$ in $\bar{K}$ with the invariants $\overline{j(k_1)}$, $\overline{j(k_2)}$. The congruence $j(k_1)\equiv j(k_2) \pmod{\mathfrak{p}_1 \cap \Sigma(j(k_1), j(k_2))}$ is equivalent to the statement that $\bar{K}_1$ and $\bar{K}_2$ have identical invariants. Suppose that $j(k_1)\neq j(k_2)$; then K_1 and K_2 are not isomorphic. One may assume that $K_2 \subset K_1$. Thus the determination of the prime factors of D_Σ is equivalent to the consideration of the multiplicators μ (not in $\mathfrak{o}$) of $\bar{K}_1$ with $\bar{K}_2=\bar{K}_1^\mu$. The detailed investigation, depending on the factorization of p in Σ, leads to the following results: (1) D_Σ is divisible only by primes p which do not decompose into distinct prime ideals of Σ; (2) a prime p divides D_Σ if there exist nonprincipal ideals $\mathfrak{a}$ of $\mathfrak{o}$ which become principal, $\mathfrak{a}R=\alpha R$, in a maximal order $R \supset \mathfrak{o}$ of the rational quaternion algebra $Q_{\infty, p}$ with the sole ramifications p and ∞.

O. F. G. Schilling (Chicago, Ill.).

Citations: MR 3, 104g = G20-4.

Referred to in G15-4.

G15-4 **(9, 13c)**

Deuring, Max. Teilbarkeitseigenschaften der singulären Moduln der elliptischen Funktionen. Ber. Math.-Tagung Tübingen 1946, pp. 62–63 (1947).

This is a brief résumé of results published by the author in Comment. Math. Helv. **19**, 74–82 (1946) [these Rev. **8**, 318]. *O. F. G. Schilling* (Chicago, Ill.).

Citations: MR 8, 318d = G15-3.

G15-5 **(10, 5a)**

Deuring, Max. Zur Theorie der elliptischen Funktionenkörper. Abh. Math. Sem. Univ. Hamburg **15**, 211–261 (1947).

An algebraic function field of one variable K with the coefficient field k is called elliptic if (i) it is separably generated and has genus one and (ii) the genus is preserved for any extension of the coefficient field. Let $\bar{k}$ denote the algebraic completion of k and suppose that $\bar{R}=\{\mu, \cdots\}$ is the ring of (normalized) meromorphisms of $K\bar{k}$. If $k(x, y)=K$ with a normalized equation $f(x, y)=0$ (depending on the characteristic p of k and the value of the absolute invariant j of $K\bar{k}$), the author determines for a meromorphism μ the field of definition k_μ, that is, the smallest (separable) extension of k such that the transforms x^μ and y^μ lie in $k_\mu(x, y)$. The author's computations are carried out in complete detail, and are based upon the structure of the (finite) unit group of $\bar{R}$; the explicit method consists in expressing the invariant j of the elliptic field under consideration in terms of the coefficients of corresponding normalized equations; e.g., for a unit μ and $p\neq 2, 3$ with $j\neq 0, 2^6 3^3$ one has to consider $k_\mu=k(a)$, where $a^2=g_2g_3^{-1}g_{12}^{-1}g_{13}$ with $y^2=4x^3-g_2x-g_3$ and $(y^\mu)^2=4(x^\mu)^3-g_{12}x^\mu-g_{13}$. In this fashion the author also determines the extension k' of k such that an isomorphism between $K\bar{k}$ and $K_1\bar{k}$ (K and K_1 elliptic over k) can be expressed rationally over k'. It turns out that $[k':k]$ is a divisor of the number of units in $\bar{R}$, provided K and K_1 contain prime divisors of degree one. This result depends upon a kind of Galois correspondence between certain subfields of $\bar{k}/k$ and certain subrings of $\bar{R}$. Each extension k_1 of k determines for Kk_1 the set $R(k_1)$ of meromorphisms $\mu\varepsilon\bar{R}$ which are rationally expressible in Kk_1, and conversely each subset $R_1 \subseteq \bar{R}$ determines a subfield

$$k\{R_1\} = \bigcup_{\mu\varepsilon R_1} k_\mu$$

of $\bar{k}$. Then $R(k_1) \cup R(k_2)=R(k_1 \cup k_2)$, $\cdots$, $k\{R_1\} \cap k\{R_2\} = k\{R_1 \cap R_2\}$. It is then shown that $k^*=k\{\bar{R}\}$ is a finite normal extension of k whose Galois group $G=\{\sigma, \cdots\}$ determines on $\bar{R}$ a group of automorphisms by the relation $\mu\to\sigma\mu\sigma^{-1}$ which is an isomorphism between $R(k_\mu)$ and $R(k_\mu{}^\sigma)$, and thus G has a crossed representation in the unit group of $\bar{R}$. Detailed computations indicate precisely which groups G and extensions of k can occur; the results are obtained for the various combinations of values for the characteristic p and the absolute invariant. For imaginary quadratic $\bar{R}$ and quadratic k^*/k, $p=0$, $\mu\to\sigma\mu\sigma^{-1}$ means the passage to the conjugate imaginary in $\bar{R}$, and for $p\neq 0$ always $G=1$ with $R(k)=\bar{R}$. The cases in which $\bar{R}$ is the maximal order of a rational quaternion algebra (ramified at p and at infinity), present serious computational handicaps for the determination of the complete correspondence between subrings of $\bar{R}/R(k)$ and subfields of k^*/k; it is shown in detail precisely which subrings and subfields do occur and correspond to each other. *O. F. G. Schilling* (Chicago, Ill.).

Referred to in G15-6.

G15-6 **(11, 314d)**

Deuring, Max. Algebraische Begründung der komplexen Multiplikation. Abh. Math. Sem. Univ. Hamburg **16**, nos. 1–2, 32–47 (1949).

The theory of complex multiplication, i.e., the description of the Abelian extensions of an imaginary quadratic field Σ by means of special (singular) values of the modular invraiant $j(z)$ and Weber's elliptic τ-function, is based upon identities and congruences between the Fourier coefficients of $j(z)$ at infinity and rather explicit formulas for the multiplication of the τ-function. In the classical treatment the use of the modular group and the transformation groups modulo an integer is essential; such an approach has no obvious analogue in the theory of moduli for abstract function fields. In this paper a more algebraic method of presentation is described and Weber's definition of a class field is emphasized. Thus the primary aim is to obtain an algebraic proof of the decomposition law for almost all prime ideals of Σ. The author leans heavily on his previous work on the moduli of (abstract) elliptic function fields [Abh. Math. Sem. Hansischen Univ. **14**, 197–272 (1941); Math. Z. **47**, 47–56 (1940); same Abh. **15**, 211–261 (1947); these Rev. **3**, 104, 266; **10**, 5] and the reduction of coefficient fields modulo discrete rank one valuations [Math. Z. **47**, 643–654 (1942); these Rev. **7**, 362]. The procedure for the absolute class field of a given field Σ with the maximal order of integers $\mathbf{R}$ is about the following. The analytic theory of elliptic functions furnishes the existence of an elliptic field $\hat{K}=\hat{k}(x, y)$ over the complex number field $\hat{k}$ with $\mathbf{R}$ for the multiplication ring. Then algebraic reasoning may be used in order to show that $\hat{K}$ is characterized, to within isomorphisms over $\hat{k}$, by a complex number j, the module of $\hat{K}$. This number is in the classical case the value of $j(z)$ for a basis of **R**. This value j is adjoined to the rational number field so as to obtain the smallest field of definition for $\hat{K}$ over the rational number field. Similarly any abstract elliptic field is determined by its module in a strictly algebraic manner; the abstract modules are algebraic over the respective prime fields, a result which was proved by the author by an algebraization of the classical reasoning based upon Fourier expansions. Next each ideal **a** of **R** gives rise to an elliptic subfield $\hat{K}^{\mathbf{a}}=\bigcup_{\mu\varepsilon\mathbf{a}}\hat{K}^{\mu}$, where $\hat{K}^{\mu}$ is defined algebraically as a subfield of $\hat{K}$, which is isomorphic to $\hat{K}$. The field $\hat{K}^{\mathbf{a}}$ has an invariant $j(\mathbf{k})$, where **k** is the absolute ideal class of **a**, and where the independence of **a** as a representative of **k** is established algebraically. (Note that this kind of independence is proved in the classical theory by means of the invariantive properties of $j(z)$ with respect to the modular group.) Furthermore an algebraic proof is given to show that all fields $\Sigma(j(\mathbf{k}))$, for variable **k**, are equal to $\Omega=\Sigma(j)$. Next the field $\Omega(x, y)=K$ with $K\hat{k}=\hat{K}$ is considered and a prime ideal P of Ω with contraction p to Σ is used for the reduction of the elements in Ω to $\bar{\Omega}$ and of K to a field $\bar{K}$. For almost all primes P the corresponding fields $\bar{K}$ are elliptic and their corresponding multiplication rings contain isomorphic images of the given ring **R**. Moreover $\bar{K}$ is inseparable over $\overline{K^{\mu}}$ if and only if μ lies in the ideal generated by p. If p has the absolute degree 1, then the abstract theory of multiplication implies $\overline{K^{\mathbf{a}p}}=(\overline{K^{\mathbf{a}}})^p$ for all ideals **a**. Repeated application of the algebraic theory of moduli yields the basic congruence $j(\mathbf{k}p)\equiv j(\mathbf{k})^p \pmod p$ for all but a finite number of primes, for the residues of the moduli are the moduli of the reduced elliptic fields. Thus the correct decomposition law holds for Ω/Σ and Weber's definition implies that Ω is the absolute class field of Σ. Finally the author treats the (more complicated) theory of ray class fields by means of further refinements of the procedure indicated above. *O. F. G. Schilling* (Chicago, Ill.).

Citations: MR 3, 104g = G20-4; MR 7, 362c = R58-5; MR 10, 5a = G15-5.

G15-7 (14, 356g)

Deuring, Max. Die Struktur der elliptischen Funktionenkörper und die Klassenkörper der imaginären quadratischen Zahlkörper. Math. Ann. **124**, 393–426 (1952).

This paper deals with a more or less complete arithmetic treatment of the celebrated theory of "complex multiplication", that is, the description of generating elements of abelian extensions Ω of an imaginary quadratic field Σ as "singular modules" of the modular j-function and "division values" of elliptic functions whose arguments are related to the bases of well-defined ideals in rings of Σ. The author rebuilds the approach to complex multiplication in the manner of one of Hasse's earlier papers [J. Reine Angew. Math. **157**, 115–139 (1926)] in which the proof of the law of reciprocity for Ω/Σ is a consequence of the theory of elliptic fields. The essential components of the author's theory are the following. (I) The theory of invariants of elliptic fields K over coefficient fields k of arbitrary characteristic, as presented in the author's paper (1) [Math. Z. **47**, 47–56 (1940); these Rev. **3**, 266]. There it is shown that elliptic fields K/k and K_1/k whose extensions by the algebraic completion of k coincide are uniquely determined by a quantity j, the so-called modular invariant which has for characteristic distinct from 2 and 3 the classical form $j=2^6 3^3 g_2^3/\Delta$, where $y^2=4x^3-g_2x-g_3$, $\Delta=g_2^3-27g_3^2\neq 0$, is the Weierstrass defining equation of K. Here it is important that there exists for each value of j an elliptic field K whose smallest possible coefficient field equals $P(j)$, P the prime field of the given field k. (II) The theory of coefficient reduction as started by the author in (2) [Math. Z. **47**, 643–654 (1942); these Rev. **7**, 362] and (3) [Abh. Math. Sem. Hansischen Univ. **14**, 197–272 (1941); these Rev. **3**, 104]. Briefly this entails the following: Suppose that k is an algebraic number field and let **p** be a prime ideal of k, then the residue class mapping $k\rightarrow\{k/\mathbf{p}, \infty\}$ can be extended to a residue class mapping of the elliptic field, for almost all **p**, so that the residue class field $\bar{K}$ is an elliptic field with the coefficient field $k/\mathbf{p}$ and the invariant $\bar{j}=j \bmod \mathbf{p}$. Furthermore the ring of multiplications **R** (meromorphisms, i.e., isomorphisms of K/k into itself which are the identity on k) is mapped isomorphically into the ring of multiplications $\bar{\mathbf{R}}$ of $\bar{K}$ (see §4 of (3)). (III) The theory of elliptic subfields of K/k (theory of division), for example in (3) loc. cit., stating that each elliptic subfield $K_0\subset K$ is a join $K^{\mathbf{a}}=\bigcup_{\mu\varepsilon\mathbf{a}}K^{\mu}$, **a** an ideal in **R** (a left ideal if **R** is a ring of quaternions). In the present paper the author reexamines and extends his former results of the division theory from the viewpoint of module theory with respect to **R** and in connection with the reduction theory. This is a preliminary step in the direction of the desired law of reciprocity. Furthermore, as a combination of results in (1) and (2), it follows that the invariants j and j_0 of K and K_0, respectively, satisfy the "invariant" equation $F(j, j_0)=0$ with highest coefficients in j and j_0 powers equaling ± 1, and integral coefficients for characteristic 0, if j is absolutely transcendental. (This furnishes the algebraization of the classical principle of "q-expansions".) Furthermore we find the crucial result that singular invariants j, i.e., those whose corresponding elliptic fields K have multiplication rings **R** which are orders in imaginary quadratic fields Σ, are absolutely algebraic over the respective prime field of K. This means, in particular, for characteristic 0, that $F(j, j)=0$, F as above for a suitable $K_0\subset K$. Finally there exist in K as many non-isomorphic elliptic subfields K_0 as there are ideal classes with respect to **R** (§10 loc. cit. (3)). Basic for the theory of the author is a heretofore unexplored concept, namely, that of the "generalized meromorphism" Φ of an elliptic field K/k, that is, an isomorphism of K into itself which maps k not necessarily trivially upon itself, i.e., induces a possibly nontrivial isomorphism φ on k. These generalized meromorphisms (playing later the role of symbolic generators of the ideals $\mathbf{a}\subset\mathbf{R}$ (page 410) and referring to the proof of the principal ideal theorem for imaginary quadratic fields) are of utmost significance. It is shown in §4 how a given isomorphism φ of k can be extended to a generalized meromorphism Φ of K; although the concept is of algebraic nature, the whole theory of invariants (see I and III above) is used to secure the existence theorem. If the automorphism φ of k has finite order and has the fixed field k_0, then there exists a finite normal extension k_1/k such that a prolongation of φ to an isomorphism φ_1 of k_1 can be extended to a general meromorphism Φ_1 of Kk_1. The proof involves that the conjugate j^{φ} of the invariant j of K (it is assumed that **R** is imaginary quadratic) determines an elliptic field $K^{\mathbf{a}}$, **a** an ideal in **R** (see III above) which coincides after coefficient extension by the algebraic completion $\hat{k}$ of k with the field K^* defined by $f^{\varphi}(X, Y)=0$, φ being applied to the coefficients of a suitable defining equation $f(x, y)=0$ of K. Then $K^*\hat{k}$ is isomorphic with $K^{\mathbf{a}}\hat{k}$ and hence $K^{\mathbf{a}}\hat{k}$ can be defined by $f^{\varphi}(x', y')=0$, and one can set $x^{\Phi_1}=x'$, $y^{\Phi_1}=y'$ as desired. In addition, it is shown precisely how many extensions Φ_1 exist, leading to the fact that each automorphism φ of k determines uniquely an ideal class with respect to **R**, to wit, the class of **a**. On page 412 appears the statement that the Frobenius mapping $z\rightarrow z^p=z^{\Pi}$ on a field K/k with absolutely algebraic coefficient field of characteristic $p\neq 0$ is a meromorphism which commutes with all multiplications and all generalized meromorphisms so that the corresponding ideal **a** of **R** is prime. Furthermore, the reduction theory II is extended with the result that the prolongation $\mathbf{P}^*$ of a discrete rank-one valuation **P** of k satisfies $\mathbf{P}^{*\Phi}=\mathbf{P}^*$ for an extension Φ of φ to K provided $\mathbf{P}^\varphi=\mathbf{P}$. The proof of the principal theorem of complex multiplication unfolds now as follows in the simplest case for which **R** is the maximal order in the given imaginary quadratic field Σ. Start with an elliptic field K of characteristic 0 with the multiplication ring **R**, its field of definition is to be $\Sigma=\Omega(j)$, j the invariant of K (see III above). Then the distinct nonisomorphic subfields of K have invariants which are in 1-1 correspondence with the ideal classes $\mathfrak{k}$ of R. Now let φ be an automorphism of the Galois group $G(\Omega/\Sigma)$ (Ω is recognized as a normal extension of Σ as a consequence of the theory of the invariant and the fact that each conjugate of j is again a suitable class invariant $j(\mathfrak{k})$). Then φ determines a generalized meromorphism Φ_1 on a suitable extension $K\Omega_1$, Ω_1 normal over Σ; Φ_1 in turn determines (see III) an ideal **a** of **R**, which in turn determines the ideal class $\mathfrak{k}$. Since distinct prolongations Φ_1 of the same φ give ideals in the same class $\mathfrak{k}$, the mapping $\varphi\to\mathfrak{k}(\varphi)$ is single-valued and (using the effect of the meromorphism Φ_1 on the multiplication ring §4 #4) it follows that the mapping is an isomorphism of $G(\Sigma/\Omega)$ into the class group of Σ with respect to **R**. Next, to obtain the full law of reciprocity, the reduction theory (II and its extension to generalized meromorphisms) is used to prove that, given a prime ideal **p** of Σ with the Frobenius automorphism φ for Ω/Σ, the class $\mathfrak{k}(\varphi)$ is the class of **p**. This fact is established by showing that the residue of Φ_1 (passage to a sufficiently large extension Ω_1 of Ω with $\mathbf{P}_1|\mathbf{p}$, and subsequent reduction of $K_1=K\Omega_1$ modulo a prolongation of $\mathbf{P}_1$) is a power of the cited meromorphism Π times an element of Σ. Thus, proceeding as in the classical theory, it follows that $\varphi\to\mathfrak{k}(\varphi)$ is indeed the isomorphism of the law of reciprocity for Ω/Σ. The theory of ray classes, though technically more involved, is carried out in a similar manner. *O. F. G. Schilling.*

Citations: MR 3, 104g = G20-4; MR 7, 362c = R58-5.

G15-8 (16, 677c)

Deuring, Max. Zur Transformationstheorie der elliptischen Funktionen. Akad. Wiss. Mainz. Abh. Math.-Nat. Kl. **1954**, 95–104 (1954).

Let $\wp\left(z;\begin{matrix}\omega_1\\ \omega_2\end{matrix}\right)$ denote the Weierstrass elliptic function with periods ω_1, ω_2 and let g_1, g_2 and Δ be the corresponding invariants. The function τ defined by

$$\tau(z;\omega_1,\omega_2)=N\begin{pmatrix}\omega_1\\ \omega_2\end{pmatrix}\wp^{w/2}\left(z;\begin{matrix}\omega_1\\ \omega_2\end{matrix}\right),$$

is basic in the study of the class-fields of imaginary quadratic fields. The factor $N\begin{pmatrix}\omega_1\\ \omega_2\end{pmatrix}$ is a normalizing factor depending on the invariants g_2, g_3 and Δ, and w is the number of units of the field. If P is a 2×2 matrix with integral entries having no factor in common and with determinant p, then a simple argument on zeros and poles yields the identity

$$\tau\left(pz;P\begin{pmatrix}\omega_1\\ \omega_2\end{pmatrix}\right)=\frac{\tau\left(z;\begin{matrix}\omega_1\\ \omega_2\end{matrix}\right)^p+A_{p-1}^{(P)}\tau\left(z;\begin{matrix}\omega_1\\ \omega_2\end{matrix}\right)^{p-1}+\cdots+A_0^{(P)}}{p^w\tau\left(z;\begin{matrix}\omega_1\\ \omega_2\end{matrix}\right)^{p-1}+B_{p-2}^{(P)}\tau\left(z;\begin{matrix}\omega_1\\ \omega_2\end{matrix}\right)^{p-2}+\cdots+B_0^{(P)}}.$$

The author investigates the nature of the coefficients $A_n^{(P)}$, $B_n^{(P)}$. If $\omega=\omega_1/\omega_2$ and if $j(\omega)=1728g_2^3/\Delta$, then $A_n^{(P)}$ and $B_n^{(P)}$ belong to the field $R(j(\omega),j(P(\omega)))$. In the case where p is a prime, each matrix P can be expressed uniquely in the form $P=MP_\mu$, where M belongs to the full modular group and P_μ is one of the canonical matrices

$$P_0=\begin{pmatrix}p&0\\0&1\end{pmatrix}\quad\text{or}\quad P_\mu=\begin{pmatrix}1&\mu\\0&p\end{pmatrix}\quad(\mu=1,2,\cdots,p).$$

The author proves that the Fourier coefficients of the functions $B_n^{(P)}$ are algebraic integers if $P=P_\mu$, $1\leqq\mu\leqq p$, and rational integers if $P=P_0$. In the special case $P=P_0$, $p=\text{prime}>3$, he also shows that the functions $A_n^{(P)}$ and $B_n^{(P)}$ can be expressed as rational functions of $j(\omega)$ and $j(p\omega)$ using rational coefficients. Furthermore, the Fourier coefficients of $A_n^{(P)}$, $0\leqq n\leqq p-1$, $B_n^{(P)}$, $1\leqq n\leqq p-2$, and $1-B_0^{(P)}$, are rational numbers whose numerators are divisible by p and whose denominators have only the prime factors 2 and 3. A similar result is also obtained for more general P. *T. M. Apostol* (Pasadena, Calif.).

G15-9 (18, 601b)

Taniyama, Yutaka. Jacobian varieties and number fields. Proceedings of the international symposium on algebraic number theory, Tokyo & Nikko, 1955, pp. 31–45. Science Council of Japan, Tokyo, 1956.

Soit A une variété abélienne. Nous noternons $\mathfrak{A}(A)$ so anneau d'endomorphismes (dont le groupe additif est libre de type fini), $\mu\to\mu'$ son antiautomorphisme involutif, et $\mathfrak{A}_0(A)$ la Q-algèbre $\mathfrak{A}(A)\otimes Q$. Etude des sous corps commutatifs R_0 de $\mathfrak{A}_0(A)$ qui sont globalement invariants par cet antiautomorphisme; ce sont des corps totalement réels ou des extensions quadratiques totalement imaginaires de corps totalement réels. Construction, pour tout idéal $\mathfrak{b}$ de $R_0\cap\mathfrak{A}(A)$, d'une variété abélienne $A_\mathfrak{b}$; celle ci est isogène à A et ne dépend que de la classe de $\mathfrak{b}$. Lorsque $[R_0:Q]=2\cdot\dim(A)$ et que A est définie sur un corps de nombres k contenant la clôture galoisienne K' de R_0 sur Q, l'étude des réductions modulo $\mathfrak{p}$ de A permet de calculer la fonction $\zeta_A(s)$ au moyen de fonctions L à „Grössencharaktere" de k; ceci généralise des résultats de Deuring [voir ci-dessous] et de Weil [Trans. Amer. Math Soc. **73** (1952), 487–495; MR **14**, 452]. Si K est une extension quadratique totalement imaginaire d'un corps totalement réel K_0 de degré g sur K, et moyennant une hypothèse sur les isomorphismes de K_0 dans C, l'étude des variétés abéliennes correspondant aux classes d'idéaux de K permet de déterminer les extensions abéliennes non ramifiées de K, et de donner une forme explicite à la loi de réciprocité d'Artin. *P. Samuel* (Clermont-Ferrand).

Citations: MR 14, 452d = G30-10.
Referred to in G15-16, G15-43.

G15-10 (18, 601c)

Deuring, Max. On the zeta-function of an elliptic function field with complex multiplications. Proceedings of the international symposium on algebraic number theory, Tokyo & Nikko, 1955, pp. 47–50. Science Council of Japan, Tokyo, 1956.

Soient k un corps de nombres algébriques, K un corps de fonctions elliptiques sur k. Un diviseur premier $\mathfrak{p}$ de k est dit régulier s'il existe un diviseur premier $\mathfrak{p}'$ de K étendant $\mathfrak{p}$ tel que le corps $K/\mathfrak{p}'$ obtenu par réduction modulo $\mathfrak{p}'$ soit un corps de fonctions elliptiques sur les corps fini $k/\mathfrak{p}$; alors $\mathfrak{p}'$ est unique; notons dans ce cas $\zeta(s,K,\mathfrak{p})$ la fonction ζ de $K/\mathfrak{p}'$. Les diviseurs premiers non réguliers $\mathfrak{q}$ de k sont en nombre fini; pour un tel diviseur on pose $\zeta(s,K,\mathfrak{q})$ égal à la fonction ζ de l'extension transcendante simple de $k/\mathfrak{q}$. On pose $\zeta(s,K)=\prod\zeta(s,K,\mathfrak{p})$ (produit étendu à tous les diviseurs premiers $\mathfrak{p}$ de k, réguliers ou non). Alors $\zeta(s,K)$ s'exprime simplement au moyen de la fonction ζ du corps k et d'une fonction L déduite d'un „Grössencharakter" qui est défini exactement modulo son conducteur. *P. Samuel.*

G15-11 (18, 673a)

Weil, André. On the theory of complex multiplication. Proceedings of the international symposium on algebraic number theory, Tokyo & Nikko, 1955, pp. 9–22. Science Council of Japan, Tokyo, 1956.

Etant donnés une variété complète non singulière V et un diviseur positif X sur V, notons $C(X)$ l'ensemble des diviseurs positifs X' sur V pour lesquels il existe deux entiers m, $m'>0$ tels que $m'X'$ soit algébriquement équivalent à mX; on dit que $C(X)$ est une polarisation de V s'il existe, dans $C(X)$, au moins un système linéaire complet ample; une variété polarisée est donc une variété munie d'une classe privilégiée de plongements projectifs. Etude des variétés abéliennes polarisées; notion de rang d'une telle variété. Soit K_0 un corps totalement réel de degré n sur Q; on appelle CM-extension de K_0 la donnée d'une extension quadratique totalement imaginaire K de K_0 et de n isomorphismes φ_i de K dans $\bar{Q}$ dont les restrictions à K_0 sont toutes distinctes; une CM-extension de K_0 détermine une classe d'isogénie de variétés abéliennes A de dimension n, telles que $\mathfrak{A}_0(A)$ contienne K et que la restriction à K de la trace de la représentation de $\mathfrak{A}_0(A)$ définie par l'algèbre de Lie de A soit $\sum \varphi_i$. Les variétés abéliennes polarisées A de rang donné, d'anneau d'endomorphismes donné et correspondant à une CM-extension donnée, sont en nombre fini; caractérisation des corps K_0 correspondants; étude des extensions de K_0 engendrées par les points d'ordre fini de A.

P. Samuel.

G15-12 (18, 673c)

Shimura, Goro. On complex multiplications. Proceedings of the international symposium on algebraic number theory, Tokyo & Nikko, 1955, pp. 23–30. Science Council of Japan, Tokyo, 1956.

Soient K un corps de nombres de degré $2n$, et A une variété abélienne de dimension n dont l'anneau d'endomorphismes $\mathfrak{A}(A)$ contient l'anneau des entiers de K. Au moyen de la théorie de la réduction modulo $\mathfrak{p}$ l'auteur démontre une généralisation de la relation de congruence de Kronecker sur les fonctions elliptiques, et en déduit des renseignements explicites sur les extensions abéliennes de K. Lorsque K est un corps quadratique imaginaire, ceci donne une forme explicite de la loi de réciprocité.

P. Samuel (Clermont-Ferrand).

G15-13 (19, 123e)

Eichler, Martin. Der Hilbertsche Klassenkörper eines imaginärquadratischen Zahlkörpers. Math. Z. **64** (1956), 229–242.

Let k be an imaginary quadratic field and $\mathfrak{o}$ the ring of integers of k. Let $\mathfrak{M}$ be the algebra of rational matrices of degree 2 and $\mathfrak{O}$ the ring of integral matrices in $\mathfrak{M}$. Let J be the set of isomorphisms φ of $\mathfrak{o}$ with subrings of $\mathfrak{O}$. Two isomorphisms φ, φ' in J are called equivalent if $\varphi'(x)=\varepsilon\varphi(x)\varepsilon^{-1}$ ($x\in\mathfrak{o}$), where ε is an element of determinant $+1$ in $\mathfrak{O}$. For any inversible α in $\mathfrak{M}$, let S_α be the corresponding homographic substitution on a complex variable τ; if $\varphi\in J$, the elements $S_{\varphi(x)}$ ($x\in\mathfrak{o}$) have the same fixed points, of which one, say $\tau(\varphi)$, is in the upper half-plane. If φ and φ' are equivalent, then $\tau(\varphi)$ and $\tau(\varphi')$ may be transformed into each other by an operation of the modular group Γ_1, whence $j(\tau(\varphi'))=j(\tau(\varphi))$, if j is the modular function. The common value of the $j(\tau(\varphi))$ for all φ in an equivalence class $\mathfrak{K}$ is called the class-invariant of $\mathfrak{K}$ and denoted by $j(\mathfrak{K})$. The main theorem of classical complex multiplication asserts that the field K obtained by adjunction to k of the numbers $j(\mathfrak{K})$ (for all classes $\mathfrak{K}$) is the absolute class field of k. The present paper gives a simplified proof of this result. Let Γ_n be the set of all S_α, for $\alpha\in\mathfrak{o}$, det $\alpha=n$ (where n is an integer >0); Γ_n decomposes into a finite number of cosets $\Gamma_1 S_i$ modulo the modular group Γ_1. The polynomial $\prod_i(X-j(S_i\tau))$ may be expressed as $F_n(X, j(\tau))$, where F_n is a polynomial in two letters with rational coefficients; moreover, the denominators of the coefficients of F_n involve only a finite number of primes (if p is a prime which is not involved in the denominators of the coefficients of the Fourier expansion of j, then p is not involved in the denominators of the coefficients of any one of the F_n). Except for perhaps a finite number of primes p, one has the congruences

$$F_p(X, X')\equiv(X-X'^p)(X^p-X') \pmod p,$$

$$F_{p^2}(X, X')\equiv(X-X'^{p^2})(X^{p^2}-X')(X-X')^p \pmod p.$$

These are the only function-theoretic facts whose knowledge is required for the present proof. The algebraic character of the numbers $j(\mathfrak{K})$ follows from the fact that $F_n(j(\mathfrak{K}), j(\mathfrak{K}))=0$ whenever n is the norm of an element $\neq 0$ in $\mathfrak{o}$. The main tool in the proof consists in representing the ideal class group of k as a group of permutations of the equivalence classes $\mathfrak{K}$ in the following manner. Let $\mathfrak{K}$ be any equivalence class, φ a representant of $\mathfrak{K}$ and $\mathfrak{a}$ an ideal in $\mathfrak{o}$; then $\varphi(\mathfrak{a})$ generates a left-ideal in $\mathfrak{O}$; the left-ideals in $\mathfrak{O}$ being principal, $\mathfrak{O}\varphi(\mathfrak{a})$ may be written as $\mathfrak{O}\alpha$ ($\alpha\in\mathfrak{O}$), and it is clear that α has the property that $\alpha\varphi(\mathfrak{o})\alpha^{-1}$ lies in $\mathfrak{O}$; we may further take α in such a way that det $\alpha>0$; the mapping $\varphi': x\to\alpha\varphi(x)\alpha^{-1}$ is then an element of J, and its class is easily seen to depend only on $\mathfrak{K}$ and on the ideal class of $\mathfrak{a}$; this makes the ideal class group of k operate on the set of equivalence classes $\mathfrak{K}$. It is easily seen that the ideal class group actually operates on the set of the class invariants $j(\mathfrak{K})$. The author proves that the permutations of the numbers $j(\mathfrak{K})$ which correspond in this manner to the ideal classes of k are induced by automorphisms of the field K. Using these automorphisms, it is proved that (with possibly a finite number of exceptions) a prime ideal $\mathfrak{p}$ of k whose ideal class is of order f decomposes into prime ideals of relative degree f in K, which proves that K is the absolute class field.

The author points out that his method does not yield the Artin reciprocity law for K, essentially because it does not allow us to distinguish between prime ideals of k which are conjugate to each other over the rationals.

The proof offered by the author may still be substantially simplified if one is willing to use the fact that a normal extension M of a field L of algebraic numbers is uniquely determined when one knows (with possibly a finite number of exceptions) all prime ideals of the first degree of L which split completely in M.

A certain number of corrections to the present paper have been published by the author in a subsequent note [see the paper listed below]. *C. Chevalley* (Paris).

G15-14 (19, 124a)

Eichler, Martin. Berichtigung zu meiner Arbeit über den Hilbertschen Klassenkörper eines imaginärquadratischen Zahlkörpers. Math. Z. **65** (1956), 214.

G15-15 (19, 396e)

Terada, Fumiyuki. Complex multiplication and principal ideal theorem. Tôhoku Math. J. (2) **6** (1954), 21–25.

Let $\mathfrak{m}$ be an integral ideal of the imaginary quadratic field Ω, relatively prime to the discriminant of Ω and decomposable into a product of prime ideals of first degree.

In the absolute field of classes K over Ω we have $\mathfrak{m}=(\gamma)$, $\gamma \in K$. In the case $N(\mathfrak{m})\equiv 1 \pmod{12}$ Hasse gave an explicit formula for the number γ, using complex multiplication of elliptic functions [Monats. Math. Phys. **38** (1931), 315–322]. In the present article, following the method of Hasse, the author sets up an explicit formula for γ in the case $N(\mathfrak{m})\equiv 5 \pmod{12}$.

Z. I. Borevič (RŽMat **1955**, no. 4851).

G15-16 (20# 1667)

Taniyama, Yutaka. *L*-functions of number fields and zeta functions of abelian varieties. J. Math. Soc. Japan 9 (1957), 330–366.

In this paper, the author (whose death, recently announced, has cut short prematurely a most promising career) not only gives a new proof, free from artificial restrictions, of his earlier theorem on the zeta-function of Abelian varieties with sufficiently many complex multiplications [cf. Y. Taniyama, Proc. internat. symposium algebraic number theory, Tokyo-Nikko (1955), pp. 31–45, Science Council of Japan, Tokyo, 1956; MR **18**, 601], but develops, in relation with that problem, a number of new ideas of far-reaching importance. Their motivation will appear most clearly if the sections of the paper are discussed in reverse order. Let k be an algebraic number-field; call $\mathfrak{g}$ the Galois group over k of its algebraic closure $\bar{k}$. Let A be an abelian variety of dimension n, defined over k; for each rational prime l, call G_l the group of the points of A whose order is a power of l, and k_l the extension of k generated by the coordinates of these points. As all the k_l are contained in $\bar{k}$, $\mathfrak{g}$ operates on G_l for every l; as G_l is the product of $2n$ groups isomorphic to the additive group of l-adic integers, this defines, for each l, a representation M_l of $\mathfrak{g}$ by l-adic matrices of order $2n$, whose kernel is the subgroup $\mathfrak{g}_l$ of $\mathfrak{g}$ attached to k_l. Now the author applies the reduction-theory (due to Shimura and himself) to this situation; this shows, first of all, that, for all prime ideals $\mathfrak{p}$ of k except for a finite number of "exceptional" ones, the reduction of A modulo $\mathfrak{p}$ determines an abelian variety of dimension n, defined over the field with $N\mathfrak{p}$ elements; it also shows that the so-called Hasse zeta-function of A can be expressed in terms of the matrices attached, in the representations M_l, to the Frobenius substitutions over k of the prime divisors in $\bar{k}$ of the non-exceptional primes of k. The author derives now from the reduction-theory some rather precise results on the latter matrices (including the fact that every non-exceptional prime $\mathfrak{p}$ is unramified in k_l for every rational prime l which is not a multiple of $\mathfrak{p}$).

The results thus obtained (§ 4, nos. 17–18) are formulated as a set of abstract conditions which the representations M_l of $\mathfrak{g}$ have to satisfy. At this point the author takes a step involving what is perhaps the most original idea of the whole paper; he considers any system (M_l) of l-adic representations of $\mathfrak{g}$, all of the same degree (l ranging over all primes) satisfying the same set of conditions. To such a system, he attaches a "zeta-function" (reducing to that of A in the case described above); and, among other results, he proves that this can be written as an infinite product of L-functions of Artin type, attached to the extensions k_l of k (abelian or not) determined by the kernels $\mathfrak{g}_l$ of the representations M_l (§ 3, no. 15, theorem 3).

Much more precise results are given for the abelian case (i.e. when all fields k_l are abelian over k); a deep analysis, based of course on class-field theory, shows that, in this case, the system (M_l) determines a "Grössencharakter of type (A_0)" [as defined by the reviewer, ibid., pp. 1–7] of the idèle-class group C_k of k; such a character has in particular the property that the Hecke L-function attached to it has algebraic coefficients; more precisely (as the author shows) the field K generated by the coefficients is either the rational field Q, or a totally imaginary quadratic extension of a totally real field. It is in fact one of the paper's main results that there is essentially a one-to-one correspondence between abelian systems of representations (M_l) of $\mathfrak{g}$ and characters of C_k of type (A_0) (§ 3, no. 11, theorem 1′); this depends upon a characterization of the latter, quite different from their original definition, by properties involving only their local behavior at $\mathfrak{p}$-adic places of k and at "sufficiently many" $\mathfrak{P}$-adic places of the field K where the coefficients of the corresponding Hecke L-function take their values (§ 1, no. 6, theorem 1). From this, it follows that the zeta-function of an abelian system of representations (M_l) of $\mathfrak{g}$ is a product of finitely many Hecke L-functions. This applies in particular to the zeta-function of an abelian variety of dimension n, defined over k, whose ring of endomorphisms over k contains an order of a number-field of degree $2n$ over Q; for it is an easy consequence of reduction-theory that the system of representations (M_l) attached to such a variety is abelian. A special case is that of any curve $ax^n+by^m=1$, since the Jacobian variety of such a curve is isogenous to a product of abelian varieties of the type described above. *A. Weil* (Princeton, N.J.)

Citations: MR 18, 601b = G15-9.
Referred to in G15-53.

G15-17 (22# 5621)

Jenner, W. E. On arithmetical properties of Riemann matrices. Monatsh. Math. **64** (1960), 110–118.

A few remarks (rather simpler in substance than might appear from the text) are made on the discriminant of the order of complex multiplications of abelian function-fields of some special types. *A. Weil* (Princeton, N.J.)

G15-18 (23# A889)

Reichardt, Hans

Ein Beweis des Hauptidealsatzes für imaginär-quadratische Zahlkörper.

Math. Nachr. **17** (1959), 318–329.

The author applies the theory of complex multiplication to give a proof of the principal-ideal theorem for imaginary quadratic fields. The paper was written before the publication of M. Deuring's account of complex multiplication [Enzyklopädie der mathematischen Wissenschaften, 2te Aufl. Bd. I 2, no. 23, Teubner, Stuttgart, 1958] which includes a detailed treatment of this and more general results. *A. Weil* (Princeton, N.J.)

G15-19 (23# A2419)

Shimura, Goro; Taniyama, Yutaka

Complex multiplication of abelian varieties and its applications to number theory.

Publications of the Mathematical Society of Japan, 6. *The Mathematical Society of Japan, Tokyo,* 1961. xi + 159 *pp.* $3.20.

According to the preface this book is a revised version, prepared by the first author (the second being deceased), of the first six chapters of the book *Modern number theory* [(Japanese) Kyōritsu Shuppan, Tokyo, 1957]. It consists of four chapters, of uneven depth and difficulty.

In Chapter 1 the basic facts concerning abelian varieties are assumed, and part of the chapter is devoted to fixing the notations (one should be aware of the fact that λ^{-1}, as used in formula (3), p. 3, and in the sequel, is not the same as the λ^{-1} defined on top of p. 2). A very brief outline of the theory of abelian varieties over the complex field (classical case) follows; finally, abelian varieties are taken to be polarized, i.e., embedded in a projective space, and a definition is given for the field of moduli.

Chapter 2 contains the tools for the later development of the theory of complex multiplication. The emphasis is on those abelian varieties, in characteristic 0, whose algebra of endomorphisms is commutative and of maximal degree. Let F be an algebraic number field of degree $2n$, and let $\varphi_1, \cdots, \varphi_n$ be distinct isomorphisms of F into the complex field; let A be an abelian variety of dimension n over a field of characteristic 0, such that there exist an isomorphism ι of $\mathscr{A}_0(A)$ (= algebra of endomorphisms of A over the field of rationals) onto F (with $\iota 1 = 1$), and a basis $\{\omega_1, \cdots, \omega_n\}$ of the invariant differentials on A, with the property $(d\iota\alpha)\omega_i = (\varphi_i\alpha)\omega_i$. Then (A, ι) is called of type $(F; \{\varphi_i\})$, and $(F; \{\varphi_i\})$ is called a CM (= complex multiplication) type. (Thus, the field F must be isomorphic to the whole algebra of endomorphisms of some abelian variety in characteristic 0; the differentials provide an "analytic representation" of the ring of endomorphisms.) By classical means (complex tori) it is then proved that $(F; \{\varphi_i\})$ is a CM type if and only if F contains subfields K, K_0 such that: K_0 is totally real; K is an imaginary quadratic extension of K_0: no two among the restrictions of the φ_i to K are complex conjugate. The chapter takes up next the study of the ring of endomorphisms $\mathscr{A}(A)$, which is, of course, an array (= order) in the algebra $\mathscr{A}_0(A)$; particular attention is paid to the cases of maximal arrays, and of characteristic 0; the methods pivot around the notions of $\mathfrak{a}$-multiplications and ideal section points: if $\mathfrak{a}$ is a left ideal of $\mathscr{A}(A)$ (or also in more general cases), an $\mathfrak{a}$-multiplication is a homomorphism λ of A such that $k(\lambda A)$ is the composite of the $k(\alpha A)$ for $\alpha \in \mathfrak{a}$, where k is a field of definition of A (in the reviewer's nomenclature, λ is a highest common divisor of all the $\alpha \in \mathfrak{a}$); a point t of A, belonging to the kernels of all the $\alpha \in \mathfrak{a}$, is a proper $\mathfrak{a}$-section point if it does not belong to the kernel of any $\beta \notin \mathfrak{a}$. Conditions for the existence of proper $\mathfrak{a}$-section points are given (and are usually weaker in characteristic $p \neq 0$).

So far the emphasis has been on characteristic 0, and on essentially complex-manifold methods. Chapter 3 provides the link with characteristic $p \neq 0$, by means of the theory of reduction of (abelian) varieties modulo a rank 1 discrete valuation of the field of constants; although the theory is far from complete, the part of it which does exist is by now well known, and no description will be given here.

Chapter 4 is the raison d'être of the book; maximal arrays and characteristic 0 are again emphasized, and four main theorems of class field theory are proved; the first one reads: Let $(K^*; \{\psi_a\})$ be a CM type such that an abelian variety (over the complex field) of that type is simple; let $(K; \{\varphi_i\})$ be the dual of $(K^*; \{\psi_a\})$; let H_0 be the group of all the ideals $\mathfrak{a}$ of K^* (that is, of the maximal array of K^*) such that there exists a $\mu \in K$ for which $\prod_a \mathfrak{a}^{\psi_a} = (\mu)$, $N\mathfrak{a} = \mu\bar{\mu}$; let (A, ι) be of type $(K; \{\varphi_i\})$, and let $\mathscr{C}$ be a polarization of A. Let k_0 be the field of moduli of $(A, \mathscr{C})$. Then H_0 is an ideal-group of K^*, defined mod (1); and the composite of k_0 and K^* is the unramified class field over K^* corresponding to H_0.

The second main theorem links the class fields of ideal-groups mod (b), where b is a rational integer, with ideal section points and Kummer varieties. Theorem 3 drops the condition of maximality for arrays of K^*. Finally, Theorem 4 deals with the zeta-function of A- and L-functions. The exposition is interrupted in a few points by "examples", which are very illuminating, and are essentially modern expositions of classical parts of the theory. One practical criticism applies to this book as well as to a large part of contemporary mathematical production: the various statements are called by different names, such as Lemma, Theorem, Proposition, Corollary; the first three are numbered independently of each other, while the numbers assigned to corollaries are functions of several variables; in addition, numbered formulae have their own separate numeration. The strain placed on the reader by this partial ordering is obvious, but apparently readers seek vengeance on other readers when they turn into authors. *I. Barsotti* (Pisa)

Referred to in G10-20, G15-25, G15-27, G15-30, G15-33, G15-36, G15-42, G15-43, G15-49, Z02-67.

G15-20 (24# A3136)

Shimura, Goro

Automorphic functions and number theory. I. (Japanese)

Sûgaku **11** (1959/60), 193–205.

An expository paper on recent developments in the theory of complex multiplication.

K. Iwasawa (Cambridge, Mass.)

Referred to in F02-16.

G15-21 (27# 4790)

Chowla, S.

Remarks on class-invariants and related topics.

Calcutta Math. Soc. Golden Jubilee Commemoration Vol. (1958/59), *Part II, pp.* 361–372. *Calcutta Math. Soc., Calcutta,* 1963.

Inter alia, some results on special Diophantine equations are proved. *B. Stolt* (Stockholm)

G15-22 (28# 3995)

Baily, Walter L., Jr.

On the moduli of Abelian varieties with multiplications.

J. Math. Soc. Japan **15** (1963), 367–386.

Let $\mathfrak{k}$ denote either a totally real number field or a purely imaginary quadratic extension of such a field, and let $\mathfrak{o}$ be the ring of integers of $\mathfrak{k}$. It is known [see Shimura, Ann. of Math. (2) **70** (1959), 101–144; MR **21** #6370; ibid. (2) **78** (1963), 149–192; MR **27** #5934] that the isomorphism classes of polarized abelian varieties of a given dimension of type σ (i.e., roughly, whose endomorphism ring contains a faithful image of σ) are parametrized by the points of the quotient space H/Γ of a bounded symmetric domain H by an arithmetically defined group Γ of automorphisms of H. It is shown here that H/Γ may be identified with a Zariski $\mathbf{Q}$-open subset of a projective variety V^* defined over the field $\mathbf{Q}$ of rational numbers, in such a way that the coordinates of a point $x \in H/\Gamma$ generate over $\mathbf{Q}$ the field of moduli of the polarized abelian variety of type σ represented by x. This generalizes earlier results of Shimura [Séminaire H. Cartan, 1957/58, Exp. 18–20, Secrétariat mathématique, Paris, 1958; MR **21** #2750] and of the author [Ann. of Math. (2) **75** (1962), 342–381; MR **29** #103] pertaining respectively to the Hilbert and Hilbert-Siegel groups. The method is a suitable generalization of that used before by the author, and in several points of the proof, the author just refers to the paper quoted above, or indicates how the corresponding step there has to be modified. He assumes the existence of a compactification V^* of H/Γ with properties similar to those known in the case of the Hilbert-Siegel group, also with respect to the operator Φ on automorphic forms, to be discussed elsewhere. The proof is based on the use of Θ-functions, whose discussion, including transformation formulae, addition theorem, etc., takes up the greater part of the paper. The embedding is defined first over the maximal abelian extension A of $\mathbf{Q}$ by means of Θ-functions (for suitable subgroups of finite index of Γ) with Fourier coefficients in A. It is then shown that by letting the Galois group of $A/\mathbf{Q}$ operate on the coefficients of these functions, one gets other mappings whose images satisfy Weil's conditions for the field descent from A to **Q**.

A. Borel (Princeton, N.J.)

Citations: MR 21# 2750 = F02-5; MR 21# 6370 = F55-11; MR 27# 5934 = F55-16; MR 29# 103 = G15-24.

Referred to in G15-23.

G15-23 (29# 5825)

Baily, Walter L., Jr.

A correction to "On the moduli of Abelian varieties with multiplications".

J. Math. Soc. Japan **16** (1964), 182.

The author remarks that G. Shimura pointed out that Lemma 1, p. 370, of the author's paper [same J. **15** (1963), 367–386; MR **28** #3995] does not hold when k is an imaginary extension. He indicates the modifications in subsequent results. *R. J. Crittenden* (Providence, R.I.)

Citations: MR 28# 3995 = G15-22.

G15-24 (29# 103)

Baily, Walter L., Jr.

On the theory of θ-functions, the moduli of abelian varieties, and the moduli of curves.

Ann. of Math. (2) **75** (1962), 342–381.

The familiar Torelli theorem establishes a natural one-to-one correspondence between the conformal equivalence classes of compact Riemann surfaces and the points of the set $\mathscr{E}$ of equivalence classes of normalized period matrices of the curves [Andreotti, Amer. J. Math. **80** (1958), 801–828; MR **21** #1309; Weil, Nachr. Akad. Wiss. Göttingen Math.-Phys. Kl. IIa **1957**, 33–53; MR **19**, 683]; the author demonstrated in an important previous paper [Ann. of Math. (2) **71** (1960), 303–314; MR **22** #1583] that the set $\mathscr{E}$ is a Zariski-open subset of an irreducible algebraic variety $\mathscr{E}'$. The present paper contains a more purely algebraic proof of the main result of the preceding paper; and this result is also extended and in a sense completed in the present paper as follows. It is shown that the set $\mathscr{E}'$ is defined over the rational field Q, and that $\mathscr{E}$ is Q-open on $\mathscr{E}'$. Further, the field $Q(e)$ generated over Q by the coordinates of a point $e \in \mathscr{E}$ is precisely the field of moduli $F(S_e)$ of the corresponding Riemann surface S_e; this follows from the corresponding result for polarized abelian varieties. Still further, there is a projective variety $\mathscr{F}'$ defined over Q, and a regular map $\lambda: \mathscr{F}' \to \mathscr{E}'$, also defined over Q, such that $\lambda^{-1}(e)$ is the quotient of S_e by the group of all conformal automorphisms of S_e for any point $e \in \mathscr{E}$. The proofs rest heavily on the classical theory of theta functions; a convenient summary of the results required from that theory is also included.

R. C. Gunning (Princeton, N.J.)

Referred to in G15-22.

G15-25 (29# 109)

Doi, Koji

On the field of moduli of an abelian variety with complex multiplication.

J. Math. Soc. Japan **15** (1963), 237–243.

The theory of complex multiplication as developed by Shimura and Taniyama [*Complex multiplication of abelian varieties and its applications to number theory*, Math. Soc. Japan, Tokyo, 1961; MR **23** #A2419] is concerned in its main part with simple abelian varieties. The author proposes to consider also composite varieties. As a first step in this direction, he considers in this paper an abelian variety A which is a direct product $B_1 \times \cdots \times B_h$ of simple abelian varieties of the same type, where the "type" of a simple abelian variety is defined as in Shimura and Taniyama's book [loc. cit.]. The main result of the author implies the following theorem: The field of moduli of A (with respect to any polarization of A) is contained in the class field of the field of moduli of the factors B_i. See also Shimura [Osaka Math. J. **14** (1962), 33–44, Proposition 1]. *P. Roquette* (Tübingen)

Citations: MR 23# A2419 = G15-19.

G15-26 (29# 2241)

Ramachandra, K.

Some applications of Kronecker's limit formulas.

Ann. of Math. (2) **80** (1964), 104–148.

This paper contains some remarkable new results on the construction of the ray class fields of an imaginary quadratic number field. The proofs depend largely on calculations involving special modular functions in connection with Kronecker's limit formulae. Let

$$\vartheta(z; u, v) = \sum_{n=-\infty}^{+\infty} e^{\pi iz(n-v)^2 + 2\pi inu - \pi iuv}$$

with rational u, v of common denominator f and

$$\Phi(z; u, v) = \{\vartheta(z; u, v)\eta(z)^{-1}\}^{12},$$

where $\eta(z)$ is the classical eta function. The functional equation due to Kronecker,

$$\Phi^f(M(z); M(u, v)) = \Phi^f(z; u, v),$$

for each substitution M of the elliptic modular group, is the basis of the following considerations.

Notations: P is the field of rational numbers; Σ an imaginary quadratic extension of P with discriminant d and different $\mathfrak{d}$; $\mathfrak{f}$, $\mathfrak{g}$ integral ideals of Σ; $\mathfrak{g}$ a divisor of $\mathfrak{f}$; $\bar{\mathfrak{f}}$ the complex conjugate ideal; $\Sigma_{\mathfrak{f}}$, $\Sigma_{\bar{\mathfrak{f}}}$ the class fields over Σ for the ray class groups mod $\mathfrak{f}$, $\bar{\mathfrak{f}}$; f the smallest positive rational integer divisible by $\mathfrak{f}$.

For a ray class R mod f put

$$\Phi_{\mathfrak{f},\mathfrak{g}}(R) = \Phi^f\left(\frac{\beta_2}{\beta_1}; s(\beta_1), s(\beta_2)\right),$$

where β_1, β_2 is a basis of $\mathfrak{b}\mathfrak{g}/\mathfrak{d}\mathfrak{f}$, $\mathfrak{b}$ being an ideal of the ray class R, and where s denotes the trace with respect to P. This is an invariant of R. The author also defines $\Phi_{\mathfrak{f},\mathfrak{f}}(R)$; however, the reviewer does not understand why that expression is also an invariant of R. Perhaps a correction is necessary. Kronecker's limit formula now yields (1) $\sum_R \bar{\chi}(R) \log|\Phi_{\mathfrak{f},\mathfrak{g}}(R)| = 0$ if $\mathfrak{g}$ does not divide $\mathfrak{f}/\mathfrak{f}_\chi$, $r(\mathfrak{f}, \mathfrak{g}, \chi)L(1, \chi_0) \neq 0$ otherwise, the sum to be extended over all ray classes R mod $\mathfrak{f}$, where $\chi \neq 1$ is a character of the ray class group, $\mathfrak{f}_\chi$ the conductor of χ, χ_0 the proper character mod $\mathfrak{f}_\chi$ defined by χ, and $r(\mathfrak{f}, \mathfrak{g}, \chi)$ an elementary factor. Similarly for the principal character

$$(2) \qquad \sum_R \log|\Phi_{\mathfrak{f},\mathfrak{g}}(R)| = 0$$

if $\mathfrak{f}/\mathfrak{g}$ is not a power of a prime ideal, and is $r(\mathfrak{f}, \mathfrak{g})L_d(1)$ otherwise, where $L_d(s) = \sum (d/n)n^{-s}$.

The $\Phi_{\mathfrak{f},\mathfrak{g}}(R)$ are conjugate algebraic numbers contained in $\Sigma_{\bar{\mathfrak{f}}}$. As a consequence of (2) they are units if $\mathfrak{g} = (1)$ and $\mathfrak{f}$ is a power of a prime ideal. Otherwise, suitable power products $\varepsilon(R)$ of them are units. Under the Galois group G of $\Sigma_{\bar{\mathfrak{f}}}/\Sigma$ they behave as follows:

$$\Phi_{\mathfrak{f},(1)}(R)^\sigma = \Phi_{\mathfrak{f},(1)}(R\bar{S}_\sigma), \quad \varepsilon(R)^\sigma = \varepsilon(R\bar{S}_\sigma), \quad \sigma \in G,$$

where S_σ is the ray class mod $\bar{\mathfrak{f}}$ associated with σ in the sense of class field theory. The proof uses Hasse's foundation of complex multiplication [J. Reine Angew. Math. **157** (1926), 115–139; ibid. **165** (1931), 64–88]. As a consequence, the relative norms $\eta_{\Sigma_{\bar{\mathfrak{f}}}/K}(\varepsilon(R))$ with respect to an intermediate field K between Σ and $\Sigma_{\bar{\mathfrak{f}}}$ generate that field.

The units $\varepsilon(R)^{\sigma-1}$ $(\sigma \in G)$ generate a subgroup of finite index in the total unit group of $\Sigma_{\bar{\mathfrak{f}}}$. Combining (1) and (2) with the class number formula, this index turns out to be the class number $H_{\mathfrak{f}}$ of $\Sigma_{\mathfrak{f}}$ times a factor consisting of the numbers h of absolute ideal classes, $h_{\mathfrak{f}}$ of ray classes mod $\mathfrak{f}$ in Σ, and of elementary expressions. This formula generalizes one given by Fueter [Rend. Circ. Mat. Palermo **29** (1910), 380–395] and Siegel [*Lectures on advanced analytic number theory*, Tata Inst. Fund. Res., Bombay, 1961].

In the last section the author proves that the values taken by a modular form $f(z)$ and its derivatives $f'(z)$, $f''(z)$, $\cdots$ for $z \in \Sigma$ are rationally expressible by algebraic numbers, by π, and by $\Delta^{1/u}(\sqrt{d})$, i.e., a suitable root of the delta function. Furthermore, $\Delta(\sqrt{d})$ is expressed in terms of $\Gamma(m/d)$, $m = 1, \cdots, |d|-1$. The paper closes with some applications on the algebraic nature of certain elliptic integrals, one of which was first stated by Chowla and Selberg [Proc. Nat. Acad. Sci. U.S.A. **35** (1949), 371–374; MR **11**, 84]. *M. Eichler* (Basel)

Citations: MR 11, 84d = E44-5.
Referred to in E44-45, R20-68, R20-81.

G15-27 (29# 4739)

Shimura, Goro
On the field of definition for a field of automorphic functions.
Ann. of Math. (2) **80** (1964), 160–189.

As shown in detail by the author in a series of earlier publications [see, for example, same Ann. (2) **79** (1964), 369–409; MR **28** #2104], the study of families of polarized abelian varieties with prescribed algebras of endomorphisms is directly related to certain discontinuous groups and the fields of automorphic functions belonging to these groups. This study is continued here, and leads to the determination of the arithmetical field of definition for the field of moduli of such families in several important cases, viz., the following: (i) The given algebra of endomorphisms L is a totally real algebraic number-field F; (ii) L is a totally indefinite quaternion algebra over F; (iii) L is a totally imaginary quadratic extension of F. In each one of these cases, the family of abelian varieties can be defined by data consisting of a vector-space V over L, an anti-hermitian form T on V, and a lattice M in V; these data determine a semisimple Lie group G and an "arithmetical" discrete subgroup Γ of G; if H is the Riemannian symmetric space belonging to G (with its natural complex structure), the field of moduli of the family in question is in many cases the field of automorphic functions for $\Gamma\backslash G$, or else it is a suitably determined subfield of that field. The purpose of the paper is to show, under suitable restrictions (sometimes of rather delicate arithmetical nature) on the lattice M, that the arithmetical field of definition for the field of moduli is the rational number-field in cases (i) and (ii) and in a certain subcase of (iii), and that otherwise, in case (iii), it is an unramified class-field over a totally imaginary quadratic extension of a totally real field, whose explicit description is given in terms of class-field theory. The proof relies heavily on previous work by the same author, and particularly upon his earlier results on the arithmetical theory of the groups in question. Case (iii), involving, as it does, a generalization of the main result in the theory of complex multiplication for abelian varieties [cf. the author and Y. Taniyama, *Complex multiplication of abelian varieties and its applications to number theory*, Chapter IV, § 15, Math. Soc. Japan, Tokyo, 1961; MR **23** #A2419] and of the concept of "dual CM-types" [ibid., Chapter II, § 8], is by far the most difficult one; a decisive step in the proof consists in showing that a "generic" abelian variety in the family under consideration can be specialized, over an arbitrarily large number-field, to an abelian variety with complex multiplication [as defined, loc. cit., Chapter II, § 6], to which the theory of complex multiplication can then be applied. *A. Weil* (Princeton, N.J.)

Citations: MR 23# A2419 = G15-19; MR 28# 2104 = E12-102.
Referred to in F50-38, F50-42, G15-29, G15-34, G15-47.

G15-28 (29# 4754)

Deuring, M.
Die Klassenkörper der komplexen Multiplikation.
Enzyklopädie der mathematischen Wissenschaften: Mit Einschluss ihrer Anwendungen, Band I 2, Heft 10, Teil II (Article I 2, 23).
B. G. Teubner Verlagsgesellschaft, Stuttgart, 1958. 60 *pp.* *DM* 15.00.

Table of contents: (A) Funktionentheoretische Grundlagen; (B) Zahlentheoretische Grundlagen; (C) Der erste Hauptsatz; (D) Der zweite Hauptsatz; (E) Bemerkungen und Literatur.

Referred to in G15-48.

G15-29 (30# 65)

Shimura, Goro
Class-fields and automorphic functions.
Ann. of Math. (2) **80** (1964), 444–463.

Let F be a totally real algebraic number field of degree $[F:Q]=g$ and D a quaternion algebra over F. Then $D \otimes_Q R = M(R) \times \cdots \times K \times \cdots$, where Q, R, K denote the fields of rationals, of reals, and of the Hamilton quaternions, and $M_2(R)$ is the matrix algebra of degree 2. If D/F is ramified at t infinite prime spots, K occurs t times and $M_2(R)$ occurs $g-t$ times. Let $\mathfrak{o}$ be a maximal order in D and $\Gamma(\mathfrak{o})$ the group of units of $\mathfrak{o}$ of norm 1 with respect to F. $\Gamma(\mathfrak{o})$ has a representation as a discontinuous group of transformations of $g-t$ copies of the upper half-plane. The author considers the field of automorphic functions $Y(\mathfrak{o})$ with respect to this group over the complex field C. If $t=0$, $Y(\mathfrak{o})$ can be defined over Q. If $t>0$, there exists a "bottom field" $B \subset C$ of $Y(\mathfrak{o})$ defined in the following way: (1) Each field of definition $A \subseteq C$ of $Y(\mathfrak{o})$ (such that there exists an algebraic function field $Y_A(\mathfrak{o})$ with the constant field A and with $Y_A(\mathfrak{o})C = Y(\mathfrak{o})$) contains B; (2) Each automorphism of such an A leaves all elements of B fixed. There exists a certain absolute class field $K(D)$ over F which contains B and, under certain assumptions on D, the composite of F and B is equal to $K(D)$. Moreover, let $\mathfrak{o}'$ be another maximal order of D and $\mathfrak{a}$ an ideal in D with left order $\mathfrak{o}$ and right order $\mathfrak{o}'$. If σ is the element of the Galois group of $K(D)/F$ belonging to the class of $n_{D/F}(\mathfrak{a})$, then $Y(\mathfrak{o})^\sigma = Y(\mathfrak{o}')$. The complete description of the class group belonging to $K(D)$ is somewhat lengthy. The proof is based on earlier papers of the author, especially that in same Ann. (2) **80** (1964), 160–189 [MR **29** #4739]. *M. Eichler* (Basel)

Citations: MR 29# 4739 = G15-27.
Referred to in F50-38.

G15-30 (30# 1128)

Shimura, Goro
On the class-fields obtained by complex multiplication of abelian varieties.
Osaka Math. J. **14** (1962), 33–44.

Since Hecke's early work, it was well known that complex multiplication, for abelian varieties of dimension > 1, fails to generate the full class-fields of the algebraic number-fields under consideration; the book by the author and Y. Taniyama, *Complex multiplication of abelian varieties and its applications to number theory* [Math. Soc. Japan, Tokyo, 1961; MR **23** #A2419] contains all that is required for a precise determination of the class-fields which can be so generated, but the results had not yet been made explicit; this is done here. Roughly speaking, if F is a totally imaginary quadratic extension of a totally real field F_0, "almost all" of the maximal abelian extension of F can be generated by the maximal abelian extension of F_0 (as to which the theory of complex multiplication offers no clue) and by complex multiplication. Special attention is given to the case where F is a cyclotomic field. Two typical special applications may be quoted here: (a) Let F be an imaginary cyclotomic field with odd relative class-number over its maximal real subfield F_0; then the absolute class-field of F is generated by that of F_0 and by the unramified extensions of F obtained by the fields of moduli of two suitable polarized abelian varieties having subfields of F as endomorphism algebras; (b) Let F be a totally imaginary quadratic extension, with odd class-number, of a totally real field $F_0 \neq Q$; let s be a positive integer such that $\sqrt{-s} \notin F$; then the absolute class-field of F is contained in the field generated by the absolute class-field of F_0 and the field of moduli of a suitable polarized abelian variety having $F(\sqrt{-s})$ as its algebra of endomorphisms. *A. Weil* (Princeton, N.J.)

Citations: MR 23# A2419 = G15-19.
Referred to in G15-33.

G15-31 (30# 3083)

Kempfert, H.

Zum allgemeinen Hauptidealsatz.

J. Reine Angew. Math. **210** (1962), 38–64.

Sei $k=P(\sqrt{l})$ ein imaginär-quadratischer Zahlkörper, $\mathfrak{f}\neq 1$ der Führer einer Strahlklasseneinteilung in k und $K_{\mathfrak{f}}$ der Strahlklassenkörper mod $\mathfrak{f}$ von k. Verfasser beweist mit den Mitteln der komplexen Multiplikation, d.h. ohne wesentlichen Rückgriff auf die allgemeine Klassenkörpertheorie, den folgenden verschärften Hauptidealsatz: Jeder zu $\mathfrak{f}$ prime Divisor von k ist in $K_{\mathfrak{f}}$ ein im Strahl mod $\mathfrak{F}(K_{\mathfrak{f}}/k)$ gelegener Hauptdivisor, wobei $\mathfrak{F}(K_{\mathfrak{f}}/k)$ der als Quotient aus Führer und Differente definierte Geschlechtermodul ist. Dieser Beweis erfolgt mit den aus dem Fueterschen Buche [*Vorlesungen über die singulären Moduln und die komplexe Multiplikation der elliptischen Funktionen*, Bänder I, II, Teubner, Leipzig, 1924/27] bekannten Methoden und benutzt die dort verwendeten gegenüber Basistransformationen der Periodenmoduln nicht invarianten elliptischen Funktionen zweiter Stufe.

K. Alber (Zbl **109**, 267)

Referred to in R38-42.

G15-32 (32# 2413)

Kuga, Michio; Shimura, Goro

On the zeta function of a fibre variety whose fibres are abelian varieties.

Ann. of Math. (2) **82** (1965), 478–539.

The main purpose of this paper is to express the Hasse-Weil zeta-function, or more generally L-functions, of certain projective varieties in terms of Dirichlet series associated with rings of Hecke operators on spaces of automorphic forms for certain fuchsian groups. This generalizes earlier work of the second author [J. Math. Soc. Japan **13** (1961), 275–331; MR **26** #84] devoted to zeta-functions of certain curves, and involves traces of Hecke operators on spaces of automorphic forms of weight >2. Let Φ be an indefinite quaternion division algebra over $\mathbf{Q}$, $\mathfrak{o}$ a maximal order of Φ, Γ_1 the group of units of $\mathfrak{o}$, and Γ_b a congruence subgroup of Γ_1 (b a positive integer; in the paper it may be a two-sided ideal). In a natural way, Γ_b may be identified with a properly discontinuous group of automorphisms of the upper-half plane $\mathfrak{H}$, which acts freely if $b>2$, as is assumed, and the quotient $V=\mathfrak{H}/\Gamma_b$ is compact. V is the base space of a fibre system W of polarized two-dimensional abelian varieties whose endomorphism ring contains $\mathfrak{o}$. Let $W_{m,b}$ be the fibre product over V of m copies of W if $m\geqq 1$, and let $V=W_{0,b}$. Results of the second author [Ann. of Math. (2) **81** (1965), 124–165; MR **30** #2010] imply that $W_{m,b}$ has a projective model defined over the cyclotomic field $\mathbf{Q}(\zeta)$ ($\zeta=\exp 2\pi i/b$), or over $\mathbf{Q}$ if b is prime to the discriminant $d(\Phi)$ of Φ. On the other hand, there is a natural representation $(\Gamma\cdot\xi\cdot\Gamma)\rightarrow(\Gamma\cdot\xi\cdot\Gamma)_k$ of the Hecke algebra generated over $\mathbf{C}$ by the double cosets $\Gamma_b\cdot\xi\cdot\Gamma_b$ ($\xi\in\Delta_1=\{\xi\in\mathfrak{o}: \det\xi>0\}$) on the space $\mathfrak{S}_k(\Gamma_b)$ of automorphic forms of weight k for Γ_b. The Dirichlet series $D(s; k, b)=\sum(\Gamma_b\cdot\xi\cdot\Gamma_b)_k\cdot(\det\xi)^{-s}$ (where ξ runs through a suitable subset of Δ_1) is known to extend on the s-plane to a holomorphic function with functional equation and Euler product, $D(s,k,b)=\prod_p H(p^{-s},k,b)^{-1}$, where $H(u,k,b)$ is a polynomial of degree 1 or 2 [Shimura, ibid. (2) **78** (1963), 149–192; MR **27** #5934]. Let the prime p be such that the reduction mod p of the fibre system $W_{m,b}$ is good. Let $(p, d(\Phi))=1$. A special case of a main result of the paper expresses the zeta function $Z(u, p(W_{m,b}))$ over the prime field of the reduced variety $p(W_{m,b})$ as a power product of determinants of Hecke polynomials $H(p^i u, k, b)$ (i half-integer, $k\leqq 4m+2$) by an explicitly given factor, with exponents independent of p. This implies that the global zeta function $Z(s, W_{m,b})=\prod_p Z(p^{-s}, p(W_{m,b}))$ of $W_{m,b}$ is the product of rational functions of p^{-s} for finitely many p's by a power product of determinants of Dirichlet series of the form $D(s-i, k, b)$. In fact, the authors consider more generally vector-valued automorphic forms for Γ_1, with respect to automorphy factors which are products of $(cz+d)^{-k}$ by some representation of Γ_1/Γ_b, and Dirichlet series over double cosets of Γ_1 associated to such spaces of automorphic forms, and relate them similarly to local and global L-functions of $W_{m,b}$ with respect to real-valued characters of a certain subgroup of the group of units of $\mathfrak{o}/b\mathfrak{o}$, viewed as a group of birational transformations of $W_{m,b}$. This allows them to discuss the zeta function of $\mathfrak{p}(W_{m,b})$ also when b divides $d(\Phi)$. This shows that the L-functions considered extend to meromorphic functions on the s-plane. On the other hand, Weil's conjectures (or Weil's theorem if $m=0$) imply estimates for the modulus of the eigenvalues of Hecke operators.

The proofs are, in principle, analogous to those given earlier, but are technically much more involved, and new problems have to be solved. A double coset $\Gamma_b\cdot\alpha\cdot\Gamma_b$ ($\alpha\in\Delta_1$) defines a correspondence $X_m(\Gamma_b\cdot\alpha\cdot\Gamma_b)$ of $W_{m,b}$. The first main step is to compute its intersection number $I_0(X_m(\Gamma_b\cdot\alpha\cdot\Gamma_b))$ with the diagonal. This has been done by the first author [*Fibre varieties over a symmetric space whose fibres are abelian varieties*, Math. Lecture Notes, Univ. Chicago, Chicago, Ill., 1964], via the Lefschetz fixed point theorem; the cohomology spaces of $W_{m,b}$ are identified with cohomology spaces of Γ, and the latter with spaces of automorphic forms by results of Eichler and Shimura; this relates I_0 to traces of Hecke operators. The second main step is to determine the reduction mod p of $X_m(\Gamma\cdot\alpha\cdot\Gamma)$ for the $\Gamma\cdot\alpha\cdot\Gamma$ which occur in Hecke polynomials. It is expressed in terms of the Frobenius correspondence, and of a correspondence related to it. Since I_0 is invariant under reduction, this allows one to connect I_0 with numbers of points of $p(W_{m,b})$ over finite fields, and then leads to the main results.

A. Borel (Princeton, N.J.)

Citations: MR 26# 84 = G30-31; MR 27# 5934 = F55-16; MR 30# 2010 = F50-38.
Referred to in F55-21, G15-47.

G15-33 (32# 7558)

Kubota, Tomio

On the field extension by complex multiplication.

Trans. Amer. Math. Soc. **118** (1965), 113–122.

Sei F ein algebraischer Zahlkörper mit $[F:\mathbf{Q}]=2n$ und $\varphi_1, \cdots, \varphi_n$ n verschiedene Isomorphismen $F\to\mathbf{C}$, so daß zwei Unterkörper K, K_0 von F existieren, für die folgende Bedingungen erfüllt sind: (1) K_0 ist ein total-reeller Zahlkörper und K ist eine rein-imaginäre quadratische Erweiterung von K_0; (2) für $i\neq j$ sind $\varphi_i|K$ und $\varphi_j|K$ nicht komplex-konjugiert. Weiter sei $(F^*;(\psi_i))$ der duale CM-Typ von dem CM-Typ $(F;(\varphi_i))$ [siehe G. Shimura und J. Taniyama, *Complex multiplication of Abelian varieties and its applications to number theory*, The Math. Soc. of Japan, Tokyo, 1961; MR **23** #A2419] und A eine zu $(F^*;(\psi_i))$ gehörige abelsche Mannigfaltigkeit.

Zu jedem ganzen Ideal $\mathfrak{b}$ des Zahlkörpers F^* bilde man die Gruppe $H(\mathfrak{b})$ aller gebrochenen Ideale $\mathfrak{a}$ von F, welche zu b (b ist die kleinste natürliche Zahl $\neq 0$ aus $\mathfrak{b}$) prim sind und für die ein $\mu\in F^*$ mit $\prod_{i=1}^n \mathfrak{a}^{\varphi_i}=(\mu)_{F^*}$, $\mu\bar{\mu}=N\mathfrak{a}$ und $\mu\equiv 1 \pmod{\mathfrak{b}}$ existiert. Mit $K_\mathfrak{b}$ bezeichne man den zu $H(\mathfrak{b})$ gehörigen Klassenkörper über F.

Falls A eine elliptische Kurve ist, ist $\bigcup_\mathfrak{b} K_\mathfrak{b}$ die größte abelsche Erweiterung von F. Eine Verallgemeinerung dieses Ergebnisses hat G. Shimura in Osaka Math. J. **14** (1962), 33–44 [MR **30** #1128] bewiesen.

Der Verfasser der vorliegenden Arbeit beweist ein Analogon des obigen Sachverhalts.

Für jede Primzahl p wird die p-Dimension $\dim_p(K|F)$ von einer beliebigen abelschen Erweiterung K von F definiert. Weiter definiert der Verfasser, daß eine abelsche Erweiterung K von F eine divisible p-Erweiterung von F ist, wenn die Charaktergruppe von der Galoisgruppe $\Gamma(K, F)$ eine divisible p-Gruppe ist. Der Hauptsatz der Arbeit (vgl. Theorem 1) lautet: Sei $(F;(\varphi_i))$ ein CM-Typ und $K_c=\bigcup_\mathfrak{b} K_\mathfrak{b}$ ($\mathfrak{b}$ durchläuft alle ganzen Ideale des Zahlkörpers F^*). Weiter sei A eine zu dem dualen CM-Typ $(F^*;(\psi_i))$ von $(F;(\varphi_i))$ gehörige abelsche Mannigfaltigkeit. Unter diesen Voraussetzungen gilt für jede Primzahl p die Ungleichung $\dim_p(K_c|F)\leqq\dim(A)+1$. Das Gleichheitszeichen gilt genau dann, wenn $(F;(\varphi_i))$ nicht ausgeartet ist.

Aus dem Hauptsatz folgt: Ist $(F;(\varphi_i))$ nicht ausgeartet, dann gilt für jede Primzahl p, $K_{a,p}=K_{c,p}$, wobei $K_{a,p}$ $[K_{c,p}]$ die maximale divisible p-Erweiterung von F ist, welche in K_a $[K_c]$ enthalten ist. (K_a ist die maximale abelsche Erweiterung von F.) *N. Guthschmidt* (Berlin)

Citations: MR 23# A2419 = G15-19; MR 30# 1128 = G15-30.

G15-34 (33# 7339)

Shimura, Gorô

Moduli and fibre systems of abelian varieties.

Ann. of Math. (2) **83** (1966), 294–338.

This is a sequel to the author's papers [same Ann. (2) **70** (1959), 101–144; MR **21** #6370; ibid. (2) **78** (1963), 149–192; MR **27** #5934; ibid. (2) **80** (1964), 160–189; MR **29** #4739; ibid. (2) **81** (1965), 124–165; MR **30** #2010] and seems to be the concluding one in algebro-geometric parts. The paper consists of the following seven sections: (1) Generalities on a fibre system of abelian varieties; (2) Maximal families of polarized abelian varieties; (3) The family Σ_Ω of PEL-structures; (4) Deformation of PEL-structures; (5) Main theorems concerning fibre systems; (6) Moduli of PEL-structures; (7) The number field k_Ω and concluding remarks. Let L be a division algebra over $\mathbf{Q}$. A PEL-structure $\mathcal{Q}=(A, \mathcal{C}, \theta; t_1, \cdots, t_s)$ with endomorphism ring L is defined as a combination of a polarized abelian variety $(A, \mathcal{C})$, an isomorphism θ of L into $\mathrm{End}_\mathbf{Q}(A)$, and points $t_1, \cdots, t_s$ of A of finite order, where the involution of $\mathrm{End}_\mathbf{Q}(A)$ determined by $\mathcal{C}$ induces a positive involution on $\theta(L)$. On the other hand, a PEL-type $\Omega=(L, \Phi, \rho; T, \mathcal{M}; v_1, \cdots, v_s)$ is formed by a division algebra L over $\mathbf{Q}$ with a positive involution ρ, a representation Φ of L by complex matrices, an L-valued ρ-anti-hermitian form T on $L^m\times L^m$, a lattice $\mathcal{M}$ in L^m and points $v_1, \cdots, v_s$ of L^m. The author defines in a natural way that $\mathcal{Q}$ be of type Ω.

In his previous paper [ibid. (2) **78** (1963), 149–192; MR **27** #5934], the author discussed a symmetric domain $\mathcal{H}(\Omega)$ which is a space of analytic moduli of PEL-structures of type Ω and a discontinuous subgroup $\Gamma(\Omega)$ of the automorphism-group of $\mathcal{H}(\Omega)$ related to the type Ω in the case with no level. The main results in the paper under review are as follows. (I) Sections 1–3: After a general theory of fibre systems and an expository section, it is shown that any PEL-structure $\mathcal{Q}$ belongs to one and only one type Ω (up to equivalence). If the level of type Ω is sufficiently high and if the dimension of $\mathcal{H}(\Omega)$ is not equal to one or $\mathcal{H}(\Omega)/\Gamma(\Omega)$ is compact, then there is a fibre system $\mathcal{F}(\Omega)$ of PEL-structures of type Ω, of which two fibres are not isomorphic, and which covers all PEL-structures of the type Ω. Moreover, the fibre system $\mathcal{F}(\Omega)$ is constructed as a Zariski open subset of a projective variety. The proof is based on the author's theorem about holomorphic property of Chow points [discussed by Shimura in Séminaire Henri Cartan, 1957/1958, Exposés 18, 19, 20, Secrétariat mathématique, Paris, 1958; MR **21** #2750], transformation formulas of ϑ-functions and the Baily-Borel theorem on quotient spaces of symmetric domains by arithmetically defined discontinuous groups. (II) Sections 4 and 5: After proving that all members belonging to a fibre system of PEL-structures are of the same type Ω, the author verifies the existence of an algebraic number field k_Ω which has properties such as those of the "field of moduli of the type Ω" (although he does not use the term "fields of moduli of types"). (III) Section 5: Applying Weil's criterion to lower fields of rationality, the field of rationality of $\mathcal{F}(\Omega)$ in (I) is descended to k_Ω. Each point of the parameter variety of $\mathcal{F}(\Omega)$ generates, over k_Ω, the field of moduli of the corresponding PEL-structure. It is also proved that $\mathcal{F}(\Omega)$ has a universal property as fibre system of PEL-structures of type Ω. (IV) Section 6: Even when the fibre system $\mathcal{F}(\Omega)$ does not exist, the author constructs a variety of moduli of PEL-structures of type Ω with as nice properties as those of the above $\mathcal{F}(\Omega)$. (V) The final section 7 is devoted to number-theoretic interest and to directions of further research in this line.

Though quite a few authors have recently discussed the same kind of problems (e.g., D. Mumford [*Geometric invariant theory*, Springer, Berlin, 1965], C. L. Siegel [Nachr. Akad. Wiss. Göttingen Math.-Phys. Kl. II **1963**, 365–427; MR **29** #3473], etc.), the reviewer thinks that among others, the determination of fields of rationality of varieties of moduli, and the exact relationships between the field of moduli of a PEL-structure and coordinates of its corresponding point on the variety of moduli are proper and remarkable results in the paper. *S. Koizumi* (Tokyo)

Citations: MR 21# 2750 = F02-5; MR 21# 6370 = F55-11; MR 27# 5934 = F55-16; MR 29# 3473 = F50-29; MR 29# 4739 = G15-27; MR 30# 2010 = F50-38.

Referred to in G15-45, G15-47, G15-51.

G15-35 (34# 1278)

Borel, A.; Chowla, S.; Herz, C. S.; Iwasawa, K.; Serre, J.-P.

Seminar on complex multiplication.

Seminar held at the Institute for Advanced Study,

Princeton, N.J., 1957–58. Lecture Notes in Mathematics, No. 21.
Springer-Verlag, Berlin-New York, 1966. ii + 102 *pp.* (*not consecutively paged*) *DM* 8.00.
Table of contents: J.-P. Serre, Statement of results; J.-P. Serre, Modular forms; A. Borel, Class invariants. I; A. Borel, Class invariants. II; K. Iwasawa, Class fields; S. Chowla, Remarks on class-invariants and related topics; C. S. Herz, Construction of class fields; C. S. Herz, Computation of singular j-invariants.

Referred to in R14-59, R26-45, Z02-67.

G15-36 **(34# 4254)**

Kubota, Tomio

An application of the power residue theory to some abelian functions.

Nagoya Math. J. **27** (1966), 51–54.

Example (2) on page 129 of G. Shimura and S. Taniyama's *Complex multiplication of abelian varieties and its applications to number theory* [Math. Soc. Japan, Tokyo, 1961; MR **23** #A2419], contains a proof of a particular case of Stickelberger's relation in the theory of Gauss's sums. One considers the Jacobian variety of the curve $y^2 = 1 - x^l$, where l is an odd prime, and the result is then an immediate consequence of class field theory and the product relation of their main Theorem 1 on page 128. In this paper, the author initiates a deeper study of such product relations for abelian functions at points of finite order of an abelian variety, by considering varieties which are "like" the one in the example (to quote the details would involve copying out the paper). This product is reminiscent of Stickelberger's relation and the author hopes that his theorem may lead to a "Stickelberger's relation" for abelian functions. *J. V. Armitage* (Durham)

Citations: MR 23# A2419 = G15-19.

G15-37 **(34# 4268)**

Shimura, Goro

Construction of class fields and zeta functions of algebraic curves.

Ann. of Math. (2) **85** (1967), 58–159.

Let F be a totally real algebraic number field of degree g and B a quaternion algebra over F which is not ramified at r infinite prime spots. Furthermore, denote by $\mathfrak{o}$ a maximal order of B and by $\Gamma(\mathfrak{o})$, $\Gamma_1(\mathfrak{o})$ the groups of units of $\mathfrak{o}$ whose norms with respect to F are either totally positive or even 1. To each unramified infinite prime spot of F there corresponds a representation of B by real matrices $\begin{pmatrix} a_v & b_v \\ c_v & d_v \end{pmatrix}$ whose coefficients lie in some quadratic extension of F. Now take r copies $\mathfrak{H}_v$ of the complex upper half plane $\mathfrak{H}$ and transform r variables z_v ranging in $\mathfrak{H}_v$ into $z_v' = (a_v z_v + b_v)(c_v z_v + d_v)^{-1}$, where $\begin{pmatrix} a_v & b_v \\ c_v & d_v \end{pmatrix}$ represent the elements of $\Gamma(\mathfrak{o})$ or $\Gamma_1(\mathfrak{o})$. There exist fundamental domains $\prod \mathfrak{H}_v/\Gamma(\mathfrak{o})$ or $\prod \mathfrak{H}_v/\Gamma_1(\mathfrak{o})$. The author treats the extreme cases $r = 1$ and $r = g$, of which the first is by far the most interesting.

Let $r = 1$. Then $\mathfrak{H}/\Gamma(\mathfrak{o})$ is conformally equivalent with a complete nonsingular algebraic curve V which can be defined over the absolute (Hilbert) class field $C(F)$ of F. If M is a totally imaginary quadratic extension of F, there exists an optimal imbedding of M in one of the maximal orders $\mathfrak{o}$ (in the sense of E. Noether), and this in turn generates a family of correspondences of V with itself having the same fixed points $z_M \in \mathfrak{H}$. If $\varphi(z)$ is a function defined at the same time over V, the adjunction of $\varphi(z_M)$ generates the absolute class field over M. For each prime ideal $\mathfrak{P}$ in M whose norm with respect to F is principal, there exists an element $\pi \in \mathfrak{o}_\sigma$ having the same norm and (under some further restrictions) $\varphi(z_M)^\sigma = \varphi(\pi^{-1}(z_M))$, where σ is the Frobenius automorphism of the prime factors of $\mathfrak{P}$ in the class field $C(M)$. A number of interesting examples can be carried out explicitly, in which F is either a real quadratic field or the real subfield of a cyclotomic field and $\Gamma_1(\mathfrak{o})$ is a simple "triangle group".

The proof is difficult and lengthy. It is based on a family $\{A\}$ of Abelian varieties, parametrized by V in a specific way, without V being the variety of moduli of these A. To each totally imaginary extension K/F, there corresponds such a family $\{A\}_K$, whose elements have endomorphism rings $\supseteq K \otimes_F B$. From all these a subfamily can be extracted. The details are too involved to be explained here.

Now let $r = g$. One reason why in this case the theory encounters far smaller difficulties may be stated as follows: the groups $\Gamma_1(\mathfrak{o})$ can be obtained simply by specialisations of the Siegel modular group. Now V is a g-dimensional variety, defined over $\mathbf{Q}$, specifically the variety of moduli of a family of Abelian varieties. Again the fixed points of correspondences generate absolute class fields over totally imaginary quadratic extensions M/F which are imbedded in B, or of some other fields closely related to M and depending on the way of embedding M in B. If $\Gamma_1(\mathfrak{o})$ is replaced by a congruence subgroup, one gets in this way ray class fields. A complete formulation of the final results would be rather lengthy.

For the cases $1 < r < g$, only conjectures are given.

Let again $r = 1$. The correspondences used so far are in principle of Hecke's type. Let $T(\mathfrak{a})$ be the matrix representation of the Hecke operator corresponding to an integral ideal $\mathfrak{a}$ of F in the space of differentials of first kind. (If the class number of F is > 1, it may be necessary to consider several $\mathfrak{o}$ and their corresponding V.) Then $Z(s) = \sum_{\mathfrak{a}} T(\mathfrak{a}) N(\mathfrak{a})^{-s}$ is a zeta function with conventional properties; in particular, it has an Euler product. Take a prime factor $\mathfrak{P}$ in $C(F)$ of a prime ideal $\mathfrak{p}$ in F and reduce V mod $\mathfrak{P}$. Then, for almost all $\mathfrak{P}$, the determinant of the Euler factor $Z_{\mathfrak{p}}(s)$ is the inverse of the denominator of the zeta function of $V/\mathfrak{P}$. As in special cases treated earlier by the author, the proof is based on the identity $T(\mathfrak{p})/\mathfrak{P} = \pi + \pi^*$, where π is the Frobenius correspondence and $T(\mathfrak{p})$ means this time the Hecke correspondence in the abstract sense. Since $Z(s)$ can be continued holomorphically to the whole s-plane and satisfies a functional equation [the author, same Ann. (2) **76** (1962), 237–294; MR **33** #1292], this last result entails the Hasse conjecture for V.

M. Eichler (Basel)

Citations: MR 33# 1292 = F65-16.

Referred to in F15-24, G15-38, G15-40, G15-45, G15-52.

G15-38 **(40# 1396)**

Shimura, Gorô

Number fields and zeta functions associated with discontinuous groups and algebraic varieties.

Proc. Internat. Congr. Math. (*Moscow*, 1966), *pp.* 290–299. *Izdat. "Mir", Moscow*, 1968.

Das Vorliegende ist im wesentlichen ein Bericht über eine frühere Arbeit des Autors [Ann. of Math. (2) **85** (1967), 58–159; MR **34** #4268]. *H. Popp* (Heidelberg)

Citations: MR 34# 4268 = G15-37.

G15-39 **(35# 1559)**

Doi, Koji; Naganuma, Hidehisa

On the Jacobian varieties of the fields of elliptic modular functions. II.

J. Math. Kyoto Univ. **6** (1967), 177–185.

The authors consider algebraic curves uniformized by elliptic modular functions which have the additional property that their endomorphism algebra is a real quadratic field $\mathbf{Q}(\sqrt{d})$. For a prime ideal $\mathfrak{l}$ of $\mathbf{Q}(\sqrt{d})$, they form the extension $K(\mathfrak{l})/\mathbf{Q}$ generated by the coordinates of the $\mathfrak{l}$-section points. The Galois group of this field is either $\mathrm{GL}(2, \mathrm{GF}(l))$ or $\mathrm{GF}(l)^* \cdot \mathrm{SL}(2, \mathrm{GF}(l^2))$ according as $(d/l) = 1$ or -1 (where l is the rational prime divisible by $\mathfrak{l}$). Actually, a more general but also more technical result on the Galois group of $K(\mathfrak{l})/\mathbf{Q}$ is proved where $\mathbf{Q}(\sqrt{d})$ is replaced by an arbitrary totally real number field. Now the genus of the curve is assumed to be 1, and the curve is reduced modulo a rational prime p not dividing the level. It is proved that the characteristic polynomial of the Frobenius correspondence is either exactly once divisible by $\mathfrak{l}$ or it is a quadratic non-residue mod $\mathfrak{l}$.

The paper is a sequel to one by the first author [Osaka J. Math. **15** (1963), 249–256; MR **32** #5655]. Furthermore, it is closely related to a paper of G. Shimura [J. Reine Angew. Math. **221** (1966), 209–220; MR **32** #5637].

M. Eichler (Basel)

Citations: MR 32# 5637 = R40-20; MR 32# 5655 = F10-90.

G15-40 (36# 5100)

Shimura, Gorô

Algebraic number fields and symplectic discontinuous groups.

Ann. of Math. (2) **86** (1967), 503–592.

With this paper a monumental series comes to a conclusion. As in the last paper [the author, same Ann. (2) **85** (1967), 58–159; MR **34** #4268] F is a totally real algebraic number field of degree g and B a quaternion algebra over F which is not ramified at r prime spots. Let $\mathfrak{o}$ be a maximal order in B and Γ the group of units of $\mathfrak{o}$ which are congruent 1 modulo an ideal $\mathfrak{c}$ of F. The group Γ can be represented as a discontinuous group acting on the product of r copies of the upper half plane. The automorphic functions with respect to this representation yield an algebraic variety $V(\mathfrak{c})$ of dimension r which is defined over a certain class field C over the smallest extension of F which is normal over $\mathbf{Q}$. It is impossible to formulate here the description of C which is explicitly given. The methods applied are essentially the same as in the paper quoted above, among which the consideration of isolated fixed points of elements of B plays a decisive rôle. But there also arise additional difficulties. For a particularly interesting result of the paper we quote from the author's introduction: "In the final § 11, we consider an infinite sequence of Galois coverings $V(\mathfrak{c}) \leftarrow V(\mathfrak{c}\mathfrak{l}) \leftarrow V(\mathfrak{c}\mathfrak{l}^2) \leftarrow \cdots$ for a prime ideal $\mathfrak{l}$ in F. Given an algebraic point y on $V(\mathfrak{c})$, take all the points on $V(\mathfrak{c}\mathfrak{l}^m)$ lying on y, and adjoin their coordinates to C. Then we obtain an infinite normal extension $\mathfrak{K}$ of $C(y)$ whose Galois group has a certain $\mathfrak{l}$-adic representation. We shall prove a few elementary properties of this representation for the Frobenius automorphism of $\mathfrak{K}$, which are analogous to those known for the points of finite order of an abelian variety. Actually if $r = g$, the former is essentially a paraphrase of the latter. But in the case $r < g$, our extension and its $\mathfrak{l}$-adic representation are new, though they are loosely connected with abelian varieties. When y is an isolated fixed point of some element of B, we know that $C(y)\mathfrak{K}$ is abelian over $C(y)$, and the $\mathfrak{l}$-adic representation of the Frobenius automorphism can be described by means of a Grössencharakter of $C(y)$. {Reviewer's remark: At this point we simplify, with some incorrectness, the original version.} However, if y is an arbitrary algebraic point on $V(\mathfrak{c})$, the nature of $\mathfrak{K}$ is quite mysterious. We have no way of even obtaining an example in the case $r < g$, for which the Frobenius automorphisms are explicitly given. It might be too early to predict how far one would be able to proceed in this direction. But it is at least certain that our canonical models should not be regarded only as a tool of constructing abelian extensions, since it is hoped that they will play some rôle in the study of non-abelian extensions. In this sense, the title of the previous paper may not have been the most appropriate one."

M. Eichler (Basel)

Citations: MR 34# 4268 = G15-37.

Referred to in G15-45, G15-52, R32-72.

G15-41 (36# 5103)

Shiratani, Katsumi

Über singuläre Invarianten elliptischer Funktionenkörper.

J. Reine Angew. Math. **226** (1967), 108–115.

A complex number j is called a "singular invariant" if the elliptic curve E (defined over the field of complex numbers) having j as its invariant admits complex multiplication. It is well known that then the endomorphism ring $\mathfrak{O}$ of E is an order in an imaginary quadratic number field Ω, that $\mathfrak{O}$ is uniquely determined, as an order of Ω, by its conductor m, and that the field $\Omega(j)$ is the ring class field of conductor m over Ω, in the sense of class field theory. Now let p be a prime number, and $\mathbf{F}_p$ the field of p elements. The author proves: Every algebraic element j_0 over $\mathbf{F}_p$ is the reduction modulo p of a singular invariant j such that $p \nmid m$. More precisely: Let f denote the degree of j_0 over $\mathbf{F}_p$. Then there exists a singular invariant j with $p \nmid m$ such that p has a prime divisor $\mathfrak{P}$ of degree f in $\Omega(j)$ and $j_0 = j \bmod \mathfrak{P}$ after a suitable identification of $\mathbf{F}_p(j_0)$ with the residue class field $\Omega(j) \bmod \mathfrak{P}$. The elliptic curve E_0 (defined over the algebraic closure of $\mathbf{F}_p$) having j_0 as its invariant always admits complex multiplication; its endomorphism ring $\mathfrak{O}_0$ is either an order in an imaginary quadratic number field Ω_0 or a maximal order in a quaternion algebra. According to these cases, j_0 is called "singular" or "supersingular"; in the latter case $j_0 \in \mathbf{F}_p$ or j_0 is of degree 2 over $\mathbf{F}_p$. The author proves: If j_0 is singular then j is uniquely determined, up to automorphisms over $\mathbf{Q}$, by the conditions stated above, and $\mathfrak{O} = \mathfrak{O}_0$. (If j_0 is supersingular then this uniqueness statement does not hold.) The case of a singular j_0 can be described by saying that p splits in $\Omega_0 = \Omega$. The proof of the author uses the algebraic theory of elliptic function fields and their reductions modulo p as developed by Deuring. Another proof, restricted to the cases $p \neq 2, 3$ and $f \equiv 1 \bmod 2$, and based on the analytic theory of modular functions, has recently been published by H. Hasse, in connection with his first proof of the Riemann hypothesis for elliptic curves [Simpos. Internaz. Geom. Algebr. (Roma, 1965), pp. 248–266, Edizioni Cremonese, Rome, 1967; see MR **35** #5441; = Rend. Mat. e Appl. (5) **25** (1966), 248–266; MR **35** #6681].

P. Roquette (Heidelberg)

Citations: MR 35# 5441 = Z10-27; MR 35# 6681 = G20-30.

Referred to in S99-12.

G15-42 (37# 1370)

Honda, Taira

On the Jacobian variety of the algebraic curve $y^2 = 1 - x^l$ over a field of characteristic $p > 0$.

Osaka J. Math. **3** (1966), 189–194.

Let J be the Jacobian variety of the curve $y^2 = 1 - x^l$, where l is an odd prime, and suppose that the ground field has characteristic $p \neq 2, l$. Then J is an abelian variety of dimension $\frac{1}{2}(l-1)$. The object of this paper is the study of the endomorphism ring $\mathscr{A}(J)$ of J and of $\mathscr{A}_0(J) = \mathscr{A}(J) \otimes \mathbf{Q}$. Denote by Z the endomorphism $(x, y) \to (\zeta x, y)$, where ζ is a primitive lth root of unity, and by Π the pth power endomorphism (the Frobenius). The author approaches $\mathscr{A}_0(J)$ via the ring $R = \mathbf{Q}(\Pi, Z)$ generated by Π

and Z, and uses the arithmetic characterization of Π^f, where f is the exponent of p modulo l, which was obtained by H. Davenport and H. Hasse [J. Reine Angew. Math. **172** (1934), 151–182] and is a special case of results of G. Shimura and Y. Taniyama [*Complex multiplication of abelian varieties and its applications to number theory*, Math. Soc. Japan, Tokyo, 1961; MR **23** #A2419]. The cases f even and f odd behave differently. When f is even, the structure of R is rather simple and the zeta-function of J coincides essentially with that of a direct product of elliptic curves of Hasse invariant zero. It is conjectured that J is isogenous to such a product (cf. Tate's Woods Hole conjectures [Uspehi Mat. Nauk **20** (1965), no. 6 (126), 27–40; MR **34** #1329; English version, #1371 below]), although $R=\mathbf{Q}(\Pi, Z)$ is smaller than the endomorphism ring of the latter. On the other hand, when f is odd the ring $\mathscr{A}_0(J)$ is just R and is a cyclic algebra over the decomposition field of ϕ in $\mathbf{Q}(Z)$. Its local invariants are determined completely by the prime ideal composition of Π^f. Since this also determines the formal structure of J [Ju. I. Manin, Uspehi Mat. Nauk **18** (1963), no. 6 (114), 3–90; MR **28** #1200], this produces simple abelian varieties with differing formal structures.

J. W. S. Cassels (Cambridge, England)

Citations: MR 23# A2419 = G15-19; MR 28# 1200 = G10-21; MR 34# 1329 = G02-18.

G15-43 (37# 2757)

Giraud, Jean

Remarque sur une formule de Shimura-Taniyama.

Invent. Math. **5** (1968), 231–236.

Let (A, i) be an abelian variety of CM-type $(F, (\varphi_i))$ defined over an algebraic number field K. Assume that A has non-degenerate reduction at the prime P of K. Then (with certain additional restrictions) there will exist an integer π of F such that the reduction of $i(\pi)$ is the Frobenius endomorphism of the reduction of A. The formula of the title then describes the decomposition of (π) into a product of prime ideals [G. Shimura and Y. Taniyama, *Complex multiplication of abelian varieties and its applications to number theory*, Math. Soc. Japan, Tokyo, 1961; MR **23** #A2419; see also Y. Taniyama, Proc. Internat. Sympos. Algebraic Number Theory (Tokyo and Nikko, 1955), pp. 31–45, Sci. Council of Japan, Tokyo, 1956; MR **18**, 601].

The formula is proved, in this paper, by a new method, the basis of which is the following result concerning an abelian variety A over a finite field k. Let R be a commutative subring of $\mathrm{End}_k(A)$ whose rank over $\mathbf{Z}$ is twice the dimension of A and which is such that $R\otimes_{\mathbf{Z}}\mathbf{Q}$ is semi-simple. Assume that the Frobenius endomorphism π of A over k is in R. Then the class of the Lie algebra of A in the Grothendieck group of the category of R-modules of finite length is the same as that of $R/\pi R$.

J. S. Milne (London)

Citations: MR 18, 601b = G15-9; MR 23# A2419 = G15-19.

G15-44 (37# 4080)

Pohlmann, Henry

Algebraic cycles on abelian varieties of complex multiplication type.

Ann. of Math. (2) **88** (1968), 161–180.

Let X be a non-singular projective algebraic variety defined over an algebraic number field. J. T. Tate [*Arithmetical algebraic geometry* (Proc. Conf. Purdue Univ., 1963), pp. 93–110, Harper & Row, New York, 1965; MR **37** #1371] has conjectured that for any p, the $2p$th factor of the Hasse zeta function of X has a pole at $s=1+p$ whose order is the rank of $\mathscr{A}^p(X)$, the subspace of $H^{2p}(X, Q)$ generated by the algebraic cohomology classes of codimension p. W. V. D. Hodge [Proc. Internat. Congr. Math. (Cambridge, Mass., 1950), Vol. 1, pp. 182–192, Amer. Math. Soc., Providence, R.I., 1952; MR **13**, 679] has conjectured that for any p, $\mathscr{A}^p(X)=H^{p,p}\cap H^{2p}(X, Q)$, where $H^{p,p}$ is the subspace of the $2p$th de Rham cohomology group represented by differential forms of type (p, p).

In the special case where X is an abelian variety A with "sufficiently many" endomorphisms (more precisely, A is of CM-type), the author proves that Tate's conjecture is equivalent to Hodge's conjecture.

Since Lefschetz proved the case $p=1$ of Hodge's conjecture in 1921, Tate's conjecture is verified for divisors on abelian varieties of CM-type.

The methods of this paper are those of Shimura and Taniyama.

Hodge's conjecture for any p would follow immediately from Lefschetz' theorem if it were true that every rational class of type (p, p) were in the subalgebra generated by $\mathscr{A}^1(X)$; the paper includes a counter-example to this possibility, due to Mumford.

M. J. Greenberg (Santa Cruz, Calif.)

Citations: MR 37# 1371 = G35-45.

Referred to in G10-40.

G15-45 (37# 6289)

Shimura, Gorô

Discontinuous groups and abelian varieties.

Math. Ann. **168** (1967), 171–199.

We summarize one of the four cases the author deals with in this paper. Let B be any quaternion algebra over a totally real algebraic number field F. Let $\tau_1, \tau_2, \cdots, \tau_g$ be the infinite primes of F and suppose that B is unramified at exactly the first h of them. Let σ be the main involution of B, V a free B-module of dimension r over B, H a σ-hermitian B-valued form on V, $\mathfrak{M}\subseteq\mathfrak{N}$ two lattices in V. Assume H is positive-definite at the last $(g-h)$ primes of F. Then the group $\mathfrak{G}(H)$ of B-linear similitudes of H with some positivity condition acts on $\mathscr{H}_1$, the product of h generalized upper half-planes, and the arithmetic subgroup $\Gamma(H)=\Gamma(H, \mathfrak{N}/\mathfrak{M})=\{U\in\mathfrak{G}(H)\,|\,U\cdot\mathfrak{M}\subseteq\mathfrak{M}, (1-U)\cdot\mathfrak{N}\subseteq\mathfrak{M}\}$ acts discontinuously. ($\mathfrak{G}(H)$ acts through the first h factors of $\mathfrak{G}(H)_{\mathbf{R}}$, which are isomorphic to $\mathrm{Sp}(r, \mathbf{R})$.)

In the case $h=g$, a previous result of the author [Ann. of Math. (2) **83** (1966), 294–338; MR **33** #7339] is that $V_1=\mathscr{H}_1/\Gamma(H)$ is an algebraic variety defined over a certain algebraic number field. Roughly, the technique he uses is the construction of a family of abelian varieties parametrized by V_1 and characterized by what he calls a PEL type of structure, which includes an injection of the algebra B into the rational holomorphic endomorphisms of members of the family.

In this paper, he treats the case $h<g$. Here, also, he uses families of abelian varieties, but they are obtained and characterized in a more complicated fashion: Let K be any imaginary quadratic extension of F included in B. Then $B=\{x+\omega\cdot y\,|\,x, y\in K\}$ for some ω with $\omega^2=\kappa$, κ some element of F positive at the first h infinite primes and negative at the others. σ restricted to K is the conjugation over F. V is a K-module from the inclusion in B, and there is a unique s-hermitian form T on V with values in K such that $\mathrm{Tr}_{K/F}(T(x, y))=\mathrm{Tr}_{B/F}(H(x, y))$ for all $x, y\in V$. K, T, $\mathfrak{M}$, $\mathfrak{N}$ determine a similitude group $\mathfrak{G}(T)$ and an arithmetic subgroup $\Gamma(T)=\Gamma(T, \mathfrak{N}/\mathfrak{M})$ as before which acts on $\mathscr{H}$, the product of h bounded symmetric domains isomorphic to $\{z\in M_r(\mathbf{C})\,|\,1-{}^t\bar{z}z$ positive-definite$\}$. There

are suitable inclusions and consequently a morphism $\mu: V_1 \to V = \mathscr{H}/\Gamma(T)$. V is a parameter family for a certain PEL type, and the map μ gives rise to a family of abelian varieties on V_1. However, if $r > 1$ the dimension of V_1 is less than that of V, and the complete characterization of those abelian varieties appearing in this family is not trivial. It is one of the main results of this paper, and is as follows: The algebra B is contained in the set of real-analytic but only partially holomorphic rational endomorphisms in a specified way. As the author remarks, this indicates that the family is not one of Mumford-Hodge-Tate type [see D. Mumford, *Algebraic groups and discontinuous subgroups* (Proc. Sympos. Pure Math., Boulder, Colo., 1965), pp. 347–351, Amer. Math. Soc., Providence, R.I., 1966; MR **34** #5828].

Now $\mu(V_1)$ is an analytic, and hence an algebraic, subvariety of the (complete) algebraic variety V. If $\mathfrak{N}$ is large enough (i.e., if the "level" is high enough) then μ is an embedding, and this implies that V_1 itself is always an algebraic variety. The author then shows it is defined over some algebraic number field. The steps are: (1) to reduce the problem to high enough level; (2) to show that there is at least one algebraic point on V_1 as a subvariety of V, in fact, the moduli point of an abelian variety of a certain C.M. type; (3) to obtain a dense set of algebraic points from this one by transformations in the algebraic group $\mathfrak{G}(H)$; (4) to show that if s is any automorphism of **C** leaving the algebraic numbers fixed, then $V_1{}^s = V_1$.

The author also handles three situations other than the one discussed here, which is his case $\nu = q = 1$. The second concerns the same type of $\mathfrak{G}(H)$ but a different type of family of abelian varieties. The third and fourth treat analogously the group of similitudes of a skew-σ-hermitian form over B, which acts on a different kind of bounded symmetric domain.

A slightly specialized case of the first two cases above has been treated with much stronger results by the author in two subsequent papers [Ann. of Math. (2) **85** (1967), 58–159; MR **34** #4268; ibid. (2) **86** (1967), 503–592; MR **36** #5100] and in his talk at the Moscow Math. Congress.

W. Casselman (Berkeley, Calif.)

Citations: MR 33# 7339 = G15-34; MR 34# 4268 = G15-37; MR 36# 5100 = G15-40.

Referred to in G15-47, G15-50.

G15-46 (38# 2125)

Hayashida, Tsuyoshi

A class number associated with the product of an elliptic curve with itself.

J. Math. Soc. Japan **20** (1968), 26–43.

In this paper the author wishes to determine the number H of the isomorphism classes of canonically polarized Jacobian varieties $(E \times E, C)$, C being a theta divisor, and E an elliptic curve with ring of endomorphisms isomorphic to the principal order $\mathfrak{o}$ of an imaginary quadratic field $Q(\sqrt{-m})$, m a positive integer. By certain correspondences between the positive divisors on $E \times E$ and the 2×2 matrices with coefficients in $\mathfrak{o}$, and between the classes of matrices and the classes of right ideals of certain orders of a quaternion algebra, the determination is reduced to that of the number of classes and singular classes of right ideals of certain orders of a quaternion algebra. Then the author uses the method of M. Eichler [J. Reine Angew. Math. **195** (1955), 127–151 (1956); MR **18**, 297]. In this way he determines H completely.

M. Miwa (Tokyo)

Citations: MR 18, 297c = F15-3.

G15-47 (38# 5789)

Shimura, Gorô

Moduli of abelian varieties and number theory.

Algebraic Groups and Discontinuous Subgroups (*Proc. Sympos. Pure Math., Boulder, Colo.*, 1965), *pp.* 312–332. *Amer. Math. Soc., Providence, R.I.*, 1966.

This report is a brief explanation of the author's recent works on the theory of moduli of abelian varieties. The main themes are: (i) the existence of a nice moduli variety and a nice fibre variety for the family Σ_Ω (of abelian varieties of type Ω in the author's terminology) defined over a well defined algebraic number field k_Ω, (ii) the description of k_Ω as a class field, and (iii) the Hasse zeta function of the fibre variety in a special case, which are discussed in the author's papers [Ann. of Math. (2) **83** (1966), 294–338; MR **33** #7339; ibid. (2) **80** (1964), 160–189; MR **29** #4739; ibid. (2) **81** (1965), 124–165; MR **30** #2010; ibid. (2) **83** (1966), 377–385; MR **32** #7514; the author and M. Kuga, ibid. (2) **82** (1965), 478–539; MR **32** #2413]. Beginning with the fundamental facts on abelian varieties, the author develops a clear-cut explanation of the context and the substance of these theories without the proofs. As for the author's latest paper [Math. Ann. **168** (1967), 171–199; MR **37** #6289], there is a brief comment about the hyper-PEL-structure but no detailed explanation of the contents of the paper. There are no new results which are not contained in the above papers, but there are some conjectures. This report is a bird's eye view of recent important work on the theory of moduli of abelian varieties.

M. Miwa (Tokyo)

Citations: MR 29# 4739 = G15-27; MR 30# 2010 = F50-38; MR 32# 2413 = G15-32; MR 32# 7514 = F50-42; MR 33# 7339 = G15-34; MR 37# 6289 = G15-45.

Referred to in F15-29.

G15-48 (39# 5516)

Serre, J.-P.

Complex multiplication.

Algebraic Number Theory (*Proc. Instructional Conf., Brighton*, 1965), *pp.* 292–296. *Thompson, Washington, D.C.*, 1967.

From the author's introduction: "A central problem of algebraic number theory is to give an explicit construction for the abelian extensions of a given field K. For instance, if K is Q, the field of rationals, the theorem of Kronecker-Weber tells us that the maximal abelian extension Q^{ab} of Q is precisely Q^{cycl}, the union of all cyclotomic extensions. ... If K is an imaginary quadratic field, complex multiplication does essentially the same. We get the extensions $K^{ab} \supset \tilde{K} \supset K$ ($\tilde{K}$ is the absolute class field, the maximum unramified abelian extension) essentially by adjoining points of finite order on an elliptic curve with the right complex multiplication." The author proceeds to state the standard important theorems in complex multiplication, and sketches M. Deuring's algebraic proofs of these theorems in *Die Klassenkörper der komplexen Multiplikation* [Teubner, Stuttgart, 1958; MR **29** #4754]. A "stop press" note at the end of this paper mentions the recent proofs by Stark and Baker of the theorem that there are exactly 9 imaginary quadratic fields with class-number 1. In recent months there have been additional proofs by Deuring, Siegel, C. Meyer and Birch. Except for Baker, all lean heavily on Heegner. The reviewer has also submitted a rather short version of Stark's proof to J. Reine Angew. Math. (to appear).

{See H. M. Stark, Proc. Amer. Math. Soc. **21** (1969), 254–255 [MR **38** #5743].}

S. Chowla (University Park, Pa.)

Citations: MR 29# 4754 = G15-28; MR 38# 5743 = R14-79.

Referred to in Z10-29.

G15-49 (40# 1365)

Shiratani, Katsumi

On the Lubin-Tate reciprocity law.

J. Number Theory **1** (1969), 494–499.

The author refers to J. Lubin and J. Tate [Ann. of Math. (2) **81** (1965), 380–387; MR **30** #3094], who gave an explicit formula for norm residue symbols in certain cases by making use of formal complex multiplication in local fields. We quote: "Our aim in this note is to generalize the Lubin-Tate formula in the number-field case by means of formal groups having sufficiently many multiplications. Namely, we consider formal groups on one parameter which are defined over the integer ring in an extension of a given ground field k of degree n. Then we extend the Lubin-Tate reciprocity law to the case of such a formal group of height n that its absolute endomorphism ring is an order in k, which is not necessarily a maximal order. This procedure is entirely parallel to the multiplication theory of abelian varieties with sufficiently many complex multiplications. Our argument in the sequel owes much to the method used in the proof of the main theorem of G. Shimura and Y. Taniyama's book [*Complex multiplication of abelian varieties and its applications to number theory*, Math. Soc. Japan, Tokyo, 1961; MR **23** #A2419]."

S. Chowla (University Park, Pa.)

Citations: MR 23# A2419 = G15-19; MR 30# 3094 = S35-3.

G15-50 (40# 1400)

Mumford, D.

A note of Shimura's paper "Discontinuous groups and abelian varieties".

Math. Ann. **181** (1969), 345–351.

The author starts out by reformulating (and generalizing somewhat) Kuga's construction of families of abelian varieties parametrized by quotients of bounded symmetric domains. The starting point is the observation that a complex structure on an **R**-vector space $V\otimes_{\mathbf Q}\mathbf R$ of even dimension may be interpreted as a homomorphism of algebraic groups $\phi: T\to \mathrm{GL}(V)$ defined over **R**, where T is the one-dimensional anisotropic torus over **R**, provided a certain restriction on weights of ϕ is imposed. It is further observed that the Riemann conditions making a polarized abelian variety out of the complex torus $(V\otimes_{\mathbf Q}\mathbf R)/$(given lattice L) are stated in terms of such ϕ. Thus, possessing one such abelian variety X_ϕ with Riemann form A on one hand and a faithful symplectic representation $\rho: G\to \mathrm{Sp}(V, A)$ over **Q** of an algebraic group G on the other, one can "deform" X_ϕ to obtain a new abelian variety $X(g)$ for each $g\in G$ by merely substituting $\rho(g)\phi\rho(g)^{-1}$ for ϕ in the above construction of X_ϕ. It turns out that, under suitable assumptions on ϕ, ρ and an arithmetic subgroup $\Gamma\subset G$, the abelian variety $X(g)$ depends only on the canonical image of g in the double coset space $\Gamma\backslash G_{\mathbf R}{}^0/K_{\mathbf R}{}^0$, where $K_{\mathbf R}{}^0$ is a maximal compact subgroup of $G_{\mathbf R}{}^0$, and $G_{\mathbf R}{}^0/K_{\mathbf R}{}^0$ is a Hermitian symmetric space. In fact, one obtains in this fashion a complex analytic fibre system of abelian varieties over the base space $\Gamma\backslash G_{\mathbf R}{}^0/K_{\mathbf R}{}^0$. It is denoted by $\mathfrak X(G,\rho,\phi)$. Now, returning to an abelian variety X_ϕ as above, define the Hodge group $\mathrm{Hg}(X_\phi)$ of X_ϕ to be the smallest algebraic subgroup of $\mathrm{Sp}(V, A)$ containing $\phi(T)$. A family $\mathfrak X(G,\rho,\phi)$ is said to be of Hodge type if and only if $G=\mathrm{Hg}(X_\phi)$ and $\rho: \mathrm{Hg}(X_\phi)\to\mathrm{Sp}(V, A)$ is the inclusion. The main theorem of the paper states that a family $\mathfrak X(G,\rho,\phi)$ is (isomorphic to one) of Hodge type if and only if it contains as its member an abelian variety of CM-type. As a corollary, it follows that the families G. Shimura constructed in the paper mentioned in the title [same Ann. **168** (1967), 171–199; MR **37** #6289] are, in fact, of Hodge type. The main theorem is arrived at via the equivalence: (X_ϕ is of CM-type) if and only if ($\mathrm{Hg}(X_\phi)$ is a torus). At the end of the paper is appended an example of a Hodge type family of 4-dimensional abelian varieties whose generic member has no nontrivial endomorphism; one can thus say that the family is not characterized by its endomorphism rings.

T. Kambayashi (De Kalb, Ill.)

Citations: MR 37# 6289 = G15-45.

G15-51 (40# 2684)

Hano, Jun-ichi

On theta functions and Weil's generalized Poisson summation formula.

Trans. Amer. Math. Soc. **141** (1969), 195–210.

Let V be a vector space of dimension $2n$ over the reals and D a lattice in V. Put $T=V/D$. Fix a non-degenerate antisymmetric bilinear form A on $V\times V$ which takes integral values on $D\times D$. Consider all complex structures J on V for which there exists a positive divisor on the complex torus T_J whose cohomology class is A. For any such J, let H_J denote the Riemann form of the polarized abelian variety (T_J, A). Assume all elementary divisors of A with respect to D are $\geqq 3$. Let e be the Pfaffian of A with respect to D. We have the following known results: (A) The space of all theta functions on V_J of type (H_J,ψ), where ψ is any semicharacter of D attached to A, has dimension e. (B) Moreover, for a certain special semicharacter ψ_0 one can write down explicitly e linearly independent theta functions of type (H_J,ψ_0) and define in that way a holomorphic map $\theta(J)$ of T_J into the complex projective space P of dimension $e-1$. The image of the cohomology class of hyperplane sections on P under $\theta(J)^*$ is the cohomology class determined by A. (C) Let S be the symplectic group of A and $S(D)$ the subgroup of S consisting of the elements σ such that $\sigma D=D$. If J is a complex structure as above and if $\sigma\in S(D)$, one defines in an obvious way the complex structure ${}^\sigma J$. The mappings $\theta(J)$ and $\theta({}^\sigma J)$ are then defined, and we have $\theta({}^\sigma J)=\theta(J)\circ\sigma$ if σ belongs to the congruence subgroup of level $2e$ of $S(D)$ (with respect to an appropriate base of D).

The last assertion is Proposition 2.5. of G. Shimura [Ann. of Math. (2) **83** (1966), 294–338, especially p. 308; MR **33** #7339].

The author gives new proofs of these results using the ideas of A. Weil [Acta Math. **111** (1964), 143–211; MR **29** #2324].

J. G. M. Mars (Utrecht)

Citations: MR 29# 2324 = E12-104; MR 33# 7339 = G15-34.

G15-52 (41# 1686)

Shimura, Gorô

On canonical models of arithmetic quotients of bounded symmetric domains.

Ann. of Math. (2) **91** (1970), 144–222.

Given a bounded symmetric domain $\mathscr H$, the author considers the problem of the construction of a system of models over algebraic number fields for the quotients of $\mathscr H$ by all arithmetic subgroups of congruence type of a semi-simple algebraic group. The problem is deeply related to class field theory. Specifically, we consider the following situation: Let F be a totally real algebraic number field, B a quaternion algebra over F with the main involution ι, X a left B-module of rank n, h a non-degenerate B-valued ι-hermitian form, G a reductive algebraic group defined by $G_{\mathbf{Q}}=\{\alpha \in \mathrm{GL}(X, B) | h(x\alpha, y\alpha)=\nu(\alpha)h(x, y), \nu(\alpha) \in F\}$. Then the semi-simple part U of G is $\mathbf{Q}$-simple, and $U_{\mathbf{C}}$ is isomorphic to a product of copies of $\mathrm{Sp}(n, \mathbf{C})$. Let $\tau_1, \cdots, \tau_g$ be all the isomorphisms of F into $\mathbf{R}$, and assume that $B^{\tau_i} \otimes \mathbf{R}=M_2(\mathbf{R})$ for $i=1, \cdots, r$, $B^{\tau_j} \otimes \mathbf{R}=$ the division algebra of Hamiltonian quaternions for $j=r+1, \cdots, g$ $(1 \leqq r \leqq g)$. Then $U_{\mathbf{R}}$ modulo a maximal compact subgroup has the structure of a bounded symmetric domain $\mathscr{H}$ which is isomorphic to $\mathscr{H}_n{}^r$, where $\mathscr{H}_n$ is the Siegel upper half space of degree n. We consider the adelization $G_A=G_0 \cdot G_\infty$ of the group G and identify G_∞ with the Lie group $G_{\mathbf{R}}$. We denote the identity component of G_∞ by $G_{\infty+}$, and we put $G_{A+}=G_0 \cdot G_{\infty+}$, $G_{\mathbf{Q}+}=G_{\mathbf{Q}} \cap G_{A+}$. Let F' be the algebraic number field generated (over $\mathbf{Q}$) by $\sum_{i=1}^r x^i$, $x \in F$. We have a suitable $\mathbf{Q}$-rational homomorphism λ: $F'^\times \to F^\times$ which satisfies $N_{F/\mathbf{Q}}(\lambda(x))=N_{F'/\mathbf{Q}}(x)^r$, $x \in F'$. We put

$$\mathbf{G}_+ = \{x \in G_{A+} | \nu(x) \in \lambda(F_A{}'^\times)F^\times F_{\infty+}{}^\times\}.$$

We construct a family $\mathscr{Z}$ of subgroups of G_{A+} satisfying the following conditions (a) and (b): (a) For any element S in $\mathscr{Z}$, we have $S=S_0 \cdot G_{\infty+}$, where S_0 is a compact subgroup of G_0, (b) S contains the projection to G_A of an open subgroup of $\tilde{D}_A=\{(x, c) \in G \times F'^\times | \nu(x)=\lambda(c)\}_A$. For every $S \in \mathscr{Z}$, the group $\Gamma_S=S \cap G_{\mathbf{Q}}$ modulo its center acts discontinuously on the space $\mathscr{H}$; S determines a subgroup $\mathscr{X}_S=\{c \in F_A{}'^\times | \lambda(c) \in F^\times \cdot \nu(S)\}$ of $F_A{}'$ containing $F'^\times F_{\infty+}{}'$; $\mathscr{X}_S$ corresponds to an abelian extension k_S of F' of finite degree. Let $\mathfrak{k}$ denote the composite of the k_S for all $S \in \mathscr{Z}$. Then for each $x \in \mathscr{G}_+$ we can determine an element $\sigma(x)$ of the Galois group $\mathrm{Gal}(\mathfrak{k}/F')$. We can now construct the following system: $\{V_S, \varphi_S, J_{TS}(x), (S, T \in \mathscr{Z}, x \in \mathscr{G}_+)\}$, satisfying the following conditions: (1) (V_S, φ_S) is a model of $\mathscr{H}/\Gamma_S$ (i.e., V_S is an algebraic variety and φ_S is a Γ_S-invariant holomorphic map of $\mathscr{H}$ into V_S which induces a biregular isomorphism of $\mathscr{H}/\Gamma_S$ to V_S). (2) V_S is defined over k_S. (3) $J_{TS}(x)$ is a morphism of V_S onto $V_T{}^{\sigma(x)}$, defined if $xSx^{-1} \subset T$ (hence, $k_T \subset k_S$). $J_{TS}(x)$ is rational over k_S, and has the following properties: (a) $J_{SS}(x)=\mathrm{id}$ if $x \in S \cap \mathscr{G}_+$; (b) $J_{TS}(x)^{\sigma(y)} \circ J_{SR}(y)=J_{TR}(xy)$; (c) $J_{TS}(\alpha)(\varphi_S(z))=\varphi_T(\alpha(z))$ if $\alpha \in G_{\mathbf{Q}+}$ and $\alpha S\alpha^{-1} \subset T$. (4) If $z \in \mathscr{H}$ is an isolated fixed point of $G_{\mathbf{Q}+}$, then using the result obtained by the author in same Ann. (2) **86** (1967), 503–592 [MR **36** #5100], one can obtain a suitable algebraic number field P' (which is the composite of certain CM-fields) and a map η: $P_A{}'^\times \to \mathscr{G}_+$ such that for every $S \in \mathscr{Z}$, the point $\varphi_S(z)$ is rational over $P_{ab}{}'$ which is the maximal abelian extension of P'. Moreover, if v is an element of $P_A{}'^\times$ and τ is the element of $\mathrm{Gal}(P_{ab}{}'/P')$ canonically associated with v, then we have $\varphi_T(z)^\tau=J_{TS}(\eta(v)^{-1})(\varphi_S(z))$. (5) In the same situation as above, we put $G_{\mathbf{Q}+}{}^z=\{\alpha \in G_{\mathbf{Q}+} | \alpha(z)=z\}$, and let $C(S)$ be the abelian extension of P' corresponding to the subgroup $\{v \in P_A{}'^\times | \eta(v) \in G_{\mathbf{Q}+}{}^z \cdot S\}$ of $P_A{}'^\times$. Then we have $P' \cdot k_S(\varphi_S(z))=C(S)$. The proof of the above theorem depends heavily on the author's previous works [ibid. (2) **85** (1967), 58–159; MR **34** #4268; loc. cit.].

For an element S of $\mathscr{Z}$, let $\mathscr{L}_S$ be the field of all automorphic functions d on $\mathscr{H}$ with respect to Γ_S of the form $d=e \circ \varphi_S$, where e is a function on V_S rational over k_S, and let $\mathscr{L}$ be the union of the $\mathscr{L}_S$ for all $S \in \mathscr{Z}$. Let x be an element of $\mathscr{G}_+$ and put $T=x^{-1}Sx$. Then, for any function f on V_S defined over k_S, the formula: $(f \circ \varphi_S)^{\tau(x)}=f^{\sigma(x)} \circ J_{ST}(x) \circ \varphi_T$ gives rise to a homomorphism τ of G_+ into $\mathrm{Aut}(\mathscr{L}/F')$ whose kernel is $\bigcap_{S \in \mathscr{Z}} S \cdot F^\times$. In particular, if $r=1$ and either $\mathscr{H}/\Gamma_S$ is compact or $G_{\mathbf{Q}}=\mathrm{GL}_2(\mathbf{Q})$, then $\mathscr{G}_+=G_{A+}$ and τ induces an isomorphism of $G_{A+}/(\bigcap_{S \in \mathscr{Z}} S \cdot F^\times)$ onto $\mathrm{Aut}(\mathscr{L}/F')$.

We obtain a "proper correspondence" $\tilde{J}_{TS}(x)$ which is the graph of $J_{TS}(x)$. The author gives theorems concerning the correspondence $X_{TS}(x)=\tilde{J}_{TU}(x) \circ {}^t\tilde{J}_{SU}(1)$; the latter correspondence depends only on the double coset $(T \cap \mathscr{G}_+)x\Gamma_S$.

Let $\mathscr{Z}'$ be the suitable subfamily of $\mathscr{Z}$ such that any two members of $\mathscr{Z}'$ are commensurable to each other (when $r=1$, we have $\mathscr{Z}'=\mathscr{Z}$). We fix a member S of $\mathscr{Z}'$ and a point u of V_S, and consider the set $\mathscr{W}$ of all normal subgroups T of S contained in $\mathscr{Z}'$. A system of points $\{u_T\}_{T \in \mathscr{W}}$ is called coherent if $u_T \in V_T$, $u_S=u$, $J_{TR}(1)(u_R)=u_T (R \subset T)$. The union K_u of the fields $k_T(u_T)$ for all $T \in \mathscr{W}$ is an infinite Galois extension of $k_S(u)$, which is independent of the choice of the coherent system $\{u_T\}$. In particular, we consider the case where $u_T=\varphi_T(z)$ for a point z in $\mathscr{H}$. Let $\mathscr{C}$ be the closure of $\{\gamma \in \Gamma_S | \gamma(z)=z\}_0$ in S_0, $\mathscr{N}$ the normalizer of $\mathscr{C}$ in S_0. Then there exists a continuous isomorphism h of $\mathrm{Gal}(K_u/k_S(u))$ into $\mathscr{N}/\mathscr{C}$ determined by $h(\tau)=x \bmod \mathscr{C}$, $u_T{}^\tau=J_{TT}(x)(u_T)$ and $\tau=\sigma(x)$ on $\mathfrak{k}$. Moreover, if the point u is generic on V_S over k_S, then we have $\mathscr{N}=S_0$, $\{\gamma \in \Gamma_S | \gamma(z)=z\}=F^\times \cap S$, and the map h is surjective. For every finite subset M of prime ideals in F, we denote the M-part of $\mathscr{N}$, $\mathscr{C}$ by $\mathscr{N}_M$, $\mathscr{C}_M$. Using the natural homomorphism of $\mathscr{N}/\mathscr{C}$ onto $\mathscr{N}_M/\mathscr{C}_M$ and combining it with the map h, we obtain a homomorphism h_M whose kernel determines a subfield $K_u{}^M$ of K_u. Then there exists a finite set Y of prime ideals of $k_S(u)$, which depends only on u, such that if M consists of all prime factors in F of a rational integer, then every prime ideal in $k_S(u)$ which is prime to the members of M and Y is unramified in $K_u{}^M$. We obtain results concerning the Frobenius automorphisms of K_u over $k_S(u)$ by considering certain rational representations of G. *K. Iyanaga* (Tokyo)

Citations: MR 34# 4268 = G15-37; MR 36# 5100 = G15-40.

G15-53 (41# 8422)

Serre, Jean-Pierre

Abelian *l*-adic representations and elliptic curves.

McGill University lecture notes written with the collaboration of Willem Kuyk and John Labute.

W. A. Benjamin, Inc., New York-Amsterdam, 1968. xvi+177 *pp.* (*not consecutively paged*)

There are four chapters. The first two chapters reflect the work of Y. Taniyama [J. Math. Soc. Japan **9** (1957), 330–366; MR **20** #1667]; a study of relations among characters of type (A_0) of the idele class group $C=I/k^\times$ of a number field k, a system of representations of the Galois group G^{ab} of the maximal abelian extension of k in (non-archimedean) local fields of a certain number field and the Hasse zeta-function of an abelian variety A defined over k; and a proof of the Hasse conjecture when A has complex multiplications. Chapter I contains definitions and examples of l-adic representations, l being any prime number. Let G be the Galois group of the algebraic closure of k over k and V_l be a vector space over $\mathbf{Q}_l$ of finite dimension. A continuous homomorphism $\rho_l: G \to \mathrm{GL}(V_l)$ is called an l-adic representation of k. When $\rho_l(G)$ is abelian, ρ_l is called abelian; in this case ρ_l may be considered as a representation of G^{ab}. When characteristic polynomials of Frobenius elements have coefficients in $\mathbf{Q}$ instead of in $\mathbf{Q}_l$, ρ_l is called rational. A "strictly compatible system" $\rho=(\rho_l)$ of rational ρ_l's for all l is the one for which the rational characteristic polynomials of Frobenius elements are the same for almost all places of k. To such a system, one can attach an L-function. A typical example of such a system is given by $V_l=\mathbf{Q}_l \otimes_{\mathbf{Z}_l} \varprojlim A_m$ with the natural action of G, where A_m is the l^mth division point of A. Chapter II gives the construction of some abelian l-adic representations. As mentioned above, this is essentially due to Taniyama. However, the author first defines an algebraic group $S_{\mathfrak{m}}$ over $\mathbf{Q}$, where $\mathfrak{m}$ denotes a modulus in k. The employment of algebraic groups makes it easy to separate purely algebraic arguments from those involving arithmetic; it also makes arguments stay in the ground field and releases us from creating new notations owing to the field extension. Put $T=R_{k/\mathbf{Q}}(G_m)$, where G_m is the multiplicative group considered over k and R is Weil's functor lowering the field of definition. Let E be the group of units of k, $U_{\mathfrak{m}}$ the open subgroup of I, the idele group, defined by congruence mod $\mathfrak{m}$, $E_{\mathfrak{m}}=E\cap U_{\mathfrak{m}}$, $C_{\mathfrak{m}}=I/k^\times U_{\mathfrak{m}}$, this being finite, and $T_{\mathfrak{m}}=T/\bar{E}_{\mathfrak{m}}$, where the bar means the Zariski closure. In this situation, one shows the existence of a commutative algebraic group $S_{\mathfrak{m}}$ which is an extension of the torus $T_{\mathfrak{m}}$ by the finite group $C_{\mathfrak{m}}$, and a homomorphism $\varepsilon: I_{\mathfrak{m}}=I/U_{\mathfrak{m}}\to S_{\mathfrak{m}}(\mathbf{Q})$. Then, by class field theory, one finds an abelian representation $\varepsilon_l: G^{\mathrm{ab}}\to S_{\mathfrak{m}}(\mathbf{Q}_l)$. Now, let ϕ be an algebraic representation $S_{\mathfrak{m}}\to \mathrm{GL}(V)$ defined over $\mathbf{Q}$. Then, for each l, ϕ induces a homomorphism $\phi_l: S_{\mathfrak{m}}(\mathbf{Q}_l)\to \mathrm{GL}(V_l)$, with $V_l=\mathbf{Q}_l\otimes_{\mathbf{Q}} V$, and one ends up with an l-adic representation $\rho_l=\phi_l\circ\varepsilon_l: G^{\mathrm{ab}}\to\mathrm{GL}(V_l)$. It is proved that $\rho=(\rho_l)$ forms a system of strictly compatible rational abelian semi-simple representations. The last two chapters come from recent work of the author and Tate. In Chapter III, the author conjectures that every rational semi-simple abelian l-adic representation ρ_l of k should come from an algebraic representation ϕ over $\mathbf{Q}$ of $S_{\mathfrak{m}}$ for some $\mathfrak{m}$ in the manner described in Chapter II. He shows that this is the case when k is a composition of quadratic extensions of $\mathbf{Q}$ (including $k=\mathbf{Q}$). In general, it is shown that the conjecture is true if one assumes, in addition to the above conditions, that ρ_l is "locally algebraic". Relations among local algebraicity and the existence of a "Hodge-Tate" decomposition are studied. The author says that proving these additional properties (and hence the conjecture) seems to require stronger results on transcendental numbers than the ones now available. Chapter IV is concerned with the representation ρ_l for $A=E$, an elliptic curve defined over k. It is proved that when E has no complex multiplication the Lie algebra of the l-adic Lie group $\rho_l(G)$ is isomorphic to $M_2(\mathbf{Q}_l)$. This is based on a finiteness theorem of Šafarevič on the good reduction and Tate's local theory of elliptic curves with non-integral modular invariant.

T. Ono (Baltimore, Md.)

Citations: MR 20# 1667 = G15-16.
Referred to in R24-42.

G20 CURVES OVER FINITE AND LOCAL FIELDS

See also Section R58.
See also reviews F15-40, G05-15, G05-38, G05-56, G05-59, G05-75, G05-77, G05-120, G30-54, L10-25, N76-6, Q25-37, R58-9, S35-3, T25-5, T25-12, T25-22, T25-29.

G20-1 **(1, 166f)**

Châtelet, François. Points exceptionnels d'une cubique de Weierstrass. C. R. Acad. Sci. Paris **210**, 90–92 (1940).

The theorem that the rational points of an elliptic cubic curve with rational coefficients are integers was generalized by Miss Lutz [J. Reine Angew. Math. **177**, 238–247 (1937)] to the case in which the coefficients are integers in a p-adic algebraic field K. They form an infinite abelian group G. The present paper applies similar methods to determine the coordinates of the points of each finite sub-group of G (exceptional points). *V. Snyder* (Ithaca, N. Y.).

Referred to in G05-43.

G20-2 **(2, 123d)**

Weil, André. Sur les fonctions algébriques à corps de constantes fini. C. R. Acad. Sci. Paris **210**, 592–594 (1940).

The author sketches in this note a proof of Riemann's hypothesis for function fields $K=k(x, y)$ of one variable and genus g over a finite field k of q elements. For the proof, it is necessary to generalize the theory of fixed points of algebraic correspondences C on $\bar{K}=\bar{k}K$, where $\bar{k}$ denotes the algebraic closure of k. The multiplicative group of all $\omega\neq 0$ in $\bar{k}$ is isomorphic to the additive group of all elements mod 1 in the universal ring $\mathfrak{R}$ over the field of rationals with respect to all primes different from the characteristic of k. By means of such a fixed isomorphism and the representation of divisors in $\bar{K}$ by residue classes of functions in $\bar{K}$, the group G of all classes in $\bar{K}$ whose orders are prime to q can be mapped upon the additive group of all $2g$-dimensional vectors with components in $\mathfrak{R}$ mod 1. The automorphism of $\bar{K}|K$ which extends the Frobenius automorphism $\omega\to\omega^q$ induces a linear transformation I on the vector group. The transformation I can be interpreted as a $2g$-dimensional matrix with coefficients in $\mathfrak{R}$. A (m_1, m_2) correspondence C of K induces a homomorphism on G which can be described by a matrix L operating on the representation of G by vectors. The number of fixed points of C is "in general" equal to $m_1+m_2-T_r(L)$. The key to the author's investigation is the fact that the trace $T_r(LL')$ is a positive rational integer, where L' denotes the matrix of the inverse correspondence of C. This result is a generalization of the fundamental relation for the periods of abelian integrals of first kind on an algebraic Riemann surface. A careful analysis of the ring of correspondences on $\bar{K}$ shows that the latter is a finite hypercomplex order over the ring of rational integers. The actual proof of Riemann's hypothesis consists of the investigation of the correspondence $\Sigma=(x\to x^q, y\to y^q)$. The matrix representing this correspondence is equal to I and its characteristic polynomial $|E-uI|$ coincides with the polynomial factor of the zeta function of K. The fundamental inequality $T_r(LL')>0$ applied to the correspondences $a_0+a_1\Sigma+\cdots+a_{2g-1}\Sigma^{2g-1}$, a_i rational integers, proves that all the characteristic roots have $\sqrt{q}$ as absolute value. Finally, the author mentions that his methods prove Artin's series for a finite extension of K to be polynomials. The reviewer hopes that a detailed account of these important results will soon be accessible. *O. F. G. Schilling.*

Referred to in G20-3, G20-9.

G20-3 **(2, 345b)**

Weil, André. On the Riemann hypothesis in function-fields. Proc. Nat. Acad. Sci. U. S. A. **27**, 345–347 (1941).

Let K/k be a field of algebraic functions of one variable over the algebraically closed field k. The field K has a projective non-singular model Γ since it has separable generations. The correspondences $C, D, \cdots$ on K may be represented by elements of the additive group of divisors $\mathfrak{C}$ on the product surface $\Gamma\times\Gamma$. The surface can be considered as the ordered pair (P, Q) of two generic points P, Q of Γ. To fixed points $A, B\varepsilon\Gamma$ there correspond by means of the varieties (P, A), (B, P) singular correspondences Γ_A, Γ_B' of $\mathfrak{C}$. A rational function ϕ on $\Gamma\times\Gamma$ determines uniquely with respect to $\Gamma\times\Gamma$ a divisor C_ϕ consisting of its zeros and poles. Since $\Gamma\times\Gamma$ is free from singularities the intersection number $[C, D]$ is defined for any two distinct irreducible elements C, D of $\mathfrak{C}$. Then the degrees $r(C)$, $s(C)$ and the coincidence number $f(C)$ of a correspondence C can be interpreted by means of intersection numbers. The divisors C_0 which are linear combinations of divisors C_ϕ, Γ_A, Γ_B' form a two-sided ideal $\mathfrak{C}_0$ of $\mathfrak{C}$, where multiplication in $\mathfrak{C}$ is defined by successive application of correspondences. The difference ring $\mathfrak{R}=\mathfrak{C}-\mathfrak{C}_0=\{\gamma, \delta, \cdots\}$ is the ring of complex multiplications in K. The unit 1 of $\mathfrak{R}$ is the map of correspondence $\Delta=(P, P)$. Since $(P, Q)\rightleftarrows(Q, P)$ is a birational transformation of $\Gamma\times\Gamma$ it follows that R has an anti-automorphism $\gamma\to\gamma'$. By a judicious selection of the representative C for a given element γ it can be achieved that the components of $r(C)+s(C)-f(C)=\sigma(\gamma)$ are defined. The integral-valued function σ has the following properties: (i) $\sigma(n\cdot 1)=2gn$, where g is the genus of K and n an integer; (ii) $\sigma(\gamma)=\sigma(\gamma')$; and (iii) $\sigma(\gamma\delta)=\sigma(\delta\gamma)$. All these properties are derived by means of the theory of intersection numbers. The author indicates next that $\sigma(\gamma\gamma')\geqq 0$, $\sigma(\gamma\gamma')=0\Leftrightarrow\gamma=0$. The proof of this fundamental inequality [see C. R. Acad. Sci. Paris **210**, 592–594 (1940); these Rev. **2**, 123] uses the notion of the generic complementary correspondence. The final proof of the Riemann hypothesis then follows readily.

O. F. G. Schilling (Chicago, Ill.).

Citations: MR 2, 123d = G20-2.

Referred to in D80-27, G02-1, G20-9, L20-22, N76-8, T10-4, T10-6.

G20-4 (3, 104g)

Deuring, Max. Die Typen der Multiplikatorenringe elliptischer Funktionenkörper. Abh. Math. Sem. Hansischen Univ. **14**, 197–272 (1941).

This is an investigation of the exact structure of the "complex multiplications" of an elliptic function field K in the case when the field k of constants is not the classical field of complex numbers, but is a field of prime characteristic p. These multiplications are defined in terms of meromorphisms. A meromorphism μ of K is an isomorphism which leaves all constants fixed and which maps K onto a subfield of itself. All such μ can be combined from automorphisms of K and meromorphisms "normalized" with respect to a fixed prime divisor (corresponding to a fixed choice of the point at ∞). The normalized meromorphisms form a ring R; addition is performed by multiplying certain corresponding divisor classes, multiplication by multiplying the isomorphisms. R contains the ring of all rational integers ("natural" multiplications), and is an integral domain. Hasse has shown [J. Reine Angew. Math. **175**, 55–62, 69–88, 193–208 (1936)] that the quotient field of R is either (1) the rational numbers, (2) an imaginary quadratic number field F or (3) a definite quaternion algebra Q. Deuring completely determines the structure of R: (1) R is the ring of all integers; (2) F is a field in which the characteristic p of K is a product of two distinct ideals, and R is an order in F with conductor prime to p; (3) Q is ramified at p and ∞, and R is a maximal order in Q. Furthermore, each of these cases is possible, and Deuring determines for given R exactly how many values are possible for the (usual) invariant j of K. For types (2) and (3) j is absolutely algebraic (over the prime field of K), and for type (3) it has at most the degree 2. Tables of these invariants are given. Type (3) does not arise in the classical theory, and it is present here if and only if the given field K has no divisor classes of order p. The proofs of these results depend on the standard method of representing multiplications by matrices, as developed for the general case by Deuring [J. Reine Angew. Math. **183**, 25–36 (1940); these Rev. **2**, 246] on the relation between multiplications of a field and those of one of its subfields, and on a transition from an elliptic field K of characteristic 0 to one of characteristic p, found by reducing the coefficient field of K modulo a suitable prime divisor. Relations of the results to class field theory and to the class invariants of an imaginary quadratic field will be studied in a later paper. *S. Mac Lane* (Cambridge, Mass.).

Citations: MR 2, 246c = R58-1.

Referred to in D80-71, F25-13, G15-3, G15-6, G15-7, G20-13, R52-19, S15-32.

G20-5 (9, 55h)

Châtelet, François. Les courbes de genre 1 dans un champ de Galois. C. R. Acad. Sci. Paris **224**, 1616–1618 (1947).

The Galois methods of the author's earlier paper [Ann. Univ. Lyon. Sect. A. (3) **9**, 40–49 (1946); these Rev. **8**, 565] are used to give a simple proof of the theorem that if a curve defined in a Galois field R is irreducible and of genus one in every finite extension of R, then it contains a point of R. Earlier proofs of this result required a theorem of F. K. Schmidt [Math. Z. **33**, 1–32 (1931)] demonstrated by transcendental methods involving zeta functions.

D. B. Scott (Aberdeen).

Citations: MR 8, 565b = G05-13.

Referred to in G25-6.

G20-6 (9, 411j)

Châtelet, François. Utilisation des congruences en analyse indéterminée. Ann. Univ. Lyon. Sect. A. (3) **10**, 5–22 (1947).

Let C be a rational cubic of genus one with group G of rational points and, C reducing to a cubic Γ over the finite field k of integers modulo p, let Γ have no double points. Using a modification of a method of E. Lutz [J. Reine Angew. Math. **177**, 238–247 (1937)] the author proves that the points of G whose homogeneous coordinates are congruent modulo p to those of the identity element of G (point at infinity) form a subgroup G_p, and that the quotient group G/G_p is isomorphic to a subgroup of G_k, the group of points of the cubic Γ in k. A new proof is given of the known result that the elements of G of finite order (the exceptional points) have integral nonhomogeneous coordinates. Three numerical examples are discussed. *I. Niven* (Eugene, Ore.).

G20-7 (9, 411k)

Châtelet, François. Intérêt et signification de l'analyse indéterminée. Rev. Gén. Sci. Pures Appl. N. S. **54**, 199–201 (1947).

G20-8 (10, 262c)

Weil, André. Sur les courbes algébriques et les variétés qui s'en déduisent. Actualités Sci. Ind., no. 1041 = Publ. Inst. Math. Univ. Strasbourg **7** (1945). Hermann et Cie., Paris, 1948. iv+85 pp.

Suppose that Ω_k is a field of algebraic functions of one variable with a finite field k of q elements for a coefficient field. Let p be a prime divisor of Ω_k which is trivial on k, i.e., a homomorphism of a suitable subring of Ω_k upon an algebraic extension $k(p)$ of k with $[k(p):k]=d(p)$. Then the zeta function of Ω_k can be defined as $Z(u)=\prod_p(1-u^{d(p)})^{-1}$, where u is a complex variable, and the product is extended over all distinct prime divisors. Artin formulated the analogue of the Riemann hypothesis as the statement that the zeros of $Z(u)$ lie on the circle $|u|=q^{-\frac{1}{2}}$. The author gives in this paper the first complete proof of this Riemann hypothesis for function fields of arbitrary genus. His proof depends on a reformulation of the hypothesis as an assertion on the positiveness of a quadratic form [corollary 3 on page 70]. This quadratic form is derived from a trace function σ acting on a subring of the ring of correspondences of Ω_k. Thus the author requires a complete treatment of the theory of correspondences, and the major portion of the present paper is devoted to it.

For the unity of method and in order to establish a clear-cut connection with the original papers of Castelnuovo, Enriques, Severi and others, it is found convenient to discuss "curves Γ over k" instead of the function field Ω_k. The concept of "curve" as used by the author requires a careful explanation as given in his book "Foundations of Algebraic Geometry" [Amer. Math. Soc. Colloquium Publ., v. 29, New York, 1946; these Rev. **9**, 303], where it is not required that k be a finite field. (Naturally the author shows how the connection can be made between his theory and the slightly different theory of the field Ω_k.) For the treatment of the algebraic geometry on a curve the author permits himself to draw freely upon his book. Thus in the definition of the canonical divisors and in the proof of the theorem of Riemann-Roch the geometry of the 2-fold product of Γ by itself is used, and thereby tools like the intersection product, etc., are employed. Such tools are not absolutely necessary if one just desires to demonstrate the theorem of Riemann-Roch. However, for the discussion of the all-important trace function it is preferable to have available, for example, the author's definition of a canonical divisor [theorem 8 on page 42]. The correspondences on Γ are introduced as divisors on $\Gamma\times\Gamma$, and the uniqueness of the product of correspondences is established [theorem 6 on page 35] leading to a simple formula for the latter. This work and the discussion of the additive group of correspondences with the concept of equivalence require a comprehensive part of the general theory of cycles and of the intersection product in chapters VII and VIII of the author's book.

The ring of correspondences $\mathfrak{A}=\{\xi,\cdots\}$ is introduced by means of the equivalence relation and a symmetry operator $\xi\rightarrow\xi'$ is defined on it essentially by the interchange of the factors in $\Gamma\times\Gamma$; the trace $\sigma(\xi)$ is defined by means of intersection multiplicities. The function σ has all the formal properties of a trace [theorem 7 on page 41]. The most complicated part of the paper consists in proving that $\sigma(\xi\xi')>0$ for nonzero ξ. Application of this basic inequality yields the positiveness of the quadratic form $\sigma(\xi\xi')=2gx^2+2\sigma(\iota^n)xy+2gq^ny^2$, where $\xi=x\delta+y\iota^n$ with integers x, y. In this formula g denotes the genus of Γ, δ denotes the identity correspondence and ι is the class of the correspondence $I(P)=P^\omega$, for each point P of Γ, where ω is the normalized automorphism of the algebraic completion $\bar{k}$ of k, $a^\omega=a^q$ for a in $\bar{k}$. The points P of Γ are essentially the same thing as the prime divisors of the coefficient extension $\Omega_k\bar{k}$. To each P there belongs, relative to k, a smallest field of definition $k(P)$. Then $d\log Z(u)=\sum_{n=1}^\infty \nu_n u^n du/u$, where ν_n is the number of distinct points P_j with $k(P_j)\subseteq k_n$ for the extension k_n of degree n over k. The numbers ν_n are identified with the numbers of components of certain intersection cycles related to $P\rightarrow P^{\omega^n}$. Thus the author shows $\nu_n=1+q^n-\sigma(\iota^n)$ and the expansion $d\log[(1-u)(1-qu)Z(u)]=\sum_{n=1}^\infty\sigma(\iota^n)u^n du/u$ together with the positiveness of $\sigma(\xi\xi')$ imply the Riemann hypothesis by means of a simple argument on analytic functions.

In the last paragraph further consequences of the structure of the ring $\mathfrak{A}$ are developed. Implications on the theory of L-series of function fields are given, and the connections with the groups of Hilbert and Artin's theory of the conductor are established. The higher ramification groups are given an interesting definition by means of the multiplicity of a point in a transformed cycle. These results depend on the identification of σ with the trace of a matrix representation of $\mathfrak{A}$ in a field of characteristic 0. The author announces the early publication of the pertinent facts which depend on the structure of the class group of Ω_k and further properties of the Jacobian variety attached to Γ, which incidentally already had to be used for the proof of the positiveness of $\sigma(\xi\xi')$ [pages 49–53]. *O. F. G. Schilling.*

Citations: MR 9, 303c = G02-2.

Referred to in D80-24, G10-1, G20-9, G20-11, G20-14, G20-15, G20-19, G20-42, G25-25, L25-16, N68-28, S02-3, S15-32, T10-9, T10-48, T25-5, T25-37, Z02-44.

G20-9 (11, 231a)

Igusa, Jun-ichi. On the theory of algebraic correspondences and its application to the Riemann hypothesis in function-fields. J. Math. Soc. Japan **1**, 147–197 (1949).

The author presents in this paper his elaboration of the specified outline for the proof of the Riemann hypothesis of function fields as presented by A. Weil [C. R. Acad. Sci. Paris **210**, 592–594 (1940); Proc. Nat. Acad. Sci. U. S. A. **27**, 345–347 (1941); Foundations of Algebraic Geometry, Amer. Math. Soc. Colloquium Publ., v. 29, New York, 1946; these Rev. **2**, 123, 345; **9**, 303]. The author's details were arrived at independently and differ somewhat from Weil's final presentation [Sur les courbes algébriques et les variétés qui s'en déduisent, Actual. Sci. Ind., no. 1041, Hermann, Paris, 1948 = Publ. Inst. Math. Univ. Strasbourg **7** (1945); these Rev. **10**, 262]; e.g., only the Riemann-Roch theorem for nonspecial linear series is used. Furthermore Schubert's formula is developed in full detail and the Picard number for products of curves is discussed. *O. F. G. Schilling.*

Citations: MR 2, 123d = G20-2; MR 2, 345b = G20-3; MR 9, 303c = G02-2; MR 10, 262c = G20-8.

G20-10 (12, 47d)

Hasse, Helmut. Punti razionali sopra curve algebriche a congruenze. Reale Accademia d'Italia, Fondazione Allessandro Volta, Atti dei Convegni, v. 9 (1939), pp. 85–140, Rome, 1943.

This is an extensive report on the author's work on the Riemann hypothesis for elliptic fields. Extensive use is made of Deuring's presentation of the theory of algebraic correspondences. The background for Abelian functions is developed, though the restriction to the elliptic case is forced because of the lack of a general intersection theory. The author's aim is stated thus. "Pubblico questo lavoro in lingua italiana per facilitare alla scuola algebrico-geometrica italiana l'accesso ad un campo, coltivato in Germania da diverse parti, in cui la geometria algebrica e l'aritmetica si danno la mano." *O. F. G. Schilling* (Chicago, Ill.).

Referred to in G25-25.

G20-11 (14, 848d)

Roquette, Peter. Riemannsche Vermutung in Funktionenkörpern. Arch. Math. **4**, 6–16 (1953).

This paper comprises the outline of a proof of the Riemann hypothesis for function fields, whose methods center around properties of the twofold product of the function field by itself without specific reference to a general intersection theory. The author shows how a proof of the all-important positive-definiteness of A. Weil's trace function (which was introduced by the latter in his "Sur les courbes algébriques et les variétés qui s'en déduisent" [Hermann, Paris, 1948; these Rev. **10**, 262]) may be constructed with the arithmetic of suitable discrete rank one valuations for a basic tool. Suppose now that K and K' are fields of algebraic functions of one variable over a perfect field Ω with respect to which they are algebraically independent. In order to consider the algebraic correspondences between K and K' the author introduces (as Severi did in the Trattato di geometria algebrica, v. 1, pt. 1, Zanichelli, Bologna, 1926) the composite $\Delta=KK'$ which is a function field of 2 variables over Ω. In the field Δ valuations $w_{\mathfrak{m}}$ (in the sequel the symbol $\mathfrak{m}$ shall be used to denote the prime divisor and its attached homomorphism $z \to z\mathfrak{m}$, for $z \in \Delta$, $\{z\mathfrak{m} \neq \infty\} = \Delta\mathfrak{m}$, as well) are considered and with them the additive group of divisors which is generated by them over the integers. As in the work of Severi and Weil, for example, the prime divisors $\mathfrak{m}$ (or irreducible correspondences if one prefers a more geometric terminology) are classified on the basis of their effect on the component fields K and K'; constant prime divisors are those which are trivial on K' or K, that is, they are prolongations of prime divisors of K or K' to Δ, and the non-constant prime divisors which are trivial on both components. For the divisors of the latter type isomorphisms $K \to K\mu$ and $K' \to K'\mu'$ are then induced by residuation modulo $\mathfrak{m}$, and $\Delta\mathfrak{m}$ is a suitably defined dependent composite of $K\mu$ and $K'\mu'$. It is important for the subsequent work that the non-constant prime divisors are in one-to-one correspondence with the types of dependent composites of K and K' over Ω ($K\mu K'\mu'$ and $K\nu K'\nu'$ belong to the same type if there exists an isomorphism τ between them for which $\mu\tau = \nu$ and $\mu'\tau = \nu'$; the author indicates how these concepts have to be modified so as to have uniform statements for the constant prime divisors as well). Next, divisors $\mathfrak{a}$ and $\mathfrak{b}$ of Δ are placed in the same $\approx$-class if they differ by a divisor which is composed of constant prime divisors (see the $\equiv$-equivalence of Weil [loc. cit. p. 29]). Weil showed then that the Riemann hypothesis is a consequence of the existence of a positive-definite linear functional $\sigma(\mathfrak{a}, \mathfrak{b})$ on the group of $\equiv$-classes ($\sigma(\mathfrak{a}, \mathfrak{a}) > 0$ if $\mathfrak{a} \neq 0$). In order to demonstrate this key result the author develops a theory of intersection numbers which avoids explicit reference to the full geometric theory of products of correspondences and projections on an algebraic variety of Δ/Ω, though it must be said the differences of approach, compared with Weil, are not as deep as it may appear; occasionally they amount only to a difference in terminology. Using Deuring's arithmetic description of Severi's theory of correspondences [see Deuring, J. Reine Angew. Math. **177**, 161–191 (1937); **183**, 25–36 (1940); these Rev. **2**, 246], and thus a generalization of Hasse's work for elliptic fields, for a given prime divisor $\mathfrak{p}$ of Δ the properties and existence of an arithmetic homomorphism of the group of divisors of Δ, which are prime to $\mathfrak{p}$, into the divisor group of $\Delta\mathfrak{p}$ are examined; the details of this existence proof by means of an explicit construction are very important (see also Deuring, Math. Z. **47**, 643–654 (1942) [these Rev. **7**, 362] for similar, though in nature quite different, problems). Suppose next that the divisor (z) of an element $z \in \Delta$ is defined as $(z) = \sum_{\mathfrak{q}} w_{\mathfrak{q}}(z)\mathfrak{q}$, $\mathfrak{a} \dashv \mathfrak{b}$ means $w_{\mathfrak{q}}(\mathfrak{a}) \leqq w_{\mathfrak{q}}(\mathfrak{b})$ for all $\mathfrak{q}$, and $\mathfrak{a} \sim \mathfrak{b}$ means that $\mathfrak{a} - \mathfrak{b}$ is the divisor of a function (this is the $\sim$-equivalence of Weil [loc. cit. p. 29]). Then the afore-mentioned homomorphism $\mathfrak{a} \to \mathfrak{a}\mathfrak{p}$ satisfies (1) $\mathfrak{a} + \mathfrak{b} = \mathfrak{c}$ implies $\mathfrak{a}\mathfrak{p} + \mathfrak{b}\mathfrak{p} = \mathfrak{c}\mathfrak{p}$, $\mathfrak{a} \dashv \mathfrak{b}$ implies $\mathfrak{a}\mathfrak{p} \dashv \mathfrak{b}\mathfrak{p}$, $\mathfrak{a} \sim \mathfrak{b}$ implies $\mathfrak{a}\mathfrak{p} \sim \mathfrak{b}\mathfrak{p}$; (2) $(z)\mathfrak{p} = (z\mathfrak{p})$ (the divisor of the image $z\mathfrak{p}$ in the field $\Delta\mathfrak{p}$); (3) if $\Delta\mathfrak{p} = K\pi K'\pi'$ and $\mathfrak{k}$, $\mathfrak{k}'$ are constant divisors (prime to $\mathfrak{p}$) from K, K', respectively, then $\mathfrak{k}\mathfrak{p} = \mathfrak{k}\pi$, $\mathfrak{k}'\mathfrak{p} = \mathfrak{k}'\pi'$ (with proper modifications in case that $K \to K\pi$ is not an isomorphism; in this connection see, especially for the properties of this homomorphism, Weil, loc. cit. pp. 31–35, for example, theorems 2 and 3, where its importance is made clear). As a next step the author defines the so-called residual product $\langle \mathfrak{a}, \mathfrak{p} \rangle$ of two divisors $\mathfrak{a}$ and $\mathfrak{p}$ (in this order!) as the divisor $N(\Delta\mathfrak{p}/K'\pi'; \mathfrak{a}\mathfrak{p})\pi'^{-1}$ of K'. (See proposition 2 on p. 38 of Weil, loc. cit.) Then the first property of (1) implies that $\langle \mathfrak{a}, \mathfrak{p} \rangle$ is linear in the first argument, while the third property of (1) implies that $\langle \mathfrak{a}, \mathfrak{p} \rangle \sim \langle \mathfrak{a}', \mathfrak{p} \rangle$ in K' if $\mathfrak{a} \sim \mathfrak{a}'$ in Δ, i.e., it enables one to relax the original assumption that $\mathfrak{a}$ be prime to $\mathfrak{p}$. The symbol $\langle \mathfrak{a}, \mathfrak{b} \rangle$ for composite $\mathfrak{b}$ is defined by linearity. Furthermore, the degree of $\langle \mathfrak{a}, \mathfrak{b} \rangle$ is denoted by $\chi(\mathfrak{a}, \mathfrak{b})$ and $\varphi(\mathfrak{a}, \mathfrak{b})$ is defined as

$$\deg(\Delta/K'; \mathfrak{a}) \deg(\Delta/K; \mathfrak{b}) + \deg(\Delta/K; \mathfrak{a}) \deg(\Delta/K'; \mathfrak{b}),$$

where $\deg(\Delta/K; \mathfrak{p})$, for example, denotes $[\Delta\mathfrak{p} : K\pi]$, using the terminology which was introduced above. Then

$$\sigma(\mathfrak{a}, \mathfrak{b}) = \psi(\mathfrak{a}, \mathfrak{b}) - \chi(\mathfrak{a}, \mathfrak{b})$$

is the desired functional of Weil (see p. 42, loc. cit.), which is easily seen to depend only on the $\sim$-classes of $\mathfrak{a}$ and $\mathfrak{b}$. Moreover, making suitable provisions for constant divisors, it follows that $\sigma(\mathfrak{a}, \mathfrak{b})$ is a one-valued function on the group of $\approx$-classes of Δ. The author's approach makes clearly the proof of the symmetric law $\langle \mathfrak{a}, \mathfrak{b} \rangle = \langle \mathfrak{b}, \mathfrak{a} \rangle$ an essential item of the theory. Because of the linearity and the behavior of divisors and multiplicities under coefficient extensions it suffices to prove $\langle \mathfrak{m}, \mathfrak{p} \rangle = \langle \mathfrak{p}, \mathfrak{m} \rangle$ for prime divisors $\mathfrak{m}$ and $\mathfrak{p}$ of degree 1. As noted at the outset, the divisors $\mathfrak{p}$ and $\mathfrak{m}$ determine essentially unique types of composites $\Delta\mathfrak{p} = K\pi K'\pi'$ and $\Delta\mathfrak{m} = K\mu K'\mu'$. One may then identify $K'\pi'$, $K'\mu'$ and K' so that $K\pi$ and $K\mu$ are subfields of K'. Then distinct prime divisors $\mathfrak{p}$ and $\mathfrak{m}$ determine distinct homomorphisms $K \to K\pi$ and $K \to K\mu$ into K'. For each prime divisor $\mathfrak{q}'$ of K' the author defines $\pi\mathfrak{q}' = N(K'/K\pi; \mathfrak{q}')\pi^{-1}$ and $\mu\mathfrak{q}' = N(K'/K\mu; \mathfrak{q}')\mu^{-1}$ in K. Next let $\{a\}$ be the set of elements in K which are integral for the valuations $\pi\mathfrak{q}'$ and $\mu\mathfrak{q}'$; it then follows that $\min w_{\mathfrak{q}'}(a\pi - a\mu)$ exists, and that it is zero for all but a finite number of valuations $\mathfrak{q}'$. Thus each minimum can be interpreted as the $\mathfrak{q}'$-adic value $w_{\mathfrak{q}'}(D'_{\pi,\mu})$ of a divisor $D'_{\pi,\mu} = D'_{\mu,\pi}$ of K'. Using the construction of the homomorphism $\mathfrak{a} \to \mathfrak{a}\mathfrak{p}$ it is indicated that this divisor is precisely $\langle \mathfrak{m}, \mathfrak{p} \rangle$; it is at this juncture that modifications of Weil's general intersection theory begin. Finally $\langle \mathfrak{p}, \mathfrak{p} \rangle \sim -W\pi$, where W is the canonical class of K, with $K'\pi' = K'$ and $K\pi \subseteq K'$ for initial assumptions. The actual proof for $\sigma(\mathfrak{a}, \mathfrak{a}) > 0$ involves the choice of an integral divisor $\sum_i \mathfrak{b}_i = \mathfrak{b} \approx \mathfrak{a}$, which contains no constant divisors from K' and has degree g (the genus of K) over K' (see Weil., loc. cit., proposition 3 on p. 43). If then the prime divisors $\mathfrak{b}_i$ have degree 1 over K', then there are given g homomorphisms $K \to K\beta_i \subseteq K'$. For these the author defines $d_\beta' = \sum_{i \neq k} D'_{\beta_i, \beta_k}$ and $N_\beta(W) = \sum_i W\beta_i$, and he asserts as a consequence of the symmetry property and the evaluation of $\langle \mathfrak{p}, \mathfrak{p} \rangle$ that $\langle \mathfrak{b}, \mathfrak{b} \rangle > d_\beta' - N_\beta(W)$. In this manner the positive-definiteness of the trace σ amounts to

$$\deg d_\beta' < 2 \deg(\Delta/K; \mathfrak{b})(2g-1).$$

The slightly stronger inequality

$$\deg d_\beta' \leqq 2 \deg(\Delta/K; \mathfrak{b})(2g-2)$$

can then be proved by means of the theorem of Riemann-Roch (for a useful comparison with Weil's work one may note that the author's $\mathfrak{b}$ corresponds to the former's X, pp. 53–54, $\deg(\Delta/K; \mathfrak{b}) = \sum_i [K' : K\beta_i]$ corresponds to Weil's $e = d'(X)$, and finally $\deg d_\beta' \leqq 2 \deg(\Delta/K; \mathfrak{b})(2g-2)$ is Weil's final inequality $\deg(Y \cdot \text{diagonal}) \leqq 2e(2g-2)$ where $X \circ X' = Y + e \cdot \text{diagonal}$ on the middle of p. 54 in Weil, loc. cit.). The author sketches his proof, which in essence will correspond to portions of Weil's work on pp. 43–53, loc cit., and it is at this crucial mark that connections with general product varieties in one form or the other, though not necessarily as facts for abelian functions proper, will enter into the discussion. In the second part of the paper the Riemann hypothesis is proved, via the Frobenius automorphism of the coefficient field and its prolongation to the function field, essentially along the lines of Weil's original proof, loc. cit. pp. 68–72. *O. F. G. Schilling.*

Citations: MR 2, 246c = R58-1; MR 7, 362c = R58-5; MR 10, 262c = G20-8.

Referred to in G20-12.

G20-12 **(15, 203a)**

Roquette, Peter. Arithmetischer Beweis der Riemannschen Vermutung in Kongruenzfunktionenkörpern beliebigen Geschlechts. J. Reine Angew. Math. **191**, 199–252 (1953).

This paper comprises the complete detailed account of a new proof of the Riemann hypothesis for function fields of one variable. A brief comparison of the author's method of proof with the original proof of A. Weil was already made in the review of the author's brief description of his approach [Arch. Math. **4**, 6–16 (1953); these Rev. **14**, 848]. As indicated [loc. cit.] the outstanding feature may be found in the combination of Deuring's divisor-theoretic version of the classical correspondence theory with a novel theory of discriminants of systems of isomorphisms. In this manner all work can be carried out on the product of the underlying function field by itself, or in fully equivalent terminology, of the given non-singular curve by itself. This means in turn that the author succeeds in getting along with the concepts and theorems belonging to the theory of rank one valuations (the Riemann-Roch theorem included). The author's presentation, based on the aforementioned background, is self-contained and leads quite rapidly to the proof of the positive definiteness of Weil's trace function. [Still another shortcut to Weil's theorem, using divisors one product varieties, and not the full machinery of the general intersection theory, is presented in the unpublished Chicago thesis of F. Quigley, "An elementary proof of the Riemann hypothesis in function fields."] *O. F. G. Schilling.*

Citations: MR 14, 848d = G20-11.
Referred to in G20-14.

G20-13 **(20# 5183)**

Igusa, Jun-ichi. Class number of a definite quaternion with prime discriminant. Proc. Nat. Acad. Sci. U.S.A. **44** (1958), 312–314.

M. Eichler [Math. Z. **43** (1938), 102–109] showed that the class number for a definite quaternion algebra of prime discriminant, ramified only at p, is

$$h=(1/3)(1-(-3/p))+(1/4)(1-(-4/p))+(1/12)(p-1).$$

M. Deuring [Abh. Math. Sem. Hansischen Univ. **14** (1941), 197–272; MR **3**, 104] observed that this class number is the number of birationally distinct elliptic curves of characteristic p having no points of order p. The author computes this number directly, getting a purely algebraic proof of the class number formula. The crucial point is that the Hasse invariant of such an elliptic curve (when $p\neq 2$) satisfies a differential equation of Gauss-Legendre type. *G. Whaples* (Bloomington, Ind.)

Citations: MR 3, 104g = G20-4.
Referred to in G20-17.

G20-14 **(20# 5202)**

Mattuck, Arthur; and Tate, John. On the inequality of Castelnuovo-Severi. Abh. Math. Sem. Univ. Hamburg 22 (1958), 295–299.

Die in Rede stehende Ungleichung von Castelnuovo und Severi ist diejenige, welche dem Beweis der Riemannschen Vermutung für Kurven zugrundeliegt [vgl. A. Weil, Publ. Inst. Math. Univ. Strasbourg **7** (1945); MR **10**, 262; P. Roquette, J. Reine Angew. Math. **191** (1953), 199–252; MR **15**, 203]. Sie bezieht sich auf Divisoren D einer Fläche der Form $V=C\times C'$, Produkt zweier vollständiger, singularitätenfreier Kurven C und C'. Sie lautet [vgl. Severi, *Trattato di geometrica algebra*, Bologna, 1926]:

(1) $$\tfrac{1}{2}[D\cdot D]\leqq dd';$$

dabei sind $d=[D\cdot(P\times C')]$ und $d'=[D\cdot(C\times P')]$ die Grade von D über C bezw. C'. Verff. zeigen nun, daß (1) direkt aus dem Riemann-Rochschen Satz für V hergeleitet werden kann. Dieser läßt sich zufolge der besonderen Struktur von V als Produkt zweier Kurven in der Form

(2) $$\chi(D)=\tfrac{1}{2}[D\cdot D]-dd'+(d+1-g')(d'+1-g)$$

schreiben; dabei sind g, g' die Geschlechter von C bezw. C', und $\chi(D)$ bedeutet wie üblich die Eulersche Charakteristik von D, also die alternierende Summe $\chi(D)=\dim D-\sup D+\dim(K-D)$ (K ein kanonischer Divisor auf V). Ihrer Natur nach sind die in $\chi(D)$ eingehenden Terme nichtnegativ; daher ergibt sich die Ungleichung (1) aus der Tatsache, daß $dd'-\frac{1}{2}[D\cdot D]$ als "superabundance" sup E eines geeigneten Divisors E dargestellt werden kann. Und zwar leistet (bei hinreichend großen d, d') der Divisor $E=D-\sum_{i=1}^{d'}(C\times P_i')$ das Verlangte, falls nur die Punkte P_i' auf C' in hinreichend allgemeiner Lage sind. Der Nachweis, daß $\sup E=dd'-\frac{1}{2}[D\cdot D]$, geschieht mit Hilfe von (2), angewandt auf E.

Sind φ_1, $\varphi_2:C'\to C$ zwei rationale Abbildungen, und sind D_1, D_2 die zugehörigen Graphen, so ergibt sich aus (1), angewandt auf die Divisoren der Form $n_1D_1+n_2D_2$, die Formel

(3) $$|\mathrm{Grad}\,\varphi_1+\mathrm{Grad}\,\varphi_2-N|\leqq 2g(\mathrm{Grad}\,\varphi_1\cdot\mathrm{Grad}\,\varphi_2)^{\frac{1}{2}},$$

wobei $N=[D_1\cdot D_2]$ die Anzahl der Lösungen P' von $\varphi_1(P')=\varphi_2(P')$ bedeutet, gezählt mit den Multiplizitäten der algebraischen Geometrie. Diese Formel (3) enthält als Spezialfall die Riemannsche Vermutung für eine Kurve C über einem endlichen Körper k mit q Elementen: dazu hat man $C'=C$ zu wählen, φ_1 als die identische Abbildung, und φ_2 als diejenige Abbildung, welche alle Koordinaten mit q potenziert.

Literatur: zum Riemann-Rochschen Satz für Flächen: Zariski, Ann. of Math. (2) **55** 1952), 552–592 [MR **14**, 80]; Bull. Amer. Math. Soc. **62** (1956), 117–143. Vgl. auch die Arbeit von Grothendieck: J. Reine Angew. Math. **200** (1958), 208–215. *P. Roquette* (Hamburg)

Citations: MR 10, 262c = G20-8; MR 15, 203a = G20-12.
Referred to in G20-18.

G20-15 **(22# 2612)**

Hasse, Helmut. The Riemann hypothesis for function fields over finite fields of constants. Univ. Madrid. Publ. Sec. Mat. Fac. Ci. **1**, no. 2 (1957), 142 pp. (Spanish)

Ce travail est un cours, fait à l'Université de Madrid, où l'auteur expose une démonstration de l'hypothèse de Riemann dans le corps des fonctions algébriques d'une variable sur un corps fini [on sait que la première démonstration générale de cette hypothèse (qu'on va écrire, par abréviation, "F-hypothèse de Riemann") est due à A. Weil; voir A. Weil, *Foundations of algebraic geometry*, Amer. Math. Soc., New York, 1946; *Sur les courbes algébriques et les variétés qui s'en déduisent*; Hermann, Paris, 1948; MR **9**, 303; **10**, 262]. On sait que la démonstration de ce théorème se réduit, d'une manière classique aujourd'hui, à la démonstration de la propriété suivante de "positivité" de la trace (au sens de Weil) $\sigma(\xi)$ de classe ξ de correspondances: si ξ' est la classe transposée de $\xi\neq 0$, on a $\sigma(\xi\xi')>0$. Il s'agit donc, finalement, d'un théorème de la théorie des correspondances, et Weil développe cette théorie à partir de sa théorie des intersections, exposée dans ses *Foundations of algebraic geometry*. Mais, de cette manière, on ne peut parvenir à la démonstration de la F-hypothèse de Riemann sans avoir assimilé, au préalable, les 250 pages des "Foundations", et on sait combien est malaisée (malgré la profondeur de sa conception et sa cohérence interne) la lecture de ce livre. La démonstration de l'auteur (très différente de celle de Weil) exige moins de connaissances préalables de géométrie algébrique et est plus accessible que celle de Weil pour ceux qui ne s'occupent pas spécialement de ce domaine. L'auteur, dans son exposé, fonde la théorie des correspondances sur celle des "restes de diviseurs" (due aux recherches de Deuring, Roquette, etc., et qu'il serait trop long d'exposer ici), au lieu de la fonder sur celle (plus compliquée, mais de portée plus grande) des intersections, ce qui lui permet d'arriver à la démonstration de la F-hypothèse de Riemann au bout de 140 pages seulement. Mais ce raccourci ne va pas sans compensations, car dans la méthode de Weil, d'inspiration plus géométrique, on sent mieux que dans celle de Hasse les raisons profondes des résultats et des notions employées.

Remarques du référent : L'auteur emploie (et, semble-t-il, délibérément) une même notation, celle de produit, pour désigner 3 opérations différentes : le composé d'un diviseur (considéré comme un homomorphisme du corps dans celui des constantes) avec une application, le transformé d'un diviseur par un isomorphisme et le reste d'un diviseur par rapport à un autre diviseur. Malgré ce que le contexte permet toujours de décider, après réflexion, de quelle opération il s'agit dans chaque cas particulier, cette manière de faire impose au lecteur un travail de vérification à mon avis superflu et peut désorienter un lecteur inexpérimenté.

D'autre part, le travail comporte un certain nombre d'errata, dont certains sont très mal placés et peuvent empêcher la compréhension des définitions. En voici quelques-uns : p. 28, lignes 15 et 18 : lire $\mathrm{gr}_{\tilde{K}'/\Omega}(\mu)$ au lieu de $\mathrm{gr}_{\tilde{K}'/\Delta}(\mu)$; p. 57, lignes 13, 15 : la lettre n joue, dans le texte, deux rôles différents, ce qui rend les formules incompréhensibles ; il faudrait, par exemple, les écrire "$\Delta n = \Omega(\theta)$ donde $t\nu = \theta^3$, $t'\nu' = \theta^2$" et "$\bar{v}$ numerador de θ" ; p. 71, ligne 21 : lire Δ/Ω au lieu de K/Ω ; p. 76, ligne 29 : lire $v'\mu'$ au lieu de $v\mu'$; p. 82, lignes 14, 25 : lire $D_{\mu,\nu}$ au lieu de $D_{v,\mathbf{v}}$, ; p. 87, ligne 9 : lire "$(\underline{\mu}, \underline{\nu})$-resultante" au lieu de "$(\mu, \underline{\nu})$-resultante" ; p. 105, ligne 6 : lire $\mathrm{gr}_{\tilde{K}'/\Omega}(\underline{\mu}) = \mathrm{gr}_{\tilde{\Delta}/K}(\mathfrak{a}) = m'$ au lieu de $\mathrm{gr}_{\tilde{K}'/\Omega}(\underline{\mu})\mathrm{gr}_{\tilde{\Delta}/K}(\mathfrak{a}) = m'$; p. 125, ligne 18 : lire "numerador" au lieu de "denominador".

M. Krasner (Paris)

Citations: MR 9, 303c = G02-2; MR 10, 262c = G20-8.

G20-16 (22# 4717)

Mattuck, Arthur. Reduction mod p **of** p**-adic divisor classes.** J. Reine Angew. Math. **200** (1958), 45–51.

Es sei K ein Funktionenkörper einer Variablen über einem $\mathbf{p}$-adischen Zahlkörper k. Vorausgesetzt wird, daß K/k eine nichtausgeartete (= "reguläre") Spezialisierung $K \to K'$ über $\mathbf{p}$ besitzt, im Sinne der Deuringschen Reduktionstheorie. [Vgl. Deuring, Math. Z. **47** (1942), 643–654; MR **7**, 362.] Es wird gezeigt, daß jeder separable Primdivisor $\mathfrak{p}'$ von K' als Bild eines Primdivisors $\mathfrak{p}$ von K auftritt. Als Folgerung ergibt sich, daß die Divisorklassengruppe 0-ten Grades $\mathfrak{D}$ von K bei der Spezialisierung $K \to K'$ auf die entsprechende Gruppe $\mathfrak{D}'$ von K' abgebildet wird.—$\mathfrak{D}$ läßt eine direkte Zerlegung $\mathfrak{D} = \mathfrak{D}_0 \oplus \mathfrak{E}$ zu, wobei $\mathfrak{D}_0$ die Gruppe der Elemente von endlicher und zu p primer Ordnung aus $\mathfrak{D}$ bezeichnet (p ist die zu $\mathbf{p}$ gehörige Primzahl), und wo $\mathfrak{E}$ eine endliche p-Erweiterung einer Gruppe $\mathfrak{Z}$ ist, die ihrerseits isomorph ist zu einem Vektorraum über den ganzen $\mathbf{p}$-adischen Zahlen ; man nennt $\mathfrak{Z}$ eine "Lutzsche Untergruppe" von $\mathfrak{D}$. Es wird gezeigt, daß $\mathfrak{D}_0$ bei der Spezialisierung $K \to K'$ auf die entsprechende Gruppe $\mathfrak{D}_0'$ abgebildet wird, während $\mathfrak{E}$ auf die Gruppe $\mathfrak{D}_p'$ der Elemente mit durch p teilbarer Ordnung aus $\mathfrak{D}'$ abgebildet wird.—Diese Resultate werden im elliptischen Spezialfall diskutiert. Aus Resultaten von Lutz [dasselbe J. **177** (1937), 238–247] läßt sich ablesen, daß $\mathfrak{Z}$ der genaue Kern in $\mathfrak{D}$ der Spezialisierungsabbildung ist ; hieraus ergeben sich gewisse Strukturaussagen über $\mathfrak{E}$, und insbesondere über die Gruppe $\mathfrak{D}_p$ der Elemente mit durch p teilbarer endlicher Ordnung aus $\mathfrak{D}$.

P. Roquette (Tübingen)

Citations: MR 7, 362c = R58-5.

G20-17 (23# A1638)

Manin, Ju. I.

The Hasse-Witt matrix of an algebraic curve. (Russian)
Izv. Akad. Nauk SSSR Ser. Mat. **25** (1961), 153–172.

This paper gives two interesting theorems about the Hasse-Witt matrix A [H. Hasse and E. Witt, Monatsh. Math. Phys. **43** (1936), 477–492] of a curve Γ over a field k with prime characteristic p. For the first theorem the field $k = k_0$ has a finite number $q = p^a$ elements, and the author shows that there is an intimate connection between A and the characteristic polynomial of the endomorphism $(x) \to (x^q)$ of the Jacobian of Γ. For the second theorem the ground field k is one on which differentiations can be defined. The author shows that the rows of the Hasse-Witt matrix satisfy those differential relations which in the classical case would be satisfied by the periods of abelian integrals of the first kind. In a particular case this was already noted by Igusa [Proc. Nat. Acad. Sci. U.S.A. **44** (1958), 312–314; MR **20** #5183]. We now discuss the two theorems in more detail.

Theorem I : Let Γ be a curve of genus $g > 0$ defined over the field k_0 of $q = p^a$ elements (p prime). Suppose that there exist g k_0-rational points P_j on Γ such that the divisor $\sum_j P_j$ is non-special, and let A be the corresponding Hasse-Witt matrix. Let $A^{(p^j)}$ be the matrix obtained from A by the automorphism $F^j : x \to x^{p^j}$ ($x \in k_0$) and write

$$A_\pi = AA^{(p)} \cdots A^{(p^{a-1})}.$$

Then

$$\bar{\pi}(\lambda) = (-1)^g \lambda^g |A_\pi - \lambda E|,$$

where E is the unit matrix and $\bar{\pi}(\lambda)$ is the reduction mod p of the characteristic polynomial $\pi(\lambda)$ of the endomorphism $\pi : (x) \to (x^q)$ of the Jacobian variety J of Γ.

In particular, when $g = 1$, then A is a scalar and $\bar{\pi}(\lambda) = \lambda(\lambda - A)$.

The proof uses results of Serre [Amer. J. Math. **80** (1958), 715–739; MR **20** #4562]. Let $\Lambda = W(k_0)$ be the field of Witt vectors of k_0. Let X be any abelian variety of dimension g defined over k_0. Then Serre shows that the characteristic polynomial $\pi(\lambda)$ of the Frobenius automorphism on X is the characteristic polynomial of the endomorphism induced by the Frobenius automorph on the Λ-module

$$L(X) = H^1(X, \mathfrak{W}) + T'(X^*).$$

Here $H^1(X, \mathfrak{W})$ is the module constructed by Serre [Internat. Sympos. Algebraic Topology, pp. 24–53, Univ. Nac. Autónoma México, Mexico City, 1958; MR **20** #4559] and $T'(X^*)$ is the module of Tate vectors constructed from the p-th power division points on the dual variety X^*. The author now considers this endomorphism modulo p. The contribution of $T'(X^*)$ to the reduced polynomial $\bar{\pi}(\lambda)$ is shown to be a power of λ. Using Serre's exact sequence

$$H^1(X, \mathfrak{W}) \xrightarrow{\Gamma} H^1(X, \mathfrak{W}) \xrightarrow{p} H^1(X, O) \to 0$$

where O is the sheaf of local rings on X, he also shows that the reduced mod p characteristic polynomial for $H^1(X, \mathfrak{W})$ is that for $H^1(X, O)$ multiplied by a power of λ. If now X is the Jacobian of the curve Γ we have $H^1(X, O) = H^1(\Gamma, O_\Gamma)$, where O_Γ is the sheaf of local rings on Γ. Since the Hasse-Witt matrix gives the representation of the action of the Frobenius automorphism on $H^1(\Gamma, O_\Gamma)$ (with respect to an appropriate basis) the required result readily follows.

The author also gives an elementary proof of Theorem I when $g=1$.

In the second part of the paper the author considers a ground field k with a Lie algebra $\mathfrak{G}$ of differentiations ∂. Let K be a regular extension of k with separating transcendence-base $(x_1, \cdots, x_k)$. Then each $\partial \in \mathfrak{G}$ can be uniquely extended to a differentiation ∂_x of K by the condition $\partial_x x_j = 0$ $(1 \leqq j \leqq k)$. Let

$$\omega = \sum_{i_1 < \cdots < i_r} a_{i_1 \cdots i_r}\, dx_{i_1} \wedge \cdots \wedge dx_{i_r}$$

be any differential form of K/k and let d denote the ordinary operation of differentiation on differential forms (the elements of k being treated as constants). For any $\partial \in \mathfrak{G}$ define also an operator $r(\partial_x)$ on differential forms by putting

$$r(\partial_x)\omega = \sum_{i_1 < \cdots < i_r} \partial_x a_{i_1 \cdots i_r}\, dx_{i_1} \wedge \cdots \wedge dx_{i_r}$$

Then $r(\partial_x)$ commutes with d and hence takes closed forms into closed forms and complete differentials into complete differentials. Further, following Chevalley [*Introduction to the theory of algebraic functions of one variable*, Amer. Math. Soc., New York, 1951; MR **13**, 64] the author shows that if ω is any closed form and $(x_1, \cdots, x_k)$, $(y_1, \cdots, y_k)$ are any two separating transcendence-bases, then $r(\partial_x)\omega - r(\partial_y)\omega$ is a complete differential. Hence $\mathfrak{G}$ acts in a uniquely determined way on the factor space $H(K)$ of closed differentials modulo complete differentials. This can be extended in the obvious way to make $H(K)$ a U-module, where $U = U(\mathfrak{G})$ is the universal covering algebra of the Lie algebra $\mathfrak{G}$.

Now let K be in particular the function-field of a curve Γ of genus $g>0$ defined over k. Suppose that there exist distinct k-rational points P_j $(1 \leqq j \leqq g)$ such that the divisor $\sum P_j$ is non-special. Let r_k be the repartition with the value t_k^{-1} at P_k (where t_k is a local uniformizer) and is 0 elsewhere. Then $r_1, \cdots, r_g$ form a base for $\mathfrak{R}$ modulo $\mathfrak{R}(0)+K$, where $\mathfrak{R}$ [resp., $\mathfrak{R}(0)$] is the space of all [resp., all integral] repartitions. The Hasse-Witt matrix $A=(a_{ij})$ is defined by the relations $r_i^p \equiv \sum_j a_{ij} r_j \pmod{\mathfrak{R}(0)+K}$. Further, there exists a basis $\omega_1, \cdots, \omega_g$ of the differentials of the first kind such that

$$(1) \qquad (\omega_i, r_j) = \delta_{ij} \quad (\text{Kronecker } \delta).$$

Let $m_1, \cdots, m_g$ be the images of $\omega_1, \cdots, \omega_g$ in $H(K)$, and let $n_1, \cdots, n_g$ be the rows of A.

Theorem II: Let $u_1, \cdots, u_g \in U$ be such that

$$(2) \qquad \sum_{1 \leqq i \leqq g} u_i m_i = 0.$$

Then

$$(3) \qquad \sum_{1 \leqq i \leqq g} u_i n_i = 0.$$

The proof runs as follows. The relation (2) is equivalent to

$$\sum r(u_i)_x \omega_i = d\phi,$$

where the operator $r(u_i)_x$ is composed of the operations $r(\partial_x)$ in the same way as u_i is composed of the ∂. Hence for each repartition r_j of the canonical base we have

$$\sum (r(u_i)_x\, \omega_i, Fr_j) = (d\varphi, Fr_j),$$

where F is the Frobenius operation. Now $(\omega, Fr_j) = (C\omega, r_j)^p$, where C is Cartier's operation. Hence

$$(4) \qquad \sum_i (Cr(u_i)_x \omega_i, r_j)^p = 0 \quad (1 \leqq j \leqq g)$$

since C annihilates all complete differentials. Now $Cr(u_i)_x\omega_i$ is independent of the choice of separating base x, because a change of base changes $r(u_i)_x\omega_i$ by a complete differential. Hence in the ith term of (3) we may take x to be the uniformizing variable t_i. Then

$$(Cr(u_i)_x\omega_i, r_j) = (F^*u_i)(C\omega_i, r_j),$$

where F^* acting on U is the adjoint of the Frobenius transformation. Hence the ith term in (4) is

$$u_i((C\omega_i, r_j))^p = u_i(\omega_i, Fr_j).$$

Thus (4) gives $\sum_i u_i(\omega_i, Fr_j) = 0$, which is the same as (3), by (1). *J. W. S. Cassels* (Cambridge, England)

Citations: MR 13, 64a = R58-12; MR 20# 5183 = G20-13.

G20-18 (25# 75)

Grothendieck, A.
Sur une note de Mattuck-Tate.
J. Reine Angew. Math. **200** (1958), 208–215.

Mattuck und Tate [Abh. Math. Sem. Univ. Hamburg **22** (1958), 295–299; MR **20** #5202] haben die Riemannsche Vermutung für algebraische Kurven hergeleitet aus dem Riemann-Rochschen Satz für algebraische Flächen. Den Methoden von Mattuck-Tate liegt, wie Verfasser hier zeigt, ein allgemeiner Satz über die Gruppe der Divisorklassen bez. algebraischer Äquivalenz auf einer singularitätenfreien, projektiven algebraischen Fläche X zugrunde (Néron-Severische Gruppe; Bezeichnung: N). Der Grad $D \cdot D'$ des Durchschnittsproduktes zweier Divisoren D und D' von X hängt nur von den Klassen von D und D' in N ab; die Abbildung $(D, D') \rightarrow D \cdot D'$ induziert in N eine Bilinearform f. Diese Bilinearform wird nun in dem durch N erzeugten reellen Vektorraum E betrachtet, dessen Dimension n gleich dem Rang der Gruppe N ist. Der in Rede stehende Satz besagt nun, daß f als quadratische Form von E nicht ausgeartet ist und den Typus $(1, n-1)$ besitzt. Es wird dafür ein Beweis angegeben; jedoch ist der Satz aus der algebraischen Geometrie seit längerer Zeit bekannt [Hodge, J. London Math. Soc. **12** (1937), 58–63; B. Segre, Ann. Mat. Pura Appl. (4) **16** (1937), 157–163; Bronowski, J. London Math. Soc. **13** (1938), 86–90]. Der Verfasser zeigt, wie man aus seinem Satz die fundamentale Ungleichung von Castelnuovo-Severi-Weil herleiten kann, die dem Beweis der Riemannschen Vermutung für Kurven zugrunde liegt. Darüber hinaus werden noch weitere Ungleichungen für die Invarianten von Divisoren auf X hergeleitet. Beispielsweise sei hier das folgende Ergebnis angegeben: Es sei C eine irreduzible, singularitätenfreie Kurve auf X, für welche $C^2 = \alpha > 0$, und für welche der durch Durchschnittsbildung mit C definierte Homomorphismus $P(X) \rightarrow P(C)$ der Picardschen Mannigfaltigkeiten von X bzw. C surjektiv ist. Dann gilt: $\chi(X) \leqq \frac{1}{2}\alpha^{-1}(g-1-\frac{1}{2}\alpha)^2$, wo $\chi(X)$ das arithmetische Geschlecht von X ist, und g das (geometrische) Geschlecht von C. *P. Roquette* (Zbl **84**, 169)

Citations: MR 20# 5202 = G20-14.
Referred to in G25-57.

G20-19 (25# 76)

Mattuck, Arthur
On symmetric products of curves.
Proc. Amer. Math. Soc. **13** (1962), 82–87.

Let C be a complete non-singular curve over an algebraically closed field of genus $g \geqq 2$. Let $C(g)$ be the g-fold symmetric product of C with itself. $C(g)$ gives a representation of the positive divisors of degree g on C. The author translates the proof of Weil [*Sur les courbes algébriques et les variétés qui s'en déduisent*, Actualités Sci. Ind., No. 1041, Hermann, Paris, 1948; MR **10**, 262] of the inequality of Castelnuovo about the number of "coincidences" of an irreducible algebraic correspondence of degrees g, e in terms of intersection numbers of a curve and a $(g-1)$-dimensional subvariety of $C(g)$. He also gives a proof of the Severi formulation of the above inequality. The use of $C(g)$ permits the author to give a geometric interpretation of the concept of weight of a point used in the proof of the inequality for the number of Weierstrass points of C. *P. Abellanas* (Madrid)

Citations: MR 10, 262c = G20-8.

G20-20 (30# 1129)

Vvedenskiĭ, O. N.

Duality in elliptic curves over a local field. I. (Russian)

Izv. Akad. Nauk SSSR Ser. Mat. **28** (1964), 1091–1112.

From the author's introduction: "Let K be a local field, i.e., a discretely normed field complete with respect to the topology induced by the norm, and let k be its residue field. Denote by A an abelian variety defined over K, by A_K the group of points on A defined over K and by $\bar{A}$ the Picard variety of A.

"When k is finite, it is known [Tate, Proc. Internat. Congr. Mathematicians (Stockholm, 1962), pp. 288–295, Mittag-Leffler, Djursholm, 1963] that the group of principal homogeneous spaces over A is dual to the group $\bar{A}_K$ except for the p-component, where p is the characteristic of K. When k is algebraically closed, it was shown by Šafarevič [Trudy Mat. Inst. Steklov. **64** (1961), 316–346; MR **29** #110] and independently by Ogg [Ann. of Math. (2) **76** (1962), 185–212; MR **27** #5758] that the group of principal homogeneous spaces over A is dual to the group $\pi_1(\bar{A}_K)$, i.e., the fundamental group of the pro-algebraic group $\bar{A}_K$ in the sense of Serre [Inst. Hautes Études Sci. Publ. Math. No. 7 (1960); MR **22** #9493], except for the p-component, where p is the characteristic of k. It was conjectured that the duality holds also for the p-component. In the present work this conjecture is proved for the special case when A is an elliptic curve whose reduction has a Hasse invariant other than 0. We should remark that we do not find explicitly a natural pairing between $\pi_1(\bar{A}_K)$ and the group of principal homogeneous spaces, although the proof of the duality, which is done in a purely computational way, permits us to deduce that one exists."

J. W. S. Cassels (Cambridge, England)

Citations: MR 27# 5758 = G10-19; MR 29# 110 = G10-23.

Referred to in G20-27.

G20-21 (31# 161)

Bombieri, Enrico

Sull'analogo della formula di Selberg nei corpi di funzioni.

Atti Accad. Naz. Lincei Rend. Cl. Sci. Fis. Mat. Natur. (8) **35** (1963), 252–257.

Let C be an algebraic curve of genus g defined over the Galois field $[q]$ of q elements. Let N_m be the number of points of C (including those at infinity) with coordinates in $[q^m]$. The author obtains an analogue of Selberg's formula for the curve C, viz., $mN_m+\sum_{i=0}^m N_iN_{m-i}=2mq^m+O(q^m)$, where the constant implied by the O depends only on C. The proof depends on an ingenious use of some simple facts about divisors on C. Using this formula and a lemma of E. Wirsing, an elementary proof is given that $N_m \sim q^m$ as $m\to\infty$. It is indicated that the method can be refined to give an improved error term. The definitive result in this direction is the inequality $|N_m-(q^m+1)|\leqq 2gq^{m/2}$, proved by A. Weil using deep theorems from algebraic geometry.

B. Gordon (Los Angeles, Calif.)

Referred to in G20-46, G25-46.

G20-22 (31# 5862a; 31# 5862b)

Hellegouarch, Yves

Une propriété arithmétique des points exceptionnels rationnels d'ordre pair d'une cubique de genre 1.

C. R. Acad. Sci. Paris **260** (1965), 5989–5992.

Hellegouarch, Yves

Applications d'une propriété arithmétique des points exceptionnels d'ordre pair d'une cubique de genre 1.

C. R. Acad. Sci. Paris **260** (1965), 6256–6258.

Let Γ be an elliptic curve, and suppose that Γ has a rational point of order $2p$, where $p\geqq 5$ is a prime. Using π-adic elliptic functions, where π is prime, the author obtains very detailed information about Γ and about the coordinates of its $2p$-division points.

In the second note, the author illustrates his result very prettily by the curve $y^2=x(x^2+190x-1215)$, which has points of order 10. He also gives a new proof that there are no curves with points of order 14. Presumably the object is to show that there are no curves with points of order $2p$ for prime $p\geqq 7$; but this seems very distant.

B. J. Birch (Cambridge, England)

Referred to in G05-112.

G20-23 (33# 2636)

Vvedens'kiĭ, O. M.

Elliptic curves with a degenerate reduction. (Ukrainian)

Vestnik L'vov. Politehn. Inst. No. 8 (1965), 70–72.

Let K be a complete discrete normed field with an algebraically closed field of residues of characteristic $p>3$, O_K the ring of integers in K, P a maximal ideal in O_K, U_K the group of units, T a prime of K.

Let A be an elliptic curve $y^2=(x-\varepsilon)^2(x+2\varepsilon)+\delta T^n$ ($\varepsilon, \delta\in U_K$; $n\geqq 1$), A_K the group of points of A rational over K, τ_K a Lutz-subgroup of points of A_K. Using standard notation, the author states, without proof, the following theorem: There exists an isomorphism between the group of principal homogeneous spaces over A and the group $\pi_1(A_K)^*$ (* means duality); there exist isomorphisms between $H^m(g, A_L)$ and $[H^{1-m}(g, \pi_1(A_L))]^*$ for all $m\in Z$.

G. Biriuk (Ann Arbor, Mich.)

G20-24 (34# 176)

Medvedev, P. A.

The order and the index of an elliptic curve. (Russian)

Izv. Akad. Nauk SSSR Ser. Mat. **30** (1966), 1179–1192.

It is known that the order of a principal homogeneous space over an abelian variety divides the index, and that the order and index have the same prime factors [I. R. Šafarevič, Dokl. Akad. Nauk SSSR **114** (1957), 267–270; MR **20** #867; S. Lang and J. Tate, Amer. J. Math. **80** (1958), 659–685; MR **21** #4960]. In this paper the author considers the special case when the ground-field is a finite algebraic extension of a p-adic field with $p\neq 2, 3$ and when the abelian variety has dimension 1 (so the principal homogeneous space is an elliptic curve with a structure of homogeneous space over its jacobian). He shows that the index is the same as the order provided that the order is odd, and gives examples when the order is 2 and the index 4.

J. W. S. Cassels (Cambridge, England)

Citations: MR 20# 867 = G05-56; MR 21# 4960 = G10-10.

Referred to in G20-25.

G20-25 (36# 6415)

Medvedev, P. A.

A remark on my paper: "The order and the index of an elliptic curve". (Russian)

Izv. Akad. Nauk SSSR Ser. Mat. **32** (1968), 247.

The original paper appeared in same Izv. **30** (1966), 1179–1192 [MR **34** #176]. Stephen Lichtenbaum has pointed out to the author that the example of an elliptic curve of order 2 and index 4 over a p-adic field is erroneous, and that, in fact, no such curve exists.

J. W. S. Cassels (Cambridge, England)

Citations: MR 34# 176 = G20-24.

G20-26 (34# 4253)

Elistratov, I. V.

Elementary proof of Hasse's theorem. (Russian)

Studies in Number Theory, No. I (Russian), pp. 21–26. *Izdat. Saratov. Univ., Saratov,* 1966.

Ju. I. Manin hat in einer Arbeit [Izv. Akad. Nauk SSSR Ser. Mat. **20** (1956), 673–678; MR **18**, 380] einen gänzlich elementaren Beweis der Riemannschen Vermutung für die Zetafunktion eines elliptischen Funktionenkörpers über einem endlichen Körper der Charakteristik $p>3$ als Grundkörper gegeben. Der Autor zeigt, dass dieser Beweis in völlig analoger Weise auch für endliche Grundkörper der Charakteristik $p>2$ geführt werden kann. {Dabei versäumt er es leider, den Maninschen Fehlschluss (vergleiche das zitierte Referat) zu beheben.}

H. G. Zimmer (Tübingen)

Citations: MR 18, 380e = D80-24.

G20-27 (34# 5818)

Vvedenskiĭ, O. N. [Vvedens'kiĭ, O. M.]

Duality in elliptic curves over a local field. II. (Russian)

Izv. Akad. Nauk SSSR Ser. Mat. **30** (1966), 891–922.

{For background, see the review of Part I [same Izv. **28** (1964), 1091–1112; MR **30** #1129].} The author extends the results of Part I to the case of degenerate multiplicative reduction and also to nondegenerate reduction with zero Hasse invariant of the reduced curve, provided that in the second case the ground field has characteristic zero.

The main results of the two papers are summed up as follows (Theorems 4 and 5). Let K be a discretely valued field complete with respect to its valuation and suppose that the residue field is algebraically closed of characteristic $p>3$. Denote by $G(K)$ the galois group of the separable closure of K. Let A be an abelian variety of dimension 1 defined over K and denote by $\pi_1(A)$ the inductive limit of the $\pi_1(A_L)$, where L runs through all finite (separable) extensions of K, and where A_L is the group of points on A defined over L, and $\pi_1(A_L)$ is the homotopy group of a proalgebraic group over the residue field [cf. J.-P. Serre, Inst. Hautes Études Sci. Publ. Math. No. 7 (1960); MR **22** #9493]. Then $G(K)$ acts continuously on $\pi_1(A)$. Denote the corresponding cohomology groups by $H^s(K, \pi_1(A))$. Similarly, denote the cohomology groups for $G(K)$ acting on the algebraic points of A by $H^s(K, A)$. Consider the three cases: (1) nondegenerate reduction, Hasse invariant of the reduced curve $\neq 0$; (2) multiplicative reduction; (3) nondegenerate reduction, the Hasse invariant of the reduced curve $=0$, and K of zero characteristic.

In all three cases, $H^s(K, A)$ $(s \geqq 2)$ and $H^s(K, \pi_1(A))$ $(s \geqq 3)$ are trivial. In all three cases, the dual group of $H^0(K, \pi_1(A))$ is isomorphic to $H^1(K, A)$. In cases (1) and (2), the group $H^1(K, \pi_1(A))$ is trivial and $H^2(K, \pi_1(A))$ is naturally isomorphic to $H^1(K, A)$. In case (3), however, the group $H^1(K, \pi_1(A))$ is nontrivial, and indeed the power of its set of elements is not less than the power of the residue field; and $H^2(K, \pi_1(A))$ is infinitely divisible.

J. W. S. Cassels (Cambridge, England)

Citations: MR 30# 1129 = G20-20.

G20-28 (34# 7509)

Ogg, A. P.

Elliptic curves and wild ramification.

Amer. J. Math. **89** (1967), 1–21.

Let A be an elliptic curve defined by a third degree equation $F(x, y) = y^2 + x^3 + \cdots = 0$ with coefficients in a complete discrete valuation ring with quotient field k, and with algebraically closed residue field of characteristic $p \geqq 0$. By suitable transformations, F is normalized so that $\operatorname{ord}(\Delta)$ is as small as possible, where Δ, the discriminant, is the function of the coefficients obtained by eliminating x, y from $F=0$, $F_x=0$, $F_y=0$. A can be thought of as a two-dimensional scheme; there exists a minimal birationally equivalent non-singular model whose closed fibre $\bar{A}$ is a curve having one of the forms enumerated by Kodaira and Néron [see A. Néron, Inst. Hautes Études Sci. Publ. Math. No. 21 (1964); MR **31** #3423]. In the classical case, one checks that the Euler number of $\bar{A}$ is $n+\varepsilon-1$, where n is the number of components of $\bar{A}$, and $\varepsilon = 0$, 1 or 2 is an integer depending on the singularities of the reduction of A [cf. the author, Ann. of Math. (2) **76** (1962), 185–212, 194; MR **27** #5758]. J. Tate has found, by checking cases, that $n+\varepsilon-1 = \operatorname{ord}(\Delta)$.

To extend this result to the general case, the author makes use of the following number δ: let l be a prime number $\neq p$, let $M = A_l$ be the group of points on A of order dividing l, let $G_0 \supseteq G_1 \supseteq G_2 \supseteq \cdots$ be the higher ramification groups for the field extension $k(M)/k$ (so that M is a G_i-module for all i) and set

$$\delta = \sum_i [G : G_i]^{-1} \dim_{\mathbf{Z}/l\mathbf{Z}} M/M^{G_i}.$$

(δ is shown to be equal to an integer defined by Serre to measure the wild ramification of M; $\delta = 0$ if and only if $k(M)/k$ is tamely ramified.) The first principal result is that δ is independent of l. The main result is that $n+\varepsilon-1 = \operatorname{ord}(\Delta) - \delta$. (Difficulties occur only when $p=3$ and—especially—$p=2$; otherwise $\delta = 0$.)

As an application, an interpretation of Picard's invariant $\rho_0 = B_2 - \rho$ in terms of principal homogeneous spaces, given previously by the author [loc. cit., p. 211] when $\delta = 0$, is now shown to hold for a pencil of elliptic curves also when $\delta \neq 0$.

Joseph Lipman (Lafayette, Ind.)

Citations: MR 27# 5758 = G10-19; MR 31# 3423 = G10-25.

Referred to in G10-36.

G20-29 (35# 1597)

Vvedens'kiĭ, O. M.

Proalgebraic groups with reduction height two. (Ukrainian. Russian summary)

Vīsnik L'vīv. Derž. Unīv. Ser. Meh.-Mat. **1965**, *vyp.* 2, 24–29.

Author's summary: "Elementary properties of the Lutz subgroup of an elliptic curve are studied."

G20-30 (35# 6681)

Hasse, Helmut

Modular functions and elliptic curves over finite fields.

Rend. Mat. e Appl. (5) **25** (1966), 248–266.

The author proves the following theorem. Let a finite field F of p^f elements be given, where p is a prime and f is assumed odd. Furthermore, let α be an element of F of degree f over the prime field. Then there exists an imaginary quadratic field Ω, a lattice $\mathfrak{a}$ in Ω, a prime divisor $\mathfrak{p}/p$ of degree f in the ring class field $K = \Omega(j(\mathfrak{a}))$ (where j is the absolute invariant) and an isomorphism of F onto the residue field $K/\mathfrak{p}$ which maps α on $j(\mathfrak{a})$. A further property

of the lattice which plays a rôle in the proof is omitted here. In general a is uniquely determined up to a scalar factor in Ω. The only exception is when $f=1$ and p is ramified in Ω, in which case there may be two lattices with this property in Ω. As is pointed out in the introduction, this theorem yields the basis for a proof of the Riemann hypothesis for an elliptic curve over a finite field. Indeed, it was the first proof ever given, though only sketched [the author, Nachr. Gesellsch. Wiss. Göttingen Math.-Phys. Kl. **1933**, 253–262]. The salient point in the proof of this theorem is of course the basic well-known congruence property mod p of the equation $F_{p^f}=0$ expressing the modular correspondence attached to p^f, and the fact that all elements of the field F are roots of $F_{p^f}(j,j)\equiv 0 \bmod p$.
M. Eichler (Basel)

Referred to in G15-41.

G20-31 (35# 6683)

Shatz, Stephen S.
The cohomology of certain elliptic curves over local and quasi-local fields.
Illinois J. Math. **11** (1967), 234–241.

One of the purposes of this paper is to check the fact that the Tate pairing $H^0(k,A)\times H^1(k,A)\to H^2(k,G_m)=Q/Z$, for a p-adic field k and an elliptic curve A defined over k whose j-invariant is not integral in k, is the duality of p-adic topological groups. The other is to answer the problem raised by J.-P. Serre [*Cohomologie galoisienne*, second edition, Springer, Berlin, 1964; MR **31** #4785; third edition, 1965; MR **34** #1328, Chapter II, p. 29] in the following case. Let k be a quasi-local field and A an elliptic curve defined over k whose j-invariant is not integral in k. Then $H^r(k,A)=(0)$ for $r=2$.
M. Miwa (Tokyo)

Citations: MR 31# 4785 = R02-39; MR 34# 1328 = R02-40.
Referred to in G25-56.

G20-32 (36# 5137)

Hirschfeld, James W. P.
A curve over a finite field, the number of whose points is not increased by a quadratic extension of the field, and sub-Hermitian forms. (Italian summary)
Atti Accad. Naz. Lincei Rend. Cl. Sci. Fis. Mat. Natur. (8) **42** (1967), 365–367.

The equation $x_0\bar{x}_0+x_1\bar{x}_1+x_2\bar{x}_2=0$, where $\bar{x}=x^{p^k}$, defines a projective non-singular curve H over the finite field $GF(p)$; the equation itself is Hermitian over $GF(p^{2k})$, "sub-Hermitian" over $GF(p^{4k})$. B. Segre [Ann. Mat. Pura Appl. (4) **70** (1965), 1–202; MR **35** #4802] showed that $N(p^{2k})=p^{3k}+1$, where $N(q)$ denotes the number of points of H which are rational over $GF(q)$. This note proves by simple geometric methods that all points of H which are rational over $GF(p^{4k})$ are already rational over $GF(p^{2k})$. With regard to Weil's general inequalities for curves of genus g $[q+1-2g\sqrt{q}\leqq N(q)\leqq q+1+2g\sqrt{q}]$, it is remarked that $N(p^{2k})$ takes on the maximum value, $N(p^{4k})$ the minimum. A generalization by Segre is discussed.
W. E. Fulton (Waltham, Mass.)

G20-33 (36# 6417)

Vvedens'kiĭ, O. M.
Torsion of elliptic curves over a local field. (**Ukrainian. Russian summary**)
Vīsnik L'vīv. Derž. Unīv. Ser. Meh.-Mat. **1965**, *vyp.* 1, 3–6.

Author's summary: "Based on an investigation of division equations on elliptic curves which are near (in the p-adic topology) to curves with singular points, it is shown that the torsion of elliptic curves over the p-adic number field is divisible by any previously assigned number."
(RŽMat **1965** #9 A239)

G20-34 (37# 213)

Yamada, Toshihiko
On the Jacobian varieties of Davenport-Hasse curves.
Proc. Japan Acad. **43** (1967), 407–411.

For a prime p, and a positive integer a, let C_a be the "Davenport-Hasse curve" $y^p-y=x^{p^a-1}$ and J_a its Jacobian. The group G of $(p-1)(p^a-1)$th roots of 1 operates on C_a. The author determines the l-adic representation of G on J_a. He then shows that J_a has a certain simple component A of multiplicity one (the "main component"), and determines the l-adic representation of G on A, and the endomorphism algebra of A. Detailed proofs and further results have appeared elsewhere [the author, J. Math. Soc. Japan **20** (1968), 403–410; MR **37** #1375].
A. P. Ogg (Berkeley, Calif.)

Citations: MR 37# 1375 = G20-35.

G20-35 (37# 1375)

Yamada, Toshihiko
On the Davenport-Hasse curves.
J. Math. Soc. Japan **20** (1968), 403–410.

Let p be a rational prime and let c_2 be the curve over $GF(p)$ having $y^p-y=x^{p^a-1}$ as its equation. Let θ be a primitive $(p^a-1)/(p-1)$ root of unity in the algebraic closure of $GF(p)$; the map $\sigma\colon(x,y)\to(\theta x,\theta^{p^a-1}y)$ is an automorphism on C_a and generates a cyclic group G of order $(p^q-1)(p-1)$. The author determines the l-adic representation of the group G as the direct sum of certain irreducible representations of multiplicity 1. If J_a is the Jacobian variety of C_a, then J_a is isogenous to the product $A_1\times\cdots\times A_h$, $A_i=B_i\times\cdots\times B_i$ $(i=1,\cdots,h)$, where the B_i are simple abelian varieties not isogenous to each other. J. Tate [Invent. Math. **2** (1966), 134–144; MR **34** #5829] has shown that the A_i are in one-to-one correspondence with the conjugacy classes (as algebraic numbers) of the characteristic roots of the p^ath power endomorphism of J_a. Let $A=A_1$ correspond to the conjugacy class of

$$\textstyle\sum_{u\in GF(p^a);\,u\neq 0}\chi(u)\exp(2\pi ip^{-1}\operatorname{tr}(u)),$$

where χ is a character of order p^a-1 of the multiplicative group of $GF(p^a)$. The author proves that A is a simple abelian variety and for $a=1$ he gives the complete decomposition of J_1 into simple factors. Finally, the l-adic representation of G on A is determined and from this one sees that the endomorphism algebra of A is generated by the pth power endomorphism and the endomorphism induced by the automorphism σ. The proof depends heavily on the methods of the above mentioned paper of Tate.
D. J. Lewis (Ann Arbor, Mich.)

Citations: MR 34# 5829 = G10-32.
Referred to in G20-34.

G20-36 (37# 5223)

Cassels, J. W. S.
Elliptic curves over local fields.
Proc. Conf. Local Fields (Driebergen, 1966), pp. 37–39. *Springer, Berlin*, 1967.

A very brief sketch of basic definitions, results, and problems in the arithmetic theory of elliptic curves.
N. Greenleaf (Rochester, N.Y.)

G20-37 **(39# 4158)**

Lichtenbaum, Stephen

Duality theorems for curves over p-adic fields.

Invent. Math. **7** (1969), 120–136.

X is a proper, smooth, geometrically connected curve over Spec k, and $\bar{X}=X\times_{\mathrm{Spec}\,k}\mathrm{Spec}\,\bar{k}$, where $\bar{k}$ is the separable closure of k with the Galois group G over k. K and $\bar{K}$ are the fields of rational functions on X and $\bar{X}$, respectively. $\mathrm{Pic}_0(X)$ denotes the subgroup of Pic X consisting of divisor classes of degree zero; $\mathrm{Br}(X)$ is the Brauer group of X. The author constructs functorial pairings ρ_0, ρ, ψ from $H^1(G,\mathrm{Pic}_0(\bar{X}))\times H^0(G,\mathrm{Pic}_0(\bar{X}))$, $H^1(G,\mathrm{Pic}(\bar{X}))\times\mathrm{Pic}_0(X)$, and $\mathrm{Br}(X)\times\mathrm{Pic}(X)$ to $\mathrm{Br}(k)=H^2(G,\bar{k}^*)$.

If k is a p-adic field (and therefore $\mathrm{Br}(k)\cong\mathbf{Q}/\mathbf{Z}$), then ρ_0 induces an isomorphism $\rho_0{}^*$ of $H^1(G,\mathrm{Pic}_0(\bar{X}))$ with the dual abelian group of $H^0(G,\mathrm{Pic}_0(\bar{X}))$. If X has a k-rational point, this follows from the fact that ρ_0 is, up to sign, identical to the dualizing Tate pairing on the Jacobian of X. In the case of arbitrary X one can utilize, in a certain imitation of Tate, the G-isomorphism between $\mathrm{Pic}_0(\bar{X})$ and $J(\bar{k})$, where J is the k-Albanese variety of X. The pairing ρ_0 induces ρ and, accordingly, one can prove that ρ^*, induced by ρ, is an isomorphism of $H^1(G,\mathrm{Pic}(\bar{X}))$ with the dual of $\mathrm{Pic}_0(X)$. Furthermore, the author shows that the following theorem of P. Roquette [Nagoya Math. J. **27** (1966), 625–642; MR **34** #1319] is a conclusion from the fact that $\rho_0{}^*$ is an isomorphism: "X and K the same as above, k a p-adic field; then the order of the kernel $(\mathrm{Br}(k)\to\mathrm{Br}(K))$ is equal to the index I of X." {Note that X need not contain a k-rational point.} Now, Roquette's theorem yields directly the following statement: ψ^* coming from ψ and mapping $\mathrm{Br}(X)$ to the dual of $\mathrm{Pic}(X)$ is an isomorphism. From this one obtains—as supplement to a theorem of Tate—that for an arbitrary complete non-singular curve X over a p-adic field the idèle-class cohomology $H^1(G,\bar{C})$ is vanishing ($\bar{C}$ = idèle-class group of $\bar{X}$).

Finally some applications of the duality-theorems are given to period-index questions on curves over p-adic fields and over arbitrary k.

The author notes that the isomorphism ψ^*, stated in terms of étale cohomology ($\mathrm{Br}(X)=H^2(X,G_m)$ and $\mathrm{Pic}(X)=H^1(X,G_m)$), can be generalized to: $H^2(X,G_m)\otimes_{\mathbf{Z}}\hat{\mathbf{Z}}$ is isomorphic to the dual of $H^{3-i}(X,G_m)$, where G_m is the sheaf which associates to each U over X the group of units in $\Gamma(U,O_U)$. *Manfred Herrmann* (Halle a.d. Saale)

Citations: MR 34# 1319 = R34-18.

G20-38 **(40# 2646)**

Vvedens'kiĭ, O. M.

Local class fields of elliptic curves. **(Ukrainian. Russian and English summaries)**

Dopovīdī Akad. Nauk Ukraïn. RSR Ser. A **1968**, 876–880.

Let K_s be the separable closure of a local field K with the characteristic of the residue class field equal to $p>3$. Denote by A_s the group of K_s-rational points on an elliptic curve A defined over K. Suppose that the Hasse invariant of the reduced curve is equal to zero. The paper under review contains an outline of the proof of the following generalization of J. Tate's result [cf. Séminaire Bourbaki, 1957/1958, *Textes des conférences*, Exposé 156, deuxième édition, Secrétariat mathématique, Paris, 1958; MR **21** #4162; facsimile reproduction, Benjamin, New York, 1966; see MR **33** #5420e]: groups $H^0(G(K_s/K),A_s)$ and $H^1(G(K_s/K),A_s)$ are dual with respect to the Tate pairing. *J. Browkin* (Warsaw)

Citations: MR 21# 4162 = G10-8.

Referred to in G20-39, G20-40.

G20-39 **(42# 5993)**

Vvedens'kiĭ, O. M.

"Local class fields" of elliptic curves. **(Ukrainian. English and Russian summaries)**

Dopovīdī Akad. Nauk Ukraïn. RSR Ser. A **1969**, 393–396, 472.

The author proves the same result as in his previous paper [same Dopovīdī **1968**, 876–880; MR **40** #2646] for elliptic curves in Weierstrass form such that the Hasse invariant of the reduced curve is equal to zero.

{See also #5994 below.} *J. Browkin* (Warsaw)

Citations: MR 40# 2646 = G20-38.

G20-40 **(42# 5994)**

Vvedens'kiĭ, O. M.

"Local class fields" of elliptic curves. **(Ukrainian. English and Russian summaries)**

Dopovīdī Akad. Nauk Ukraïn. RSR Ser. A **1969**, 966–969, 1051.

The author proves the same result as in his previous papers [same Dopovīdī **1968**, 876–880; MR **40** #2646; #5993 above] for another class of elliptic curves.

J. Browkin (Warsaw)

Citations: MR 40# 2646 = G20-38.

G20-41 **(40# 4269)**

Miller, Leonhard

Elementarer Beweis eines Satzes von H. Hasse über die Punkte der Ordnung p auf einer elliptischen k-Kurve, p = char k.

Nachr. Akad. Wiss. Göttingen Math.-Phys. Kl. II **1969**, 1–8.

The author gives an "elementary" proof, à la Chevalley-Warning, of Hasse's theorem that an elliptic curve over a field k of characteristic $p>0$ has a k-rational point of order p if and only if its Hasse invariant is a non-zero $(p-1)$th power in k; he assumes k is finite, and $p\neq 2,3$.

A. P. Ogg (Berkeley, Calif.)

G20-42 **(40# 5620)**

Stepanov, S. A.

The number of points of a hyperelliptic curve over a finite prime field. **(Russian)**

Izv. Akad. Nauk SSSR Ser. Mat. **33** (1969), 1171–1181.

In dieser Arbeit wird eine zahlentheoretische Abschätzung von H. Hasse [Abh. Math. Sem. Univ. Hamburg **10** (1934), 325–348] und A. Weil [*Sur les courbes algébriques et les variétés qui s'en déduisent*, Actualités Sci. Indust., No. 1041, Hermann, Paris, 1948; MR **10**, 262] mit neuen Methoden verbessert. Sei $n\geqq 3$ eine ungerade Zahl und $p>9n^2$ eine beliebige Primzahl. Sei k_p der Körper mit p Elementen. Man betrachtet die Kurve $y^2=f(x)$, mit $f(x)=x^n+a_1x^{n-1}+\cdots+a_{n-1}x+a_n\in k_p[x]$. Mit I_p bezeichnet man die Lösungsanzahl der Gleichung $y^2=f(x)$ in k_p. Es wird die folgende Abschätzung bewiesen: $|I_p-p|\leqq\sqrt{(3n)}n\sqrt{p}$. *W. Vogel* (Halle a.d. Saale)

Citations: MR 10, 262c = G20-8.

Referred to in D80-75, T25-35.

G20-43 **(41# 3481)**

Ogg, A. P.

A remark on the Sato-Tate conjecture.

Invent. Math. **9** (1969/70), 198–200.

Let A be an elliptic curve defined over a number field k. At a prime v of k where A has good reduction, let $\pm\Theta_v$ be the argument of the zeros of the zeta-function of the reduced elliptic curve. The conjecture of the title says the angles Θ_v are uniformly distributed in $[0,\pi]$ relative to the measure $2\pi^{-1}\sin^2\Theta\, d\Theta$ [cf. J. T. Tate, *Arithmetical algebraic geometry* (Proc. Conf. Purdue Univ., 1963), pp. 93–110, Harper-Row, New York, 1965; MR **37** #1371]. This problem is closely related to certain Euler products. The product $L_n(s)=\prod_v(1\text{-}\exp(ni\Theta_v)(Nv)^{-s})^{-1}$ converges for $\sigma=\mathrm{Re}(s)>1$, where $n\in\mathbf{Z}$ and Nv is the norm of the finite prime v. Taking $M_n=L_nL_{n-2}\cdots L_{-n}$ for $n\geqq 1$, the conjecture would follow if the functions M_n had analytic continuations without zeros on the line $\sigma=1$. The author shows, using elementary facts about Dirichlet series, that the existence of a holomorphic continuation beyond the line $\sigma=\frac{1}{2}$ (which is unfortunately unknown) implies the non-existence of zeros on the line $\sigma=1$.

W.-D. Geyer (Heidelberg)

G20-44 (41# 5376)

Roquette, Peter

Analytic theory of elliptic functions over local fields.

Hamburger Mathematische Einzelschriften (N.F.), Heft 1.

Vandenhoeck & Ruprecht, Göttingen, 1970. 90 *pp.* *DM* 28.00.

This work is devoted to the study of elliptic function fields F/K, where K is a local field (a field which is complete for a non-archimedean valuation) and F a field of periodic functions over K. Some of the necessary algebraic background of this theory is given in an appendix; here the defining relations, the absolute invariant j, the Hasse invariant γ and the cohomological invariant ξ of an arbitrary elliptic function field are defined and discussed. It is shown that for a field K there is one and, up to a K-isomorphism, only one elliptic function field over K having given invariants j, γ, ξ (if $j\neq 0, 12^3$).

In case K is a local field, Laurent series $\sum_{n\in Z} a_nX^n$ ($a_n\in K$) are considered which converge for each element $\alpha\neq 0$ of the algebraic closure Ω of K. A meromorphic function is the quotient of two Laurent series. For $q\in K$, $0<|q|<1$, a meromorphic function f is called q-periodic if $f(q^{-1}X)=f(X)$. These functions are to be considered as the nonarchimedean analogues of the doubly periodic complex functions. The q-periodic functions form an elliptic function field $F_K(q)$. This was first shown by J. Tate, who initiated the whole theory. It seems that the results of Tate are published here for the first time in detail.

Using the analytic representation of the field $F_K(q)$, it is possible to compute explicitly many algebraic invariants of $F_K(q)$ and to study their relations. It is therefore of interest to know which elliptic function fields F/K are of the form $F_K(q)/K$ for some $q\in K$, $0<|q|<1$. The author proves that this is the case if and only if the following conditions hold: (i) F/K has a prime divisor of degree 1, (ii) the absolute invariant j satisfies $|j|>1$, (iii) the Hasse invariant γ is trivial.

Next the question is discussed of which elliptic function fields E/K have $F_K(q)$ as their Jacobian field, i.e., have the same absolute and Hasse invariant as $F_K(q)$ (but not necessarily a prime divisor of degree 1). This question leads to the notion of semiperiodic function: If L/K is a cyclic extension, σ a generator of the galois group of L/K and $Q\in L$ an element with norm q, then a meromorphic function f over L is called semiperiodic if $\tau_Q\sigma f=f$ (here σ operates on the coefficients of f and τ_Q is the translation automorphism $f(X)\to f(Q^{-1}X)$). The semiperiodic functions form an elliptic function field $F_K(L,\sigma,Q)$ and each elliptic function field E/K with Jacobian field $F_K(q)$ is isomorphic to some $F_K(L,\sigma,Q)$. L is determined by E as the unique minimal splitting field of E/K (L is a splitting field of E/K if the constant field extension EL/L has a prime divisor of degree 1).

The properties of semiperiodic function fields are discussed in detail. Furthermore, the author determines the elliptic subfields of the fields of periodic and semiperiodic functions.

The book contains several recommendations for further investigations. It is very clearly written and is a pleasure to read.

Ernst Kunz (Regensburg)

Referred to in Q25-37.

G20-45 (41# 6854)

Oort, F.

Hensel's lemma and rational points over local rings.

Symposia Mathematica, Vol. III (INDAM, Rome, 1968/69), pp. 217–232. *Academic Press, London*, 1970.

Let A be a local domain with maximal ideal M, and let F be a set of polynomials over A in a fixed number of variables. Consider the following statement (S): "If F has a zero modulo all powers of M, then F has a zero in A." Statement (S) was proved by the reviewer [Inst. Hautes Études Sci. Publ. Math. No. 31 (1966), 59–64; MR **34** #7515] in the case where A is a Henselian discrete valuation ring over which its completion is separable—in particular, the special case where A is complete of dimension one. The author generalizes the latter result to complete local domains of arbitrary dimension, but only in the special case where the set F consists of a single polynomial in a single variable.

The key lemma in this paper states that there exists an integer function $f(i,j)$ such that $x\notin M^i$ and $y\notin M^j$ imply $xy\notin M^{f(i,j)}$. The proof of this lemma involves a clever use of the structure of an algebraic ring on the quotients A/M^n and the technique of constructible sets of Chevalley-Grothendieck.

M. J. Greenberg (Santa Cruz, Calif.)

Citations: MR 34# 7515 = G25-33.

G20-46 (41# 8419)

Andrews, George E.

A note on the Bombieri-Selberg formula for algebraic curves.

Portugal. Math. **27** (1968), 75–81.

Let Γ be an absolutely irreducible and nonsingular curve of genus $g>0$ over the Galois field GF(q). Let N_m denote the number of points of Γ in GF(q^m). E. Bombieri [Atti Accad. Naz. Lincei Rend. Cl. Sci. Fis. Mat. Natur. (8) **35** (1963), 252–257; MR **31** #161] has proved $mN_m+\sum_{i=0}^m N_iN_{m-i}=2mq^m+O(q^m)$, $\sum_{i=1}^m q^iN_{m-i}=mq^m+O(q^m)$ by means of a Tauberian theorem of P. Erdős [J. Indian Math. Soc. (N.S.) **13** (1949), 131–144; MR **11**, 420; ibid. (N.S.) **13** (1949), 145–147; MR **11**, 420]. The author shows here that these formulas can be derived in a relatively simple way by means of generating functions and partial fraction decomposition related to the zeta function of Γ.

K. Shiratani (Fukuoka)

Citations: MR 11, 420a = N20-8; MR 11, 420b = N20-9; MR 31# 161 = G20-21.

G20-47 (42# 241)

Ivanov, A. F.

A boundary value problem for Dirichlet characters. (Russian. English summary)

Vestnik Leningrad. Univ. **25** (1970), *no.* 1, 30–38.

Let $\mathbf{P}_1,\cdots,\mathbf{P}_s$ be a set of prime divisors of an algebraic function field k in one variable over a finite field $[q]$, $q=p^m$, and let $\varepsilon_1,\cdots,\varepsilon_s$ be a set of complex roots of unity, so that $\varepsilon_i^n=1$ for some natural n ($i=1,\cdots,s$). It is proved that in case $n=p^an'n''$, where $a=0,1,2$; $n'|q-1$, $(n'',p(|q-1))=1$, and n'' is square-free, there exists a Dirichlet character χ for k such that $\chi(\mathbf{P}_i)=\varepsilon_i$. The largest part of the paper is concerned with the description of the character χ of order p^2.

T. Metsänkylä (Turku)

G20-48 **(42# 276)**

Rienzo, Bruce L.

Elliptic curves over local fields.

Pi Mu Epsilon J. **5** (1969/70), 56–70.

The author gives an exposition of the theorem of Lutz on elliptic curves over local fields. Some numerical examples of elliptic curves defined over finite prime fields are also discussed. *M. L. Madan* (Columbus, Ohio)

G20-49 **(42# 4551)**

Greenleaf, Newcomb

Fields in which varieties have rational points: A note on a problem of Ax.

Proc. Amer. Math. Soc. **27** (1971), 139–140.

J. Ax [Ann. of Math. (2) **88** (1968), 239–271; MR **37** #5187] a démontré que si k est un champ parfait tel que le groupe de Galois $G(k)$ sur k de la clôture algébrique de k est abélien et si toute variété absolument irréductible définie sur k possède un point k-rationnel, alors $G(k)$ est procyclique. L'auteur construit un exemple montrant que l'abélianité de $G(k)$ est bien nécessaire.

B. d'Orgeval (Beaune)

Citations: MR 37# 5187 = U05-38.

G20-50 **(43# 219)**

Vvedenskiĭ, O. N.

Subgroups of norms in elliptic curves defined over a local field. (Russian)

Ukrain. Mat. Ž. **22** (1970), 531–533.

In dieser Note werden zwei Sätze von S. Lichtenbaum [Amer. J. Math. **90** (1968), 1209–1223; MR **38** #5788] für den Fall hergeleitet, daß der zugrunde gelegte lokale Körper eine Charakteristik $p>0$ besitzt.

W. Vogel (Halle a.d. Saale)

Citations: MR 38# 5788 = G05-94.

G20-51 **(43# 4833)**

Vvedenskiĭ, O. N. [Vvedens'kiĭ, O. M.]

The Galois cohomology of elliptic curves defined over a local field. (Russian)

Mat. Sb. (*N.S.*) **83** (**125**) (1970), 474–484.

In dieser Arbeit werden einige Voraussetzungen von A. Néron [Proc. Conf. Local Fields (Driebergen, 1966), pp. 66–77, Springer, Berlin, 1967; MR **39** #209] zur Berechnung der Galois-Kohomologie von prinzipialen homogenen Räumen über elliptischen Kurven abgeschwächt. Hierbei sind die elliptischen Kurven über einem lokalen Körper definiert. Ferner werden in diesem Zusammenhang Voraussetzungen diskutiert, die von I. R. Šafarevič [Trudy Mat. Inst. Steklov. **64** (1961), 316–346; MR **29** #110] angegeben worden sind.

{This article has appeared in English translation [Math. USSR-Sb. **12** (1970), 477–488].}

W. Vogel (Halle a.d. Saale)

Citations: MR 29# 110 = G10-23.

G20-52 **(44# 1668)**

Zimmer, Horst G.

An elementary proof of the Riemann hypothesis for an elliptic curve over a finite field.

Pacific J. Math. **36** (1971), 267–278.

This is a new version of the proof of the Riemann hypothesis for the congruence-zeta-function of an elliptic curve, given by $\varphi(x,y)=y^2+(a_0x+a_1)y+x^3+b_1x^2+b_2x+b_3=0$. It is closely related to Ju. I. Manin's proof [Izv. Akad. Nauk SSSR Ser. Mat. **20** (1956), 673–678; MR **18**, 380], unified for any positive characteristic. Let k be the ground field of q elements, $K=k(x,y)$ the function field of the curve. The author considers the curve C with the same equation as above but defined over K. The function $d(P)=-\frac{1}{2}\sum f_{\mathfrak p}\omega_{\mathfrak p}(x_p)$ on the group of K-rational points $P=(x_p,y_p)$ of C is a quadratic form, and the sum is taken over all prime divisors $\mathfrak p$ of K/k with $\omega_{\mathfrak p}(x_p)<0$, $\omega_{\mathfrak p}$ being the order function on K associated with $\mathfrak p$. The discriminant of $d(P)$ $\Delta_{P,Q}=[d(P+Q)-d(P)-d(Q)]^2-4d(P)\,d(Q)$ is proved to be $\leqq 0$, and is applied to $P=(x,y)$, $Q=(x^q,y^q)$; the author computes $d(P)=1$, $d(Q)=q$, $d(P+Q)-d(P)-d(Q)=q-N$, N the number of k-rational points, and hence $|N-q|\leqq 2\sqrt{q}$. *H. Kurke* (Berlin)

Citations: MR 18, 380e = D80-24.

G25 VARIETIES OVER FINITE AND LOCAL FIELDS

For abelian varieties, see **G10**, **G15**.

See also Sections D80, T40.

See also reviews F15-30, G02-18, G02-20, G10-20, G30-17, G35-45, T25-23, T45-2, T55-19, U10-16, Z02-69, Z10-66.

G25-1 **(14, 848c)**

Carlitz, L. Note on a conjecture of André Weil. Proc. Amer. Math. Soc. **4**, 5–9 (1953).

Let V be a variety of dimension n without singular points defined over the finite field $GF(q)$, $q=p^n$ and N_m the number of rational points on V over the extended field $GF(q^m)$. A. Weil has made the conjecture that $\sum_{m=1}^{\infty}N_mu^{m-1}=d\log Z(u)/du$ where (1) $Z(u)$ is a rational function satisfying a simple functional equation and (2) having zeros and poles that satisfy some simple relations. The author shows that this conjecture holds when the variety is an equation of the form $Q(x_1,\cdots,x_s)=\alpha$, where Q denotes a quadratic form. The conjecture also holds for an equation of the form $\alpha_1x_1^ey_1^f+\cdots+\alpha_sx_s^ey_s^f=0$, $(e,f)=1$. In this case the variety contains singular points when $ef>1$. The conjecture (1) doesn't hold for an equation $\alpha_1x_1^ey_1^fz_1^g+\cdots+\alpha_sx_s^ey_s^fz_s^g=0$, $(e,f,g)=1$. The author gives another example where the conjecture holds.

H. Bergström (Göteborg).

G25-2 **(16, 398d)**

Lang, Serge, and Weil, André. Number of points of varieties in finite fields. Amer. J. Math. **76**, 819–827 (1954).

Let k denote a finite field, of order q, and $V=V_{n,d,r}$ be an algebraic variety defined over k, in a projective space P^n, having the dimension r and the order d. Then it is proved that the number N of points of V which are in k satisfies the inequality

$$|N-q^r|\leqq(d-1)(d-2)q^{r-1/2}+Aq^{r-1},$$

where $A=A(n,d,r)$ is a constant depending only on n, d, r. This theorem for $r=1$, i.e. if V is a curve, is a reformulation of the Riemann hypothesis in function fields; for $r>1$, the proof of the theorem is carried out by an induction on r, leading to evaluation in two different ways of the number of pairs consisting of a point of V in k and a hyperplane in P^n containing this point.

The theorem above leads at once to an asymptotic result. For, if k_ν is the extension of degree ν over k and $N^{(\nu)}$ is the number of points of V in k_ν, then

$$N^{(\nu)}=q^{\nu r}+O(q^{\nu(r-1/2)})\quad\text{for}\quad\nu\to\infty;$$

and so $N^{(\nu)}\to\infty$ if $\nu\to\infty$. The same asymptotic behaviour is proved to hold for abstract varieties, and applications are obtained to the analytic zeta function $Z(U)$, associated with such a variety V, defined by $d \log Z(U)/dU = \sum_{\nu=1}^{\infty} N^{(\nu)} U^{\nu-1}$. It is shown that $Z(U)$ has no pole or zero in the circle $|U| < q^{-r}$, has exactly one pole in the circle $|U| < q^{-r+1/2}$, namely a pole of order 1 at $U = q^{-r}$, and that the zeros and poles of $Z(U)$ in the circle $|U| < q^{-r+1}$ are birational invariants of V. Finally, some conjectures are stated concerning the behaviour of $Z(U)$ for $|U| \geqq q^{-r+1/2}$. [In the first formula of p. 823, the κ_n in parentheses has to be replaced by κ_{n+1}.] *B. Segre* (Rome).

Referred to in D72-21, D80-54, D80-77, G25-5, G25-7, G25-8, G30-17, G30-19, G35-47, L05-37, N72-32, P44-31, R08-44.

G25-3 (16, 743b)

Nisnevič, L. B. On the number of points of an algebraic manifold in a prime finite field. Dokl. Akad. Nauk SSSR (N.S.) **99**, 17–20 (1954). (Russian)

The author considers an absolutely irreducible variety V in n-dimensional projective space; the field of definition of V is k and has characteristic p; dim $V=d$; degree $V=m$; N is the number of points V whose coordinates are in the prime field of k. It is shown that

$$|N-p^d| \leqq cp^{d-\frac{1}{2}},$$

where c depends on m and n but not on p or d. The proof is by induction on d and uses the well-known case $d=1$ studied by A. Weil. It should be observed that in Th. 3 seemingly both h and R denote dim H. *F. J. Terpstra.*

Referred to in G25-8.

G25-4 (18, 672b)

Lang, Serge. Unramified class field theory over function fields in several variables. Ann. of Math. (2) **64** (1956), 285–325.

Let K be a field of algebraic functions of several variables over a finite field k, and let L/K be a finite Abelian extension of K. Let $\mathfrak{o}$ be a regular locality in K (i.e. the local ring in K of a simple point of a model of the field K/k), and let $\mathfrak{p}$ be its maximal ideal. If $\mathfrak{o}$ is unramified in L, then we may attach in the usual manner to $\mathfrak{o}$ (or to $\mathfrak{p}$) a Frobenius symbol $(\mathfrak{p}, L/K)$ which is an element of the Galois group G of L/K; this mapping may be extend to a homomorphism φ (the reciprocity map) into G of the free group $\mathfrak{Z}$ generated by all regular localities of K which are unramified in L. The study of the reciprocity map is the main object of class-field theory; the main problems are to determine its image and its kernel. From analogy with class field theory, we expect the image of φ to be the whole of G. As for its kernel, there is a group which is trivially contained in it: let $\mathfrak{o}$ be regular and unramified in L, and let $\mathfrak{O}$ be a locality of L above $\mathfrak{o}$; then the residue field of $\mathfrak{O}$ is an algebraic extension of degree d of that of $\mathfrak{o}$, and d is the order of $(\mathfrak{p}, L/K)$ if $\mathfrak{p}$ is the maximal prime ideal of $\mathfrak{o}$; the kernel of φ therefore contains $d\mathfrak{o}$. Let us call trace group the group generated by the elements $d\mathfrak{o}$ for all regular localities $\mathfrak{o}$ which are unramified in L. From now on, let us assume that the extension L/K is unramified, which means that every normal locality in K is unramified in L (the author proves that it is sufficient that the condition be satisfied for all localities which belong to some normal complete model of K). Then, from analogy with class-field theory, we expect the kernel of the reciprocity map to contain, besides the trace group, a certain subgroup of $\mathfrak{Z}$ which would be analogous to the group of principal ideals in number theory. In the present paper, the author constructs such a group for a certain type of unramified abelian extensions L/K which will be described presently. From now on let there be given a fixed normal projective model V of K/k, and let us restrict $\mathfrak{Z}$ to be the group generated by the local rings of the simple points of V (this entails no serious loss of generality). Let A be the Albanese variety of V and α a canonical mapping (defined over k) of V into A. Let B be an Abelian variety defined over k and which admits a surjective homomorphism λ of finite kernel onto A, defined over k. Then we may associate to B and λ an unramified extension as follows: the set $\lambda^{-1}(\alpha(V))$ turns out to be a variety C; if U is the set of points $(x, y) \in V \times C$ such that $\alpha(x) = \lambda(y)$ (x simple on V), then the projection $V \times C \to V$ induces a map $U \to V$ which is an unramified covering of the set of simple points of V; if L is the field of functions on U rational over k, then L/K is an Abelian unramified extension. Such extensions, and those which may be obtained from these by combination with extensions of the basic field, are called extensions of the Albanese type. Let $\mathfrak{Z}_0$ be the group of elements of degree 0 in $\mathfrak{Z}$; then α defines a homomorphism of $\mathfrak{Z}_0$ into the group A_k of rational points over k of A; the kernel of this homomorphism is called the Albanese kernel. This is the group which takes the place of the group of principal ideals in number theory. In fact, the author proves the following statements, which constitute a complete generalisation of class-field theory: if L/K is of Albanese type, the reciprocity mapping is surjective and its kernel is generated by the trace group and the Albanese kernel; to every subgroup Γ in $\mathfrak{Z}$ containing the Albanese kernel and of finite index, there is associated a unique extension L/K of the Albanese type such that Γ is the kernel of the reciprocity map of L/K; there is a limitation theorem for every Galois extension of K.

The extensions of the Albanese type are certainly not all the unramified Abelian extensions of K. Let for instance X be a rational divisor of V such that, for some $n>0$, nX is linearly equivalent to 0; set $nX=(\varphi)$, $\varphi \in K$; assume that n is prime to the characteristic of K and that k contains the nth roots of unity. Then $K(\varphi^{1/n})$ will be an unramified Abelian extension of K, but will not be of the Albanese type if X is not algebraically equivalent to 0. However, the author proves a result which implies that, if there is no torsion in the Neron-Severi group, then every Abelian unramified extension of degree prime to the characteristic is of the Albanese type; an exemple due to Serre shows that the condition of the degree being prime to the characteristic cannot be omitted from this statement. *C. Chevalley* (Paris).

Referred to in G25-6, G25-8, G25-11, G25-12, L10-15.

G25-5 (18, 719h)

Lustig, Gerhard. Über die Zetafunktion einer arithmetischen Mannigfaltigkeit. Math. Nachr. **14** (1955), 309–330 (1956).

The results of this paper are related to some of the work of Lang and Weil on the radius of convergence for the zeta function of absolutely irreducible varieties without singularities over a finite field [Amer. J. Math. **76** (1954), 819–827; MR **16**, 398]. The author considers zeta functions of rings in fields of Kroneckerian dimension 2 which are determined by consistent collections of local rings (which are nonsingular in the sense of Krull). The latter assumption permits the enumeration of the number of residue classes of an ideal in a component local ring in terms of the number of elements of the residue class field belonging to the associated maximal ideal (part I). A reduction to dimension 1 is used to show that his functions converge absolutely if $\mathrm{Re}(s) \geqq 2$.

O. F. G. Schilling.

Citations: MR 16, 398d = G25-2.

G25-6 (19, 174a)

Lang, Serge. Algebraic groups over finite fields. Amer. J. Math. **78** (1956), 555–563.

Es sei k ein endlicher Körper mit q Elementen, und es

sei G eine über k definierte algebraische Gruppe. [Für die Grundlagen der Theorie algebraischer Gruppen siehe Weil, Amer. J. Math. **77** (1955), 355–391, 493–512; MR **17**, 533.] Ist x ein Punkt von G, so bezeichne mann mit $x^{(q)}$ denjenigen Punkt von G, welcher entsteht, wenn man die Koordinaten von x mit q potenziert. Die Abbildung $f(x)=x^{-1}x^{(q)}$ ist eine rationale Abbildung von G in sich; Verf. zeigt, daß sie sogar eine Abbildung auf G ist. Bedeutet x einen allgemeinen Punkt von G, so ist die Körpererweiterung $k(x)/k(f(x))$ algebraisch, separabel und galoissch, wobei die galoissche Gruppe isomorph ist zu der Gruppe G_1 der in k rationalen Punkte von G.

Setzt man allgemeiner $F(x, y)=x^{-1}yx^{(q)}$, so erscheint dadurch G als homogener Darstellungsraum bezüglich G selbst. Unter Benutzung dieser Tatsache zeigt Verf., daß jeder homogene Raum H bezüglich G, welcher über k definiert ist, einen rationalen Punkt besitzt. Dieser Satz kann als Verallgemeinerung des vom Verf. früher bewiesenen Satzes angesehen werden, welcher folgendes besagt: Ist V eine über k definierte algebraische Mannigfaltigkeit, welche über der algebraisch-abgeschlossenen Hülle $\bar{k}$ von k biregulär äquivalent zu einer abelschen Mannigfaltigkeit ist, so besitzt V einen rationalen Punkt und ist also selbst eine abelsche Mannigfaltigkeit über k. [Siehe dazu Lang, Proc. Nat. Acad. Sci. **41** U.S.A. (1955), 174–176; MR **17**, 87.]

Weiter gibt Verf. einen neuen Beweis eines Resultates von Châtelet: Wenn eine algebraische Mannigfaltigkeit V/k biregulär äquivalent über $\bar{k}$ zum projektiven Raum ist, so ist sie bereits über k biregulär äquivalent zum projektiven Raum [C. R. Acad. Sci. Paris **224** (1947), 1616–1618; MR **9**, 55]. Beim Beweis benutzt Verf. den Satz, daß die einzigen biregulären Korrespondenzen des projektiven Raumes mit sich selbst die projektiven Abbildungen sind. Chow hat gezeigt, daß diese Eigenschaft außer dem projektiven Raum auch noch gewissen anderen Mannigfaltigkeiten zukommt [Ann. of Math. (2) **50** (1949), 32–67; MR **10**, 396]. Es ergibt sich daraus, daß auch der Satz von Châtelet für diese anderen Mannigfaltigkeiten gültig ist.

Schließlich betrachtet Verf. noch die Klassenkörpertheorie für die galoissche Erweiterung $k(x)/k(f(x))$. Es wird ein gewisses nicht-abelsches Reziprozitätsgesetz aufgestellt, und gezeigt, daß die zugehörigen Artinschen L-Reihen für Nichthauptcharaktere trivial sind. Hieraus wird das folgende Resultat gefolgert: Sei $\mathfrak{g}$ eine Untergruppe von G, welche nur aus rationalen Punkten über k besteht, und sei H der homogene Raum der Nebenklassen von G modulo $\mathfrak{g}$. Dann besitzen G und H die gleiche Anzahl von rationalen Punkten. In einer weiteren Arbeit [Ann. of Math. (2) **64** (1956), 285–325; MR **18**, 672] entwickelt Verf. eine abelsche Klassenkörpertheorie.

P. Roquette (Hamburg).

Citations: MR 9, 55h = G20-5; MR 17, 87e = G10-3; MR 18, 672b = G25-4.

Referred to in S02-3.

G25-7 (19, 320b)

Lang, Serge. *L*-series of a covering. Proc. Nat. Acad. Sci. U.S.A. **42** (1956), 422–424.

In this note the author makes use of the fact that the algebraic analogue of the theory of topological transformation groups is the theory of Galois coverings of algebraic varieties in order to draw some statements and conjectures about the behavior of the Artin L-series in such a Galois covering.

From every linear representation of a finite group an L-series is obtained. Let U, V be two algebraic varieties over a finite field with q elements and suppose that U is a Galois cover of V with finite group G. Let $H_1(U)$ denote the l-adic representation space of G arising from the Albanese variety $A(U)$ of U. Its dimension $B_1(U)$ equals $2g$, where g is the irregularity of U. We let F be the Frobenius transformation of U, and f the Frobenius transformation of V. The L-series obtained from this representation, it may be conjectured, should give exactly the contribution in the circle $|t|<q^{-(n-1)}$ to the L-series defined by the prime rational cycles of V. This extends the Weil conjectures on the zeta-function for varieties over a finite field [S. Lang and A. Weil, Amer. J. Math. **76** (1954), 819–827; MR **16**, 398].

P. E. Conner.

Citations: MR 16, 398d = G25-2.

G25-8 (19, 578c)

Lang, Serge. Sur les séries *L* d'une variété algébrique. Bull. Soc. Math. France **84** (1956), 385–407.

L'auteur rapporte deux compléments à la "théorie du corps de classes" qu'il a développée dans son mémoire dédié à Artin [Ann. of Math. (2) **64** (1956), 285–325; MR **18**, 672].

Il étudie d'abord les zéros et les pôles des séries L; soient k un corps fini à q éléments, K un corps de fonctions algébriques à r variables sur k, E une extension galoisienne finie de K, et M une représentation linéaire de son groupe de Galois. Si l'on choisit un schéma ("modèle") U de K, non singulier, et tel que E/K soit non ramifié sur U, on peut définir (loc. cit.) la substitution de Frobenius $\sigma_{\mathfrak{p}}$ d'un cycle premier $\mathfrak{p}$ de dimension zéro de U; d'où, par la formule d'Artin, une fonction L:

$$L_{M,U}(t)=\prod_{\mathfrak{p}} 1/\det(1-t^{\deg(\mathfrak{p})}M(\sigma_{\mathfrak{p}})).$$

Supposons alors que la représentation M soit irréductible et non triviale, et que k soit algébriquement fermé dans E (c'est le cas "géométrique" — il est dommage que le cas général ne soit pas traité). L'auteur démontre alors que la fonction $L_{M,U}$ est holomorphe et partout non nul dans le disque $|t|<q^{-(r-\frac{1}{2})}$. La démonstration, assez délicate, consiste à ramener la question au cas des courbes au moyen de sections planes convenable; c'est là un procédé voisin de celui qu'avait déjà employé l'auteur pour l'étude de la fonction zêta [S. Lang et A. Weil, Amer. J. Math. **72** (1954), 819–827; MR **16**, 398; voir aussi L. B. Nisnevic, Dokl. Akad. Nauk SSSR (N.S.) **99** (1954), 17–20; MR **16**, 743].

Dans une seconde partie, l'auteur étend sa théorie du corps de classes à de nouveaux types d'extensions. Si $\alpha:U\to G$ est une application rationnelle de U dans un groupe algébrique commutatif G (α, U et G étant définis sur k), on dit que U et G sont bien adaptés pour α si α ne peut pas se factoriser en $U\to G'\to G$, où $G'\to G$ est une isogénie non triviale de G (définie sur une extension k' de k). Dans ce cas, l'image réciproque ("pull-back") par α d'une isogénie séparable $G'\to G$ de degré n est un revêtement abélien irréductible et de degré n de U; les revêtements $V\to U$ qui peuvent être obtenus de cette manière (sur une extension de k) sont dits "de type α". L'auteur indique (le plus souvent sans démonstration) comment les résultats de son mémoire cité plus haut s'étendent aux revêtements de type α (qui remplacent ceux "du type d'Albanese"); le principal intérêt de cette extension provient de ce que tout revêtement abélien est de type α pour un α convenable (appliquer Kummer ou Artin-Schreier-Witt). Dans le cas où U est une courbe, on peut prendre pour G une jacobienne généralisée de U (au sens de Rosenlicht); les relations de ces jacobiennes avec le groupe des classes d'idèles redonnent alors la théorie du corps de classes sous sa forme usuelle, et cela sans qu'il ait été nécessaire de faire aucun calcul d'indices, ni de démontrer aucune de ces pénibles "inégalités" qui déparent le cas des corps de nombres.

J.-P. Serre (Paris).

Citations: MR 16, 398d = G25-2; MR 16, 743b = G25-3; MR 18, 672b = G25-4.

Referred to in G25-12, G25-17, G25-22, L10-15.

G25-9 **(20# 2329)**

Morikawa, Hisasi. On the existence of unramified separable infinite solvable extensions of function fields over finite fields. Nagoya Math. J. **13** (1958), 95–100.

If K is an algebraic function field of one variable of genus >1 over the constant field k, which is finite and has at least 11 elements, there exists an unramified separable solvable extension of infinite degree of K which is regular over k. The proof uses previous results of the author [#2340 below] and an inequality, based on the Riemann hypothesis, whose application gives rise to the restriction on the cardinality of k.

M. Rosenlicht (Evanston, Ill.)

Citations: MR 20# 2340 = G25-11.
Referred to in G25-10.

G25-10 **(21# 671)**

Morikawa, Hisasi. Correction to my paper "On the existence of unramified separable infinite solvable extensions of function fields over finite fields". Nagoya Math. J. **14** (1959), 53–57.

Nine necessary technical lemmas are added to the proof of the title result of the author's previous paper [same J. **13** (1958), 95–100; MR **20** #2329].

M. Rosenlicht (Evanston, Ill.)

Citations: MR 20# 2329 = G25-9.

G25-11 **(20# 2340)**

Morikawa, Hisasi. Generalized jacobian varieties and separable abelian extensions of function fields. Nagoya Math. J. **12** (1957), 231–254.

Lang has shown how the class field theory for unramified abelian coverings of an algebraic curve is related to the separable isogenies of the jacobian variety of the curve [Ann. of Math. (2) **64** (1956), 285–325; MR **18**, 672]. This paper first shows that any separable abelian covering of an algebraic curve may be obtained as a "pull back" of a separable isogeny of a commutative algebraic group onto a suitable generalized jacobian variety of the curve. This had been previously noted by Lang and proved by Serre [Groupes algébriques et théorie du corps de classes, Collège de France, 1957, (mimeographed)] by using the universal mapping property of generalized jacobians [see Rosenlicht, Ann. of Math. (2) **66** (1957), 80–88; MR **19**, 579]; here the result is obtained by first showing the existence of a separable homomorphism from a suitable generalized jacobian of the covering onto a generalized jacobian of the base curve. As a consequence, the author obtains (as does Serre, loc. cit.) a full class field theory à la Lang for arbitrary separable abelian extensions of a function field of one variable over a finite constant field.

M. Rosenlicht (Evanston, Ill.)

Citations: MR 18, 672b = G25-4.
Referred to in G25-9.

G25-12 **(21# 1973)**

Serre, Jean-Pierre. Groupes algébriques et corps de classes. Publications de l'institut de mathématique de l'université de Nancago, VII, Actualités Sci. Indust., No. 1264, Hermann, Paris, 1959. 202pp. 3000 francs.

This is mainly an exposition of the theory of generalized Jacobian varieties by Rosenlicht [Ann. of Math. (2) **59** (1954), 505–530; **66** (1957), 80–88; MR **15**, 823; **19**, 579] and the class field theory over function fields by Lang [ibid. **64** (1956), 285–325; Bull. Soc. Math. France **84** (1956), 385–407; MR **18**, 672; **19**, 578].

Very little knowledge (mainly the sheaf-theoretic definition of algebraic varieties by Serre [Ann. of Math. (2) **61** (1955), 197–278; MR **16**, 953]) is preassumed, so that this will be an easy text book on these subjects.

In Chapter I, some important results in this book are prestated.

Basic results on algebraic curves (Riemann-Roch theorem, residue formula, duality theorem) are proved in Chapter II. Some further preliminary results are proved in Chapters III and IV (Chap. III: the theorem that if f is a rational map from a non-singular curve X into an additive group G such that it is regular outside of a closed set S, then there is a module $\mathfrak{m}$ of divisors on X with support S such that, for any divisor $D=(\varphi)$ with $\varphi\equiv 1 \bmod \mathfrak{m}$, $f(D)=0$; Chap. IV: the theory of curves with singular points), and the theory of generalized Jacobian varieties is expounded in Chapter V.

The class field theory over function fields is expounded in Chapter VI.

Homological properties of abelian varieties, proved by Barsotti [Ann. Mat. Pura Appl. (4) **38** (1955), 77–119; MR **17**, 193; Rend. Circ. Mat. Palermo (2) **5** (1956), 145–169; MR **18**, 673; and the article reviewed above]* and by Rosenlicht [Amer. J. Math. **80** (1958), 685–714; MR **20** #5780] are expounded.

M. Nagata (Kyoto)

*I.e. MR 21 #1972.

Citations: MR 18, 672b = G25-4; MR 19, 578c = G25-8.

G25-13 **(21# 1975)**

Chow, Wei-Liang. The criterion for unit multiplicity and a generalization of Hensel's lemma. Amer. J. Math. **80** (1958), 539–552.

V/k is a variety over a complete discretely-valued field k and $\bar{V}/\bar{k}$ is its reduction mod p. Then every simple $\bar{k}$-rational point of $\bar{V}$ has a foreimage in the reduction which is a simple k-rational point of V (generalized Hensel's lemma). The proof is elementary, and gives also the criterion of multiplicity one, phrased roughly: if $\bar{X}$ and $\bar{Y}$ are transversal at $\bar{\alpha}$, there exists in $X\cdot Y$ a unique $\alpha\to\bar{\alpha}$, and $i(\alpha, X\cdot Y)=1$. Non-elementary generalization, using multiplicity theory of local rings, to analogous statement asserting preservation of intersection multiplicities under reduction mod p at a proper intersection of $\bar{X}$ and $\bar{Y}$, together with uniqueness and rationality of the foreimage cycle.

A. P. Mattuck (Cambridge, Mass.)

G25-14 **(21# 4156)**

Sampson, J. H.; and Washnitzer, G. Numerical equivalence and the zeta-function of a variety. Amer. J. Math. **81** (1959), 735–748.

The authors consider a non-singular projective variety V of dimension r, defined over a finite field k. It is shown that, if the group of r-cycles on $V\times V$, modulo numerical equivalence, is finitely generated (or even if a suitable subgroup of that group is finitely generated) the zeta-function of V is a rational function and satisfies a functional equation. On the other hand, it is shown that, if the logarithmic derivative of the zeta-function is a rational function, it has only simple poles. The paper includes a summary in cohomological language.

A. Weil (Princeton, N.J.)

Referred to in G25-22.

G25-15 **(21# 4958)**

Taniyama, Yutaka. Distribution of positive 0-cycles in absolute classes of an algebraic variety with finite constant field. Sci. Papers Coll. Gen. Ed. Univ. Tokyo **8** (1958), 123–137.

Let V be a projective variety, normal over a field k and non-singular in codimension 1. Let α be a mapping of V into an abelian variety A, defined over k and such that it cannot be factored non-trivially as $\alpha = \lambda \circ \beta$, where β is a mapping of V into an abelian variety B and λ is an isogeny of B onto A. Let r and a be the dimensions of V and A, respectively. Let $V^{(m)}$ be the m-fold symmetric product of V; every positive 0-cycle $\mathfrak{a} = P_1 + \cdots + P_m$ of degree m on V determines a point of $V^{(m)}$, and, by putting $\alpha(\mathfrak{a}) = \sum_i \alpha(P_i)$, one defines a mapping α_m of $V^{(m)}$ into A. One main purpose of the present paper is to prove the following theorem: if $m \geqq 2a+1$, then, for all points y of A, the cycle $\alpha_m^{-1}(y)$ is defined, has only one (irreducible) component, and its degree (as a cycle in the ambient projective space) is independent of y; moreover, if A is the Albanese variety of V, α the canonical mapping of V into A, and y a generic point of A, then the unique component of $\alpha_m^{-1}(y)$ is of multiplicity 1.

The method of proof, as novel as it is surprising, consists in first considering the case when k is the finite field with q elements; if k_ν is the extension of k of degree ν, and if the number of rational points over k_ν on a closed algebraic set, known to have no component of dimension $<d$, is asymptotically equal to $q^{d\nu}$, then that set can consist of only one component of dimension d. In applying this idea to the situation described above, essential use is made of the isogeny $x \to x^{q^\nu} - x$ of A onto itself, whose kernel g_ν consists of the points of A which are rational over k_ν; this may be viewed as defining an abelian non-ramified covering of A, isomorphic to A, whose Galois group is isomorphic to g_ν, and therefore, by "pull-back" by means of α, a similar covering of V, hence also of "almost all" the curves obtained by intersecting V with linear varieties of the appropriate dimension. Once the theorem is obtained for finite groundfields, the method of reduction modulo $\mathfrak{p}$ enables the author to extend it to the general case. At the same time, his estimates for finite ground fields yield valuable new information concerning zeta-functions, in the direction of the conjecture according to which the number of rational points of V over k_ν is uniquely determined, up to a remainder term of order $O(q^{(r-1)\nu})$, by r and by the zeta-function of the Albanese variety of V. A final corollary says that, for any groundfield k, the Albanese variety of V remains such under reduction modulo almost all valuations of k.

A. Weil (Princeton, N.J.)

Referred to in G25-17.

G25-16 (22# 6808a; 22# 6808b; 22# 6808c)

Ishida, Makoto. On zeta-functions and *L*-series of algebraic varieties. Proc. Japan Acad. **34** (1958), 1–5.

Ishida, Makoto. On zeta-functions and *L*-series of algebraic varieties. II. Proc. Japan Acad. **34** (1958), 395–399.

Ishida, Makoto. Remarks on my previous paper on congruence zeta-functions. Proc. Japan Acad. **35** (1959), 321–322.

In this series of papers, known facts on zeta-functions of abelian varieties are extended to varieties having an abelian variety as a Galois covering, and to L-functions attached to such coverings; some of the existing conjectures on zeta-functions and L-functions can be verified in that case. Part of the author's results are restricted to the case in which the Galois group of the covering is abelian. *A. Weil* (Princeton, N.J.)

Referred to in G25-22.

G25-17 (22# 6809)

Ishida, Makoto. On congruence *L*-series. J. Math. Soc. Japan **12** (1960), 22–33.

Earlier conjectures, chiefly due to S. Lang [Bull. Soc. Math. France **84** (1956), 385–407; MR **19**, 578] are further considered, in the light of results due to Y. Taniyama [Sci. Papers Coll. Gen. Ed. Univ. Tokyo **8** (1958), 123–137; MR **21** #4958]. One should note, however, that the author has chosen to modify Lang's definition of an L-series (loc. cit.); it is asserted that both definitions are equivalent for unramified coverings of non-singular varieties. The main result says in substance that Lang's conjecture on the "first layer" of zeros of the L-function for such coverings would follow from a certain assumption on families of "regular" varieties (which amounts to saying that Lang's conjecture is "uniformly" true for a suitable family of such varieties). *A. Weil* (Princeton, N.J.)

Citations: MR 19, 578c = G25-8; MR 21# 4958 = G25-15.

G25-18 (24# A1272)

Ishida, Makoto

On Galois coverings of algebraic varieties and Albanese varieties attached to them.

J. Fac. Sci. Univ. Tokyo Sect. I 8, 577–604 (1960).

Es sei V eine normale (= ganzabgeschlossene) algebraische Mannigfaltigkeit mit dem Funktionenkörper L. Ferner sei K ein endlicher Galoisscher Erweiterungskörper von L. Die normale (= ganzabgeschlossene) Hülle U von V in K ist eine normale algebraische Mannigfaltigkeit mit dem Funktionenkörper K. Zufolge der Inklusion $L \subset K$ hat man eine rationale Abbildung $f: U \to V$. In dieser Situation nennt man U eine Galoissche Überlagerung der Mannigfaltigkeit V [Lang und Serre, Amer. J. Math. **79** (1957), 319–330; MR **19**, 320]. Der Verfasser untersucht das Verhalten der zu U bzw. zu V gehörigen Albaneseschen Mannigfaltigkeiten. (Für die Theorie der Albaneseschen Mannigfaltigkeiten vergleiche etwa das Buch von Lang, *Abelian varieties*, Interscience, New York, 1959 [MR **21** #4959].) Es sei $\alpha: U \to A$ eine kanonische Abbildung von U in die zugehörige Albanesesche Mannigfaltigkeit A. Jedem Automorphismus σ von K/L ist ein Endomorphismus η_σ und ein Punkt a_σ von A zugeordnet durch die Formel $\alpha(\sigma u) = \eta_\sigma(\alpha u) + a_\sigma$ für einen allgemeinen Punkt u von U. Man setze $C_\sigma = (\eta_\sigma - 1)A$; dies ist eine Abelsche Teilmannigfaltigkeit von A. Es sei C die von allen C_σ erzeugte Abelsche Teilmannigfaltigkeit von A. Die Vereinigung von C und den Nebenklassen $C + a_\sigma$ ist eine algebraische Untergruppe C^* von A. Satz 1: die Faktorgruppe $A_0 = A/C^*$ ist die zu V gehörige Albanesesche Mannigfaltigkeit; die zugehörige kanonische Abbildung $\alpha_0: V \to A_0$ wird gegeben durch $\alpha_0 = \alpha f^{-1}$ modulo C^*. Satz 2: die 'Norm' $\rho A = (\sum_\sigma \eta_\sigma)A$ ist isogen zu A_0. Falls der Grad $n = (K:L)$ prim zur Charakteristik p des Grundkörpers ist, so gibt es separable Isogenien zwischen ρA und A_0. Es sei l eine von p verschiedene Primzahl. Bekanntlich lässt der Endomorphismenring von A eine Darstellung vom Grad $2g$ ($g = \dim A$) über dem Ring der ganzen l-adischen Zahlen zu (vergleiche dazu das oben zitierte Buch von Lang). Diese Darstellung werde mit M_1 bezeichnet. Als Folgerung aus Satz 2 wird bewiesen:

$$2ng_0 = 2g + \sum_{\sigma \neq 1} \operatorname{Spur} M_1(\eta_\sigma).$$

(Hierbei ist $g_0 = \dim A_0$.) Wenn U und V singularitätenfreie algebraische Kurven sind, so geht diese Formel über in die bekannte Riemann-Hurwitzsche Relativgeschlechtsformel. Nun wird vorausgesetzt, dass U, also auch V projektiv ist. Für jede Untergruppe H der Galoisschen Gruppe G gibt es ein projektives Modell U_H des zu H gehörigen Invariantenkörpers, derart, dass die natürliche Abbildung $f_H: U \to U_H$ eine Galoissche Überlagerung in dem obigen Sinne ist. Es sei g_H die Dimension der Albaneseschen Mannigfaltigkeit von U_H, insbesondere also

$g_1 = g$ und $g_G = g_0$. Satz 3: es bedeute χ_H denjenigen Charakter von G, der von dem Hauptcharakter von H induziert wird. Aus einer Relation der Form $\sum_H c_H\chi_H = 0$ mit ganzen rationalen Koeffizienten c_H folgt die entsprechende Relation $\sum_H c_H g_H = 0$. Satz 4: wenn $n = q^m$ eine Primzahlpotenz ist, so ist $g - g_0 \equiv 0 \bmod \frac{1}{2}(q-1)$. An einem Beispiel wird für $m = 1$ gezeigt, dass $g - g_0 = \frac{1}{2}(q-1)$ sein kann. In dem Falle, wo die Galoissche Gruppe G Abelsch ist, wird eine direkte Zerlegung (bis auf Isogenie) von A in Abelsche Teilmannigfaltigkeiten angegeben, wobei ein Faktor gleich A_0 ist (Satz 5). Nun werde vorausgesetzt, dass U und V singularitätenfrei und vollständig sind. Es bedeute $D_0(U)$ den Modul der ganzen Differentialformen erster Stufe. Der Abbildung $\alpha: U \to A$ entspricht eine Abbildung $\delta\alpha: D_0(A) \to D_0(U)$. Diese ist im allgemeinen injektiv, aber nicht notwendig surjektiv. Satz 6: Es werde vorausgesetzt, dass $p \nmid n$. Wenn die Abbildung $\delta\alpha$ surjektiv ist, so ist es auch die Abbildung $\delta\alpha_0$. Ohne die Voraussetzung $p \nmid n$ ist dieser Satz nicht mehr allgemein richtig, wofür auf ein Beispiel von Igusa verwiesen wird [Proc. Nat. Acad. Sci. U.S.A. **41** (1955), 964–967; MR **17**, 534]. Schliesslich wird noch eine Abschätzung bewiesen, welche g mit Hilfe von V, n und der Verweigungssituation von U über V abzuschätzen gestattet. Es bedeute g_0^* das Geschlecht der allgemeinen Kurve auf V. Ferner sei Z_0 eine algebraische Teilmenge von V derart, dass die Punkte aus $V - Z_0$ unverzweigt sind in $f: U \to V$. Mit $d(Z_0)$ werde der Grad der Komponente Z_0' der Kodimension 1 von Z_0 bezeichnet, d.h. der Grad des Schnittproduktes von Z_0' mit einer allgemeinen Kurve von V. Satz 8: $g \leqq g_0 + (n-1)(g_0^* + \frac{1}{2}d(Z_0) - 1)$. Ist insbesondere U über V unverzweigt, so gilt: $g \leqq g_0 + (n-1)(g_0^* - 1)$. Alle oben angeführten Sätze werden auch unter Berücksichtigung von Rationalitätsfragen über einem vorgegebenen Grundkörper k bewiesen.

P. Roquette (Tubingen)

Citations: MR 21# 4959 = G10-9.

G25-19 (25# 3913)

Dwork, Bernard M.

On the congruence properties of the zeta function of algebraic varieties.

J. Reine Angew. Math. **203** (1960), 130–142.

V sei eine algebraische Mannigfaltigkeit im projektiven n-dimensionalen Raum S_n über dem Körper k von $q = p^c$ Elementen (p Primzahl). N_i sei die Anzahl der Punkte von V mit Koordinaten im Körper k_i von q^i Elementen ($[K_i : k] = i$), also $\zeta(V, t) = \exp[\sum_{i=1}^{\infty} N_i t^i / i]$ die Weilsche Zetafunktion von V. V kann reduzibel und singularitätenbehaftet sein. Hauptergebnis: $\zeta(V, t)$ ist Quotient zweier t-Potenzreihen mit rationalen, p-ganzen Koeffizienten, die im p-adischen Sinne im Kreise $|t| < |q^{-1}|$ konvergieren. Durch einfache kombinatorische Überlegungen kann dies auf den Fall zurückgeführt werden, daß V eine Hyperfläche ist, etwa durch $f(X_0, X_1, \cdots, X_n) \equiv 0 \bmod p$ definiert, wo f ein Polynom über dem vollständigen unverzweigten diskret bewerteten Körper K der Charakteristik 0 mit dem Restklassenkörper k ist, dessen Koeffizienten p-ganz, aber nicht sämtlich durch p teilbar sind. Zuerst wird unter V' die Hyperfläche $\prod_{i=0}^{n} X_i = 0$ verstanden, nach der Anzahl M_i der über k_i rationalen Punkte von $S_n - V \cup V'$ gefragt. Verallgemeinerung eines Ansatzes von Warning [Abh. Math. Sem Hamburg. Univ. **11** (1935), 76–83] ergibt M_i als p-adischen Grenzwert

$$M_i(q^i - 1) \equiv \alpha_{i,r} = \sum_{x_\mu \in k_i^\times} \prod_{j=0}^{i-1} f(x_0^{q^j}, \cdots, x_n^{q^j})^{(q-1)p^r} \bmod p^{r+1}.$$

Die rechte Seite dieser Kongruenz kann nun anders gedeutet werden:

$$\alpha_{i,r} = (q^i - 1)^{n+1} \operatorname{Sp}(\psi \circ f(X)^{(q-1)p^r}).$$

ψ ist die K-lineare Transformation von $K[X_0, \cdots, X_n]$ in sich, die durch $\psi(X_0^{\nu_0} \cdots X_n^{\nu_n}) = X_0^{\nu_0/q} \cdots X_n^{\nu_n/q}$, falls alle ν_μ/q ganz sind, sonst $= 0$, definiert ist, und für $g(X)$ aus $K[X]$: $(\psi \circ g)h(X) = \psi(g(X)h(X))$. Die Spur der linearen Transformation $\psi \circ g$ wird als die Spur ihrer Einschränkung $(\psi \circ g)_m$ auf den endlichdimensionalen Vektorraum der Polynome höchstens m-ten Grades definiert, die sich für hinreichend große m als von m unabhängig erweist. Also kann man auf

$$\sum_{i=1}^{\infty} \frac{M_i t^i}{i(q^i - 1)^n} = \lim_{r \to \infty} \sum_{i=1}^{\infty} \operatorname{Sp}(\psi \circ f^{(q-1)p^r}) \frac{t^i}{i}$$
$$= -\lim_{r \to \infty} \log \det [I - t(\psi \circ f^{(q-1)p^r})]$$

schließen. $\det(I - t(\psi \circ f^{(q-1)p^r}))$ ist wieder durch $\det(I - t(\psi \circ f^{(q-1)p^r})_m)$ für hinreichend großes m definiert. Der Limes ist im Ring der Potenzreihen $K\{t\}$ als koeffizientenweiser p-adischer Limes gemeint ("schwacher Limes"). Daraus

$$(*) \quad \exp\left[-\sum_{i=1}^{\infty} \frac{M_i}{i(q^i - 1)^n} t^i\right] = \lim_{r \to \infty} \det(I - t(\psi \circ f^{(q-1)p^r})) = \langle f, t \rangle.$$

Eine Analyse der Koeffizienten der charakteristischen Polynome $\det(I - t(\psi \circ f^{(q-1)p^r}))$ auf Teilbarkeit durch Potenzen von p zeigt nun, daß der Limes rechts in (*) auch im "starken" Sinne gilt, das heißt gleichmäßig über alle Koeffizienten der Potenzreihen; außerdem, daß die durch (*) definierte Potenzreihe $\langle f, t \rangle$ p-adisch in $|t| < |q^{-1}|$ konvergiert. Um von $\exp[-\sum_{i=1}^{\infty} (M_i / i(q^i - 1)^n) t^i]$ zu $\exp[\sum_{i=1}^{\infty} (M_i/i) t^i] = \zeta(S_n - V \cup V', t)$ überzugehen, benutzt man den Operator $\delta: h(t)^\delta = h(t)/h(qt)$ in der Gruppe der Potenzreihen $h(t) = 1 + c_1 t + c_2 t^2 + \cdots$; es ist

$$\zeta(S_n - V \cup V', t)^{(-\delta)^n} = \exp\left[\sum_{i=1}^{\infty} \frac{M_i}{i(q^i - 1)^n} t^i\right],$$

$\zeta(S_n - V \cup V', t) = \langle f, t \rangle^{-(-\delta)^{-n}}$, und hieraus folgt schließlich

$$(**) \quad \zeta(V, t) = \frac{\zeta(S_n, t)}{\zeta(S_n - V, t)} = \frac{\prod_{A \subset S} \langle A; f, t \rangle^{(-\delta)^{m(A)}}}{\prod_{i=0}^{n} (1 - q^i t)},$$

wo A alle Teilmengen der Indexmenge $S = \{0, 1, \cdots, n\}$ durchläuft und $\langle A; f, t \rangle$ die für den Durchschnitt V_A von V mit dem $m(A)$-dimensionalen projektiven Teilraum: $X_i = 0$ für $i \notin A$, gebildete, $\langle f, t \rangle$ entsprechende Potenzreihe ist. Das genannte Hauptergebnis folgt daraus. Man kann aber ein etwas besseres Resultat gewinnen, indem man mittels der Einschränkung $[\psi \circ f^{(q-1)p^r}]$ von $\psi \circ f^{(q-1)p^r}$ auf das Ideal $X_0 \cdots X_n K[X]$ von $K[X]$ entsprechend $\langle f, t \rangle$ die ebenfalls für $|t| < |q^{-1}|$ konvergente Potenzreihe $[f, t]$ (mit ganzen p-adischen Koeffizienten) und ihre Analoga für die den A zugeordneten Teilräume einführt; $[f, t] = \lim_{r \to \infty} \det(I - t[\psi \circ f^{(q-1)p^r}])$:

$$\zeta(V, t) = \frac{\prod_{A \subset S} [A; f, q^{n-m(A)} t]^{(-\delta)^{m(A)}}}{\prod_{i=0}^{n} (1 - q^i t)},$$

also

$$\zeta(V, t) = \frac{[f, t]}{1 - t} \frac{H_1(qt)}{H_2(qt)},$$

wo die Potenzreihen $H_i(t)$ für $|t| < |q^{-1}|$ konvergieren, und ganze Koeffizienten haben, $H_i(t) = 1 + c_1 t + c_2 t^2 + \cdots$. Also hat $\zeta(V, t)$ für gerade $\dim V = n - 1$ einen Pol bei $t = 1$ aber keine Nullstelle in $|t|<|q^{-1}|$, für ungerade dim V kann es keinen Pol $\neq 1$ in diesem Kreise geben. Nimmt man an, daß $\zeta(V,t)$ rational ist, so schließt man leicht, daß die Reziproken der Nullstellen und Pole von $\zeta(V,t)$ ganze algebraische Zahlen sind; ferner, daß, wenn α eine ganze algebraische Zahl ist, deren Norm einen (gewöhnlichen) absoluten Betrag $<q^{\operatorname{grad}\alpha}$ hat, α^{-1} für gerade dim V nicht Nullstelle und für ungerade dim V nicht Pol von $\zeta(V,t)$ sein kann (von dem möglichen Pol $t=1$ abgesehen). Definiert man für eine Hyperfläche $V, f(X)\equiv 0 \bmod p$, im S_n:

$$P(V,t)^{(-1)^n} = \zeta(V,t)\prod_{i=0}^{n-1}(1-q^it)$$

so besagt eine Vermutung von A. Weil (unter anderem), daß $P(V,t)$ ein Polynom ist, wenn V irreduzibel und singularitätenfrei ist. Man findet nun leicht aus (**):

$$\langle f,t\rangle^{\delta^n} = (1-t)^{1+\delta+\cdots+\delta^n}\cdot\prod_{A\subset S}P(V_A,t).$$

Nimmt man nun an, dass alle V_A bis herunter zu Indexmengen A von mindestens drei Elementen (so daß die zugehörigen Räume mindestens von der Dimension 2 sind) irreduzibel und singularitätenfrei sind, und weiter, daß V durch keine Ecke des Koordinatensimplexes geht, so ergibt sich (unter Annahme der Weilschen Vermutung), daß $\prod_{A\subset S}P(V_A,t)$ ein Polynom und daher $\langle f,t\rangle$ eine p-adisch ganze Funktion (beständig konvergente Potenzreihe) mit der Eigenschaft ist, daß aus $\langle f,\alpha\rangle=0$ stets $\langle f,q^{-1}\alpha\rangle=0$ folgt und daß jeder Kreis $|t|<\rho$ nur endlich viele Nullstellen von $\langle f,t\rangle$ enthält. (Offenbar sind alle Nullstellen und alle Pole aller $\zeta(V_A,t)$ Nullstellen von $\langle f,t\rangle$.) Es wird daher für jedes f mit p-adischen ganzen Koeffizienten vermutet, daß $\langle f,t\rangle$ eine ganze Funktion ist [vgl. das folgende Referat #3914].

Schließlich wird noch für die Anzahl N_i der über k_i rationalen Punkte einer V die folgende p-adische Annäherungsformel bewiesen: Ist b eine positive Zahl, so gibt es ganze p-adische Zahlen $y_1,\cdots,y_r$ und Zahlen $\delta_\nu=\pm 1$, so daß

$$N_i \equiv y_1{}^i\,\delta_1+\cdots+y_r{}^i\delta_r \bmod q^{(1-b)i-\log i}$$

gilt. Der log ist zur Basis q zu nehmen, r hängt möglicherweise von b, aber nicht von i ab.

M. Deuring (Göttingen)

Referred to in G25-50.

G25-20 (25# 3914)

Dwork, Bernard

On the rationality of the zeta function of an algebraic variety.

Amer. J. Math. **82** (1960), 631–648.

Das Hauptergebnis ist der folgende Satz: Die Zetafunktion $\zeta(V,t)$ einer algebraischen Mannigfaltigkeit V über einem endlichen Körper k ist eine rationale Funktion von t (Vermutung von Weil). $\zeta(V,t)$ ist durch

$$(1)\qquad \zeta(V,t) = \exp\Big[\sum_{i=1}^{\infty}N_it^i/i\Big]$$

definiert, wo N_i die Anzahl der Punkte von V bedeutet, die Koordinaten in der Erweiterung i-ten Grades k_i von k haben. V mag eine affine, projektive oder allgemeiner eine abstrakte Mannigfaltigkeit im Sinne von Weil sein, V darf auch reduzibel und singularitätenbehaftet sein. Durch naheliegende kombinatorische Überlegungen wird der Beweis auf den Fall zurückgeführt, daß V die Differenz einer Hyperfläche $f(x_1,\cdots,x_n)=0$ im n-dimensionalen affinen Raume über k und der reduziblen Hyperfläche $\prod_{i=1}^n x_i=0$ ist, so daß also N_i die Anzahl der Lösungen $x_1,\cdots,x_n$ von $f(x_1,\cdots,x_n)=0$ mit $x\in k_i^\times$ (Multiplikativgruppe von k_i) ist. Mit irgend einem nichttrivialen Charakter Θ der Additivgruppe von k_i gilt

$$(2)\qquad q^iN_i = (q^i-1)^n+\sum_{x_\nu\in k_i;\ \nu=0,1,\cdots,n}\Theta(x_0f(x_1,\cdots,x_n)),$$

wo $q=p^a$ die Elementezahl von k sei, p die Charakteristik von k. Dies wird in die p-adische Approximationsformel

$$(3)\qquad q^iN_i = (q^i-1)^n+\sum_{\xi_\nu\in T_i;\ \nu=0,1,\cdots,n}\ \prod_{j=0}^{i-1}F_r(\xi_0{}^{q^j},\cdots,\xi_n{}^{q^j}) \bmod p^r,\ r=1,2,3,\cdots,$$

übergeführt, $F_r(X_0,\cdots,X_n)$ ist ein Polynom mit ganzen Koeffizienten in dem Körper Ω, der vollständigen und algebraisch abgeschlossenen Hülle des Körpers $\mathbf{Q}_p$ der rationalen p-adischen Zahlen und T_i ist die Gruppe der (q^i-1)-ten Einheitswurzeln in Ω. Diese Umformung verläuft folgendermaßen: $\xi\to x$ sei der Isomorphismus von $k_i^\times$ auf T_i, der ξ seine Restklasse x nach dem maximalen Ideal zuordnet, oder umgekehrt: $\xi=\xi(x)$ ist der multiplikative (Teichmüller-) Repräsentant von x in Ω. Ist ζ eine primitive p-te Einheitswurzel und ist L_i die unverzweigte Erweiterung i-ten Grades von $\mathbf{Q}_p$, so ist $\Theta(x)=\zeta^{\operatorname{Spur}_{L_i/\mathbf{Q}_p}(\xi(x))}$ ein nichtrivialer Charakter von $k_i{}^+$. Für diesen wird eine Aufspaltung $\Theta(x)=\prod_{j=0}^{i-1}\theta(\xi(x)^{p^j})$ hergeleitet, in der $\theta(t)=\sum_{m=0}^{\infty}\beta_mt^m$ eine Potenzreihe bedeutet, deren Koeffizienten β_m (aus Ω) die Abschätzung $|\beta_m|\leqq|p|^{m/(p-1)}$ erfüllen ($|\ |$ bedeutet den Betrag im bewerteten Körper Ω). Wird dies noch dem Körper k durch Einführung von $\Lambda(t)=\prod_{j=0}^{a-1}\theta(t^{p^j})=\sum_{m=0}^{\infty}\lambda_mt^m$ angepaßt—es gilt wieder (4) $|\lambda_m|\leqq|p|^{m/(p-1)}$—so folgt aus (2)

$$q^iN_i = (q^i-1)^n+\sum_{\xi_\mu\in T_i}\prod_{\nu=1}^{\rho}\prod_{j=0}^{i-1}\Lambda(A_\nu M_\nu\xi_\mu{}^{q^j})$$

wenn $X_0F(X_1,\cdots,X_n)=\sum_{\nu=1}^{\rho}A_\nu M_\nu$ mit $A_\nu\in k$, M_ν Potenzprodukt der X_μ ist. Da die $\Lambda(A_\nu M_\nu{}^{q^j})$ keine Polynome sind, ist es nötig $\sum_{m=0}^{r(q-1)}\lambda_mt^m=\Lambda_r(t)$ gesetzt, für $=1,2,\cdots$, Polynome (5) $F_r(X)=\sum_r\Lambda_r(A_\nu M_\nu)$ einzuführen, mit diesen gilt dann (beachte (4)) die Formel (3). Für die Summe rechts in (3) hat man nun nach des Verfassers Arbeit [siehe #3913] einen Ausdruck als Spur einer linearen Transformation des Polynomrings $\Omega[X]$ in sich

$$\sum_{\xi_\nu\in T_i;\ \nu=0,1,\cdots,n}\ \prod_{j=0}^{i-1}F_r(\xi_0{}^{q^j},\cdots,\xi_n{}^{q^j}) = (q^i-1)^{n+1}\operatorname{Spur}(\psi\circ F_r)^i.$$

Ähnlich wie [loc. cit.] schließt man jetzt auf die Existenz des Grenzwertes (6) $\lim_{r\to\infty}\det(I-t\psi\circ F_r)=\Delta(t)$, dabei ist die Konvergenz—im Potenzreihenring $\Omega\{t\}$—koeffizientenweise p-adisch gemeint; weiter, daß (7) $\zeta(V,qt)=(1-t)^{-(-\delta)^n}\Delta(t)^{-(-\delta)^{n+1}}$ gilt, wo δ den loc. cit. erklärten (in der eben erwähnten Topologie) topologischen Automorphismus der multiplikativen Gruppe $1+t\Omega\{t\}$ bedeutet. Man kann nun die Koeffizienten von $\det(I-t\psi\circ F_r)$ aus der Definition (5) von F_r berechnen und dann, dank der Abschätzung (4), zeigen, daß für die Koeffizienten von $\det(I-t\psi\circ F_r)=\sum_{m=0}^{\infty}\gamma_{r,m}t^m$ eine Abschätzung $|\gamma_{r,m}|^{1/m}\leqq\varepsilon_m$; $r=1,2\cdots$, mit $\lim_m\varepsilon_m=0$ gilt. Für $\Delta(t)=\sum_{m=0}^{\infty}\gamma_mt^m$ folgt $|\gamma_m|^{1/m}\leqq\varepsilon_m$, und also ist $\Delta(t)$ (in Ω) beständig konvergent; (7) ergibt, daß $\zeta(V,t)$ p-adisch meromorph (Quotient von zwei beständig konvergenten Potenzreihen in Ω) ist.

Bemerkt man nun noch, daß $\zeta(V,t)$ zufolge der Definition (1) eine Potenzreihe mit ganzen rationalen Koeffizienten ist, so folgt die Rationalität von $\zeta(V,t)$ mit Hilfe des auch an sich interessanten Kriteriums: Eine Potenzreihe $F(t)=\sum_{i=0}^{\infty}A_it^i$ mit Koeffizienten A_i aus einem endlichen algebraischen Zahlkörper L ist genau dann rational, wenn die Menge der Primstellen $\mathfrak{p}$ von L so in eine endliche

Menge S und ihr Komplement S' eingeteilt werden kann, daß (i) $|A_i|_{\mathfrak{p}} \leqq 1$, $i=0, 1, 2, \cdots$, gilt für $\mathfrak{p} \in S'$; (ii) $F(t)$ als Funktion einer $\mathfrak{p}$-adischen Variabeln $\tau_{\mathfrak{p}}$ in $\Omega_{\mathfrak{p}}$ (der algebraisch abgeschlossenen und $\mathfrak{p}$-adisch vollständigen Hülle von L) in einem Kreise $|\tau_{\mathfrak{p}}|_{\mathfrak{p}} \leqq R_{\mathfrak{p}}$ meromorph (d.h. Quotient zweier dort konvergenter Potenzreihen) ist, und es gilt $\prod_{\mathfrak{p}\in S} R_{\mathfrak{p}} > 1$. Die $\mathfrak{p}$-Beträge sind dabei so normiert zu denken, daß für $A \neq 0$ aus L die Produktformel $\prod_{\mathfrak{p}} |A|_{\mathfrak{p}} = 1$ gilt. Der Beweis beruht auf dem klassischen Kriterium für die Rationalität einer Potenzreihe $\sum_{i=0}^{\infty} A_i t^i$ mit Koeffizienten aus einem Körper (von É. Borel): Genau dann ist $F(t)$ rational, wenn es ein $m=1, 2, \cdots$ und ein $i_0 = 1, 2, \cdots$, gibt, so daß die Hankelschen Determinanten $N_{i,m} = \det (A_{i+j+l})_{j,l=0,\ldots,m}$ null sind für $i \geqq i_0$. Es wird übrigens nur der einfachste Fall $L=\mathbf{Q}$ und $S=\{p, p_\infty\}$ dieses Kriteriums gebraucht. Zum Schluß wird noch auf die loc. cit. nur unter der Annahme der Rationalität von $\zeta(V, t)$ bewiesenen Aussagen hingewiesen.

Die Aufspaltung des additiven Charakters Θ mittels der gut konvergenten Potenzreihe θ, die ein wesentliches Hilfsmittel des Beweises bildet, ist, wie der Verfasser bemerkt, keinesweges die einzig mögliche und es wird angedeutet, wie man sie auch auf anderem Wege gewinnen kann; ferner wird bemerkt, daß die genannte Aufspaltung auch für die Theorie der Gaußschen Summen nützlich ist, es wird eine Kongruenz von Stickelberger [Math. Ann. **37** (1890), 321–367] mit ihrer Hilfe hergeleitet.

M. Deuring (Göttingen)

Referred to in G25-24, G25-31, G25-32, G25-50, G25-57, G25-58, L10-15, Q25-15, T25-23.

G25-21 (25# 5055)

Segre, Beniamino

Geometry and algebra in Galois spaces.

Abh. Math. Sem. Univ. Hamburg **25** (1961/62), 129–139.

Questo lavoro riproduce una conferenza letta ad Amburgo dall'autore il 4-XI-1960 al "Fest-Kolloquium" in onore di W. Blaschke. L'autore vi riassume, applica e commenta risultati di recenti ricerche sue e della sua scuola [vedi, e.g., Acta Arith. **5** (1959), 315–332; MR **22** #4980; Conv. Internaz. di Teoria dei Gruppi Finiti (Firenze, 1960), pp. 66–80, Edizioni Cremonese, Rome, 1960; MR **22** #12102].

Nella parte I, col Teor. 1, si stabilisce che affinchè l forme di ordini $n_1, \cdots, n_l$ dello spazio proiettivo ad r dimensioni $S_{r,q}$ (costrutto su di un campo di Galois $\gamma = \mathrm{GF}(q)$ di ordine $q=p^h$; $p>2$, $h \geqq 1$, p primo) possano non avere punti in comune occorre che sia $n = n_1 + \cdots + n_l > r$. Se $n \leqq r$, quelle forme hanno almeno $1+q+\cdots+q^{r-n}$ punti distinti in comune, ed il numero totale delle loro intersezioni distinte è sempre $\equiv 1 \pmod p$.

Per quanto riguarda un sistema di equazioni algebriche i cui primi membri siano polinomi non omogenei coi coefficienti in γ la cui somma dei gradi sia n, l'autore dimostra fra l'altro (Cor. 2) che, se $n<r$, in γ il numero delle soluzioni distinte del sistema è sempre multiplo di p. Se invece $n=r$, c'è sempre (Cor. 3) in γ qualche soluzione comune, ed il numero totale delle soluzioni distinte è $\equiv 1 \pmod p$.

Nella parte II l'autore ricorda come la ricerca del numero k delle soluzioni $(x) = (x_1, \cdots, x_r)$ in γ di un arbitrario sistema di $l \geqq 1$ equazioni algebriche coi coefficienti in γ si possa ricondurre al calcolo del rango $\rho = q^r - k$ di una matrice quadrata M del tipo $q^r \times q^r$. L'autore ricorda anche i suoi eleganti risultati relativi al caso di una sola equazione in una sola incognita ($l=r=1$).

Nella parte III l'autore fornisce qualche esempio di applicazione dei risultati esposti precedentemente alla caratterizzazione di alcune varietà di $S_{r,q}$ (coniche, k-archi completi o meno, loro tangenti, ovali).

E. Morgantini (Padova)

Citations: MR 22# 12102 = T40-24.

G25-22 (27# 146)

Yanagihara, Hiroshi

On L-series of normal varieties.

J. Math. Soc. Japan **13** (1961), 120–135.

Es seien U und V normale (=ganzabgeschlossene) Mannigfaltigkeiten über einem endlichen Körper, und es sei U eine Galoissche Überlagerung von V mit der Galoisschen Gruppe G. Der Verfasser gibt hier eine Definition der zu den Charakteren von G gehörigen L-Reihen, wobei auch die singulären Punkte und die Verzweigungspunkte von V gebührend berücksichtigt werden. Hierin unterscheidet sich die Definition des Verfassers von der bei Lang [Bull. Soc. Math. France **84** (1956), 385–407; MR **19**, 578] gegebenen Definition. Es wird eine Funktionalgleichung für diese L-Reihen hergeleitet, unter der Voraussetzung, dass U singularitätenfrei ist. [Vgl. dazu auch: Sampson und Washnitzer, Amer. J. Math. **81** (1959), 735–748; MR **21** #4156; Ishida, Proc. Japan Acad. **34** (1958), 1–5; MR **22** #6808a; ibid. **34** (1958), 395–399; MR **22** #6808b].

P. Roquette (Tübingen)

Citations: MR 19, 578c = G25-8; MR 21# 4156 = G25-14; MR 22# 6808a = G25-16; MR 22# 6808b = G25-16.

G25-23 (28# 1198)

Manin, Ju. I.

On the arithmetic of rational surfaces. (Russian)

Dokl. Akad. Nauk SSSR **152** (1963), 46–49.

A rational surface is by definition a nonsingular projective algebraic surface which is birationally equivalent to the projective plane over the algebraic closure of the ground field. Swinnerton-Dyer [Mathematika **9** (1962), 54–56; MR **25** #3413] has given an example of a rational surface defined over an algebraic number field which has points defined over every local closure of the ground field but none defined over the ground field. Here the author gives an example of two rational surfaces which are biregularly equivalent over every local closure of the ground field but not over the ground field. He shows, however, that neither sort of pathology is exhibited by the relatively minimal forms of rational surfaces [cf. Nagata, Mem. College Sci. Univ. Kyoto Ser. A Math. **32** (1960), 351–370; MR **23** #A3739].

In the second part of the paper the author proves Weil's conjecture [Proc. Internat. Congr. Mathematicians (Amsterdam, 1954), Vol. III, pp. 550–558, Noordhoff, Groningen, 1956; MR **19**, 1078] that the number of points on a rational surface F defined over the field of q elements is $q^2 + q$ Trace $\Phi + 1$, where Φ is the endomorphism of the group of divisor classes modulo linear equivalence induced by the Frobenius automorph. This follows from the lemma that the group of cycles on $E \times F$ modulo linear equivalence, where E and F are rational surfaces, is generated by the classes of cycles of the type $x \times y$, where x, y are cycles on E, F, respectively.

An almost immediate consequence is that the Hasse-Weil zeta-function of a rational surface defined over an algebraic number field (i.e., the product of the local zetas) is substantially $\zeta(s, k)\ \zeta(s-2, k)\ L(s, k)$, where L is an

Artin zeta-function.

J. W. S. Cassels (Cambridge, England)

Citations: MR 19, 1078a = G02-8; MR 25# 3413 = D32-68.

Referred to in G25-31.

G25-24 (28# 3039)

Dwork, Bernard

On the zeta function of a hypersurface.

Inst. Hautes Études Sci. Publ. Math. No. 12 (1962), 5–68.

The author continues his strikingly original work on the zeta function of an algebraic variety defined over a finite field. Here he considers a nonsingular hypersurface H of degree d in projective n-space over the field $k = GF(q)$. The Weil conjectures predict that its zeta function has the form

$$(1) \qquad \zeta(H, t) = P(t)^{(-1)^n} / \prod_0^{n-1} (1 - q^i t),$$

where $P(t)$ is a polynomial of predicted degree. This paper gives a proof covering all cases except when $\mathrm{char}(k) = 2$ and d is even. The object studied is a certain linear operator α acting on a space of p-adic power series, whose connection with the ζ-function is taken over from an earlier paper (cited below), with the addition of (2) below. A partial spectral theory is developed for α here, and a key role is also played by a Koszul-type complex associated with a set of differential operators on the space of power series. Some theorems in p-adic analysis are included.

Let Q_p be the rational p-adic field, and Ω the completion of the algebraic closure of Q_p. We consider first an operator α of the general type needed for the problem. This α can be defined on the space of all power series $\Omega(X_0, \cdots, X_{n+1})$, but in order that its spectrum not be all of Ω^*, its action is restricted to a subspace $L(\kappa)$ of series whose coefficients grow in ordinal at least at rate κ (a real number). Fix a suitable series F in $L(\kappa)$, and define an operator α on $L(q\kappa)$ by $\alpha(G) = \Psi \cdot (F \cdot G)$, where Ψ is the qth root operator on $\Omega(X)$, sending monomials of the form $X^{(qu)}$ into $X^{(u)}$ and the others into 0. A "characteristic series" χ_F is introduced as the limit of the characteristic polynomials of α acting on truncations of $L(q\kappa)$. The spectral theory for α is now done assuming that the coefficients of F lie in a finite extension K_0 of Q_p. To each zero λ^{-1} of χ_F of multiplicity s_λ, it associates the primary subspace W_λ, of dim s_λ, which is the kernel of $(I - \lambda^{-1})^s$ for all $s \geqq s_\lambda$. If we restrict the coefficient field to K_0, then if λ^{-1} is not a zero of χ_F, then $I - \lambda^{-1}\alpha$ is surjective, with the obvious generalization using s_λ. {This spectral theory was subsequently generalized and simplified by Serre [same Publ. No. 12 (1962), 69–85; MR **26** #1733].}

For the application to $\zeta(H, t)$, various choices for F may be made. If $\bar{f}(X)$ is the defining polynomial for H over k, let $f(X)$ be the unique polynomial over Ω reducing mod p to $\bar{f}$ and whose coefficients are $(q-1)$st roots of unity. Put $H = \gamma X_0 f$, where $\gamma^{q-1} = 1$, and then we fix $F = (\exp H)^\delta$, where in general $G(X)^\delta$ is defined to be $G(X)/G(X^q)$. Actually, other F's are usable and later one must switch from one to another.

From the author's earlier paper [Amer. J. Math. **82** (1960), 631–648; MR **25** #3914] the basic connection between $\zeta(H, t)$ and α is (letting H' be the hypersurface $X_1 X_2 \cdots X_{n+1} = 0$)

$$\zeta(H - H', qt) = \chi_F^{-(-\delta)^{n+1}} (1-t)^{-(-\delta)^n}.$$

Let A be a nonempty subset of $S = \{1, \cdots, n+1\}$ and H_A be the hyperplane obtained by intersecting H with the hyperplanes $X_i = 0$, $i \in A$. We can assume that H_A is nonsingular for all A. Letting the equation (1) for H_A define the rational function $P_A(t)$, one can deduce formally that

$$(2) \qquad \chi_F^{\delta^{n+1}} = (1-t) \prod_A P_A(qt).$$

Says the author: "We believe this equation is quite significant since χ_F is entire even if H is singular."

To show $P_S(qt)$ is a polynomial, the essential first step is to show that $\chi_F^{\delta^{n+1}}$ is a polynomial of degree d^n. This is true because there is a finite-dimensional quotient space $\mathfrak{W}$ of $L(q\kappa)$ on which α acts (as $\bar{\alpha}$, say) and

$$(3) \qquad \chi_F^{\delta^{n+1}} = \det(I - t\bar{\alpha}).$$

The idea of the proof of this is to introduce differential operators on $L(q\kappa)$: $D_i G = X_i\, \partial G / \partial X_i + HG$ $(i = 1, \cdots, n+1)$. We have easily $\alpha \circ D_i = q D_i \circ \alpha$, showing that if λ^{-1} is an eigenvalue of α, so is $q\lambda^{-1}$, and in fact $D_i(W_\lambda) \subset W_{\lambda/q}$; thus α acts (as $\bar{\alpha}$) on $\mathfrak{W} = L(q\kappa)/\sum D_i L(q\kappa)$. The natural projection $L(q\kappa) \to \mathfrak{W}$ carries a primary subspace W_λ onto the eigenspace $\mathfrak{W}_\lambda$ if λ^{-1} is also an eigenvalue of $\bar{\alpha}$ (otherwise onto 0), and all eigenspaces of $\bar{\alpha}$ arise this way. Moreover, it induces an isomorphism $W_\lambda / \sum D_i W_{\lambda/q} \to \mathfrak{W}_\lambda$. All this follows from the spectral theory. Letting $\dim \mathfrak{W}_\lambda = b_\lambda$, what must be proved is therefore the first equality of

$$(3) \qquad \chi_F^{\delta^{n+1}} = \prod_\lambda (1 - \lambda^{-1} t)^{b_\lambda} = \det(I - t\bar{\alpha})$$

the product being taken over the spectrum of α. To do this the author uses a complex which is a modification of the exterior algebra complex (here apparently invented ab ovo)

$$0 \to F_{n+1} \to F_n \to \cdots \to F_0 \to W_\lambda \to 0,$$

where $F_r = W_{\lambda/q^r} \otimes \Lambda^r E$. The differentiations in the complex are the usual ones, employing the $n+1$ commuting endomorphisms D_i. If one knows the sequence is exact, the equality (3) follows trivially; but by the usual formalism of these complexes, exactness follows if one knows that for all k, $D_k \beta = \sum D_i \beta_i \Rightarrow \beta = \sum D_i \beta_i'$, where $\beta_i, \beta_i' \in W_{\lambda/q}$ and $\beta \in W_\lambda$. This last statement is the crux of the matter; it is proved first when β, β_i, β_i' are simply in $L(q\kappa)$, using elementary but long computations, then the spectral theory is used to put the elements in the right primary subspaces.

It still must be shown that $P_S(qt)$ is a polynomial. For this purpose a decomposition $W = \sum W_A{}^A$ is given so that $\bar{\alpha}$ induces an $\bar{\alpha}_A{}^A$ on each summand, and

$$(4) \qquad \det(I - t\bar{\alpha}) = \prod_{A \subset S} \det(I - t\alpha_A{}^A) = \prod P_A(qt),$$

where the second equality follows from the first, (2), and (3). Now (4) is still valid if S is replaced by any subset $B \subset S$; the resulting system of relations shows easily that $P_S(qt) = \det(I - t\bar{\alpha}_S{}^S)$, which completes the proof, the degree being calculated via the Koszul resolution. The $W_A{}^A$ are obtained as natural quotients (via the D_i) of spaces $L_A{}^A(q\kappa)$ obtained by taking the power series in $L(q\kappa)$, setting $X_i = 0$ for all $i \notin A$, and then taking just the series divisible by X_i, for all $i \in A$. This last condition causes technical complications in the rather involved (in algebra and convergence) calculations in $L(q\kappa)$ which establish both the decomposition of W and (4) above. The case $p | d$ is particularly troublesome and is excluded entirely when $p = 2$.

Subsequent work by the author has established the missing case (p and d even) mentioned above, and proved the conjectured functional equation for $\zeta(H, t)$. The location of the zeros of $P(t)$ remains open.

A. Mattuck (Cambridge, Mass.)

Citations: MR 25# 3914 = G25-20; MR 26# 1733 = Q25-15.

Referred to in G25-28, G25-31, G25-35, G25-41, T25-23.

G25-25 (29# 2697)

Segre, Beniamino

Arithmetische Eigenschaften von Galois-Räumen. I.

Math. Ann. **154** (1964), 195–256.

Con questa memoria dei Math. Annalen e con le altre due pubblicate negli [Ann. Mat. Pura Appl. (4) **64** (1964), 1–76] e nelle [Math. Notae **19** (1964), 1–10], l'autore fornisce una brillante ed interessante esposizione degli ultimi risultati delle sue ricerche sui legami tra le teoria algebriche e geometriche [per i risultati precedenti vedasi il volume: *Lectures on modern geometry*, Edizioni Cremonese, Rome, 1961; MR **24** #A1045].

Come l'autore dichiara nella introduzione, in questa memoria (per la cui traduzione in lingua tedesca Egli ringrazia W. Groebner) si occupa soprattutto di problemi di carattere numerico ed aritmetico relativi alle varietà algebriche di uno spazio di Galois $S_{r,q}$, ossia di uno spazio proiettivo di dimensione r su di un corpo finito di dimensione q.

Il lavoro è diviso in tre parti. Nella parte I, dedicata alle equazioni algebriche in una variabile, l'autore si occupa dapprima (§ 1) del carattere quadratico del discriminante D di un polinomio $f(x)$ di grado n sopra un corpo γ, tanto nel caso che la caratteristica p di γ sia 2, oppure $\neq 2$. Nel caso $p \neq 0$, si ritrova per altra via un teorema di L. Carlitz [Simon Stevin **31** (1956), 27–30; MR **18**, 285]. Nel § 2 l'autore considera i casi singolari per il determinante Hessiano di una forma binaria e fa vedere come in un corpo di caratteristica $p \neq 0$ ogni equazione algebrica di grado p, il cui gruppo Hessiano svanisca identicamente ($a = 0$) o si riduca ad un unico punto (contato $2p-4$ volte), si possa con una sostituzione lineare (che manda quel punto all' ∞) trasformare in una equazione trinomia del tipo (10): $x^p = ax + b$. Nel § 3 si esamina in modo particolare il caso in cui il corpo γ è finito e di ordine $q = p^h$, determinando una condizione necessaria e sufficiente perchè la (10) non abbia soluzioni in γ. Se invece ne ha, puo averne una ($p \neq 2$) oppure p, che possono esprimersi razionalmente mediante b, una radice $(p-1)$-esima di a ed una arbitraria delle p radici che ha in γ l'equazione fissa (nella incognita k):

$$k^{p^h-1} + k^{p^h-2} + \cdots + k^p + 1 = 0.$$

Nel § 4 si esamina il caso in cui il corpo finito γ sia di caratteristica $p = 2$ e perciò di ordine $q = 2^h$. Allora gli elementi del corpo γ ed i polinomi $f(x)$ su γ si suddividono in due categorie distinte e non vuote, che per i polinomi irriducibili in γ sono quelle dei polinomi di grado dispari o di grado pari. Se invece $f(x)$ è riducibile (e a discriminante non nullo) appartiene alla 1ª od alla 2ª categoria se tra i suoi fattori irriducibili ve n'è un numero pari o dispari di grado pari. Fra l'altro se ne deduce che, anche se $p = 2$, un polinomio su γ a discriminante non nullo si spezza, in una qualsiasi estensione quadratica di γ, in un prodotto di fattori irriducibili, tutti di grado dispari. Comunque le cosiderazioni precedenti si applicano nel § 5 alla deduzione di alcune proprietà delle equazioni algebriche su un corpo finito γ, in forma indipendente dalla caratteristica. In particolare (se $p \neq 3$) per un polinomio cubico $f(x)$ a discriminante non nullo, se x_1, x_2, x_3 sono i suoi zeri e z_1, z_2 quelli del determinante hessiano $h(x)$ di $f(x)$, questi 5 numeri distinti si ripartiscono in γ ed in alcune sue estensioni quadratiche o cubiche in quattro modi possibili, secondo che $q \equiv 1 \pmod 3$, oppure $q \equiv 2 \pmod 3$, oppure z_1, z_2 appartengano o no a γ. Da questo teorema si deduce un procedimento per il calcolo effettivo di x_1, x_2, x_3 che ha molte analogie con le classiche formule di Cardano. Nel § 6 l'autore si occupa diffusamente delle equazioni biquadratiche $f(x) = 0$ a discriminante non nulle e della distribuzione in γ delle radici di una equazione siffatta e di quelle della sua risolvente cubica $\varphi(\lambda)$, con particolare riferimento al caso equianarmonico.

Nella parte II, dedicata alle equazioni omogenee di grado n, del tipo $f(x_1, \cdots, x_r) = g(y_1, \cdots, y_s)$, l'autore si occupa dapprima in generale (§ 7) del numero N delle soluzioni di un'equazione siffatta (determinate a meno di un fattore non nullo) che cadono nel corpo finito γ di ordine $q = nt + 1$ dei coefficienti. Le formule ottenute vengono applicate nel § 8 al caso particolare in cui la forma f si riduce ad una costante $k \in \gamma$ e, in una estensione di ordine n di γ, la forma g si spezzi nel prodotto di n forme lineari coniugate e linearmente indipendenti. Si passa poi al caso in cui f è una forma arbitraria su γ, ottenendo per N una espressione in cui figura come parametro il numero F dei punti di $S_{r,q}$ giacenti sulla forma $f = 0$. Nel § 9 si considera la superficie cubica $f(x_1, x_2) = f(y_1, y_2)$ dell' $S_{3,q} = \{(x_1, x_2, y_1, y_2)\}$. Quando $(q-1, 3) = 1$ e la superficie non è singolare, il numero N dei punti (con le coordinate in γ) che giacciono su di essa è dato da $N = q^2 + q[(F-1)^2 + 1] + 1$, dove $F = 0, 1, 2, 3$ è il numero degli zeri, contenuti in γ, della forma f, ciascuno contato una sola volta. Se il discriminante D della f è $\neq 0$, e $q \equiv 1 \pmod 3$, la formula precedente va sostituita con l'altra: $N = q^2 + q[(F-1)^2 + 3] + 1$.

Infine l'autore fa vedere nel § 10 come dalle precedenti considerazioni si possa dedurre (limitatamente ai valori 0, 1 del genere g) una semplice dimostrazione di un teorema di H. Hasse [Convegno Sci. Fis. Mat. Natur. [1939], pp. 85–140, Reale Accad. Italia, Rome, 1943; MR **12**, 47] ed A. Weil [*Sur les courbes algébriques et les variétés qui s'en déduisent*, Actualités Sci. Indust., No. 1041, Hermann, Paris, 1948; MR **10**, 262] su una limitazione superiore del numero dei punti appartenenti ad una curva algebrica assolutamente irriducibile su di un corpo finito.

Nella parte III si studiano gli stessi problemi già affrontati nella parte II, nel caso particolare che le forme f, g siano combinazioni lineari di potenze n-esime. Sfruttando un algoritmo opportuno, introdotto nel § 11, si studiano successivamente nei §§ 12, 13, 14, 15 i casi in cui $n = 2, 3, 4$ ed $n \geqq 5$. È praticamente impossibile riassumere in breve i numerosi risultati conseguiti dall'autore, che ne illustra anche i collegamenti con altre teorie, cosicchè sembra preferibile lasciarli degustare al Lettore interessato.

E. Morgantini (Padova)

Citations: MR 10, 262c = G20-8; MR 12, 47d = G20-10; MR 18, 285g = A36-21.

Referred to in T40-39.

G25-26 (31# 171)

Dwork, Bernard

A deformation theory for the zeta function of a hypersurface.

Proc. Internat. Congr. Mathematicians (Stockholm, 1962), pp. 247–259. *Inst. Mittag-Leffler, Djursholm,* 1963.

From the author's introduction: "The main object of this report is to give a method by which diagonal forms (defining hypersurfaces) may be deformed into more general homogeneous forms in such a way that results valid for diagonal forms can be carried over to the general case."

G25-27 **(32# 4120)**

Perel'muter, G. I.

On some sums and manifolds connected with them. (Russian)

Works of Young Scientists (Russian), pp. 69–72. *Izdat. Saratov. Univ., Saratov,* 1964.

A few straightforward remarks about the zeta-functions of the hypersurfaces $y^2 = f(x_1, \cdots, x_n)$ and $y^q - y = f(x_1, \cdots, x_n)$ over the field of q elements (q a prime).

J. W. S. Cassels (Cambridge, England)

G25-28 **(32# 5654)**

Dwork, Bernard

On the zeta function of a hypersurface. II.

Ann. of Math. (2) **80** (1964), 227–299.

The author here continues his work on the Weil conjectures for the zeta function of a non-singular projective hypersurface H defined over GF(q). In Part I of this paper [Inst. Hautes Études Sci. Publ. Math. No. 12 (1962), 5–68; MR **28** #3039] (cited below as (I), and a prerequisite for this paper), he identified the zeta function $P(t)$ of H as the characteristic polynomial of a certain endomorphism $\bar{\alpha}$ acting on a space $\mathfrak{W}^S$ of q-adic power series. In this paper, he proves that $P(t)$ satisfies the right functional equation. (The location of its zeros is the deep remaining question.)

The functional equation is a duality statement, asserting that $P(t)$ is essentially unchanged by the substitution $t \to q^{n-1}/t$, where $n-1 =$ dimension H. The idea of the paper is to prove this by getting a dual theory to the one given in (I). A space $\mathfrak{K}$ of q-adic Laurent series (i.e., negative exponents, and growth conditions) is defined; a quotient space $\mathfrak{K}/\mathfrak{K}^S$ is naturally dual to $\mathfrak{W}^S$, an endomorphism α^* dual to α is naturally defined on $\mathfrak{K}/\mathfrak{K}^S$, and one gets (1) $P(t) = \det(1 - t\alpha^*)$. The main point is now to give a certain isomorphism (2) $\bar{\theta}: \mathfrak{K}/\mathfrak{K}^S \to \mathfrak{W}^S$ satisfying the condition (3) $\bar{\theta} \circ \alpha^* \circ \bar{\theta}^{-1} = q^{n+1}(\bar{\alpha})^{-1}$. The functional equation then follows immediately from (1), (2), and (3).

The definition of a $\bar{\theta}$ satisfying (3) is done in several steps. First one assumes the hypersurface H (or rather, a lifting of it to the q-adics) is given by a diagonalized equation (4) $f(X) = \sum a_i X_i^d = 0$, $i = 1, \cdots, n+1$, where the definition of $\bar{\theta}$ and proof of (3) use the partial differentiation operators D_i of (I) and their duals D_i^*. Here everything is very explicit.

For a general hypersurface, one gives $\bar{\theta}$ by viewing H as a deformation of (4), writing its equation in the form (5) $f(X) = a_i X_i^d + \Gamma h(X)$, where Γ is a q-adic variable. Thus, (4) corresponds to $\Gamma = 0$. For each Γ, one gets the corresponding spaces $\mathfrak{K}_\Gamma/\mathfrak{K}_\Gamma{}^S$ and $\mathfrak{W}_\Gamma{}^S$.

Now if Γ is near 0 q-adically, then by using the q-adic exponential function, the author defines an isomorphism (6) $T_\Gamma: \mathfrak{K}_0/\mathfrak{K}_0{}^S \to \mathfrak{K}_\Gamma/\mathfrak{K}_\Gamma{}^S$ which enables him to define $\bar{\theta}_\Gamma$ as the composite map: (7) $\bar{\theta}_\Gamma: \mathfrak{K}_\Gamma/\mathfrak{K}_\Gamma{}^S \to \mathfrak{K}_0/\mathfrak{K}_0{}^S \xrightarrow[\theta_0]{} \mathfrak{W}_0{}^S \to \mathfrak{W}_\Gamma{}^S$, the last map being the dual to T_Γ. The proof of (3) is easy now.

Finally, for arbitrary values of Γ, he takes bases for the two spaces $\mathfrak{K}_\Gamma/\mathfrak{K}_\Gamma{}^S$ and $\mathfrak{W}_\Gamma{}^S$ and shows that the matrix giving $\bar{\theta}$ has entries which are rational functions of Γ. This enables him to extend the definition of $\bar{\theta}$ to all but a finite number of values of Γ. Since $\bar{\theta}$ satisfies (3) (using α_Γ and $\alpha_\Gamma{}^*$) for Γ near 0, it follows by Krasner's p-adic analytic continuation theory that it satisfies (3) for all Γ.

Some final remarks. (1) The matrix C_Γ representing the map (6) satisfies a Picard-Fuchs equation $\partial C_\Gamma/\partial\Gamma = C_\Gamma B$. When the hypersurface is a curve, it has been checked for low values of the genus (in this paper, for genus 1 only) that C_Γ is actually the period matrix for the normalized integrals of the second kind on the curve. (2) A second, less restrictive proof of (3), not using analytic continuation but instead some involved combinatorial arguments, is also given. (3) A final section gives a method for determining the doubtful sign in the functional equation; in particular, if $n-1$ is odd, the sign depends only on the degree d, $n-1$, and on q.

In subsequent work the author considers singular hypersurfaces. Recent unpublished work by Washnitzer, Monsky, and Katz sheds new light on Dwork's methods.

A. Mattuck (Cambridge, Mass.)

Citations: MR 28# 3039 = G25-24.

Referred to in G25-35, G25-44, G25-57, T25-23.

G25-29 **(33# 124)**

Greenberg, Marvin J.

Rational points in Henselian discrete valuation rings.

Bull. Amer. Math. Soc. **72** (1966), 713–714.

The author announces two theorems and some corollaries concerning the existence of zeros $(x_1, x_2, \cdots, x_n)$ of finite sets $F_1, \cdots, F_r$ of polynomials in $R[X_1, \cdots, X_n]$ such that $x_i \in R$. Here R is a Henselian discrete valuation ring. Detailed proofs are to appear elsewhere.

H. T. Muhly (Iowa City, Iowa)

G25-30 **(34# 174)**

Bombieri, Enrico

On Galois coverings over finite fields.

Proc. Internat. Colloq. Algebraic Geometry (Madrid, 1965) *(Spanish), pp.* 23–30. *Inst. Jorge Juan del C. S. I. C.-Internat. Math. Union, Madrid,* 1966.

Let X be an algebraic variety defined over a finite field k and G a finite group of automorphisms of X acting over k. Assume (1) the variety X is normal, (2) the quotient space is in a natural way an algebraic variety, and (3) the covering $f: X \to X/G$ is separable and unramified. The author proves under these conditions several nice identities between Artin L-functions associated to the covering $f: X \to X|G$ and to the characters of G and zeta functions of certain algebraic varieties canonically related to the variety X and to the group G.

H. Popp (Tübingen)

G25-31 **(34# 4256)**

Swinnerton-Dyer, H. P. F.

The zeta function of a cubic surface over a finite field.

Proc. Cambridge Philos. Soc. **63** (1967), 55–71.

Let k be a field of q elements and let k_n be its unique extension of degree n. If $\mathscr{S}$ is a nonsingular variety defined over k, then the zeta function of $\mathscr{S}$ is given by $\zeta(s) = \exp(\sum_{n=1} n^{-1} N_n q^{-ns})$, where N_n denotes the number of points on $\mathscr{S}$ defined over k. It follows from results of B. Dwork [Amer. J. Math. **82** (1960), 631–648; MR **25** #3914; Inst. Hautes Études Sci. Publ. Math. No. 12 (1962), 5–68; MR **28** #3039] that ζ is a rational function in q^s, and if $\mathscr{S}$ is a nonsingular cubic variety then $\zeta(s) = \{(1-q^{-s})(1-q^{1-s})(1-q^{2-s}) \prod_1^6 (1-w_i q^{-s})\}^{-1}$; whence $N_n = 1 + q^n + q^{2n} + \sum w_i{}^n$.

H. Davenport and the reviewer [Quart. J. Math. Oxford Ser. (2) **14** (1963), 153–159; MR **26** #6117] showed that there is an integer ν such that for all n which are multiples of ν, $N_n = q^{2n} + O(q^n)$; whence $|w_i| < q$. The author points out that they had implicitly proved that for such n, $N_n = q^{2n} + 7q^n + 1$; whence $w_i = q\eta_i$, where the η_i are νth roots of 1. In this paper the author determines the η_i. He does so in terms of the conjugacy class of the permutation σ^* in the permutation group on the 27 lines on the cubic surface $\mathscr{S}$, where σ^* is the permutation induced by the Frobenius automorphism $\sigma(a) = a^q$. The conjugacy classes were previously enumerated by J. S. Frame [Ann. Mat. Pura Appl. (4) **32** (1951), 83–119; MR **13**, 817]. In most instances the η_i are determined in an elementary way, but in two instances the result is obtained by averaging over a linear system of cubic surfaces. In doing so, one needs to know the possible rational singular cubic surfaces on a linear system of cubic surfaces through 9 given lines.

This is a definitive work which covers the many special cases examined by various authors over the years. As the author indicates, these results are special cases of a theorem of Ju. I. Manin [Dokl. Akad. Nauk SSSR **152** (1963), 46–49; MR **28** #1198], but Manin's proof requires considerably more geometry and this "relatively" simpler argument will appeal to many number theorists.

D. J. Lewis (Ann Arbor, Mich.)

Citations: MR 25# 3914 = G25-20; MR 26# 6117 = D80-40; MR 28# 1198 = G25-23; MR 28# 3039 = G25-24.

G25-32 (34# 4271)

Perel'muter, G. I.

Rationality of L-functions of a class of algebraic varieties. (Russian)

Studies in Number Theory, No. 1 (Russian), pp. 59–62. Izdat. Saratov. Univ., Saratov, 1966.

The L-functions of the title are those of the cyclic covering $Y^p - Y = f(X_1, \cdots, X_n)$ of the affine space with coordinates $X_1, \cdots, X_n$, where the ground field k is finite of characteristic p and where $f \in k[X_1, \cdots, X_n]$. Appealing to results of B. Dwork [Amer. J. Math. **82** (1960), 631–648; MR **25** #3914], the author sketches a proof that the L-functions are rational.

J. W. S. Cassels (Cambridge, England)

Citations: MR 25# 3914 = G25-20.

G25-33 (34# 7515)

Greenberg, Marvin J.

Rational points in Henselian discrete valuation rings.

Inst. Hautes Études Sci. Publ. Math. No. 31 (1966), 59–64.

Let R be a Henselian discrete valuation ring, t a generator of the maximal ideal, and K the field of fractions. Let R^* be the completion of R, K^* its field of fractions. Then, under the assumption that K^* is separable over K, the author gives the following result. Let Z be a prescheme of finite type over R; then there are integers $N \geqq 1$, $c \geqq 1$, $s \geqq 0$ depending on Z such that for $\nu \geqq N$ and for any point x of Z in R/t^ν, the image of x in $Z(R/t^{[\nu/c]-s})$ lifts to a point of Z in R. The proof is reduced to the case where Z is affine over R and this is proved by induction on the dimension of Z. Moreover, Z may be assumed to be integral. Then two cases arise. If Z is separable over R, the proof is reduced to Newton's lemma for a system of polynomials with coefficients in R; otherwise, extending the base ring R to a ring R' and using a nice functor $\mathscr{F}$ from the category of affine schemes of finite type over R' to that of R, the proof is reduced to the case of lower dimensions. As an application, a generalization of S. Lang's result on C_i fields [cf. Ann. of Math. (2) **55** (1952), 373–390; MR **13**, 726] is given: If k is a C_i field then the field $k((t))$ of formal power series in one variable t over k is C_{i+1}.

H. Yanagihara (Hiroshima)

Citations: MR 13, 726d = D72-6.

Referred to in D72-52, G20-45, G25-42, U10-16.

G25-34 (34# 7516)

Tamagawa, Tsuneo

On rational points on projective varieties defined over a complete valuation field.

Algebraic Groups and Discontinuous Subgroups (Proc. Sympos. Pure Math., Boulder, Colo., 1965), *pp.* 84–89. *Amer. Math. Soc., Providence, R.I.*, 1966.

Let k be a complete and perfect field with a nonarchimedean valuation $|\ |$, $P_k{}^n$ the corresponding n-dimensional projective space. Define the norm of $x = (x_0, \cdots, x_n)$ by $\|x\| = \max\{|x_0|, \cdots, |x_n|\}$. If $f(x_0, \cdots, x_n)$ is homogeneous of degree d in k, the value $\|x\|^{-d}|f(x)|$ is uniquely determined by the point $P \in P_k{}^n$ with coordinates x; denote this value by $|f(P)|$. A set of homogeneous polynomials $f_1, \cdots, f_N$ in k is a zero set if

$$\inf_{P\in P_k{}^n} \max\{|f_1(P)|, \cdots, |f_n(P)|\} = 0.$$

The following properties are proved. (A) If a set $\{f_1, \cdots, f_N\}$ of homogeneous polynomials in k is a zero set, there exists a point $P_0 \in P_k{}^n$ such that $f_1(P_0) = 0, \cdots, f_N(P_0) = 0$. (B) Let G be a reductive algebraic group defined over k such that there is no subtorus of G which splits over k. Then the group G_k of all k-rational elements of G is bounded.

A. Evyatar (Gutwirth) (Haifa)

G25-35 (35# 194)

Dwork, Bernard M.

On the zeta function of a hypersurface. III.

Ann. of Math. (2) **83** (1966), 457–519.

In Parts I and II [Inst. Hautes Études Sci. Publ. Math. No. 12 (1962), 5–68; MR **28** #3039; Ann. of Math. (2) **80** (1964), 227–299; MR **32** #5654] the author showed that the zeta-function of a non-singular hypersurface defined over GF(q) has the overall form predicted by the Weil conjectures and satisfies the right functional equation. The present paper breaks fresh ground by considering the singular hypersurfaces; except for the rationality, little is known (or even conjectured) about the zeta-function of these.

The notations, ideas, and to some extent the methods of the previous papers are assumed as a prerequisite. In the first two papers, finite-dimensional quotient spaces of p-adic power series were introduced which served as p-adic cohomology groups for the non-singular hypersurface. {An explicit isomorphism with the deRham cohomology has since been constructed by N. Katz ["On the differential equations satisfied by period matrices", Ph.D. thesis, Princeton Univ., Princeton, N.J., 1966].} In this paper, analogous cohomology spaces $H^s(\mathfrak{L}^*)$ are introduced for the singular hypersurface, and the bulk of the paper is devoted to proving they are finite-dimensional. These spaces $H^s(\mathfrak{L}^*)$ are constructed, as before, from a space $\mathfrak{L}^*$ of p-adic Laurent series in several variables, the cohomology being defined via the differential operators D_i derived from the polynomial f defining the hypersurface. The proof that the spaces $H^s(\mathfrak{L}^*)$ are finite-dimensional is by induction on s, the space $H^s(\mathfrak{L}^*)$ being related to the cohomology space $H^{s-1}(\mathfrak{L}_\Gamma{}^*)$ of a higher-dimensional hypersurface—essentially a one-parameter family H_Γ of hypersurfaces, all non-singular except for the given hypersurface H_0. (Thus, the deformation theory given in Part II plays an essential role here, too.) The finite-dimensionality of the space $H^1(\mathfrak{L}^*)$ comes from results in p-adic ordinary differential equations, to which a brief chapter is devoted.

A second type of cohomology space $\hat{\mathfrak{R}}_\infty \subset \mathfrak{L}^*$ is introduced on which the basic endomorphism α^* acts, and which is spanned by the eigenvectors of α^*. (In the non-singular case, the characteristic polynomial of α^* is essentially the zeta-function.) Its cohomology is also proved to be finite-dimensional, provided f has coefficients in an algebraic number field. The representation of α^* on the spaces $H^s(\hat{\mathfrak{R}}_\infty)$ leads to a decomposition of $\det(I - t\alpha)^{\delta^{1+n}}$ into the characteristic polynomials of the endomorphism acting on these spaces.

The relation of these cohomology spaces to classical ones is left open, nor are any explicit conjectures about the zeta-function offered, for singular hypersurfaces. In this connection, however, the author remarks that the mapping between the cohomology space and its dual which gave the functional equation for non-singular hypersurfaces still exists in this new theory, and has the same formal relation with α^*; however, it is no longer an isomorphism. This as well as other clues to the future direction of the theory are offered at the end of the introduction.

A. Mattuck (Cambridge, Mass.)

Citations: MR 28# 3039 = G25-24; MR 32# 5654 = G25-28.

Referred to in G25-36, G25-44, G25-53.

G25-36 (35# 2895)

Dwork, B.

On zeta functions of hypersurfaces. (French summary)

Les Tendances Géom. en Algèbre et Théorie des Nombres, pp. 77–82. Édition du Centre National de la Recherche Scientifique, Paris, 1966.

The results and conjectures which are briefly sketched in this note have appeared in full detail [the author, Ann. of Math. **83** (1966), 457–519; MR **35** #194].

N. Greenleaf (Rochester, N.Y.)

Citations: MR 35# 194 = G25-35.

G25-37 (35# 2894)

Bombieri, E.; Swinnerton-Dyer, H. P. F.

On the local zeta function of a cubic threefold.

Ann. Scuola Norm. Sup. Pisa (3) **21** (1967), 1–29.

Let F_q denote the finite field of q elements, let V be a complete non-singular threefold in projective four-space, defined over F_q, and let r_n denote the number of points of V defined over F_{q^n}. The authors give a canonical form of the zeta function of V and show, among other things, that it satisfies the Riemann-Weil hypothesis, i.e., the algebraic integers ω_h occurring in the formula $r_n=(q^{4n}-1)/(q^n-1)-\sum_{h=1}^{10}\omega_h{}^n$ are all of absolute value $q^{3/2}$. This is proved by reducing the problem to the corresponding one about the zeta function of a curve, to which Weil's well-known results can be applied.

O. H. Körner (Marburg)

Referred to in G25-51.

G25-38 (35# 4219)

Perel'muter, G. I.

The Z-function of a class of cubic surfaces. (Russian)

Studies in Number Theory, No. I (Russian), pp. 49–58. *Izdat. Saratov. Univ., Saratov,* 1966.

Let k be a finite field of characteristic not 2 or 3, and let V be a non-singular cubic surface, defined by an equation $tz^2=x^3+ay^3+abxyt+a^2bt^3$, a, b, c in k. V is then a rational surface. Using a method of L. J. Mordell [J. London Math. Soc. **38** (1963), 351–355; MR **27** #3625] for counting rational points, the author computes the zeta-function $Z(V)$ of V explicitly and verifies the conjectures of A. Weil [Bull. Amer. Math. Soc. **55** (1949), 497–508; MR **10**, 592] concerning the absolute values of the zeros and poles of $Z(V)$ and the functional equation for $Z(V)$.

N. Greenleaf (Rochester, N.Y.)

Citations: MR 10, 592e = T50-8; MR 27# 3625 = D80-45.

G25-39 (35# 6688)

Elistratov, I. V.

The number of classes and the location of zeros of the $Z(u)$-function. (Russian)

Volž. Mat. Sb. Vyp. 4 (1966), 58–65.

Let K be an algebraic function field in one variable over a finite field of q elements. Let $Z(u)=\sum_G u^{\deg G}$ (where G runs through the integral divisors of K) be the zeta function of K, g the genus of K, and h the class number. The author studies the relation between g, h, and the zeros of $Z(u)$. When $g=1$ he shows that $Z(u)$ has just two zeros $u=e^{\pm i\varphi}/\sqrt{q}$, where $m=2(\sqrt{q})\cos\varphi$ is an integer satisfying $-2\sqrt{q}\leqq m\leqq\min(q, 2\sqrt{q})$. If both zeros are real, then they have the same sign, and q is a square. From now on suppose $g=2$. In this case it is shown that every divisor class has dimension 0, 1, or 3. If some class has dimension 3, then the others have dimension 0; moreover $q=2$, $h=25$, and $Z(u)$ has $-\frac{1}{2}\pm\frac{1}{2}i$ as double zeros. If all classes have dimension 1 or 0, then $Z(u)$ has four zeros $e^{\pm i\varphi_1}/\sqrt{q}$, $e^{\pm i\varphi_2}/\sqrt{q}$, where $\cos\varphi_1+\cos\varphi_2=m/2\sqrt{q}$, $\cos\varphi_1\cos\varphi_2=n/4q$. Here m and n are integers satisfying $-4\sqrt{q}\leqq m\leqq\min(q, 4\sqrt{q})$, $|n|\leqq 4\sqrt{q}$, $m^2\geqq 4n$. If the zeros are all real, and q is not a square, then their signs are $(--++)$. If q is a square $\geqq 16$, then all three sign combinations $(----)$, $(--++)$, $(++++)$ are possible, but when $q=4$ or 9, $(++++)$ cannot occur.

B. Gordon (Los Angeles, Calif.)

G25-40 (36# 1446)

Lubkin, S. [Lubkin, Saul]

On a conjecture of André Weil.

Amer. J. Math. **89** (1967), 443–548.

This important paper contains proofs of Weil's conjectures on the factorization and functional equation of the zeta function of a complete non-singular variety X liftable to characteristic zero and defined over a finite field of characteristic $p>0$. The author also proves Weil's conjecture that the group of numerical equivalence classes of cycles on X is finitely generated. As Weil himself showed [Proc. Internat. Congr. Math. (Amsterdam, 1954), Vol. III, pp. 550–558, Noordhoff, Groningen, 1956; MR **19**, 1078], the afore-mentioned results on the zeta function follow from the existence of a "good" cohomology theory for X having a Lefschetz fixed point theorem. Thus the main task is to construct such a theory.

This construction was first sketched by A. Grothendieck [see M. Artin, "Grothendieck topologies", mimeographed notes, Harvard Univ., Cambridge, Mass., 1962], using the cohomology of sheaves on the étale Grothendieck topology. In this paper, the étale topology is also used, but the cohomology is obtained from a projective system of semi-simplicial complexes (simplicial sets). This has the advantage of giving a homology and homotopy theory as well, but the author does not explore that here beyond giving the definitions. The analogue of his construction for ordinary topological spaces is the Alexander-Spanier cohomology theory.

The cohomology required must have characteristic zero. Both Grothendieck and the author construct it as a module over the q-adic numbers, where q is any prime different from p. Of greater interest is a later paper [Ann. of Math. (2) **87** (1968), 105–194; ibid. (2) **87** (1968), 195–255] in which the author purports to construct a p-adic cohomology theory, using only the Zariski topology, which gives an alternative proof of Weil's conjectures.

In an appendix, the author sketches an intersection theory on singular varieties. This theory is defined for cohomological "cycles" in terms of the cup product, and gives integral intersection multiplicities. This theory can be used to give a cohomological definition of the zeta function of a complete singular variety.

An annoying facet of this paper is the presence of several statements which the author says he "can prove", but for which no proof is even sketched.

Note that (1) the hypothesis "X liftable to characteristic zero" will not be needed if Poincaré duality can be proved directly in characteristic p, and (2) Weil's conjecture about the location of the zeros of the zeta function still remains to be proved. *M. J. Greenberg* (Santa Cruz, Calif.)

Citations: MR 19, 1078a = G02-8; MR 37# 215 = G25-43.
Referred to in G25-45, G25-47.

G25-41 **(36# 1447)**

Ireland, K. F.

On the zeta function of an algebraic variety.

Amer. J. Math. **89** (1967), 643–660.

In connection with his work on the Weil conjectures, B. Dwork proved a series of results about the zeta function of a nonsingular projective hypersurface [Inst. Hautes Études Sci. Publ. Math. No. 12 (1962), 5–68; MR **28** #3039]. This paper extends some of these results to hypersurfaces in multiprojective space and to complete intersections in projective space. Of particular interest is that in both cases, mysterious new eigenvalues enter into the Dwork-type zeta functions.

To give details in a reasonable space seems impossible. The notation generally follows that of Dwork, and one gets for a hypersurface V in $P^m \times P^n$ a relation $\chi_F^{\delta^{1+n+m}}(t) = \prod_j (1-q^jt)^{\binom{n}{j}\binom{m}{j}} \prod_{A_1,A_2} P_{A_1\times A_2}(qt)$, where $A_1 \subset \{1, \cdots, m+1\}$ and $A_2 \subset \{1, \cdots, n+1\}$. The left side (let's call it $X(t)$) is constructed from $\det(1-t\alpha)$, where α is an endomorphism of a certain p-adic Banach space $L(b)$ of power series (determined by the hypersurface V), while on the right side, $P_{A_1\times A_2}$ is essentially the zeta-function of the projection of V onto the linear variety where the coordinates "in $A_1 \times A_2$" are non-zero. (These projections are assumed nonsingular.)

Thus, the $P_{A_1\times A_2}$ are known to be rational functions. The author does not prove they are polynomials, but is able to show at least that they have the right degree (= appropriate Betti number) and that $X(t)$ is a polynomial. This comes about because, as in the Dwork theory, one gets that $X(t)$ is a characteristic polynomial of the image $\bar{\alpha}$ of α on a finite-dimensional quotient space of $L(b)$ Certain differential operators on $L(b)$ are used to form a Koszul complex (see the review cited above), and from this complex is deduced the degree of $X(t)$. Dwork's original argument, in particular the acyclicity of the complex, is vastly simplified and clarified here.

The factors $(1-q^jt)$, with their multiplicities, are unexplained as yet.

Complete intersections $f_1 = \cdots = f_r = 0$ in projective space are handled by the classical trick of introducing indeterminates $Z_1, \cdots, Z_r$ and considering the semi-projective hypersurface $Z_1f_1 + \cdots + Z_rf_r = 0$. The results are similar. Throughout, details of proofs are sketched or omitted, the reader being referred to Dwork's paper.

A. Mattuck (Cambridge, Mass.)

Citations: MR 28# 3039 = G25-24.

G25-42 **(36# 3787)**

Eršov, Ju. L.

Rational points over Hensel fields. **(Russian. English summary)**

Algebra i Logika Sem. **6** (1967), *no.* 3, 39–49.

In this paper the author proves two theorems about the existence of rational points on algebraic varieties defined over Henselian fields and rings. The second generalizes a result of M. J. Greenberg [Inst. Hautes Études Sci. Publ. Math. No. 31 (1966), 59–64; MR **34** #7515] but is less explicit in the case considered by Greenberg. The proofs use logical methods, in particular "ultrapowers".

We now describe the results in more detail. They are described in terms of a category in which the objects are fields and a morphism $\phi: F_0 \to F_1$ is an F_1-valued place on F_0, i.e., a ring-homomorphism of a ring $R \subset F_0$, whose field of fractions is F_0, into F_1, the kernel being a maximal ideal of R. A morphism thus induces in a canonical way a valuation on F_0. If $i: F_0 \to F_1$ is a monomorphism in this category, the author calls a morphism $\rho: F_1 \to F_0$ a retract over i if ρi is the identity map of F_0. For example, if i is the natural injection of F_0 into the function field F_1 of a variety V defined over F_0, then a simple rational point on V induces a retract over i in an obvious way. The first theorem gives conditions under which the converse of this statement is true. The author introduces the class $\mathfrak{F}_0$ of fields F which possess a nontrivial valuation with respect to which they satisfy Hensel's lemma. For $F \in \mathfrak{F}_0$, a necessary and sufficient condition that V should have a simple rational point is that there should exist a retract over i whose associated valuation has a discrete group of finite rank. Immediate corollaries are that if one such point exists, then they are Zariski-dense and that the existence of such a point is a property of the function-field F_0, not merely of the model V.

For the second theorem the author says that the triplet $\langle F, v, \Gamma\rangle$, consisting of a field F, and a valuation v on it with value-group Γ, has property (†) if every extension $\langle F_1, v_1\Gamma_1\rangle$ of it for which the completion F_v is separable over F_{1v_1} and the group Γ is a serving group of Γ_1 is such that F_1 is separable over F. He shows that an algebraically complete valuation in the sense of the author [Algebra i Logika Sem. **5** (1966), no. 1, 5–40; MR **34** #4134] has the property (†). He then proves the following generalization of Greenberg's theorem. Let $\langle F, v, \Gamma\rangle$ be a Henselian valuation satisfying the condition (†) and let A_v be the ring of integers of F for v. Let (*) $G_1(x_1, \cdots, x_n)$, $\cdots$, $G_m(x_1, \cdots, x_n)$ be a system of equations with coefficients in A_v. Suppose that for every $\gamma > 0$, $\gamma \in \Gamma$, there exists a system $y_1, \cdots, y_n \in A_v$ such that $v(G_i(y_1, \cdots, y_n)) > \gamma$ for $i = 1, \cdots, m$. Then (*) has a solution in A_v. Further, there is a $\gamma_0 \in \Gamma^+$ (where Γ^+ is the set of positive elements of Γ) and a monotone map $\phi: \{\gamma | \gamma \in \Gamma, \gamma \geqq \gamma_0\} \to \Gamma^+$ such that if $y_1, \cdots, y_n \in A_v$, $v(G_i(y_1, \cdots, y_n)) > \gamma \geqq \gamma_0$ $(i = 1, \cdots, m)$, then there exist $x_1, \cdots, x_n \in A_v$ such that $G_i(x_1, \cdots, x_n) = 0$ $(i = 1, \cdots, m)$ and $v(x_i - y_i) > \phi(\gamma)$ $(i = 1, \cdots, n)$. *J. W. S. Cassels* (Cambridge, England)

Citations: MR 34# 7515 = G25-33.

G25-43 **(37# 215)**

Lubkin, Saul

A p-adic proof of Weil's conjectures.

Ann. of Math. (2) **87** (1968), 105–194; *ibid.* (2) **87** (1968), 195–255.

Let X be a complete smooth variety of dimension n defined over the finite field with q elements. Weil's conjectures about the zeta function $Z(t)$ of X are generally considered as follows: (1) (Rationality) $Z(t)$ is a rational function of t. (2) (Functional equation) $Z(1/q^nt) = (\pm 1)q^{nx/2}t^xZ(t)$, where x is the self-intersection number of the diagonal on $X \times X$. (3) (Riemann hypothesis) The zeros and poles of $Z(t)$ have absolute value equal to an integral power of $\sqrt{q}$.

Rationality was first proved by Dwork without speaking of cohomology. However, both rationality and the functional equation are simple formal consequences of a "Weil cohomology" theory $X \mapsto H^*(X)$, which has coefficients in a field of characteristic zero, satisfies Poincaré duality and the Künneth formula and receives a functorial ring homomorphism from the algebraic cycles modulo rational equivalence $C^*_{\text{rat}}(X)$. Moreover, a Weil cohomology implies the finite generation of the algebraic cycles modulo numerical equivalence. {It is incorrectly asserted on page 236, however, that any two closed points of X, taken with suitable multiplicity, are rationally equivalent.} The Riemann hypothesis remains unproved in general.

Let $\mathcal{O}$ be a complete discrete valuation ring with quotient field K of characteristic zero and residue field k. The author constructs a Weil cohomology on the category of k-varieties X which lift to smooth proper $\mathcal{O}$-schemes $\mathbf{X}$ as follows. Let $H_{\mathbf{X}}^*(X, K)$ be the hypercohomology of the complex $\Omega_{\mathbf{X}_K}{}^*$ of differential forms on the generic fibre $\mathbf{X}_K$. If, by Lefschetz's principle, we assume K is contained in the complex numbers $\mathbf{C}$, then $H_{\mathbf{X}}^*(X, K) \otimes_K \mathbf{C}$ is canonically isomorphic to the classical cohomology of $\mathbf{X}_{\mathbf{C}}$; hence, $H_{\mathbf{X}}^*(X, K)$ satisfies Poincaré duality and the Künneth formula: $H^*_{\mathbf{X}\times\mathbf{Y}}(X \times Y, K) = H_{\mathbf{X}}^*(X, K) \otimes H_{\mathbf{Y}}^*(Y, K)$. The construction of a ring homomorphism $C^*_{\text{rat}}(X) \to H_{\mathbf{X}}^*(X, K)$ is the most delicate part of the article. With the construction completed, if $f: X \to Y$ is a morphism, then its graph gives rise to an element of $H^*_{\mathbf{X}\times\mathbf{Y}}(X \times Y, K)$; thence, by the Künneth formula and Poincaré duality, to a map $f^* = H_{\mathbf{X}}^*(X, K) \to H_{\mathbf{Y}}^*(Y, K)$. It follows easily that $H_{\mathbf{X}}^*(X, K)$ depends not on the lifting $\mathbf{X}$ of X and depends functorially on X.

The cohomology class of a subvariety Y of X is constructed with the aid of the Washnitzer-Monsky completion $\Omega_K{}^{*+}$, which is a certain subsheaf of

$$[\lim \text{proj}_{\nu \geq 0}(\Omega_{\mathbf{X}}{}^*/t^\nu\Omega_{\mathbf{X}}{}^*)] \otimes_{\mathcal{O}} K,$$

where t is a uniformizing parameter of $\mathcal{O}$. Let x be the generic point of Y, A the local ring of x on $\mathbf{X}$, $Z = \text{Spec}(A/tA)$ and $t_1, \cdots, t_d$ elements which, together with t, form a system of regular parameters of A. Then it is proved that the relative hypercohomology group $H^{2d}(Z, Z-x, \Omega_K{}^{*+})$ may be computed as the Čech cohomology group $H^{2d}(U_{t_1,\cdots,t_d}, (Z, Z-x), \Omega_K{}^{*+})$ and that the Čech cochain which associates the value $(1/t_1\cdots t_d)(dt_1 \wedge\cdots\wedge dt_n)$ to the n-simplex $X-(t_1, \cdots, t_n=0), \cdots, X-(t_n=0)$, X and zero to the others, defines a cohomology class in $H^{2d}(Z, Z-x, \Omega_K{}^{*+})$ which is independent of the choice of $t_1, \cdots, t_d$. Finally, this class gives rise to the cohomology class of Y in $H_{\mathbf{X}}{}^{2d}(X, K)$ by means of isomorphisms

$$H^{2d}(Z, Z-x, \Omega_K{}^{*+}) \simeq H^{2d}(X, X-Y, \Omega_0{}^{*+}) \otimes_{\mathcal{O}} K,$$

$$[\lim \text{proj}_{\nu\geq 0} H^{2d}(X, \Omega_{\mathbf{X}}{}^*/t^\nu\Omega_{\mathbf{X}}{}^*)] \otimes_{\mathcal{O}} K \simeq H_{\mathbf{X}}{}^{2d}(X, K).$$

Chapter I deals entirely with relative hypercohomology. It involves no algebraic geometry and may be of wider interest. *S. L. Kleiman* (New York)

Referred to in G25-40, G25-45, G25-47.

G25-44 (37# 216)

Dwork, Bernard M.

Analytic theory of the zeta function of algebraic varieties.

Arithmetical Algebraic Geometry (Proc. Conf. Purdue Univ., 1963), *pp.* 18–32. *Harper & Row, New York,* 1965.

A useful summary of the author's proof of the rationality and functional equation for the zeta function of a hypersurface over a finite field (see Ann. of Math. (2) **80** (1964), 227–299 [MR **32** #5654] and earlier work cited there). His more recent work on the zeta function of singular hypersurfaces [ibid. (2) **83** (1966), 457–519; MR **35** #194] is not included. *A. Mattuck* (Cambridge, Mass.)

Citations: MR 32# 5654 = G25-28; MR 35# 194 = G25-35.

G25-45 (38# 1095)

Barshay, Jacob

On the zeta function of biprojective complete intersections.

Trans. Amer. Math. Soc. **135** (1969), 447–458.

It is shown once again by a highly computational method that the degree of the zeta function of a biprojective complete intersection is equal to the negative of the Euler-Poincaré characteristic of certain liftings. This is a very special case of the Lefschetz theorem, proved by the reviewer [Amer. J. Math. **89** (1967), 443–548; MR **36** #1446; Ann. of Math. (2) **87** (1968), 105–194; ibid. (2) **87** (1968), 195–255; MR **37** #215] in two different ways, q-adic and p-adic. *S. Lubkin* (Berkeley, Calif.)

Citations: MR 36# 1446 = G25-40; MR 37# 215 = G25-43.

G25-46 (38# 4420)

Chowla, S.; Hasse, H.

On a paper of Bombieri.

Norske Vid. Selsk. Forh. (Trondheim) **41** (1968), 30–33.

The zeta-function $\zeta_K(s)$ of an algebraic function field K of genus $\geqq 1$ over a constant field of q elements is a rational function of the variable $z = q^{-s}$ whose zeros ω satisfy $|\omega| = q^{-1/2}$, as A. Weil proved with deep-lying theorems of algebraic geometry. For the much weaker inequality $1 > |\omega| > q^{-1}$, an elementary proof was given by E. Bombieri [Atti Accad. Naz. Lincei Rend. Cl. Sci. Fis. Mat. Natur. (8) **35** (1963), 252–257; MR **31** #161] using an analogue of Selberg's prime number formula. In the present paper it is shown that this result can be obtained in a much simpler and more natural way. Namely, only elementary properties of $\zeta_K(s)$ suffice for this. *O. H. Körner* (Marburg)

Citations: MR 31# 161 = G20-21.

G25-47 (39# 4159)

Lubkin, Saul

A result on the Weil zeta function.

Trans. Amer. Math. Soc. **139** (1969), 297–300.

Sei X eine projektive singularitätenfreie algebraische Varietät der Dim n über einen GF(q), die sich zu einer projektiven Varietät über einem Körper der Charakteristik 0 liften läßt, $Z_X(T) = \prod_{i=0}^n P_{2i}(T)/\prod_{i=1}^n P_{2i-1}(T)$ die Zetafunktion von X (siehe den Verfasser [Amer. J. Math. **89** (1967), 443–548; MR **36** #1446; Ann. of Math. (2) **87** (1968), 105–194; ibid. (2) **87** (1968), 195–255; MR **37** #215]), $P_h = \prod_{i=1}^{\beta_h}(1-\alpha_{hi}T)$ Weilpolynom. Aus Weil's Vermutungen [A. Weil, Bull. Amer. Math. Soc. **55** (1949), 497–508; MR **10**, 592], daß P_h ganzzählige Koeffizienten hat und $|\alpha_{hi}| = q^{h/2}$ (Riemannsche Vermutung) würde folgen: $P_h(T) = \pm q^{h\beta_h/2}T^{\beta_h}P_h(1/q^hT)$. Der Verfasser beweist diese Tatsache ohne Benutzung dieser (noch offenen) Vermutungen mittels seiner in den oben zitierten Arbeiten entwickelten Kohomologietheorien und einiger elementarer Überlegungen über nichtausgeartete Bilinearformen auf Vektorräumen. *H. Kurke* (Berlin)

Citations: MR 10, 592e = T50-8; MR 36# 1446 = G25-40; MR 37# 215 = G25-43.

G25-48 (39# 4173)

Verdier, J. L.

The Lefschetz fixed point formula in étale cohomology.

Proc. Conf. Local Fields (Driebergen, 1966), *pp.* 199–214. *Springer, Berlin,* 1967.

The usual Lefschetz number can be defined as the image of the number 1 for the composite homomorphism (X compact, connected, oriented manifold of dim n, H_* singular homology): $(\mathbf{Z} \simeq)\ H_n(X) \xrightarrow{D} H_n(X \times X) \xrightarrow{1\times f_*}$

$H_n(X\times X)\to H_n(X\times X,\ X\times X-\Delta)\cong H_0(X)\ (\simeq \mathbf{Z})$, where D is the diagonal map, $f: X\to X$ is a morphism with only isolated fixed points, Δ the diagonal in $X\times X$. The computation of this number requires a finiteness theorem for the homology, a Künneth formula, Poincaré duality and Alexander-Pontrjagin duality.

The author shows that this plan can be followed (modulo some non-trivial ideas and theorems) also in "étale cohomology" for a scheme X smooth and complete over an algebraically closed field k. Thus he gets a general Lefschetz formula, which, however, he is able to compute only in case X is a curve.

Precisely, let L be an étale sheaf of Q_l-vector spaces (l prime to char(k)) and assume that L is such that $H^q(X, L)$ are finite-dimensional Q_l-vector spaces (a condition for this: L constructible in a suitable sense). Let $f: X\to X$ be a morphism, $\phi: f^*(L)\to L$ a lifting of f to the sheaf L. Then one has maps $(f, \varphi)^q: H^q(X, L)\to H^q(X, L)$. Assume that f has only isolated fixed points of multiplicity one. At each fixed point P consider the map φ_P induced by ϕ on the stalk L_P. By the hypothesis of constructibility, L_P is a finite-dimensional vector space, so that φ_P possesses a trace. Then $\sum_q(-1)^q \operatorname{Tr}(f,\varphi)^q=\sum_P \operatorname{Tr}(\varphi_P)$. *F. Gherardelli* (Florence)

G25-49 (40# 4271)

Baily, Walter L., Jr.

On Hensel's lemma and exponential sums.

Global Analysis (Papers in Honor of K. Kodaira), pp. 85–100. Univ. Tokyo Press, Tokyo, 1969.

Let k be an algebraic number field, and V a nonsingular d-dimensional variety in affine n-space, defined over k. For any prime ideal $\mathfrak{p}$ in k, one denotes by $k_\mathfrak{p}$ the $\mathfrak{p}$-adic completion of k and by $\mathfrak{o}_\mathfrak{p}$ its valuation ring. One first studies now a point $a\in k_\mathfrak{p}{}^n$ at which the equations of V vanish modulo $\mathfrak{p}^m$ can be refined to a point b at which they vanish modulo $\mathfrak{p}^{m+1}$. Let then $V(\mathfrak{o}_\mathfrak{p})$ be the set of points of V with coordinates in $\mathfrak{o}_\mathfrak{p}$; for $a\in V(\mathfrak{o}_\mathfrak{p})$ the quotient $V(a,\mathfrak{p}^m)$ of $(a+\mathfrak{p}^m\mathfrak{o}_\mathfrak{p}{}^n)\cap V$ by the relation of congruence modulo $\mathfrak{p}^{m+1}$ is isomorphic to $(\mathfrak{o}_\mathfrak{p}/\mathfrak{p}\mathfrak{o}_\mathfrak{p})^d$ for any large enough m, say $m\geqq m_\mathfrak{p}$; one can take $m_\mathfrak{p}=1$ for almost all primes $\mathfrak{p}$. Also, if V_a is the tangent linear variety to V at a, then the quotients $V(a,\mathfrak{p}^m)$ and $V_a(a,\mathfrak{p}^m)$ are isomorphic for m large. Now let h be a $k_\mathfrak{p}$-linear form on $k_\mathfrak{p}{}^n$, and $g(a)$ be the norm of its restriction to the tangent space V_a; then the mapping $a\mapsto g(a)$ from $V(\mathfrak{o}_\mathfrak{p})$ to $\mathbf{R}$ is continuous. If Ker(h) is nowhere tangent to V, if ε is a character of $k_\mathfrak{p}/\mathfrak{o}_\mathfrak{p}$ which is nontrivial on $\mathfrak{p}^{-1}$, and if π denotes a uniformizing element at $\mathfrak{p}$, then the sum $\sum_a \varepsilon(\pi^{-j}h(a))$ (summation extended to the congruence classes of $V(\mathfrak{o}_\mathfrak{p})$ modulo $\mathfrak{p}^j$) is 0 for j large enough; if the multiplicative group $k_\mathfrak{p}{}^*$ operates on $V(k_\mathfrak{p})$ in a reasonable way, this sum is a rational number for all $j\geqq 0$.

One applies these results to the direct computation of the Fourier coefficients of Eisenstein series for the Siegel modular group $\mathrm{Sp}(n,\mathbf{Z})$. Gaussian sums are not needed for this computation. *P. Samuel* (Cambridge, Mass.)

G25-50 (41# 210)

Reich, Daniel

A p-adic fixed point formula.

Amer. J. Math. **91** (1969), 835–850.

The author shows that the space F of functions of n variables over a p-adic universal domain which are p-adically holomorphic on the complement D within a polydisc of a tubular neighborhood of a hypersurface $f=0$, forms a p-adic Banach space with respect to the uniform norm. An orthonormal basis for F is determined and under appropriate conditions F is shown to be the space of formal power series, with growth conditions, in $(X_1, X_2, \cdots, X_n, 1/f)$. The author then deduces [as per B. M. Dwork, J. Reine Angew. Math. **203** (1960), 130–142; MR **25** #3913] that certain completely continuous operators $\mathbf{\Psi}$ on F possess well defined characteristic power series and therefore $\mathbf{\Psi}\circ g$ have a trace which can be expressed in terms of values of g at the fixed points of D relative to the Frobenius map on D. From this he shows [as did Dwork, Amer. J. Math. **82** (1960), 631–648; MR **25** #3914] that the zeta function of an algebraic variety defined over a finite field is a rational function. The approach here is such as to eliminate the need for the additive characters on the finite field. The paper concludes with a discussion of L-series of finite Galois coverings of varieties over finite fields extending some observations of J.-P. Serre [Inst. Hautes Études Sci. Publ. Math. No. 12 (1962), 69–85; MR **26** #1733]. *D. J. Lewis* (Ann Arbor, Mich.)

Citations: MR 25# 3913 = G25-19; MR 25# 3914 = G25-20; MR 26# 1733 = Q25-15.

G25-51 (41# 3482)

Manin, Ju. I.

Correspondences, motifs and monoidal transformations. (Russian)

Mat. Sb. (N.S.) **77** (**119**) (1968), 475–507.

This paper is concerned with Grothendieck's theory of "motifs", that is, the most general cohomology theory conceivable for algebraic varieties over an arbitrary ground field. It gives a clear exposition of the fundamental notion and investigates the behaviour of motifs under various geometric operations, in particular, under monoidal transformations. As an application the author shows that the zeta-function of a unirational projective threefold over a finite field satisfies the "Riemann-Weil" conjectures. For cubic threefolds this had already been proved by E. Bombieri and H. P. F. Swinnerton-Dyer by entirely different methods [Ann. Scuola Norm. Sup. Pisa (3) **21** (1967), 1–29; MR **35** #2894]. As with the Bombieri–Swinnerton-Dyer proof, there is an auxiliary abelian variety (at least up to isogeny) but the author's treatment does not give their interpretation of it in terms of the grassmannian of lines on the threefold.

The attention of the cultivated reader may be drawn to the quotation from Herbert Read motivating the term "motif" and to the author's comment on the role of functoriality in the arts (page 478).

We now discuss the contents of the paper in more detail. It is concerned with the category of algebraic varieties over a fixed ground field k. The first five sections are devoted to the definition from first principles of the contravariant functor h from this category to the category of motifs (over k) and to the additive, multiplicative and graded structure of the latter. (More technically, only "effective motifs" in Grothendieck's terminology are considered.) The sixth section introduces the "Tate motif" $\mathbf{L}$, which plays a role analogous to that of the Tate module in l-adic cohomology. It is now shown (§ 6) that the motif $h(\mathbf{P}^r)$ of r-dimensional projective space is $1\oplus\mathbf{L}\oplus\cdots\oplus\mathbf{L}^r$, and, more generally (§ 7), that the motif of a fibre space $\mathbf{P}(\mathscr{E})$ over a variety X, where $\mathscr{E}$ is a locally free sheaf of dimension r, is given by $h(\mathbf{P}(\mathscr{E}))=h(X)\otimes h(\mathbf{P}^r)$. After a discussion of "twisting" by $\mathbf{L}$ (§ 8) the ninth section considers a monoidal transformation $X'\to X$ with centre Y of codimension r and shows that $h(X')=h(X)\oplus(\sum_{i=1}^{r-1} h(Y)\otimes\mathbf{L}^i)$. In § 10 the motif of a curve X is shown to be of the shape $h(X)=1\oplus X^+\oplus\mathbf{L}$, where X^+ corresponds to the jacobian of X up to isogeny.

The final section gives the applications to unirational

three-folds X. By theorems of Abhyankar the morphism $\mathbf{P}^3 \xrightarrow{\phi} X$ of algebraic varieties can be embedded in a commutative triangle

$$\begin{array}{ccc} & X' & \\ {}^{\chi}\swarrow & & \searrow^{\psi} \\ \mathbf{P}^3 & \xrightarrow[\phi]{} & X \end{array}$$

where ψ is of finite degree and χ can be decomposed over a finite extension k' of the ground field k into a product of monoidal transformations whose centre is either a point or an irreducible curve. On taking k' as the new ground field, $h(X')$ can be found from the results of §§ 9, 10. But now the existence of ψ shows that $h(X)$ is a direct summand of $h(X')$ and so its form can be determined. Finally, the assertions about the zeta-function of X follow by the application of the frobenius in the traditional fashion.

The sensitive reader will wince at the use of a superior O at the foot of page 477 merely as a label after it has been used tacitly in the middle of the same page to change the direction of arrows after the manner of Bures-sur-Yvette.

{This article has appeared in English translation [Math. USSR-Sb. **6** (1968), 439–470].}

J. W. S. Cassels (Cambridge, England)

Citations: MR 35# 2894 = G25-37.
Referred to in G25-55.

G25-52 (41# 6856)

Harder, G.

Eine Bemerkung zu einer Arbeit von P. E. Newstead.

J. Reine Angew. Math. **242** (1970), 16–25.

Let X be a nonsingular projective variety defined over the field $\mathbf{F}(q)$ with $q=p^r$ elements. A prime number $l\neq p$ determines l-adic cohomology groups $H^i(X, \mathbf{Q}_l)$ and homomorphisms $f^i: H^i(X, \mathbf{Q}_l)\to H^i(X, \mathbf{Q}_l)$ induced by the Frobenius map. The Weil conjectures imply that the eigenvalues $c_{i,t}$ of $(f^i)^{-1}$ are algebraic integers with absolute value $q^{i/2}$. Their importance is due to the fact that the number of rational points on X over the field $\mathbf{F}(q^n)$ is the sum $\sum_{i,t}(-1)^i c_{i,t}^n$, where t varies from 1 to $b_i=\dim H^i(X, Q_l)$. The Weil conjectures have been checked only for a rather small list of varieties: the contribution of the present paper is to check them for a new class of varieties X by a most ingenious chain of reasoning.

The varieties in question arise as follows. The algebraic vector bundles over a nonsingular irreducible curve of genus g have been studied by D. Mumford [*Geometric invariant theory*, Springer, Berlin, 1965; MR **35** #5451], M. S. Narasimhan and C. S. Seshadri [Ann. of Math. (2) **82** (1965), 540–567; MR **32** #1725] and Seshadri [#6858 below]. Their results are particularly explicit for vector bundles of fibre dimension 2: in this case E is stable if for every line bundle $L\subset E$ the Chern classes satisfy $c(L)< c(E/L)$, and the stable bundles are parametrised by a projective variety X (unfortunately, the paper under review misprints this inequality). Moreover, the variety X obtained by considering curves and vector bundles over $\mathbf{F}(q)$ is a reduction of the variety $X_{\mathbf{C}}$ obtained by considering curves and holomorphic vector bundles over the field $\mathbf{C}$ of complex numbers, and $\dim H^i(X, \mathbf{Q}_l)= \dim H^i(X_{\mathbf{C}}, \mathbf{C})$. In a recent paper [Topology **6** (1967), 241–262; MR **38** #341] a full calculation of the Betti numbers $\dim H^i(X_{\mathbf{C}}, \mathbf{C})$ was performed by P. E. Newstead (whose name is unfortunately misprinted throughout the paper under review).

The author uses the properties of various algebraic group actions and Tamagawa numbers to obtain information about the number of stable vector bundles (i.e., points of X) over the field $\mathbf{F}(q^n)$. This is a delicate task because the group action in question sometimes maps stable vector bundles to unstable vector bundles. He then uses an induction argument, which depends on Poincaré duality and the explicit values of b_i found by Newstead, to count the number of points of X over $\mathbf{F}(q^n)$ and to check the correctness of Weil's conjectures in this case.

R. L. E. Schwarzenberger (Coventry)

G25-53 (41# 8423)

Dwork, Bernard M.

On the zeta function of a hypersurface. IV: A deformation theory for singular hypersurfaces.

Ann. of Math. (2) **90** (1969), 335–352.

In a previous article [same Ann. (2) **83** (1966), 457–519; MR **35** #194] the author studied the zeta function theory of a family of p-adic hypersurfaces parametrized by A^1 whose general member was nonsingular. The present paper extends the theory to hypersurfaces with singular general member, and to parameter spaces of higher dimension (A^m for the finer results).

The work runs more or less parallel to that in the work cited. As before, for each parameter value (λ), there is a finite dimensional space $\mathfrak{R}_\lambda$ of power series defined by growth conditions, together with an endomorphism whose characteristic polynomial is connected with the zeta function. The author constructs bases for the spaces $\mathfrak{R}_\lambda$ depending rationally on the (λ), and when A^m is the parameter space, he demonstrates the existence of a polynomial $G(\lambda)$ forming the denominator in the coefficients of the bases which vanishes for a particular (λ) if and only if the corresponding space $\mathfrak{R}_\lambda$ has less than the generic dimension. As in the previous work, a system of linear differential equations is obtained, which in the nonsingular case turned out to be essentially the classical Picard-Fuchs equations satisfied by the moving cohomology classes. Their interpretation here is apparently unknown.

A. Mattuck (Cambridge, Mass.)

Citations: MR 35# 194 = G25-35.

G25-54 (42# 279)

Waterhouse, William C.

Abelian varieties over finite fields.

Ann. Sci. École Norm. Sup. (4) **2** (1969), 521–560.

Tate, Serre and Honda have classified abelian varieties over a finite field k—up to isogeny; this paper reviews their results in Chapters 1 and 2, then adds some further results on the precise endomorphism rings and isomorphism types of abelian varieties.

The main technique is presented in Chapter 3. Let A be an abelian variety over k, R its endomorphism ring, which is an order in a semi-simple algebra E. Let I be a left ideal in R which is also a lattice in E, $H(I)$ the intersection of all the kernels of endomorphisms in I; since I contains an isogeny, $H(I)$ is a finite subgroup and $A/H(I)$ is an abelian variety isogenous to A. I is called a kernel ideal if it contains all the endomorphisms annihilating $H(I)$; in this case it is shown that the isomorphism class of $A/H(I)$ is completely determined by the isomorphism class of I as an R-module. The author also shows that every maximal order in E is the endomorphism ring of an abelian variety of the form $A/H(I)$. (However, even for curves, not every member of the isogeny class of A has this form in general.)

In Chapter 4, Deuring's results on elliptic curves are derived, where the classification is very explicit. In Chapter 5 the author proves that over a finite field separable isogeny gives an equivalence relation. He also considers the case where A is principal, meaning E is a number field and R its full ring of integers. In that case he proves that the ideal class group of R acts freely on the set of isomorphism classes of principal abelian varieties isogenous to A, that each orbit is just a separable isogeny class of principal varieties, and that the number of orbits can be calculated from local invariants of E. Chapter 6 considers the special case where k is the prime field of characteristic p, and in this case a complete classification of the elementary abelian varieties is achieved. Chapter 7 considers the special case of elementary abelian varieties which are ordinary, i.e., which have the maximum number p^g of points killed by p; the main result states roughly that all conceivable endomorphism rings actually occur. Finally, in the appendix, the author shows that his $A/H(I)$ is the connected component of a group scheme $\mathrm{Hom}_R(I, A)$ constructed by Serre, and gives an example to show they are not in general equal.

M. J. Greenberg (Santa Cruz, Calif.)

G25-55 (42# 3088)

Grothendieck, A.

Standard conjectures on algebraic cycles.

Algebraic Geometry (Internat. Colloq., Tata Inst. Fund. Res., Bombay, 1968), *pp.* 193–199. *Oxford Univ. Press, London,* 1969.

This note briefly discusses two fundamental conjectures about algebraic cycles on a smooth projective variety X isolated independently by Bombieri and the author to explain the Weil conjectures. (They are discussed in more detail in the reviewer's report [*Dix exposés sur la cohomologie des schémas*, pp. 359–386, North-Holland, Amsterdam, 1968].) Let $X \mapsto H^*(X)$ be a Weil cohomology such as l-adic cohomology and $y \in H^2(X)$ the class of a hyperplane section. The conjecture of Lefschetz type asserts that the operator $\cup\, y^{n-i}: H^i(X) \to H^{2n-i}(X)$ is an isomorphism for $i \leqq n = \dim(X)$ and that its "quasi-inverse" the Λ-operator of Hodge theory is induced by an algebraic cycle λ, which does not depend on the choice of Weil cohomology. The conjecture holds for abelian varieties (after Lieberman), for curves, surfaces and flag manifolds, and it is stable under product, hyperplane section and specialization. In characteristic zero, it holds for all X if and only if numerical equivalence is the same as homological equivalence. A possible way to verify the conjecture (alluded to on p. 197) would be to consider the various projections p of X as a projectively embedded variety and to determine the cohomology classes of the "critical" cycles such as $Z = \{(x, y) | p(x) = p(y)\}$, for these are the cycles arising canonically from the embedded variety X. The cohomology class of λ plays such an important role that should the conjecture turn out to be false, one would want to enlarge the notion of algebraic cycle in some intrinsic way to include λ (just as one would do over the complex numbers for the rational (p, p)-cycles should the Hodge conjecture be false, or over a finite field for the cycles left invariant by some iterate of the Frobenius morphism should Tate's conjecture fail). The conjecture of Hodge type asserts that the Q-valued symmetric bilinear form $(v, w) \mapsto (-1)^j \langle v \cup w \cup y^{n-2j} \rangle$ is positive definite on the part of $H^{2j}(X)$ killed by $\cup\, y^{n-2j+1}$. In characteristic zero, the conjecture follows easily from Hodge theory; in positive characteristic, it is only established for $j = 1$. The Weil conjectures for an X defined over the field of q elements result as follows: the existence of the Weil cohomology already implies that the zeta-function of X is a rational function $\prod_{i=1}^{2n+1} P_{i-1}(t)^{(-1)^i}$, where $P_i(t)$ is the characteristic polynomial of the Frobenius automorphism f_i of $H^i(X)$, and it satisfies a functional equation; a weak form of the conjecture of Lefschetz type, which asserts that the Künneth projections $H^n(X \times X) \to H^i(X) \otimes H^{n-i}(X)$ are defined by intrinsic algebraic cycles, implies that $\mathrm{Tr}(f_i^N) \in (1/m)\mathbf{Z}$ for every N and some fixed m, hence by a lemma of Dwork-Fatou the $P_i(t)$ have integer coefficients, which do not depend on the choice of Weil cohomology; the two "standard" conjectures imply by well-known arguments of Weil and Serre that the roots of $P_i(t)$ have absolute value $q^{i/2}$. The "standard" conjectures go further: they permit construction out of the category of smooth projective varieties and correspondence classes modulo numerical equivalence of a semisimple abelian category; this category of "motives" embodies all the arithmetic properties of varieties reflected in their Weil cohomologies, and the various Weil cohomologies factor through it and so they are all essentially the same. The category of motives has already been constructed to a certain extent and used by Manin to prove the Weil conjectures for unirational threefolds (cf. Ju. I. Manin [Mat. Sb. (N.S.) **77** (**119**) (1968), 475–507; MR **41** #3482; to appear in Amer. Math. Soc. Transl.] and M. Demazur [Séminaire Bourbaki, 1969/70, Exp. 365, Springer, Berlin, 1971]).

S. L. Kleiman (Cambridge, Mass.)

Citations: MR 41# 3482 = G25-51.

G25-56 (43# 1996)

Milne, J. S.

Weil-Châtelet groups over local fields.

Ann. Sci. École Norm. Sup. (4) **3** (1970), 273–284.

The author proves the following theorem: Let K be a local field, let A and A^D be dual abelian varieties defined over K, and assume that A has potential good reduction (i.e., after some finite separable extension L, $A \otimes_K L$ has good reduction). Then Tate's pairings $H^r(K, A) \times H^{1-r}(K, A^D) \to Br(K) = \mathbf{Q}/\mathbf{Z}$ are non-degenerate for every $r \in \mathbf{Z}$ (so that, in particular, $H^r(K, A) = (0)$ for all $r \geqq 2$).

This theorem was first proved by Tate without the reduction hypothesis but under the assumption that the characteristic of K is zero [J. Tate, Séminaire Bourbaki, 1957/58: *Textes des conférences*, deuxième édition, Exp. 156, Secrétariat mathématique, Paris, 1958; MR **21** #4162]. Later, the reviewer [Illinois J. Math. **11** (1967), 234–241; MR **35** #6683] showed that if A was an elliptic curve with bad reduction the theorem was true with no restriction on the characteristic. Consequently, the author's result closes out the case of elliptic curves for any characteristic, and it establishes the period-index theorem via S. Lichtenbaum's result [Amer. J. Math. **90** (1968), 1209–1223; MR **38** #5788].

The method of proof is, in principle, the same as that used by Tate and the reviewer. However, the novel feature is that the assumption of good reduction allows one to introduce the Oort-Tate rank p group schemes over the ring of integers in K, and then a close study of these (Lemma 5 of the paper) together with a cohomological dévissage suffices to yield the proof of the theorem.

{Reviewer's remark: The opinion of the author notwithstanding, the reviewer feels that a unified proof is possible for this theorem if only one were to count indices correctly —presumably by Haar measure.}

S. S. Shatz (Philadelphia, Pa.)

Citations: MR 21# 4162 = G10-8; MR 35# 6683 = G20-31; MR 38# 5788 = G05-94.

G25-57 (44# 215)

Monsky, Paul

p-adic analysis and zeta functions.

Lectures in Mathematics, Department of Mathematics, Kyoto University, 4.

Kinokuniya Book-Store Co., Ltd., Tokyo, 1970. iv + 117 *pp.* 700 *yen;* $2.00.

This is a short, readable exposition on the Weil conjectures for zeta functions for varieties over finite fields, based on lectures given at Kyoto University in 1969. The first half consists of proofs of several classical results: A. Weil's calculation of the zeta function for diagonal hypersurfaces [Bull. Amer. Math. Soc. **55** (1949), 497–508; MR **10**, 592], A. Grothendieck's proof of the Riemann hypothesis for curves using the Riemann-Roch theorem for surfaces [J. Reine Angew. Math. **200** (1958), 208–215; MR **25** #75], B. M. Dwork's proof of the rationality of the zeta function of a variety over a finite field [Amer. J. Math. **82** (1960), 631–648; MR **25** #3914].

In the second half the author treats p-adic analysis and discusses J.-P. Serre's theory of completely continuous operators on p-adic Banach spaces [Inst. Hautes Études Sci. Publ. Math. No. 12 (1962), 69–85; MR **26** #1733], Dwork's "Lefschetz fixed point theorem" for complete nonsingular varieties [Ann. of Math. (2) **80** (1964), 227–299; MR **32** #5654], and connections between Dwork's differential operator theory and various cohomology theories following N. Katz [Inst. Hautes Études Sci. Publ. Math. No. 35 (1968), 223–258; MR **39** #4168]. This monograph should serve to introduce many to this deep and difficult subject. *D. J. Lewis* (Ann Arbor, Mich.)

Citations: MR 10, 592e = T50-8; MR 25# 75 = G20-18; MR 25# 3914 = G25-20; MR 26# 1733 = Q25-15; MR 32# 5654 = G25-28.

G25-58 **(44# 6708)**

Dwork, B.

On the rationality of zeta functions and L-series.

Proc. Conf. Local Fields (Driebergen, 1966), pp. 40–55. Springer, Berlin, 1967.

The author discusses various approaches to the question of the rationality of zeta-functions and L-series for algebraic varieties defined over a finite field. The first proof of the rationality theorem was given by the author in 1959 [Amer. J. Math. **82** (1960), 631–648; MR **25** #3914]. He used a generalization of E. Borel's theorem which asserts that a power series with coefficients in the ring of integers of an algebraic number field is a rational function if it has positive radius of convergence at each archimedean place and for at least one finite place it is meromorphic everywhere. That and the result of J.-P. Serre show that it is enough to express the zeta-function and L-series as a ratio of Fredholm determinants of completely continuous endomorphisms of p-adic Banach spaces. In order to find such a representation the author needs a trace formula. In this paper he discusses different variants of the trace formula that he and other authors have obtained.

In Section 3 the author considers the trace formula of D. Reich ["P-adic function spaces and the theory of the zeta function", Ph.D. Thesis, Princeton Univ., Princeton, N.J., 1966]. In the last section he considers the relations of his theory to the theory of dagger spaces of G. Washnitzer and P. Monsky [Proc. Nat. Acad. Sci. U.S.A. **52** (1964), 1511–1514; MR **30** #2014] and to some results of N. Katz ["On the differential equations satisfied by period matrices", Ph.D. Thesis, Princeton Univ., Princeton, N.J., 1966]. *I. I. Pjateckiĭ-Šapiro* (Moscow)

Citations: MR 25# 3914 = G25-20.

G30 CURVES OF ARBITRARY GENUS, OR OF GENUS ≠ 1, OVER GLOBAL FIELDS

See also Section R58.

See also reviews D28-31, D32-51, D40-27, D44-45, F25-6, F25-23, G02-18, G05-42, G25-23, G35-27, J02-27, J64-19, R38-18, R54-30.

G30-1 **(3, 14d)**

Chabauty, Claude. Sur les points rationnels des courbes algébriques de genre supérieur à l'unité. C. R. Acad. Sci. Paris **212**, 882–885 (1941).

Let $f(x_0, x_1, x_2)=0$ be an algebraic curve of genus $g>0$ whose coefficients generate a finite algebraic number field K_0. The author discusses the solutions of $f=0$ by numbers in a finite extension K/K_0 and states the following theorem. The equation $f=0$ has a finite number of solutions in K if its reduced rank r with respect to K is less than g. The number r is defined as $d-1$, where d is the dimension of the additive vector group of the rational (with respect to K) g-tuples of points on $f=0$ in the g-dimensional affine space over an algebraically closed p-adic field H_p. The correspondence between the g-tuples on $f=0$ with coordinates in H_p and above affine space is set up by a generalization of Jacobi's inversion theorem. For this purpose the author proposes to use a local uniformization of $f=0$ which is p-adically convergent. On substituting such a uniformization in the differentials of first kind on the curve it is possible to define local integrals of the first kind. Finally, Mordell's conjecture that $f=0$ contains a finite number of rational points is rephrased. Some of the important details of proof are not indicated in the author's abstract.

O. F. G. Schilling (Chicago, Ill.).

G30-2 **(5, 254b)**

Chabauty, Claude. Sur les solutions de certaines équations diophantiennes en nombres algébriques, en particulier en entiers algébriques, de degré borné. C. R. Acad. Sci. Paris **217**, 127–129 (1943).

Let V be an algebraic curve whose field of coefficients is an algebraic number field K_0. A point on V is termed algebraic of degree h if its coordinates generate over K_0 an extension of degree h. Let g be the genus of V and ρ the arithmetic rank of the period matrix. The author announces, among other results, that there exists only a finite number of points of degree h provided $h\leqq g-\rho$ for a pure period matrix.

O. F. G. Schilling (Chicago, Ill.).

G30-3 **(6, 58e)**

Chabauty, Claude. Sur le théorème fondamental de la théorie des points entiers et pseudo-entiers des courbes algébriques. C. R. Acad. Sci. Paris **217**, 336–338 (1943).

C. L. Siegel has proved [Abh. Preuss. Akad. Wiss. **1929**, no. 1, 70 pp.] that an algebraic curve $f(x, y)=0$ of positive genus contains only a finite number of points with integral coordinates x, y in any given algebraic number field K; the proof uses the theory of Abelian functions and a proposition concerning simultaneous approximation of algebraic numbers. The author indicates the idea of a much simpler proof. He asserts that there exist on the curve two integral algebraic functions ξ and η, ramified only at infinity and cyclically, and satisfying an equation $\phi(\xi, \eta) = \text{const.}$, where ϕ is a binary form with at least three distinct linear factors; in virtue of A. Weil's principle of transport, the general Diophantine equation $f = 0$ is then reduced to the particular type $\phi = \text{const.}$ which had been previously discussed by A. Thue [Skrifter Vid. Selsk. Christiania **1908**, no. 3] and C. Siegel [Math. Z. **10**, 173–213 (1921)]. This proof can be extended to the case that x, y are fractional numbers in K provided all prime ideal factors of the ideal $(x, y, 1)^{-1}$ belong to a preassigned finite set.

C. L. Siegel (Princeton, N. J.).

G30-4 (6, 185g)

Chabauty, Claude. Démonstration de quelques lemmes de rehaussement. C. R. Acad. Sci. Paris **217**, 413–415 (1943).

Let C be an algebraic curve over an algebraic numberfield. A point $P \varepsilon C$ is called pseudo-integral with respect to an integer m if the denominators of its coordinates are relatively prime to m. Let $F(P)$ be the residue class field of C at P. Then an integral function f on C is called "distinguished" if the value of f at a pseudo-integral point P lies in a field $K \geqq F(P)$ such that the discriminant of $K/F(P)$ divides a constant which is independent of m. The author proves the following basic lemmas. (1) On an elliptic curve there exist for every $n \geqq 3$ two distinguished functions ω, π such that $\omega^n - \pi^n = 1$. (2) If C is unicursal and has at least three distinct points at infinity then there exists a pair of distinguished functions which are related by an elliptic relation. Using these facts the author indicates that it suffices to prove Mordell's hypothesis (each curve of genus not less than 2 has only a finite number of points with coordinates in an algebraic numberfield) for curves of genus 2.

O. F. G. Schilling (Chicago, Ill.).

G30-5 (7, 418e)

Chabauty, Claude. Approximation des nombres algébriques et points pseudo-entiers des courbes algébriques. C. R. Acad. Sci. Paris **218**, 899–901 (1944).

Indications are given for a proof of the following theorem. Let $C: f(x, y) = 0$ be a nonrational algebraic curve with at most two different points at infinity; let K be a finite algebraic field, α an integer in K, $\nu(\alpha)$ the number of different prime ideal factors of α. A constant $c > 1$ independent of α exists such that there are at most $c^{\nu(\alpha)}$ points (x, y) on C, x and y being elements of K for which $\alpha^r x$, $\alpha^s y$ are integers in K if r, s are chosen suitably.

K. Mahler.

G30-6 (9, 460h)

Châtelet, François. Sur la réalité des courbes unicursales. Revue Sci. **85**, 709–715 (1947).

M. Noether has shown [Math. Ann. **3**, 161–227, 547–580 (1871)] that any plane unicursal curve can be birationally transformed, within any field including the coefficients of its equation, into a line or conic; an arithmetical interpretation of this result was given by Hilbert and Hurwitz [Acta Math. **14**, 217–224 (1890)]. Now the author obtains an equivalent result for real unicursal curves, by using a somewhat simpler new method, which consists in first expressing the coordinates of a point describing the curve as complex rational functions of a parameter, and then determining all (generally complex) values of the parameter associated with real simple points of the curve.

B. Segre (Bologna).

G30-7 (10, 623c)

Néron, André. Un théorème sur le rang des courbes algébriques dans les corps de degré de transcendance fini. C. R. Acad. Sci. Paris **228**, 1087–1089 (1949).

Let K be any extension of finite transcendence degree of the rational field. The author states that, given any algebraic curve Γ of genus $p \geqq 1$ and finite rank r over K, there is an infinity of fields K^σ homomorphic to K and such that the homomorphism between K and K^σ transforms Γ into a curve Γ^σ having rank greater than or equal to r over K^σ.

Next he indicates three consequences of this theorem, extending one of his previous results [same C. R. **226**, 1781–1783 (1948); these Rev. **10**, 60], i.e., that, denoting by k an arbitrary finite algebraic field, (a) any pencil of plane elliptic cubics over k, no curve of which is reducible, contains some curves of rank greater than or equal to 8 over k; (b) there are some elliptic cubics of rank greater than or equal to 10 over k; (c) there are some curves of any given genus $p \geqq 2$, having rank greater than or equal to $3p+5$ over k.

B. Segre (Bologna).

Citations: MR 10, 60f = G05-18.

Referred to in G30-9.

G30-8 (12, 354d)

Châtelet, François. Application des idées de Galois à la géométrie algébrique. Colloque de géométrie algébrique, Liège, 1949, pp. 91–103. Georges Thone, Liège; Masson et Cie., Paris, 1950. 200 Belgian francs; 1400 French francs.

By a neat application of Galois Theory the author deals with the classical problem of the existence of rational points on a unicursal curve. By the example of the rational points on a rational quadric the author shows how the use of algebraic numbers is helpful and natural even in problems which can be stated entirely in terms of the rational field.

D. B. Scott (London).

G30-9 (12, 852c)

Néron, A. Les propriétés du rang des courbes algébriques dans les corps de degré de transcendance fini. Algèbre et Théorie des Nombres. Colloques Internationaux du Centre National de la Recherche Scientifique, no. 24, pp. 65–69. Centre National de la Recherche Scientifique, Paris, 1950.

Let k, K', K be three fields such that $K' = k(u_1, \cdots, u_n)$ is a purely transcendental extension of k, and $K = K'(\alpha)$ is an algebraic (simple) extension of K' as well as an extension of finite transcendental degree of the rational field. We obtain an homomorphism σ of K in a field K^σ, by giving certain values $u_1^\sigma, \cdots, u_n^\sigma$, arbitrarily chosen in k, for the variables $u_1, \cdots, u_n$. If Γ is a curve of genus $p \geqq 1$, defined in K, suppose that it has finite rank r in K (i.e., r is the rank of the Abelian group formed by the points of the Jacobi V_r of Γ belonging to K). The author shows that it is then possible to determine σ, in an infinity of different ways, so that the transform Γ^σ of Γ has rank $\geqq r$ in K^σ. Incidentally he proves that the number of points of a curve $\Phi(z, u) = 0$ of genus $\geqq 1$ and finite rank r, defined over the rational field, such that z is rational and u is an integer $< N$, has an upper bound $B(\log N)^r$, where B is a constant. He then constructs, over a finite algebraic field, plane elliptic cubic curves of ranks 8, $\geqq 9$, $\geqq 10$, and curves of arbitrary genus $p \geqq 2$ of rank $\geqq 3p+6$ [cf. Néron, C. R. Acad. Sci. Paris **226**, 1781–1783 (1948); **228**, 1087–1089 (1949); these Rev. **10**, 60, 623].

B. Segre (Rome).

Citations: MR 10, 60f = G05-18; MR 10, 623c = G30-7.

G30-10 (14, 452d)

Weil, André. Jacobi sums as "Grössencharaktere". Trans. Amer. Math. Soc. **73**, 487–495 (1952).

Let k be an algebraic number-field of degree d and let $\mathfrak{m}$ be an (integral) ideal of k. Following Hecke, a complex-valued function $f(\mathfrak{a})$ defined and $\neq 0$ for all (integral) ideals $\mathfrak{a}$ prime to $\mathfrak{m}$ is a Grössencharakter provided $f(\mathfrak{ab})=f(\mathfrak{a})f(\mathfrak{b})$ if there are rational integers e_λ and complex numbers c_λ, $1\leqq\lambda\leqq d$, such that if α is an integer of k, $\alpha\equiv 1$ $(\mathfrak{m})$, and $\alpha_1, \cdots, \alpha_d$ are the conjugates of α, then $f((\alpha))=\prod \alpha_\lambda^{e_\lambda}|\alpha_\lambda|^{c_\lambda}$; $\mathfrak{m}$ is called a defining ideal for f. In the next place let $m>1$, and ζ be a primitive mth root of unity over Q, the field of rationals. Let $\mathfrak{p}$ be any prime ideal in $Q(\zeta)$ prime to m and define the multiplicative character $\chi_\mathfrak{p}(x)\equiv x^{(q-1)/m}(\mathfrak{p})$, where $q=N\mathfrak{p}$. Now let $r\geqq 1$ and let $a=(a_1, \cdots, a_r)$ be a set of integers (mod m) and put $J_a(\mathfrak{p})=(-1)^{r+1}\sum\chi_\mathfrak{p}^{a_1}(x_1)\cdots\chi_\mathfrak{p}^{a_r}(x_r)$, the summation extending over all $x_1, \cdots, x_r$ $(\mathfrak{p})$ such that $x_1+\cdots+x_r\equiv -1$ $(\mathfrak{p})$; also let $J_a(\mathfrak{ab})=J_a(\mathfrak{a})J_a(\mathfrak{b})$ for all $\mathfrak{a}$, $\mathfrak{b}$ prime to m. The main result of the paper is contained in the theorem: For each $a\neq(0)$, the function $J_a(\mathfrak{a})$ is a Grössencharakter and m^2 is a defining ideal for it.

As an application of this theorem a proof is given of the following conjecture of Hasse. Consider the curve (*) $Y^e=\gamma X^f+\delta$, where $2\leqq e\leqq f$ and γ, δ are non-zero elements of an algebraic number-field k of characteristic prime to ef. If $\mathfrak{p}$ is a prime ideal of k, prime to $ef\gamma\delta$, then (*) reduced mod $\mathfrak{p}$ defines a curve over the finite field $GF(q)$, $q=N\mathfrak{p}$. Let $Z_\mathfrak{p}(u)$ denote the zeta-function of that curve and define $Z(s)=\prod_\mathfrak{p} Z_\mathfrak{p}(N\mathfrak{p}^{-s})$; then Hasse conjectured that $Z(s)$ is a meromorphic function that satisfies a functional equation of the usual type. *L. Carlitz* (Durham, N. C.).

Referred to in G05-42, G15-9, G30-14, G30-15, G30-18, R18-29, R18-32, R50-4.

G30-11 (14, 578a; 14, 578b)

Nagell, Trygve. Un théorème arithmétique sur les coniques. Ark. Mat. **2**, 247–250 (1952).

Nagell, Trygve. Remarques sur les corps résolvants des coniques, cubiques et quartiques. Ark. Mat. **2**, 379–384 (1952).

In the first of these two papers it is shown that, if a conic C belonging to a field Ω does not contain any point belonging to Ω, then the same occurs in any algebraic extension of Ω of odd order. Also a previous similar result concerning plane cubics is recalled [T. Nagell, Nova Acta Soc. Sci. Upsaliensis (4) **13**, no. 3 (1942); these Rev. **8**, 315], and another one on quartics is obtained. The argument of the proofs is completed in the second paper, where examples are also given and the result on quartics is modified by showing that, if a plane irreducible quartic belongs to Ω and contains a set (belonging to Ω) of an odd number of points, then the quartic contains a triplet of points belonging to Ω. [For extensions to algebraic curves of arbitrary order and genus, cf., B. Segre, Atti Accad. Naz. Lincei. Rend. Cl. Sci. Fis. Mat. Nat. (8) **13**, 335–340 (1952); MR **14**, 900.] *B. Segre* (Rome).

Citations: MR 8, 315d = G05-10; MR 14, 900b = G30-12.

G30-12 (14, 900b)

Segre, Beniamino. Sui corpi risolventi delle equazioni algebriche. Atti Accad. Naz. Lincei. Rend. Cl. Sci. Fis. Mat. Nat. (8) **13**, 335–340 (1952).

Soit C une courbe de genre g définie sur un corps k de caractéristique 0. En utilisant les notions de diviseur de C rationnel sur k et de série linéaire rationnelle sur k, l'auteur démontre divers résultats arithmétiques relatifs aux sujets suivants: existence sur C de diviseurs positifs de degré donné (en particulier g) rationnels sur k; degrés des courbes planes birationnellement équivalentes à C sur k (avec, comme cas particulier, les résultats classiques de Noether-Hurwitz-Poincaré sur les courbes de genre 0); degrés sur k des corps où C possède des points rationnels. *P. Samuel.*

Referred to in G30-11.

G30-13 (15, 151a)

Néron, André. Problèmes arithmétiques et géométriques rattachés à la notion de rang d'une courbe algébrique dans un corps. Bull. Soc. Math. France **80**, 101–166 (1952).

If U is an algebraic irreducible variety, we denote by $G(U)$ the additive Abelian group of the U-divisors and by $G_l(U)$, $G_a(U)$ the groups of the U-divisors which, on U, are linearly or algebraically equivalent to zero respectively. If K is a field of definition of U, an element of $G(U)$ is said to be rational over K if it is invariant with respect to every automorphism of the algebraic closure $\bar{K}$ of K which preserves the elements of K. The totality of the rational divisors of U is a subgroup $G(U,K)$ of $G(U)$; and we shall also consider the groups $G_l(U,K)=G_l(U)\cap G(U,K)$, $G_a(U,K)=G_a(U)\cap G(U,K)$, $\gamma(U,K)=G_a(U,K)/G_l(U,K)$.

When U is a non-singular curve C of genus g, containing a rational divisor of degree g, the minimum number r of generators of $\gamma(C,K)$ has been called by Poincaré the rank of C in K; and a reduced rank r_0 can be defined also when C is singular. The finiteness of r was proved first by Mordell [Proc. Cambridge Philos. Soc. **21**, 179–192 (1922)] for $g=1$ and assuming K to be the field of rational numbers, and then by Weil [Acta Math. **52**, 281–315 (1929)] for arbitrary g and on supposing that K is any finite algebraic field. This remarkable result is now extended to the case when, g being arbitrary, K has any characteristic p and can be generated on its prime subfield by a finite number of elements. The extension is obtained here by associating to C a suitable algebraic variety U, by showing then that $\gamma(C,K)$ is isomorphic to a subgroup of the direct product of $G(U,K)/G_a(U,K)$ and of the group of the rational points of a certain Abelian variety (related to the Picard variety of U), and finally by proving the existence of finite bases for the last two groups.

The results are attained throughout by purely algebraic methods, with the intervention of the notions of complexity (Northcott) or of height (Weil) of a point over a field of characteristic zero, and by the use of an "infinite descent". Thus algebraic proofs and extensions of two fundamental theorems by Severi and by Weil are given; the existence of a finite basis for $G(U,K)/G_a(U,K)$, obtained here for arbitrary U and K, was proved first by Severi with transcendental methods [Math. Ann. **62**, 194–225 (1906); Ist. Veneto Sci. Lett. Arti. Parte II. **75**, 1121–1162 (1916)], in the case when K is the complex field. Around these important contributions there are many other interesting results, like those of a preliminary chapter concerning intersections (both in the regular and in the irregular case), correspondences, equivalence theory, Jacobi and Abelian varieties.

The last chapter deals in detail with the question of determining the rank of a curve variable in certain linear systems, and shows its connection with the problem of finding the base-number for the Severi group of a convenient algebraic variety. It is proved that, if C is a curve of genus $g\geqq 1$ over a field K and $(A_1, A_2, \cdots, A_m)$ denotes a set of m generic independent points of C, then the reduced rank r_0 of C in $K(A_1, \cdots, A_m)$ is $\geqq m$. Moreover, curves having the rank $r\leqq 4g+4$ or $r\geqq 3g+6$ in certain fields are constructed, and the conditions for the first ones to have $r=r_0=4g+4$ are given. Thus, e.g., if we fix eight points on a plane over any field K, such that neither three of them are collinear nor six of them lie on a conic, then through those points there is an infinity of plane cubics having the reduced rank $\geqq 9$ in K; moreover, through six points subject to the same conditions there is an infinity of cubics of reduced rank $\geqq 10$ in K. *B. Segre* (Rome).

Referred to in G10-6, G30-21, G30-30.

G30-14 (15, 779e)

Hasse, Helmut. Über das Zerlegungsgesetz für einen Funktionalprimdivisor in einem zyklischen Körper von durch ihn teilbarem Primzahlpotenzgrad. Arch. Math. **5**, 216–225 (1954).

In a recent paper [Trans. Amer. Math. Soc. **73**, 487–495 (1952); these Rev. **14**, 452] Weil constructed a zeta-function for the function-field defined by $ax^m+by^n=c$ and showed that it can be expressed as the product of $2g$ Hecke L-functions, where g is the genus of the function-field. This result suggests the following problem. Let K denote an algebraic number field of finite degree over the rational field R and let $\mathfrak{p}$ be a prime divisor of K; let $\mathfrak{p}$ divide the rational prime p. Assume that $K\supset Z_n$, the field of the p^nth roots of unity. If t is an indeterminate, then the mapping $t\rightarrow t^p$ defines a meromorphism P of $R(t)$ onto $R^P=R(t^p)$. Let $u \in R(t)$, u integral (mod $\mathfrak{p}$), and define

$$K_n=K(t, (u^{P^n})^{p^{-n}}).$$

It is also assumed that if $u^p=u^P+u'p$, then u' is not a pth power residue (mod $\mathfrak{p}$). For example this condition is satisfied if $u=1+ct^m$, $p\nmid m$ and c a rational number prime to p. The author now raises the question of describing the prime factor $\mathfrak{p}_n$ of $\mathfrak{p}$ in the field K_n. We quote only the first theorem of the paper. Let ζ_ν denote a primitive p^νth root of unity, $\zeta_\nu{}^p=\zeta_{\nu-1}$ and put $\pi_\nu=1-\zeta_\nu$; let π_n be divisible by exactly $\mathfrak{p}^e$, thus defining e. Then we have the following results. If $p\nmid e$ then $\mathfrak{p}=\mathfrak{p}_1{}^p$. If $p|e$ then $p=\mathfrak{p}$.

L. Carlitz (Durham, N. C.).

Citations: MR 14, 452d = G30-10.

G30-15 (16, 116d)

Eichler, Martin. Quaternäre quadratische Formen und die Riemannsche Vermutung für die Kongruenzzetafunktion. Arch. Math. **5**, 355–366 (1954).

Let $F(x)$ be a quaternary quadratic form with rational integral coefficients whose g.c.d. $=1$ and of determinant D. The theta-function

$$\vartheta_F(\tau)=\sum_{-\infty}^{\infty}e^{2\pi iF(x)}=\sum_{n=0}^{\infty}\alpha_F(n)e^{2\pi in\tau}$$

is a modular function of degree -2 belonging to the subgroup $G(Q)$ of the modular group defined by $ad-bc=1$, $c\equiv 0$ (mod Q), where Q contains just those primes that divide D. Thus

$$\vartheta_F\left(\frac{a\tau+b}{c\tau+d}\right)=\left(\frac{D}{a}\right)(c\tau+d)^2\vartheta_F(\tau).$$

Corresponding to the condition $(D/a)=1$ we have also the subgroup $G_1(Q)$. Put $\vartheta_F(\tau)=E_F(\tau)+S_F(\tau)$, where

$$E_F(\tau)=\sum_{n=0}^{\infty}\epsilon_F(n)e^{2\pi in\tau},\quad S_F(\tau)=\sum_{n=0}^{\infty}\sigma_F(n)e^{2\pi in\tau},$$

an Eisenstein series and a cusp form. Thus

$$\alpha_F(n)=\epsilon_F(n)+\sigma_F(n).$$

The principal term $\epsilon_F(n)$ is known from the work of Siegel; if $(n, D)=1$ then

$$\epsilon_F(n)=C_F\cdot n\sum_{t|n}\left(\frac{D}{t}\right)t^{-1},$$

where C_F is independent of n. In the present paper it is proved that

$$(*)\qquad |\sigma_F(n)|<\gamma_F(\epsilon)n^{\frac{1}{2}+\epsilon}\quad(\epsilon>0),$$

where $\gamma_F(\epsilon)$ is independent of n, and indeed for p prime

$$(**)\qquad |\sigma_F(p)|<\gamma_Fp^{\frac{1}{2}}.$$

To prove (*) and (**) the author considers a certain field K of modular functions belonging to $G_1(Q)$, the field of constants is the rational field; $\bar{K}$ is the field obtained from K by replacing the field of constants by its algebraic closure. Let K_1 consist of those functions in K that are invariant under $G(Q)$ so that K is of degree 2 relative to K_1; let η denote the generator of the Galois group of K/K_1. Reduction of K (mod p) gives the field $K(p)$ with prime field of characteristic p (for all but a finite number of primes p). The Hecke operators T_n [Math. Ann. **114**, 1–28, 316–351 (1937)] define multipliers of $\bar{K}$ which generate a subring M_0 of the ring M of all multipliers of $\bar{K}$. To M_0 corresponds the subset $M_0(p)$ of $M(p)$, the multiplier ring of $\overline{K(p)}$. Denote the image of η, τ_n in $M_0(p)$ by $\eta(p)$, $\tau_n(p)$, respectively; let $\pi(p)$ denote the multiplier of $\overline{K(p)}$ obtained by taking pth powers, and let * denote the Rosati antiautomorphism. Then it is proved that

$$\tau_p(p)=\eta(p)^{\frac{1}{2}(1-(D/p))}\pi(p)+\pi(p)^*;$$

in particular, for D a square

$$\tau_p(p)=\pi(p)+\pi(p)^*.$$

The Riemann hypothesis for the zeta function of $K(p)$ may be stated in the form $|\pi_i(p)|=p^{\frac{1}{2}}$, where the $\pi_i(p)$ are the eigenvalues of the operator $\pi(p)$. This result together with $M_0\cong M_0(p)$ implies (*) and (**).

Now let D be a square. Then the Dirichlet series corresponding to the cusp forms belonging to the group $G(Q)$ have an Euler factorization $Z_p(s)=(1_g-T_pp^{-s}+1_gp^{1-2s})^{-1}$. This implies $|Z_p(s)|^{-1}=N((1-\pi(p)p^{-s})(1-\pi(p)^*p^{-s}))$. On the other hand,

$$\zeta_{K(p)}(s)=\frac{L(p^{-s})}{(1-p^{-s})(1-p^{1-s})}=\frac{N((1-\pi(p)p^{-s})(1-\pi(p)^*p^{-s}))}{(1-p^{-s})(1-p^{1-s})},$$

so that

$$(***)\qquad \prod_p\frac{1}{\zeta_{K(p)}(s)}\sim\frac{1}{\zeta(s)\zeta(s-1)}\prod_p|1_g-T_pp^{-s}+1_gp^{1-2s}|^{-1},$$

where the symbol $\sim$ indicates that a finite number of factors is possibly omitted. The left member of (***) is a meromorphic function and satisfies a functional equation of the usual sort. Thus a conjecture of Hasse is proved for the case of the field K. Previous results in this direction were obtained by Weil [Trans. Amer. Math. Soc. **73**, 487–495 (1952); these Rev. **14**, 452] for the case $K=k(x, y)$, $ax^m+by^n=1$, and Deuring [Nachr. Akad. Wiss. Göttingen. Math.-Phys. Kl. Math.-Phys.-Chem. Abt. **1953**, 85–94; these Rev. **15**, 779] for the case of an elliptic function field with singular moduli. *L. Carlitz* (Durham, N. C.).

Citations: MR 14, 452d = G30-10; MR 15, 779d = G05-42.

Referred to in E02-7, E12-96, E20-65, E28-49, E28-73, F25-11, F30-19, F30-41, F50-24, G05-99, P02-18, R40-20.

G30-16 (16, 799f)

Kawada, Y., and Tate, J. On the Galois cohomology of unramified extensions of function fields in one variable. Amer. J. Math. **77**, 197–217 (1955).

Let k be a field of algebraic functions in one variable, with an algebraically closed field of constants k_0. Let K/k be a finite Galois extension with Galois group G, and assume that K/k is everywhere unramified. Let U be the group of all elements of finite order of the multiplicative group of k_0. Let $E=E(K)$ denote the group of the divisor classes of K, and define its dual E' as the group of all homomorphisms of E into U. The Galois group G operates on E and E' in a natural fashion.

By investigating the cohomology groups $H^r(G, E')$, where r is an arbitrary integer, positive, negative, or 0, the authors establish a theory of extensions K/k as described above which is exactly analogous to class field theory, and in which the group E' takes the place of the idèle class group. In particular, they prove that there is a canonical homomorphism of $H^{r-2}(G, Z)$ (where Z is the additive group of the integers) onto $H^r(G, E')$, which is an isomorphism whenever the characteristic of k does not divide the order of G. Moreover, just as in class field theory, this homomorphism results from cup multiplication with a canonical generator of $H^2(G, E')$, the fundamental class, with the same restriction and inflation properties in field towers which hold in class field theory.

The usual divisor class norm map $E(K)\rightarrow E(k)$ yields the dual conorm N': $E'(k)\rightarrow E'(K)$ which is shown to be an isomorphism (into), and which plays the part analogous to the usual injection map of idèle classes. In particular, $N'(E'(k))$ coincides with the G-fixed part $E'(K)^G$ of $E'(K)$. On the other hand, the ordinary injection of $E(k)$ into $E(K)$ dualizes to a homomorphism N: $E'(K)\rightarrow E'(k)$ which takes the place of the idèle class norm; indeed, for any x in $E'(K)$, $N'N(x)$ is the product of the G-conjugates of x in $E'(K)$. It follows that $H^0(G, E')$ is canonically isomorphic with $E'(k)/N(E'(K))$. The above general cohomology result, specialized to $r=2$, gives a canonical homomorphism of G onto $E'(k)/N(E'(K))$ which is an isomorphism whenever G is abelian and of an order prime to the characteristic of k. This isomorphism (more generally, also the homomorphism) is made explicit by using a standard 2-cocycle representing the fundamental class. The result provides a link between this pseudo class field theory and the Kummer theory of unramified abelian extensions of degree prime to the characteristic. In particular, the Kummer theory now yields the appropriate existence theorem for the pseudo class field theory.

The second part of the paper is concerned with the classical case, where k_0 is the field of the complex numbers. In that case, the group E_0 of the divisor classes of degree 0 is isomorphic with the $2g$-dimensional torus group T^{2g}, where g is the genus of K, and T is the multiplicative group of all unimodular complex numbers. Accordingly, E_0 may be equipped with the structure of a compact topological group. Also, E/E_0 is isomorphic with Z, and E is given the structure of a locally compact topological group such that E/E_0 is discrete and the induced topology on E_0 coincides with that obtained from the isomorphism with T^{2g}. It is shown first that the group E' of the above abstract theory may here be replaced by the group E^c of all continuous homomorphisms of E into T without losing any of the former results. Then the various elements of the abstract theory are interpreted in topological and analytical terms involving the Riemann surface $R(K)$ of K.

Thus the elements of E^c are represented by functions on the divisors of K whose values are obtained by integrating certain differentials (attached uniquely to the divisors of degree 0) over 1-cycles of $R(K)$. By analyzing the connections between the differentials and homology classes of K and those of k, it is then shown that $E'(k)/N(E'(K))$ is isomorphic with $H_1(k)/p(H_1(K))$, the factor group of the 1-dimensional homology group $H_1(k)$ of $R(k)$ modulo the image under the projection map p of the 1-dimensional homology group $H_1(K)$ of $R(K)$. On the other hand, if F stands for fundamental group, the Galois group G of K/k is isomorphic with $F(k)/p(F(K))$. If G is abelian this gives the result that G is isomorphic with $H_1(k)/p(H_1(K))$. Using an explicit 2-cocycle representing the fundamental class of $H^2(G, E')$ it is finally shown that the reciprocity isomorphism of the pseudo class field theory coincides with the composite of the two isomorphisms:

$$G\approx H_1(k)/p(H_1(K))\approx E'(k)/N(E'(K)).$$

G. Hochschild (Urbana, Ill.).

Referred to in G30-43, R38-18.

G30-17 (17, 350c)

Lamprecht, Erich. Arithmetische Zetafunktionen zu zyklischen p-Körpern von zwei Veränderlichen über einem Galoisfeld. Arch. Math. **6** (1955), 266–274.

In this note the author studies generalizations of the zeta function to fields of Kroneckerian dimension 2 and prime characteristic p. For the definition of his zeta functions the author employs prolongations of valuations on subfields of Kroneckerian dimension 1 by means of Gauss' Lemma. Thus his functions depend on the fibering of the given field (problems which do not arise for zeta functions of function fields of one variable over a finite algebraic number field indicate that his definition is bound to lead to shortcomings of his approach), and obvious difficulties concerning the dependence of the zeta function on the particular fibering immediately arise. In order to secure his tentative results the author makes restrictions on the generation of his fields as p-extensions of rational function fields, so that the ramification theory may lead to simplifications of Gaussian sums involved in the discussion of his functions. The lack of generally valid functional equations (or modifications thereof) of his zeta functions indicates the tentative nature of the author's approach. [For other studies on the zeta function of fields of prime characteristic see, e.g., A. Weil, Bull. Amer. Math. Soc. **55** (1949), 497–508; MR **10**, 592; and S. Lang and A. Weil, Amer. J. Math. **76** (1954), 819–827; MR **16**, 398.] *O. F. G. Schilling.*

Citations: MR 10, 592e = T50-8; MR 16, 398d = G25-2.
Referred to in G30-18, G35-34.

G30-18 (17, 947d)

Hasse, Helmut. Zetafunktion und L-Funktionen zu einem arithmetischen Funktionenkörper vom Fermatschen Typus. Abh. Deutsch. Akad. Wiss. Berlin. Kl. Math. Nat. **1954**, no. 4, 70 pp. (1955).

Let k be a number field, t an indeterminate over k, and K a finite algebraic extension of the rational function field $R=k(t)$. The field K is called arithmetical function field. The author defines a zeta function $\zeta_K(s)=\prod_{\mathfrak{p}} \zeta_{K\mathfrak{p}}(s)$, where $\mathfrak{p}$ ranges over the "arithmetic primes" of K (i.e. those places for which the image field $k\mathfrak{p}$ is finite and $t\mathfrak{p}$ is transcendental over $k\mathfrak{p}$); $\zeta_{K\mathfrak{p}}(s)$ denotes the well-known zeta function of the image field $K\mathfrak{p}$ regarded as a function field over a finite field as field of constants. In this paper, the author first gives the foundations of a general theory of arithmetic function fields and their zeta functions. Secondly, he considers the so-called (special) Fermat function fields, defined by $K=k(u_1, u_2)$ with $u_1^{m_1}+u_2^{m_2}=1$ (m_1, m_2 are positive integers); here t is to be $t=u_1^{m_1}=1-u_2^{m_2}$. Assume that k contains the m_ith roots of unity ($i=1, 2$). In these fields he proves a decomposition law for the arithmetic primes with respect to K/R. By means of this, he shows that $\zeta_K(s)$ splits into the product of $\zeta_R(s)=\zeta_k(s)\zeta_k(s-1)$ and another factor $L_K(s)$ which in turn splits into certain L-functions $L(\chi|s)$ corresponding to the characters $\chi\neq 1$ of the Galois group of K/R. It is proved that $L(\chi|s)^{-1}$ can be represented by means of a certain "Größencharakter" $\lambda_\varkappa$ (in the sense of Hecke) as the Euler product

$$L(\chi|s)^{-1}=\prod_{\mathfrak{p}}(1-\lambda_\chi(\mathfrak{p})\mathfrak{N}(\mathfrak{p})^{s-\frac{1}{2}}),$$

where $\mathfrak{p}$ ranges over all the primes of k not dividing the order $m(\chi)$ of χ. The conductor $\mathfrak{f}(\chi)$ of λ_χ divides $m(\chi)^2$. The author determines $\mathfrak{f}(\chi)$ in certain special cases. [See also A. Weil, Trans. Amer. Math. Soc. **73** (1952), 487–495; MR **14**, 452; M. Deuring, Nachr. Akad. Wiss. Göttingen. Math. Phys. Kl. IIa. **1953**, 85–94; MR **15**, 779; E. Lamprecht, Arch. Math. **6** (1955), 266–274; MR **17**, 350; see also the paper reviewed below.] *P. Roquette.*

Citations: **MR** 14, 452d = G30-10; **MR** 15, 779d = G05-42; **MR** 17, 350c = G30-17; **MR** 17, 947e = G35-30.

G30-19 (18, 107c)

Lamprecht, Erich. Bewertungssysteme und Zetafunktionen algebraischer Funktionenkörper. I. Math. Ann. **131** (1956), 313–335.

Let A be a function field of 2 variables over a finite field of constants k. Consider a pair of subfields $K\neq K'$ of A, each of transcendence degree 1 over k, and each algebraically closed in A. Let $B(K, K')$ denote the set of those places of A which induce in K' but not in K an isomorphism. For each $\mathfrak{P}\in B(K, K')$ the image field $A\mathfrak{P}$ is an algebraic function field of 1 variable over a finite field of constants; let $Z_{A\mathfrak{P}}(s)$ be the corresponding zeta function. The author considers the zeta function

$$Z_A(s; K, K')=\prod_{\mathfrak{P}\in B(K,K')} Z_{A\mathfrak{P}}(s)$$

of A belonging to the pair K, K'. [For these zeta functions, see also Lamprecht, Math. Z. **64** (1956), 47–71; MR **17**, 947.] He first shows, if also $K''\neq K$, then the two sets $B(K, K')$ and $B(K, K'')$ differ only by a finite number of places, and hence $Z_A(s; K, K')$ and $Z_A(s; K, K'')$ differ only by a finite number of factors. As a corollary we get the following statement: The zeros and poles of $Z_A(s; K, K')$ which do not lie on the lines $\Re(s)=0, \frac{1}{2}, 1$ are already determined by A and K (and do not depend on the choice of K'). As to the lines $\Re(s)=0, 1$, it is already sufficient to exclude those zeros and poles s for which $\Im(s)\neq 2\pi i n/\log q$, where q denotes the number of elements in k and n an arbitrary integer. Furthermore, the difference of the orders of the zeros of $Z_A(s; K, K')$ in the points $s=0$ and $s=1$ does not depend on the choice of K'. [See also, Lang and Weil, Amer. J. Math. **76** (1954), 819–827; MR **16**, 398.] — A second result is the following: If $\bar{A}$ is a finite algebraic and pure inseparable extension of A, denote by $\bar{K}, \bar{K}'$ the algebraic closures of K, K' respectively in $\bar{A}$. Then $Z_A(s; K, K')=Z_{\bar{A}}(s; \bar{K}, \bar{K}')$. — In order to prove the above mentioned results on zeta functions, the author first develops a pure algebraic theory of "reduction of constants" which describes the connection of A/K and $A\mathfrak{P}/K\mathfrak{P}$ for almost all $\mathfrak{P}\in B(K, K')$. In this theory, k needs not to be assumed finite. The following two results may be mentioned: (i) Let A/K be separable. If A' is a subfield of A such that A/A' is algebraic, then $A\mathfrak{P}/A'\mathfrak{P}$ is algebraic for almost all $\mathfrak{P}\in B(K, K')$ and we have $[A:A']=[A\mathfrak{P}:A'\mathfrak{P}]$. (ii) If A is a purely transcendental extension of k (i.e. $A=k(x, y)$ with $x, y\in A$) then each K is a purely transcendental extension of k too (i.e. $K=k(z)$ with $z\in K$). [In connection with the latter theorem see also Chevalley, J. Math. Soc. Japan **6** (1954), 303–324, Lemma 2, p. 319; MR **16**, 672.] *P. Roquette.*

Citations: **MR** 16, 398d = G25-2; **MR** 17, 947e = G35-30.

Referred to in G35-34.

G30-20 (18, 107d)

Lamprecht, Erich. Bewertungssysteme und Zetafunktionen algebraischer Funktionenkörper. II. Arch. Math. **7** (1956), 225–234.

Let A be a function field of 2 variables over its field of constants k. Consider a subfield K of A, of degree of transcendency 1 over k, and algebraically closed in A. If $K'\neq K$ is another such subfield, consider the set B of all places $\mathfrak{P}$ of A which induce in K' but not in K an isomorphism. The image field $A\mathfrak{P}$ contains $K'\mathfrak{P}$ and is therefore of degree of transcendency 1 over $K\mathfrak{P}$. The author is asking for properties which belong to A/K and $A\mathfrak{P}/K\mathfrak{P}$ for almost all (i.e. all but a finite number of) $\mathfrak{P}$ in B. For the first part of these investigations, see the paper reviewed above. The main result of this paper is as follows: Let $g(A/K)$ be the genus of A/K, and $G(A/K)$ the conservative genus, defined to be the minimum of the genera of all constant extensions of A/K. Let us assume that A/K is separable. Then, for almost all $\mathfrak{P}\in B$, $K\mathfrak{P}$ is the exact field of constants of $A\mathfrak{P}$, and we have

$$G(A/K)=G(A\mathfrak{P}/K\mathfrak{P})\leq g(A\mathfrak{P}/K\mathfrak{P})\leq g(A/K).$$

Among others, there are the following corollaries of this theorem: (1) If $G(A/K)=g(A/K)$, then $G(A\mathfrak{P}/K\mathfrak{P})=g(A\mathfrak{P}/K\mathfrak{P})$ for almost all $\mathfrak{P}\in B$. [See also Deuring, Nachr. Akad. Wiss. Göttingen. Math-Phys. Kl. IIa. **1955**, 13–42; MR **17**, 17.] (2) $g(A/K)-g(A\mathfrak{P}/K\mathfrak{P})$ is a multiple of $(p-1)/2$ for almost all $\mathfrak{P}\in B$. [See Tate, Proc. Amer. Math. Soc. **3** (1952), 400–406; MR **13**, 905.] (3) Let $\bar{g}(A/k)$ be the maximum of the genera of the subfields of A of degree of transcendency 1 over k. Then, if k is perfect, we have $\bar{g}(A/k)\leq \max(g(K/k), g(A/K))$. Furthermore, if in addition $g(K/k)>G(A/K)$ then $g(K/k)=\bar{g}(A/k)$ and K is the only field with the latter property. — The author applies these results to the case where k is a finite field. He is asking for those properties of the zetafunction $Z_A(s; K, K')$ which only depend on A and not on K and K' (for the definition of the zetafunction, see his first part mentioned above). In particular, if A can be written as the independent compositum of two fields of degree of transcendency 1 over k, he succeeds to construct a zetafunction of A which is determined uniquely by A alone. [See also Lamprecht, Math. Z. **64** (1955), 47–71; MR **17**, 947.] *P. Roquette* (Hamburg).

Citations: **MR** 17, 17c = G05-50; **MR** 17, 947e = G35-30.

G30-21 (19, 321b)

Néron, A. Propriétés arithmétiques de certaines familles de courbes algébriques. Proceedings of the International Congress of Mathematicians, 1954, Amsterdam, vol. III, pp. 481–488. Erven P. Noordhoff N.V., Groningen; North-Holland Publishing Co., Amsterdam, 1956. $7.00.

The following theorem is proved. Let A, B be two abelian varieties, u a homomorphism of A on B, W a non-abelian subvariety of A such that W and B have the same dimension and B is the support of $u(W)$. Moreover, suppose that A, B, W, u are defined upon the same finite algebraic field k, and that B contains an infinity of rational points on k not lying on a proper abelian subvariety of B. Now, if h is any real number, denote by $\varphi(h)$ the number of points M of B such that the intersection $u^{-1}(M)\cdot W$ is defined and has a "highness" [according to A. Weil, Ann. of Math. (2) **53** (1951), 412–444; MR **13**, 66] or a "complexity" [according to Northcott, Proc. Cambridge Philos. Soc. **45** (1949), 502–509; MR **11**, 390] lower than h; next, denote by $\psi(h)$ the number of the above points M such that one of the components of $u^{-1}(M)\cdot W$ is rational on k. Then, for any real number $\varepsilon>0$, the inequality $\psi(h)<\varepsilon\varphi(h)$ holds for all sufficiently large values of h.

This result is similar to the famous irreducibility theorem [D. Hilbert, J. Reine Angew. Math. **110** (1892), 104–129] concerning the case when A is any algebraic variety and B is a linear space. By using it suitably in the case when B is the representative variety of a system of algebraic curves, the author establishes the existence of curves of a given genus g and of high rank on the rational field, and precisely of rank 11 for $g=1$ and of rank $3g+7$ for $g\geqq 2$. These results on the rank improve by unity the results the author himself had previously deduced [Bull. Soc. Math. France **80** (1952), 101–166; MR **15**, 151] in a similar manner, from Hilbert's theorem. *B. Segre.*

Citations: MR 11, 390a = G35-20; MR 13, 66d = G35-25; MR 15, 151a = G30-13.

G30-22 (19, 635d)

Takahashi, Shuichi. On Fermat function fields. Proceedings of the international symposium on algebraic number theory, Tokyo & Nikko, 1955, pp. 256–257. Science Council of Japan, Tokyo, 1956.

Dans cette note, l'auteur considère, du point de vue de ses propriétés arithmétiques, le corps K de fonctions algébriques, défini par l'équation $ax^l+bx^l+1=0$ (où a et b sont des nombres rationnels non nuls) avec, comme corps de définition, quelque corps k_0 de nombres algébriques (l'auteur dit avoir considéré surtout les cas, où k_0 est le corps Q des nombres rationnels ou celui des racines l-ièmes de l'unité). Il annonce que, par des spécialisations convenables de ce corps K, en se servant des méthodes des A. Weil, Siegel et Vinogradov, il a pu obtenir des résultats importants sur l'arithmétique de ce corps (en particulier, dans le cas $k_0=Q$). Il n'énonce d'ailleurs qu'un seul de ces résultats (sans donner une idée même faible de sa démonstration), qui est le suivant: il existe une borne supérieure explicitement calculable du nombre des solutions rationnelles de l'équation considérée. Ce résultat, si le référent le comprend bien, implique, en particulier, que la courbe de Fermat $x^l+y^l+1=0$ n'a qu'un nombre fini de points rationnels, et une telle proposition constitue un progrès considérable dans la théorie de l'équation de Fermat. Le référent n'a aucune raison à priori de douter de l'exactitude de ce résultat ou de sa démonstration par l'auteur, mais étant donné son importance et le caractère délicat de la question, il pense que la publication aussi rapide que possible de sa démonstration s'impose. {Le référent a remarqué une erreur, due probablement à la distraction: le cas de spécialisation employé dans les recherches de Legendre (ou de S. Germain?), de Wendt et de Dickson est à sa connaissance $p\equiv 1 \pmod l$, et non $p=l$.} *M. Krasner* (Paris).

G30-23 (20# 29)

Lamprecht, Erich. Invariante Zetafunktionen arithmetischer Funktionenkörper. Abh. Math. Sem. Univ. Hamburg 22 (1958), 71–83.

Suppose that A is an algebraic function field of one variable whose precise coefficient field is a finite algebraic number field K. Denote by $B=\{p\}$ the set of all inequivalent rank one valuations of K. A prolongation P of p to A is called a functional valuation of A provided there is an $x\in A-K$ such that (*) $v_P(\sum_{i=0}^n a_ix^i)=\mathrm{Min}_i(v_p(a_i))$ for every polynomial $\sum a_ix^i$ in $K[x]$. Furthermore, P is called regular if (K) $KP=Kp$ is the precise field of constants of AP (residue class fields being denoted by postscripts), (U) P and p have the same value group, and (G) A/K and AP/KP have the same genus g. The author reformulates results on the existence of regular prolongations P for given $p\in B$, e.g., if $g\geqq 2$ then almost all p have a uniquely determined regular P. Term then p A-regular if it possesses some regular prolongation. Then it is recalled that almost all p are A-regular, and, in particular, that the isomorphism types AP are unique. Denoting by $B_A(x)$ the subset of B consisting of p's with prolongations P such that (*) holds for fixed x, the author defines the zeta function $Z_A(s,x)$ as $\prod_P Z_{AP}(s)$, $P\in B_A(x)$. Using properties of the congruence zeta functions $Z_{AP}(s)$ and of the zeta function $Z_K(s)$ of K it follows quickly that the above product converges for $K(s)>2$ and is in this half plane free of zeros and poles, furthermore that its poles and zeros in $\mathrm{R}(s)>3/2$ are those of $Z_K(s-1)$. In order to obtain a zeta function $Z_A'(s)$ which is invariantly attached to the field A/K the author uses the set B_A' of all A-regular prime divisors of K, picks for each p a fixed regular prolongation P, and sets $Z_A'(s)=\prod_P Z_{AP}(s)$, P determined as indicated by all $p\in B_A'$. Since almost all $P\in B_A(x)$ are regular and inert over $K(x)$, it follows $Z_A'(s)$ and $Z_A(s,x)$ are related by a correction factor $\prod_P Z_{AP}(s)\prod_Q Z_{AQ}(s)^{-1}$, where P is regular and in $B_A(x)$, whereas Q is in $B_A(x)$ but not regular. This factor is regular for $\mathrm{R}(s)>1$ and has on $\mathrm{R}(s)=0, \frac{1}{2}, 1$ only a finite number of inequivalent zeros and poles; furthermore $Z_A'(s)$ converges absolutely for $\mathrm{R}(s)>2$. The author raises the important question on the modifications which are necessary to obtain an invariant zeta function or A/K which satisfies a simple functional equation; finally, special cases are discussed which illuminate the serious problems arising in this connection. *O. F. G. Schilling* (Chicago, Ill.)

G30-24 (21# 2652)

Manin, Yu. I. Algebraic curves over fields with differentiation. Izv. Akad. Nauk SSSR. Ser. Mat. **22** (1958), 737–756. (Russian)

Le but de ce travail est de construire un homomorphisme du groupe des classes de diviseurs de degré zéro d'une courbe algébrique définie sur un corps de caractéristique zéro, dans le groupe additif d'un espace vectoriel de dimension finie sur le corps de base. Quelques propriétés du noyau de cet homomorphisme sont décrites. Comme application des résultats obtenus on établit un critère de dépendence linéaire de points sur une courbe elliptique. (L'auteur estime que ce critère peut être utile en connection avec les travaux de Néron sur le rang des courbes algébriques.) *E. Lluis* (Mexico, D.F.)

Referred to in G30-30.

G30-25 (23# A1641)

Faddeev, D. K.

Group of divisor classes on the curve defined by the equation $x^4+y^4=1$.

Dokl. Akad. Nauk SSSR **134** (1960), 776–777 (*Russian*); *translated as Soviet Math. Dokl.* **1** (1961), 1149–1151.

The algebraic function field $R(x,y)$, where R is the rational field and $x^4+y^4=1$, is of genus 3 and contains the three following function fields of genus 1: $R(\xi,y)$, $R(x,\eta)$ and $R(u,v)$, where $\xi=x^2$, $\eta=y^2$ and $u=x/y$, $v=y^{-2}$. Hence there is a canonical map of the Jacobian variety J of $R(x,y)$ onto each of the Jacobian varieties J_1, J_2, J_3. The author shows that the induced mapping of J onto $J_1\times J_2\times J_3$ is onto and has as kernel a group of order 8 and of type (2, 2, 2). He deduces that the group of rational points on J is of finite order and states that this order is 32. He deduces that the only points on the title curve whose coordinates lie in a quadratic extension of the rationals are the points $(\pm i, 0)$, $(0, \pm i)$ and

$$(\sigma_1(1+\sigma_3\sqrt{(-7)})/2,\ \sigma_2(1-\sigma_3\sqrt{(-7)})/2) \qquad (\sigma_1^2=\sigma_2^2=\sigma_3^2=1).$$

Further, every point on the title curve whose coordinates lie in a cubic extension of the rationals lies on a rational line through one of the finite number of rational points on the curve. {In the translation, read "variety" instead of "multiplicity" throughout.}

J. W. S. Cassels (Cambridge, England)

Referred to in D28-41, G30-28.

G30-26 (24# A86)

Lang, Serge

Integral points on curves.

Inst. Hautes Études Sci. Publ. Math. No. 6 (1960), 27–43.

In 1929 [Abh. Preuss. Akad. Wiss. Phys.-Math. Kl. **1929**, 3–70; pp. 41–69] C. L. Siegel proved the fundamental theorem that on any algebraic curve $C: f(x, y) = 0$ of genus $p \geqq 1$ there are at most finitely many "rational" integral points (x, y), i.e., x and y are integers in a given finite algebraic extension K of the rational field Q. Siegel's proof depended (i) on the Mordell-Weil theorem [L. J. Mordell, Proc. Cambridge Philos. Soc. **21** (1922), 179–192; A. Weil, Acta Math. **52** (1928), 281–315] which states that the additive group of sets of p "rational" points on C has a finite basis; and (ii) on Siegel's general methods in Diophantine approximations. Since 1929 the theory has made progress. Already in 1935 A. Weil [*Arithmétique et géométrie sur les variétés algébriques*, Actualités Sci. Ind., No. 206, Hermann, Paris, 1935] noted that instead of (i) a weaker result on nonramified abelian extensions of high degree of the Jacobian variety of C suffices, and that Siegel's theorem is independent of the method of infinite descent. Then, in 1955, K. F. Roth [Mathematika **2** (1955), 1–20; MR **17**, 242] introduced his powerful new method for dealing with the rational approximations of algebraic numbers, a method which can be extended to the approximations of algebraic numbers by numbers in a field K [W. J. LeVeque, *Topics in number theory, Vol. II*, Addison-Wesley, Reading, Mass., 1956; Ch. 4; MR **18**, 283] and where the approximation may be either with respect to an absolute value or any p-adic value [D. Ridout, Mathematika **5** (1958), 40–48; MR **20** #3851]. In the present paper the author sketches a simplified proof of Siegel's theorem and of its analogue for function fields of characteristic 0, using these more recent developments. He shows the stronger result that there are only finitely many "rational" points (x, y) on C for which the denominators of x and y have only finitely many given prime factors; until now this had been proved only for curves of genus 1 [the reviewer, J. Reine Angew. Math. **170** (1933), 168–178]. The author further extends Siegel's theorem to any finite (not necessarily algebraic) extension K of Q [cf. the reviewer, Mathematika **2** (1955), 116–127; MR **18**, 565].

K. Mahler (Manchester)

Citations: MR 17, 242d = J68-14; MR 18, 283b = Z01-38; MR 18, 565d = D40-27; MR 20# 3851 = J68-20.

Referred to in G10-29, G30-30.

G30-27 (24# A87)

LeVeque, W. J.

Rational points on curves of genus greater than 1.

J. Reine Angew. Math. **206** (1961), 45–52.

Let K be a finite algebraic extension of the rational field Q; let $C: f(x, y) = 0$, where $f(x, y) \in K[x, y]$, be an algebraic curve of genus g; let $\mathfrak{z}(x, y) \in K(x, y)$ be a rational function on C which is not constant; and let $\mathfrak{M} = \{(x, y)\}$ be an infinite sequence of points on C with coordinates in K. C. L. Siegel showed in 1929 [Abh. Preuss. Akad. Wiss. Phys.-Math. Kl. **1929**, no. 1] that $\mathfrak{z}(x, y)$, for $g \geqq 1$, can be an integer for at most finitely many (x, y) in $\mathfrak{M}$; the reviewer further proved in 1933 [J. Reine Angew. Math. **170** (1933), 168–178] that, when $K = Q$ and $g = 1$, the greatest prime factor in the denominator of $\mathfrak{z}(x, y)$ tends to infinity when (x, y) runs over $\mathfrak{M}$. The author extends the reviewer's result to the case when $g \geqq 2$ and K is not necessarily Q; now the largest norm of any prime ideal factor of the denominator of $\mathfrak{z}(x, y)$ tends to infinity. The proof depends essentially on the ideas of Siegel and the reviewer, and makes use of a generalized $\mathfrak{p}$-adic form of Roth's theorem stated by the reviewer [*Lectures on Diophantine approximations*, Part I, Univ. of Notre Dame Press, Notre Dame, Ind., 1961; Ch. 8 and Appendix C], but proved so far only for the approximation by rational numbers. The author's result has been obtained independently, and in a more general form, by S. Lang [see preceding review, #A86].

K. Mahler (Manchester)

G30-28 (24# A723)

Faddeev, D. K.

The group of divisor classes on some algebraic curves.

Dokl. Akad. Nauk SSSR **136** (1961), 296–298 (*Russian*); *translated as Soviet Math. Dokl.* **2** (1961), 67–69.

The author sketches a proof that the number of divisor classes of degree 0 on the curve $y^l = x^k(1-x)$ defined over the field k_0 of the lth roots of 1 is finite for $l = 5, 7$, $1 \leqq k \leqq l-2$ and for $l = 11$, $k = 1, 5, 9$. The proof depends on the following map of divisors defined over k_0 into $k_0^*/(k_0^*)^l$: If $\mathfrak{A} = \prod_i P_i^{a_i}$ is a divisor, then $j(\mathfrak{A}) = \prod_i x(P_i)^{a_i}$. It turns out that the kernel of this map contains the principal divisors, and that it is a group-homomorphism. Its kernel is precisely the set of divisors in classes A of the shape $A = B^{1-\varepsilon}$, where ε is the automorphism $x \to x$, $y \to \varepsilon y$ of the curve ($\varepsilon^l = 1$). The group of divisor classes can be explicitly found for the l-adic closure of k_0. The stated result follows by a comparison of the l-adic result with the global result that the ideal $[j(\mathfrak{A})]$ is a perfect lth power. Using the author's earlier work [same Dokl. **134** (1960), 776–777; MR **23** #A1641], it follows that the group of rational divisor classes of degree 0 on $x^5 + y^5 = 1$ and $x^7 + y^7 = 1$ is finite. The author remarks that the corresponding result for $x^6 + y^6 = 1$ is false.

J. W. S. Cassels (Cambridge, England)

Citations: MR 23# A1641 = G30-25.

Referred to in G30-29.

G30-29 (24# A2577)

Faddeev, D. K.

Invariants of divisor classes for the curves $x^k(1-x) = y^l$ in an l-adic cyclotomic field. **(Russian)**

Trudy Mat. Inst. Steklov. **64** (1961), 284–293.

The author gives a detailed proof of the result stated as Theorem 2 in his note [Dokl. Akad. Nauk SSSR **136** (1961), 296–298; MR **24** #A723]. Let $A = \prod_{i=1}^m P_i^{a_i}$ be some divisor on the title curve defined over a field k of characteristic zero (P_i $(1 \leqq i \leqq m)$ are points defined over the algebraic closure of k). Write $j(A) = \prod_i' (x(P_i))^{a_i}$, where the dash indicates that points with $x = 0$ or ∞ are omitted. Then j induces a homomorphism of the group of divisor classes defined over k modulo linear equivalence into the group $k^*/(k^*)^l$ (k^* is the multiplicative group of inversible elements of k). By some rather detailed computations the author determines the image of this homomorphism when k is the field of l-adic numbers. (In the original note the kernel of the homomorphism is stated with a hint at the proof.)

J. W. S. Cassels (Cambridge, England)

Citations: MR 24# A723 = G30-28.

G30-30 **(24# A2576)**

Manin, Ju. I.

Diophantine equations over functional fields. **(Russian)**
Dokl. Akad. Nauk SSSR **139** (1961), 806–809.

There is a well-known but hitherto impregnable conjecture of Mordell that there is only a finite number of rational points on any curve of genus greater than 1 defined over the rationals. In this note the author sketches a proof that over a function field of one variable as groundfield there is an extensive class of curves of genus greater than 1 on each of which there is only a finite number of points defined over the groundfield. More precisely, the result is as follows. Let k be an algebraically closed field without characteristic, let K be a field of functions of a single variable over k and let L be a field of functions of genus 1 over the field K. Let m be an integer $\geqq 3$ and let v be a non-constant element of L without multiple zeros. Then the field $L(v^{1/m})$ has only a finite number of divisors of degree 1 defined over K. He also proves the following analogue of the theorem of Siegel and Mahler [Siegel, Abh. Preuss. Akad. Wiss. Phys.-Math. Kl. **1929**, 3–70; Mahler, J. Reine Angew. Math. **170** (1933), 168–178] that on a curve of genus $\geqq 1$ defined over an algebraic numberfield κ there are only a finite number of points defined over κ which are integral except at a given fixed set of primes of κ: Let k, K, L be as above and let S be a finite set of points of K/k. Let v be any nonconstant element of L. Then there exist only a finite number of divisors $\mathfrak{Q}$ of L/K defined over K such that the divisor of zeros of $v(\mathfrak{Q}) \in K$ contains only points of S.

Lang [Inst. Hautes Études Sci. Publ. Math. No. **6** (1960), 27–43; MR **24** #A86] had already discussed the extension to the functionfield case of the proof of the theorem of Siegel and Mahler. The proofs of Manin depend, however, on results which so far as is known have no analogue in the case when the groundfield is an algebraic numberfield. The essential tool is that if K is a field in which a differentiation can be defined and L is a functionfield of genus 1 over K then there is a homomorphic map of the group of divisors on L defined over K modulo linear equivalence into the additive group of elements of K. When K is as above, the kernel consists only of the elements of finite order [cf. Manin, Izv. Akad. Nauk SSSR **22** (1958), 737–756; MR **21** #2652]. In addition the proof uses the Mordell-Weil-Severi-Néron finite basis theorem [Néron, Bull. Soc. Math. France **80** (1952), 101–166; MR **15**, 151] and Weil's theory of distributions [Weil, Acta Math. **52** (1928), 281–315]. The paper concludes with a discussion of further generalisations to abelian varieties.

J. W. S. Cassels (Cambridge, England)

Citations: MR 15, 151a = G30-13; MR 21# 2652 = G30-24; MR 24# A86 = G30-26.

G30-31 **(26# 84)**

Shimura, Goro

On the zeta-functions of the algebraic curves uniformized by certain automorphic functions.
J. Math. Soc. Japan **13** (1961), 275–331.

This is a continuation of the general program initiated by the author [Ann. of Math. (2) **70** (1959), 101–144; MR **21** #6370]; it depends in part upon the general theorems proved in the latter paper, and in part upon the author's theory of reduction modulo p in algebraic geometry [Amer. J. Math. **77** (1955), 134–176; MR **16**, 616]. The case treated here is that of the group of units of an indefinite quaternion algebra Φ over the rational numbers, and of its congruence subgroups; as Φ is indefinite, Φ_R can be identified with $M_2(R)$, the algebra of matrices of order 2 over the reals; then the group of units of Φ appears as a discontinuous subgroup of $\mathrm{SL}(2, R)$, the factor-space being compact if and only if Φ is a division algebra (the author's treatment includes the case when this is not so). The first paragraph deals with the "Hecke ring" associated with a maximal order $\mathfrak{o}$ of Φ; calling Γ the group of the units of $\mathfrak{o}$ with norm $+1$, one defines the Hecke ring as the set of formal linear combinations (with integral coefficients) of double cosets $\Gamma\alpha\Gamma$ for Γ in the semigroup of elements of $\mathfrak{o}$ with norm >0, the multiplication law of the ring being defined in a "natural" manner. If $T(n)$, for every natural integer $n>0$, is the sum of the $\Gamma\alpha\Gamma$ for $\alpha \in \mathfrak{o}$, $N(\alpha)=n$, then the formal Dirichlet series $\sum T(n)n^{-s}$ has an Euler product. The Hecke ring operates on the space of cusp-forms of given degree d for the group Γ; if $T(n, d)$ corresponds to $T(n)$ in this representation of the ring, one can then consider the Dirichlet series $\sum T(n,d)n^{-s}$; this converges for $\mathrm{Re}(s)>d+1$, has an Euler product, can be continued in the whole s-plane, and has a functional equation; this is proved by expressing the function as an integral in the idèle-group for Φ. All this is extended to the congruence subgroups of Γ (although in that case the functional equation is given in less explicit form). The main part of the paper consists in the further investigation, by the methods of algebraic geometry, of the series $\zeta(s)=\det(\sum T(n, 2)n^{-s})$, or rather of the factors of its Euler product; if $\mathfrak{C}$ is the curve defined by the automorphic functions for the group Γ (operating as a Fuchsian group in the Poincaré half-plane), it is shown that $\mathfrak{C}$ can be identified with a curve defined over the rational numbers, and that, for almost all p, the factors of the Euler product of $\zeta(s)$ are the zeta-functions of the reduction of $\mathfrak{C}$ modulo p. This (and the corresponding facts for the congruence subgroups of Γ) depends upon the fact that $\mathfrak{C}$ parametrizes the abelian varieties of dimension 2 with the complex multiplication ring $\mathfrak{o}$ (it is the "variety of moduli" for such varieties; for well-known reasons, it is not enough to consider abelian varieties; one must put on these varieties some additional structure, the "polarization"; and, in order to deal with congruence subgroups of Γ, one must also put on these varieties the additional structure given by identifying in a prescribed manner the group of points of given order N with a fixed abstract group of type (N, N, N, N)). The Hecke operators can be interpreted as correspondences on the curve $\mathfrak{C}$ corresponding to certain operations on the abelian varieties parametrized by $\mathfrak{C}$; after reduction modulo p, relations are found between those correspondences and the Frobenius correspondence, and these give the key to the whole theory (just as Kronecker's congruences give the key to the theory of complex multiplication). {While the general outline of the proof is fairly straightforward, it is unfortunately (and unavoidably), blurred by many technical details which have to be dealt with at almost every step. It is announced that the same basic principles can be applied to more general types of arithmetically defined discontinuous groups.}

A. Weil (Princeton, N.J.)

Citations: MR 21# 6370 = F55-11.
Referred to in F50-24, G15-32, R40-20.

G30-32 **(26# 4986)**

Konno, Shuji

On Artin's L-functions of the algebraic curves uniformized by certain automorphic functions.
J. Math. Soc. Japan **15** (1963), 89–100.

Let $\mathfrak{o}$ be a maximal order in a rational indefinite quaternion algebra. If N is a positive integer prime to the discriminant, let Γ be the unit group of $\mathfrak{o}$ and Γ_N the subgroup of units γ such that $\gamma \equiv 1 \pmod N$. The algebra has a faithful matrix representation in $[Q]_2$, so that Γ and Γ_N

can be regarded as Fuchsian groups on the upper half-plane. There is an algebraic curve $\mathfrak{L}_N$ defined over Q whose function field is the field of automorphic functions with respect to Γ_N. Let ρ_1 be an absolutely irreducible representation of $\Gamma/\Gamma_N = G$ contained in the analytic representation of G on the jacobian variety of the curve. Let Ω be the group of regular elements in $[Z/NZ]_2$ reduced mod $\{\pm 1\}$, and consider G as a subgroup of Ω. Let $\rho_1, \cdots, \rho_r$ be the set of inequivalent conjugate representations of ρ_1 relative to Ω. Set deg $\rho_i = m$, $\chi = \chi_1 + \cdots + \chi_r$ where $\chi_i = \operatorname{tr} \rho_i$. The author shows that the mth power of Artin's L-function $L(\chi, s)^m$ for the curve is a product of Dirichlet series obtained from the representation of modular correspondences by automorphic cusp forms of type $(\Gamma, \rho, 2)$ in the sense of Shimura [Ann. of Math. (2) **76** (1962), 237–294]. Then $L(\chi, s)^m$ is meromorphic in the whole plane and has a functional equation. In particular, if χ is a simple character this is true for $L(\chi, s)$ itself.

W. E. Jenner (Chapel Hill, N.C.)

G30-33 (27# 1875)

Skolem, Th.

A general remark concerning the study of rational points on algebraic curves.

Norske Vid. Selsk. Forh. (Trondheim) **36** (1963), 1–3.

Using a sequence of transformations of the form $x = x_1 y$ from the (x, y)-plane to the (x_1, y)-plane with suitably chosen origin and x-axis, the author shows that for any plane algebraic curve C with a finite number of finite rational points there exists a birational transformation with rational coefficients which carries C into a plane curve with no finite rational points.

D. Kirby (Southampton)

G30-34 (27# 4812)

Manin, Ju. I.

Proof of an analogue of Mordell's conjecture for algebraic curves over function fields. (Russian)

Dokl. Akad. Nauk SSSR **152** (1963), 1061–1063.

The author sketches a proof of the following result. Let K be a function field of characteristic 0 with field of constants k. Suppose that the algebraic curve C defined over K has genus $\geqq 2$. If C_K is infinite, then there is a curve C', defined over k, and a birational transformation τ of C' onto C, defined over K, such that almost all the points in C_K lie in $\tau(C_k')$.

The proof is based on analytical and topological methods. It might be possible to replace the differentials used here by (generalized) Jacobian varieties in order to obtain a proof in characteristic p.

Details will presumably be published elsewhere.

E. C. Dade (Pasadena, Calif.)

Referred to in G30-39.

G30-35 (28# 1199)

Manin, Ju. I.

Rational points on algebraic curves over function fields. (Russian)

Izv. Akad. Nauk SSSR Ser. Mat. **27** (1963), 1395–1440.

A classical conjecture of Mordell asserts that a curve of genus $\geqq 2$ defined over a number field has only a finite number of rational points in that field. The author proves the analogue of this conjecture for curves over function fields, and his result can be stated as follows. Let K be a function field, i.e., a finitely generated regular extension of a field k of characteristic 0, and let C be a curve (algebraic, irreducible) of genus $\geqq 2$, defined over K. If C has infinitely many rational points in K, then there exists a curve C_0 defined over k, a birational transformation $F: C_0 \to C$ defined over K, such that all but a finite number of these points are images under F of points of C_0 rational over k.

It is an easy technical matter to reduce the assertion to the case where k is the field of complex numbers, and where K is of transcendence degree 1 over k. In that case, one may view K as the function field of a parameter curve T, and one may view C as the generic member of a pencil of curves on an algebraic surface. The author's theorem is then seen to be equivalent to the following statement. Let V be a projective algebraic surface, and let C_t $(t \in T)$ be a pencil of curves on the surface such that the genus of the generic curve is $\geqq 2$. If the pencil has infinitely many rational sections, then V is birationally equivalent to a product of a fixed curve and the parameter curve T, and all but a finite number of the sections arise from constant points of the fixed curve.

Finally, one can express the author's theorem in a third equivalent form. Let K be a function field over k again, and assume for simplicity that the transcendence degree is 1. Let P be a point in projective space $\mathbf{P}^n$, rational over K. Then P is the generic point over k of a variety W_P contained in $\mathbf{P}^n$. By deg W_P we shall mean the projective degree. Then the theorem is equivalent to the following assertion. Let C be a non-singular curve defined over K. Then the degrees of the varieties W_P, as P ranges over the rational points of C in K, are bounded, in a suitable projective embedding. It is actually this final statement which is proved. Its equivalence with the first statement was known [cf. the reviewer, *Diophantine geometry*, Proposition 2 and Corollary of Chapter VII, § 2, Interscience, New York, 1962; MR **26** #119; also, the reviewer and A. Néron, Amer. J. Math. **81** (1959), 95–118; MR **21** #1311].

The proof giving a bound for the above degree proceeds in two steps. The first step consists in obtaining a new theorem on abelian varieties, and the second consists in applying it to the curve, embedded in its Jacobian. It should be pointed out that they represent a major new diophantine method. Siegel's theorem concerning the finiteness of integral points (in the function field case for curves of genus 1) also follows from it. Up to now, the only known proof was Siegel's proof or variants of it, which made use of the Thue-Siegel-Roth theorem.

The theorem on abelian varieties arises from an algebraisation of the theory of Picard-Fuchs differential equations. Let L be a function field over K, assume for simplicity that the dimension of K over k is 1, and let $\partial: K \to K$ be a derivation whose constant field is k. Let $\Omega^1 = \Omega^1(L/K)$ be the K-space of differential 1-forms of L over K. If $(x) = (x_1, \cdots, x_n)$ is a transcendence base of L over K, and $\omega \in \Omega^1$, then we can write $\omega = \sum u_i \, dx_i$ with $u_i \in L$. We denote by ∂_x the unique extension of ∂ to L such that $\partial_x x_i = 0$ for all i. Then we can also define ∂_x on Ω^1 by letting $\partial_x \omega = \sum (\partial_x u_i) \, dx_i$. If $\mathscr{Z}$ denotes the group of forms ω such that $d\omega = 0$ and $\mathscr{B}$ the group of forms $d\varphi$ with $\varphi \in L$, then ∂_x is easily seen to operate on $\mathscr{Z}/\mathscr{B}$, and this operation is independent of the choice of transcendence base (x).

Let now V be a (projective) model of L over K, let V_K denote the set of rational points of V in K, and let $P \in V_K$ be a simple point. Let $\mathfrak{o}_P$ and $\mathfrak{m}_P$ be its local ring and maximal ideal in L. If $y \in \mathfrak{o}_P$, we denote by y_P or $y(P)$ the value of y at P, i.e., the residue class in K of y mod $\mathfrak{m}_P$. A transcendence base (x) as above will be called a system of quasi-parameters at P if $x_i \in \mathfrak{o}_P$ for all i, and $x_i - x_{iP}$ is a system of parameters. For such (x), we have $(\partial_x y)_P = \partial y_P$.

Let $K[\partial]$ be the ring of polynomial differential operators with coefficients in K. Then by what we said above, $K[\partial]$ operates on $\mathscr{Z}/\mathscr{B}$. If $\omega \in \mathscr{Z}$, we denote by $\bar{\omega}$ the residue class of $\omega \bmod \mathscr{B}$. Let $\omega_1, \cdots, \omega_g$ be a basis for the differential forms of first kind. A Picard-Fuchs equation is a relation of type $\mathscr{L}: \sum_{j=1}^{g} \mathscr{L}_j\bar{\omega}_j=0$ where $\mathscr{L}_j \in K[\partial]$, $\bar{\omega}_j$ is the class of a differential form of first kind $\omega_j \in \mathscr{Z}$. For each choice of transcendence base (x), such a relation has a representative $\mathscr{L}_x: \sum \mathscr{L}_{jx}\omega_j=dz_x$ where z_x lies in L.

Let P be a simple point in V_K. A system of quasi-parameters (x) will be called admissible at P if $\partial x_{iP}=0$ for all i. Given a finite number of simple points, it is easy to show that a system of quasi-parameters admissible for all of them exists. Let P, Q be two simple points in V_K. Let $\mathscr{L}$ be a Picard-Fuchs equation. If (x) is a system of quasi-parameters at P, Q, admissible at both P, Q, and if $\mathscr{L}_x$ is a representative for $\mathscr{L}$ as above, then we let $\mu_x(P, Q)=z_{xQ}-z_{xP}$. This is an element of K, which is easily proved to be independent of the choice of (x), subject to the above conditions. Hence we can denote it by $\mu_{\mathscr{L}}(P,Q)$. The symbol $\mu_{\mathscr{L}}(P,Q)$ is the algebraisation of an integral between P and Q, and in transcendental notation, we would write $\mu_{\mathscr{L}}(P,Q)=\sum_{j=1}^{g} \mathscr{L}_j \int_P^Q \omega_j$ where $\mathscr{L}_j$ is a differential operator with respect to the parameters under the integral sign. Clearly, we have $\mu(P, Q)+\mu(Q, R)=\mu(P, R)$. The symbol also satisfies some obvious functorial properties.

Let $V=A$ be an abelian variety defined over K. Let 0 be the origin. For each Picard-Fuchs relation $\mathscr{L}$, and rational point P in A_K, we define $\mu_{\mathscr{L}}(P)=\mu_{\mathscr{L}}(0, P)$. From the preceding additivity and the functorial properties, one concludes that the map $P \to \mu_{\mathscr{L}}(P)$ is a homomorphism of A_K into the additive group of K (denoted by K^+). Let (B, τ) be Chow's K/k-trace of A. It is easily seen that τB_k is contained in the kernel of this homomorphism, and so is the torsion group of A_K. The main theorem asserts: If a point P of A_K is contained in the kernel of every Picard-Fuchs homomorphism $\mu_{\mathscr{L}}$, then it lies in the group generated by τB_k and the torsion group of A_K. This is a deep statement, which is proved by showing that some integral multiple of P is infinitely divisible in A_K, and hence must lie in τB_k. The proof uses transcendental means, assuming that k is the field of complex numbers, considering algebraic families of abelian varieties parametrized by a curve T (a model of K over k), and using the theory of abelian integrals. Since the module of Picard-Fuchs relations is finitely generated over $K[\partial]$, one may actually choose a finite number of relations and corresponding homomorphisms $\mu_1, \cdots, \mu_s$. The intersection of their kernels is then the group generated as described above, and one obtains an injection of the factor group $A_K/(\tau B_k+\text{torsion})$ into the direct product $K^+ \times \cdots \times K^+$ taken s times. The main point of this injection is that it transforms the rather intractable relations of the Mordell-Weil group A_K into essentially linear differential relations in the additive group of K. The preceding theorem is then applied to a curve C of genus $\geqq 2$ defined over K, embedded in its Jacobian J, and the problem amounts to finding a finite-dimensional k-linear subspace E of L, a function field over K, having the following property. Given a point P in C_K, there exists a non-zero function f in E such that f is defined at P and $f(P)=0$. Essentially, this shows that such points are all contained in the intersection of C and a hyperplane section of a suitable projective embedding, determined by the k-space E. The proof of this final statement is again very ingenious, using repeatedly the unramified coverings of C induced by isogenies of its Jacobian, in order to eliminate the differential operators from the Picard-Fuchs relations, and end up with functional relations relative to a suitable finitely generated space E. *S. Lang* (New York)

Citations: MR 21# 1311 = G10-6; MR 26# 119 = G02-9.

Referred to in G30-52, G30-55.

G30-36 **(29# 3430)**

Chowla, S.

A remark on a conjecture of C. L. Siegel.

Proc. Nat. Acad. Sci. U.S.A. **51** (1964), 774–775.

The author states that Siegel [Abh. Preuss. Akad. Wiss. Phys.-Math. Kl. **1929**, 1–70] made the conjecture: Let $f(x, y)=0$ be the equation of an algebraic curve of genus $p>0$ over an algebraic number field; then, if the diophantine equation $f(x, y)=0$ has only finitely many (integral) solutions, a bound can be found for the number of solutions which depends only on the number of coefficients of f. The author remarks that this conjecture is false since, for example, he has proved [J. Indian Math. Soc. **20** (1934), 121–128] that, for some $c>0$ and infinitely many n, the equation $x^3+y^3=n$ has at least $c \log \log n$ solutions in positive integers. *E. S. Barnes* (Adelaide)

G30-37 **(31# 1231)**

Lamprecht, Erich

Durch Produktdarstellungen erklärte Zetafunktionen. (Russian summary)

Sammelband zu Ehren des 250. Geburtstages Leonhard Eulers, pp. 246–255. *Akademie-Verlag, Berlin,* 1959.

Author's summary: "The investigation is a contribution to a program which has been developed in recent years by many authors: finitely-generated fields, i.e., fields which are obtained from their prime subfields by adjoining a finite number of elements, have associated with them zeta-functions with properties similar to those of Dedekind zeta-functions (in the case of number fields) and the so-called zeta-functions over a finite field (in the case of a field of functions of one variable over a finite field). For these zeta-functions of higher fields the author considers, in particular, the following three questions: (1) Does there exist a full representation by Euler products, with the same properties as in the classical case? (2) Are these zeta-functions connected in an invariant manner with the fields in question? (3) What are the relations between the various definitions of similar zeta-functions to be found in the literature?

"In view of the need for brevity, consideration is in the main limited to what is from the present point of view the simplest non-trivial case, to wit, the case of a field of functions of one variable over a finite algebraic number field. In § 1, a review of results previously published elsewhere on the first two of these questions is given. In § 2, with a view to answering the third question, the author investigates relations between invariant zeta-functions defined in § 1 and a generalisation of the Dedekind zeta-function given by E. Kähler. In § 3, there is a brief account of analogous information for fields of more general types."

G30-38 **(32# 4083)**

Mumford, David

A remark on Mordell's conjecture.

Amer. J. Math. **87** (1965), 1007–1016.

A notorious conjecture of Mordell asserts that the number of points defined over an algebraic number field (finite extension of the rationals) on a curve C of genus $\geqq 2$ is finite. Here the author shows that the number of points with height $\leqq H$ is at most $A \log H + B$, where A, B are constants depending only on the curve and the field k. In particular, the number of coprime positive integral solutions of $x^n + y^n = z^n$ ($n > 3$, fixed) with $z \leqq Z$ is at most $A \log\log Z + B$. The proof depends on the comparison of heights on C and on the Jacobian J of C in which C is embedded, and uses the theorem of Néron and Tate that heights on an abelian variety are essentially given by a quadratic form. The author remarks that one cannot expect to obtain Mordell's conjecture itself by such arguments since they also apply when k is a function field of a single variable, and then there are curves of any genus with an infinity of points defined over k whose heights increase in the exact rate given by the author's theorem. The paper contains an illuminating summary of the relations between a curve and its Jacobian, and also of the properties of heights.

J. W. S. Cassels (Cambridge, England)

G30-39 (34# 4272)

Samuel, Pierre

Compléments à un article de Hans Grauert sur la conjecture de Mordell.

Inst. Hautes Études Sci. Publ. Math. No. 29 (1966), 55–62.

Mordell's conjecture asserts that an algebraic curve of genus $\geqq 2$ defined over a number field K has only a finite number of rational points (over K). The function field analogue of this has been proved by Ju. I. Manin [Izv. Akad. Nauk SSSR Ser. Mat. **27** (1963), 1395–1440; MR **27** #4812], using analytical methods, and by H. Grauert [Inst. Hautes Études Sci. Publ. Math. No. 25 (1965), 131–149], from the point of view of algebraic geometry. (See also M. Miwa [J. Math. Soc. Japan **18** (1966), 182–188; MR **32** #7559] for a generalization of Grauert's result to the case considered by the present author, which is not correct for positive characteristic, and the author's own exposé [*Séminaire Bourbaki*, 17e Année, 1964/65, fasc. 1, exposé 287, second corrected edition, Secrétariat mathématique, Paris, 1966; reprinting, Benjamin, New York, 1966; see MR **33** #5420] for an illuminating and entertaining account of the background.)

The theorem of Manin-Grauert reads as follows. Let k be an algebraically closed field of characteristic 0 and let K be a field of algebraic functions over k. Let C be a curve of genus $\geqq 2$ defined over K. Then if the set C_K of rational points (over K) is infinite, there exists a K-isomorphism $f: C \to C'$, where C' is a curve defined over k. Moreover, $C_K' - C_k'$ is finite.

Much of Grauert's proof is valid in characteristic p, and in the present paper the author completes the discussion as it applies in this case and incidentally simplifies part of the original proof.

For an absolutely non-singular curve, the theorem of Manin-Grauert is true provided that K is not isomorphic to a curve defined over a finite field. If C is birationally equivalent to such a curve, then there is a supplementary condition depending on whether or not the Frobenius endomorphism of C' commutes with a Galois descent. (There is an example given in § 6 of the Séminaire Bourbaki exposé.)

Finally, the author discusses the phenomenon of genus drop in passing from C to a curve defined over $\bar{K}$. If the absolute genus is $\geqq 2$ and if C_K is infinite, then the curve C possesses an absolutely non-singular normal model defined over K with genus equal to the absolute genus. The question of what happens if the absolute genus is 0 or 1 is left open.

J. V. Armitage (Durham)

Citations: MR 27# 4812 = G30-34; MR 32# 7559 = G30-45.

G30-40 (34# 5816)

Dem'janenko, V. A.

Rational points of a class of algebraic curves. (Russian)

Izv. Akad. Nauk SSSR Ser. Mat. **30** (1966), 1373–1396.

The author produces a wide class of algebraic curves Γ of genus $g > 1$ defined over an algebraic number field K, which have at most a finite number of points defined over K, in accordance with Mordell's conjecture. Further, all these points can be determined effectively.

More precisely, let Γ_1 be an abelian variety of dimension 1 defined over K. Then the rational maps $\phi: \Gamma \to \Gamma_1$ defined over K have a natural group-structure defined by operating on Γ_1 with the images of a generic point of Γ. Let G be the group of the ϕ modulo the constant maps. Denote by U the group of points on Γ_1 defined over K. Then if the rank of G is greater than the rank of U, there are only finitely many points on Γ defined over K, and they can be determined effectively. An example of this situation is $\Gamma: x^4 + y^4 = A$, $A \in K$, and $\Gamma_1: u^2 + v^4 = A$, provided that U has at most one generator. For, G contains the independent maps $\phi_1: u = x^2, v = y$ and $\phi_2: u = y^2, v = x$.

In the second section, the author shows how the proof of the main theorem can be modified so as to deal with Γ such as $ax^4 + by^4 + c = 0$ which have rational maps into abelian varieties (here $au^2 + bv^4 + c = 0$, $bu^2 + cv^4 + a = 0$, etc.) which only become isogenous over an extension of the ground-field K.

The gist of the maladroitly presented proof of the main theorem appears to be as follows. Let $\phi_1, \cdots, \phi_m$ be independent elements of G. Then $\deg(\sum_j n_j \phi_j) = \sum_{i,j} \beta_{ij} n_i n_j$ ($n_j \in \mathbf{Z}$) for some quadratic form β_{ij}, which is positive definite because of the independence of the ϕ's. Now let a be a point of Γ defined over K. Then $h^*(\sum_j n_j \phi_j(a)) = \sum_{i,j} b_{ij}(a) n_i n_j$ ($n_j \in \mathbf{Z}$) for some real $b_{ij}(a)$, where h^* denotes the Tate height. The properties of heights under rational maps [e.g., S. Lang, *Diophantine geometry*, Interscience, New York, 1962; MR **26** #119] show that the ratios of the $b_{ij}(a)$ tend to the corresponding ratios of the β_{ij} as the height H of a on Γ tends to infinity. In particular, the quadratic form $b_{ij}(a)$ is non-degenerate as soon as $H >$ some effectively computable C. For such a, the $\phi_j(a)$ must therefore be independent elements of U. This is impossible if rank $U < m$. {Reviewer's remarks: Unaccountably, the author works with the ordinary logarithmic height instead of Tate's height, and at the foot of p. 1379 he confuses the issue by unnecessarily and unjustifiably assuming the non-degeneracy which he is in the course of proving.}

J. W. S. Cassels (Cambridge, England)

Referred to in D02-23, G05-106, G30-42, G30-47, Z10-43.

G30-41 (35# 2893)

Dem'janenko, V. A.

Rational points of a class of algebraic curves. (Russian)

Dokl. Akad. Nauk SSSR **171** (1966), 1259–1260.

Let K be an algebraic number field and let Γ be a curve of genus greater than one defined over K. A classical conjecture of Mordell states that Γ should have only a finite number of points rational over K. Suppose that there exists an elliptic curve Γ_1 defined over K, and linearly independent morphisms $\varphi_1, \cdots, \varphi_r$ from Γ to Γ_1. The author states the following result: If the rank of the group U of points of Γ_1 rational over K is less than r, then Γ has only a finite number of points rational over K. The proof is said to depend on the height function. Similar results are obtained by considering the group $U/2U$. Several applications to particular curves are made. For example, if the elliptic curve $u^3+v^2=A$ ($A\in K$) has rank $\leqq 1$ over K, then the curve $x^4+y^4=A$ has only a finite number of rational points in K.

{This article has appeared in English translation [Soviet Math. Dokl. **7** (1966), 1626–1628].}

N. Greenleaf (Rochester, N.Y.)

G30-42 (35# 4218)

Dem'janenko, V. A.

Rational points of certain curves of higher genus. (Russian)

Acta Arith. **12** (1966/67), 333–354.

Let k be an algebraic number field. The author establishes sufficient conditions for the curves (1) $x^4+y^4=A$ and (2) $x^6+y^6=A$, where A is a fixed element of k, to have at most finitely many points defined over k, when k is either (i) the rational field, (ii) the Gaussian field, or (iii) a totally real field. The conditions relate to the k-rational points on certain elliptic curves onto which the given curves can be mapped in several ways (e.g., $u^4-A=v^2$ in case (1)). Thus the general set-up is similar to that of the author's recent paper [Izv. Akad. Nauk SSSR Ser. Mat. **30** (1966), 1373–1396; MR **34** #5816], where a wider class of curves is considered. But the conditions here seem neither to imply nor to be implied by the conditions of the earlier paper (for the special cases (1) and (2)) and the line of attack is, at least superficially, somewhat different.

J. W. S. Cassels (Cambridge, England)

Citations: MR 34# 5816 = G30-40.

G30-43 (35# 5417)

Madan, M. L.

On the Galois cohomology of tamely ramified fields of algebraic functions.

Arch. Math. (*Basel*) **17** (1966), 400–408.

Let k be an algebraically closed field of characteristic $p\geqq 0$, K a field of algebraic functions of one variable over k, F a finite Galois extension of K, G the Galois group of F over K, C the group of divisor classes of F, W the group of roots of unity in the multiplicative group of the field of constants k, and S the finite set of prime divisors of K which are ramified in F. Main theorem: Assume F/K is tamely ramified. Then for any odd integer s, there is a canonical exact sequence $1\to H^s(G,C)\to H^{s+2}(G,W)\to \prod_{\mathfrak{p}\in S} H^{s+2}(G_{\mathfrak{p}},W)\to H^{s+1}(G,C)\to H^{s+3}(G,W)\to 1$. This generalizes the isomorphism theorem of Y. Kawada and J. Tate [Amer. J. Math. **77** (1955), 197–217; MR **16**, 799] in the case S is empty.

M. J. Greenberg (Santa Cruz, Calif.)

Citations: MR 16, 799f = G30-16.

G30-44 (36# 5139)

Grauert, Hans

Mordells Vermutung über rationale Punkte auf algebraischen Kurven und Funktionenkörper.

Inst. Hautes Études Sci. Publ. Math. No. 25 (1965), 131–149.

The main result of this paper is the following: Let k be an algebraically closed field of characteristic 0, K a function field with constant field k and C a complete non-singular algebraic curve defined over K with genus $\geqq 2$. Then the set of K-rational points of C is infinite if and only if there exists an algebraic curve defined over k which is K-isomorphic to C. The proof is carried out, using the infinitesimal theory with the algebraic-geometrical method, for the fibre variety X with the affine model R of K/k as base space and C as generic fibre. In the course of the proof the following is essential: (X,π,R) is quasi-trivial on some neighbourhood of every point of R or there is a finite number of rational sections.

Concerning this theme there are results of Samuel and the reviewer. Samuel's is for the case where k is an algebraically closed field k of characteristic $p\neq 0$ and the reviewer's is for arbitrary constant field k.

M. Miwa (Tokyo)

Referred to in G30-51.

G30-45 (32# 7559)

Miwa, Megumu

On Mordell's conjecture for algebraic curves over function fields.

J. Math. Soc. Japan **18** (1966), 182–188.

Let K be a regular extension of finite type of a field k and let C be a complete non-singular curve of genus $\geqq 2$ defined over K. Then the main theorem is: The set of all rational points of C over K is a finite set or C is trivially defined, which means there is a curve C_0 defined over k that is birationally equivalent to C over K. This is a generalization of the results of H. Grauert [Inst. Hautes Études Sci. Publ. Math. No. 25 (1965), 131–149] and these results are used in the proof.

{In Lemma 1, C^* and C_0 are birationally isomorphic over K, by the construction of C_0. Hence in the proof of Theorem 1 the argument concerning the birational isomorphism of C and C_0 over K may be omitted. In the case of positive characteristic (§ 2), the proof of Proposition 3 seems to contain a point which is not correct.}

Y. Kawahara (Tokyo)

Referred to in G30-39.

G30-46 (36# 5140)

Samuel, P.

Lectures on old and new results on algebraic curves.

Notes by S. Anantharaman. Tata Institute of Fundamental Research Lectures on Mathematics, No. 36.

Tata Institute of Fundamental Research, Bombay, 1966. ii + 127 + iii *pp.* $2.00.

The main purpose of the present publication is to explain the results of Grauert and the author on Mordell's conjecture over function fields, namely, for function fields with algebraically closed constant fields of arbitrary characteristics. In order to do this the author first deals with fundamental concepts and results in algebraic geometry in Chapter I. In Chapter II he explains several classical results for algebraic curves, which are needed later, such as the theorems of Riemann-Roch, Hurwitz-Zeuthen, Schwarz-Klein, Severi and de Francis. The explanations are easy and interesting. The last chapter, III, is devoted to the proof of the results of Grauert and the author. The methods of proof are essentially the same as those used in the original papers. The descriptions are based on the author's Bourbaki talk and are simplified, dealing first with the case of function fields of one variable. There is no description of the case of function fields with arbitrary constant field, for which the main theorems of this publication are also true, as was shown by the reviewer.

M. Miwa (Tokyo)

Referred to in G30-51.

G30-47 (37# 1376)

Cassels, J. W. S.

On a theorem of Dem'janenko.

J. London Math. Soc. **43** (1968), 61–66.

This paper gives a simplified proof of a theorem of V. A. Dem'janenko [Izv. Akad. Nauk SSSR Ser. Mat. **30** (1966), 1373–1396; MR **34** #5816] which can be used to show that a certain class of curves of genus $g \geqq 2$ defined over an algebraic number field K satisfy Mordell's conjecture, i.e., they have only finitely many K-rational points. The theorem states that if $\varphi_1, \cdots, \varphi_m$ are rational maps (defined over K) from a curve Γ into an abelian variety Γ_1 of dimension 1, no non-zero linear combination of the φ's being a constant map, then, for any K-rational point a of Γ not belonging to a certain finite, explicitly computable set S, $\varphi_1(a), \cdots, \varphi_m(a)$ are independent elements of the group of K-rational points of Γ_1.

The proof uses the quadratic height of Tate, and is elegantly presented, but otherwise Paragraphs 1, 2 and 4 of the review of the paper cited above may be taken also as a review of this paper. The author does not prove the results of Section 2 of Dem'janenko's paper.

J. S. Milne (London)

Citations: MR 34# 5816 = G30-40.

G30-48 (38# 4478)

Paršin, A. N.

Algebraic curves over function fields. (Russian)

Dokl. Akad. Nauk SSSR **183** (1968), 524–526.

Soient k un corps algébriquement clos de caractéristique zéro, K un corps, extension de type fini de k de dimension 1 et de genre q, g un entier supérieur à 1, et S une partie finie de K; l'auteur étudie l'ensemble des courbes X sur K projectives, non singulières, géométriquement irréductibles de genre g et ayant bonne réduction hors de S. Soit E l'ensemble des classes d'isomorphisme des courbes sur K de genre g qui ont bonne réduction en tout point de K, qui ne sont pas de la forme $Y \otimes K$, où Y est une courbe sur k, et qui ne le deviennent pas après extension de K. Alors E est fini, et si $q \leqq 1$, E est vide.

{This article has appeared in English translation [Soviet Math. Dokl. **9** (1968), 1419–1422].} *J.-E. Bertin* (Paris)

G30-49 (39# 1459)

Ihara, Yasutaka

The congruence monodromy problems.

J. Math. Soc. Japan **20** (1968), 107–121.

This paper is a summary, without proofs, of forthcoming notes of a lecture given at Princeton University in 1967.

Let R be the field of real numbers. Let $k_\mathfrak{p}$ be a $\mathfrak{p}$-adic number field with the ring of integers $\mathfrak{o}_\mathfrak{p}$ and $N\mathfrak{p} = q$. Let $G_R = \mathrm{PSL}(R)$ and $G_\mathfrak{p} = \mathrm{PSL}(k_\mathfrak{p})$. Let $G = G_R \times G_\mathfrak{p}$. Let Γ be a subgroup of G satisfying the following conditions: (Γ1) The projection maps $\Gamma \to \Gamma_R = \Gamma \cap G_R$, $\Gamma \to \Gamma_\mathfrak{p} = \Gamma \cap G_\mathfrak{p}$ are injective and the images Γ_R and $\Gamma_\mathfrak{p}$ are dense in G_R and $G_\mathfrak{p}$, respectively. (Γ2) Γ is discrete in G and the quotient G/Γ is compact. (Γ3) Γ is torsion free. Let $\mathfrak{h} = \{z \in C \mid \mathrm{Im}\, z > 0\}$ and $\Gamma_z = \{\gamma \in \Gamma \mid \gamma_R z = z\}$. $z \in \mathfrak{h}$ is a Γ-fixed point if and only if $\Gamma_z \neq \{I\}$ (I = identity). Two points $z, z' \in \mathfrak{h}$ are Γ-equivalent if and only if there exists a $\gamma \in \Gamma$ such that $z' = \gamma_R z$; $\mathfrak{P}(\Gamma)$ is the quotient set of the set of all Γ-fixed points by the Γ-equivalence. $\gamma \in \Gamma$ is elliptic if it is contained in Γ_z for some $z \in \mathfrak{h}$. One defines $\deg\{\gamma\}_\Gamma$, where $\{\gamma\}_\Gamma$ is the Γ-conjugacy class that contains Γ, by $\deg\{\gamma\}_\Gamma = |V_\mathfrak{p}(\lambda_\mathfrak{p})|$, where $\pm\{\lambda_\mathfrak{p}, \lambda_\mathfrak{p}^{-1}\}$ are the eigenvalues of $\gamma_\mathfrak{p}$ and $V_\mathfrak{p}$ is the normalized additive valuation of $k_\mathfrak{p}$. If $P \in \mathfrak{P}(\Gamma)$, one puts $\deg P = \deg\{\gamma\}_\Gamma = \deg\{\gamma^{-1}\}_\Gamma$, $\{\gamma^{\pm 1}\}_\Gamma$ being the primitive elliptic Γ-conjugacy classes which correspond to P. One defines the ζ function $\zeta_\Gamma(u)$ of Γ by $\zeta_\Gamma(u) = \prod_{P \in \mathfrak{P}(\Gamma)} (1 - u^{\deg P})^{-1}$. The author states that $\zeta_\Gamma(u) = Q(u)((1-u)(1-q^2u))^{-1}(1-u)^{(q-1)(g-1)}$, where g is the genus of the Riemann surface $\mathfrak{h}/\Gamma_R^{\,0}$ (where $\Gamma^0 = \Gamma \cap (G_R \times \mathrm{PSL}_2(\mathfrak{o}_\mathfrak{p})))$ and $Q(u)$ is a polynomial of u of degree $2g$ with integral coefficients and with $Q(0) = 1$, satisfying the functional equation $(qu)^{2g}Q(q^{-2}u^{-1}) = Q(u)$. One states also the following theorem: Let $\{L/C, G_\mathfrak{p}\}$ be a $G_\mathfrak{p}$-field over C. Then there exists an algebraic number field k of finite degree over Q and a good subfield L_k of $\{L/C, G_\mathfrak{p}\}$ over k (i.e., a subfield L_k such that L_k is $G_\mathfrak{p}$ invariant and $L_kC = L$). If $\{L/C, G_\mathfrak{p}\}$ is irreducible (i.e., such that if Δ is a subgroup of G containing Γ as subgroup of finite index and if $\{M/C, G_\mathfrak{p}\}$ is the $G_\mathfrak{p}$-field corresponding to Δ, then $M = L$), then it has an essentially unique good subfield L_{k_0} over an algebraic number field k_0 of finite degree. The author also states four conjectures and gives some examples. *P. Abellanas* (Madrid)

G30-50 (39# 2762)

Miwa, Megumu

Mordell's conjecture on the rational points of an algebraic curve defined over a function field. (Japanese)

Sûgaku **20** (1968), 25–35.

This is a survey article on a variation of Mordell's conjecture in Diophantine problems. In the language of algebraic geometry the original Mordell conjecture is stated as follows: Let C be a non-singular curve of genus $\geqq 2$ defined over the rational number field Q. Then C contains only a finite number of Q-rational points. When C is an algebraic curve of genus $\geqq 2$ defined over a function field K/k of arbitrary characteristic, we have the following variation of Mordell's conjecture. If the set C_K of K-rational points of C is infinite, then there exists an algebraic curve C_0 defined over k and a birational correspondence u of C onto C_0 over K such that $C_K - u^{-1}(C_{0k})$ is a finite set. The original conjecture has not been proved yet but the variation has been proved affirmatively by several authors with some additional assumptions. The detailed exposition of this subject is the contents of this article. The final results are summarized in Theorem 6.4. *Y. Nakai* (Osaka)

G30-51 (39# 2763)

Miwa, Megumu

On Mordell's conjecture for the curve over function field with arbitrary constant field.

J. Math. Soc. Japan **21** (1969), 229–233.

L'auteur perfectionne les compléments apportés par le rapporteur [*Lectures on old and new results on algebraic curves*, Tata Inst. Fundamental Res., Bombay, 1966; MR **36** #5140] aux résultats de Manin-Grauert [see H. Grauert, Inst. Hautes Études Sci. Publ. Math. No. 25 (1965), 131–149; MR **36** #5139] sur la conjecture de Mordell pour les corps de fonctions. Il utilise pour cela des lemmes sur la descente, galoisienne ou inséparable, de courbes algébriques. Il montre aussi que, si C et C' sont deux courbes de genre $\geqq 2$ définies sur un corps k, tout isomorphisme de C sur C' est défini sur une extension séparable de degré fini de k.

P. Samuel (Cambridge, Mass.)

Citations: MR 36# 5139 = G30-44; MR 36# 5140 = G30-46.

G30-52 (41# 1740)

Paršin, A. N.

Algebraic curves over function fields. I. (Russian)

Izv. Akad. Nauk SSSR Ser. Mat. **32** (1968), 1191–1219.

L'auteur démontre dans un cas particulier la conjecture suivante de Šafarevič: l'ensemble des courbes algébriques non constantes définies sur un corps global K de genre donné $g > 1$ et de type S donné est fini. Toute courbe sera supposée non-singulière et géométriquement irréductible;

soient k un corps algébriquement clos de caractéristique nulle, B une courbe projective définie sur k, q le genre de B, K le corps des fonctions rationnelles de B. Par fibré $f: X \to B$ l'auteur entend un épimorphisme projectif plat f d'une surface projective irréductible non-singulière X sur B dont la fibre générique est une courbe. À un tel fibré sont attachés son genre, qui est le genre de sa fibre générique, et son type, qui est le sous-ensemble fini S de B des points en lesquels la fibre de f n'est pas une courbe (non-singulière) de genre g. Un tel fibré est dit minimal si aucune de ses fibres n'est une courbe exceptionnelle de genre 1. Toute courbe C définie sur K définit un fibré minimal $f: X \to B$ appelé modèle (minimal non-singulier) de C. La courbe C est dite non-dégénérée si son modèle f est un morphisme lisse; la courbe C est constante si et seulement si son modèle est un fibré isotrivial. Le résultat fondamental de l'article est le suivant: (a) si $q \geqq 2$, étant donné un entier $g > 1$, il n'existe qu'un nombre fini de classes d'isomorphisme de fibrés lisses non isotriviaux de base B et de genre g; (b) si $q = 0$ ou 1, tout fibré lisse de genre $g > 1$ et de base B est isotrivial. Autrement dit: (a) si $q \geqq 2$, l'ensemble des classes d'isomorphisme de courbes C non constantes non dégénérées sur K de genre donné $g > 1$ est fini; (b) si $q = 0$ ou 1, toute courbe non dégénérée C sur K de genre $g > 1$ est constante. L'auteur donne ensuite une autre démonstration du théorème suivant de Ju. I. Manin [mêmes Izv. **27** (1963), 1395–1440; MR **28** #1199]: soit C une courbe définie sur K, complète, non constante et de genre $g > 1$, alors l'ensemble des points de C rationnels sur K est fini. L'auteur montre enfin que la conjecture de L. J. Mordell [Proc. Cambridge Philos. Soc. **21** (1922), 179–192] est conséquence de la conjecture de I. R. Šafarevič [Proc. Internat. Congr. Mathematicians (Stockholm, 1962), pp. 163–176, Inst. Mittag-Leffler, Djursholm, 1963; see MR **34** #2569]. *J.-E. Bertin* (Caen)

Citations: MR 28# 1199 = G30-35; MR 34# 2569 = R02-47.

G30-53 **(41# 3477)**

Coates, J.

Construction of rational functions on a curve.

Proc. Cambridge Philos. Soc. **68** (1970), 105–123.

Let K be an algebraic function field in one variable over **Q**. Let $\mathfrak{M}$ be the vector space of functions in K having prescribed lower bounds on their orders at a specified set of values. By the Riemann-Roch theorem, one has an explicit formula for the dimension of $\mathfrak{M}$, and in principle one should be able to construct a basis for $\mathfrak{M}$. The purpose of this paper is to give a detailed explicit construction of such a basis with the intent to use that basis to determine integer points on curves of genus 1. The construction gives the functions in the basis as a power series of the form $\sum w_k(x-a)^{k\rho+\sigma}$, where $w_k = \Delta^{-k-1}\alpha_k$, Δ is a rational integer, α_k is an algebraic integer from a field K', $\max(\Delta^{k+1}, \Delta^{k+1}\operatorname{height}(w_k)) \leqq \Lambda^k$, and Λ and K' are restricted in terms of a defining equation for K. The construction is based on the proof of the Riemann-Roch theorem given by K. Hensel and G. Landsberg [*Theorie der algebraischen Funktionen einer Variablen und ihre Anwendung auf algebraische Kurven und Abelsche Integrale*, Teubner, Leipzig, 1902]. *D. J. Lewis* (Ann Arbor, Mich.)

Referred to in G05-101.

G30-54 **(43# 1992)**

Manin, Ju. I.

The fine structure of the Néron-Tate height. **(Russian)**

Mat. Sb. (*N.S.*) **83** (**125**) (1970), 331–348.

The height of a point with algebraic coordinates in a projective space, as studied by A. Weil [Ann. of Math. (2) **53** (1951), 412–444; MR **13**, 66], is unique up to a factor $e^{O(1)}$. On the other hand Tate and Néron [cf. A. Néron, ibid. (2) **82** (1965), 249–331; MR **31** #3424; S. Lang, Séminaire Bourbaki, 1963/64, Fasc. 3, Exp. 274, Secrétariat mathématique, Paris, 1964; MR **31** #1252] have shown that this indeterminacy can be removed on abelian varieties. The present article serves as a complement to Néron's work. In the first section the author describes generalizations for the local and global bilinear pairings of Néron. Here the usual norm is replaced by quasi-characters, i.e., in the local case, homomorphisms of a local field into the multiplicative group of complex numbers. In the global case the quasi-characters are defined on the idele group of the given field. In particular, for the case of Tate curves, the author gives explicit formulae expressing the Néron bilinear functions in terms of nonarchimedian theta-functions. In the second half of the paper he studies the possibility of extending the canonical height of Néron and Tate to varieties other than abelian varieties, for example to curves. Here if $\phi: X \to J_X$ is the embedding of a curve in its Jacobian, different bundles L_1 and L_2 in $\operatorname{Pic} J_X$ may induce the same bundle in Pic X. The author constructs examples to show that in this case the canonical heights $\hat{h}_{L_1} \circ \phi$, $\hat{h}_{L_2} \circ \phi$ on X may not coincide, although, according to Weil's theorem, they differ by a multiple $e^{O(1)}$. *A. H. Wallace* (Philadelphia, Pa.)

Citations: MR 13, 66d = G35-25; MR 31# 1252 = G35-42; MR 31# 3424 = G10-26.

G30-55 **(44# 6704)**

Lapin, A. I.

The integral points on curves of genus $p > 1$. **(Russian)**

Izv. Akad. Nauk SSSR Ser. Mat. **35** (1971), 754–761.

In this article, which is a continuation of an earlier article [same Izv. **29** (1965), 701–716; MR **34** #664] the author proves the following theorem: For every pair of positive integers n and p, there exists a hyperelliptic curve Γ of genus p, defined over $K = k(X)$, where k is an algebraically closed field, such that Γ has at least n integral points. This result, which extends a similar result of Manin concerning Mordell's conjecture [Ju. I. Manin, ibid. **27** (1963), 1395–1440; MR **28** #1199] represents a negative answer to Siegel's conjecture [C. L. Siegel, Abh. Preuss. Akad. Wiss.-Phys. Math. Kl. **1929**, no. 1, especially pp. 41–69]. *S. A. Basarab* (Bucharest)

Citations: MR 28# 1199 = G30-35; MR 34# 664 = G05-78.

G35 VARIETIES OVER GLOBAL FIELDS

See also Section D72.

See also reviews D32-68, E68-25, F25-13, G02-18, G02-20, G05-52, G10-7, G10-49, G25-23, G25-49, G25-51, R08-33, Z10-7.

G35-1 **(5, 154e; 5, 154f)**

Segre, B. **On ternary non-homogeneous cubic equations with more than one rational solution.** J. London Math. Soc. **18**, 88–100 (1943).

Segre, B. **A note on arithmetical properties of cubic surfaces.** J. London Math. Soc. **18**, 24–31 (1943).

The first of these two papers concerns non-singular cubic surfaces F which are rational in the sense that they are definable over the field of rational numbers. The questions treated pertain to the existence of rational points on F and, more generally, of rational lines and of non-trivial rational curves on F. The results are stated without proofs; these will be published elsewhere. Concerning the existence of rational points it is stated that F either carries no rational points or infinitely many. The existence of non-trivial rational curves (that is, curves which are not obtained as the complete intersection of F with another rational surface) is correlated to the existence of a rational line, a rational doublet, triplet or sextuplet of such lines and to the existence of a parametric rational solution of the equation of F. The paper also contains a discussion of the equation $a_1x_1^3+a_2x_2^3+a_3x_3^3+a_4x_4^3=0$ and of special cases of this equation, such as the Ryley equation $x_1^3+x_2^3+x_3^3+px_4^3=0$, p not the cube of a rational number. In the second paper the author proves by geometric considerations that a cubic rational surface F with more than one rational point necessarily carries infinitely many rational points. The essential part of the proof is that in which it is shown that, if F carries three collinear rational Eckhardt points, then it carries an infinity of rational points (compare with the next review of the paper by Mordell). *O. Zariski* (Baltimore, Md.).

Referred to in D02-1, D32-16.

G35-2 (5, 154g)

Mordell, L. J. Segre's indeterminate non-homogeneous cubic equation in three variables. J. London Math. Soc. **18**, 43–46 (1943).

If a rational cubic surface carries three collinear rational Eckhardt points then its equation can be reduced to the following form: $z(z+2+2px+2qy)=ax^3+bx^2y+xy^2+dy^3$. It has been shown by B. Segre that this equation possesses a parametric solution which involves rational functions of three parameters with rational coefficients [see the preceding review]. In this note this parametric solution is obtained by direct algebraic processes. *O. Zariski* (Baltimore, Md.).

G35-3 (6, 102e)

Chabauty, Claude. Sur les points rationnels des variétés algébriques dont l'irrégularité est supérieure à la dimension. C. R. Acad. Sci. Paris **212**, 1022–1024 (1941).

Among other results the author announces the following theorem on algebraic curves C over an algebraic number field. "If an algebraic curve of genus g and reduced rank r does not possess reducible Abelian integrals, then there exists only a finite number of inequivalent rational systems in an algebraic series on C provided its dimension is not greater than $g-r$." The sketch of the proof involves the p-adic theory of Abelian integrals and the existence of a model free from singularities for Picard varieties.
O. F. G. Schilling (Chicago, Ill.).

G35-4 (6, 117d)

Segre, B. A complete parametric solution of certain homogeneous Diophantine equations, of degree n in $n+1$ variables. J. London Math. Soc. **19**, 46–55 (1944).

Consider the function

$$\Phi(x)=\prod_{i=1}^{n+1}(x_0+x_1t_i+\cdots+x_nt_i^n)$$

of degree $n+1$ in the variables $x_0, \cdots, x_n$, where the t_i are the roots of any polynomial equation of degree $n+1$ in 1 variable with rational coefficients which is irreducible in the rational number field. The Diophantine equations studied are

$$\sum_{i=0}^{n} b_i\partial\Phi(x)/\partial x_i=0,$$

the b_i being arbitrary rational numbers. A rational parametric solution is given for any such equation. The result is extended to the case where the t_i are roots of a reducible equation, although it is still assumed that the discriminant of the equation is not zero. An application of the result to algebraic geometry is also given. *I. Niven.*

Referred to in G35-6.

G35-5 (6, 185a)

Segre, B. Arithmetic upon an algebraic surface. Bull. Amer. Math. Soc. **51**, 152–161 (1945).

A statement of various theorems concerning the existence of rational points, or one- or two-parameter systems of rational points, on a rational cubic surface. Proofs are not given, but some of the methods of proof are indicated. These, as well as the theorems themselves, are mainly of an algebro-geometric nature. *R. J. Walker.*

Referred to in G35-7, G35-32.

G35-6 (7, 52a)

Segre, B. On arithmetical properties of singular cubic surfaces. J. London Math. Soc. **19**, 84–91 (1944).

The question considered is the existence of points with rational coordinates on a cubic surface $F(x, y, z)=0$ with rational coefficients and one or more singular points. The answer depends on the configuration of the singular points. The only remaining nontrivial cases are those of two or three isolated singular points. [The four point case has been considered by the author in another paper [same J. **19**, 46–55 (1944); these Rev. **6**, 117].] For three singular points there is either no rational point or a two parameter set, both cases being possible. For two singularities there is an infinite number of rational points but not a two parameter set; proof of this last fact is not given.
R. J. Walker (Ithaca, N. Y.)

Citations: MR 6, 117d = G35-4.
Referred to in G35-26.

G35-7 (7, 71a)

Valeiras, Antonio. On Diophantine analysis on cubic surfaces. Memorias sobre Matematicas (1942–44) por Antonio Valeiras, pp. 59–79. Buenos Aires, 1944. (Spanish)

There is first a scanty historical sketch on the Diophantine equation (1) $x^3+y^3+z^3+t^3=0$, for which two complete rational parametric solutions of the third and fourth degree are obtained by means of well-known geometric arguments [all this can be found in H. W. Richmond, Trans. Cambridge Philos. Soc. **22**, 389–403 (1920), where tables of sets of small integers satisfying (1) are also given]. There follow some rather irrelevant remarks concerning the arithmetic upon general cubic surfaces [on this subject cf. B. Segre, Bull. Amer. Math. Soc. **51**, 152–161 (1945); these Rev. **6**, 185; several other recent papers are quoted there], the canonical equation (2) $ABC=A'B'C'$ for these surfaces (where A, B, C, A', B', C' are linear quaternary forms), and the dual of the surface (1). It is also shown that the number of lines lying on the surface $x^n+y^n+z^n+t^n=0$ (n an integer greater than 2) is $3n^2$. It should be noticed that the equation (2) is not new, as the author thinks, but goes back to Steiner [J. Reine Angew. Math. **53**, 133–141 (1857)=Gesammelte Werke, vol. 2, Berlin, 1882, pp. 651–659].
B. Segre (Manchester).

Citations: MR 6, 185a = G35-5.

G35-8 (7, 169d)

Wachs, Sylvain. Sur une propriété arithmétique d'une variété cubique de l'espace à quatre dimensions. Rev. Sci. (Rev. Rose Illus.) **80**, 402–406 (1942).

This paper consists of two unrelated parts. In the first part it is observed that on the general V_3^3 in [4] there are sets of three lines, two by two skew; then, by a simple construction involving such a set of three lines, the well-known result that V_3^3 is the image of an involution of order 2 in [3] is proved. [This result can also be obtained by using a single line r of V_3^3, from the remark that the lines touching V_3^3 at points of r form an ∞^3 unicursal system, whose elements are in an algebraic (2, 1)-correspondence with the points of V_3^3.] When V_3^3 and the three lines considered on it belong to the rational field, one thus obtains a rational 3-parameter solution for the Diophantine equation representing V_3^3. The author asks whether this solution is complete or not, without giving an answer. [The answer is, in general, negative, since the conic Γ considered in §2 may contain an infinity of rational points, and yet meet the line D at two irrational points.]

The second part determines all the rational lines lying on the V_3^3 (1) $x_0^3+x_1^3+x_2^3+x_3^3+x_4^3=0$, that is, all the solutions of (1) which are of the form (2) $x_i=a_ix_3+b_ix_4$ (a_i, b_i rational, $i=0, 1, 2$). The author obtains them by discussing the system of four Diophantine equations in a_0, a_1, a_2, b_0, b_1, b_2 expressing that the elimination of x_0, x_1, x_2 from (1) and (2) leads to an identity in x_3, x_4. The result is that there are only 15 such solutions, namely, the trivial ones $x_i+x_j=x_h+x_k=x_l=0$, where i, j, h, k, l are the numbers 0, 1, 2, 3, 4 taken in any order; but the author twice states erroneously that there are only the 10 solutions $x_i+x_j=x_h=x_k=x_l=0$. *B. Segre* (Manchester).

Referred to in G35-18.

G35-9 (7, 244c)

Richmond, H. W. On the Diophantine equation $F\equiv ax^4+by^4+cz^4+dw^4=0$, the product $abcd$ being a square number. J. London Math. Soc. **19**, 193–194 (1944).

It is proved that one solution of the equation of the title can be used to generate a series of solutions. *I. Niven.*

Referred to in D36-32, G35-14.

G35-10 (7, 244d)

Segre, B. On arithmetical properties of quadric and quartic surfaces. J. London Math. Soc. **19**, 195–200 (1944).

After obtaining explicitly all the quartic tetrahedral surfaces that are rational (that is, representable by an equation with rational coefficients), the author deduces two distinct methods for deriving new solutions from a known solution of quartic Diophantine equations of a certain type depending on seven parameters. One of these two methods includes that given by Richmond [see the preceding review]. One part of the proof depends on an arithmetical result for quadrics, not yet published. *I. Niven.*

Referred to in D36-32, G35-14.

G35-11 (7, 323a)

Châtelet, François. Variations sur un thème de H. Poincaré. Ann. Sci. École Norm. Sup. (3) **61**, 249–300 (1944).

It is known (R being the rational number field) that (I) a unicursal curve in R contains points in R if and only if it is birationally equivalent in R to a line and (2) a unicursal curve in R is equivalent in R either to a line or a conic in R [Poincaré, J. Math. Pures Appl. (5) **7**, 161–233 (1901); M. Noether, Math. Ann. **23**, 311–358 (1884); Hilbert and Hurwitz, Acta Math. **14**, 217–224 (1891)]. The author gives new and suggestive proofs of these results, which he is able to generalise.

Let Φ be an arbitrary field and F an r-dimensional "Brauer variety" in Φ, that is, let F be defined by equations with coefficients in Φ and let there be a Poincaré transformation (birational with only isolated critical points) $\mathfrak{F}$ of a projective space E_r into F, the coefficients of $\mathfrak{F}$ being in some algebraic extension k of Φ. Every Poincaré transformation of F into itself in k is of the form $\mathfrak{F}^{-1}\mathfrak{H}\mathfrak{F}$, where $\mathfrak{H}$ is a nondegenerate homography in k of E_r, and this lies in Φ if and only if $\mathfrak{H}$ satisfies certain equations called the "system of equivalence" of F. The aggregate of degenerate and nondegenerate solutions $\mathfrak{H}$ of these equations forms a normal simple algebra over Φ with k as a splitting field. The degenerate solutions give rise to "normal subvarieties" of F (which are themselves Brauer varieties in Φ) and solutions of rank one correspond to points of F in Φ. The conditions for equivalence (defined in terms of Poincaré transformations) between Brauer varieties or their normal subvarieties reduce to simple relations between the corresponding algebras. Among other results, the extension to Brauer varieties of the first theorem above is derived by an application of the Wedderburn structure theorem. *D. B. Scott.*

Referred to in G05-7, G35-13, G35-29, G35-32.

G35-12 (9, 135b)

Segre, B. On arithmetical properties of quartic surfaces. Proc. London Math. Soc. (2) **49**, 353–395 (1947).

Let $F(x, y, z, w)$ be a quartic form with rational coefficients. Certain phases of the general problem of finding rational solutions of $F=0$ are handled by geometric methods. The author restricts himself to the case in which the quartic surface F contains one or more rational lines and considers the possibility of finding other one-, or two-, parameter families of rational solutions. His main tools are two transformations defined as follows. Let C be a rational line of F and P a rational point of C. The tangent plane to F at P intersects F in C and a residual cubic Γ which also contains P. The tangent line to Γ at P intersects Γ again in a rational point P', generally distinct from P. The locus of P' as P describes C is a curve C', called the R-transform of C, which contains a one-parameter set of rational points of F. If C and D are two skew rational lines of F, to a general point P of F there corresponds a unique point P' of F such that the line PP' intersects both C and D. Then P' is the T-transform of P, and the T-transform of any set of rational points is a set of rational points. Using these transformations and other geometric properties of quartic surfaces the author investigates surfaces containing various configurations of lines; special attention is also given to surfaces of the form $\phi(x, y)=\psi(z, w)$. As a particularly interesting case the equation $x^4+y^4=z^4+w^4$ is shown to have an infinite number of one-parameter sets of rational points in addition to the one such set discovered by Euler. [Dickson, History of the Theory of Numbers, v. 2, Washington, 1920, p. 644.] *R. J. Walker* (Ithaca, N. Y.).

Referred to in G35-14.

G35-13 (9, 304b)

Châtelet, François. Essais de géométrie galoisienne. Bull. Soc. Math. France **74**, 69–86 (1946).

Exposition of the "Galois methods" exploited in the author's thesis [Ann. Sci. École Norm. Sup. (3) **61**, 249–300 (1944); these Rev. **7**, 323] and some later papers. *D. B. Scott* (London).

Citations: MR 7, 323a = G35-11.

G35-14 (10, 182a)

Richmond, Herbert W. A note upon an arithmetical property of quartic surfaces. J. London Math. Soc. **23**, 6–8 (1948).

Consider the equation (1) $ax^4+by^4=cz^4+dw^4$, where a, b, c, d are integers and $abcd$ is a square. The quartic tetrahedral surface represented by (1) (in homogeneous coordinates (x, y, z, w)) is such that the inflexional tangents in any of its rational points can be obtained rationally, and so from any known solution of (1) in rational numbers two other solutions may be deduced [cf. H. W. Richmond, same J. **19**, 193–194 (1944); B. Segre, same J. **19**, 195–200 (1944); Proc. Cambridge Philos. Soc. **41**, 187–209 (1945), § II; Proc. London Math. Soc. (2) **49**, 353–395 (1947), § VIII; these Rev. **7**, 244, 169; **9**, 135]. The present paper determines all the biaxial quartic surfaces (2) $F(x, y)=G(z, w)$, where $F(x, y)$ and $G(z, w)$ are two binary quartics with rational coefficients, to which the results above can be extended. There are only two types of such surfaces (2). For the first type $F(x, y)$ and $G(z, w)$ are the squares of two quadratics, so that the quartic (2) splits up into two quadrics. For the second type the cubic invariants of $F(x, y)$ and $G(z, w)$ vanish and a certain arithmetical condition is satisfied by the coefficients of these two forms; the quartic (2) is then a projective transform of (1) in the complex field, and is therefore included among those investigated arithmetically in the first of Segre's papers quoted above.

B. Segre (Bologna).

Citations: MR 7, 244c = G35-9; MR 7, 244d = G35-10; MR 9, 135b = G35-12.

G35-15 (10, 510g)

Châtelet, François. Relations entre l'arithmétique et la géométrie sur une quadrique. Bull. Soc. Math. France **76**, 108–113 (1948).

The author discusses for rational quadrics in S_3 the classical arithmetical results on the existence of rational points and the division of such quadrics into classes whose elements are transformable into one another by rational homographies of the space. His innovation is to use the representation of the reguli of a quadric by conics in S_5 to reduce the problems to known questions concerning conics over the rational field and quadratic extensions of it.

D. B. Scott (London).

G35-16 (10, 510h)

Segre, B. Proprietà algebriche ed aritmetiche di forme cubiche. I. Atti Accad. Naz. Lincei. Rend. Cl. Sci. Fis. Mat. Nat. (8) **4**, 346–352 (1948).

In this and two other papers [see the following reviews], the author considers rational solutions of $x_1^3+\cdots+x_{r+2}^3=0$. This equation defines a cubic hypersurface F_r in S_{r+1}, which is invariant under a group G of $3^{r+1}(r+2)!$ collineations. In this paper the case $r+2=2n$ is considered. The hypersurface F is shown to contain $3^n(2n)!/2^n n!$ S_{n-1}'s, obtainable from $x_1+x_{n+1}=\cdots=x_n+x_{2n}=0$ by transforming by elements of G. Of these S_{n-1}'s, $(2n)!/2^n n!$ are rational. By projecting F onto an S_{2n-2} from two suitably chosen skew S_{n-1}'s of F, F can be parametrized rationally in quadratic forms in $2n-1$ variables. This parametrization gives all rational points of F. *R. J. Walker* (Ithaca, N. Y.).

G35-17 (10, 510i)

Segre, B. Proprietà algebriche ed aritmetiche di forme cubiche. II. Atti Accad. Naz. Lincei. Rend. Cl. Sci. Fis. Mat. Nat. (8) **4**, 509–515 (1948).

On the cubic hypersurface F, $x_0^3+x_1^3+\cdots+x_{2n}^3=0$, there are $3^{n-2}(2n+1)!/2^{n-2}(n-2)!5!$ doubly infinite systems of S_{n-1}'s. Each system generates a V_{n-1}^3 which is a section of F by an S_{n-2}. The S_{n-2} is given by (*) $x_3+x_{n+3}=\cdots=x_n+x_{2n}=0$ or a transform of this by an element of G. [See the preceding review.] The corresponding section of F is the cubic defined by (*) and (**) $x_0^3+x_1^3+x_2^3+x_{n+1}^3+x_{n+2}^3=0$. The determination of the S_{n-1}'s on F is thus reduced to the determination of the doubly infinite set of lines on the F_3 given by (**). A birational representation of these lines as an 18-fold plane is given. *R. J. Walker* (Ithaca, N. Y.).

G35-18 (10, 511a)

Segre, B. Proprietà algebriche ed aritmetiche di forme cubiche. III. Atti Accad. Naz. Lincei. Rend. Cl. Sci. Fis. Mat. Nat. (8) **4**, 629–632 (1948).

A simple geometric proof is given of the following theorem due to S. Wachs [Revue Sci. (Rev. Rose Illus.) **80**, 402–406 (1942); these Rev. **7**, 169]. The only rational lines on the F_3 given by (**) [see the preceding review] are the 15 lines $x_i=x_j+x_k=x_l+x_m$, i, j, k, l, m being a permutation of 0, 1, 2, $n+1$, $n+2$. It follows that the only rational S_{n-1}'s on F_r, $r=2n-1$, are the $(2n+1)!/2^n n!$ spaces $x_{i_0}=x_{i_1}+x_{i_{n+1}}=\cdots=x_{i_n}+x_{i_{2n}}=0$, $i_0, \cdots, i_{2n}$ being a permutation of $0, \cdots, 2n$. For the case $n\geqq 5$ use is made of the existence of nontrivial integer solutions of $a_1x_1^2+\cdots+a_5x_5^2=0$, the a_i being integers not all of the same sign, to show that every rational point on F_r is either a rational point of a rational S_{n-1} or the residual intersection of a rational line tangent to F_r at such a point. From this result is obtained a complete rational parametrization of F_r in 10-ic forms in $2n+3$ variables. *R. J. Walker* (Ithaca, N. Y.).

Citations: MR 7, 169d = G35-8.

G35-19 (10, 511b)

Segre, B. Proprietà algebriche ed aritmetiche di forme cubiche. IV. Atti Accad. Naz. Lincei. Rend. Cl. Sci. Fis. Mat. Nat. (8) **5**, 3–11 (1948).

[Cf. the preceding review.] Let Φ_m be the cubic hypersurface in S_{m+1} defined by

$$x_1^3+\cdots+x_{m+3}^3=0, \quad x_1+\cdots+x_{m+2}+\lambda x_{m+3}=0,$$

where $\lambda=1$ if m is odd and $\lambda=4^{\frac{1}{3}}$ if m is even. It is shown that Φ_m has $\binom{m+2}{[(m+1)/2]}$ double points. For $m=1$, 2, 3, or 4, Φ_m is a well-known variety, which has the maximum number of double points for its order and dimension. The situation of the double points of Φ_m is investigated, and a complete rational parametrization of Φ_m is obtained.

R. J. Walker (Ithaca, N. Y.).

G35-20 (11, 390a)

Northcott, D. G. An inequality in the theory of arithmetic on algebraic varieties. Proc. Cambridge Philos. Soc. **45**, 502–509 (1949).

A point P having in n-dimensional projective space S_n homogeneous coordinates $(\xi)=(\xi_0, \cdots, \xi_n)$ is called algebraic if all the ratios ξ_i/ξ_j are algebraic numbers. Then in any given number field K containing all these ratios the ξ_i generate a fractional ideal Ω, belonging to the ring of algebraic integers in K. Moreover, denoting by R the field of rational numbers, $N_{K/R}\Omega$ is a fractional ideal in R, admitting a unique positive generator, $|N_{K/R}\Omega|$ say. Consider the positive number

$$C(P)=\{\prod_\sigma(|\xi_0^\sigma|+\cdots+|\xi_n^\sigma|)/|N_{K/R}\Omega|\}^{1/(K:R)},$$

where the product is to be extended over all the relative isomorphisms σ of K over R into the complex field, and $(\xi_0^\sigma, \cdots, \xi_n^\sigma)$ is the transform of P by σ. It is easily seen that $C(P)$, called the arithmetical complexity of P, depends only on P and not on K. The purpose of this paper is to consider how $C(P)$ varies when P undergoes a mapping T of a certain type. The main result is expressed by the inequality $A\leqq C^m(P)/C(P^T)\leqq B$, concerning an algebraic point P varying on an indivisible (i.e., absolutely irreducible) algebraic variety V embedded in S_n, free from multiple points and defined over an arbitrary number field k. The mapping T associates at P the point P^T of coordinates $(T_0(\xi), \cdots, T_n(\xi))$, where $T_0, \cdots, T_n$ are $n+1$ forms on V of the same degree m, defined on k and having no common zero on V. In the formula above A and B denote positive constants depending only on V and T.

The inequality is established by using A. Weil's "theory of distributions" [Acta Math. **52**, 281–315 (1929)], described here in detail with the addition of some new results [cf. especially lemma 3]. *B. Segre* (Bologna).

Referred to in G30-21, G35-25.

G35-21 (11, 390b)

Northcott, D. G. A further inequality in the theory of arithmetic on algebraic varieties. Proc. Cambridge Philos. Soc. **45**, 510–518 (1949).

This paper is a sequel to the previous one, and we refer to the preceding review for the notations. It proves the inequality $C^m(P) \leqq MC(P^T)$, where now T denotes a more general mapping of the variety V, called a regular mapping, m is an integer attached to it, M is a positive constant depending only on V and T, and the inequality holds for every algebraic point P of V, with only possible exceptions for the points of certain subvarieties defined by T. By introducing on an elliptic curve the Weierstrassian uniformizing parameter u, one can define on it certain mappings of the types considered in this paper and in the previous one, i.e., $u \to Nu$, $u \to u-\alpha$, $u \to 2u-\alpha$, where N is a positive integer and α corresponds to an algebraic point. The general results previously obtained give then some new arithmetical properties of the elliptic cubics. *B. Segre* (Bologna).

Referred to in G35-25.

G35-22 (11, 390c)

Northcott, D. G. The values taken by a rational function on an algebraic variety. Proc. Cambridge Philos. Soc. **45**, 675–677 (1949).

Certain rather obvious connections between divisor and specialization theory, used in the previous two papers, are established here explicitly. In particular, it is proved that a zero or infinity in the sense of divisor theory is still a zero or infinity in the sense of specialization theory, and vice versa. *B. Segre* (Bologna).

G35-23 (11, 615c)

Northcott, D. G. Periodic points on an algebraic variety. Ann. of Math. (2) **51**, 167–177 (1950).

Let F and R be any field of complex numbers and the rational field, respectively. Denote then by σ any relative isomorphism of F/R, and by ξ^σ its effect on a given element ξ of F. A point $P=(\xi_0, \cdots, \xi_n)$ of the linear space $S_n(x_0, \cdots, x_n)$ is said to be rational with respect to F if its homogeneous coordinates ξ_i are equal (or proportional) to elements of F. The degree of rationality of a point P of S_n, whose coordinates are algebraic numbers, is the degree over R of the smallest field in which P is rational. The author proves first that, given a positive number k, for any field F there are only a finite number of points $P=(\xi_0, \cdots, \xi_n)$ of S_n which are rational relative to F and such that $D_F(P) \leqq k$, where $D_F(P) = \prod_\sigma(|\xi_0^\sigma| + \cdots + |\xi_n^\sigma|)/(N_{F/R}\Omega)$, the product being taken over all different isomorphisms σ of F/R, and Ω denoting the ideal sum $(\xi_0)+\cdots+(\xi_n)$.

Consider next an algebraic variety V of S_n, and the mapping of S_n carrying the point $(x_0, \cdots, x_n)$ into

$$[L_0(x_0, \cdots, x_n), L_1(x_0, \cdots, x_n), \cdots, L_n(x_0, \cdots, x_n)],$$

where the $L_i(x)$ are forms of degree l having algebraic numbers as coefficients. Suppose that (i) $l \geqq 2$, (ii) the $L_i(x)$ never vanish simultaneously at any point of V, (iii) the mapping transforms V into itself; then it is proved that the number of points of V having a given degree of rationality and such that, by iterating the mapping, each of them generates a finite sequence, is always finite. This is obtained as a consequence of the inequality $D_F{}^l(P) \leqq M^{(F:R)} D_F(Q)$, where P is any point of V which is rational relative to F, Q is the transform of P by the mapping, and M is a constant which depends on V and the mapping, but not on F. In the particular case where V is an elliptic cubic curve, the above results are applied to the study of the division values of the Weierstrass $\wp$-function, thus extending results previously obtained in this connection by K. Mahler [Quart. J. Math., Oxford Ser. **6**, 74–77 (1935)].

Conditions (i)–(iii) above are very restrictive [cf. B. Segre, Math. Ann. **109**, 1–3 (1933); F. Severi, Math. Ann. **109**, 4–6 (1933); these papers, however, are not quoted by the author]. The author succeeds in weakening condition (ii) for the case of plane curves, by utilizing Weil's concept of a "distribution" and his "decomposition theorem" [Acta Math. **52**, 281–315 (1929)]. *B. Segre* (Bologna).

G35-24 (12, 852d)

Segre, Beniamino. Sur les points entiers des surfaces cubiques. Algèbre et Théorie des Nombres. Colloques Internationaux du Centre National de la Recherche Scientifique, no. 24, pp. 81–82. Centre National de la Recherche Scientifique, Paris, 1950.

The algebraic surface $F(x, y, z)=0$ has infinitely many integral points (x, y, z) if there is a substitution $x=a_1u+b_1v+c_1$ etc. with integer coefficients such that $F(x, y, z)=\phi(u, v)$ and $\phi(u, v)=0$ has infinitely many integer points, e.g., is a cubic with integer coefficients and a cusp at an integral point. Examples are (i) $hz^3=f(x, y)$, where h is an integer and $f(x, y)$ is an irreducible inhomogeneous quadratic form with integer coefficients such that $f(x, y)=0$ has an integer solution and (ii) $hz^2=f(x, y)$, where h is an integer and $f(x, y)$ is an irreducible inhomogeneous cubic with integral coefficients such that $f(x, y)=0$ has an integral point of inflexion. *J. W. S. Cassels* (Cambridge, England).

G35-25 (13, 66d)

Weil, André. Arithmetic on algebraic varieties. Ann. of Math. (2) **53**, 412–444 (1951).

The author has extended in his thesis [Acta Math. **52**, 281–315 (1929)] Mordell's theorem (concerning the case $p=1$), proving that any algebraic curve of genus p over any given finite algebraic field k has a finite rank r (minimum number of sets of p points, rational over k, from which all the others can be deduced by means of rational operations). The main tool in proving this deep result is a decomposition theorem (proved in loc. cit., chapter I) extending to arbitrary algebraic varieties a well known elementary result on factorization of rational functions over a curve of genus zero. This theory has been further developed by C. L. Siegel [Abh. Preuss. Akad. Wiss. Math.-Nat. Kl. **1929**, no. 1 (1930)], A. Weil [Arithmétique et géométrie sur les variétés algébriques, Actualités Sci. Ind., no. 206, Hermann, Paris, 1935] and, very recently, D. G. Northcott [Proc. Cambridge Philos. Soc. **45**, 502–509, 510–518 (1949); these Rev. **11**, 390]. In the present work (which is divided into five sections and an appendix), by making explicit some ideal-theoretic concepts implicit in the papers cited above, the proper algebraic foundations for that theory are supplied, and a comprehensive account of its results, including some new ones, is given.

In section I, after having defined specializations, specialization-rings, specialization-ideals, valuation-rings and valuation-ideals, the theorem on the extension of specializations in algebraic geometry is proved, as well as other results including Krull's identification between integrally closed ideals and valuation-ideals. Then the valuation-functions are introduced, and their relations with the divisors of an algebraic variety are investigated. Among other results, the following one is proved. Let V be a nonsingular projective variety defined over a field k; let T be a divisor on V rational over k. Then there are functions x_μ, u_ν on V, defined over k, whose divisors are $(x_\mu)=T+X_\mu-Z$, $(u_\nu)=U_\nu-Z$, where Z is a divisor and the X_μ (as well as the U_ν) are positive divisors with no point in common.

Section II contains a study of absolute values on a field and its subrings, leading to the important notions of distributions (functions conveniently attached to finite sets of elements of a field) and their size. For every point $\alpha=(\alpha_0, \alpha_1, \cdots, \alpha_n)$ with algebraic coordinates in a projective space P^n, a height $h(\alpha)$ is intrinsically defined, such that, if $d(\alpha)$ is the degree over the rational field Q of the extension of Q generated by the α_i/α_j, the number of points α in P^n for which $d(\alpha)\leqq d_0$, $h(\alpha)\leqq h_0$, is finite (when n, d_0, h_0 are given). Also the effect on heights of a change of coordinates is studied, and it is shown how, from every theorem on sizes of distributions, a theorem on heights of points can be deduced. Using the remark that a set of $n+1$ functions on V defines a mapping of V into P^n, the following theorem is proved.

Let V be an abstract algebraic variety, complete and normal, defined over an algebraic number-field k (i.e., a finite algebraic extension of Q). Let φ, ψ be two mappings of V into projective spaces, both defined over k; assume that the linear system of primals without fixed components, defined on V by φ and ψ, is both without fixed points and belongs to the same complete system. Then φ, ψ are everywhere defined on V, and there are constants γ, γ', both >0, such that

$$\gamma h[\psi(P)]\leqq h[\varphi(P)]\leqq \gamma' h[\psi(P)]$$

at all absolutely algebraic points P of V.

The following decomposition theorem is then established in section III, together with other related results. Let V be a nonsingular projective variety defined over a field k. Let v be an absolute value, everywhere $<+\infty$, on k. Then to every prime rational divisor W over k on V one can attach a function $\Delta_W(P)$, defined at all the points P of V which are rational over k, taking its values in $[0, 1]$ in such a way that the following properties hold: (a) $\Delta_W(P)$ is 0 if and only if P lies on W, and it is continuous everywhere for the topology defined by v; (b) if z is any function, defined over k on V, with the divisor $(z)=\sum_i m_iW_i$, where the W_i are prime rational divisors over k, then there are constants γ, γ', both >0, such that

$$\gamma\prod_i \Delta_{W_i}(P)^{m_i}\leqq v[z(P)]\leqq \gamma'\prod_i \Delta_{W_i}(P)^{m_i}$$

at all points P, rational over k on V, at which z is defined.

In the case of curves, no distinction has to be made between valuation-functions and divisors, and the whole theory simplifies, as it is shown in section IV. Finally, section V provides substantial motivation for the concept of valuation-functions "attached" to divisors in section I, by dealing with some further general concepts (fractional ideals, centre of a valuation, local ideals and their coherent system), and the appendix concerns divisorial valuations.

B. Segre (Rome).

Citations: MR 11, 390a = G35-20; MR 11, 390b = G35-21.

Referred to in G02-6, G05-34, G30-21, G30-54.

G35-26 (13, 678d)

Segre, Beniamino. On the rational solutions of homogeneous cubic equations in four variables. Math. Notae 11, 1–68 (1951).

A homogeneous cubic equation in four variables defines a cubic surface F in projective 3-space. This surface is assumed to be non-singular, the singular case having been treated by the author in an earlier paper [J. London Math. Soc. **19**, 84–91 (1944); these Rev. **7**, 52]. Assuming the equation has rational coefficients, the basic problem is to find points of the surface with rational coefficients; a related problem is to find on the surface curves, finite point sets, etc. which are determined by polynomial equations with rational coefficients. Such points, curves, etc. are called "rational". The point of view in the proofs is largely geometrical, much use being made of known properties of F, such as its intersections with other surfaces, the configuration of its 27 lines, and its Eckhardt points. Surfaces of the form $\sum a_ix_i^3=0$ are treated in special detail. Typical of the chief results are: (1) F has either no rational points or an infinite number; (2) F contains a non-trivial rational curve (i.e., not the complete intersection with a rational surface) if and only if it contains a rational set of 1, 2, 3, or 6 mutually skew lines; (3) F is expressible as a third order determinant of rational linear forms if and only if it has a rational point and a rational set of six mutually skew lines; (4) Ryley's equation, $F=x_1^3+x_2^3+x_3^3+px_4^3=0$, where p is rational but not the cube of a rational number, has no parametric solution $x_i=\varphi_i(t)$, the φ_i being relatively prime rational polynomials, unless the curve thus given parametrically is the complete intersection of F with another surface.

R. J. Walker (Ithaca, N. Y.).

Citations: MR 7, 52a = G35-6.

Referred to in G35-28, G35-32, G35-46.

G35-27 (14, 580a)

Néron, A. La théorie de la base pour les diviseurs sur les variétés algébriques. Deuxième Colloque de Géométrie Algébrique, Liège, 1952, pp. 119–126. Georges Thone, Liège; Masson & Cie, Paris, 1952. 375 Belgian francs; 2625 French francs.

Let V be an algebraic variety, G the group of divisors on V, and G_a the group of divisors algebraically equivalent to 0. Then the theorem of Severi states that G/G_a is a finitely generated group. This theorem has been established by Severi in the case where the basic field is that of complex numbers (by transcendental methods). The author briefly sketches a proof of the extension of this theorem to an arbitrary basic field. The proof proceeds by induction on the dimension n of V, and each step of the induction involves an argument of "infinite descent" of the type of the one which was used by A. Weil in the proof of the corresponding theorem for curves over a field of algebraic numbers.

The problem is first reduced to the case where V is fibered by a family of curves; the parameter variety of this family, say $\mathfrak{M}$, is then of dimension $n-1$, and it is to $\mathfrak{M}$ that the inductive assumption is applied. Let H_0 be the group of divisors in G which cut out a divisor of degree 0 on the generic fiber of V, H the group of divisors whose projections on $\mathfrak{M}$ are of dimensions $\leqq n-2$ and $H_a=G_a+H$. Let H' be the group of reciprocal images of divisors on $\mathfrak{M}$ under the projection of V on $\mathfrak{M}$; then $(G_a+H')/G_a$ is isomorphic to a factor group of $G(\mathfrak{M})/G_a(\mathfrak{M})$ and is therefore finitely generated by the inductive assumption. If $H_a=H+G_a$, then $H_a/(G_a+H')$ is easily seen to be finitely generated. The problem is therefore reduced to proving that H_0/H_a is finitely generated (G/H_0 being a cyclic group).

In order to do this, let $C(M)$ be the generic fiber of V (M generic on $\mathfrak{M}$), $J(M)$ its Jacobian variety, and $\mathfrak{J}$ the locus of $J(M)$ over the field of definition k of V. To every divisor in H_0 there is associated a section of the fibered variety $\mathfrak{J}$, and these sections form a group h isomorphic to H_0/H_l, where H_l is generated by H and by the group G_l of divisors linearly equivalent to 0 on V. It is first proved that, for any $s>0$, the group h/sh is finite. The proof is based on properties of abelian varieties. This paves the way for an application of the method of infinite descent. Let $Z_1, \cdots, Z_r$ be representatives for the classes of h modulo sh. To any Z in h we may associate an infinite sequence $Z^{(i)}$ such that $Z^{(i-1)} = sZ^{(i)} + Z_{l(i)}$, $1 \leq l(i) \leq r$. Let h_a be the image of H_a/H_l in h. Then the problem is reduced to showing that $Z^{(i)}$ ultimately belongs to some finite set of cosets of h modulo h_a which does not depend on Z. This is accomplished by making use of a projective model of $\mathfrak{J}$ and showing that $Z^{(i)}$ is represented on this model by a cycle of bounded degree.

As an application, the author derives a generalization of A. Weil's theorem on curves to the case of a curve defined over an arbitrary field of finite type (i.e., absolutely generated by a finite number of elements). *C. Chevalley.*

G35-28 (14, 790a)

Châtelet, François. Sur un exemple de M. B. Segre. C. R. Acad. Sci. Paris **236**, 268–269 (1953).

B. Segre [Math. Notae **11**, 1–68 (1951); these Rev. **13**, 678] proved that a non-singular cubic surface S with rational coefficients is birationally equivalent, with rational coefficients, to a plane if (1) S contains a rational set of mutually skew lines, and (2) S contains a rational point. An example is given here to show that (2) is not redundant. Also, two slight generalizations of Segre's theorem are given.
R. J. Walker (Ithaca, N. Y.).

Citations: MR 13, 678d = G35-26.
Referred to in G35-29.

G35-29 (16, 850f)

Châtelet, François. Exemples de surfaces de Brauer. C. R. Acad. Sci. Paris **239**, 1578–1579 (1954).

In an earlier paper [Ann. Sci. Ecole Norm. Sup. (3) **61**, 249–300 (1944); MR **7**, 323] the author applied some general algebraic techniques to obtain properties of algebraic varieties defined by polynomials with coefficients in a given field. Later [C. R. Acad. Sci. Paris **236**, 268–269 (1953); MR **14**, 790] he applied these methods to cubic surfaces containing a rational homoloidal net of skew cubic curves. In the present note he outlines a method of constructing all such surfaces having three conical nodes, gives an example, and comments that the method can be generalized to higher-dimensional varieties. *R. J. Walker.*

Citations: MR 7, 323a = G35-11; MR 14, 790a = G35-28.

G35-30 (17, 947e)

Lamprecht, Erich. Zetafunktionen symmetrisch-erzeugbarer algebraischer Funktionenkörper mehrerer Veränderlicher. Math. Z. **64** (1955), 47–71 (1956).

Let A be a finitely generated field and p the characteristic of A. Assume there is given a basis of transcendency $x = \{x_1, \cdots, x_n\}$ of A. The author defines a zetafunction $Z_A(s)$, depending on x, in the following recursive way [in the case $p=0$, $n=1$ see also the paper reviewed above]: If A is a finite field (i.e., $p>0$, $n=0$), put $Z_A(s) = (1-\mathfrak{N}(A)^{-s})^{-1}$, where $\mathfrak{N}(A)$ denotes the number of elements in A. If A is not finite, let A_* be the subfield of those elements in A, which are absolutely algebraic if $p=0$, and which are algebraic over the field generated by x_1 if $p>0$. Consider the places $\mathfrak{P}$ of A such that (i) $\mathfrak{P}$ induces in A_* a non-trivial place, and (ii) the images $x_i\mathfrak{P}$ ($1 \leq i \leq n$ if $p=0$; $2 \leq i \leq n$ if $p>0$) are algebraically independent over $A_*\mathfrak{P}$. By induction, assume the zetafunction $Z_{A\mathfrak{P}}(s)$ of the image field $A\mathfrak{P}$ with respect to the basis of transcendency $\{x_1\mathfrak{P}, \cdots, x_n\mathfrak{P}$ if $p=0$, and $x_2\mathfrak{P}, \cdots, x_n\mathfrak{P}$ if $p>0\}$ already defined. Then $Z_A(s)$ is defined by the product formula $Z_A(s) = \prod_{\mathfrak{P}} Z_{A\mathfrak{P}}(s)$.

The author considers mainly the case where A is the independent compositum of n fields K_i, each of degree of transcendency 1, and where x_i is a basis of transcendency for K_i. By means of general composition theorems (§ 1, 3) he shows that the properties of $Z_A(s)$ can be derived from those of the $Z_{K_i}(s)$. He discusses the following properties: (a) convergence of the defining product formula; (b) rationality of $Z_A(s)$ as function of q^s if $p>0$ and q is the number of elements in the constant field of A; (c) representation of $Z_A(s)$ by means of L-functions with „Größencharaktere" if $p=0$; (d) distribution of poles and zeros if $p>0$; (e) functional equation if $p>0$.

In § 2, the author considers the case $p>0$, and the "geometrical" zetafunction $\zeta_A(z)$, defined with respect to a projective model M of A by

$$d \log \zeta_A(z) = \sum_r N^{(r)}(M)\, z^r dz/z,$$

here $N^{(r)}(M)$ denotes the number of points of M which are rational in the extension of degree r over the constant field of A [see Weil, Bull. Amer. Math. Soc. **55** (1949), 497–508; MR **10**, 592]. He again proves a general composition theorem, similar to that for the zetafunctions described above. From this it follows, if A is the independent compositum of n fields K_i, that $\zeta_A(q^{-s}) = Z_A(s)$, if the choices of M and x, defining ζ and Z, are both adapted to the representation of A as the compositum of the K_i.

The author mentions that in general it is not true that $\zeta_A(q^{-s}) = Z_A(s)$, even if M and x are related to each other in a natural way. He computes $\zeta_A(z)$ if M is defined by the inhomogeneous equation $y^p - y = a_1x_1^m + \cdots + a_nx_n^m$ $(m|p-1)$. [For the case $n=1$, see Davenport and Hasse, J. Reine Angew. Math. **172** (1934), 151–182.] Finally, the author gives necessary and sufficient conditions for A (if $n=2$) to be represented in two different ways as independent compositum of two fields. *P. Roquette.*

Citations: MR 10, 592e = T50-8.
Referred to in G30-18, G30-19, G30-20, G35-34.

G35-31 (18, 334c)

Segre, Beniamino. Alcune osservazioni sulle superficie cubiche nel campo razionale. Atti Accad. Naz. Lincei. Rend. Cl. Sci. Fis. Mat. Nat. (8) **20** (1956), 147–149.

T. Skolem [Math. Z. **63** (1955), 295–312; MR **17**, 464] ha dato un esempio di superficie cubica razionale (e cioé, a coefficienti razionali), priva di punti multipli, che mediante un sistema omaloidico razionale di quadriche vien trasformata in una superficie cubica avente una terna razionale di punti doppi (irrazionali); ciò consente di ottenere per la data superficie una rappresentazione parametrica razionale. Alla questione, posta da T. Skolem, di vedere se un simile procedimento possa essere esteso alle superficie cubiche generali, B. Segre risponde nella Nota presente, dimostrando che: le superficie cubiche razionali alle quali può estendersi il procedimento suddetto son tutte e sole quelle dotate di tre rette a, b, c a due a due sghembe, costituenti una terna razionale e dotate di (almeno) une comune retta trasversale razionale (ciascuna delle due schiere rigate della quadrica definita da a, b, c deve cioè avere infinite generatrici razionali). In particolare la superficie cubica $\sum a_ix_i^3 = 0$ ($i = 1, 2, 3, 4$; a_i numeri razionali non nulli) può essere trasformata cremonianamente nel campo razionale in una superficie cubica dotata di tre punti doppi non allineati se il prodotto di due opportune delle a_i diviso per il prodotto delle rimanenti è il cubo di un numero razionale.
D. Gallarati (Genova).

Citations: MR 17, 464c = D32-51.

G35-32 **(18, 334d)**

Châtelet, F. Points rationnels sur les surfaces cubiques. Séminaire A. Châtelet et P. Dubreil de la Faculté des Sciences de Paris, 1953/1954. Algèbre et théorie des nombres. 2e tirage multigraphié, pp. 8-01–8-11. Secrétariat mathématique, 11 rue Pierre Curie, Paris, 1956.

The present paper begins by summarizing some of the arithmetical results on cubic surfaces expounded by B. Segre [Bull. Amer. Math. Soc. **51** (1945), 152–161; Math. Notae **11** (1951), 1–68; MR **6**, 185; **13**, 678]. One of them asserts that a rational non-singular cubic surface containing a rational sextuplet of lines can be birationally represented on a plane in the rational field if, and only if, it contains one rational point. The author now remarks that, consequently, the questions of deciding whether the surface does or does not contain such a point, and of obtaining all the rational points when they exist, can be dealt with by using the methods of his thesis [Ann. Sci. Ecole Norm. Sup. (3) **61** (1944), 249–300; MR **7**, 323]; then he applies this remark to the research of the rational solutions (x, y, z) of the equation

$$N(x+\theta y+\theta^2 z)=A,$$

where A is a rational number, θ is a cyclic cubic number, and $N(a)$ denotes the norm of a, a being a number of the field $R(\theta)$. Next the rational non-singular cubic surfaces containing a rational triplet are likewise investigated, using the fact that on the surface there are two sextuplets containing the given triplet; this is then applied to the study of the above equation in the case when θ is a non-cyclic cubic number. The same purpose is also achieved by another method, in which the theory of ideals of algebraic numbers directly intervenes. *B. Segre* (Rome).

Citations: MR 6, 185a = G35-5; MR 7, 323a = G35-11; MR 13, 678d = G35-26.

G35-33 **(18, 600c)**

Néron, André. Arithmétique et classes de diviseurs sur les variétés algébriques. Proceedings of the international symposium on algebraic number theory, Tokyo & Nikko, 1955, pp. 139–154. Science Council of Japan, Tokyo, 1956.

L'auteur précise, dans le cas des corps de fonctions, certains points de la théorie des „distributions" de Weil. Il en déduit une simplification de la méthode de descente infinie employée par lui pour montrer que $G(V)/G_a(V)$ est un groupe abélien de type fini. *P. Samuel.*

G35-34 **(19, 244a)**

Lamprecht, Erich. Bewertungssysteme und Zetafunktionen algebraischer Funktionenkörper. III. Math. Ann. **132** (1957), 373–403.

For any extension K/k of finite type of a field k, denote by $P(K)$ the set of prime divisors of K/k (classes of equivalent discrete valuations of K/k); a prime divisor M in $P(K)$ is said to be trivial on a subfield K' of K if the valuations of the class M are trivial on K'. Let A/k be a field of algebraic functions of 2 variables over k; let K, K' be two distinct subfields of A, of transcendance degree 1 over k, algebraically closed in A; A is then algebraic over KK'. The author introduces the set $P(K, K')$ of prime divisors of A/k which are trivial on K' but not on K. For each V in $P(K, K')$, let $R(V)$ be the residue field of V, which is of transcendance degree 1 over k; each prime divisor v in $P(R(V))$ determines (by the process of composition of valuations) a class of equivalent discrete valuations of rank 2 of A/k, or, what amounts to the same, a place of A/k; let $b(K, K')$ be the set of places obtained in this manner. The author introduces a notion of divisor relative to $b(K, K')$; to every element $\neq 0$ of A there is associated such a divisor. There is a simultaneous approximation theorem for any finite set of places in $b(K, K')$. On the other hand, there is a natural mapping $f_{K,K'}: b(K, K')\to P(K)\times P(K')$. If (w,w') is in $P(K)\times P(K')$, the pair (w, w') is called permutable if there is a bijection of $f_{K,K'}{}^{-1}(w, w')$ on $f_{K',K}{}^{-1}(w', w)$ such that corresponding places have isomorphic residue fields. It is proved (as a special case of a more general result) that, if k is perfect, then there is an integer N such that, for almost all w in $P(K)$, all but at most N of the elements of $P(K')$ are permutable with w.

In case k is a finite field, the author has introduced the zeta function

$$Z(s; K, K')=\prod_{V\in B(K,K')}\zeta(R(V); s),$$

where $\zeta(R(V); s)$ is the zeta function of the field $R(V)$ [Math. Ann. **131** (1956), 313–335; MR **18**, 107]. In the present paper, he legitimatizes this definition by showing that the product converges in the domain $\Re(s)>2$; it is proved that the Z-function can be continued analytically at least in the region $\Re(s)>3/2$; assuming that it can be continued in the region $\Re(s)>1$, the number, locations and orders of the zeros and poles it may have in this region are invariants of A (they do not depend on K and K'); in some examples which were computed by the author [Math. Z. **64** (1956), 47–71; Arch. Math. **6** (1955), 266–274; MR **17**, 947, 350], one actually obtains in this manner invariants of the field A. *C. Chevalley.*

Citations: MR 17, 350c = G30-17; MR 17, 947e = G35-30; MR 18, 107c = G30-19.

G35-35 **(20# 2349)**

Nishimura, Hajime. Some remarks on rational points. Mem. Coll. Sci. Univ. Kyoto. Ser. A. Math. **29** (1955), 189–192.

The following theorem is proved. Let U, V be abstract varieties, V complete, let Π be a rational function defined on U with values in V, and let k be a field of definition for U, V, Π. If U has a rational point P over k that is simple on U, then V also has a rational point over k. An example is given to show that the hypothesis, "P is simple", cannot be replaced by the weaker hypothesis, "U is normal at P". *H. T. Muhly* (Iowa City, Iowa)

G35-36 **(20# 4558)**

Morin, Ugo. Problemi di razionalità ed analisi indeterminata. Rend. Sem. Mat. Fis. Milano **27** (1957), 160–166.

The author shows how the methods of classical diophantine analysis may be applied to study the existence of a surface which unisects the rational curves of a system of curves on a variety $V_3{}^n$ in S_4.

G. B. Huff (Athens, Ga.)

G35-37 **(21# 3405)**

Roquette, Peter. Einheiten und Divisorklassen in endlich erzeugbaren Körpern. Jber. Deutsch. Math. Verein. **60** (1957), Abt. 1, 1–21.

Let K be a field. A prime divisor $\mathfrak{p}$ of K means a class of equivalent discrete valuations of rank 1. Let M be a set of prime divisors of K such that (1) for every element $a\in K^*$ (the multiplicative group of K) there exist only a finite number of $\mathfrak{p}\in M$ with $w_{\mathfrak{p}}(a)\neq 0$. The divisor group D_M is defined to be the free abelian group with free generators $\mathfrak{p}\in M$. Then the natural exact sequence

$$1\to E_M\to K^*\to D_M\to C_M\to 1$$

holds with the unit group E_M and the divisor class group

C_M. The problem is to show that under certain conditions E_M and C_M are finitely generated.

The "Stufe" of a finitely generated field K means (the transcendental degree of K) + 1 if the characteristic of K is zero, and the transcendental degree otherwise. It is denoted by St (K). For a subset x of K, St $(x)=K$ means that K is finite algebraic over (x). Then M_x means the set of all prime divisors $\mathfrak{p}$ of K such that (a) every element of x is integral for $\mathfrak{p}$ and (b) St $(x \bmod \mathfrak{p})=$ St $(K \bmod \mathfrak{p})=$ St $(K)-1$. It is proved that M_x has the above property (1) in case St $(x)=K$. In general a set M of prime divisors of K is called finitely generated if there exists a set $x \subset K$ such that St $(x)=K$, $M_x \subset M$ and $M-M_x$ is finite.

The fundamental results are the following two theorems. Unit theorem: Let K be finitely generated; then the unit group E_M with respect to a finitely generated set M of prime divisors is itself finitely generated. Class theorem: Under the same assumptions the divisor class group C_M is also finitely generated. These theorems are proved by mathematical induction on the Stufe of K. The unit theorem follows from well-known results in the case of Stufe 1. For the proof of the class theorem the deep results of Weil and Néron are used. *Y. Kawada* (Tokyo)

Referred to in G10-12.

G35-38 (24# A85)

Chatelet, F.

Points rationnels sur certaines courbes et surfaces cubiques.

Enseignement Math. (2) **5** (1959), 153–170 (1960).

Let a, a_1, a_2 be in the field $\mathbf{Q}$ of rational numbers and suppose that $\theta=a^{1/2}$ is irrational. The author sets up a theory of the rational points (x, y, z) on the surface $S: y^2-az^2=x(x-a_1)(x-a_2)$ which is reminiscent of Weil's elementary treatment of the Mordell-Weil theorem [Bull. Sci. Math. (2) **54** (1930), 182–191]. Since $y^2-az^2=(y-\theta z)(y+\theta z)$, the points of S defined over $\mathbf{Q}(\theta)$ are expressible in terms of the parameters $\lambda=(y+\theta z)/(x-a_1)$ and $\mu=(y-\theta z)/(x-a_2)$. If $M, \bar{M}$ are two conjugate points of S defined over $\mathbf{Q}(\theta)$, the line joining them cuts S in a third point, which must be rational. A necessary and sufficient condition that the rational point (x, y, z) be obtainable this way is that each of $x, x-a_1, x-a_2$ be a norm of an element of $\mathbf{Q}(\theta)$. Apparently not every rational point of S is of this shape, but at least $x=dn$, $x-a_1=d_1n_1$, $x-a_2=d_2n_2$, where n, n_1, n_2 are norms and d, d_1, d_2 are from a finite set. Further, if (x_j, y_j, z_j) $(j=1, 2, 3)$ are rational collinear points on S then $x_1x_2x_3$, $(x_1-a_1)\times(x_2-a_1)(x_3-a_1)$ and $(x_1-a_2)(x_2-a_2)(x_3-a_2)$ are all norms. Hence all the rational points on S are given by a finite number of rational parametric representations. Finally, if a rational point can be obtained from one pair of conjugate points $M, \bar{M}$, then it can be obtained from infinitely many such pairs, and the author discusses the relations of these pairs to one another. The author states that the results of the paper can be generalized to $y^2-az^2=P(x)$, where $P(x)$ is any cubic polynomial with rational coefficients.

J. W. S. Cassels (Cambridge, England)

Referred to in G35-43.

G35-39 (25# 4407)

Predonzan, Arno

Alcuni teoremi relativi all'unirazionalità di ipersuperficie algebriche non generali.

Rend. Sem. Mat. Univ. Padova **31** (1961), 281–293.

Morin has shown [Atti Secundo Congresso Un. Mat. Ital. (Bologna, 1940), pp. 298–302, Edizioni Cremonese, Rome, 1942; MR **8**, 527] that the general primal of order n in P_r is unirational over an algebraic extension of the base field for sufficiently large r (i.e., for r exceeding some integer $r(n)$). The author considers the unirationality of arbitrary primals. He first shows that an absolutely irreducible primal of order $n \geqq 2$ in P_r (defined over a field k) which contains a totally non-singular P_s is unirational over the field $k(P_s)$ provided $s>s(n)$, where $s(n)$ is a function of n which is defined inductively. From this he deduces a result which asserts the unirationality (over an algebraic extension of the field of definition) of an absolutely irreducible primal of order n in P_r for sufficiently large r, this being defined in terms of the function $s(n)$ introduced above and the dimension of the singular sub-variety. In the case of a non-singular variety this gives some improvement on Morin's result.

Finally the author proves the unirationality (over an algebraic extension of the field of definition) of any primal of order n $(\geqq 2)$ in P_r defined by a form which is the sum of $(r+1)$ nth powers of linear forms.

D. B. Scott (Brighton)

Referred to in G35-41.

G35-40 (29# 91)

Schanuel, S.

On heights in number fields.

Bull. Amer. Math. Soc. **70** (1964), 262–263.

The object of this note is to announce a proof of a generalization of the classical result due to Dedekind and Weber. A corollary is formulated as follows: K is a number field of degree N over Q. S_∞ is the set of Archimedean absolute values of K normalized to extend the absolute value of Q. For $x \in K^*$, $\nu \in S_\infty$, let $\|X\|_\nu=|X|_\nu^{N_\nu}$, where $N_\nu=[K_\nu: Q_\nu]$ so that $N_\nu=1$ or 2. Let $X=(X_1, \cdots, X_m) \in K^m$ and $\|X\|_\nu=\sup\|X_i\|$, $H_\infty(X)=\prod_{\nu\in S_\infty}\|X\|_\nu$. Let $[X]$ denote the fractional ideal generated by $X_1, \cdots, X_m$. Define the height of X to be $N[X]^{-1}H_\infty(X)$. Finally, the class of a point in projective space $P^{n-1}(K)$ is the class modulo principal ideals of the fractional ideal generated by homogeneous coordinates for X. Theorem: The number of points in $P^{m-1}(K)$ of a given class with height at most B is

$$\frac{k_m B^m}{\zeta_K(m)}+O(B^{(m-1)/N}),$$

where

$$k_m = \left(\frac{2^{r_1}(2\pi)^{r_2}}{\sqrt{d}}\right)^m \frac{R}{w}m^r.$$

R. Ayoub (University Park, Pa.)

G35-41 (31# 120)

Morin, Ugo

Risoluzione geometrica di problemi di analisi diofantea di grado superiore.

Univ. e Politec. Torino Rend. Sem. Mat. **20** (1960/61), 255–266.

Es werden Hyperflächen der Form $x_1{}^n+x_2{}^n+\cdots+x_{r+1}^n=0$ im r-dimensionalen projektiven Raum S_r $(r\geqq 5)$ diskutiert und insbesondere die Frage nach der Unirationalität dieser Hyperflächen. Definitionskörper ist der Körper Q der rationalen Zahlen. Es stellt sich zum Beispiel heraus, dass die oben angegebene Hyperfläche bei ungeradem n für hinreichend grosses r unirational ist, nämlich für $r \geqq s(n+1)/(s(n)+1)+s(n)$, wobei $s(n)$ rekursiv durch $s(2)=0$, $s(n)=\binom{s(n-1)+(n-1)}{n-1}$ definiert wird. Darüberhinaus werden auch Hyperflächen von verwandtem Typus diskutiert, z.B. $x_1^n+\cdots+x_{2s}^n=x_{2s+1}^n+\cdots+x_{r+1}^n$. Für Einzelheiten wird auf die Originalarbeiten verwiesen, insbesondere auf A. Predonzan [Rend. Sem. Mat. Univ.

Padova **31** (1961), 281–293; MR **25** #4407].

P. Roquette (Tübingen)

Citations: MR 25# 4407 = G35-39.

G35-42 (31# 1252)

Lang, Serge

Les formes bilinéaires de Néron et Tate.

Séminaire Bourbaki, 1963/64, *Fasc.* 3, *Exposé* 274, 11 *pp. Secrétariat mathématique, Paris*, 1964.

An account of two papers containing fundamental results in the theory of heights of points on algebraic varieties defined over global fields; the first, by John Tate ("non publié, comme d'habitude"), has already been partly published by proxy [Manin, Izv. Akad. Nauk SSSR Ser. Mat. **28** (1964), 1363–1390; MR **30** #3886]; in it is verified the conjecture of Néron ["Valeur asymptotique du nombre des points rationnels de hauteur bornée sur une courbe elliptique", short communication in Proc. Internat. Congr. Mathematicians (August, 1958, Edinburgh), p. xx, Cambridge Univ. Press, Cambridge, 1960] that the height is given, up to a bounded summand, by a quadratic form. The proof depends on an ingenious limiting process, which also gives a bilinear form on the points of an abelian variety and its dual. In the other paper, by Néron, which will doubtless be published in due course in the conventional way, it is shown that the quadratic form and bilinear form are, in fact, sums of summands, one for each local completion of the global field. These local summands are said to be essentially just intersection multiplicities. Results in this direction, but apparently less complete, have already been given by Manin [loc. cit.]. Néron's proof is said to depend on a reformulation of Weil's theory of distributions, and an indication of the new theory is given.

J. W. S. Cassels (Cambridge, England)

Citations: MR 30# 3886 = G10-24.

Referred to in G10-26, G30-54.

G35-43 (35# 4217)

Chatelet, François

Points rationnels sur certaines surfaces cubiques.

Les Tendances Géom. en Algèbre et Théorie des Nombres, *pp.* 67–75. *Éditions du Centre National de la Recherche Scientifique, Paris*, 1966.

The author pursues for cubic surfaces an analogue of the Poincaré-Mordell-Weil theorem for elliptic curves (see also the author's paper in Enseignement Math. (2) **5** (1959), 153–170 (1960) [MR **24** #A85]. Let S be a cubic surface defined over $\mathbf{Q}$ and let k be a quadratic extension of $\mathbf{Q}$. Since S is cubic, two points M_1, M_2 of S_k (the subset of S of points rational over k) determine a third point $M\in S_k$ as the intersection of S with the line joining M_1 and M_2. Although this rule of composition of points on S_k does not define a group structure on it for a cubic surface, we write $M=M_1+M_2$. If, in particular, M_1 and M_2 are mutually conjugate by an automorphism of k over $\mathbf{Q}$, M is rational over $\mathbf{Q}$: $M\in S_{\mathbf{Q}}$. Denote by E_0 the subset of $S_{\mathbf{Q}}$ obtained from S_k in this manner. In analogy with the theorem for elliptic curves, the author discusses the following properties: (i) $S_{\mathbf{Q}}$ is a union of a finite number of mutually disjoint subsets E_i of the form P_i+E_0, $P_i\in S_{\mathbf{Q}}$, and (ii) each E_i is unirationally representable by the k-rational points of a plane, and verifies them for the following examples: (a) S is given by $N(x+\theta y+\theta^2 z)=a$, $a\in\mathbf{Q}$, θ is a noncyclic cubic number, N is the norm of $\mathbf{Q}(\theta)$ over $\mathbf{Q}$, $k=\mathbf{Q}(\delta)$, δ being the square root of the discriminant of θ; (b) S is given by $y^2-az^2=x(x-a_1)(x-a_2)$, $a, a_1, a_2\in\mathbf{Z}$, a is square free, $k=\mathbf{Q}(\sqrt{a})$. The paper concludes with an indication of an example of S which contains a sextuplet over a biquadratic field and for which the analogous methods apply.

T. Ono (Philadelphia, Pa.)

Citations: MR 24# A85 = G35-38.

G35-44 (36# 6393)

Masuda, Katsuhiko

Application of the theory of the group of classes of projective modules to the existence problem of independent parameters of invariant.

J. Math. Soc. Japan **20** (1968), 223–232.

Let K be the rational function field $k(x_1, \cdots, x_n)$ in n variables $x_1, \cdots, x_n$ over a constant field k. Let μ be the k-automorphism on K given by $\mu(x_n)=x_1$, $\mu(x_i)=x_{i+1}$, $1\leq i<n$. If L is the fixed field of μ, it is not known whether L must always be purely transcendental over k. In case k is the field Q of rational numbers and n is a prime number, the problem has been solved for $n=2, 3, 5, 7$ (the last two cases by the author [Nagoya Math. J. **8** (1955), 59–63; MR **16**, 993], the case $n=2$ is trivial, the case $n=3$ is due to Noether). In this paper it is shown that for $n=11$, L over Q is purely transcendental also. Let γ be a primitive nth root of unity where n is a prime. If H is the Galois group of $Q[\gamma]$ over Q, a certain multiplicative subgroup M of $K[\gamma]$ is shown to be a rank 1 projective module over $Z[H]$ (=the group ring of H over the integers). It is known that L over Q is purely transcendental whenever M is free as a $Z[H]$-module. Write $A=Z[H]$ and denote by $\bar{A}$ the integral closure of A in $Q[H]$. Now the rank 1 projective class group $D(\bar{A})$ of $\bar{A}$ and the group $D(\bar{A}/A)$ of classes of rank 1 projective A-modules which are split by $\bar{A}$ both turn out to be trivial for $n=3, 5, 7, 11$. So from the exactness of the sequence $0\to D(\bar{A}/A)\to D(A)\to D(\bar{A})\to 0$ one concludes that L is purely transcendental over Q for $n=3, 5, 7, 11$.

S. Yuan (Buffalo, N.Y.)

G35-45 (37# 1371)

Tate, John T.

Algebraic cycles and poles of zeta functions.

Arithmetical Algebraic Geometry (*Proc. Conf. Purdue Univ.*, 1963), *pp.* 93–110. *Harper & Row, New York*, 1965.

This report is essentially identical to the author's article in the privately circulated Proceedings of the 1964 Woods Hole Conference in Algebraic Geometry, published in Uspehi Mat. Nauk **20** (1965), no. 6 (126), 27–40; MR **34** #1329. It is an exposition of the "Tate conjectures" relating the cycle group of codimension i on a variety V/k to the elements of $H_l^{2i}(V)$ invariant under $G(\bar{k}/k)$ if k is finite, and to the poles of the ζ-function if k is finitely generated. The most notable progress on the conjectures since this article has been the author's proof of the conjectures for k finite, $i=1$, and V an abelian variety [the author, Invent. Math. **2** (1966), 134–144; MR **34** #5829].

A. Mattuck (Cambridge, Mass.)

Citations: MR 34# 1329 = G02-18; MR 34# 5829 = G10-32.

Referred to in G05-89, G10-32, G15-44.

G35-46 **(37# 1373)**

Manin, Ju. I.

Rational surfaces over perfect fields. (Russian. English summary)

Inst. Hautes Études Sci. Publ. Math. No. 30 (1966), 55–113.

From the author's summary: "Let k be a perfect field of arbitrary characteristic. The main object of this paper is to establish some new objects associated with algebraic surfaces F defined over k which are invariants for birational transformations defined over k. There are two main applications. The first is that if K is any extension of k of degree 2, then there are infinitely many birationally equivalent rational surfaces defined over k which all become birationally equivalent to the plane over K. The second application is to a partial classification of the del Pezzo surfaces for birational equivalence over k. For our purposes a del Pezzo surface defined over k is a nonsingular rational surface with a very ample anticanonical system, so the nonsingular cubic surfaces are a special case. As we use the language of schemes, we have to prove some classical results in the new framework, notably some results of F. Enriques [Math. Ann. **49** (1897), 1–23] on the classification of rational surfaces. In the last section we produce evidence for the conjecture that if the field k is quasi-algebraically closed (in the sense of Lang), then a rational surface defined over k always has a point on it defined over k". In Section 0 some preliminaries are given: singularities of a surface, effective Cartier divisors, . . . Section 1 "generalizes results of Enriques to surfaces defined over a general perfect field k". Section 2 deals with birational invariants. Let F be a rational surface, $N(F)$ the group of divisor classes on $F \otimes \bar{k}$ for numerical equivalence. It is proved that a necessary condition for the k-surfaces F and F' to be birationally equivalent over k in the category of proper regular k-surfaces ("complete nonsingular k-surfaces" in the classical terminology) with birational morphisms is that there exist trivial G-modules M and M' such that $N(F)+M' \approx N(F')+M$ (G is the Galois group of the algebraic closure $\bar{k}$ of k over k), and this is the principal tool of this section. In Section 3 the del Pezzo surfaces are studied. It is not possible to detail here the results obtained on curves of this type of surfaces and on birational classification, some of them generalizing the results of B. Segre [Math. Notae Universidad de Rosario **11** (1951), 1–68; MR **13**, 678]. Relative to the conjecture of the last section, the following theorem is shown: The conjecture is true for rational surfaces with a pencil of curves of genus zero, for forms of the absolute minimal models and for del Pezzo surfaces of degree $n=5$. *M. L. Laplaza* (Mayaguez, Puerto Rico)

Citations: MR 13, 678d = G35-26.

Referred to in D72-66, G10-42, G35-50, Z10-27.

G35-47 **(39# 211)**

Ono, Takashi

An integral attached to a hypersurface.

Amer. J. Math. **90** (1968), 1224–1236.

The zeta function attached to a number field (for example) can be defined by an integral over the idèle group of the field. Analogously, when $F(X)=F(X_1, \cdots, X_n)$ is a nonconstant absolutely irreducible polynomial over a number field (or function field in one variable with finite constant field), the author defines a function $Y(F, \Phi; s)= \int_{V_A} \Phi(x)\|F(x)\|^s \, dV_A$, where A is the adèle ring of the ground field, V_A is the set of x in A^n such that $F(x)$ is an idèle, $\|a\|$ is the idèle-modulus of a, dV_A is a canonical measure on V_A relative to a set of convergence factors, and $\Phi(x)$ is a "standard function" on V_A. He shows that this function is always regular for $\mathrm{Re}(s)>0$ and, when the hypersurface $F(X)=0$ is nonsingular, he shows that it has an analytic continuation for $\mathrm{Re}(s)>-\frac{1}{2}$ and computes its residue at the simple pole $s=0$. The proofs use the estimates of S. Lang and A. Weil [same J. **76** (1954), 819–827; MR **16**, 398] for the number of points on a variety over a finite field. *J. S. Milne* (London)

Citations: MR 16, 398d = G25-2.

G35-48 **(39# 1456)**

Jarden, Moshe

Rational points on algebraic varieties over large number fields.

Bull. Amer. Math. Soc. **75** (1969), 603–606.

For each system $\sigma=(\sigma_1, \cdots, \sigma_s)$ of s elements of the Galois group $G=G(\overline{\mathbf{Q}}/\mathbf{Q})$ with the algebraic closure $\overline{\mathbf{Q}}$ of the rationals $\mathbf{Q}$, let $\mathbf{Q}(\sigma)$ denote the fixed field of the σ_i, $1 \leqq i \leqq s$, in $\overline{\mathbf{Q}}$ (s is any integer $\geqq 1$). The question asked is how often $\mathbf{Q}(\sigma)$ has the property (*) every non-empty absolutely irreducible algebraic variety defined over $\mathbf{Q}(\sigma)$ has at least one $\mathbf{Q}(\sigma)$-rational point. The author answers "almost always" with respect to the normalized Haar measure in the topological group G. By this, he gives affirmative answers to questions proposed by J. Ax [Ann. of Math. (2) **88** (1968), 239–271; MR **37** #5187]. Namely, the Nullstellensatz of the type (*) holds for surprisingly many "proper" subfields of $\overline{\mathbf{Q}}$, some of which are not even pseudo-finite. The author's arguments are measure-theoretic in nature, so that the existence assertions are cardinality-type. The key step (number-theoretical) is based upon the fact that $\mathbf{Q}$ is Hilbertian. In fact, the paper is written for an arbitrary "denumerable Hilbertian field of characteristic zero". *H. Hironaka* (Cambridge, Mass.)

Citations: MR 37# 5187 = U05-38.

G35-49 **(40# 2659)**

Nobusawa, Nobuo

On rationality of algebraic function fields.

Canad. Math. Bull. **12** (1969), 339–341.

The author gives an example of fields $B \supset F \supset k$ such that B is an algebraic function field over F, F is an algebraic function field over k, and k is an algebraic number field, and such that for every prime p of k, B_p/F_p is a rational function field, but B/F is not a rational function field. The construction of B is similar to that of the Brauer fields defined by P. Roquette [Math. Ann. **150** (1963), 411–439; MR **27** #4832]. *J. Ohm* (Baton Rouge, La.)

Citations: MR 27# 4832 = R34-6.

G35-50 **(40# 4272)**

Miwa, Megumu

Galois cohomology and birational invariant of algebraic varieties.

J. Math. Soc. Japan **21** (1969), 584–603.

This paper studies some birational invariants of algebraic varieties which were introduced, in the special case of rational surfaces, by Ju. I. Manin [Inst. Hautes Études Sci. Publ. Math. No. 30 (1966), 55–113; MR **37** #1373].

Let V be a complete non-singular variety over an arbitrary field K, let $N^0(V)$ be the Néron-Severi group of $V_{\bar{K}}$ modulo its torsion subgroup, and let A and $\hat{A}$ be the Albanese and Picard varieties of V ($\bar{K}$ is the algebraic closure of K). If G is the Galois group of $\bar{K}$ over K and M is a discrete G-module, then write $h^1(M)$ for the order of $H^1(G, M)$ (if finite). The author defines $h_K(V) = h^1(N^0(V))/h^1(\mathrm{Hom}_{\bar{K}}(A, \hat{A}))^{1/2}$ and shows that it has the following three properties; (a) it is a birational invariant of complete non-singular varieties over K; (b) $h_K(V_1 \times V_2) = h_K(V_1)h_K(V_2)$; (c) $h_{K_0}(R_{K/K_0}(V)) = h_K(V)$ if K is a finite separable extension of K_0 and R_{K/K_0} denotes the Weil restriction of scalars function.

Now restrict K to be a number field or a function field in one variable over a finite field, and let I_K be the idele group of K. For any G-module M, write $i(M) = \ker(H^1(G, \mathrm{Hom}_{\mathbf{Z}}(M, K^*)) \to H^1(G, \mathrm{Hom}_{\mathbf{Z}}(M, I_K)))$. The author defines $i_K(V) = i(N^0(V))/i(\mathrm{Hom}_{\bar{K}}(A, \hat{A}))^{1/2}$, and shows that this also has the properties (a), (b), and (c). It follows that the quotient, $\mu_K(V) = h_K{}^1(V)/i_K(V)$, has the same properties (a), (b), and (c).

When V is a rational surface, then A and $\hat{A}$ are trivial, and so $h_K(V) = h^1(N^0(V))$ and $i_K(V) = i(N^0(V))$. Thus, the result of T. Ono [Ann. of Math. (2) **78** (1963), 47–73; MR **28** #94] shows that, in this case, $\mu_K(V)$ is the Tamagawa number of the torus whose character module is $N^0(V)$. *J. S. Milne* (Ann Arbor, Mich.)

Citations: MR 28# 94 = E68-7; MR 37# 1373 = G35-46.

G35-51 (40# 5623)

Voskresenskiĭ, V. E.

The birational equivalence of linear algebraic groups. (Russian)

Dokl. Akad. Nauk SSSR **188** (1969), 978–981; *erratum, ibid.* **191** (1970), *nos.* 1, 2, 3, vii.

Soient k un corps de caractéristique 0, $\bar{k}$ sa clôture algébrique, $\mathscr{G}$ le groupe de Galois de $\bar{k}/k$, G un groupe algébrique linéaire connexe défini sur k, V un modèle projectif de G sur k, et $\bar{V} = V \times_k \bar{k}$. (1) Si G est résoluble, alors $\mathrm{Pic}(G) = H^1(k, \hat{G})$. (2) Si G est semi-simple, alors $\mathrm{Pic}(G) = \mathrm{Hom}(\pi, \bar{k}^*)^{\mathscr{G}}$, où π désigne le groupe fondamental de G. (3) Si G est un tore rationnel sur k, on a une suite exacte de $\mathscr{G}$-modules: $0 \to \hat{G} \to M \to N \to 0$, où $\hat{G}$ est le $\mathscr{G}$-module des caractères rationnels de G, et où M et N sont des $\mathscr{G}$-modules triviaux au sens de Manin. (4) Si G est un tore défini sur un corps de nombres k, on a la suite exacte de groupes $0 \to A(G) \to H^1(k, \mathrm{Pic}\ \bar{V}) \to Ш(G) \to 0$, où $Ш(G)$ est le groupe de Šafarevič de G, et où $A(G) = \prod_p G(k_p)/\overline{G(k)}$, et si G se décompose sur une extension cyclique de k, $A(G) = Ш(G) = 0$.

Enfin, dans le cas où G est semi-simple de revêtement simplement connexe $\tilde{G}$ et de groupe fondamental π, et défini sur un corps de nombres k, l'auteur établit une suite exacte $0 \to A \to H^1(k, \mathrm{Pic}\ \bar{V}) \to B \to 0$, où $A = \mathrm{Coker}(H^1(k, \pi) \to \Pi_{p \in S} H^1(k_p, \pi))$ où $[S] < \infty$ et $B = \mathrm{Ker}(H^2(k, \pi) \to \Pi_p H^2(k_p, \pi))$, et l'auteur énonce les conjectures suivantes:

(a) $A(\tilde{G}) = Ш(\tilde{G}) = 0$; (b) lorsque G est rationnel sur k, alors $Ш(G) = 0$ et le nombre de Tamagawa de G est égal à l'ordre de $\mathrm{Pic}(G)$.

{This article has appeared in English translation [Soviet Math. Dokl. **10** (1969), 1212–1215].}

J.-E. Bertin (Paris)

G35-52 (43# 4825)

Swinnerton-Dyer, H. P. F.

The birationality of cubic surfaces over a given field.

Michigan Math. J. **17** (1970), 289–295.

Let k be a number field, and let V be a smooth cubic surface in projective 3-space, defined over k. The author gives a criterion for V to be birationally equivalent, over k, to the plane. Let S_n denote an n element subset of the set of 27 lines on V, such that no two lines of S_n meet and any conjugate of a member of S_n lies in S_n. Then V is birationally equivalent, over k, to the plane if and only if V has at least one point in k, and at least one of S_2, S_3 or S_6. The key steps in the proof are a reduction to the case where the Neron-Severi group NS of V, i.e., the elements of the geometric Neron-Severi group left fixed by the Galois group, is generated by 3 coplanar lines defined over k, together with an arithmetical lemma on the numerical characters of a suitably chosen linear system on V.

J. C. Fogarty (Amherst, Mass.)

G35-53 (43# 6170)

Deligne, Pierre

Les constantes des équations fonctionnelles.

Séminaire Delange-Pisot-Poitou: 1969/70, *Théorie des Nombres, Fasc.* 2, *Exp.* 19 *bis*, 13 *pp. Secrétariat mathématique, Paris*, 1970.

Let $\mathbf{X}$ be a projective non-singular algebraic variety over a global field K (equipped with the usual notation: Σ the collection of places ν of K, k_ν the residue class field of K_ν, and $\bar{K}_\nu$ an algebraic closure of K_ν). The author enunciates the conjectured form for the functional equation of a Hasse-Weil type zeta function. We describe this in somewhat less generality than does the author.

Let φ_ν be the Frobenius symbol (topological generator of $G(\bar{k}_\nu/k_\nu)$ and $\mathrm{Fr}_\nu = \varphi_\nu{}^{-1}$, and let $W(\bar{K}_\nu/K_\nu))$ be the Weil group (for ν non-archimedean $1 \to I_\nu \to W(\bar{K}_\nu/K_\nu) \to Z \to 0$ where I_ν is the inertial subgroup of $G(\bar{k}_\nu/k_\nu)$, and $\mathbf{Z}$ is the subgroup of $G(\bar{k}_\nu/k_\nu)$ generated by φ_ν). The author assumes the conjecture that the characters of the representation of W on $H^m(\mathbf{X} \otimes_{K_\nu} \bar{K}_\nu, \mathbf{Q}_l) = V_1(\nu)$, and the induced representation of Fr_ν on $(V_1(\nu))^{I_\nu} = V_0(\nu)$ are independent of l, where $l \neq \mathrm{char}\ k_\nu$. Here $V_1(\nu)$ is the mth etale cohomology group of $\mathbf{X}$ (for $\mathbf{X}$ a curve think of the l-adic Tate module of the Jacobian variety of $\mathbf{X}$). For each ν, $Z_\nu(\mathbf{X}, s)$ is the zeta function obtained from $V_0(\nu)$ (for ν non-archimedian, $Z_\nu(\mathbf{X}, s) = \det(I - \mathrm{Fr}_\nu q_\nu{}^{-s}, V_0)^{-1})$, and $Z_\nu(\check{\mathbf{X}}, s)$ is the zeta function obtained from the contragrediant representation.

Let ψ be an additive (non-trivial) character of the adele classes of K, ψ_ν its νth component. Given a finite-dimensional representation V of $W(\bar{K}_\nu/K_\nu)$, Langlands has shown (unpublished, extending work of Dwork) that a generalized Gauss sum $\varepsilon(\psi_\nu, V) \in C^*$, extending the case when $\dim V = 1$, where $\varepsilon(\psi_\nu, V)$ is the Artin root number.

Let $Z(\mathbf{X}, s) = \prod_{\nu \in \Sigma} Z_\nu(\mathbf{X}, S)$. Then the conjectured relation is (*) $Z(\check{\mathbf{X}}, 1-s) = D^{-d/2} \cdot \varepsilon(\mathbf{X}, s) \cdot Z(\mathbf{X}, s)$, where $\varepsilon(\mathbf{X}, s) = \varepsilon(X, \{V_i(\nu)\}_{i=0}^1, s)$ where $d = \dim V_1(\nu)$, $\varepsilon(\mathbf{X}, \{V_i(\nu)\}_{i=0}, s)$ is a quasi-character times $\varepsilon(\psi_\nu, \{V_i(\nu)\}) \cdot \det(-\mathrm{Fr}_\nu, V_0(\nu))$, and if K is a number field $D = \mathrm{Disc}(K/\mathbf{Q})$. It is conjectured that $\varepsilon(\mathbf{X}, \{V_1(\nu)\}_{i=1}^2)$ is $\neq 1$ for only finitely many ν.

The conjectured form of the functional equation is in agreement with elliptic curves cases where the Hasse-Weil zeta function is related to automorphic functions on the upper-half plane; the work of Kuga and Shimura, and Shimura. *M. Fried* (Stony Brook, N.Y.)

G35-54 **(43# 6214)**

Neron, A.

Hauteurs et théorie des intersections.

Questions on Algebraic Varieties (*C.I.M.E., III Ciclo, Varenna*, 1969), *pp.* 101–120. *Edizioni Cremonese, Rome*, 1970.

Introduction de l'auteur: "Dans un travail précédent [Ann. of Math. (2) **82** (1965), 249–331; MR **31** #3424] nous avons étudié divers problèmes se rattachant à la notion de hauteur d'un point rationnel d'une variété algébrique définie sur un corps global. Je me propose ici d'exposer, dans ses grandes lignes, les principaux résultats de ce travail, en commençant par traiter à part, et de façon plus détaillée, le cas particulier des corps de fonctions algébriques d'une variable, mettant en évidence le lien de cette théorie avec la notion de modèle minimal au sens de notre article dans Inst. Hautes Études Sci. Publ. Math. No. 21 (1964) [MR **31** #3423]. Bien que les théorèmes fondamentaux du cas général puissent s'obtenir indépendamment de l'existence des modèles minimaux, l'introduction de ceux-ci permet de mieux préciser certains points du cas particulier envisagé, et de présenter la théorie sous une forme purement algébrique, sans recourir aux méthodes de majoration habituelles qui font intervenir la notion 'grossière' de hauteur, et sans utiliser aucun passage à la limite. Les résultats figurant dans cet exposé se trouvent déjà dans le premier article cité de l'auteur. Les variantes introduites ne concernent que leur présentation."

{Remarque du rapporteur: Malheureusement, le caractère clair et didactique de l'exposé est quelque peu troublé par la présence de quelques oublis et erreurs d'impression. Par exemple, il faut dans l'énoncé du Théorème 1 supposer A minimale, et dans sa forme équivalente (p. 110) préciser que g_φ est somme d'une forme quadratique et d'une forme linéaire.} *J.-P. Jouanolou* (Strasbourg)

Citations: MR 31# 3423 = G10-25; MR 31# 3424 = G10-26.